W9-CQU-280

Addison-Wesley

Algebra and Trigonometry

Teacher's Edition

Stanley A. Smith
Randall I. Charles
John A. Dossey
Mervin L. Keedy
Marvin L. Bittinger

ADDISON-WESLEY PUBLISHING COMPANY
Menlo Park, California · Reading, Massachusetts · New York
Don Mills, Ontario · Wokingham, England · Amsterdam · Bonn
Sydney · Singapore · Tokyo · Madrid · San Juan

Editorial Staff: Rochelle Blair, Senior Editor
Glenn Worthman
Design/Production staff: John Walker
Photo editor: Inge Kjemtrup

Photo Acknowledgments

Page	Credit
Cover	© Art Wolfe/AllStock
003	Cary Wolinsky/Stock, Boston
013	© R. Hamilton Smith
030	Cary Wolinsky/Stock, Boston
048	Bill Ross/West Light
061	Jim Brown/The Stock Market
067	W. B. Finch/Stock, Boston
100	Jim Brown/The Stock Market
105	Hank Morgan/Rainbow
127	Roy Morsch/The Stock Market
143	Leonard Lee Rue III/After-Image
144	Hank Morgan/Rainbow
153	Craig Hammell/The Stock Market
154	Roy Morsch/The Stock Market
159	Richard Pasley/Stock, Boston
170	Colin Bourke/The Stock Market
194	Richard Pasley/Stock, Boston
205	Martin Rogers/Stock, Boston
206	Martin Rogers/Stock, Boston
234	Ted Mahieu/The Stock Market
243	Jeff Hunter/The Image Bank
270	Greg Vaughn/Tom Stack & Associates
275	Jeff Hunter/The Image Bank
291	Brian Vikander/West Light
319	Brian Vikander/West Light
320	Hank Morgan/Rainbow
341	Ken Biggs/After-Image
362	Rick Blumberg/Stock, Boston
366	Ken Biggs/After Image
383	Teri Gilman/After-Image
384 C	Patti Murray/Animals, Animals
384 L	Luis Villota/The Stock Market
384 R	Robert Pearcy/Animals, Animals
415	Teri Gilman/After-Image
422	Mike Mazzaschi/Stock, Boston
429	Don & Pat Valenti/Tom Stack & Associates
438	NASA
452	Vic Huber/West Light
457	Don & Pat Valenti/Tom Stack & Associates
479	Courtesy of Apple Computer, Inc.
500	Courtesy of Apple Computer, Inc.
501	The Bettman Archive
515	Lee Boltin
546	Max Winter/Stock, Boston
555	Lee Boltin
567	Sonya Jacobs/The Stock Market
598	Sonya Jacobs/The Stock Market
604	Bill Gallery/Stock, Boston
611	E. R. Degginger/Bruce Coleman Inc.
612	E. R. Degginger/Bruce Coleman Inc.
624	Chad Slattery/After-Image
643	Michael Tamborrino/The Stock Market
649	Elliott Smith*
654	Ken Biggs/After-Image
657	Michael Tamborrino/The Stock Market
672	Tim Davis
674	© R. Hamilton Smith
683	Robert P. Carr/Bruce Coleman Inc.
689	Ted Horowitz/The Stock Market
695	Focus on Sports
697	Ted Horowitz/The Stock Market
712	Everett C. Johnson/After-Image
718	Bob Daemmrich/Stock, Boston
720	Elliott Smith*
727	N. Strung/The Stock Market
740	Wayland Lee*/Addison-Wesley Publishing Company
746	J. C. Mantilla/FOCUS Virginia
747	N. Strung/The Stock Market
775	Hank Morgan/Rainbow
781	Anthony Suau/Black Star
800	Anthony Suau/Black Star
809	Hal Clason/Tom Stack & Associates
820	Laurence Nelson/Stock, Boston
827	Rene Burri/Magnum
829	NASA

*Photographs provided expressly for the publisher.

ISBN 0-201-81253-3

1 2 3 4 5 6 7 8 9 10-VH-96 95 94 93

Authors

Stanley A. Smith served as Coordinator, Office of Mathematics (K-12), for Baltimore County Public Schools, Maryland. He has taught junior high school mathematics and science and senior high school mathematics. He earned his M.A. degree at the University of Maryland. Mr. Smith was named Outstanding Mathematics Educator by the Maryland Council of Teachers of Mathematics in 1987. He is co-author of *Addison-Wesley Essentials of Mathematics* (1989), *Addison-Wesley Consumer Mathematics* (1989), and *Addison-Wesley Informal Geometry* (1986).

Randall I. Charles is Associate Professor of Mathematics at San Jose State University. He has taught at all levels and has been an elementary and secondary school mathematics supervisor. He has recently been involved in the development and evaluation of a nationally recognized problem-solving program. Dr. Charles holds a Ph.D. in Mathematics Education from Indiana University, and is co-author of several books, including *Addison-Wesley Mathematics* (1989) for grades 7 and 8, *Addison-Wesley Essentials of Mathematics* (1989), *Addison-Wesley Pre-Algebra* (1987), and *Problem-Solving Experiences in Mathematics* (1985).

John A. Dossey is Professor of Mathematics at Illinois State University where he teaches both mathematics and methods courses for teachers. He has taught at every level from grade 7 through graduate school and has served as K-12 supervisor of mathematics. He received his Ph.D. in Mathematics Education from the University of Illinois. During 1986–1988, Dr. Dossey served as President of the National Council of Teachers of Mathematics. He is a member of the National Research Council's Mathematical Sciences Education Board. In addition to books on both methods and content, he has published a number of research papers dealing with the Second International Study of Mathematics. He is co-author of *Addison-Wesley Essentials of Mathematics* (1989).

Mervin L. Keedy is Professor of Mathematics Emeritus at Purdue University. He received his Ph.D. at the University of Nebraska and formerly taught at the University of Maryland. He has also taught mathematics and science in junior and senior high schools. Professor Keedy is the author of many books on mathematics. Most recently he is co-author of *Addison-Wesley General Mathematics* (1986), *Addison-Wesley Applying Mathematics* (1986), and *Addison-Wesley Informal Geometry* (1986).

Marvin L. Bittinger is Professor of Mathematics Education at Indiana University-Purdue University at Indianapolis. He earned his Ph.D. at Purdue University. Dr. Bittinger is the author of many books on mathematics. Most recently, he is the author of *Calculus* (Addison-Wesley, 1984) and is co-author of *Business Mathematics* (Addison-Wesley, 1987), *Addison-Wesley General Mathematics* (1986), and *Addison-Wesley Informal Geometry* (1986).

Consultants and Reviewers

Ferrill Alderfer, Cherry Hill East High School, Cherry Hill, New Jersey
Margaret Arevalo, Memorial High School, San Antonio, Texas
Otto Bielss, Dallas Independent School District, Dallas, Texas
Bruce Burt, West Chester Area School District, West Chester, Pennsylvania
Cecile Carlton, Nashua Senior High School, Nashua, New Hampshire
Gill Choi, Board of Education, Chicago, Illinois
Jim Crawford, Manchester Memorial High School, Manchester, New Hampshire
David S. Daniels, Longmeadow High School, Longmeadow, Massachusetts
Ron Davis, Lee County Schools, Fort Meyers, Florida
Paul Dillenberger, Minneapolis School District, Minneapolis, Minnesota
Charles Garabedian, Watertown High School, Watertown, Massachusetts
Susan Harder, Clark High School, Plano, Texas
Susan Heicklen, State College Area Intermediate High School, State College, Pennsylvania
Arthur C. Howard, Aldine Independent School District, Houston, Texas
Arthur Jackson, Concord High School, Concord, New Hampshire
Melleretha Johnson, City of Saginaw School District, Saginaw, Michigan
Lillian Jones, Westview Junior High School, Miami, Florida
Catherine J. Kowalski, Bellaire High School, Bellaire, Texas
Roger Larson, Anoka-Hennepin School District, Coon Rapids, Minnesota
Sandra Lindstrom, Mercer Island High School, Mercer Island, Washington
Kay Meister, Columbus School Board, Columbus, Ohio
Bert Niehius, Carlmont High School, Belmont, California
Mick O'Neil, Salem High School, Salem, New Hampshire
Roy Ramos, Kennedy High School, San Antonio, Texas
Ron Schutt, Lexington High School, Lexington, Massachusetts
Robert Scott, Sweetwater High School, Sweetwater, Texas
Edna Vasquez, Redford High School, Detroit, Michigan
Jim Wohlgehagen, Plano Independent School District, Plano, Texas

Contributors

Wayne S. Copes   William J. Sacco
Clifford W. Sloyer   Robert M. Stark

Associated with the University of Delaware and Advancement of Mathematical Education, Inc., Newark, Delaware

Contents

1 Real Numbers, Algebra, and Problem Solving

2 Equations and Inequalities

3 Relations, Functions, and Graphs

4 Systems of Equations and Problem Solving

5 Polynomials and Polynomial Equations

6 Rational Expressions and Equations

7 Powers, Roots, and Complex Numbers

8 Quadratic Equations

9 Quadratic Functions and Transformations

10 Equations of Second Degree

11 Polynomial Functions

12 Exponential and Logarithmic Functions

13 Matrices and Determinants

14 Sequences, Series, and Mathematical Induction

15 Counting and Probability

16 Statistics and Data Analysis

17 Trigonometric Functions

18 Trigonometric Identities and Equations

Appendix

Addison-Wesley *meets all of your Algebra and Trigonometry needs*

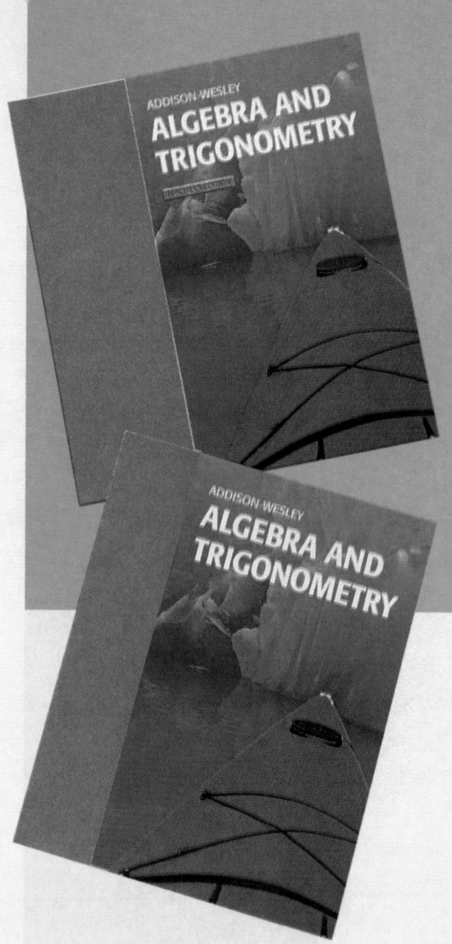

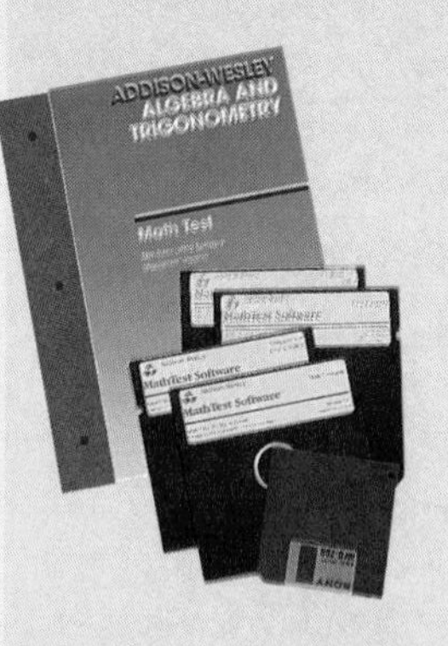

MathTest Software

Generates tests, worksheets, and problems for assessment or cooperative learning. Programmed algorithms create an unlimited number of problems in any combination as well as answer keys. Frees you to work with students. Easy to use on IBM, Apple, or Mac. Mac users select from non-routine questions and alternative assessment items, too.

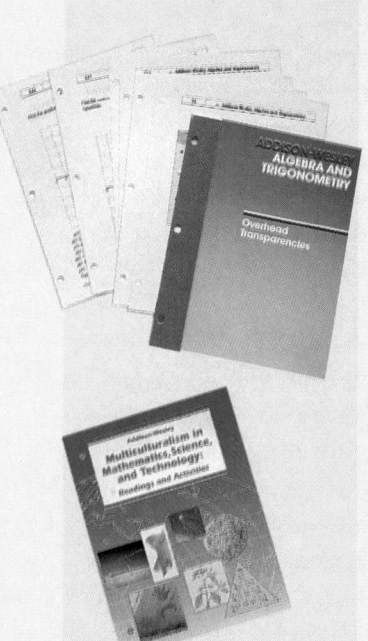

Overhead Transparencies

Crisp and accurate, they display chalkboard examples and problem strategies. Engages visual learning, lets you maintain eye contact with students.

Solutions Manual

Solutions to every exercise, parameters for every open question posed in the text, graphic solutions.

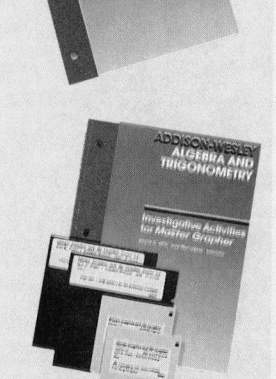

Multiculturalism in Mathematics, Science, and Technology

Celebrate diversity as you deepen understanding and motivate students from all backgrounds with this imaginative collection of activities.

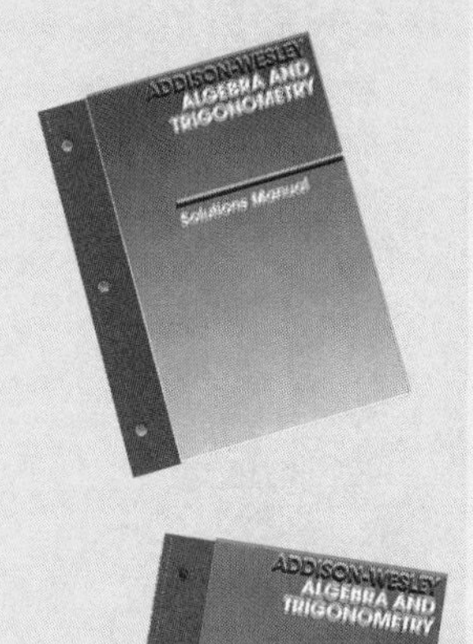

Master Grapher

An interactive graphing utility for IBM, Apple II, or Mac. *Investigative Activities for Master Grapher* includes student worksheets with keystrokes and menu choices for self-guidance. Use teacher demonstration lessons with your LCD projection panel to step up the pace of learning.

Teacher's Resource Packages

Your deep-pocket resource for management and instruction comes to you as a set of eleven supplements, each addressing a different daily teaching challenge.

Four management aids support you from student placement to final evaluation.

Management and Teaching Tools

Includes record-keeping aids, student resources, and two-year assignment guide.

Lesson Plan Book

Detailed one-page lesson plans with objectives and NCTM Standards correlations.

First Five Minutes Transparency Masters

Fast class starters from the FIRST FIVE MINUTES feature in your Teacher's Edition.

Assessment

Quizzes and cumulative tests, choice of levels for chapter tests, placement and problem-solving assessment tools.

Seven instruction supplements provide a treasury of help, motivation, and creative stimulus for every student in your class.

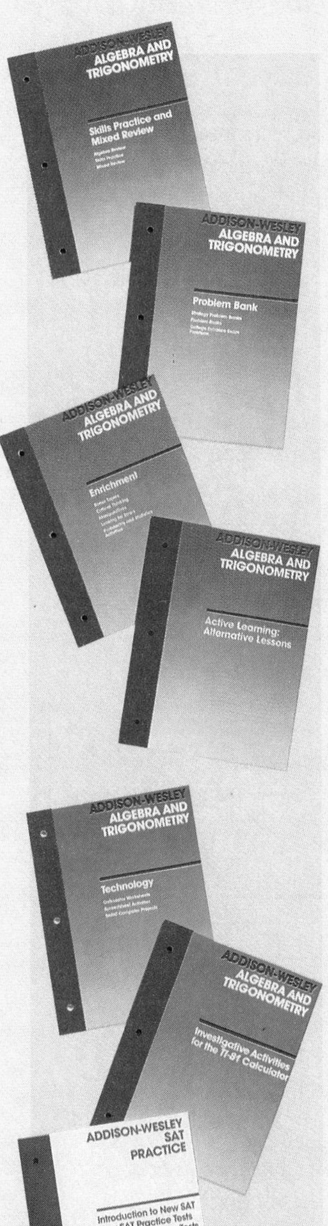

Skills Practice and Mixed Review

Includes arithmetic and geometry review as well as lesson-correlated practice.

Problem Bank

Includes strategy problem banks and college entrance exam problems.

Enrichment

Bonus topics for *all* students. Includes critical thinking, error recognition, probability, and work with manipulatives.

Active Learning

Alternative lessons include guided activities and follow-up for constructivist learning.

Technology

Calculator and spreadsheet activities; BASIC computer projects.

Investigative Activities for the TI-81 Calculator (with Teacher's Guide)

Meet the standards—yours and NCTM's—with interactive graphing explorations.

SAT Practice

For use with 1993 PSAT and 1994 SAT, includes "grid-in" practice.

Addison-Wesley Algebra and Trigonometry's content

Connections/Explorations

Encourage Students to Reach a Higher Level of Mathematical Understanding

✔ **Connections**

End-of-lesson features show connections between algebra and geometry or calculus. See pages 187, 249, 818.

The connections logo ◇◇ appears in the Teacher's Edition when the text or exercises have connections to geometry.

✔ **Explore**

Explore features give students the opportunity to try out new concepts before the lesson begins. See pages 297, 310, 400 and 433.

9-5 Graphs of $f(x) = a(x - h)^2 + k$

Explore

Graph these equations.

$y = (x - 2)^2$ $\quad y = (x - 2)^2 + 4$ $\quad y = (x - 2)^2 - 3$

Study your graphs. What are the coordinates of the vertex of each graph? Predict the coordinates of the vertex of the function $y = (x - 20)^2 + 40$.

In graphs of equations of the form $y = (x - h)^2 + k$, what effect does k have on the graph?

✔ **Writing to Learn**

Students develop a deeper understanding by verbalizing mathematical concepts. See page 37.

✔ **Master Grapher**

Students can use this software to explore graphs, draw conclusions, and to test these conclusions. See page 255.

Problem Solving/Critical Thinking

Promotes Critical Thinking in a Broad Range of Situations

✔ **Problem-Solving Guidelines**

Throughout the text, a special logo reminds students of the phases needed for effective problem solving. See page 469.

PROBLEM-SOLVING GUIDELINES
■ UNDERSTAND the problem
■ Develop and carry out a PLAN
■ Find the ANSWER and CHECK

✔ **Problem Solving for Specific Topics**

In these lessons, students translate word problems into algebraic forms. See page 598.

✔ **Problem Solving: Strategies**

Students learn to approach problems in new ways, using a variety of strategies. See page 372.

✔ **Problem Solving: College Entrance Exams**

Students learn how to successfully apply strategies on standardized tests. See page 557.

In addition, The Problem Bank supplement contains 4 exams simulating the SAT.

✔ **Problem Solving: Situational Problem Solving**

These open-ended, real-world situations elicit a wide range of thinking skills. See page 775.

✔ **Critical Thinking Problems**

Almost every exercise set offers a critical thinking problem to help develop thinking skills. See page 457.

prepares students for the twenty-first century

Technology
Motivates Students to Explore Algebra

✔ Calculator Instruction
Calculator instruction is provided, where appropriate. See page 703.

In the Teacher's Edition, calculator instruction is keyed to worksheets in the Technology supplement. See page 438.

✔ Calculator Investigation
This feature at the end of lessons allows students to explore concepts with a calculator. See page 542.

Several calculator packages to accompany Addison-Wesley Algebra and Trigonometry are available. Please see your Addison-Wesley catalog for details.

✔ TI-81 Investigations
These investigations provide opportunities for important exploration of concepts using the TI-81 Graphing Calculator. They appear in the Appendix and are referenced in the appropriate lesson. See page 855.

✔ Problem for Programmers
This feature gives students with programming experience opportunities to apply their skills. See page 503.

Problem for Programmers

Write a program that will take any values input for a, h, and k for the equation $f(x) = a(x - h)^2 + k$ and determine whether the function has a maximum or a minimum value, find the line of symmetry, and find the vertex.

Applications
Help Students Learn to Apply Mathematics

✔ Chapter Openers
Chapters begin with an application that motivates the material and is solved later in the chapter. See page 781.

✔ Lesson Openers
Select lessons begin with an application that provides a concrete frame of reference and a springboard for developing the lesson.

3-8 Mathematical Modeling: Using Linear Functions
Objective: Find a linear function and use the equation to make predictions.

Crickets are known to chirp faster at higher temperatures and slower at lower temperatures. The number of chirps is thus a function of the temperature.

The following data were collected and recorded in a table.

Temperature °C	6	8	10	15	20
Number of chirps per minute	11	29	47	75	109

Can we predict the number of chirps per minute for a temperature of 18°C? If a

✔ Problem Solving: Applications
By demonstrating the need for algebra in real life, these applications motivate students to master algebra. See page 604.

✔ Data Analysis
New data handling and analysis topics provide up-to-date and realistic statistics methods. See pages 688–721.

Addison-Wesley Algebra and Trigonometry structure

BEFORE THE CHAPTER . . .

Chapter Openers The chapter begins with an application that students can solve later as an exercise.

Ready For A pretest helps identify which lessons students need to review.

DURING THE CHAPTER . . .

Lesson Openers

Select lessons in each chapter begin the presentation of algebraic concepts within an Explore, Application, or Math History context.

Objective

The objective for each section appears on the student page.

Examples

Student understanding is enhanced by fully worked examples.

Try This Exercises

Following the examples, the Try This exercises provide students with immediate reinforcement of concepts and skills and help teachers diagnose student difficulties.

8-6 Formulas and Problem Solving

The height of an object that has been fired upward with initial velocity v_0 at any given time t is given by the formula $h = v_0t - 16t^2$, where h is in feet, t is in seconds, and v_0 is in ft/s.

How long has an object been in the air, given it is at height h and was fired with initial velocity v_0. In other words, can we determine t if we know h and v_0?

Solving Formulas

Objective: Solve second-degree formulas for a given letter.

EXAMPLE 1 Solve $h = v_0t - 16t^2$ for t, the time an object is in the air, given h, the height of the object, and v_0, the initial velocity.

$$16t^2 - v_0t + h = 0 \quad \text{Finding standard form}$$

$$a = 16, b = -v_0, c = h$$

$$t = \frac{-b \pm \sqrt{b^2 - 4ac}}{2a}$$

$$t = \frac{v_0 \pm \sqrt{(-v_0)^2 - 4 \cdot 16 \cdot h}}{2 \cdot 16} \quad \text{Substituting into the quadratic formula}$$

$$t = \frac{v_0 \pm \sqrt{v_0^2 - 64h}}{32}$$

$$t = \frac{v_0 + \sqrt{v_0^2 - 64h}}{32} \text{ or } t = \frac{v_0 - \sqrt{v_0^2 - 64h}}{32}$$

Since h is nonnegative, both of these give nonnegative values for t.

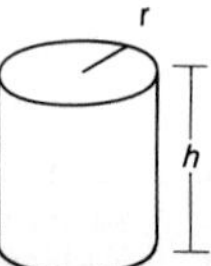

Try This Solve for the indicated letter.

a. $V = \pi r^2h$; r **b.** $2\pi r^2 + 2\pi rh = 1$; r

makes rigorous content accessible to every student

A Exercises

Students can use the A exercises to reinforce their understanding of the lesson.

B Exercises

By using the B exercises, students discover connections and integrate their understanding of concepts.

9-7 EXERCISES

A

Find the x-intercepts.

1. $f(x) = x^2 - 4x + 1$
2. $f(x) = x^2 + 6x + 10$
3. $f(x) = -x^2 + 2x + 3$
4. $f(x) = x^2 + 2x - 5$
5. $f(x) = x^2 - 3x - 4$
6. $f(x) = x^2 - 8x + 5$
7. $f(x) = -x^2 + 3x + 4$
8. $f(x) = 2x^2 - 4x + 6$
9. $f(x) = 2x^2 + 4x - 1$
10. $f(x) = x^2 - x + 2$
11. $f(x) = x^2 - x + 1$
12. $f(x) = 4x^2 + 12x + 9$
13. $f(x) = -x^2 - 3x - 3$
14. $f(x) = -5x^2 + 6x - 5$
15. $f(x) = 3x^2 - 6x + 1$
16. $f(x) = x^2 - 4x + 4$

B

17. Graph the function $f(x) = x^2 - x - 6$. Use your graph to approximate solutions to the following equations.
a. $x^2 - x - 6 = 2$ **b.** $x^2 - x - 6 = -3$

18. Graph the function $f(x) = \frac{x^2}{8} + \frac{x}{4} - \frac{3}{8}$. Use your graph to approximate solutions to the following equations.
a. $\frac{x^2}{8} + \frac{x}{4} - \frac{3}{8} = 0$ **b.** $\frac{x^2}{8} + \frac{x}{4} - \frac{3}{8} = 1$ **c.** $\frac{x^2}{8} + \frac{x}{4} - \frac{3}{8} = 2$

19. ***Critical Thinking*** Write an equation for a quadratic function that has x-intercepts of $(-3, 0)$ and $(5, 0)$.

Challenge

Find the x-intercepts.

20. $f(x) = x^4 - 10$ **21.** $f(x) = x^4 - 3x^2 + 9$

Mixed Review

Test for symmetry with respect to the origin. **22.** $y + x = 1$ **23.** $y - x^2 = 4$
24. $4y = 3x - 7$ **25.** $x^2 + y^2 = 3$

For each function graph the function, find the vertex, and find the line of symmetry.
26. $f(x) = x^2$ **27.** $f(x) = -2(x + 3)^2$

Graph the following relations. **28.** $y = |x|$ **29.** $y = |x + 4|$

30. The distance s that an object falls when dropped from some point above the ground varies directly as the square of the time t it falls. The object falls 19.6 meters in 2 seconds.
a. Find the equation of variation.
b. How far will the object fall in 15 seconds?
c. How long will it take for the object to fall 122.5 meters?

Critical Thinking Problems

These problems provide students with opportunities to develop thinking skills.

Challenge Exercises

Challenge exercises encourage honors students to apply their knowledge at the highest level.

Mixed Review

Through daily review of the basic course material, students maintain their previously learned skills.

AFTER THE CHAPTER . . .

Chapter Summary and Review A summary of each lesson is combined with its own review exercises. This unique format provides students with important theorems and vocabulary and with ideal test preparation.

Chapter Test Problems in the Chapter Test parallel those in the Chapter Summary and Review, so students can test themselves after reviewing.

Addison-Wesley Algebra and Trigonometry provides

BEFORE THE CHAPTER . . .

Four special chapter planning guide pages provide for planning, assignment, and assessment.

Chapter Overview Provides a quick summary of the chapter's content.

Chapter Objectives List all objectives for the chapter.

Teaching Guide Provides suggestions for cooperative learning, alternative assessment, and communication ideas for each chapter. A multicultural note and possible investigations or projects are also included.

Multi-Level Management Guide Helps teachers adjust plans appropriately for different level classes. The guides include suggestions for planning each lesson and utilize all of the supplementary materials.

DURING THE CHAPTER . . .

Essential Elements

The Essential Elements are keyed to appropriate lessons.

First Five Minutes

To start every lesson, there is a quick review of skills needed for the day.

Teaching Notes

Notes and suggestions are provided to help teach every objective.

Math Point

This feature contains useful background information for perspective and anecdotes for human interest.

Avoiding Common Errors

By using these suggestions, teachers can guide students to avoid error patterns.

Key Questions

The key questions can be used to stimulate class discussion and promote discovery of concepts.

FIRST FIVE MINUTES

1. Write an equation of the line with slope 5 and y-intercept (0, 3).
   $y = 5x + 3$
2. Write an equation of the line with slope 4 containing the point (2, 3).
   $y - 3 = 4(x - 2)$
   This can be simplified to
   $y = 4x - 5$.
3. Write an equation for the line containing the points (4, 7), (6, 11).
   The slope is $\frac{11 - 7}{6 - 4} = 2$.
   The equation of the line is
   $y = 2x - 1$.

Point out that not all situations can be described by linear relationships. However, when a relationship is linear, we can use the best fit line to make predictions.

Other considerations also may limit the domain of a function. For example, a negative number of chirps would be meaningless. Also, imagine what would happen to a cricket at $-40°C$ or $100°C$.

Math Point

Why is m used for slope? One theory is that it is short for the French word "monter," which means "to mount, to climb, to slope up." Since Descartes, the creator of the coordinate system, was French, this is a plausible explanation.

Avoiding Common Errors

Students should not fit a line between two points that are close together on the ordinate axis. If we had fit the line using (8, 29) and (10, 47), we would have found the equation $c = 9t - 43$. From this we would have predicted that crickets chirp *119* times at 18°C. This is not a reasonable prediction (they chirp *less* often at 20°C) and the point (18, 119) is not close to the line we fit.

Key Questions

- How many points do you need to find the slope of a line?
  Two
- Is the slope the same between any two points on a line?
  Yes

3-8 Mathematical Modeling: Using Linear Functions

Objective: Find a linear function and use the equation to make predictions.

Crickets are known to chirp faster at higher temperatures and slower at lower temperatures. The number of chirps is thus a function of the temperature.

The following data were collected and recorded in a table.

Temperature °C	6	8	10	15	20
Number of chirps per minute	11	29	47	75	109

Can we predict the number of chirps per minute for a temperature of 18°C? If a linear equation fits the data reasonably well, we can develop a **linear function** as a **mathematical model** of the situation. We can then use the model (the linear function) to make predictions.

EXAMPLE 1

Use the data collected in the table to predict the number of chirps per minute when the temperature is 18°C.

UNDERSTAND the problem

Question: Can a linear function fit the data, and, if so, what is the approximate number of chirps per minute for a temperature of 18°C?

Data: Crickets chirp 11 times per minute at 6°C, 29 times per minute at 8°C, and so on, as listed in the table.

Develop and carry out a PLAN

First, we plot the data to determine whether a linear equation gives an approximate fit. We make a graph with a t-axis (temperature) and a c-axis (chirps per minute), and plot the data. We see that they lie approximately on a straight line. Thus, we can use a linear function to model the situation.

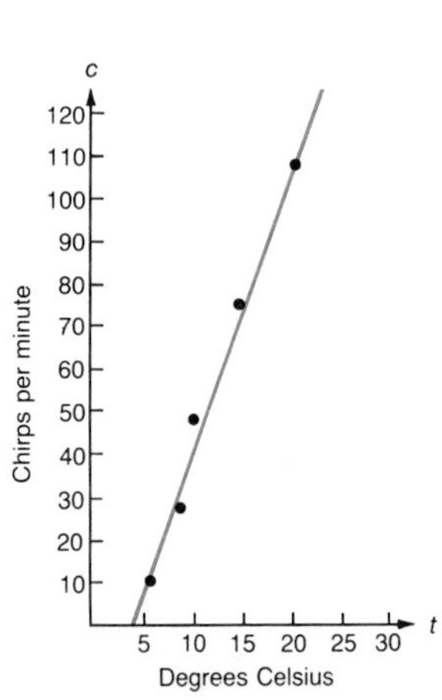

The line is placed so that some points are above and some are below the line, and so that each point is close to the line.

tools for heightening teaching effectiveness

Answers

Teacher's Edition answers are printed in blue.

Try This Multiply or divide and write scientific notation for the answer.

g. $(9.1 \times 10^{-17})(8.2 \times 10^3)$ 7.462×10^{-13} **h.** $\frac{4.2 \times 10^5}{2.1 \times 10^2}$ 2.0×10^3 **i.** $\frac{1.1 \times 10^{-4}}{2.0 \times 10^{-7}}$ 5.5×10^2

Estimating and Approximating

Objective: Use scientific notation in approximating and estimating.

Scientific notation is helpful in estimating or approximating. Such estimating is an important skill in problem solving.

EXAMPLE 8 Estimate $780{,}000{,}000 \times \frac{0.00071}{0.000005}$.

$\frac{(7.8 \times 10^8)(7.1 \times 10^{-4})}{(5 \cdot 10^{-6})}$ Converting to scientific notation and multiplying

$= \frac{7.8 \times 7.1}{5} \times \frac{(10^8)(10^{-4})}{10^{-6}}$ Regrouping

$\approx \frac{8 \times 7}{5} \times 10^{8+(-4)-(-6)}$ Rounding

$\approx \frac{56}{5} \times 10^{10}$

$\approx 11 \times 10^{10}$ Rounding

$\approx 1.1 \times 10^{11}$ Converting to scientific notation

We now have an approximation of 1.1×10^{11}.

Try This Estimate. Answer may vary depending on how you round.

j. $830{,}000{,}000 \times \frac{0.0000012}{3{,}100{,}000}$ 3×10^{-4}

Using Scientific Notation

Many calculators switch their displays automatically to scientific notation when results are greater than the capacity of the display. If we multiply 20,820,000 by 5000 on a calculator, the display will show 1.041 11. This means 1.041×10^{11}. Calculators with keys EXP or EE allow you to enter numbers in scientific notation. To enter 0.0035698 in scientific notation, press

3.5698 [EXP] 3 [+/−]

Calculate $34{,}700{,}000 \times 5000$ using scientific notation.

3.47 [EXP] 7 [×] 5 [EXP] 3 [=] → 1.735 11

For additional calculator practice, see Calculator Worksheet 3.

Chalkboard Examples

1. Estimate.
$\frac{0.000345 \cdot 41300}{5980}$
Write in scientific notation.
$\frac{(3.45 \cdot 10^{-4})(4.1300 \cdot 10^4)}{(5.98 \cdot 10^3)}$
Round to one significant digit.
$\frac{(3.0 \cdot 10^{-4})(4.0 \cdot 10^4)}{(6.0 \cdot 10^3)}$
Simplify.
$\frac{3 \cdot 4}{6} \cdot 10^{-4+4-3}$
$\approx 2 \cdot 10^{-3}$

LESSON ENRICHMENT

Change the problem in Example 2. See how quickly students can see the pattern.

Five plus twice a number is

six times the number. $x = \frac{5}{4}$

five times the number. $x = \frac{5}{3}$

four times the number. $x = \frac{5}{2}$

three times the number. $x = \frac{5}{1} = 5$

two times the number. $x = \frac{5}{0}$, no solution

LESSON QUIZ

Convert to scientific notation.
1. 67,000,000
$6.7 \cdot 10^7$
2. 0.000039
$3.9 \cdot 10^{-5}$

Convert to standard notation.
3. $5.32 \cdot 10^5$
532,000
4. $4.65 \cdot 10^{-4}$
0.000465
5. Multiply and write in scientific notation.
$(3.0 \cdot 10^6)(4.0 \cdot 10^7)$
$12.0 \cdot 10^{13} = 1.2 \cdot 10^{14}$

ADDITIONAL ANSWERS

Try This

d. $(0, -2), (0, 2)$
e. $(-2, -3), (-2, 3), (2, -3), (2, 3)$
f. $(2, -3), \left(-\frac{14}{3}, \frac{1}{3}\right)$

Chalkboard Examples

These additional examples are accompanied by worked-out answers.

Lesson Enrichment

This feature provides suggestions for extending the lesson.

Lesson Quiz

Teachers can use the quiz supplied at the end of every lesson as a quick assessment tool.

References to Calculator Worksheets

Calculator instruction is keyed to additional calculator worksheets in the **Technology** supplement.

Cooperative Learning Groups

Benefits of Cooperative Learning

Students benefit in several ways from small group instruction. Progress and success are the responsibility of the group, so an individual is less likely to be frozen by anxiety about "getting the right answer." Group work also demonstrates that there is more than one way to solve a problem—one of the most important ideas students can learn.

Setting up Cooperative Learning Groups

To set up cooperative learning groups, you should first determine group size and make-up. If your students are not experienced with cooperative learning groups, you may want to begin with groups of two students. Most teachers find the optimum group size to be three or four. You should allow a group at least three sessions before making a change.

Before the first group lesson, post a set of cooperative learning rules in the room and discuss them with the class. Consistently enforce and reinforce these rules. Some possible rules are:

1. All students must participate.
2. Each group member must be willing to help any other member.
3. Show respect for one another; criticize ideas, not people.
4. Ask the teacher for help only if every member of the group has the same question.
5. Do not talk to other groups.
6. Everyone in the group must agree on the answer.

Student's Role in Cooperative Learning Groups

Each student in a group should have a designated task. Tasks can include spokesperson or reporter, writer or recorder, checker, technology person, time keeper, and others as needed. Tasks can change daily or weekly, but students should get an opportunity to routinely do every task.

Teacher's Role in Cooperative Learning Groups

When students are working in small groups, the teacher can serve as a coach. Circulate through the room, listening to group discussions and interact as needed. Observe whether all students are involved, and question those who appear to be passive.

If an entire group appears to be struggling, ask the spokesperson what the group is discussing and what is giving difficulty. Ask questions that refocus the students' attention. A question can make students discern a weak point in their approach, recognize misinterpreted information, or evaluate the reasonableness of an assumption or answer.

Using Cooperative Learning Groups

A. Review
   1. Use the **First Five Minutes** for a review of skills needed for the day's lesson.
   2. Have students work in groups and compare their homework answers to determine errors. The **Selected Answers** can be used if the group cannot agree on an answer for an odd-numbered problem. The group should agree on one answer.
   3. Ask one member from each group to present "common errors" found in each group. Use the suggestions given in **Avoiding Common Errors** to insure understanding of the material.

B. Motivation and Development of Lesson
   1. Use the *application* presented on the opening page of each chapter to motivate topics in the chapter. Use **Explore, Math History,** and **Application** to motivate specific lessons. Exploration activities may be completed independently or with students working in small groups. Some of the **Explore** activities involve graphing and may be completed with the help of a computer or graphing calculator. Discuss the conclusions reached by the students.
   2. Focus on promoting student understanding using the suggestions found with each subsection. Use the **Key Questions** to promote student involvement. Use **Investigative Activities** to demonstrate graphing concepts.

C. Seatwork
   1. Ask student groups to work the **Try This** exercises. Have students compare answers within the group, give help where needed, and agree on an answer and method.
   2. Choose one group to present the **Try This** exercises to the class.
   3. The **Lesson Quiz** can be used to assess understanding of the day's lesson, and a bonus may be assigned to the group with the highest average score.

D. Homework Assignments
   1. Assign both reading and written assignments. Students should always read the lesson covered.
   2. The **Assignment Guide** gives suggested written assignments for three levels of classes. Writing the assignment on the chalkboard in the same place every day is an effective way to assure that an assignment is not overlooked.
   3. **Critical Thinking** exercises should be assigned whenever possible to give students the opportunity to reverse their thinking, to apply multiple skills, to analyze and synthesize, to evaluate, and to create. These exercises should be thoroughly discussed as there may be a variety of correct answers. The answers for the **Critical Thinking** exercises are never included in the student **Selected Answer** section.
   4. **Mixed Review** *exercises* should be assigned every day. They are found at the end of every lesson. In addition **Mixed Review** *worksheets* can be found in the supplemental package when further review is necessary.

Teaching Problem Solving

Developing a Positive Classroom Atmosphere

The teacher's role in creating an atmosphere conducive to successful problem solving cannot be overemphasized. Your actions affect the classroom atmosphere in several ways. First, your attitude toward problem solving will affect your students' attitudes. If you demonstrate that problem solving is not only important but also exciting and fun, students are likely to develop similar attitudes. Your own beliefs are crucial; here are some ways to convey them.

- Join enthusiastically in the problem-solving experience, exploring problems along with your students. "Think aloud" as you examine and solve, and encourage students to do the same.
- Create problems based on your students' own situations to demonstrate that problem solving is an ongoing, everyday experience.
- Encourage students to write problems themselves.
- Personalize problems from the book whenever possible (use students' names and familiar locations, for example).
- Discuss interesting inventions and games as examples of problem solving in real life.

Active Involvement

Research has shown that successful problem solvers have active involvement with problems; those who remain passive will not develop their problem-solving skills. Show that you value each student's contribution, even when his or her skills still need development. Your comments can help elicit and promote desirable problem-solving habits.

- Recognize and reinforce willingness and perseverance.
- Reward risk-takers.
- Encourage students to play hunches.
- Accept unusual solutions.
- Emphasize persistence and creativity rather than speed.
- Have students analyze their solutions; show that verification and interpretation are part of the answer process.

Evaluating Problem-Solving Performance

Problem-solving experiences provide for alternative assessment if evaluation involves the process in addition to the answer.

- Ask students to write an explanation, as well as a complete solution, for each problem situation describing why he or she thinks that this is the correct way to solve the problem. Students can keep these in a journal.
- Observe each student in a class as he or she solves problems in a whole-class setting.

A scheme for analyzing a student's problem-solving performance is provided in the **Management and Teaching Tools** supplement.

Using Problem-Solving Guidelines

Problem-solving guidelines give both teacher and student a structure for solving problems. In *Addison-Wesley Algebra and Trigonometry* the process of solving problems is described as a series of three phases:

Phase 1: UNDERSTAND the problem
Phase 2: Develop and carry out a PLAN
Phase 3: Find the ANSWER and CHECK

In Phase 1, students need to identify the question and the data. You can try the following techniques to help students with this phase:

- Ask questions that focus on what the unknown quantities are, what the data are, what data are needed to answer the question, and what data is extraneous.
- Ignoring the numbers for the moment, discuss the situation and action involved in the problem.
- Have students identify and state the question.
- Have students state the problem in their own words.

Phase 2, the planning stage, involves selecting and implementing one or more strategies for solving the problem. While the strategy *Write an Equation* is important to the algebra curriculum, students should be formally introduced to a variety of nonroutine strategies. The book presents lessons in the following strategies:

Page 54 *Draw a Diagram*	Page 98 *Guess, Check, Revise*
Page 152 *Make an Organized List*	Page 285 *Make a Table, Look for a Pattern*
Page 372 *Use Logical Reasoning*	Page 472 *Simplify the Problem*
Page 509 *Work Backward*	Page 637 *Combine Strategies*

As often as possible, demonstrate more than one strategy for solving a single problem, or show how one strategy could be applied in different ways.

Phase 3 involves a review and check of procedures and commitment to an answer. Have students write the answer in a complete sentence. This makes them relate the numerical part of the solution to the narrative setting and consider reasonableness, and helps them determine whether they have answered the question being asked. Teach them to reread the problem and check whether all relevant information was used and all the conditions were met. Have them check for computational errors and compare their answers to an estimate.

Extending a Problem-Solving Lesson

"Checking back" is the final stage in solving a particular problem, but a problem-solving lesson should not end there. You can extend the problem-solving experience in several ways. Show a second solution method, either a new strategy or a different use of the same strategy. Showing variations in the way a strategy is used to solve a single problem extends students' knowledge about the strategy.

Have students write problems similar to the one they have just solved. They can change the setting and numbers. They can change certain conditions, change the question being asked, or change a problem that asks for a final quantity so that the final quantity is known and a beginning quantity is asked for. Activities like these help students focus on how the conditions in a problem affect the way one goes about finding the solution.

Teaching with Technology

Calculator

Students should be encouraged to use calculators when the emphasis is on algebraic concepts and skills rather than arithmetic proficiency. The calculator boxes give simple instructions that will work on most calculators. If your students are using many different calculators, you may want to spend a day having students familiarize themselves with their calculators. The first *Calculator Worksheet* in the **Technology** supplement provides a format for "learning about your calculator." The other *Calculator Worksheets* provide additional practice using each key introduced in the book.

Graphing Calculator

Graphing calculator investigations are provided in the appendix as well in the supplement **Investigative Activities for the TI-81 Calculator**. These investigations provide opportunities for the student to investigate algebraic concepts and perceive spatial relationships of these concepts. All activities are keyed to lessons in the book.

In addition to graphing activities, investigations are provided for analyzing statistical data and for solving systems of equations using both Cramer's rule and inverse matrices.

Computer Graphing Utility

Master Grapher is an interactive graphing software package. This graphing utility has a zoom option that can be used to find coordinates of points of intersection to several decimal places. This program can be used to graph equations given in *Explore* lesson openers.

You may wish to have students use this program to graph equations and functions in Chapter 3, systems of equations in Chapter 4, quadratic equations and functions in Chapters 8–10, conics in Chapter 10, higher-degree functions in Chapter 11, and exponential and logarithmic functions in Chapter 12. In Chapter 11, for example, students can use Master Grapher to estimate roots of higher-degree equations by graphing the corresponding function and locating the x-intercepts using the zoom option.

Investigative Activities for Master Grapher is a supplement designed to assist students in investigating algebraic concepts and in perceiving spatial relationships of many of these concepts. These activities are designed to take advantage of the power of the computer by allowing the students to "discover" many algebraic concepts and relationships through making and testing their own conjectures. The activities can be used to supplement specific lessons, keyed in the Teacher's Edition. Sample lessons show how Master Grapher can be used for teacher demonstration in a one-computer classroom.

Computer-Assisted Problem Solving

Computer-Assisted Problem Solving in the Appendix contains BASIC programs that allow the student to use a computer to solve problems. These programs require no programming experience. They are simply to be entered and run. For students with some understanding of the commands, the Extension to the problem involves a simple one- to two-line modification to the program. Programs to find equations of lines, perform synthetic division, find matrix inverses, and find measures of central tendency and variation, make an excellent bank of programs that can be used to solve many other problems.

Spreadsheets

The **Technology** supplement contains *Calculator Worksheets* (described above), *Spreadsheet Activities*, and BASIC *Computer Projects*. Each *Spreadsheet Activity* illustrates how to use a spreadsheet to work with algebraic concepts, and each activity presents problems for the student to solve and explore. The *BASIC Computer Projects* do the same with the BASIC computer language.

MathTest Software

This software package can generate an almost infinite number of tests, worksheets, mixed review sheets, etc. As this test-generating software is algorithm based, you can give each student in the class a different test, if you wish, and the answers will be provided for you by the software.

Course Options for Algebra Two

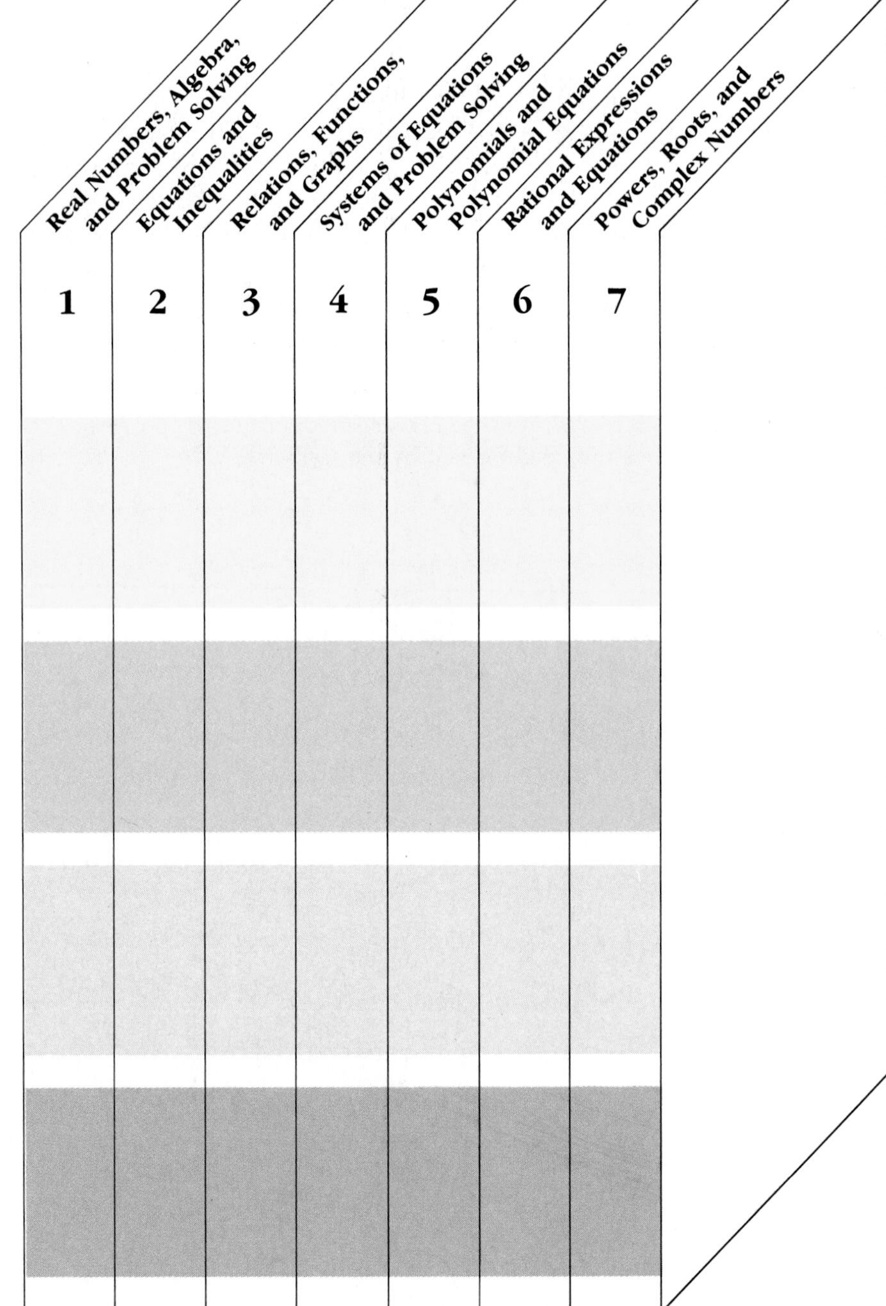

Algebra Two
Standard second-year algebra topics

Algebra Two with Finite Math
Finite math strand continues from algebra through matrices, sequence and series, induction, and probability and statistics.

Algebra Two with Trigonometry
Trigonometry strand continues from algebra through trigonometry topics from simple triangles to DeMoivre's Theorem.

Comprehensive Algebra Two
Comprehensive Course covers all topics of algebra, finite math, and trigonometry.

8	9	10	11	12	13	14	15	16	17	18
Quadratic Equations	Quadratic Functions and Transformations	Equations of Second Degree	Polynomial Functions	Exponential and Logarithmic Functions	Matrices and Determinants	Sequences, Series, and Mathematical Induction	Counting and Probability	Statistics and Data Analysis	Trigonometric Functions	Trigonometric Identities and Equations

Using the Assignment Guide

Addison-Wesley Algebra and Trigonometry contains all second-year algebra topics and solid introductions to finite math and trigonometry. Assignment schedules are provided for four course options—a regular algebra course, a regular algebra course covering topics in finite math, a regular algebra course covering topics in trigonometry, and a comprehensive algebra course covering topics in finite math and trigonometry. All four courses provide for 170 teaching days and include review and testing days.

Daily assignments and optional supplementary assignments are given for each chapter in the Chapter Planning guide prior to each chapter. Specific assignments for each lesson are also provided in the teacher's margin notes.

The assignment guide lists supplement pages that can be used with a particular lesson. These pages are suggested to provide flexibility for individual classroom situations. It is not intended that *every* listed supplement page be used in every class.

The following chart summarizes the number of days allocated for each chapter for the four courses, and includes chapter reviews and tests.

Chapter	**1**	**2**	**3**	**4**	**5**	**6**	**7**	**8**	**9**	**10**	**11**	**12**	**13**	**14**	**15**	**16**	**17**	**18**
Algebra	13	13	16	13	13	14	15	14	14	14	12	15	0	0	0	0	0	0
Algebra with Finite math	10	10	14	13	11	12	14	10	11	11	8	10	9	7	7	9	0	0
Algebra with Trigonometry	10	10	14	13	11	12	14	10	11	11	8	10	0	0	0	0	17	17
Comprehensive	7	7	8	11	8	10	13	9	10	10	8	9	8	7	7	8	13	12

Semester

Teacher's Answer Section

Page 77 EXERCISE SET 2-4

4. 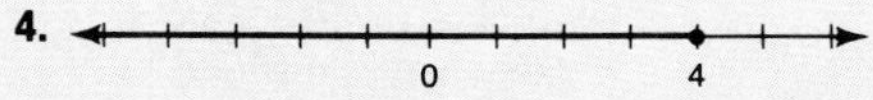

5.

6.

7.

Page 91 EXERCISE SET 2-7

You may wish to have students write answers in set notation. For example, the answer to Exercise 25 would be $\{-3, 3\}$ and the answer to Exercise 27 would be $\{x \mid -3 < x < 3\}$.

21. $-3, 3$

22. $-5, 5$

23. $-3 < x < 3$

24. $-5 \le x \le 5$

25. $x \le -2$ or $x \ge 2$

26. $y < -8$ or $y > 8$

27. $t \le -5.5$ or $t \ge 5.5$

28. $m \ne 0$

29. $-9, 15$

30. $-\frac{4}{3}, \frac{8}{3}$

31. $-\frac{1}{2} \le x \le \frac{7}{2}$

32. $-1 \le x \le \frac{1}{5}$

33. $y < -\frac{3}{2}$ or $y > \frac{17}{2}$

34. $y < -\frac{4}{3}$ or $y > 4$

35. $x \le -\frac{5}{4}$ or $x \ge \frac{23}{4}$

36. $y < -\frac{15}{9}$ or $y > \frac{19}{9}$

37. $x > -\frac{3}{5}$ or $x < -1$

43. All real numbers 44. No solution 45. $-\frac{13}{54} < x < -\frac{7}{54}$

46. $-33 < x < -31$ 47. All real numbers

48. $3 \le x \le 6$ or $-4 \le x \le -1$ 49. $-\frac{1}{4}, 1$ 50. No solution

51. $x \le 1$

Page 96 EXERCISE SET 2-8

1. $7x - 12 = 37$

$7x = 49$	Add. property
$x = 7$	Mult. property

2. $5y + 16 = 88 - 3y$

$8y + 16 = 88$	Add. property
$8y = 72$	Add. property
$y = 9$	Mult. property

3. $15x - 5 \ge 11 - 2x$

$17x \ge 16$	Add. property
$x \ge \frac{16}{17}$	Mult. property

4.

$13x + 12 < 15x - 7$	
$-2x < -19$	Add. property
$x > \frac{19}{2}$	Mult. property

5. If $6y = 10$, then $3y = 5$. 6. If $2x + 5 = 14$, then $5x + 3 = 17$. 7. If $x < 20$, then $x < 12$. 8. If $4y + 2 < 8y + 1$, then $3y + 5 > 17 - y$. 9. If $x = 7$, then $7x - 12 = 37$. 10. If $y = 9$, then $5y + 16 = 88 - 3y$. 11. If $x \geq \frac{16}{17}$, then $15x - 5 \geq 11 - 2x$. 12. If $x > \frac{19}{2}$, then $13x + 12 < 15x - 7$.

29.

1. $a = b$	Hypothesis
2. $a - a = 0$	Prop. of additive inverses
3. $a - b = 0$	Statements 1 and 2 (substitution)
4. $a - b + 0 = 0$	Additive identity property
5. $a - b + c - c = 0$	Prop. of additive inverses
6. $a + c - b - c = 0$	Commutative property
7. $a + c - (b + c) = 0$	Inverse of a sum property
8. $a + c = b + c$	Prop. of additive inverses

30.

1. $a = b$	Hypothesis
2. $a(1) = b(1)$	Mult. identity property
3. $a\left(\frac{c}{c}\right) = b\left(\frac{c}{c}\right)$	Property of 1
4. $\frac{ac}{c} = \frac{bc}{c}$	Multiplication
5. $\frac{ac}{c} - \frac{bc}{c} = 0$	Addition property
6. $\frac{1}{c}(ac - bc) = 0$	Distributive property
7. $c\left[\frac{1}{c}(ac - bc)\right] = 0$	Prin. of zero products
8. $\frac{c}{c}[(ac - bc)] = 0$	Associative property
9. $1(ac - bc) = 0$	Property of 1
10. $ac - bc = 0$	Mult. identity property
11. $ac = bc$	Addition property

31. Part 1. If $a = 0$ or $b = 0$ then $ab = 0$

1. $a = 0$	Hypothesis
2. $ab = 0(b)$	Mult. property
3. $ab = 0$	Mult. prop. of zero
4. If $a = 0$ then $ab = 0$	Statements 1–3
5. $b = 0$	Hypothesis
6. $ab = a(0)$	Mult. property
7. $ab = 0$	Mult. prop. of zero
8. If $b = 0$ then $ab = 0$	Statements 5–7
9. If $a = 0$ or $b = 0$ then $ab = 0$	Statements 4 and 8

Part 2. If $ab = 0$ then $a = 0$ or $b = 0$

1. $ab = 0$ $(a \neq 0)$	Hypothesis
2. $\frac{1}{a} \cdot ab = \frac{1}{a} \cdot 0$	Mult. property
3. $1(b) = 0$	Prop. of reciprocals
4. $b = 0$	Mult. identity prop.
5. If $ab = 0$ and $a \neq 0$ then $b = 0$	Statements 1–4
6. $ab = 0$ $(b \neq 0)$	Hypothesis
7. $ab \cdot \frac{1}{b} = 0 \cdot \frac{1}{b}$	Mult. property
8. $a(1) = 0$	Prop. of reciprocals
9. $a = 0$	Mult. identity prop.
10. If $ab = 0$ and $b \neq 0$ then $a = 0$	Statements 6–9
11. If $ab = 0$ then $a = 0$ or $b = 0$	Statements 5 and 10

33.

1. $a < b$	Hypothesis
2. $a - a < b - a$	Addn. prop. for ineq.
3. $0 < b - a$	Additive inv. prop.
4. $b < c$	Hypothesis
5. $b - b < c - b$	Addn. prop. for ineq.
6. $0 < c - b$	Additive inv. prop.
7. $0 < (b - a) + (c - b)$	Addn. of pos. #'s is pos.
8. $0 < c - a + b - b$	Comm. prop.
9. $0 < c - a$	Additive inverse prop.
10. $0 + a < c - a + a$	Addn. prop. for ineq.
11. $a < c$	Add. ident, add. inv. prop.
12. If $a < b$ and $b < c$ then $a < c$	Statements 1, 4, 11

34.

1. $a < b$	Hypothesis
2. $0 < b - a$	Defn. of $<$
3. $0 < b - a + 0$	Add. identity
4. $0 < b - a + c - c$	Add. inverse prop.
5. $0 < (b + c) - (a + c)$	Comm. and dist. props.
6. $a + c < b + c$	Defn. of $<$
7. If $a < b$ then $a + c < b + c$	Statements 1–6

35. Part 1. $(c > 0)$

1. $a < b$	Hypothesis
2. $0 < b - a$	Defn. of $<$
3. $0 < c(b - a)$	Prod. of pos. #'s is pos.
4. $0 < cb - ca$	Dist. prop.
5. $ca < cb$	Defn. of $<$
6. If $a < b$ and $c > 0$ then $ac < bc$	Statements 1–5

Part 2. $(c < 0)$

1. $a < b$	Hypothesis
2. $0 < b - a$	Defn. of $<$
3. $0 > c(b - a)$	Prod. of neg. and pos. # is neg.
4. $0 > cb - ca$	Dist. prop.
5. $ca > cb$	Defn. of $>$
6. If $a < b$ and $c < 0$ then $ac > bc$	Statements 1–5

36. If x is an integer, then x is a rational number. If x is a rational number, then x is an integer.

37. If x is a quitter, then x never wins. If x never wins, then x is a quitter.

38. Part 1.

1. $a > b$	Hypothesis
2. $0 > b - a$	Add. prop.
3. $-b > -a$	Add. prop.
4. $-a < -b$	Commut. prop.
5. If $a > b$, then $-a < -b$.	Statements 1–4

Part 2.

1. $-a < -b$	Hypothesis
2. $0 < -b + a$	Add. prop.

3. $b < a$ | Add. prop.
4. $a > b$ | Commut. prop.
5. If $-a < -b$, then $a > b$. | Statements 1–4

Combining the two parts of the proof, $a > b$ if and only if $-a < -b$. Thus the two statements are equivalent.

Page 108 EXERCISE SET 3-1

30. a. {(−1, −1), (−1, 0), (−1, 1), (−1, 2), (0, −1), (0, 0), (0, 1), (0, 2), (1, −1), (1, 0), (1, 1), (1, 2), (2, −1), (2, 0), (2, 1), (2, 2)}
    b. {(−1, 0), (−1, 1), (−1, 2), (0, −1), (0, 1), (0, 2), (1, −1), (1, 0), (1, 2), (2, −1), (2, 0), (2, 1)}
    c. Domain {−1, 0, 1, 2}; range {−1, 0, 1, 2}
    d. {(−1, −1), (−1, 1), (0, 0), (1, 1), (1, −1), (2, 2)}
31. a. {(−1, −1), (−1, 1), (−1, 3), (−1, 5), (1, −1), (1, 1), (1, 3), (1, 5), (3, −1), (3, 1), (3, 3), (3, 5), (5, −1), (5, 1), (5, 3), (5, 5)}
    b. {(−1, −1), (−1, 1), (−1, 3), (−1, 5), (1, 1), (1, 3), (1, 5), (3, 3), (3, 5), (5, 5)}
    c. Domain {−1, 1, 3, 5}; range {−1, 1, 3, 5}
    d. {(−1, 3), (−1, 5), (1, 3), (1, 5), (3, 5)}
33. Possible answers: (3, 1, 1), (3, 2, 4), (3, 3, 9), (3, 4, 16), (3, 5, 25)
34. Possible answers: (−2, −1, −1), (−4, −2, −8), (−6, −3, −27), (−8, −4, −64), (−10, −5, −125)

Page 114 EXERCISE SET 3-2

1.
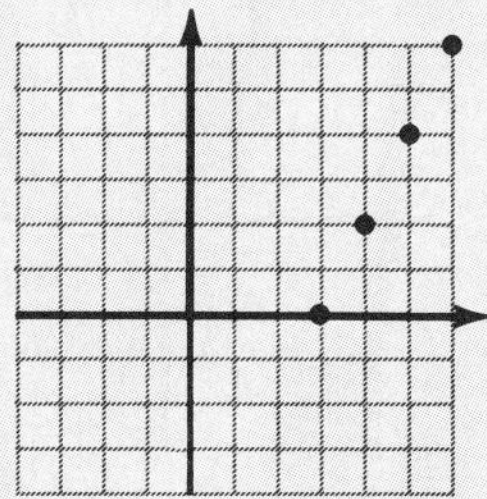

2.
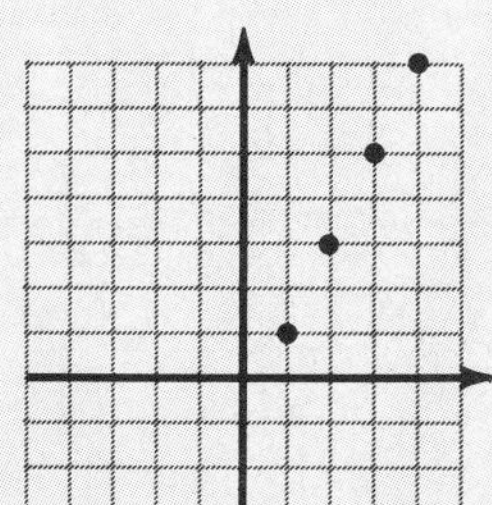

3.
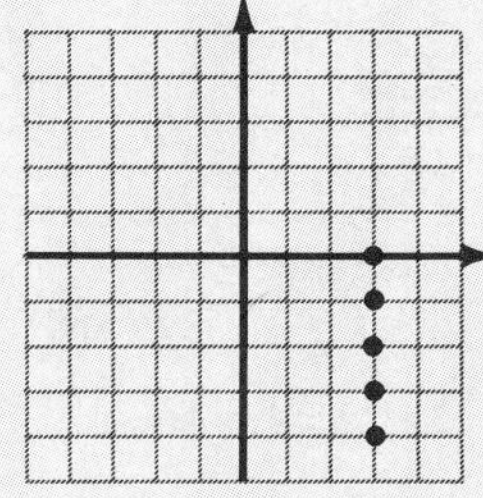

4.
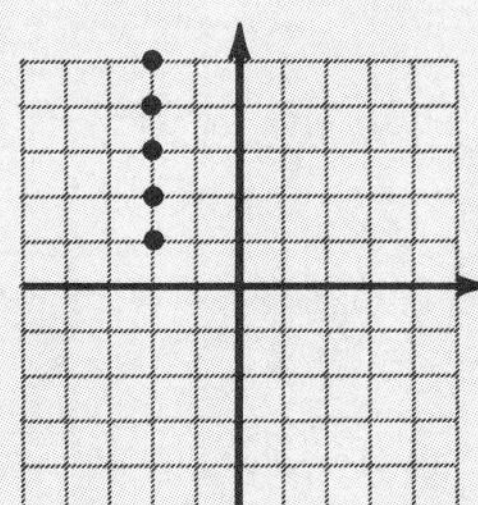

5.
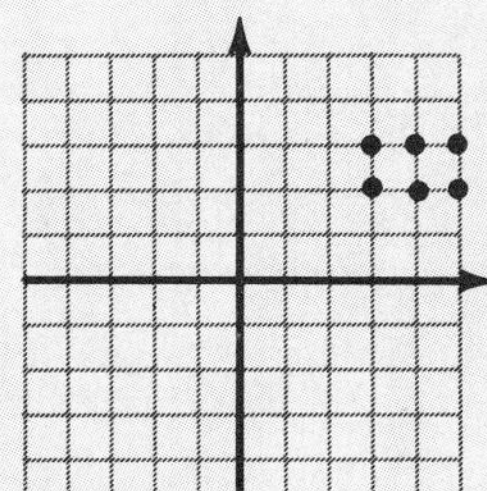

6.
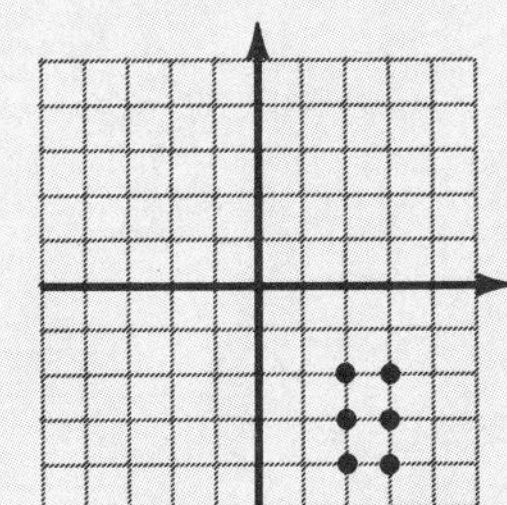

7.
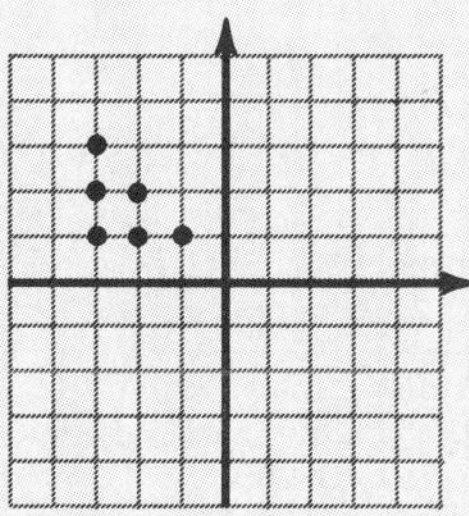

8.
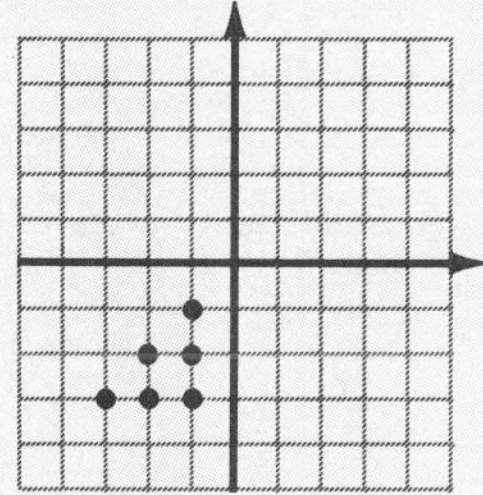

21.
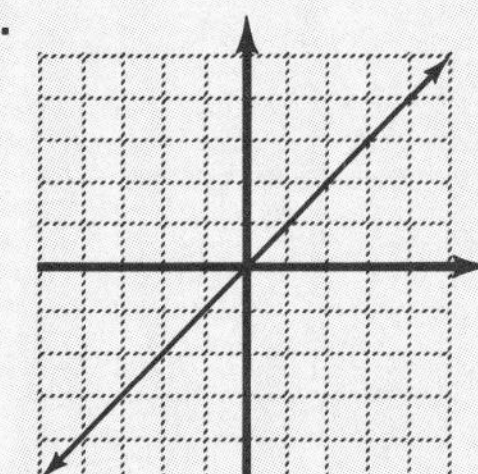

22.
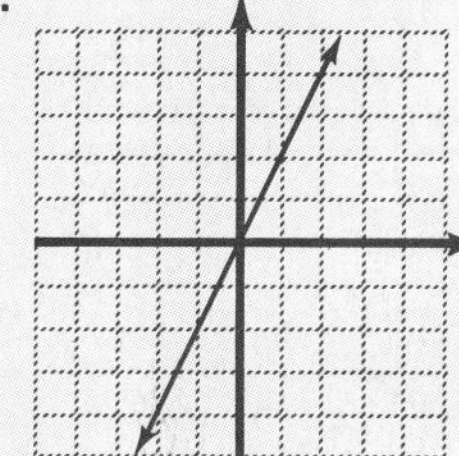

23.
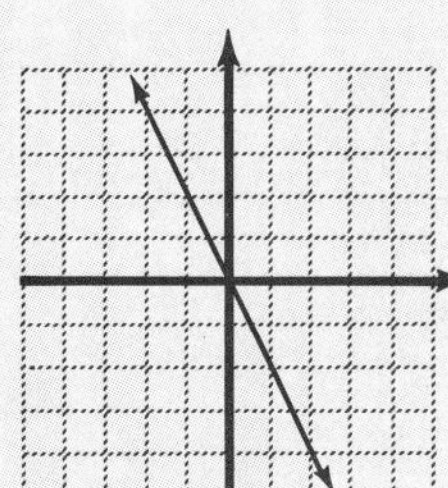

24.
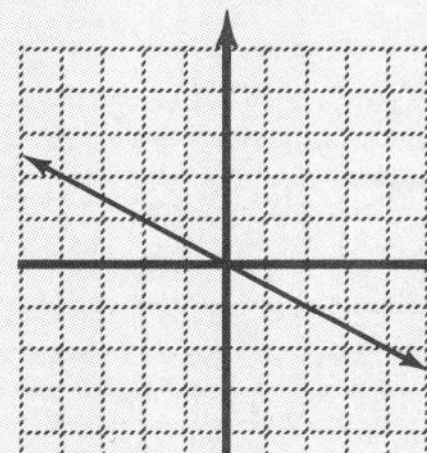

25.
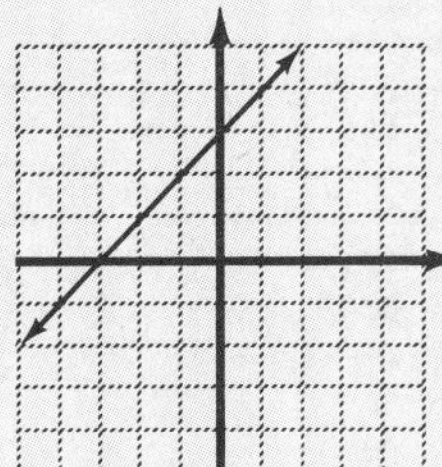

26.
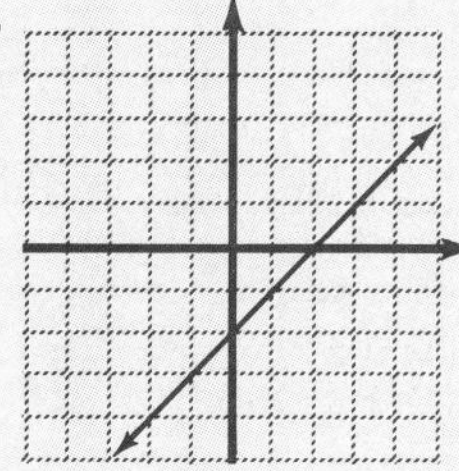

27.
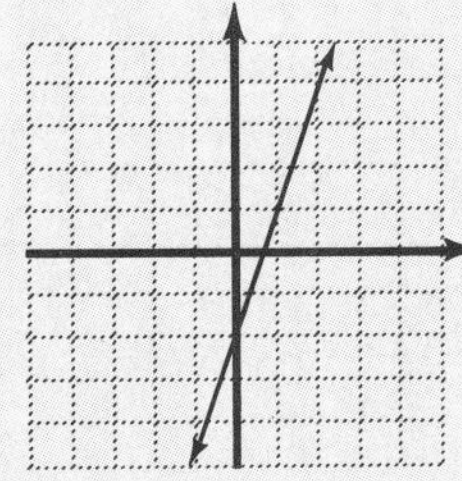

28.
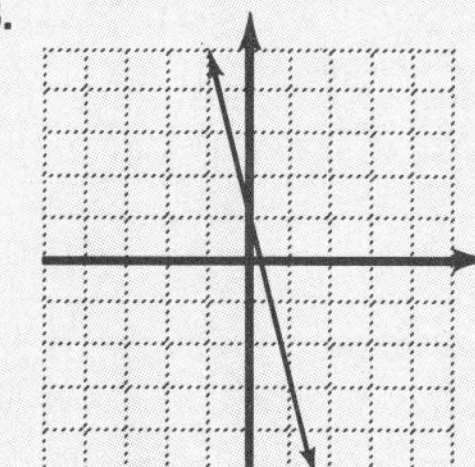

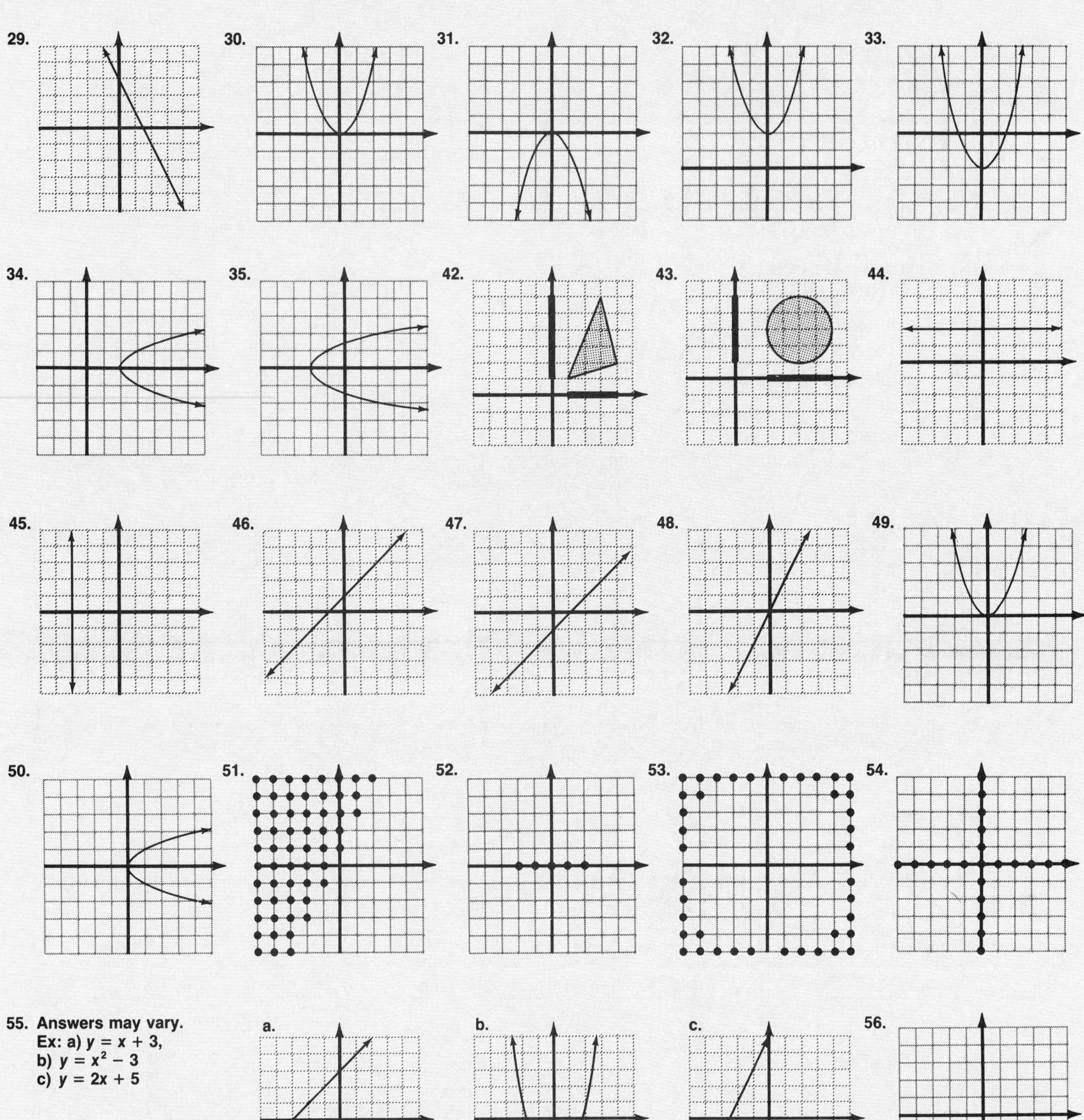

55. **Answers may vary.**
Ex: a) $y = x + 3$,
b) $y = x^2 - 3$
c) $y = 2x + 5$

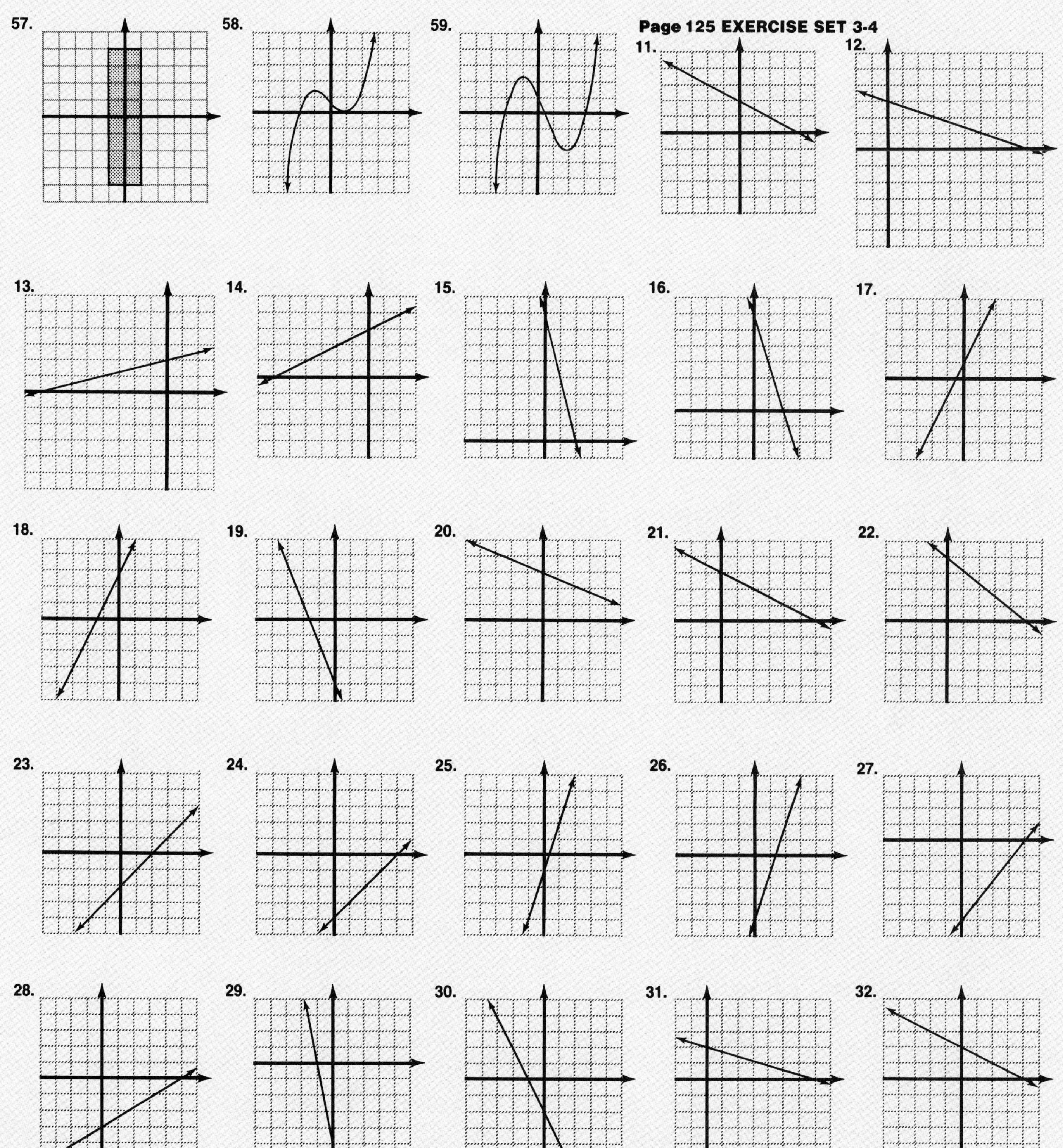
57.
58.
59.
Page 125 EXERCISE SET 3-4
11.
12.
13.
14.
15.
16.
17.
18.
19.
20.
21.
22.
23.
24.
25.
26.
27.
28.
29.
30.
31.
32.

33.

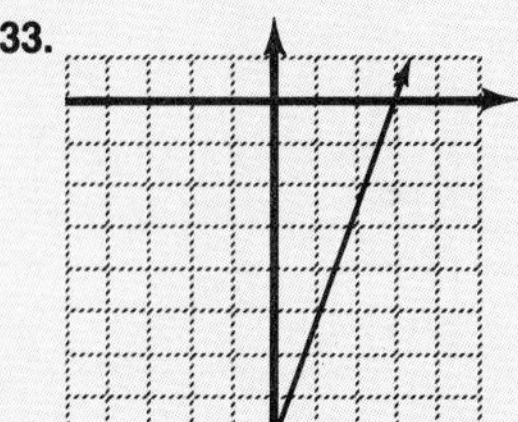

34.

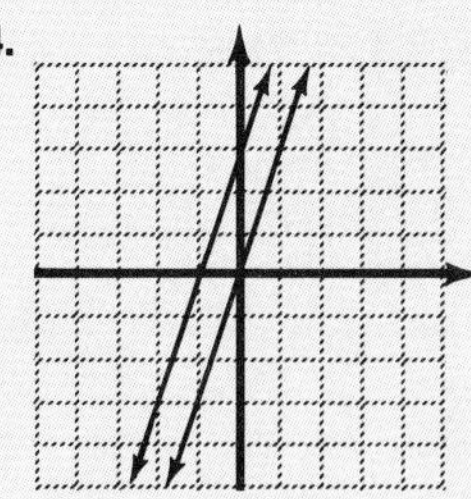

35.

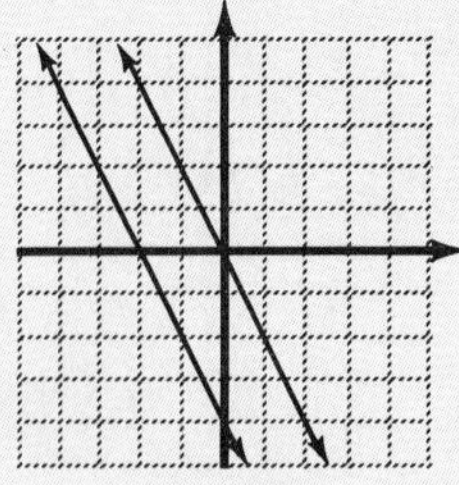

36.

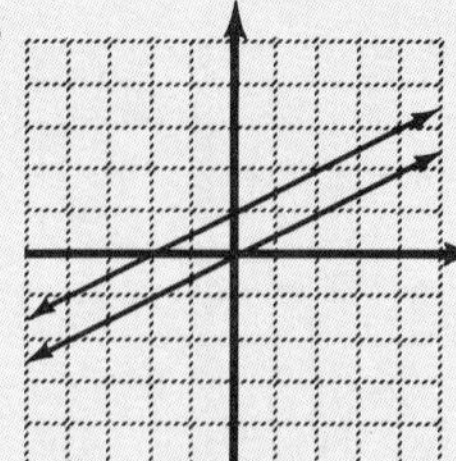

37.

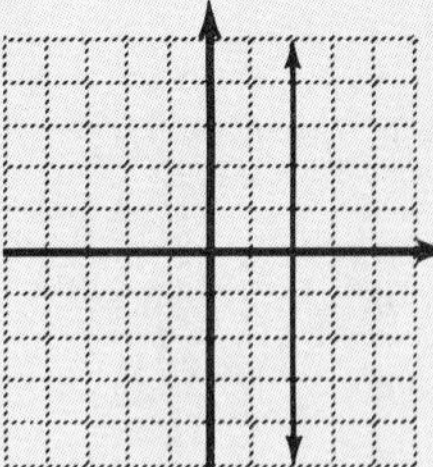

38.

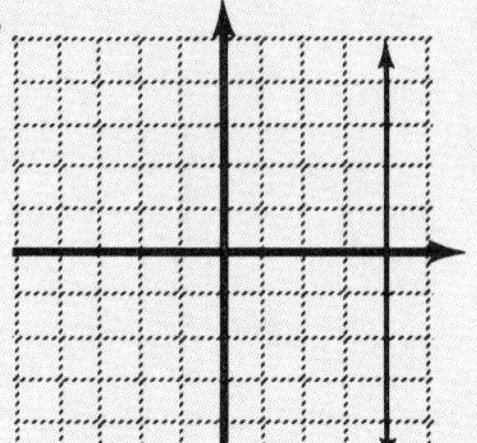

39.

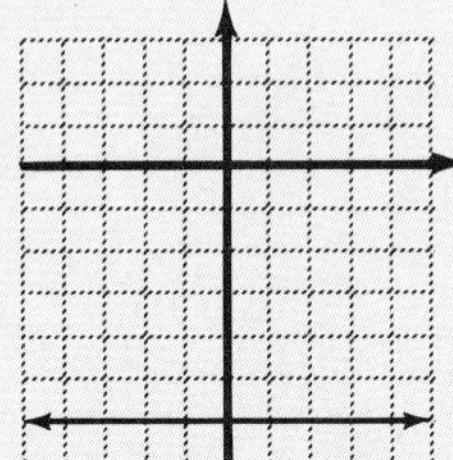

40.

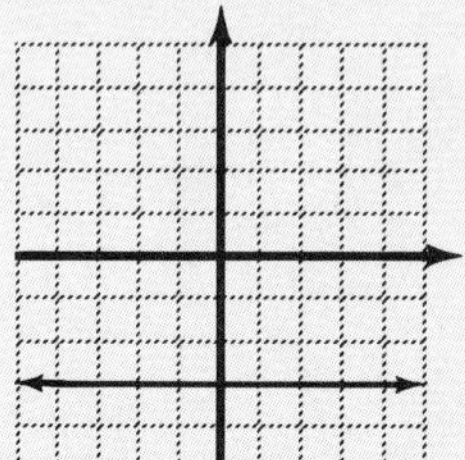

41.

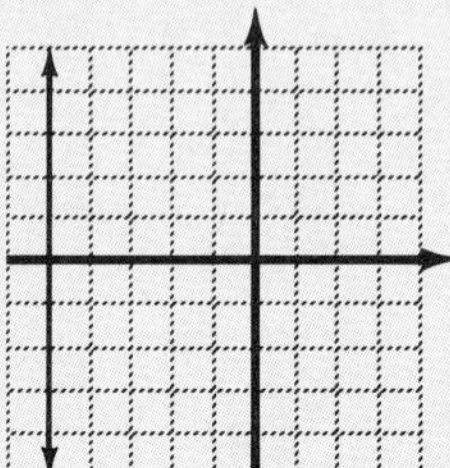

42.

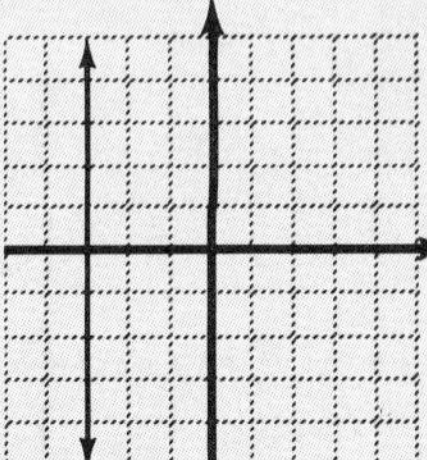

43.

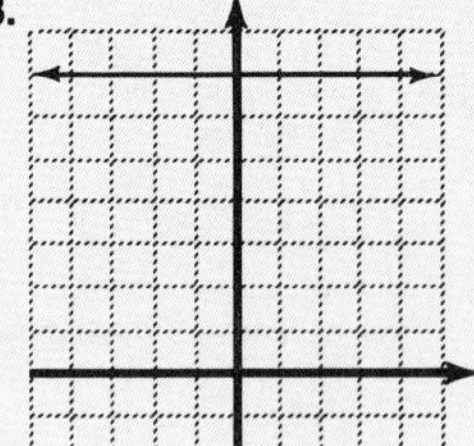

44.

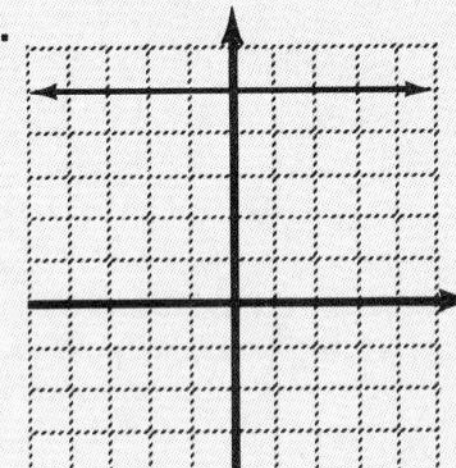

45.

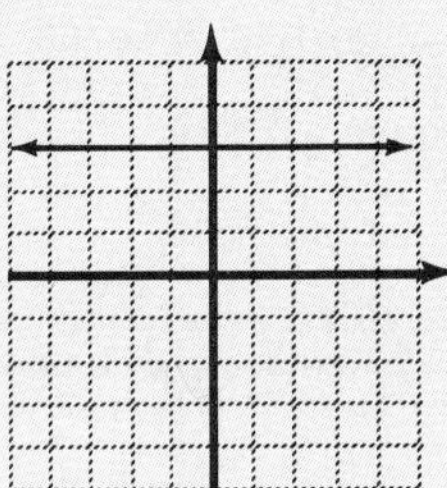

46.

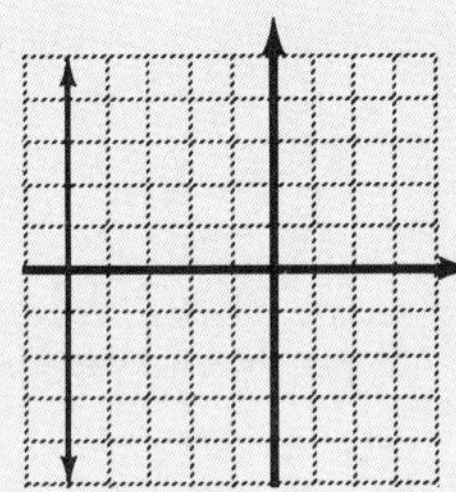

47.

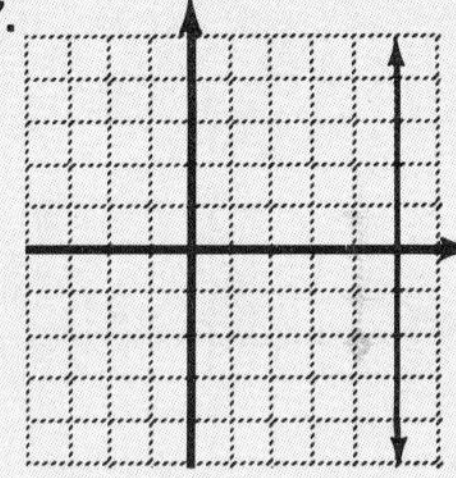

48.

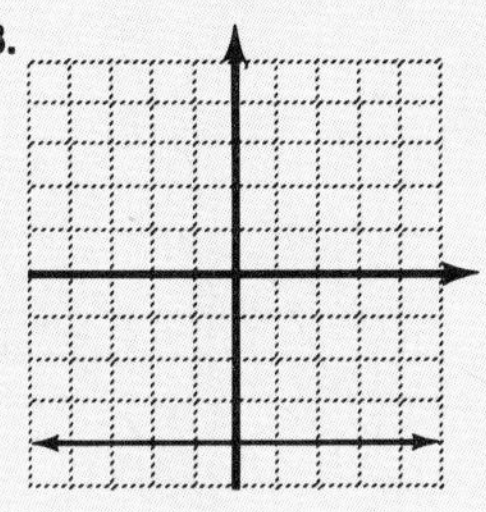

Page 136 EXERCISE SET 3-6

31.

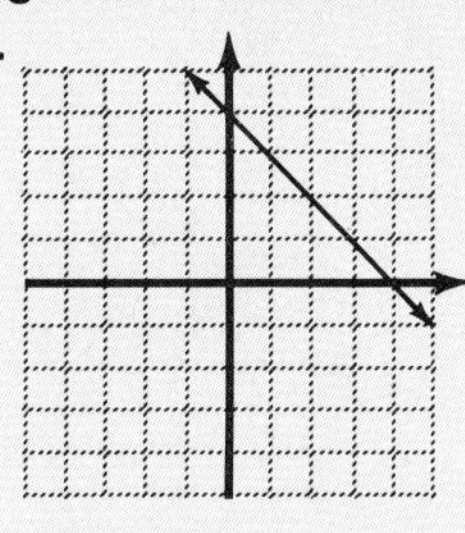

32.

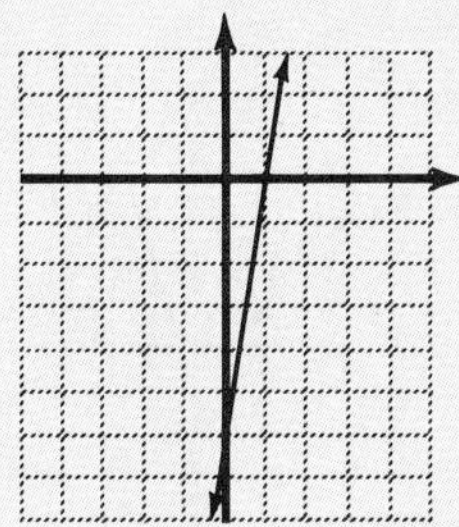

33.

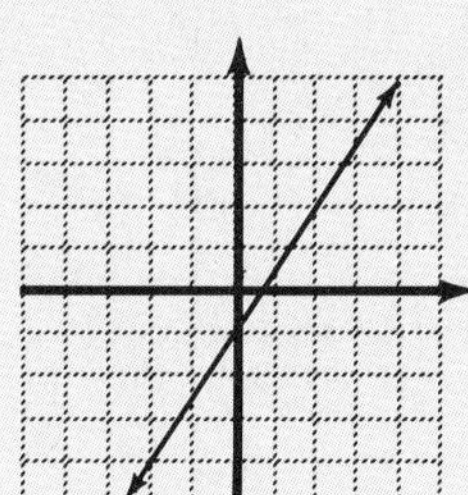

34.

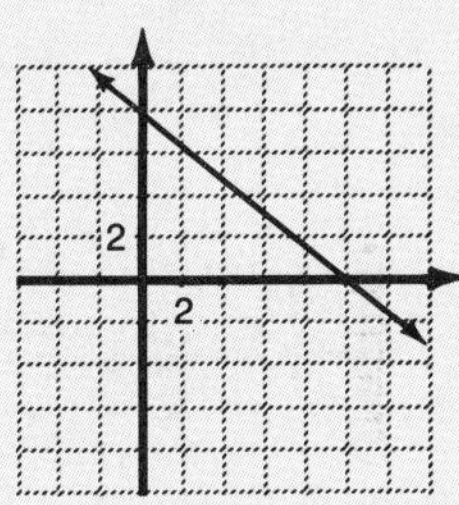

35.

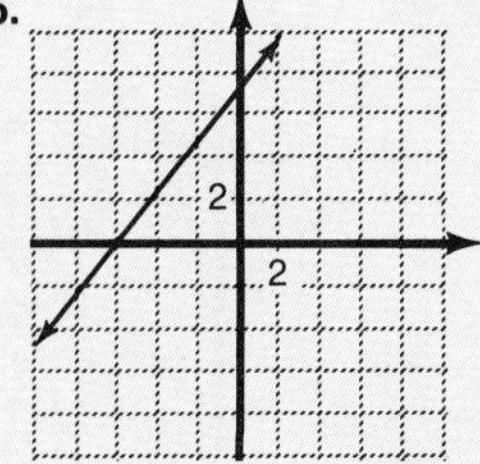

36.

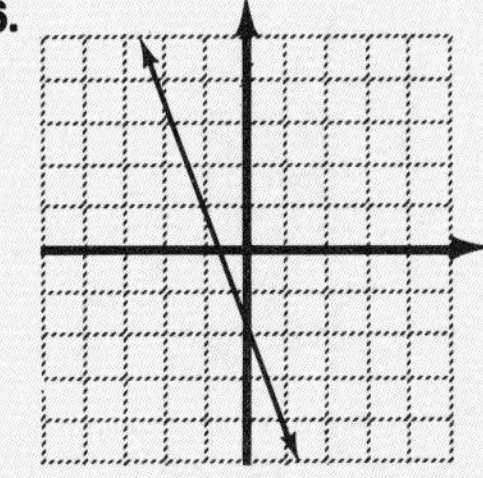

58. $\frac{x}{a} + \frac{y}{b} = 1$; $bx + ay = ab$, multiplying both sides by ab; $y = -\frac{b}{a}x + b$, solving for y; y-intercept is b; setting $y = 0$, $x = a$; x-intercept is a

62. $Ax + By + C = 0$; $By = -Ax - C$; $y = \frac{A}{B}x - \frac{C}{B}$; this is slope-intercept equation of the line, so $m = -\frac{A}{B}$, where $B \neq 0$.

Page 150 EXERCISE SET 3-9

1.

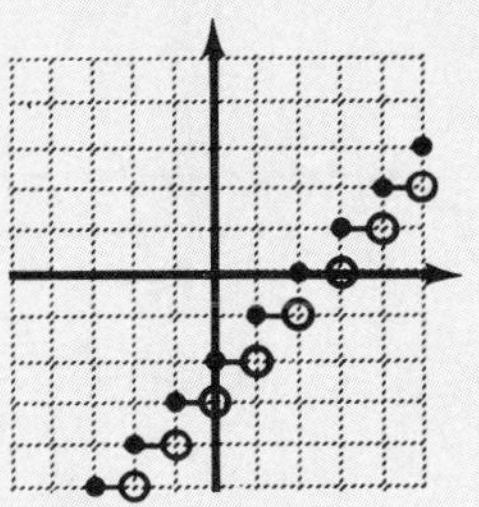

2–3.

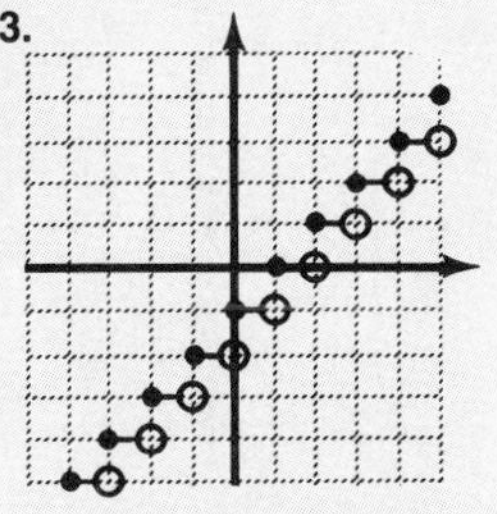

4.

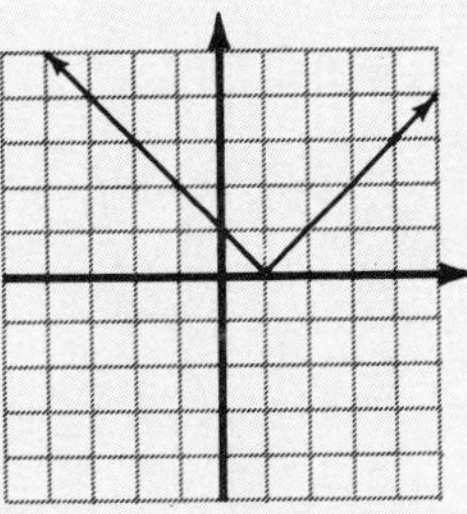

5.

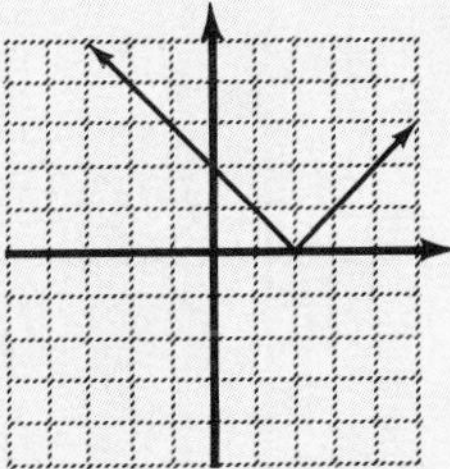

6.

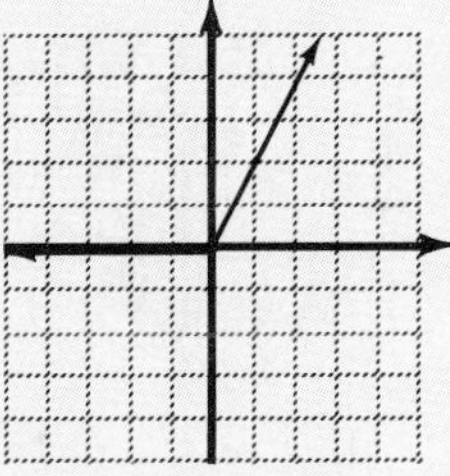

7.

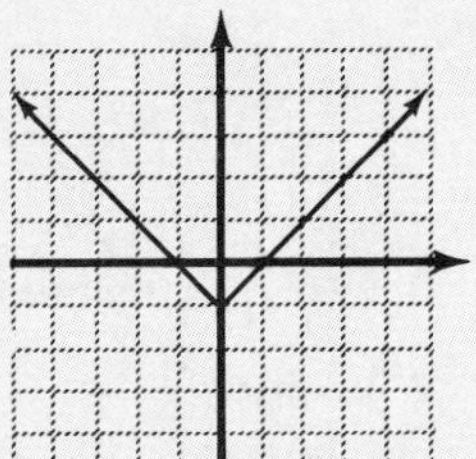

8.

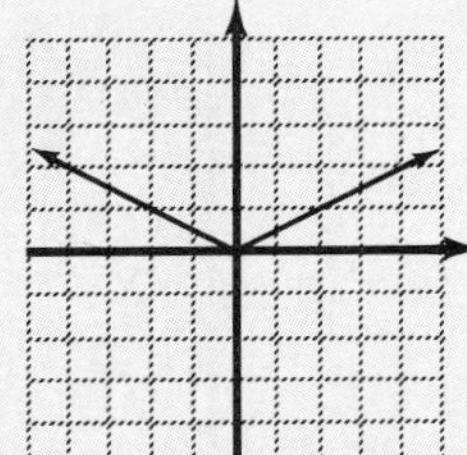

9.

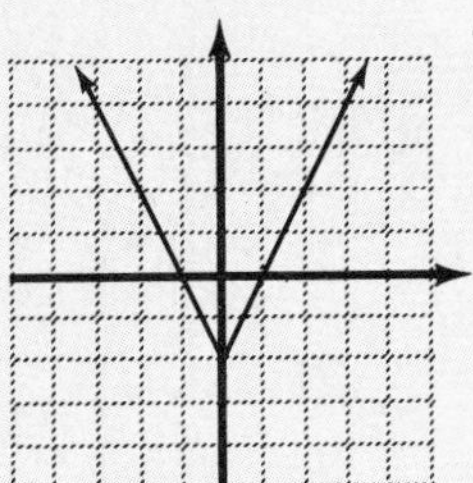

45.

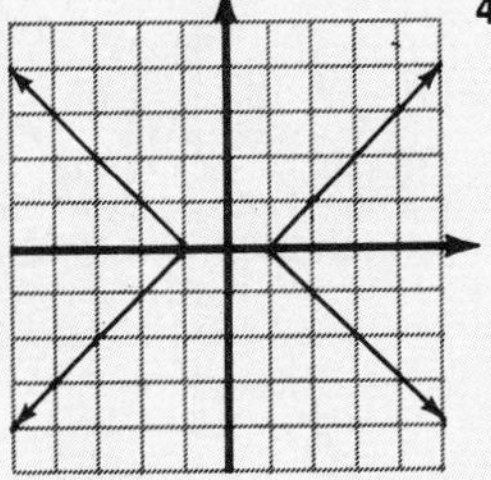

46.

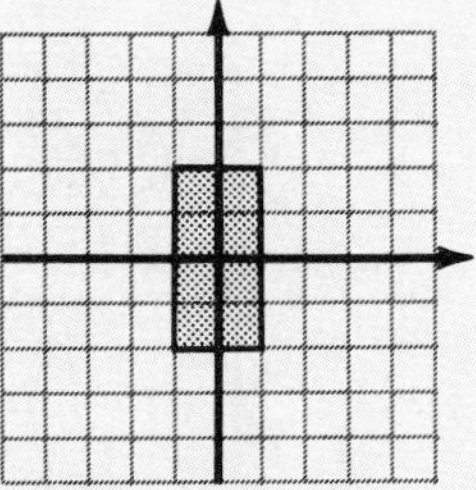

48.

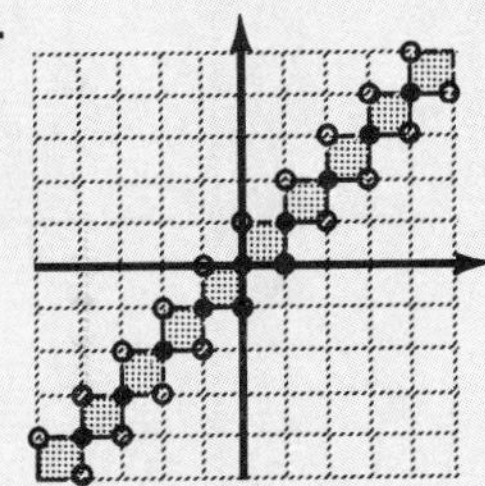

Page 157 CHAPTER 3 TEST

6.

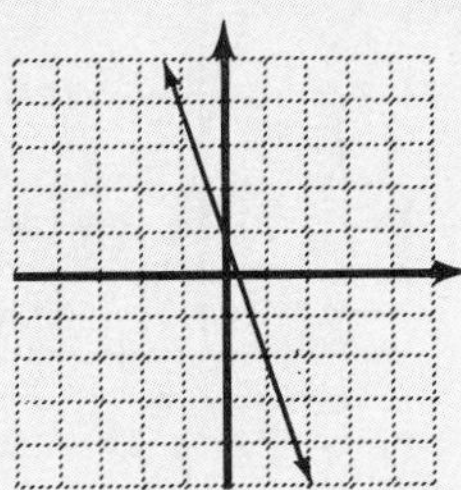

7.

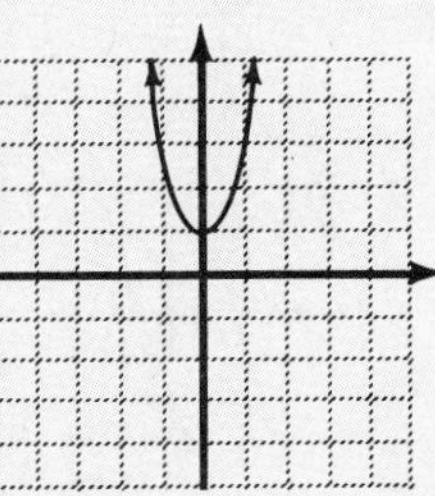

14.

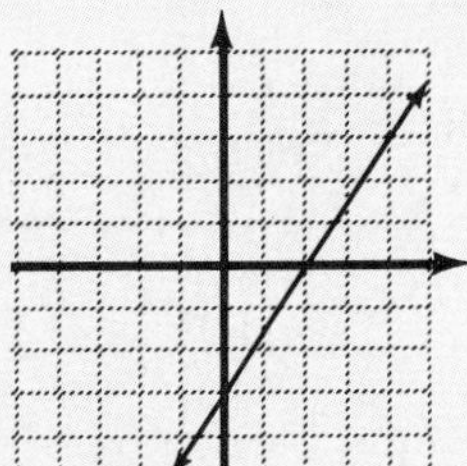

15.

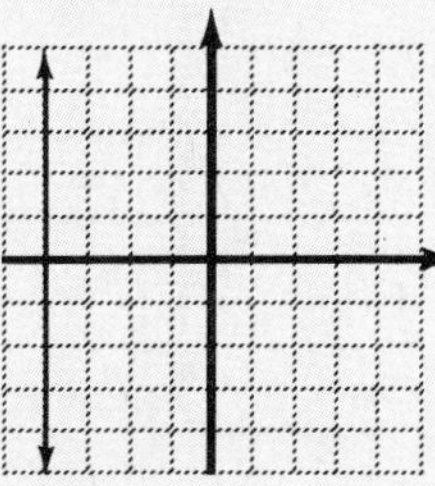

16.

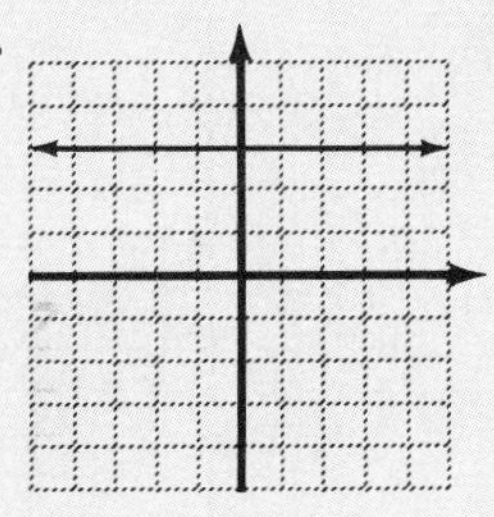

25.

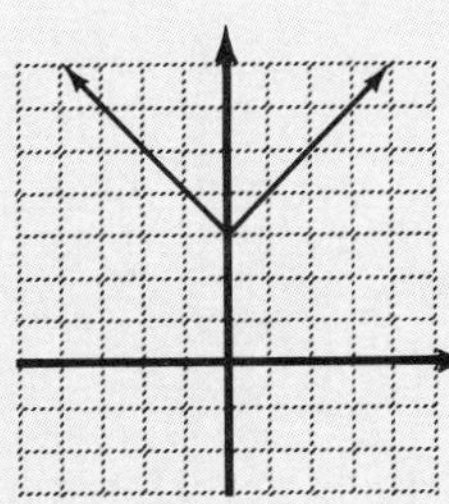

26.

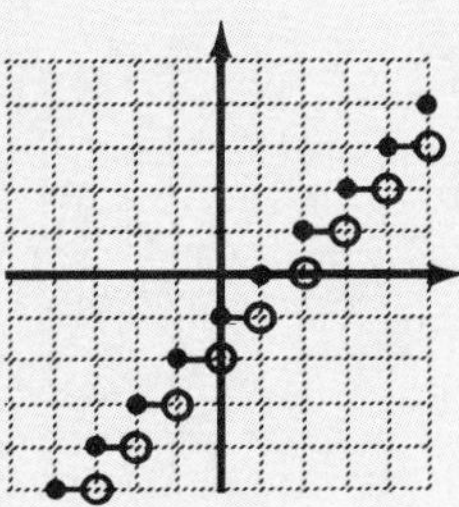

Page 158 READY FOR CHAPTER 4?

11.

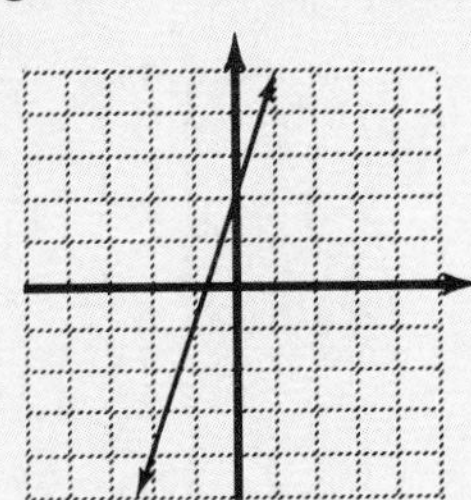

12.

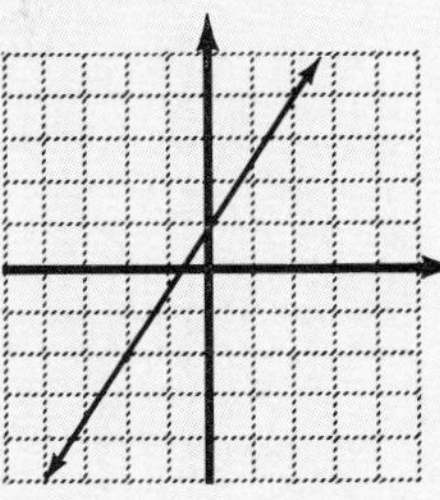

13.

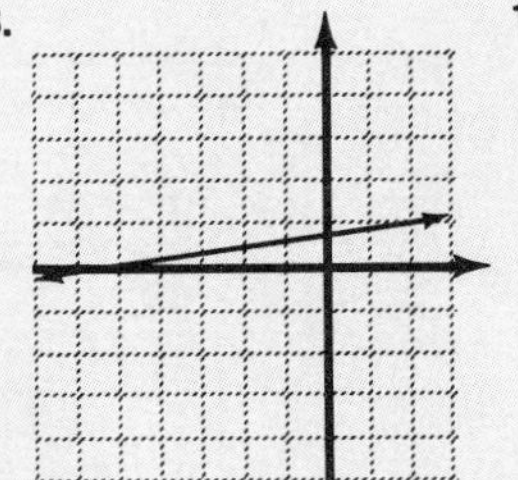

14.

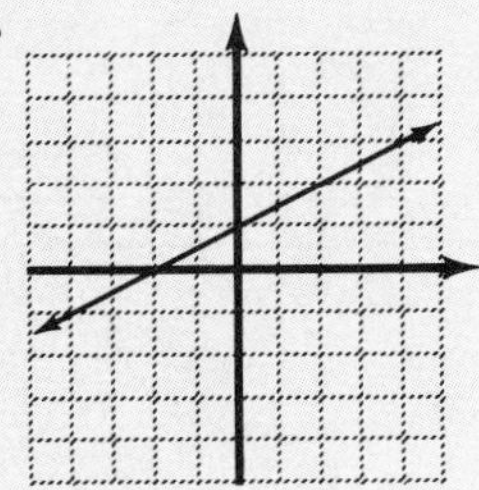

15.

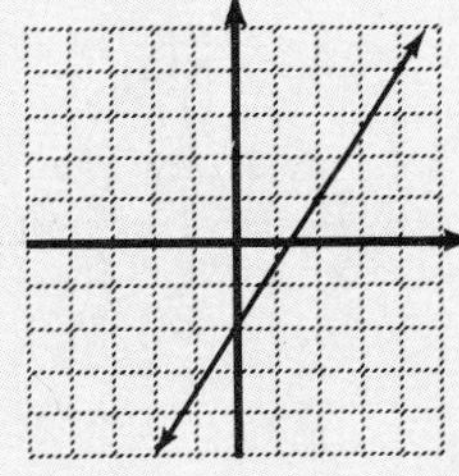

16.

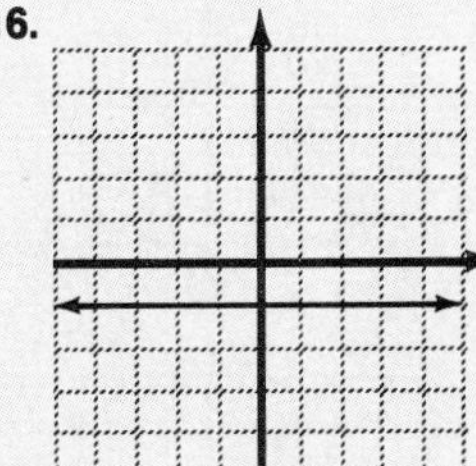

Page 161 EXERCISE SET 4-1

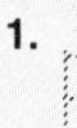

1.
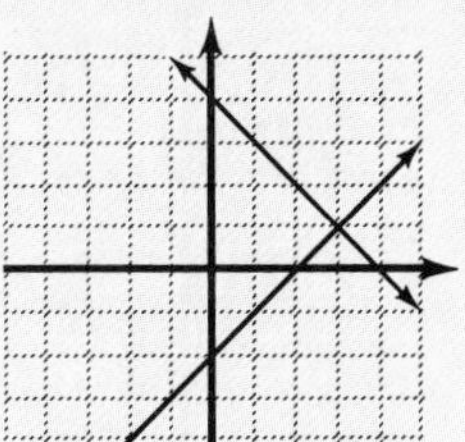

2.
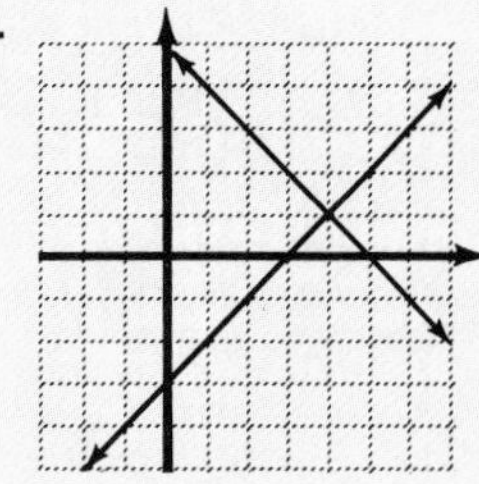

3.
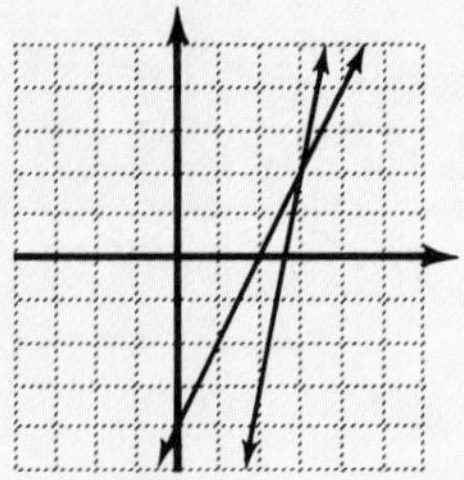

4.
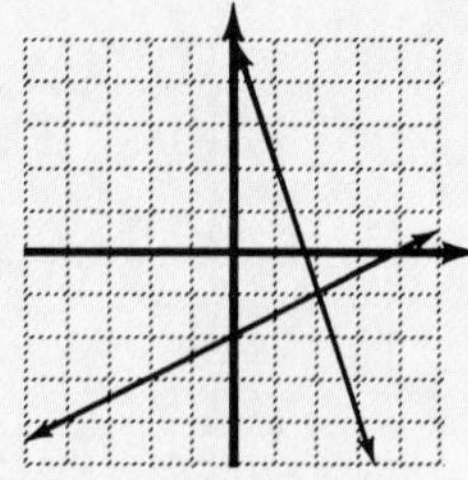

5.
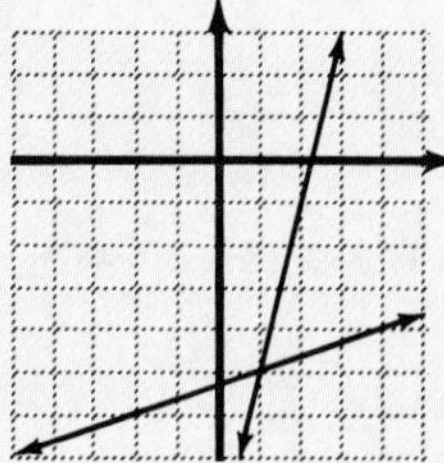

6.
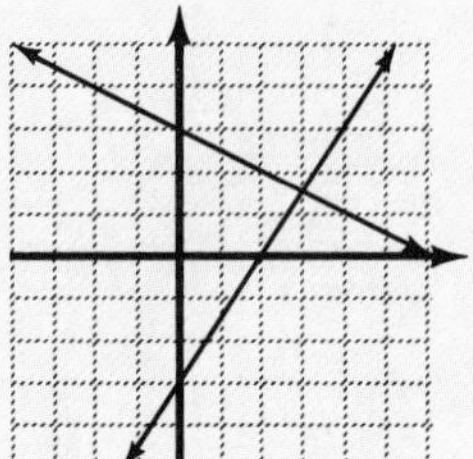

7.
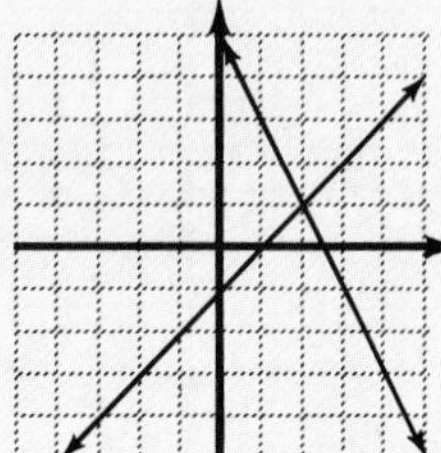

8.
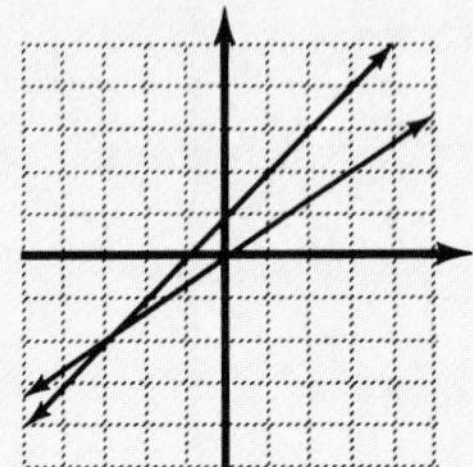

9.
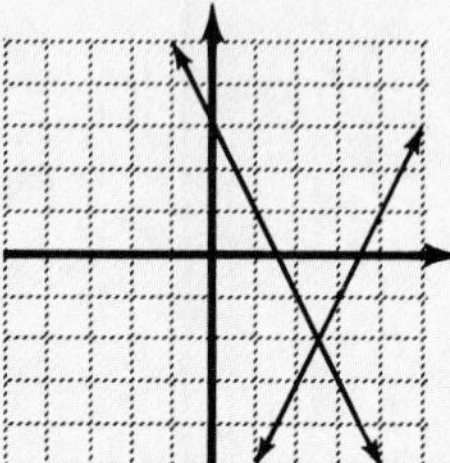

10.
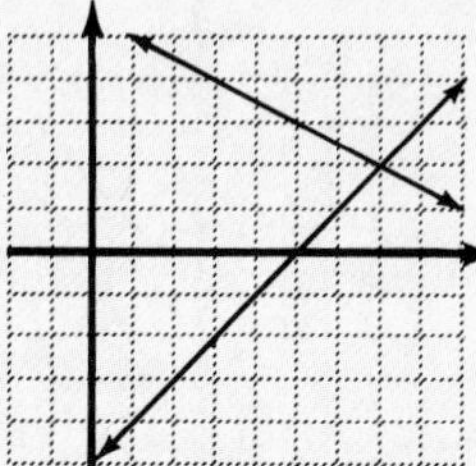

11.
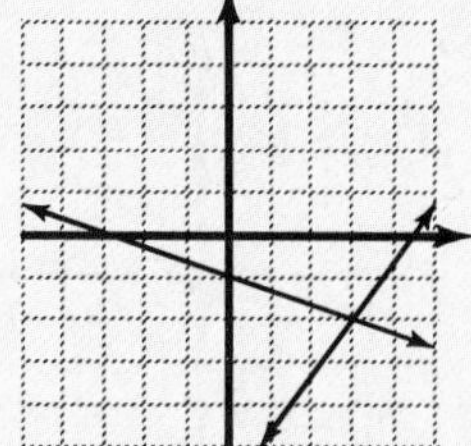

12.
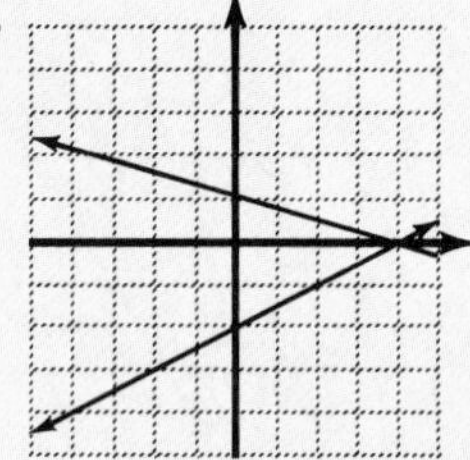

13.
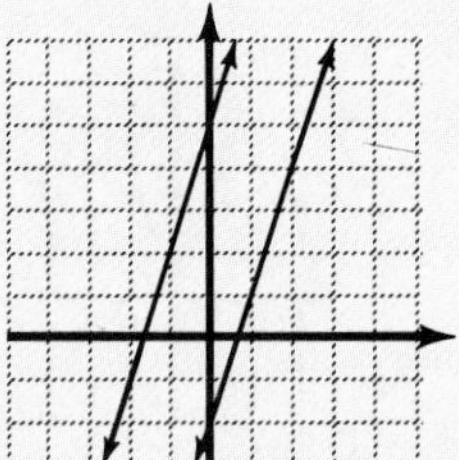

14.
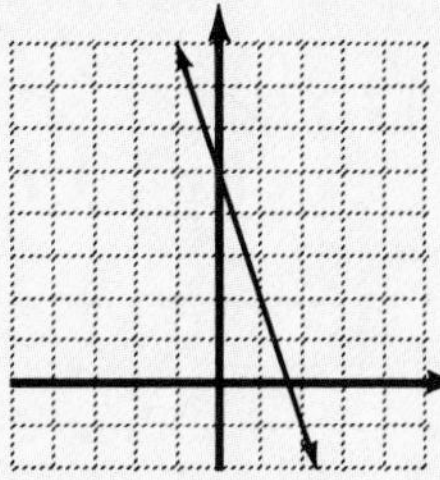

16.
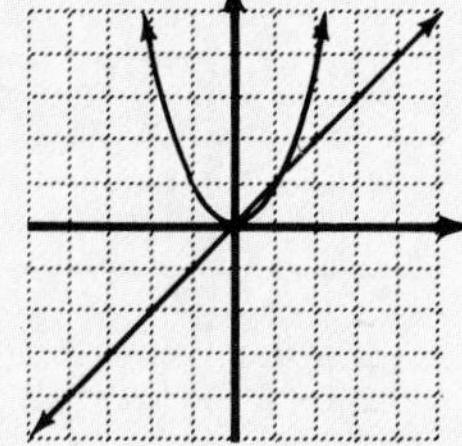

17.
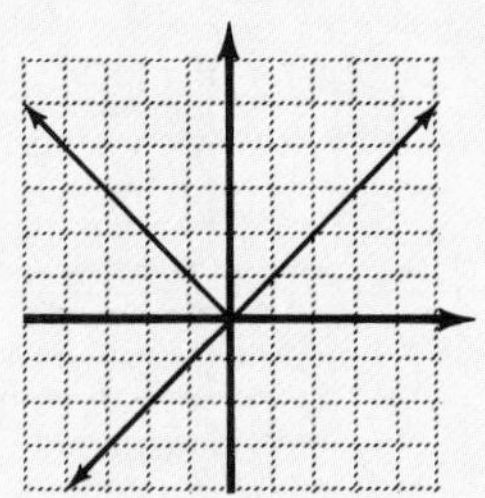

Page 192 EXERCISE SET 4-7

1.
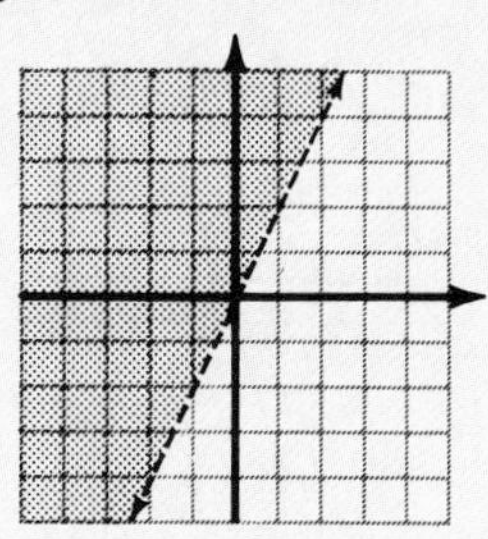

2.
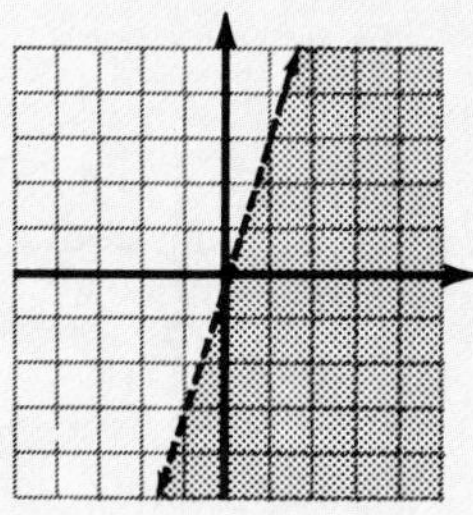

3.
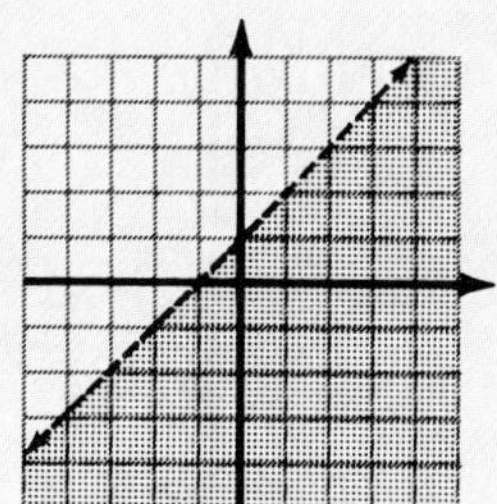

4.
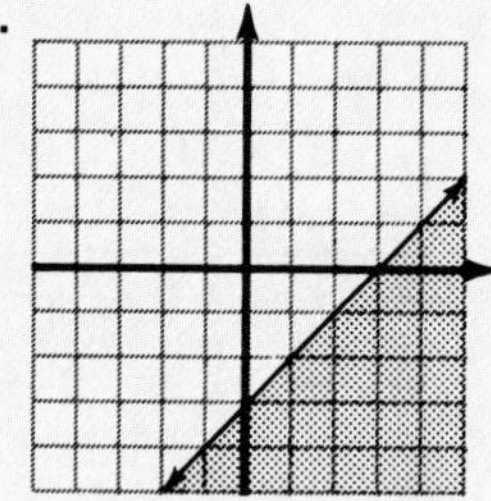

5.
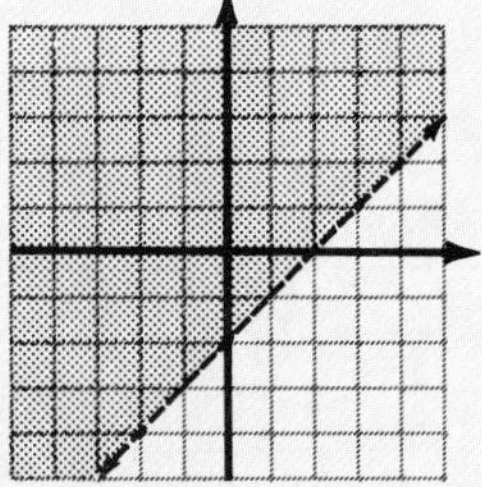

6.
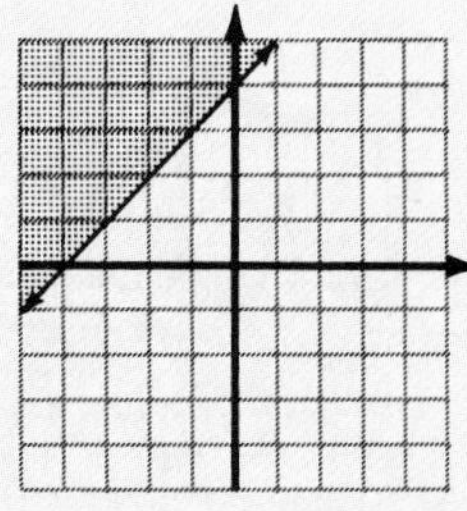

7.
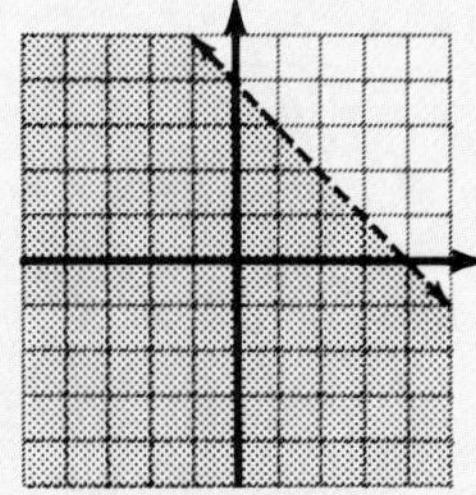

8.
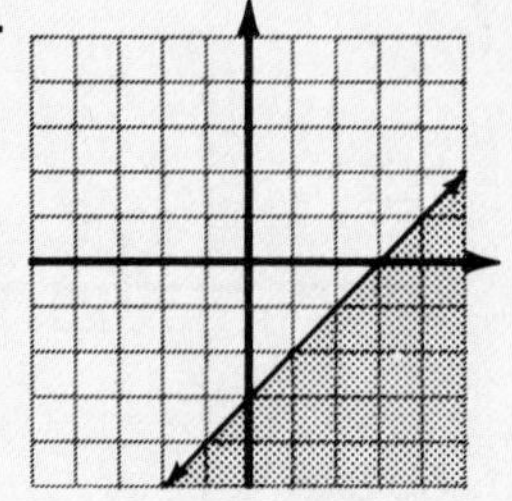

9.
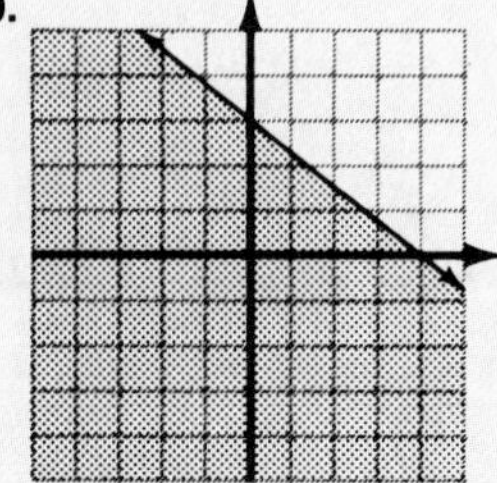

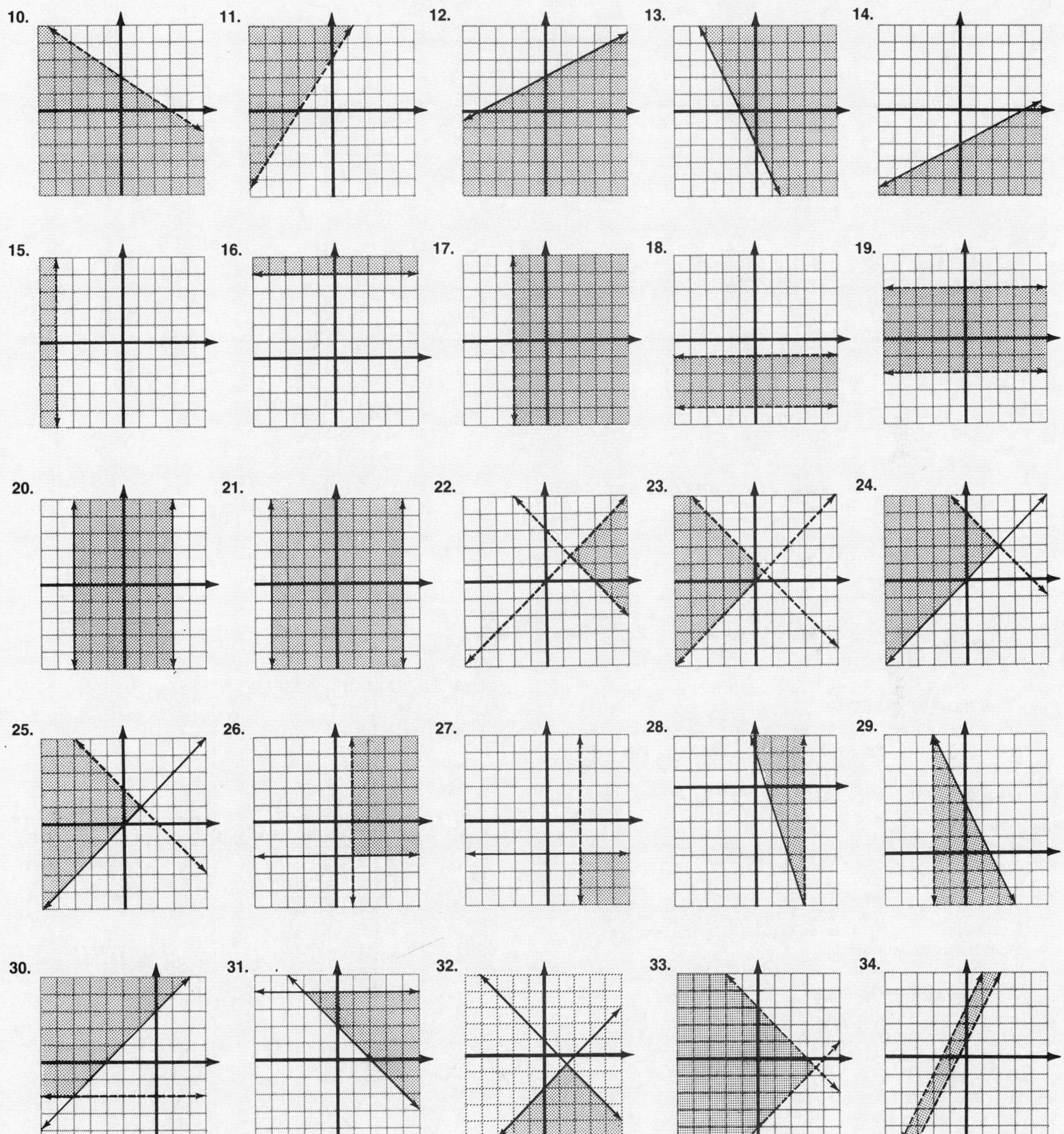
10.
11.
12.
13.
14.
15.
16.
17.
18.
19.
20.
21.
22.
23.
24.
25.
26.
27.
28.
29.
30.
31.
32.
33.
34.

35.

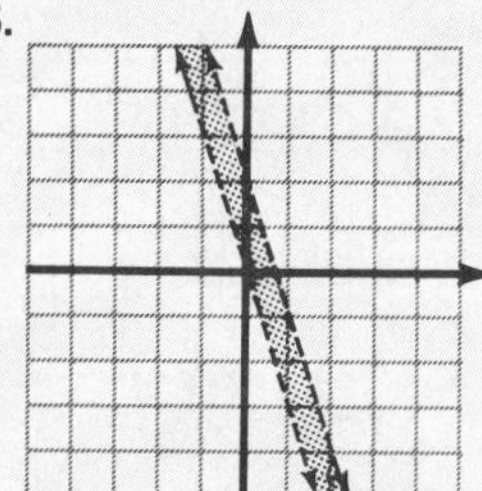

36.

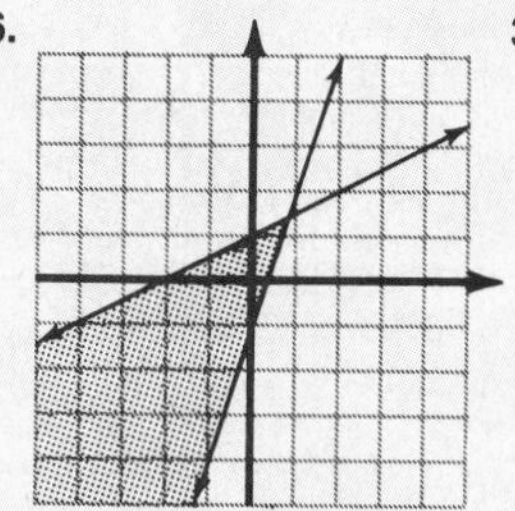

37.

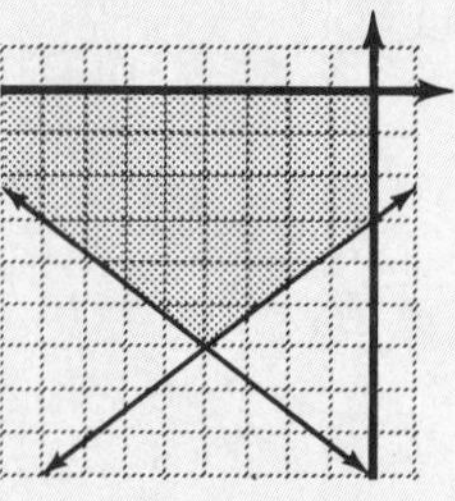

38.

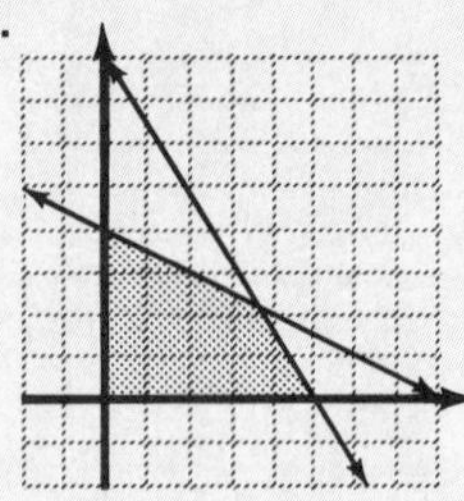

39.

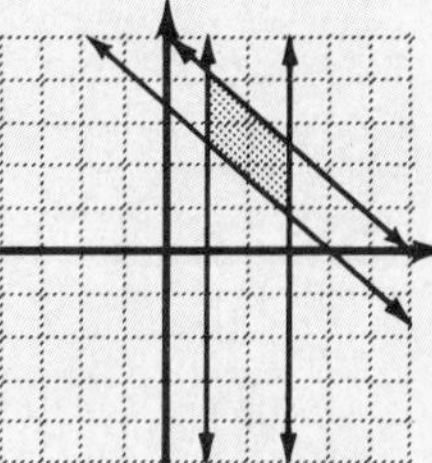

40.

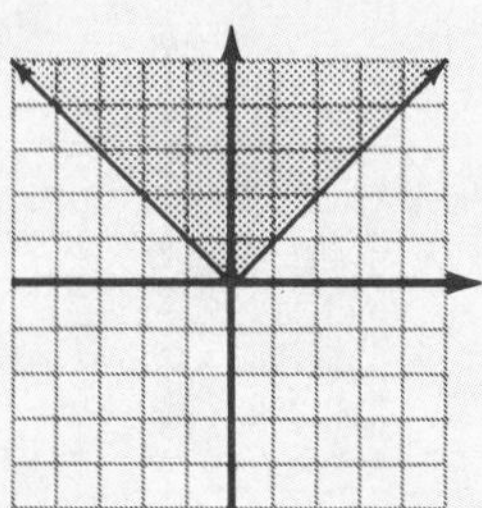

41.

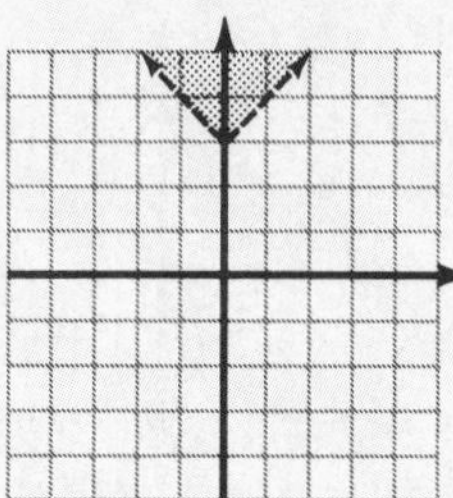

42.

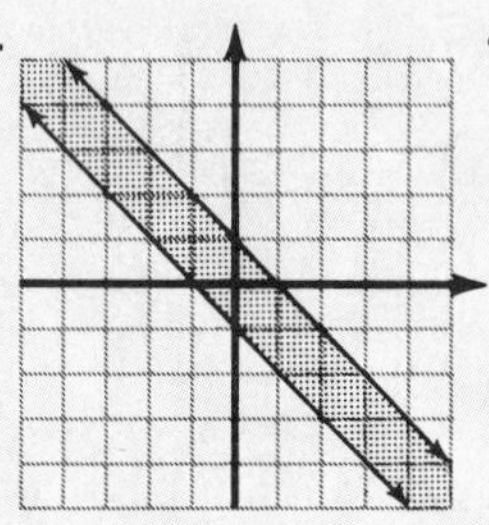

43.

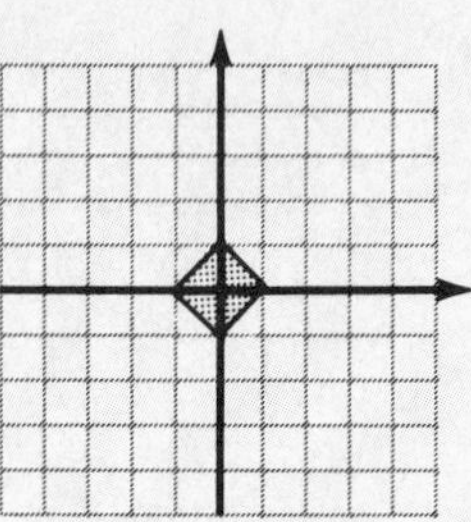

44.

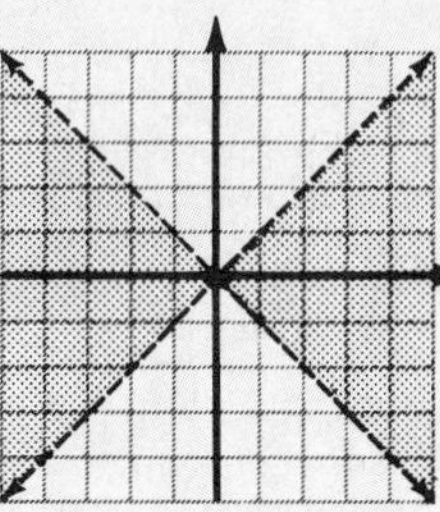

45.

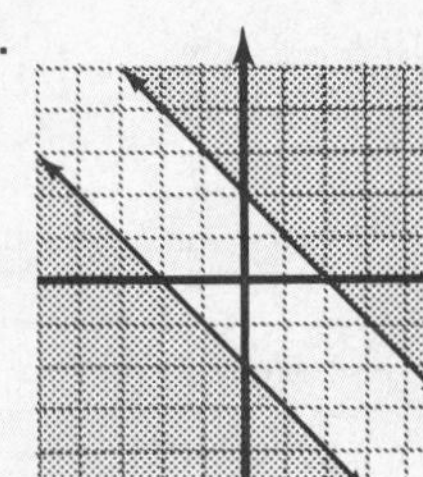

Page 223 EXERCISE SET 5-4

71. $(a^8 + 1)(a^4 + 1)(a^2 + 1)(a + 1)(a - 1)$
72. $(x^a - y)(x^a + y)$
73. $(y^{16} + 1)(y^8 + 1)(y^4 + 1)(y^2 + 1)(y + 1)(y - 1)$
74. $(x + a)(x + b)$
75. $\left(\frac{1}{2}p - \frac{2}{5}\right)^2$
76. $(bx + a)(dx + c)$
77. $x(x + 15)(x - 15)$
78. $\frac{1}{3}\left(\frac{2}{3}r + \frac{1}{2}s\right)^2$
79. $(81x^4 + 16y^8)(9x^2 + 4y^4)(3x + 2y^2)(3x - 2y^2)$
80. $x^{a-b}(4x^{2b} + 7)$
81. $y^{a+b}(7y^a - 5 + 3y^b)$

Page 228 EXERCISE SET 5-5

94. $3(x - 11)(x + 15)$ 95. $(x^{2a} + y^b)(x^{4a} - x^{2a}y^b + y^{2b})$
96. $4y(y - 12)^2$ 97. $3x(y - 25)^2$ 98. $(ax - by)(a^2x^2 + abxy + b^2y^2)$
99. $12(x - 3y)^2$ 100. $15t(t - 7)(t + 3)$ 101. $6x(x + 9)(x + 4)$
102. $(x^a + 8)(x^a - 3)$ 103. $\left(\frac{2}{3}x + \frac{1}{4}y\right)\left(\frac{4}{9}x^2 - \frac{1}{6}xy + \frac{1}{16}y^2\right)$
104. $(2x^a - 3)(2x^a + 1)$
105. $\frac{1}{2}\left(\frac{1}{2}x^a + y^{2a}z^{3b}\right)\left(\frac{1}{4}x^{2a} - \frac{1}{2}x^a y^{2a}z^{3b} + y^{4a}z^{6b}\right)$
106. $(4x + 1)(2x - 3)$; if we include negative factors
$(-4x - 1)(-2x + 3) = -1(4x + 1)(-2x + 3)$
$= (-1)^2(4x + 1)(2x - 3) = (4x + 1)(2x - 3)$. The negative factorization is equivalent.

Page 231 EXERCISE SET 5-6

48. $x^6 - y^6 = (x^2)^3 - (y^2)^3 = (x^2 - y^2)(x^4 + x^2y^2 + y^4)$
But $(x^2 + xy + y^2)(x^2 - xy + y^2) = [(x^2 + y^2) + xy][(x^2 + y^2) - xy]$
$= x^4 + 2x^2y^2 + y^4 - x^2y^2 = x^4 + x^2y^2 + y^4$
So $x^6 - y^6 = (x^2 - y^2)(x^2 + xy + y^2)(x^2 - xy + y^2)$
49. $(x - 1)^3(x^2 + 1)(x + 1)$ 50. $y(y - 1)^2(y - 2)$
51. $(3x^{2s} + 4y^t)(9x^{4s} - 12x^{2s}y^t + 16y^{2t})$
52. $c(c^w + 1)^2$ 53. $6(2x^a - 1)(2x^a + 1)$

Page 325 EXERCISE SET 7-8

1.

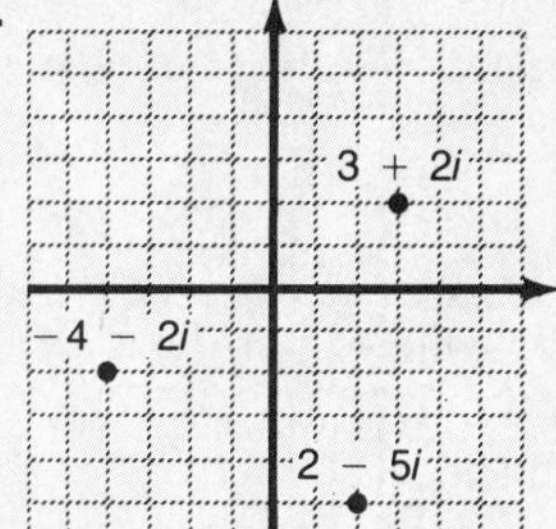

2.

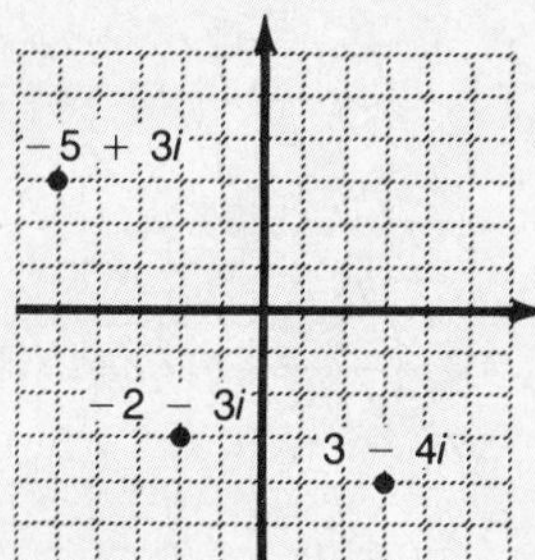

3.

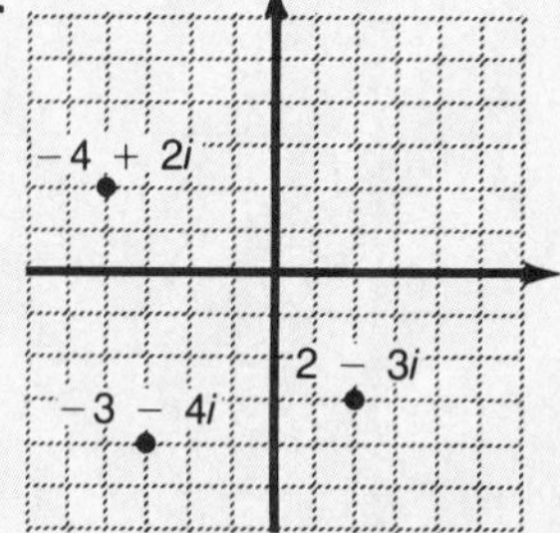

4.

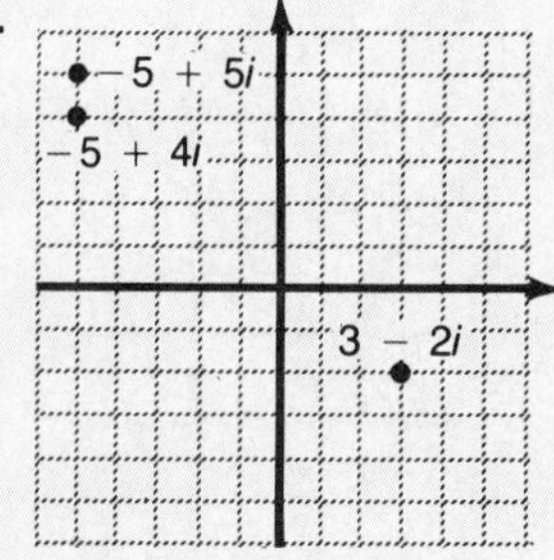

5.

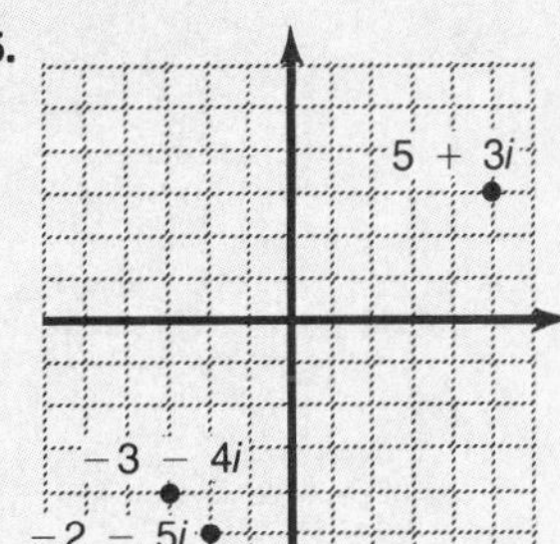

6.

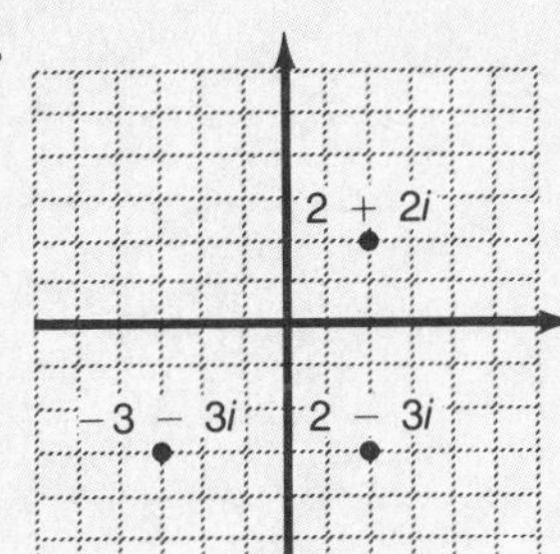

19. a.

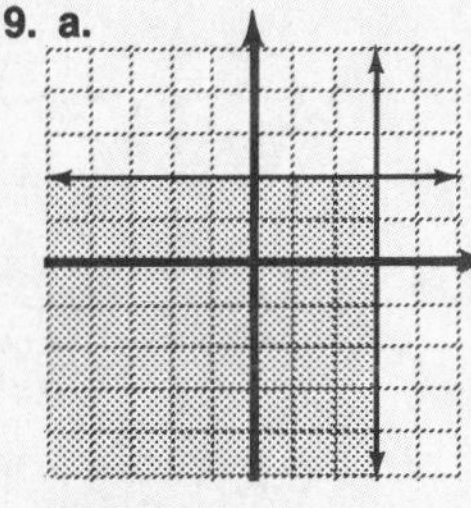

19. b.

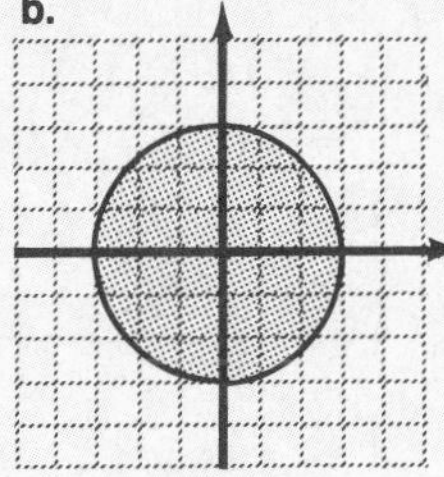

19. c.

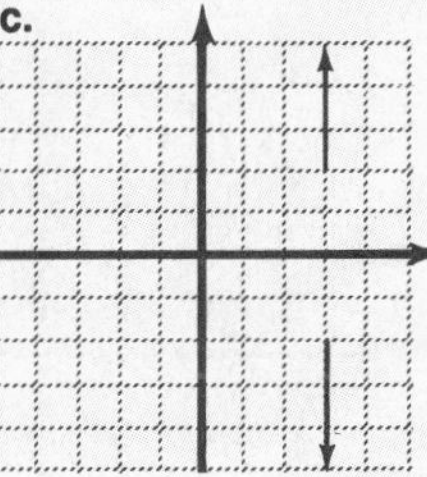

Page 393
EXERCISE SET 9-2

5.

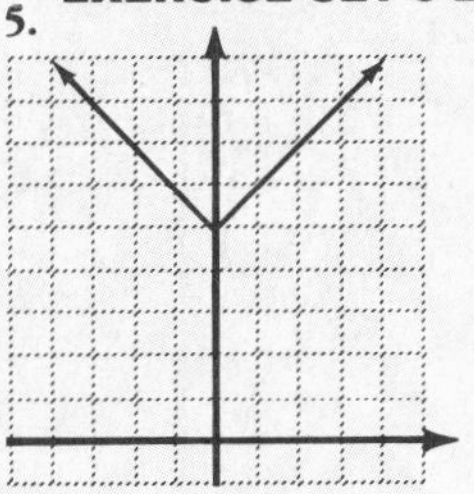

6.

7.

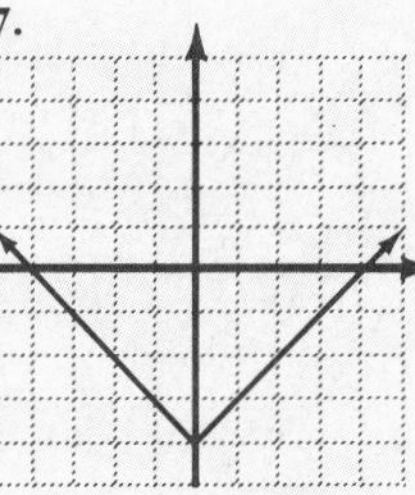

8.

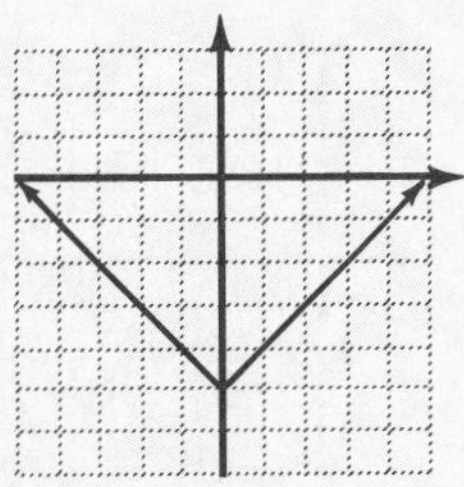

9.

10.

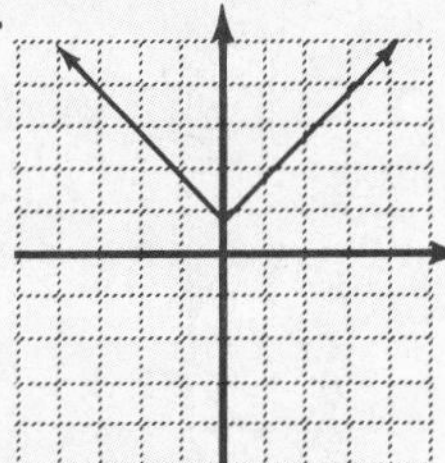

11.

12.

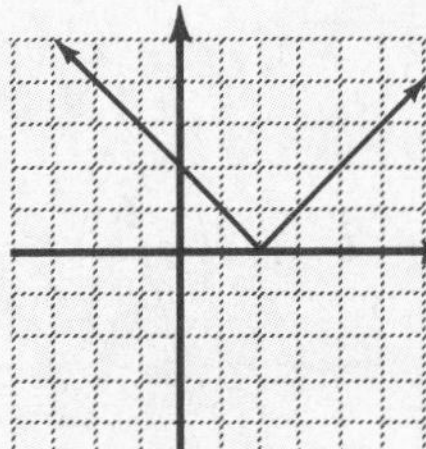

13.

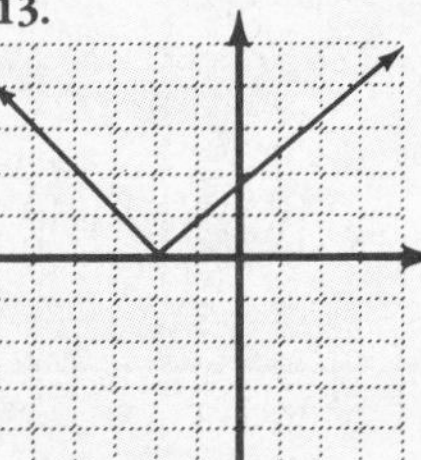

14.

15.

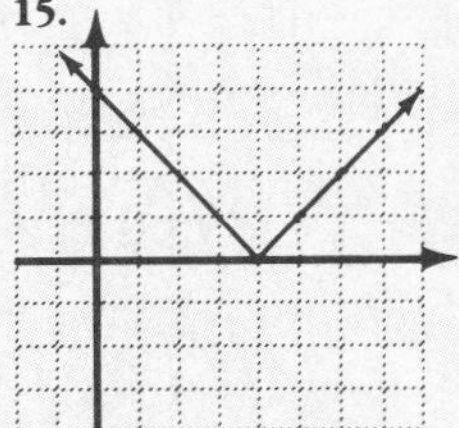

16.

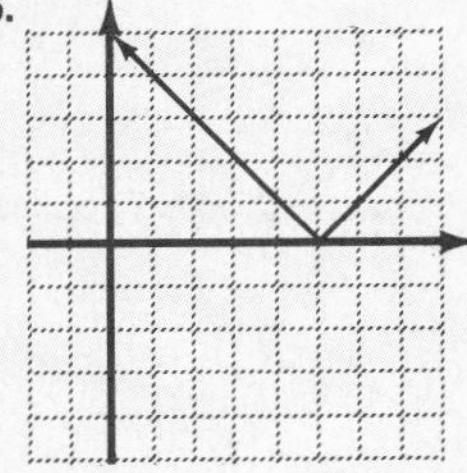

Page 357 EXERCISE SET 8-4

69. The solutions of $ax^2 + bx + c = 0$ can be written as

$$-\frac{b}{2a} + \frac{\sqrt{b^2 - 4ac}}{2a} \text{ or } -\frac{b}{2a} - \frac{\sqrt{b^2 - 4ac}}{2a}$$

The solutions of $ax^2 - bx + c = 0$ are

$$\frac{b \pm \sqrt{(-b)^2 - 4ac}}{2a}, \text{ or } \frac{b}{2a} \pm \frac{\sqrt{b^2 - 4ac}}{2a}$$

$$\left(\frac{b}{2a} - \frac{\sqrt{b^2 - 4ac}}{2a}\right) + \left(-\frac{b}{2a} + \frac{\sqrt{b^2 - 4ac}}{2a}\right) = 0$$

$$\left(\frac{b}{2a} + \frac{\sqrt{b^2 - 4ac}}{2a}\right) + \left(-\frac{b}{2a} - \frac{\sqrt{b^2 - 4ac}}{2a}\right) = 0$$

Thus the solutions are additive inverses

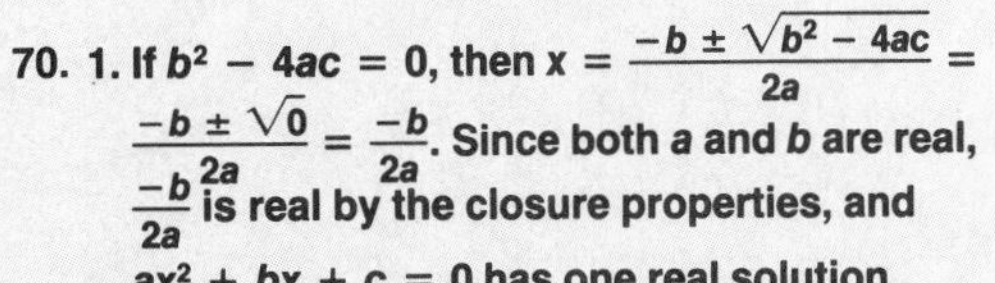

70. 1. If $b^2 - 4ac = 0$, then $x = \frac{-b \pm \sqrt{b^2 - 4ac}}{2a} = \frac{-b \pm \sqrt{0}}{2a} = \frac{-b}{2a}$. Since both a and b are real, $\frac{-b}{2a}$ is real by the closure properties, and $ax^2 + bx + c = 0$ has one real solution.

2. If a, b, and c are real and $b^2 - 4ac > 0$, then $\sqrt{b^2 - 4ac}$ represents a positive real number (let $\sqrt{b^2 - 4ac} = d$). Thus $x = \frac{-b \pm \sqrt{b^2 - 4ac}}{2a} = \frac{-b \pm d}{2a}$. By the closure properties in the reals, both $\frac{-b + d}{2a}$ and $\frac{-b - d}{2a}$ are real. Since $\frac{-b + d}{2a} \neq \frac{-b - d}{2a}$, there exist two real solutions.

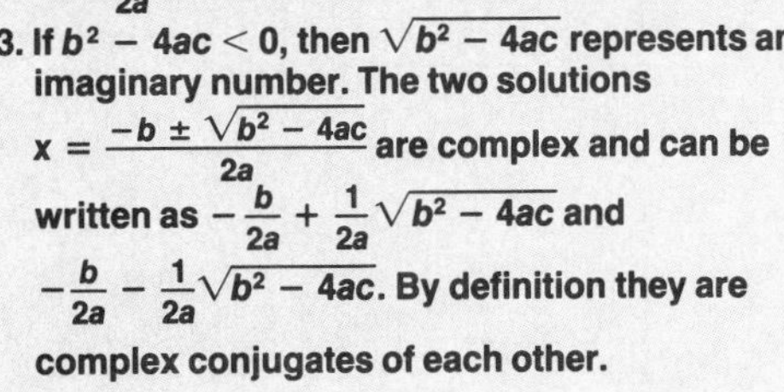

3. If $b^2 - 4ac < 0$, then $\sqrt{b^2 - 4ac}$ represents an imaginary number. The two solutions $x = \frac{-b \pm \sqrt{b^2 - 4ac}}{2a}$ are complex and can be written as $-\frac{b}{2a} + \frac{1}{2a}\sqrt{b^2 - 4ac}$ and $-\frac{b}{2a} - \frac{1}{2a}\sqrt{b^2 - 4ac}$. By definition they are complex conjugates of each other.

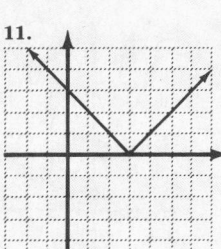

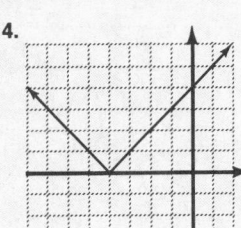

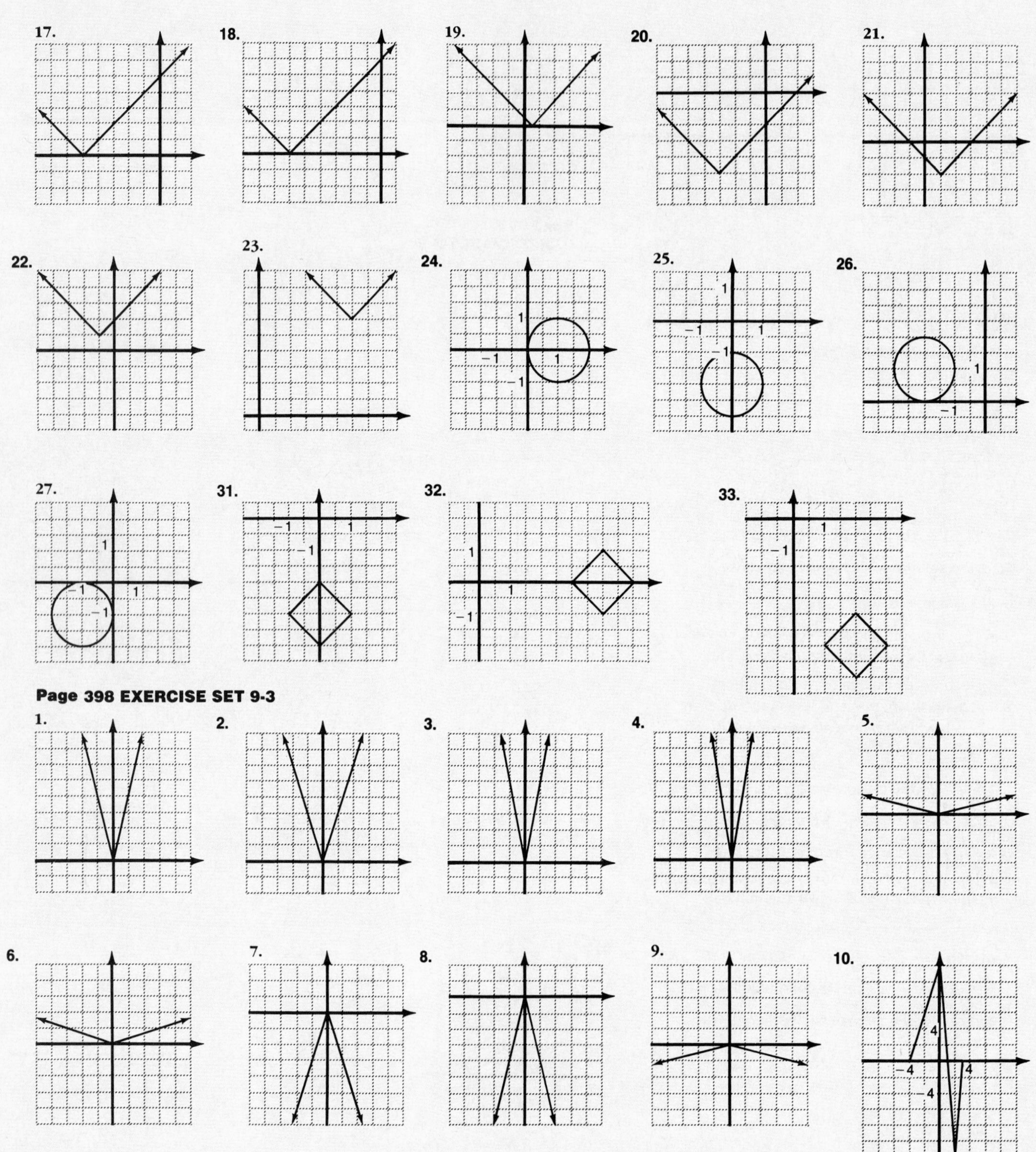
17.
18.
19.
20.
21.
22.
23.
24.
25.
26.
27.
31.
32.
33.
Page 398 EXERCISE SET 9-3
1.
2.
3.
4.
5.
6.
7.
8.
9.
10.

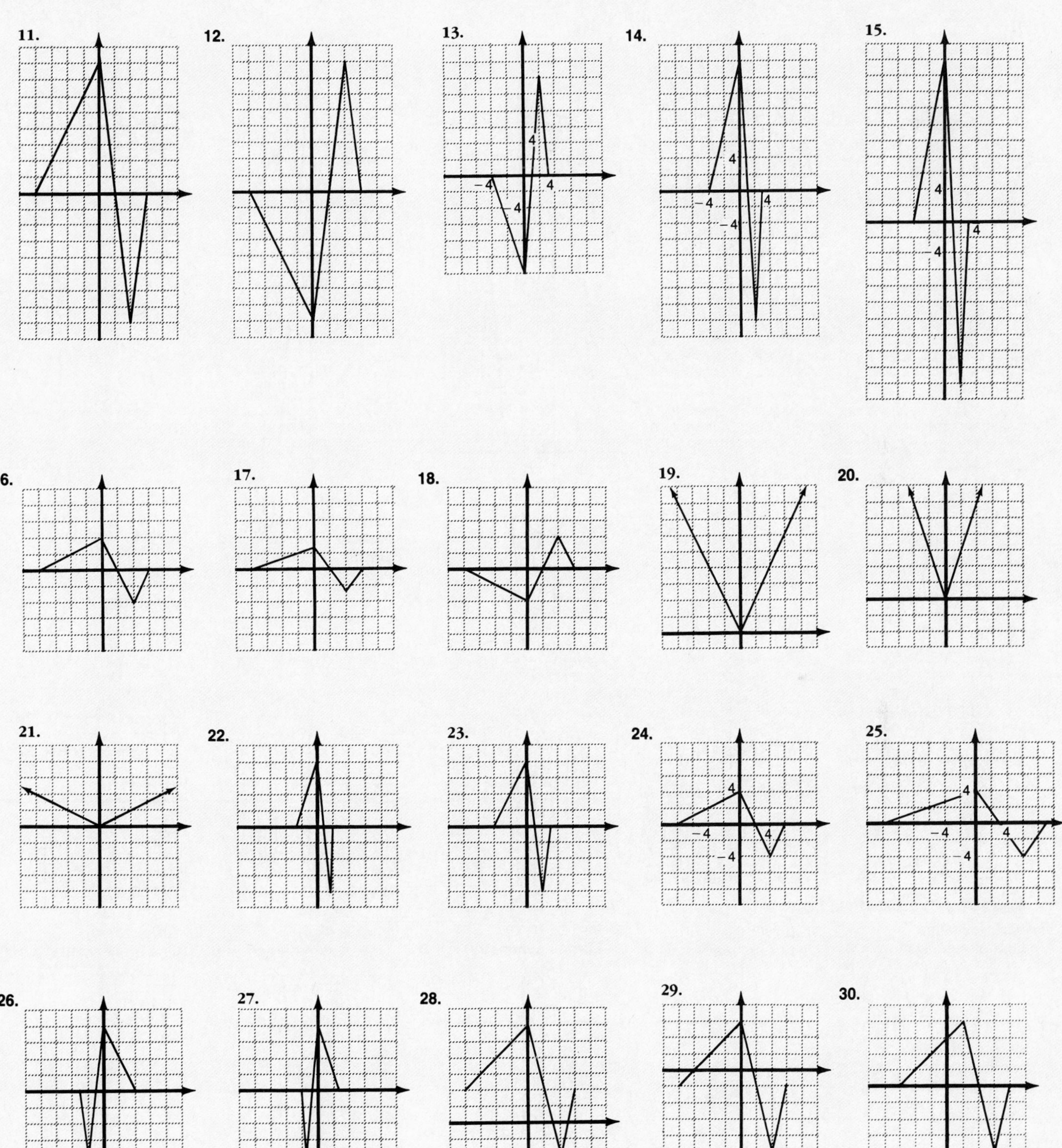
11.
12.
13.
4
−4
−4
4
14.
4
−4
4
−4
15.
4
−4
4
16.
17.
18.
19.
20.
21.
22.
23.
24.
4
−4
4
−4
25.
4
−4
4
−4
26.
27.
28.
29.
30.

31.

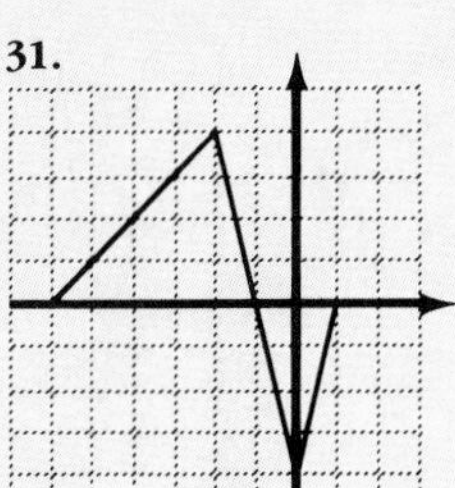

32.

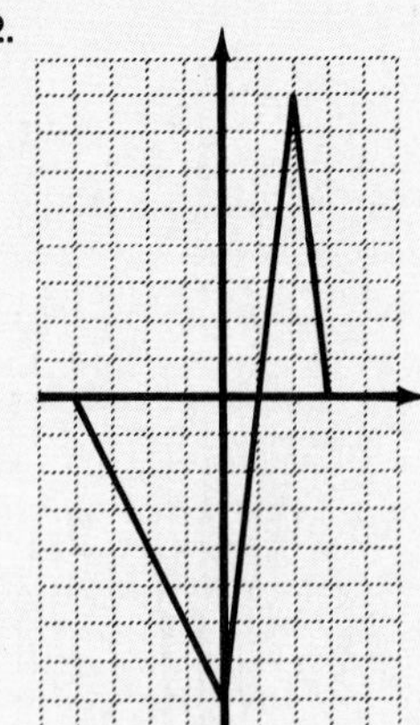

33.

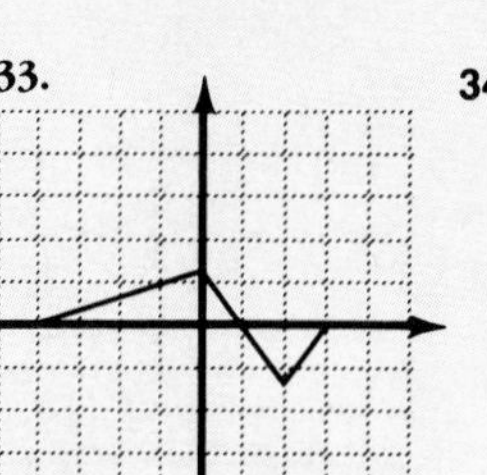

34.

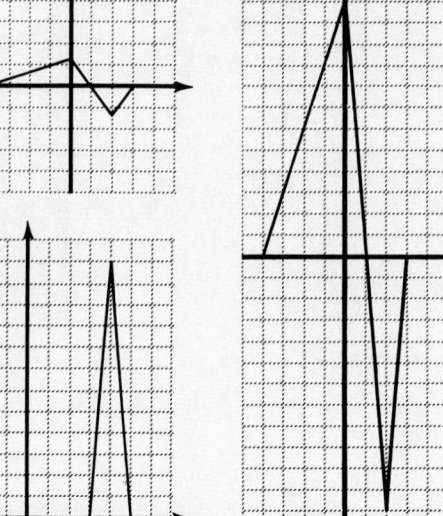

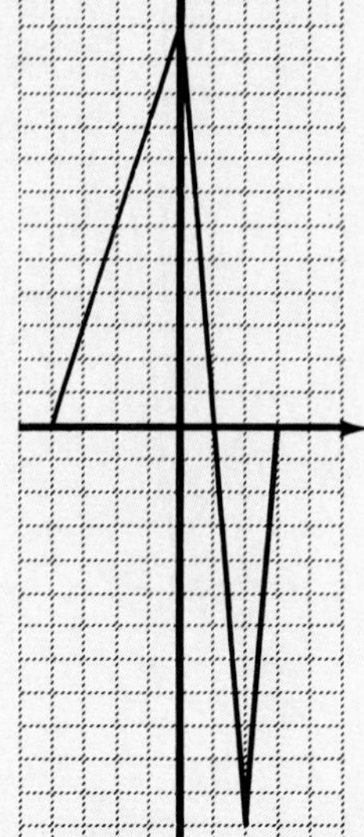

35.

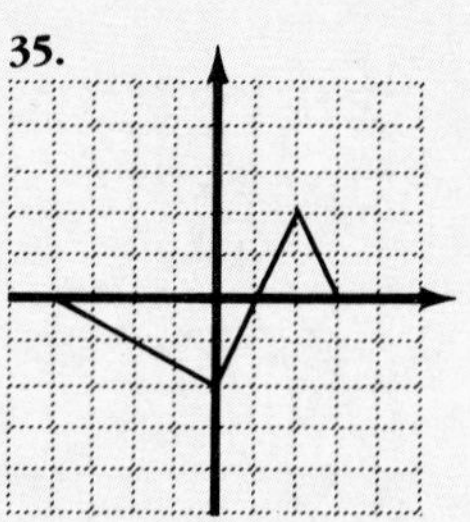

36.

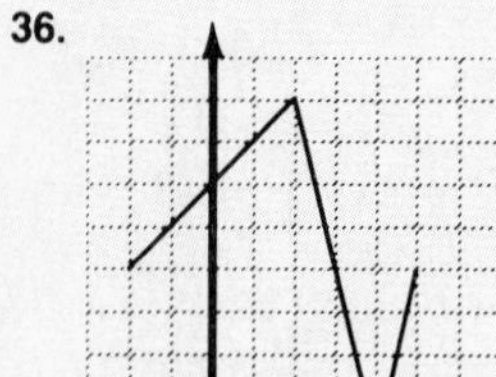

37.

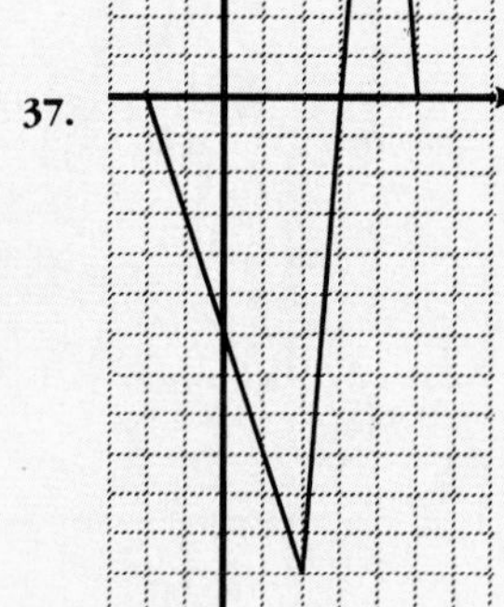

38. The graph is stretched horizontally, shrunk vertically and reflected across both the x-axis and y-axis.

39.

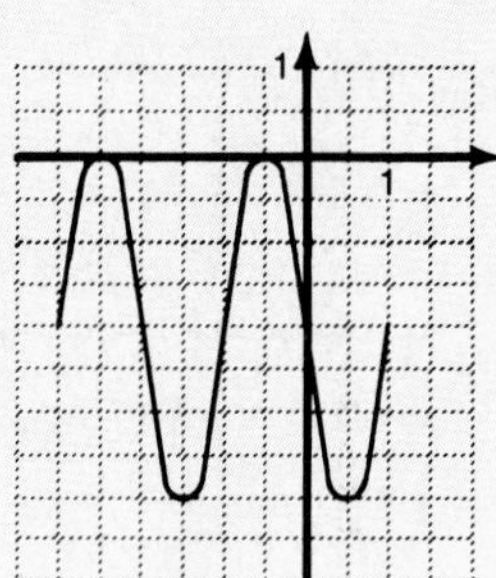

40.

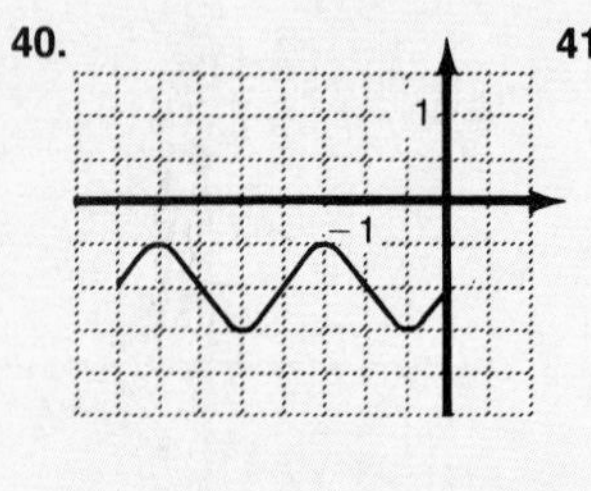

41.

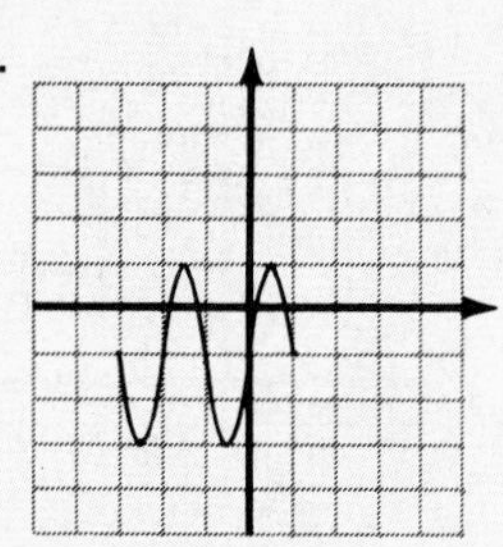

42.

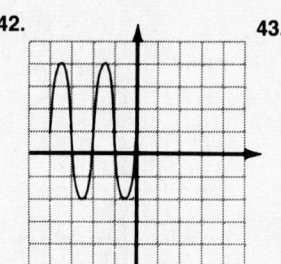

43.

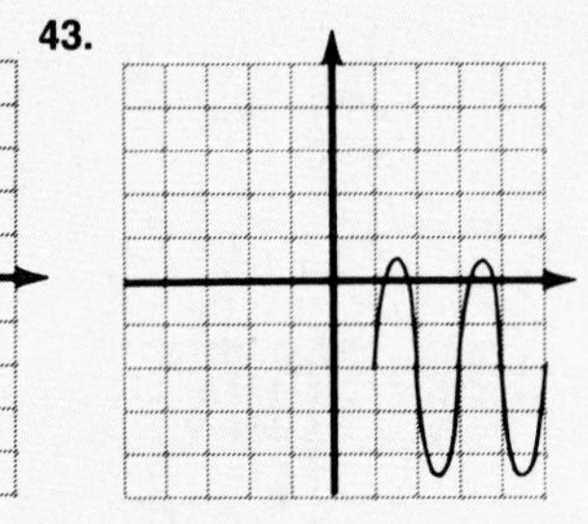

44.

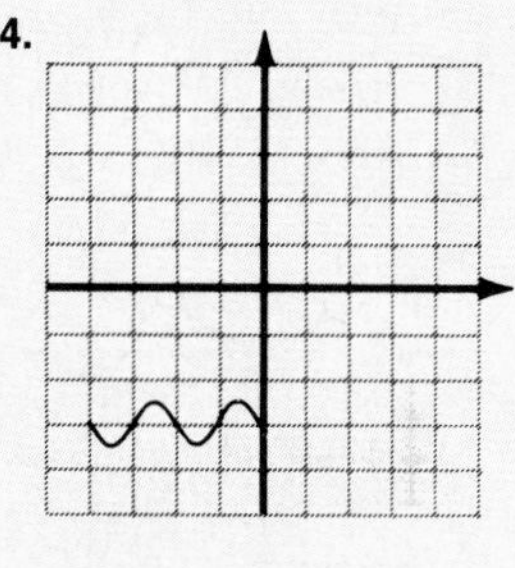

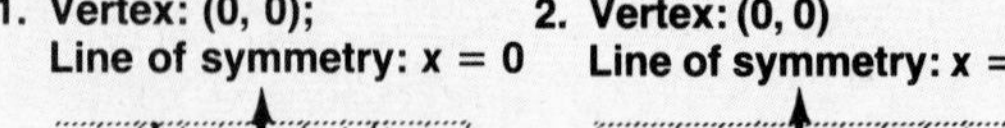

Page 402 EXERCISE SET 9-4

1. Vertex: (0, 0); Line of symmetry: $x = 0$

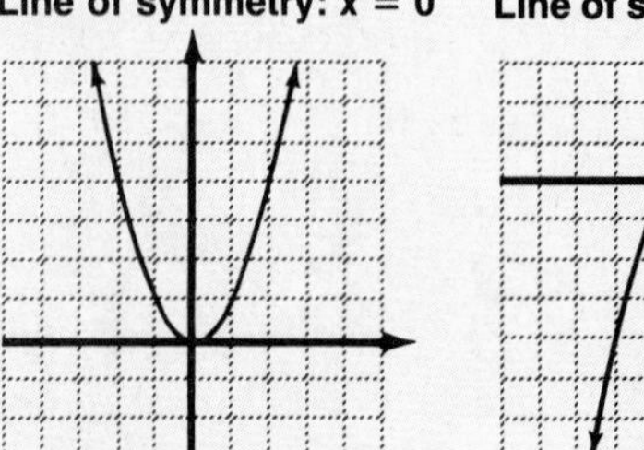

2. Vertex: (0, 0) Line of symmetry: $x = 0$

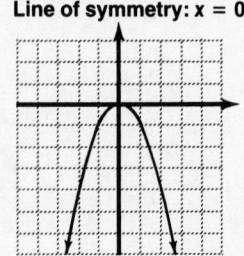

3. Vertex: (0, 0); Line of symmetry; $x = 0$

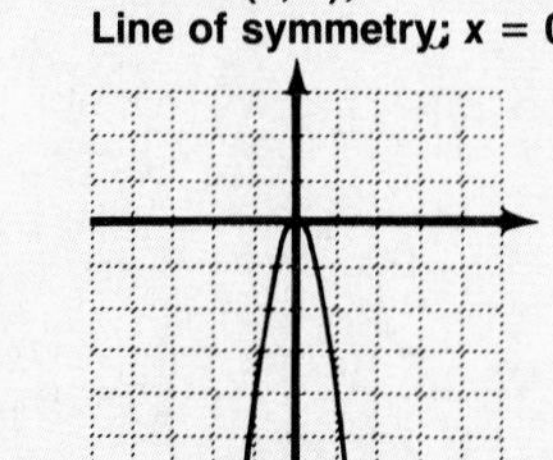

4. Vertex: (0, 0) Line of symmetry: $x = 0$

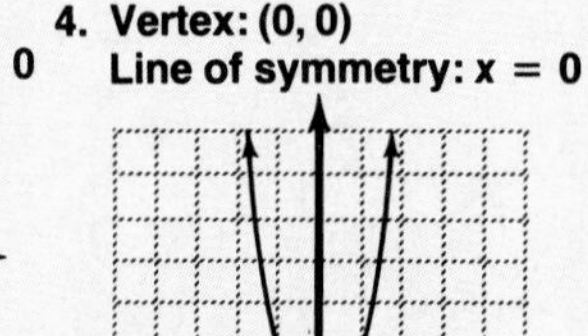

5. Vertex: (0, 0); Line of symmetry: $x = 0$

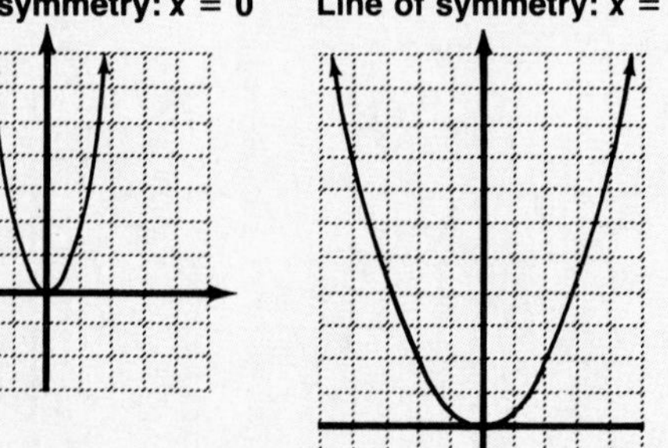

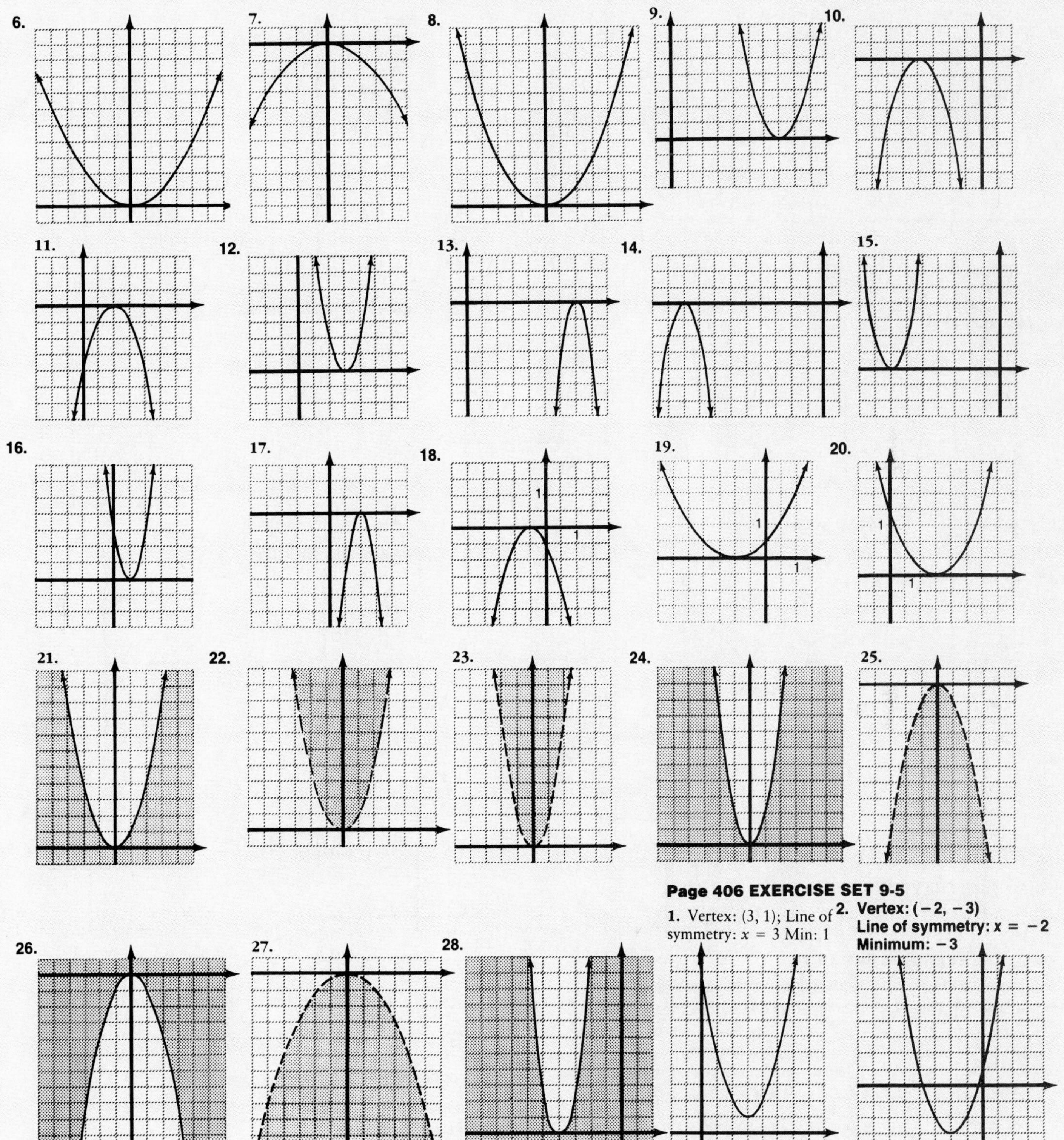

Page 406 EXERCISE SET 9-5

1. Vertex: (3, 1); Line of symmetry: $x = 3$ Min: 1

2. Vertex: $(-2, -3)$
Line of symmetry: $x = -2$
Minimum: -3

3. Vertex: $(-1, -2)$; Line of symmetry: $x = -1$ Min: -2

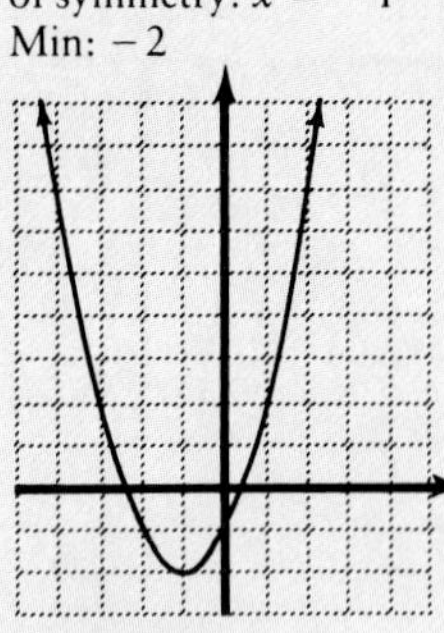

4. Vertex: (1, 2)
Line of symmetry: $x = 1$
Minimum: 2

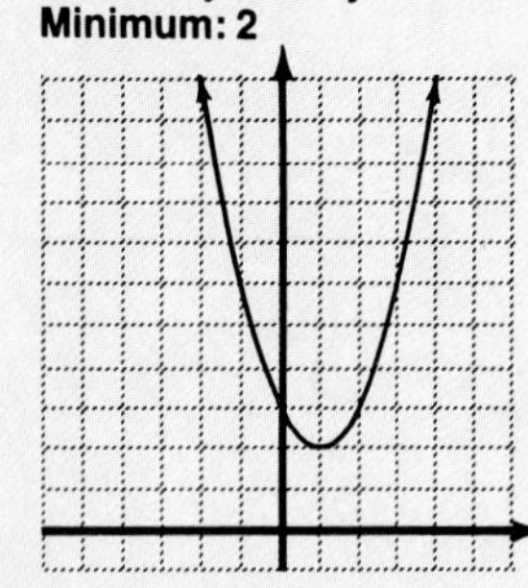

5. Vertex: $(1, -3)$; Line of symmetry: $x = 1$ Min: -3

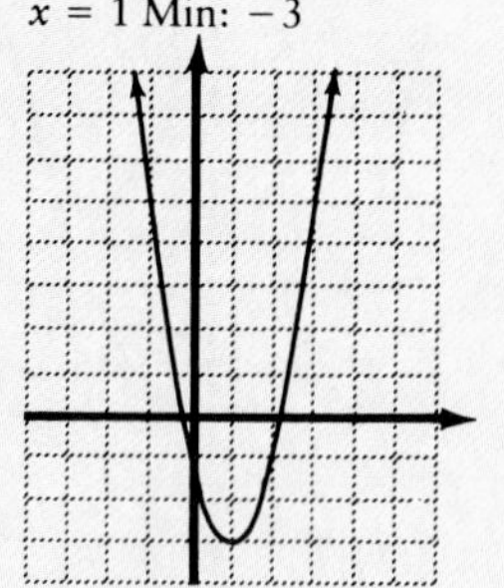

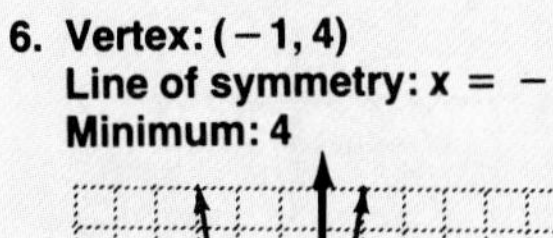

6. Vertex: $(-1, 4)$
Line of symmetry: $x = -1$
Minimum: 4

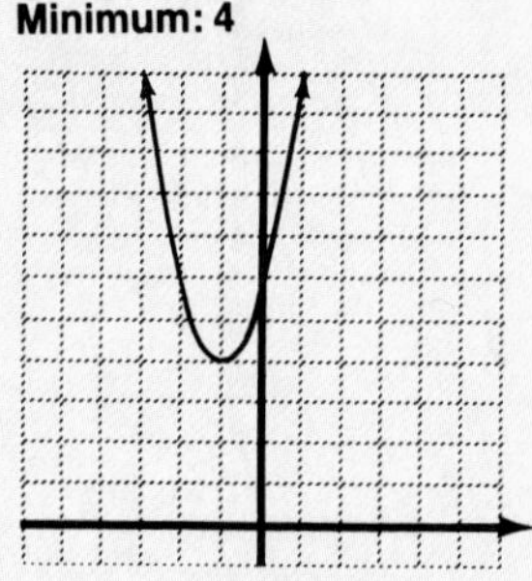

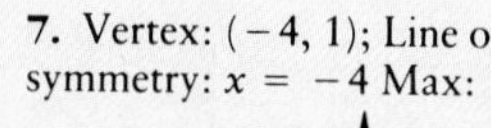

7. Vertex: $(-4, 1)$; Line of symmetry: $x = -4$ Max: 1

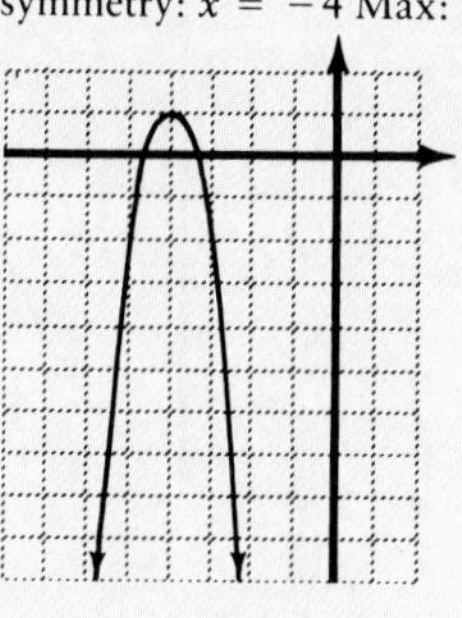

8. Vertex: $(5, -3)$
Line of symmetry: $x = 5$
Maximum: -3

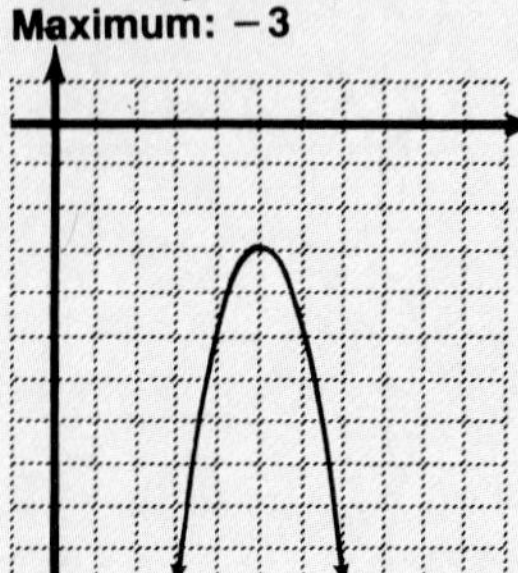

Page 410 EXERCISE SET 9-6

22.

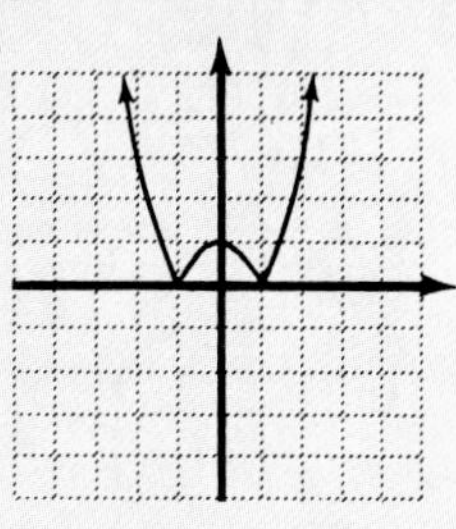

23.

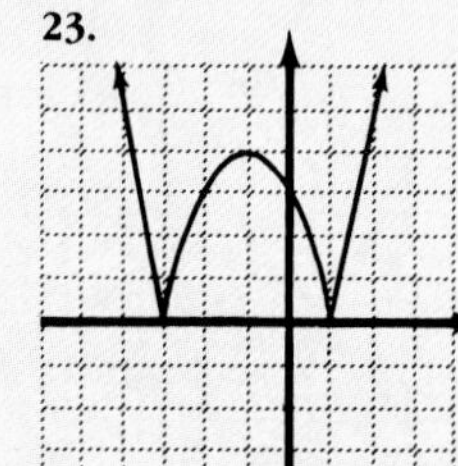

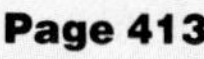

Page 413 EXERCISE SET 9-7

26.

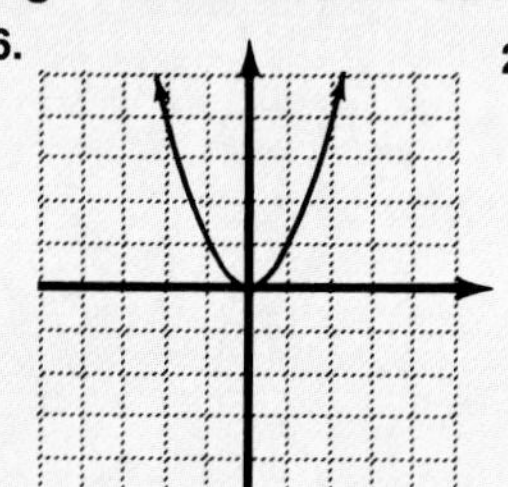

27.

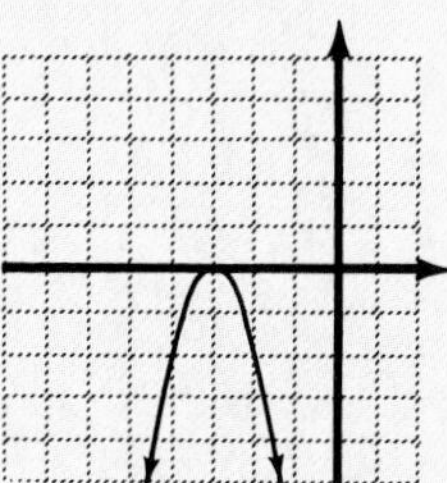

28.

29.

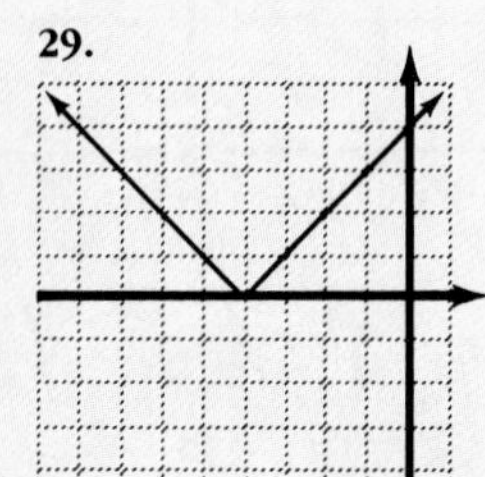

Page 424 CHAPTER 9 SUMMARY AND REVIEW

20.

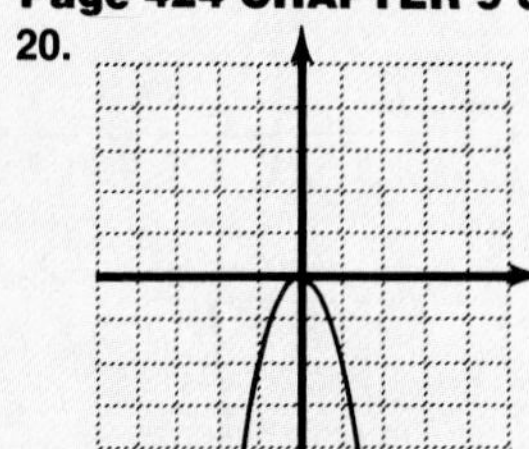

21.

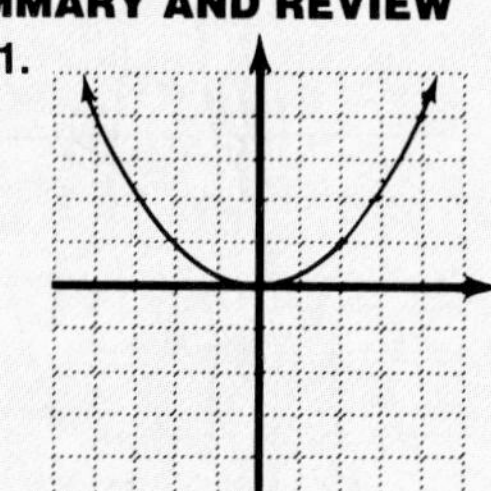

22.

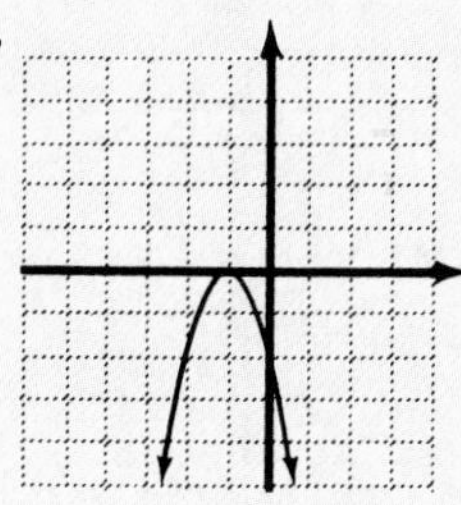

23.

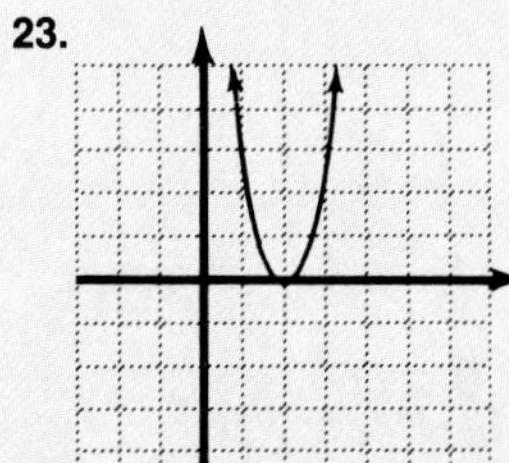

24.

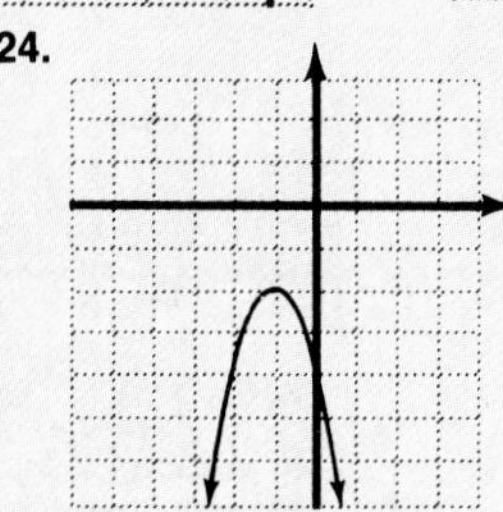

25.

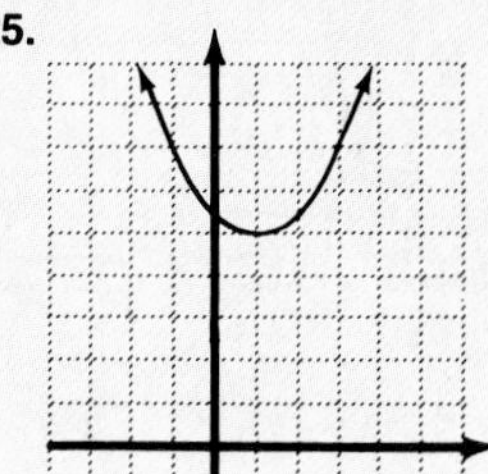

26.

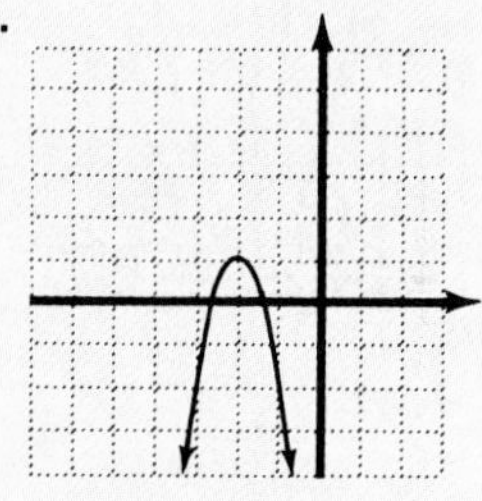

Page 432 EXERCISE SET 10-1

25. If two points are on a vertical line, they have coordinates (a, y_1) and (a, y_2). Thus, the distance from one to the other is $|y_2 - y_1|$. Now $\sqrt{(a-a)^2 + (y_2 - y_1)^2} = \sqrt{0 + (y_2 - y_1)^2} = \sqrt{(y_2 - y_1)^2} = |y_2 - y_1|$. The proof for a horizontal line is similar.

26. Let $P_1(x_1, y_1)$ and $P_2(x_2, y_2)$ be the endpoints of a segment and let M be the point $\left(\frac{x_1 + x_2}{2}, \frac{y_1 + y_2}{2}\right)$. If $P_1M = MP_2 = \frac{1}{2}P_1P_2$, then M is the midpoint of $\overline{P_1P_2}$. $P_1M = \sqrt{\left(\frac{x_1 + x_2}{2} - x_1\right)^2 + \left(\frac{y_1 + y_2}{2} - y_1\right)^2}$ $= \frac{1}{2}\sqrt{(x_2 - x_1)^2 + (y_2 - y_1)^2}$. $MP_2 = \sqrt{\left(x_2 - \frac{x_1 + x_2}{2}\right)^2 + \left(y_2 - \frac{y_1 + y_2}{2}\right)^2}$ $= \frac{1}{2}\sqrt{(x_2 - x_1)^2 + (y_2 - y_1)^2}$. $P_1P_2 = \sqrt{(x_2 - x_1)^2 + (y_2 - y_1)^2}$. M is the midpoint of $\overline{P_1P_2}$.

27. The midpoint of $\overline{DB}$ has coordinates $\left(\frac{a}{2}, \frac{b}{2}\right)$, which is the same as the midpoint of $\overline{AC}$.

Page 436 EXERCISE SET 10-2

5.
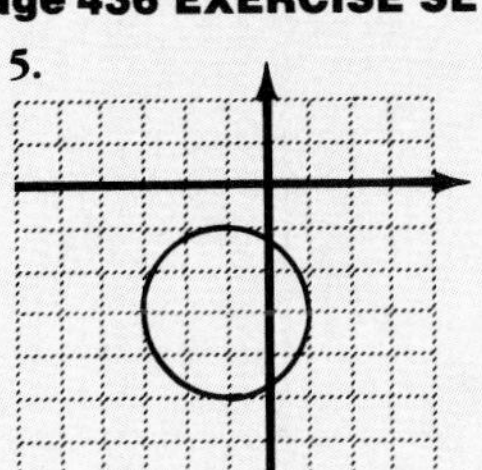

6.
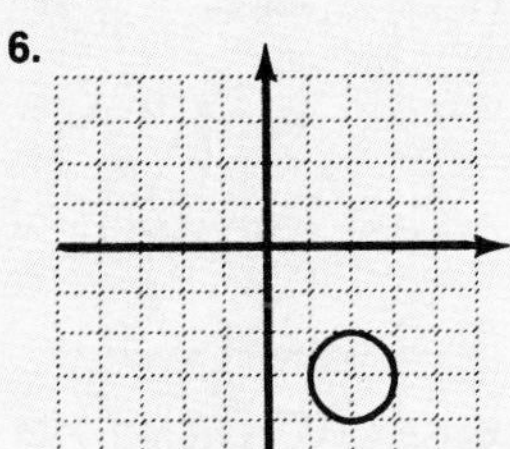

7.
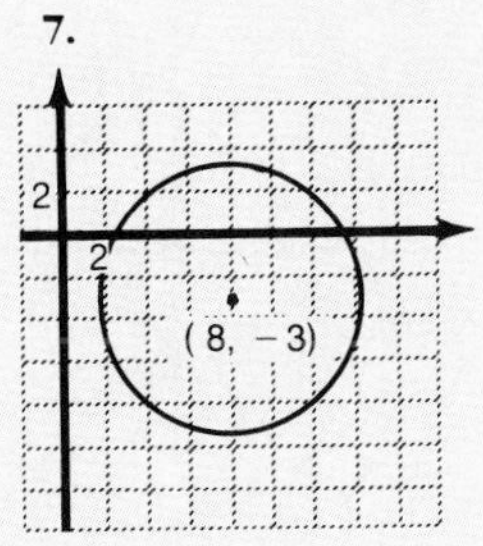

8.
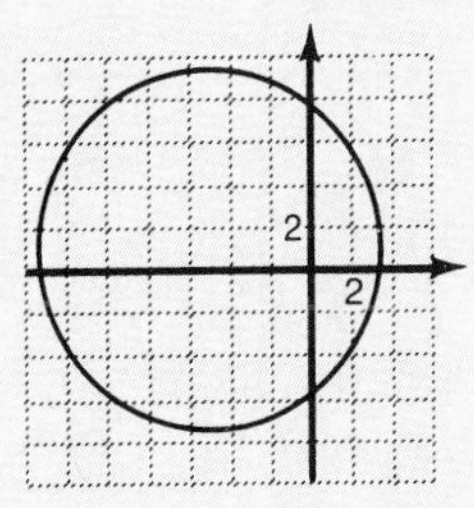

9.
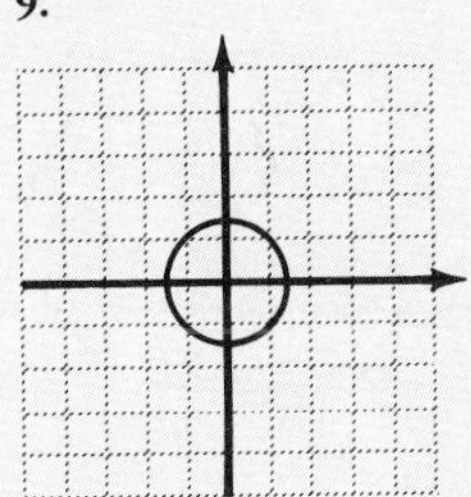

10.
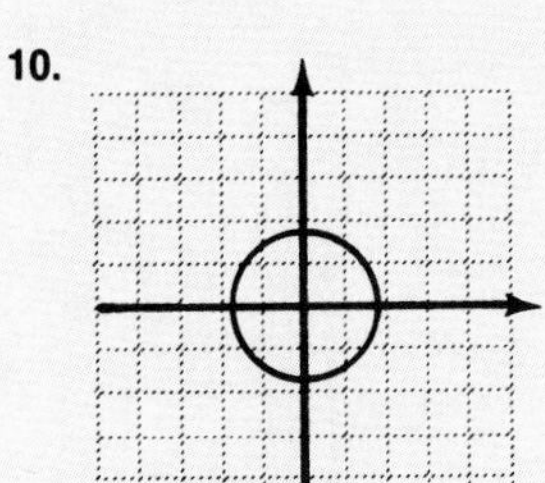

11.
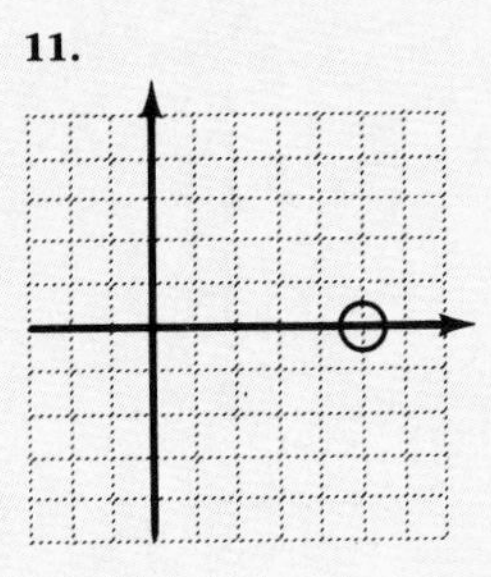

12.
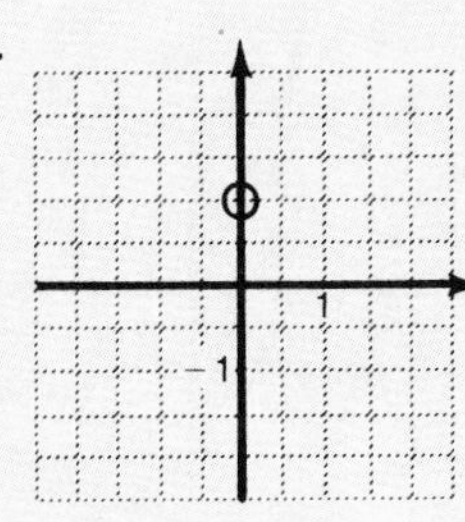

28. a.
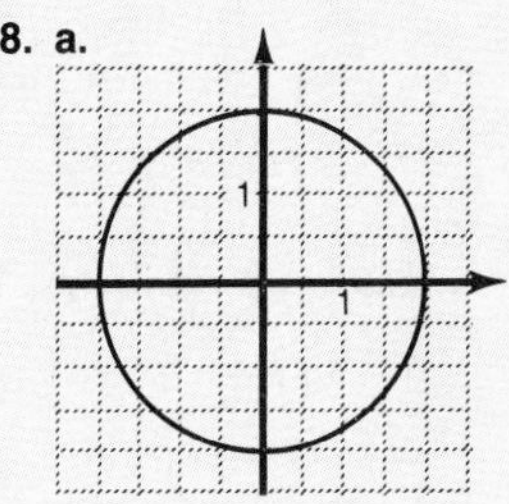

b.
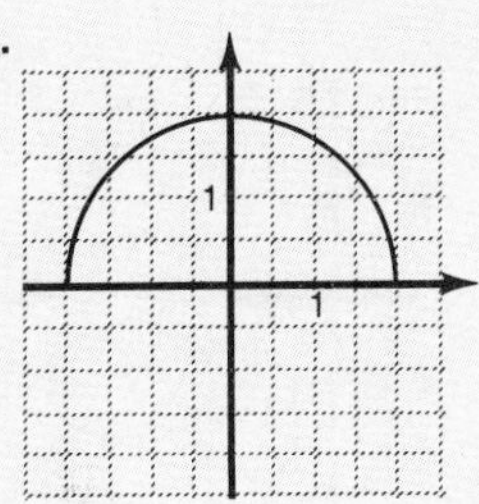

c.
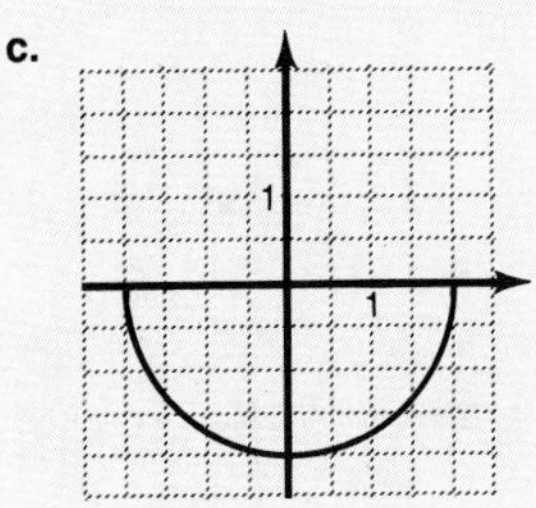

31.
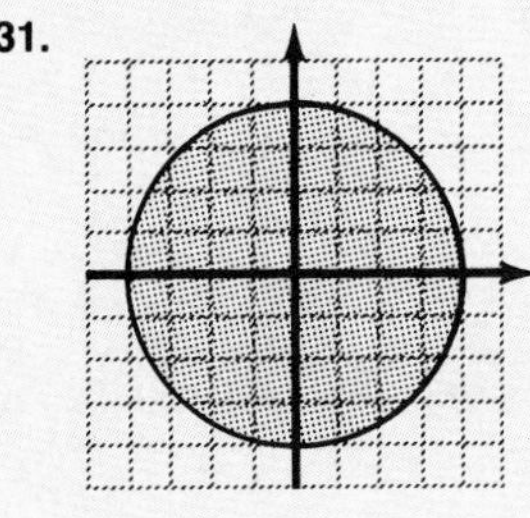

32.
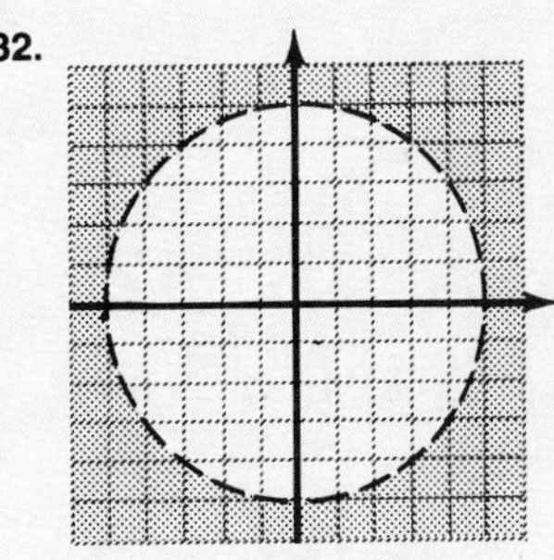

33.
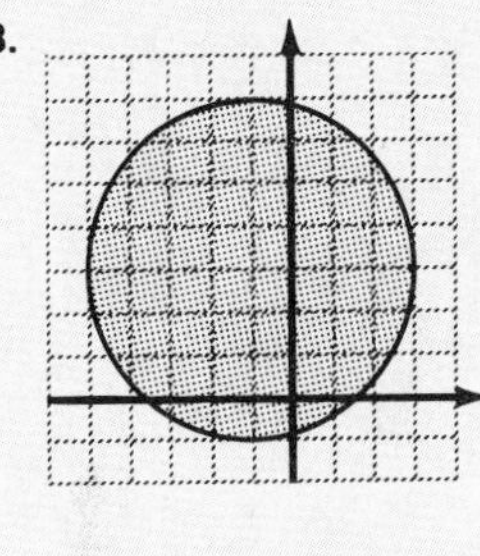

Page 442 EXERCISE SET 10-3

1.
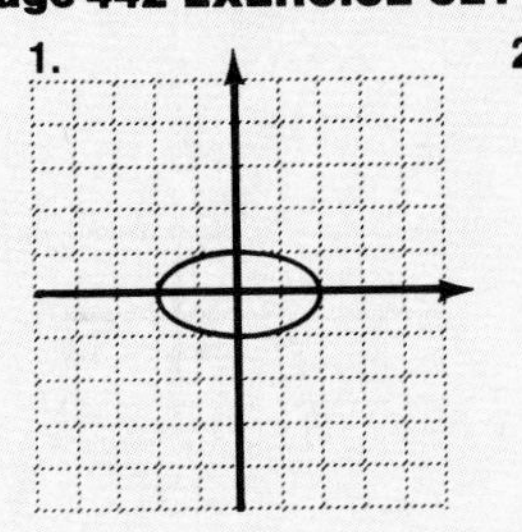

2.
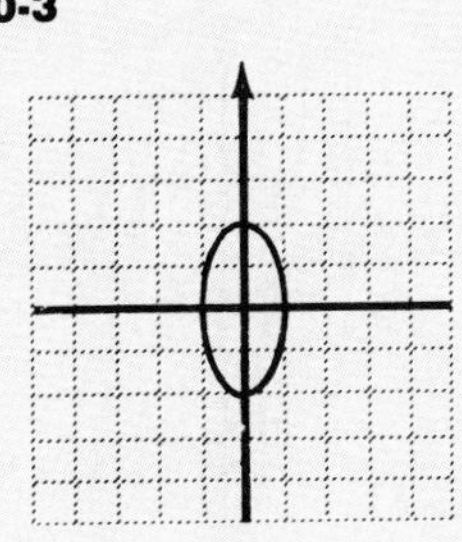

3.
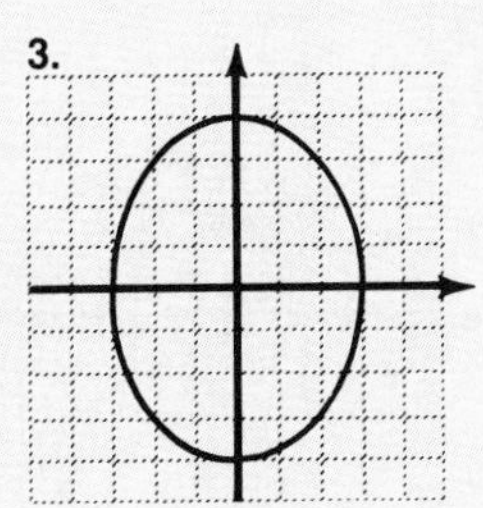

4.
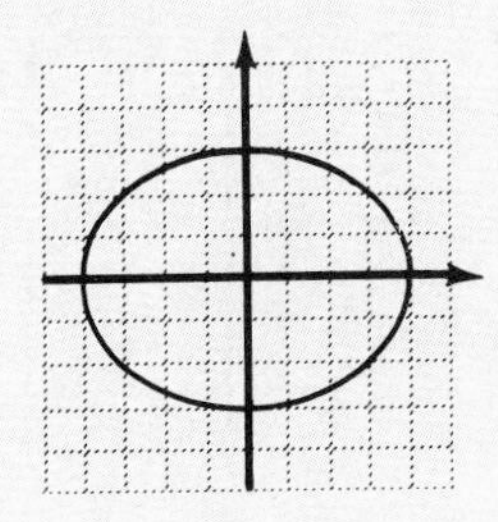

5.
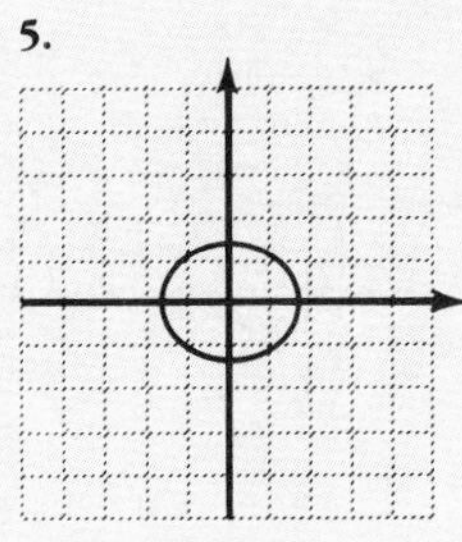

6.
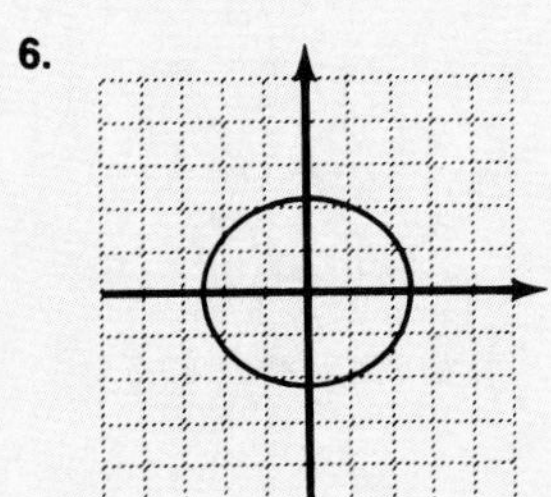

7.
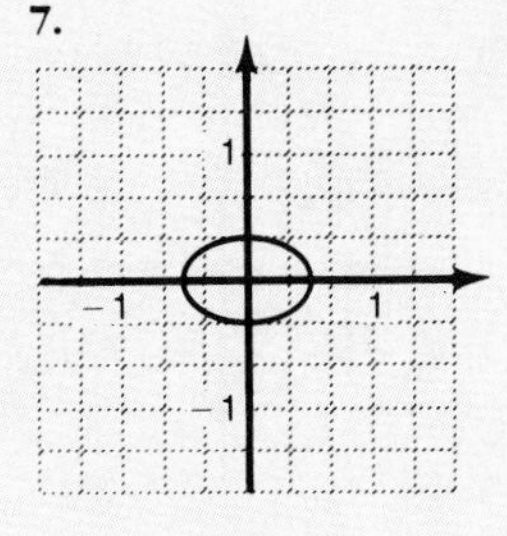

8.
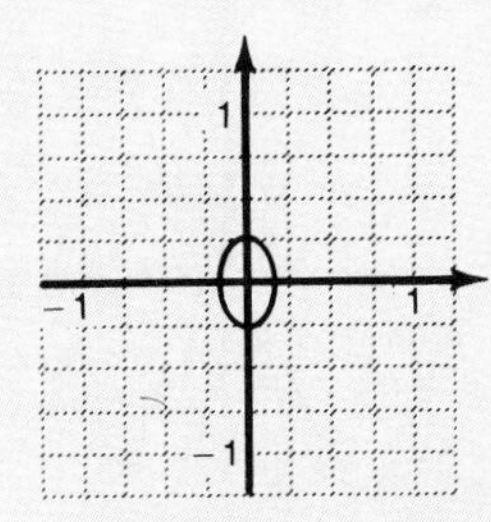

9.
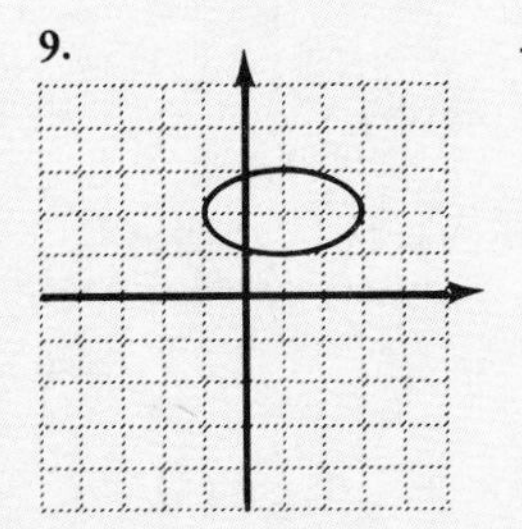

10.
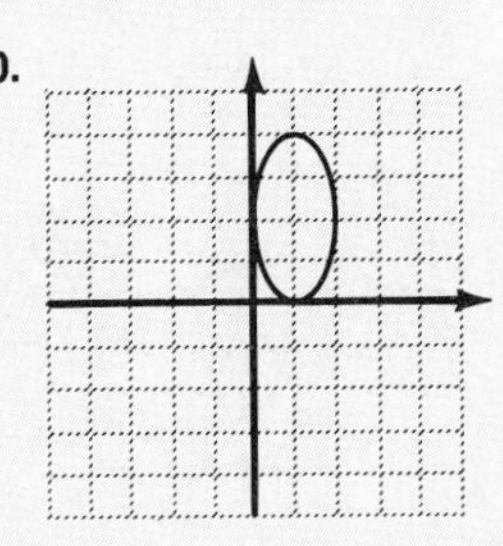

11.

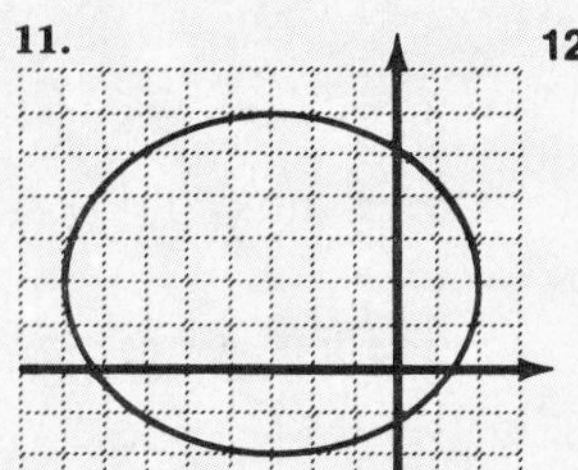

12.

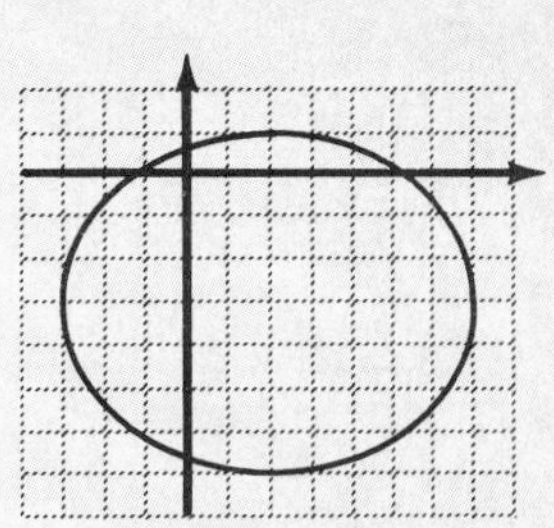

13.

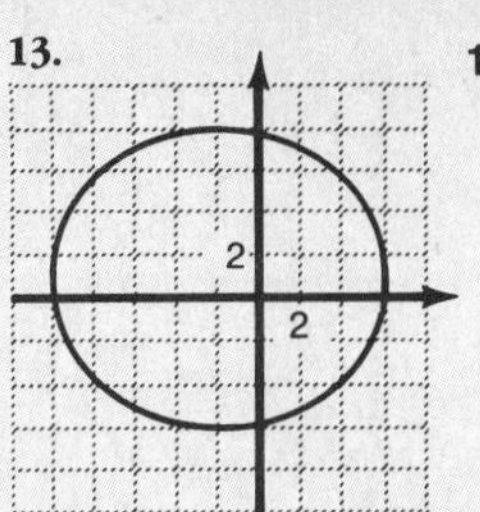

14.

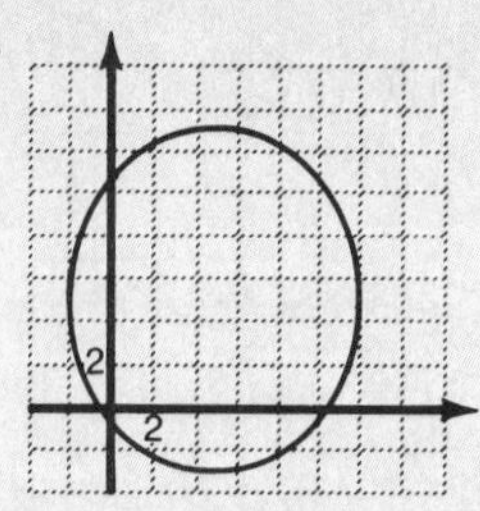

15.

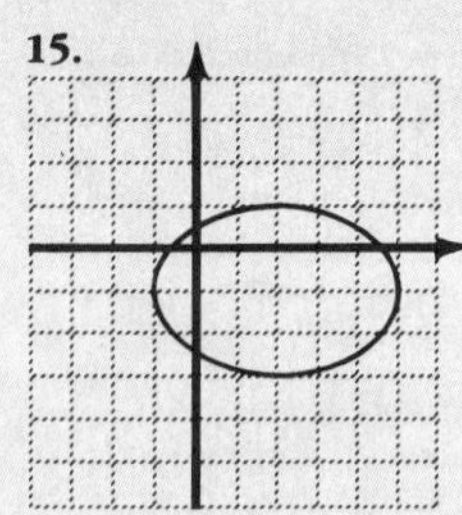

16.

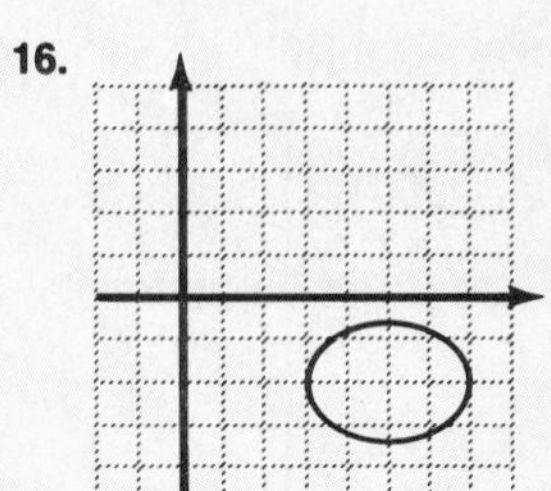

17.

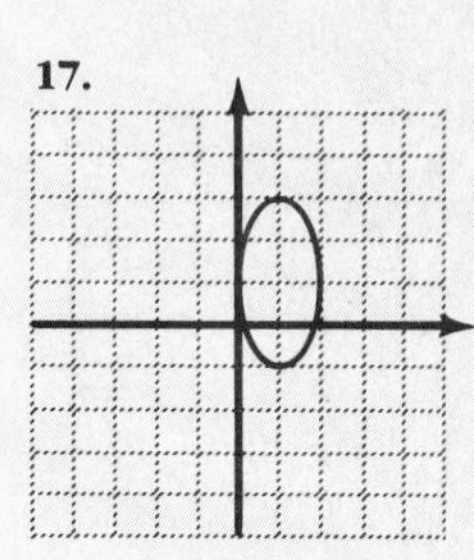

18.

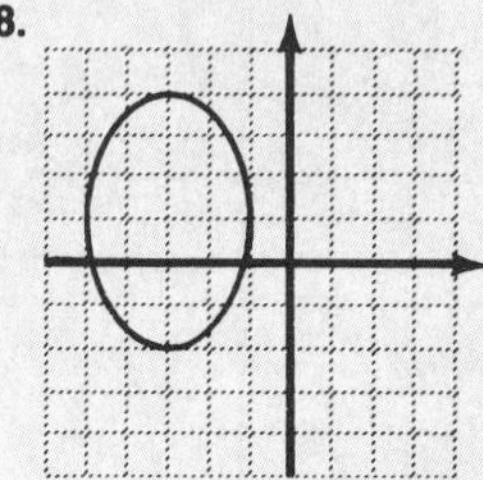

27. a) No

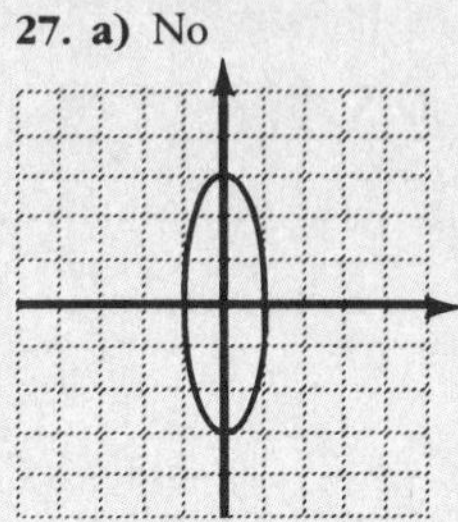

c.

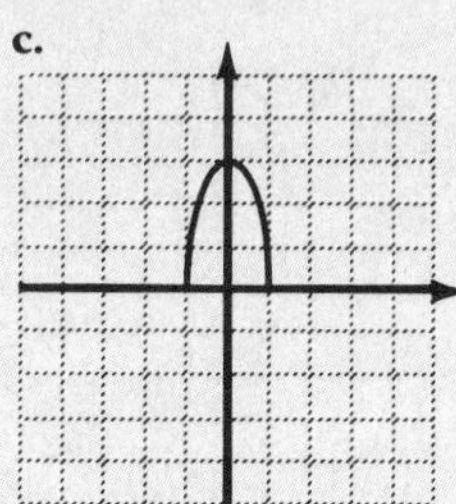

d.

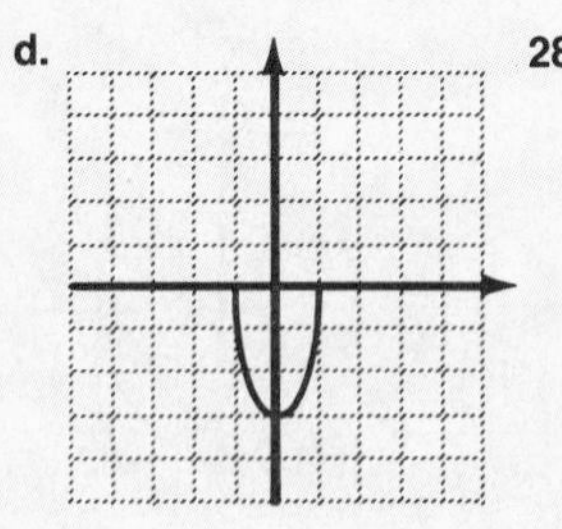

28.

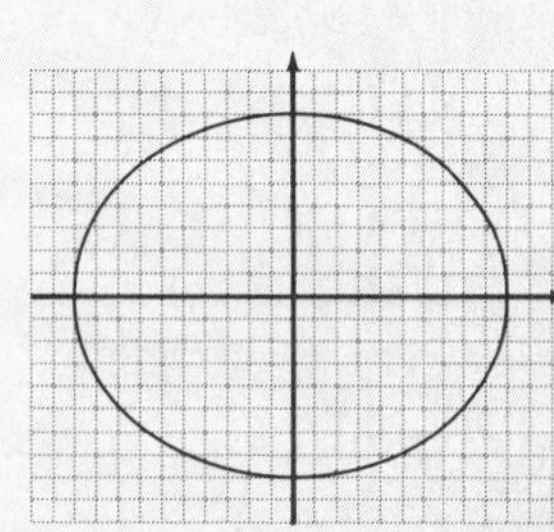

32. $F_1P + F_2P = 2a$; by the distance formula
$\sqrt{(x + c)^2 + y^2} + \sqrt{(x - c)^2 + y^2} = 2a$;
$\sqrt{(x + c)^2 + y^2} = 2a - \sqrt{(x - c)^2 + y^2}$;
$x^2 + 2cx + c^2 + y^2 = 4a^2 - 4a\sqrt{(x - c)^2 + y^2} + x^2 - 2cx + c^2 + y^2$;
$-4a^2 + 4cx = -4a\sqrt{(x - c)^2 + y^2}$; $-a^2 + cx = -a\sqrt{(x - c)^2 + y^2}$;
$a^4 - 2a^2cx + c^2x^2 = a^2x^2 - 2a^2cx + a^2c^2 + a^2y^2$;
$x^2(a^2 - c^2) + a^2y^2 = a^2(a^2 - c^2)$; with P at $(0, b)$, it follows that $b^2 = a^2 - c^2$.
Substituting b^2 for $a^2 - c^2$ in the last equation, we have the equation of the ellipse $b^2x^2 + a^2y^2 = a^2b^2$, or $\frac{x^2}{a^2} + \frac{y^2}{b^2} = 1$.

37.

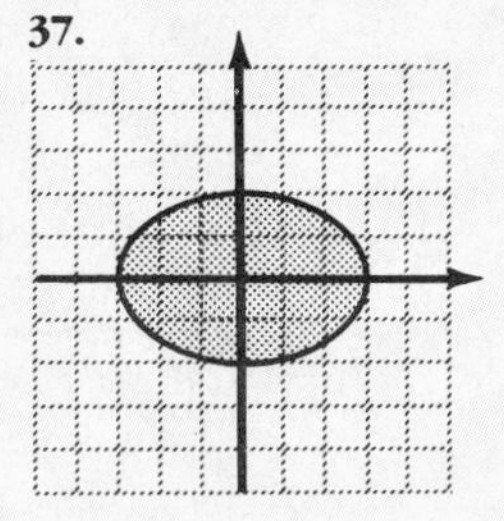

38.

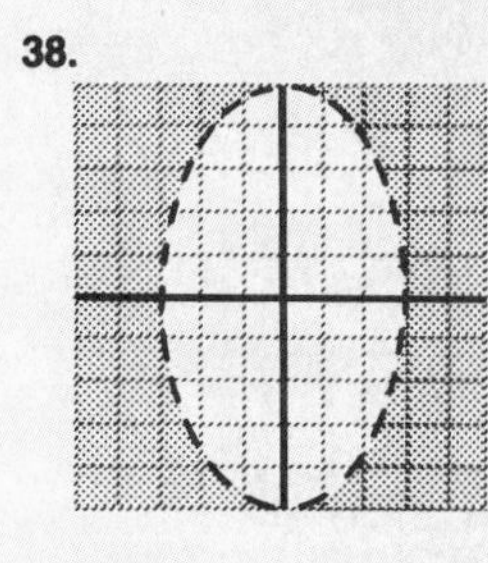

39.

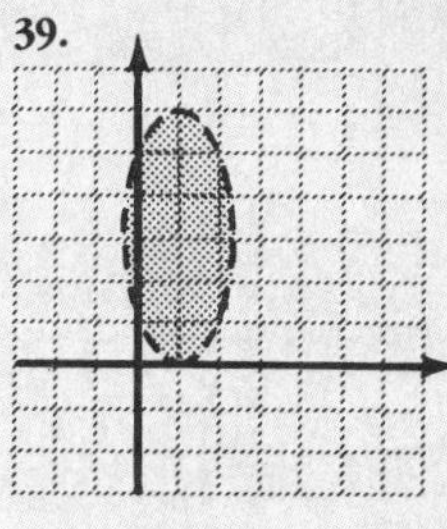

Page 450 EXERCISE SET 10-4

1.

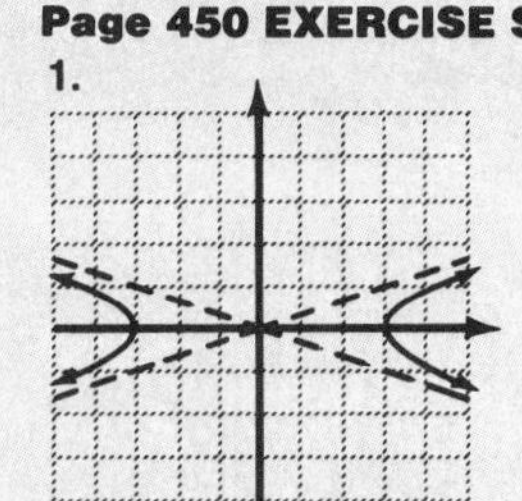

2.

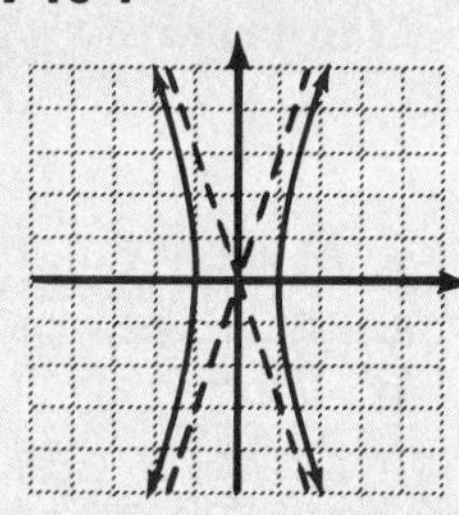

3.

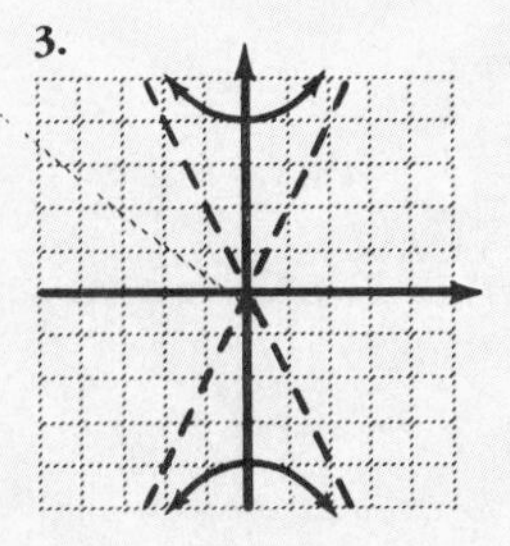

4.

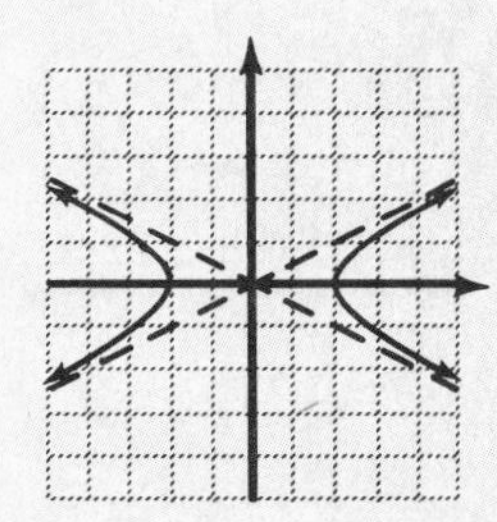

5.

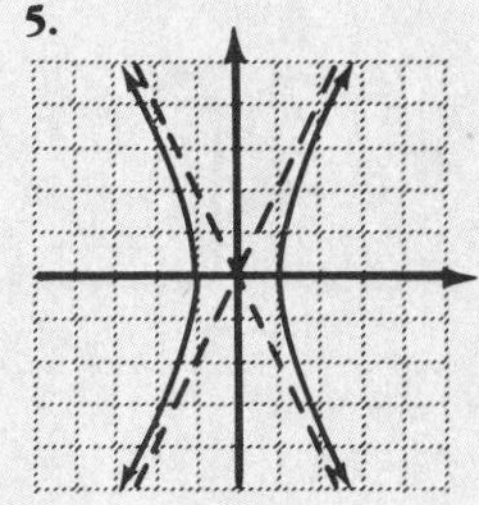

6.

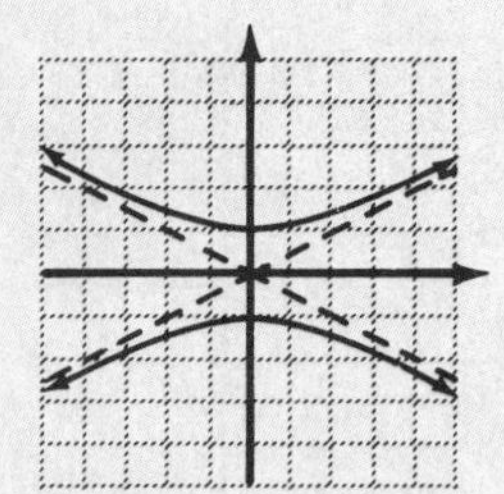

7.

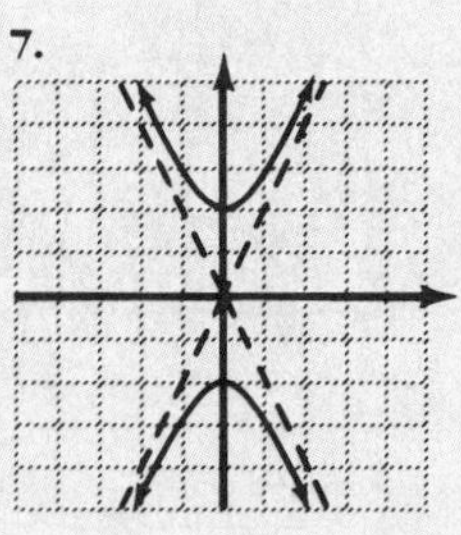

8.

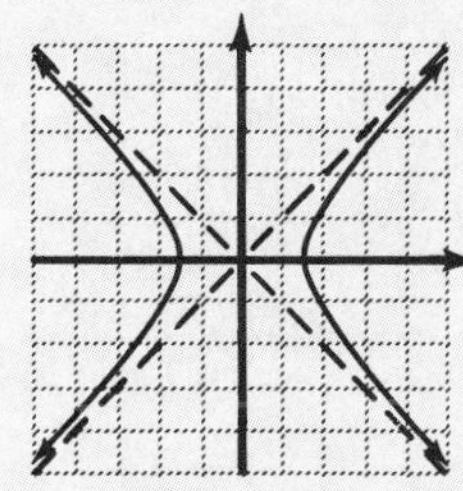

9.

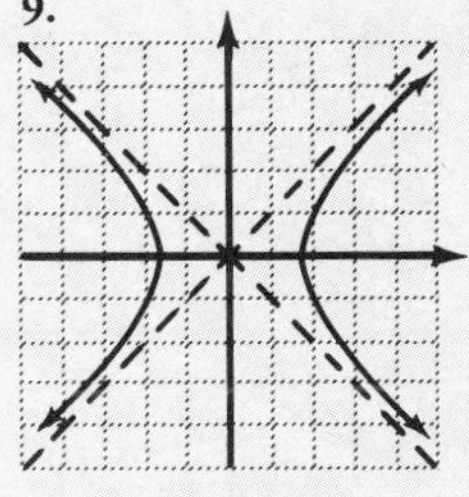

10.

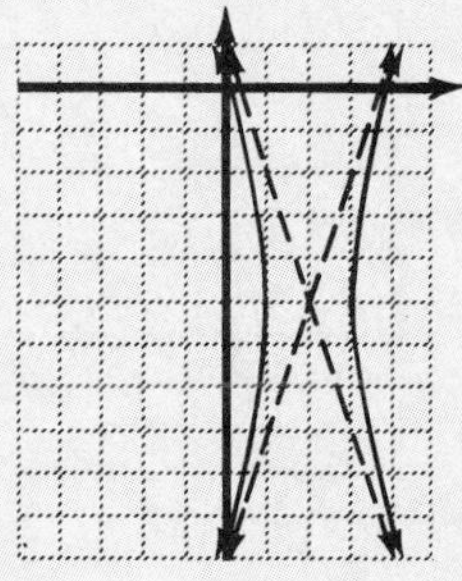

11.

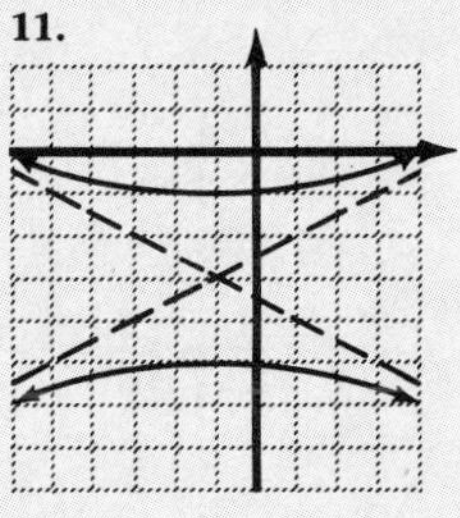

12.

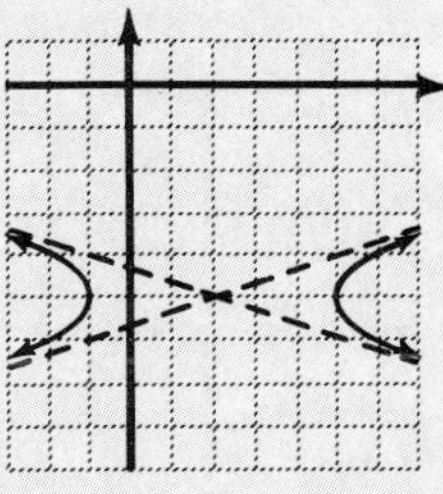

13.

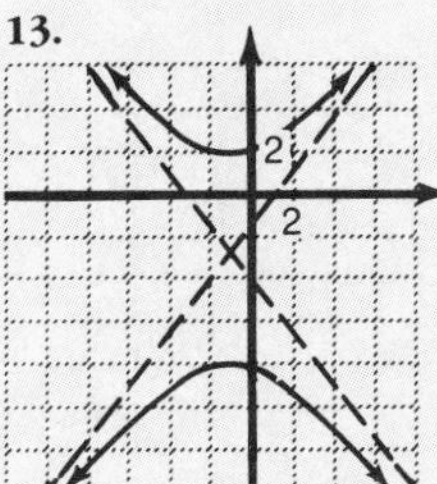

14.

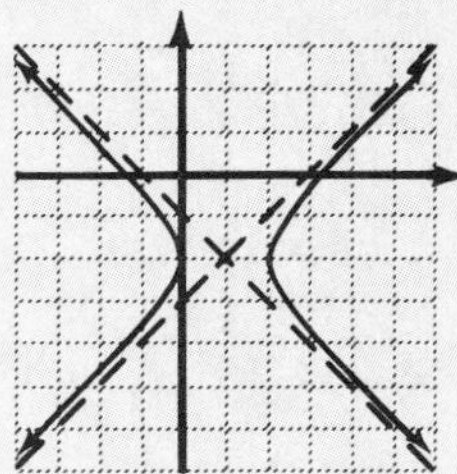

15.

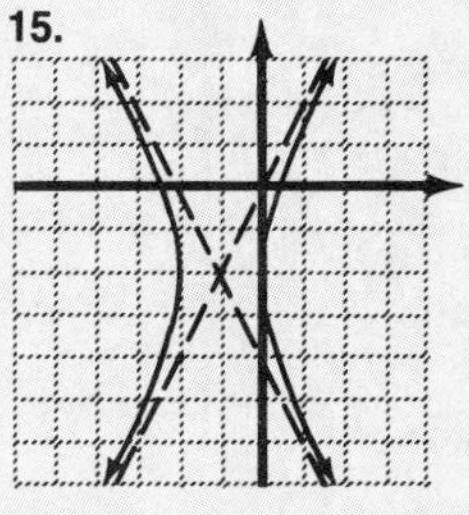

16.

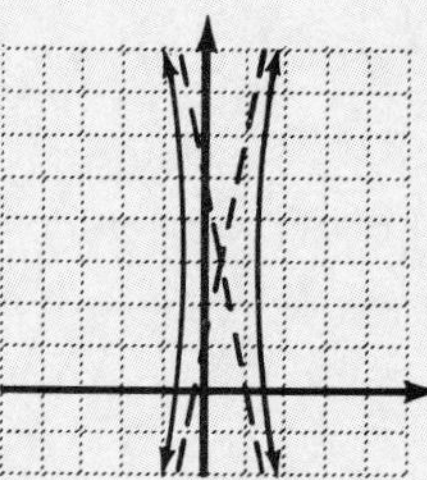

17.

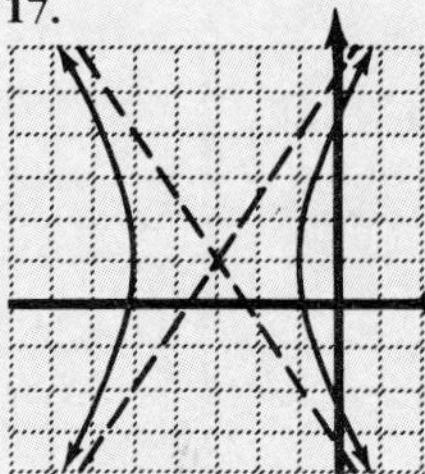

18.

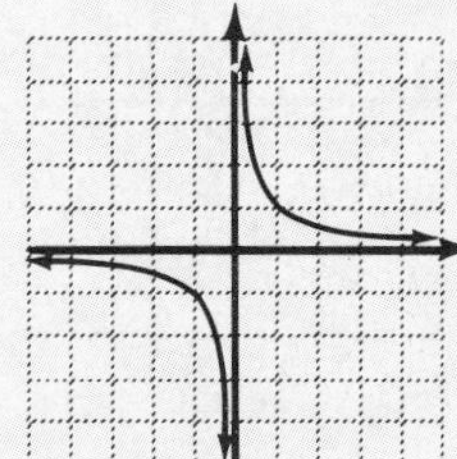

19.

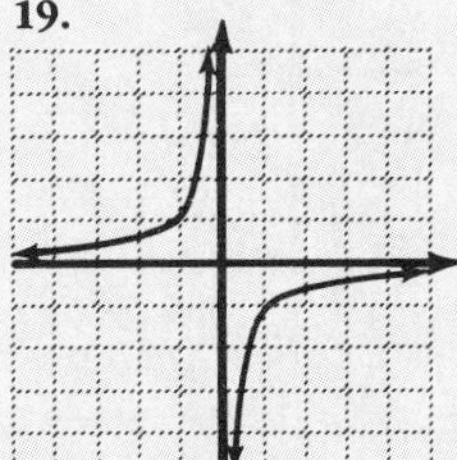

20.

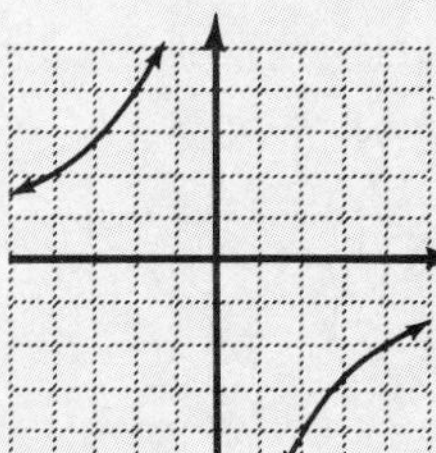

21.

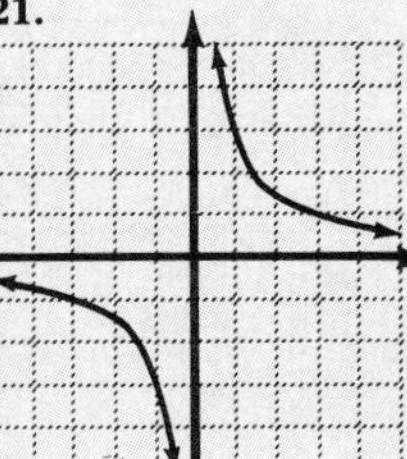

24. The graph of $\frac{x^2}{a^2} - \frac{y^2}{b^2} = 1$ is the graph of $\frac{x^2}{b^2} - \frac{y^2}{a^2} = 1$ rotated 90°.

25. $PF_1 - PF_2 = 2a$; by the distance formula, $\sqrt{(x + c)^2 + y^2} - \sqrt{(x - c)^2 + y^2} = 2a$; $\sqrt{(x + c)^2 + y^2} = 2a + \sqrt{(x - c)^2 + y^2}$; $x^2 + 2xc + c^2 + y^2 = 4a^2 + 4a\sqrt{(x - c)^2 + y^2} + x^2 - 2xc + c^2 + y^2$; $4cx - 4a^2 = 4a\sqrt{(x - c)^2 + y^2}$; $cx - a^2 = a\sqrt{(x - c)^2 + y^2}$; $c^2x^2 - 2a^2cx + a^4 = a^2x^2 - 2cxa^2 + a^2c^2 + a^2y^2$; $x^2(c^2 - a^2) - a^2y^2 = a^2(c^2 - a^2)$; In the triangle F_1PF_2, $PF_1 - PF_2 < F_1F_2$, or $2a < 2c$, so $a < c$, and $c^2 > a^2$, so $c^2 - a^2 > 0$. We represent $c^2 - a^2$ by b^2: $x^2b^2 - a^2y^2 = a^2b^2$, or $\frac{x^2}{a^2} - \frac{y^2}{b^2} = 1$.

26. $y^2 = 9\left(\frac{x^2}{16} - 1\right)$; y^2 gets large as $|x|$ gets large.

Asymptotes: $y = \pm\frac{3}{4}x$

30.

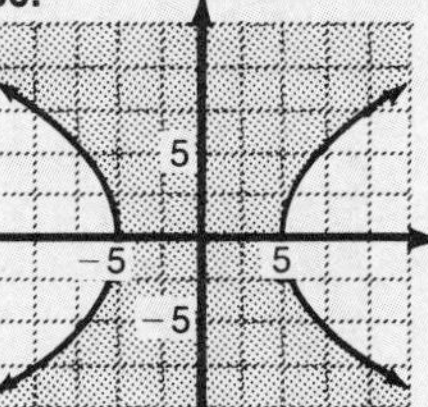

31.

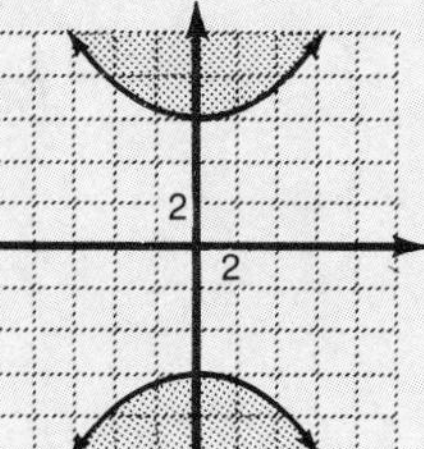

32.

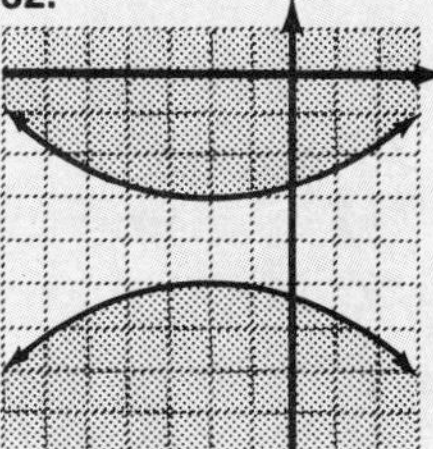

Page 456 EXERCISE SET 10-5

1.

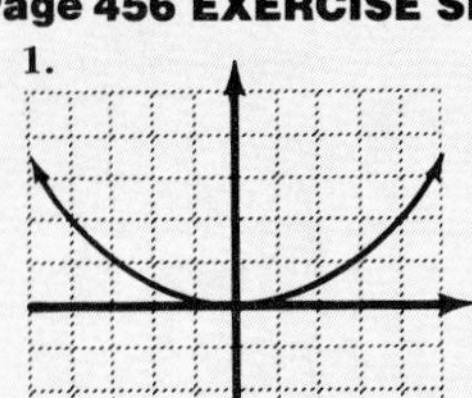

2.

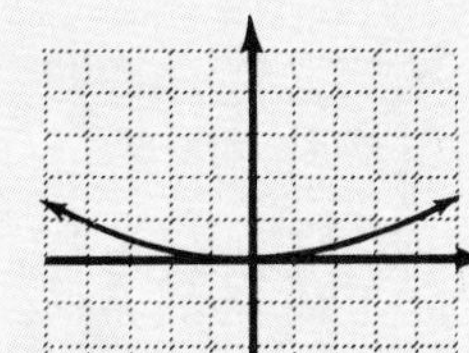

3.

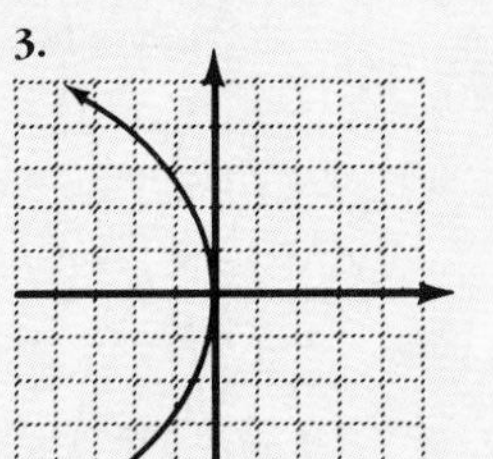

4.

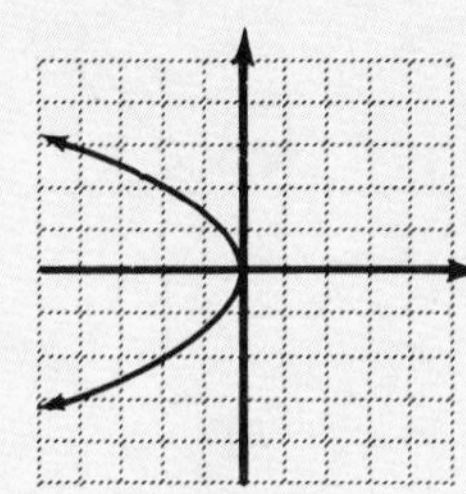

5.

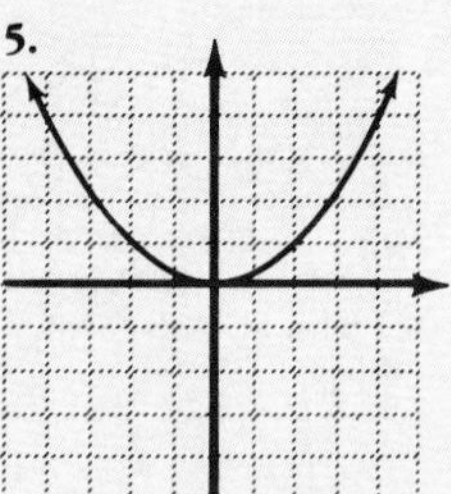

6.

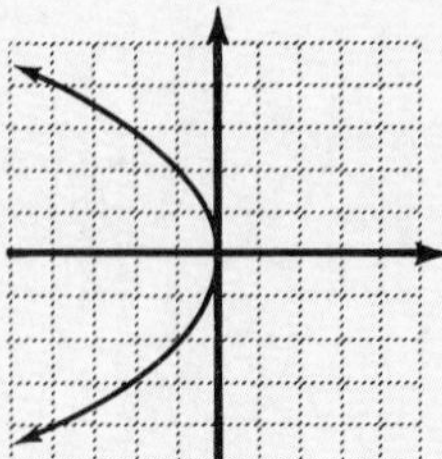

7.

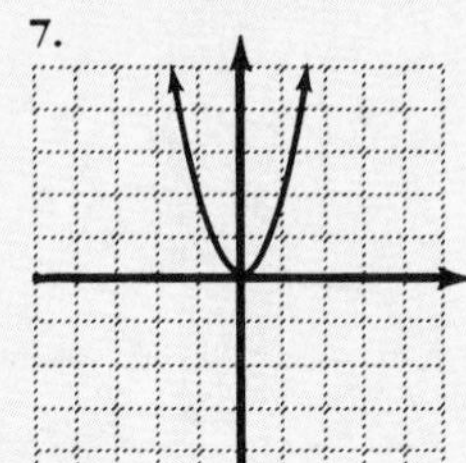

8.

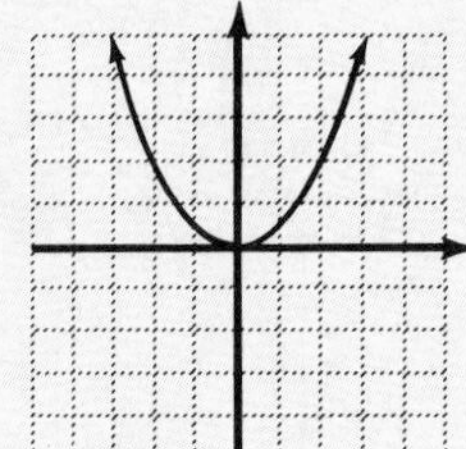

9.

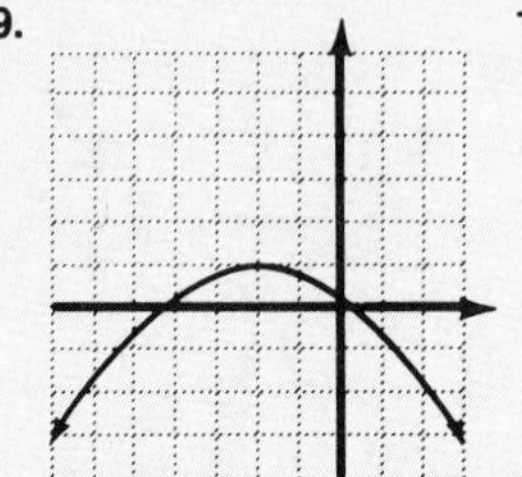

10.

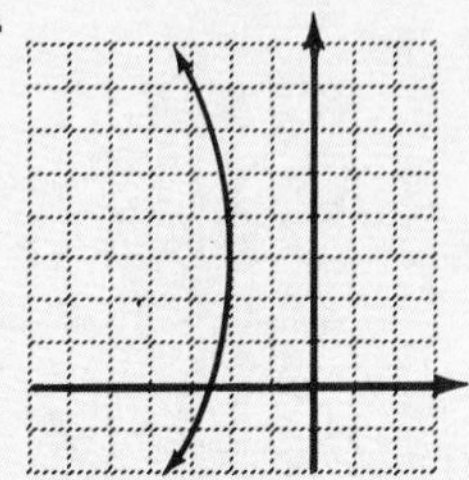

11.

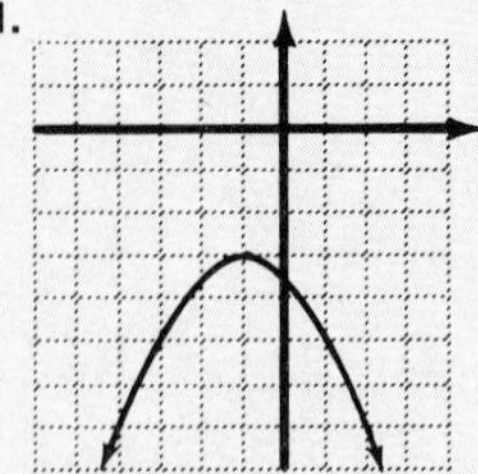

12.

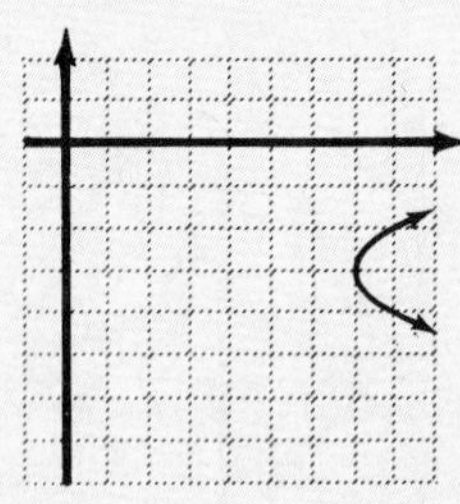

13.

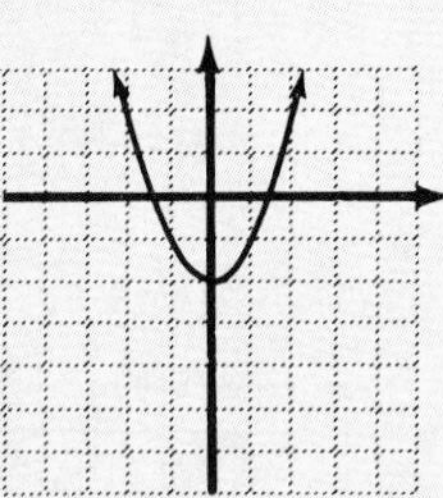

14.

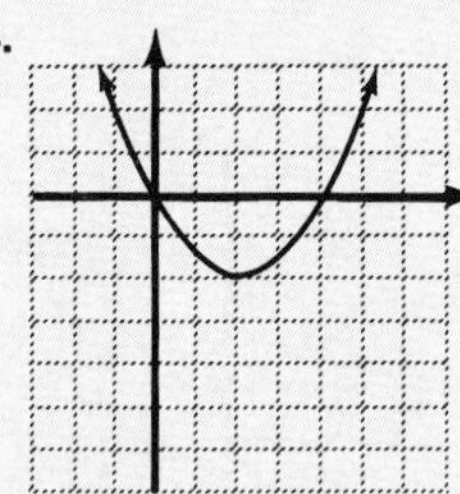

15.

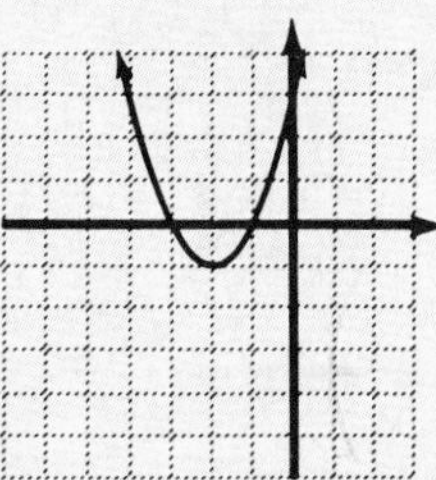

16.

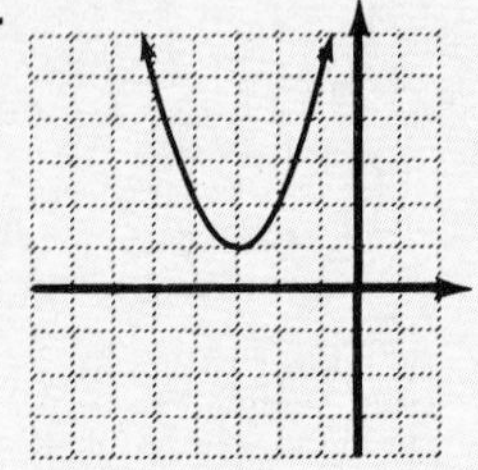

17.

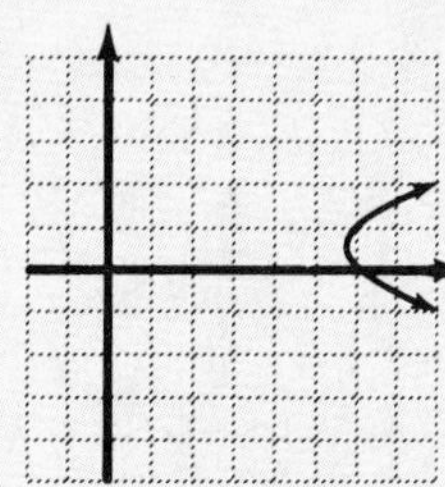

18.

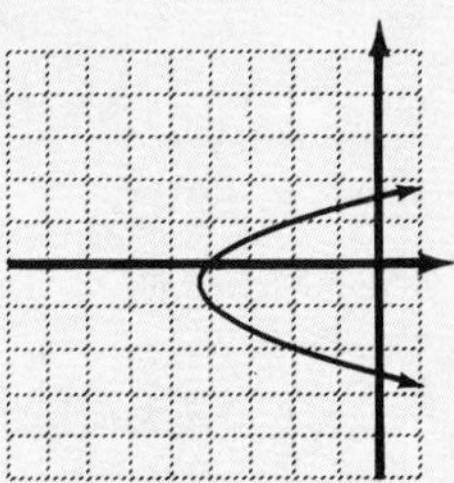

31.

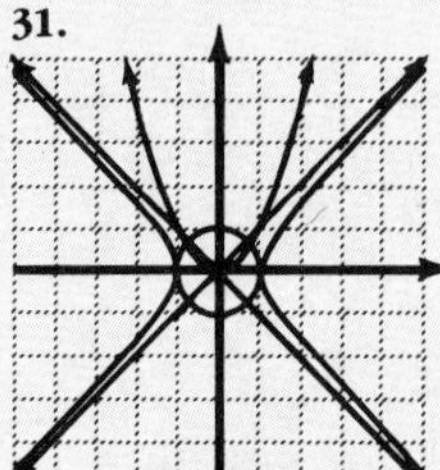

32.

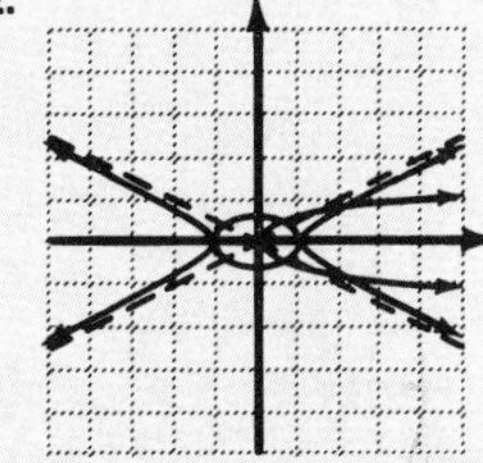

34. a.

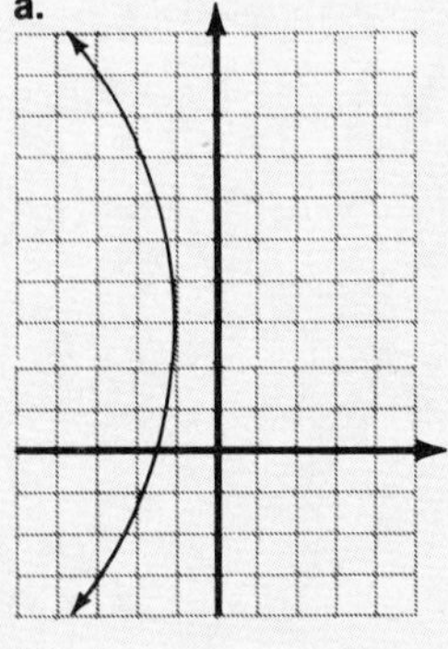

37. a. *OF* is the distance of *P* to the directrix. By the definition this equals *PF*, the distance of *P* to the focus. Hence, $\angle POF$ measures 45°.

b. $\angle PFO$ measures 45°, so the segment PP' intersects the axis of symmetry at the focus. The vertex will be the midpoint of the segment *OF*. If the vertex is 3 units from the segment, the segment has length 12.

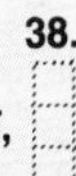

38.

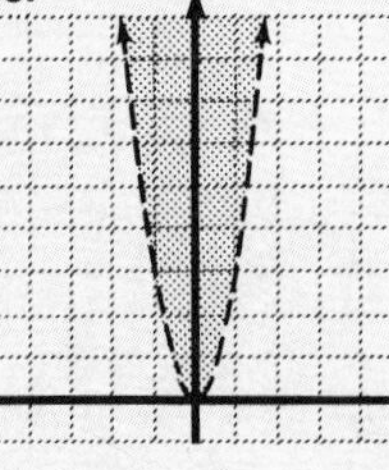

39.

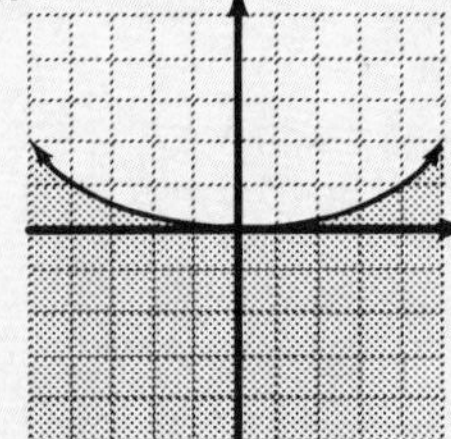

40.

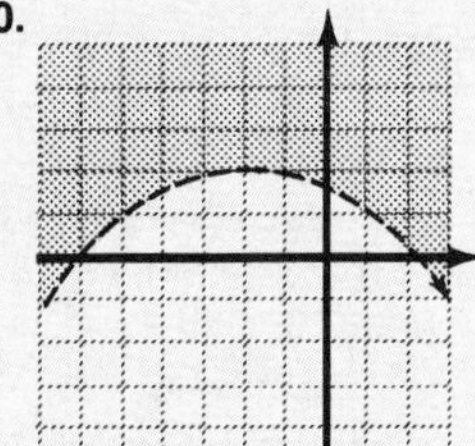

Page 462 EXERCISE SET 10-6

20.

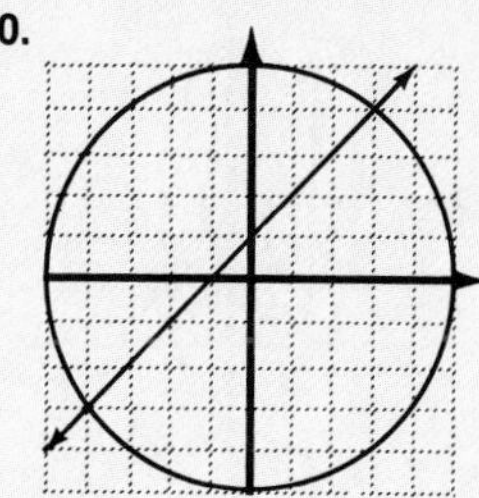

21.

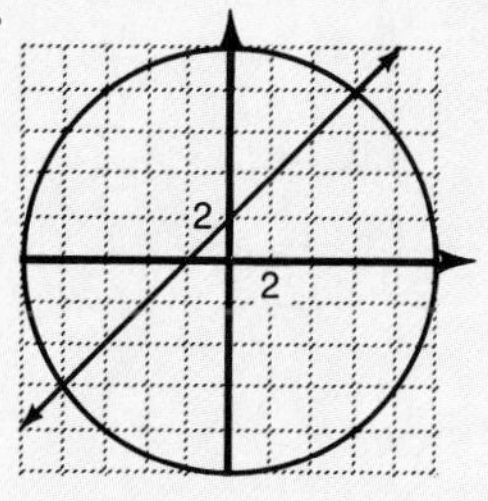

22.

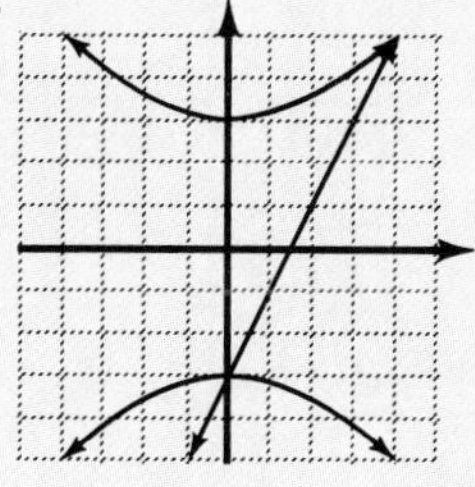

23.

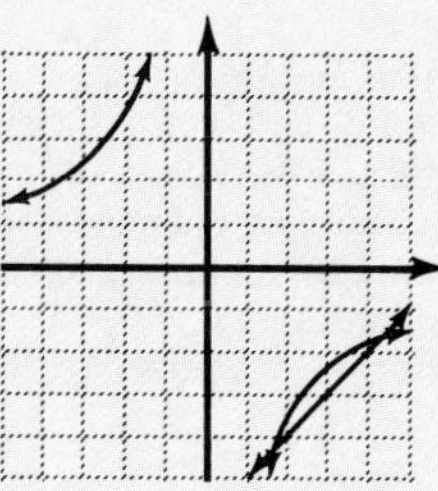

24.

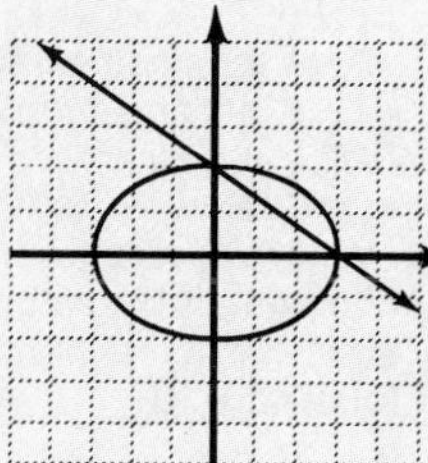

25.

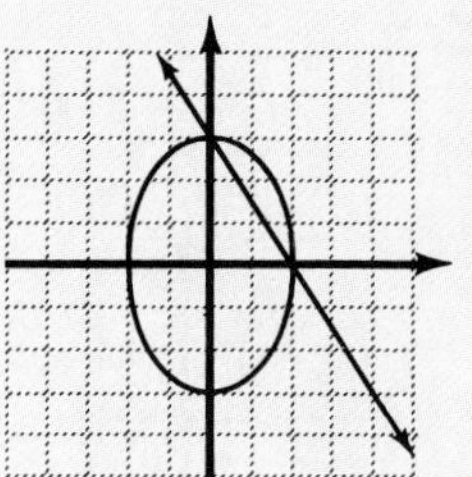

26.

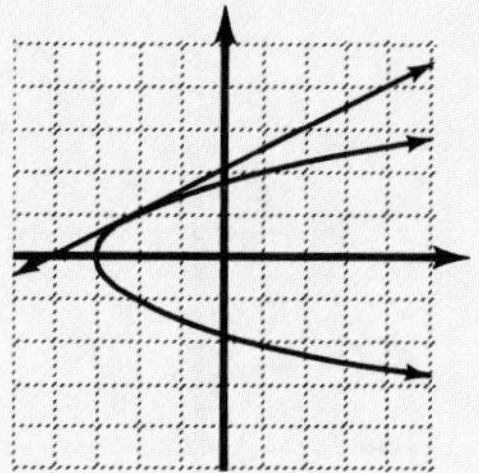

27.

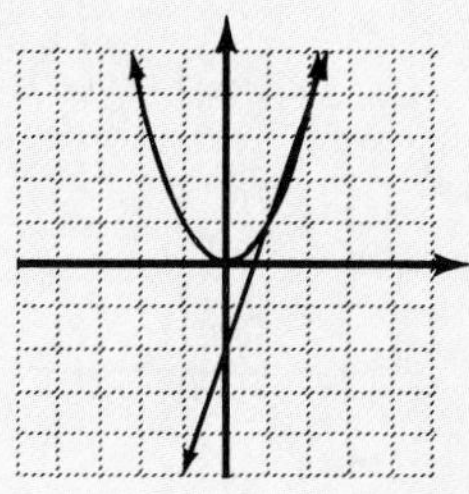

28.

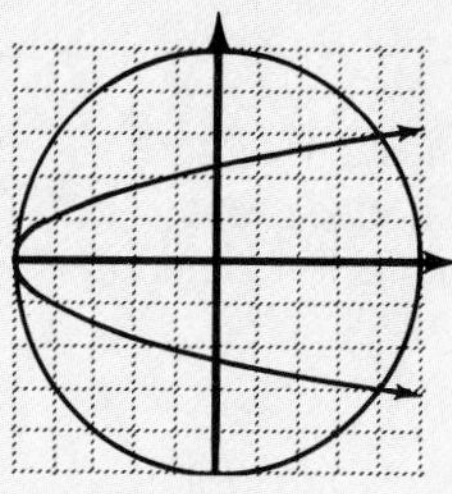

29.

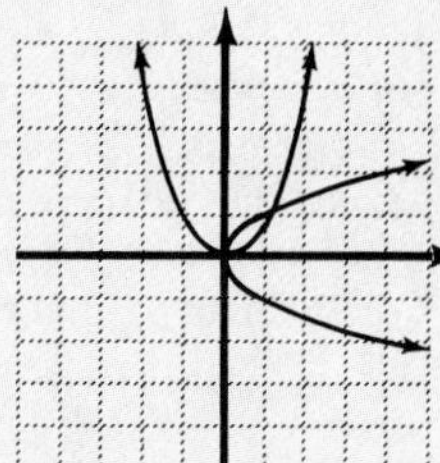

30

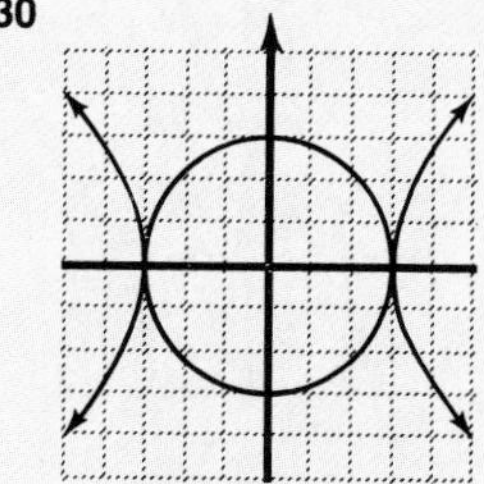

31.

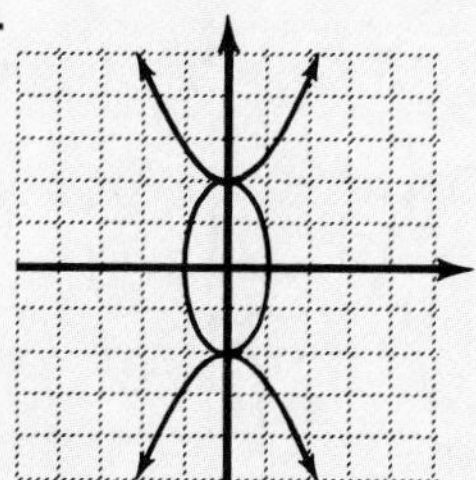

32

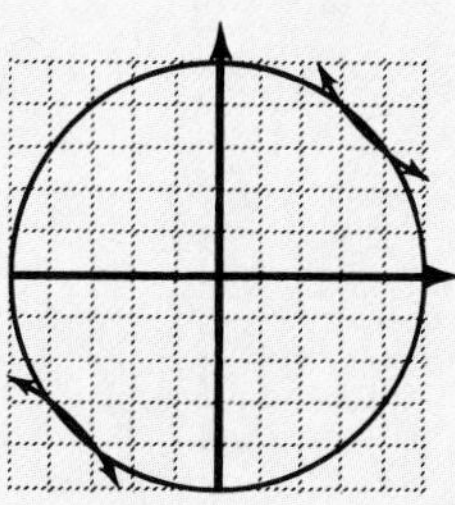

33.

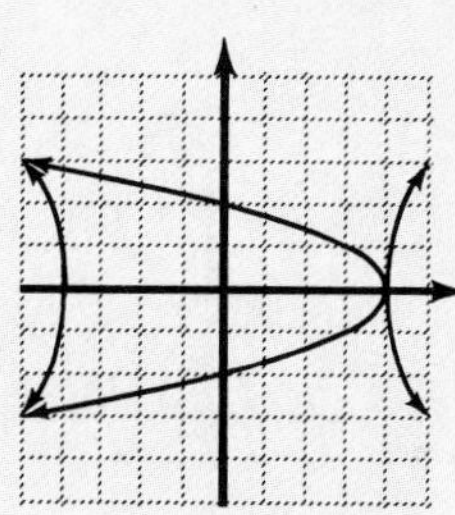

34.

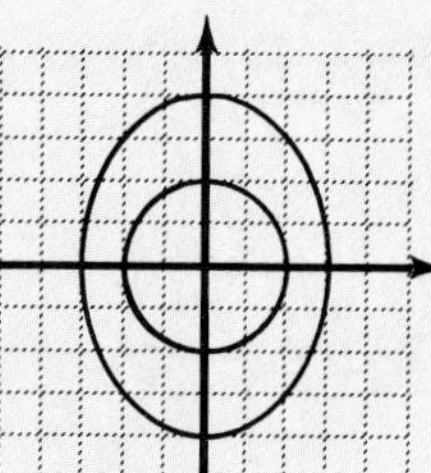

35.

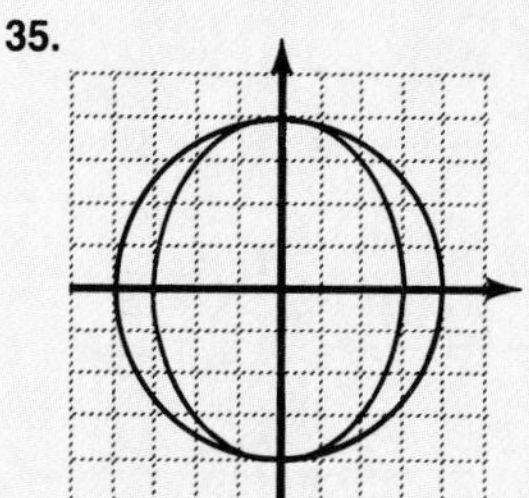

36.

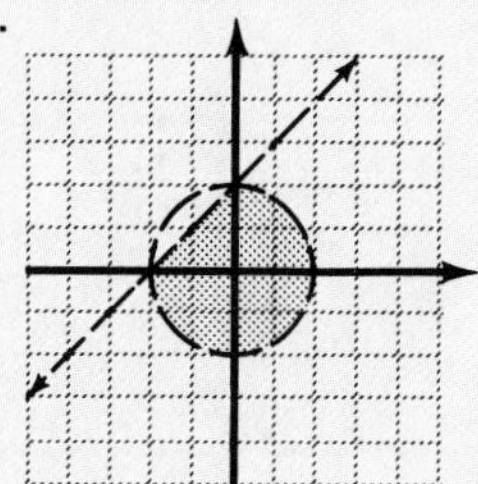

37.

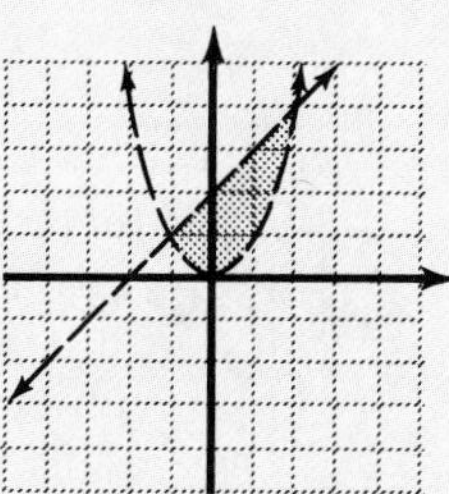

38.

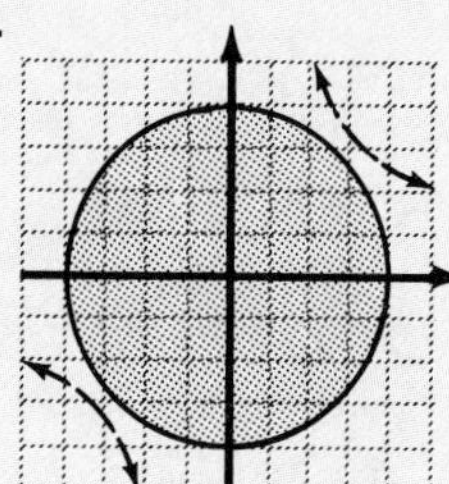

39.

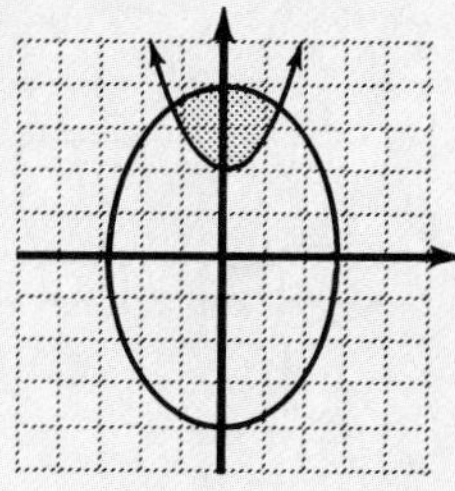

40.

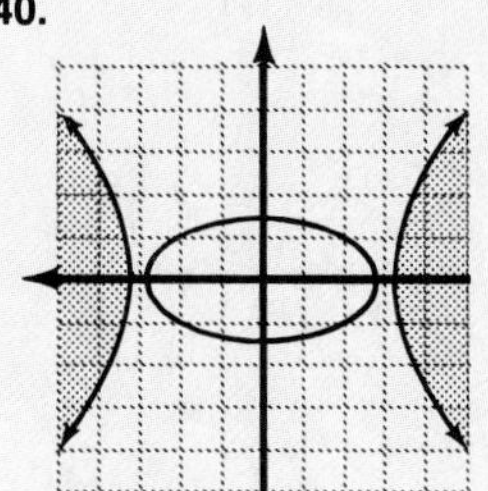

42.

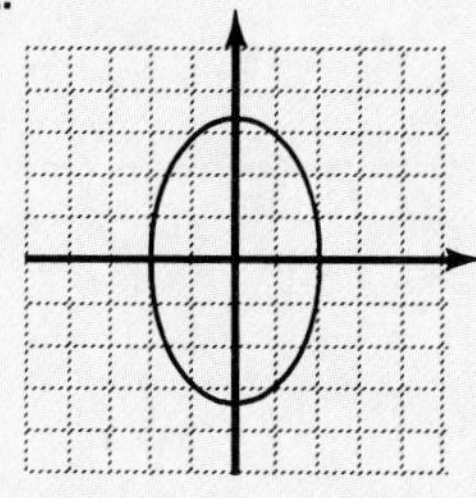

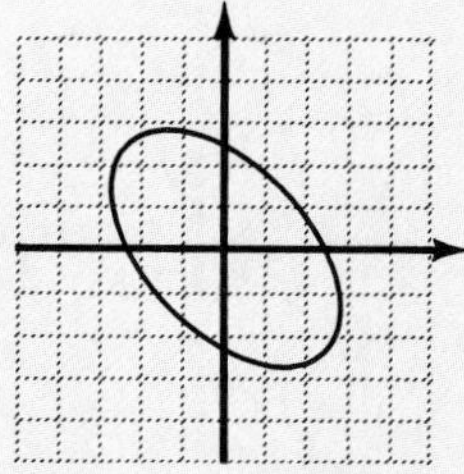

The first equation is for an ellipse whose major axis is along the y-axis. The second equation produces an ellipse that is a 45° rotation of the first ellipse, with its major axis along the line $y = -x$.

Page 494 EXERCISE SET 11-3

52. Let $P(x) = a_nx^n + a_{n-1}x^{n-1} + \cdots + a_1x + a_0$, where the coefficients are real numbers. Let $z = a + bi$ be a complex root of $P(x)$. Then $P(z) = 0$, or $a_nz^n + a_{n-1}z^{n-1} + \cdots + a_1z + a_0 = 0$. Now let us find the conjugate of each side of the equation. We can represent the conjugate using a bar. First note that $\overline{0} = 0$, since 0 is a real number. Then we have the following.

$$\begin{aligned} 0 &= \overline{0} \\ &= \overline{a_nz^n + a_{n-1}z^{n-1} + \cdots + a_1z + a_0} \\ &= \overline{a_nz^n} + \overline{a_{n-1}z^{n-1}} + \cdots + \overline{a_1z} + \overline{a_0} \\ &= \overline{a_n}\cdot\overline{z^n} + \overline{a_{n-1}}\cdot\overline{z^{n-1}} + \cdots + \overline{a_1}\cdot\overline{z} + \overline{a_0} \\ &= a_n\overline{z^n} + a_{n-1}\overline{z^{n-1}} + \cdots + a_1\overline{z} + a_0 \\ &= a_n\overline{z}^n + a_{n-1}\overline{z}^{n-1} + \cdots + a_1\overline{z} + a_0 \end{aligned}$$

Since $P(\overline{z}) = 0$, $\overline{z} = a - bi$ is also a root.

53. Let $z = a + c\sqrt{b}$. The proof is like the proof of Theorem 11-5 in Exercise 52.

Page 507 EXERCISE SET 11-6

1.
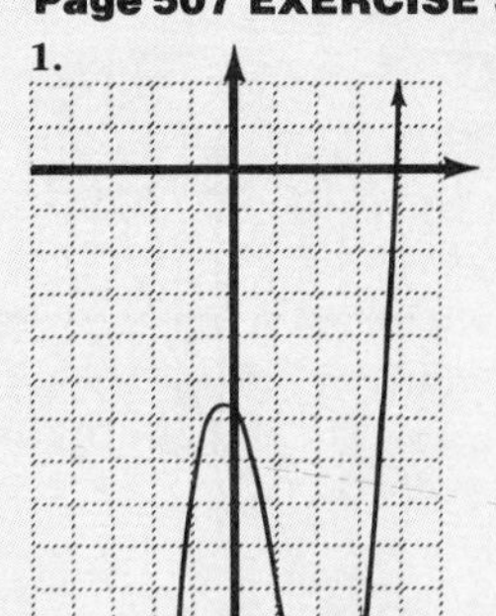

2.
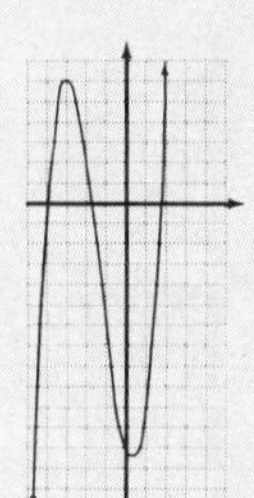

3.
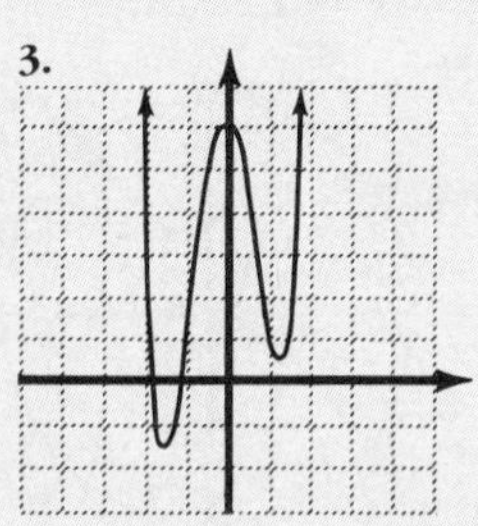

4.
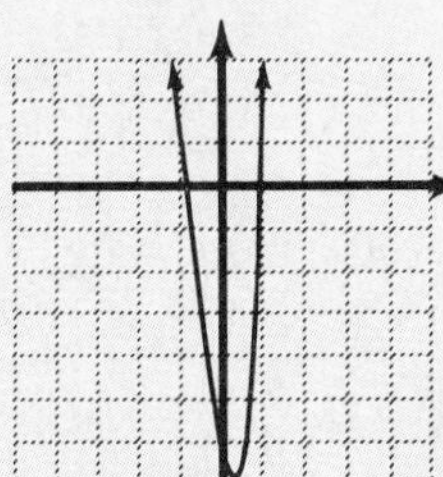

5.
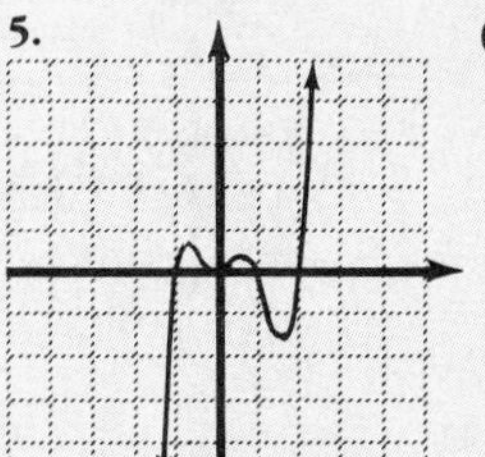

6.
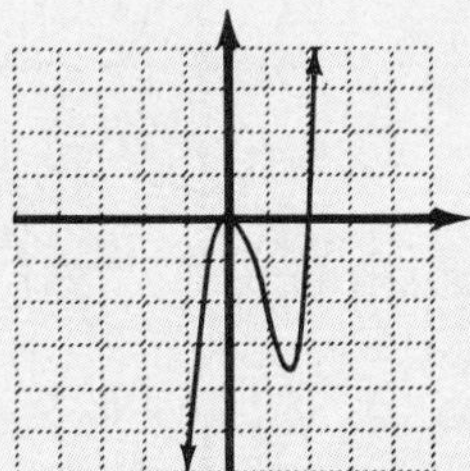

7. $-1, 2$
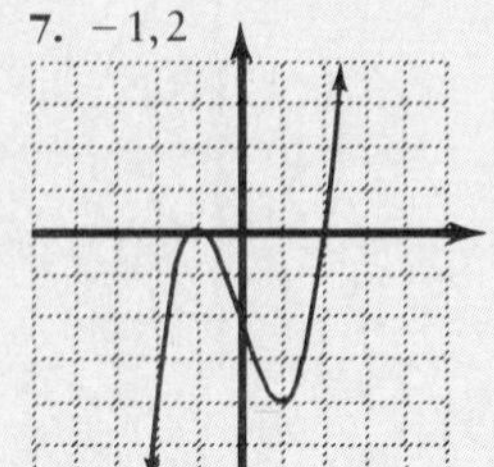

8.
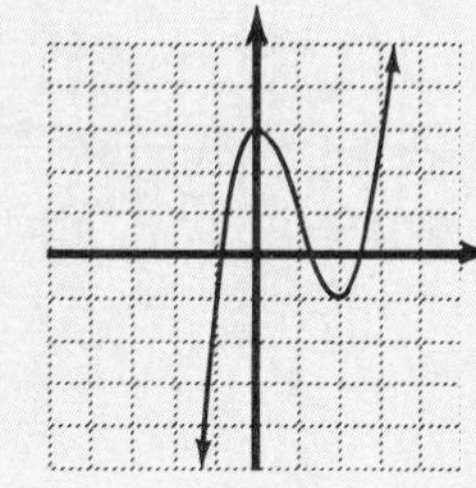

9.
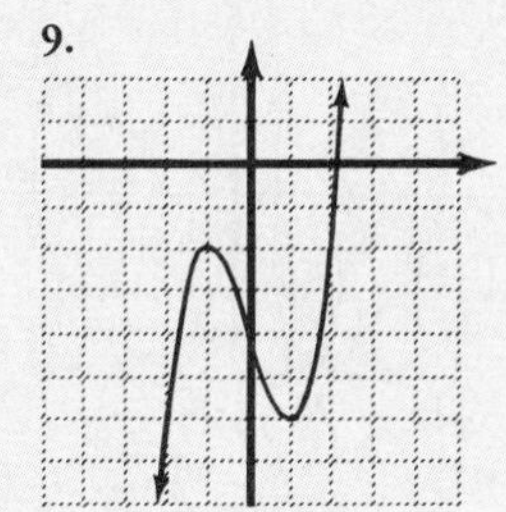

10.
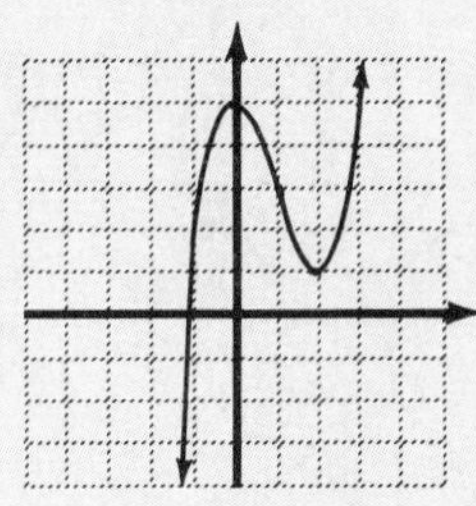

11.
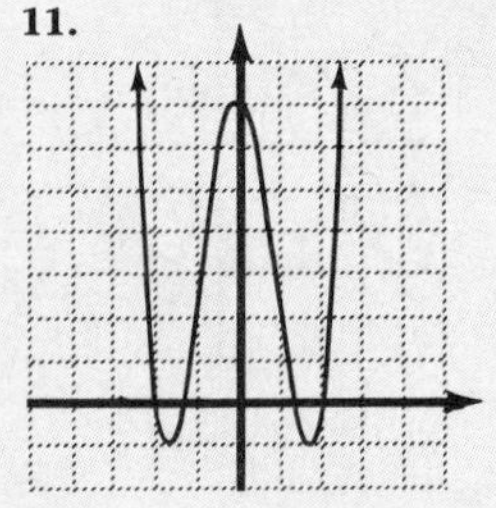

12.
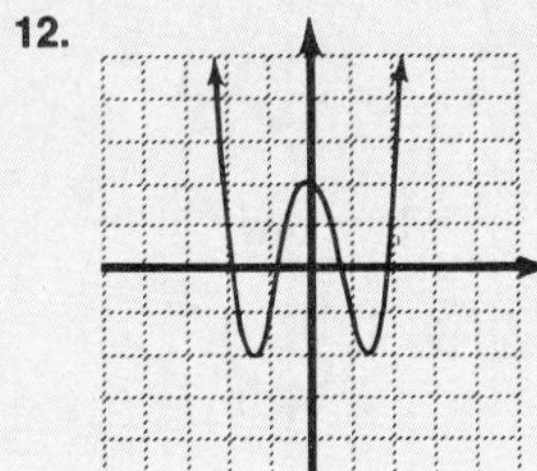

13.
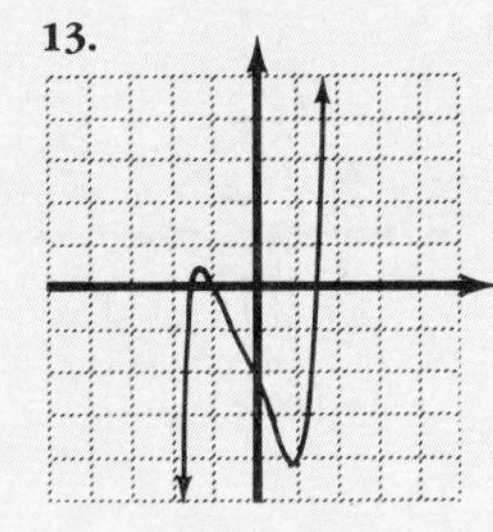

14.
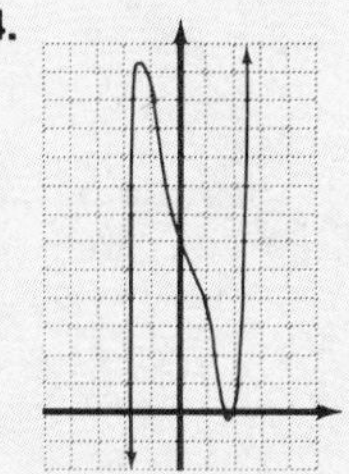

15.
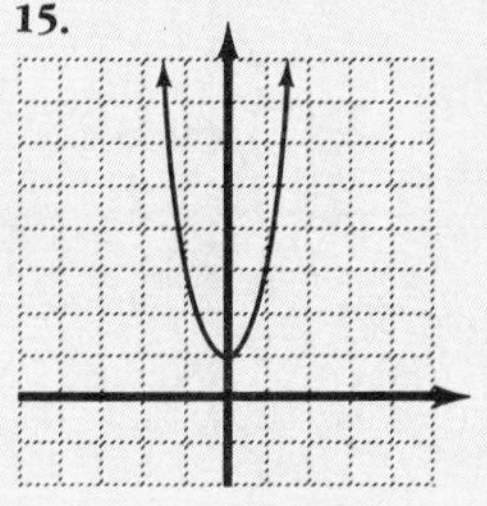

16.
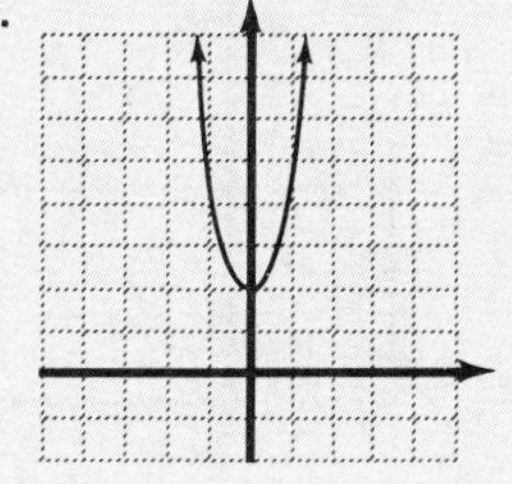

19. -1.27
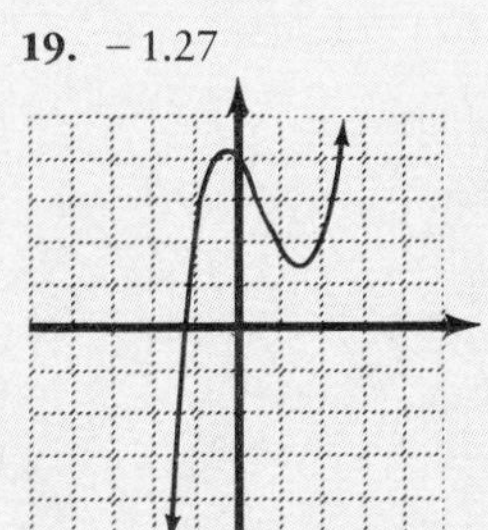

20.
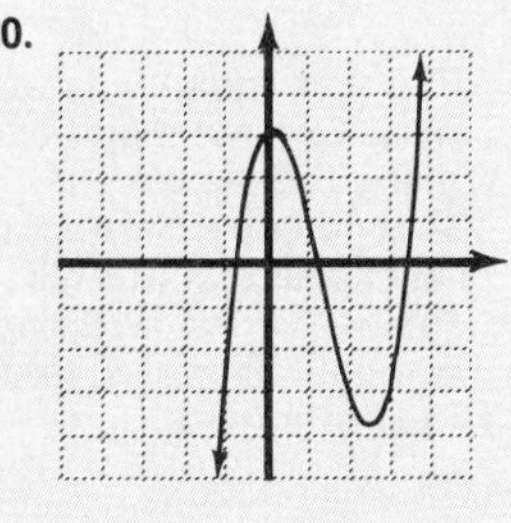

Page 519 EXERCISE SET 12-1

44.
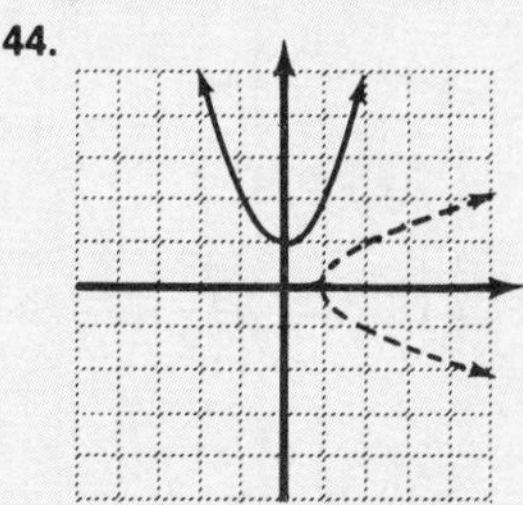

45.
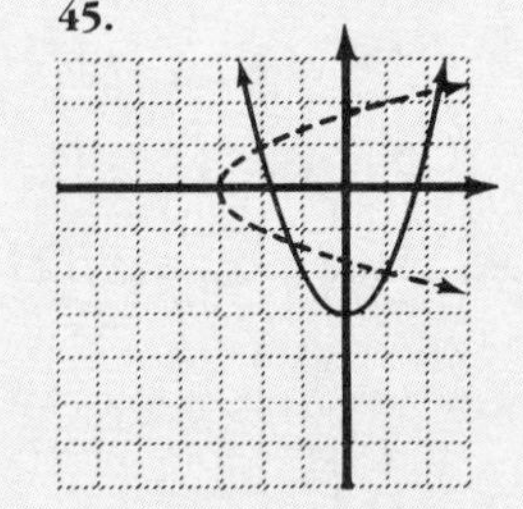

46.
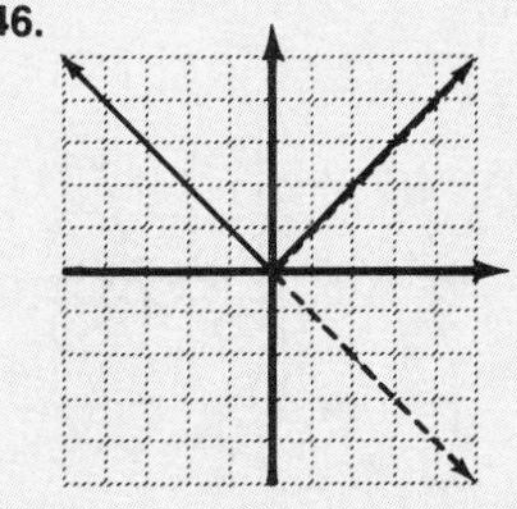

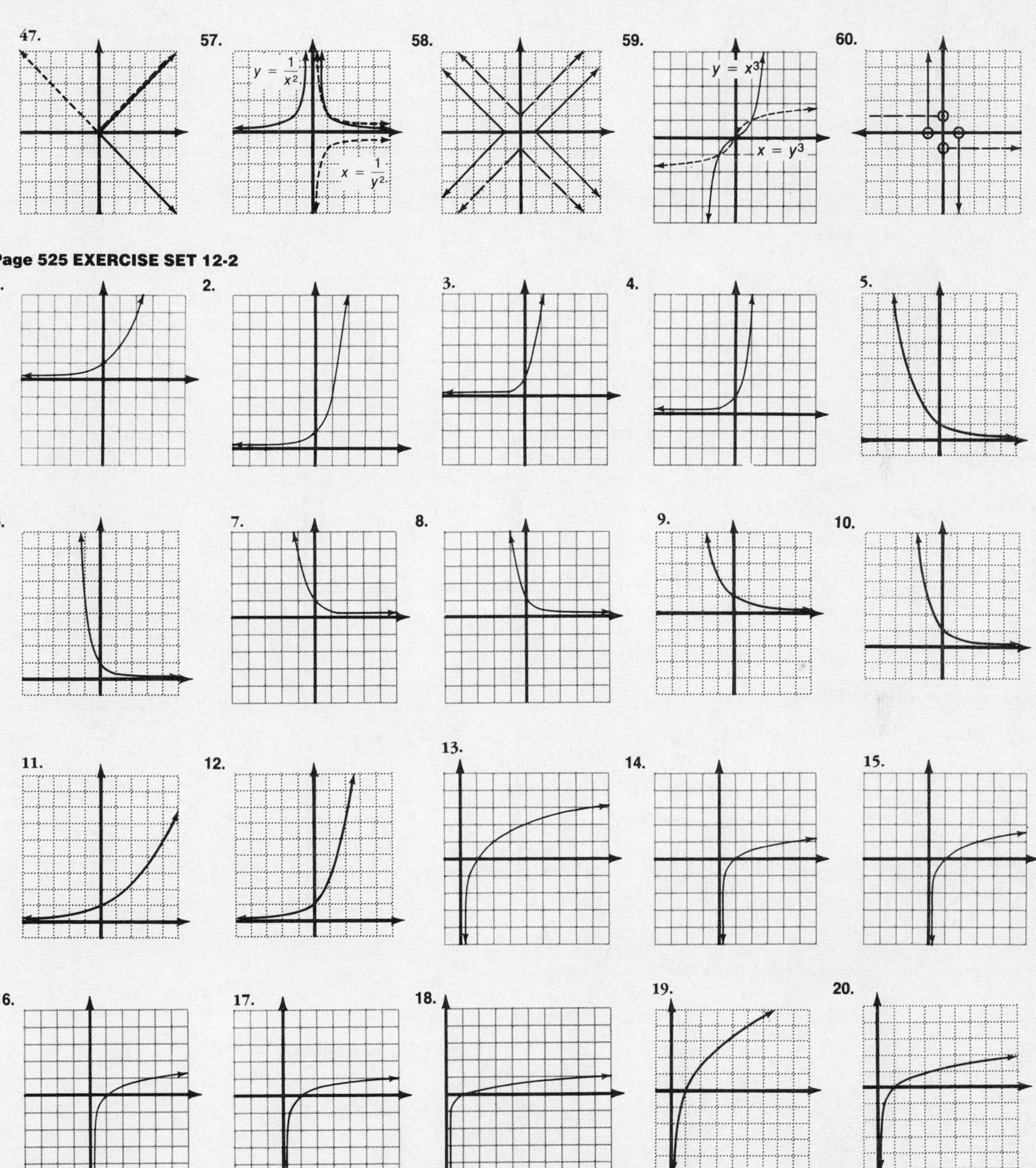
47.
57.
$y = \frac{1}{x^2}$
$x = \frac{1}{y^2}$
58.
59.
$y = x^3$
$x = y^3$
60.
Page 525 EXERCISE SET 12-2
1.
2.
3.
4.
5.
6.
7.
8.
9.
10.
11.
12.
13.
14.
15.
16.
17.
18.
19.
20.

25.

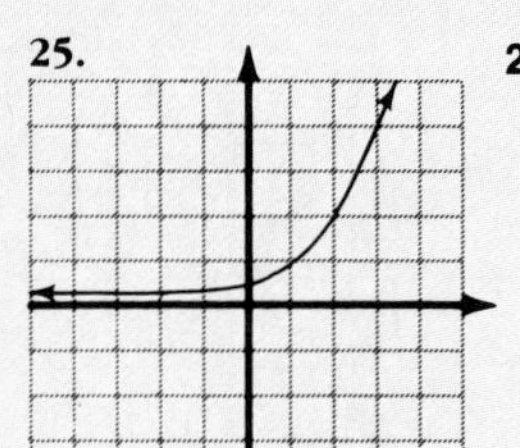

26.

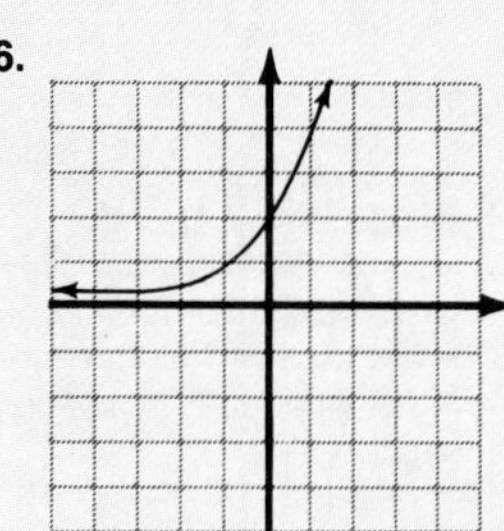

27.

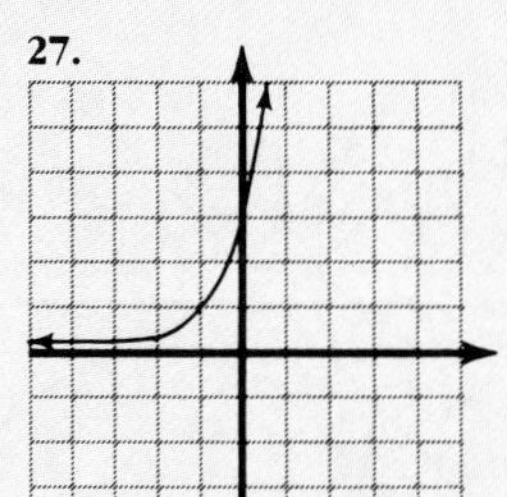

28.

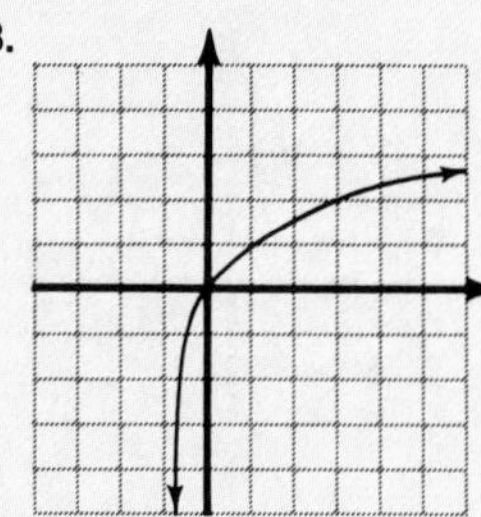

29.

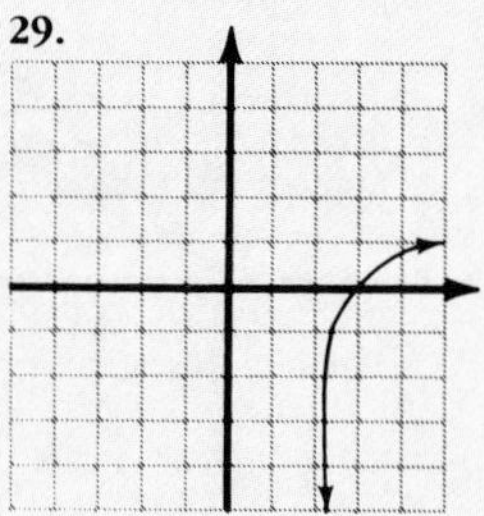

30.

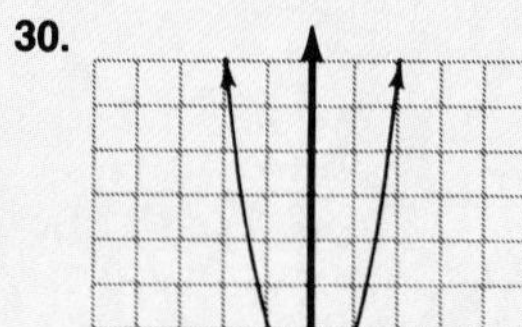

31.

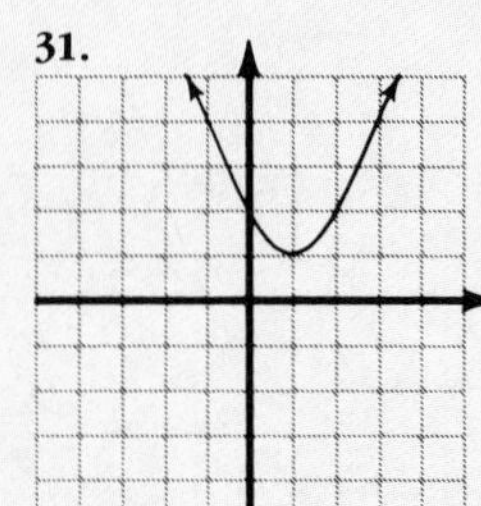

32.

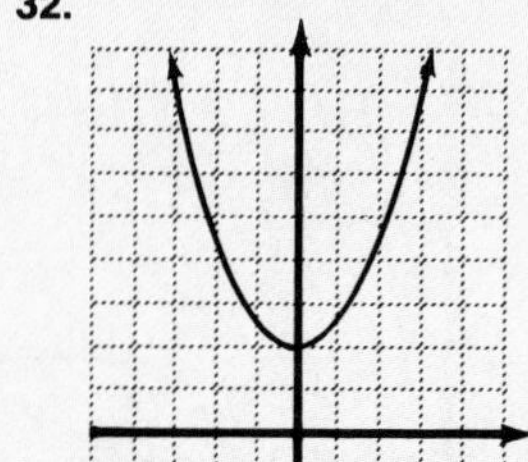

33.

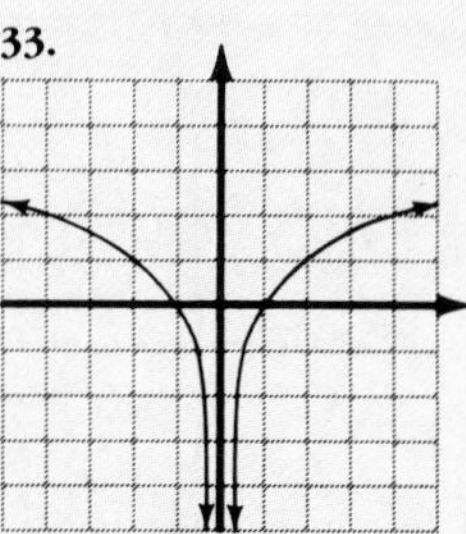

34. All real numbers **35.** $\{x \mid x > 0\}$

36. $\{x \mid x \neq 0\}$ **37.** $\{x \mid x > 0\}$ **38.** $\left\{x \mid x > \frac{4}{3}\right\}$

39. $\{x \; x \neq 0\}$

40. a. 8 b. 8.574188 c. 8.815241
d. 8.821353 e. 8.824411 f. 8.824962

44.

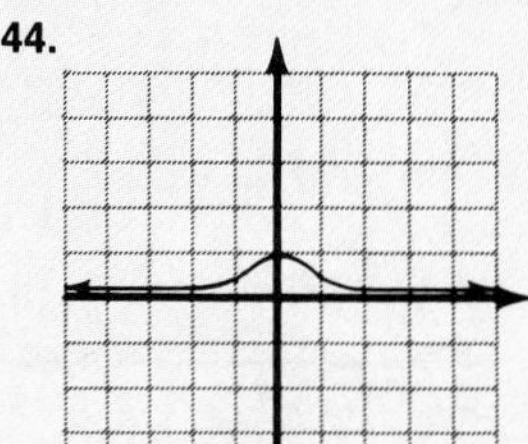

45.

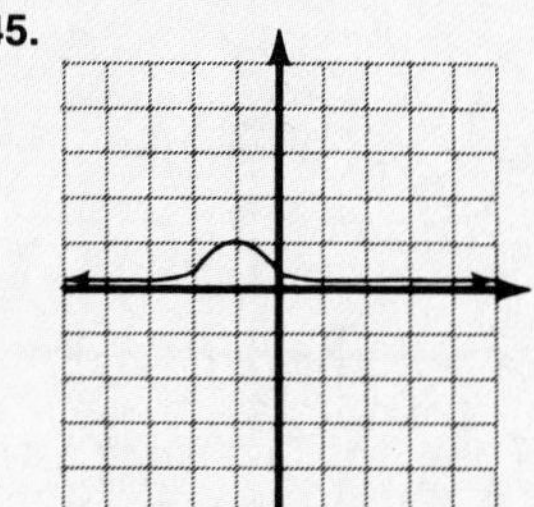

46.

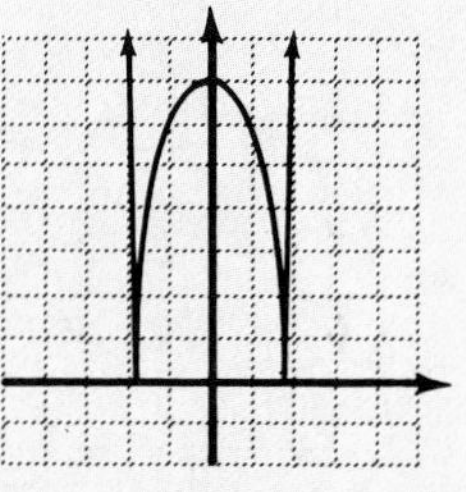

Page 555 EXERCISE SET 12-8

1.

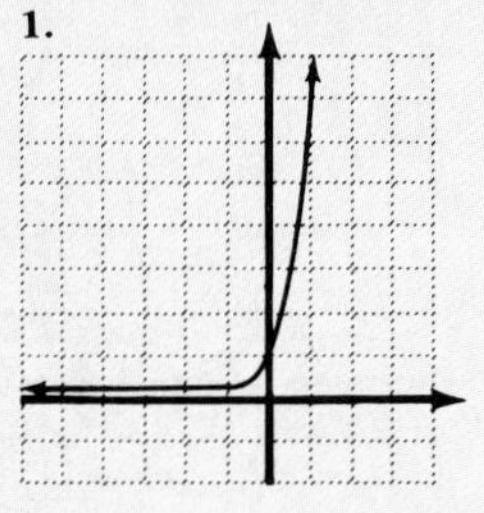

2.

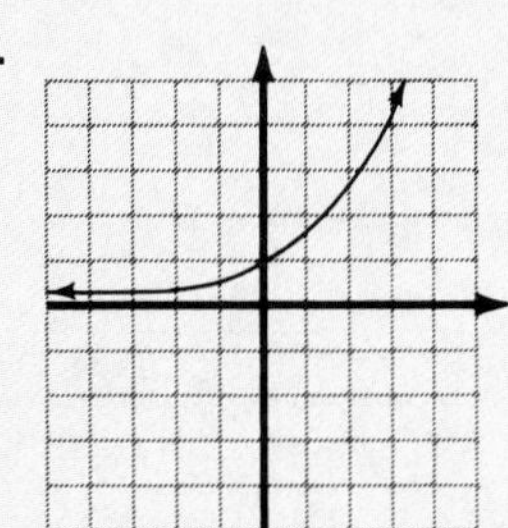

3.

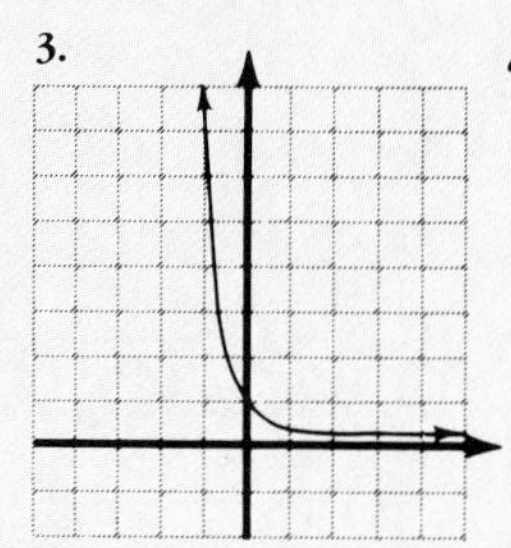

4.

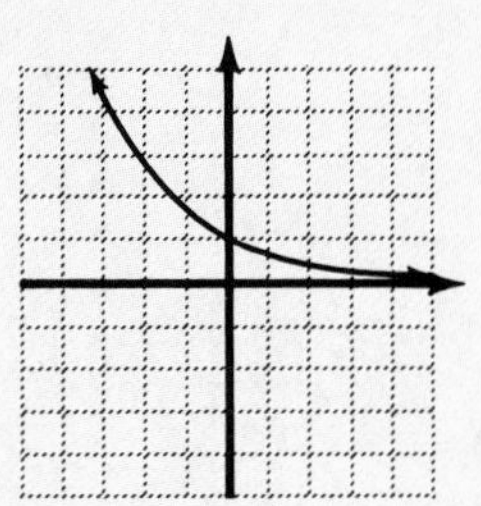

5.

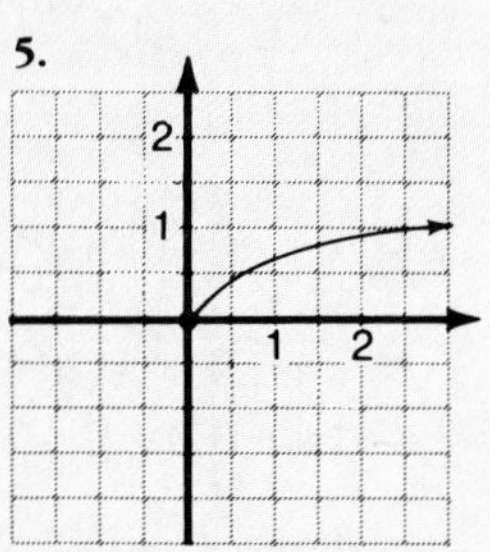

6.

Page 575 EXERCISE SET 13-2

20. $\begin{bmatrix} -1 & -1 \\ -1 & -1 \end{bmatrix}$ **21.** $\begin{bmatrix} 3 & 3 & -7 \\ 5 & -2 & -1 \end{bmatrix}$ **22.** $\begin{bmatrix} -1 & -3 \\ -2 & -6 \end{bmatrix}$ **23.** $\begin{bmatrix} 4 & -5 & 2 \\ -1 & 0 & 4 \\ 2 & 3 & 5 \end{bmatrix}$ **24.** $\begin{bmatrix} 0 & 2 \\ 2 & 0 \end{bmatrix}$

25. $\begin{bmatrix} -3 & 7 & -7 \\ 0 & 0 & -3 \\ 0 & 0 & -6 \end{bmatrix}$ **26.** $\begin{bmatrix} 1 & 6 & -3 \\ 13 & -2 & -2 \end{bmatrix}$ **27.** Cannot be subtracted

28. $(A + B) + C = A + (B + C) = \begin{bmatrix} -1 & -4 \\ 5 & -3 \end{bmatrix}$ **29.** $(G + H) + M = (M + H) + G = \begin{bmatrix} -4 & 3 & 1 \\ 2 & -1 & -2 \\ -1 & -8 & 0 \end{bmatrix}$

31. Let $A = \begin{bmatrix} a_{11} & \cdots & a_{1n} \\ \vdots & & \vdots \\ a_{m1} & \cdots & a_{mn} \end{bmatrix}$ $B = \begin{bmatrix} b_{11} & \cdots & b_{1n} \\ \vdots & & \vdots \\ b_{m1} & \cdots & b_{mn} \end{bmatrix}$

$A - B = \begin{bmatrix} a_{11} - b_{11} & \cdots & a_{1n} - b_{1n} \\ \vdots & & \vdots \\ a_{m1} - b_{m1} & \cdots & a_{mn} - b_{mn} \end{bmatrix} = \begin{bmatrix} a_{11} + (-b_{11}) & \cdots & a_{1n} + (-b_{1n}) \\ \vdots & & \vdots \\ a_{m1} + (-b_{m1}) & \cdots & a_{mn} + (-b_{mn}) \end{bmatrix}$

$= A + (-B)$

32. Let $A = \begin{bmatrix} a_{11} & \cdots & a_{1n} \\ \vdots & & \vdots \\ a_{m1} & \cdots & a_{mn} \end{bmatrix}$ $B = \begin{bmatrix} b_{11} & \cdots & b_{1n} \\ \vdots & & \vdots \\ b_{m1} & \cdots & b_{mn} \end{bmatrix}$

$A + B = \begin{bmatrix} a_{11} + b_{11} & \cdots & a_{1n} + b_{1n} \\ \vdots & & \vdots \\ a_{m1} + b_{m1} & \cdots & a_{mn} + b_{mn} \end{bmatrix} = \begin{bmatrix} b_{11} + a_{11} & \cdots & b_{1n} + a_{1n} \\ \vdots & & \vdots \\ b_{m1} + a_{m1} & \cdots & b_{mn} + a_{mn} \end{bmatrix}$

$= B + A$

Page 587 EXERCISE SET 13-4

40. a. $(A + B)(A - B) = \begin{bmatrix} 0 & -1 \\ 2 & 3 \end{bmatrix} \begin{bmatrix} -2 & 1 \\ 2 & -1 \end{bmatrix} = \begin{bmatrix} -2 & 1 \\ 2 & -1 \end{bmatrix}$,

$A^2 - B^2 = \begin{bmatrix} 1 & 0 \\ 0 & 1 \end{bmatrix} - \begin{bmatrix} 1 & -3 \\ 0 & 4 \end{bmatrix} = \begin{bmatrix} 0 & 3 \\ 0 & -3 \end{bmatrix}$

b. $(A + B)(A + B) = \begin{bmatrix} 0 & -1 \\ 2 & 3 \end{bmatrix} \begin{bmatrix} 0 & -1 \\ 2 & 3 \end{bmatrix} = \begin{bmatrix} -2 & -3 \\ 6 & 7 \end{bmatrix}$,

$(A^2 + 2AB + B^2) = \begin{bmatrix} 1 & 0 \\ 0 & 1 \end{bmatrix} + 2\begin{bmatrix} -1 & 1 \\ 2 & 0 \end{bmatrix} + \begin{bmatrix} 1 & -3 \\ 0 & 4 \end{bmatrix} = \begin{bmatrix} 0 & -1 \\ 4 & 5 \end{bmatrix}$

41. $A + B = \begin{bmatrix} a + e & c + g \\ b + f & d + h \end{bmatrix}$, $B + A = \begin{bmatrix} a + e & c + g \\ b + f & d + h \end{bmatrix}$

42. $(A + B) + C = \begin{bmatrix} a + e & c + g \\ b + f & d + h \end{bmatrix} + \begin{bmatrix} p & r \\ q & s \end{bmatrix} = \begin{bmatrix} a + e + p & c + g + r \\ b + f + q & d + h + s \end{bmatrix}$,

$A + (B + C) = \begin{bmatrix} a & c \\ b & d \end{bmatrix} + \begin{bmatrix} e + p & g + r \\ f + q & h + s \end{bmatrix} = \begin{bmatrix} a + e + p & c + g + r \\ b + f + q & d + h + s \end{bmatrix}$

43. $A - B = \begin{bmatrix} a & c \\ b & d \end{bmatrix} - \begin{bmatrix} e & g \\ f & h \end{bmatrix} = \begin{bmatrix} a - e & c - g \\ b - f & d - h \end{bmatrix}$,

$A + (-B) = \begin{bmatrix} a & c \\ b & d \end{bmatrix} + \begin{bmatrix} -e & -g \\ -f & -h \end{bmatrix} = \begin{bmatrix} a - e & c - g \\ b - f & d - h \end{bmatrix}$

44. $(-1)A = (-1)\begin{bmatrix} a & c \\ b & d \end{bmatrix} = \begin{bmatrix} -a & -c \\ -b & -d \end{bmatrix}$,

$-A = -\begin{bmatrix} a & c \\ b & d \end{bmatrix} = \begin{bmatrix} -a & -c \\ -b & -d \end{bmatrix}$

45. $k(A + B) = k\begin{bmatrix} a + e & c + g \\ b + f & d + h \end{bmatrix} = \begin{bmatrix} ka + ke & kc + kg \\ kb + kf & kd + kh \end{bmatrix}$,

$kA + kB = \begin{bmatrix} ka & kc \\ kb & kd \end{bmatrix} + \begin{bmatrix} ke & kg \\ kf & kh \end{bmatrix} = \begin{bmatrix} ka + ke & kc + kg \\ kb + kf & kd + kh \end{bmatrix}$

46. $(k + m)A = (k + m)\begin{bmatrix} a & c \\ b & d \end{bmatrix} = \begin{bmatrix} (k + m)a & (k + m)c \\ (k + m)b & (k + m)d \end{bmatrix}$

$= \begin{bmatrix} ka + ma & kc + mc \\ kb + mb & kd + md \end{bmatrix}$,

$kA + mA = k\begin{bmatrix} a & c \\ b & d \end{bmatrix} + m\begin{bmatrix} a & c \\ b & d \end{bmatrix} = \begin{bmatrix} ka & kc \\ kb & kd \end{bmatrix} + \begin{bmatrix} ma & mc \\ mb & md \end{bmatrix}$

$= \begin{bmatrix} ka + ma & kc + mc \\ kb + mb & kd + md \end{bmatrix}$

Page 622 EXERCISE SET 14-2

39. $S_n = a_1 + a_2 + a_3 + \cdots + a_{n-2} + a_{n-1} + a_n$
Group terms as follows. $S_n = (a_1 + a_n) + (a_2 + a_{n-1}) + (a_3 + a_{n-2}) + \cdots$ If n is odd, the middle term $a_{\left(\frac{n+1}{2}\right)}$ will be left over.
Now $a_2 = a_1 + d$ and $a_{n-1} = a_n - d$, so $(a_1 + a_n) = (a_2 + a_{n-1})$. Likewise the sums of all the pairs are equal, so $S_n = (a_1 + a_n) + (a_1 + a_n) + \cdots$. If n is even, there are $\frac{n}{2}$ pairs, so
$S_n = \frac{n}{2}(a_1 + a_n)$. If n is odd, there are $\frac{n-1}{2}$ pairs, so
$S_n = \frac{n-1}{2}(a_1 + a_n) + a_{\left(\frac{n+1}{2}\right)} = \frac{n-1}{2}(a_1 + a_n) + \frac{1}{2}(a_1 + a_n) = \frac{n}{2}(a_1 + a_n)$

40. Given Problem 39, $S_n = \frac{n}{2}(a_1 + a_n)$, but $a_n = a_1 + (n - 1)d$.
Thus $S_n = \frac{n}{2}[a_1 + a_1 + (n - 1)d]$ or
$S_n = \frac{n}{2}[2a_1 + (n - 1)d]$.

41. $x + d = y$ or $x = y - d$
$z = y + d$
$x + y + z = y - d + y + y + d = 3y$

42. For n odd the middle term is $\frac{a_1 + a_n}{2}$ but $S_n = \frac{n}{2}(a_1 + a_n)$ or
$\frac{S_n}{n} = \frac{1}{2}(a_1 + a_n) = \frac{a_1 + a_n}{2}$. For n even, the sum of the middle two terms is equal to the sum of the first and last terms or $a_1 + a_n$, but $S_n = \frac{n}{2}(a_1 + a_n) = \frac{2S_n}{n} = a_1 + a_n$.

Page 636 EXERCISE SET 14-5

1. A. $\frac{1}{2} \cdot 1(1 + 5) = \frac{6}{2} = 3$

B. Assume true for $n = k$, show true for $n = k + 1$.

$3 + 4 + 5 + \cdots + (k + 2) + (k + 3) = \frac{k(k + 5)}{2} + k + 3$

$= \frac{k(k + 5) + 2(k + 3)}{2} = \frac{k^2 + 7k + 6}{2} = \frac{(k + 1)(k + 6)}{2}$

$= \frac{1}{2}(k + 1)[(k + 1) + 5]$

2. A. $1(1 + 2) = 1 \cdot 3 = 3$

B. Assume true for $n = k$, show true for $n = k + 1$.
$3 + 5 + 7 + \cdots + (2k + 1) + (2k + 3) = k(k + 2) + (2k + 3)$
$= k^2 + 4k + 3 = (k + 1)(k + 3) = (k + 1)[(k + 1) + 2]$

3. A. $-\frac{1(1 + 3)}{2} = \frac{-4}{2} = -2$

B. Assume true for $n = k$, show true for $n = k + 1$.

$-2 - 3 - 4 - \cdots - (k + 1) - (k + 2)$

$= \frac{-k(k + 3)}{2}$

$- (k + 2) = \frac{-k(k + 3) - 2(k + 2)}{2}$

$= \frac{-(k^2 + 5k + 4)}{2}$

$= \frac{-(k + 1)(k + 4)}{2}$

$= -\frac{1}{2}(k + 1)[(k + 1) + 3]$

4. A. $\frac{4}{3}(4^1 - 1) = \frac{4}{3}(3) = 4$

B. Assume true for $n = k$, show true for $n = k + 1$.

$$4 + 4^2 + \cdots + 4^k + 4^{k+1} = \frac{4(4^k - 1)}{3} + 4^{k+1}$$
$$= \frac{4(4^k - 1) + 3 \cdot 4^{k+1}}{3} = \frac{4}{3}(4^k - 1 + 3 \cdot 4^k) = \frac{4}{3}[(1 + 3)\, 4^k - 1]$$
$$= \frac{4}{3}(4^{k+1} - 1)$$

5. A. $\frac{1(1 + 1)(2 \cdot 1 + 1)}{6} = 1.$

B. Assume true for $n = k$, show true for $n = k + 1$.

$$1^2 + 2^2 + 3^2 + \cdots + k^2 + (k + 1)^2$$
$$= \frac{k(k + 1)(2k + 1)}{6} + (k + 1)^2$$
$$= \frac{(k + 1)(2k^2 + 7k + 6)}{6}$$
$$= \frac{(k + 1)(k + 2)(2k + 3)}{6} = \frac{(k + 1)(k + 2)[2(k + 1) + 1]}{6}$$

6. A. $\frac{1^2(1 + 1)^2}{4} = 1.$

B. Assume true for $n = k$, show true for $n = k + 1$.

$$1^3 + 2^3 + 3^3 + \cdots + k^3 + (k + 1)^3 = \frac{k^2(k + 1)^2}{4} + (k + 1)^3$$
$$= \frac{k^2(k + 1)^2 + 4(k + 1)^3}{4} = \frac{(k + 1)^2[k^2 + 4(k + 1)]}{4}$$
$$= \frac{(k + 1)^2(k^2 + 4k + 4)}{4} = \frac{(k + 1)^2(k + 2)^2}{4}$$
$$= \frac{(k + 1)^2[(k + 1) + 1]^2}{4}$$

7. A. $\frac{1}{1 + 1} = \frac{1}{2}$

B. Assume true for $n = k$, show true for $n = k + 1$.

$$\frac{1}{1 \cdot 2} + \frac{1}{2 \cdot 3} + \cdots \frac{1}{k(k + 1)} + \frac{1}{(k + 1)(k + 2)}$$
$$= \frac{k}{k + 1} + \frac{1}{(k + 1)(k + 2)} = \frac{k(k + 2)}{(k + 1)(k + 2)} + \frac{1}{(k + 1)(k + 2)}$$
$$= \frac{(k + 1)^2}{(k + 1)(k + 2)} = \frac{(k + 1)}{(k + 2)} = \frac{(k + 1)}{[(k + 1) + 1]}$$

8. A. $\frac{1}{2}(3 \cdot 1 + 1) = 2$

B. Assume true for $n = k$, show true for $n = k + 1$.

$$2 + 5 + 8 + \cdots + (3k - 1) + [3(k + 1) - 1]$$
$$= \frac{k(3k + 1)}{2} + [3(k + 1) - 1] = \frac{3k^2 + 7k + 4}{2} = \frac{(k + 1)(3k + 4)}{2}$$
$$= \frac{1}{2}(k + 1)[3(k + 1) + 1]$$

9. A. $\frac{1(9 - 1)}{2} = 4$

B. Assume true for $n = k$, show true for $n = k + 1$.

$$4 + 3 + 2 + \cdots + (5 - k) + [5 - (k + 1)]$$
$$= \frac{k(9 - k)}{2} + (4 - k) = \frac{-k^2 + 7k + 8}{2}$$
$$= \frac{(k + 1)(-k + 8)}{2} = \frac{1}{2}(k + 1)[9 - (k + 1)]$$

10. A. $\frac{3\left(1 - \frac{1}{3}\right)}{2} = \frac{3\left(\frac{2}{3}\right)}{2} = 1.$

B. Assume true for $n = k$, show true for $n = k + 1$.

$$1 + \frac{1}{3} + \frac{1}{9} + \cdots + 3^{1-k} + 3^{1-(k+1)}$$
$$= \frac{3}{2}\left(1 - \left(\frac{1}{3}\right)^k\right) + 3^{-k} = \frac{3\left(1 - \left(\frac{1}{3}\right)^k\right) + 2\left(\frac{1}{3}\right)^k}{2}$$
$$= \frac{3 - \frac{3}{3}\left(\frac{1}{3}\right)^k}{2} = \frac{3}{2}\left(1 - \left(\frac{1}{3}\right)^{k+1}\right)$$

11. A. $2 \cdot 1 + 3 = 5;\ 1(1 + 4) = 5$

B. Assume true for $n = j$, show true for $n = j + 1$.

$$\sum_{k=1}^{j} (2k + 3) + [2(j + 1) + 3] = j(j + 4) + (2j + 5)$$
$$= j^2 + 6j + 5 = (j + 1)[(j + 1) + 4]$$

12. A. $2^1 = 2;\ 2(2^1 - 1) = 2$

B. Assume true for $n = j$, show true for $n = j + 1$.

$$\sum_{k=1}^{j} 2^k + 2^{j+1} = 2(2^j - 1) + 2^{j+1} = 2^{j+1} - 2 + 2^{j+1}$$
$$= 2(2^{j+1}) - 2 = 2(2^{j+1} - 1)$$

13. Proving that the proposition is true for 1 is like knocking over the first domino. Proving that if the proposition is true for k, then it is true for $k + 1$ is like knowing that knocking over a given domino guarantees that the next domino will also fall.

14. A. $1 + \frac{1}{1} = 1 + 1$

B. Assume true for $n = k$, show true for $n = k + 1$.

$$\left(1 + \frac{1}{1}\right)\left(1 + \frac{1}{2}\right)\cdots\left(1 + \frac{1}{k}\right)\left(1 + \frac{1}{k + 1}\right)$$
$$= (k + 1)\left(1 + \frac{1}{k + 1}\right) = k + \frac{k}{k + 1} + 1 + \frac{1}{k + 1}$$
$$= \frac{k^2 + 3k + 2}{k + 1} = \frac{(k + 1)(k + 2)}{k + 1} = (k + 1) + 1.$$

15. A. $1^5 = \frac{1^2 \cdot 2^2 \cdot 3}{12}$

B. Assume true for $n = j$, show true for $n = j + 1$.

$$\sum_{k=1}^{j} k^5 + (j + 1)^5 = \frac{j^2(j + 1)^2(2j^2 + 2j - 1)}{12} + (j + 1)^5$$
$$= \frac{(j + 1)^2[2j^4 + 2j^3 - j^2 + 12(j + 1)^3]}{12}$$
$$= \frac{(j + 1)^2(2j^4 + 14j^3 + 35j^2 + 36j + 12)}{12}$$
$$= \frac{(j + 1)^2(j + 2)^2(2j^2 + 6j + 3)}{12}$$
$$= \frac{(j + 1)^2(j + 2)^2(2(j + 1)^2 + 2(j + 1) - 1)}{12}$$

16. $\sum_{k=1}^{n} k^3 - \sum_{k=1}^{n} k^2 = \frac{n(n^2 - 1)(3n + 2)}{12} = \frac{n(n - 1)(n + 1)(3n + 2)}{12}$

A. $1 - 1 = 0$

B. Assume true for $n = j$, show true for $n = j + 1$.

$$\sum_{k=1}^{j} k^3 - \sum k^2 + (j + 1)^3 - (j + 1)^2$$
$$= \frac{j(j^2 - 1)(3j + 2)}{12} + (j + 1)^3 - (j + 1)^2$$

$$\sum_{k=1}^{j+1} k^3 - \sum_{k=1}^{j+1} k^2 = \frac{(j+1)[j(j-1)(3j+2) + 12(j+1)^2 - 12(j+1)]}{12}$$
$$= \frac{(j+1)(j)(3j^2 + 11j + 10)}{12}$$
$$= \frac{(j+1)(j)(j+2)(3j+5)}{12}$$
$$= \frac{(j+1)(j+1-1)(j+1+1)(3(j+1)+2)}{12}$$

PAGE 663 EXERCISE SET 15-4

28. (A) Check for $n = 1$.

$$(a+b)^1 = \binom{1}{0}a^1 + \binom{1}{1}b^1$$
$$a + b = a + b$$

(B) Assume true for $n = k$.

$$(a+b)^k = \binom{k}{0}a^k + \binom{k}{1}a^{k-1}b + \cdots + \binom{k}{k-1}ab^{k-1} + \binom{k}{k}b^k$$

Show true for $n = k + 1$.

$$(a+b)^k(a+b) = \left[\binom{k}{0}a^k + \binom{k}{1}a^{k-1}b + \cdots + \binom{k}{k-1}ab^{k-1} + \binom{k}{k}b^k\right](a+b)$$
$$(a+b)^{k+1} = \binom{k}{0}a^{k+1} + \binom{k}{1}a^kb + \cdots + \binom{k}{k-1}a^2b^{k-1} + \binom{k}{k}ab^k + \binom{k}{0}a^kb + \binom{k}{1}a^{k-1}b^2 + \cdots + \binom{k}{k-1}ab^k + \binom{k}{k}b^{k+1}$$
$$= \binom{k}{0}a^{k+1} + \left[\binom{k}{1} + \binom{k}{0}\right]a^kb + \cdots + \left[\binom{k}{k} + \binom{k}{k-1}\right]ab^k + \binom{k}{k}b^{k+1}$$
$$= \binom{k}{0}a^{k+1} + \binom{k+1}{1}a^kb + \cdots + \binom{k+1}{k}ab^k + \binom{k}{k}b^{k+1}$$
$$= \binom{k+1}{0}a^{k+1} + \binom{k+1}{1}a^kb + \cdots + \binom{k+1}{k}ab^k + \binom{k+1}{k+1}b^{k+1}$$

Note: $\binom{k}{0} = \binom{k+1}{0}$ and $\binom{k}{k} = \binom{k+1}{k+1}$.

Therefore by A and B the statement

$$(a+b)^n = \binom{n}{0}a^n + \binom{n}{1}a^{n-1}b + \cdots + \binom{n}{n-1}ab^{n-1} + \binom{n}{n}b^n$$

is true for all natural numbers n.

Page 692 EXERCISE SET 16-1

2.

Stem	Leaf
4	9, 9, 9, 6, 8
5	6, 6, 5, 8, 9, 7, 6, 5, 4, 3, 8, 6
6	3, 1, 0, 3, 0, 8, 5, 7, 3, 1, 4, 4

3.

Stem	Leaf
3	9, 8
4	5, 6, 8, 9, 0, 8, 9, 9
5	5, 6, 9, 6, 9
6	5, 7, 7, 7, 8, 9, 8, 5, 8, 9, 5, 7
7	0, 1, 0, 2, 0

6.

Interval	Frequency	Rel f
24.6–25.0	2	0.07
25.1–25.5	2	0.07
25.6–26.0	7	0.25
26.1–26.5	2	0.07
26.6–27.0	5	0.18
27.1–27.5	4	0.14
27.6–28.0	4	0.14
28.1–28.5	1	0.04
28.6–29.0	1	0.04

7.

Interval	Frequency	Rel f
9,001 – 10,000	1	0.03
10,001 – 11,000	2	0.07
11,001 – 12,000	6	0.21
12,001 – 13,000	6	0.21
13,001 – 14,000	4	0.134
14,001 – 15,000	0	0
15,001 – 16,000	2	0.07
16,001 – 17,000	1	0.03
17,001 – 18,000	2	0.07
18,001 – 19,000	1	0.03
19,001 – 20,000	4	0.134

8.

Interval	Frequency	Rel f
61–65	2	0.05
66–70	7	0.17
71–75	5	0.12
76–80	9	0.21
81–85	1	0.02
86–90	13	0.31
91–95	0	0.00
96–100	4	0.10
101–105	1	0.02

9. If the stem-and-leaf diagram is rotated $\frac{1}{4}$ turn counterclockwise, it approximates a bar graph.
10. A stem-and-leaf diagram can be constructed quickly but it is not as informative as a frequency distribution. However, a frequency distribution can take longer to construct.
11. Scan the tally column until you find the median entries. The average height of the 20 waterfalls is about 1900 feet.
12. 0.3

13. 14.

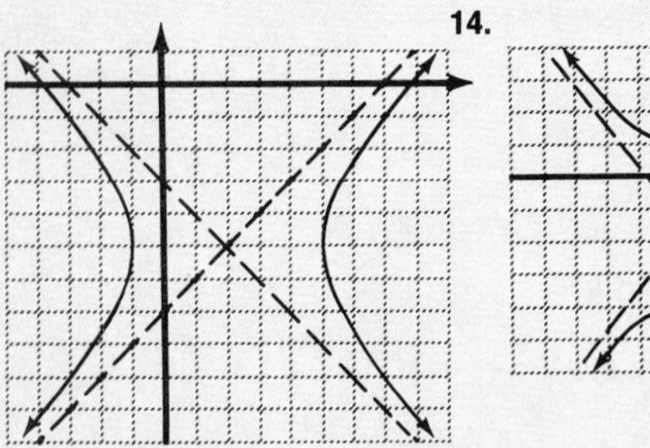

Page 771 EXERCISE SET 17-7

1, 3, 5.

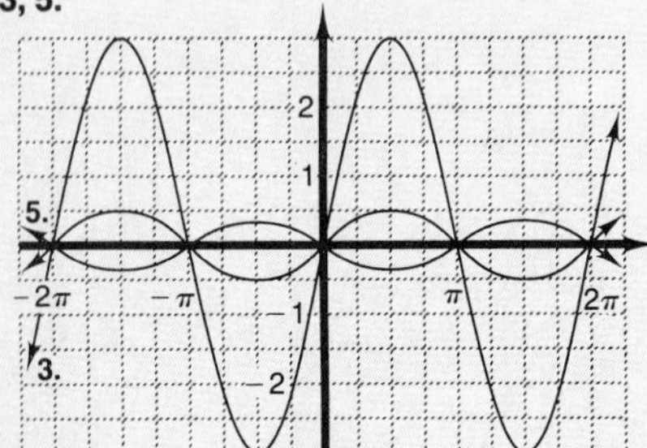

2, 4, 6.

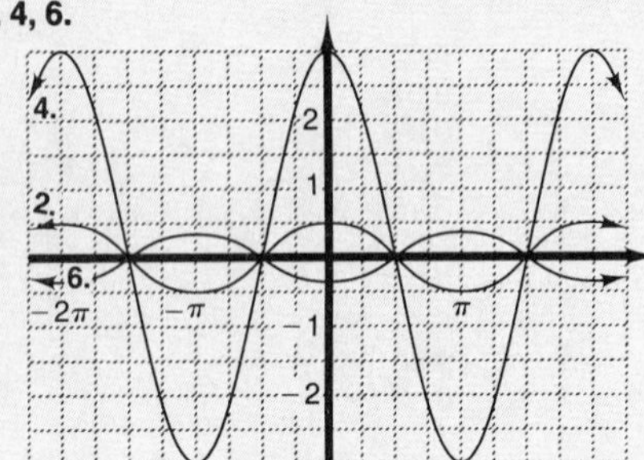

7, 8, 9.

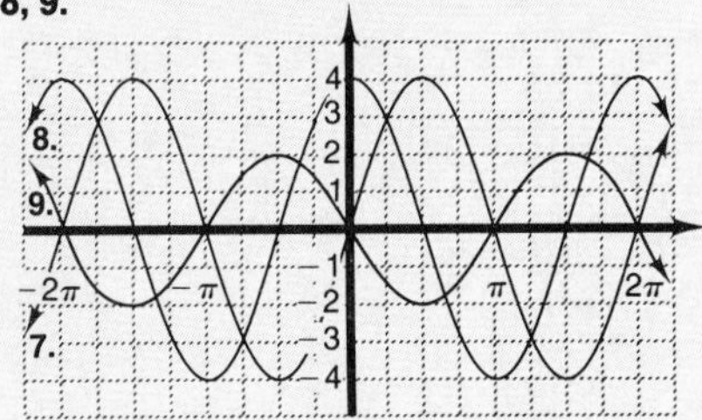

10.

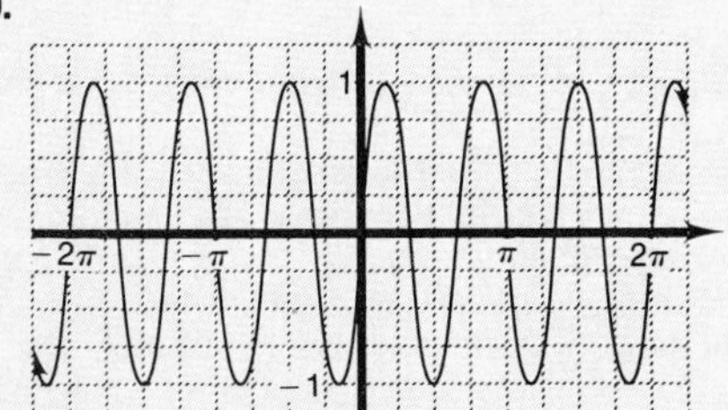

11.

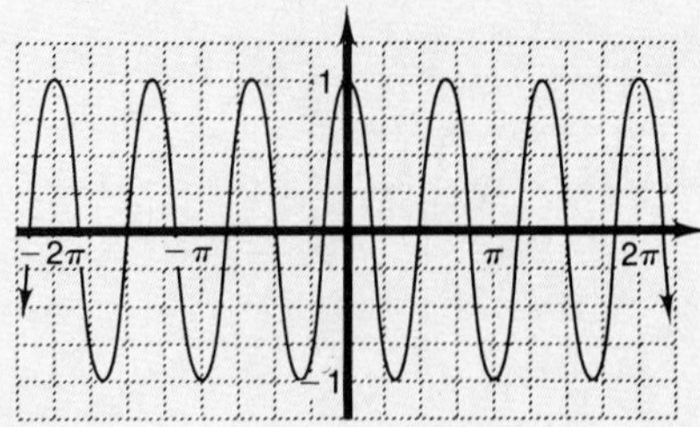

12, 14.

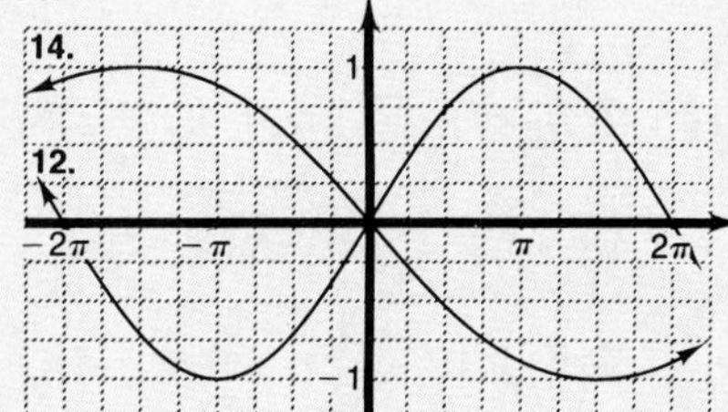

13, 15.

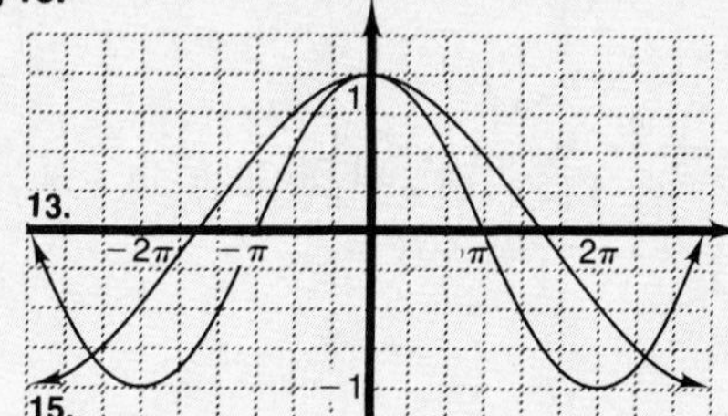

16, 17.

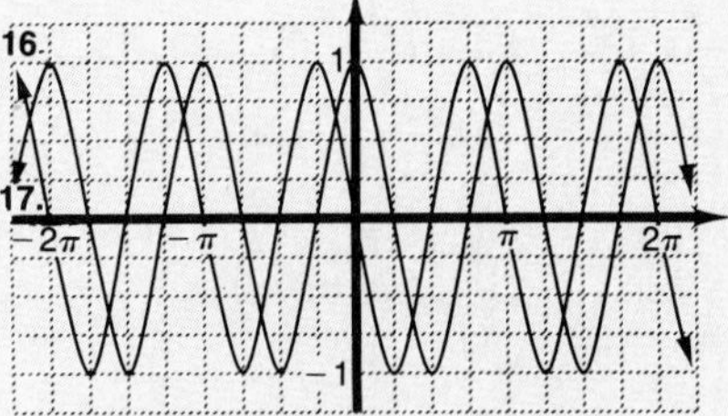

18.

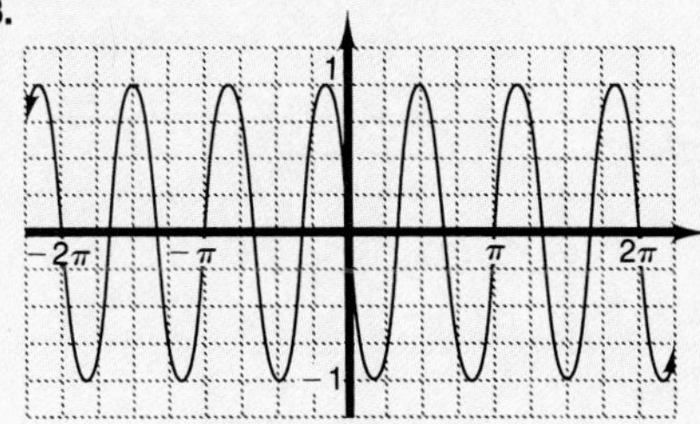

25, 27.

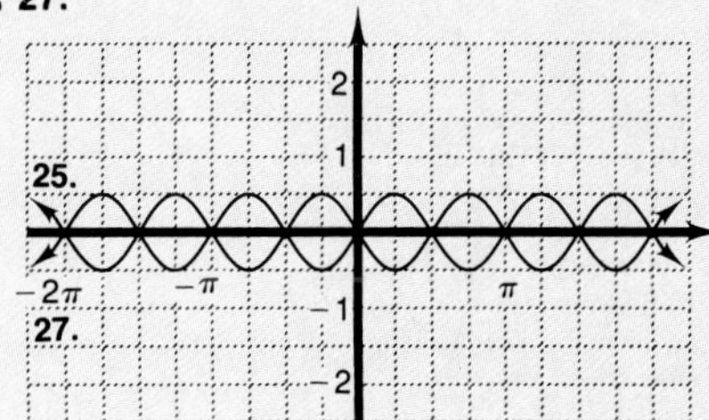

23. $A = 2$, period $= 4\pi$
24. $A = 2$, period $= 4\pi$
25. $A = \frac{1}{2}$, period $= \pi$
26. $A = \frac{1}{2}$, period $= \pi$
27. $A = \frac{1}{2}$, period $= \pi$

19, 21.

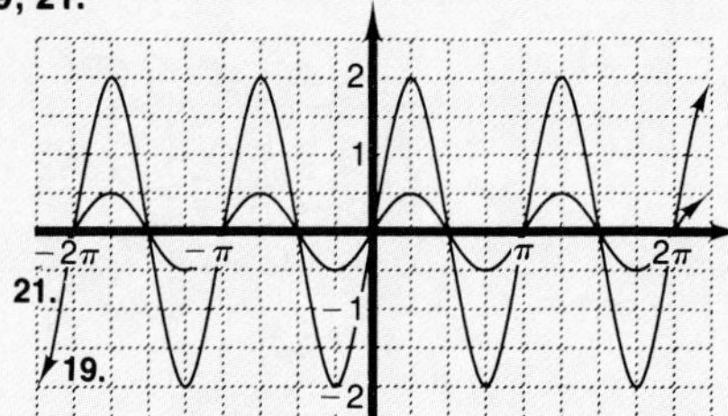

19. $A = 2$, period $= \pi$
20. $A = 2$, period $= \pi$
21. $A = \frac{1}{2}$, period $= \pi$
22. $A = \frac{1}{2}$, period $= \pi$

26.

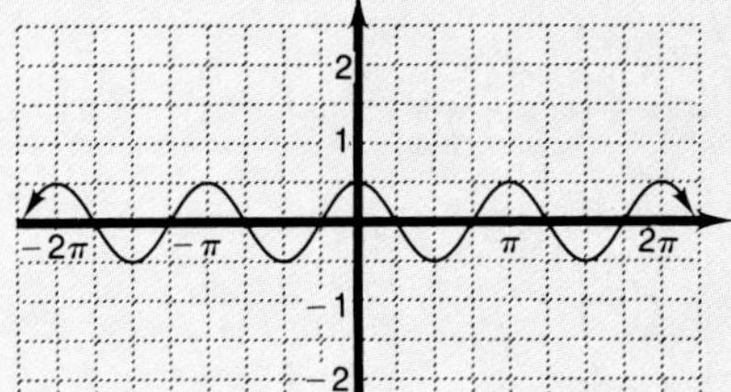

20, 22.

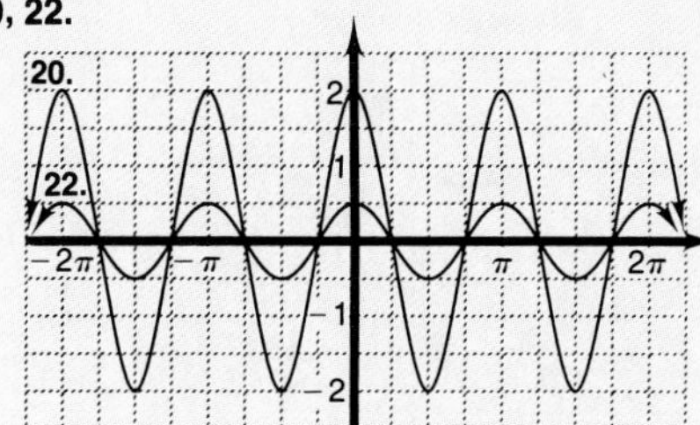

28, 29.

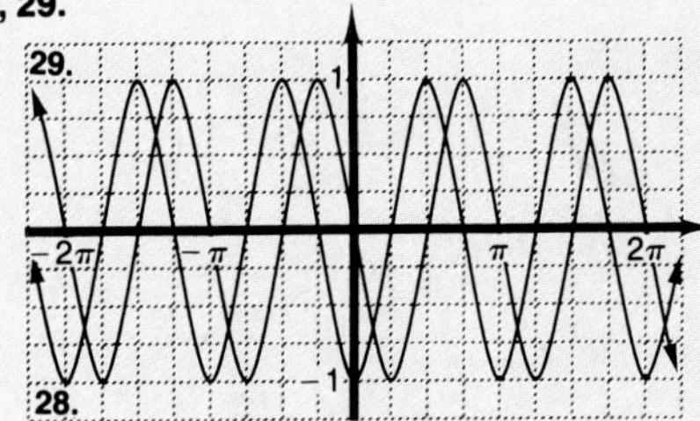

23, 24.

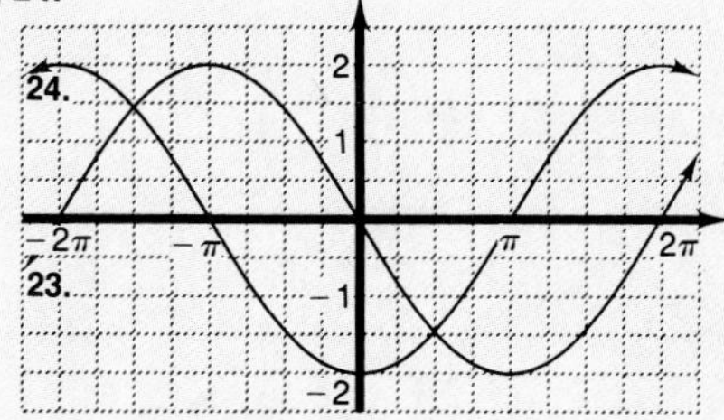

30.

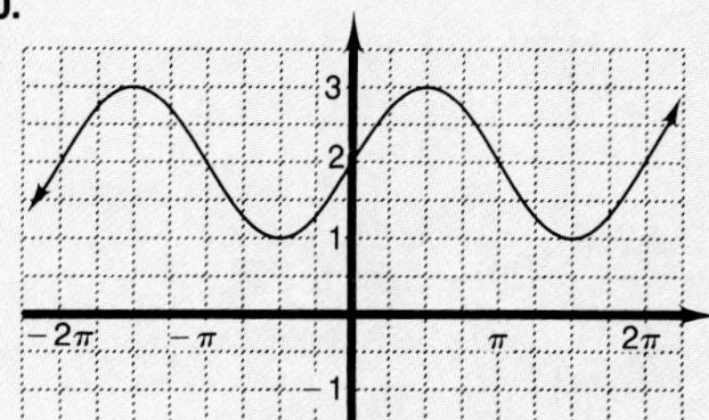

32.

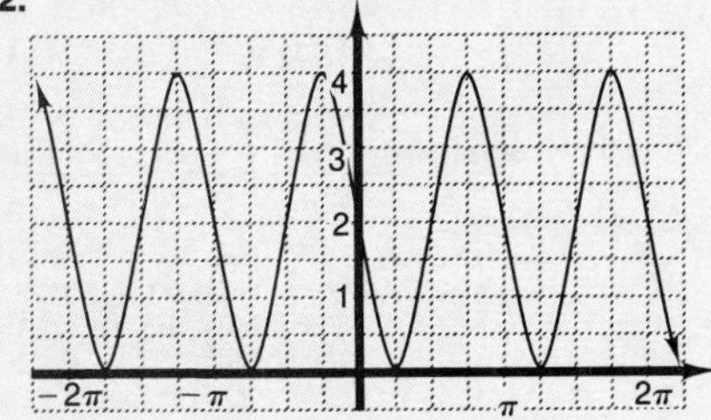

33.

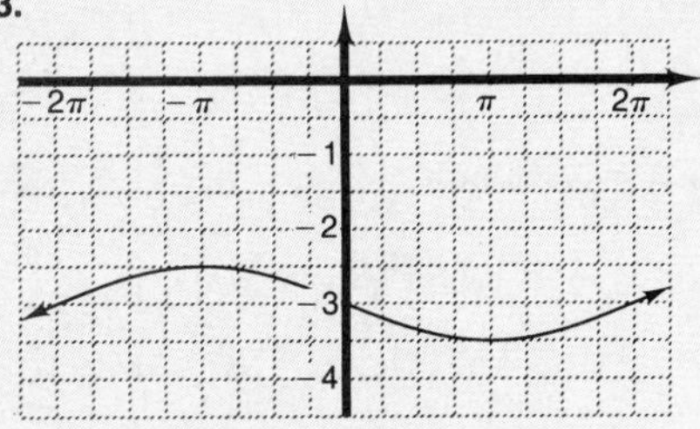

11.

$$\frac{1+\tan\theta}{1-\tan\theta}+\frac{1+\cot\theta}{1-\cot\theta}\equiv 0$$

$$\begin{array}{c|c}
\dfrac{1+\dfrac{\sin\theta}{\cos\theta}}{1-\dfrac{\sin\theta}{\cos\theta}}+\dfrac{1+\dfrac{\cos\theta}{\sin\theta}}{1-\dfrac{\cos\theta}{\sin\theta}} & 0 \\
\dfrac{\dfrac{\cos\theta+\sin\theta}{\cos\theta}}{\dfrac{\cos\theta-\sin\theta}{\cos\theta}}+\dfrac{\dfrac{\sin\theta+\cos\theta}{\sin\theta}}{\dfrac{\sin\theta-\cos\theta}{\sin\theta}} & \\
\dfrac{\cos\theta+\sin\theta}{\cos\theta-\sin\theta}+\dfrac{\sin\theta+\cos\theta}{\sin\theta-\cos\theta} & \\
\dfrac{\cos\theta+\sin\theta}{\cos\theta-\sin\theta}-\dfrac{\cos\theta+\sin\theta}{\cos\theta-\sin\theta} &
\end{array}$$

12.

$$\frac{\cos^2\theta+\cot\theta}{\cos^2\theta-\cot\theta}\equiv\frac{\cos^2\theta\tan\theta+1}{\cos^2\theta\tan\theta-1}$$

$$\begin{array}{c|c}
\dfrac{\cos^2\theta+\dfrac{\cos\theta}{\sin\theta}}{\cos^2\theta-\dfrac{\cos\theta}{\sin\theta}} & \dfrac{\cos^2\theta\dfrac{\sin\theta}{\cos\theta}+1}{\cos^2\theta\dfrac{\sin\theta}{\cos\theta}-1} \\
\dfrac{\dfrac{\cos^2\theta\sin\theta+\cos\theta}{\sin\theta}}{\dfrac{\cos^2\theta\sin\theta-\cos\theta}{\sin\theta}} & \dfrac{\cos\theta\sin\theta+1}{\cos\theta\sin\theta-1} \\
\dfrac{\cos^2\theta\sin\theta+\cos\theta}{\cos^2\theta\sin\theta-\cos\theta} & \\
\dfrac{\cos\theta(\cos\theta\sin\theta+1)}{\cos\theta(\cos\theta\sin\theta-1)} & \\
\dfrac{\cos\theta\sin\theta+1}{\cos\theta\sin\theta-1} &
\end{array}$$

13.

$$\frac{1+\cos 2\theta}{\sin 2\theta}\equiv\cot\theta$$

$$\begin{array}{c|c}
\dfrac{1+2\cos^2\theta-1}{2\sin\theta\cos\theta} & \dfrac{\cos\theta}{\sin\theta} \\
\dfrac{\cos\theta}{\sin\theta} &
\end{array}$$

14.

$$\frac{2\tan\theta}{1+\tan^2\theta}\equiv\sin 2\theta$$

$$\begin{array}{c|c}
\dfrac{2\dfrac{\sin\theta}{\cos\theta}}{1+\dfrac{\sin^2\theta}{\cos^2\theta}} & 2\sin\theta\cos\theta \\
\dfrac{2\dfrac{\sin\theta}{\cos\theta}}{\dfrac{\cos^2\theta+\sin^2\theta}{\cos^2\theta}} & \\
2\dfrac{\sin\theta}{\cos\theta}\cdot\dfrac{\cos^2\theta}{\cos^2\theta+\sin^2\theta} & \\
2\sin\theta\cos\theta &
\end{array}$$

Page 794 EXERCISE SET 18-3

7.

$$\frac{1+\tan\theta}{1+\cot\theta}\equiv\frac{\sec\theta}{\csc\theta}$$

$$\begin{array}{c|c}
\dfrac{1+\dfrac{\sin\theta}{\cos\theta}}{1+\dfrac{\cos\theta}{\sin\theta}} & \dfrac{\dfrac{1}{\cos\theta}}{\dfrac{1}{\sin\theta}} \\
\dfrac{\dfrac{\cos\theta+\sin\theta}{\cos\theta}}{\dfrac{\sin\theta+\cos\theta}{\sin\theta}} & \dfrac{\sin\theta}{\cos\theta} \\
\dfrac{\sin\theta}{\cos\theta} &
\end{array}$$

8.

$$\frac{\cot\theta-1}{1-\tan\theta}\equiv\frac{\csc\theta}{\sec\theta}$$

$$\begin{array}{c|c}
\dfrac{\dfrac{\cos\theta}{\sin\theta}-1}{1-\dfrac{\sin\theta}{\cos\theta}} & \dfrac{\dfrac{1}{\sin\theta}}{\dfrac{1}{\cos\theta}} \\
\dfrac{\dfrac{\cos\theta-\sin\theta}{\sin\theta}}{\dfrac{\cos\theta-\sin\theta}{\cos\theta}} & \dfrac{\cos\theta}{\sin\theta} \\
\dfrac{\cos\theta}{\sin\theta} &
\end{array}$$

15.

$$\sec 2\theta\equiv\frac{\sec^2\theta}{2-\sec^2\theta}$$

$$\begin{array}{c|c}
\dfrac{1}{\cos 2\theta} & \dfrac{\dfrac{1}{\cos^2\theta}}{2-\dfrac{1}{\cos^2\theta}} \\
\dfrac{1}{2\cos^2\theta-1} & \dfrac{\dfrac{1}{\cos^2\theta}}{\dfrac{2\cos^2\theta-1}{\cos^2\theta}} \\
 & \dfrac{1}{2\cos^2\theta-1}
\end{array}$$

16.

$$\cot 2\theta\equiv\frac{\cot^2\theta-1}{2\cot\theta}$$

$$\begin{array}{c|c}
\dfrac{\cos 2\theta}{\sin 2\theta} & \dfrac{\dfrac{\cos^2\theta}{\sin^2\theta}-1}{2\dfrac{\cos\theta}{\sin\theta}} \\
 & \dfrac{\dfrac{\cos^2\theta-\sin^2\theta}{\sin^2\theta}}{2\dfrac{\cos\theta}{\sin\theta}} \\
 & \dfrac{\cos^2\theta-\sin^2\theta}{\sin^2\theta}\cdot\dfrac{\sin\theta}{2\cos\theta} \\
 & \dfrac{\cos 2\theta}{\sin 2\theta}
\end{array}$$

17.

$$\frac{\sin(\alpha+\beta)}{\cos\alpha\cos\beta}\equiv\tan\alpha+\tan\beta$$

$$\begin{array}{c|c}
\dfrac{\sin\alpha\cos\beta+\cos\alpha\sin\beta}{\cos\alpha\cos\beta} & \dfrac{\sin\alpha}{\cos\alpha}+\dfrac{\sin\beta}{\cos\beta} \\
 & \dfrac{\sin\alpha\cos\beta+\cos\alpha\sin\beta}{\cos\alpha\cos\beta}
\end{array}$$

9.

$$\frac{\sin x+\cos x}{\sec x+\csc x}\equiv\frac{\sin x}{\sec x}$$

$$\begin{array}{c|c}
\dfrac{\sin x+\cos x}{\dfrac{1}{\cos x}+\dfrac{1}{\sin x}} & \dfrac{\sin x}{\dfrac{1}{\cos x}} \\
\dfrac{\sin x+\cos x}{\dfrac{\sin x+\cos x}{\cos x\sin x}} & \cos x\sin x \\
\cos x\sin x &
\end{array}$$

10.

$$\frac{\sin x-\cos x}{\sec x-\csc x}\equiv\frac{\cos x}{\csc x}$$

$$\begin{array}{c|c}
\dfrac{\sin x-\cos x}{\dfrac{1}{\cos x}-\dfrac{1}{\sin x}} & \dfrac{\cos x}{\dfrac{1}{\sin x}} \\
\dfrac{\sin x-\cos x}{\dfrac{\sin x-\cos x}{\cos x\sin x}} & \cos x\sin x \\
\cos x\sin x &
\end{array}$$

18.

$$\frac{\cos(\alpha-\beta)}{\cos\alpha\sin\beta}\equiv\tan\alpha+\cot\beta$$

$$\begin{array}{c|c}
\dfrac{\cos\alpha\cos\beta+\sin\alpha\sin\beta}{\cos\alpha\sin\beta} & \dfrac{\sin\alpha}{\cos\alpha}+\dfrac{\cos\beta}{\sin\beta} \\
\dfrac{\sin\alpha\sin\beta+\cos\alpha\cos\beta}{\cos\alpha\sin\beta} & \dfrac{\sin\alpha\sin\beta+\cos\alpha\cos\beta}{\cos\alpha\sin\beta}
\end{array}$$

19. $\dfrac{\tan\theta + \sin\theta}{2\tan\theta} \equiv \cos^2\dfrac{\theta}{2}$

$\dfrac{\frac{\sin\theta}{\cos\theta} + \sin\theta}{2\frac{\sin\theta}{\cos\theta}}$	$\dfrac{1+\cos\theta}{2}$
$\dfrac{\frac{\sin\theta + \sin\theta\cos\theta}{\cos\theta}}{2\frac{\sin\theta}{\cos\theta}}$	
$\dfrac{\sin\theta + \sin\theta\cos\theta}{2\sin\theta}$	
$\dfrac{1+\cos\theta}{2}$	

20. $\dfrac{\tan\theta - \sin\theta}{2\tan\theta} \equiv \sin^2\dfrac{\theta}{2}$

$\dfrac{\frac{\sin\theta}{\cos\theta} - \sin\theta}{2\frac{\sin\theta}{\cos\theta}}$	$\dfrac{1-\cos\theta}{2}$
$\dfrac{\frac{\sin\theta - \sin\theta\cos\theta}{\cos\theta}}{2\frac{\sin\theta}{\cos\theta}}$	
$\dfrac{1-\cos\theta}{2}$	

21. $\cos^4 x - \sin^4 x \equiv \cos 2x$

$(\cos^2 x - \sin^2 x)(\cos^2 x + \sin^2 x)$	$\cos^2 x - \sin^2 x$
$\cos^2 x - \sin^2 x$	

22. $\dfrac{\cos^4 x - \sin^4 x}{1 - \tan^4 x} \equiv \cos^4 x$

$\dfrac{\cos^4 x - \sin^4 x}{1 - \frac{\sin^4 x}{\cos^4 x}}$	$\cos^4 x$
$\dfrac{\cos^4 x - \sin^4 x}{\frac{\cos^4 x - \sin^4 x}{\cos^4 x}}$	
$\cos^4 x$	

23. $\dfrac{\tan 3\theta - \tan\theta}{1 + \tan 3\theta\tan\theta} \equiv \dfrac{2\tan\theta}{1 - \tan^2\theta}$

$\tan(3\theta - \theta)$	$\tan 2\theta$
$\tan 2\theta$	

24. $\left(\dfrac{1+\tan\theta}{1-\tan\theta}\right)^2 \equiv \dfrac{1+\sin 2\theta}{1-\sin 2\theta}$

$\left(\dfrac{\cos\theta + \sin\theta}{\cos\theta - \sin\theta}\right)^2$	$\dfrac{1+\sin 2\theta}{1-\sin 2\theta}$
$\dfrac{\sin^2\theta + 2\sin\theta\cos\theta + \cos^2\theta}{\sin^2\theta - 2\sin\theta\cos\theta + \cos^2\theta}$	
$\dfrac{1+\sin 2\theta}{1-\sin 2\theta}$	

25. $\sin(\alpha + \beta)\sin(\alpha - \beta) \equiv \sin^2\alpha - \sin^2\beta$

$(\sin\alpha\cos\beta + \cos\alpha\sin\beta)(\sin\alpha\cos\beta - \cos\alpha\sin\beta)$

$\sin^2\alpha\cos^2\beta - \cos^2\alpha\sin^2\beta$

$\sin^2\alpha(1 - \sin^2\beta) - (1 - \sin^2\alpha)(\sin^2\beta)$

$\sin^2\alpha - \sin^2\alpha\sin^2\beta - \sin^2\beta + \sin^2\alpha\sin^2\beta$

$\sin^2\alpha - \sin^2\beta$

26. $\cos(\alpha + \beta)\cos(\alpha - \beta) \equiv \cos^2\alpha - \sin^2\beta$

$(\cos\alpha\cos\beta - \sin\alpha\sin\beta)(\cos\alpha\cos\beta + \sin\alpha\sin\beta)$

$\cos^2\alpha\cos^2\beta - \sin^2\alpha\sin^2\beta$

$\cos^2\alpha(1 - \sin^2\beta) - (1 - \cos^2\alpha)\sin^2\beta$

$\cos^2\alpha - \cos^2\alpha\sin^2\beta - \sin^2\beta + \cos^2\alpha\sin^2\beta$

$\cos^2\alpha - \sin^2\beta$

27. $\cos(\alpha + \beta) + \cos(\alpha - \beta) \equiv 2\cos\alpha\cos\beta$

$(\cos\alpha\cos\beta - \sin\alpha\sin\beta) + (\cos\alpha\cos\beta + \sin\alpha\sin\beta)$

$2\cos\alpha\cos\beta$

28. $\sin(\alpha + \beta) + \sin(\alpha - \beta) \equiv 2\sin\alpha\cos\beta$

$(\sin\alpha\cos\beta + \cos\alpha\sin\beta) + (\sin\alpha\cos\beta - \cos\alpha\sin\beta)$

$2\sin\alpha\cos\beta$

29. Answers may vary.

30. $\log(\cos x - \sin x) + \log(\cos x + \sin x)$
$= \log[(\cos x - \sin x)(\cos x + \sin x)]$
$= \log(\cos^2 x - \sin^2 x)$
$= \log(\cos 2x)$

31. $\sin\theta = \cos\phi$

32. $$\frac{1}{\omega C(\tan\theta + \tan\phi)} = \frac{1}{\omega C\left(\frac{\sin\theta}{\cos\theta} + \frac{\sin\phi}{\cos\phi}\right)} = \frac{1}{\omega C\left(\frac{\sin\theta\cos\phi + \sin\phi\cos\theta}{\cos\theta\cos\phi}\right)} = \frac{\cos\theta\cos\phi}{\omega C\sin(\theta + \phi)}$$

33. $$\frac{E_1 + E_2}{2} = \frac{\sqrt{2}E_t\cos\left(\theta + \frac{\pi}{p}\right) + \sqrt{2}E_t\cos\left(\theta - \frac{\pi}{p}\right)}{2}$$
$$= \sqrt{2}\,E_t\,\frac{\cos\theta\cos\frac{\pi}{p} - \sin\theta\sin\frac{\pi}{p} + \cos\theta\cos\frac{\pi}{p} + \sin\theta\sin\frac{\pi}{p}}{2}$$
$$= \sqrt{2}\,E_t\cos\theta\cos\frac{\pi}{p}.$$

Similarly for $\frac{E_1 - E_2}{2}$

34.

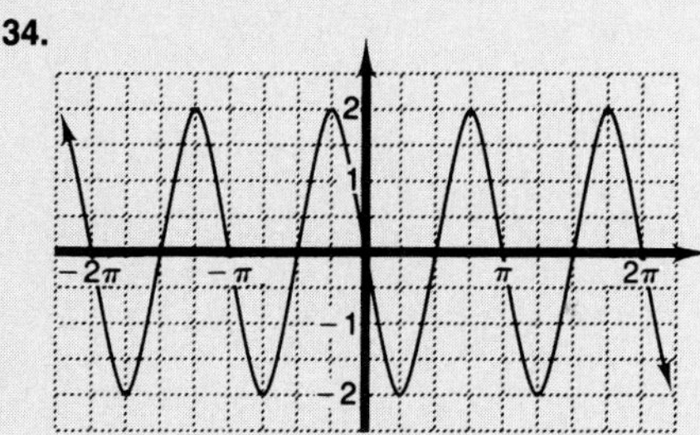

35.

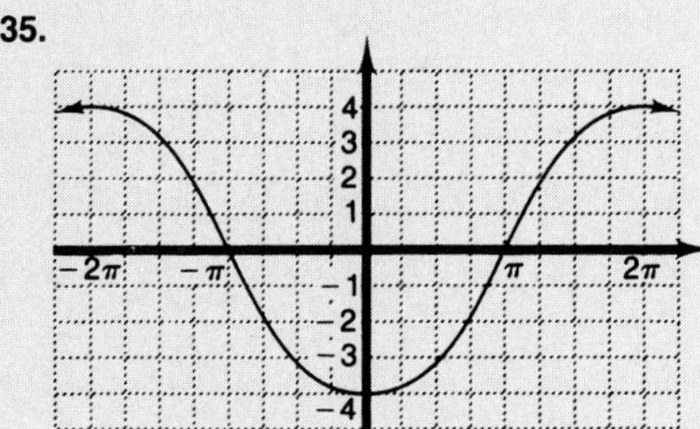

36.

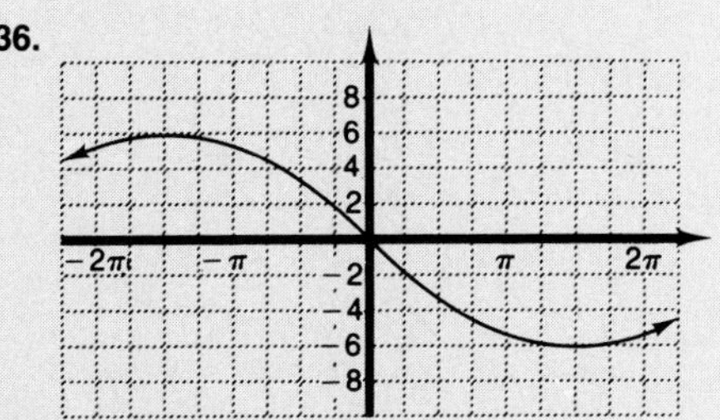

Page 825 EXERCISE SET 18-9

62. $|z \cdot w| = |r_1 r_r \text{ cis } (\theta_1 + \theta_2)| = |r_1 r_2 \cos(\theta_1 + \theta_2) + r_1 r_2 i \sin(\theta_1 + \theta_2)| = \sqrt{r_1^2 r_2^2 \cos^2(\theta_1 + \theta_2) + r_1^2 r_2^2 \sin^2(\theta_1 + \theta_2)} = \sqrt{r_1^2 r_2^2} = r_1 r_2$

$|z| \cdot |w| = |r_1 \text{ cis } \theta_1| = |r_2 \text{ cis } \theta_2|$

$= |r_1 \cos\theta_1 + r_1 i \sin\theta_1| \cdot |r_2 \cos\theta_2 + r_2 i \sin\theta_2|$

$= \sqrt{r_1^2 \cos^2\theta_1 + r_1^2 \sin^2\theta_1} \cdot \sqrt{r_2^2 \cos^2\theta_2 + r_2^2 \sin^2\theta_2} = \sqrt{r_1^2} \cdot \sqrt{r_2^2} = r_1 r_2$

63. $\left|\frac{z}{w}\right| = \left|\frac{r_1}{r_2} \text{ cis } (\theta_1 - \theta_2)\right|$

$= \left|\frac{r_1}{r_2} \cos(\theta_1 - \theta_2) + \frac{r_1}{r_2} i \sin(\theta_1 - \theta_2)\right|$

$= \sqrt{\frac{r_1}{r_2^2} \cos^2(\theta_1 - \theta_2) + \frac{r_1^2}{r_2^2} \sin^2(\theta_1 - \theta_2)}$

$= \sqrt{\frac{r_1^2}{r_2^2}} = \frac{r_1}{r_2}$

$\left|\frac{z}{w}\right| = \left|\frac{r_2 \text{ cis } \theta_1}{r_2 \text{ cis } \theta_2}\right| = \left|\frac{r_1 \cos\theta_1 + r_1 i \sin\theta_1}{r_2 \cos\theta_2 + r_2 i \sin\theta_2}\right|$

$= \frac{\sqrt{r_1^2 \cos^2\theta_1 + r_1^2 \sin^2\theta_1}}{\sqrt{r_2^2 \cos^2\theta_2 + r_2^2 \sin^2\theta_2}} = \frac{\sqrt{r_1^2}}{\sqrt{r_2^2}} = \frac{r_1}{r_2}$

Addison-Wesley Algebra and Trigonometry

Teacher's Edition

Addison-Wesley

Algebra

and Trigonometry

Stanley A. Smith
Randall I. Charles
John A. Dossey
Mervin L. Keedy
Marvin L. Bittinger

ADDISON-WESLEY PUBLISHING COMPANY
Menlo Park, California · Reading, Massachusetts · New York
Don Mills, Ontario · Wokingham, England · Amsterdam · Bonn
Sydney · Singapore · Tokyo · Madrid · San Juan

CHAPTER **1**

Real Numbers, Algebra, and Problem Solving

Chapter Overview

Chapter 1 is a comprehensive review of the key facts and methods of elementary algebra. Number properties and principles are presented with more formality than in previous courses. Problem solving is introduced using simple linear equations. Properties of exponents and scientific notation are detailed. An optional section on proofs based on number axioms completes the chapter's lessons. Problem-solving strategies continue developing problem-solving skills, adding the strategy *Draw a Diagram.*

Although Chapter 1 is one of the longer chapters, it may be used effectively to gauge the abilities of the students. Teachers may then choose to move on to Chapter 2 quickly.

Objectives

1-1
- Show that a number is rational and distinguish between rational and irrational numbers.
- Add positive and negative numbers.
- Subtract positive and negative numbers.

1-2
- Multiply positive and negative numbers.
- Divide positive and negative numbers.
- Recognize division by zero as impossible.

1-3
- Evaluate algebraic expressions.
- Use number properties to write equivalent expressions.

1-4
- Use the distributive property to multiply.
- Use the distributive property to factor expressions.
- Collect like terms.
- Write the inverse of a sum.
- Use the distributive property to simplify expressions.

1-5
- Solve equations using the addition and multiplication properties.

1-6
- Become familiar with and solve simple algebraic problems.

1-7
- Simplify expressions with integer exponents.

1-8
- Multiply or divide with exponents.
- Use exponential notation in raising powers to powers.
- Use the rules for order of operations to simplify expressions.

1-9
- Convert between scientific and standard notation.
- Use scientific notation in multiplication and division.
- Use scientific notation in approximating and estimating.

1-10
- Use axioms and properties to justify algebraic statements.
- Write column proofs.

1-11
- Solve nonroutine problems using the strategy *Draw a Diagram.*

TEACHING CHAPTER 1

Cooperative Learning Opportunities

It will be helpful, starting with Chapter 1, for students to realize that the **Challenge** exercises can provide interesting insights into mathematics. The **Challenge** exercises in Lessons 1-1 and 1-8 are well suited to cooperative work in pairs. Assign pairs, have students do the exercises together and then, as time permits, ask them what else they can discover about the topic.

As a follow up to the **Challenge** exercises on page 8, you might ask students to write a repeating decimal in which three or four numerals repeat, and then find the fractional equivalent. You could also ask them to find the fractional equivalent of $0.\overline{9}$. If they are not happy with the answer, ask them to find the fraction for $0.\overline{3}$ and determine how this affects their thinking about $0.\overline{9}$.

In the **Challenge** exercises on page 43, some students may be uncomfortable with variables as exponents. Working in pairs, students can explain the material to each other and come up with appropriate solutions.

Multicultural Note: *Giuseppe Peano*

In geometry we prove practically everything. But arithmetic and algebra are different. Most of the basic results are verified using examples rather than formal proofs. For thousands of years merchants, scientists, and mathematicians used numbers and were satisfied with the predictable results. What worked for the natural numbers continued to work for the integers, rational numbers, and real numbers.

At various times mathematicians wanted to build a foundation for the house of arithmetic but it was really not until the nineteenth century that construction was begun. Giuseppe Peano (1858–1932) listed five axioms for the natural numbers. From these he established the basic properties of natural numbers and then the real numbers.

The discussion continues about the relationship between mathematics and logic. Some believe that all of mathematics is simply a sub-topic of logic, while others say that symbolic logic is a branch of mathematics.

Alternative Assessment and Communication Ideas

The **Writing to Learn** activity on page 37, offers a method to assess understanding by exploring the connection between symbols and words. As a follow up to this activity you might ask students to write several paragraphs explaining the advantages of using mathematical symbols to do math and to express mathematical rules, as opposed to using words, which are also symbols. Ask them to devise categories for some of the symbols found in Chapter 1. Categories might be: numbers standing for quantities; variables representing numbers; symbols for operations.

A related oral assessment would be to ask students to explain, in words, the axioms, properties, and theorems found in Lesson 1-10.

Finally, as an alternative form of assessment, you might ask students to explain the meaning of *simplify* and to show, with examples, how to simplify an algebraic expression. This activity forces students to look closely at the various operations and relationships of Chapter 1.

Investigations and Projects

It is sometimes difficult for students to appreciate the various properties of real numbers. This is probably because these properties seem obvious and it is difficult to imagine numbers behaving in any other way.

As a project, students can define an operation based on a combination of arithmetic operations, and then test to see whether the operation is commutative and/or associative.

To get them started, you can suggest the following: $a \cdot b = a^2 + b^2$
This is commutative and associative.
$x \cdot y = \frac{x+y}{2}$ This is commutative but not associative.

$r \cdot s = 2r + s$ This is neither commutative nor associative.

After students have invented some operations and successfully tested them, ask them if they can invent two operations such that both are commutative and associative and one is distributive over the other.

MANAGING CHAPTER 1

Lesson	PACING CHART (DAYS) Algebra	Algebra w/Finite	Algebra w/Trig	Comprehensive	Opening Activity	Cooperative Activity	Seat or Group Work
1-1	1	1	1	0.5	First Five Minutes 1-1: **TE** p.4 or ***FFM Transparency Masters*** p.1	Critical Thinking: **SE** p.8	Try This a–o
1-2	1	0.5	0.5	0.5	First Five Minutes 1-2: **TE** p.9 or ***FFM Transparency Masters*** p.1	Critical Thinking: **SE** p.12 Critical Thinking 1: ***Enrichment*** p.22	Try This a–m
1-3	1	0.5	0.5	0.5	First Five Minutes 1-3: **TE** p.14 or ***FFM Transparency Masters*** p.2	Critical Thinking: **SE** p.19	Try This a–l
1-4	2	1	1	0.5	First Five Minutes 1-4: **TE** p.20 or ***FFM Transparency Masters*** p.2	Critical Thinking: **SE** p.25 Critical Thinking 1: ***Enrichment*** p.22	Try This a–t
1-5	1	1	1	0.5	First Five Minutes 1-5: **TE** p.26 or ***FFM Transparency Masters*** p.3	Explore: **SE** p.26 Critical Thinking: **SE** p.29 ✂ Manipulative Activity 1: ***Enrichment*** p.42	Try This a–f
1-6	1	1	1	0.5	First Five Minutes 1-6: **TE** p.30 or ***FFM Transparency Masters*** p.3	Critical Thinking: **SE** p.34 Bonus Topic 1: ***Enrichment*** p.2	Try This a–d
1-7	1	1	1	0.5	First Five Minutes 1-7: **TE** p.35 or ***FFM Transparency Masters*** p.4	Explore: **SE** p.35 Critical Thinking: **SE** p.37	Try This a–l
1-8	2	1	1	0.5	First Five Minutes 1-8: **TE** p.38 or ***FFM Transparency Masters*** p.4	Critical Thinking: **SE** p.43	Try This a–t
1-9	1	1	1	0.5	First Five Minutes 1-9: **TE** p.44 or ***FFM Transparency Masters*** p.5	Critical Thinking: **SE** p.48	Try This a–j
1-10	0	0	0	0.5	First Five Minutes 1-10: **TE** p.49 or ***FFM Transparency Masters*** p.5	Critical Thinking: **SE** p.53 Looking for Errors 1: ***Enrichment*** p.62	Try This a–g
1-11	0.5	0.5	0.5	0.5	First Five Minutes 1-11: **TE** p.54 or ***FFM Transparency Masters*** p.6	Looking for Errors 1: ***Enrichment*** p.62 Strategy Problem Bank 1: ***Problem Bank*** p.2	Problems 1–2: **SE** p.55
Review	0.5	0.5	0.5	0.5			
Test	1	1	1	1			

FFM: First Five Minutes SPMR: Skills Practice Mixed Review

MANAGING CHAPTER 1

Enrichment	Review/Assess	Reteach	Technology	Lesson
Math Point: **TE** p.4, p.6 Lesson Enrichment: **TE** p.6	Lesson Quiz: **TE** p.7	Skillls Practice 1, #1–21: ***SPMR*** p.13		**1-1**
Critical Thinking 1: ***Enrichment*** p.22	Lesson Quiz: **TE** p.11	Skills Practice 1, #22–33: ***SPMR*** p.13	Finding Reciprocals: **SE** p.11 Calculator Investigation: **SE** p.13 Calculator Wkst 1: ***Technology*** p.3	**1-2**
Calculator Investigation: **SE** p.19	Lesson Quiz: **TE** p.17	Algebraic Expressions: **TE** p.14 Skills Practice 1, #34–45: ***SPMR*** p.13	Calculator Investigation: **SE** p.19	**1-3**
Critical Thinking 1: ***Enrichment*** p.22	Lesson Quiz: **TE** p.23 Quiz 1: ***Assessment*** p.9	Skills Practice 2, #1–26: ***SPMR*** p.14		**1-4**
✂ Manipulative Activity 1: ***Enrichment*** p.42	Lesson Quiz: **TE** p.28 Mixed Review 1: ***SPMR*** p.65	Skills Practice 2, #27–43: ***SPMR*** p.14	Problem for Programmers: **SE** p.29	**1-5**
Bonus Topic 1: ***Enrichment*** p.2	Lesson Quiz: **TE** p.32	Problem Bank 1: ***Problem Bank*** p.22 Skills Practice 3, #1–2: ***SPMR*** p.15		**1-6**
Math Point: **TE** p.35 Writing to Learn: **SE** p.37	Lesson Quiz: **TE** p.36	Skills Practice 3, #3–14: ***SPMR*** p.15		**1-7**
Lesson Enrichment: **TE** p.41	Lesson Quiz: **TE** p.42 Quiz 2: ***Assessment*** p.10	Skills Practice 3, #15–29: ***SPMR*** p.15	The Exponential Key: **SE** p.42 Order of Operations: **TE** p.41 Calculator Wkst 2: ***Technology*** p.4	**1-8**
Math Point: **TE** p.44	Lesson Quiz: **TE** p.46	Skills Practice 3, #30–31: ***SPMR*** p.15	Using Scientific Notation: **SE** p.46 Calculator Wkst 3: ***Technology*** p.5	**1-9**
Looking for Errors 1: ***Enrichment*** p.62	Lesson Quiz: **TE** p.51			**1-10**
Problem 1: Computer Assisted Problem Solving, **SE** p.839	Mixed Review 2: ***SPMR*** p.66	Strategy Problem Bank 1: ***Problem Bank*** p.2	Problem 1: Computer Assisted Problem Solving, **SE** p.839	**1-11**
	Summary and Review: **SE** pp.56–58 Test: **SE** pp.58–59			**Review**
	Chapter 1 Test: ***Assessment*** pp.47–52(reg.), pp.157–158 (adv.); Assessing Strategies 1: ***Assessment*** pp. 195–196			**Test**

The solution to the problem posed on the facing page can be found on page 30.

Ready for Real Numbers, Algebra, and Problem Solving?

Write fractional notation for each number.

1. 3.2 $\frac{16}{5}$ **2.** 5.15 $\frac{103}{20}$ **3.** 0.04 $\frac{1}{25}$ **4.** 1.001 $\frac{1001}{1000}$

Write decimal notation for each number.

5. $\frac{11}{20}$ 0.55 **6.** $\frac{18}{25}$ 0.72 **7.** $3\frac{3}{5}$ 3.6 **8.** $4\frac{1}{7}$ $4.\overline{142857}$

Calculate.

9. $31.3 + 6.07$ 37.37 **10.** $6.79 + 3.4$ 10.19 **11.** $3 - 1.53$ 1.47 **12.** $4.055 - 3.889$ 0.166

13. 16×0.8 12.8 **14.** 2.21×1.8 3.978 **15.** $0.6 \div 0.24$ 2.5 **16.** $2.7 \div 7.2$ 0.375

17. $\frac{3}{5} + \frac{1}{3}$ $\frac{14}{15}$ **18.** $1\frac{2}{3} + 3\frac{1}{4}$ $4\frac{11}{12}$ **19.** $\frac{5}{7} - \frac{9}{14}$ $\frac{1}{14}$ **20.** $8\frac{3}{4} - 7\frac{5}{6}$ $\frac{11}{12}$

21. $\frac{1}{6} \times \frac{5}{8}$ $\frac{5}{48}$ **22.** $3\frac{3}{8} \times \frac{2}{3}$ $2\frac{1}{4}$ **23.** $\frac{4}{5} \div \frac{3}{4}$ $\frac{16}{15}$ **24.** $1\frac{9}{16} \div \frac{5}{8}$ $2\frac{1}{2}$

Find each percent.

25. 36% of 92 33.12 **26.** 25% of 25 6.25 **27.** 130% of 64 83.2 **28.** $\frac{1}{2}$% of 400 2

Write the correct symbol $=$, $<$, or $>$.

29. 3.5 □ 3.36 $>$ **30.** 0.074 □ 0.703 $<$

31. $\frac{3}{13}$ □ $\frac{3}{16}$ $>$ **32.** $\frac{12}{25}$ □ $\frac{36}{75}$ $=$

Write each ratio. Simplify if possible.

33. 28 astronauts for 4 missions 7:1 **34.** 52 weeks in 12 months 13:3

35. 92 kilometers in 8 hours 23:2 **36.** 16 runs in 44 innings 4:11

CHAPTER

1 Real Numbers, Algebra, and Problem Solving

Many factors determine the placement and timing of traffic signals on city streets and intersections. Typically, studies are done regarding the direction and speed of traffic, road conditions, and other factors, before signals are placed and cycle times set.

The time that any traffic light remains yellow in one town is 1 second more than 0.05 times the speed limit of the street the light faces. What is the yellow time for a traffic light on a street with a speed limit of 30 miles per hour?

1-1

FIRST FIVE MINUTES

Write each using fractional, decimal, and percent notation.

1. $\frac{1}{2}$ 0.5, 50%
2. 1% 0.01, $\frac{1}{100}$
3. 0.25 $\frac{1}{4}$, 25%
4. 2 $\frac{2}{1}$, 2.0, 200%
5. $\frac{1}{3}$ $0.\overline{3}$, $33\frac{1}{3}$%; also $33.\overline{3}$%

Rational and Irrational Numbers

You may wish to draw a diagram to illustrate the different sets of numbers and their relationships.

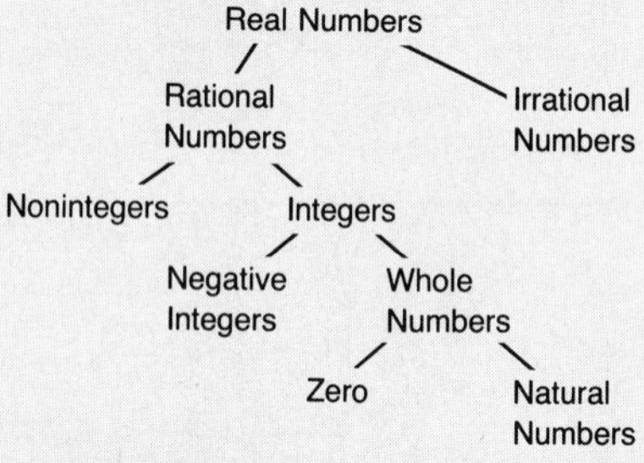

Math Point
The philosopher Pythagoras was born on the Greek island of Samos around 580 B.C. He traveled widely in his youth and later founded a religious order. He and his followers based their philosophy on the idea that ratio and proportion are the keys to understanding the world. The Pythagoreans discovered an astounding and troubling fact: There are points on the number line that cannot be named as a ratio of two integers. This undermined the central tenet of their doctrine. It is reported that the penalty for revealing this secret to outsiders was death.

The square root of two is a real number that cannot be written as a ratio of two integers. It took mathematicians nearly 2000 years to fully understand this fact.

1-1 Real Numbers and Operations

The most important set of numbers in algebra is the set of real numbers. There is exactly one real number for each point on a number line.

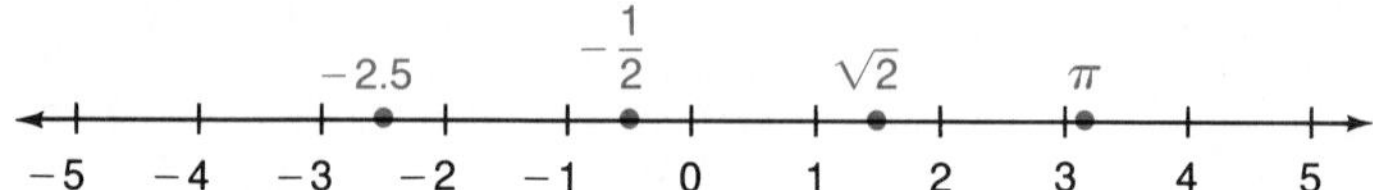

The positive numbers are shown to the right of zero, and the negative numbers to the left. Zero is neither positive nor negative. The sets of natural numbers {1, 2, 3, 4, . . .}, whole numbers {0, 1, 2, 3, 4, . . .}, and integers {. . . , −3, −2, −1, 0, 1, 2, 3, . . .} are all subsets of the set of real numbers.

Rational and Irrational Numbers

Objective: Show that a number is rational and distinguish between rational and irrational numbers.

The real numbers consist of the rational and irrational numbers.

Definition

Rational numbers are those that can be expressed as a ratio $\frac{a}{b}$, where a and b are integers and $b \neq 0$.

These are rational numbers: $-\frac{2}{7}$ 4 9.6 0 $0.\overline{6}$

Since they can be written as: $\frac{-2}{7}$ $\frac{4}{1}$ $\frac{96}{10}$ $\frac{0}{1}$ $\frac{2}{3}$

If a real number cannot be expressed as a ratio of integers $\frac{a}{b}$, $b \neq 0$, then it is called irrational. For instance, we can prove that there is no rational number that is a square root of 2. That is, we cannot find integers a and b for which $\frac{a}{b} \cdot \frac{a}{b} = 2$. We can come close, but there is no rational number whose square is *exactly* 2. Thus $\sqrt{2}$ is not a rational number. It is irrational. Unless a whole number is a perfect square, its square root is irrational. The following numbers are irrational.

$$\sqrt{3}, \quad \sqrt{8}, \quad -\sqrt{45}, \quad \sqrt{11}, \quad \pi$$

Decimal notation for rational numbers either ends or repeats. Decimal notation for irrational numbers never ends and never repeats.

EXAMPLES Determine which are rational and which are irrational.

1. 8.974974974 . . . (numeral repeats) Since the numeral repeats, the number is rational. We can express it as $8.\overline{974}$. The bar indicates that those digits repeat.

2. 3.12112111211112 . . . (numeral does not repeat) Since the numeral does not end or repeat, the number is irrational.

3. 4.325 Since the numeral ends, the number is rational.

4. $\sqrt{17}$ Since 17 is not a perfect square, the number $\sqrt{17}$ is irrational.

Try This Determine which of the following are rational and which are irrational.

a. 7.42 Rational **b.** $\sqrt{49}$ Rational **c.** 0.47646464 . . . (numeral repeats) Rational

d. $-\sqrt{32}$ Irrational **e.** $\frac{59}{37}$ Rational **f.** 2.5734107656631 . . . (numeral does not repeat) Irrational

The absolute value of a number is its distance from 0 on a number line. We denote the absolute value of x as $|x|$.

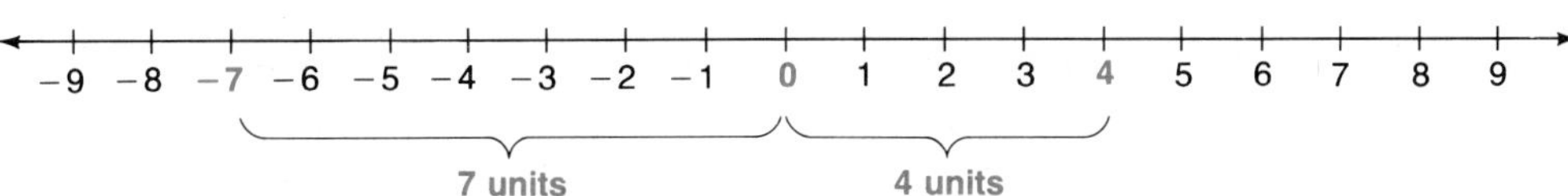

Since 4 is four units from 0, $|4| = 4$. Since -7 is seven units from 0, $|-7| = 7$. The absolute value of 0, $|0|$, is 0. We will define absolute value algebraically in Chapter 2.

Addition of Real Numbers

Objective: Add positive and negative numbers.

Recall the rules of signs for adding real numbers.

Rules for Addition of Real Numbers

1. To add when there are like signs, add the absolute values. The sum has the same sign as the addends.
2. To add when there are unlike signs, subtract the absolute values. The sum has the sign of the addend with the greater absolute value.

EXAMPLES Add.

5. $-5 + (-9) = -14$ Adding absolute values, the sum is negative.

6. $23 + (-11) = 12$ Subtracting absolute values; the positive addend has greater absolute value.

Key Questions

Draw a number line representing all real numbers. Label a few simple fractions: $\frac{1}{2}, \frac{1}{3}, \frac{2}{3}$.

- Will there always be a rational number between any two rational numbers? Yes
- If you were to remove all rational numbers, would there be any numbers left on this number line? Yes, irrational numbers; for example, the square root of 2

Chalkboard Examples

Is the number rational or irrational? Why?

1. 0.19191919...(repeats)
   Rational, since the digits repeat a pattern
2. 0.011000111100000111111 . . .
   Irrational, since the digits don't continually repeat any pattern
3. 8.714
   Rational, since the digits end
4. $\sqrt{5}$
   Since 5 does not have a whole number square root, the number $\sqrt{5}$ is irrational.

Addition of Real Numbers

Chalkboard Examples

Add.

1. $-12 + (-7)$
   The result will be negative.
   $-(12 + 7) = -19$
2. $32 + (-6)$
   The larger addend is positive, so the result is positive. $32 - 6 = 26$
3. $-3.4 + 2.1$
   The larger addend is negative, so the result is negative.
   $-3.4 + 2.1 = -1.3$
4. $-\frac{5}{3} + \frac{1}{6}$
   Rewrite with a common denominator.
   $-\frac{10}{6} + \frac{1}{6}$
   The larger addend is negative, so the result is negative.
   $-\frac{10}{6} + \frac{1}{6} = -\frac{9}{6} = -\frac{3}{2}$

Subtraction of Real Numbers

Math Point
The "invention" of 0 and negative numbers is considered by historians to be one of the great advances in mathematics. Knowledge of 0 and the advanced methods of addition, multiplication, and division first used by Arabs were transmitted to Europe around the year 1200 A.D. by Leonardo Fibonacci. He had learned the methods while traveling as a boy with his father in the Arab world. At that time, understanding how to add, multiply, and divide in the Hindu-Arabic number system marked one as well-educated.

Key Questions

- What is the additive inverse of $-\frac{1}{2}$? $\frac{1}{2}$
- What is the additive inverse of 0? 0

Chalkboard Examples

Subtract by adding an inverse.

1. $7 - 10$ $\quad 7 + (-10) = -3$
2. $8 - (-5)$
   $8 + [-(-5)] = 8 + 5 = 13$
3. $-3.8 - 4.1$
   $-3.8 + (-4.1) = -7.9$
4. $-\frac{7}{2} - \left(-\frac{4}{5}\right)$
   $-\frac{7}{2} + \frac{4}{5} = -\frac{35}{10} + \frac{8}{10} = -\frac{27}{10}$

LESSON ENRICHMENT

Any repeating decimal can be written as a ratio. For example:

$$n = 0.23\overline{23}$$
$$(100 - 1)n = (100 - 1)(0.23\overline{23})$$
$$99n = 23.23\overline{23} - 0.23\overline{23}$$
$$99n = 23$$
$$n = \frac{23}{99}$$

Write as a ratio.

1. $0.65\overline{65}$ $\quad \frac{65}{99}$
2. $0.\overline{369}$ $\quad \frac{41}{111}$

7. $-9.2 + 3.1 = -6.1$ The negative addend has greater absolute value.

8. $-\frac{5}{4} + \frac{1}{7} = -\frac{35}{28} + \frac{4}{28} = -\frac{31}{28}$ The negative addend has greater absolute value.

Try This Add.

g. $-8 + (-9)$ -17 **h.** $-8.9 + (-9.7)$ -18.6 **i.** $-\frac{6}{5} + \left(-\frac{23}{10}\right)$ $-\frac{7}{2}$

j. $14 + (-28)$ -14 **k.** $-4.5 + (7.8)$ 3.3 **l.** $\frac{3}{8} + \left(-\frac{5}{6}\right)$ $-\frac{11}{24}$

Subtraction of Real Numbers

Objective: Subtract positive and negative numbers.

Every real number has an **additive inverse** or **opposite.** The additive inverse of a number is the number added to it to get 0. The additive inverse of a number x is symbolized by $-x$. Every real number has exactly one additive inverse.

The Property of Additive Inverses

For each real number a, there is exactly one number b for which $a + b = 0$.

The additive inverse of a number is the number opposite it, with respect to 0, on a number line.

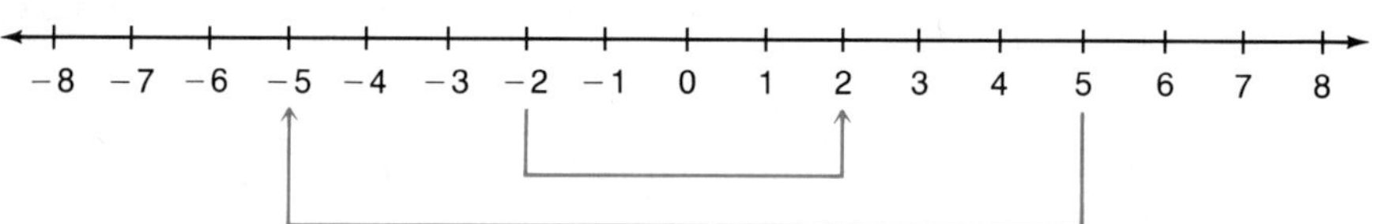

To find the additive inverse of 5, we reflect to the opposite side of 0. The additive inverse of 5 is -5. (We read -5 as "the additive inverse of 5" or "negative 5.") The additive inverse of -2 is $-(-2)$, or 2.

To find the additive inverse of a number quickly, merely change its sign.

Subtraction is defined in terms of addition. Subtraction and addition are inverse operations.

Definition

Subtraction

The **difference** $a - b$ is the number c such that $c + b = a$.

We can always subtract by adding an inverse. This fact can be proved, and we shall prove it later. If a statement can be proved, we call it a **theorem.**

Theorem 1-1

The Subtraction Theorem

For all real numbers a and b, $a - b = a + (-b)$.
(To subtract, we can add the inverse.)

The number subtracted is called the **subtrahend.** To subtract, we can change the sign of the subtrahend and then add it to the other number.

EXAMPLES Subtract by adding an inverse.

9. $5 - (-4) = 5 + 4 = 9$ Adding the inverse of the subtrahend, or changing the sign and adding

10. $-\frac{4}{3} - \left(-\frac{2}{5}\right) = -\frac{4}{3} + \frac{2}{5} = -\frac{20}{15} + \frac{6}{15} = -\frac{14}{15}$

Try This Subtract by adding an inverse.

m. $8 - (-9)$ 17 **n.** $23.7 - 5.9$ 17.8 **o.** $-\frac{11}{16} - \left(-\frac{23}{12}\right)$ $\frac{59}{48}$

1-1 EXERCISES

A

Determine which of the following are rational and which are irrational.

1. $\frac{3}{17}$ **2.** -13.91 **3.** -25 **4.** 42

5. $\sqrt{36}$ **6.** $\sqrt{19}$ **7.** $-\sqrt{16}$ **8.** $-\sqrt{37}$

9. $-12.3333\ldots$ (numeral repeats)

10. $4.123123412345123456\ldots$ (numeral does not repeat)

11. $2.714285714285\ldots$ (numeral repeats)

12. $-5.01001000100001\ldots$ (numeral does not repeat)

Add.

13. $-12 + (-16)$ −28 **14.** $-11 + (-18)$ −29 **15.** $-8 + (-8)$ −16

16. $8 + (-3)$ 5 **17.** $9 + (-4)$ 5 **18.** $-16 + 9$ −7

19. $-23 + 8$ −15 **20.** $-24 + 0$ −24 **21.** $-34 + 0$ −34

22. $-8.4 + 9.6$ 1.2 **23.** $-5.83 + (-7.43)$ −13.26 **24.** $-\frac{2}{7} + \frac{3}{7}$ $\frac{1}{7}$

25. $-\frac{5}{6} + \frac{1}{6}$ $-\frac{2}{3}$ **26.** $-\frac{11}{12} + \left(-\frac{5}{12}\right)$ $-\frac{4}{3}$ **27.** $\frac{2}{5} + \left(-\frac{3}{10}\right)$ $\frac{1}{10}$

LESSON QUIZ

Determine which of the following are rational and which are irrational.

1. $\sqrt{29}$ Irrational
2. 0.315215 Rational
3. $\frac{17}{19}$ Rational

Evaluate.

4. $-11 + 7$ −4
5. $-14 - 23$ −37
6. $-\frac{1}{5} + \frac{3}{2}$ $-\frac{2}{10} + \frac{15}{10} = \frac{13}{10}$
7. $-18.73 + 4.11$ −14.62

Assignment Guide
Algebra: 1–42 e/o, MR

Alg w/Finite or Trig: 1–46 e/o, 47, MR

Comprehensive: 1–46 m4, 47–50, MR, assign w. 1-2

*Codes: e/o Even *or* odd exercises
m3 Exercises that are multiples of 3 (i.e., 3, 6, 9,...)
m4 Exercises that are multiples of 4 (i.e., 4, 8, 12,...)
MR Mixed Review exercises
assign w. Indicates that two lessons are assigned

ADDITIONAL ANSWERS

Exercises

1. Rational
2. Rational
3. Rational
4. Rational
5. Rational
6. Irrational
7. Rational
8. Irrational
9. Rational
10. Irrational
11. Rational
12. Irrational

For Exercises 43–46, answers may vary.

43. II, $\sqrt{4}, (\sqrt{2})^2, \sqrt[3]{8}, \frac{8}{4}$

44. X, $\sqrt{100}, (\sqrt{10})^2, \sqrt[3]{1000}, \frac{20}{2}$

45. $\frac{1}{2}, \sqrt{\frac{1}{4}}, \frac{8}{16}, \sqrt[3]{\frac{1}{8}}, \frac{2}{4}$

46. $-\sqrt{9}, -(\sqrt{3})^2, -(\sqrt[3]{27}), -\frac{18}{6}, \left(-\frac{1}{3}\right)^{-1}$

47. Two unrelated sets of digits appear, each six times, with a different starting digit for every ratio.

$\frac{1}{13} = 0.\overline{076923}$

$\frac{10}{13} = 0.\overline{769230}$

$\frac{9}{13} = 0.\overline{692307}$

$\frac{12}{13} = 0.\overline{923076}$

$\frac{3}{13} = 0.\overline{230769}$

$\frac{4}{13} = 0.\overline{307692}$

Similarly, $\frac{2}{13} = 0.\overline{153846}$

Beginning one place to the right, we find $\frac{7}{13}, \frac{5}{13}, \frac{11}{13}, \frac{6}{13}, \frac{8}{13}$.

48. a. $\frac{2}{3}$ b. $\frac{7}{9}$ c. $\frac{37}{45}$

49. For example, 0.909009000900009....

50. a. No
b. No
c. No
d. No
e. Densely ordered
f. Densely ordered

Mixed Review

51. $\frac{7}{24}$ **52.** 4.011
53. $\frac{43}{40}$ **54.** 56.5
55. 259.08 **56.** $\frac{2}{11}$
57. $\frac{1}{4}$ **58.** $\frac{23}{12}$
59. 2 **60.** 4
61. 1 **62.** 256
63. 60 **64.** 105
65. 396

Subtract.

28. $5 - 7$ -2 **29.** $9 - 12$ -3 **30.** $-5 - 7$ -12
31. $-9 - 12$ -21 **32.** $-6 - (-11)$ 5 **33.** $-7 - (-12)$ 5
34. $10 - (-5)$ 15 **35.** $28 - (-16)$ 44 **36.** $15.8 - 27.4$ -11.6
37. $17.2 - 24.9$ -7.7 **38.** $-18.01 - 11.24$ -29.25 **39.** $-19.04 - 15.76$ -34.8
40. $-\frac{21}{4} - \left(-\frac{7}{4}\right)$ $-\frac{7}{2}$ **41.** $-\frac{16}{5} - \left(-\frac{3}{5}\right)$ $-\frac{13}{5}$ **42.** $-\frac{1}{2} - \left(-\frac{1}{12}\right)$ $-\frac{5}{12}$

B

The number 3 can be represented by the symbols 3, III, $\sqrt{9}$, $\frac{36}{12}$, $\left(\sqrt{3}\right)^2$, $\sqrt[3]{27}$, and so on.

Write five different representations for each of the following numbers.

43. 2 **44.** 10 **45.** 0.5 **46.** -3

47. ***Critical Thinking*** Find decimal notation for $\frac{1}{13}, \frac{2}{13}, \frac{3}{13}, \ldots, \frac{12}{13}$. What pattern do you find?

Challenge

48. Suppose that $n = 0.\overline{8}$. We can find rational notation for n by finding $10n$ and then $10n - n$ as follows.

$$\begin{aligned} 10n &= 8.\overline{8} \\ n &= 0.\overline{8} \\ \hline 10n - n &= 8 \qquad 9n = 8, n = \frac{8}{9} \end{aligned}$$

Find rational notation for each of the following.

a. $0.\overline{6}$ **b.** $0.\overline{7}$ **c.** $0.8\overline{2}$ (Hint: Find $100n$, $10n$, and $100n - 10n$.)

49. Write decimal notation for an irrational number using only the digits 0 and 9.

50. A set of numbers is said to be **densely ordered** if between any two numbers there is another that is also in the set. Which of the following sets are densely ordered?

a. natural numbers **b.** integers **c.** multiples of 10
d. even integers **e.** rational numbers **f.** real numbers

Mixed Review

Calculate. **51.** $\frac{5}{12} - \frac{1}{8}$ **52.** $1.103 + 2.908$ **53.** $\frac{7}{10} + \frac{3}{8}$

54. $38.9 + 17.6$ **55.** $12.7 \cdot 20.4$ **56.** $\frac{2}{7} \cdot \frac{7}{11}$ **57.** $\frac{1}{2} \cdot \frac{2}{3} \cdot \frac{3}{4}$

58. $\frac{1}{2} + \frac{2}{3} + \frac{3}{4}$ **59.** $\frac{2}{3} \div \frac{1}{3}$

Find the greatest common factor (GCF) for each pair of numbers.

60. 8 and 20 **61.** 27 and 64 **62.** 256 and 512

Find the least common multiple (LCM) for each pair of numbers.

63. 6 and 20 **64.** 15 and 35 **65.** 11 and 36

1-2 Multiplication and Division of Real Numbers

Multiplication of Real Numbers

Objective: Multiply positive and negative numbers.

When multiplying real numbers, we multiply the absolute values. Use the following rules to determine the sign of the product.

Multiplication of Real Numbers

1. If both numbers are positive or both negative, their product is positive.
2. If one number is positive and the other is negative, their product is negative.

EXAMPLES Multiply.

1. $6(-7) = -42$ Multiplying absolute values, the product is negative.

2. $-5.2(-10) = 52$ Multiplying absolute values, the product is positive.

3. $-8 \times -7 \times 6 = 56 \times 6 = 336$

Try This Multiply.

a. $-4 \cdot 6$ -24 **b.** -8.1×-3.5 28.35 **c.** $9.1(-4.7)$ -42.77 **d.** $\left(-\frac{3}{4}\right)\left(-\frac{5}{6}\right)$ $\frac{5}{8}$

Division of Real Numbers

Objective: Divide positive and negative numbers.

Every nonzero real number has a multiplicative inverse or reciprocal. The reciprocal of a number is the number we multiply it by to get 1.

The Property of Multiplicative Inverses

For each nonzero number a, there is exactly one number b for which $ab = 1$.

To find the reciprocal of a number, we divide 1 by that number. The reciprocal of 8 is $\frac{1}{8}$, or 0.125 because $8\left(\frac{1}{8}\right) = 1$. If the number is in rational notation, we can find the reciprocal by inverting. The reciprocal of $-\frac{2}{3}$ is $-\frac{3}{2}$ since $\left(-\frac{2}{3}\right)\left(-\frac{3}{2}\right) = 1$. Note that the reciprocal of a negative number is negative.

1-2

FIRST FIVE MINUTES

Simplify.

1. $\frac{42}{20}$ $\frac{21}{10}$
2. $|-7.5|$ 7.5
3. $-8 + 3$ -5
4. $-12 + (-5)$ -17
5. $13 - 17$ -4

Multiplication of Real Numbers

You may want to show students the following pattern to illustrate the rule for determining the sign of the product of a positive and a negative number.

$2 \cdot 5 = 10$
$1 \cdot 5 = 5$
$0 \cdot 5 = 0$
$-1 \cdot 5 = -5$
$-2 \cdot 5 = -10$

The sign of the product of two negative numbers also fits a pattern.

$2 \cdot -5 = -10$
$1 \cdot -5 = -5$
$0 \cdot -5 = 0$
$-1 \cdot -5 = 5$
$-2 \cdot -5 = 10$

Key Questions

- Does $-3 \cdot -3 = 3 \cdot 3$? Yes
- Does $-3 \cdot 0 = 3 \cdot 0$? Yes
- Does $1 \cdot -1 = -1 \cdot 1$? Yes

Chalkboard Examples

Multiply.

1. $-9 \cdot 11$
   -99; multiply absolute values and change the sign.
2. $(-7)(-4)$
   28; multiply absolute values.
3. $(-1)(-1)(-1)$
   -1

Division of Real Numbers

Emphasize that dividing by a number is the same as multiplying by its reciprocal.

Key Questions

- Is $-\frac{3}{4}$ the reciprocal of $\frac{4}{3}$?

  No; $\left(-\frac{3}{4}\right)\left(\frac{4}{3}\right) \neq 1$

- Is $\frac{3}{-4}$ the reciprocal of $\frac{4}{-3}$?

  Yes; $\left(\frac{3}{-4}\right)\left(\frac{4}{-3}\right) = 1$

Chalkboard Examples

Divide.

1. $-\frac{24}{3}$

   -8

2. $\frac{-15}{-3}$

   5

3. $\frac{2}{9} \div \frac{5}{7}$

   $\frac{2}{9} \cdot \frac{7}{5} = \frac{14}{45}$

4. $\frac{4}{5} \div \left(-\frac{6}{11}\right)$

   $\frac{4}{5} \cdot \left(-\frac{11}{6}\right) = -\frac{44}{30} = -\frac{22}{15}$

Division and multiplication are inverse operations. In fact, division is defined in terms of multiplication.

Definition

Division

The **quotient** $\frac{a}{b}$, where $b \neq 0$, is the number c such that $c \cdot b = a$.

To subtract, we can add the additive inverse. To divide, we can multiply by the multiplicative inverse. The following theorem parallels the subtraction theorem.

Theorem 1-2

The Division Theorem

For all real numbers a and b, $b \neq 0$,

$$\frac{a}{b} = a \cdot \frac{1}{b}$$

(To divide a by b, we multiply a by the reciprocal of b.)

When dividing real numbers, we divide the absolute values. Use the following rules to determine the sign of the quotient.

Division of Real Numbers

1. If both numbers are positive or both negative, the quotient is positive.
2. If one number is positive and the other is negative, the quotient is negative.

EXAMPLES Divide.

4. $\frac{10}{-2} = -5$ The quotient is negative.

5. $\frac{-5.6}{-7} = 0.8$ The quotient is positive.

Try This Divide.

e. $\frac{24}{-8}$ -3

f. $-\frac{10}{5}$ -2

g. $\frac{-10}{-40}$ $\frac{1}{4} = 0.25$

EXAMPLES Divide.

6. $\frac{1}{4} \div \frac{3}{5} = \frac{1}{4} \cdot \frac{5}{3}$ Using the division theorem

$= \frac{5}{12}$ Multiplying numerators and denominators

7. $\frac{2}{3} \div \left(-\frac{4}{9}\right) = \frac{2}{3} \cdot \left(-\frac{9}{4}\right)$ Using the division theorem

$= -\frac{18}{12} = -\frac{3}{2}$ Multiplying and simplifying

Try This Divide.

h. $-\frac{3}{4} \div \frac{7}{8}$ $-\frac{6}{7}$

i. $-\frac{12}{5} \div \left(-\frac{7}{15}\right)$ $\frac{36}{7}$

Division and Zero

Objective: Recognize division by zero as impossible.

We can divide zero by any nonzero number. The answer is always zero. On the other hand, we can never divide by zero. By the definition of division, we would have $\frac{n}{0} = c$ such that $c \cdot 0 = n$. But $c \cdot 0 = 0$ for any number c, so the only possible number that n could be is 0. Let's consider what $\frac{0}{0}$ might be.

$\frac{0}{0}$ might be 5 because $0 = 0 \cdot 5$ $\frac{0}{0}$ might be 267 because $0 = 0 \cdot 267$

It looks as if $\frac{0}{0}$ could be any number. Thus we cannot define and must exclude division by 0. Zero is the only real number that does not have a reciprocal.

EXAMPLES Which of the following divisions are possible?

8. $\frac{7}{0}$ Not possible

9. $\frac{0}{7}$ Possible

10. $\frac{4}{x-x}$ Not possible

Try This Which of the following divisions are possible?

j. $\frac{0}{8}$ Possible

k. $\frac{0}{0}$ Not possible

l. $\frac{8}{0}$ Not possible

m. $\frac{17}{2x-2x}$ Not possible

Finding Reciprocals

Many scientific calculators have a reciprocal key $1/x$
Find the reciprocal of 63.

63 $1/x$ → 0.015873

For additional calculator practice, see Calculator Worksheet 1.

Division and Zero

You may want to have students use their calculators to evaluate $\frac{0}{1}$ (to obtain 0) and then $\frac{1}{0}$ (to obtain an error message).

Chalkboard Examples

Which of the following divisions are possible?

1. $\frac{6}{2 \cdot 3 - 6}$
Not possible
2. $\frac{4 - 2^2}{8}$
$\frac{0}{8} = 0$
3. $\frac{7 + (-1)7}{7 + (-1)7}$
Not possible

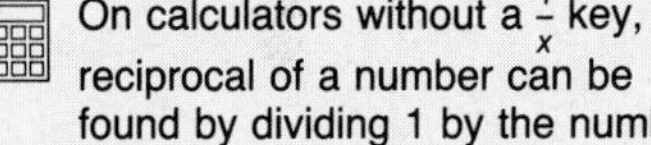

On calculators without a $\frac{1}{x}$ key, the reciprocal of a number can be found by dividing 1 by the number.

LESSON QUIZ

Multiply.

1. $8(-3)$ -24
2. $-6(7)$ -42
3. $(-4)(-7)$ 28
4. $-9\left(-\frac{3}{2}\right)$ $\frac{27}{2}$
5. $(-1)(-2)(-3)(-4)$ 24
6. $-\frac{7}{11}\left(\frac{4}{5}\right)$ $-\frac{28}{55}$

Divide.

7. $-\frac{34}{2}$ -17
8. $\frac{-14}{-7}$ 2
9. $-\frac{7}{6} \div \frac{3}{5}$
$-\frac{7}{6} \cdot \frac{5}{3} = -\frac{35}{18}$
10. $-\frac{7}{3} \div -\frac{5}{11}$
$-\frac{7}{3} \cdot \left(-\frac{11}{5}\right) = \frac{77}{15}$

Assignment Guide
Algebra: 1–49 e/o, MR

Alg w/Finite or Trig: 1–55 m4, 56, MR, assign w. 1-3

Comprehensive: 1–55 m4, 56–58, MR, assign w. 1-1

ADDITIONAL ANSWERS

Exercises

50. $\frac{1}{8}$
51. $-\frac{1}{2}$
52. $-\frac{9}{25}$
53. -2
54. No
55. Yes
56. Multiply all pairs of numbers whose absolute values are reciprocals: $\left(-\frac{1}{6}\right)(-6)\cdot\left(\frac{1}{5}\right)(5)\cdot\left(\frac{1}{4}\right)(-4)\cdot\left(-\frac{1}{3}\right)(-3)\cdot\left(-\frac{1}{2}\right)(2)\cdot(-1) = 1\cdot 1\cdot(-1)\cdot 1\cdot(-1)\cdot(-1)$ Then multiply out. The result is -1.

1-2 EXERCISES

A

Multiply.

1. $3(-7)$ -21
2. $5(-8)$ -40
3. $-2\cdot 4$ -8
4. $-5\cdot 9$ -45
5. $(-8)(-2)$ 16
6. $(-7)(-3)$ 21
7. $(-9)(-14)$ 126
8. $(-8)(-17)$ 136
9. $(-6)(5.7)$ -34.2
10. $(-7)(-6.1)$ 42.7
11. $-4.2(-6.3)$ 26.46
12. $-7.4(9.6)$ -71.04
13. $-3\left(\frac{2}{-3}\right)$ 2
14. $-5\left(-\frac{3}{5}\right)$ 3
15. $-3(-4)(5)$ 60
16. $-6(-8)(9)$ 432
17. $4(-3)\cdot(-2)(1)$ 24
18. $-3\cdot(-6)(8)(0)$ 0
19. $-\frac{3}{5}\cdot\frac{4}{7}$ $-\frac{12}{35}$
20. $-\frac{5}{4}\cdot\frac{11}{3}$ $-\frac{55}{12}$
21. $-\frac{9}{11}\cdot\left(-\frac{11}{9}\right)$ 1
22. $-\frac{13}{7}\cdot\left(-\frac{5}{2}\right)$ $\frac{65}{14}$
23. $-\frac{2}{3}\cdot\left(-\frac{2}{3}\right)\cdot\left(-\frac{2}{3}\right)$ $-\frac{8}{27}$
24. $-\frac{4}{5}\cdot\left(-\frac{4}{5}\right)\cdot\left(-\frac{4}{5}\right)$ $-\frac{64}{125}$
25. $-\frac{1}{2}\left(\frac{2}{3}\right)\left(-\frac{3}{4}\right)\left(\frac{4}{5}\right)$ $\frac{1}{5}$

Divide.

26. $\frac{-8}{4}$ -2
27. $-\frac{16}{2}$ -8
28. $\frac{56}{-8}$ -7
29. $\frac{-28}{7}$ -4
30. $\frac{63}{-7}$ -9
31. $\frac{-77}{-11}$ 7
32. $\frac{-48}{-6}$ 8
33. $\frac{84}{-12}$ -7
34. $\frac{-5.4}{-18}$ 0.3
35. $\frac{-8.4}{-12}$ 0.7
36. $18.6\div(-3.1)$ -6
37. $39.9\div(-13.3)$ -3
38. $(-75.5)\div(-15.1)$ 5
39. $(-12.1)\div(-0.11)$ 110
40. $\frac{2}{7}\div\left(-\frac{4}{3}\right)$ $-\frac{3}{14}$
41. $\frac{3}{5}\div(-6)$ $-\frac{1}{10}$
42. $-\frac{12}{5}\div\left(-\frac{3}{10}\right)$ 8
43. $-\frac{5}{6}\div\left(-\frac{2}{3}\right)$ $\frac{5}{4}$
44. $-\frac{8}{3}\div\left(\frac{4}{7}\right)$ $-\frac{14}{3}$
45. $\frac{6}{7}\div\left(-\frac{9}{14}\right)$ $-\frac{4}{3}$

Which of these divisions are possible?

46. $\frac{9}{0}$ Not possible
47. $\frac{0}{16}$ Possible
48. $\frac{(a-a)}{28}$ Possible
49. $\frac{(2x-2x)}{(2x-2x)}$ Not possible

B

Find the reciprocal of each number.

50. $|-8|$
51. $\frac{|7-19|}{-6}$
52. $-\frac{|25|}{|-9|}$
53. $-\left|\frac{1}{-2}\right|$
54. Are 0.025 and -40 reciprocals?
55. Are 6 and $0.1\overline{6}$ reciprocals?
56. ***Critical Thinking*** Describe how you would perform the following multiplication:

$$\left(-\frac{1}{6}\right)\left(\frac{1}{5}\right)\left(\frac{1}{4}\right)\left(-\frac{1}{3}\right)\left(-\frac{1}{2}\right)(-1)(2)(-3)(-4)(5)(-6)$$

Challenge

57. Find the product of any nonzero number and the reciprocal of its inverse. −1
58. Is the reciprocal of a nonzero rational number rational or irrational? Explain.
59. a. How might you define the reciprocal of a percent?
    b. What would be the reciprocal of 40%?
    c. What would be the reciprocal of 125%?
60. Find the number, which when multiplied by the reciprocal of $-\frac{1}{8}$ gives a product that is the absolute value of -2.

Mixed Review

Write decimal notation for each number. **61.** $7\frac{7}{8}$ **62.** $\frac{81}{16}$ **63.** $-4\frac{2}{3}$

Determine which are rational and which are irrational. **64.** $\sqrt{24}$ **65.** $-\sqrt{25}$ **66.** 0.0013

Simplify. **67.** $3 + (-6)$ **68.** $-5.1 + (-4.3)$ **69.** $8 - 11$

70. $3 - (-4)$ **71.** $\frac{2}{9} + \left(-\frac{7}{9}\right)$ **72.** $-\frac{2}{3} - \left(-\frac{2}{3}\right)$ **73.** $\frac{3}{5} - \frac{1}{10}$

74. $\frac{2}{3} + \left(-\frac{1}{6}\right)$ **75.** $|-37| + |12|$ **76.** $-\frac{5}{6} + \frac{2}{3}$

77. $|0| - |1| - |2|$ **78.** $-\frac{1}{2} + \frac{1}{3} - \frac{1}{4} + \frac{1}{5}$

Find each percent.

79. 90% of 90 **80.** 180% of 45

81. Tickets for the state fair cost \$5.75 for adults and \$3.50 for children. Children under the age of 3 are admitted free. What would it cost for a family of two adults, an eighteen-month old boy, and twin ten-year old girls to enter the fair?

Calculator Investigation

A **binary operation** assigns to each pair of numbers of a set another number of the set. The operations of addition and multiplication are examples of binary operations on the set of real numbers. Addition assigns a **sum** to a pair of numbers and multiplication a **product.** A **unary operation** takes a single number and assigns another number to it.

How can a calculator be thought of as an operation machine? What unary operations can be performed using your calculator?

---

58. Rational; the reciprocal of a rational number $\frac{p}{q}$, where p and q are integers, and $p \neq 0$ and $q \neq 0$, is $\frac{q}{p}$.

59. a. The reciprocal of a, where a is a percent, is the percent b such that $a \cdot b = 100\%$.
b. 250%
c. 80%

60. $-\frac{1}{4}$

Mixed Review

61. 7.875
62. 5.0625
63. $-4.\overline{6}$
64. Irrational
65. Rational
66. Rational
67. −3
68. −9.4
69. −3
70. 7
71. $-\frac{5}{9}$
72. 0
73. $\frac{1}{2}$
74. $\frac{1}{2}$
75. 49
76. $-\frac{1}{6}$
77. −3
78. $-\frac{13}{60}$
79. 81
80. 81
81. \$18.50

Calculator Investigation

A calculator can be thought of as an operation machine because it takes the entered number(s) and returns the result determined by the chosen operation. Unary operations could include:

$\frac{1}{x}$, x^2, $\sqrt{x}$, lnx, %, x!, sinx, cosx, tanx

1-3

FIRST FIVE MINUTES

Simplify.

1. $-5 - 7$
   -12
2. $7 + (-4)$
   3
3. $-6 \cdot 7$
   -42
4. $(-5)(-4)$
   20
5. $-\frac{3}{7} \cdot \frac{4}{5}$
   $-\frac{12}{35}$
6. $-\frac{4}{5} \div \frac{11}{3}$
   $-\frac{4}{5} \cdot \frac{3}{11} = -\frac{12}{55}$
7. The area A of a rectangle with width w and length l is given by the formula $A = lw$. Find the area of a rectangle with width 5 and length 7.
   $A = 5 \cdot 7 = 35$

Algebraic Expressions

You may want to review for this lesson by asking students to give examples of numerals, symbols, constants, and variables.

Key Questions

- In the expression $3m + m$, can the first $m = 3$ and the second $m = 2$?
  No
- In the expression $x + y$, can $x = 2$ and $y = 2$?
  Yes

Chalkboard Examples

Evaluate.

1. $3x - 7$ for $x = 4$
   $3 \cdot 4 - 7 = 5$
2. $(-1)(-x)$ for $x = -3$
   $(-1)[-(-3)] = -1 \cdot 3 = -3$
3. $|x - 7|$ for $x = 5$
   $|5 - 7| = |-2| = 2$

1-3 Algebraic Expressions and Properties of Numbers

In algebra we use letters to represent numbers. For example, in the formula for the area of a circle

$$A = \pi r^2$$

A stands for the area and r stands for the radius. The Greek letter π stands for the ratio of circumference to diameter of a circle. A and r can represent various numbers, so they are called variables. The letter π represents only one number, so it is called a constant.

Algebraic Expressions

Objective: Evaluate algebraic expressions.

Algebraic expressions consist of numerals, variables, and other mathematical symbols such as $+$ or $\sqrt{\ }$. Here are some examples of algebraic expressions.

$$x \qquad -8|, \qquad \sqrt{x + 6}, \qquad y^2 - 2y + 9$$

When we substitute numbers for the variables in an expression and then calculate, the number we get is the value of the expression for those replacements. We say that we are evaluating the expression.

EXAMPLE 1 Evaluate $2y + x$ for $x = 3$ and $y = 5$.

$$\begin{aligned} 2y + x &= 2 \cdot 5 + 3 && \text{Substituting 3 for } x \text{ and 5 for } y \\ &= 10 + 3 && \text{Calculating} \\ &= 13 \end{aligned}$$

The value of the expression is 13.

EXAMPLE 2 Evaluate $-(-x)$ for $x = -7$.

$$\begin{aligned} -(-x) &= -(-(-7)) && \text{Substituting } -7 \text{ for } x \\ &= -(7) && \text{Calculating within the parentheses} \\ &= -7 && \text{Finding the inverse of 7} \end{aligned}$$

The value of the expression is -7.

EXAMPLE 3 Evaluate $|x| + 2|y|$ for $x = 15$ and $y = -10$.

$$\begin{aligned} |x| + 2|y| &= |15| + 2|-10| && \text{Substituting 15 for } x \text{ and } -10 \text{ for } y \\ &= 15 + 2 \cdot 10 && \text{Finding absolute values} \\ &= 15 + 20 = 35 \end{aligned}$$

The value of the expression is 35.

Try This Evaluate each expression.

a. $5x - y$ for $x = 10$ and $y = 5$ 45 b. $-(-y)$ for $y = -8$ -8

c. $|x| - 2|y|$ for $x = -16$ and $y = -4$ 8

Expressions and Number Properties

Objective: Use number properties to write equivalent expressons.

The subtraction theorem tells us that the expressions $m - n$ and $m + (-n)$ will always have the same value whenever we make the same substitutions in both expressions. Expressions that always have the same value for all acceptable replacements are equivalent expressions.

EXAMPLES Use the subtraction theorem to write equivalent expressions.

4. $4y - x = 4y + (-x)$ Adding an inverse

5. $3p + 5q = 3p - (-5q)$ Using the subtraction theorem in reverse

Try This Use the subtraction theorem to write equivalent expressions.

d. $-5x - 3y$ $-5x + (-3y)$ e. $17m - 45$ $17m + (-45)$ f. $-6p + 5t$ $-6p - (-5t)$

A number that does not give us a value when substituted in an expression is not an *acceptable* replacement. For example, the number 1 is not an acceptable replacement for x in the expression

$$\frac{4 + x}{x - 1}$$

because it gives us a divisor of 0, and division by 0 is undefined.

Number properties help us identify equivalent expressions. The commutative properties tell us that we can change order when adding or multiplying and obtain an expression equivalent to the original one.

The Commutative Properties

Addition
For any real numbers a and b, $a + b = b + a$.

Multiplication
For any real numbers a and b, $a \cdot b = b \cdot a$.

The associative properties tell us that we can change grouping when adding or multiplying and obtain an equivalent expression.

Expressions and Number Properties

Illustrate the number properties with arithmetic examples. For example,

a. $3 + 4 = 4 + 3$ Commutative property of addition
b. $2 \cdot (4 \cdot 3) = (2 \cdot 4) \cdot 3$ Associative property of multiplication
c. $5 + 0 = 5$ Identity property of addition

Avoiding Common Errors

$(a + b) + c = c + (a + b)$ illustrates the commutative property, not the associative property.

Key Questions

- Is $3x - 3$ equivalent to $-3 + 3x$?
Yes
- Is 3 an acceptable replacement for $\frac{x-3}{3x}$?
Yes
- Does $a \div b = b \div a$?
No; $\frac{1}{4} \neq \frac{4}{1}$
- If you say $\frac{x}{x} = 1$, what must you specify?
That $x \neq 0$

Chalkboard Examples

Use the subtraction theorem to write equivalent expressions.

1. $x - 4$
$x + (-4)$
2. $|x + 3|$
$|x - (-3)|$
3. Use the commutative property of addition to write an equivalent expression.
$2ab + 7bc$
$7bc + 2ab$
4. Use the commutative property of multiplication to write an equivalent expression.
$5(x + y)$
$(x + y) \cdot 5$
5. Use the associative property of addition to write an equivalent expression.
$7a + (ab + c)$
$(7a + ab) + c$
6. Use the associative property of multiplication to write an equivalent expression.
$(8x^3)y^2$
$8(x^3y^2)$

7. Use the commutative and associative properties to justify the claim that $(a \cdot 5 + 3) + b$ is equivalent to $3 + (b + 5a)$
$(a \cdot 5 + 3) + b$
$= (5a + 3) + b$ Comm.
$= 5a + (3 + b)$ Assoc.
$= (3 + b) + 5a$ Comm.
$= 3 + (b + 5a)$ Assoc.

8. Write an expression equivalent to $\frac{3}{5}$. Use $\frac{7}{7}$ for 1.
$\frac{3}{5} \cdot 1 = \frac{3}{5} \cdot \frac{7}{7} = \frac{21}{35}$

9. Write an expression for $\frac{3ab}{6ac}$ by simplifying.
$\frac{3ab}{6ac} = \frac{(3a)b}{(3a)2c}$
$= \frac{3a}{3a} \cdot \frac{b}{2c} = 1 \cdot \frac{b}{2c}$
$= \frac{b}{2c}$

10. Show that $ab - ac$ is equivalent to $ab - bc + bc - ac$.
Add 0 in the form $-bc + bc$.

The Associative Properties

Addition
For any real numbers a, b, and c, $a + (b + c) = (a + b) + c$.
Multiplication
For any real number a, b, and c, $a \cdot (b \cdot c) = (a \cdot b) \cdot c$.

EXAMPLE 6 Use the commutative property of addition to write an expression equivalent to $3x + 4y$.

$$3x + 4y = 4y + 3x \quad \text{Changing order}$$

EXAMPLE 7 Use the associative property of multiplication to write an expression equivalent to $3x(7y \cdot 9z)$.

$$3x(7y \cdot 9z) = (3x \cdot 7y) \cdot 9z \quad \text{Changing grouping}$$

We can use both the commutative and associative properties to write equivalent expressions.

EXAMPLE 8 Use the commutative and associative properties of addition to write an expression equivalent to $\left(\frac{5}{x} + 2y\right) + 3z$.

$$\left(\frac{5}{x} + 2y\right) + 3z = \frac{5}{x} + (2y + 3z) \quad \text{Using the associative property}$$
$$= \frac{5}{x} + (3z + 2y) \quad \text{Using the commutative property}$$

Try This

g. Use the associative property of addition to write an expression equivalent to $(8m + 5n) + 6p$. $8m + (5n + 6p)$

h. Use the commutative property of multiplication to write an expression equivalent to $(17x)(-9t)$. $(-9t)(17x)$

i. Use the commutative and associative properties of multiplication to write an expression equivalent to $9p(4q \cdot 16r)$. $16r(4q \cdot 9p)$

We can use the identity properties of addition and multiplication to write equivalent expressions.

The Identity Properties

Addition
For any real number a, $a + 0 = a$.
Multiplication
For any real number a, $a \cdot 1 = a$.

The number 0 is the additive identity, and the number 1 is the multiplicative identity. Recall that the ratio $\frac{b}{b}$ is equivalent to 1 for any nonzero number b. Also, the difference $b - b$ is equivalent to 0 for any number b.

EXAMPLE 9 Write an expression equivalent to $\frac{x}{3y}$. Use $\frac{8}{8}$ for 1.

$$\frac{x}{3y} = \left(\frac{x}{3y}\right)\left(\frac{8}{8}\right) \quad \text{Multiplying by 1}$$

$$= \frac{8x}{24y} \quad \text{Multiplying numerators and denominators}$$

The expressions $\frac{x}{3y}$ and $\frac{8x}{24y}$ are equivalent. They will represent the same number for any acceptable replacements for x and y.

Try This

j. Write an expression equivalent to $\frac{19t}{3x}$. Use $\frac{9}{9}$ for 1. $\frac{171t}{27x}$

EXAMPLE 10 Write an expression equivalent to $\frac{6xy}{2x}$ by simplifying.

$$\frac{6xy}{2x} = \frac{2 \cdot 3 \cdot xy}{2x} \quad \text{Factoring the numerator}$$

$$= \left(\frac{2x}{2x}\right) \cdot \frac{3y}{1} \quad \text{Factoring the rational expression}$$

$$= 1 \cdot \frac{3y}{1}$$

$$= 3y$$

The expressions $\frac{6xy}{2x}$ and $3y$ are equivalent. They will represent the same number for any acceptable replacements for x and y.

Try This

k. Write an expression equivalent to $\frac{10yz}{5z}$ by simplifying. $2y$

EXAMPLE 11 Write an expression equivalent to $4x - 2$ by adding 0. Use $7y - 7y$ for 0.

$$4x - 2 = 4x - 2 + (7y - 7y) \quad \text{Adding 0}$$

$$= 4x + 7y - 2 - 7y \quad \text{Rearranging}$$

The expressions $4x - 2$ and $4x + 7y - 2 - 7y$ are equivalent.

Try This

l. Write an expression equivalent to $8a - b$ by adding 0. Use $x - x$ for 0. $8a + x - b - x$

LESSON QUIZ

1. Evaluate $5x + 2$ for $x = 7$.
   37
2. Evaluate $3x + 2y$ for $x = 5, y = 7$.
   29
3. Write an equivalent expression that does not use subtraction.
   $5x - 7y$
   $5x + (-7y)$
4. Use the commutative property of addition to write an equivalent expression for $8x + 3y$.
   $3y + 8x$
5. Use the associative property of multiplication to write an equivalent expression for $[5(x + y^2)]z$.
   $5[(x + y)^2z]$
6. Write an equivalent expression for $\frac{2x}{y}$ using $\frac{6}{6}$ for 1.
   $\frac{12x}{6y}$
7. Simplify.
   $\frac{9uv}{3vw}$
   $\frac{3u}{w}$

Assignment Guide
Algebra: 1 – 42 e/o, MR
Alg w/Finite or Trig: 1–50 m4, 51, MR, assign w. 1-2
Comprehensive: 1–50 m4, 51–53, MR, assign w. 1-4

ADDITIONAL ANSWERS

Exercises

21. $8y + (-9x)$
22. $16m + (-56)$
23. $t + (-34s)$
24. $-18x + (-5y)$
25. $9x - (-7)$
26. $23x - (-12y)$
27. $-18m - (-n)$
28. $-65k - (-15h)$

1-3 EXERCISES

A

Evaluate each expression.

1. $3x + y$ for $x = 16$ and $y = 6$ 54
2. $5y - x$ for $x = 8$ and $y = -11$ −63
3. $2p + 3t$ for $p = -20$ and $t = 17$ 11
4. $5s - 3t$ for $s = -14$ and $t = 13$ −109
5. $3x + 5y + z$ for $x = 18$, $y = 9$, and $z = 4$ 103
6. $8x + 4y - 2z$ for $x = 5$, $y = 17$, and $z = -8$ 124
7. $-y$ for $y = 4$ −4
8. $-x$ for $x = -8$ 8
9. $-(-x)$ for $x = -17$ −17
10. $-(-m)$ for $m = 12$ 12
11. $-(y + 4a)$ for $y = 2$ $-2 - 4a$
12. $-(y + 20)$ for $y = -6$ −14
13. $-(x - 2)$ for $x = 17$ −15
14. $-(y + 2)$ for $y = 1$ −3
15. $3|x + 2|$ for $x = -4$ 6
16. $|p| + |q|$ for $p = -31$ and $q = -12$ 43
17. $5|y|$ for $y = -23$ 115
18. $|p + q|$ for $p = 21$ and $q = -9$ 12
19. $|p| + |q|$ for $p = 21$ and $q = -9$ 30
20. $|p - q|$ for $p = 31$ and $q = -6$ 37

Use the subtraction theorem to write equivalent expressions.

21. $8y - 9x$
22. $16m - 56$
23. $t - 34s$
24. $-18x - 5y$
25. $9x + 7$
26. $23x + 12y$
27. $-18m + n$
28. $-65k + 15h$
29. Use the commutative property of addition to write an expression equivalent to $9y + 73x$. $73x + 9y$
30. Use the associative property of multiplication to write an expression equivalent to $9a \cdot (6b \cdot 12c)$. $(9a \cdot 6b) \cdot 12c$
31. Use the associative property of addition to write an expression equivalent to $12x + (9y + 89z)$. $(12x + 9y) + 89z$
32. Use the commutative property of multiplication to write an expression equivalent to $(32a)(-12b)$. $(-12b)(32a)$
33. Use the commutative and associative properties of addition to write an expression equivalent to $\left(\frac{y}{8} + 90\right) + 6x$. $(6x + 90) + \frac{y}{8}$, etc.
34. Use the commutative and associative properties of multiplication to write an expression equivalent to $(9x \cdot 12y)\, 8z$. $9x \cdot (8z \cdot 12y)$, etc.

Write an expression equivalent to each of the following. Use the ratio given for 1.

35. $\frac{12x}{23y}$; $\frac{8}{8}$ $\frac{96x}{184y}$
36. $\frac{19a}{b}$; $\frac{9}{9}$ $\frac{171a}{9b}$
37. $\frac{102}{5xy}$; $\frac{7}{7}$ $\frac{714}{35xy}$
38. $\frac{90z}{16y}$; $\frac{x}{x}$ $\frac{90xz}{16xy}$

Write an expression equivalent to each of the following by simplifying.

39. $\frac{4y}{4x}$ $\frac{y}{x}$
40. $\frac{8xy}{16y}$ $\frac{x}{2}$
41. $\frac{5y}{-2xy}$ $\frac{5}{-2x}$
42. $\frac{3(y + 1)}{21(y + 1)}$ $\frac{1}{7}$

B

Write as an algebraic expression.

43. five more than the absolute value of a number $5 + |x|$

44. the additive inverse of a number increased by its absolute value $-x + |x|$

45. the additive inverse of the absolute value of twice some number $-|2a|$

46. the absolute value of the sum of two numbers $|a + b|$

47. the sum of the absolute value of two numbers $|p| + |q|$

48. The absolute value of the difference of x and y is greater than 5. $|x - y| > 5$

49. Three times the absolute value of a number is 8. $3|p| = 8$

50. The absolute value of the sum of two numbers is less than the square of their sum. $|x + y| < (x + y)^2$

51. ***Critical Thinking*** Write an algebraic expression in x and y that has a value of 20 when $x = 2$ and $y = -6$. Answers may vary. Examples are $x - 3y$, $4x - 2y$, $7x - y$

Challenge

52. Suppose we define a new operation @ on the set of real numbers as follows: $a @ b = 3a - b$. Thus $9 @ 2 = 3(9) - 2 = 25$. Is @ commutative? That is, does $a @ b = b @ a$ for all real numbers a and b? No; $2 @ 9 = 3(2) - 9 = -3 \neq 25$

53. Suppose we define a new operation $\oplus$ on the set of real numbers as follows: $a \oplus b = a^2 + b^2$. Thus $4 \oplus 2 = 4^2 + 2^2 = 16 + 4 = 20$. Is $\oplus$ commutative? Yes

Mixed Review

Simplify. **54.** $4.2 + (-6.8)$ **55.** $6(-9)$ **56.** $-3.2(-4.1)$

57. $-8 \div 2$ **58.** $-4 - 9$ **59.** $-9(-3)$ **60.** $40 \div (-5)$

61. $-8 + 27$ **62.** $7 - 11$ **63.** $-\frac{3}{16} + \frac{8}{16}$ **64.** $\frac{3}{5} - \frac{3}{10}$ **65.** $-\frac{4}{5} \cdot \frac{1}{2}$

Express as a ratio of integers. **66.** -5 **67.** 9.1 **68.** $\frac{2.8}{4.5}$ **69.** $-\frac{0.2}{0.05}$

Determine which of the following are rational and which are irrational.

70. $\sqrt{25}$ **71.** $3.454554555\ldots$ **72.** 3.45455 **73.** $-\frac{1}{7}$ **74.** $\sqrt{8}$

Calculator Investigation

a. Evaluate the expression $\frac{1}{x}$ for $x = 0.1$, $x = 0.01$, $x = 0.001$, $x = 0.0001$, and so on. What happens as the value of x gets smaller and smaller?

b. Evaluate the expression $5\left(\frac{1}{n}\right)$ for $n = 0.001$, $n = 0.01$, $n = 0.1$, $n = 1$, and so on. What happens as the value of n gets larger and larger?

Mixed Review

54. -2.6
55. -54
56. 13.12
57. -4
58. -13
59. 27
60. -8
61. 19
62. -4
63. $\frac{5}{16}$
64. $\frac{3}{10}$
65. $-\frac{2}{5}$
66. $\frac{-5}{1}$
67. $\frac{91}{10}$
68. $\frac{28}{45}$
69. $\frac{-4}{1}$
70. Rational
71. Irrational
72. Rational
73. Rational
74. Irrational

Calculator Investigation

a. As x gets smaller, the value of $\frac{1}{x}$ gets larger and larger.

b. As n gets larger and larger, the value of $5\left(\frac{1}{n}\right)$ gets smaller and smaller.

1-4

FIRST FIVE MINUTES

Simplify.

1. $5(4 + 7)$ $5 \cdot 11 = 55$
2. $7(8 - 2)$ $7 \cdot 6 = 42$
3. Evaluate $3(x + 5)$ for $x = 6$.
   $3(6 + 5) = 3 \cdot 11 = 33$
4. Evaluate $|x - y|$ for $x = 2$ and $y = 4$.
   $|2 - 4| = |-2| = 2$
5. Simplify $\frac{4xy}{2x}$.
   $2y$
6. Factor 91 into the product of two numbers.
   $7 \cdot 13$

Multiplying

You may want to show the proof of Theorem 1-3, which is sometimes called the distributive property of multiplication over subtraction.

$$\begin{aligned} a(b - c) &= a[b + (-c)] \\ &= ab + a(-c) \\ &= ab + a(-1)c \\ &= ab + (-1)ac \\ &= ab - ac \end{aligned}$$

Avoiding Common Errors

Students may make the mistake of writing

$3(x + y)$ as $3x + y$

rather than $3x + 3y$.
Remind students to use the distributive property when removing parentheses.

Key Questions

- When calculating $51(19 + 17)$ do you add first or multiply first?
  Add first
- When calculating $51 \cdot 19 + 51 \cdot 17$ do you add first or multiply first?
  Multiply first

Chalkboard Examples

Multiply.

1. $5(y + 3)$
   $5y + 5 \cdot 3 = 5y + 15$
2. $r(a + b + c)$
   $ra + rb + rc$
3. $-a(z + 2)$
   $(-a)z + (-a) \cdot 2$
   $-az - 2a$
4. $-5z(x - 7)$
   $-5zx - (-5z) \cdot 7$
   $-5zx + 35z$

1-4 The Distributive Property

Multiplying

Objective: Use the distributive property to multiply.

The distributive property tells us that when multiplying a number by a sum, we can add first and then multiply, or multiply first and then add.

The Distributive Property of Multiplication Over Addition

For any real numbers a, b, and c, $a(b + c) = ab + ac$.

In stating this property, we have used an agreement about parentheses. Parentheses show us which calculations are to be done first. We agree to omit them around products, however. Thus the expression $ab + ac$ is equivalent to $(ab) + (ac)$, since multiplications are performed before additions.

The following theorem can be proved with the help of the subtraction theorem.

Theorem 1-3

For any real numbers a, b, and c, $a(b - c) = ab - ac$.

We can also use the distributive property to write equivalent expressions.

EXAMPLES Multiply.

1. $4(x + 2) = 4x + 4 \cdot 2$ Using the distributive property
   $= 4x + 8$ Simplifying
2. $b(s - t + f) = bs - bt + bf$
3. $-3(y + 4) = (-3)(y) + (-3)(4)$
   $= -3y - 12$
4. $-2x(y - 1) = -2x \cdot y - (-2x) \cdot 1$
   $= -2xy + 2x$

Try This Multiply.

a. $5(x + 9)$ $5x + 45$ **b.** $8(y - 10)$ $8y - 80$ **c.** $a(x + y - z)$ $ax + ay - az$

Factoring
Objective: Use the distributive property to factor expressions.

The reverse of multiplying is factoring. To factor an expression is to find an equivalent expression that is a product. The parts of an expression like $3x + 4y + 8z$, separated by plus signs, are called terms of the expression. In this expression the terms are $3x$, $4y$, and $4z$. In the term $3x$, 3 and x are factors. The coefficient of x is 3.

If all the terms of an expression have a factor in common, we can factor it out using the distributive property. We usually factor out the greatest common factor of all the terms.

EXAMPLES Factor.

5. $cx - cy = c(x - y)$ Using the distributive property

6. $9x + 27y = 9x + 9 \cdot (3y) = 9(x + 3y)$

7. $P + Prt = P \cdot 1 + Prt = P(1 + rt)$

Try This Factor.

d. $2l + 2w$ $2(l + w)$ **e.** $ac - ay$ $a(c - y)$ **f.** $6x - 12$ $6(x - 2)$ **g.** $-25y + 15w + 5$ $5(-5y + 3w + 1)$

Collecting Like Terms
Objective: Collect like terms.

Terms whose variables are the same, such as $9y$ and $23y$, are called like terms. Similarly, $8a^5$ and $17a^5$ are like terms. Terms such as $23x$ and $9x^2$ are not like terms. Using the distributive property, we can simplify by collecting like terms. An expression with like terms collected is equivalent to the original expression.

EXAMPLES Collect like terms.

8. $x - 3x = 1 \cdot x - 3 \cdot x = (1-3)x = -2x$

9. $2x + 3y - 5x - 2y$

$= 2x + 3y + (-5x) + (-2y)$ Adding an inverse to subtract

$= 2x + (-5x) + 3y + (-2y)$ Using the commutative and associative properties

$= (2 - 5)x + (3 - 2)y$ Using the distributive property

$= -3x + y$

Try This Collect like terms.

h. $9x + 11x$ $20x$ **i.** $5x - 12x$ $-7x$ **j.** $22x - 2.5 + 1.4x + 6.4$ $23.4x + 3.9$

Factoring

Show that factoring is the reverse of multiplying. Stress that multiplying also serves as a check.

Chalkboard Examples

Factor.
1. $9x + 9y$
   $9(x + y)$
2. $18a + 21b$
   $3(6a + 7b)$
3. $a + 3ay$
   $a \cdot 1 + 3ay = a(1 + 3y)$

Collecting Like Terms

Emphasize that two terms are *like terms* if they have the same variables with exactly the same exponents. For example, $3x^3y^2$ and $5x^3y^2$ are like terms because they have the same variables with the same exponents. The terms $3xy$ and $5xy^2$ are *not* like terms, because the exponents of the y factors are different. Similarly x, x^2, x^3, etc., are not like terms.

Key Questions

- Are $-3x$ and $3x$ like terms?
  Yes
- Are 1 and $1x$ like terms?
  No

Chalkboard Examples

Collect like terms.
1. $5x + 4x + 2x$
   $(5 + 4 + 2)x = 11x$
2. $5a + 7b - 8a - 2b$
   $5a - 8a + 7b - 2b$
   $= (5 - 8)a + (7 - 2)b$
   $= -3a + 5b$

Inverses of Sums

Multiplication can be thought of as a "stretching" or a "shrinking" operation on the number line. For example, multiplication of a number by 2 stretches the number out to a position twice as far from the origin. Multiplication by $\frac{1}{2}$ shrinks the number to a position half as far from the origin. Multiplication by 0 shrinks the number down to 0. Multiplication by -1 can be thought of as rotating or flipping the number to its mirror image on the other side of the origin.

Chalkboard Examples

Simplify.

1. $-(-1)$
   1
2. $-(z - 7)$
   $-1(z + (-7))$
   $= -1z + (-1)(-7)$
   $= -z + 7$
3. $-(-3a + 2b - c)$
   $-1(-3a + 2b + (-c))$
   $= -1(-3a) + (-1)2b + (-1)(-c)$
   $= 3a - 2b + c$
4. $-(9a - 4b - c + d)$
   $-9a + 4b + c - d$
5. $-\left(-\frac{1}{2} + \frac{2}{3}x - \frac{4}{7}x^2\right)$
   $\frac{1}{2} - \frac{2}{3}x + \frac{4}{7}x^2$

Inverses of Sums

Objective: Write the inverse of a sum.

When we multiply a number by -1, we get the additive inverse of that number.

Theorem 1-4

The Multiplicative Property of -1

For any real number a, $-1 \cdot a = -a$.

(Negative 1 times a is the additive inverse of a, or multiplying a number by -1 changes its sign.)

Using the multiplicative property of -1, we can replace an inverse sign by -1.

EXAMPLES Simplify.

10.
$$\begin{aligned} -(-9y) &= -1(-9y) && \text{Using the property of } -1 \\ &= [-1(-9)]y && \text{Using the associative property} \\ &= 9y \end{aligned}$$

11.
$$\begin{aligned} -(3x - 2y + 4) &= -1(3x - 2y + 4) && \text{Using the property of } -1 \\ &= -1(3x) - (-1)(2y) + (-1)(4) && \text{Using the distributive property} \\ &= -3x - (-2y) + (-4) && \text{Using the property of } -1 \\ &= -3x + 2y - 4 && \text{Using the subtraction theorem} \end{aligned}$$

Try This Simplify.

k. $-(7x)$ $-7x$ **l.** $-(y + 10)$ $-y - 10$ **m.** $-(-3x - 2y + 1)$ $3x + 2y - 1$

Example 11 illustrates another important property of real numbers.

Theorem 1-5

The Inverse of a Sum Property

For any real numbers a and b, $-(a + b) = -a + (-b)$.

(The inverse of a sum is the sum of the inverses.)

This property holds when there is a sum of more than two terms. It also holds for differences because any difference is equivalent to a sum. The property gives us a rule for finding the additive inverse of an expression with more than one term. To find the additive inverse of an expression with more than one term, change the sign of every term.

EXAMPLES Simplify.

12. $-(3x - 4y + 59) = -3x + 4y - 59$ Changing the sign of each term

13. $-\left(-9t + 7z - \frac{1}{4}w\right) = 9t - 7z + \frac{1}{4}w$ Changing the sign of each term

Try This Simplify.

n. $-(-2x - 5z + 24)$ $2x + 5z - 24$ **o.** $-\left(\frac{1}{4}t + 41w - rd + 23\right)$ $-\frac{1}{4}t - 41w + rd - 23$

Using the Distributive Property

Objective: Use the distributive property to simplify expressions.

When a sum or difference is being subtracted, we can subtract by adding an inverse. We can simplify, using the distributive property to remove parentheses.

EXAMPLES Simplify.

14. $6x - (4x + 2) = 6x + [-(4x + 2)]$ Adding an inverse
$= 6x + [(-4x) + (-2)]$ Using the inverse of a sum property
$= 6x - 4x - 2$ Using the subtraction theorem
$= 2x - 2$ Collecting like terms

When an expression in parentheses is preceded by a subtraction sign or additive inverse sign, the sign of each term inside the parentheses is changed.

15. $x - 5(x + y) = x + [-5(x + y)]$ Adding the inverse of $5(x + y)$
$= x + [-5x - 5y]$ Using the distributive property
$= x - 5x - 5y$
$= -4x - 5y$ Collecting like terms

When parentheses are needed within parentheses, we may use other grouping symbols. Computations are done within the innermost symbols first.

16. $6y - \{4[3(y - 2) - 4(y + 2)] - 3\}$
$= 6y - \{4[3y - 6 - 4y - 8] - 3\}$ Multiplying to remove the innermost parentheses
$= 6y - \{4[-y - 14] - 3\}$ Collecting like terms in the brackets
$= 6y - \{-4y - 56 - 3\}$ Multiplying to remove the brackets
$= 6y + 4y + 59 = 10y + 59$

Try This Simplify.

p. $6x - (3x - 8)$ $3x + 8$ **q.** $x - 2(y + x)$ $-x - 2y$

r. $3x - 5(2y - 4x)$ $23x - 10y$ **s.** $15x - \{2[2(x - 5) - 6(x + 3)] + 4\}$ $23x + 52$

t. $9a + \{3a - 2[(a - 4) - (a + 2)]\}$ $12a + 12$

Using the Distributive Property

The expression $-(4x + 2)$ can be rewritten as $-1(4x + 2)$ prior to using the distributive property if students have any difficulty with this section.

Key Questions

- Does $-(a - b) = (-a - b)$? No
- Does $(a - b) = -(-a + b)$? Yes

Chalkboard Examples

Simplify.

1. $4a - (a + 5)$
   $4a - a - 5 = 3a - 5$
2. $2z - 4w - (5z - 3w)$
   $2z - 4w - 5z + 3w$
   $= -3z - w$
3. $3z - 4(z + 2)$
   $3z - 4z - 8$
   $= -z - 8$
4. $9 - 2[2 - 3(x + 1)]$
   $9 - 2[2 - 3x - 3]$
   $= 9 - 2[-1 - 3x]$
   $= 9 + 2 + 6x$
   $= 11 + 6x$
5. $4 + a\{3 + b[c + 2(d + 1)]\}$
   $= 4 + a\{3 + b[c + 2d + 2]\}$
   $= 4 + a\{3 + bc + 2bd + 2b\}$
   $= 4 + 3a + abc + 2abd + 2ab$

LESSON QUIZ

1. Multiply $-4(3x - 7)$.
   $-12x + 28$
2. Factor $6x + 3y + 9$.
   $3(2x + y + 3)$
3. Collect like terms.
   $8z - 3x - 2z + x$
   $6z - 2x$
4. Simplify.
   $-(3z - 4w + 8)$
   $-3z + 4w - 8$
5. Simplify.
   $8r - 3(2r - 7) + 4$
   $= 8r - 6r + 21 + 4$
   $= 2r + 25$
6. Simplify.
   $3[2x + 4(x + 1)] - 2$
   $3[2x + 4x + 4] - 2$
   $= 3[6x + 4] - 2$
   $= 18x + 12 - 2$
   $= 18x + 10$

Assignment Guide
Algebra: Day 1: 1 – 46 e/o
Day 2: 47 – 80 e/o, MR
Alg w/Finite or Trig: 1–80 m4, 81–87 e/o, 88, MR
Comprehensive: 1–87 m4, 88–92, MR, assign w. 1-3

ADDITIONAL ANSWERS

Exercises

1. $3a + 3$
2. $8x + 8$
3. $4x - 4y$
4. $9a - 9b$
5. $-10a - 15b$
6. $-6c - 10d$
7. $2ab - 2ac + 2ad$
8. $5xy - 5xz + 5xw$
9. $2\pi rh + 2\pi r$
10. $P + Prt$
11. $\frac{1}{2}ha + \frac{1}{2}hb$
12. $\pi r + \pi rs$
13. $8(x + y)$
14. $7(a + b)$
15. $9(p - 1)$
16. $12(x - 1)$
17. $7(x - 3)$
18. $6(y - 6)$
19. $x(y + 1)$
20. $a(b + 1)$
21. $2(x - y + z)$
22. $3(x + y - z)$
23. $3(x + 2y - 1)$
24. $4(a + 2b - 1)$
25. $a(b + c - d)$
26. $x(y - z - w)$
27. $\pi r(r + s)$
28. $\frac{1}{2}h(a + b)$
47. $4b$
48. $5x$
49. $-a - 2$
50. $-b - 9$
51. $-b + 3$
52. $-x + 8$
53. $-t + y$
54. $-r + s$
55. $-a - b - c$
56. $-x - y - z$
57. $-8x + 6y - 13$
58. $-9a + 7b - 24$
59. $2c - 5d + 3e - 4f$
60. $4x - 8y + 5w - 9z$
61. $-a - 5$
62. $-4x - 9$
63. $m + 1$
64. $a + 3$
65. $5d - 12$
66. $13x - 16$
67. $-7x + 14$
68. $-15y - 45$
69. $-9x + 21$
70. $-12y + 24$

1-4 EXERCISES

A

Multiply.

1. $3(a + 1)$
2. $8(x + 1)$
3. $4(x - y)$
4. $9(a - b)$
5. $-5(2a + 3b)$
6. $-2(3c + 5d)$
7. $2a(b - c + d)$
8. $5x(y - z + w)$
9. $2\pi r(h + 1)$
10. $P(1 + rt)$
11. $\frac{1}{2}h(a + b)$
12. $\pi r(1 + s)$

Factor.

13. $8x + 8y$
14. $7a + 7b$
15. $9p - 9$
16. $12x - 12$
17. $7x - 21$
18. $6y - 36$
19. $xy + x$
20. $ab + a$
21. $2x - 2y + 2z$
22. $3x + 3y - 3z$
23. $3x + 6y - 3$
24. $4a + 8b - 4$
25. $ab + ac - ad$
26. $xy - xz - xw$
27. $\pi rr + \pi rs$
28. $\frac{1}{2}ah + \frac{1}{2}bh$

Collect like terms.

29. $4a + 5a$ $9a$
30. $9x + 3x$ $12x$
31. $8b - 11b$ $-3b$
32. $9c - 12c$ $-3c$
33. $14y + y$ $15y$
34. $13x + x$ $14x$
35. $12a - a$ $11a$
36. $15x - x$ $14x$
37. $t - 9t$ $-8t$
38. $x - 6x$ $-5x$
39. $5x - 3x + 8x$ $10x$
40. $3x - 11x + 2x$ $-6x$
41. $9a - 10b + 4a$ $13a - 10b$
42. $7c + 8d - 5c + 2d$ $2c + 10d$
43. $12a + 3b - 5a + 6b$ $7a + 9b$
44. $4x - 7 + 18x + 25$ $22x + 18$
45. $13p + 5 - 4p + 7$ $9p + 12$
46. $17a + 17b - 12a - 38b$ $5a - 21b$

Simplify.

47. $-(-4b)$
48. $-(-5x)$
49. $-(a + 2)$
50. $-(b + 9)$
51. $-(b - 3)$
52. $-(x - 8)$
53. $-(t - y)$
54. $-(r - s)$

Find the additive inverse.

55. $a + b + c$
56. $x + y + z$
57. $8x - 6y + 13$
58. $9a - 7b + 24$
59. $-2c + 5d - 3e + 4f$
60. $-4x + 8y - 5w + 9z$

Simplify.

61. $a - (2a + 5)$
62. $x - (5x + 9)$
63. $4m - (3m - 1)$
64. $5a - (4a - 3)$
65. $3d - 7 - (5 - 2d)$
66. $8x - 9 - (7 - 5x)$
67. $-2(x + 3) - 5(x - 4)$
68. $-9(y + 7) - 6(y - 3)$
69. $5x - 7(2x - 3)$
70. $8y - 4(5y - 6)$

71. $9a - [7 - 5(7a - 3)]$

72. $12b - [9 - 7(5b - 6)]$

73. $5\{-2 + 3[4 - 2(3 + 5)]\}$

74. $7\{-7 + 8[5 - 3(4 + 6)]\}$

75. $2y + \{7[3(2y - 5) - (8y + 7)] + 9\}$

76. $7b - \{6[4(3b - 7) - (9b + 10)] + 11\}$

77. $[8(x - 2) + 9x] - \{7[3(2y - 5) - (8y + 7)] + 9\}$

78. $[11(a - 3) + 12a] - \{6[4(3b - 7) - (9b + 10)] + 11\}$

79. $-3[9(x - 4) + 5x] - 8\{3[5(3y + 4)] - 12\}$

80. $-6[8(y - 7) + 9y] - 7\{5[7(4z + 3)] - 14\}$

B

Simplify.

81. $-[-(-(-9))]$

82. $-\{-[-(-(-10))]\}$

83. $-\{-[-(-(-(-8)))]\}$

84. $\frac{2}{3}[2(x + y) + 4(x + 4y)]$

85. $-4[3(x - y - z) - 3(2x + y - 5z)]$

The expression $P + Prt$ gives the value of an account of P dollars principal, invested at a rate r (in percent) for a time t (in years). Find the value of an account under the following conditions.

86. $P = \$120 \quad r = 12\% \quad t = 1$ yr

87. $P = \$500 \quad r = 14\% \quad t = \frac{1}{2}$ yr

88. ***Critical Thinking*** Decide whether finding the absolute value is distributive over addition. That is, can we add first and then find the absolute value or find the absolute value and then add?

Challenge

Simplify.

89. $[-(7a - b) - (a + 5b)] - \left[2\left(a + \frac{1}{2}b\right) + 3\left(7a - \frac{5}{3}b\right)\right]$

90. $0.01\{0.1(x - 2y) - [0.001(3x + y) - (0.2x - 0.1y)]\} - (x - y)$

91. Find a rule for simplifying problems like 81-83.

92. Show that $(x - y)(y - x)$ is equivalent to $-(x - y)^2$.

Mixed Review

93. Evaluate $-(s - 4t)$ for $s = -4$ and $t = 15$.

94. Use the commutative property of addition to write an expression equivalent to $-3x + 6y$.

95. Use the commutative and associative properties of multiplication to write an expression equivalent to $8x(9y \cdot 17z)$.

Write decimal notation. **96.** 12% **97.** 50% **98.** $\frac{2}{5}$ **99.** $\frac{1}{0.7}$

Write rational notation. **100.** 10% **101.** 0.45 **102.** 10.5 **103.** 125%

71. $44a - 22$
72. $47b - 51$
73. -190
74. -1449
75. $-12y - 145$
76. $-11b + 217$
77. $17x + 14y + 129$
78. $23a - 18b + 184$
79. $-42x - 360y - 276$
80. $-102y - 980z - 301$

81. 9
82. -10
83. 8
84. $4x + 12y$
85. $12x + 24y - 48z$
86. \$134.40
87. \$535.00
88. No; for example $|2 + (-1)| = 1$ but $|2| + |-1| = 3$
89. $-31a$
90. $-0.99703x + 0.99699y$
91. The answer is positive for an even number of minus signs, negative for an odd number of minus signs.
92. $(x-y)(y-x) = (x-y)(y+(-x))$
$= (x-y)(-x+y)$
$= (x-y)(-1)(x-y)$
$= (-1)(x-y)(x-y)$
$= -(x-y)(x-y)$
$= -(x-y)^2$

Mixed Review

93. 64
94. $6y - 3x$
95. $(9y \cdot 8x)17z$
96. 0.12
97. 0.5
98. 0.4
99. $1.\overline{428571}$
100. $\frac{1}{10}$
101. $\frac{9}{20}$
102. $10\frac{1}{2}$ or $\frac{21}{2}$
103. $\frac{5}{4}$

1-5

FIRST FIVE MINUTES

In each of the following equations, find a number x which makes the equation a true statement.

1. $x + 1 = 3$
   2
2. $3x = 12$
   4
3. $\frac{x}{5} = 5$
   25
4. Evaluate $4x + 7$ for $x = 3$.
   19
5. Evaluate $3(x + 1) + x$ for $x = 4$.
   19
6. Simplify.
   $8\left(\frac{1}{8}\right) + \frac{3}{7}\left(-\frac{7}{3}\right)$
   0

Point out that while there may be more than one way to transform an equation to a simpler equation, there is only one solution set. Remind students to check their solutions by substituting them into the original equations.

Avoiding Common Errors

An equation such as

$3x + 6 - 3x = 6$

can be simplified to

$6 = 6$

Students may think that 6 is the solution. Point out that any value for x will make the equation true.

Key Questions

- Is 3 a member of the solution set for $x - 3 = 0$? Yes

Suppose $x = y$.

- Does $x \cdot 17 = y \cdot 17$? Yes
- Does $x - 17 = y - 17$? Yes
- Does $x \cdot x = y \cdot y$? Yes
- Does $x \cdot x = y \cdot z$? Only if $x = z$

1-5 Solving Equations

Objective: Solve equations using the addition and multiplication properties.

Explore

A scale has several weights on one side and an object on the other. The scale is balanced. Suppose we add a two-pound weight to each side of the scale. Must the scale still balance?

A mathematical sentence $A = B$ says that the symbols A and B are equivalent. Such a sentence is an equation. The set of all acceptable replacements is the replacement set. The replacements that make an equation true are its solutions. The set of all solutions is the solution set. Unless otherwise stated, the replacement set we will use for solving equations and inequalities is the set of real numbers.

When we have found all the solutions of an equation, we say that we have **solved** the equation. One approach to solving an equation is to transform it to a simpler equation whose solution set is obvious. The addition and multiplication properties of equality can be used when transforming equations.

Theorem 1-6

The Addition Property of Equality

If $a = b$, then $a + c = b + c$ for any real number c.

Using the addition property, we can assume that the scale above will balance. Suppose we triple the weight on each side of the scale. Will the scale balance?

Theorem 1-7

The Multiplication Property of Equality

If $a = b$, then $a \cdot c = b \cdot c$ for any real number c.

Using the multiplication property, we can assume that the scale will balance.

We often need to use the addition and multiplication properties together. We usually use the addition property first.

EXAMPLE 1 Solve.

$$3x - 4 = 13$$
$$3x - 4 + 4 = 13 + 4 \quad \text{Using the addition property; adding the inverse of } -4$$
$$3x = 17$$
$$\frac{1}{3} \cdot 3x = \frac{1}{3} \cdot 17 \quad \text{Using the multiplication property; multiplying by the reciprocal of 3}$$
$$x = \frac{17}{3} \quad \text{Simplifying}$$

Check:

$3x - 4$	$= 13$
$3\left(\frac{17}{3}\right) - 4$	13
$17 - 4$	13
13	13 ✓

The solution is $\frac{17}{3}$.

Try This Solve.

a. $13 = -25 + y$ $y = 38$ **b.** $-4x = 64$ $x = -16$ **c.** $9x - 4 = 8$ $x = 4/3$ **d.** $-\frac{1}{4}y + \frac{3}{2} = \frac{1}{2}$ $y = 4$

If there are like terms in an equation, they should be collected first. If there are like terms on opposite sides of an equation, we can get them on the same side using the addition property and then collect them.

EXAMPLE 2 Solve.

$$-12y + 22 = -y$$
$$-12y + y + 22 + (-22) = -y + y + (-22) \quad \text{Adding } -22 \text{ and } y \text{ to both sides}$$
$$-11y = -22$$
$$-\frac{1}{11}(-11y) = -\frac{1}{11}(-22) \quad \text{Multiplying both sides by } -\frac{1}{11}$$
$$y = \frac{22}{11}, \text{ or } y = 2$$

Check:

$-12y + 22$	$= -y$
$-12(2) + 22$	-2
-2	-2 ✓

EXAMPLE 3 Solve.

$$8x + 6 - 2x = -12 - 4x + 5$$
$$6x + 6 = -7 - 4x \quad \text{Collecting like terms}$$
$$6x = -13 - 4x \quad \text{Adding } -6 \text{ to both sides and simplifying}$$
$$10x = -13 \quad \text{Adding } 4x \text{ to both sides and simplifying}$$
$$x = -\frac{13}{10} \quad \text{Multiplying both sides by } \frac{1}{10} \text{ and simplifying}$$

Chalkboard Examples

Solve using the addition and multiplication properties.

1. $6x + 3 = 27$
$6x + 3 + (-3) = 27 + (-3)$
$6x = 24$
$\frac{1}{6}(6x) = \frac{1}{6} \cdot 24$
$x = 4$

2. $-4x - 3 = 7$
$-4x - 3 + 3 = 7 + 3$
$-4x = 10$
$-\frac{1}{4}(-4x) = -\frac{1}{4} \cdot 10$
$x = -\frac{10}{4}$
$x = -\frac{5}{2}$

3. $-11x + 6 = 42 - 2x$
$-11x + 6 + (-6) = 42 + (-6) - 2x$
$-11x = 36 - 2x$
$-11x + 2x = 36 - 2x + 2x$
$-9x = 36$
$-\frac{1}{9}(-9x) = -\frac{1}{9}(36)$
$x = -4$

4. $15y - 5 = 6y + 3 - y$
$15y - 5 = 5y + 3$
$15y = 5y + 8$
$10y = 8$
$y = \frac{8}{10}$
$y = \frac{4}{5}$

LESSON QUIZ

Solve.

1. $t - 7 = 31$
   $t = 38$
2. $8x + 3 = 9$
   $x = \frac{6}{8} = \frac{3}{4}$
3. $0.2x - 1.2 = 1.8$
   $x = \frac{3}{0.2} = 15$
4. $5x + 4 = 19$
   $x = 3$
5. $7x + 5 = 3x + 9$
   $x = 1$
6. $3r + 2 - 8r = 2r - 6$
   $r = \frac{8}{7}$

Assignment Guide
Algebra: 1–40 e/o, MR

Alg w/Finite or Trig: 1–52 m3, 53, MR

Comprehensive: 1–52 m4, 53, 54–57, MR, assign w. 1-6

Check:

$8x + 6 - 2x$	$= -12 - 4x + 5$
$8\left(-\frac{13}{10}\right) + 6 - 2\left(-\frac{13}{10}\right)$	$-12 - 4\left(-\frac{13}{10}\right) + 5$
$\left(-\frac{52}{5}\right) + 6 + \left(\frac{13}{5}\right)$	$-12 - \left(-\frac{26}{5}\right) + 5$
$-\frac{39}{5} + 6$	$-7 + \frac{26}{5}$
$-\frac{9}{5}$	$-\frac{9}{5}$ ✓

The solution is $-\frac{13}{10}$.

Try This Solve using the addition and multiplication properties.

e. $5y - 8 = -8 - 4y - 4$ $y = -\frac{4}{9}$ **f.** $5x - 12 - 3x = 7x - 2 - x$ $x = -\frac{5}{2}$

1-5 EXERCISES

A

Solve using the addition and multiplication properties.

1. $y + 11 = 8$ −3
2. $t + 13 = 4$ −9
3. $x - 18 = 22$ 40
4. $p - 15 = 11$ 26
5. $x + 9 = -6$ −15
6. $p + 14 = -42$ −56
7. $t - 9 = -23$ −14
8. $y - 7 = -3$ 4
9. $x - 26 = 13$ 39
10. $5x = 20$ 4
11. $3x = 21$ 7
12. $8y = -72$ −9
13. $9t = -81$ −9
14. $-24x = -192$ 8
15. $-13y = 117$ −9
16. $\frac{1}{5}y = 8$ 40
17. $\frac{1}{4}x = 9$ 36
18. $\frac{2}{3}x = 27$ $\frac{81}{2}$
19. $4x - 12 = 60$ 18
20. $4x - 6 = 70$ 19
21. $5y + 3 = 28$ 5
22. $7t + 11 = 74$ 9
23. $2y - 11 = 37$ 24
24. $3x - 13 = 29$ 14
25. $-4x - 7 = -35$ 7
26. $-9y + 8 = -91$ 11
27. $5x + 2x = 56$ 8
28. $3x + 7x = 120$ 12
29. $9y - 7y = 42$ 21
30. $8t - 3t = 65$ 13
31. $-6y - 10y = -32$ 2
32. $-9y - 5y = 28$ −2
33. $7y - 1 = 23 - 5y$ 2
34. $15x + 20 = 8x - 22$ −6
35. $5 - 4a = a - 13$ $\frac{18}{5}$
36. $8 - 5x = x - 16$ 4
37. $3m - 7 = -7 - 4m - m$ 0
38. $5x - 8 = -8 + 3x - x$ 0
39. $5r - 2 + 3r = 2r + 6 - 4r$ $\frac{4}{5}$
40. $5m - 17 - 2m = 6m - 1 - m$ −8

B

Solve.

41. $0x = 0$ **42.** $4x = 0$ **43.** $0x = 5$ **44.** $7y = 7y$ **45.** $7w = -7w$

46. $4x - 2x - 2 = 2x$ **47.** $2x + 4 + x = 4 + 3x$

48. $-\frac{3}{4}x + \frac{1}{8} = -2$ $\frac{17}{6}$ **49.** $y - \frac{1}{3}y - 15 = 0$ $\frac{45}{2}$ **50.** $\frac{3x}{2} + \frac{5x}{3} - \frac{13x}{6} - \frac{2}{3} = \frac{5}{6}$ $\frac{3}{2}$

51. $3x + 2^2 = x + 3^2$ $\frac{5}{2}$ **52.** $2^3 \cdot x + 9 = 2^2 \cdot x - 23$ -8

53. ***Critical Thinking*** Determine whether the following statement is true or false. If true, tell why. If false, give a counterexample.

If a statement $a \neq b$ is true, then $a + c \neq b + c$ is true for any real number c.

Challenge

An identity is an equation that is true for all acceptable replacements. Determine which of the following are identities.

54. $2(x - 3) + 5 = 3(x - 2) + 5$ No **55.** $3(x - 4) = 3x - 4$ No

56. $\frac{3y - 1}{y^2 - y} - \frac{2}{y - 1} = \frac{1}{y}$ Yes **57.** $7(x - 3) \cdot \frac{1}{7} = x - 3$ Yes

Mixed Review

Simplify.

58. $4a - 7(3a - 9)$ **59.** $[5(a + 2) + 6a] - \{8[2(5a - 4)] + 17a\}$

Factor.

60. $9c + 12b - 3a$ **61.** $8n - 8m$ **62.** $14t - 7$ **63.** $6n + 12$

Evaluate.

64. $2m + 4n$ for $m = -6, n = 2$ **65.** $4(m + 3) - 15$ for $m = 2$

66. Use the commutative and associative properties of multiplication to write an expression equivalent to $\left(\frac{1}{2}x \cdot 5y\right)\left(\frac{1}{5}y \cdot 2x\right)$.

67. Use the commutative and associative properties of addition to write an expression equivalent to $\left(\frac{1}{2}x + 5y\right) + \left(\frac{1}{5}y + 2x\right)$.

Problem for Programmers

Write a program that will solve an equation of the form $ax + b = c$. Test your program using the equations in Exercises 19-26 of Lesson 1-5. The program should allow input of a, b, and c, and output the solution.

ADDITIONAL ANSWERS

Exercises

41. All real numbers
42. $x = 0$
43. No solution
44. All real numbers
45. $w = 0$
46. No solution
47. All real numbers
53. True; suppose $a + c = b + c$. Add $-c$ to both sides. Then $a = b$. This is false, so $a + c \neq b + c$.

Mixed Review

58. $-17a + 63$
59. $-86a + 74$
60. $3(3c + 4b - a)$
61. $8(n - m)$
62. $7(2t - 1)$
63. $6(n + 2)$
64. -4
65. 5
66. Answers may vary. Ex: $2x \cdot \frac{1}{2}x \cdot 5y \cdot \frac{1}{5}y$
67. Answers may vary. Ex: $2x + \frac{1}{2}x + 5y + \frac{1}{5}y$

Problem for Programmers

This program can be written using any programming language (BASIC, PASCAL, LOGO, etc.). The programming ability of the student will determine how the values of a, b, and c are input (from the keyboard or within the program), and how the answer is output. Encourage more capable programmers to output answers as "x = solution."

This program can also be written on a spreadsheet where a, b, and c are entered in separate columns, and the solution is computed in another column.

1-6

FIRST FIVE MINUTES

1. Solve.
   $4x + 7 = 12$
   $x = \frac{5}{4}$
2. Solve.
   $4x + 5 = 2x + 9$
   $x = 2$

Write an expression for each.

3. Twice the number *n*
   $2n$
4. 5 more than *x*
   $x + 5$
5. 7 less than *y*
   $y - 7$
6. Twenty percent of *b*
   $0.20b$

Encourage students to use the Problem-Solving Guidelines when solving problems. A copy of these guidelines is also available on Overhead Transparency 1 (*T1*). You may want them to write out the steps as shown or to verbalize the steps. The objective is to get students to break the problem up into little steps so that solving "word problems" is not feared.

When the use of the guidelines becomes automatic, it is no longer necessary to write them down or verbalize them.

Key Questions

- What is the yellow time for a speed limit of 50 mi/h?
  3.5 s
- Can you use the equation in Example 1 to find the yellow time for any speed limit?
  Yes
- If you knew how long the light remained yellow, how would you find the speed limit?
  Substitute for *y* and solve for *s*.

1-6 Problem Solving: Writing Equations

Objective: Become familiar with and solve simple algebraic problems.

In your studies of mathematics, you have had considerable experience solving problems. The following guidelines make up a process that can help with many algebra problems.

PROBLEM-SOLVING GUIDELINES

■ **Phase 1: UNDERSTAND the problem**

What am I trying to find?
What data am I given?
Have I ever solved a similar problem?

■ **Phase 2: Develop and carry out a PLAN**

What strategies might I use to solve the problem?
How can I correctly carry out the strategies I selected?

■ **Phase 3: Find the ANSWER and CHECK**

Does the proposed solution check?
What is the answer to the problem?
Does the answer seem reasonable?
Have I stated the answer clearly?

EXAMPLE 1

The time that a traffic light remains yellow is 1 second more than 0.05 times the speed limit. What is the yellow time for a traffic light on a street with a speed limit of 30 mi/h?

■ **UNDERSTAND the problem**

Question: What is the time that the traffic light remains yellow? — Clarifying the question

Data: The yellow time is 0.05 times the speed limit plus 1 second. — Identifying the data

■ **Develop and carry out a PLAN**

Choose the strategy *Write an Equation.*

Yellow time is 1 second more than 0.05 times the speed limit.

$$y = 1 + 0.05 \cdot s$$

$$y = 1 + 0.05s$$

Translating to an equation

For a speed limit of 30 mi/h, s will be 30. Thus we have the following.

$$y = 1 + 0.05(30)$$

$$y = 1 + 1.5$$

$$y = 2.5$$

Solving the equation

■ **Find the ANSWER and CHECK**

On a 30 mi/h street, 2.5 seconds is a reasonable time for the light to remain yellow.

The yellow time is 2.5 seconds.

Stating the answer clearly

EXAMPLE 2

It has been found that the world record for the 10,000-meter run has been decreasing steadily since 1940. The record is approximately 30.18 minutes minus 0.07 times the number of years since 1940. Assume the record continues to decrease in this way. Predict what it will be in 1995.

■ **UNDERSTAND the problem**

Question: What will the record probably be in 1995?

Clarifying the question

Data: The record was 30.18 min in 1940. It decreases 0.07 times the number of years since 1940.

Identifying the important data

■ **Develop and carry out a PLAN**

Record is 30.18 minutes minus 0.07 times the number of years since 1940.

$$R = 30.18 - 0.07 \cdot (1995 - 1940)$$

Translating to an equation

$$R = 30.18 - 0.07(1995 - 1940)$$

Solving the equation

$$R = 30.18 - 0.07(55) = 26.33$$

■ **Find the ANSWER and CHECK**

The number checks in the equation.

It is less than the original record and makes sense in the problem.

We predict that the record in 1995 will be 26.33 min.

Stating the answer clearly

Chalkboard Examples

1. 31 is 9 more than twice a number. Find the number.
   Let n = the number. Translate to an equation.
   $31 = 9 + 2n$
   Solve.
   $22 = 2n$
   $11 = n$
   The number is 11.
   31 is 9 more than twice 11.
2. The final exam in a course will count as 30% of the total. Prior to the final exam, 245 points are possible. How many points will the final be worth?
   Let x = the points on the final.
   Total points = 245 + x
   $0.30(245 + x) = x$
   $73.5 + 0.30x = x$
   $73.5 = 0.70x$
   $105 = x$
   The final exam will be worth 105 points. This is 30% of the total (105 + 245). The answer checks.
3. The Acme Widget Company has $13,000 available for making widgets. Part of the money is spent on an advanced widget-bending machine costing $1000. The manufacturing cost for each widget is $3. How many widgets can be made with the money available?
   Let x = number of widgets made.
   3x = manufacturing cost
   3x + 1000 = total spent
   $3x + 1000 = 13{,}000$
   $3x = 12{,}000$
   $x = 4000$
   4000 widgets can be made.

LESSON QUIZ

Solve.

1. The number 12 is 14 greater than twice a number. Find the number. The number is − 1.
2. Six percent of some number equals 12. Find the number. The number is 200.
3. A rental car cost $24 per day plus 25 cents per mile. The total trip cost $54. How many miles were traveled if the trip lasted one day? 120 miles were traveled.

Try This

a. The County Cab Company charges 70¢ plus 12¢ per $\frac{1}{4}$ kilometer for each ride. What will be the total cost of a 14-km ride? $7.42

b. It has been found that the world record for the 800-m run has been decreasing steadily since 1930. The record is approximately 1.82 min minus 0.0035 times the number of years since 1930. Predict what the record will be in 1995. ≈1.593 min

---

EXAMPLE 3

An insecticide originally contained $\frac{1}{2}$ ounce of pyrethrins. The new formula contains $\frac{5}{8}$ oz of pyrethrins. What percent of the pyrethrins of the original formula does the new formula contain?

■ **UNDERSTAND the problem**

Question: What percent of the original amount of pyrethrins does the new formula contain? — Clarifying the question

Data: The original formula contained $\frac{1}{2}$ oz., the new formula is $\frac{5}{8}$ oz. — Identifying the data

■ **Develop and carry out a PLAN**

We may translate to an equation and solve.
What percent of $\frac{1}{2}$ oz is $\frac{5}{8}$ oz?

$$y \times \frac{1}{100} \cdot \frac{1}{2} = \frac{5}{8}$$ Translating percent to "$\times \frac{1}{100}$"

$$y \times \frac{1}{200} = \frac{5}{8}$$ Multiplying

$$y = \frac{5}{8} \times 200$$ Multiplying by the reciprocal of $\frac{1}{200}$

$$y = 125$$ Simplifying

■ **Find the ANSWER and CHECK**

We must find out whether 125% of $\frac{1}{2}$ is $\frac{5}{8}$.

$$\frac{125}{100} \times \frac{1}{2} = \frac{125}{200} = \frac{5}{8}$$

The number checks. This is reasonable, since $\frac{5}{8}$ is greater than $\frac{1}{2}$, the percent must be greater than 100.

The amount of pyrethrins in the new formula $\frac{5}{8}$ oz., is 125% of the original amount of $\frac{1}{2}$ oz. — Stating the answer clearly

Try This

c. A public television station set a goal of \$350,000 in pledges during a certain month. The total pledged was \$525,000. What percent of the station's goal was reached?
150%

d. A bread recipe calls for $\frac{2}{3}$ cup of rye flour. You only have $\frac{3}{4}$ cup on hand. What percent of your original amount of rye flour will remain after baking the bread?
≈ 11.1%

1-6 EXERCISES

A

1. Tony's Baby-Sitting Service charges \$2.50 per job plus \$1.75 per hour. What is the cost of a 7-hour baby-sitting job?
2. The cost of renting a rug shampooer is \$4.25 per hour plus \$3.25 for the shampoo. Find the cost of shampooing a rug when the time required is 3.5 hours.
3. The Jalopy Car Rental charges \$32 per day plus \$0.23 per mile. Find the cost of renting a car for a 3-day trip of 320 miles.
4. A phone company charges 40¢ per long distance call plus 20¢ per minute. Find the cost of an 18-minute phone call.
5. The distance from Earth to the moon is about 240,000 mi. That is about 0.005 the distance from Earth to Mars. Find the approximate distance from Earth to Mars.
6. Jamie gave Laura \$3 more than Laura already had. Now Laura has \$19. How much did Jamie give her?
7. The height of the Statue of Liberty is 92 m. This is about 0.27 the height of the Hancock Building in Chicago. What is the approximate height of the Hancock Building?
8. The area of the Red Sea is about 18% of the area of the Mediterranean Sea. The area of the Red Sea is about 453,000 km. Find the approximate area of the Mediterranean Sea.
9. The melting point of aluminum is 1.96 times the melting point of lead. The melting point of aluminum is 1220 degrees Farenheit. What is the melting point of lead?
10. The area of the Pacific Ocean is about 239,000,000 km^2. This represents 46% of the earth's area. What is the approximate area of the earth?
11. The Olympic time for men's 500-m speed skating has been decreasing by about 0.1 seconds per year since 1924, when the record was 44.0 seconds. Predict what the time will be in 1992.
12. The Olympic time for women's 500-m speed skating has been decreasing by about 0.2 seconds per year since 1920, when the record was 54 seconds. Predict what the time will be in 1992.
13. The Olympic time for men's 400-m hurdles has been decreasing by about 0.14 seconds per year since 1920, when the record was 54 seconds. Predict what the time will be in 1992.

Assignment Guide
Algebra: 1–18 e/o, MR

Alg w/Finite or Trig: 1–18 m3, 19–22, MR

Comprehensive: 1–21 m4, 22–24, MR, assign w. 1-5

ADDITIONAL ANSWERS

Exercises

1. $C = 2.50 + 7 \cdot 1.75$; \$14.75
2. $C = 3.5 \cdot 4.25 + 3.25$; \$18.13
3. $C = 3 \cdot 32 + 320 \cdot 0.23$; \$169.60
4. $C = 0.40 + 18 \cdot 20$; \$4.00
5. $0.005D = 240{,}000$; ≈48,000,000 mi
6. $J - 3 + J = 19$; \$11
7. $92 = 0.27h$; ≈341 m
8. $0.18a = 453{,}000$; ≈2,516,667 km^2
9. $1.96m = 1220$; 622.45°F
10. $239{,}000{,}000 = 0.46a$; ≈520,000,000 km^2
11. $t = 44.0 - 0.1(1992 - 1924)$; 37.2 s
12. $t = 54 - 0.2(1992 - 1920)$; 39.6 s
13. $t = 54 - 0.14(1992 - 1920)$; 43.92 s

14. $p = 334{,}000 + 14{,}000 \cdot (2005 - 1960)$; 964,000

15. $p \cdot 26\frac{3}{8} = 22\frac{1}{2}$; $\approx 85.3\%$

16. $p = \dfrac{2.8}{55.7 - 2.8}$; $\approx 5.3\%$

17. $p = \dfrac{25.968 - 6689}{6689}$; $\approx 288.2\%$

18. $338 = \frac{1}{2}c - 34$; \$744

19. $5p + 9 = 10(p - 0.5)$; \$2.80

20. $\dfrac{R + (R + 2) + \frac{1}{6}R}{3} = 9\frac{1}{3}$;
Reggie 12, Kirra 14, Delia 2

21. $p = \dfrac{\frac{1}{3}}{1 - \frac{2}{5}}$; $\approx 55.6\%$

22. Answers may vary.

23. $80 + 40t = 55t$; $t = 5\frac{1}{3}$ hrs; 1:20 p.m.

24. $2(10a + b) - \frac{1}{2}(10b + a) = 108$, substitute $a = b + 3$; 63

Mixed Review

25. $15t$
26. $-2c$
27. $-8x$
28. 8
29. $-\frac{1}{2}$
30. $\frac{1}{2}$
31. 14
32. 6
33. -3
34. -11
35. -3
36. 2
37. 1
38. 2

14. The number of physicians in the United States has been rising at the rate of about 14,000 per year since 1960, when there were about 334,000 physicians. Predict how many physicians there will be in the year 2005.

15. A person invested in stock selling for $\$26\frac{3}{8}$ per share. The stock value is now $\$22\frac{1}{2}$ per share. What percent of the original investment is the current stock value?

16. In 1984 the average American ate 55.7 lb of chicken. This was 2.8 lb more than the average in 1982. What was the percent of increase in chicken consumption from 1982 to 1984?

17. Between 1970 and 1980, the population of Sierra Vista, Arizona, grew from 6689 to 25,968. By what percent did the population increase?

18. The price of a computer was cut in half. Then it was cut another \$34. The new price was \$338. What was the original price?

B

19. On Monday, Ramon bought five computer disks. Two days later the price of the disks was decreased by 50¢ per disk. Leticia bought ten disks at the sale price and paid \$9 more than Ramon paid for five disks. What was the original price of a disk?

20. Kirra is two years older than Reggie. Reggie is six times as old as Delia. The average of their ages is nine years and four months. How old is each of them?

21. A gallon of one brand of paint covers approximately $\frac{2}{5}$ of the total wall area of a room. A gallon of a different brand will cover about $\frac{1}{3}$ of the total wall area. After the first gallon is used, what percent of the remaining wall area will the second gallon cover?

22. ***Critical Thinking*** Write a problem that can be solved using the equation $y = \frac{1}{2}x + 10$.

Challenge

23. At 6:00 a.m., the Wong family left for a vacation trip and drove south at an average speed of 40 mi/h. Their friends, the Heisers, left two hours later and traveled the same route at an average speed of 55 mi/h. At what time could the Heisers expect to overtake the Wongs?

24. The tens digit of a two-digit number is three greater than the ones digit. The difference between twice the original number and half the number obtained after reversing the digits is 108. What is the original number?

Mixed Review

Collect like terms. **25.** $11t + 4t$ **26.** $3c + 4c - 9c$ **27.** $x - 9x$

Solve. **28.** $y + 6 = 14$ **29.** $2m + 5 = 4$ **30.** $34t - 7 = 10$

31. $\frac{1}{2}r + 13 = 20$ **32.** $6a + 18 = 54$ **33.** $-9w = 27$

34. $5(n - 2) = -65$ **35.** $9c + 4 = 31 + 18c$ **36.** $4w + 5 = 6w + 1$

37. $8 - 5y = 11y - 8$ **38.** $7c + 15 = 16c - 3$

1-7 Exponential Notation

Objective: Simplify expressions with integer exponents.

Explore

The ability to write numbers in different forms is a powerful problem-solving tool. For example, 81 can be written as $8(10) + 1$ or as 3^4. The first form is standard form, the second is exponential notation. In exponential notation a^n, a is the base and n is the exponent. We say 3^4 is a power of 3 because it can be written as a product where all of the factors are 3: $81 = 3^4 = 3 \cdot 3 \cdot 3 \cdot 3$.

How might we define an integer exponent?

Consider the following table of equivalencies. What is the pattern?

10^3	10^2	10^1	10^0	10^{-1}	10^{-2}	10^{-3}
1000	100	10	1	?	?	?

First we define whole number exponents.

Definition

Whole number exponents

Exponential notation a^n, where n is an integer greater than 1, means

$$\underbrace{a \cdot a \cdot a \cdot \ldots \cdot a \cdot a}_{n \text{ factors}}$$

Exponential notation a^1 means a.
Exponential notation a^0 means 1, provided $a \neq 0$.

EXAMPLES Simplify.

1. $(-6)^2 = (-6)(-6) = 36$
2. $-6^2 = -(6 \cdot 6) = -36$
3. $(4x)^2 = 4x \cdot 4x = 16x^2$
4. $(-3y)^3 = (-3y)(-3y)(-3y) = -27y^3$
5. $-5^3 = -(5^3) = -125$
6. $7(2x)^2 = 7(2x)(2x) = 7(4x^2) = 28x^2$

Try This Simplify.

a. $(8x)^3$ $512x^3$ **b.** $(-3m)^4$ $81m^4$ **c.** 9^2 81 **d.** $9(3y)^3$ $243y^3$

1-7

FIRST FIVE MINUTES

Simplify.
1. $(2x)(2x)$ $4x^2$
2. $(-1)(-1)(-1)$ -1
3. $\frac{1}{3} \cdot \frac{1}{3}$ $\frac{1}{9}$
4. $(2 \cdot 2)(2 \cdot 2 \cdot 2)$ $4 \cdot 8 = 32$

Emphasize that -3^2 means $-(3)(3)$ and that $3x^2$ means $3 \cdot x \cdot x$.

Math Point
0^0 is undefined. The following patterns give an intuitive understanding of why this is so.
$3^0 = 1; 2^0 = 1; 1^0 = 1$,
so we might write $0^0 = 1$.
$0^3 = 0 \cdot 0 \cdot 0 = 0; 0^2 = 0; 0^1 = 0$,
so we might write $0^0 = 0$.
Since the two patterns give different results, we say that 0^0 is undefined.

Avoiding Common Errors

Students may make the following mistakes.
$3^{-2} = -6$
or
$3^{-2} = -9$
Emphasize that a negative exponent never affects the sign of the base.

Key Questions

- Does $(-2)^0 = (2)^0$? Yes
- Does $3^{-1} = -3^1$? No
- Is 8^{-6} greater than 1 or less than 1? Less than 1
- Does $0^{-1} = -0^{-1}$? No; both are undefined.
- Does a negative exponent ever make an expression negative? No

Chalkboard Examples

Simplify.
1. $(-2x)^4$
   $(-2x)(-2x)(-2x)(-2x) = 16x^4$
2. $4(3y)^3$
   $4(27y^3) = 108y^3$

Write equivalent expressions without negative exponents.

3. $(2x)^{-1}$ $\frac{1}{2x}$
4. $(-2a)^{-3}$
   $\frac{1}{(-2a)^3} = \frac{1}{-8a^3} = -\frac{1}{8a^3}$

Write equivalent expressions using negative exponents.

5. $\frac{1}{4^3}$ 4^{-3}

6. $\frac{1}{(2a)^7}$ $(2a)^{-7}$

LESSON QUIZ

Simplify.
1. $(3a)^2$ $9a^2$
2. $(-3x)^3$ $-27x^3$
3. -3^2 $-(3^2) = -9$

Write an equivalent expression without using negative exponents.

4. 4^{-2} $\frac{1}{4^2} = \frac{1}{16}$
5. $(-2x)^{-3}$ $\frac{1}{(-2x)^3} = \frac{1}{-8x^3} = -\frac{1}{8x^3}$

Write an equivalent expression using negative exponents.

6. $\frac{1}{7^3}$ 7^{-3}
7. $\frac{1}{(3x)^5}$ $(3x)^{-5}$

Assignment Guide
Algebra: 1–28 e/o, MR

Alg w/Finite or Trig: 1–35 e/o, 36, MR

Comprehensive: 1–35 m4, 36–41, MR, assign w. 1-8

ADDITIONAL ANSWERS

Exercises

9.	$\frac{1}{9^5}$	**10.**	$\frac{1}{16^2}$
11.	$\frac{1}{11^1}$	**12.**	$\frac{1}{(-4)^3}$
13.	$\frac{1}{(6x)^3}$	**14.**	$\frac{1}{(-5y)^2}$
15.	$\frac{1}{(3m)^4}$	**16.**	$\frac{x^2}{y^3}$
17.	$\frac{2a^2}{b^5}$	**18.**	$\frac{a^2c^4}{b^3d^5}$
19.	x^2y^2	**20.**	$\frac{a^2y^2}{x^3b^3}$

At the beginning of the lesson, you looked for a pattern in the table. As each exponent decreased by 1, each value was multiplied by $\frac{1}{10}$. So for the pattern to continue, the missing values in the table are $\frac{1}{10}$, $\frac{1}{100}$, and $\frac{1}{1000}$. This suggests the following definition.

Definition

Integer Exponents

For any nonzero real number b and integer n, b^{-n} means $\frac{1}{b^n}$.

This definition tells us that b^n and b^{-n} are reciprocals.

EXAMPLES Write equivalent expressions without negative exponents.

7. $(-2)^{-3} = \frac{1}{(-2)^3}$, or $-\frac{1}{8}$

8. $(3x)^{-2} = \frac{1}{(3x)^2}$, or $\frac{1}{9x^2}$

Try This Write equivalent expressions without negative exponents.

e. 10^{-4} $\frac{1}{10{,}000}$ **f.** $(-4)^{-3}$ $-\frac{1}{64}$ **g.** $(5y)^{-3}$ $\frac{1}{125y^3}$ **h.** $(-5)^{-4}$ $\frac{1}{625}$

EXAMPLES Write equivalent expressions using negative exponents.

9. $\frac{1}{5^2} = 5^{-2}$

10. $\frac{1}{(3x)^5} = (3x)^{-5}$

Try This Write equivalent expressions using negative exponents.

i. $\frac{1}{4^3}$ 4^{-3} **j.** $\frac{1}{(-5)^4}$ $(-5)^{-4}$ **k.** $\frac{1}{(2x)^6}$ $(2x)^{-6}$ **l.** $\frac{1}{(-8x)^{-5}}$ $(-8x)^5$

1-7 EXERCISES

A

Simplify.

1. $(3y)^3$ $27y^3$ **2.** $(-2x)^4$ $16x^4$ **3.** $(-6)^0$ 1 **4.** -3^4 -81

5. $3(2m)^1$ $6m$ **6.** $5(-6x)^2$ $180x^2$ **7.** -5^3 -125 **8.** -8^2 -64

Write equivalent expressions without negative exponents.

9. 9^{-5} **10.** 16^{-2} **11.** 11^{-1} **12.** $(-4)^{-3}$

13. $(6x)^{-3}$ **14.** $(-5y)^{-2}$ **15.** $(3m)^{-4}$ **16.** x^2y^{-3}

17. $2a^2b^{-5}$ **18.** $a^2b^{-3}c^4d^{-5}$ **19.** $\frac{x^2}{y^{-2}}$ **20.** $\frac{a^2b^{-3}}{x^3y^{-2}}$

Write equivalent expressions using negative exponents.

21. $\frac{1}{3^4}$ 3^{-4}
22. $\frac{1}{9^2}$ 9^{-2}
23. $\frac{1}{(-16)^2}$ $(-16)^{-2}$
24. $\frac{1}{(-8)^6}$ $(-8)^{-6}$

25. $\frac{1}{(5y)^3}$ $(5y)^{-3}$
26. $\frac{1}{(5x)^5}$ $(5x)^{-5}$
27. $\frac{1}{3y^4}$ $\frac{y^{-4}}{3}$
28. $\frac{1}{4b^3}$ $\frac{b^{-3}}{4}$

B

Write an equivalent expression without rational notation.

29. $\frac{x^2y}{z^7}$
30. $\frac{20}{4xy}$
31. $\frac{b^{-10}}{x^{10}y^{10}}$
32. $\frac{a^2b^{-3}}{x^3y^{-2}}$

Evaluate each of the following.

33. x^{-4} for $x = 2$ $\frac{1}{16}$
34. $m^{-3} + 7$, for $m = -0.25$ -57
35. $x^3 + y^{-2}$, for $x = -3$ and $y = 4$ $-26\frac{15}{16}$
36. ***Critical Thinking*** Find several pairs of numbers such that the second power of the first is the same as the fourth power of the second.

Challenge

Simplify.

37. $(-2)^0 - (-2)^3 - (-2)^{-1} + (-2)^4 - (-2)^{-2}$ $25\frac{1}{4}$
38. $2(6^1 \cdot 6^{-1} - 6^{-1} \cdot 6^0)$ $\frac{5}{3}$
39. $\frac{(-8)^{-2} \cdot (8 - 8^0)}{2^{-6}}$ 7
40. Evaluate $(x - y)(x^{y-x} - y^{x-y})$ when $x = 1$ and $y = -2$. 27
41. About 3500 years ago, this problem appeared in one of the earliest known arithmetic books:

    Each of 7 persons owns 7 cats, each cat eats 7 mice, each mouse eats 7 ears of barley, each ear of barley yields 7 measures. How many measures is this? 16,807

    Solve the problem. Then write a problem similar to this one.

Mixed Review

Factor. 42. $ab + mb - xb$ 43. $17 - 51y^2$ 44. $20k^3a^2 - 16k^2a^3$

Solve. 45. $9 - 3y = 5y - 23$ 46. $5c + 3c = 16$ 47. $-21t = 21$

WRITING TO LEARN

Suppose you read the following definition of a whole number exponent:

A whole number exponent tells how many times to multiply a number by itself.

Is this definition equivalent to the one stated at the beginning of this lesson? Write a paragraph to support your position.

29. x^2yz^{-7}
30. $5x^{-1}y^{-1}$
31. $b^{-10}x^{-10}y^{-10}$
32. $a^2b^{-3}x^{-3}y^2$

36. Answers may vary. Examples are 1, 1; 4, 2; 9, 3.

Mixed Review

42. $b(a + m - x)$
43. $17(1 - 3y^2)$
44. $4k^2a^2(5k - 4a)$
45. 4
46. 2
47. -1

Writing to Learn

The definitions are not equivalent. Since 0 is a whole number, this definition says that a zero exponent means that the number is multiplied by itself 0 times (thus *not* multiplied by itself). This does not mean that a number to the 0 power is 1.

1-8

FIRST FIVE MINUTES

Simplify.

1. $a \cdot a$
   a^2
2. $\frac{3^3}{3}$
   $\frac{27}{3} = 9$
3. $(2^2)(2^2)(2^2)$
   $4 \cdot 4 \cdot 4 = 64$
4. $2^3 \cdot \frac{1}{2}$
   $8 \cdot \frac{1}{2} = 4$
5. $\frac{1}{2} \cdot \frac{1}{2} \cdot \frac{1}{2}$
   $\frac{1}{8}$
6. $2 \cdot 2 \cdot 2 \cdot \frac{1}{2} \cdot \frac{1}{2} \cdot \frac{1}{2}$
   $8 \cdot \frac{1}{8} = 1$

Multiplication and Division

Stress that exponents are added only when the bases are the same.

You may wish to derive Theorem 1-9 as follows.

$$\frac{a^m}{a^n} = (a^m)(a^{-n})$$

By Theorem 1-8,

$$(a^m)(a^{-n}) = a^{m+(-n)} = a^{m-n}$$

Key Questions

- Does $4^{-2} \cdot 4^3 = 4$?
  Yes
- Does $1^3 \cdot 1^3 = 1^5$?
  Yes, by evaluation
- Does $3^2 \cdot 2^2 = 6^4$?
  No
- Does $3^4 - 3^{-4} = 0$
  No

1-8 Properties of Exponents

Multiplication and Division

Objective: Multiply or divide with exponents.

To multiply using exponential notation when we have the same base, we add the exponents. For example, $x^3 \cdot x^2 = x^{3+2} = x^5$. Let us consider a case in which one exponent is positive and one is negative.

$$b^5 b^{-2} = b \cdot b \cdot b \cdot b \cdot b \cdot \frac{1}{b \cdot b}$$ Using the definition of exponents

$$= \frac{b \cdot b}{b \cdot b} \cdot b \cdot b \cdot b$$ Using the associative property

$$= 1 \cdot b \cdot b \cdot b$$

$$= b \cdot b \cdot b$$ Using the identity property of multiplication

$$= b^3$$

Notice that adding the exponents gives the correct result.

Theorem 1-8

For any real number a and integers m and n, $a^m a^n = a^{m+n}$.
(We can add exponents if the bases are the same.)

EXAMPLES Multiply and simplify.

1. $4^5 \cdot 4^{-3} = 4^{5+(-3)} = 4^2 = 16$ Adding exponents
2. $(-2)^{-3}(-2)^7 = (-2)^{-3+7} = (-2)^4 = 16$
3. $(8x^4y^{-2})(-3x^{-3}y) = 8 \cdot (-3) \cdot x^4 \cdot x^{-3} \cdot y^{-2} \cdot y^1$
   $= -24(x^{4-3})(y^{-2+1})$
   $= -24xy^{-1}$, or $\frac{-24x}{y}$
4. $(4x^a \cdot y^b)(2x^2y^3) = 4 \cdot 2(x^{a+2})(y^{b+3})$
   $= 8(x^{a+2})(y^{b+3})$

Try This Multiply and simplify.

a. $8^{-3}8^7$ 4,096
b. $(-3x^{-4})(25x^{-10})$ $-75x^{-14}$
c. $(5x^{-3}y^4)(-2x^{-9}y^{-2})$ $-10x^{-12}y^2$
d. $(5x^m y^n)(6x^7y^4)$ $30x^{m+7}y^{n+4}$

We now consider division using exponential notation.

$\frac{8^5}{8^3}$ means $\frac{8 \cdot 8 \cdot 8 \cdot 8 \cdot 8}{8 \cdot 8 \cdot 8}$. This simplifies to $8 \cdot 8$, or 8^2.

We can obtain the result by subtracting exponents. This is always true, even if exponents are negative or zero.

Theorem 1-9

For any real number $a \neq 0$ and integers m and n, $\frac{a^m}{a^n} = a^{m-n}$.

(We can subtract exponents if the bases are the same.)

EXAMPLES Divide and simplify.

5. $\frac{5^7}{5^{-3}} = 5^{7-(-3)}$ Subtracting exponents
$= 5^{7+3}$
$= 5^{10}$

6. $\frac{9^{-2}}{9^5} = 9^{-2-5}$
$= 9^{-7}$, or $\frac{1}{9^7}$

7. $\frac{7^{-4}}{7^{-5}} = 7^{-4-(-5)}$
$= 7^{-4+5} = 7^1 = 7$

8. $\frac{16x^4y^7}{-8x^3y^9} = \frac{16}{-8} \cdot \frac{x^4}{x^3} \cdot \frac{y^7}{y^9} = -2xy^{-2}$, or $-\frac{2x}{y^2}$

9. $\frac{14x^4y^7}{4x^5y^{-5}} = \frac{14}{4} \cdot \frac{x^4}{x^5} \cdot \frac{y^7}{y^{-5}} = \frac{7}{2}x^{-1}y^{12}$, or $\frac{7y^{12}}{2x}$

10. $\frac{18x^{5a}}{2x^{3a}} = \frac{18}{2} \cdot \frac{x^{5a}}{x^{3a}} = 9x^{5a-3a} = 9x^{2a}$

We do not define 0^0. Notice the following.

$$0^0 = 0^{1-1} = \frac{0^1}{0^1} = \frac{0}{0}$$

We have seen that $\frac{0}{0}$ is undefined, so 0^0 is also undefined.

Try This Divide and simplify.

e. $\frac{5^4}{5^{-2}}$ 5^6

f. $\frac{10^{-2}}{10^{-8}}$ 10^6

g. $\frac{42y^7x^6}{-21y^{-3}x^{10}}$ $-2y^{10}x^{-4}$, or $-\frac{2y^{10}}{x^4}$

h. $\frac{33a^5b^{-2}}{22a^7b^{-4}}$ $\frac{3}{2}a^{-2}b^2$, or $\frac{3b^2}{2a^2}$

i. $\frac{56y^{ab}}{-7y^{ab}}$ -8

Chalkboard Examples

Multiply and simplify.

1. $5^2 \cdot 5^4$
$5^{2+4} = 5^6$
2. $7^{-5} \cdot 7^8$
$7^{-5+8} = 7^3$
3. $6^{-4} \cdot 6^{-3}$
$6^{-4-3} = 6^{-7}$ or $\frac{1}{6^7}$
4. $(-1)^{10} \cdot (-1)^4$
$(-1)^{10+4} = (-1)^{14} = 1$
5. $x^5 \cdot x^{-7}$
$x^{5-7} = x^{-2} = \frac{1}{x^2}$
6. $(a^2b^3)(a^4b^2)$
$a^2a^4b^3b^2 = a^{2+4}b^{3+2} = a^6b^5$
7. $(x^cy^d)(x^2y^3)$
$x^{c+2}y^{d+3}$

Divide and simplify.

8. $\frac{7^5}{7^3}$
$7^{5-3} = 7^2$
9. $\frac{6^5}{6^7}$
$6^{5-7} = 6^{-2}$, or $\frac{1}{6^2}$
10. $\frac{3^{-2}}{3^{-5}}$
$3^{-2-(-5)} = 3^{-2+5} = 3^3$

Raising Powers to Powers

Point out that certain conditions have to be met in order to avoid division by 0. For example, in Theorem 1-11, both *a* and *m* cannot equal 0. Likewise, in Theorem 1-12, *a* cannot equal zero if *m* is negative.

Chalkboard Examples

Simplify.

1. $(2^3)^5$
   $2^{3\cdot 5} = 2^{15}$
2. $(a^3)^{-4}$
   $a^{3\cdot(-4)} = a^{-12}$ or $\frac{1}{a^{12}}$
3. $(x^2y^3)^5$
   $x^{2\cdot 5}y^{3\cdot 5} = x^{10}y^{15}$
4. $\left(\frac{3^2}{2^4}\right)^3$
   $\frac{3^{2\cdot 3}}{2^{4\cdot 3}} = \frac{3^6}{2^{12}}$
5. $\left(\frac{x^{-1}}{y^3}\right)^4$
   $\frac{x^{-1\cdot 4}}{y^{3\cdot 4}} = \frac{x^{-4}}{y^{12}}$
   $= \frac{1}{x^4y^{12}}$, or $x^{-4}y^{-12}$
6. $\left(\frac{3a^2b^3}{5c^4}\right)^2$
   $\frac{3^2a^4b^6}{5^2c^8} = \frac{9a^4b^6}{25c^8}$

Raising Powers to Powers

Objective: Use exponential notation in raising powers to powers.

Consider the expression $(5^2)^4$. It means $5^2 \cdot 5^2 \cdot 5^2 \cdot 5^2$, or 5^8. We can obtain the result by multiplying the exponents.

$$5^{2\cdot 4} = 5^8$$

Consider $(8^{-2})^3$. It means $\frac{1}{8^2} \cdot \frac{1}{8^2} \cdot \frac{1}{8^2}$, or $\frac{1}{8^6}$, which is 8^{-6}.

Again, we could obtain the result by multiplying the exponents.

Theorem 1-10

For any real number *a* and integers *m* and *n*, $(a^m)^n = a^{m\cdot n}$.

(To raise a power to a power, we can multiply exponents.)

EXAMPLES Simplify.

11. $(3^5)^7 = 3^{5\cdot 7} = 3^{35}$ Multiplying exponents

12. $(x^{-5})^4 = x^{-5\cdot 4} = x^{-20}$, or $\frac{1}{x^{20}}$

Try This Simplify.

j. $(3^7)^6$ 3^{42} **k.** $(x^2)^{-7}$ x^{-14}, or $\frac{1}{x^{14}}$ **l.** $(t^{-3})^{-2}$ t^6

When there are several factors inside the parentheses, we can use the next theorem.

Theorem 1-11

For any real numbers *a* and *b* and integers *m*, *n*, and *p*, $(a^mb^n)^p = a^{m\cdot p} \cdot b^{n\cdot p}$

(To raise an expression with several factors to a power, raise each factor to the power by multiplying exponents.)

EXAMPLES Simplify.

13. $(3x^2y^{-2})^3 = 3^3(x^2)^3(y^{-2})^3 = 3^3x^6y^{-6} = 27x^6y^{-6}$, or $\frac{27x^6}{y^6}$

14. $(5x^3y^{-5}z^2)^4 = 5^4(x^3)^4(y^{-5})^4(z^2)^4 = 625x^{12}y^{-20}z^8$, or $\frac{625x^{12}z^8}{y^{20}}$

Try This Simplify.

m. $(2xy)^3$ $8x^3y^3$ **n.** $(-2x^4y^2)^5$ $-32x^{20}y^{10}$ **o.** $(10x^{-4}y^7z^{-2})^3$ $1000x^{-12}y^{21}z^{-6}$, or $\frac{1000y^{21}}{x^{12}z^6}$

We now consider raising a quotient to a power. Consider $\left(\frac{5^5}{3^4}\right)^3$.

$$\left(\frac{5^5}{3^4}\right)^3 = \frac{5^5}{3^4}\cdot\frac{5^5}{3^4}\cdot\frac{5^5}{3^4} = \frac{5^{15}}{3^{12}}$$

Once more, we can obtain the result by multiplying the exponents. This is true in general, for positive, negative, or zero exponents.

Theorem 1-12

For any real numbers a and b ($b \neq 0$) and any integers m, n, and p, $\left(\frac{a^m}{b^n}\right)^p = \frac{a^{m\cdot p}}{b^{n\cdot p}}$.

To raise a quotient to a power, raise both the numerator and denominator to the power by multiplying exponents.

EXAMPLES Simplify.

15. $\left(\frac{x^2}{y^{-3}}\right)^{-5} = \frac{x^{2(-5)}}{y^{-3(-5)}} = \frac{x^{-10}}{y^{15}} = x^{-10}y^{-15}$, or $\frac{1}{x^{10}y^{15}}$

16. $\left(\frac{2x^3y^{-2}}{3y^4}\right)^5 = \frac{(2x^3y^{-2})^5}{(3y^4)^5} = \frac{2^5x^{15}y^{-10}}{3^5y^{20}}$

$= \frac{2^5x^{15}}{3^5y^{30}} = \frac{32x^{15}}{243y^{30}}$, or $\frac{32}{243}x^{15}y^{-30}$

Try This Simplify.

p. $\left(\frac{x^{-3}}{y^4}\right)^{-3}$ x^9y^{12}

q. $\left(\frac{3x^2y^{-3}}{2y^{-1}}\right)^2$ $\frac{9x^4}{4y^4}$, or $\frac{9}{4}x^4y^{-4}$

Order of Operations

Objective: Use the rules for order of operations to simplify expressions.

When several operations, including raising to powers, are to be done in a calculation, we must decide in what order they are to be done. The agreements made about such calculations are given by the following rules.

Order of Operations

1. Calculate within innermost parentheses first.
2. Evaluate exponential expressions.
3. Multiply and divide in order from left to right.
4. Add and subtract in order from left to right.

Order of Operations

You may want to point out that computer languages such as BASIC are programmed to use the order of operations. Many calculators are also programmed to use the correct order of operations. However, there are some calculators that are not.

Chalkboard Examples

1. $-5^2 + 3\cdot 5$
   $-25 + 15$
   $= -10$
2. $5\cdot(2^3 - 5) + 2$
   $5(8 - 5) + 2$
   $= 5\cdot 3 + 2$
   $= 15 + 2$
   $= 17$
3. $2\cdot 3^2 + 4\cdot 5 - (2 - 7)$
   $2\cdot 3^2 + 4\cdot 5 - (-5)$
   $= 2\cdot 9 + 20 + 5$
   $= 18 + 20 + 5$
   $= 38 + 5$
   $= 43$

Some calculators will not calculate exponential expressions with negative bases. Students should use the change sign key to give the expression the correct sign.

LESSON ENRICHMENT

Let $a = 2$. Calculate b, c, and d.

1. $b = 2^a$
   4
2. $c = 2^b$
   16
3. $d = 2^c$
   65,536

Determine the sign of the following expressions.

4. -1^4 Negative
5. -1^{-3} Negative
6. -1^{-8} Negative
7. $\frac{-1^{11}}{-5^3}$ Positive
8. -6^{21} Negative
9. $(-15^{-14})(-15^{20})$ Positive

LESSON QUIZ

Multiply and simplify.

1. $7^{-4} \cdot 7^9$
   7^5
2. $(4x^2)(3x^5)$
   $12x^7$
3. $(2a^{-3}b^6)(3a^5b^{-2})$
   $6a^2b^4$

Divide and simplify.

4. $\frac{5^7}{5^{-2}}$
   5^9
5. $\frac{y^{-4}}{y^{-3}}$
   y^{-1} or $\frac{1}{y}$
6. $\frac{8x^3y^4}{2xy^2}$
   $4x^2y^2$

Simplify.

7. $(5^{-4})^{-5}$
   5^{20}
8. $(2x^3y^{-1})^3$
   $8x^9y^{-3}$, or $8\frac{x^9}{y^3}$
9. $\left(\frac{x^{-3}}{y^2}\right)^4$
   $x^{-12}y^{-8}$ or $\frac{1}{x^{12}y^8}$

Assignment Guide
Algebra: Day 1: 1 – 30, MR
Day 2: 31 – 58
Alg w/Finite or Trig: 1–63 e/o, 64, MR
Comprehensive: 1–63 m3, 64, 65–71 e/o, MR, assign w. 1-7

EXAMPLES Simplify.

17. $3^2 - 9 \cdot 6$

$= 9 - 9 \cdot 6$ Evaluating exponential expression first

$= 9 - 54$ Multiplying

$= -45$ Subtracting

18. $[2(8 - 13 + 2)^3 \div 6 + 2]^2$

$= [2(-3)^3 \div 6 + 2]^2$ Calculating within parentheses

$= [2(-27) \div 6 + 2]^2$ Simplifying the exponential expression

$= [-54 \div 6 + 2]^2$ Calculating within brackets

$= [-9 + 2]^2$ Dividing

$= [-7]^2$ Adding

$= 49$ Simplifying the exponent

Try This Simplify.

r. $3 \cdot 2^2 + 4$ 16 **s.** $3 \cdot (2^2 + 4)$ 24 **t.** $\{[(3 + 2)^2 - 3 + 2^2 + 1] \div 9\}^3$ 27

The Exponential Key

Scientific calculators have an exponential key y^x
Calculate 5^7.

5 y^x 7 = → 78125

Calculate 3^{-4}.

3 y^x 4 +/− = → 0.012345679

For additional calculator practice, see Calculator Worksheet 2.

1-8 EXERCISES

A

Multiply and simplify.

1. $5^6 \cdot 5^3$ 5^9 **2.** $6^2 \cdot 6^6$ 6^8 **3.** $8^{-6} \cdot 8^2$ 8^{-4} or $\frac{1}{8^4}$ **4.** $9^{-5} \cdot 9^3$ 9^{-2} or $\frac{1}{9^2}$

5. $8^{-2} \cdot 8^{-4}$ 8^{-6} or $\frac{1}{8^6}$ **6.** $9^{-1} \cdot 9^{-6}$ 9^{-7} or $\frac{1}{9^7}$ **7.** $b^2 \cdot b^{-5}$ b^{-3} or $\frac{1}{b^3}$ **8.** $a^4 \cdot a^{-3}$ a

9. $a^{-3} \cdot a^4 \cdot a^2$ a^3 **10.** $x^{-8} \cdot x^5 \cdot x^3$ 1 **11.** $(2x^3)(3x^2)$ $6x^5$ **12.** $(9y^2)(2y^3)$ $18y^5$

13. $(14m^2n^3)(-2m^3n^2)$ $-28m^5n^5$ **14.** $(6x^5y^{-2})(-3x^2y^3)$ $-18x^7y$

15. $(-2x^{-3})(7x^{-8})$ $-14x^{-11}$ or $-\frac{14}{x^{11}}$ **16.** $(6x^{-4}y^3)(-4x^{-8}y^{-2})$ $-24x^{-12}y$ or $-\frac{24y}{x^{12}}$

17. $(5x^ay^b)(-6x^5y^9)$ $-30(x^{a+5})(y^{b+9})$ **18.** $(-9x^my^6)(-8x^ny^p)$ $72(x^{m+n})(y^{p+6})$

Divide and simplify.

19. $\frac{6^8}{6^3}$ 6^5 20. $\frac{7^9}{7^4}$ 7^5 21. $\frac{4^3}{4^{-2}}$ 4^5 22. $\frac{5^8}{5^{-3}}$ 5^{11}

23. $\frac{10^{-3}}{10^6}$ $\frac{1}{10^9}$ 24. $\frac{12^{-4}}{12^8}$ $\frac{1}{12^{12}}$ 25. $\frac{9^{-4}}{9^{-6}}$ 9^2 26. $\frac{2^{-7}}{2^{-5}}$ $\frac{1}{4}$

27. $\frac{a^3}{a^{-2}}$ a^5 28. $\frac{y^4}{y^{-5}}$ y^9 29. $\frac{9a^2}{(-3a)^2}$ 1 30. $\frac{24a^5b^3}{-8a^4b}$ $-3ab^2$

31. $\frac{-24x^6y^7}{18x^{-3}y^9}$ $\frac{-4x^9}{3y^2}$ 32. $\frac{14a^4b^{-3}}{-8a^8b^{-5}}$ $\frac{-7b^2}{4a^4}$ 33. $\frac{-18x^{-2}y^3}{-12x^{-5}y^5}$ $\frac{3x^3}{2y^2}$ 34. $\frac{-14a^{14}b^{-5}}{-18a^{-2}b^{-10}}$ $\frac{7a^{16}b^5}{9}$

35. $\frac{20x^{6a}}{-2x^a}$ $-10x^{5a}$ 36. $\frac{-18x^{5y}}{-3x^{-6y}}$ $6x^{11y}$ 37. $\frac{36x^ay^b}{-12x^2y^5}$ 38. $\frac{-100x^{3a}y^{-5}}{-25x^{-a}y^6}$

Simplify.

39. $(4^3)^2$ 40. $(5^4)^5$ 41. $(8^4)^{-3}$ 42. $(9^3)^{-4}$

43. $(6^{-4})^{-3}$ 44. $(7^{-8})^{-5}$ 45. $(3x^2y^2)^3$ 46. $(2a^3b^4)^5$

47. $(-2x^3y^{-4})^{-2}$ 48. $(-3a^2b^{-5})^{-3}$ 49. $(-6a^{-2}b^3c)^{-2}$ 50. $(-8x^{-4}y^5z^2)^{-4}$

51. $\left(\frac{4^{-3}}{3^4}\right)^3$ 52. $\left(\frac{5^2}{4^{-3}}\right)^{-3}$ 53. $\left(\frac{2x^3y^{-2}}{3y^{-3}}\right)^3$ 54. $\left(\frac{-4x^4y^{-2}}{5x^{-1}y^4}\right)^{-4}$

55. $3 \cdot 2 + 4 \cdot 2^2 - 6(3 - 1)$ 10 56. $3[(2 + 4 \cdot 2^2) - 6(3 - 1)]$ 18

57. $4(8 - 6)^2 + 4 \cdot 3 - 2 \cdot 8 \div 4$ 24 58. $[4(8 - 6)^2 + 4] \cdot (3 - 2 \cdot 8) \div 4$ -65

B

Simplify.

59. $\frac{(2^{-2})^{-4}(2^3)^{-2}}{(2^{-2})^2(2^5)^{-3}}$ 2^{21} 60. $\left[\frac{(-3x^2y^5)^{-3}}{(2x^4y^{-8})^{-2}}\right]^2$ $\frac{2^4x^4}{3^6y^{62}}$ 61. $\left[\left(\frac{a^{-2}}{b^7}\right)^{-3} \cdot \left(\frac{a^4}{b^{-3}}\right)^2\right]^{-1}$ $\frac{1}{a^{14}b^{27}}$

62. $\left[\frac{(-4x^2y^3)(-2xy)^{-2}}{(4x^4y^2)(-2x^5y)}\right]^{-2}$ $64x^{18}y^4$ 63. $\frac{(3xy)^2(6x^2y^2) \times 4x^4y^4}{(4xy)^2 \times 13x^2y^2}$ $\frac{27x^4y^4}{26}$

64. ***Critical Thinking*** How can you use the definition of a negative exponent to make Theorem 1-12 a special case of Theorem 1–11?

Challenge

Simplify.

65. $(x^y \cdot x^{2y})^3$ x^{9y} 66. $(y^x \cdot y^{-x})^4$ 1 67. $(a^{b+x} \cdot a^{b-x})^3$ a^{6b}

68. $(m^{a-b} \cdot m^{2b-a})^p$ m^{bp} 69. $(x^by^a \cdot x^ay^b)^c$ $x^{ca+cb}y^{ca+cb}$ 70. $(m^{x-b}n^{x+b})^x(m^bn^{-b})^x$ $m^{x^2}n^{x^2}$

71. $\left[\frac{(2x^ay^b)^3}{(-2x^ay^b)^2}\right]^2$ $4x^{2a}y^{2b}$ 72. $\left[\left(\frac{x^r}{y^s}\right)^2\left(\frac{x^{2r}}{y^{3s}}\right)^{-2}\right]^{-2}$ $\frac{x^{4r}}{y^{8s}}$

Mixed Review

Evaluate. 73. $t(3t + 5)$, for $t = 4$ 74. $-3x + 7 + 2x$, for $x = 5$

Simplify. 75. $\left(-\frac{1}{2}\right)\left(-\frac{2}{3}\right)\left(-\frac{3}{4}\right)\left(-\frac{4}{5}\right)$ 76. $(200)(-4)\left(-\frac{3}{2}\right)(0)(0.974)$

77. $3(x + 17) - 3(17 + x)$ 78. $7(14x - 15x) + 4(x + x)$

ADDITIONAL ANSWERS

Exercises

37. $-3x^{a-2}y^{b-5}$
38. $4x^{4a}y^{-11}$ or $\frac{4x^{4a}}{y^{11}}$
39. 4^6
40. 5^{20}
41. 8^{-12} or $\frac{1}{8^{12}}$
42. 9^{-12} or $\frac{1}{9^{12}}$
43. 6^{12}
44. 7^{40}
45. $3^3x^6y^6$ or $27x^6y^6$
46. $2^5a^{15}b^{20}$ or $32a^{15}b^{20}$
47. $(-2)^{-2}x^{-6}y^8$ or $\frac{y^8}{4x^6}$
48. $(-3)^{-3}a^{-6}b^{15}$ or $-\frac{b^{15}}{27a^6}$
49. $(-6)^{-2}a^4b^{-6}c^{-2}$ or $\frac{a^4}{36b^6c^2}$
50. $(-8)^{-4}x^{16}y^{-20}z^{-8}$ or $\frac{x^{16}}{4096y^{20}z^8}$
51. $\frac{1}{4^9 \cdot 3^{12}}$
52. $\frac{1}{5^6 \cdot 4^9}$
53. $\frac{8x^9y^3}{27}$
54. $\frac{5^4y^{24}}{(-4)^4x^{20}}$
64. Suppose we substitute $-n$ for n in Theorem 1-11, which states $(a^mb^n)^p = a^{mp}b^{np}$. Then $(a^mb^{-n})^p = a^{mp}b^{-np}$. Since $b^{-n} = \frac{1}{b^n}$ and $b^{-np} = \frac{1}{b^{np}}$, we have $\left(a^m \cdot \frac{1}{b^n}\right)^p = a^{mp} \cdot \frac{1}{b^{np}}$, or $\left(\frac{a^m}{b^n}\right)^p = \frac{a^{mp}}{b^{np}}$.

Mixed Review

73. 68
74. 2
75. $\frac{1}{5}$
76. 0
77. 0
78. x

1-9

FIRST FIVE MINUTES

Calculate.

1. $3.1 \cdot 10$
   31
2. $5.4 \cdot 10^{-1}$
   0.54
3. 10^6
   1,000,000
4. 10^{-4}
   0.0001

Write using exponential notation.

5. 1,000,000,000
   10^9
6. $10^7 \cdot 10^5$
   10^{12}
7. $10^{-4} \cdot 10^{-3}$
   10^{-7}

Conversions

Math Point
Scientific notation often shows how accurate a quantity is. For example, 2025 kg can be rounded to 2000 kg. In scientific notation, this would be written as 2.0×10^3 kg to show that there are only two significant digits. Scientists use special rules for calculating with significant digits so that rounding will not introduce any errors into their results.

Key Questions

- Does $34.5 = 34.5 \cdot 10^0$?
  Yes
- Does $34.5 = 3.45 \cdot 10^{-1}$?
  No
- Is $10 \cdot 10^3$ in scientific notation?
  No

Chalkboard Examples

1. Convert 45,600 to scientific notation.
   $4.56 \cdot 10^4$
2. Convert 0.0000368 to scientific notation.
   $3.68 \cdot 10^{-5}$
3. The distance from the earth to the sun is 93,000,000 miles. Write in scientific notation.
   $9.3 \cdot 10^7$

Convert to standard notation.

4. $3.87 \cdot 10^4$
   38,700
5. $5.876 \cdot 10^{-3}$
   0.005876

1-9 Scientific Notation

Scientific notation is useful for calculating with very large or very small numbers. It is also helpful for estimating. Scientific notation for 2,800,000,000 miles, the distance from the planet Neptune to the sun, is 2.8×10^9; for 0.000000022 cm, the diameter of a helium atom, is 2.2×10^{-8}; and for 100 is 1×10^2.

Definition

Scientific notation for a number is notation of the form $a \times 10^n$ where $1 \leq a < 10$ and n is an integer.

Conversions

Objective: Convert between scientific and standard notation.

We can convert to scientific notation by multiplying by 1, choosing $10^b \cdot 10^{-b}$ for the number 1, where b is the number of decimal places to be moved.

EXAMPLE 1 The temperature near the sun's center is about 20,000,000° Kelvin. Write scientific notation for this number.

We need to move the decimal point 7 places to the left, so that it is between the digits 2 and 0, so we choose $10^7 \times 10^{-7}$ for 1 and then multiply.

$$20{,}000{,}000 \times (10^7 \times 10^{-7}) \quad \text{Multiplying by 1}$$
$$= (20{,}000{,}000 \times 10^{-7}) \times 10^7 \quad \text{Using the associative and commutative properties}$$
$$= 2.0 \times 10^7$$

EXAMPLE 2 The wave length of a certain red light is 0.000066 cm. Write scientific notation for this number.

We need to move the decimal point 5 places to the right. We choose $10^5 \times 10^{-5}$ for 1, and then multiply.

$$0.000066 \times (10^5 \times 10^{-5}) \quad \text{Multiplying by 1}$$
$$= (0.000066 \times 10^5) \times 10^{-5} \quad \text{Using the associative property}$$
$$= 6.6 \times 10^{-5}$$

EXAMPLE 3 Light travels about 9,460,000,000,000 km in one year. Write scientific notation for this number.

$$9{,}460{,}000{,}000{,}000 \times 10^{-12} \times 10^{12} \quad \text{Multiplying by 1}$$
$$= 9.46 \times 10^{12} \quad 10^{-12} \text{ moved the decimal point 12 places to the left.}$$

Try This

a. Convert 460,000,000,000 to scientific notation. 4.6×10^{11}

b. Convert 0.000000001235 to scientific notation. 1.235×10^{-9}

c. The mass of a hydrogen atom is 0.0000000000000000000000017 grams. Write scientific notation for this number. 1.7×10^{-24}g

d. The distance from the earth to the sun is about 150,000,000 km. Write scientific notation for this number. 1.5×10^{8}km

---

You should try to make conversions between standard and scientific notation mentally.

EXAMPLES Convert to standard notation.

4. $7.893 \times 10^5 = 789{,}300$ Moving the decimal point 5 places to the right

5. $4.7 \times 10^{-8} = 0.000000047$ Moving the decimal point 8 places to the left

Try This Convert to standard notation.

e. 7.893×10^{11} 789,300,000,000 **f.** 5.67×10^{-5} 0.0000567

Multiplying and Dividing

Objective: Use scientific notation in multiplication and division.

To multiply and divide using scientific notation, we use the commutative and associative properties and then use the properties of exponents to simplify the powers of ten.

EXAMPLE 6 Multiply and write scientific notation for the answer.

$$(3.1 \times 10^5)(4.5 \times 10^{-3})$$

We apply the commutative and associative properties.

$$\begin{aligned}(3.1 \times 10^5)(4.5 \times 10^{-3}) &= (3.1 \times 4.5)(10^5 \times 10^{-3})\\ &= 13.95 \times 10^2\end{aligned}$$

We convert 13.95 to scientific notation and then simplify.

$$\begin{aligned}13.95 \times 10^2 &= (1.395 \times 10^1) \times 10^2\\ &= 1.395 \times 10^3\end{aligned}$$

EXAMPLE 7 Divide and write scientific notation for the answer.

$$\begin{aligned}\frac{7.2 \times 10^{-7}}{8.0 \times 10^6} &= \frac{7.2}{8.0} \times \frac{10^{-7}}{10^6} && \text{Factoring}\\ &= 0.9 \times 10^{-13} && \text{Dividing}\\ &= (9.0 \times 10^{-1}) \times 10^{-13} && \text{Converting 0.9 to scientific notation}\\ &= 9.0 \times 10^{-14}\end{aligned}$$

Multiplying and Dividing

Chalkboard Examples

Multiply. Write the answer in scientific notation.

1. $(4.1 \cdot 10^7)(2.0 \cdot 10^5)$
   $8.2 \cdot 10^{12}$
2. $(9 \cdot 10^{-4})(4 \cdot 10^8)$
   $3.6 \cdot 10^5$
3. $\dfrac{1.1 \cdot 10^9}{5.5 \cdot 10^6}$
   $2.0 \cdot 10^2$

Estimating and Approximating

Students can obtain a quick estimate by rounding to one significant digit. For example, $3.245 \cdot 10^7$ can be rounded to $3 \cdot 10^7$. If the decimal part is 0.5 or greater, then round upward. If the decimal part is less than 0.5, then round downward. For example, the number 3.245 rounds down to 3, whereas the number 3.512 rounds up to 4.

Chalkboard Examples

1. Estimate.

$$\frac{0.000345 \cdot 41300}{5980}$$

Write in scientific notation.

$$\frac{(3.45 \cdot 10^{-4})(4.1300 \cdot 10^{4})}{(5.98 \cdot 10^{3})}$$

Round to one significant digit.

$$\frac{(3.0 \cdot 10^{-4})(4.0 \cdot 10^{4})}{(6.0 \cdot 10^{3})}$$

Simplify.

$$\frac{3 \cdot 4}{6} \cdot 10^{-4+4-3}$$

$$\approx 2 \cdot 10^{-3}$$

LESSON QUIZ

Convert to scientific notation.

1. 67,000,000
   $6.7 \cdot 10^7$
2. 0.000039
   $3.9 \cdot 10^{-5}$

Convert to standard notation.

3. $5.32 \cdot 10^5$
   532,000
4. $4.65 \cdot 10^{-4}$
   0.000465
5. Multiply and write in scientific notation.
   $(3.0 \cdot 10^6)(4.0 \cdot 10^7)$
   $12.0 \cdot 10^{13} = 1.2 \cdot 10^{14}$
6. Divide and write in scientific notation.
   $\frac{1.4 \cdot 10^4}{4 \cdot 10^5}$
   $3.5 \cdot 10^{-2}$

Try This Multiply or divide and write scientific notation for the answer.

g. $(9.1 \times 10^{-17})(8.2 \times 10^3)$ 7.462×10^{-13}
h. $\frac{4.2 \times 10^5}{2.1 \times 10^2}$ 2.0×10^3
i. $\frac{1.1 \times 10^{-4}}{2.0 \times 10^{-7}}$ 5.5×10^2

Estimating and Approximating

Objective: Use scientific notation in approximating and estimating.

Scientific notation is helpful in estimating or approximating. Such estimating is an important skill in problem solving.

EXAMPLE 8 Estimate $780{,}000{,}000 \times \frac{0.00071}{0.000005}$.

$$\frac{(7.8 \times 10^8)(7.1 \times 10^{-4})}{(5 \cdot 10^{-6})}$$ Converting to scientific notation and multiplying

$$= \frac{7.8 \times 7.1}{5} \times \frac{(10^8)(10^{-4})}{10^{-6}}$$ Regrouping

$$\approx \frac{8 \times 7}{5} \times 10^{8+(-4)-(-6)}$$ Rounding

$$\approx \frac{56}{5} \times 10^{10}$$

$$\approx 11 \times 10^{10}$$ Rounding

$$\approx 1.1 \times 10^{11}$$ Converting to scientific notation

We now have an approximation of 1.1×10^{11}.

Try This Estimate. Answer may vary depending on how you round.

j. $830{,}000{,}000 \times \frac{0.0000012}{3{,}100{,}000}$ 3×10^{-4}

Using Scientific Notation

Many calculators switch their displays automatically to scientific notation when results are greater than the capacity of the display. If we multiply 20,820,000 by 5000 on a calculator, the display will show 1.041   11. This means 1.041×10^{11}. Calculators with keys EXP or EE allow you to enter numbers in scientific notation. To enter 0.0035698 in scientific notation, press

3.5698 EXP 3 +/–

Calculate $34{,}700{,}000 \times 5000$ using scientific notation.

3.47 EXP 7 × 5 EXP 3 = → 1.735   11

For additional calculator practice, see Calculator Worksheet 3.

1-9 EXERCISES

A

Convert to scientific notation.

1. 47,000,000,000
2. 2,600,000,000,000
3. 863,000,000,000,000,000
4. 957,000,000,000,000,000
5. 0.000000016
6. 0.000000263
7. 0.00000000007
8. 0.00000000009

Write scientific notation for the number.

9. The mass of an electron is 0.000000000000000000000000000911 g.
10. The population of the United States is about 270,000,000.
11. An electron carries a charge of 0.00000000048 electrostatic units.
12. The volume of a grain of sand is about 0.0000000013 ft^3.
13. An oxygen atom is about 0.000000001 times the size of a drop of water.
14. The distance from the sun to Pluto is 3,664,000,000 miles.
15. The weight of a blue whale is 306,990 pounds.
16. The gross national product (GNP) of the United States in 1984 was \$3,662,800,000,000.

Convert to decimal notation.

17. 4×10^{-4} 0.0004
18. 5×10^{-5} 0.00005
19. 6.73×10^{8} 673,000,000
20. 9.24×10^{7} 92,400,000
21. 8.923×10^{-10} 0.0000000008923
22. 7.034×10^{-2} 0.07034

Multiply or divide, and write scientific notation for the answer.

23. $(2.3 \times 10^{6})(4.2 \times 10^{-11})$
24. $(6.5 \times 10^{3})(5.2 \times 10^{-8})$
25. $(2.34 \times 10^{-8})(5.7 \times 10^{-4})$
26. $(3.26 \times 10^{-6})(8.2 \times 10^{-6})$
27. $(3.2 \times 10^{6})(2.6 \times 10^{4})$
28. $(3.11 \times 10^{3})(1.01 \times 10^{13})$

Divide, and write scientific notation for the answer.

29. $\frac{8.5 \times 10^{8}}{3.4 \times 10^{5}}$ 2.5×10^{3}
30. $\frac{5.1 \times 10^{6}}{3.4 \times 10^{3}}$ 1.5×10^{3}
31. $\frac{4.0 \times 10^{-6}}{8.0 \times 10^{-3}}$ 5×10^{-4}
32. $\frac{7.5 \times 10^{-9}}{2.5 \times 10^{-4}}$ 3×10^{-5}
33. $\frac{12.6 \times 10^{8}}{4.2 \times 10^{-3}}$ 3×10^{11}
34. $\frac{3.2 \times 10^{-7}}{8.0 \times 10^{8}}$ 4×10^{-16}

Estimate.

35. $\frac{(6.1 \times 10^{4})(7.2 \times 10^{-6})}{9.8 \times 10^{-4}}$ 4.5×10^{2}
36. $\frac{(8.05 \times 10^{-11})(5.9 \times 10^{7})}{3.1 \times 10^{14}}$ 1.6×10^{-17}
37. $\frac{780{,}000{,}000 \times 0.00071}{0.000005}$ 1.1×10^{11}
38. $\frac{830{,}000{,}000 \times 0.12}{3{,}100{,}000}$ 3×10^{1}
39. $\frac{43{,}000{,}000 \times 0.095}{63{,}000}$ 6.5×10^{1}
40. $\frac{0.0073 \times 0.84}{0.000006}$ 1×10^{3}

Assignment Guide

Algebra: 1 – 40 e/o, MR

Alg w/Finite or Trig: 1–46 e/o, 47, MR

Comprehensive: 1–46 m4, 47, 48–55 e/o, MR, assign w. 1-10

ADDITIONAL ANSWERS

Exercises

1. 4.7×10^{10}
2. 2.6×10^{12}
3. 8.63×10^{17}
4. 9.57×10^{17}
5. 1.6×10^{-8}
6. 2.63×10^{-7}
7. 7×10^{-11}
8. 9×10^{-11}
9. 9.11×10^{-28} grams
10. 2.7×10^{8}
11. 4.8×10^{-10} eu
12. 1.3×10^{-9}
13. 1×10^{-9}
14. 3.664×10^{9} mi
15. 3.0699×10^{5} lb
16. \$$3.6628 \times 10^{12}$

23. 9.66×10^{-5}
24. 3.38×10^{-4}
25. 1.3338×10^{-11}
26. 2.6732×10^{-11}
27. 8.32×10^{10}
28. 3.1411×10^{16}

41. 3.8715403×10^3
42. 5.100036×10^2
43. 2.0000000029×10^7
44. 7.1428571×10^1

Mixed Review

56. $105y + 36$
57. $35y + 98$
58. $\frac{1}{5^{24}3^8}$ or $5^{-24}3^{-8}$
59. -132
60. $64t^3$
61. t^2
62. $45m^2$
63. $-2(a + b)$
64. $-(3m + 2n)$
65. $(w - y)\left(\frac{x}{2}\right)$

B

Convert to scientific notation.

41. 3,871.5403 **42.** 510.0036 **43.** 20,000,000.029 **44.** $71.\overline{428571}$

45. The distance light travels in 100 years is about 5.8×10^{14} miles. How far does light travel in 13 weeks? $\approx 1.4 \times 10^{12}$ mi

46. The average distance of the earth from the sun is around 9.3×10^7 miles. About how far does the earth travel in its yearly orbit about the sun? (Hint: Assume the orbit is circular.) $\approx 5.8 \times 10^8$ mi

47. ***Critical Thinking*** Scientific notation for a number is $a \times 10^n$, where a is an odd prime number that is a factor of 845 and n is the greatest multiple of 4 that is less than 11. Find standard notation for the number. 500,000,000

Challenge

48. Compare $8 \cdot 10^{-90}$ and $9 \cdot 10^{-91}$. Which is larger and by how much? Write scientific notation for the difference. 8×10^{-90} is larger by 7.1×10^{-90}.

Use the table below for Exercises 49 – 55. Write the answers using scientific notation.

Feet in a mile	5.28×10^3	Minutes in an hour	6×10^1
Yards in a mile	1.76×10^3	Hours in a day	2.4×10^1
Seconds in a minute	6×10^1	Days in a year	3.6525×10^2

49. One foot per second is how many miles per hour? $\approx 6.82 \times 10^{-1}$ mi/h

50. Find miles per hour for a speed of 25 feet per second. 1.70×10^1 mi/h

51. The world record for the mile in 1987 was 3 min 46.32 seconds. Find the record in feet per second. 2.33×10^1 ft/sec

52. The world record for the 100 yard dash was 9.0 seconds. Find the average speed in feet per second. 3.33×10^1 ft/sec

53. What percent faster was the record for the 100 yard dash than for the mile? 42.9%

54. The speed of light is about 186,282 miles per second. A light year is the distance light travels in one year. How many feet does light travel per day? 8.5×10^{13} ft/day

55. How many seconds does it take for light to travel 100 yards? 3.05×10^{-7} sec

Mixed Review

Simplify. **56.** $6y - [8 - 11(9y + 4)]$

57. $[9(y + 2) + 8y] - \{6[(3y - 5) - (6y + 11)] + 16\}$ **58.** $\left(\frac{5^{-6}}{3^2}\right)^4$

59. $[6(9 - 4) + 3] \cdot (4 - 3 \cdot 8) \div 5$ **60.** $(4t)^3$ **61.** $(-t)^2$ **62.** $5(-3m)^2$

Collect like terms. **63.** $4a - 5b - 6a + 3b$ **64.** $9m - 5n + 3n - 12m$

Factor. **65.** $\frac{wx}{2} - \frac{yx}{2}$

1-10 Field Axioms, Theorems, and Proofs

Field Axioms and Properties

Objective: Use axioms and properties to justify algebraic statements.

Properties that we accept without proof are called **axioms.** We try to choose the more obvious and acceptable properties as axioms. Different mathematicians may make different choices. Following is a list of properties that we accept as axioms in this text.

Axioms for Real Numbers

The Properties of Closure
Addition: For every real number a and b, $a + b$ is a real number.
Multiplication: For every real number a and b, ab is a real number.

The Commutative Properties of Addition and Multiplication
For any real numbers a and b, $a + b = b + a$ and $a \cdot b = b \cdot a$.

The Associative Properties of Addition and Multiplication
For any numbers a, b, and c, $a + (b + c) = (a + b) + c$ and $a(bc) = (ab)c$.

The Distributive Property of Multiplication over Addition
For any numbers a, b, and c, $a(b + c) = ab + ac$.

The Identity Properties
Addition: For any number a, $a + 0 = a$.
Multiplication: For any number a, $a \cdot 1 = a$.

The Properties of Inverses
Addition: For each real number a, there is one and only one additive inverse b for which $a + b = 0$.
Multiplication: For each nonzero number a, there is one and only one multiplicative inverse b for which $ab = 1$.

The following properties can be derived from the definition of equality.

Properties of Equality

For any real numbers a, b, and c,

Reflexive Property	$a = a$.
Symmetric Property	if $a = b$, then $b = a$.
Transitive Property	if $a = b$ and $b = c$, then $a = c$.

1-10

FIRST FIVE MINUTES

Write an equivalent expression for each of the following.

1. ab
   ba
2. $u + v$
   $v + u$
3. $a + (b + c)$
   $(a + b) + c$
   There are other possibilities. For example, $a + (c + b)$ or $(b + c) + a$, etc.
4. $x(yz)$
   $(xy)z$
   There are other possibilites. For example, $x(zy)$ or $(yz)x$, etc.
5. $r(s + t)$
   $rs + rt$
   There are other possibilities. For example, $r(t + s)$ or $(s + t)r$, etc.
6. $z + 0$
   z
7. $w \cdot 1$
   w
8. $a + (-a)$
   0
9. $b \cdot b^{-1}$
   1

Field Axioms and Properties

You may want to make the analogy between algebra and a game. The axioms are rules that tell us what "moves" are allowed. The object is to use the axiom rules to transform expressions and statements into new expressions and statements.

Chalkboard Examples

Which axioms or properties of equality, if any, justify the following statements?

1. $4 + x^2 = x^2 + 4$
   Commutative property of addition
2. $a(u + v) = au + av$
   Distributive property
3. If $3x = 4y$, then $4y = 3x$.
   Symmetric property of equality
4. $3a + (-3a) = 0$
   Inverse property of addition
5. Does the set of positive real numbers form a field with addition and multiplication?
   No; there is no additive inverse.

Proofs

Many proofs require that one expression be replaced by an equivalent expression. For example, when we replace $-3 + 3$ with 0 within an expression, we are substituting equivalent expressions. You may wish to prove Theorems 1-14, 1-15, or 1-16 in class. Here is a proof of Theorem 1-14.

1. $a \cdot 0 = a \cdot 0 + 0$
2. $a \cdot 0 + 0 = a \cdot 0 + a + (-a)$
3. $a \cdot 0 + a + (-a) = a \cdot 0 + a \cdot 1 + (-a)$
4. $a \cdot 0 + a \cdot 1 + (-a) = a(0 + 1) + (-a)$
5. $a(0 + 1) + (-a) = a \cdot 1 + (-a)$
6. $a \cdot 1 + (-a) = a + (-a)$
7. $a + (-a) = 0$

Hence,

8. $a \cdot 0 = 0$, 1–7 by transitivity of equality.

Chalkboard Examples

1. Prove that $(a + b)c = ac + bc$.

   The distributive axiom only guarantees distribution from the left.
   1. $(a + b)c = c(a + b)$, by commut. property of mult.
   2. $c(a + b) = ca + cb$, by the distributive property.
   3. $ca + cb = ac + bc$, by two applications of the commut. property of multiplication.
   4. $(a + b)c = ac + bc$, by Statements 1–3 and the transitive property of equality.

2. Prove that $(a + b)(c + d) = ac + ad + bc + bd$.

   Note that the grouping parentheses have been omitted for clarity on the right side.
   1. $(a + b)(c + d) = (a + b)c + (a + b)d$, by distributing $(a + b)$ from the left.
   2. $(a + b)c + (a + b)d = ac + bc + ac + bd$, by distributing c from the right and d from the right, using Chalkboard Example 1.
   3. $(a + b)(c + d) = ac + ad + bc + bd$, by Statements 1–2 using the transitive property of equality.

EXAMPLES Which axioms or properties of equality, if any, justify the following statements?

1. $6(x + 3) = 6x + 18$ — Distributive property
2. $5y - x = 5y - x$ — Reflexive property of equality
3. $3x^2 \cdot 1 = 3x^2$ — Identity property of multiplication
4. If $2 + 3 = 5$ and $5 = 4 + 1$, then $2 + 3 = 4 + 1$ — Transitive property of equality

Try This Which axioms or properties of equality, if any, justify the following statements? See Additional Answers.

a. $5 + (a + b) = (5 + a) + b$ **b.** $5(x - 2) = 5x - 10$

c. $5y^3 + 0 = 5y^3$ **d.** $(x + 2)\left(\frac{1}{x + 2}\right) = 1$

Any number system with two operations defined in which the axioms on page 49 hold is called a **field.** The axioms are known as **field axioms.** The set of real numbers with addition and multiplication form a field.

EXAMPLE 5 Does the set of integers with addition and multiplication form a field?

The set of integers does not satisfy the property of multiplicative inverses. It is not a field.

Try This Tell whether each of these sets with addition and multiplication form a field. If not, tell why.

e. the set of whole numbers No; no multiplicative inverse

f. the set of rational numbers Yes

Proofs

Objective: Write column proofs.

Number properties that can be proved by using axioms and definitions are called theorems. The following theorem may be called an "extended distributive property."

> **Theorem 1-13**
>
> **An Extended Distributive Property**
>
> For any real numbers a, b, c, and d, $a(b + c + d) = ab + ac + ad$.

To prove a theorem we write a sequence of statements. Each must be supported by an axiom, definition, or previously-proved statement. Proofs are sometimes written in columns to make sure that every statement is supported.

EXAMPLE 6 Prove Theorem 1-13.

An Extended Distributive Property

For any real numbers a, b, c, and d, $a(b + c + d) = ab + ac + ad$.

1. $a(b + c + d) = a[(b + c) + d]$	1. Associative property of addition
2. $= a(b + c) + ad$	2. Distributive property
3. $= ab + ac + ad$	3. ? Distributive property
4. $a(b + c + d) = ab + ac + ad$	4. Transitive property of equality

Try This

g. Supply the reason for step 3 of the proof in Example 6. See above.

Here are some further number properties, stated as theorems. You will be asked to prove them in the exercises. To prove a specific theorem, you may use any preceding theorem for its proof.

Theorem 1-14

The Multiplicative Property of 0

For any real number a, $a \cdot 0 = 0$.

Theorem 1-15

Additive Inverses of Products

For any real numbers a and b, $-(ab) = -a \cdot b = a(-b)$.

(The additive inverse of a product of two numbers is equivalent to the product of either one of them and the additive inverse of the other.)

Theorem 1-16

Products of Additive Inverses

For any real numbers a and b, $(-a)(-b) = ab$.

(The product of the inverse of two numbers is the product of those numbers.)

LESSON QUIZ

Which axiom or property justifies the following statements?

1. $(4x)(3y) = (3y)(4x)$
   Commut. property of mult.
2. $\frac{5}{2}[a + (-b)] = \frac{5}{2}a + \frac{5}{2}(-b)$
   Distributive property
3. If $a = b$ and $b = 3$, then $a = 3$.
   Transitive property of equality
4. Supply the reasons for the following proof steps.
   a. $ax = ax$
   Reflexive property of equality
   b. $ax = ax + 0$
   Additive identity
   c. $ax + 0 = ax + a + (-a)$
   Additive inverse property
   d. $ax + a + (-a)$
   $= ax + a \cdot 1 + (-a)$
   Multiplicative identity property
   e. $ax + a \cdot 1 + (-a)$
   $= a(x + 1) + (-a)$
   Distributive property

Assignment Guide
Algebra: Omit

Alg w/Finite or Trig: Omit

Comprehensive: 1–26 e/o, 27, 28, MR, assign w. 1-9

ADDITIONAL ANSWERS

Try This

a. Associative property of addition
b. Distributive property
c. Identity property of addition
d. Identity property of multiplication and property of multiplicative inverses

Exercises

1. Distributive property
2. Associative property of addition
3. Property of additive inverses
4. Distributive property
5. None; subtraction theorem
6. Associative property of multiplication
7. Associative property of addition
8. None; division theorem
9. Symmetric property of equality
10. Reflexive property of equality
11. Commutative property of addition
12. Associative property of addition
13. None; subtraction theorem
14. Distributive property
15. Commutative property of addition
16. Transitive property of equality
17. No; there is no additive inverse or multiplicative inverse.
18. No; there is no multiplicative inverse.
19. Yes
20. No; there is no additive inverse.

1-10 EXERCISES

A

Which axioms or properties of equality, if any, justify each statement?

1. $6(x + 3) = 6x + 18$

2. $4x + (2y + 5) = (4x + 2y) + 5$

3. $a(-b + b) = a \cdot 0$

4. $x(a + b) = xa + xb$

5. $3x - 2y = 3x + (-2y)$

6. $-1 \cdot 3x = -3x = (-3) \cdot x$

7. $5x - (y - 2) = (5x - y) + 2$

8. $\frac{2}{x+1} = 2 \cdot \frac{1}{x+1}$

9. If $2 = x$, then $x = 2$.

10. $a + b = a + b$

11. $x^2 + y^2 = y^2 + x^2$

12. $(a + b) + c = a + (b + c)$

13. $x^3 - y^3 = x^3 + (-y^3)$

14. $\frac{1}{2}(x + y) = \frac{1}{2}x + \frac{1}{2}y$

15. $x + y = y + x$

16. If $-1 \cdot x = -x$ and $-x = y$, then $-1 \cdot x = y$.

Tell whether each of these sets with addition and multiplication form a field. If not, tell why.

17. The set of natural numbers

18. The set of even numbers

19. The set of rational numbers

20. The set $\{0,1\}$

21. Theorem 1-1, the subtraction theorem Complete the proof.

For any real numbers a and b, $a - b = a + (-b)$.

To prove the subtraction theorem, we will use the definition of subtraction. It says that $a - b$ is the number c such that $c + b = a$. We will show that $a + (-b)$ works the same way.

1. $[a + (-b)] + b = a + [(-b) + b]$	1. ? Associative property of addition
2. $= a + 0$	2. Property of additive inverses
3. $= a$	3. ? Identity property for addition
4. $[a + (-b)] + b = a$	4. Transitive property of equality
5. $a + (-b) = a - b$	5. Definition of subtraction

22. Theorem 1-5 Complete the proof.

For any real numbers a and b, $-(a + b) = -a + (-b)$.

1. $(a + b) + [-a + (-b)]$ $= [a + (-a)] + [b + (-b)]$	1. Commutative, associative properties for addn.
2. $= 0 + 0$	2. Property of additive inverses
3. $= 0$	3. Identity property for addition
4. Thus $-a + (-b)$ is the inverse of $(a + b)$; in other words, $-a + (-b) = -(a + b)$.	4. Property of additive inverses

B

Prove the following.

23. For any real numbers a and b, $-(a - b) = b - a$.

24. For any real number a, $-(-a) = a$.

25. Theorem 1-2, the division theorem

26. For any nonzero real number a, $\frac{a}{a} = 1$.

27. ***Critical Thinking*** A set is *closed* under an operation if, whenever the operation is performed on elements within the set, the result is also in the set. Determine which of the following sets are closed under the given operation.

- **a.** the set of whole numbers; addition Yes
- **b.** the set of whole numbers; subtraction No
- **c.** the set of odd integers; addition No
- **d.** the set of even integers; multiplication Yes
- **e.** the set of rational numbers; multiplication Yes

Challenge

28. A number system consists of {0,1,2} and the operation of + and × defined by these tables. For example, in this system, $1 + 2 = 0$, and $2 \times 2 = 1$.

Determine whether this number system is a field. Yes

+	0	1	2
0	0	1	2
1	1	2	0
2	2	0	1

×	0	1	2
0	0	0	0
1	0	1	2
2	0	2	1

Mixed Review

Multiply. **29.** $5x(y + 3z)$ **30.** $3a(2b - 3c)$ **31.** $2w(1 - 3x)$

Simplify. **32.** $6^2 \cdot 6^4$ **33.** $m^{-8} \cdot m^5$ **34.** $y^3 \cdot y^{-7} \cdot y^2$ **35.** $x^{13} \cdot x^{-9}$

Solve. **36.** $m - 31 = 19$ **37.** $z - 64 = 241$ **38.** $23x = 368$

39. $-\frac{7}{16}y = \frac{7}{4}$

40. Alfredo has saved \$238 to buy a racing bicycle. This represents 85% of the cost of the bike. Find the cost of the bike.

41. The fine for speeding in one town is \$10 plus \$2 for each mile per hour exceeding the speed limit. What is the fine for a driver stopped for driving 44 miles per hour in a 25 mile-per-hour zone? \$48

Divide and write scientific notation for the answer.

42. $\frac{1.28 \times 10^{-3}}{6.4 \times 10^{-1}}$ **43.** $\frac{7.29 \times 10^{2}}{8.1 \times 10^{4}}$ **44.** $\frac{10^4}{8 \times 10^4}$

23. $-(a - b) = -(a + (-b))$ Theorem 1-1
$= -1 \cdot (a + (-b))$ Ident. prop. of mult.
$= (-1)(a) + (-1)(-b)$ Dist. prop.
$= -a + b$ Mult. prop. of -1
$= b + (-a)$ Commut. prop. of addition
$= b - a$ Theorem 1-1
$-(a - b) = b - a$ Statements 1 – 6

24. $a - a = a + (-a)$ Theorem 1 – 1
$a - a = 0$ Add. inverse prop.
$a + (-a) - (-a) = -(-a)$ Theorem 1-5
$a = -(-a)$ Reflexive prop. of equality, Statements 1 – 3

25. $\frac{a}{b} = \frac{a \cdot 1}{1 \cdot b}$ Identity property of multiplication
$= \frac{a}{1} \cdot \frac{1}{b}$ Assoc. prop. of mult.
$= a \cdot \frac{1}{b}$ Ident. prop. of mult.
$\frac{a}{b} = a \cdot \frac{1}{b}$ Statements 1 – 3

26. $\frac{a}{a} = a \cdot \frac{1}{a}$ Division theorem
$= 1$ Mult. inverse prop.
$\frac{a}{a} = 1$ Statements 1 – 2

Mixed Review

29. $5xy + 15xz$
30. $6ab - 9ac$
31. $2w - 6wx$
32. 6^6
33. m^{-3}
34. y^{-2}
35. x^4
36. 50
37. 305
38. 16
39. -4
40. \$280
42. 2×10^{-3}
43. 9×10^{-3}
44. 1.25×10^{-1}

1-11

FIRST FIVE MINUTES

1. Joel got 73% on his first test and 80% on his second test. What must Joel score on his third test to average 80%? 87%
2. Chang cuts a 1.4 meter board into three pieces; each half as long as the last one he cut. How long is each piece? 0.8m, 0.4m, 0.2m
3. Three gears are connected so that they all mesh. Can they be turned? No
4. Becky has $7 less than Elaine. Elaine has $5 more than Lynn. They have $51 altogether. How much does each one have? Becky $14, Elaine $21, Lynn $16

Draw a Diagram

Many of the problem solving-strategies that will be introduced can be used to help students write an equation for solving. It is also important, however, for students to experience working problems that cannot be solved by writing and solving equations, and to know other strategies that can be used to solve problems. Formally introducing students to a variety of problem-solving strategies can give them a larger repertoire of techniques for solving nonroutine problems as well as routine problems.

Emphasize that drawing a diagram that describes a problem can be very helpful in understanding the problem. Demonstrate with the example how drawing a diagram helps you sort out and visualize the information in the problem. Drawing a diagram can be a useful intermediate step toward writing an equation to solve a problem.

Key Questions

- What does the unshaded part of the rectangle represent? 80% of the rainfall
- How would you check the answer in Example 1? Multiply M by 0.2 to see if 0.5 is 20% of M.

1-11 Problem Solving: Strategies

Draw a Diagram

Objective: Solve nonroutine problems using the strategy *Draw a Diagram.*

PROBLEM-SOLVING GUIDELINES
■ UNDERSTAND the problem
■ Develop and carry out a PLAN
■ Find the ANSWER and CHECK

Problem-Solving Guidelines were introduced in this chapter to help you solve problems. The three phases in the guidelines can be helpful in solving all problems.

The planning phase involves selecting and implementing *strategies* for solving problems. The problem-solving strategy called Write an Equation is the one you will work with often in your study of algebra.

There are many other strategies you can use to solve problems in mathematics. Usually, some combination of strategies is used. For example, the strategy called Draw a Diagram can often be used to help you understand a problem for which you will also write an equation to find a solution.

EXAMPLE 1

The average rainfall in May in one western city is 0.5 in. This amount is only 20% of the average amount of rainfall in one midwestern city in May. How much rainfall does the midwestern city average in May?

Drawing a diagram helps show the relationship between the numbers in the problem and the unknown quantity.

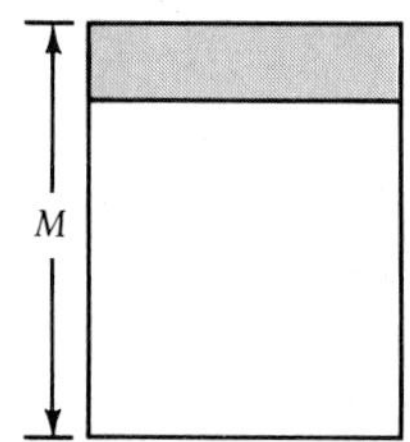

20% of the midwestern city's average rainfall is 0.5 in.

The midwestern city's average rainfall is unknown.

From the diagram, we can see that the equation $20\% \times M = 0.5$ expresses the relationship between the total amount of rainfall in the midwestern city and the 20%, or 0.5 in. of rainfall in the western city. Solve the equation to finish carrying out your plan.

$$0.20 \times M = 0.5 \quad \text{Writing 20\% as 0.20}$$

$$M = \frac{0.5}{0.20} = 2.5$$

The average amount of rainfall in the midwestern city is 2.5 in. The answer checks.

EXAMPLE 2

A professional decorator can hang wallpaper on a square wall with sides of 10 feet in 30 minutes. How long would it take this person to cover a square section of wall with sides of 5 feet? Assume the wallpaper was hung at the same rate of speed.

An incorrect assumption is that it will take half as long to cover the smaller wall, since the side of the square is half the side of the larger square. Drawing a picture shows why this is incorrect and helps show the correct answer.

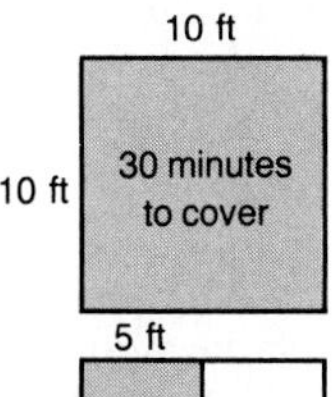

The diagram shows the information given in the problem. The square is 10 ft on each side, and it takes 30 min to cover this square.

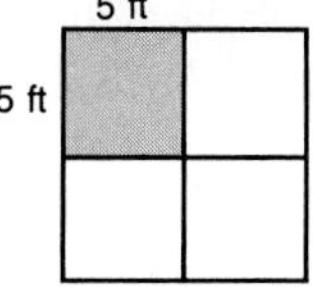

We can use the original diagram to show that a square with sides of 5 ft is $\frac{1}{4}$ the area of the original square. Thus it will take only $\frac{1}{4}$ as long to cover this section.

It will take $7\frac{1}{2}$ min to cover the square section with sides of 5 ft.

Problem-Solving Strategies		
Write an Equation	Draw a Diagram	Guess, Check, Revise
Make an Organized List	Make a Table	Look for a Pattern
Use Logical Reasoning	Simplify the Problem	Work Backward

1-11 PROBLEMS

Solve using one or both of the strategies presented so far.

1. How many spokes does a wheel have if there are 16 spaces between the spokes?
2. An adult dosage of a medicine uses 280 grams of one ingredient. A child's dosage uses 125 grams. What percent of the adult dosage is needed for the child's dosage?
3. Two train shipments reached the same factory from different cities. The distance from each city to the factory was 900 miles. One train travelled 600 miles in the same time that the other travelled only 400 miles. How much of a head start, in miles, was the slower train given if both trains arrived at the same time?
4. The population in a certain city is 35% greater than it was 10 years ago. If the population in this city today is 105,000, what was the population 10 years ago?
5. A chemical compound evaporates in a predictable way. In the first hour, $\frac{1}{2}$ of the amount in the jar at the beginning of the hour evaporates. In the second hour, $\frac{1}{3}$ of the amount in the jar at the beginning of the second hour evaporates. In the third hour, $\frac{1}{4}$ of the amount in the jar at the beginning of the third hour evaporates, and so on. If a container started with 60 L of compound, after how many hours would the amount of the compound be less than 10 L?

Chalkboard Example

1. It costs $132 to carpet a room that is 12 ft × 12 ft. How much does it cost to carpet a closet that is 4 ft × 6 ft? Draw a diagram.

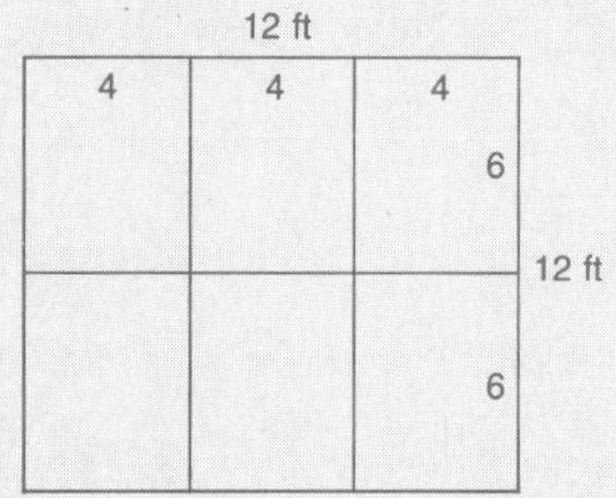

4 ft × 6 ft is $\frac{1}{6}$ of 12 ft × 12 ft.

$\frac{1}{6} \cdot 132 = \$22$

Hints For Problems

1. Draw a wheel with 3 spaces and count the number of spokes. Try 4 spaces. Look for a pattern.
2. Which operation can you use to find what percent one number is of another?
3. Draw a diagram showing the factory and the position of each city. Use the diagram to find the time needed to travel from each city to the factory.
4. 135% of the population 10 years ago will give the current population.
5. Draw a jar showing the amount there after each hour.

ANSWERS

1. There are 16 spokes for a wheel with 16 spaces.
2. The child's dosage is about 45% of the adult dosage.
3. Train A goes 600 miles in the same time train B goes 400 miles, so train A goes 900 miles in the time train B goes 600 miles. Thus, train B needs a 300-mile head start.
4. The population 10 years ago was about 77,800.
5. There will be 10 liters at 5 hours, so there would be less than 10 liters after 5 hours.

ANSWERS

1. No, no, yes, yes
2. Rational
3. Rational
4. Rational
5. $-\frac{27}{10}$
6. 0.8
7. $-\frac{1}{24}$
8. $-\frac{16}{35}$
9. -19.7
10. 32.28
11. -8.4
12. $2\frac{1}{7}$
13. 6010
14. -5.2
15. $\frac{7}{6}$
16. $-\frac{5}{12}$
17. $7y \cdot 4x$

Chapter 1 Summary and Review

1-1

A rational number can be expressed as a ratio $\frac{a}{b}$, where a and b are integers and $b \neq 0$.

1. Is -3 a natural number? a whole number? an integer? a rational number?

Determine which are rational and which are irrational.

2. $-\sqrt{49}$ **3.** -0.733 **4.** $6.5\overline{27}$

To add when there are like signs, add the absolute values. The sum has the same sign as the addends. To add when there are unlike signs, subtract the absolute values. The sum has the sign of the addend with the greater absolute value.

Add.

5. $-\frac{7}{5} + \left(-\frac{13}{10}\right)$ **6.** $8.7 + (-7.9)$ **7.** $-\frac{7}{8} + \frac{5}{6}$

To subtract a rational number, add its inverse.

Subtract.

8. $-\frac{6}{7} - \left(-\frac{2}{5}\right)$ **9.** $-13.8 - 5.9$ **10.** $16.56 - (-15.72)$

1-2

When multiplying or dividing rational numbers, multiply or divide their absolute values. If both numbers are positive or both are negative, then the answer is positive. If one number is positive and the other is negative, then the answer is negative.

Multiply.

11. $-4(2.1)$ **12.** $-\frac{5}{6}\left(-\frac{18}{7}\right)$ **13.** $(-6.01)(-1000)$

The quotient $\frac{a}{b}$ is the number c such that $c \cdot b = a$.

Divide.

14. $\frac{-18.72}{3.6}$ **15.** $-\frac{7}{8} \div \left(-\frac{3}{4}\right)$ **16.** $\frac{2}{3} \div \left(-\frac{8}{5}\right)$

1-3

The commutative properties, $a + b = b + a$ and $ab = ba$, and associative properties, $a + (b + c) = (a + b) + c$ and $a(bc) = (ab)c$, are used to write equivalent expressions

17. Use the commutative property of multiplication to write an expression equivalent to $4x \cdot 7y$.

18. Use the associative property of addition to write an expression equivalent to $\left(\frac{x}{3} + 5\right) + 2y$.

19. Write an equivalent expression by simplifying $\frac{10(x-2)}{24(x-2)}$.

Evaluate each expression for $x = 3$ and $y = -2$.

20. $2x + 1 - 3y$

21. $-(x - 1 - y)$

22. $2|x-4| - |y|$

1-4

The distributive property, $a(b + c) = ab + ac$, tells us that when multiplying a number by a sum, we can add first and then multiply, or multiply first and then add.

Multiply.

23. $6(x - y + z)$

24. $-3(k - 2t + w)$

25. $12\left(\frac{a}{2} - \frac{b}{3} + \frac{c}{4}\right)$

Factor.

26. $ax - ay$

27. $-20x + 5y - 10z$

28. $2ab - 6ac - 8ad$

Combine like terms.

29. $-6y - 8z - 4y + 3z$

30. $2.3y - 8 - 4y + 7.6x - 5.8x$

Simplify.

31. $-(r - t)$

32. $-(-4x + 3y)$

Simplify.

33. $2a - (3a - 4)$

34. $y - 3(2y - 4x)$

35. $5x - [2x - (3x + 2)]$

36. $8x - \{2x - 3[(x - 4) - (x + 2)]\}$

1-5

We use the addition property of equality (if $a = b$, then $a + c = b + c$) and the multiplication property of equality (if $a = b$, then $ac = bc$) to solve equations.

Solve.

37. $5x - 3 = 27$

38. $6y + 3 = y - 12$

39. $3t - 8 - t = 7t - 8 + 2t$

1-6

The three phases of the Problem-Solving Guidelines are: UNDERSTAND the problem, develop and carry out a PLAN, and find the ANSWER and CHECK.

40. Ace Car Rental charges \$27 per day plus \$0.35 per mile to rent a car. Find the cost of renting a car for a 7-day trip of 840 miles.

1-7

For any nonzero number b and integer n, b^{-n} means $\frac{1}{b^n}$.
Write equivalent expressions using negative exponents.

41. $\frac{1}{8^3}$

42. $\frac{1}{(-3)^2}$

43. $\frac{1}{3y^5}$

44. $\frac{1}{(3y)^5}$

18. $\frac{x}{3} + (5 + 2y)$
19. $\frac{5}{12}$
20. 13
21. -4
22. 0
23. $6x - 6y + 6z$
24. $-3k + 6t - 3w$
25. $6a - 4b + 3c$
26. $a(x - y)$
27. $-5(4x - y + 2z)$
28. $2a(b - 3c - 4d)$
29. $-10y - 5z$
30. $1.8x - 1.7y - 8$
31. $-r + t$
32. $4x - 3y$
33. $-a + 4$
34. $-5y + 12x$
35. $6x + 2$
36. $6x - 18$
37. 6
38. -3
39. 0
40. \$483
41. 8^{-3}
42. $(-3)^{-2}$
43. $\frac{y^{-5}}{3}$
44. $(3y)^{-5}$

45. $\frac{1}{(-4)^3}$, or $-\frac{1}{64}$
46. x^3y^4
47. $\frac{3a^3}{c^5}$
48. $\frac{w^3y^5}{x^2z^6}$
49. $-\frac{14}{x}$
50. a^2
51. $-\frac{3y^5}{x^8}$
52. $81x^8y^{12}$
53. $-\frac{1}{8x^9}$
54. $\frac{4x^6}{9y^{20}}$
55. 8.0×10^7
56. 7.4×10^{-7}
57. 3.78×10^9
58. 2.5×10^{-9}

Write equivalent expressions without negative exponents.

45. $(-4)^{-3}$ **46.** $\frac{x^3}{y^{-4}}$ **47.** $3a^3c^{-5}$ **48.** $w^3x^{-2}y^5z^{-6}$

1-8

For any real number $a \neq 0$, and integers m, n, and p, $a^m \cdot a^n = a^{m+n}$, $\frac{a^m}{a^n} = a^{m-n}$, and $(a^mb^n)^p = a^{m \cdot p}b^{n \cdot p}$.

Simplify.

49. $(7x^3y^{-1})(-2x^{-4}y)$ **50.** $\frac{a^{-2}}{a^{-4}}$ **51.** $-\frac{54x^{-5}y^4}{18x^3y^{-1}}$

52. $(-3x^2y^3)^4$ **53.** $(-2x^3)^{-3}$ **54.** $\left(-\frac{2x^3y^{-6}}{3y^4}\right)^2$

1-9

Scientific notation for a number is notation of the form $a \times 10^n$ where $1 \leq a < 10$ and n is an integer.

Write scientific notation.

55. 80,000,000 **56.** 0.00000074

57. $(1.8 \times 10^{12})(2.1 \times 10^{-3})$ **58.** $\frac{6.25 \times 10^{-6}}{2.5 \times 10^3}$

See also Problem 1, Computer-Assisted Problem Solving, page 839.

ANSWERS

1. Irrational
2. Rational
3. Irrational
4. Rational
5. Irrational
6. Rational
7. Irrational
8. Rational
9. −7.98
10. $-\frac{11}{80}$
11. $\frac{5}{36}$
12. 11.06
13. $\frac{31}{18}$
14. −36.8
15. −2.79
16. $\frac{20}{21}$
17. −43

Chapter 1 Test

Which of the following numbers are rational and which are irrational?

1. $\sqrt{5}$ **2.** $0.\overline{153846}$ **3.** 0.1121231234...

4. 0 **5.** $\sqrt{10}$ **6.** $\frac{1.7}{2.9}$

7. 3.14159265 ... (numeral does not repeat)

8. $3.142857\overline{142857}$... (numeral repeats)

Add.

9. $-4.9 + (-3.08)$ **10.** $\frac{9}{16} + \left(-\frac{7}{10}\right)$ **11.** $-\frac{4}{9} + \frac{7}{12}$

Subtract.

12. $-0.74 - (-11.8)$ **13.** $\frac{8}{9} - \left(-\frac{5}{6}\right)$ **14.** $-30.7 - 6.1$

Multiply.

15. $-0.9(3.1)$ **16.** $-\frac{2}{7}\left(-\frac{10}{3}\right)$ **17.** $0.43(-100)$

Divide.

18. $\frac{4}{3} \div \left(-\frac{8}{15}\right)$ **19.** $-\frac{6.09}{0.29}$ **20.** $\frac{-7.2}{-0.4}$

21. Use the associative property of multiplication to write an expression equivalent to $(x \cdot 2y) \cdot 8z$.

22. Use the commutative property of addition to write an expression equivalent to $5y + 3x$.

23. Write an equivalent expression by simplifying $\frac{12xyz}{8y}$.

Evaluate each expression for $x = -1$ and $y = 5$.

24. $3x - y + 7$ **25.** $-(y - x + 1)$ **26.** $3|x + 1| - |y|$

Multiply.

27. $-4(x - y + 8)$ **28.** $a(3b - c - d)$ **29.** $6\left(3x - \frac{y}{2} - \frac{z}{4}\right)$

Factor.

30. $2xy - xz$ **31.** $6ab - 8bc - 4bd$ **32.** $3xy - 6xyz$

Combine like terms.

33. $9x - 5x - 6x + 7x$ **34.** $3.2y - 9 - 5y + 4.8x - 5.7x$

Simplify.

35. $-(-2t)$ **36.** $-(-5 - 3x)$ **37.** $-(6 - 5y)$

Simplify.

38. $3t - (5t - 6)$ **39.** $9y - [4y - (2y - 5)]$ **40.** $2x - 5(3 - 2x) - 5$

Solve.

41. $3 - 2x = 7$ **42.** $5y - 2 = y - 10$ **43.** $5x - 2 + 3x = 9 - 2x - 11$

44. A housecleaning service charges $10.00 a visit plus $7.50 an hour. How much would this service charge if it took $3\frac{1}{2}$ hours to clean a house?

Write using negative exponents.

45. $\frac{1}{a^3}$ **46.** 3^2 **47.** x^n **48.** $\frac{1}{3x^2}$

Write without negative exponents.

49. $(-2)^{-2}$ **50.** $x^{-2}y^3$ **51.** $2a^{-2}c^4$ **52.** $\frac{1}{-x^{-5}}$

Simplify using positive exponents.

53. $(-5x^3)(-6x^5)$ **54.** $\frac{63y^4z^9}{9y^2z^{-3}}$ **55.** $\frac{2x^{-4}}{8x^{-2}}$

56. $(-4x^2y^4)^3$ **57.** $(-3x^4y)^{-3}$ **58.** $\left(\frac{3x^2y^3}{12x^{-1}y^{-6}}\right)^2$

Write scientific notation.

59. 90,400,000 **60.** 0.00000752 **61.** $\frac{2 \times 10^{-4}}{5 \times 10^3}$

18. $-\frac{5}{2}$
19. -21
20. 18
21. $x \cdot (2y \cdot 8z)$
22. $3x + 5y$
23. $\frac{3xz}{2}$
24. -1
25. -7
26. -5
27. $-4x + 4y - 32$
28. $3ab - ac - ad$
29. $18x - 3y - \frac{3z}{2}$
30. $x(2y - z)$
31. $2b(3a - 4c - 2d)$
32. $3xy(1 - 2z)$
33. $5x$
34. $-1.8y - 0.9x - 9$
35. $2t$ **36.** $5 + 3x$
37. $-6 + 5y$ **38.** $-2t + 6$
39. $7y - 5$ **40.** $12x - 20$
41. -2 **42.** -2
43. 0 **44.** $36.25
45. a^{-3} **46.** $\frac{1}{3^{-2}}$
47. $\frac{1}{x^{-n}}$ **48.** $\frac{x^{-2}}{3}$
49. $\frac{1}{(-2)^2}$ **50.** $\frac{y^3}{x^2}$
51. $\frac{2c^4}{a^2}$ **52.** $-x^5$
53. $30x^8$ **54.** $7y^2z^{12}$
55. $\frac{1}{4x^2}$ **56.** $-64x^6y^{12}$
57. $-\frac{1}{27x^{12}y^3}$ **58.** $\frac{x^6y^{18}}{16}$
59. 9.04×10^7
60. 7.52×10^{-6}
61. 4×10^{-8}

Test Item Analysis

Item	Lesson
1-14	1-1
15-20	1-2
21-26	1-3
27-40	1-4
41-43	1-5
44	1-6
45-52	1-7
53-58	1-8
59-61	1-9

CHAPTER 2

Equations and Inequalities

Chapter Overview

Chapter 2 continues covering techniques for solving equations. The principle of zero products, used throughout the course and in higher mathematics, is introduced here. Formulas and problem solving complete the earlier discussion of linear equations.

The properties of inequalities make up the core of Chapter 2, including principles that parallel those for equations, graphing on a number line, and problem solving. Conjunction, disjunction, and absolute value are discussed in the context of inequalities. Properties of absolute value are discussed in detail. An optional proof lesson covers conditional statements, converses, and equivalence. The problem-solving strategy *Guess, Check, Revise* is added to the student's bank of problem-attack methods.

Objectives

2-1
- Solve equations containing fractions or decimals.
- Solve equations containing parentheses.
- Use the principle of zero products to solve equations.

2-2
- Solve problems by translating to equations.

2-3
- Solve a formula for a specified letter.

2-4
- Determine if a number is a solution of an inequality and graph the solution set.
- Solve inequalities using the addition property.
- Solve inequalities using the multiplication property.
- Solve inequalities using both the addition and multiplication properties.

2-5
- Solve problems by translating to inequalities.

2-6
- Solve and graph conjunctions of inequalities.
- Solve and graph disjunctions of inequalities.

2-7
- Simplify absolute value expressions.
- Find the distance between two points using absolute value.
- Solve and graph equations and inequalities involving absolute value.

2-8
- Prove conditional statements.
- Write and prove converses of statements.
- Solve equations and inequalities by proving a statement and its converse.
- Recognize whether an operation will produce equivalent statements.

2-9
- Solve problems using the strategy *Guess, Check, Revise,* and other strategies.

TEACHING CHAPTER 2

Cooperative Learning Opportunities

The sequenced problem solving strategy first outlined by Polya and used throughout the text is the best general model available. But some students are reluctant to follow a routine; they want to just get the answer as quickly as possible. One method of assuring that the method is followed is to assign 3-person cooperative groups in which each student is responsible for one of the three steps.

In Lesson 2-2, you might assign Exercises 9, 11, and 13 to be done by 3-person groups. Assign the following roles. (1) Reads the problem; then restates the problem and identifies what must be found; (2) writes the necessary equation, substitutes known quantities, solves. (3) Considers whether the result of the equation answers the original question. If a student gets stuck, he or she may be helped by the others in the group. Rotate roles after each exercise.

The same groups might meet again to review some of the homework exercises.

Multicultural Note: *Emmy Noether*

Solving equations and inequalities depends on certain assumptions about the structure of mathematics, that is, the rules governing different procedures. Some mathematicians, particularly in the past 200 years, have worked to determine the nature of these structures and how one algebraic structure such as the real numbers might compare with another set of mathematical objects for which different operations are assigned.

Emmy Noether (1882–1935) was one of the very great mathematicians who worked in the field of abstract algebra. Exploring Einstein's theory of general relativity, she developed "Noether's Theorem," which made a lasting contribution to the theory (of invariants and conservation laws) that supported Einstein's work. Her work, in fact, was so fundamental and "structural" that it is said to have placed the theory of invariants in the field of abstract algebra.

Alternative Assessment and Communication Ideas

Some students have trouble with inequality notation. Two approaches to alternative assessment and communication can help remedy the difficulties and also give you a clearer understanding of the basis for some student difficulties.

Have a question and answer session in which you work in reverse. That is, draw an inequality on the chalkboard and then ask a student to explain in words, not symbols, the numbers in the set. Follow this activity with a quiz in which you ask students to write an inequality for each of the following.

(1) 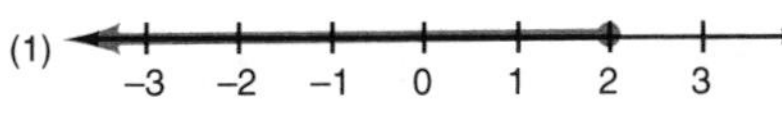

Ans: $x \leq 2$

(2) 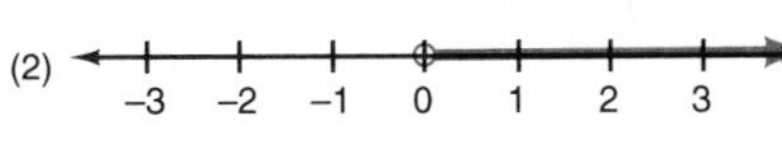

Ans: $x > 0$

(3) 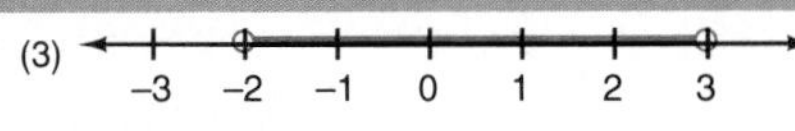

Ans: $-2 < x < 3$

(4) 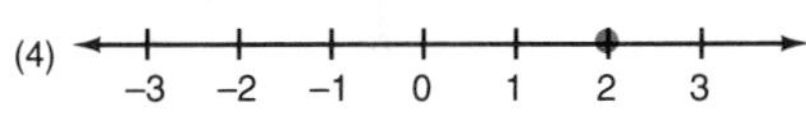

Ans: $x = 2$

(5) 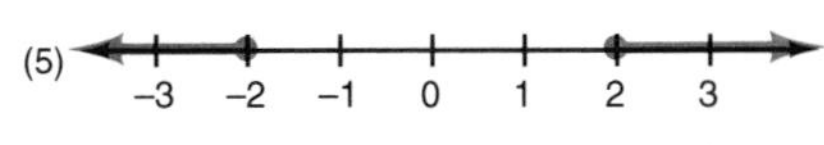

Ans: $-2 \geq x \geq 2$

Investigations and Projects

The logic of Venn diagrams is closely related to that of inequalities. Have students investigate the basic rules governing the union and intersection of sets and the use of Venn diagrams. Then introduce them to the complement of a set and ask them to consider the relationships governing the complements of unions and complements of intersections. Some may discover DeMorgan's Law, which states that the complement of the union of sets is equivalent to the intersections of the complements.

Finally, you might offer Venn diagrams such as the one shown below and ask students to describe the shaded area in set notation.

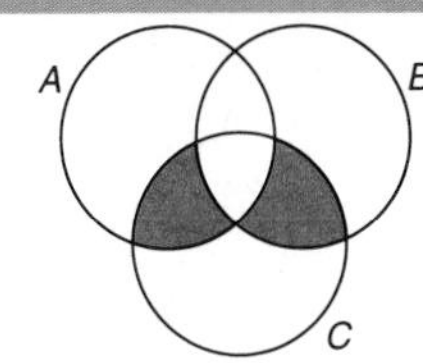

Ans: $((A \cap C) \cap \overline{B}) \cup ((B \cap C) \cap \overline{A})$

MANAGING CHAPTER 2

Lesson	PACING CHART (DAYS) Algebra	Algebra w/Finite	Algebra w/Trig	Compre-hensive	Opening Activity	Cooperative Activity	Seat or Group Work
2-1	1	1	1	0.5	First Five Minutes 2-1: **TE** p.62 or ***FFM Transparency Masters*** p.6	Critical Thinking: **SE** p.65 ✂ Manipulative Activity 2: ***Enrichment*** p.43	Try This a–f
2-2	2	1	1	0.5	First Five Minutes 2-2: **TE** p.66 or ***FFM Transparency Masters*** p.7	Critical Thinking: **SE** p.70	Try This a–g
2-3	1	1	1	0.5	First Five Minutes 2-3: **TE** p.71 or ***FFM Transparency Masters*** p.7	Critical Thinking: **SE** p.72 Critical Thinking 2: ***Enrichment*** p.23	Try This a–f
2-4	2	1	1	0.5	First Five Minutes 2-4: **TE** p.73 or ***FFM Transparency Masters*** p.8	Critical Thinking: **SE** p.77	Try This a–o
2-5	1	1	1	0.5	First Five Minutes 2-5: **TE** p.78 or ***FFM Transparency Masters*** p.8	Critical Thinking: **SE** p.81 Looking for Errors: **SE** p.81	Try This a–b
2-6	1	1	1	0.5	First Five Minutes 2-6: **TE** p.82 or ***FFM Transparency Masters*** p.8	Critical Thinking: **SE** p.86	Try This a–h
2-7	1	1	1	1	First Five Minutes 2-7: **TE** p.87 or ***FFM Transparency Masters*** p.9	Critical Thinking: **SE** p.91	Try This a–q
2-8	0	0	0	1	First Five Minutes 2-8: **TE** p.92 or ***FFM Transparency Masters*** p.9	Critical Thinking: **SE** p.97	Try This a–n
2-9	2	1	1	0.5	First Five Minutes 2-9: **TE** p.98	Problem Solving: **SE** pp.100–101 Strategy Problem Bank 2: ***Problem Bank*** p.3	Problem 1: **SE** p.99
Review	1	1	1	0.5			
Test	1	1	1	1			

FFM: First Five Minutes SPMR: Skills Practice Mixed Review

MANAGING CHAPTER 2

Enrichment	Review/Assess	Reteach	Technology	Lesson
Lesson Enrichment: **TE** p.64 Math Point: **TE** p.63 ✂ Manipulative Activity 2: ***Enrichment*** p.43	Lesson Quiz: **TE** p.64	Skills Practice 4, #1–10: ***SPMR*** p.16		**2-1**
Lesson Enrichment: **TE** p.67	Lesson Quiz: **TE** p.68	Problem Bank 2: ***Problem Bank*** p.23 Skills Practice 4, #11–14: ***SPMR*** p.16		**2-2**
Critical Thinking 2: ***Enrichment*** p.23	Lesson Quiz: **TE** p.72 Quiz 3: ***Assessment*** p.11	Skills Practice 4, #15–20: ***SPMR*** p.16	Calculator Worksheet 4: ***Technology*** p.6	**2-3**
Problem 2: Computer Assisted Problem Solving, **SE** pp.839–840	Lesson Quiz: **TE** p.76	Skills Practice 4, #21–33: ***SPMR*** p.16	Problem 2: Computer Assisted Problem Solving, **SE** pp.839–840	**2-4**
Looking for Errors: **SE** p.81	Lesson Quiz: **TE** p.79 Mixed Review 3: ***SPMR*** p.67	Skills Practice 5, #1–2: ***SPMR*** p.17		**2-5**
College Entrance Exam 1, Section I: ***Problem Bank*** pp.47–50	Lesson Quiz: **TE** p.84 Quiz 4: ***Assessment*** p.12	Skills Practice 5, #3–14: ***SPMR*** p.17	Problem for Programmers: **SE** p.86	**2-6**
College Entrance Exam 1, Section II: ***Problem Bank*** pp.51–54	Lesson Quiz: **TE** p.90	Skills Practice 5, #15–35: ***SPMR*** p.17		**2-7**
Math Point: **TE** p.95	Lesson Quiz: **TE** p.96	Problem Bank 3: ***Problem Bank*** p.24		**2-8**
Problem Solving: **SE** pp.100–101	Mixed Review 4: ***SPMR*** p.68	Strategy Problem Bank 2: ***Problem Bank*** p.3		**2-9**
	Summary and Review: **SE** pp.102–103 Test: **SE** p.103			**Review**
	Chapter 2 Test: ***Assessment*** pp.53–58(reg.), pp.159–160 (adv.) Assessing Strategies 2: ***Assessment*** pp.197–198			**Test**

The solution to the problem posed on the facing page can be found on page 100.

Ready for Equations and Inequalities?

1-1 Write the correct symbol $=$, $<$, or $>$.

1. $-8.09 \square -8.11$ $>$ **2.** $-0.001 \square -\frac{1}{1000}$ $=$ **3.** $-\frac{2}{7} \square \frac{6}{7}$ $<$

1-1 Add.

4. $3.8 + (-3.8)$ 0 **5.** $-4.8 + 1.2$ -3.6 **6.** $-\frac{3}{8} + \left(-\frac{1}{6}\right)$ $-\frac{13}{24}$

1-1 Subtract.

7. $8 - (-5)$ 13 **8.** $-18.2 - 4.7$ -22.9 **9.** $-\frac{2}{3} - \left(-\frac{4}{7}\right)$ $-\frac{2}{21}$

1-2 Multiply.

10. $3 \cdot (-8)$ -24 **11.** $-4.7 \cdot 10$ -47 **12.** $-8 \cdot \left(-\frac{3}{4}\right)$ 6

1-4 Factor.

13. $3x - 18$ $3(x - 6)$ **14.** $5x - 10y + 15$ $5(x - 2y + 3)$

15. $4x - 8 + 6y$ $2(2x - 4 + 3y)$ **16.** $12ab + 4ac - 16ad$ $4a(3b + c - 4d)$

1-4 Multiply.

17. $5(y - 4)$ $5y - 20$ **18.** $a(2 - b)$ $2a - ab$

19. $c(x + y - z)$ $cx + cy - cz$ **20.** $-3(x - y + 1)$ $-3x + 3y - 3$

1-4 Collect like terms.

21. $x + 3x - 5x$ $-x$ **22.** $2y + 3 + 5y - 1$ $7y + 2$

CHAPTER 2

Equations and Inequalities

Some helicopters can carry cargo internally, inside the body of the aircraft, or externally, strapped beneath or to the side of the body. When the cargo is carried externally, the airspeed is decreased because of drag on the helicopter. However, loading and unloading for cargo carried externally is much faster. When transporting cargo, how can delivery time be minimized?

2-1

FIRST FIVE MINUTES

Simplify.

1. $\frac{3}{7} \cdot 7$ 3
2. $\frac{1}{2} + \frac{1}{4}$ $\frac{2}{4} + \frac{1}{4} = \frac{3}{4}$
3. $10(35.5x)$ $355x$

Clearing Fractions or Decimals

Have students multiply the equation by the smallest power of ten that will clear the equation of decimals.

When using a calculator, clearing decimals may not be necessary. For example,

$$0.80a = 0.25$$
$$a = \frac{0.25}{0.80} = 0.3125$$

Key Questions

- What multiplier would you use to simplify the following?
  $214x + 21.4x = 0.214$ 1000
- What multiplier would you use to simplify the following?
  $\frac{x}{2} + \frac{3}{16} = \frac{5}{8}$ 16

Chalkboard Examples

Solve.

1. $\frac{1}{7}z + \frac{3}{14} = \frac{5}{14}$
$$14\left(\frac{1}{7}z + \frac{3}{14}\right) = 14 \cdot \frac{5}{14}$$
$$14 \cdot \frac{1}{7}z + 14 \cdot \frac{3}{14} = 5$$
$$2z + 3 = 5$$
$$z = 1$$
2. $0.5a + 0.75a + 1.2 = 1.45$
$$1.25a + 1.2 = 1.45$$
$$1.25a = 0.25$$
$$(100)1.25a = (100)0.25$$
$$125a = 25$$
$$a = \frac{25}{125}$$
$$a = \frac{1}{5} \text{ or } 0.2$$

2-1 More on Solving Equations

Clearing Fractions or Decimals

Objective: Solve equations containing fractions or decimals.

When an equation contains fractions or decimals, we can use the multiplication property to eliminate them. The process is called clearing the equation of fractions or decimals.

EXAMPLE 1 Solve.

$$\frac{3}{4}x + \frac{1}{2} = \frac{3}{2}$$

We multiply both sides of the equation by the least common denominator, in this case 4.

$$4\left(\frac{3}{4}x + \frac{1}{2}\right) = 4 \cdot \frac{3}{2} \quad \text{Multiplying by 4}$$
$$4 \cdot \frac{3}{4}x + 4 \cdot \frac{1}{2} = 4 \cdot \frac{3}{2} \quad \text{Using the distributive property}$$
$$3x + 2 = 6 \quad \text{Simplifying}$$
$$3x = 4$$
$$x = \frac{4}{3}$$

Check:

$\frac{3}{4}x + \frac{1}{2}$	$= \frac{3}{2}$
$\frac{3}{4}\left(\frac{4}{3}\right) + \frac{1}{2}$	$\frac{3}{2}$
$1 + \frac{1}{2}$	$\frac{3}{2}$
$\frac{3}{2}$	$\frac{3}{2}$ ✓

The solution is $\frac{4}{3}$.

EXAMPLE 2 Solve.

$$12.4 - 3.64x = 1.48$$

We multiply both sides of the equation by a power of ten.

$$100(12.4 - 3.64x) = 100 \cdot 1.48 \quad \text{Multiplying by 100}$$
$$1240 - 364x = 148$$
$$-364x = 148 + (-1240)$$
$$-364x = -1092$$
$$x = 3$$

Since $12.4 - 3.64(3) = 1.48$, the solution is 3.

Try This Solve.

a. $\frac{2}{3} - \frac{5}{6}y = \frac{1}{3}$ $y = \frac{2}{5}$

b. $6.3x - 9.6 = 3$ $x = 2$

Equations with Parentheses

Objective: Solve equations containing parentheses.

When an equation contains parentheses, we first use the distributive property to remove them. Then we proceed as before.

EXAMPLE 3 Solve.

$$3(7 - 2x) = 14 - 8(x - 1)$$

$$21 - 6x = 14 - 8x + 8 \quad \text{Using the distributive property}$$

$$21 - 6x = 22 - 8x$$

$$8x - 6x = 22 + (-21) \quad \text{Using the addition principle}$$

$$2x = 1 \quad \text{Collecting like terms and simplifying}$$

$$x = \frac{1}{2} \quad \text{The number checks, so the solution is } \tfrac{1}{2}.$$

Guidelines for Solving Equations

1. Use the distributive property to remove parentheses, if necessary.
2. Clear fractions or decimals, if necessary.
3. Collect like terms on both sides of the equation.
4. Use the addition and multiplication properties to get the variable alone.

Try This Solve.

c. $3(y - 1) - 1 = 2 - 5(y + 5)$ $y = -\frac{19}{8}$

The Principle of Zero Products

Objective: Use the principle of zero products to solve equations.

When we multiply two numbers, the product will be zero if one of the factors is zero. Furthermore, if a product is zero, then at least one of the factors must be zero.

A statement that both A and B must be true or both must be false can be abbreviated as A if and only if B. This is equivalent to if A then B, and if B then A.

Theorem 2-1

The Principle of Zero Products

For any real numbers a and b, $ab = 0$ if and only if $a = 0$ or $b = 0$.

Equations with Parentheses

This lesson continues the review of elementary algebra concepts, combining order of operations and the distributive property.

Chalkboard Example

1. Solve.
   $5(3 + 2x) = 12 - 4(x - 6)$
   $15 + 10x = 12 - 4x + 24$
   $10x + 4x = 12 + 24 - 15$
   $14x = 21$
   $x = \frac{3}{2}$

The Principle of Zero Products

The expression "if and only if" is sometimes abbreviated "iff." Point out that P iff Q is equivalent to Q iff P.

Math Point
Alexander Calder (1898 – 1976) was an American artist noted for his invention of the mobile. Mobiles are perfectly balanced, and they follow mathematical principles relating mass and distance.

Key Questions

- If $x = 0$ and $y = 0$, must $xy = 0$?
  Yes
- If $x = 0$ or $y = 0$, must $xy = 0$?
  Yes
- If $xy = 0$, must $x = 0$ and $y = 0$?
  No

Chalkboard Examples

1. Solve.
   $(a - 3)(a - 1) = 0$
   $a - 3 = 0$ or $a - 1 = 0$
   $a = 3$ or $a = 1$
   There are two solutions, 3 and 1.
   The solution set is $\{3, 1\}$.
2. Solve.
   $(2x - 4)(3x - 15) = 0$
   $2x - 4 = 0$ or $3x - 15 = 0$
   $2x = 4$ or $3x = 15$
   $x = 2$ or $x = 5$
   The solutions are 2 and 5.
   The solution set is $\{2, 5\}$.

LESSON ENRICHMENT
Will this mobile balance?

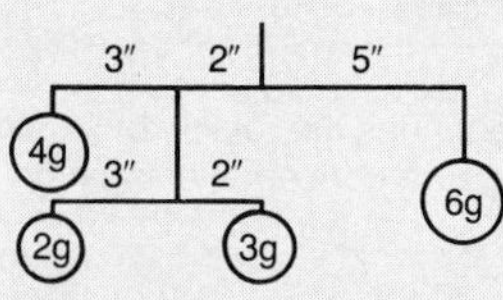

Students may need to construct this mobile to find the answer. The mobile balances, and this can be explained mathematically.

$2 \cdot 3 = 3 \cdot 2$ and
$4(3 + 2) + (2 + 3)2 = 6 \cdot 5$

LESSON QUIZ

Solve.

1. $\frac{2}{3}x - \frac{1}{2} = \frac{1}{6}$
   $6\left(\frac{2}{3}\right)x - 6\left(\frac{1}{2}\right) = 6\left(\frac{1}{6}\right)$
   $4x - 3 = 1$
   $4x = 4$
   $x = 1$
2. $3(x - 7) = 3$
   $3x - 21 = 3$
   $3x = 24$
   $x = 8$
3. $(x - 7)(2x - 6) = 0$
   $x - 7 = 0$ or $2x - 6 = 0$
   $x = 7$ or $2x = 6$
   $x = 7$ or $x = 3$

Assignment Guide

Algebra: Day 1: 1 – 12, MR
Day 2: 13 – 28

Alg w/Finite or Trig: 1–40 e/o, 41, MR

Comprehensive: 1–40 m4, 41, 42–45 e/o, MR, assign w. 2-2

EXAMPLE 4 Solve.

$$(x + 4)(x - 2) = 0$$
$$x + 4 = 0 \text{ or } x - 2 = 0 \quad \text{Using the principle of zero products}$$
$$x = -4 \text{ or } x = 2 \quad \text{Solving each equation separately}$$

Check:

$(x + 4)(x - 2)$	$= 0$
$(-4 + 4)(-4 - 2)$	0
$0 \cdot (-6)$	0
0	0 ✓

$(x + 4)(x - 2)$	$= 0$
$(2 + 4)(2 - 2)$	0
$6 \cdot 0$	0
0	0 ✓

There are two solutions, -4 and 2. We can show the solutions as a set by listing them inside braces. The solution set is $\{-4, 2\}$.

EXAMPLE 5 Solve.

$$7x(4x + 2) = 0$$
$$7x = 0 \text{ or } 4x + 2 = 0 \quad \text{Using the principle of zero products}$$
$$x = 0 \text{ or } 4x = -2$$
$$x = 0 \text{ or } x = -\frac{1}{2} \quad \text{Solving each equation separately}$$

The solutions are 0 and $-\frac{1}{2}$. The solution set is $\left\{0, -\frac{1}{2}\right\}$.

EXAMPLE 6 Solve.

$$(-2x + 5)(5x + 1) = 0$$
$$-2x + 5 = 0 \text{ or } 5x + 1 = 0$$
$$-2x = -5 \text{ or } 5x = -1$$
$$x = \frac{5}{2} \text{ or } x = -\frac{1}{5}$$

The solution set is $\left\{\frac{5}{2}, -\frac{1}{5}\right\}$.

Try This Solve.

d. $(x - 19)(x + 5) = 0$ $\{19, -5\}$
e. $x(3x - 17) = 0$ $\left\{0, \frac{17}{3}\right\}$
f. $(9x + 2)(-6x + 3) = 0$ $\left\{-\frac{2}{9}, \frac{1}{2}\right\}$

2-1 EXERCISES

A

Solve.

1. $\frac{1}{4} + \frac{3}{8}y = \frac{3}{4}$ $\frac{4}{3}$
2. $\frac{1}{5} + \frac{3}{10}x = \frac{4}{5}$ 2
3. $-\frac{5}{2}x + \frac{1}{2} = -18$ $\frac{37}{5}$
4. $0.9y - 0.7 = 4.2$ $\frac{49}{9}$
5. $0.8t - 0.3t = 6.5$ 13
6. $1.4x + 5.02 = 0.4x$ $-\frac{502}{100}$
7. $2(x + 6) = 8x$ 2
8. $3(y + 5) = 8y$ 3
9. $80 = 10(3t + 2)$ 2
10. $27 = 9(5y - 2)$ 1
11. $180(n - 2) = 900$ 7
12. $210(x - 3) = 840$ 7

13. $5y - (2y - 10) = 25$ 5

14. $8x - (3x - 5) = 40$ 7

15. $0.7(3x + 6) = 1.1 - (x + 2)$ $-\frac{51}{31}$

16. $0.9(2x + 8) = 20 - (x + 5)$ $\frac{39}{14}$

17. $\frac{1}{8}(16y + 8) - 17 = -\frac{1}{4}(8y - 16)$ 5

18. $\frac{1}{6}(12t + 48) - 20 = -\frac{1}{8}(24t - 144)$ 6

19. $a + (a - 3) = (a + 2) - (a + 1)$ 2

20. $0.8 - 4(b - 1) = 0.2 + 3(4 - b)$ $-\frac{37}{5}$

21. $(x + 2)(x - 5) = 0$ $\{-2, 5\}$

22. $(x + 4)(x - 8) = 0$ $\{-4, 8\}$

23. $(y - 8)(y - 9) = 0$ $\{8, 9\}$

24. $(t - 3)(t - 7) = 0$ $\{3, 7\}$

25. $(2x - 3)(3x - 2) = 0$ $\left\{\frac{3}{2}, \frac{2}{3}\right\}$

26. $(3y - 4)(4y - 1) = 0$ $\left\{\frac{4}{3}, \frac{1}{4}\right\}$

27. $m(m - 8) = 0$ $\{0, 8\}$

28. $p(p - 5) = 0$ $\{0, 5\}$

B

Solve.

29. $x(x - 1)(x + 2) = 0$ $\{0, 1, -2\}$

30. $y(y - 4)(y + 2) = 0$ $\{0, 4, -2\}$

31. $\frac{1}{7}(a - 3)(7a + 4) = 0$

32. $24\left(\frac{x}{6} - \frac{1}{3}\right) = x - 24$

33. $0.5(x - 2) - 2(x - 5) = 0.4(x - 5) - 5(x - 2)$

Solve for x.

34. $8x + 3 = c$

35. $16x - 4 = f$

36. $cx + 3h = 5a$

37. $7x - 3 = ax + 5b$

38. $ax - bx = 12$

39. $5x + ax = 19$

40. Contrast solving $0.8y - 1.2 = -1.6y$ by first clearing decimals with solving without first clearing decimals. Which would you do using a calculator? Why?

41. ***Critical Thinking*** Write an equation that has both 7 and -8 as solutions.

Challenge

Solve.

42. $x \cdot x = 1$ $\{1, -1\}$

43. $x \cdot x = x$ $\{1, 0\}$

44. $x(x - 1) = x$ $\{0, 2\}$

45. $x(x - 1) = x(x + 1)$ $\{0\}$

46. What is the solution set for each equation?

   a. $x(x - 1)(x - 2)(x - 3) \cdots = 0$
   b. $(x - 1)(x - 2)(x - 3) \cdots = 0$
   c. $(x + 1)(x + 2)(x + 3) \cdots = 0$
   d. $x(x - 2)(x - 4)(x - 6) \cdots = 0$
   e. $x(x - 10)(x - 20)(x - 30) \cdots = 0$
   f. $\cdots (x + 3)(x + 2)(x + 1)x(x - 1)(x - 2)(x - 3) \cdots = 0$

Mixed Review

Simplify **47.** $4^2 \cdot 4^3 \cdot x^0$ **48.** $(-y)^3(-y)^2$ **49.** $x^3 \cdot x^{-5}$ **50.** $(3c^2)^3$

Convert to scientific notation. **51.** 390,040 **52.** 0.000421 **53.** 24.072

Convert to standard notation. **54.** 4.03×10^{-6} **55.** -8.22×10^6

ADDITIONAL ANSWERS

Exercises

31. $\left\{3, -\frac{4}{7}\right\}$
32. $-\frac{16}{3}$
33. $-\frac{10}{31}$
34. $\frac{c - 3}{8}$
35. $\frac{f + 4}{16}$
36. $\frac{5a - 3h}{c}$
37. $\frac{3 + 5b}{7 - a}$
38. $\frac{12}{a - b}$
39. $\frac{19}{5 + a}$
40. You should solve the equation without clearing the decimals because the calculator can do computations with decimals easily.
41. Answers may vary: Ex: $x^2 + x - 56 = 0$
46. **a.** {the whole numbers}
   b. {the positive integers}
   c. {the negative integers}
   d. {the even whole numbers}
   e. {the whole number multiples of 10}
   f. {the integers}

Mixed Review

47. 4^5
48. $(-y)^5$
49. x^{-2}
50. $27c^6$
51. 3.9004×10^5
52. 4.21×10^{-4}
53. 2.4072×10^1
54. 0.00000403
55. $-8,220,000$

2-2

FIRST FIVE MINUTES

Write an algebraic expression for each of the following phrases.

1. twice the number x
   $2x$
2. 5 more than n
   $n + 5$
3. 7 fewer than w
   $w - 7$
4. The total of x and y
   $x + y$
5. 8 less than y
   $y - 8$
6. 40 percent of b
   $0.40 \cdot b$
7. the average of x and y
   $\frac{(x + y)}{2}$
8. one third of z
   $\frac{1}{3} \cdot z$

Problem Solving: Using Equations

Many of the problem-solving strategies, such as *draw a diagram,* are useful in solving problems. Encourage students to find many ways to set up and solve a problem.

In Try This e., "return" refers to the total amount, principal and interest, after the investment.

Avoiding Common Errors

Students often assign unknowns without specifying the units. This is a common source of confusion. For example, in Chalkboard Example 1, a student might write, "Let x be before lunch." Require a specific unit of measure, like "Let x be the time, in hours."

2-2 Problem Solving: Using Equations

Objective: Solve problems by translating to equations.

PROBLEM-SOLVING GUIDELINES
■ UNDERSTAND the problem
■ Develop and carry out a PLAN
■ Find the ANSWER and CHECK

Many problems can be solved by translating them into mathematical language. Often this means translating a problem into an equation. When appropriate, *drawing a diagram* usually helps us to understand the problem.

EXAMPLE 1

A 28-ft rope is cut into two pieces. One piece is 3 ft longer than the other. How long are the pieces?

■ **UNDERSTAND the problem**

Question: What are the lengths of the two pieces of rope? — *Clarifying the question*

Data: The total length of the rope is 28 ft. One piece of rope is 3 ft longer than the other piece. — *Identifying the data*

A diagram can help translate the problem to an equation.

28 ft

One piece | 3 ft longer piece — *Drawing a diagram*

■ **Develop and carry out a PLAN**

Here is one way to translate.

Length of one piece plus length of other is 28. — *Translating to an equation*

$$x + (x + 3) = 28$$

Using x for the length of one piece and $x + 3$ for the other

$$2x + 3 = 28$$
$$2x = 25$$
$$x = \frac{25}{2}, \text{ or } 12\frac{1}{2}$$

Solving the equation

■ **Find the ANSWER and CHECK**

One piece is $12\frac{1}{2}$ ft long, and the other piece is 3 ft longer, or $15\frac{1}{2}$ ft long. — *The answer checks in the problem.*

The sum of the lengths is 28 ft.

Try This

a. A 23-ft cable is cut into two pieces, one three times as long as the other. How long are the pieces? $5\frac{3}{4}$ ft; $17\frac{1}{4}$ ft

EXAMPLE 2

Five plus twice a number is seven times the number. What is the number?

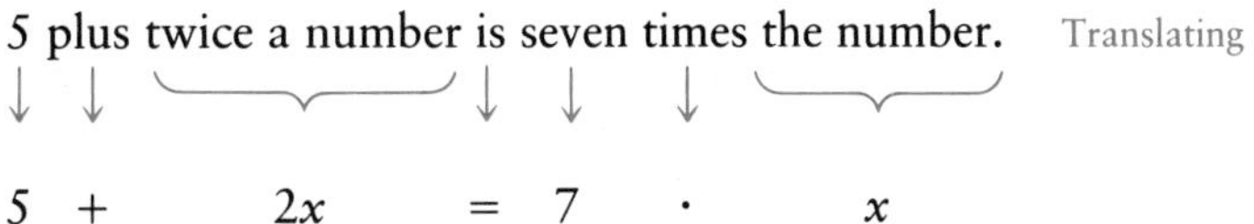

5 plus twice a number is seven times the number.

Translating

$$5 + 2x = 7 \cdot x$$

We have used x to represent the unknown number.

$$\begin{aligned} 5 + 2x &= 7x \\ 5 &= 7x - 2x \\ 5 &= 5x \\ x &= 1 \end{aligned}$$

Twice 1 is 2. If we add 5, we get 7. Seven times 1 is also 7. Checking
This checks, so the answer to the problem is 1.

Try This

b. If seven times a certain number is subtracted from 6, the result is five times the number. What is the number? $\frac{1}{2}$

c. Chris bought a baseball card in 1975. By 1985, the value of the card had tripled. Since 1985, the value has increased by another $30. The card is now worth 5 times its original value. How much was the card worth when Chris bought it? $3x + 30 = 5x$; $15

EXAMPLE 3

The price of a mobile home was cut 11% to a new price of $48,950. What was the original price?

Original price minus 11% of original price is new price.

$$x - 11\% \cdot x = 48{,}950$$ Translating

We have used x to represent the original price.

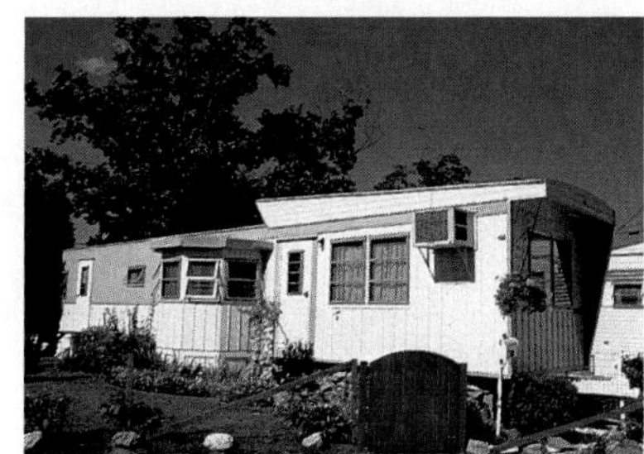

$$\begin{aligned} x - 0.11 \cdot x &= 48{,}950 && \text{Replacing 11\% by 0.11} \\ 1x - 0.11x &= 48{,}950 \\ (1 - 0.11)x &= 48{,}950 && \text{Factoring} \\ 0.89x &= 48{,}950 \\ x &= 55{,}000 \end{aligned}$$

The solution of the equation is 55,000.
Check: 11% of 55,000 is 6050. Subtracting from 55,000 we get 48,950. The number checks, so the original price was $55,000.

Chalkboard Examples

1. A carpenter works one third as long after lunch as she worked before lunch. If she works a total of 8 hours, how long did she work before lunch?

   Draw a picture:

   x | $\frac{1}{3}x$

   Let x = time (hrs) worked before lunch.
   $\frac{1}{3}x$ = time (hrs) worked after lunch

   $x + \frac{1}{3}x = 8$

   $\frac{4}{3}x = 8$

   $x = 6$

   She worked 6 hours before lunch.

2. The giant economy size of Wheat Wiffles is 25% larger than the regular size. The giant economy size is 500 grams. How large is the regular size?
   Let x = grams in regular size.
   $x + 0.25x$ = grams in giant size
   $x + 0.25x = 500$
   $1.25x = 500$
   $x = 400$
   The regular size is 400 grams.

3. The sum of two consecutive even integers is 50. What are the integers?
   Let e = the first even integer.
   $e + 2$ = the second even integer
   $e + (e + 2) = 50$
   $2e + 2 = 50$
   $2e = 48$
   $e = 24$
   The first even integer is 24.
   $e + 2 = 26$
   The second even integer is 26.
   The total is 50. The answers check.

LESSON ENRICHMENT

Change the problem in Example 2. See how quickly students can see the pattern.

Five plus twice a number is

six times the number. $x = \frac{5}{4}$

five times the number. $x = \frac{5}{3}$

four times the number. $x = \frac{5}{2}$

three times the number. $x = \frac{5}{1} = 5$

two times the number. $x = \frac{5}{0}$, no solution

LESSON QUIZ

1. A straight racetrack is 100 meters long. A white line has been drawn across the track, dividing it into two sections. The first section is 15 meters longer than the second section. How long are the sections? The sections are 42.5 m and 57.5 m.
2. A certain amount of money was deposited in a bank. The value of the money increased by 25% to a final value of \$100. How much was originally invested? \$80 was originally invested.

Try This

d. A clothing store drops the price of a suit 25% to a sale price of \$93. What was the original price of the suit? \$124

e. An investment is made at 12% simple interest. It grows to \$812 at the end of 1 year. How much was invested originally? (Hint: Recall the expression $P + Prt$ regarding the return on a principal of P dollars.) \$725

EXAMPLE 4

The sum of two consecutive integers is 35. What are the integers?

$$\underbrace{\text{First integer}} + \underbrace{\text{second integer}} = 35$$

$$x \quad + \quad (x+1) \quad = 35 \qquad \text{Translating}$$

Since the integers are consecutive, we know that one of them is 1 greater than the other. We call one of them x and the other $x + 1$.

$$\begin{aligned} x + (x + 1) &= 35 \qquad \text{Solving the equation} \\ 2x + 1 &= 35 \\ 2x &= 34 \\ x &= 17 \end{aligned}$$

Since x is 17, then $x + 1$, the second integer, is 18. The answers are 17 and 18. These are both integers and consecutive. Their sum is 35, so the answers check in the problem.

Guidelines for Solving Problems Using Equations.

1. If two numbers are consecutive, call one x and the other $x + 1$.
2. If two numbers are consecutive odd or consecutive even numbers, call one x and the other $x + 2$.
3. If a number x is increased by $n\%$, the new number is $x + \frac{1}{100} n \cdot x$.

Try This

f. The sum of two consecutive odd integers is 36. What are the integers? 17, 19

g. Field goals in basketball count two points each. In one game, Harold had one less field goal than Gunther. Together they scored 46 points on field goals.
(1) How many points did each player score on field goals? Harold 22, Gunther 24
(2) How many field goals did each player make? Harold 11, Gunther 12

2-2 EXERCISES

Assignment Guide
Algebra: Day 1: 1 – 10 MR
Day 2: 11 – 20

Alg w/Finite or Trig: 1–27 e/o, 28, MR

Comprehensive: 1–27 m4, 28, 29, MR, assign w. 2-1

A

Solve.

1. A 12-cm piece of tubing is cut into two pieces. One piece is 4 cm longer than the other. How long are the pieces? 8 cm; 4 cm
2. A 10-m piece of wire is cut into two pieces. One piece is 2 m longer than the other. How long are the pieces? 6 m; 4 m
3. A piece of wire 4-m long is cut into two pieces so that one piece is two thirds as long as the other. Find the length of each piece. $1\frac{3}{5}$ m; $2\frac{2}{5}$ m
4. A piece of rope 5-m long is cut into two pieces so that one piece is three fifths as long as the other. Find the length of each piece. $1\frac{7}{8}$ m; $3\frac{1}{8}$ m
5. Five more than three times a number is the same as ten less than six times the number. What is the number? 5
6. Six more than nine times a number is the same as two less than ten times the number. What is the number? 8
7. A pro shop in a bowling alley drops the price of bowling balls 24% to a sale price of \$34.20. What was the original price? \$45
8. An appliance store drops the price of a certain type of TV 18% to a sale price of \$410. What was the original price? \$500
9. Money is borrowed at 11% simple interest. After 1 year \$721.50 pays off the loan. How much was borrowed originally? \$650
10. Money is borrowed at 12% simple interest. After 1 year \$896 pays off the loan. How much was borrowed originally? \$800

For Exercises 11 and 12, the measures of the angles of a triangle add up to 180°. 

Symbolizes connections to other math disciplines, such as geometry.

11. The second angle of a triangle is three times the first and the third is 12° less than twice the first. Find the measures of the angles. 32°, 96°, 52°
12. The second angle of a triangle is four times the first and the third is 5° more than twice the first. Find the measures of the angles. 25°, 100°, 55°

For Exercises 13 and 14, the area of a rectangle is $l \times w$, and the perimeter is $2l + 2w$.

13. The perimeter of a college basketball court is 96 m and the length is 14 m more than the width. What are the dimensions? Length is 31 m; width is 17 m
14. The perimeter of a certain soccer field is 310 m. The length is 65 m more than the width. What are the dimensions? Length is 110 m; width is 45 m
15. Find three consecutive odd integers such that the sum of the first, two times the second, and three times the third is 82. 11, 13, 15
16. Find two consecutive even integers such that two times the first plus three times the second is 76. 14, 16
17. After a person gets a 20% raise in salary, the new salary is \$18,000. What was the old salary? \$15,000

ADDITIONAL ANSWERS

28. Answers may vary. Ex: A 36-ft rope is cut into two pieces. One piece is 3 ft longer than the other. How long are the pieces?

Mixed Review

30. $-x^2 + 7$
31. $3x^4 + 3x^2y - xy^2$
32. $-2a^3b + a^2b - 4ab^2$
33. $2a^2 + 2b^2 + 2c^2$
34. $2x(x + 1)$
35. $3ab^2(a - 3)$
36. $4a^2(3 - a)$
37. $6xy(5x + y - 2x^2)$
38. -1
39. $1.64 \cdot 10^3$

18. A person gets a 7.5% raise, bringing the salary to \$46,225. What was the salary before the raise? \$43,000

19. The total cost for tuition plus room and board at Southern State University is \$6584. Tuition costs \$704 more than room and board. What is the tuition fee? \$3644

20. The cost of a private pilot course is \$2250. The flight portion costs \$1500 more than the ground school portion. What is the cost of each? Ground school portion costs \$375; flight portion costs \$1875

B

21. A student's scores on five tests are 93%, 89%, 72%, 80%, and 96%. What must the student score on the sixth test so that the average will be 88%? 98%

22. The yearly changes in the population of a city for three consecutive years are, respectively, 20% increase, 30% increase, and 20% decrease. What is the total percent change from the beginning to the end of the third year? 25% increase

23. Three numbers are such that the second is 6 less than three times the first and the third is 2 more than $\frac{2}{3}$ the second. The sum of the three numbers is 172. Find the largest number. 84

24. An appliance store is having a sale on 13 VCR models. They are displayed left to right in order of increasing price. The price of each VCR differs by \$60 from that of each adjacent VCR. For the price of the VCR at the extreme right, a customer can buy both the second and the sixth models. What is the price of the least expensive VCR? \$360

25. A tank at a marine exhibit contains 2000 gallons of sea water. The sea water is 7.5% salt. How many gallons, to the nearest gallon, of fresh water must be added to the tank so that the mixture contains only 7% salt? 143 gallons

26. The sum of two consecutive odd integers is 137. Find the integers. No solution

27. The perimeter of a square is 12 cm greater than that of another square. Its area exceeds the area of the other by 39 cm^2. Find the perimeter of each square. 20 cm, 32 cm

28. ***Critical Thinking*** Rewrite the problem of Example 1 so that in the solution the shorter piece of rope has a length of $16\frac{1}{2}$ feet.

Challenge

29. Diophantus spent one sixth of his life as a child, one twelfth as a young man, and one seventh as a bachelor. Five years after he was married he had a son who died 4 years before his father at half his father's final age. How long did Diophantus live? 84 years

Mixed Review

Collect like terms. **30.** $x^2 + 3 + (-2x^2) + 4$ **31.** $x^4 + x^2y + 2x^4 + 2yx^2 - xy^2$

32. $a^3b + 2a^2b - 6ab^2 - 3a^3b + 2ab^2 - a^2b$ **33.** $a^2 + b^2 + c^2 - (-a^2 - b^2 - c^2)$

Factor. **34.** $2x^2 + 2x$ **35.** $3a^2b^2 - 9ab^2$ **36.** $12a^2 - 4a^3$

37. $30x^2y + 6xy^2 - 12x^3y$ **38.** $3x - [2x - 3 - (-x - 4)]$

Multiply. **39.** $(8.2 \times 10^{-3})(2 \times 10^5)$

2-3 Solving Formulas

Objective: Solve a formula for a specified letter.

A **formula** is a rule for doing a specific calculation. Formulas are often given as equations. A formula for finding wattage is $W = EI$ where E represents voltage and I represents resistance. Suppose we know the wattage and voltage and want to find the resistance. We can solve the formula for a specific variable, following the same steps we use to solve an equation.

EXAMPLE 1 Solve the formula $W = EI$ for I.

$$W = EI \quad \text{We want the letter } I \text{ alone.}$$

$$\frac{1}{E} \cdot W = \frac{1}{E} \cdot EI \quad \text{Multiplying both sides by } \frac{1}{E}$$

$$\frac{W}{E} = I$$

EXAMPLE 2 Solve for b.

$$A = \frac{5}{2}(b - 20)$$

$$\frac{2}{5}A = b - 20 \quad \text{Multiplying both sides by } \frac{2}{5}$$

$$\frac{2}{5}A + 20 = b \quad \text{Adding 20 to both sides}$$

Try This Solve.

a. $A = \frac{1}{2}bh$, for b. $b = \frac{2A}{h}$

b. $P = \frac{3}{5}(c + 10)$, for c $c = \frac{5}{3}P - 10$

c. $H = 2r + 3m$, for m $m = \frac{H - 2r}{3}$

d. $Q = 3r + 5p$, for p $p = \frac{Q - 3r}{5}$

EXAMPLE 3 Solve for P.

$$A = P + Prt \quad \text{An interest formula}$$

$$A = P(1 + rt) \quad \text{Factoring}$$

$$A \cdot \frac{1}{1 + rt} = P(1 + rt) \cdot \frac{1}{1 + rt} \quad \text{Multiplying on both sides by } \frac{1}{1 + rt}$$

$$\frac{A}{1 + rt} = P \quad \text{Simplifying}$$

Try This Solve.

e. $T = Q + Qiy$, for Q $Q = \frac{T}{1 + iy}$

f. $x = G - Gr^2p$, for G $G = \frac{x}{1 - r^2p}$

2-3

FIRST FIVE MINUTES

Write each of the following statements as an equation.

1. The circumference c of a circle with radius r is two times π times r.
   $c = 2\pi r$
2. The area A of a rectangle with width w and length l is the product of w and l.
   $A = wl$
3. The area A of a triangle with base b and height h is one half the product of b and h.
   $A = \frac{1}{2}bh$

You may want to review some common formulas with students before beginning this section.

Key Question

- To solve $C = 2\pi(r - 2)$ for r, what would you do first? **Multiply both sides by $\frac{1}{2\pi}$, or distribute the 2π over $r - 2$.**

Chalkboard Examples

1. Solve the formula $A = wl$ for w.
   Multiply both sides by $\frac{1}{l}$.
   $\frac{A}{l} = w$
2. Solve $w = 3(x - 2)$ for x.
   $\left(\frac{1}{3}\right)w = x - 2$
   $\left(\frac{1}{3}\right)w + 2 = x$
3. Solve the formula $A = P + Prt$ for r.
   $A - P = Prt$
   $\frac{A - P}{Pt} = r$

LESSON QUIZ

Solve.

1. $m = 2(n - 3)$, for n

   $\frac{m+6}{2} = n$

2. $V = \frac{T}{P}$, for T

   $VP = T$

3. $I = \frac{E}{R}$, for R

   $R = \frac{E}{I}$

> ***Assignment Guide***
> Algebra: 1 – 24 e/o, MR
>
> Alg w/Finite or Trig: 1–28 e/o, 29, MR
>
> Comprehensive: 1–28 m4, 29–31, MR, assign w. 2-4

ADDITIONAL ANSWERS

Exercises

11. $l = \frac{P - 2w}{2}$ 12. $w = \frac{P - 2l}{2}$
13. $a^2 = c^2 - b^2$
14. $b^2 = c^2 - a^2$
15. $r^2 = \frac{A}{\pi}$ 16. $\pi = \frac{A}{r^2}$
17. $F = \frac{9}{5}C + 32$
18. $h = \frac{2}{11}W + 40$
19. $r^3 = \frac{3V}{4\pi}$ 20. $\pi = \frac{3V}{4r^3}$
21. $h = \frac{2A}{(a + b)}$ 22. $b = \frac{2A - ha}{h}$
23. $m = \frac{rF}{v^2}$ 24. $v^2 = \frac{rF}{m}$
29. Answers may vary. Enter the numerical value of a^2, then press the square root function key. The value of r^3 can be found in a similar way.

Mixed Review

32. x^4 33. 6^{-6}
34. $4m^4n^2$ 35. 8^6
36. $\frac{13}{10}$ 37. $\frac{19}{11}$
38. 2 39. 5
40. 6 41. 4 or −5

2-3 EXERCISES

A

Solve.

1. $A = lw$, for l (an area formula) $l = \frac{A}{w}$
2. $A = lw$, for w $w = \frac{A}{l}$
3. $W = EI$, for I (an electricity formula) $I = \frac{W}{E}$
4. $W = EI$, for E $E = \frac{W}{I}$
5. $F = ma$, for m (a physics formula) $m = \frac{F}{a}$
6. $F = ma$, for a $a = \frac{F}{m}$
7. $I = Prt$, for t (an interest formula) $t = \frac{I}{Pr}$
8. $I = Prt$, for P $P = \frac{I}{rt}$
9. $E = mc^2$, for m (a relativity formula) $m = \frac{E}{c^2}$
10. $E = mc^2$, for c^2 $c^2 = \frac{E}{m}$
11. $P = 2l + 2w$, for l (a perimeter formula)
12. $P = 2l + 2w$, for w
13. $c^2 = a^2 + b^2$, for a^2 (a geometry formula)
14. $c^2 = a^2 + b^2$, for b^2
15. $A = \pi r^2$, for r^2 (an area formula)
16. $A = \pi r^2$, for π
17. $C = \frac{5}{9}(F - 32)$, for F (a temperature formula)
18. $W = \frac{11}{2}(h - 40)$, for h
19. $V = \frac{4}{3}\pi r^3$, for r^3 (a volume formula)
20. $V = \frac{4}{3}\pi r^3$, for π
21. $A = \frac{1}{2}ha + \frac{1}{2}hb$, for h (an area formula)
22. $A = \frac{1}{2}ha + \frac{1}{2}hb$, for b
23. $F = \frac{mv^2}{r}$, for m (a physics formula)
24. $F = \frac{mv^2}{r}$, for v^2

B

Solve.

25. $s = v_i t + \frac{1}{2}at^2$, for a $a = \frac{2s - 2v_i t}{t^2}$
26. $A = \pi rs + r^2$, for s $s = \frac{A - r^2}{\pi r}$
27. In Exercise 7, you solved the formula $I = Prt$ for t. Use it to find how long it will take a deposit of \$75 to earn \$3 interest when invested at 10% simple interest. 0.4 yr
28. In Exercise 8, you solved the formula $I = Prt$ for P. Use it to find how much principal would be needed to earn \$6 in two thirds of a year at 12% simple interest. \$75
29. ***Critical Thinking*** In Exercises 13 and 19 you solved for a^2 and r^3, respectively. Tell how you could use a calculator to find a and r.

Challenge

30. A gas formula from physics is $\frac{P_1V_1}{T_1} = \frac{P_2V_2}{T_2}$. Solve it for V_1. $V_1 = \frac{T_1P_2V_2}{P_1T_2}$
31. Solve the gas formula of Exercise 30 for T_2. $T_2 = \frac{P_2V_2T_1}{P_1V_1}$

Mixed Review

Simplify. **32.** $(x^2)^2$ **33.** $(6^3)^{-2}$ **34.** $(2m^2n)^2$ **35.** $(8^{-2})^{-3}$

36. $\frac{3}{5} + \frac{t}{2} = \frac{5}{4}$ **37.** $\left(\frac{11}{2}\right)m - 3 = \frac{13}{2}$ **38.** $\left(-\frac{1}{8}\right)t + \frac{1}{6} = -\frac{1}{12}$

39. $4n - (3n + 6) = -1$ **40.** $0.4n + 2.7 = 5.1$ **41.** $(x - 4)(x + 5) = 0$

2-4 Solving Inequalities

Solutions and Graphs

Objective: Determine if a number is a solution of an inequality and graph the solution set.

The order of the real numbers is often pictured on a number line.

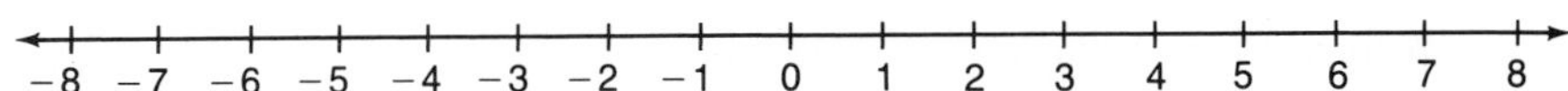

If a number occurs to the left of another on the number line, the first number **is less than** the second, and the second **is greater than** the first. We use the symbol $<$ to mean "is less than" and $>$ to mean "is greater than."

The symbol $\leq$ means "is less than or equal to," and the symbol $\geq$ means "is greater than or equal to."

Mathematical sentences containing $<$, $>$, $\leq$, or $\geq$ are called **inequalities**. A solution of an inequality is any number that makes it true. The set of all solutions is called the **solution set**. When we have found all solutions of an inequality, we say we have **solved** the inequality.

EXAMPLES Determine whether the given number is a solution of the inequality.

1. $x + 3 < 6; 5$

We substitute and get $5 + 3 < 6$, or $8 < 6$, a false sentence. Thus, 5 is not a solution.

2. $2x - 3 > -3; 1$

We substitute and get $2(1) - 3 > -3$, or $-1 > -3$, a true sentence. Thus, 1 is a solution.

3. $4x - 1 \leq 3x + 2; 3$

We substitute and get $4(3) - 1 \leq 3(3) + 2$, or $11 \leq 11$, a true sentence. Thus, 3 is a solution.

Try This Determine whether the given number is a solution of the inequality.

a. $3 - x < 2; 4$ Solution

b. $3y + 2 > -1; -2$ Not a solution

c. $3x + 2 \leq 4x - 3; 5$ Solution

A graph of an inequality is a drawing that shows all of its solutions on a number line. The graph is a picture of the solution set.

2-4

FIRST FIVE MINUTES

Solve.

1. $3x - 5 = 2$
   $3x = 7$
   $x = \frac{7}{3}$
2. $2x - 3 + 4x = 7$
   $6x = 10$
   $x = \frac{5}{3}$
3. $3(2x - 4) = 6$
   $6x - 12 = 6$
   $6x = 18$
   $x = 3$
4. $-2(3x - 5) = -2$
   $-6x + 10 = -2$
   $-6x = -12$
   $x = 2$

Solutions and Graphs

Since inequalities have infinitely many solutions, it is impossible to check all of them. However, it is possible to check the boundary point to see whether the mathematics was done correctly, and to check one other point to see whether the inequality symbol is correct.

In Example 6, we would let $x = 3$ in the equation $x + 4 = 7$. Since $3 + 4 = 7$, 3 is the boundary point. Then we choose a number that is greater than 3, say 4. Since $4 + 4 > 7$, the inequality symbol is correct.

Key Questions

- If $a \leq -2$ and $b > -2$, can $a = b$? No
- If $a \geq -1$ and $b < 1$, can $a = b$? Yes

Chalkboard Examples

Determine whether the given number is a solution of the inequality.

1. $x + 7 < 9$; 1
   Yes
   $1 + 7 < 9$
   This is a true statement. 1 is a solution.
2. $4x - 2 > 7$; 2
   $4(2) - 2 > 7$
   $6 > 7$
   This is a false statement. 2 is not a solution.
3. $6x + 4 \geq 2x + 8$; 0
   $6(0) + 4 \geq 2(0) + 8$
   $4 \geq 8$
   This is a false statement. 0 is not a solution.
4. Graph $x > -1$ on the number line.

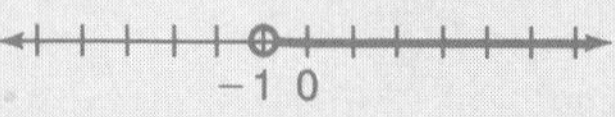

5. Graph $x \geq 0$ on the number line.

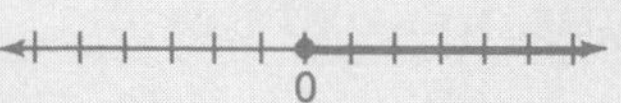

The Addition Property

Chalkboard Examples

1. Solve $x - 7 < -5$. Graph the solution set.
   $x - 7 + 7 < -5 + 7$
   $x < 2$

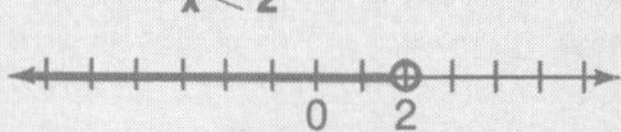

EXAMPLE 4 Graph $x < 2$ on a number line.

The solutions consist of all numbers less than 2, so we shade all numbers less than 2. Note that 2 is not a solution. We indicate this by using an open circle at 2.

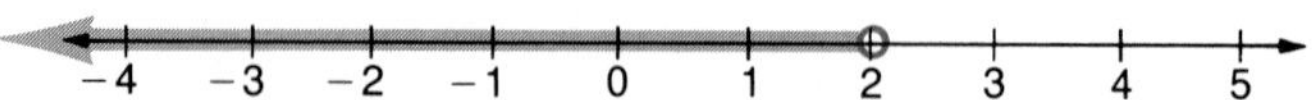

The solution set graphed in Example 4 can be written $\{x \mid x < 2\}$. This is called **set-builder notation.** The notation is read "the set of all x such that x is less than 2." Set notation of this type is written using braces. The symbol | is read "such that."

EXAMPLE 5 Graph $x \geq -3$ on a number line.

We draw a picture of the solutions $\{x \mid x \geq -3\}$.

This time the solution set consists of all the numbers greater than -3, including -3. We shade all numbers greater than -3 and use a solid circle at -3 to indicate that it is also a solution.

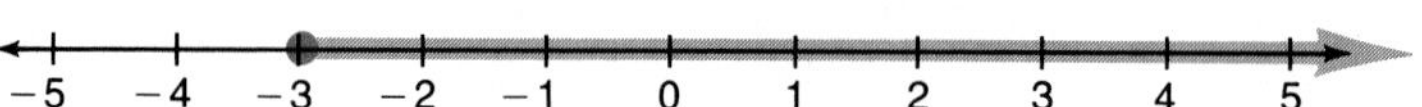

Try This Graph on a number line. See Additional Answers.

d. $x < -2$ **e.** $x \geq 1$ **f.** $x \leq 5$

The Addition Property

Objective: Solve and graph inequalities using the addition property.

There is an addition property for inequality similar to the one for equality.

Theorem 2-2

The Addition Property of Inequality

If $a < b$ is true, then $a + c < b + c$ is true for any real number c.

Similar statements hold for $>$, $\leq$, and $\geq$.

If any number is added to both sides of a true inequality, another true inequality is obtained.

To solve an inequality using the addition property, we transform the inequality into a simpler one by adding the same number to both sides, as we do in solving equations.

EXAMPLE 6 Solve. Then graph.

$$x + 4 > 7$$

$$x + 4 + (-4) > 7 + (-4) \quad \text{Using the addition property, adding } -4$$

$$x > 3$$

The solution set is $\{x \mid x > 3\}$.
The graph is as follows.

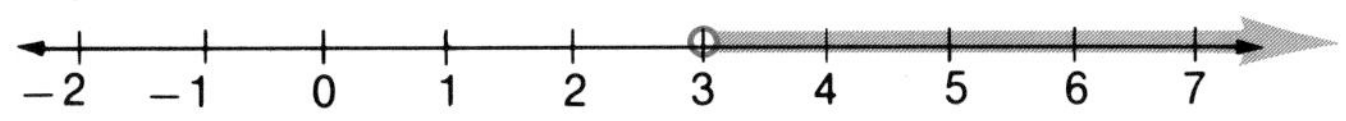

In Example 6, every number greater than 3 was a solution. Because there are many solutions to an inequality, we cannot check all the solutions by substituting into the original inequality as we do for equations. We can check our calculations by substituting a few values for the variable into the original inequality.

Try This Solve. Then graph. See Additional Answers.

g. $x + 6 > 9$ $x > 3$ **h.** $10 \geq x + 7$ $3 \geq x$ **i.** $3x - 1 \leq 2x - 3$ $x \leq -2$

The Multiplication Property

Objective: Solve inequalities using the multiplication property.

Consider the true inequality $4 < 9$.

If we multiply both numbers by 2, we get the true inequality $8 < 18$.

If we multiply both numbers by -3, we get the false inequality $-12 < -27$.

If we reverse the inequality symbol, we get the true inequality $-12 > -27$.

If we multiply both sides of a true inequality by a positive number, we get another true inequality. If we multiply by a negative number and reverse the inequality symbol, we get another true inequality.

Theorem 2-3

The Multiplication Property of Inequality

If $a < b$ is true, then
$ac < bc$ is true for any positive real number c, and
$ac > bc$ is true for any negative real number c
Similar statements hold for $>$, $\leq$, and $\geq$.

When we solve an inequality using the multiplication property, we can multiply by any number except zero.

The Multiplication Property

Stress that the inequality symbol changes if the multiplication property is used to multiply by a negative number. Use several examples like the introductory one to illustrate this point.

Avoiding Common Errors

The most common error is the obvious one, forgetting to reverse the inequality. A simple check catches this error. Pick any simple number from the proposed solution set, and check it in the original inequality. Use the number 0 if it is a possible solution.

Chalkboard Examples

1. Solve and graph.
$5x > 12$
$\frac{1}{5}(5x) > \frac{1}{5}(12)$
$x > 2.4$
0 2.4

2. Solve and graph.
$-5x < 15$
$-\frac{1}{5}(-5x) > -\frac{1}{5}(15)$
$x > -3$
−3 0

3. $-3x \leq -6$
$-\frac{1}{3}(-3x) \geq -\frac{1}{3}(-6)$
$x \geq 2$
0 2

Using the Properties Together

Math Point
Here is a proof that if $a < b$, then $-a > -b$.
1. $a < b$, hypothesis
2. $a + (-a) < b + (-a)$, addition property
3. $0 < b + (-a)$, additive inverse
4. $-b + 0 < -b + b + (-a)$, addition property
5. $-b < -a$, identity and inverse properties
6. $-a > -b$, reversing the inequality

Key Questions
- If $-x < 10$, can $x = 20$?
  Yes
- If $-x + 8 \leq 2$, can $x = -6$?
  No
- If $a < b$, is $10a < 10b$?
  Yes
- If $a < b$, is $-10a < -10b$?
  No

Chalkboard Example
1. Solve and graph.
   $3 - 5x < 3x + 7$
   $-8x < 4$
   $x > -\frac{1}{2}$

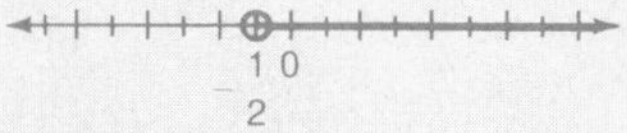

LESSON QUIZ
1. Determine whether the given number is a solution of the inequality.

$3(2) - 3 < 5$
$3 < 5$
This is a true statement. 2 is a **solution.**

Solve.
2. $x - 4 > 0$
   $x > 4$
3. $7x < 28$
   $x < 4$
4. $5x + 7 \leq 12$
   $5x \leq 5$
   $x \leq 1$
5. $-6x \geq 18$
   $x \leq -3$
6. $3 - 4x < 8 + 6x$
   $-10x < 5$
   $x > -\frac{1}{2}$

EXAMPLES Solve.

7.
$$3y < \frac{3}{4}$$
$$\frac{1}{3} \cdot 3y < \frac{1}{3} \cdot \frac{3}{4} \quad \text{Multiplying by } \tfrac{1}{3}$$
$$y < \frac{1}{4}$$

Any number less than $\frac{1}{4}$ is a solution. The solution set is $\left\{y \mid y < \frac{1}{4}\right\}$.

8.
$$-4x < \frac{4}{5}$$
$$-\frac{1}{4} \cdot (-4x) > -\frac{1}{4} \cdot \frac{4}{5} \quad \text{Multiplying by } -\tfrac{1}{4} \text{ and reversing the inequality symbol}$$
$$x > -\frac{1}{5}$$

Any number greater than $-\frac{1}{5}$ is a solution. The solution set is $\left\{x \mid x > -\frac{1}{5}\right\}$.

Try This Solve.

j. $5y \leq \frac{3}{2}$ $y \leq \frac{3}{10}$ **k.** $-2y > \frac{5}{6}$ $y < -\frac{5}{12}$ **l.** $-\frac{1}{3}x \leq -4$ $x \geq 12$

Using the Properties Together

Objective: Solve inequalities using both the addition and multiplication properties.

We use the addition and multiplication properties together in solving inequalities in much the same way as for equations.

EXAMPLE 9 Solve.

$$16 - 7y \geq 10y - 4$$
$$-16 + 16 - 7y \geq -16 + 10y - 4 \quad \text{Adding } -16$$
$$-7y \geq 10y - 20$$
$$-10y - 7y \geq -10y + 10y - 20 \quad \text{Adding } -10y$$
$$-17y \geq -20$$
$$-\frac{1}{17} \cdot (-17y) \leq -\frac{1}{17} \cdot (-20) \quad \text{Multiplying by } -\tfrac{1}{17} \text{ and reversing the inequality sign}$$
$$y \leq \frac{20}{17} \quad \text{The solution set is } \left\{y \mid y \leq \tfrac{20}{17}\right\}.$$

Try This Solve.

m. $6 - 5y \geq 7$ $y \leq -\frac{1}{5}$ **n.** $3x + 5x < 4$ $x < \frac{1}{2}$ **o.** $17 - 5y \leq 8y - 5$ $y \geq \frac{22}{13}$

2-4 EXERCISES

A

Determine whether the specified number is a solution of the inequality.

1. $2y - 5 > -10; 3$ Yes **2.** $5y - 2 > 3y + 8; 8$ Yes **3.** $6 - y < 9; -3$ No

You may wish to have students write answers in set notation. For example, the answer to Exercise 8 would be $\{x \mid x > -5\}$.

Graph.

4. $x \le 4$ **5.** $y < -1$ **6.** $x > 5$ **7.** $x \ge 3$

Solve.

8. $x + 8 > 3$ $x > -5$ **9.** $x + 5 > 2$ $x > -3$ **10.** $y + 3 < 9$ $y < 6$

11. $y + 4 < 10$ $y < 6$ **12.** $a + 9 \le -12$ $a \le -21$ **13.** $a + 7 \le -13$ $a \le -20$

14. $t + 14 \ge 9$ $t \ge -5$ **15.** $x - 9 \le 10$ $x \le 19$ **16.** $y - 8 > -14$ $y > -6$

17. $y - 9 > -18$ $y > -9$ **18.** $x - 11 \le -2$ $x \le 9$ **19.** $y - 18 \le -4$ $y \le 14$

20. $8x \ge 24$ **21.** $9t < -81$ **22.** $0.3x < -18$ **23.** $0.5x < 25$

24. $-9x \ge -8.1$ **25.** $-8y \le 3.2$ **26.** $-\frac{3}{4}x \ge -\frac{5}{8}$

27. $-\frac{5}{6}y \le -\frac{3}{4}$ **28.** $2x + 7 < 19$ **29.** $5y + 13 > 28$

30. $5y + 2y \le -21$ **31.** $-9x + 3x \ge -24$ **32.** $2y - 7 < 5y - 9$

33. $8x - 9 < 3x - 11$ **34.** $0.4x + 5 \le 1.2x - 4$ **35.** $0.2y + 1 > 2.4y - 10$

B

Solve.

36. $3x - \frac{1}{8} \le -\frac{3}{8} + 3x$ No solution **37.** $2x - 3 < \frac{13}{4}x + 10 - 1.25x$ Real Numbers

38. $4(3y - 2) \ge 9(2y + 5)$ $y \le -\frac{53}{6}$ **39.** $4m + 5 \ge 14(m - 2)$ $m \le \frac{33}{10}$

40. ***Critical Thinking*** Find two different inequalities whose solution set contains all real numbers less than -5.

Challenge

Solve.

41. $(y + 3)(y - 3) < 0$ **42.** $y(y + 5) > 0$ **43.** $\frac{x + 3}{x - 3} > 0$ **44.** $\frac{x - 2}{x + 1} < 0$

45. Determine whether the statement is true. If false, give a counterexample.
a. For any real numbers, a, b, c, and d, if $a < b$ and $c < d$, then $a - c < b - d$.
b. For any real numbers x and y, if $x < y$ then $x^2 < y^2$.

Mixed Review

Simplify. **46.** $a^5 \cdot a^{-3} \cdot a^2$ **47.** $(6x^3y^5)^2$ **48.** $(2m^5)^2$ **49.** $\frac{20n^{3t}}{5n^t}$ **50.** $\left(\frac{x^2}{y^2}\right)^3$

51. The sum of three consecutive integers is 65 more than twice the first integer. Find the three integers.

Assignment Guide
Algebra: Day 1: 1 – 17, MR
Day 2: 18 – 35

Alg w/Finite or Trig: 1–39 e/o, 40, MR

Comprehensive: 1–39 m4, 40, 41–45 e/o, MR, assign w. 2-3

ADDITIONAL ANSWERS

Try This

d. 

e. 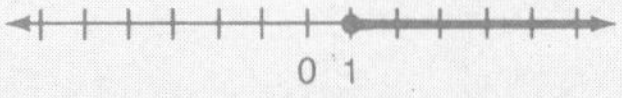

f. 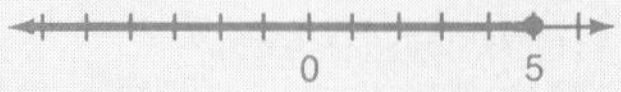

g. 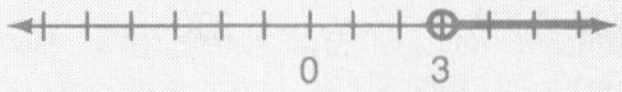

h. 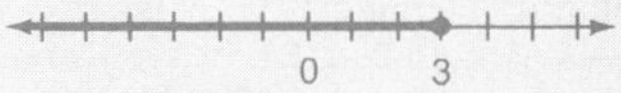

i. 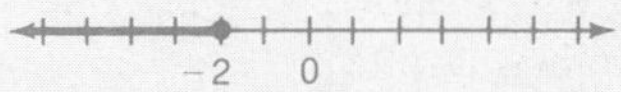

Exercises

For Exercises 4–7, see Teacher's Answer Section.

20. $x \ge 3$ **21.** $t < -9$
22. $x < -60$ **23.** $x < 50$
24. $x \le 0.9$ **25.** $y \ge -0.4$
26. $x \le \frac{5}{6}$ **27.** $y \ge \frac{9}{10}$
28. $x < 6$ **29.** $y > 3$
30. $y \le -3$ **31.** $x \le 4$
32. $y > \frac{2}{3}$ **33.** $x < -\frac{2}{5}$
34. $x \ge 11.25$ **35.** $y < 5$
40. Answers may vary. Ex: $x < -5$, $3x + 2 < -13$
41. $-3 < y < 3$
42. $y > 0$ or $y < -5$
43. $x < -3$ or $x > 3$
44. $-1 < x < 2$
45. a. False, because $a = 4$, $b = 5$, $c = 1$, $d = 4$.
b. False, because $-3 < -2$, but $9 > 4$.

Mixed Review

46. a^4 **47.** $36x^6y^{10}$
48. $4m^{10}$ **49.** $4n^{2t}$
50. $\frac{x^6}{y^6}$ **51.** 62, 63, 64

2-5

FIRST FIVE MINUTES

Write an equation for each of the following. Do not solve.

1. A number n plus 5 equals 7.
   $n + 5 = 7$
2. Twice the number x, plus 2, equals three times x.
   $2x + 2 = 3x$
3. Twenty percent of b, plus one, equals b.
   $0.20b + 1 = b$
4. 5 more than m equals one half m.
   $m + 5 = \left(\frac{1}{2}\right)m$
5. Twice c is 5 less than c.
   $2c = c - 5$

Problem Solving: Using Inequalities

This section is similar to problem solving with equations. You may want to point out that if a quantity is "at least 3," it can be 3 or more than 3 (not less), and thus $\geq$ is the correct inequality sign to use.

Key Questions

- If x is not more than 10,
  can $x = 10$? Yes
  can $x < 10$? Yes
  can $x > 10$? No
  What is the correct inequality sign to use? $\leq$
- If y is at least 15,
  can $y = 15$? Yes
  can $y < 15$? No
  can $y > 15$? Yes
  What is the correct inequality sign to use? $\geq$

2-5 Problem Solving: Using Inequalities

Objective: Solve problems by translating to inequalities.

The Problem-Solving Guidelines can help when solving problems that translate to inequalities rather than to equations.

PROBLEM-SOLVING GUIDELINES

■ **Phase 1: UNDERSTAND the problem**

What am I trying to find?
What data might I need?
Have I ever solved a similar problem?

■ **Phase 2: Develop and carry out a PLAN**

What strategies might I use to solve the problem?
How can I correctly carry out the strategies I selected?

■ **Phase 3: Find the ANSWER and CHECK**

Does the proposed solution check?
What is the answer to the problem?
Does the answer seem reasonable?
Have I stated the answer clearly?

EXAMPLE 1

In a history course there will be three tests. You must get a total score of 270 for an A. You get 91 and 86 on the first two tests. What score on the last test will give you an A?

■ **UNDERSTAND the problem**

Question: What test score will make the total 270 or more? — Clarifying the question

Data: The first two test scores are 91 and 86. — Identifying the given data

■ **Develop and carry out a PLAN**

Let x be your score on the last test. — Using a variable to represent what you are trying to find

$$\text{Total score} \geq 270 \quad \text{Translating to an inequality}$$
$$91 + 86 + x \geq 270 \quad \text{Solving the inequality}$$
$$177 + x \geq 270$$
$$x \geq 93$$

■ **Find the ANSWER and CHECK**

If the third score is 93, — *Replacing x with 93*

$91 + 86 + 93 = 270$

If the third score is greater than 93, say 95,

$91 + 86 + 95 = 272$

The score on the third test must be at least 93 for you to receive an A. — *The answer makes sense in the problem.*

Try This

a. In a chemistry course, there will be five tests. To get a B, a total of 400 points is needed. You get scores of 91, 86, 73, and 79 on the first four tests. What score on the last test will give you a B? Score ≥ 71

EXAMPLE 2

On your new job you can be paid in one of two ways.

Plan A: A salary of \$600 per month plus a commission of 4% of total sales

Plan B: A salary of \$800 per month plus a commission of 6% of total sales over \$10,000

For what amount of total sales is Plan A better than Plan B, assuming that total sales are always more than \$10,000?

■ **UNDERSTAND the problem**

Question: What total sales will make the pay for Plan A greater than the pay for Plan B? — *Clarifying the question*

Data: Plan A: \$600/month salary plus 4% commission — *Identifying the given data*

Plan B: \$800/month salary plus 6% commission on sales over \$10,000 — *Interpreting the assumption*

■ **Develop and carry out a PLAN**

Use x to represent the sales for the month.

Income from Plan A = $600 + 4\%\ x$ — *Writing an expression for the income from each plan*

Income from Plan B = $800 + (x - 10{,}000)\ 6\%$

Income from Plan A > Income from Plan B — *Translating to an inequality*

$600 + 0.04x > 800 + (x - 10{,}000)0.06$ — *Recalling that % means times 0.01*

$600 + 0.04x > 200 + 0.06x$

$400 > 0.02x$

$20{,}000 > x$

■ **Find the ANSWER and CHECK**

For total sales under \$20,000, Plan A is better than Plan B. — *The answer checks and makes sense in the problem.*

Chalkboard Examples

1. To set the record in the local triathalon, you must have a total time under 10 hours. Your running time was 3.2 hours and your bicycling time was 5.4 hours. What is the needed time for the swimming section?
   Let s be the swimming time in hours.
   $3.2 + 5.4 + s < 10$
   $8.6 + s < 10$
   $s < 1.4$
   Check a number in the solution set, say $s = 1$.
   $3.2 + 5.4 + (1) < 10$
   $9.6 < 10$ True
2. Two medical insurance plans are available. Plan A pays 80% of all medical bills over \$100. Plan B pays 60% of all medical bills over \$10. For what range of bills is the amount paid by plan A less than the amount paid by plan B?
   Let b be the dollar amount of medical bills.
   The amount paid by plan A is $0.80(b - 100)$.
   The amount paid by plan B is $0.60(b - 10)$.
   The solution set satisfies
   $0.80(b - 100) < 0.60(b - 10)$
   $8(b - 100) < 6(b - 10)$
   $8b - 800 < 6b - 60$
   $2b < 740$
   $b < 370$
   Therefore plan A pays less than plan B for bills less than \$370.

LESSON QUIZ

1. Electricity costs \$8 per month, plus \$0.03 per kilowatt hour of electricity used. What amount of electricity will keep the bill below \$20?
   $e < 400$
   Any amount less than 400 kilowatt hours will keep the bill below \$20.
2. A writer can be paid in one of two ways.
   Plan A: \$12,000 plus \$2 for each book sold
   Plan B: \$18,000 plus \$1 for each book sold
   For what number of books does plan A pay less than plan B?
   Plan A pays less than plan B if fewer than 6000 books are sold.

Assignment Guide
Algebra: 1 – 8 e/o, MR

Alg w/Finite or Trig: 1–12 e/o, 13, MR, assign w. Application

Comprehensive: 1–12 m4, 13, 14–17 e/o, MR, assign w. 2-6

Try This

b. A painter can be paid in two ways.
Plan A: \$500 plus \$15 per hour
Plan B: \$20 per hour
Suppose the job takes n hours. For what values of n is Plan A better for the painter?
$n < 100$ hours

2-5 EXERCISES

A

1. A car rents for \$13.95 per day, plus \$0.10 per mile. You are on a daily budget of \$76.00. Within what mileage must you stay to remain within budget?
Less than 620.5 miles
2. You are taking a history course. There will be four tests. You have scores of 89, 92, and 95 on the first three. You must earn a total of 360 points to get an A. What score on the last test will give you an A? 84 or more
3. You are going to invest \$25,000, part at 14% and part at 16%. What is the most that can be invested at 14% to make at least \$3600 interest per year? \$20,000
4. You are going to invest \$20,000, part at 12% and part at 16%. What is the most that can be invested at 12% in order to make at least \$3000 interest per year? \$5000
5. In planning for a school dance, you find that one band will play for \$250, plus 50% of the total ticket sales. Another band will play for a flat fee of \$550. In order for the first band to produce more profit for the school than the other band, what is the highest price you can charge per ticket, assuming 300 people attend? Less than \$2 (\$1.99)
6. On your new job, you can be paid in one of two ways.

   Plan A: A salary of \$500 per month plus a commission of 4% of total sales
   Plan B: A salary of \$750 per month plus a commission of 5% of total sales over \$8000

   For what amount of total sales is Plan B better than Plan A, assuming that total sales are always more than \$8000? More than \$15,000
7. A mason can be paid in two ways.

   Plan A: \$500.00 plus \$9.00 per hour
   Plan B: \$14.00 per hour

   Suppose that the job takes n hours. For what values of n is Plan A better for the mason than Plan B? Less than 100 hours
8. A mason can be paid in two ways.

   Plan A: \$300.00 plus \$11.00 per hour
   Plan B: \$18.50 per hour

   Suppose that the job takes n hours. For what values of n is Plan B better for the mason than plan A? More than 40 hours

B

9. An investment of P dollars made at the simple interest rate (r) for t years will grow to a total $T = P + Prt$. For an investment of \$10,000 to grow to at least \$12,000 in two years, what is the minimum interest rate at which it can be invested? 10%

In a science course, you must average 89 for an A. Your first three tests were 75, 95, and 91.

10. If you have only one test remaining, what score do you need for an A? 95
11. If you have two tests remaining, what do you need to average on the two tests? 92
12. After the first three tests, you find that you must average 90 or better on your remaining tests for an A. How many tests do you have left? 6
13. ***Critical Thinking*** Suppose that a machinist is manufacturing rectangular boxes of various sizes. The length of any box must exceed the width by at least 3 cm, but the perimeter cannot exceed 24 cm. What widths are possible? $w \leq 4.5$ cm and cannot be negative

Challenge

The formula $S = -16t^2 + v_0t + S_0$ tells the height at time t of a projectile fired vertically from height S_0 with initial velocity v_0.

Suppose a projectile is fired vertically from ground level at an initial velocity of 448 ft per second.

14. When will the projectile be higher than 3072 ft?
15. When, if ever, will the projectile's height exceed 10,000 ft?

A carpenter makes either a certain hourly rate of r dollars per hour, or a special rate that is \$5 per hour less if a fee of f dollars is paid first.

16. For what number of hours is the hourly rate cheaper?
17. Next year the fee will be doubled, but the discount will be \$7.50 per hour. For what number of hours will the special rate be cheaper?

Mixed Review

Solve. **18.** $2a + b = c$, for a **19.** $x = \frac{1}{yz}$, for z

20. $ab + cd + ef = g$, for c **21.** $A = 2\pi r + 2\pi rh$, for r

LOOKING FOR ERRORS

A student gave "2, 4, 6" as the answer to the problem
"Find three consecutive even integers such that 10 times the largest value exceeds the product of the other two by more than 40."
Is the student's answer correct? Explain.

ADDITIONAL ANSWERS

Exercises

14. $12 < t < 16$; between 12 and 16 seconds
15. Never; maximum height is 3136 ft
16. Less than $\frac{f}{5}$ hours
17. Greater than $\frac{f}{3.75}$ hours

Mixed Review

18. $a = \frac{c - b}{2}$
19. $z = \frac{1}{xy}$
20. $c = \frac{g - ab - ef}{d}$
21. $r = \frac{A}{2\pi(1 + h)}$

Looking for Errors

Not entirely. There are two additional answers: 4, 6, 8; and 6, 8, 10. Simply checking one answer may miss other solutions.

2-6

FIRST FIVE MINUTES

Graph the following inequalities.

1. $x \le 1$

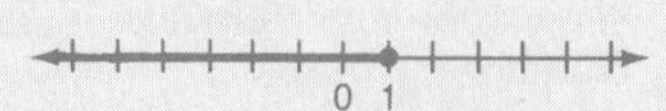

2. $x < 2$

0 2

Solve and graph.

3. $-4x - 3 < -11$
   $-4x < -8$
   $x > 2$

0 2

4. $2(1 - x) \ge 3$
   $2 - 2x \ge 3$
   $-2x \ge 1$
   $x \le -\frac{1}{2}$

$-\frac{1}{2}$ 0

Conjunctions and Intersections

Stress the relationship between "and" and the symbol $\cap$.

You may want to graph one statement above the graph of another statement, and then use vertical lines to illustrate the intersection of the two solution sets, which leads to the solution set of the conjunction.

Key Questions

- Can the following conjunction be true: $x \le 5$ and $x < -3$?
  Yes
- Can the following conjunction be true: $x \ge 3$ and $x \le 1$?
  No
- What is the intersection of the two sets $x < 5$ and $x \ge 3$?
  $3 \le x < 5$

2-6 Compound Inequalities

In mathematics and elsewhere, a compound statement may be composed of several shorter statements, each connected by the word and or the word or. A statement such as *The moon is red and the night is cold* may be true, depending upon whether the individual statements are true. Similarly, the compound inequality $x < 2$ *or* $x > 0$ may be true for a value of x, depending upon the truth of the individual statements.

Conjunctions and Intersections

Objective: Solve and graph conjunctions of inequalities.

When two or more statements are joined by the word and to make a compound statement, the new statement is called a conjunction. Here are some examples.

The moon is red and the night is cold.

$x + y = 5$ and $x - y = 2$

$-2 < x$ and $x < 1$

For a conjunction to be true, all of the individual statements must be true. Let's look at the solution sets of graphs of a conjunction and their individual statements.

$-2 < x$ and $x < 1$

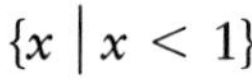

$\{x \mid -2 < x\}$

$\{x \mid x < 1\}$

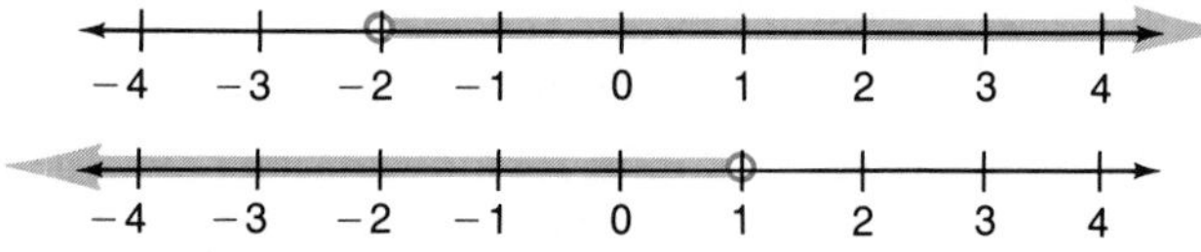

For a number to be a solution of the conjunction, it must be in both solution sets. The solution set of the conjunction contains the elements common to both of the individual solution sets.

$\{x \mid -2 < x \text{ and } x < 1\}$

−4 −3 −2 −1 0 1 2 3 4

The conjunction "$-2 < x$ and $x < 1$" can be abbreviated $-2 < x < 1$.

The elements of two or more sets that are common is called their intersection. For two sets A and B, we can represent the intersection by $A \cap B$. If sets have no common members, the intersection is the empty set, which can be represented by the symbol $\emptyset$.

The solution set of $-2 < x$ and $x < 1$ is the intersection of the solution sets.

$\{x \mid -2 < x\} \cap \{x \mid x < 1\}$

EXAMPLE 1 Graph $-3 \le x < 4$.

The conjunction corresponds to an intersection of sets. The solution set is the intersection of the solution sets.

$$\{x \mid -3 \le x\} \cap \{x \mid x < 4\}$$

The graph is the intersection of both individual graphs.

Graph of $\{x \mid -3 \le x\}$

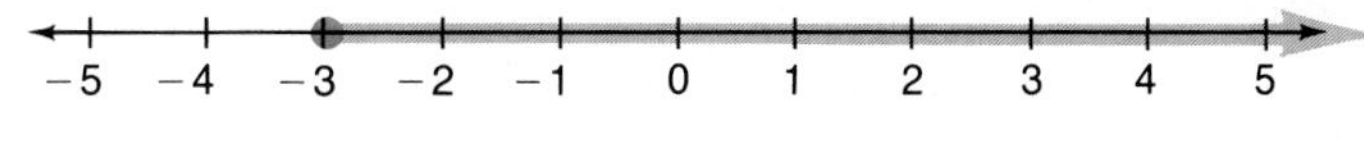

Graph of $\{x \mid x < 4\}$

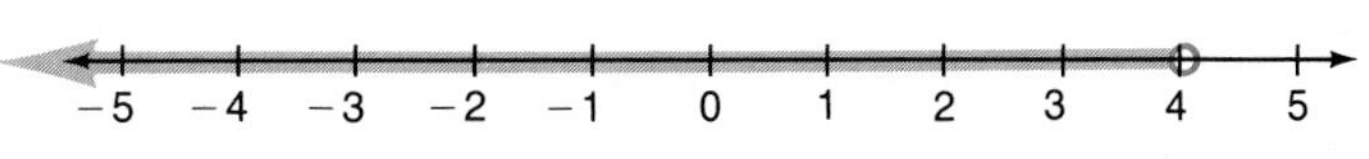

Graph of the intersection, $\{x \mid -3 \le x < 4\}$

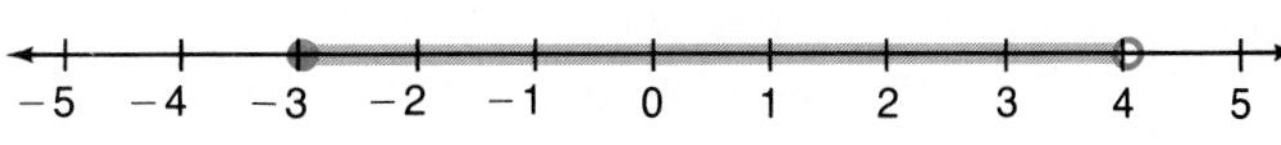

Try This Graph. See Additional Answers.

a. $-1 \le x < 4$ **b.** $-2 < y < 5$

EXAMPLE 2 Solve.

$$-3 < 2x + 5 < 7$$

We write the conjunction with the word and.

$$-3 < 2x + 5 \text{ and } 2x + 5 < 7$$

We could solve the individual inequalities separately and abbreviate the answer.

$$\begin{array}{lcl} -3 < 2x + 5 & \text{and} & 2x + 5 < 7 \\ -3 + (-5) < 2x + 5 + (-5) & \text{and} & 2x + 5 + (-5) < 7 + (-5) \quad \text{Adding } -5 \\ -8 < 2x & \text{and} & 2x < 2 \\ -4 < x & \text{and} & x < 1 \quad \text{Multiplying by } \tfrac{1}{2} \\ & -4 < x < 1 & \end{array}$$

Note that we did the same thing to each inequality in every step. We can simplify the procedure as follows.

$$\begin{array}{lll} -3 & < 2x + 5 & < 7 \\ -3 + (-5) & < 2x + 5 + (-5) & < 7 + (-5) \quad \text{Adding } -5 \\ -8 & < 2x & < 2 \\ -4 & < x & < 1 \quad \text{Multiplying by } \tfrac{1}{2} \end{array}$$

The solution set is $\{x \mid -4 < x < 1\}$.

Try This Solve.

c. $-2 \le 3x + 4 \le 7$ $\{x \mid -2 \le x \le 1\}$ **d.** $4 \ge -x + 3 > -6$ $\{x \mid -1 \le x < 9\}$

Chalkboard Examples

1. Graph.
   $2 < x < 5$
   This is really the conjunction of the two statements $2 < x$ and $x < 5$.
   The solution set is the intersection of the two solution sets $\{x \mid 2 < x\} \cap \{x \mid x < 5\}$.

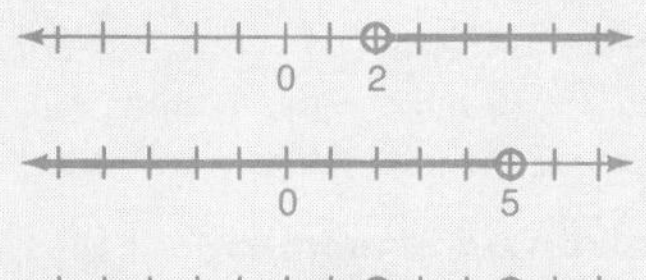

2. Solve.
   $3 < 4x - 5 < 7$
   Write the conjunction with the word "and," and solve each inequality.
   $3 < 4x - 5$ and $4x - 5 < 7$
   $8 < 4x$ and $4x < 12$
   $2 < x$ and $x < 3$
   $2 < x < 3$
   The solution set is $\{x \mid 2 < x < 3\}$.

Disjunctions and Unions

Point out that the word "or" cannot be left out. Rewriting "$x < 1$ or $x > 4$" as "$1 > x > 4$" makes the statement a conjunction. The former has many solutions, the latter has no solution.

Key Questions

- If $x < 2$ or $x > 1$, can $x = 44$? Yes
- If $x > 2$ or $x < 2$, can $x = 2$? No

Chalkboard Examples

1. Graph.
   $x > 2$ or $x < 5$

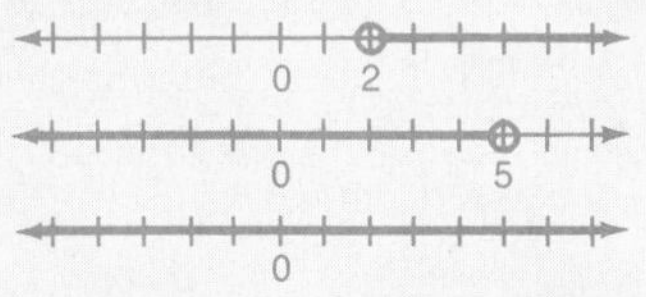

Every number is included in either one, the other, or both of the solution sets. Therefore the union is all real numbers.

2. Solve.
   $3x - 2 < 4$ or $2x > 10$
   Solve the individual inequalities.
   $x < 2$ or $x > 5$

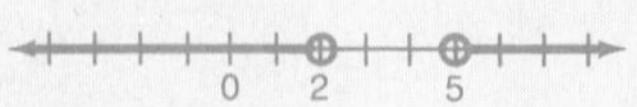

The solution set is $\{x \mid x < 2 \text{ or } x > 5\}$.

LESSON QUIZ

1. Graph.
   $-2 < x < 3$

   −2 0 3

2. Solve.
   $4 < 3x + 1 < 7$
   $4 < 3x + 1$ and $3x + 1 < 7$
   $3 < 3x$ and $3x < 6$
   $1 < x$ and $x < 2$
   The soultion set is $\{x \mid 1 < x < 2\}$.
3. Graph.
   $x > 4$ or $x < 3$

4. Solve.
   $5x + 1 < 11$ or $2x + 3 > 9$
   $5x < 10$ or $2x > 6$
   $x < 2$ or $x > 3$
   The solution set is $\{x \mid x < 2 \text{ or } x > 3\}$.

Disjunctions and Unions

Objective: Solve and graph disjunctions of inequalities.

When two or more statements are joined by the word **or** to make a compound statement, the new statement is called a **disjunction.** Here are some examples of disjunctions.

It is raining or the wind is blowing.
y is an even number or y is a prime number
$x < -3$ or $x > 3$

For a disjunction to be true, *at least* one of the individual statements must be true. Let's look at the solution sets and graphs of a disjunction and its individual statements.

$x < -3$ or $x > 3$

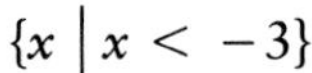

$\{x \mid x < -3\}$

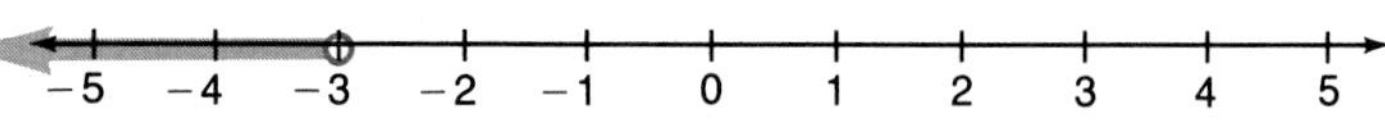

$\{x \mid x > 3\}$

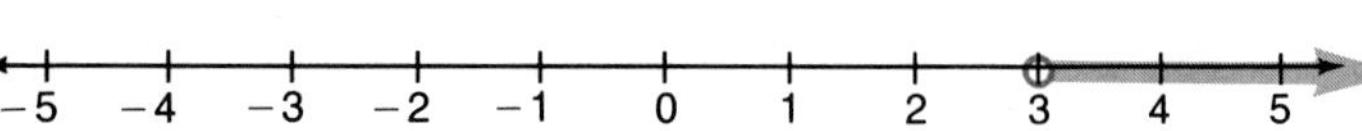

If a number is in *either* or *both* of the solution sets, it is in the solution set of the disjunction. The solution set of the disjunction is the set we get by joining the other two sets.

$\{x \mid x < -3 \text{ or } x > 3\}$

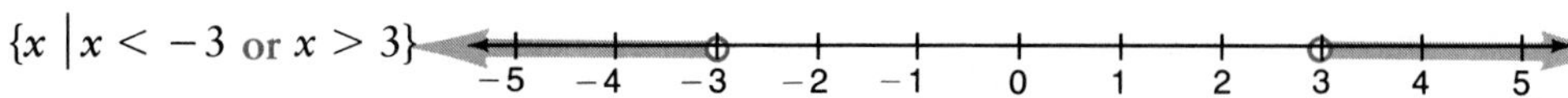

The set obtained by joining two or more sets is called their **union.** For two sets A and B, we can name the union $A \cup B$. The solution set of $x < -3$ or $x > 3$ is the union.

$\{x \mid x < -3\} \cup \{x \mid x > 3\}$

EXAMPLE 3 Graph $x \leq 2$ or $x \geq 5$.

The graph consists of the union of their individual graphs.

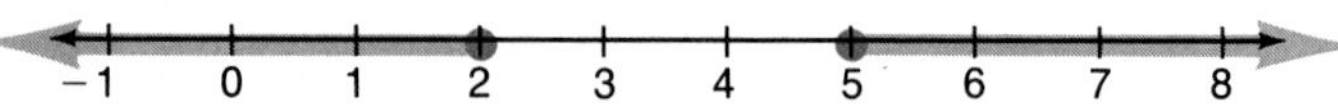

Try This Graph. See Additional Answers.

e. $x \leq -2$ or $x > 4$

f. $x < -4$ or $x \geq 6$

EXAMPLE 4 Solve $-2x - 5 \geq -2$ or $x - 3 > 2$.

We solve the individual inequalities separately, but we continue writing the word or.

$$-2x - 5 + 5 \leq -2 + 5 \text{ or } x - 3 + 3 > 2 + 3$$
$$-2x \geq 3 \text{ or } x > 5$$
$$x \leq -\frac{3}{2} \text{ or } x > 5$$

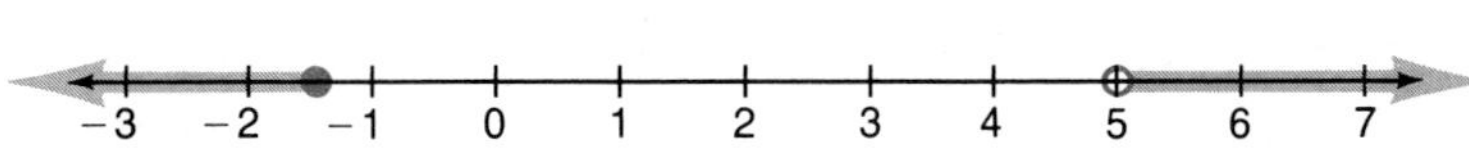

The solution set is $\left\{x \middle| \ x \leq -\frac{3}{2} \text{ or } x > 5\right\}$

Try This Solve. See Additional Answers.

g. $x - 4 < -3$ or $x - 4 \geq 3$

h. $-2x + 4 \leq -3$ or $x + 5 < 3$

2-6 EXERCISES

A

Graph. You may wish to have students write answers in set notation. For example, the answer to Exercise 5 would be $\{x \mid -4 < x < 6\}$.

1. $1 < x < 6$ **2.** $0 \leq y \leq 3$ **3.** $-7 \leq y \leq -3$ **4.** $-9 \leq x < -5$

Solve.

5. $-2 < x + 2 < 8$ $-4 < x < 6$

6. $-1 < x + 1 \leq 6$ $-2 < x \leq 5$

7. $1 < 2y + 5 \leq 9$ $-2 < y \leq 2$

8. $3 \leq 5x + 3 \leq 8$ $0 \leq x \leq 1$

9. $-10 \leq 3x - 5 \leq -1$ $-\frac{5}{3} \leq x \leq \frac{4}{3}$

10. $-18 \leq -2x - 7 < 0$ $\frac{11}{2} \geq x > -\frac{7}{2}$

11. $7 > -x + 7 > -7$ $0 < x < 14$

12. $-5 \geq -3x - 20 > -35$ $-5 \leq x < 5$

Graph.

13. $x < -1$ or $x > 2$

14. $x < -2$ or $x > 0$

15. $x \leq -3$ or $x > 1$

16. $x \leq -1$ or $x > 3$

17. $x < -8$ or $x > -2$

18. $t \leq -10$ or $t \geq -5$

Solve.

19. $x + 7 < -2$ or $x + 7 > 2$

20. $x + 9 < -4$ or $x + 9 > 4$

21. $2x - 8 \leq -3$ or $x - 8 \geq 3$

22. $x - 7 \leq -2$ or $3x - 7 \geq 2$

23. $3x - 9 < -5$ or $x - 9 > 6$

24. $4x - 4 < -8$ or $x - 4 > 12$

B

Solve.

25. $x \geq 2$ and $x > 5$ **26.** $x \geq 3$ and $x < -1$ **27.** $x \geq 4$ or $x > 1$

28. $x < 1$ or $x > -1$ **29.** ($x < 5$ or $x > 9$) and $x < 0$

Assignment Guide
Algebra: 1–24 e/o, MR

Alg w/Finite or Trig: 1–41 e/o, 42, MR

Comprehensive: 1–41 m4, 42 43–48 e/o, MR, assign w. 2-5

ADDITIONAL ANSWERS

Try This

a. −1 0 4

b −2 0 5

e. −2 0 4

f. −4 0 6

g. $\{x \mid x < 1 \text{ or } x \geq 7\}$

h. $\left\{x \mid x < -2 \text{ or } x \geq \frac{7}{2}\right\}$

Exercises

1. 0 1 6

2. 0 3

3. −7 −3 0

4. −9 −5 0

13. −1 0 2

14. −2 0

15. −3 0 1

16. −1 0 3

17. −8 −2 0

18. −10 −5 0

19. $x < -9$ or $x > -5$

20. $x < -13$ or $x > -5$

21. $x \leq \frac{5}{2}$ or $x \geq 11$

22. $x \leq 5$ or $x \geq 3$ (any real number)

23. $x < \frac{4}{3}$ or $x > 15$

24. $x < -1$ or $x > 16$

25. $x > 5$

26. no solution

27. $x > 1$

28. all real numbers

29. $x < 0$

30. $-\frac{3}{2} \le a \le 1$
31. $m < \frac{6}{5}$
32. $\frac{2}{5} \le x < \frac{4}{5}$
33. $x < \frac{13}{40}$ or $x > \frac{17}{40}$
34. $-\frac{1}{8} < x < \frac{1}{2}$
35. $x > \frac{21}{4}$
36. True
37. True
38. False
39. False
40. False
41. False
42. Answers may vary. Ex: $(x < 0$ or $x > 2)$ and $(x > 1$ or $x < -1)$
43. $-\frac{2}{5} \le x \le 2$
44. $-\frac{5}{4} \le m < 1$
45. $10 < x \le 18$
46. $x \le -\frac{1}{5}$ or $x \ge 0$

Mixed Review

49. 3
50. 24
51. -16
52. 54
53. $9w^2$
54. $-96c^2$
55. $-64a^6b^3$
56. 2048
57. $121

Problem for Programmers

This program can be written using any programming language. The student's programming ability will determine how the numbers (*a*, *b*, and *c*) are input. Students may write 4 separate programs for <, >, ≤, and ≥, or one program for all four if they are more experienced programmers.

Solve.

30. $4a - 2 \le a + 1 \le 3a + 4$

31. $4m - 8 > 6m + 5$ or $5m - 8 < -2$

32. $-\frac{2}{15} \le \frac{2}{3}x - \frac{2}{5} < \frac{2}{15}$

33. $2x - \frac{3}{4} < -\frac{1}{10}$ or $2x - \frac{3}{4} > \frac{1}{10}$

34. $3x < 4 - 5x < 5 + 3x$

35. $(x + 6)(x - 4) > (x + 1)(x - 3)$

Which of the following are true for all real numbers *a, b, c*?

36. If $b > c$, then $b \nleq c$.

37. If $-b < -a$, then $a < b$.

38. If $c \neq a$, then $a < c$.

39. If $a < c$, and $c < b$, then $b \ngeq a$.

40. If $a < c$ and $b < c$, then $a < b$.

41. If $-a < c$ and $-c > b$, then $a < b$.

42. ***Critical Thinking*** Write a compound inequality that is the conjunction of two disjunctions.

Challenge

Solve.

43. $[4x - 2 < 8$ or $3(x - 1) < -2]$ and $-2 \le 5x \le 10$

44. $-2 \le 4m + 3 < 7$ and $[m - 5 \le 4$ or $3 - m > 12]$

45. $x + 4 < 2x - 6 \le x + 12$

46. $x + \frac{1}{10} \le -\frac{1}{10}$ or $x + \frac{1}{10} \ge \frac{1}{10}$

47. A certain conjunction is made up of p statements each separated by the word *and.*

a. How many statements must be false for the conjunction to be false? 1

b. How many statements must be true for the conjunction to be true? p

48. A certain disjunction is made up of q statements, each separated by the word *or.*

a. How many statements must be false for the disjunction to be false? q

b. How many statements must be true for the disjunction to be true? 1

Mixed Review

Evaluate. **49.** $-3t - 21$, for $t = -8$ **50.** $4|x + y|$, for $x = 3, y = -9$

51. $3(m - 5) + 2$, for $m = -1$ **52.** $3a(2b - 3c)$, for $a = 2, b = 3, c = -1$

Simplify. **53.** $(-3w)^2$ **54.** $-6(-4c)^2$ **55.** $(-4a^2b)^3$ **56.** $|-2048|$

57. To run an ad in a local newspaper, it costs $25 for the design and $4 per issue for each column-inch. How much does it cost to run a 3-column-inch ad for 8 issues?

Problem for Programmers

Write a program that will solve an inequality of the form $ax + b > c$ or $ax + b < c$. The program should allow input of *a, b,* and *c* and output the solution. Expand the program to include $ax + b \le c$ and $ax + b \ge c$. Test your program using Exercises 8–29 in Lesson 2-4.

2-7 Absolute Value

Properties of Absolute Value

Objective: Simplify absolute value expressions.

We know that the absolute value of a number is its distance from 0 on a number line. We make our formal definition of absolute value as follows.

Definition

Absolute Value

For any real number x,

$|x| = x$ if x is nonnegative, and

$|x| = -x$ (the inverse of x) if x is negative.

The absolute value of a nonnegative number is the number itself. The absolute value of a negative number is the additive inverse of that number, which is always positive.

$|5| = 5 \qquad |0| = 0 \qquad |-8| = 8$

There are certain properties of absolute value that can be proved using the definition. They are stated in the next theorem.

Theorem 2-4

Properties of Absolute Value

A. For all real numbers a and b, $|ab| = |a| \cdot |b|$.
(The absolute value of a product is the product of the absolute values.)

B. $\left|\frac{a}{b}\right| = \frac{|a|}{|b|}$ assuming that $b \neq 0$.
(The absolute value of a quotient is the quotient of the absolute values.)

C. $|a^n| = a^n$ if n is an even integer.
(The absolute value of an even power is that power.)

Theorem 2-4 can be used to simplify expressions containing absolute value. To simplify, leave as little as possible within absolute value signs.

2-7

FIRST FIVE MINUTES

Graph.

1. $x \geq 0$

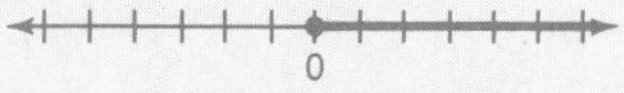

2. $x - 1 \leq 0$
   $x \leq 1$

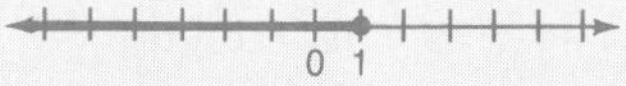

3. $-2 < x < 2$

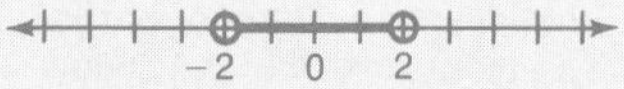

4. $-1 < x - 2 < 1$
   $-1 < x - 2$ and $x - 2 < 1$
   $1 < x$ and $x < 3$

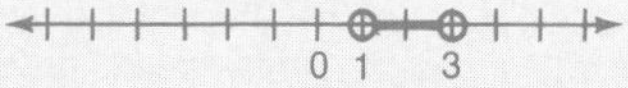

Properties of Absolute Value

Remind students that the geometric definition of the absolute value of x is its distance from 0 on a number line, and that the algebraic definition is

$|x| = x$ if $x \geq 0$
$|x| = -x$ if $x < 0$

You may want to illustrate the properties of absolute value by using numerical examples, for example

$|-3 \cdot 5| = |-15| = 15$
$|-3| \cdot |5| = 3 \cdot 5 = 15$

Key Questions

- Is $-x$ always a negative number?
  No, if $x = -3$, then $-x = 3$
- Does $-|-3| = -|3|$?
  Yes
- Does $|-3| = -|3|$?
  No

Chalkboard Examples

Simplify.

1. $|3 \cdot y|$ $\quad |3| \cdot |y| = 3|y|$
2. $|a^3|$ $\quad |a^2| \cdot |a| = a^2|a|$
3. $|a^4b^2|$
   a^4b^2 is always positive, hence $|a^4b^2| = a^4b^2$
4. $\left|\frac{y}{z^2}\right|$ $\quad \frac{|y|}{z^2}$
5. $|-3y|$ $\quad |-3||y| = 3|y|$

Distance on a Number Line

Point out that the distance from a to b is the same as the distance from b to a. Therefore, we expect that

$$|a - b| = |b - a|$$

This is true, since

$$|a - b| = |1|\,|a - b| = |-1|\,|a - b| = |(-1)(a - b)| = |b - a|$$

Avoiding Common Errors

A common error in algebra is to believe you've made a mistake when you haven't. More than one sequence of steps can yield a correct solution, and a student may obtain a correct solution by a method different from the teacher's, the book's, or another student's. In such circumstances, students need to have confidence in their own work.

Remind students that checking their answers can often verify whether they are correct.

Chalkboard Examples

1. Find the distance between the points having coordinates 9 and 3.
   The distance is $|9 - 3| = |6| = 6$.
2. Find the distance between the points having coordinates 7 and -5.
   The distance is $|7 - (-5)| = |7 + 5| = 12$.

EXAMPLES Simplify.

1. $|5x| = |5| \cdot |x| = 5|x|$
2. $|x^2| = x^2$
3. $|x^2y^3| = |x^2y^2y| = |x^2| \cdot |y^2| \cdot |y| = x^2y^2|y|$
4. $\left|\dfrac{x^2}{y}\right| = \dfrac{|x^2|}{|y|} = \dfrac{x^2}{|y|}$
5. $|-5x| = |-5| \cdot |x| = 5|x|$

Try This Simplify.

a. $|7x|$ $7|x|$ **b.** $|x^8|$ x^8 **c.** $|5a^2b|$ $5a^2|b|$ **d.** $\left|\dfrac{7a}{b^2}\right|$ $\dfrac{7|a|}{b^2}$ **e.** $|-9x|$ $9|x|$

Distance on a Number Line

Objective: Find the distance between two points using absolute value.

On a number line, the number that corresponds to a point is called its coordinate. To find the distance between two points, we can subtract their coordinates and take the absolute value of the result, since distance is always nonnegative. For example, the distance from 2 to -3 on a number line is $|-3 - 2|$ or $|-5|$, which is 5.

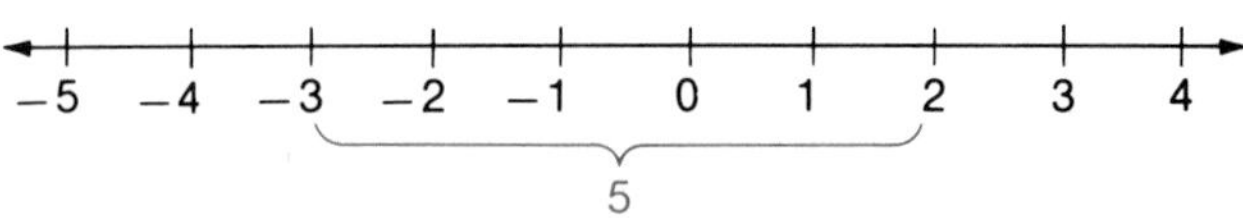

Note that we could have found this distance by subtracting in the reverse order, $|2 - (-3)| = |5| = 5$.

Definition

The **distance** between any two points on a number line having coordinates a and b is $|a - b|$ or $|b - a|$.

EXAMPLE 6 Find the distance between points having coordinates 10 and 3.

The distance is $|10 - 3|$, or $|7|$, which is 7.

EXAMPLE 7 Find the distance between points having coordinates -92 and -8.

The distance is $|-92 - (-8)|$, which is $|-84|$, or 84.

Try This Find the distance between points having the given coordinates.

f. $-6, -35$ 29 **g.** 19, 14 5 **h.** $-3, 17$ 20

Equations and Inequalities with Absolute Value

Objective: Solve and graph equations and inequalities involving absolute value.

To solve equations or inequalities with absolute value, it may help to think about distance on a number line.

EXAMPLE 8 Solve $|x| = 4$. Then graph the solution set using a number line.

The solutions of the equation are those numbers x whose distance from 0 is 4. The solution set is $\{4, -4\}$. The graph consists of just two points as shown.

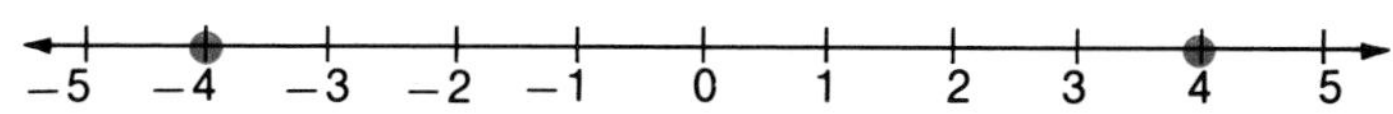

Try This Solve. Then graph using a number line. See Additional Answers.

i. $|x| = 6$ $\{6, -6\}$ **j.** $|x| = \frac{1}{2}$ $\left\{\frac{1}{2}, -\frac{1}{2}\right\}$

EXAMPLE 9 Solve $|x| < 4$. Then graph the solution set.

The solutions of $|x| < 4$ are those numbers whose distance from 0 is less than 4. The solution set is $\{x \mid -4 < x < 4\}$. The graph is as follows.

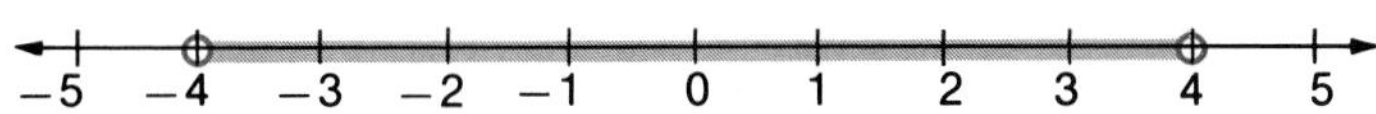

Try This Solve. Then graph. See Additional Answers.

k. $|x| < 5$ $\{x \mid -5 < x < 5\}$ **l.** $|x| \leq 6.5$ $\{x \mid -6.5 \leq x \leq 6.5\}$

EXAMPLE 10 Solve $|x| \geq 4$. Then graph the solution set.

The solutions of $|x| \geq 4$ are those numbers whose distance from 0 is greater than or equal to 4; in other words, those numbers x such that $x \leq -4$ or ≥ 4. The solution set is $\{x \mid x \leq -4 \text{ or } x \geq 4\}$. The graph is as follows.

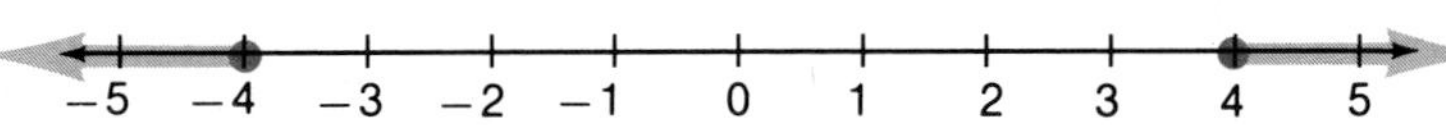

Try This Solve. Then graph the solution set. See Additional Answers.

m. $|y| \geq 8$ $\{y \mid y \leq -8 \text{ or } y \geq 8\}$ **n.** $|x| > \frac{1}{2}$ $\left\{x \mid x < -\frac{1}{2} \text{ or } x > \frac{1}{2}\right\}$

Equations and Inequalities with Absolute Value

The solutions of

$|N| \leq b$

are those numbers that satisfy

$-b \leq N \leq b$

while the solutions of

$|N| \geq b$

are those numbers that satisfy

$N \geq b$ or $N \leq -b$.

In parts A and C of Theorem 2-5, the solution set is a union of two sets, as indicated by the word *or.*

$N = b$ or $N = -b$

$N < -b$ or $N > b$

In part B, the solution set is understood to be an intersection of two sets.

$-b < N$ and $N < b$

Theorem 2-5 B and C are also true if $<$ and $>$ are replaced by $\leq$ and $\geq$, respectively.

Chalkboard Examples

Overhead Transparency 2 (*T2*)

1. Solve $|a| = 2$.

   This is the set of points a whose distance from 0 is exactly 2. There are two such numbers, 2 and -2. The solution set is $\{2, -2\}$.

   −2 0 2

2. Solve $|a| < 2$.

   The solution set consists of all those points a whose distance from 0 is less than 2. The solution set satisfies the conditions $a > -2$ and $a < 2$.

   −2 0 2

3. Solve $|a| \geq 2$.

   The solution set consists of all those points a whose distance from 0 is 2 or greater. The solutions satisfy the conditions $a \leq -2$ or $a \geq 2$.

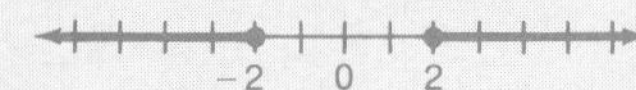

4. Solve and graph.
$|2x - 4| = 2$

Use Theorem 2-5A.

$2x - 4 = 2$ or $2x - 4 = -2$

$2x = 6$ or $2x = 2$

$x = 3$ or $x = 1$

5. Solve and graph.
$|2x - 4| < 2$

Use Theorem 2-5B.

$-2 < 2x - 4$ and $2x - 4 < 2$

$2 < 2x$ and $2x < 6$

$1 < x$ and $x < 3$

6. Solve and graph.
$|2x - 5| \geq 1$

Use Theorem 2-5C.

$2x - 5 \leq -1$ or $2x - 5 \geq 1$

$2x \leq 4$ or $2x \geq 6$

$x \leq 2$ or $x \geq 3$

LESSON QUIZ

Simplify, leaving as little as possible inside the absolute value signs.

1. $|-3x^2|$

$3x^2$

2. $|5x^3y|$

$5x^2|xy|$

Solve and graph.

3. $|x| < 3$

$-3 < x < 3$

4. $|2x + 3| \leq 1$

$-1 \leq 2x + 3$ and $2x + 3 \leq 1$

$-4 \leq 2x$ and $2x \leq -2$

$-2 \leq x$ and $x \leq -1$

5. $|2x - 1| > 3$

$2x - 1 < -3$ or $2x - 1 > 3$

$2x < -2$ or $2x > 4$

$x < -1$ or $x > 2$

Examples 8 – 10 illustrated three cases of solving equations and inequalities with absolute value. The following theorem gives the general principles for solving.

Theorem 2-5

Principles for Solving Absolute Value Equations

For any positive number b and any expression $|N|$

A. The solutions of $|N| = b$ satisfy $N = -b$ or $N = b$.

B. The solutions of $|N| < b$ satisfy $-b < N < b$.

C. The solutions of $|N| > b$ satisfy $N < -b$ or $N > b$.

EXAMPLES Solve. Then graph.

11. $|5x - 4| = 11$ — $|N| = b$, where N is $5x - 4$ and b is 11.

$5x - 4 = 11$ or $5x - 4 = -11$ — Using Theorem 2-5A

$5x = 15$ or $5x = -7$ — Adding 4 to both sides

$x = 3$ or $x = -\frac{7}{5}$ — Multiplying both sides by $\frac{1}{5}$

The solution set is $\left\{3, -\frac{7}{5}\right\}$.

Here is the graph of the solution set.

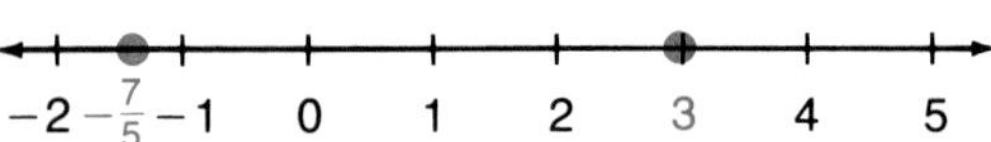

12. $|3x - 2| < 4$ — $|N| < b$, where N is $3x - 2$ and b is 4.

$-4 < 3x - 2 < 4$ — Using Theorem 2-5B

$-2 < 3x < 6$ — Adding 2

$-\frac{2}{3} < x < 2$ — Multiplying by $\frac{1}{3}$

The graph is as follows.

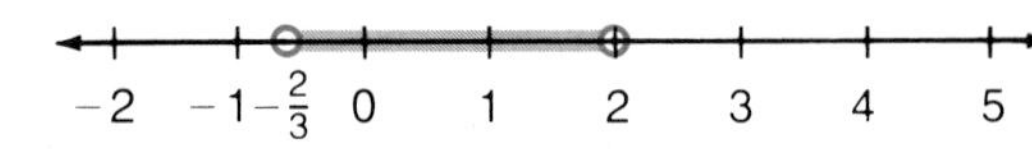

13. $|4x + 2| \geq 6$ — $|N| \geq b$, where N is $4x + 2$ and b is 6.

$4x + 2 \leq -6$ or $4x + 2 \geq 6$ — Using Theorem 2-5C

$4x \leq -8$ or $4x \geq 4$ — Adding -2

$x \leq -2$ or $x \geq 1$ — Multiplying by $\frac{1}{4}$

The graph is as follows.

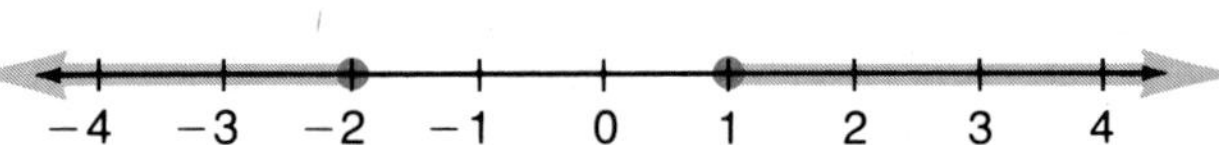

Try This Solve. Then graph. See Additional Answers.

o. $|3x + 4| = 9$ **p.** $|2x - 3| \leq 7$ **q.** $|2x - 4| > 7$

2-7 EXERCISES

A

Simplify, leaving as little as possible inside absolute value signs.

1. $|3x|$ $3|x|$ 2. $|4x|$ $4|x|$ 3. $|y^8|$ y^8 4. $|x^6|$ x^6

5. $|9x^2y^3|$ $9x^2y^2|y|$ 6. $|10a^4b^7|$ $10a^4b^6|b|$ 7. $\left|\frac{a^2}{b}\right|$ $\frac{a^2}{|b|}$ 8. $\left|\frac{y^4}{m}\right|$ $\frac{y^4}{|m|}$

9. $|-16m|$ $16|m|$ 10. $|-9t|$ $9|t|$ 11. $|t^3|$ $t^2|t|$ 12. $|p^5|$ $p^4|p|$

Find the distance between the points having the given coordinates.

13. $-8, -42$ 34 14. $-9, -36$ 27 15. 26, 15 11 16. 54, 18 36
17. $-9, 24$ 33 18. $-18, -37$ 19 19. $-5, 0$ 5 20. 0, 23 23

Solve. Then graph.

21. $|x| = 3$ 22. $|x| = 5$ 23. $|x| < 3$ 24. $|x| \leq 5$
25. $|x| \geq 2$ 26. $|y| > 8$ 27. $|t| \geq 5.5$ 28. $|m| > 0$
29. $|x - 3| = 12$ 30. $|3x - 2| = 6$ 31. $|2x - 3| \leq 4$
32. $|5x + 2| \leq 3$ 33. $|2y - 7| > 10$ 34. $|3y - 4| > 8$
35. $|4x - 9| \geq 14$ 36. $|9y - 2| > 17$ 37. $|10x + 8| > 2$

B

Solve.

38. $|m + 5| + 9 \leq 16$ $-12 \leq m \leq 2$ 39. $|t - 7| + 3 \geq 4$ $t \leq 6$ or $t \geq 8$
40. $|g + 7| + 13 = 4$ No solution 41. $2|2x - 7| + 11 = 25$ 0, 7

42. ***Critical Thinking*** Determine whether the absolute value of a difference is always the same as the difference of the absolute values. No; ex. $|3 - 5| \neq |3| - |5|$

Challenge

Solve.

43. $|3x - 4| > -2$ 44. $|x - 6| \leq -8$ 45. $\left|\frac{5}{9} + 3x\right| < \frac{1}{6}$

46. $1 - \left|\frac{1}{4}x + 8\right| > \frac{3}{4}$ 47. $|x + 5| > x$ 48. $2 \leq |x - 1| \leq 5$

49. $|7x - 2| = x + 4$ 50. $|x - 1| - 2 = |2x - 5|$ 51. $|x + 1| \leq |x - 3|$

Mixed Review

Simplify. 52. $n^{-8} \cdot n^{12}$ 53. $\frac{m^3}{m^5}$ 54. $\frac{y^5}{y^{-3}}$ 55. $\frac{-56w^8}{7n^6}$

Solve. 56. $1.8t = -3.6$ 57. $12c + 6 = 9c$ 58. $5a - (3a - 10) = 4a$

Use the commutative and associative properties to write three equivalent expressions for each. 59. $ab + (c + d)$ 60. $x^2(yz \times xy)$

Assignment Guide
Algebra: 1–37 e/o, MR

Alg w/Finite or Trig: 1–41 e/o, 42, MR

Comprehensive: 1–41 m3, 42, 43–51 e/o, MR, assign w. Application

ADDITIONAL ANSWERS

Try This

i. -6 0 6
j. $-\frac{1}{2}$ 0 $\frac{1}{2}$
k. -5 0 5
l. -6.5 0 6.5
m. -8 0 8
n. $-\frac{1}{2}$ 0 $\frac{1}{2}$
o. $\{x \mid x = -\frac{13}{3}$ or $x = \frac{5}{3}\}$
$-\frac{13}{3}$ 0 $\frac{5}{3}$
p. $\{x \mid -2 \leq x \leq 5\}$
-2 0 5
q. $\{x \mid x < -\frac{3}{2}$ or $x > \frac{11}{2}\}$
$-\frac{3}{2}$ 0 $\frac{11}{2}$

Exercises

For Exercises 21–37 and 43–51, see Teacher's Answer Section.

Mixed Review

52. n^4 53. m^{-2}
54. y^8 55. $-8w^8n^{-6}$
56. $t = -2$ 57. $c = -2$
58. $a = 5$
59. Answers may vary. $ab + (d + c)$; $(c + d) + ab$; $ba + (c + d)$
60. Answers may vary. $(yz \times xy)x^2$; $x^2(zy \times yx)$; $x^2(xy \times yz)$

2-8

FIRST FIVE MINUTES

Solve.

1. $3x - 1 < 5$
   $3x < 6$
   $x < 2$
2. $3 > 5x - 7$
   $10 > 5x$
   $2 > x$
3. $|x| \geq 5$
   $x \leq -5$ or $x \geq 5$
4. $|2x - 2| \leq 4$
   $-4 \leq 2x - 2$ and $2x - 2 \leq 4$
   $-2 \leq 2x$ and $2x \leq 6$
   $-1 \leq x$ and $x \leq 3$

Conditional Statements

An if-then statement is only false when the antecedent is true and the consequent is false. If the antecedent is false, then nothing is asserted about the consequent. This is sometimes used to make a point. For example, someone says, "If Thomas is telling the truth, then I'm a monkey's uncle." The speaker is emphasizing that the statement "Thomas is telling the truth" is false. Since the antecedent is false, nothing is asserted about the consequent "I'm a monkey's uncle."

Key Questions

Consider the sentence "If Todd plays first base, then Sam plays shortstop."

- What is the antecedent?
  Todd plays first base.
- What is the consequent?
  Sam plays shortstop.
- If Sam plays shortstop and Todd plays third base, is the sentence true?
  Yes
- If Sam plays right field and Todd plays first base, is the sentence true?
  No

Chalkboard Example

1. Prove that if $2x - 5 > 7$, then $x > 6$.
   1. $2x - 5 > 7$ Hypothesis
   2. $2x > 12$ Add. property
   3. $x > 6$ Mult. property
   4. If $2x - 5 > 7$, then $x > 6$ Statements 1 – 3

2-8 Proofs in Solving Equations

Optional

Conditional Statements

Objective: Prove conditional statements.

If-then statements are important in mathematics. Here are some examples.

If $x = 1$, then $x + 1 = 2$.

If $x < 5$, then $x < 10$.

If a figure is a square, then it has four sides.

In a statement If P, then Q,

P is a sentence that follows if, and Q is a sentence that follows *then.* The sentence P is called the antecedent, and the sentence Q is called the consequent. If-then statements are also called conditionals.

To prove a conditional, we *suppose* or *assume* that the antecedent P is true. Then we try to show that it leads to Q. That allows us to conclude that the statement *If P, then Q* is true. Solving equations provides a good example of proving conditionals.

EXAMPLE 1 Prove the statement: If $5x + 4 = 24$, then $x = 4$.

We first assume that $5x + 4 = 24$ is true. We call such an assumption a hypothesis. Then we use equation-solving principles to arrive at $x = 4$. We use a column proof to list each statement and the theorems or axioms that allow us to make this statement.

1. $5x + 4 = 24$	1. Hypothesis (assumed true)
2. $5x = 20$	2. Using the addition property
3. $x = 4$	3. Using the multiplication property
4. If $5x + 4 = 24$, then $x = 4$.	4. Statements 1 – 3

Here is a proof written in paragraph form, called a narrative proof.

Suppose that $5x + 4 = 24$ is true. Then, by the addition property, adding -4 to both sides, it follows that $5x = 20$. By the multiplication property, multiplying both sides by $\frac{1}{5}$, we then obtain $x = 4$.
Therefore, if $5x + 4 = 24$, then $x = 4$, which was to be shown.

Try This Prove the following statements. See Additional Answers.

a. If $3x + 5 = 20$, then $x = 5$. **b.** If $-3x + 8 > 23$, then $x < -5$.

Converses

Objective: Write and prove converses of statements.

From a statement *If P, then Q*, we can make a new statement by interchanging the antecedent and consequent. We get *If Q, then P*. The two statements are called converses of each other.

EXAMPLES Write the converse of each statement.

2. If $x = 2$, then $x + 3 = 5$. The converse is: If $x + 3 = 5$, then $x = 2$.
3. If $x < 5$, then $x < 10$. The converse is: If $x < 10$, then $x < 5$.
4. If an animal is a cat, then it has four legs. The converse is: If an animal has four legs, then it is a cat.

Try This Write the converse of each statement.

c. If $3x + 7 = 37$, then $x = 10$. If $x = 10$, then $3x + 7 = 37$.

d. If $x > 15$, then $x > 12$. If $x > 12$, then $x > 15$.

What does an if-then statement tell us? Consider the statement If $x < 5$, then $x < 10$.

This statement is true. It tells us that any replacement for x that makes the antecedent true, also must make the consequent true. It does *not* tell us what happens if the antecedent is false. Let's try some substitutions.

	Antecedent	Consequent
x	$x < 5$	$x < 10$
3	$3 < 5$ true	$3 < 10$ true
6	$6 < 5$ false	$6 < 10$ true
15	$15 < 5$ false	$15 < 10$ false

Now let's look at the converse: If $x < 10$, then $x < 5$. This converse is false.

	Antecedent	Consequent
x	$x < 10$	$x < 5$
20	$20 < 10$ false	$20 < 5$ false
7	$7 < 10$ true	$7 < 5$ false
3	$3 < 10$ true	$3 < 5$ true

For the replacement 7, we have a true antecedent and a false consequent. That can happen only when the conditional is *false*. Converses of true conditionals may not be true. We have just seen an example in which the converse is not true.

Converses

Emphasize that the truth of the original if-then statement does not guarantee the truth of its converse.

Chalkboard Examples

Write the converse of each statement.

1. If $x < 3$, then $x < 4$.
   If $x < 4$, then $x < 3$.
2. If $2x + 1 > 5$, then $x > 2$.
   If $x > 2$, then $2x + 1 > 5$.
3. Prove: If $x > 2$, then $5x - 7 > 3$.
   1. $x > 2$ — Hypothesis
   2. $5x > 10$ — Mult. property
   3. $5x - 7 > 3$ — Add. property
   4. If $x > 2$, then $5x - 7 > 3$ — Statements 1 – 3

Solving Equations and Inequalities

Chalkboard Examples

1. Solve $4x + 3 < 11$.

   $4x + 3 < 11$ Hypothesis
   $4x < 8$ Add. property
   $x < 2$ Mult. property
   Each step is reversible, hence the first statement is equivalent to the last statement.

2. Solve $6x + 7 < 37$ by proving a statement and its converse.

   a. If $6x + 7 < 37$, then $x < 5$.
   $6x + 7 < 37$
   $6x < 30$
   $x < 5$

   b. If $x < 5$, then $6x + 7 < 37$.
   $x < 5$
   $6x < 30$
   $6x + 7 < 37$
   We have shown that $6x + 7 < 37$ is equivalent to $x < 5$.

Consider the statement *If* $5x + 4 = 24$, *then* $x = 4$. We know this statement is true because we proved it in Example 1. Therefore, any number that makes $5x + 4 = 24$ true must also make $x = 4$ true. Let's prove the converse.

EXAMPLE 5 Prove: If $x = 4$, then $5x + 4 = 24$.
We reverse the steps of Example 1.

1. $x = 4$	1. Hypothesis
2. $5x = 20$	2. Using the multiplication property
3. $5x + 4 = 24$	3. Using the addition property
4. If $x = 4$, then $5x + 4 = 24$.	4. Statements 1 – 3

Any number that makes $x = 4$ true must also make $5x + 4 = 24$ true.

Try This See Additional Answers.

e. In Try This **a**, you proved *if* $3x + 5 = 20$, *then* $x = 5$. Prove the converse.

f. In Try This **b**, you proved *if* $-3x + 8 > 23$, *then* $x < -5$.
(1) Prove the converse.
(2) Describe the solution sets of the antecedent and consequent.

Solving Equations and Inequalities

Objective: Solve equations and inequalities by proving a statement and its converse.

When we solve an equation or inequality, in effect we write a proof. We start with the sentence to be solved, using it as a hypothesis. From that hypothesis, we try to obtain a very simple statement with an obvious solution set.

EXAMPLE 6 Solve.

$6x - 2 = 28$ Hypothesis
$6x = 30$ Using the addition property
$x = 5$ Using the multiplication property

The statement $x = 5$ has an obvious solution set, $\{5\}$. What about the solution set of $6x - 2 = 28$? We can prove the converse or we can check by substituting. For inequalities we cannot check by substituting because the solution sets are infinite.

EXAMPLE 7 Solve $3x + 5 < 29$ by proving a statement and its converse.

(a) We prove this statement: If $3x + 5 < 29$, then $x < 8$. We abbreviate the writing as we ordinarily do in solving.

$3x + 5 < 29$ Hypothesis
$3x < 24$ Using the addition property
$x < 8$ Using the multiplication property

(b) We prove this statement: If $x < 8$, then $3x + 5 < 29$, also abbreviating the writing.

$x < 8$ Hypothesis

$3x < 24$ Using the multiplication property

$3x + 5 < 29$ Using the addition property

Since we have proved a statement and its converse, we know $3x + 5 < 29$ and $x < 8$ have the same solution set. Therefore, the solution set of $3x + 5 < 29$ is $\{x \mid x < 8\}$.

Try This See Additional Answers.

g. Solve $7x - 1 > 34$ by proving a statement and its converse.

h. Solve $9x - 5 = 103$
(1) by proving a statement and its converse.
(2) by proving a statement and then substituting.

Equivalent Statements

Objective: Recognize whether an operation will produce equivalent statements.

If two equations or inequalities have the same solution set, they are said to be equivalent. If in solving we know which manipulations give us equivalent statements, we can cut down on the work of proving converses.

Theorem 2-6

The use of the addition and multiplication properties of equality and inequality produces equivalent statements under the following conditions.

A. The expression added or multiplied must be defined for all replacements.

B. The expression by which we multiply must never have the value 0.

According to Theorem 2-6, whenever we add any constant or multiply by any nonzero constant, we obtain equivalent statements. Thus when solving simple equations or inequalities, we can depend on Theorem 2-6 and need not actually prove a converse.

EXAMPLE 8

To show that multiplying by 0 can be troublesome, "prove" that $x = 1$ and $x^2 = x$ are equivalent.

$x = 1$

$x^2 = x$ Multiplying both sides by x

The solution set of $x = 1$ is $\{1\}$. The solution set of $x^2 = x$ is $\{0, 1\}$. The statements are *not* equivalent.

Equivalent Statements

There are two kinds of steps in the derivation of a solution set: reversible steps and non-reversible steps. For example, the step from

$x > 2$

to

$x + 1 > 2 + 1$

is reversible. The two statements are equivalent. On the other hand, the step from

$x = 2$

to

$|x| = 2$

is not reversible, since

$|x| = 2$

does not imply that $x = 2$. The value of x may be -2.

Math Point
If an if-then statement is false, what can be said about the truth or falsity of its converse?

The only way an if-then statement can be false is for its antecedent to be true and its consequent to be false. The antecedent and consequent change places in the converse. The converse has a false antecedent and a true consequent. The converse is therefore a true statement.

Chalkboard Examples

Will each step be certain to produce an equivalent equation or inequality?

1. multiplying both sides by x
   No, x may be 0.
2. adding $\frac{1}{x^2}$ to both sides
   No, undefined at $x = 0$
3. adding $2x$ to both sides
   Yes
4. multiplying both sides by $\frac{1}{(x^2 + 1)}$
   Yes, the denominator can't be 0.
5. adding $2x + 1$ to both sides
   Yes
6. adding $\frac{x}{(x + 1)}$ to both sides
   No, $x + 1$ may be 0.

LESSON QUIZ

1. Prove.
   If $6x - 7 < 5$, then $x < 2$.
   1. $6x - 7 < 5$ Hypothesis
   2. $6x < 12$ Add. property
   3. $x < 2$ Mult. property
   4. If $6x - 7 < 5$, then $x < 2$ Statements 1–3
2. Solve by proving the statement and its converse.
   $7x + 5 < 19$
   a. If $7x + 5 < 19$, then $x < 2$.
      $7x + 5 < 19$ Hypothesis
      $7x < 14$ Add. property
      $x < 2$ Mult. property
   b. If $x < 2$, then $7x + 5 < 19$.
      $x < 2$ Hypothesis
      $7x < 14$ Mult. property
      $7x + 5 < 19$ Add. property
   The statements are equivalent, thus the solution set of $x < 2$ equals the solution set of $7x + 5 < 19$.

Assignment Guide
Algebra: omit

Alg w/Finite or Trig: omit

Comprehensive: 1–31 e/o, 32, 33–38 e/o, MR

ADDITIONAL ANSWERS

Try This

a. 1. $3x + 5 = 20$ Hypothesis (assumed true)
   2. $3x = 15$ Add. property
   3. $x = 5$ Mult. property
   4. If $3x + 5 = 20$, then $x = 5$. Statements 1–3

b. 1. $-3x + 8 > 23$ Hypothesis (assumed true)
   2. $-3x > 15$ Add. prop. for inequalities
   3. $x < -5$ Mult. prop. for inequalities
   4. If $-3x + 8 > 23$, then $x < -5$ Statements 1–3

e. 1. $x = 5$ Hypothesis
   2. $3x = 15$ Mult. property
   3. $3x + 5 = 20$ Add. property
   4. If $x = 5$, then $3x + 5 = 20$ Statements 1–3

EXAMPLES

Which of the following will be certain to produce an equivalent equation or inequality?

9. adding $\frac{1}{x}$ to both sides — No, x cannot be zero.

10. adding $3x - 3x$ to both sides — Yes

11. multiplying both sides by $x + 2$ — No, the expression could have the value 0.

12. multiplying both sides by $x^2 + 1$ — Yes, the expression will always be nonzero.

13. multiplying both sides by $\frac{3}{x} + 2$ — No, the expression could be undefined.

Try This Which of the following will be certain to produce an equivalent equation or inequality?

i. multiplying both sides by 5 Yes

j. multiplying both sides by $3x - 3x$ No

k. adding $\frac{x}{1} - x$ to both sides Yes

l. adding 7 to both sides Yes

m. multiplying both sides by $x + 5$ No

n. multiplying both sides by $\frac{1}{x} + 27$ No

2-8 EXERCISES

A

Prove the following.

1. If $7x - 12 = 37$, then $x = 7$.

2. If $5y + 16 = 88 - 3y$, then $y = 9$.

3. If $15x - 5 \geq 11 - 2x$, then $x \geq \frac{16}{17}$.

4. If $13x + 12 < 15x - 7$, then $x > \frac{19}{2}$.

Write the converse of each statement.

5. If $3y = 5$, then $6y = 10$.

6. If $5x + 3 = 17$, then $2x + 5 = 14$.

7. If $x < 12$, then $x < 20$.

8. If $3y + 5 > 17 - y$, then $4y + 2 < 8y + 1$.

Write the converse of each statement, and then prove it. Compare with Exercises 1–4.

9. If $7x - 12 = 37$, then $x = 7$.

10. If $5y + 16 = 88 - 3y$, then $y = 9$.

11. If $15x - 5 \geq 11 - 2x$, then $x \geq \frac{16}{17}$.

12. If $13x + 12 < 15x - 7$, then $x > \frac{19}{2}$.

Solve by proving a statement and its converse.

13. $3x - 2 < 5x + 7$ $\left\{x \mid -\frac{9}{2} < x\right\}$

14. $4y + 5 \geq 7y - 2$ $\left\{y \mid \frac{7}{3} \geq y\right\}$

15. $16x + 3 = 2x - 5$ $-\frac{4}{7}$

16. $6y - 12 = 8y + 2$ -7

Solve by proving a statement and then substituting.

17. $14x - 12 = 16x + 5$ $-\frac{17}{2}$

18. $7y + 5 = 5y + 7$ 1

19. $-6x - 10 = 6x + 10$ $-\frac{5}{3}$

20. $-5y + 7 = 10y - 14$ $\frac{7}{5}$

Which of the following will be certain to produce an equivalent equation or inequality?

21. multiplying both sides by 7 Yes

22. multiplying both sides by x^2 No

23. adding $x^2 + 3$ to both sides Yes

24. adding $3 - x^2$ to both sides Yes

25. adding $\frac{x-2}{x+3}$ to both sides No

26. multiplying both sides by $x^2 + 2$ Yes

27. adding 5 to both sides Yes

28. multiplying both sides by $\frac{1}{x^2+1}$ Yes

B

29. Prove the addition property of equality.

30. Prove the multiplication property of equality.

31. Prove the property of zero products.

32. ***Critical Thinking*** Write a conditional statement that has a true converse; a false converse. Answers may vary.

Challenge

To prove the addition property and the multiplication property of inequality, we need another theorem and an additional axiom for real numbers. We may also need to use the fact that $a > b$ and $b < a$ are equivalent statements.

Theorem 2-7

For any real numbers a and b, $a < b$ is true if and only if $b - a > 0$.

Trichotomy

For any real number a, one and only one of the following is true.

a. $a > 0$ **b.** $a = 0$ **c.** $a < 0$

33. Prove the transitive property of inequality. (For any real numbers a, b, and c, if $a < b$ and $b < c$, then $a < c$.)

34. Prove the addition property of inequality.

35. Prove the multiplication property of inequality.

For each statement, rewrite in *if . . . then* form and then write the converse.

36. Integers are rational numbers.

37. Quitters never win.

38. Use the addition property to prove that $a > b$ and $-a < -b$ are equivalent.

Mixed Review

Evaluate for $m = \frac{1}{2}$. **39.** m^3 **40.** $m - \frac{4}{5}$ **41.** $\frac{m}{3}$ **42.** $\frac{1}{3} + 3m$

Solve. **43.** $16n + 8n = 312$ **44.** $-16 = 4c + 6$ **45.** $r - 16r = 645$

f. (1)
1. $x < -5$ Hypothesis
2. $-3x > 15$ Multiply both sides by -3
3. $-3x + 8 > 23$ Add 8 to both sides

(2) Solution set of antecedent and consequent: $\{x \mid x < -5\}$ since the consequent is the solution set of the antecedent.

g. Statement
$7x - 1 > 34$
$7x > 35$ Add. property
$x > 5$ Mult. property
Converse
$x > 5$
$7x > 35$ Mult. property
$7x - 1 > 34$ Add. property

h. (1) Statement
$9x - 5 = 103$
$9x = 108$ Add. property
$x = 12$ Mult. property
Converse
$x = 12$
$9x = 108$ Mult. property
$9x - 5 = 103$ Add. property

(2) $9x - 5 = 103$
$9x = 108$
$x = 12$
$9(12) - 5 = 103$ Substituting
$108 - 5 = 103$
$103 = 103$

Exercises

For Exercises 1–12 and 29–38, see Teacher's Answer Section.

Mixed Review

39. $\frac{1}{8}$

40. $-\frac{3}{10}$

41. $\frac{1}{6}$

42. $\frac{11}{6}$

43. 13

44. $-5\frac{1}{2}$

45. -43

2-9

FIRST FIVE MINUTES

1. Play the game Hi-Lo. Think of a number for students to guess. The only clues you should give are "high" or "low." The first student to guess the number correctly wins. Suggested numbers to use are 39, 738, −13, 2.73.
2. Use the Hi-Lo method to find the first 3 digits of the square root of 300. $\sqrt{300} \approx 17.3$

Guess, Check, Revise

Every day, problems are solved by the Guess, Check, Revise method. Emphasize that the key is to make intelligent guesses. That is, first make a "ballpark" guess based on the data in the problem, then evaluate the accuracy of that guess and use this information to make increasingly "educated" guesses and focus on a correct answer.

Key Questions

- In Example 1, how much would 600 kWh cost? $24
- How much would each 100 kWh cost after the first 600? $10
- Guess how many kWh would cost $34. 700
- Guess how many kWh would cost $124. 1600

2-9 Problem Solving: Strategies

Guess, Check, Revise

Objective: Solve problems using the strategy *Guess, Check, Revise* and other strategies.

PROBLEM-SOLVING GUIDELINES
■ UNDERSTAND the problem
■ Develop and carry out a PLAN
■ Find the ANSWER and CHECK

Some problems can be solved by guessing a solution, checking the guess, and, if necessary, using information gained from the check to revise the guess. This strategy for solving problems is called **Guess, Check, Revise.**

EXAMPLE 1

Use the *Guess, Check, Revise* strategy to solve this problem.

ELECTRIC BILL		
1st 600 kWh @ 4¢ each	=	$ 24
Next 850 kWh @ 10¢ each	=	$ 85
TOTAL	=	$109

A company received an electric bill for one month of $109. The bill is shown at the left. The manager of the company told the employees that the electric bill needed to be cut exactly in half the next month. How many kilowatt hours did they need to use to have a bill half as large?

You can see that the number of kilowatt hours used must be greater than 600, since $24.00 is less than half of $109.00. Half of $109.00 is $54.50 (109 ÷ 2 = 54.5).

Guess: 800 kWh

600 kWh @ 4¢ each = 600 (0.04) = 24.00
200 kWh @ 10¢ each = 200 (0.10) = 20.00
TOTAL = $44

Since $44.00 is less than $54.50, the guess of 800 kWh was too low. The next guess should be higher.

Guess: 1000 kWh

600 kWh @ 4¢ each = 600 (0.04) = 24.00
400 kWh @ 10¢ each = 400 (0.10) = 40.00
TOTAL = $64

Since $64.00 is greater than $54.50, the guess of 1000 kWh was too high. The next guess should be less than 1000 but greater than 800.

If you continue this process of *guessing, checking, and revising*, you can quickly find that the correct number of kilowatt hours used is 905.

Example 1 shows an important fact about solving problems in mathematics. The missing number in this problem was found using the *Guess, Check, Revise* strategy. The missing number could have also been found using equation-solving techniques. Many problems in mathematics can be solved correctly in more than one way.

For some problems, there may be no solution. For others, several solutions are possible. In the following example, the strategy *Guess, Check, Revise* is used to show that no solution is possible.

EXAMPLE 2

The cost of 3 different sandwiches on a menu are roast beef \$3.25, cheese \$2.75, and reuben \$3.75. Carola bought 2 sandwiches with a \$10 bill and received \$4.25 change. Which sandwiches did she buy?

Guess: 2 cheese sandwiches $2 \times \$2.75 = \$5.50, \$10 - \$5.50 = \$4.50$

\$4.50 is too much change. The next most expensive sandwich is roast beef.

Guess: 1 cheese sandwich, 1 roast beef sandwich $\$3.25 + \$2.75 = \$6, \$10 - \$6 = \$4$

\$4 is not enough change. Every other combination of sandwiches is more expensive, so less change than \$4 is returned. Thus there is no solution.

Problem-Solving Strategies		
Write an Equation	Draw a Diagram	Guess, Check, Revise
Make an Organized List	Make a Table	Look for a Pattern
Use Logical Reasoning	Simplify the Problem	Work Backward

2-9 PROBLEMS

Solve using one or more of the strategies presented so far.

1. Solve Example 1 above using the strategy *Write an Equation.*
2. Three computers were on sale. Model E computer was priced at $\frac{1}{3}$ the price of Model C, and Model P was priced at $\frac{1}{2}$ the price of Model E. One business bought one of each type of computer on sale and paid a total of \$1800, not including tax. What was the sale price of each computer?
3. The number of cable television subscribers in a particular city has been increasing at a rate of about 15% every 2 years. The company expects this rate to continue for at least the next 10 years. There are 275 subscribers in the city this year. About how many subscribers does the company predict there will be in 4 years?
4. What is the greatest number of pieces into which a pie can be cut with four straight cuts? (The pieces may not be stacked.)
5. Two friends planned an 80 km walk/bike-a-thon. They wanted to start and arrive at the same time. The bike would only carry one person at a time. They decided that one of them would ride a certain distance, then leave the bike for the other and continue walking. Both walk and ride at the same rate of speed. At what distances should the bicycle be left so that each person walks twice and rides twice?

Chalkboard Example

1. A computer service costs 12¢ per minute for the first hour of use and 6¢ for each minute after that. Greenberg Inc. received a bill for \$59.10 for its first month of the service. How much did it use the service?

Use the Guess, Check, and Revise strategy.

1st guess: 10 hours or 600 min

60 min @ 12¢ = 60(0.12) = 7.20
540 min @ 6¢ = 540(0.06) = 32.40
Total = \$39.60

Guess is too low. Guess 15 hours or 900 min.

60(0.12) = 7.20
840(0.06) = 50.40
Total = \$57.60

Guess is close but too low. Try 925 min.

60(0.12) = 7.20
865(0.06) = 51.90
Total = \$59.10

Greenberg Inc. used the system for 925 min, or 15 h 25 min.

Hints for Problems

1. Let x equal the number of kWh over 600.
2. Let C be the price of model C. Give each model in terms of C.
3. Find the total number of customers after 2 years, then 4 years.
4. Draw a diagram.
5. Draw a diagram and guess some locations that might work. Revise your guesses as needed.

ANSWERS

1. They would use 905 kWh.
2. Model C = \$1,200
   Model E = \$ 400
   Model P = \$ 200
3. There might be about 364 customers after 4 years.
4. 11
5. Some possible solutions: 20 km, 40 km, 60 km, 30 km, 60 km, 70 km

Problem Solving: Application

You may need to review the formula $D = rt$, and show how flight time is thus miles divided by mi/h (distance divided by rate). You may wish to discuss some other considerations, such as whether unloading might actually be faster than loading, the maximum distance a helicopter can fly without refueling, and the effect of loading only a part of the cargo internally.

Problem Solving: Application

Helicopter Flight Time

Some helicopters can carry cargo internally, inside the body of the aircraft, or externally, strapped beneath or to the side of the body. When the cargo is carried externally, the airspeed is decreased because of drag on the helicopter. However, loading and unloading for cargo carried externally is much faster.

Suppose that cargo can be loaded by either of the two methods, but not by a combination. When transporting cargo, how can delivery time be minimized?

Example

A load of medical equipment is to be carried a distance of 80 miles and delivery time is to be minimized. Assume the following data.

	Average Speed (mi/h)	Loading Time (hr)	Unloading Time (hr)
Internal Load	140	$\frac{1}{4}$	$\frac{1}{4}$
External Load	100	$\frac{1}{12}$	$\frac{1}{12}$

The average speed when carrying the load internally is 140 mi/h. Thus it will take $\frac{80}{140}$ hours to travel 80 miles with only an internal load.

The total delivery time for an inside load is

loading time + flight time + unloading time =

$$\frac{1}{4} + \frac{80}{140} + \frac{1}{4} = \frac{15}{14} \approx 1.07 \text{ hr}$$

The average speed when carrying the load externally is 100 mi/h. Thus it will take $\frac{80}{100}$ hours to travel 80 miles with only an external load.

The total delivery time for an outside load is

loading time + flight time + unloading time =

$$\frac{1}{12} + \frac{80}{100} + \frac{1}{12} = \frac{29}{30} \approx 0.97 \text{ hr}$$

Therefore, to ship this cargo 80 miles external loading is preferable.

Suppose we want to ship this same cargo 200 miles. We then have the following.

	Loading Time	+	Flight Time	+	Unloading Time	=	Delivery Time
Internal Load	$\frac{1}{4}$	+	$\frac{200}{140}$	+	$\frac{1}{4}$	=	$\frac{27}{14} \approx 1.9$ hr
External Load	$\frac{1}{12}$	+	$\frac{200}{100}$	+	$\frac{1}{12}$	=	$\frac{13}{6} \approx 2.2$ hr

Therefore, to ship this cargo 200 miles internal loading is preferable.

Problems

1. Determine the preferable loading for shipping this cargo 140 miles.
2. Determine the preferable loading for shipping this cargo 110 miles.
3. Determine the preferable loading for shipping this cargo 118 miles.

Suppose the helicopter is to carry this cargo D miles. For which distances is internal loading preferable? For which distances is external loading preferable?

Total delivery time for external load

$$\frac{1}{12} + \frac{D}{100} + \frac{1}{12}$$

Total delivery time for internal load

$$\frac{1}{4} + \frac{D}{140} + \frac{1}{4}$$

Therefore, external loading is preferable to internal loading whenever

$$\frac{1}{12} + \frac{D}{100} + \frac{1}{12} < \frac{1}{4} + \frac{D}{140} + \frac{1}{4}$$

Solving this inequality we have

$$\frac{D}{100} + \frac{1}{6} < \frac{D}{140} + \frac{1}{2}$$

$$21D + 350 < 15D + 1050$$ Multiplying both sides by 2100, the LCM of 100, 6, 140 and 4.

$$6D < 700$$

$$D < \frac{700}{6} \approx 117 \text{ miles.}$$

Therefore, for distances less than 117 miles external loading is preferable. For distances of 117 miles or greater, internal loading is preferable.

Problems

Assume the following data for a helicopter with a load of forest firefighting equipment.

	Average Speed (mi/h)	Loading Time (hr)	Unloading Time (hr)
Internal Load	200	$\frac{1}{4}$	$\frac{1}{4}$
External Load	150	$\frac{1}{8}$	$\frac{1}{8}$

4. Determine the preferable loading for shipping this cargo 100 miles.
5. Determine the preferable loading for shipping this cargo 250 miles.
6. Suppose the helicopter is to carry this cargo D miles. For which distances is internal loading preferable? For which distances is external loading preferable?

ANSWERS

1. Internal loading
2. External loading
3. Internal loading
4. External loading
5. Internal loading
6. Internal: $D > 150$ mi
   External: $D < 150$ mi

Chapter 2 Summary and Review

2-1

When **solving equations**, use the distributive property to remove parentheses, clear fractions or decimals, collect like terms on both sides of the equation, and use the addition and multiplication properties to get the variable alone on one side.

Solve.

1. $\frac{1}{4} + \frac{1}{2}x = \frac{5}{4}$ **2.** $\frac{2}{3}x + \frac{1}{6} = 9$ **3.** $0.6x + 1.5 = 2.1$

4. $2.9y - 4.6 = 0.6y$ **5.** $300(x + 7) = 350$ **6.** $\frac{1}{4}(3x - 5) = 10 - \frac{3}{4}(x - 1)$

The **principle of zero products** states that $ab = 0$, if and only if $a = 0$ or $b = 0$.

Solve.

7. $(x + 4)(x - 3) = 0$ **8.** $(2x - 5)(3x + 4) = 0$

2-2

Drawing a diagram often helps when solving problems.

9. One angle of a triangle is five times as large as the first angle. The measure of the third angle is 2° less than that of the first angle. The sum of the angles in a triangle is 180°. How large are the three angles?

10. A retail store decreases the price of suits 20% to \$120. What is the former price?

2-3

To solve a **formula** for a given letter, use the same methods as for solving any equation.

11. Solve $A = \frac{1}{2}bh$, for b **12.** Solve $V = ab + at$, for a

2-4

If we multiply both sides of a true **inequality** by a positive number, we get another true inequality; if we multiply by a negative number, we must reverse the inequality symbol.

Solve and graph on a number line.

13. $y + 3 \geq 4$ **14.** $2x + 7 > x - 9$ **15.** $\frac{1}{3}x \geq -9$

16. $-9y \geq -45$ **17.** $-\frac{2}{3}x \geq -20$ **18.** $3x - 8 \leq 7x + 5$

2-5

Use the Problem-Solving Guidelines to solve problems involving inequalities.

19. Find all sets of three consecutive positive odd integers whose sum is less than 20 but greater than 10.

ANSWERS

1. 2 **2.** $13\frac{1}{4}$
3. 1 **4.** 2
5. $-5\frac{5}{6}$ **6.** 8
7. $-4, 3$ **8.** $2\frac{1}{2}, -\frac{4}{3}$
9. 26°, 130°, 24° **10.** \$150
11. $\frac{2A}{h}$ **12.** $\frac{V}{b+t}$
13. $y \geq 1$
14. $x > -16$
15. $x \geq -27$
16. $y \leq 5$

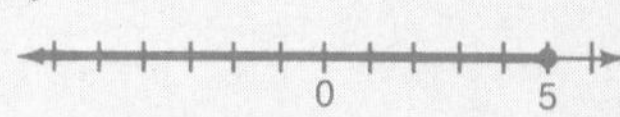

17. $x \leq 30$

18. $x \geq -\frac{13}{4}$

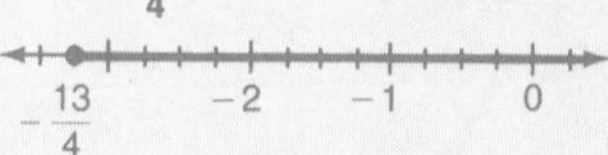

19. 3, 5, 7
20. $-3 < x < 5$

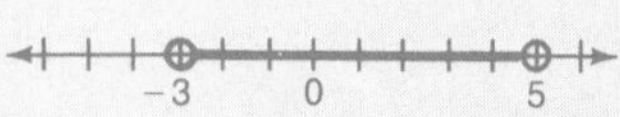

21. $x < -5$ or $x > 3$
22. $-3 < x < 2$
23. $x < -2$ or $x > 1$
24. $y^2|y|$ **25.** $x^2|xy|$
26. $3x^2y^2$ **27.** 26
28. 17 **29.** 21
30. $x = 6$ or $x = -6$

31. $-4 < y < 4$

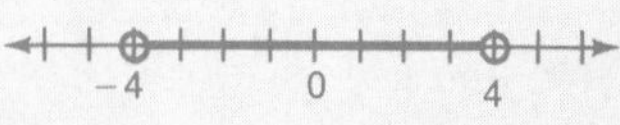

2-6

For a **conjunction** to be true, all of its individual statements must be true. For a **disjunction** to be true, at least one of its statements must be true.

Graph on a number line.

20. $-3 < x < 5$ **21.** $x < -5$ or $x > 3$

Solve. Then graph.

22. $-7 < 2x - 1 < 3$ **23.** $x + 1 < -1$ or $x + 1 > 2$

Simplify.

24. $|y^3|$ **25.** $|x^3y|$ **26.** $|3x^2y^2|$

Find the **distance** between points having these **coordinates**.

27. -9 and 17 **28.** -23 and -40 **29.** -18 and 3

2-7

The solutions of $|N| = b$ satisfy $N = -b$ or $N = b$, the solutions of $|N| < b$ satisfy $-b < N < b$, the solutions of $|N| > b$ satisfy $N < -b$ or $N > b$.

Solve. Then graph.

30. $|x| = 6$ **31.** $|y| < 4$ **32.** $|x| \geq 2$

33. $|x - 3| \geq 5$ **34.** $|3x + 5| < 7$

See also Problem 2, Computer-Assisted Problem Solving, page 839.

Chapter 2 Test

Solve.

1. $r - 17 = 20$ **2.** $-9n = 450$ **3.** $3y + 10 = 16$

4. $-2z + 5 = 7$ **5.** $0.8x - 3.7 = 0.3$ **6.** $\frac{1}{5}y - \frac{2}{3} = 6$

7. $8(x + 9) = 112$ **8.** $8y - (5y - 9) = -160$ **9.** $(3x + 5)(2x - 6) = 0$

10. $y + 5 \geq 8$ **11.** $4x \geq 28$ **12.** $-8y \leq -40$

13. $4 + 7y \leq 39$ **14.** $2x - 9 \leq 9x + 4$ **15.** $-4x - 6 > 7x - 14$

16. A 14-m piece of cable is cut into 2 pieces. One piece is 4 m longer than the other. How long are the pieces?

17. Solve $Q = P - Prt$, for P. **18.** Simplify $|x^5y^4|$.

19. You have made scores of 81, 76, and 82 on three quizzes. What is the least you can make on the fourth quiz to have an average of at least 80?

20. Find the distance between points with coordinates 33 and -12.

Solve. Then graph.

21. $-3 < x + 1 < 8$ **22.** $|y| \geq 8$ **23.** $|x - 2| \leq 6$ **24.** $|2x + 7| < 9$

32. $x \geq 2$ or $x \leq -2$

33. $x \geq 8$ or $x \leq -2$

34. $-4 < x < \frac{2}{3}$

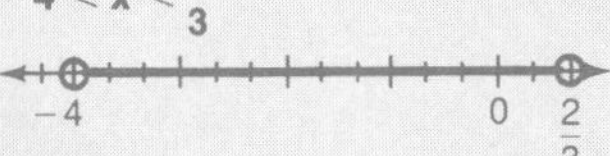

ANSWERS

1. 37 **2.** -50

3. 2 **4.** -1

5. 5 **6.** $\frac{100}{3}$

7. 5 **8.** $-\frac{169}{3}$

9. $-\frac{5}{3}, 3$ **10.** $y \geq 3$

11. $x \geq 7$ **12.** $y \geq 5$

13. $y \leq 5$ **14.** $x \geq -\frac{13}{7}$

15. $x < \frac{8}{11}$ **16.** 9m, 5m

17. $P = \frac{Q}{1 - rt}$ **18.** $x^4y^4|x|$

19. 81 **20.** 45

21. $-4 < x < 7$

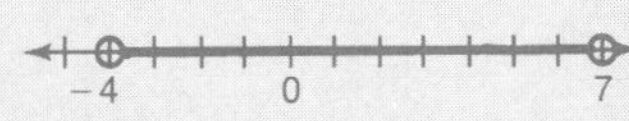

22. $y \leq -8$ or $y \geq 8$

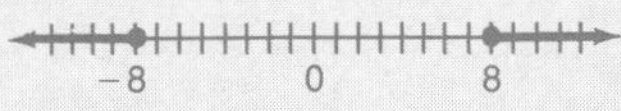

23. $-4 \leq x \leq 8$

24. $-8 < x < 1$

Test Item Analysis

Item	Lesson
1–9	2-1
10–15	2-4
16	2-2
17	2-3
18, 20, 21	2-6
22–24	2-7

CHAPTER 3

Relations, Functions, and Graphs

Chapter Overview

Relations, functions, and elementary set theory are the new topics in Chapter 3, which are introduced as they relate to the familiar topics of graphs and linear equations. A relation is defined as a set of ordered pairs and is graphed in a coordinate plane. A function is defined as a special relation whose graph passes the vertical-line test. Linear equations and their graphs are examined in detail, including slope, standard forms, and parallel and perpendicular lines. Problem solving includes linear functions fitted to data. The strategy *Make an Organized List* is introduced to develop systematic methods to find solutions.

Objectives

3-1
- Find the Cartesian product of two sets.
- List ordered pairs from a Cartesian product that satisfy a given relation.
- List the domain and the range of a relation.
- Use set-builder notation to describe a relation.

3-2
- Graph the ordered pairs of relation.
- Determine whether an ordered pair is a solution of an equation.
- Graph equations by plotting several solutions.

3-3
- Recognize functions and their graphs.
- Use function notation to find function values.
- Find the domain of a function, given a formula for the function.

3-4
- Recognize a linear equation.
- Graph linear equations.
- Graph equations whose graphs are parallel to the x- or y-axes.

3-5
- Find the slope of a line containing a given pair of points.
- Find the slopes of horizontal and vertical lines.
- Use the point-slope equation to find an equation of a line.

3-6
- Use the two-point equation to find an equation of a line, given two points on the line.
- Find the slope and y-intercept of a line, given the slope-intercept equation for the line.
- Graph linear equations in slope-intercept form.
- Find the standard form of a linear equation.

3-7
- Use equations to determine whether two lines are parallel.
- Write an equation of the line that contains a given point and is parallel to a given line.
- Use equations to determine whether two lines are perpendicular.
- Write an equation of the line that contains a given point and is perpendicular to a given line.

3-8
- Find a linear function and use the equation to make predictions.

3-9
- Graph special functions.
- Find the composite of two functions.

3-10
- Solve problems using the strategy *Make an Organized List* and other strategies.

TEACHING CHAPTER 3

Cooperative Learning Opportunities

A general principle in cooperative learning is that less group time translates to smaller groups. If you are just beginning to use cooperative groups, there is nothing wrong with spending only 5 to 10 minutes on an activity. But, if this is the case, then you should work with pairs.

Paired review of homework is an easy way to get into cooperative learning. The exercises in Lessons 3-5, 3-6, and 3-7 are suitable to paired review. The skills are important for future work and not too difficult. In most cases students will be able to correct each other's mistakes and provide explanations.

At the start of class, or after the five-minute quiz, assign students in pairs. Have them exchange homework papers and review each exercise. When their answers do not agree, they should rework the exercise until they have a solution that satisfies both students.

Multicultural Note: *Egyptian Coordinates*

Although our coordinate system did not appear until the 17th century, the Egyptians did have a type of coordinate measurement.

In the markings shown in the diagram, the top mark represents a bent arm (the cubit) and the 3 tallies beneath it means there are 3 cubits. The straight line represents a palm, and the 3 lines beneath it indicate 3 palms. The two bent lines represent 2 fingers.

The relationship between the measurements is: 1 cubit = 7 palms; 1 palm = 4 fingers. You might ask students to

Horizontal (fingers)	**Vertical**	**Vertical** (fingers)
0	3 cu, 3 pa, 2 fi	
28	3 cu, 1 pa, 3 fi	
56	2 cu, 3 fi	

complete the table and draw a graph for the following coordinates.

For more information, see page 60 of **Multiculturalism in Mathematics, Science, and Technology**.

Alternative Assessment and Communication Ideas

The **Writing to Learn** activities on pages 115 and 151 offer the opportunity for assessment that is more verbal than the usual tests and that also explores general concepts. For the activity on page 151, have students draw the graph and also explain it. This will encourage them to think about the meaning of function.

The **Critical Thinking** exercises in Lesson 3-3 can form an alternative assessment because most of the exercises ask questions about graphs but do not require a graph as part of the solution (except in Lesson 3-2). These exercises require that students internalize the concepts associated with graphs and use these notations without having a graph in front of them.

In addition to the alternative assessments mentioned, you might ask students to write a paragraph explaining function and/or a paragraph on the importance of mathematical notation.

Investigations and Projects

Graphs are widely used in newspapers and magazines to report data in science, politics, business, sports, personal preferences, and other areas.

As a project ask students to collect graphs from newspapers and magazines. Have them categorize these by type of graph and report on the types of graphs used for particular kinds of information. What kind of data is best reported using a bar graph, circle graph, and line graph?

Have students also report on how the graphs they have collected differ from those in the text. They might consider the way the coordinates are used; whether there is a break in either of the scales; whether the graph is an actual line graph, a broken line graph, or a best fit; whether the graph is used to project into the future.

Ask students to complete their report by writing about the advantages of presenting information in the form of graphs.

MANAGING CHAPTER 3

Lesson	PACING CHART (DAYS) Algebra	Algebra w/Finite	Algebra w/Trig	Comprehensive	Opening Activity	Cooperative Activity	Seat or Group Work
3-1	1	1	1	1	First Five Minutes 3-1: **TE** p.106 or ***FFM Transparency Masters*** p.9	Critical Thinking: **SE** p.109	Try This a–g
3-2	1	1	1	0.5	First Five Minutes 3-2: **TE** p.110 or ***FFM Transparency Masters*** p.10	Critical Thinking: **SE** p.115	Try This a–i
3-3	1	1	1	0.5	First Five Minutes 3-3: **TE** p.116 or ***FFM Transparency Masters*** p.10	Critical Thinking: **SE** p.121 Critical Thinking 3: ***Enrichment*** p.24	Try This a–j
3-4	2	2	2	0.5	First Five Minutes 3-4: **TE** p.122 or ***FFM Transparency Masters*** p.10	Critical Thinking: **SE** p.126 ✂ Manipulative Activity 3: ***Enrichment*** p.44	Try This a–o
3-5	2	1	1	0.5	First Five Minutes 3-5: **TE** p.127 or ***FFM Transparency Masters*** p.10	Critical Thinking: **SE** p.132	Try This a–i
3-6	2	1	1	0.5	First Five Minutes 3-6: **TE** p.133 or ***FFM Transparency Masters*** p.11	Critical Thinking: **SE** p.137 Looking for Errors 2: ***Enrichment*** p.63	Try This a–j
3-7	2	1	1	0.5	First Five Minutes 3-7: **TE** p.138 or ***FFM Transparency Masters*** p.11	Critical Thinking: **SE** p.142 Looking for Errors: **SE** p.142	Try This a–h
3-8	1	1	1	1	First Five Minutes 3-8: **TE** p.143 or ***FFM Transparency Masters*** p.12	Critical Thinking: **SE** p.147 Looking for Errors 3: ***Enrichment*** p.64	Try This a–b
3-9	1	1	1	1	First Five Minutes 3-9: **TE** p.148 or ***FFM Transparency Masters*** p.12	Critical Thinking: **SE** p.151	Try This a–l
3-10	1	1	1	0.5	First Five Minutes 3-10: **TE** p.152 or ***FFM Transparency Masters*** p.12	Problem Solving: **SE** p.154 Strategy Problem Bank 3: ***Problem Bank*** p.4	Problems 1, 2: **SE** p.153
Review	1	1	1	0.5			
Test	1	1	1	1			

 FFM: First Five Minutes SPMR: Skills Practice Mixed Review

MANAGING CHAPTER 3

Enrichment	Review/Assess	Reteach	Technology	Lesson
Lesson Enrichment: **TE** p.108 Bonus Topic 2: ***Enrichment*** p.3	Lesson Quiz: **TE** p.108	Skills Practice 6, #1–8: ***SPMR*** p.18		**3-1**
Math Point: **TE** p.112 Writing to Learn: **SE** p.115	Lesson Quiz: **TE** p.114	Skills Practice 6, #9–15: ***SPMR*** p.18	Calculator Worksheet 5: ***Technology*** p.7	**3-2**
Critical Thinking 3: ***Enrichment*** p.24	Lesson Quiz: **TE** p.119 Quiz 5: ***Assessment*** p.13	Skills Practice 6, #16–21: ***SPMR*** p.18	Problem for Programmers: **SE** p.121	**3-3**
✂ Manipulative Activity 3: ***Enrichment*** p.44	Lesson Quiz: **TE** p.125	Skills Practice 7, #1–12: ***SPMR*** p.19	BASIC Computer Project 1: ***Technology*** p.81	**3-4**
Lesson Enrichment: **TE** p.128 Math Point: **TE** p.129 Math Point: **TE** p.130	Lesson Quiz: **TE** p.131 Mixed Review 5: ***SPMR*** p.69	Skills Practice 7, #13–28: ***SPMR*** p.19	Worksheet 1: ***TI-81 Activities*** pp.5–8; Worksheet 2: ***TI-81 Activities*** pp.9–12; Worksheet 1: ***Master Grapher*** pp.13–16, pp.147–150 or pp.283–286	**3-5**
Looking for Errors 2: ***Enrichment*** p.63	Lesson Quiz: **TE** p.136	Skills Practice 7, #29–44: ***SPMR*** p.19	Worksheet 2: ***Master Grapher*** pp.17–20, pp.151–154, or pp.287–290	**3-6**
Looking for Errors: **SE** p.142	Lesson Quiz: **TE** p.141 Quiz 6: ***Assessment*** p.14	Skills Practice 8, #1–10: ***SPMR*** p.20	Worksheet 3: ***TI-81 Activities*** pp.13–16; Worksheet 3: ***Master Grapher*** pp.21–24, pp.155–158, or pp.291–294	**3-7**
Math Point: **TE** p.143 Looking for Errors 3: ***Enrichment*** p.64	Lesson Quiz: **TE** p.146	Skills Practice 8, #11–12: ***SPMR*** p.20 Problem Bank 4: ***Problem Bank*** p.25	Spreadsheet Activity 1: ***Technology*** pp.45–47	**3-8**
Special Functions: **TE** p.148 Writing to Learn: **SE** p.151	Lesson Quiz: **TE** p.150	Skills Practice 8, #13–27: ***SPMR*** p.20	Special Functions: **TE** p.148 BASIC Computer Project 2: ***Technology*** p.82	**3-9**
Problem 3: Computer Assisted Problem Solving, **SE** pp.840–841	Mixed Review 6: ***SPMR*** p.70	Strategy Problem Bank 3: ***Problem Bank*** p.4	Problem 3: Computer Assisted Problem Solving, **SE** pp.840–841	**3-10**
	Summary and Review: **SE** pp.155–156; Test: **SE** p.157			**Review**
	Chapter 3 Test: ***Assessment*** pp.59–64(reg.), pp.161–162 (adv.); Assessing Strategies 3: ***Assessment*** pp.199–200			**Test**

The solution to the problem posed on the facing page can be found on page 144.

Ready for Relations, Functions, and Graphs?

1-1 Add.

1. $-4 + 0$ -4

2. $-2 + (-7)$ -9

3. $-2.7 + (-3.5)$ -6.2

4. $15 + (-8)$ 7

5. $-8.1 + 2.4$ -5.7

6. $\frac{2}{3} + \left(-\frac{3}{5}\right)$ $\frac{1}{15}$

1-3 Evaluate each expression when $x = -2, y = 3$, and $z = -4$.

7. $y - xz$ -5

8. $3x + 2y - z$ 4

2-1 Solve.

9. $x + 8 = -12$ -20

10. $3x = 21$ 7

11. $4x - 5 = 11$ 4

12. $9x - 2x = 21$ 3

13. $7x - 4 + 2x = -8 - 3x + 6$ $\frac{1}{6}$

14. $r + \frac{5}{6} = -\frac{3}{12}$ $-\frac{13}{12}$

15. $5t = -12$ $-\frac{12}{5}$

16. $\frac{2}{3}x = 16$ 24

17. $-4y - 3y = 28$ -4

18. $8 - 5x = x - 14$ $\frac{11}{3}$

19. $8a = 3(a + 5)$ 3

2-4 Solve.

20. $x + 2 < 6$ $x < 4$

21. $y - 8 \geq 0$ $y \geq 8$

22. $4y \leq -8$ $y \leq -2$

23. $-5x > 10$ $x < -2$

24. $3x - 1 > 8$ $x > 3$

25. $2 + 7y \leq 3$ $y \leq \frac{1}{7}$

26. $4y - 1 < y + 2$ $y < 1$

27. $x - 6 \geq 3x - 10$ $x \leq 2$

CHAPTER 3

Relations, Functions, and Graphs

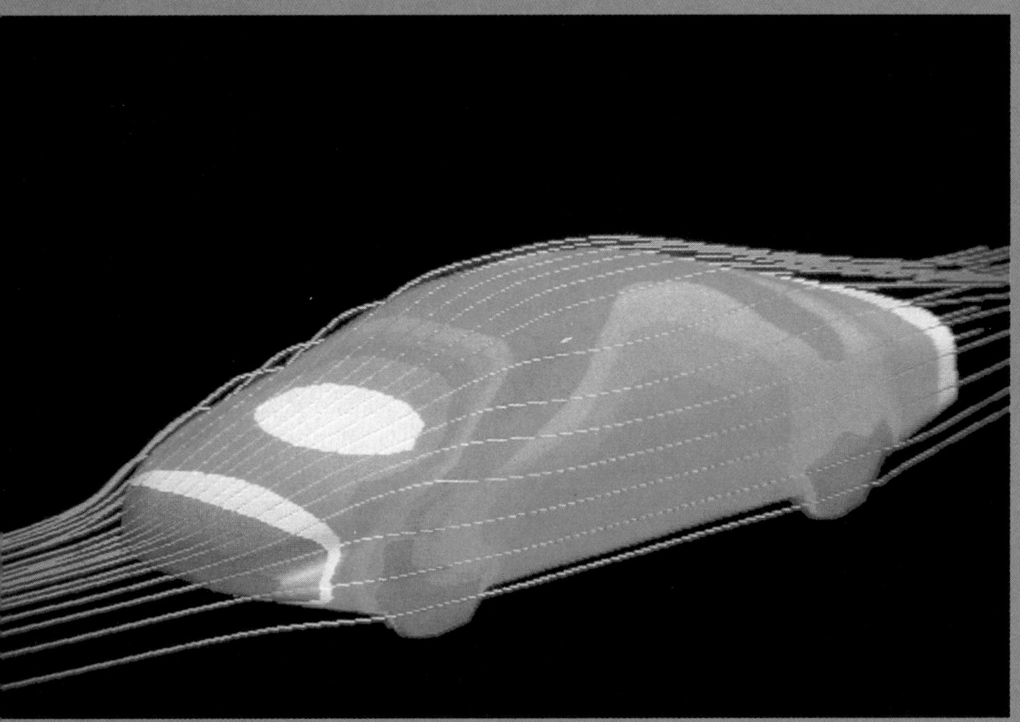

Speed (km/h)	Resistance (kg)
10	3.2
21	4.8
34	7.2
40	8.0
45	15.1
55	29.6

Wind tunnel experiments are used to test the wind friction, or resistance, of an automobile at various speeds. Is resistance a linear function of speed? Can we predict the resistance of an automobile traveling 50 km/h?

3-1

FIRST FIVE MINUTES

1. Sara has three pairs of shoes, 1, 2, and 3. She has two hats, a and b. Write down all the possible combinations of shoes and hats by writing pairs, such as $(1, a)$, $(3, b)$, etc.
   There are 6 possibilities.
   $(1, a), (1, b), (2, a), (2, b), (3, a), (3, b)$
2. A coin is thrown twice. Write down all the possible ordered outcomes, such as (H, H), (H, T), etc.
   There are 4 possibilities.
   $(H, H), (H, T), (T, H), (T, T)$

Cartesian Products

Students may choose to write relations in rows and columns for organization.

Have students find $B \times A$, where A and B are the same sets as in the introduction, and compare the results with $A \times B$.

Key Questions

- a. Does $A \times B = B \times A$?
  No
  b. Is the Cartesian product commutative?
  No
  c. If $C \times D = D \times C$, what must be true about C and D?
  $C = D$
- If E has 4 elements and F has 5 elements, how many pairs does $E \times F$ have?
  20
- If $H \times G$ has 12 pairs and H has 2 elements, how many elements does G have?
  6

Chalkboard Examples

1. Find the Cartesian product $E \times F$, where $E = \{H, T\}$ and $F = \{0, 1\}$.
   $\{(H, 0), (H, 1), (T, 0), (T, 1)\}$
2. Find the Cartesian product $F \times E$, where $E = \{H, T\}$ and $F = \{0, 1\}$.
   There are 4 pairs.
   $\{(0, H), (0, T), (1, H), (1, T)\}$

3-1 Relations and Ordered Pairs

Cartesian Products

Objective: Find the Cartesian product of two sets.

Consider the following sets:

A = {Justin, Ramon, Yung Su} B = {jeans, tee shirt}

From these sets we can form a set of ordered pairs choosing the first element from set A and the second element from set B.

{(Justin, jeans), (Justin, tee shirt),
(Ramon, jeans), (Ramon, tee shirt),
(Yung Su, jeans), (Yung Su, tee shirt)}

The set of all ordered pairs formed as above is called the **Cartesian product** and is denoted $\boldsymbol{A \times B}$. We read $A \times B$ as "A cross B." In general, $A \times B$ will not produce the same set of ordered pairs as $B \times A$.

Definition

The **Cartesian product** of two sets A and B, symbolized $A \times B$, is the set of all ordered pairs having the first member from set A and the second member from set B.

The two sets used to find a Cartesian product may be the same.

EXAMPLE 1 Find the Cartesian product $Q \times Q$, where $Q = \{2, 3, 4, 5\}$.

The Cartesian product $Q \times Q$ is as follows.

$$\{(2, 2), (2, 3), (2, 4), (2, 5),\\ (3, 2), (3, 3), (3, 4), (3, 5),\\ (4, 2), (4, 3), (4, 4), (4, 5),\\ (5, 2), (5, 3), (5, 4), (5, 5)\}$$

Try This Find the following Cartesian products.

a. $A \times B$, where $A = \{d, e\}$ and $B = \{1, 2\}$ $\{(d, 1), (d, 2), (e, 1), (e, 2)\}$

b. $C \times C$, where $C = \{x, y, z\}$ $\{(x, x), (x, y), (x, z), (y, x), (y, y), (y, z), (z, x), (z, y), (z, z)\}$

Relations

Objective: List ordered pairs from a Cartesian product that satisfy a given relation.

In some Cartesian products we can select ordered pairs that make up a common relation, such as <, as in the following example.

EXAMPLE 2

In the Cartesian product {(1, 1), (1, 2), (1, 3), (2, 1), (2, 2), (2, 3)} list the set of ordered pairs for which the first member is less than the second member.

{(1, 2), (1, 3), (2, 3)}

This set of ordered pairs is the relation *less than.*

Try This

c. In the Cartesian product of Example 2, list the set of ordered pairs for which the first member is the same as the second member. This is the relation *equals.* {(1, 1), (2, 2)}

Any set of ordered pairs selected from a Cartesian product is a relation.

Definition

A **relation** from a set A to a set B is any set of ordered pairs in $A \times B$.

Domain and Range

Objective: List the domain and the range of a relation.

Definition

The set of all first members in a relation is the **domain** of the relation. The set of all second members in a relation is the **range** of the relation.

EXAMPLE 3 List the domain and the range of the relation < in Example 2.

Domain: {1, 2}; Range: {2, 3}

Try This

d. List the domain and the range of the relation {(a, 1), (b, 2), (c, 3), (e, 2)}.
Domain {a, b, c, e}; range {1, 2, 3}

e. List the domain and the range of the relation {(2, 2), (1, 1), (1, 2), (1, 3)}.
Domain {1, 2}; range {1, 2, 3}

Relations

The definition of a relation applies beyond the realm of numbers. For example, two people can be related as parent and child, and this relationship can be represented by a set of ordered pairs. In this case, the ordered pairs are pairs of people. The domain and range sets are sets of people.

Key Question

- If A has 4 elements and B has 5 elements, what are the minimum and maximum numbers of ordered pairs in a relation from set A to set B?
  0, 20

Chalkboard Example

1. In the Cartesian product shown in Example 2, list the set of ordered pairs for which the second number is greater than or equal to the first number.
   {(1, 1), (2, 3), (2, 2), (1, 2), (1, 3)}

Domain and Range

Chalkboard Examples

List the domain and range of the following relations.

1. {(a, b), (a, d), (b, c)}
   Domain {a, b};
   range {b, d, c}
2. {(1, x), (1, y), (2, z), (2, w)}
   Domain {1, 2};
   range {x, y, z, w}

Using Set-Builder Notation

Students will better understand set-builder notation if they consider its meaning rather than its symbols. For example, when reading or writing $\{x \mid x > 3\}$ students should say to themselves, "the set of all x such that x is greater than 3."

Before working Try This *g*, you may suggest to students that they form the cross product $Q \times Q$.

Chalkboard Examples

1. Use the set $\{0, 2, 4, 6, 8\}$. Find $\{x \mid x \leq 4\}$.
   $\{x \mid x \leq 4\} = \{0, 2, 4\}$
2. Use the relation $R \times R$, where $R = \{1, 3, 5, 7\}$. Find $\{(x, y) \mid y = x + 2\}$.
   $\{(x, y) \mid y = x + 2\}$
   $= \{(1, 3), (3, 5), (5, 7)\}$

LESSON ENRICHMENT

Consider each of the following "relations." Express each as a Cartesian product.

1. x is married to y people × people
2. A owns b people × things

LESSON QUIZ

1. Find $A \times B$, where $A = \{1, 2, 3\}$ and $B = \{x, y.\}$
   $\{(1, x), (1, y), (2, x), (2, y), (3, x), (3, y)\}$
2. $E = \{1, 3, 5\}$. List the Cartesian product $E \times E$ determined by the relation $\leq$.
   $\{(1, 1), (1, 3), (1, 5), (3, 3), (3, 5), (5, 5)\}$
3. List the domain and range of the relation $\{(1, a), (3, b)\}$.
   Domain $\{1, 3\}$; range $\{a, b\}$
4. In the set $\{1, 3, 5, 7, 9\}$, find $\{x \mid 2 < x < 8\}$. $\{3, 5, 7\}$
5. $S = \{1, 2\}$. List all the pairs in $S \times S$ that are in $\{(x, y) \mid x < y\}$.
   $(1, 2)$

Assignment Guide

Algebra: 1–29 e/o, MR

Alg w/Finite or Trig: 1–31 e/o, 32, MR

Comprehensive: 1–31 e/o, 32–34, MR

Using Set-Builder Notation

Objective: Use set-builder notation to describe a relation.

In a set or relation, we often need to refer to those elements that satisfy a certain condition. With respect to the set $\{1, 2, 3, 4, 5, 6\}$, we may refer to the set of all x such that x is greater than 3. The numbers 4, 5, and 6 satisfy this condition. Thus we write

$$\{x \mid x > 3\} = \{4, 5, 6\}$$

$\{x \mid x > 3\}$ is set-builder notation.

EXAMPLE 4

Use the set $\{1, 2, 3, 4, 5, \ldots, 10\}$. Find $\{x \mid 2 < x < 8\}$.

The numbers 3, 4, 5, 6, and 7 satisfy both conditions, $x < 8$ and $x > 2$.

$$\{x \mid 2 < x < 8\} = \{3, 4, 5, 6, 7\}$$

EXAMPLE 5

Use the relation $Q \times Q$, where $Q = \{2, 3, 4, 5\}$. Find $\{(x, y) \mid y > x + 1\}$.

We check each ordered pair to find those that satisfy $y > x + 1$.

$$\{(x, y) \mid y > x + 1\} = \{(2, 5), (2, 4), (3, 5)\}$$

Try This

f. Use the set $\{1, 2, 3, \ldots, 10\}$. Find $\{x \mid 5 < x < 7\}$ $\{6\}$

g. Use the set $Q \times Q$, where $Q = \{2, 3, 4, 5\}$. Find $\{(x, y) \mid x > 2 \text{ and } y > 3\}$.
$\{(3, 4), (3, 5), (4, 4), (4, 5), (5, 4), (5, 5)\}$

3-1 EXERCISES

A

Find the following Cartesian products.

1. $A \times B$ where $A = \{$chili, pizza, salad$\}$ and $B = \{$cheese, onions, peppers$\}$

2. $A \times B$ where $A = \{$omelette, scrambled$\}$ and $B = \{$bacon, sausage$\}$

3. $B \times C$, where $B = \{x, y, z\}$ and $C = \{1, 2\}$

4. $B \times C$, where $B = \{5, 7, 10\}$ and $C = \{a, z\}$

5. $D \times D$, where $D = \{5, 6, 7, 8\}$

6. $E \times E$, where $E = \{-2, 0, 2, 4\}$

Consider the relation $E \times E$, where $E = \{-7, -3, 1, 2, 5\}$. List the set of ordered pairs determined by the relations.

7. $<$ (less than)

8. $>$ (greater than)

9. $\leq$ (less than or equal)

10. $\geq$ (greater than or equal)

11. $=$ (equal)

12. $\neq$ (not equal)

List the domain and the range for each of the following relations.

13. $\{(5, 2), (6, 4), (8, 6)\}$

14. $\{(7, 1), (8, 2), (9, 5)\}$

15. $\{(6, 0), (7, 5), (8, 5)\}$

16. $\{(8, 2), (10, 1), (6, 3)\}$

17. $\{(8, 1), (8, 1), (5, 1)\}$

18. $\{(6, 2), (2, 0), (-3, 0)\}$

19. $\{(5, 6)\}$

20. $\{(7, -4)\}$

Use the set C, where $C = \{2, 4, 6, 8, 10, 12\}$. Find the set indicated by each of the following.

21. $\{x|x > 7\}$ {8, 10, 12} **22.** $\{x|3 < x < 10\}$ {4, 6, 8} **23.** $\{x|x > 6 \text{ or } x < 3\}$ {2, 8, 10, 12}

Consider the relation $A \times A$, where $A = \{2, 3, 4, 5\}$. Find the sets indicated by each of the following.

24. $\{(x, y)|x \leq 2 \text{ and } y \leq 3\}$

25. $\{(x, y)|x > 4 \text{ and } y < 4\}$

26. $\{(x, y)|2 \leq x \leq 3 \text{ and } y = 3\}$

27. $\{(x, y)|x < 4 \text{ and } 4 \leq y \leq 5\}$

28. $\{(x, y)|x = 3 \text{ and } y = 2\}$

29. $\{(x, y)|2 < x < 4 \text{ and } 2 < y < 5\}$

B For Exercises 30-31, and 33-34, see Teacher's Answer Section.

30. a. Find the Cartesian product $D \times D$ where $D = \{-1, 0, 1, 2\}$.
b. Find the set of ordered pairs determined by the relation $\neq$.
c. List the domain and the range of this relation.
d. Find $\{(x, y)|x^2 = y^2\}$.

31. a. Find the Cartesian product $E \times E$, where $E = \{-1, 1, 3, 5\}$.
b. Find the set of ordered pairs determined by the relation $\leq$.
c. List the domain and the range of this relation.
d. Find $\{(x, y) \mid |x| < |y|\}$.

32. ***Critical Thinking*** List three different relations that have the same domain and range. Answers may vary.

Challenge

Consider the set of all ordered triples (x, y, z) where x, y, and z are real numbers. Every subset of $R \times R \times R$ is called a relation in $R \times R \times R$.

33. List any five ordered triples in $A = \{(x, y, z)|x = 3, y > 0 \text{ and } z = y^2\}$.

34. List any five ordered triples in $B = \{(x, y, z)|x = 2y, y < 0 \text{ and } z = y^3\}$.

Mixed Review

Evaluate for $a = 3, b = -5$. **35.** $(a + b)^2$ **36.** $4a - 3b$

Evaluate for $a = 4, b = -1$. **37.** b^a **38.** $-a|2b|$

Simplify. **39.** $c^{-4} \cdot c^3 \cdot c^7$ **40.** $(-4x^2y^{-3})(2x^3y^2)$

Solve and graph. **41.** $\left(\frac{1}{3}\right)y + 5 > \left(\frac{3}{4}\right)y$ **42.** $-4 < x - 3 < 5$

Solve. **43.** $-5t - \frac{1}{8} < \frac{1}{2} - 3t$

ADDITIONAL ANSWERS

Exercises

1. {(chili, cheese), (chili, onions), (chili peppers), (pizza, cheese), (pizza, onions), (pizza, peppers), (salad, cheese), (salad, onions), (salad, peppers)}

2. {(omelette, bacon), (omelette, sausage), (scrambled, bacon), (scrambled, sausage)}

3. {(x, 1), (x, 2), (y, 1), (y, 2), (z, 1), (z, 2)}

4. {(5, a), (5, z), (7, a), (7, z), (10, a), (10, z)}

5. {(5, 5), (5, 6),(5, 7), (5, 8), (6, 5), (6, 6), (6, 7), (6, 8), (7, 5), (7, 6), (7, 7), (7, 8), (8, 5), (8, 6), (8, 7), (8, 8)}

6. {(−2, −2), (−2, 0), (−2, 2), (−2, 4), (0, −2), (0, 0), (0, 2), (0, 4), (2, −2), (2, 0), (2, 2), (2, 4), (4, −2), (4, 0), (4, 2), (4, 4)}

7. {(−7, −3), (−7, 1), (−7, 2), (−7, 5), (−3, 1), (−3, 2), (−3, 5), (1, 2), (1, 5), (2, 5)}

8. {(−3, −7), (1, −3), (1, −7), (2, 1), (2, −3), (2, −7), (5, 2), (5, 1), (5, −3), (5, −7)}

9. {(−7, −7), (−7, −3), (−7, 1), (−7, 2), (−7, 5), (−3, −3), (−3, 1), (−3, 2), (−3, 5), (1, 1), (1, 2), (1, 5), (2, 2), (2, 5), (5, 5)}

10. {(−7, −7), (−3, −3), (−3, −7), (1, 1), (1, −3), (1, −7), (2, 2), (2, 1), (2, −3), (2, −7), (5, 5), (5, 2), (5, 1), (5, −3), (5, −7)}

11. {(−7, −7), (−3, −3), (1, 1), (2, 2), (5, 5)}

12. {(−7, −3), (−7, 1), (−7, 2), (−7, 5), (−3, −7), (−3, 1), (−3, 2), (−3, 5), (1, −7), (1, −3), (1, 2), (1, 5), (2, −7), (2, −3), (2, 1), (2, 5), (5, −7), (5, −3), (5, 1), (5, 2)}

13. Domain {5, 6, 8}; range {2, 4, 6}

14. Domain {7, 8, 9}; range {1, 2, 5}

15. Domain {6, 7, 8}; range {0, 5}

16. Domain {8, 10, 6}; range {2, 1, 3}

17. Domain {8, 5}; range {1}

18. Domain {6, 2, −3}; range {2, 0}

19. Domain {5}; range {6}

20. Domain {7}; range {−4}

24. {(2, 2) (2, 3)} **25.** {(5, 2), (5, 3)}

26. {(2, 3), (3, 3)}

27. {(2, 4), (2, 5), (3, 4), (3, 5)}

28. {(3, 2)} **29.** {(3, 3), (3, 4)}

Mixed Review

35. 4 **36.** 27

37. 1 **38.** −8

39. c^6 **40.** $-8x^5y^{-1}$

41. $y < 12$ **42.** $-1 < x < 8$

43. $t > -\frac{5}{16}$

3-2

FIRST FIVE MINUTES

Use $R = \{0, 1, 2, 3, 4, 5, 6, 7, 8, 9\}$.
List the Cartesian product $R \times R$.

1. $\{(x, y) \mid x = y\}$
   $\{(0, 0), (1, 1), (2, 2), (3, 3), (4, 4), (5, 5), (6, 6), (7, 7), (8, 8), (9, 9)\}$
2. $\{(x, y) \mid y = 2x\}$
   $\{(0, 0), (1, 2), (2, 4), (3, 6), (4, 8)\}$
3. $\{(x, y) \mid x > 8 \text{ and } y > 8\}$
   $\{(9, 9)\}$

Graphing Relations

The decision to associate the first coordinate, or x-coordinate, with the horizontal axis is completely arbitrary. Nevertheless this convention is almost universally adopted.

When letters other than x or y are used for coordinates, the letter which comes first in the alphabet is used for the horizontal axis.

Avoiding Common Errors

Students often associate the coordinates with the wrong axes. Remind students that the first coordinate indicates a distance right or left and the second coordinate indicates a distance up or down.

Key Questions

- Is (3, 6) the same point as (6, 3)?
  No
- Is the first member of an ordered pair the x-coordinate or the y-coordinate?
  The x coordinate

Chalkboard Example

1. Graph the relation $\{(2, 1), (-1, 2), (-2, -1), (1, -2)\}$.

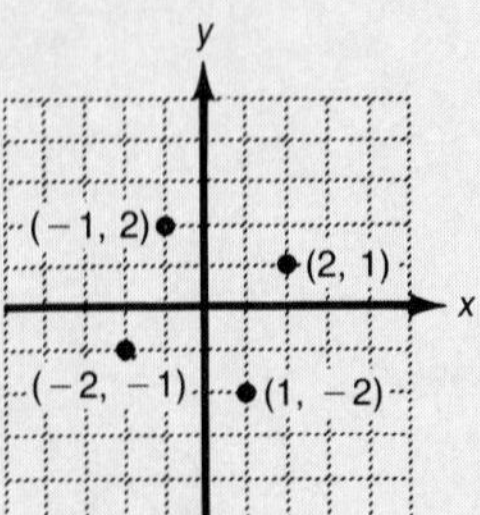

3-2 Graphs

Graphing Relations

Objective: Graph the ordered pairs of a relation.

Most of the relations we will work with involve $R \times R$, where R is the set of real numbers. The set R is infinite. Thus relations involving R may be infinite and therefore cannot be indicated by listing the ordered pairs. We can indicate such relations with a **graph.**

On a number line each point corresponds to a number. On a plane each point corresponds to an ordered pair of numbers from $R \times R$. To represent $R \times R$, we draw an **x-axis** and a **y-axis** perpendicular to each other. Their intersection is called the **origin** and is labeled 0. The arrows show the positive directions. This is called the **Cartesian coordinate system.** The figure below shows the graph of the relation $\{(4, 3), (-3, 5), (-4, -2), (3, -4)\}$.

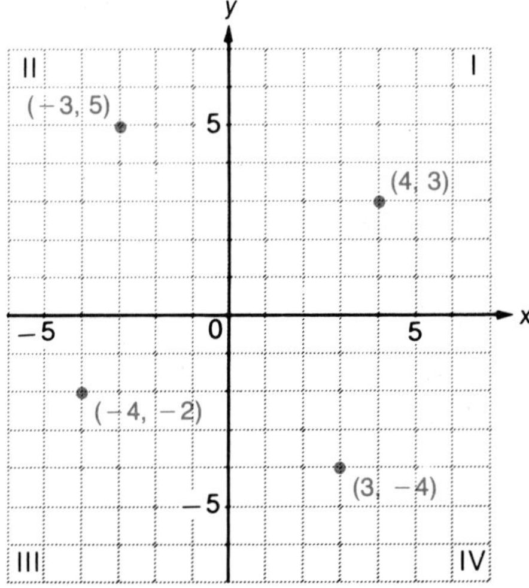

The first member of an ordered pair is called the **x-coordinate,** or **abscissa.** The second member is called the **y-coordinate,** or **ordinate.** Together these are called the **coordinates of a point.**

The axes divide the plane into four regions called **quadrants,** indicated by the Roman numerals numbered counterclockwise from the upper right.

To graph the relation, we plot the points that correspond to the ordered pairs in the relation.

EXAMPLE 1 Graph the relation $\{(-3, 2), (-1, -4), (4, 3), (5, 5)\}$.

For the ordered pair $(-3, 2)$, the x-coordinate tells us to move 3 units to the left of the y-axis. The y-coordinate tells us to move 2 units up from the x-axis.

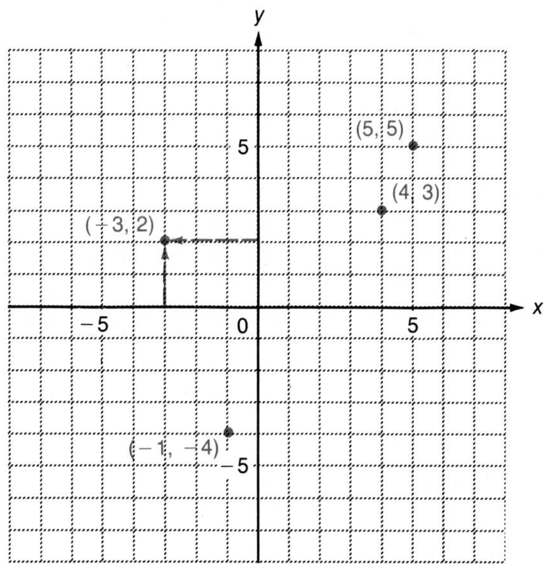

Try This Graph each relation. See Additional Answers.

a. $\{(-2, -2), (1, -4), (5, 6), (-3, 5), (0, 8)\}$

b. $\{(3, 2), (-5, 2), (-4, 3), (-4, 0), (3, -7)\}$

Solutions of Equations

Objective: Determine whether an ordered pair is a solution of an equation.

If an equation has two variables, its solutions are ordered pairs of numbers. A **solution** is an ordered pair such that when the numbers are substituted for the variables, a true equation is produced.

EXAMPLE 2 Determine whether the given ordered pairs are solutions of this equation.

$(-1, -4)$ and $(7, 5)$; $y = 3x - 1$

y	$= 3x - 1$	
-4	$3(-1) - 1$	Substituting -1 for x and -4 for y
-4	$-3 - 1$	
-4	-4 ✓	

The equation becomes true, so $(-1, -4)$ is a solution.

Solutions of Equations

Avoiding Common Errors

When an equation is written in the form $y = 5x - 2$, students will occasionally substitute the first coordinate of (1, 3) in the variable y because it appears first in the equation. Emphasize that the first coordinate replaces the variable x and the second coordinate replaces the variable y.

Chalkboard Example

1. Determine whether the ordered pair (1, 3) is a solution of the equation $y = 5x - 2$.
   Substitute 1 for x and 3 for y. Check the equation.
   $(3) = 5(1) - 2$
   $3 = 5 - 2$
   $3 = 3$
   The pair (1, 3) does satisfy the equation $y = 5x - 2$.

Graphing Equations

Students will need to plot enough points to determine the pattern of the graph. Linear equations require only 2 points, while equations of higher degree can require many points.

Point out that there is an infinite number of pairs of points for each equation and that the same graph can be determined from a wide variety of points.

Math Point
The first person to fully appreciate and exploit the graphing method described in this chapter was René Descartes (Re-nay Day-cart), (1596 – 1650), a French mathematician, philosopher, and scientist. Descartes was concerned with the correct methods for obtaining true knowledge. He questioned everything, even his own existence. His most famous saying is, "I think, therefore I am."

Avoiding Common Errors
Students will commonly find two or three points and then connect them with jagged straight-line segments. Emphasize that it is known that equations of degree 2 or greater generally have smoothly curved graphs. Such equations may require many pairs to identify the nature of the curve.

y	$= \; 3x - 1$	
5	$3 \cdot 7 - 1$	Substituting 7 for x and 5 for y
5	$21 - 1$	
5	20	

The equation becomes false, so (7, 5) is not a solution.

Try This Determine whether the given ordered pairs are solutions of the indicated equation.

c. $(1, 7), (2, 9); y = 2x + 5$ Yes; yes

d. $(-1, 4), (0, 6); y = -2x + 5$ No; no

e. $(-2, 5), (3, 9); y = x^2$ No; yes

Graphing Equations

Objective: Graph equations by plotting several solutions.

The solutions of an equation with two variables are ordered pairs and thus determine a relation. Here are some general suggestions for graphing an equation.

Guidelines for Graphing

1. Use graph paper.
2. Label axes with symbols for the variables.
3. Use arrows to indicate positive directions.
4. Mark numbers on the axes for scale.
5. Plot solutions and complete the graph.
6. Label the equation or relation being graphed.

EXAMPLE 3 Graph $y = 3x - 1$.

Find some ordered pairs that are solutions. We can choose *any* number that is a possible replacement for x and then determine y.

Let $x = 0$. Then $y = 3(0) - 1 = -1$.
So $(0, -1)$ is a solution.

Let $x = 1$. Then $y = 3(1) - 1 = 2$.
So $(1, 2)$ is a solution.

Let $x = 2$. Then $y = 3(2) - 1 = 5$.
So $(2, 5)$ is a solution.

Let $x = -1$. Then $y = 3(-1) - 1 = -4$.
So $(-1, -4)$ is a solution.

Let $x = -2$. Then $y = 3(-2) - 1 = -7$.
So $(-2, -7)$ is a solution.

We record the solutions in a table.

x	y
0	−1
1	2
2	5
−1	−4
−2	−7

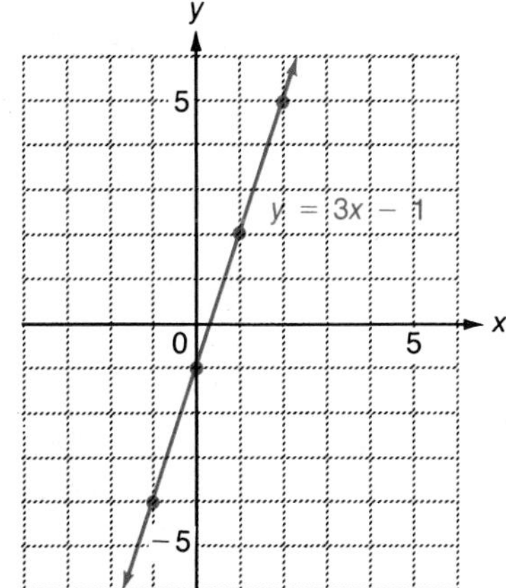

Next we plot these points. If we could plot all solutions, they would form a line. We can draw the line with a straightedge, and label it $y = 3x - 1$. The relation consists of all pairs (x, y) such that $y = 3x - 1$ is true. That is, $\{(x, y) | y = 3x - 1\}$.

Note that the equation $y = 3x - 1$ has an infinite set of solutions. The graph of the equation is a drawing of the solution set.

Try This Graph each of the following. See Selected Answers.

f. $y = -3x + 1$ **g.** $y = \frac{1}{2}x + 2$

EXAMPLE 4 Graph $y = x^2 - 5$.

We select numbers for x and find the corresponding values for y. The table gives us the ordered pairs $(0, -5)$, $(-1, -4)$, and so on.

x	y
0	−5
1	−4
2	−1
3	4
−1	−4
−2	−1
−3	4

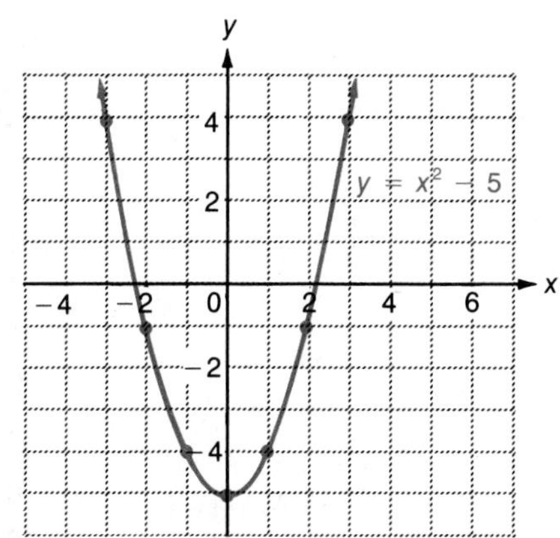

Next we plot these points. We note that as the absolute value of x increases, $x^2 - 5$ also increases. Thus the graph is a curve that rises gradually on either side of the y-axis, as shown above. This graph shows the relation $\{(x, y) | y = x^2 - 5\}$.

Chalkboard Examples

1. Graph $y = 2x - 1$.
   Find some ordered pairs. Choose some values for x; compute the corresponding value for y.
   Let $x = 0$, then $y = -1$.
   Let $x = 1$, then $y = 1$.
   Let $x = -1$, then $y = -3$.
   Here are the values written in a table.

x	y
−1	−3
0	−1
1	1

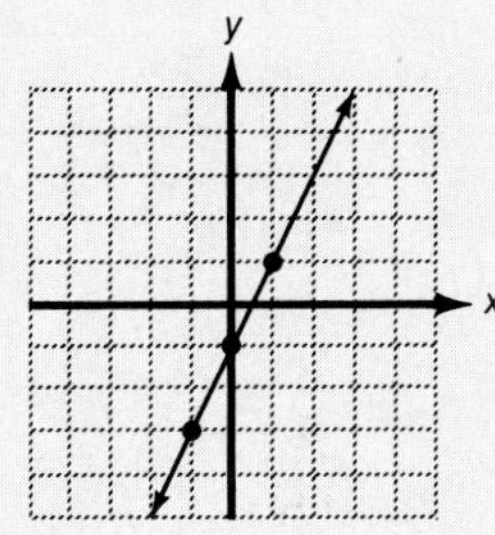

2. Graph $y = -x^2$.
   Choose some x values and compute the corresponding y values.

x	y
−2	−4
$-\frac{3}{2}$	$-\frac{9}{4}$
−1	−1
$-\frac{1}{2}$	$-\frac{1}{4}$
0	0
$\frac{1}{2}$	$-\frac{1}{4}$
1	−1
$\frac{3}{2}$	$-\frac{9}{4}$
2	−4

Plot these points and connect them with a smooth curved line.

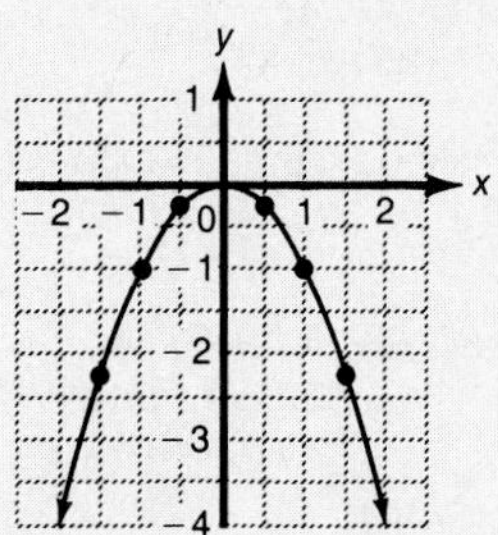

LESSON QUIZ

1. Plot the points of the following relation. $\{(2, 1), (0, 2), (-1, -1), (1, -1)\}$

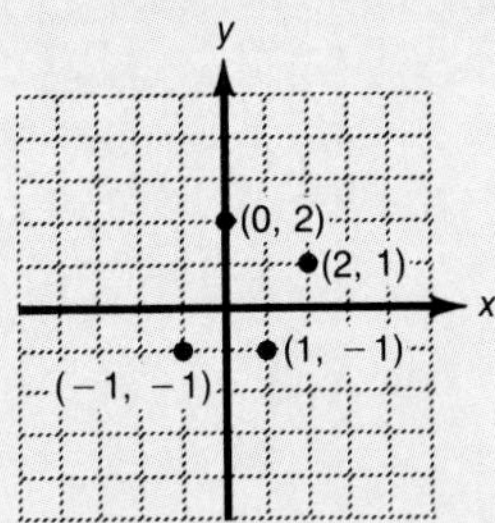

2. Determine whether the ordered pair $(2, -1)$ is a solution of the equation $y = 4x - 9$.
$-1 = 4(2) - 9$
$-1 = -1$
The pair is a solution.
3. Graph $y = 3x + 2$

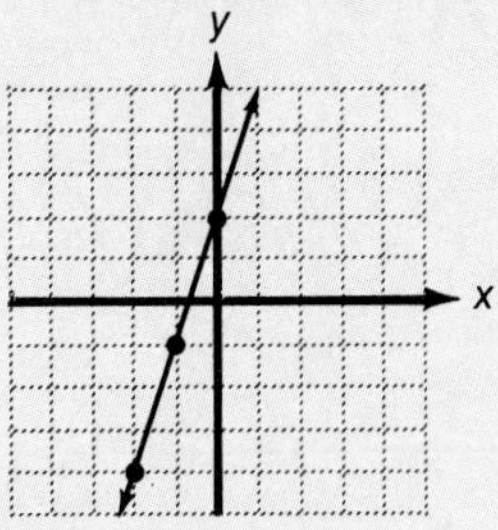

4. Graph the curve $y = x^2 - 3$.

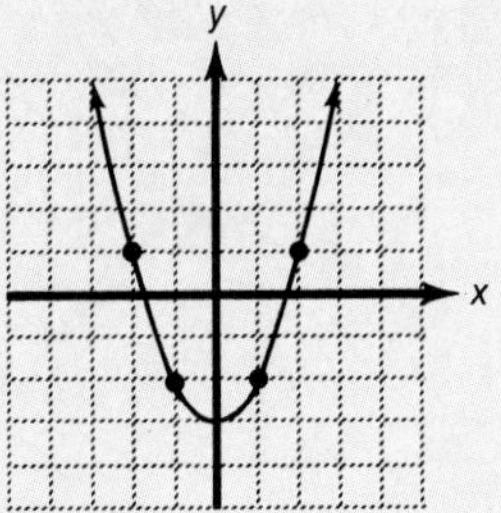

Assignment Guide
Algebra: 1–35 e/o, MR

Alg w/Finite or Trig: 1–35 m3, 36–54 e/o, 55, MR

Comprehensive: 1–54 m3, 55, 56–59 e/o, MR, assign w. 3-3

Try This Graph each of the following. See Selected Answers.

h. $y = 3 - x^2$ **i.** $x = y^2 - 5$ (Hint: Select values for y.)

3-2 EXERCISES

A

Graph each relation.

1. $\{(3, 0), (4, 2), (5, 4), (6, 6)\}$
2. $\{(1, 1), (2, 3), (3, 5), (4, 7)\}$
3. $\{(3, -4), (3, -3), (3, -2), (3, -1), (3, 0)\}$
4. $\{(-2, 1), (-2, 2), (-2, 3), (-2, 4), (-2, 5)\}$
5. $\{(4, 3), (4, 2), (3, 2), (3, 3), (5, 2), (5, 3)\}$
6. $\{(2, -2), (3, -2), (2, -3), (3, -3), (2, -4), (3, -4)\}$
7. $\{(-1, 1), (-2, 1), (-2, 2), (-3, 1), (-3, 2), (-3, 3)\}$
8. $\{(-1, -1), (-1, -2), (-1, -3), (-2, -2), (-2, -3), (-3, -3)\}$

Determine whether the given ordered pairs are solutions of the indicated equation.

9. $(1, -1), (0, 3)$; $y = 2x - 3$ Yes; no
10. $(2, 5), (-2, -7)$; $y = 3x - 1$ Yes, yes
11. $(3, 4), (-3, 5)$; $3s + t = 4$ No; no
12. $(2, 3), (-5, 15)$; $2p + q = 5$ No; yes
13. $(3, 5), (-2, -15)$; $4x - y = 7$ Yes; yes
14. $(2, 7), (-1, 8)$; $5x - y = 3$ Yes; no
15. $\left(0, \frac{3}{5}\right), \left(-\frac{1}{2}, -\frac{4}{5}\right)$; $2a + 5b = 3$ Yes; no
16. $\left(0, \frac{3}{2}\right), \left(\frac{2}{3}, 1\right)$; $3f + 4g = 6$ Yes; yes
17. $(2, -1), (-0.75, 2.75)$; $4r + 3s = 5$ Yes; no
18. $(2, -4), (2.4, -5)$; $5w + 2z = 2$ Yes; yes
19. $(3, 2), (22, 31)$; $-3x + 2y = -4$ No; yes
20. $(1, 2), (-40, 14)$; $2x - 5y = -6$ No; no

Graph each of the following.

21. $y = x$
22. $y = 2x$
23. $y = -2x$
24. $y = -\frac{1}{2}x$
25. $y = x + 3$
26. $y = x - 2$
27. $y = 3x - 2$
28. $y = -4x + 1$
29. $y = -2x + 3$
30. $y = x^2$
31. $y = -x^2$
32. $y = x^2 + 2$
33. $y = x^2 - 2$
34. $x = y^2 + 2$
35. $x = y^2 - 2$

B

36–41. Indicate the domain and range for each relation in Exercises 30–35.

42. Draw a triangle with vertices at (1, 1), (4, 2), and (3, 6). Shade the triangle and its interior.
a. Shade (on the x-axis) the domain. Describe the domain. $\{x \mid 1 \le x \le 4\}$
b. Shade (on the y-axis) the range. Describe the range. $\{y \mid 1 \le y \le 6\}$

43. Draw a circle with radius of length 2, centered at (4, 3). Shade its interior.
   a. Shade (on the x-axis) the domain. Describe the domain. $\{x \mid 2 \le x \le 6\}$
   b. Shade (on the y-axis) the range. Describe the range. $\{y \mid 1 \le y \le 5\}$

Graph each relation. All relations are in $R \times R$, where R is the set of real numbers.

	First Coordinate	Second Coordinate
44.	any real number	2
45.	-3	any real number
46.	any real number	1 more than the first coordinate
47.	any real number	1 less than the first coordinate
48.	any real number	twice the first coordinate
49.	any real number	the square of the first coordinate
50.	the second coordinate squared	any real number

Consider $M \times M$, where $M = \{-5, -4, -3, \ldots, 4, 5\}$. Graph each relation.

51. $\{(x, y) \mid y > 2x\}$

52. $\{(x, y) \mid -3 < x < 3 \text{ and } y = 0\}$

53. $\{(x, y) \mid x^2 + y^2 > 25\}$

54. $\{(x, y) \mid x \cdot y = 0\}$

55. ***Critical Thinking*** Find and graph three equations that have $(-2, 1)$ as a solution.

Challenge

Graph the following relations in $R \times R$.

56. $\{(x, y) \mid 1 \le x \le 4 \text{ and } -3 \le y \le -1\}$

57. $\{(x, y) \mid -1 \le x \le 1 \text{ and } -4 \le y \le 4\}$

Use a calculator to find ordered pairs. Graph using 20 values of x between -5 and 5.

58. $y = \frac{1}{3}x^3 - x + \frac{2}{3}$

59. $y = \frac{1}{3}x^3 - \frac{1}{2}x^2 - 2x + 1$

Mixed Review

Solve. **60.** $|a - 11| - 7 = -2$ **61.** $2(y^2 - y) = \frac{1}{2}(4y^2 + 10)$

62. The sum of three consecutive odd integers is 41 more than twice the smallest. Find the three integers.

63. A $2\frac{1}{2}$-ft ribbon is cut in two so that the shorter piece is $\frac{1}{4}$ the length of the longer piece. How long is each piece of ribbon?

64. Rae invested \$500. The money she deposited in account A earned 6% annual interest, while the amount in account B earned 8%. At the end of the year, she had a total of \$535 in the two accounts. How much had she invested in each account?

WRITING TO LEARN

Write a paragraph in which you explain how the idea of a Cartesian coordinate system allows us to think of a plane as an infinite sheet of graph paper.

ADDITIONAL ANSWERS

Try This

a.

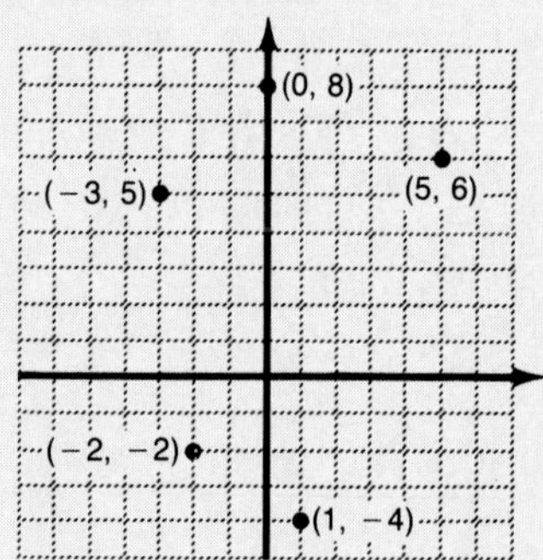

b.

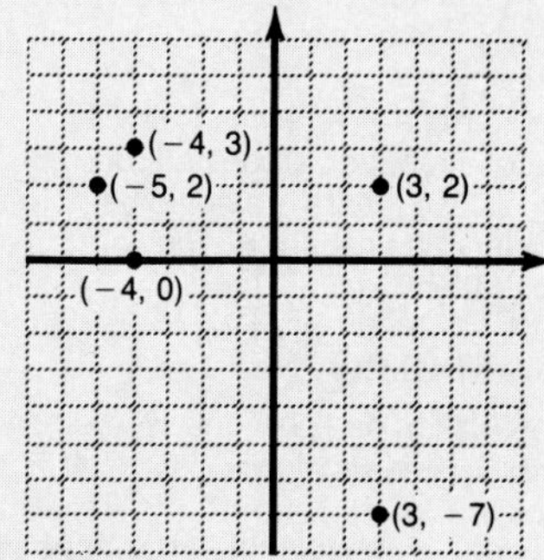

Exercises

For Exercises 1 – 8 and 21 – 35, see Teacher's Answer Section.

36. Domain R; range $\{y \mid y \ge 0\}$
37. Domain R; range $\{y \mid y \le 0\}$
38. Domain R; range $\{y \mid y \ge 2\}$
39. Domain R; range $\{y \mid y \ge -2\}$
40. Domain $\{x \mid x \ge 2\}$; range R
41. Domain $\{x \mid x \ge -2\}$; range R

For Exercises 42 – 59, see Teacher's Answer Section.

Mixed Review

60. 6, 16
61. $y = -\frac{5}{2}$
62. 35, 37, 39
63. 6 in., 24 in.
64. \$250 in *A*, \$250 in *B*

Writing to Learn

Paragraph should include the idea that the coordinate system sets up a one-to-one correspondence with the axes and the real number system. Since the real numbers are infinite, so are the coordinate axes.

3-3

FIRST FIVE MINUTES

In the following, use $S \times S$ where $S = \{0, 1, 2, 3\}$.

1. $\{(x, y) \mid y = x + 1\}$
   (0, 1), (1, 2), (2, 3)
2. $\{(x, y) \mid x > 1 \text{ and } y > 2\}$
   (2, 3), (3, 3)
3. $\{(x, y) \mid y = x^2\}$
   (0, 0), (1, 1)

Recognizing Functions

Point out that graphs such as $y = x^4$ have no vertical segments even though they seem to be vertical when $|x|$ is very large.

In Example 1, relations S and T include letters as part of the ordered pairs. These letters are not to be considered as variables. They are simply letters.

Key Questions

- If a relation has only one ordered pair, must it be a function?
  Yes
- If every member in the range appears only once in the relation, must the relation be a function?
  No

3-3 Functions

The number of innings credited to a baseball pitcher is based upon the number of outs recorded. One out corresponds to $\frac{1}{3}$ inning, two outs to $\frac{2}{3}$ inning, three outs to 1 inning, and so on. The number of innings is thus a function of the number of outs recorded. Relations where each member of the domain is matched with exactly one member of the range are called functions.

Recognizing Functions

Objective: Recognize functions and their graphs.

In a function, no two ordered pairs can have the same first coordinate and a different second coordinate. Thus each member of the domain determines exactly one member of the range.

The relation $A = \{(2, 3), (5, 9), (1, 0), (10, -2)\}$ is a function because no two ordered pairs have the same first coordinate and different second coordinates.

The relation $B = \{(4, 5), (4, 0), (-1, 9)\}$ is not a function because the ordered pairs (4, 5) and (4, 0) have the same first coordinate and different second coordinates.

EXAMPLE 1 Which of the following relations are functions?

$$R = \{(9, 1), (-5, -2), (2, -1), (3, -9)\}$$
$$S = \{(6, a), (8, f), (6, b), (-2, p)\}$$
$$T = \{(z, 7), (y, -5), (r, 7), (z, 0), (k, 0)\}$$
$$M = \{(2, 3), (4, 3), (7, 3), (0, 3), (17, 3), (-3, 3)\}$$

Relations R and M are functions. Relations S and T have ordered pairs with the same first coordinate and different second coordinates, and thus are not functions.

Try This

a. Which of the following relations are functions?

$A = \{(9, 0), (3, 8), (5, 8), (9, -1)\}$ Not a function
$B = \{(0, t), (9, e), (-2, q), (-5, b)\}$ Function
$C = \{(-3, 5), (7, -2), (4, -6)\}$ Function
$D = \{(0, 1), (1, 0), (-1, 1)\}$ Function
$E = \{(5, -5), (5, -5)\}$ Function

Suppose a relation has two ordered pairs with the same first coordinate, but different second coordinates. The graphs of these two ordered pairs would be points on the same vertical line. This gives us a method to test whether a graph is the graph of a function.

The Vertical Line Test

If it is possible for a vertical line to intersect a graph at more than one point, then the graph is not the graph of a function.

EXAMPLE 2 Which of the following are graphs of functions?

(a)

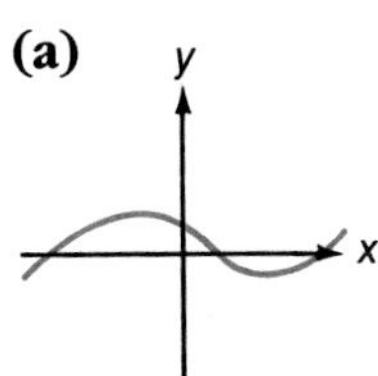

(b)

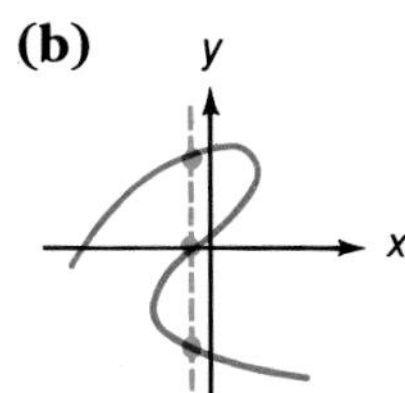

(c)

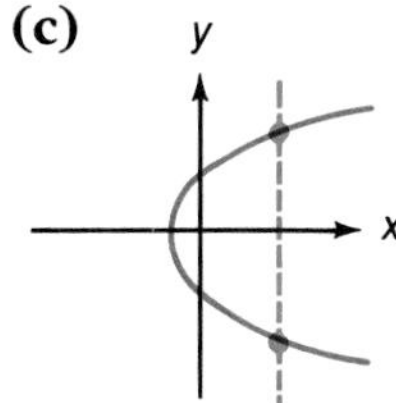

(d)

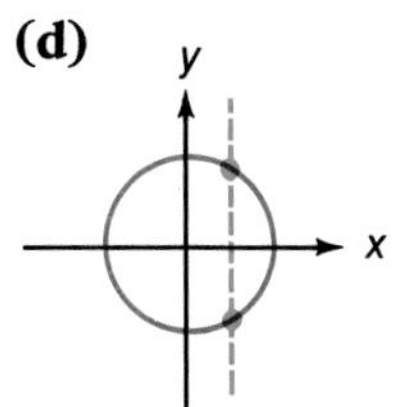

(e)

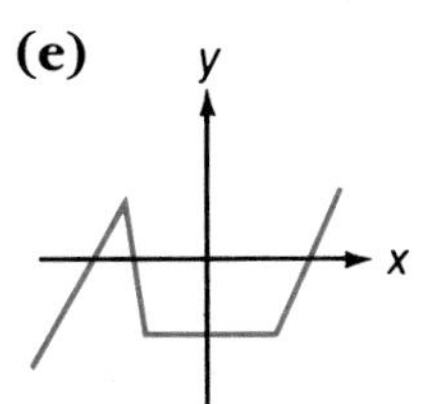

(f)

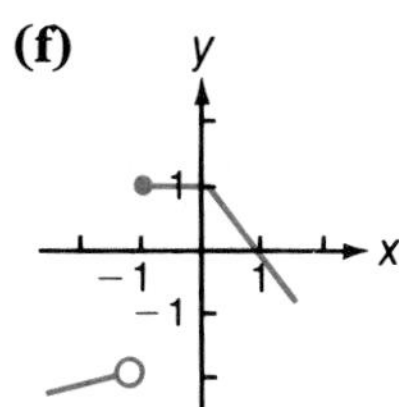

In graph f, the solid dot shows that $(-1, 1)$ belongs to the graph. The open dot shows that $(-1, 2)$ does not belong to the graph.

Examples a, e, and f are graphs of functions. Graphs b, c, and d fail the vertical line test.

Try This

b. Which of the following are graphs of functions?

(1)

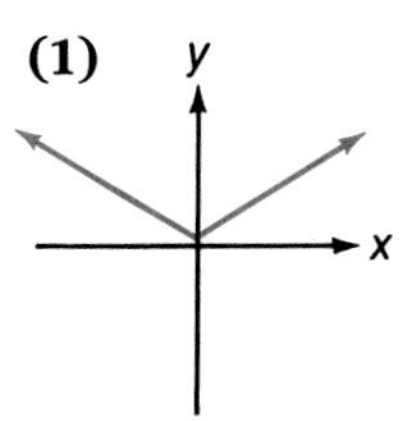

Yes

(2)

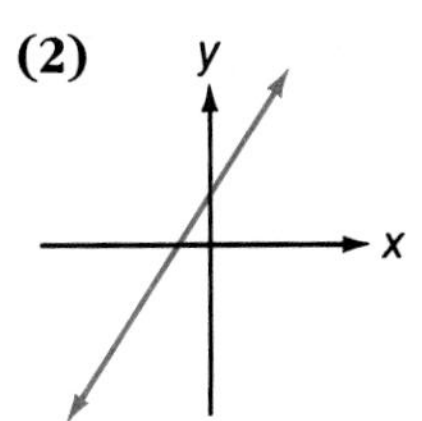

Yes

(3)

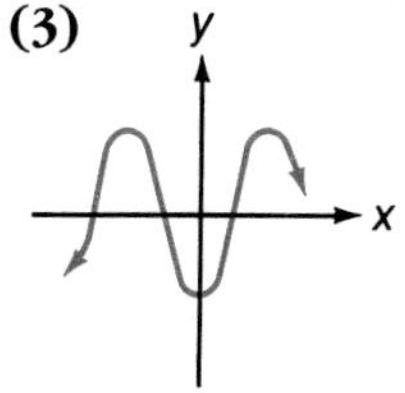

Yes

(4)

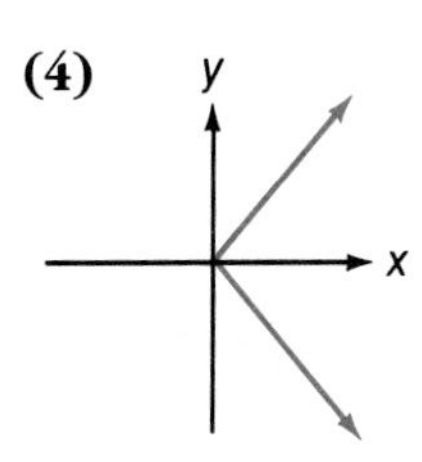

No

Chalkboard Examples T3

1. Which of the following are functions?
   $A = \{(1, 1), (1, 2), (1, 3)\}$
   No, this is not a function. Three different y-coordinates correspond to the x-coordinate 1.
   $B = \{(1, 3), (2, 3), (3, 3)\}$
   Yes, this is a function. No x-coordinate corresponds to more than one y-coordinate.
   $C = \{(1, 2), (2, 3), (3, 4)\}$
   Yes, this is a function. No x-coordinate corresponds to more than one y-coordinate.
   $D = \{(1, 2), (2, 2), (1, 0)\}$
   No, this is not a function. Two different y-coordinates correspond to the x-coordinate 1.
2. Which of the following are graphs of functions? b and c

a.

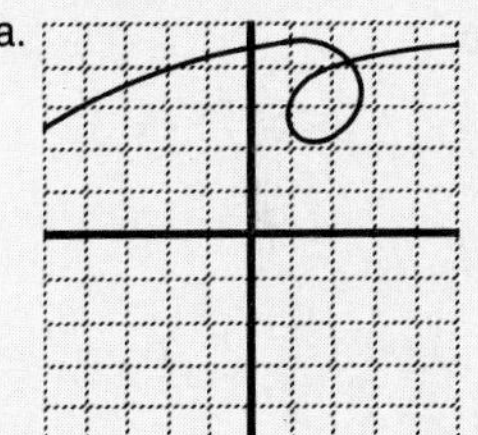

b.

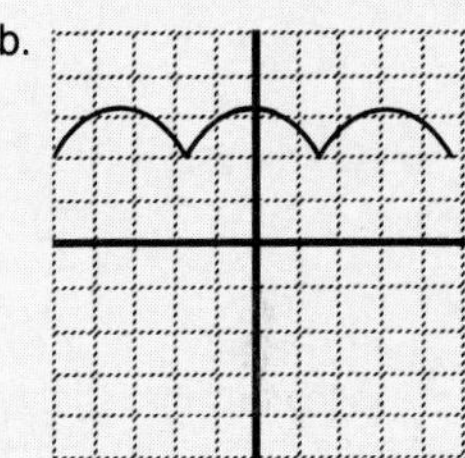

c.

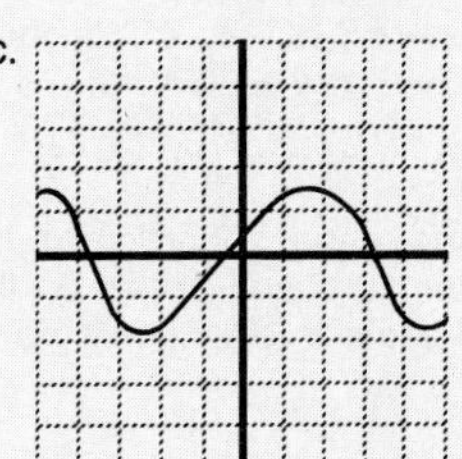

d.

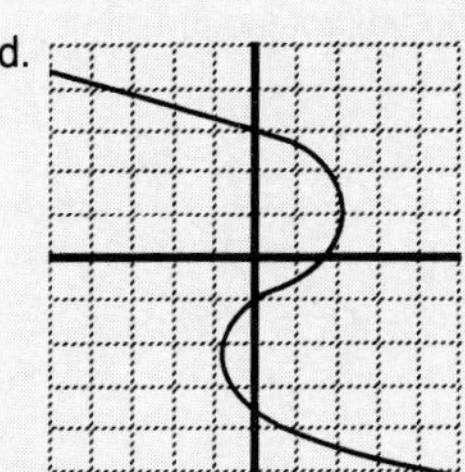

Function Notation

Point out that (x, y) and $(x, f(x))$ are interchangeable notations.

Emphasize that the function notation $f(x)$ is not multiplication and that $f(x)$ is read as "f of x."

Key Questions

- If $f(a) = f(b)$, must $a = b$? No
- If $f(x) = 0$, must $x = 0$? No
- If $a = b$, must $f(a) = f(b)$? Yes

Chalkboard Examples

1. Consider the function $f = \{(1, 1), (2, 4), (3, 9)\}$. Find $f(1)$, $f(2)$, $f(3)$.
   $f(1) = 1$
   $f(2) = 4$
   $f(3) = 9$
2. $g(x) = 1 + x + x^2$. Find each of the following.
   a. $g(0)$
      $g(0) = 1 + (0) + (0)^2 = 1$
   b. $g(1)$
      $g(1) = 1 + (1) + (1)^2 = 3$
   c. $g(-2)$
      $g(-2) = 1 + (-2) + (-2)^2$
      $= 1 - 2 + 4 = 3$
   d. $g(b^2)$
      $g(b^2) = 1 + (b^2) + (b^2)^2$
      $= 1 + b^2 + b^4$

Finding the Domain of a Function

Point out that the domain is part of the definition of a function and that changing the domain changes the function. For example, if the domain is the set of positive integers less than 7, then the function defined by $y = \frac{6}{x}$ is the set $\{(1, 6), (2,3), (3, 2), (4, 1.5), (5, 1.2), (6, 1)\}$.

On the other hand, if the domain is the set of real numbers (except 0), then the function consists of infinitely many pairs.

Chalkboard Example

1. Find the domain of the function $y = \frac{x}{x - 1}$.
   The domain is the set of real numbers, except $x = 1$. In the case $x = 1$, the denominator is 0 and the function is undefined.

Function Notation

Objective: Use function notation to find function values.

Functions are often named by letters. Since a function is a relation, a function f is thus a set of ordered pairs. We can represent the first coordinate of a pair by x, the second coordinate y by $f(x)$. The ordered pair is then $(x, f(x))$. The symbol $f(x)$ is read "f of x." The number represented by $f(x)$ is called the value of the function at x.

EXAMPLE 3 Find $g(2)$ and $g(5)$ for $g = \{(1, 4), (2, 3), (3, 2), (4, -8), (5, 2)\}$.

Since we have the ordered pair $(2, 3)$, $g(2) = 3$. Similarly, $(5, 2)$ gives us $g(5) = 2$.

Try This

c. Consider the function $h = \{(-4, 0), (9, 1), (-3, -2) (6, 6), (0, -2)\}$. Find $h(9)$, $h(6)$, and $h(0)$. $h(9) = 1$; $h(6) = 6$; $h(0) = -2$

Some functions can be defined by formulas or equations. Function values can be obtained by making substitutions for the variables.

EXAMPLE 4 $f(x) = 2x^2 - 3$. Find each of the following.

	$f(x) = 2x^2 - 3$
(a) $f(0)$	$f(0) = 2 \cdot 0^2 - 3 = -3$
(b) $f(-3)$	$f(-3) = 2(-3)^2 - 3 = 18 - 3 = 15$
(c) $f(5a)$	$f(5a) = 2(5a)^2 - 3 = 2(25a^2) - 3 = 50a^2 - 3$

Try This Find each of the following for $f(x) = 3x^2 + 1$.

d. $f(0)$ 1 **e.** $f(1)$ 4 **f.** $f(-1)$ 4 **g.** $f(2a)$ $12a^2 + 1$

Finding the Domain of a Function

Objective: Find the domain of a function, given a formula for the function.

When a function in $R \times R$ is given by a formula, the domain is understood to be all real numbers that are acceptable replacements.

EXAMPLE 5 What is the domain of f for $f(x) = \frac{x - 4}{x + 3}$?

To find the domain of f, we must determine whether there are any unacceptable replacements. Notice what happens when $x = -3$.

$$f(-3) = \frac{-3 - 4}{-3 + 3} = \frac{-7}{0}$$

Since we cannot divide by 0, the replacement -3 is not acceptable. When a replacement is not acceptable, that number is not in the domain of the function. Thus the domain of f is $\{x \mid x \neq -3\}$.

Try This

h. $g(x) = \frac{x}{(x-1)(x+3)}$. What is the domain of g? $\{x \mid x \neq 1 \text{ and } x \neq -3\}$

i. $h(x) = 3x + 9$. What is the domain of h? $\{x \mid x \text{ is a real number}\}$

j. $p(x) = \frac{x-2}{3} - \frac{1}{3x}$. What is the domain of p? $\{x \mid x \neq 0\}$

3-3 EXERCISES

A

Which of the following relations are functions?

1. $K = \{(1, 2), (2, 3), (3, 4), (4, 1)\}$ Yes
2. $L = \{(3, -5), (0, 0), (-5, 3), (-3, -5)\}$ Yes
3. $T = \{(-4, -4), (-1, -6), (-4, 4), (-6, -1)\}$ No
4. $V = \{(2, -9), (4, 2), (0, 5), (4, -9)\}$ No
5. $B = \{(6, -6), (-2, 2), (0, 0), (2, -2), (-6, 6)\}$ Yes
6. $F = \{(0, a), (1, a), (-1, a), (1, -1), (-1, -1)\}$ No, unless $a = -1$

Which of the following are graphs of functions?

7. Yes

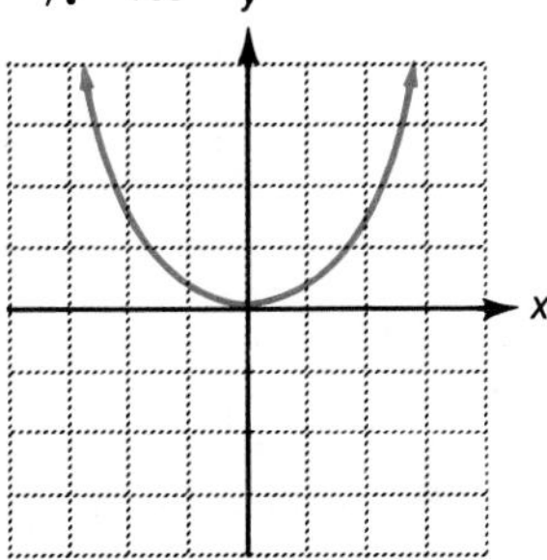

8. Yes

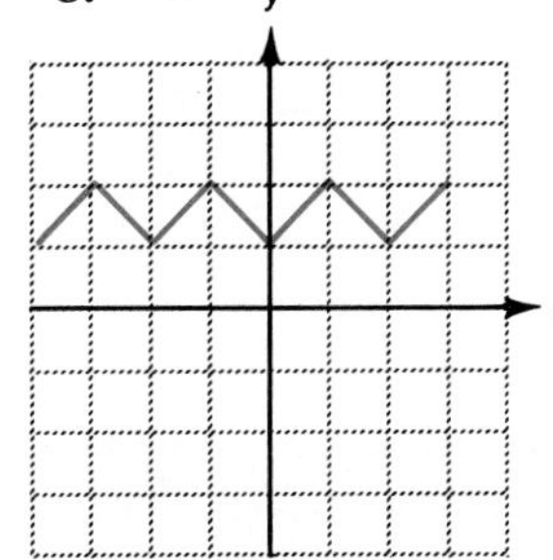

9. No

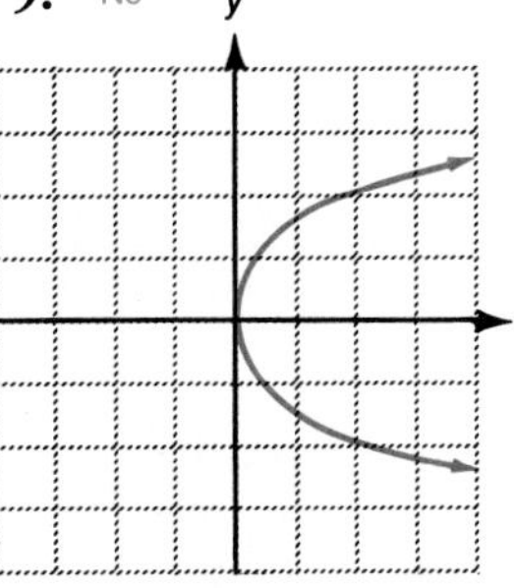

10. No

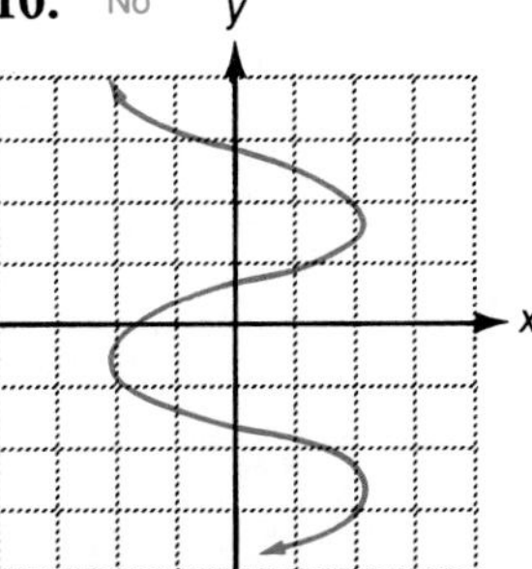

11. Yes

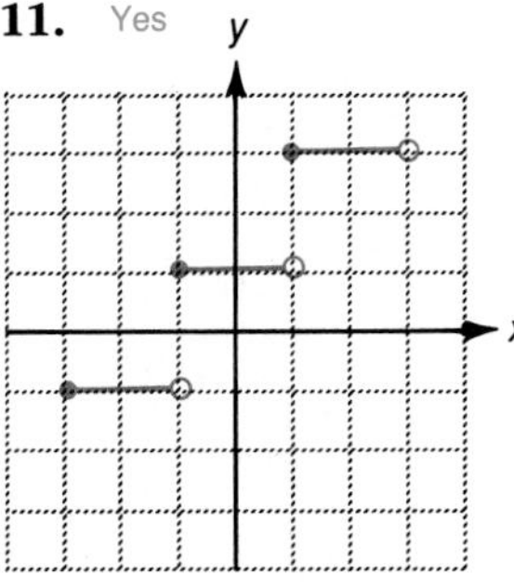

12. Yes

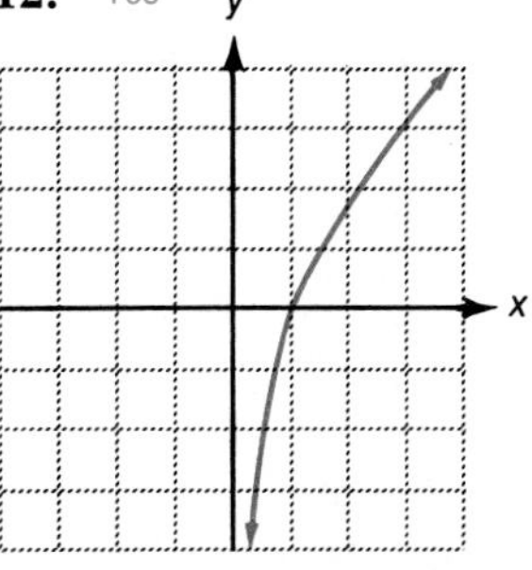

LESSON QUIZ

1. Is the following the graph of a function?

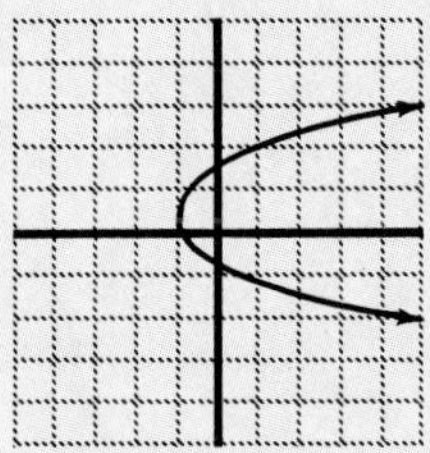

No, this is not the graph of a function, since a vertical line cuts the graph twice, showing that a first coordinate is paired with more than one second coordinate.

The function g is defined by $g(x) = 2x + 3$.
Find the values of the following.

2. $g(0)$
   $g(0) = 2(0) + 3 = 3$
3. $g(5)$
   $g(5) = 2(5) + 3 = 13$
4. $g(5x)$
   $g(5x) = 2(5x) + 3 = 10x + 3$
5. Find the domain of the function $h(x) = \frac{2x}{x-3}$.
   The domain is all real numbers, except $x = 3$. In this case, the function has a zero denominator.

Assignment Guide

Algebra: 1–28 e/o, MR

Alg w/Finite or Trig: 1–32 e/o, 33, MR

Comprehensive: 1–32 m4, 33, 34–36, MR, assign w. 3-2

ADDITIONAL ANSWERS

Exercises

25. $\left\{x \mid x \neq -\frac{8}{5}\right\}$
26. $\{x \mid x \neq 3 \text{ and } x \neq 0\}$
27. $\{x \mid x \neq 0, x \neq -2, \text{ and } x \neq 1\}$
28. R
29. a. $\frac{1}{2}$
 b. $\frac{1}{3}$
 c. $-\frac{1}{2}$
 d. Not possible

Consider the following functions. Find the indicated function values.

13. $g(x) = x + 1$
a. $g(0)$ 1 **b.** $g(-4)$ −3 **c.** $g(-7)$ −6 **d.** $g(8)$ 9

14. $h(x) = x - 4$
a. $h(4)$ 0 **b.** $h(8)$ 4 **c.** $h(-3)$ −7 **d.** $h(-4)$ −8

15. $f(x) = 5x^2 + 4x$
a. $f(0)$ 0 **b.** $f(-1)$ 1 **c.** $f(3)$ 57 **d.** $f(t)$ $5t^2 + 4t$

16. $g(x) = 3x^2 - 2x$
a. $g(0)$ 0 **b.** $g(-1)$ 5 **c.** $g(3)$ 21 **d.** $g(t)$ $3t^2 - 2t$

17. $f(x) = 3x^2 + 2x - 1$
a. $f(2)$ 15 **b.** $f(3)$ 32 **c.** $f(-3)$ 20 **d.** $f(1)$ 4

18. $h(x) = 4x^2 - x + 2$
a. $h(3)$ 35 **b.** $h(0)$ 2 **c.** $h(-1)$ 7 **d.** $h(-2)$ 20

19. $f(x) = \dfrac{x^2 - x - 2}{2x^2 - 5x - 3}$
a. $f(0)$ $\frac{2}{3}$ **b.** $f(4)$ $\frac{10}{9}$ **c.** $f(-1)$ 0 **d.** $f(3)$ Not possible

20. $s(x) = \dfrac{3x - 4}{2x + 5}$
a. $s(10)$ $\frac{26}{25}$ **b.** $s(2)$ $\frac{2}{9}$ **c.** $s\left(-\frac{5}{2}\right)$ Not possible **d.** $s(-1)$ $-\frac{7}{3}$

What is the domain of each of the following functions?

21. $f(x) = 7x + 4$ R

22. $f(x) = |3x - 2|$ R

23. $f(x) = 4 - \dfrac{2}{x}$ $\{x \mid x \neq 0\}$

24. $f(x) = \dfrac{1}{x - 3}$ $\{x \mid x \neq 3\}$

25. $f(x) = \dfrac{1}{5x + 8}$

26. $f(x) = \dfrac{1}{(3 - x)(x + x)}$

27. $f(x) = \dfrac{4x^3 + 4}{x(x + 2)(x - 1)}$

28. $f(x) = x^3 - x^2 + x - 2$

B

Think of a function as a machine. *Inputs* are entered into the machine. The machine then gives the proper *output*. The inputs that are acceptable to the machine are the elements of the domain of the function. The outputs of the machine are the elements of the range of the function.

29. Find the indicated outputs.
a. $f(2)$ **b.** $f(3)$ **c.** $f(-2)$ **d.** $f(0)$

input x

$f(x) = \frac{1}{x}$ → $\frac{1}{x}$ output

What inputs would not be accepted by the following machines?

30. input x

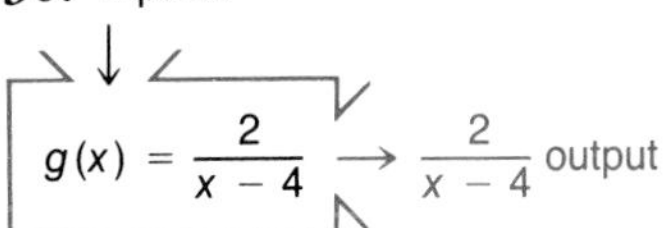

$g(x) = \frac{2}{x-4} \rightarrow \frac{2}{x-4}$ output

31. input x

$h(x) = \frac{x+3}{x^2-x} \rightarrow \frac{x+3}{x^2-x}$ output

32. input x

$f(x) = \frac{1}{-x} \rightarrow \frac{1}{-x}$ output

33. ***Critical Thinking*** The ordered pair (3, 2) is a solution to an equation describing a function from set A to set B. Is 3 in the domain of every function from set A to set B?

Challenge

The sum of two functions f and g (denoted by $f \oplus g$) is defined as $(f \oplus g)(x) = f(x) + g(x)$, for every x that is in the domain of f and the domain of g.

34. Suppose $f(x) = 2x + 3$ and $g(x) = x - 5$.

a. What is $(f \oplus g)(5)$? 13

b. What is $(f \oplus g)(-6)$? −20

c. What is $(f \oplus g)(0)$? −2

d. What is the domain of $(f \oplus g)$? R

e. Is $(f \oplus g)(x) = (g \oplus f)(x)$ for all x in the domain of f and g? Yes

35. Suppose $f(x) = \frac{1}{x}$ and $g(x) = \frac{1}{(x-2)}$.

a. What is $(f \oplus g)(1)$? 0

b. What is $(f \oplus g)(2)$? Not possible

c. What is $(f \oplus g)(0)$? Not possible

d. What is the domain of $(f \oplus g)$? $\{x \mid x \neq 0 \text{ and } x \neq 2\}$

36. How do you think the products of two functions would be defined?
For x in the domain of f and g, $(f \otimes g)(x) = [f(x)][g(x)]$

Mixed Review

Find the distance between points on a number line having the given coordinates.

37. −14, −22 **38.** −2, 8 **39.** 0, 47.5 **40.** −24, −2

Solve. Then graph. **41.** $-x + 2 < -1$ or $0.3x < 0.6$ **42.** $2x + 4 < 3x + 2 < 29$

43. $-\frac{9}{2} < -\frac{1}{2}x + 1 < -2$

For what replacements for x are the divisions possible? **44.** $x \div \frac{0}{x}$

45. $\frac{2(3x-6)}{2(3x-6) - 3(2x-4)}$ **46.** $\frac{1}{x-2} + \frac{1}{2-x}$

Problem for Programmers

Write a program that will determine whether a set of 10 ordered pairs (a relation) is a function. Test your program using Exercises 1–6 in Lesson 3-3.

30. 4
31. 0, 1
32. 0
33. No. For example, if A = {the rational numbers} and B = {the rational numbers}, the function $y = \frac{1}{x-3}$ is a function from A to B, but is not defined when $x = 3$.

Mixed Review

37. 8
38. 10
39. 47.5
40. 22
41. $x > 3$ or $x < 2$

42. $2 < x < 9$

43. $11 > x > 6$

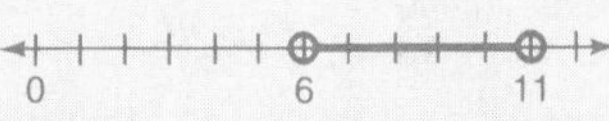

44. None
45. None
46. All real numbers except $x = 2$

Problem for Programmers

This program can be written using any programming language (BASIC, PASCAL, LOGO, etc.). The programming ability of the student will determine how the ordered pairs are input (from the keyboard or within the program), and how the answers are output. Encourage more capable programmers to output answers as complete sentences.

3-4

FIRST FIVE MINUTES

1. Graph $y = 2x - 2$.

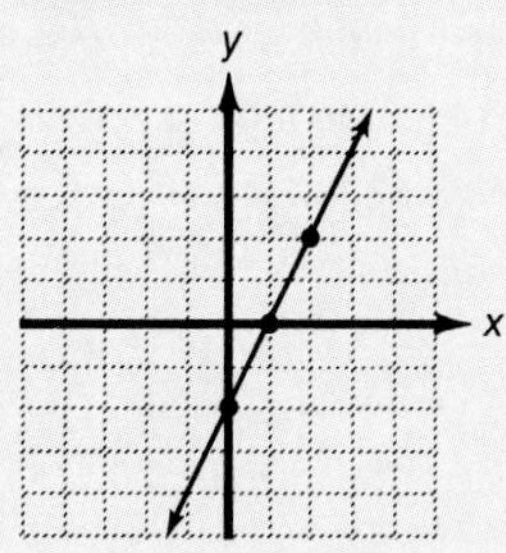

Recognizing Linear Equations

Chalkboard Example

1. Which of the following are linear equations?
   a. $3x + 2y = 7$
   Yes
   b. $5x = 1$
   Yes
   c. $3xy = 1$
   No, the product xy occurs.
   d. $y = \frac{1}{x}$
   No, there is a variable in the denominator.
   e. $x^2 + y^2 = 1$
   No, x^2 and y^2 occur.
   f. $y = 3x + 1$
   Yes

Graphing Linear Equations

Emphasize that two points determine a straight line. Students should, however, plot three points as a check. If all three points do not lie on a straight line, either an error has been made or the equation is not linear.

Avoiding Common Errors

Choosing two points that are close together can lead to an inaccurate graph. Points for determining a linear graph should be chosen so that they are spaced apart from each other.

3-4 Graphs of Linear Equations

The equation $K = C + 273$, which gives the relationship between the Kelvin and Celsius temperature scales, has a graph that is a straight line. Such equations are called linear or first-degree equations.

Recognizing Linear Equations

Objective: Recognize a linear equation.

An equation is linear if there are no products of variables, the variables occur to the first power only, and there are no variables in a denominator.

EXAMPLE 1 Which of the following equations are linear? If an equation is not linear, give the reason.

(a) $xy = 9$ **(b)** $2r + 7 = 4s$ **(c)** $4x^3 = 7y$

(d) $8x - 17y = y$ **(e)** $q = \frac{3}{p}$ **(f)** $4x = -3$

Equations b, d, and f are linear equations. Equations a, c, and e are not linear.

Equation a has a product of two variables. Equation c has a variable to the third power. Equation e has a variable in a denominator. It is equivalent to $q = 3p^{-1}$, which has a variable to a power other than 1.

Try This Which of the following equations are linear? If an equation is not linear, give the reason. See Additional Answers.

a. $5y + 8x = 9$ **b.** $7y = 11$ **c.** $5y^2x = 13$

d. $x = 4 + \frac{7}{y}$ **e.** $xy = 0$ **f.** $3x - 2y + 5 = 0$

Graphing Linear Equations

Objective: Graph linear equations.

Theorem 3-1

The graph of any linear equation is a straight line.

Since two points determine a line, we can graph a linear equation by finding two points that belong to the graph. Then we draw a line containing those points.

A third point should always be used as a check. Often the easiest points to find are the points where the graph crosses the axes.

Definition

The **y-intercept** of a graph is the y-coordinate of the point where the graph intersects the y-axis. The **x-intercept** is the x-coordinate of the point where the graph crosses the x-axis.

To find the y-intercept, let $x = 0$ and solve for y. To find the x-intercept, let $y = 0$ and solve for x.

EXAMPLE 2 Graph $4x + 5y = 20$.

First find the intercepts.

To find the y-intercept, let $x = 0$ and solve for y. We find $y = 4$, the y-intercept. We plot the point $(0, 4)$.

To find the x-intercept, let $y = 0$ and solve for x. We find $x = 5$, the x-intercept. We plot the point $(5, 0)$. The point $\left(1, 3\frac{1}{5}\right)$ was used as a check.

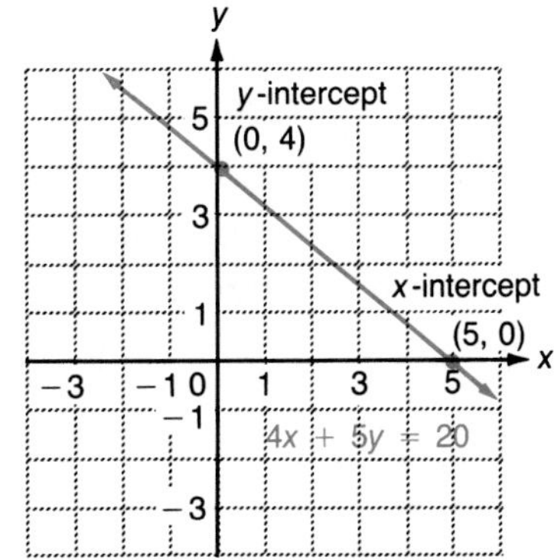

Try This Graph. See Selected Answers.

g. $2x - 6y = -2$

h. $3y = 2x - 6$

The graph of any equation of the form $y = mx$ contains the origin. Thus the x-intercept and the y-intercept occur at the same point, $(0, 0)$. Other points will be needed to graph.

EXAMPLE 3 Graph $y = 2x$.

x	y (or $2x$)
0	0
1	2
−1	−2

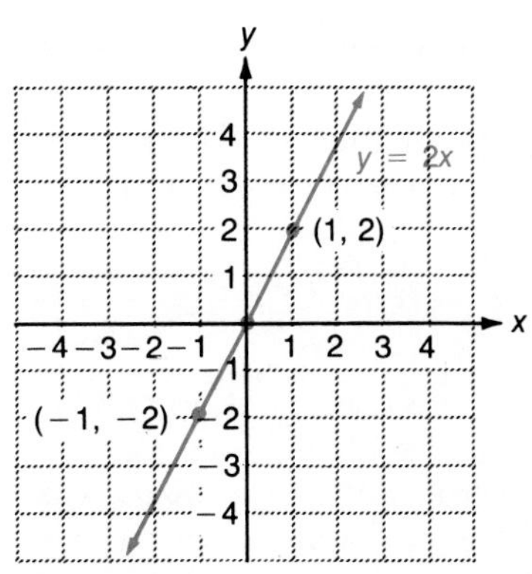

Chalkboard Examples

1. Graph $5x + 3y = 1$.

   Let $x = 0$, then $y = \frac{1}{3}$.
   The point $(0, \frac{1}{3})$ is on the graph.
   Let $y = 0$, then $x = \frac{1}{5}$.
   The point $\left(\frac{1}{5}, 0\right)$ is on the graph.
   Find another point on the line.
   Let $x = 2$, then $y = -3$.
   The point $(2, -3)$ allows us to accurately graph the line.

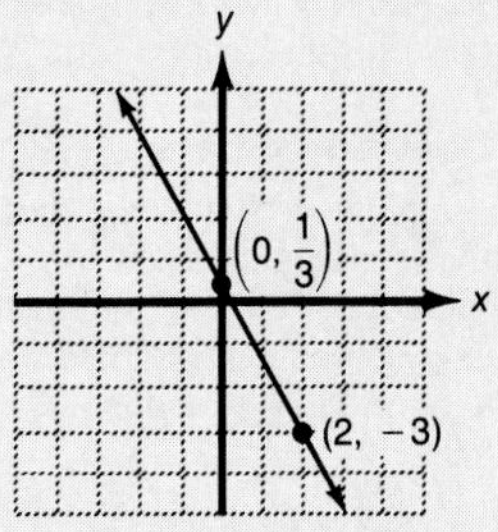

2. Graph $y = -2x + 1$ and compare it with $y = -2x$.

   Make a table of values.

x	y ($y = -2x + 1$)
0	1
1	−1
2	−3

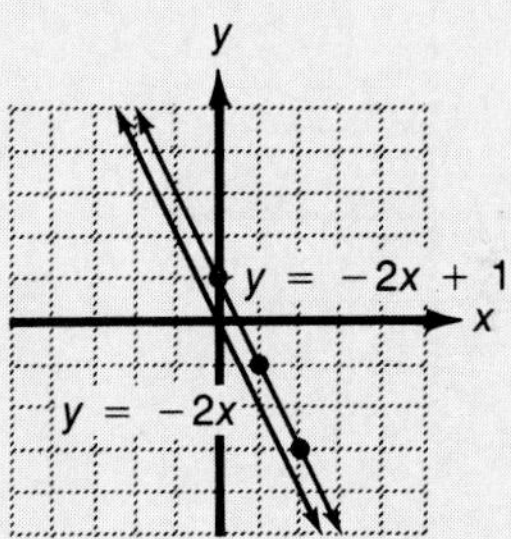

The graph of $y = -2x + 1$ is a line moved up 1 unit from the line $y = -2x$

Lines Parallel to the Axes

Students usually remember that $y = a$ and $x = a$ are lines that are parallel to the axes; however, they often forget which is parallel to which axis. Stress that in the equation $y = a$, x can be assigned any value and in the equation $x = b$, y can be assigned any value. They can make a table of values and plot them if necessary.

Point out the graph of $x = b$ is not a function. This is the only form of linear equation whose graph is not a function.

Avoiding Common Errors

Many students plot $y = 0$ as the y-axis and $x = 0$ as the x-axis because they seem to "match up." Point out that every point on the x-axis has y-coordinate 0, and every point on the y-axis has x-coordinate 0.

Chalkboard Examples

1. Graph $y = -2$.
   Any ordered pair of the form $(x, -2)$ satisfies the equation. The line is parallel to the x-axis with y-intercept -2.

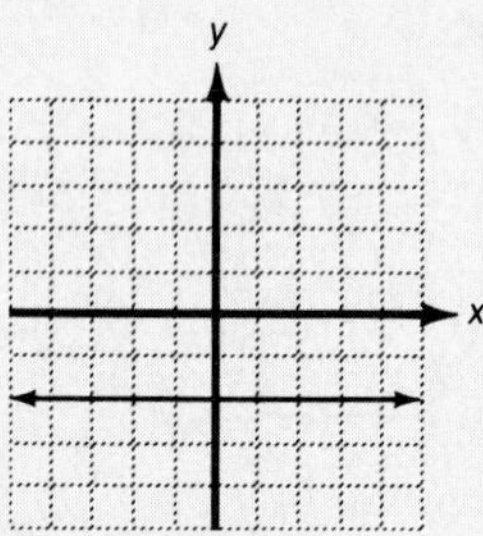

2. Graph $x = 3$.
   Any ordered pair of the form $(3, y)$ is a solution. The line is parallel to the y-axis with x-intercept 3.

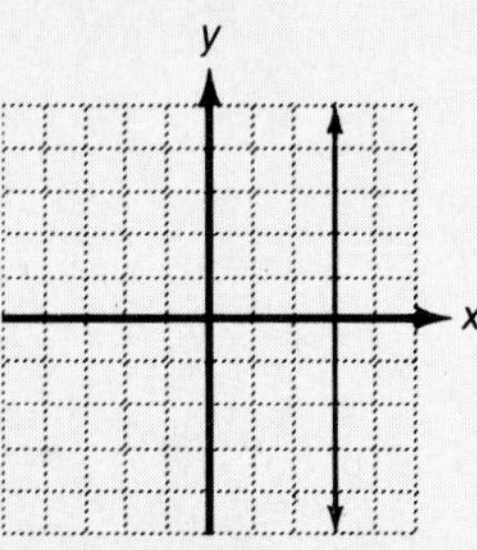

Try This Graph. See Selected Answers.

i. $y = -x$

j. $y = \frac{5}{2}x$

We have seen that the graph of $y = mx$ is a straight line containing the origin. Notice what happens if we add a number b to the right-hand side to get $y = mx + b$.

EXAMPLE 4

Graph $y = 2x - 3$ and compare it with the graph of $y = 2x$. First make a table of values. Then graph and compare.

x	y (or $2x - 3$)
0	-3
1	-1
3	3
-2	-7

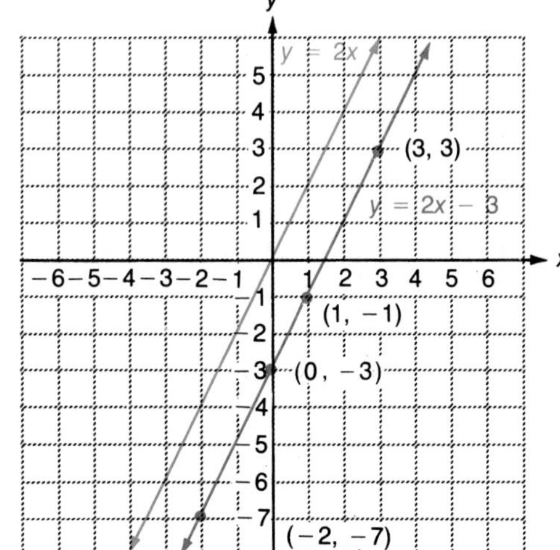

The graph of $y = 2x - 3$ is a line moved down 3 units from the graph of $y = 2x$.

Try This Graph and compare with the graph of $y = 2x$. See Additional Answers.

k. $y = 2x + 1$

l. $y = 2x - 4$

Theorem 3-2

The graph of an equation $y = mx$ is a line containing the origin. The graph of $y = mx + b$ is a line parallel to $y = mx$ and has b as the y-intercept.

Lines Parallel to the Axes

Objective: Graph equations whose graphs are parallel to the x- or y-axes.

Consider the equation $y = 4$, or $y = 0 \cdot x + 4$. No matter what number we choose for x, the value of y is 4. Thus $(x, 4)$ is a solution regardless of the value chosen for x.

Theorem 3-3

For constants a and b, the graph of an equation of the form $y = b$ is a line parallel to the x-axis with y-intercept b. The graph of an equation of the form $x = a$ is a line parallel to the y-axis with x-intercept a.

EXAMPLES

5. Graph $y = 4$.
Any ordered pair $(x, 4)$ is a solution. Thus the line is parallel to the x-axis, and the y-intercept is 4.

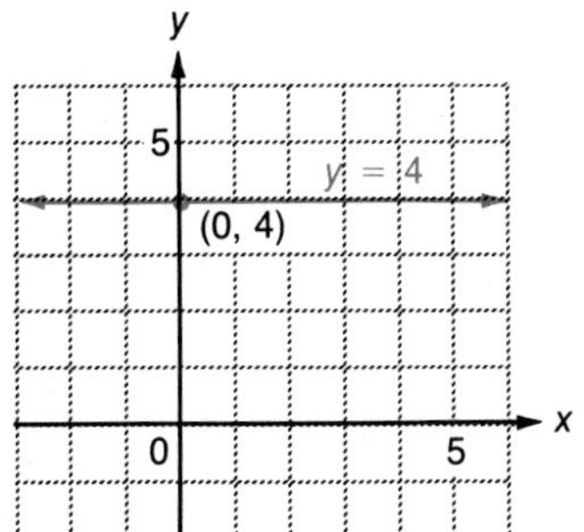

6. Graph $x = -2$.
Any ordered pair $(-2, y)$ is a solution. Thus the line is parallel to the y-axis, and the x-intercept is -2.

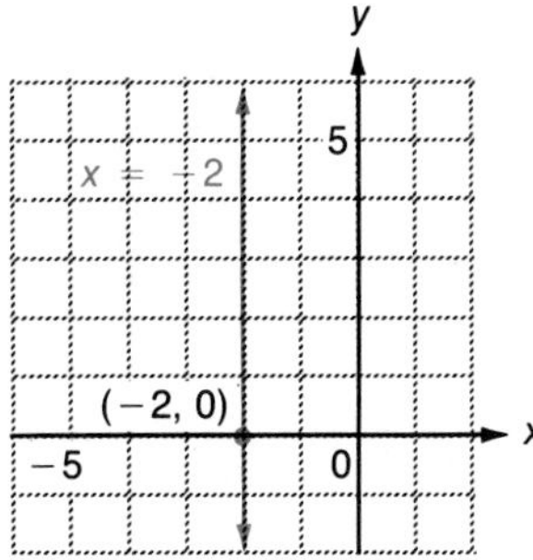

Try This Graph these equations. See Selected Answers.

m. $x = 4$ **n.** $y = -3$ **o.** $y = 0$

Graphing Linear Equations

1. If there is a variable missing, solve for the other variable. The graph will be a line parallel to an axis.
2. If no variable is missing, find the intercepts. Use the intercepts to graph.
3. If the intercept points are too close together, or are the same point, choose another point farther from the origin.
4. Use a third point as a check.

3-4 EXERCISES

A

Which of the following equations are linear? If an equation is not linear, give the reason.

1. $3x - 4 = y$ Yes
2. $x = 9$ Yes
3. $4r^2 = 2r + 1$ No; 2nd degree
4. $2 + 3pq = -9$ No; product of variables
5. $y = 7$ Yes
6. $3x^2 + 4y^2 = 16$ No; 2nd degree
7. $4x - 5y = 20$ Yes
8. $5 = \frac{1}{x}$ No; variable in denominator
9. $3p - 4 = q - 1$ Yes
10. $5 = r + 4t$ Yes

LESSON QUIZ

Graph the following.

1. $3x + 4y = 12$

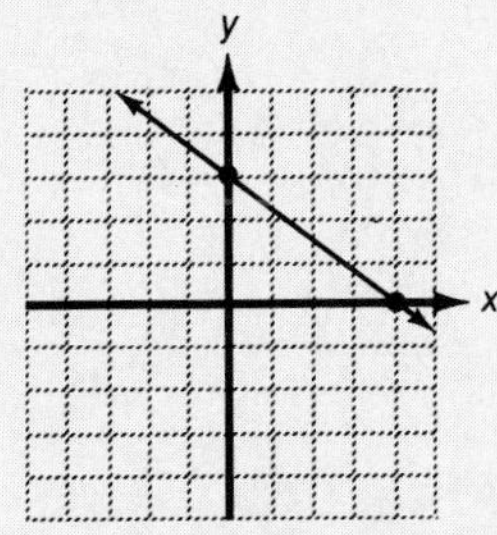

2. $x = -1$

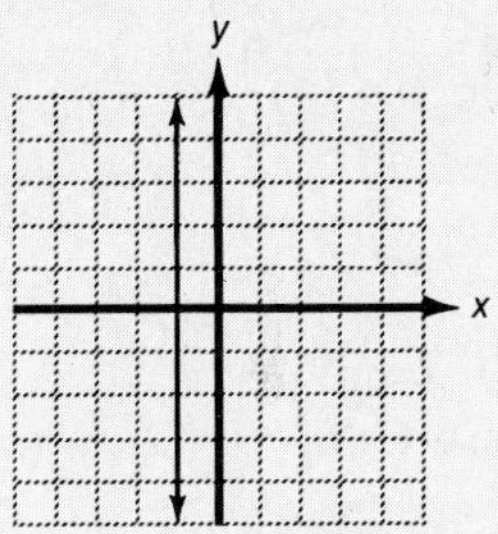

Assignment Guide
Algebra: Day 1: 1–22, MR
Day 2: 23–48

Alg w/Finite or Trig: Day 1: 1–22, MR
Day 2: 23–53 e/o, 54

Comprehensive: 1–53 m4, 54–55, MR, assign w. 3-5

ADDITIONAL ANSWERS

Try This

a. Yes
b. Yes
c. No, has a variable to a power
d. No, has a variable in a denominator
e. No, has a product of variables
f. Yes

k. The graph of $y = 2x + 1$ is a line moved up 1 unit from the graph of $y = 2x$.
l. The graph of $y = 2x - 4$ is a line moved down 4 units from the graph of $y = 2x$.

Exercises

For Exercises 11 – 48, see Teacher's Answer Section.

49. $\left(0, -\frac{2}{3}\right), \left(\frac{10}{3}, 0\right)$
50. $\left(0, -\frac{7}{2}\right), \left(-\frac{7}{16}, 0\right)$
51. $(0, -0.1), (10, 0)$
52. $\left(0, -\frac{6}{77}\right), \left(-\frac{2}{11}, 0\right)$
53. Exercises 39, 40, 43, 44, 45 and 48 are horizontal lines and, therefore, functions.
54. Answers may vary.
55. a. Answers may vary.
b. All contain (3, 2).
c. $y - 3 = k(x + 5)$

Mixed Review

56. $4x^{14}y^{10}$
57. $\frac{1}{a^{-6}}$ or a^6
58. 1
59. $\{(a, 0), (a, 1), (b, 0), (b, 1), (c, 0), (c, 1)\}$
60. $\{(0, a), (0, b), (0, c), (1, a), (1, b), (1, c)\}$
61. $\{(-1, 0), (-1, 1), (0, 1)\}$

Graph each of the following linear equations.

11. $x + 2y = 4$ **12.** $x + 3y = 9$ **13.** $-x + 4y = 8$
14. $-x + 2y = 6$ **15.** $4x + y = 8$ **16.** $3x + y = 6$
17. $3y - 3 = 6x$ **18.** $2y - 6 = 4x$ **19.** $y = -\frac{5}{2}x - 4$
20. $y = -\frac{2}{5}x + 3$ **21.** $3x + 6y = 18$ **22.** $4x + 5y = 20$
23. $x - 2 = y$ **24.** $x - 4 = y$ **25.** $3a - 1 = b$
26. $3a - 4 = b$ **27.** $5x - 4y = 20$ **28.** $3x - 5y = 15$
29. $y = -5 - 5x$ **30.** $y = -2 - 2x$ **31.** $2p + 7q = 14$
32. $3p + 6q = 12$ **33.** $8r - 3t = 24$

Graph and compare.

34. $y = 3x + 3$ and $y = 3x$ **35.** $y = -2x - 4$ and $y = -2x$
36. $y = \frac{1}{2}x + 1$ and $y = \frac{1}{2}x$

Graph.

37. $x = 2$ **38.** $x = 4$ **39.** $y = -6$ **40.** $y = -3$
41. $x = -5$ **42.** $x = -3$ **43.** $y = 7$ **44.** $y = 5$
45. $3y - 9 = 0$ **46.** $3x + 15 = 0$ **47.** $2x - 10 = 0$ **48.** $6y + 24 = 0$

B

Find the coordinates of the intercept points for the following equations.

49. $2x + 5y + 2 = 5x - 10y - 8$ **50.** $\frac{1}{8}y = -x - \frac{7}{16}$
51. $0.4y - 0.004x = -0.04$ **52.** $x = -\frac{7}{3}y - \frac{2}{11}$

53. Which of the graphs in Exercises 37 – 48 are graphs of functions?

54. ***Critical Thinking*** *Write a convincing argument* that the equation $y = 0$ has a graph that is the x-axis.

Challenge

55. Consider the equation $y - 2 = k(x - 3)$. The set of all lines that results from replacing k with different values is a family of lines, and k is the parameter of the family.
a. Replace k with any four numbers and graph the resulting equations.
b. What do you observe about these lines?
c. Graph four lines containing the point $(-5, 3)$. Write an equation with parameter k that describes these lines.

Mixed Review

Simplify. **56.** $(-2x^3y^2)^2(-xy)^4(x^{-2}y^{-1})^{-2}$ **57.** $\left(\frac{1}{a^{-2}}\right)^3$ **58.** $b^3\left(\frac{b}{b^{-2}}\right)^{-1}$

Consider the following sets. $A = \{a, b, c\}$, $B = \{0, 1\}$, $C = \{-1, 0, 1\}$. Find the sets determined by each of the following. **59.** $A \times B$ **60.** $B \times A$ **61.** $<$ for $C \times C$

3-5 Slope

Master Grapher Worksheet 1, *Graphing Lines: Slope and y–Intercept*, can be used as a lesson opener. Worksheet 2, *Graphing Functions: Absolute Value*, can be used for lesson closure.

The grade of a road is a measure of its steepness. The grade is the ratio of the rise of the road to every 100 feet of distance.

It is usually given as a percent. For instance, a road can have a 2% grade. In much the same manner we can describe the steepness of a line.

Finding the Slope of a Line

Objective: Find the slope of a line containing a given pair of points.

Here is a line with two points marked. As we go from P_1 to P_2, the change in x is $x_2 - x_1$. Similarly, the change in y is $y_2 - y_1$.

The ratio of the change in y to the change in x is called the slope of the line.

We usually use the letter m to designate slope.

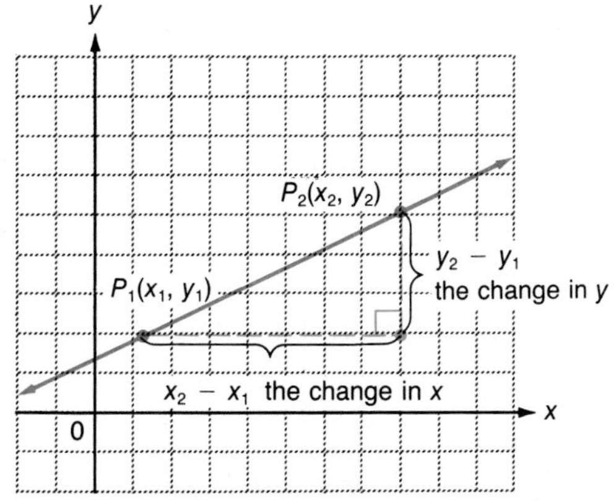

Definition

The **slope** m of a line is the change in y divided by the change in x, or

$$m = \frac{y_2 - y_1}{x_2 - x_1}$$

where (x_1, y_1) and (x_2, y_2) are any two points on the line, and $x_2 \neq x_1$.

To find the slope of a line, use the coordinates of any two points to determine the change in y and the change in x. Then divide the change in y by the change in x.

3-5

FIRST FIVE MINUTES

Graph the following lines on the same graph.

1. $y = x$
2. $y = 2x$
3. $y = \frac{1}{2}x$
4. $y = -2x$

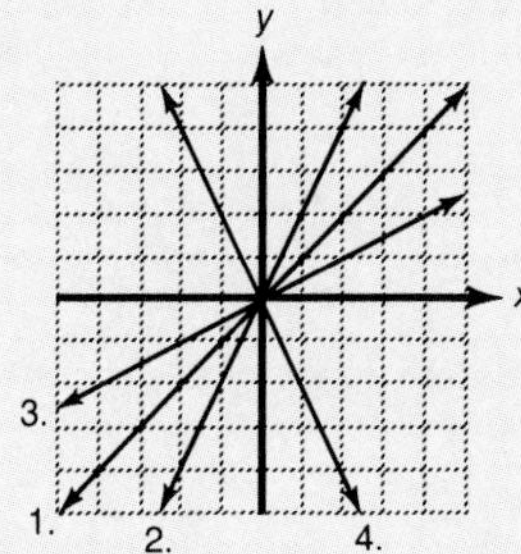

Finding the Slope of a Line

The slope can also be defined as "rise over run" where the rise is the change in the y-direction and the run is the change in the x-direction.

Point out that the slope of a line does not depend on which two points are chosen. You can illustrate this by choosing a third point, say (2, 4) in Example 1, and find the slope using (1, 2) and (3, 4), or (2, 4) and (3, 6). In either case, you will find the slope to be 2.

Avoiding Common Errors

Some students will calculate the change in x divided by the change in y. Stress that the slope is *rise divided by run*; that is, the y-change divided by the x-change.

Other students may use $\frac{y_2 - y_1}{x_1 - x_2}$.
Point out that the coordinates must be subtracted in the same order.

Key Questions

- How many points do you need to find the slope of a line?
  Two
- Is the slope the same between any two points on a line?
  Yes

Chalkboard Examples

1. The points (3, 5) and (7, 11) are on a line. Find the slope of the line.

   Slope $= \frac{y_2 - y_1}{x_2 - x_1}$

   $= \frac{11 - 5}{7 - 3}$

   $= \frac{6}{4} = \frac{3}{2}$

2. The points (5, 3) and (2, 8) are on a line. Find the slope of the line.

   Slope $= \frac{y_2 - y_1}{x_2 - x_1}$

   $= \frac{8 - 3}{2 - 5}$

   $= \frac{5}{-3} = -\frac{5}{3}$

   The negative slope means that the line slopes downward as we move from left to right.

LESSON ENRICHMENT

What is the range of angles that a line of slope m makes with the positive x-axis?

1. For $0 \le m \le 1$? $0° \le \theta \le 45°$
2. For $1 \le m \le \infty$? $45° < \theta \le 90°$
3. For $-1 \ge m \ge -\infty$? $90° \le \theta \le 135°$
4. For $0 \ge m \ge -1$? $135° \le \theta \le 180°$

EXAMPLE 1 The points (1, 2) and (3, 6) are on a line. Find its slope.

$$\text{The slope, } m = \frac{y_2 - y_1}{x_2 - x_1} \qquad \frac{\text{change in } y}{\text{change in } x}$$

$$= \frac{6 - 2}{3 - 1}$$

$$= \frac{4}{2}, \text{ or } 2$$

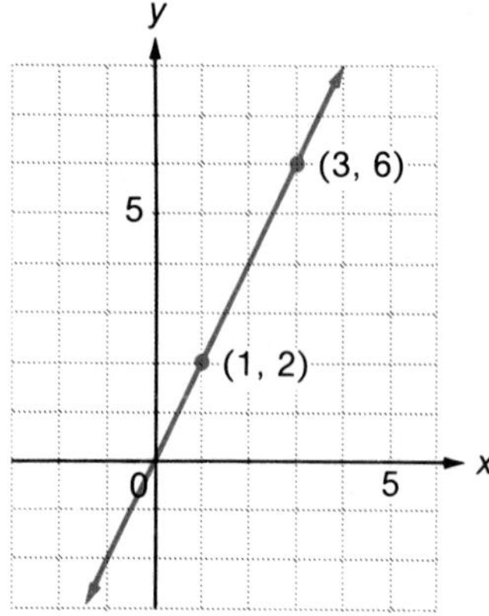

If we use the points (1, 2) and (3, 6) in opposite order, we find that the change in y is negative and the change in x is negative. We get the same number for the slope.

$$m = \frac{2 - 6}{1 - 3} = \frac{-4}{-2}, \text{ or } 2$$

When we compute slope, the order of the points does not matter as long as we take the same order for finding the differences.

The points (0, 0) and $(-1, -2)$ are also on the line. If we use those points to compute the slope, we get the following.

$$m = \frac{-2 - 0}{-1 - 0} = 2$$

The slope will be the same no matter what pair of points we use.

Try This Find the slope of the line containing each pair of points.

a. (1, 1) and (12, 14) $\frac{13}{11}$

b. (3, 9) and (4, 10) 1

c. (0, −4) and (5, 7) $\frac{11}{5}$

d. (7, 2) and (6, 3) −1

If a line slants up from left to right, it has positive slope, as in Example 1. If a line slants down from left to right, it has negative slope.

The following graphs show the relative positions of lines with different positive and negative slopes.

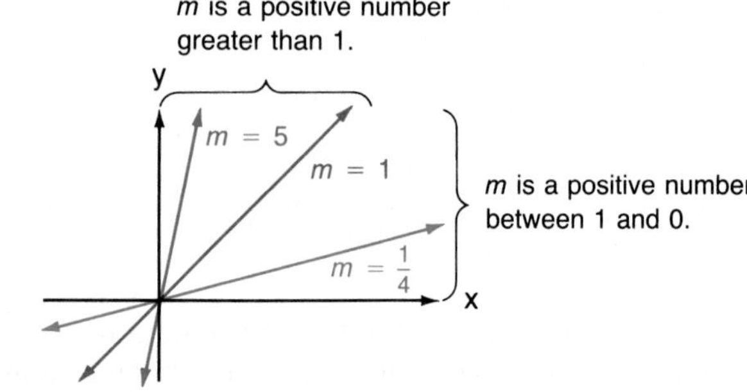

m is a negative number less than −1.

m is a negative number between 0 and −1.

y

x

$m = -\frac{1}{2}$

$m = -6$

$m = -1$

Horizontal and Vertical Lines

Objective: Find the slopes of horizontal and vertical lines.

Vertical and horizontal lines do not slant. Let us apply the definition of slope to them.

EXAMPLE 2 Find the slope of the line $y = 3$.

$$m = \frac{y_2 - y_1}{x_2 - x_1} = \frac{3 - 3}{-2 - 4} = \frac{0}{-6} = 0$$

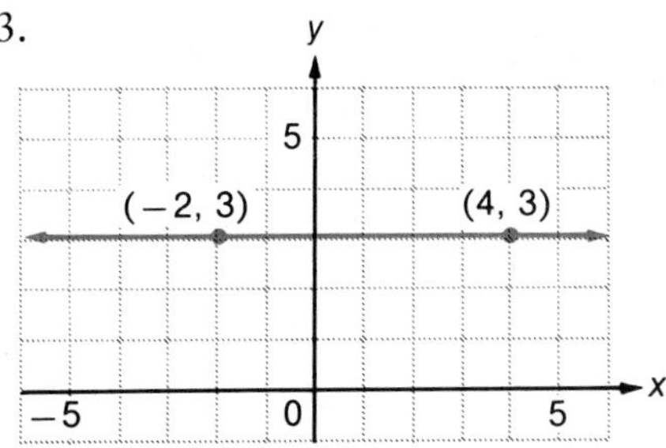

Any two points on a horizontal line have the same y-coordinate. The change in y is 0, so the slope is 0.

EXAMPLE 3 Find the slope of the line $x = -4$.

$$m = \frac{y_2 - y_1}{x_2 - x_1} = \frac{-2 - 3}{-4 - (-4)} = \frac{-5}{0}$$

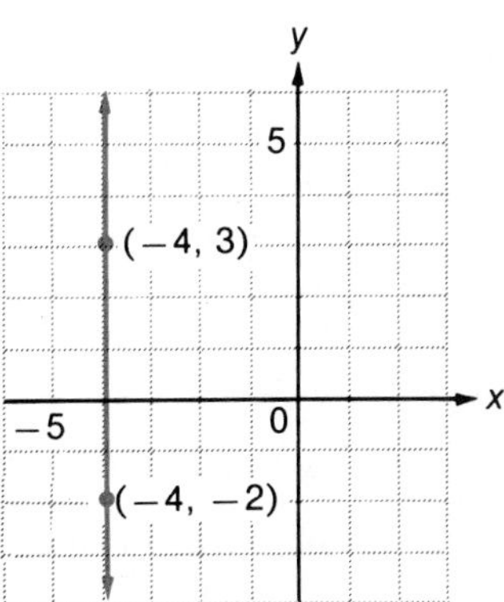

Since division by 0 is not defined, we say that this line has *no slope.*

Any two points on a vertical line have the same x-coordinates. The change in x is 0, so the denominator in the formula for slope is 0. Thus a vertical line has no slope.

Horizontal and Vertical Lines

Emphasize that there is a difference between a line with no slope and a line with zero slope.

Math Point
Calculus, developed in the 17th century by Isaac Newton and Gottfried Leibniz, was one of the most influential mathematical discoveries. A key topic in the study of calculus is finding the slope of a curve, such as $y = x^2$, at a single point.

Key Questions

- Which is less steep, a line with slope 10, or a line with slope −20?
  The line with slope 10
- Is there a limit to how large a slope can be?
  No

Chalkboard Examples

1. Find the slope of the line $y = -1$.
   For any choice of x_1 and x_2, $y_1 = -1$, and $y_2 = -1$. Hence, the slope is
   $$m = \frac{y_2 - y_1}{x_2 - x_1} = \frac{-1 - (-1)}{x_2 - x_1} = 0$$
2. Find the slope of the line $x = 2$.
   Any pairs of the form $(2, y_1)$, $(2, y_2)$ satisfy the condition. The slope equation is
   $$m = \frac{y_2 - y_1}{x_2 - x_1} = \frac{y_2 - y_1}{2 - 2}$$
   Since the denominator is 0, the slope is not defined.

Point-Slope Equations of Lines

In Example 4, you may want to substitute the original point, $\left(\frac{1}{2}, -1\right)$, into the final equation, $y = 5x - \frac{7}{2}$, to assure students the equation contains the point $\left(\frac{1}{2}, -1\right)$.

Here is a proof of Theorem 3-5. Think of a fixed point P with coordinates (x, y) on a nonvertical line. Suppose we have a movable point P on the line with coordinates (x, y). The slope m is $\frac{y - y_1}{x - x_1}$.

By the multiplication principle,
$\frac{(y - y_1)}{x - x_1} \cdot (x - x_1) = m(x - x_1)$

Simplifying,
$(y - y_1) \cdot \frac{(x - x_1)}{(x - x_1)} = m(x - x_1)$

So, $(y - y_1) = m(x - x_1)$

Math Point
Why is m used for slope? One theory is that it is short for the French word "monter," which means "to mount, to climb, to slope up." Since Descartes, the creator of the coordinate system, was French, this is a plausible explanation.

Chalkboard Examples

1. Find the equation of the line with slope 2 and passing through the point (3, 5).
   $(y - y_1) = m(x - x_1)$
   $(y - 5) = 2(x - 3)$
   This can be put into simpler form.
   $y - 5 = 2x - 6$
   $y = 2x - 1$
   Check that (3, 5) is on the line.
   $(5) = 2(3) - 1$. True.
2. Find the equation of the line with x-intercept (3, 0) and slope 4.
   $(y - y_1) = m(x - x_1)$
   $(y - 0) = 4(x - 3)$
   $y = 4x - 12$
   Notice that (0, −12) is the y-intercept.

Theorem 3-4

A horizontal line has slope 0. A vertical line has no slope.

Try This Find the slope, if it exists.

e. $y = -5$ 0 **f.** $x = 17$ No slope

Point-Slope Equations of Lines

Objective: Use the point-slope equation to find an equation of a line.

If we know the slope of a line and the coordinates of a point on the line, we can find an equation of the line.

Theorem 3-5

The Point-Slope Equation

A line containing (x_1, y_1) with slope m has an equation $(y - y_1) = m(x - x_1)$.

EXAMPLE 4 Find an equation of the line containing $\left(\frac{1}{2}, -1\right)$ with slope 5.

$$(y - y_1) = m(x - x_1)$$
$$y - (-1) = 5\left(x - \frac{1}{2}\right) \quad \text{Substituting}$$
$$y + 1 = 5\left(x - \frac{1}{2}\right)$$
$$y = 5x - \frac{7}{2} \quad \text{Simplifying}$$

EXAMPLE 5 Find an equation of the line with y-intercept 4 and slope $\frac{3}{5}$.

$$(y - y_1) = m(x - x_1)$$
$$y - 4 = \frac{3}{5}(x - 0) \quad \text{Substituting}$$
$$y = \frac{3}{5}x + 4 \quad \text{Simplifying}$$

Try This

g. Find an equation of the line containing the point $(-2, 4)$ with slope -3. $y = -3x - 2$

h. Find an equation of the line containing the point $(-4, -10)$ with slope $\frac{1}{4}$. $y = \frac{1}{4}x - 9$

i. Find an equation of the line with x-intercept 5 and slope $-\frac{1}{2}$. $y = -\frac{1}{2}x + \frac{5}{2}$

3-5 EXERCISES

A

Find the slope, if it exists, of the line containing each pair of points.

1. $(5, 0)$ and $(6, 8)$ 8
2. $(4, 0)$ and $(7, 3)$ 1
3. $(0, 7)$ and $(-2, 9)$ -1
4. $(0, 8)$ and $(3, 8)$ 0
5. $(4, -3)$ and $(6, -4)$ $-\frac{1}{2}$
6. $(5, -7)$ and $(8, -3)$ $\frac{4}{3}$
7. $(0, 0)$ and $(-4, -8)$ 2
8. $(0, 0)$ and $(-5, -6)$ $\frac{6}{5}$
9. $(-2, -4)$ and $(-9, -7)$ $\frac{3}{7}$
10. $(-3, -7)$ and $(-8, -5)$ $-\frac{2}{5}$
11. $\left(\frac{1}{2}, \frac{1}{4}\right)$ and $\left(\frac{3}{2}, \frac{3}{4}\right)$ $\frac{1}{2}$
12. $\left(\frac{3}{5}, \frac{1}{2}\right)$ and $\left(\frac{1}{5}, -\frac{1}{2}\right)$ $\frac{5}{2}$
13. $\left(\frac{1}{8}, \frac{1}{4}\right)$ and $\left(\frac{3}{4}, \frac{1}{2}\right)$ $\frac{2}{5}$
14. $\left(\frac{1}{3}, -\frac{1}{8}\right)$ and $\left(\frac{5}{6}, -\frac{1}{4}\right)$ $-\frac{1}{4}$
15. $(3.2, -12.8)$ and $(3.2, 2.4)$ No slope
16. $(-16.3, 12.4)$ and $(8.3, 12.4)$ 0

Find the slope, if it exists, of each line.

17. $x = 7$ No slope
18. $x = -4$ No slope
19. $y = -3$ 0
20. $y = 18$ 0
21. $x = 6$ No slope
22. $x = -17$ No slope
23. $y = 20$ 0
24. $y = -31$ 0
25. $5x - 6 = 15$ No slope
26. $-12 = 4x - 7$ No slope
27. $5y = 6$ 0
28. $19 = -6y$ 0
29. $y - 6 = 14$ 0
30. $12 - 4x = 9 + x$ No slope
31. $15 + 7x = 3x - 5$ No slope
32. $3y - 2x = 5 + 9y - 2x$ 0

Find the equation of the line containing the given points with the indicated slope.

33. $(3, 2)$; $m = 4$ $y = 4x - 10$
34. $(4, 7)$; $m = -2$ $y = -2x + 15$
35. $(-5, -2)$; $m = -1$ $y = -x - 7$
36. $(-2, -4)$; $m = 3$ $y = 3x + 2$
37. $(-6, 4)$; $m = \frac{1}{2}$ $y = \frac{1}{2}x + 7$
38. $(3, -1)$; $m = -\frac{4}{3}$ $y = -\frac{4}{3}x + 3$
39. $(0, -7)$; $m = 0$ $y = -7$
40. $(3, 0)$; $m = 0$ $y = 0$

B

Use a calculator to find the slope of the line containing the given pair of points.

41. $(0.04, 0.08)$ and $(0.47, 0.83)$ 1.7441860
42. $(0.02, 0.8)$ and $(-0.2, -0.04)$ $3.\overline{81}$

Use a calculator to find an equation of each line.

43. The line containing the point $(3.014, -2.563)$ with slope 3.516 $y = 3.516x - 13.1602$
44. The line containing the points $(1.103, 2.443)$ and $(8.114, 11.012)$ $y = 1.2222x + 1.0949$
45. Determine whether these three points are on a line. (Hint: Compare the slopes of $\overline{AB}$ and $\overline{BC}$. $\overline{AB}$ refers to the segment from A to B.)
    $A(9, 4)$, $B(-1, 2)$, $C(4, 3)$ Yes

LESSON QUIZ

1. Find the slope of the line containing the points (2, 4) and (6, 9).
   $\frac{(9-4)}{6-2} = \frac{5}{4}$

   Find the slope, if it exists, of the following lines
2. $y = 5$.
   The slope = 0.
3. $x = -4$
   The slope is undefined.
4. Find the equation of the line with slope 4 and passing through the point (2, 3).
   $(y - 3) = 4(x - 2)$
   $y - 3 = 4x - 8$
   $y = 4x - 5$

Assignment Guide

Algebra: Day 1: 1 – 16, MR
Day 2: 17 – 40

Alg w/Finite or Trig: 1 – 40 m3, 41–51 e/o, 52, MR

Comprehensive: 1 – 50 m4, 52 – 54, MR, assign w. 3-4

48a. $\frac{-5c}{4b}$

b. No Slope

c. $\frac{a+d}{f}$

52. Their graphs are either entirely in the 1st and 3rd quadrants or entirely in the 2nd and 4th quadrants.
53. Figure $ABCD$ is a parallelogram and its opposite sides are parallel.
54. Figure $EFGH$ is a rhombus and its diagonals are perpendicular. The slopes of $\overline{EG}$ and $\overline{FH}$ are negative reciprocals.
55. a. Grade = 4%; $y = 0.04x$
b. Grade = 6.7%; $y = 0.067x$

Mixed Review

56. $\{x \mid x \neq 0\}$
57. R
58. 42
59. 15
60. 144
61. $-\frac{1}{6}$
62. $\frac{9}{10}$
63. $-\frac{36}{5}$
64. $\frac{2}{45}$

46. Determine whether these three points are on a line. (See hint for Exercise 45.)
$A(-1, -1), B(2, 2), C(-3, -4)$ No
47. Determine a so that the slope of the line containing this pair of points has the given value. $\frac{5}{8}$
$(-2, 3a), (4, -a); m = -\frac{5}{12}$
48. Find the slope of the line that contains the given pair of points.
a. $(5b, -6c), (b, -c)$ **b.** $(b, d), (b, d + e)$ **c.** $(c + f, a + d), (c - f, -a - d)$
49. A line contains the points $(-100, 4)$ and $(0, 0)$. List four more points of the line.
Answers may vary. $(-25, 1), (-50, 2), (-75, 3), (25, -1)$

Find two solutions of each equation. Use these to find the slope.

50. $2x + 3y = 6$ $m = -\frac{2}{3}$
51. $2x + 5y + 2 = 5x + 10y - 8$ $m = -\frac{3}{5}$
52. ***Critical Thinking*** Suppose that the product of the slopes of two lines through the origin is positive. What can you say about the location of the lines?

Challenge

53. Plot the points $A(0, 0)$, $B(8, 2)$, $C(11, 6)$, and $D(3, 4)$. Draw $\overline{AB}$, $\overline{BC}$, $\overline{CD}$, and $\overline{DA}$. Find the slopes of these four segments. Compare the slopes of $\overline{AB}$ and $\overline{CD}$. Compare the slopes of $\overline{BC}$ and $\overline{DA}$.
54. Plot the points $E(-2, -5)$, $F(2, -2)$, $G(7, -2)$, and $H(3, -5)$. Draw $\overline{EF}$, $\overline{FG}$, $\overline{GH}$, $\overline{HE}$, $\overline{EG}$, and $\overline{FH}$. Compare the slopes of $\overline{EG}$ and $\overline{FH}$.
55. Numbers like 2%, 3%, and 6% are often used to represent the *grade* of a road. Such a number tells how steep a road is. For example, a 3% grade means that for every horizontal distance of 100 ft, the road rises or descends 3 ft. In each case, find the road grade and an equation giving the height y of a vehicle in terms of a horizontal distance x.

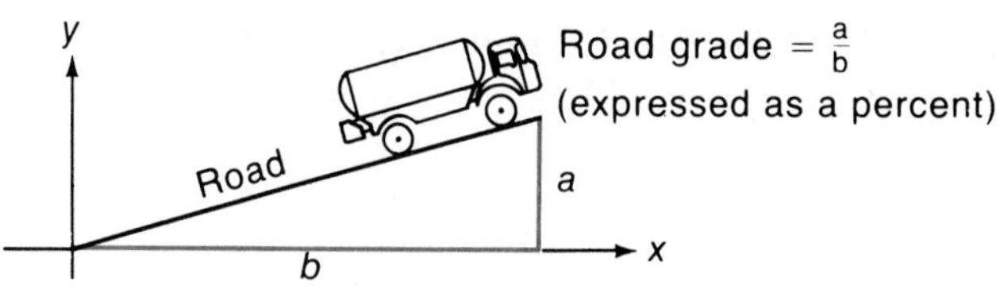

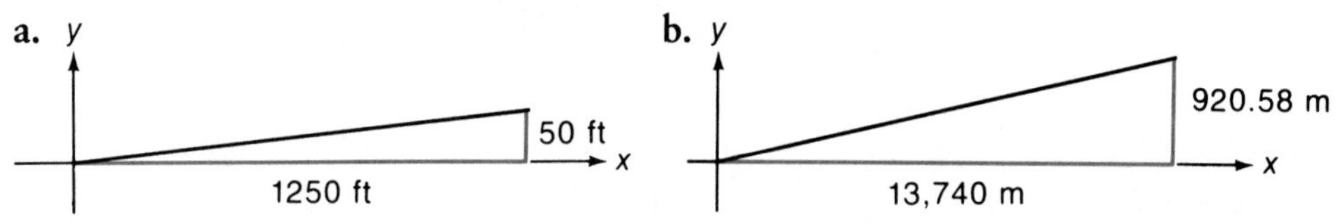

Mixed Review

Find the domain of each function. **56.** $f(x) = 12 + \frac{3}{x}$ **57.** $f(x) = |x + 2|$

Evaluate for $n = 4$. **58.** $5(n + 2) + 12$ **59.** $n(6 - n) + 7$ **60.** $(3n)^2$

Solve. **61.** $c + \frac{2}{3} = \frac{1}{2}$ **62.** $r - \frac{1}{2} = \frac{2}{5}$ **63.** $-\frac{k}{9} = \frac{4}{5}$ **64.** $9c = \frac{2}{5}$

3-6 More Equations of Lines

Two-Point Equations of Lines

Objective: Use the two-point equation to find an equation of a line, given two points on the line.

Given two points, we can find an equation of the line containing them. If we find the slope of a line by dividing the change in y by the change in x and substitute this value for m in the point-slope equation, we obtain the two-point equation.

Theorem 3-6

The Two-Point Equation

Any nonvertical line containing the points (x_1, y_1) and (x_2, y_2) has an equation

$$y - y_1 = \frac{y_2 - y_1}{x_2 - x_1}(x - x_1)$$

EXAMPLE 1 Find an equation of the line containing the points (2, 3) and (1, −4).

We find the slope and then substitute in the two-point equation. We take (2, 3) as (x_1, y_1) and (1, −4) as (x_2, y_2).

$$y - 3 = \frac{-4 - 3}{1 - 2}(x - 2) \quad \text{Substituting}$$

$$y - 3 = \frac{-7}{-1}(x - 2)$$

$$y - 3 = 7(x - 2)$$

$$y - 3 = 7x - 14$$

$$y = 7x - 11$$

In Example 1, we could have taken (1, −4) as (x_1, y_1) and (2, 3) as (x_2, y_2) and have arrived at the same equation.

$$y - (-4) = \frac{3 - (-4)}{2 - 1}(x - 1)$$

$$y = 7x - 11 \quad \text{Simplifying}$$

Try This Find an equation of the line containing the following pairs of points.

a. (1, 4) and (3, −2) $y = -3x + 7$ **b.** (3, −6) and (0, 4) $y = -\frac{10}{3}x + 4$

3-6

FIRST FIVE MINUTES

1. Determine whether the point (2, 7) is on the line $y = 3x + 1$.
   (7) = 3(2) + 1, Yes
2. Find the slope of the line containing the points (4, 2) and (7, 5).
   $m = \frac{5 - 2}{7 - 4} = \frac{3}{3} = 1$
3. Find the equation of the line with slope 3 and containing the point (2, 5).
   $(y - 5) = 3(x - 2)$
   $y - 5 = 3x - 6$
   $y = 3x - 1$

Two-Point Equations of Lines

Point out that there are many equivalent equations for the same line and that no one form is more correct than others. Different forms are more useful for different purposes. For example, the form

$(y - 1) = 3(x - 3)$

gives us the slope, 3, and a point, (3, 1). The form

$y = 3x - 8$

gives us the slope, 3, and the y-intercept, −8. The form

$-3x + y = -8$

is useful for certain applications involving symmetry.

Chalkboard Example

1. Find the equation of the line containing the points (3, 1) and (5, 7).
   The slope is $\frac{7 - 1}{5 - 3} = 3$.
   The equation is
   $y - 1 = 3(x - 3)$.
   This can be rewritten as
   $y - 1 = 3x - 9$
   $y = 3x - 8$

Slope-Intercept Equations of Lines

Have students look at the graphs they drew in Exercises 3-4. Then ask them to find the slopes and y-intercepts of some of these equations. Finally, ask them to write the equations in slope-intercept form by solving for y, and compare the equation with the slope and the y-intercept to see whether they can determine for themselves that the coefficient of x is the slope and the value of b is the y-intercept.

Point out that each point on a line will yield a different but equivalent point-slope equation. Each of these equations will describe the original line. However, a line can be described by only *one* slope-intercept equation.

Key Questions

- What form of equation would you find if you wanted to know the y-intercept and the slope?
  Slope-intercept
- What form of equation would you find if you wanted to know the slope of the line and a point that the line contains?
  Point-slope

Chalkboard Examples

1. Find the slope and y-intercept of the line whose equation is $y = 6x + 9$.
   The slope is 6.
   The y-intercept is 9.
2. Find the slope and y-intercept of the line whose equation is $6x + 2y = 24$.
   Solve for y.
   $2y = -6x + 24$
   $y = -3x + 12$
   The slope is -3.
   The y-intercept is 12.

Slope-Intercept Equations of Lines

Objective: Find the slope and y-intercept of a line, given the slope-intercept equation for the line.

If we know the slope and y-intercept of a line, we can find an equation for the line. Suppose a line has slope 4 and y-intercept -2. From the point-slope equation we have

$$\begin{aligned} y - (-2) &= 4(x - 0) \\ y + 2 &= 4x \\ y &= 4x - 2 \end{aligned}$$

This is the slope-intercept equation of the line.

Theorem 3-7

The Slope-Intercept Equation

A nonvertical line with slope m and y-intercept b has an equation $y = mx + b$.

From any equation for a nonvertical line, we can find the slope-intercept equation by solving for y. There is no slope-intercept equation for a vertical line because the line has no slope.

EXAMPLE 2 Find the slope and y-intercept of the line whose equation is $y = 2x - 3$.

$$y = 2x - 3$$

slope 2 y-intercept -3

EXAMPLE 3 Find the slope and y-intercept of the line whose equation is $3x - 6y - 7 = 0$.

First solve for y. This puts the equation into slope-intercept form.

$$\begin{aligned} -6y &= -3x + 7 \\ -\frac{1}{6} \cdot (-6y) &= -\frac{1}{6} \cdot (-3x) + \left(-\frac{1}{6}\right) \cdot 7 \\ y &= \frac{1}{2}x - \frac{7}{6} \end{aligned}$$

The slope is $\frac{1}{2}$, the y-intercept is $-\frac{7}{6}$.

Try This Find the slope and y-intercept of each line. See Additional Answers.

c. $y = -5x + \frac{1}{3}$ **d.** $-2x + 3y - 6 = 0$ **e.** $2y - 6 = 0$

Graphing Using Slope-Intercept Form

Objective: Graph linear equations in slope-intercept form.

EXAMPLE 4 Graph $5y - 20 = -3x$.

Solving for y, we find the slope-intercept form $y = -\frac{3}{5}x + 4$. Thus the y-intercept is 4 and the slope is $-\frac{3}{5}$.

We plot (0, 4) and then find another point by moving 5 units to the right and 3 units down. The point has coordinates (5, 1). We can then draw the line.

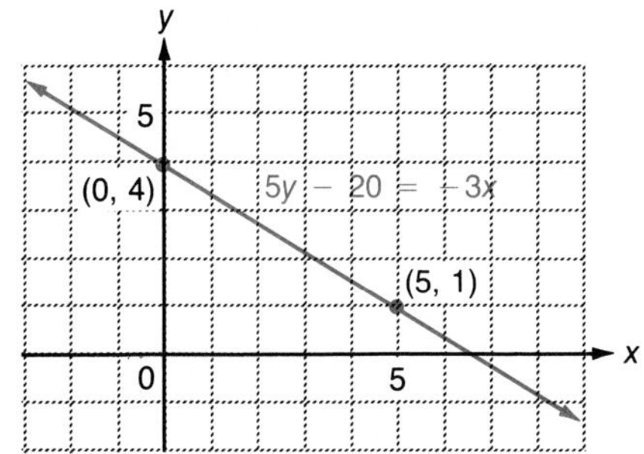

Try This Graph each equation using slope-intercept form. See Additional Answers.

f. $y = 3x - 1$ **g.** $7y = -4x - 21$ **h.** $6x = -5y - \frac{5}{2}$

Finding the Standard Form

Objective: Find the standard form of a linear equation.

Any linear equation can be written so that 0 is on the right side. This is called the standard form of a linear equation.

Definition

The **standard form** of a linear equation is $Ax + By + C = 0$, where A and B are not both zero.

In standard form, A, B, and C represent constants.

We can change the standard form of a linear equation to the slope-intercept equation by solving for y. This leads to the following theorem.

Theorem 3-8

The slope of a line whose equation is $Ax + By + C = 0$ is $-\frac{A}{B}$ if $B \neq 0$.

Graphing Using Slope-Intercept Form

Point out that each method of graphing is useful for specific situations. Graphing using the slope-intercept form is particularly useful when the equation can be easily transformed to the slope-intercept form and when the y-intercept is an integer.

Chalkboard Example

1. Graph $3y - 9x = -3$.
   Solve for y.
   $y = 3x - 1$
   The slope is 3, the y-intercept is -1.

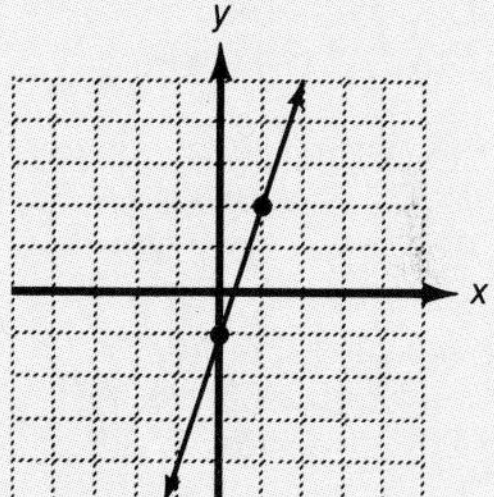

Finding the Standard Form

You may want to show the steps leading to Theorem 3-8.

$$Ax + By + C = 0$$
$$By = -Ax - C$$
$$y = -\frac{A}{B}x - \frac{C}{B}$$
$$y = -\frac{A}{B}x + \left(-\frac{C}{B}\right)$$

This is the slope intercept form and we can determine from this that

slope $= -\frac{A}{B}$

Chalkboard Example

1. Find the standard form of the equation $5y = \frac{2}{3}x + 1$.

   $5y = \frac{2}{3}x + 1$
   $15y = 2x + 3$
   $-2x + 15y - 3 = 0$
   which is of the form
   $Ax + By + C = 0$, where
   $A = -2, B = 15, C = -3$.
   The slope is $-\left(-\frac{2}{15}\right)$ or $\frac{2}{15}$.

LESSON QUIZ

1. Find the equation, in slope-intercept form, of the line containing the points (6, 1) and (9, 7).
   $y = 2x - 11$
2. Find the slope and y-intercept of the line.
   $y = 5x + 8$
   The slope is 5.
   The y-intercept is 8.
3. Find the slope of the line.
   $4x + 3y = 7$
   The slope is $-\frac{4}{3}$.
4. Find the equation of the line with slope 4 and y-intercept (0, 5).
   $y = 4x + 5$

Assignment Guide

Algebra: Day 1: 1–30
Day 2: 31–47, MR

Alg w/Finite or Trig: 1–47 m3, 48–56 e/o, 57, MR

Comprehensive: 1–56 m4, 57, 58–62 e/o, MR, assign w. 3-7

ADDITIONAL ANSWERS

Try This

c. $m = -5; b = \frac{1}{3}$

d. $m = \frac{2}{3}; b = 2$

e. $m = 0; b = 3$

f.

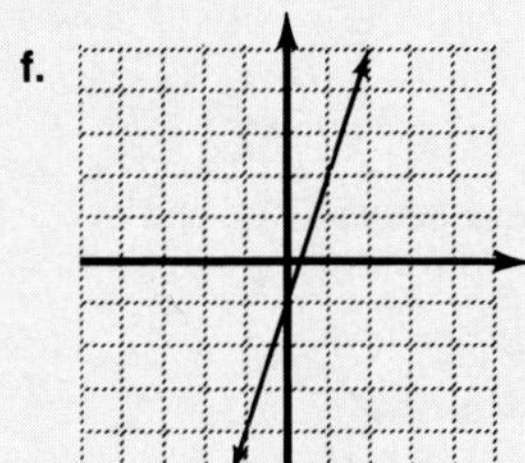

g.

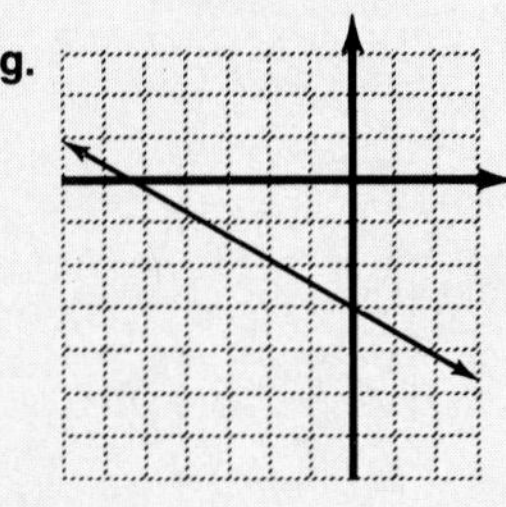

EXAMPLE 5 Find the standard form and slope of the equation $7x = \frac{1}{4} - 5y$.

$$7x = \frac{1}{4} - 5y$$

$$7x + 5y - \frac{1}{4} = 0 \qquad \text{Using the addition principle, adding } 5y - \tfrac{1}{4}$$

This equation is of the form $Ax + By + C = 0$, where $A = 7$, $B = 5$, and $C = -\frac{1}{4}$. The slope is $-\frac{A}{B} = -\frac{7}{5}$.

Try This Find the standard form and slope of each equation.

i. $5y = \frac{1}{2} + 5x$ $5x - 5y + \frac{1}{2} = 0; m = 1$

j. $8x = 10 + 5y$ $8x - 5y - 10 = 0; m = \frac{8}{5}$

3-6 EXERCISES

A

Find an equation of the line containing the following pairs of points.

1. (1, 4) and (5, 6) $y = \frac{1}{2}x + \frac{7}{2}$
2. (2, 6) and (4, 1) $y = -\frac{5}{2}x + 11$
3. $(-1, -1)$ and (2, 2) $y = x$
4. $(-3, -3)$ and (6, 6) $y = x$
5. $(-2, 0)$ and (0, 5) $y = \frac{5}{2}x + 5$
6. (6, 0) and $(0, -3)$ $y = \frac{1}{2}x - 3$
7. (3, 5) and $(-5, 3)$ $y = \frac{1}{4}x + \frac{17}{4}$
8. (4, 6) and $(-6, 4)$ $y = \frac{1}{5}x + \frac{26}{5}$
9. (0, 0) and (5, 2) $y = \frac{2}{5}x$
10. (0, 0) and (7, 3) $y = \frac{3}{7}x$
11. $(-4, -7)$ and $(-2, -1)$ $y = 3x + 5$
12. $(-2, -3)$ and $(-4, -6)$ $y = \frac{3}{2}x$

Find the slope and y-intercept of each line.

13. $y = 2x + 3$ $m = 2; b = 3$
14. $y = 3x + 4$ $m = 3; b = 4$
15. $y = -4x + 9$ $m = -4; b = 9$
16. $y = -5x - 7$ $m = -5; b = -7$
17. $y = 6 - x$ $m = -1; b = 6$
18. $y = 7 - x$ $m = -1; b = 7$
19. $2y = -6x + 10$ $m = -3; b = 5$
20. $-3y = -12x + 6$ $m = 4; b = -2$
21. $3x - 4y = 12$ $m = \frac{3}{4}; b = -3$
22. $5x + 2y = -7$ $m = -\frac{5}{2}; b = -\frac{7}{2}$
23. $6x + 2y - 8 = 0$ $m = -3; b = 4$
24. $3y - 2x + 5 = 0$ $m = \frac{2}{3}; b = -\frac{5}{3}$
25. $-7x - 3y - 9 = 0$ $m = -\frac{7}{3}; b = -3$
26. $-8x - 5y - 7 = 0$ $m = -\frac{8}{5}; b = -\frac{7}{5}$
27. $y = 7$ $m = 0; b = 7$
28. $y = 9$ $m = 0; b = 9$
29. $3y + 10 = 0$ $m = 0; b = -\frac{10}{3}$
30. $4y + 11 = 0$ $m = 0; b = -\frac{11}{4}$

Graph each equation using slope-intercept form. For Exercises 31 – 36, see **Teacher's Answer Section**

31. $y = -x + 4$
32. $6x - 6 - y = 0$
33. $-2y = -3x + 2$
34. $4x = -5y + 40$
35. $7x - 6y + 42 = 0$
36. $3y = -8x - 5$

Find the standard form and slope, if it exists, of each equation.

37. $4x - 8 = y$ **38.** $y = 6x - 2$ **39.** $y = 2x + 3$

40. $x = 2y - 1$ **41.** $x = 6$ **42.** $y = 9$

43. $5x = -5y + 10$ **44.** $y + 4 = 4x + 8$ **45.** $3x - 8 = x - 2$

46. $9x + 7 = 9x + 7 + y$ **47.** $3(x + 2y) = \frac{1}{2}(6x + 12y)$

B

Find an equation of a line with the given slope and *y*-intercept.

48. $m = -4$; *y*-intercept 3 **49.** $m = \frac{2}{5}$; *y*-intercept -4

50. $m = 75$; *y*-intercept $- 18$ **51.** $m = - 0.36$; *y*-intercept 10

Find an equation of the line containing each pair of points.

52. $(-0.2, 0.7)$ and $(-0.7, -0.3)$ **53.** $\left(\frac{1}{11}, \frac{1}{2}\right)$ and $\left(-\frac{10}{11}, -2\right)$

54. Find an equation of the line containing $(2, -3)$ and having the same slope as the line $3x + 4y = 10$.

55. Find an equation of the line containing $(3, -4)$ and having slope -2. If the line contains the points $(a, 8)$ and $(5, b)$, find a and b.

56. Write an equation of the line that has *x*-intercept -3 and *y*-intercept $\frac{2}{5}$.

57. ***Critical Thinking*** Consider the following equations. Tell which equation does **not** belong in the group and why.
a. $y = 5x + 3$ **b.** $2x + 3 = 5y - 9 + 4x$ **c.** $3x - 5y + 9 = 0$
d. $3(x + 9) = 4y - 7$

Challenge

58. Prove that $\frac{x}{a} + \frac{y}{b} = 1$ has *x*-intercept a and *y*-intercept b.

Use the result of Exercise 58 to find *a*, *b*, and the slope of each line.

59. $5x - 4y - 7 = 0$ $a = \frac{7}{5}, b = -\frac{7}{4}, m = \frac{5}{4}$ **60.** $2y - 3x = 4$ $a = -\frac{4}{3}, b = 2, m = \frac{3}{2}$

61. $1.25y + 7.8x = 4.2x - 18$ $a = -5, b = -14.4, m = -2.88$

62. Prove Theorem 3-8.

Mixed Review

Which of the following relations are functions? **63.** $\{(0, 0), (1, 7), (2, 0), (-1, 7)\}$

64. $\{(1, 6), (1, 2)\}$ **65.** $\{(x, y) | y = 2x + 1\}$ **66.** $\{(x, y) | y = 3\}$

67. $\{(x, y) | x = 2\}$

68-72. List the domain and the range for each of the above relations.

73. Lucinda needed an average score of 9.45 to win a jump competition. The first 3 judges gave her 9.35, 9.40, and 9.25. What score did she need from the fourth judge to win?

h.

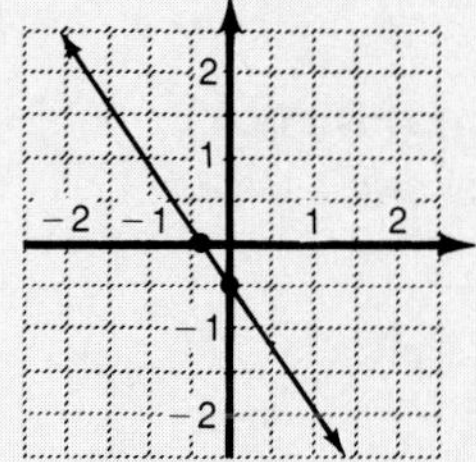

Exercises

37. $4x - y - 8 = 0; m = 4$
38. $6x - y - 2 = 0; m = 6$
39. $2x - y + 3 = 0; m = 2$
40. $x - 2y + 1 = 0; m = \frac{1}{2}$
41. $x - 6 = 0$; no slope
42. $y - 9 = 0; m = 0$
43. $x + y - 2 = 0; m = -1$
44. $4x - y + 4 = 0; m = 4$
45. $2x - 6 = 0$; no slope
46. $y = 0; m = 0$
47. Not a linear equation
48. $y = -4x + 3$
49. $y = \frac{2}{5}x - 4$
50. $y = 75x - 18$
51. $y = -0.36x + 10$
52. $y = 2x + 1.1$
53. $y = \frac{5}{2}x + \frac{3}{11}$
54. $y = -\frac{3}{4}x - \frac{3}{2}$
55. $y = -2x + 2; a = -3, b = -8$
56. $y = \frac{2}{15}x + \frac{2}{5}$
57. Equation (b) does not belong because it has a negative slope.

For Exercises 58 and 62, see Teacher's Answer Section.

Mixed Review

63. Function
64. Not a function
65. Function
66. Function
67. Not a function
68. Domain $\{-1, 0, 1, 2\}$; range $\{0, 7\}$
69. Domain $\{1\}$; range $\{2, 6\}$
70. Domain R; range R
71. Domain R; range $\{3\}$
72. Domain $\{2\}$; range R
73. 9.80 or more

3-7

FIRST FIVE MINUTES

Graph the following three lines on the same axes.

1. $y = 2x$
2. $y = 2x - 3$
3. $4x - 2y = 4$

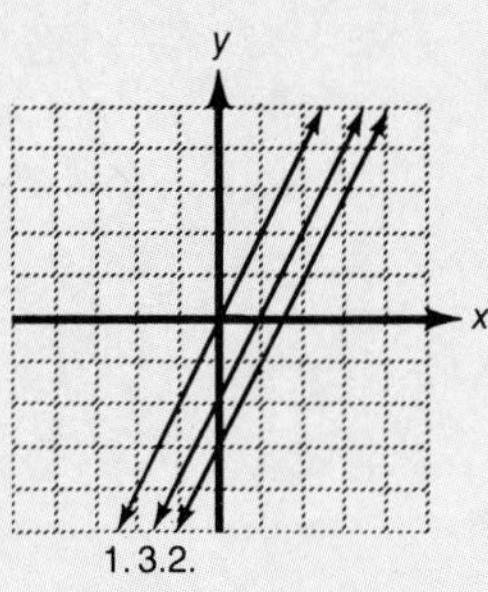

Graph the following two lines on the same axes.

4. $y = 3x$
5. $y = -\frac{1}{3}x$

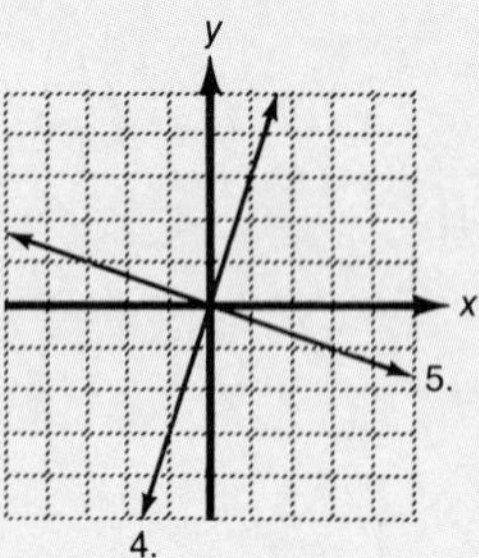

Parallel Lines

Have students look at the graphs they drew for Warm-Up Exercises 1-3, find the slopes and y-intercepts, and compare.

Point out that graphing is not necessary to determine whether the graphs of two equations are parallel. However, students may want to use graphs as visual aids.

Key Questions

- Can two different lines have two points in common? No
- Can two parallel lines have one point in common? No
- Can two parallel lines have different slopes? No
- Can two parallel lines have different y-intercepts? Yes

3-7 Parallel and Perpendicular Lines 

Master Grapher Worksheet 3, *Graphing Functions: Parallels and Perpendiculars*, can be used as a lesson opener.

Parallel Lines

Objective: Use equations to determine whether two lines are parallel.

When we graph a pair of linear equations on the same axes, there are three possibilities.

1. The equations have the same graph.
2. The graphs intersect at exactly one point.
3. The graphs are parallel lines.

Theorem 3-9

Two nonvertical lines are parallel if and only if they have the same slope and different y-intercepts.

EXAMPLE 1 Determine whether the graphs of $y = -3x + 5$ and $4y = -12x + 20$ are parallel.

We find the slope-intercept equations by solving for y.

$y = -3x + 5$ is in slope-intercept form.

For $4y = -12x + 20$ we have

$$y = -\frac{12x}{4} + \frac{20}{4}$$

$$y = -3x + 5$$

The equation is now in slope-intercept form. The slope-intercept equations are the same. This tells us that the graphs are the same line. Thus the lines are not parallel.

EXAMPLE 2

Determine whether the graphs of $y - 3x = 1$ and $-2y = 3x + 2$ are parallel.

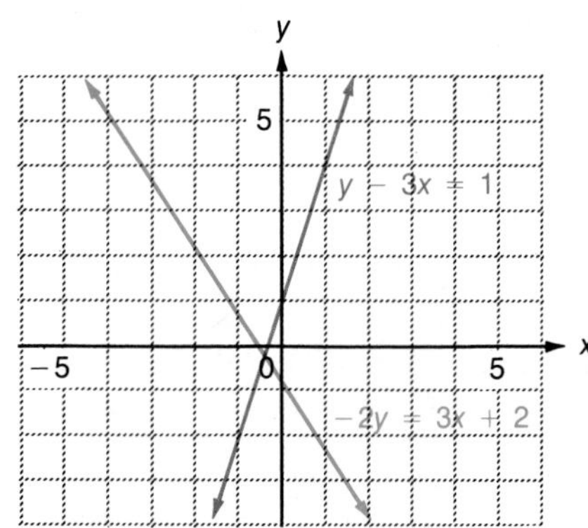

First find the slope-intercept form for each equation.

$$y = 3x + 1, y = -\frac{3}{2}x - 1$$

The slopes are different. Thus the lines are not parallel.

EXAMPLE 3 Determine whether the graphs of $3x - y = -5$ and $y - 3x = -2$ are parallel.

Solving for y in each equation

$$y = 3x + 5, y = 3x - 2$$

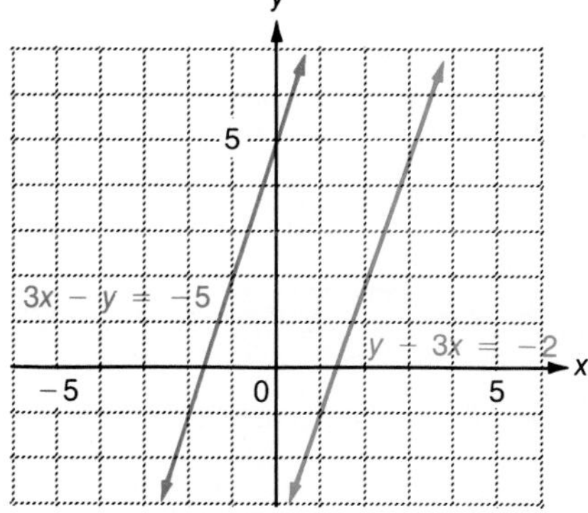

The slopes are the same, but the y-intercepts are different. Thus the lines are parallel.

Try This Determine whether the graphs of each pair of equations are parallel.

a. $x + 4 = y$
$y - x = -3$ Yes

b. $y + 4 = 3x$
$4x - y = -7$ No

c. $y = 4x + 5$
$2y = 8x + 10$ No

Finding Equations of Parallel Lines

Objective: Write an equation of the line that contains a given point and is parallel to a given line.

EXAMPLE 4

Write an equation of the line containing the point $(-1, 3)$ and parallel to the line $2x + y = 10$.

We first find the slope-intercept equation.

$$y = -2x + 10$$

Now we see that the parallel line must have slope -2.

Next we find the point-slope equation of the line with slope -2 and containing the point $(-1, 3)$.

$y - y_1 = m(x - x_1)$ Theorem 3-5

$y - 3 = -2[x - (-1)]$ Substituting

$y = -2x + 1$ Simplifying

The equations $y = -2x + 10$ and $y = -2x + 1$ have the same slope and different y-intercepts. Hence their graphs are parallel.

Try This

d. Write an equation of the line containing the point $(-2, -4)$ and parallel to the line $2y + 8x = 6$. $y = -4x - 12$

Chalkboard Examples

1. Determine whether the graphs of $y = 4x - 2$ and $y = 4x + 7$ are parallel.
   Yes, the slopes are both equal to 4.
2. Determine whether the graphs of $6x + 2y = 5$ and $3x + y = 7$ are parallel.
   Yes
   Method 1: The slopes are
   $m = -\frac{6}{2} = -3$ and $m = -\frac{3}{1}$
   Method 2: Solve for y.
   $6x + 2y = 5$
   $2y = -6x + 5$
   $y = -3x + \frac{5}{2}$
   The slope of the first line is -3.
   $3x + y = 7$
   $y = -3x + 7$
   The slope of the second line is -3. The lines have the same slope and different intercepts; therefore, the lines are parallel.
3. Determine whether the graphs of $6x - 2y = 12$ and $y = 3x - 6$ are parallel.
   Solving the first equation for y yields
   $-2y = -6x + 12$
   $y = 3x - 6$
   This is the same equation as the second line. The lines are coincident.

Finding Equations of Parallel Lines

Chalkboard Example

1. Write an equation of the line parallel to the line $y = 5x + 4$ and containing the point (1, 3).
   The slope of the given line is 5. We want a line with slope 5 and containing (1, 3). Using the point-slope equation
   $y - y_1 = m(x - x_1)$
   $y - 3 = 5(x - 1)$
   This simplifies to
   $y = 5x - 2$

Perpendicular Lines

Have students look at the graphs they drew for Warm-Up Exercises 3-5, find the slopes and compare.

Point out that if a line has slope m, then a second line perpendicular to the first has slope $-\frac{1}{m}$. In other words, the slope of a perpendicular line is the *negative reciprocal* of the slope of the original line.

Key Questions

Suppose that line a is perpendicular to line b.

- If the slope of line a is 3, what is the slope of line b?

  $-\frac{1}{3}$
- If the slope of line b is $-\frac{3}{2}$, what is the slope of line a?

  $\frac{2}{3}$

Chalkboard Example

1. Determine whether the lines $y = 5x + 2$ and $y = -5x + 2$ are perpendicular.
   We need only test whether the product of the slopes equals -1.

   $5(-5) = -25$

   The product is not -1, hence the lines are not perpendicular.

Perpendicular Lines

Objective: Use equations to determine whether two lines are perpendicular.

If two lines meet at right angles, they are **perpendicular.**

Theorem 3-10

Two nonvertical lines are perpendicular if and only if the product of their slopes is -1.

EXAMPLE 5 Determine whether the graphs of lines $5y = 4x + 10$ and $4y = -5x + 4$ are perpendicular.

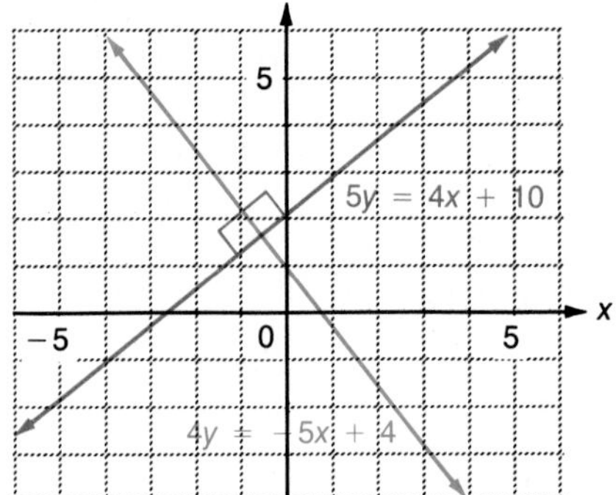

We find the slope-intercept equations by solving for y.

$$y = \frac{4}{5}x + 2, \quad y = -\frac{5}{4}x + 1$$

The product of the slopes is -1; that is,

$$\frac{4}{5}\cdot\left(-\frac{5}{4}\right) = -1$$

The lines are perpendicular.

Proof of Theorem 3-10

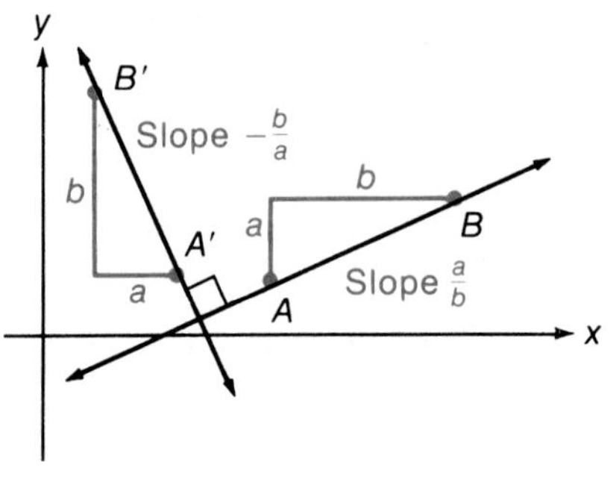

Consider a line $\overleftrightarrow{AB}$ as shown, with slope $\frac{a}{b}$. Then think of rotating the entire figure 90° to get a line perpendicular to $\overleftrightarrow{AB}$. For the new line the roles of a and b are interchanged, but a is now negative. Thus the slope of the new line is $-\frac{b}{a}$. Let us multiply the slopes $\frac{a}{b}\left(-\frac{b}{a}\right) = -1$.

This is the condition under which lines will be perpendicular.

Try This Determine whether the graphs of each pair of equations are perpendicular.

e. $2y - x = 2$ and $y + 2x = 4$ Yes **f.** $3y = 2x + 15$ and $2y = 3x + 10$ No

Finding Equations of Perpendicular Lines

Objective: Write an equation of the line that contains a given point and is perpendicular to a given line.

EXAMPLE 6 Write an equation of the line perpendicular to $4y - x = 20$ and containing the point $(2, -3)$.

We find the slope-intercept equation for $4y - x = 20$.

$$y = \frac{1}{4}x + 5$$

We know that the slope of the perpendicular line must be -4 because $\frac{1}{4}(-4) = -1$. Next we find the point-slope equation of the line having slope -4 and containing the point $(2, -3)$.

$$y - y_1 = m(x - x_1) \quad \text{Theorem 3-5}$$
$$y - (-3) = -4(x - 2) \quad \text{Substituting}$$
$$y = -4x + 5 \quad \text{Simplifying}$$

Try This Write an equation of the line containing the given point and perpendicular to the given line.

g. $(-1, 2); y = \frac{7}{8}x - 3$ $y = -\frac{8}{7}x + \frac{6}{7}$ **h.** $(3, 4); 4 - y = 2x$ $y = \frac{1}{2}x + \frac{5}{2}$

3-7 EXERCISES

A

Determine whether the graphs of each pair of equations are parallel.

1. $x + 6 = y$, $y - x = -2$ Yes **2.** $2x - 7 = y$, $y - 2x = 8$ Yes **3.** $y + 3 = 5x$, $3x - y = -2$ No

4. $y + 8 = -6x$, $-2x + y = 5$ No **5.** $y = 3x + 9$, $2y = 6x - 2$ Yes **6.** $y = -7x - 9$, $-3y = 21x + 7$ Yes

Write an equation of the line containing the given point and parallel to the given line.

7. $(3, 7); x + 2y = 6$ **8.** $(0, 3); 3x - y = 7$

9. $(2, -1); 5x - 7y = 8$ **10.** $(-4, -5); 2x + y = -3$

11. $(-6, 2); 3x - 9y = 2$ **12.** $(-7, 0); 5x + 2y = 6$

Determine whether the graphs of each pair of equations are perpendicular.

13. $y = 4x - 5$ and $4y = 8 - x$ Yes

14. $2x - 5y = -3$ and $2x + 5y = 4$ No

15. $x + 2y = 5$ and $2x + 4y = 8$ No

16. $y = -x + 7$ and $y = x + 3$ Yes

Finding Equations of Perpendicular Lines

Chalkboard Example

1. Write an equation for the line perpendicular to the line $y = 3x + 2$ and having y-intercept 4.
   The slope of the given line is 3. The slope of the line perpendicular to the given line is $-\frac{1}{3}$. The equation of the line, in slope-intercept form, is
   $y = -\frac{1}{3}x + 4$

LESSON QUIZ

Determine whether the given pairs of lines are parallel, perpendicular, the same line, or none of the above.

1. $y = 6x + 2$
   $y = 3(2x + 1)$
   The lines are parallel. The second equation may be written as
   $y = 6x + 3$
   The two lines have the same slope, but different y-intercepts.
2. $6x + 2y = 8$
   $y = 4 - 3x$
   Solve the first equation for y.
   $2y = -6x + 8$
   $y = -3x + 4$
   The second equation can be rewritten as $y = -3x + 4$.
   The two equations are equivalent, hence the lines are the same.
3. $y = 2x + 7$
   $y = -\frac{1}{2}x + 8$
   The slopes are 2 and $-\frac{1}{2}$.
   The product of the slopes is -1, hence the lines are perpendicular.
4. Write the equation of the line parallel to $y = 5x - 7$ and containing $(2, 4)$.
   The slope of the given line is 5. The required line is
   $y - 4 = 5(x - 2)$, or $y = 5x - 6$

Assignment Guide

Algebra: Day 1: 1–12
Day 2: 13–22, MR

Alg w/Finite or Trig: 1–27 e/o, 28, MR

Comprehensive: 1–27 m4, 28–31, MR, assign w. 3-6

ADDITIONAL ANSWERS

Exercises

7. $y = -\frac{1}{2}x + \frac{17}{2}$
8. $y = 3x + 3$
9. $y = \frac{5}{7}x - \frac{17}{7}$
10. $y = -2x - 13$
11. $y = \frac{1}{3}x + 4$
12. $y = -\frac{5}{2}x - \frac{35}{2}$
17. $y = \frac{1}{2}x + 4$
18. $y = -3x + 12$
19. $y = \frac{4}{3}x - 6$
20. $y = -\frac{2}{5}x - \frac{31}{5}$
21. $y = \frac{5}{2}x + 9$
22. $y = -2x - 10$
25. The side that contains (3, 4) and (6, 9) has slope $\frac{5}{3}$. The side that contains $(-2, 7)$ and (3, 4) has slope $-\frac{3}{5}$. Since $\frac{5}{3} \cdot \left(-\frac{3}{5}\right) = -1$, these two sides are perpendicular.

Mixed Review

32. No
33. Yes
34. No
35. Yes
36. No
37. 6
38. 22
39. 27
40. 7
41. 126
42. 102

Write an equation of the line containing the given point and perpendicular to the given line.

17. $(2, 5)$; $2x + y = -3$

18. $(4, 0)$; $x - 3y = 0$

19. $(3, -2)$; $3x + 4y = 5$

20. $(-3, -5)$; $5x - 2y = 4$

21. $(0, 9)$; $2x + 5y = 7$

22. $(-3, -4)$; $-3x + 6y = 2$

B

23. Find an equation of the line containing $(4, -2)$ and parallel to the line containing $(-1, 4)$ and $(2, -3)$. $y = -\frac{7}{3}x + \frac{22}{3}$

24. Find an equation of the line containing $(-1, 3)$ and perpendicular to the line containing $(3, -5)$ and $(-2, 7)$. $y = \frac{5}{12}x + \frac{41}{12}$

25. Use slopes to show that the triangle with vertices $(-2, 7)$, $(6, 9)$, and $(3, 4)$ is a right triangle.

26. Write an equation of the line that has y-intercept $\frac{5}{7}$ and is parallel to the graph of $6x - 3y = 1$. $y = 2x + \frac{5}{7}$

27. Write an equation of the line that has x-intercept -1.2 and is perpendicular to the graph of $6x - 3y = 1$. $y = -0.5x - 0.6$

28. ***Critical Thinking*** Two lines are perpendicular, and neither is vertical. How many quadrants must the lines pass through? All 4 quadrants

Challenge

29. Line l is perpendicular to line m, and line m is perpendicular to line n. Lines l and n do not coincide.

a. What is the relationship between the slopes of lines l and n? They are the same.

b. How many points do lines l and n have in common? None; the lines are parallel.

c. If line l has an equation $y = mx + b$, write an equation for line n. $y = mx + c, c \neq b$

30. Find a so that the graphs of $5y = ax + 5$ and $\frac{1}{4}y = \frac{1}{10}x - 1$ are parallel. 2

31. Find k so that the graphs of $x + 7y = 70$ and $y + 3 = kx$ are perpendicular. 7

Mixed Review

Determine whether the following ordered pairs are solutions of $y = 3x + 5$.

32. $(5, 0)$ **33.** $(-1, 2)$ **34.** $(0, 8)$ **35.** $(-50, -145)$ **36.** $(50, 145)$

Consider the function $f(x) = 3x^2 - 2x + 6$. Find each function value.

37. $f(0)$ **38.** $f(-2)$ **39.** $f(3)$ **40.** $f(1)$ **41.** $f(-6)$ **42.** $f(6)$

LOOKING FOR ERRORS

Jessie rewrote Theorem 3-10 as follows. "Two nonvertical lines are perpendicular if and only if their slopes are negative reciprocals of each other." Is Jessie's statement equivalent to the statement on page 140? Yes

3-8 Mathematical Modeling: Using Linear Functions

Objective: Find a linear function and use the equation to make predictions.

Crickets are known to chirp faster at higher temperatures and slower at lower temperatures. The number of chirps is thus a function of the temperature.

The following data were collected and recorded in a table.

Temperature °C	6	8	10	15	20
Number of chirps per minute	11	29	47	75	109

Can we predict the number of chirps per minute for a temperature of 18°C? If a linear equation fits the data reasonably well, we can develop a linear function as a mathematical model of the situation. We can then use the model (the linear function) to make predictions.

EXAMPLE 1

Use the data collected in the table to predict the number of chirps per minute when the temperature is 18°C.

UNDERSTAND the problem

Question: Can a linear function fit the data, and, if so, what is the approximate number of chirps per minute for a temperature of 18°C?

Data: Crickets chirp 11 times per minute at 6°C, 29 times per minute at 8°C, and so on, as listed in the table.

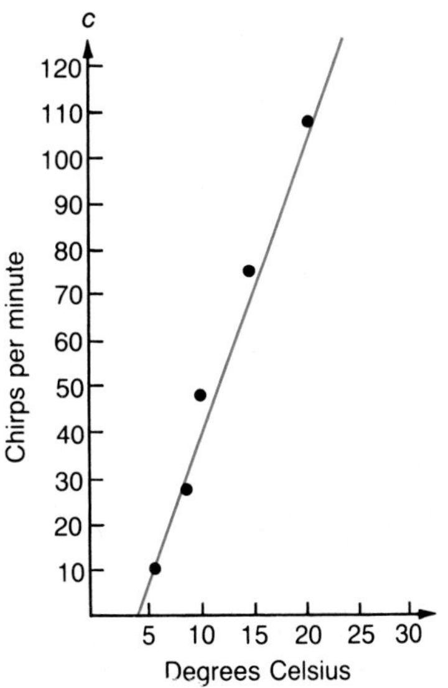

Develop and carry out a PLAN

First, we plot the data to determine whether a linear equation gives an approximate fit. We make a graph with a t-axis (temperature) and a c-axis (chirps per minute), and plot the data. We see that they lie approximately on a straight line. Thus, we can use a linear function to model the situation.

The line is placed so that some points are above and some are below the line, and so that each point is close to the line.

3-8

FIRST FIVE MINUTES

1. Write an equation of the line with slope 5 and y-intercept (0, 3).
   $y = 5x + 3$
2. Write an equation of the line with slope 4 containing the point (2, 3).
   $y - 3 = 4(x - 2)$
   This can be simplified to
   $y = 4x - 5$.
3. Write an equation for the line containing the points (4, 7), (6, 11).
   The slope is $\frac{11 - 7}{6 - 4} = 2$.
   The equation of the line is
   $y = 2x - 1$.

Point out that not all situations can be described by linear relationships. However, when a relationship is linear, we can use the best fit line to make predictions.

Other considerations also may limit the domain of a function. For example, a negative number of chirps would be meaningless. Also, imagine what would happen to a cricket at −40°C or 100°C.

Avoiding Common Errors

Students should not fit a line between two points that are close together on the ordinate axis. If we had fit the line using (8, 29) and (10, 47), we would have found the equation $c = 9t - 43$. From this we would have predicted that crickets chirp *119* times at 18°C. This is not a reasonable prediction (they chirp *less* often at 20°C) and the point (18, 119) is not close to the line we fit.

Math Point

There are a number of ways to draw a line. One possibility is to draw a line from the lower left point to the upper right point. Another possibility is to draw the line that minimizes the sum of vertical distances between the points and the line; or one could draw the line that minimizes the sum of perpendicular distances between the points and the line.

Statisticians often use a "least squares line," which minimizes the sum of the squares of the vertical distances between the points and the line. Statisticians may also use a "factor analysis line," which minimizes the sum of the squares of the perpendicular distances between the points and the line.

Chalkboard Examples

1. Suppose that a person who is 6 feet tall weighs 180 pounds and that a person who is 4 feet tall weighs 80 pounds. Fit a linear equation to the points and estimate the weight of a person who is 5.5 feet tall.
   The pairs of the form (h, w) represent a height h and a weight w. The line contains the points (6, 180) and (4, 80). The slope of the line is
   $m = \frac{180 - 80}{6 - 4} = 50.$
   The equation is
   $w - 80 = 50(h - 4)$.
   This simplifies to
   $w = 50h - 120$.
   If $h = 5.5$, then
   $w = 50(5.5) - 120 = 155$.
2. During an experiment, the following data were generated:

Time (sec.)	Temperature(C)
0	20.1
10	26.8
20	36.0
30	41.6
40	50.2
50	55.9

a. Can a linear function fit the data? Yes
b. Graph the data.
c. Graph a line so that the same number of points are above as below the line.

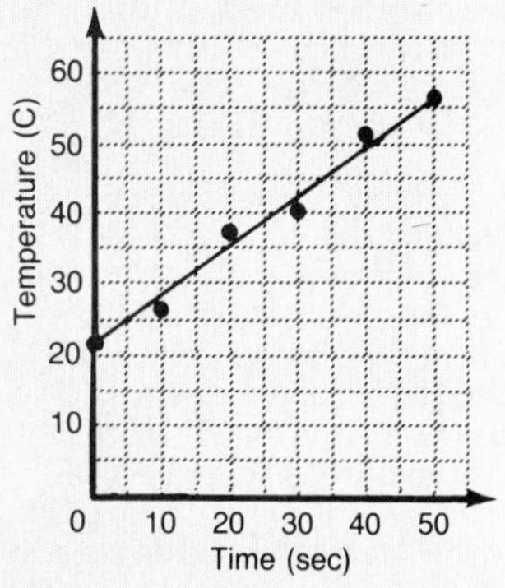

d. Choose 2 points that are close to the line. The end points are a good choice.
e. Fit a linear function through the points. $T = 20.1 + 0.716t$
f. Use the function to predict the temperature after 2 minutes. 106°C after 120 sec.

We can use two of the data points that are close to the line to find a two-point equation. We choose the points given by (6, 11) and (20, 109) since the line through these points is very close to the line we fit, over the domain of the data.

$$c - c_1 = \frac{c_2 - c_1}{t_2 - t_1}(t - t_1) \quad \text{Using the two-point equation, } c \text{ is chirps, } t \text{ is temperature.}$$

$$c - 11 = \frac{109 - 11}{20 - 6}(t - 6) \quad \text{Substituting}$$

$$c - 11 = 7(t - 6)$$

$$c = 7t - 31$$

Using this equation as a formula, we find that when $t = 18$, $c = 7(18) - 31 = 95$. When the temperature is 18°C, crickets chirp about 95 times per minute. The answer is reasonable, since 95 falls between 47 and 109, and is closer to 109.

EXAMPLE 2

Wind tunnel experiments are used to test the wind friction, or resistance, of an automobile at various speeds. If resistance is a linear function of speed, predict the resistance of an automobile traveling 50 km/h.

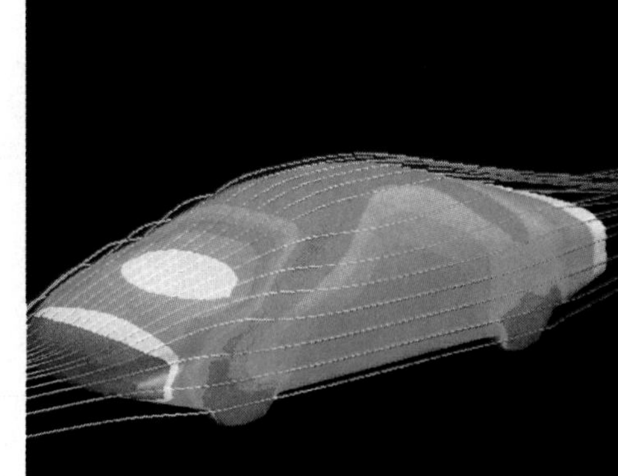

Speed (km/h)	Resistance (kg)
10	3.2
21	4.8
34	7.2
40	8.0
45	15.1
55	29.6

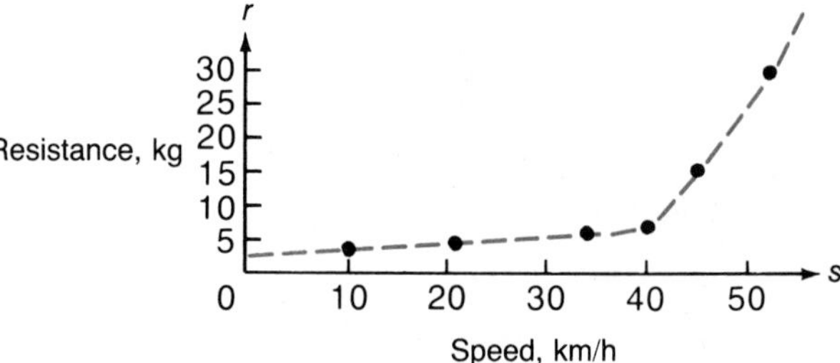

When graphed, the data do not approximate one straight line. However, there appear to be two linear parts to the graph: for speeds up to 40 km/h and for speeds of 40 km/h and above. We use (10, 3.2) and (40, 8.0) to find $r = 0.16s + 16$ for $s \leq 40$, and use (40, 8.0) and (55, 29.6) to find $r = 1.44s - 49.6$ for $s \geq 40$.

For $s = 50$, $r = 1.44(50) - 49.6 = 22.4$. Thus the resistance at 50 km/h is approximately 22.4 kg. Note that a nonlinear function might fit the data better.

Try This

a. It has been found that certain running records have changed with time, according to linear functions. In 1920 the record for the 100-m dash was 10.43 seconds. In 1983 it was 9.93 seconds. Let R represent the record in the 100-m dash and t the number of years since 1920.

1. Fit a linear function to the data points. $R = -0.0079t + 10.43$

2. Use your function to predict the record in 2000; in 2050. ≈9.79 s, ≈9.39 s

3. In what year will the record be 9.0 seconds? ≈2099

b. A chemistry experiment generated the following temperatures for a solution over time.

Time (minutes)	5	15	25	30	32
Temperature °F	75	130	175	200	210

Answers may vary. $T = 5t + 50$; 90°; 2 min

If a linear function fits the data, determine the function, predict the temperature of the solution after 8 minutes, and predict the time it takes for the temperature to reach 60°F.

Guidelines for Finding Linear Functions

1. Graph the data.
2. If the data lie approximately on a straight line, a linear function can be used.
3. Graph a line so that approximately half the points are above and half are below the line.
4. Find the coordinates for two of the data points on or close to the line.
5. Apply the two-point equation to find a linear function.

3-8 EXERCISES

A

Solve.

1. In 1950 the life expectancy of women was 72 years. In 1970 it was 75 years. Let E represent the life expectancy and t the number of years since 1950 ($t = 0$ gives 1950 and $t = 10$ gives 1960).

a. Fit a linear function to the data points. [They are (0, 72) and (20, 75).] $E = \frac{3}{20}t + 72$

b. Use the function to predict the life expectancy of women in 1993 in 2008. 78.45 years in 1993, 80.7 in 2008

2. In 1950 the life expectancy of men was 65 years. In 1970 it was 68 years. Let E represent the life expectancy and t the number of years since 1950.

a. Fit a linear function to the data points. $E = \frac{3}{20}t + 65$

b. Use the function to predict the life expectancy of men in 1996; in 2007. 71.9 years in 1996, 73.55 in 2007

Assignment Guide
Algebra: 1–9 e/o, MR

Alg w/Finite or Trig: 1–14 e/o, 15, MR

Comprehensive: 1–14 e/o, 15–17, MR

LESSON QUIZ

1. The cost of a cord is a linear function of its length. 3 ft of cord costs \$13. 9 ft of cord costs \$25. Fit a linear function to the data and estimate the cost of 20 ft of cord.
A pair of the form (l, c) relates the length l of a piece of cord with its cost c. The line contains the points (3, 13) and (9, 25). The slope of the line is
$$m = \frac{25 - 13}{9 - 3} = 2$$
The equation of the line is
$c - 13 = 2(l - 3)$
This simplifies to
$c = 2l + 7$
If $l = 20$, then
$c = 2(20) + 7 = 47$

3. In 1950 natural gas demand in the United States was 20 quadrillion joules. In 1960 the demand was 22 quadrillion joules. Let D represent the demand for natural gas t years after 1950.
   a. Fit a linear function to the data points. $D = \frac{1}{5}t + 20$
   b. Use the function to predict the natural gas demand in 1991; in 2005. 28.2 in 1991, 31 in 2005
4. In 1930 the record for the 1500-m run was 3.85 minutes. In 1950 it was 3.70 minutes. Let R represent the record in the 1500-m run and t the number of years since 1930.
   a. Fit a linear function to the data points. $R = -0.0075t + 3.85$
   b. Use the function to predict the record in 1994; in 2001. 3.37 min in 1994, 3.3175 in 2001
   c. When will the record be 3.3 minutes? $\approx$ 2003
5. In 1930 the record for the 400-m run was 46.8 seconds. In 1970 it was 43.8 s. Let R represent the record in the 400-m run and t the number of years since 1930.
   a. Fit a linear function to the data points. $R = -0.075t + 46.8$
   b. Use the function to predict the record in 1996; in 2003. 41.85 sec in 1996, 41.325 in 2003
   c. When will the record be 40 seconds? 2021
6. The cost of a taxi ride for the first $\frac{1}{5}$ mi is \$1.50. For 3 mi the cost is \$4.30.
   a. Fit a linear function to the data points. $C = m + 1.3$
   b. Use the function to find the cost of a 7-mi ride. \$8.30
   c. How far could a person ride for \$20? 18.7 mi
7. If you rent a car for 1 day and drive it 100 mi, the cost is \$30.00. If you drive it 150 mi, the cost is \$37.50.
   a. Fit a linear function to the data points. $C = 0.15m + 15$
   b. Use the function to find how much it will cost to rent the car for 1 day if you drive it 200 mi. \$45.00
8. An accountant located five different city tax returns for a specific year. These were the city taxes for some different incomes.

Income (in \$000)	8	15	25	40	75
Taxes (in dollars)	24	70	180	300	560

Answers may vary.
$T = 8I - 40$; \$400; \$35,000

If a linear function fits the data, determine the function, predict the tax amount for an income of \$55,000, and predict the income for a tax amount of \$240.

9. An instant coffee comes in several size jars. These were the prices for each size at one supermarket.

Ounces	2	6	10	16	32
Price	\$0.95	\$2.15	\$3.29	\$4.89	\$8.99

Answers may vary.
$P = 0.268o + 0.414$; \$6.85; 50.7 oz

If a linear function fits the data, determine the function, predict the price of a 24-oz jar, and predict the size of a jar that would sell for \$13.99.

B

Solve, assuming a linear function fits the situation.

10. The value of a copy machine is \$5200 when it is purchased. After 2 years its value is \$4225. Find its value after 8 years. \$1300

11. Water freezes at 32° Fahrenheit and at 0° Celsius. Water boils at 212° F and at 100° C. What Celsius temperature corresponds to a room temperature of 70° F? 21.1°C

12. A business determines that when it sells 7000 units of a product it will take in \$22,000. For the sale of 8000 units it will take in \$25,000. How much will it take in for the sale of 10,000 units? \$31,000

13. A piece of copper pipe has a length of 100 cm at 18°C. At 20°C the length of the pipe changes to 100.00356 cm. Find the length of the pipe at 40°C and at 0°C. 100.03916 cm; 99.96796 cm

14. For a linear function f, $f(-1) = 3$ and $f(2) = 4$.
a. Find an equation for f. **b.** Find $f(3)$. **c.** Find a such that $f(a) = 100$.

15. ***Critical Thinking*** Suppose in Example 1 that the temperature is actually determined by the number of times the crickets chirp. How could you quickly develop a linear function to determine the temperature for a specific number of chirps per minute?

Challenge

16. A person applying for a sales position is offered alternative salary plans.
Plan A: a base salary of \$600 per month plus a commission of 4% of the gross sales for the month
Plan B: a base salary of \$700 per month plus a commission of 6% of the gross sales for the month in excess of \$10,000
a. For each plan, formulate a function that expresses monthly earnings as a function of gross sales x. Plan A: $E = 600 + 0.04x$; Plan B: $E = 100 + 0.06x$
b. For what gross sales values is Plan B preferable? $x \geq 25{,}000$

17. An anthropologist can use linear functions to estimate the height of a male or female, given the length of certain bones. A *humerus* is the bone from the elbow to the shoulder. The height, in centimeters, of a male with a humerus of length x is given by $M(x) = 2.89x + 70.64$. The height, in centimeters, of a female with a humerus of length x is given by $F(x) = 2.75x + 71.48$. A 45-cm humerus was uncovered in some ruins.
a. Assuming it was from a male, how tall was he? 200.69 cm
b. Assuming it was from a female, how tall was she? 195.23 cm
c. For what height would the lengths of a female humerus and a male humerus be equal? 87.98 cm

Mixed Review

Find the slope, if it exists, of each line. **18.** $3y = -12$ **19.** $x = 4$

Find the equation of the lines containing the given points, with the indicated slopes.
20. $(-1, -4)$; $m = 1$ **21.** $(2, 3)$; $m = -1$ **22.** $(4, 2)$; $m = 0$

Simplify. **23.** $9c - 16c$ **24.** $4m + 2m - m$ **25.** $7x + 5 + (4 - 2x)$
26. $t + t + t$ **27.** $4(3r) - 12s + 2r$ **28.** $6(y + 4y) + 3y$ **29.** $(p^2 \cdot p^2)^2 \cdot p^{-4}$

ADDITIONAL ANSWERS

14a. $f(x) = \frac{1}{3}x + 3\frac{1}{3}$
b. $4\frac{1}{3}$
c. 290
15. Answers may vary. By solving the equation for t, the equation would become $t = \frac{1}{7}c + \frac{32}{7}$.

Mixed Review

18. 0
19. No slope
20. $y = x - 3$
21. $y = -x + 5$
22. $y = 2$
23. $-7c$
24. $5m$
25. $5x + 9$
26. $3t$
27. $14r - 12s$
28. $33y$
29. p^4

3-9

FIRST FIVE MINUTES

1. Evaluate the function $y = 3x - 4$ when $x = 7$.
   $y = 3(7) - 4 = 17$
2. If $f(x) = \frac{12}{x}$, what is $f(3)$?
   $f(3) = \frac{12}{(3)} = 4$
3. Simplify $|-3| - |-(-3)|$.
   $3 - 3 = 0$
4. Given that y is a linear function of x and that $y = 4$ when $x = 2$, and that $y = 8$ when $x = 3$, find y when $x = 5$.
   The line contains the points (2, 4) and (3, 8). The slope of the line is
   $m = \frac{8-4}{3-2} = 4$
   The equation is
   $y - 4 = 4(x - 2)$.
   This simplifies to
   $y = 4x - 4$
   When $x = 5$, $y = 16$.

Special Functions

You may want to point out the following commands for computer programming.

In BASIC, we use y = ABS(X) for absolute value and y = INT(x) for the greatest integer function.

In PASCAL, we use y: = abs(x) for absolute value and y: = trunc(x) for the greatest integer function.

Key Questions

- Does [2] = [2.8]?
  Yes
- Does [−2] = [−2.8]?
  No

3-9 More about Functions

First class postage for letters or packages is a function of weight. For one ounce or less, the postage is 25¢. For each additional ounce *or fraction of an ounce* 20¢ is due. Such a function is called a step function since at each integral ounce, the price steps to the next value. Another example of a step function is the greatest integer function $f(x) = [x]$.

Special Functions

Objective: Graph special functions.

The greatest integer function, $f(x) = [x]$, is the greatest integer that is less than or equal to x. For example, $[4.5] = 4$, $[-1] = -1$, and $[-3.9] = -4$.

EXAMPLE 1 Graph $f(x) = [x]$.

For $0 \le x < 1$, $f(x) = 0$.
For $1 \le x < 2$, $f(x) = 1$.
For $2 \le x < 3$, $f(x) = 2$, and so on.

We can use the pattern above to graph $f(x)$ for x between any two integers, and thus graph the function for all real numbers.

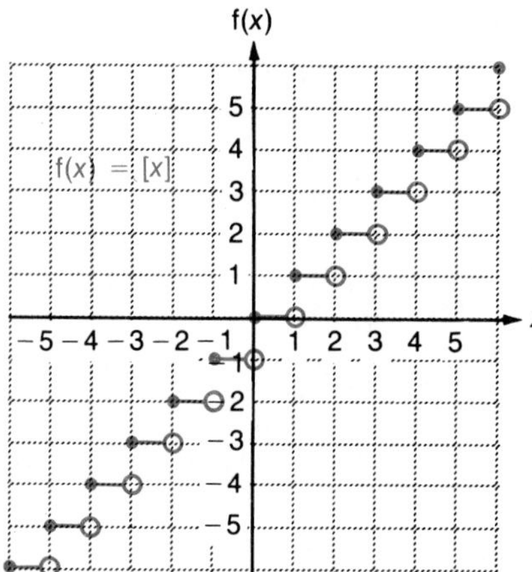

EXAMPLE 2 Graph $f(x) = |x|$.

Finding the absolute value of a number can also be thought of in terms of a function, the absolute value function $f(x) = |x|$. The domain of the absolute value function is the set of real numbers; the range is the set of positive real numbers.

The graph has two parts,

For $x \ge 0$, $f(x) = x$.
For $x < 0$, $f(x) = -x$.

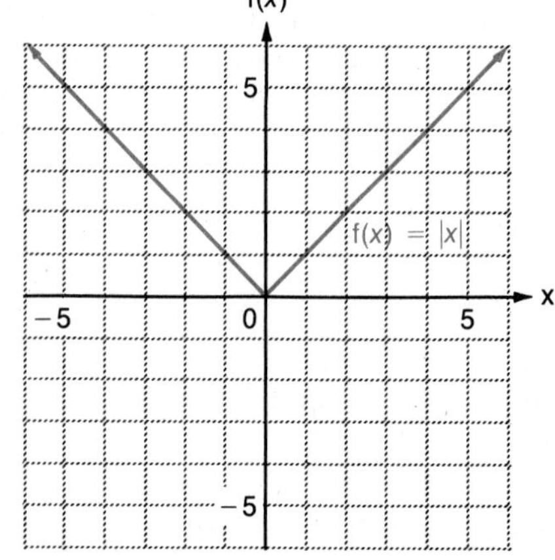

Try This Graph. See Selected Answers.

a. $y = [x] + 1$ **b.** $y = [x + 1]$ **c.** $f(x) = |x| + 1$ **d.** $f(x) = |x + 1|$

Composition of Functions

Objective: Find the composite of two functions.

Functions can be combined in many ways. One such way is called composition.

Definition

Let f and g be any two functions such that the range of g is in the domain of f. The **composition** of f and g is the function given by $f(g(x))$.

EXAMPLES Suppose $f(x) = x^2$ and $g(x) = x + 2$.

3. Find $f(g(3))$.

First find $g(3)$.

$g(3) = 3 + 2$ Substituting 3 for x in $g(x) = x + 2$
$= 5$

Then find $f(g(3))$.

$f(g(3)) = f(5)$ Substituting 5 for $g(3)$
$= 5^2$ Substituting 5 for x in $f(x) = x^2$
$= 25$

We can find compositions of functions by working within inner parentheses first.

4. Find $g(f(3))$.

$g(f(x)) = g(x^2)$ Substituting x^2 for $f(x)$
$g(f(3)) = g(3^2)$ Substituting 3 for x
$= g(9)$
$= 9 + 2 = 11$ Substituting 9 for x in $g(x) = x + 2$

Try This Suppose $f(x) = 2x$ and $g(x) = x - 7$.

e. Find $f(g(2))$. −10 **f.** Find $g(f(2))$. −3 **g.** Find $g(f(0))$. −7 **h.** Find $f(g(-5))$. −24

We can find expressions that represent the composite of two functions.

EXAMPLES Suppose $f(x) = 4x$ and $g(x) = x + 3$.

5. Find an expression for $f(g(x))$.

$f(g(x)) = f(x + 3)$ Substituting $x + 3$ for $g(x)$
$= 4(x + 3)$
$= 4x + 12$ Using the distributive property

Chalkboard Examples

1. Graph the function $y = x - [x]$.
The function returns the decimal part of the number.

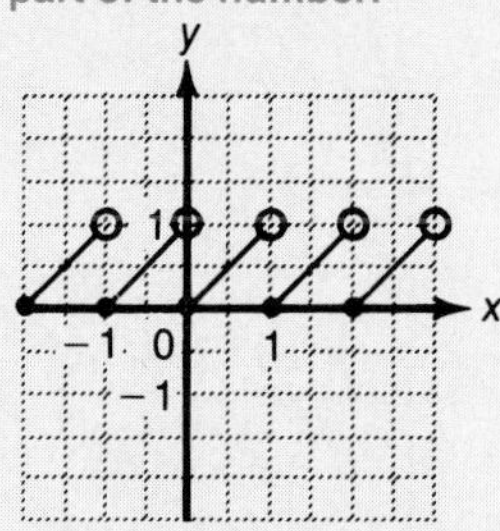

2. Graph the function $y = \frac{x}{|x|}$.

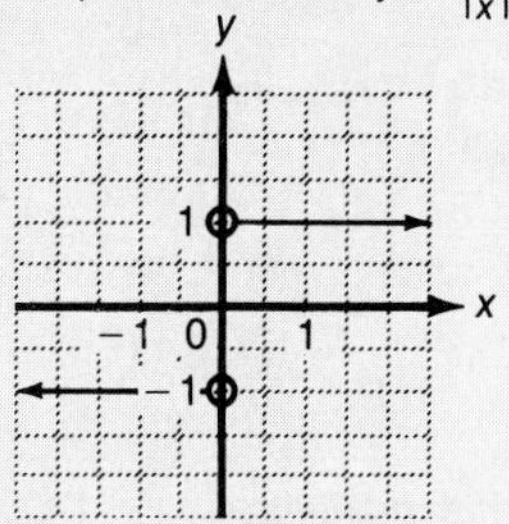

Composition of Functions

Examples 3 and 4 illustrate the fact that $f(g(x))$ does not necessarily have the same value as $g(f(x))$.

Some students may still confuse function notation with multiplication. Emphasize that
a. $f(x)$ is not fx, xf or $(x)f$.
b. $f(-x)$ is not $-fx$.
c. $f(x + z)$ is not $fx + fz$.

Stress that it is acceptable to replace a single variable with an expression.

Chalkboard Examples

Suppose $f(x) = 3x$ and $g(x) = x + 2$.
1. Find $f(g(4))$.
$g(4) = (4) + 2 = 6$
$f(g(4)) = f(6) = 3(6) = 18$
2. Find $g(f(4))$.
$f(4) = 3(4) = 12$
$g(f(4)) = g(12) = (12) + 2 = 14$

Suppose $f(x) = 2x$ and $g(x) = x + 5$.
3. Find an expression for $f(g(x))$.
$f(g(x)) = f(x + 5) = 2(x + 5)$
4. Find an expression for $g(f(x))$.
$g(f(x)) = g(2x) = 2x + 5$

LESSON QUIZ

1. Suppose $y = [x + 5]$. Find the value of y when $x = 1.3$.
   $y = [1.3 + 5] = [6.3] = 6$
2. Graph $y = |x + 2|$.

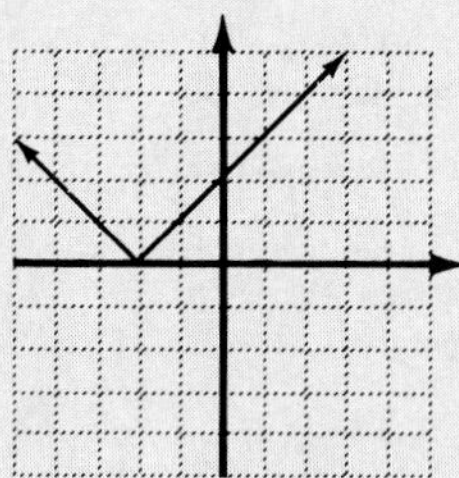

Suppose $f(x) = x^2$ and $g(x) = 2x$.

3. Find $f(g(3))$.
   $f(g(3)) = f(2(3)) = f(6) = (6)^2 = 36$
4. Find $f(x + 1)$.
   $f(x + 1) = (x + 1)^2$
5. Find $f(g(x))$.
   $f(g(x)) = f(2x) = (2x)^2 = 4x^2$

Assignment Guide

Algebra: 1 – 25 e/o, MR

Alg w/Finite or Trig: 1–25 m3, 26–43 e/o, 44, MR

Comprehensive: 1–40 m3, 44, 45–50 e/o, MR

6. Find an expression for $g(f(x))$.

$$g(f(x)) = g(4x) \quad \text{Substituting } 4x \text{ for } f(x)$$
$$= 4x + 3$$

Try This Suppose $f(x) = -3x$ and $g(x) = x - 4$.

i. Find an expression for $f(g(x))$. $-3x + 12$
j. Find an expression for $g(f(x))$. $-3x - 4$
k. Find an expression for $f(f(x))$. $9x$
l. Find an expression for $g(g(x))$. $x - 8$

3-9 EXERCISES

A

Graph.

1. $f(x) = [x - 2]$
2. $f(x) = [x] - 1$
3. $f(x) = [x - 1]$
4. $f(x) = |x - 1|$
5. $f(x) = |x - 2|$
6. $f(x) = |x| + x$
7. $f(x) = |x| - 1$
8. $f(x) = \frac{1}{2}|x|$
9. $f(x) = 2|x| - 2$

For Exercises 10-25 suppose $f(x) = x^2$, $g(x) = x - 1$ and $h(x) = 4x$. Find the following.

10. $f(g(2))$ 1
11. $g(f(-1))$ 0
12. $h(g(3))$ 8
13. $f(h(-2))$ 64
14. $h(g(0))$ -4
15. $g(h(9))$ 35
16. $f(g(-5))$ 36
17. $h(g(-12))$ -52

Find expressions for the following.

18. $f(g(x))$ $(x - 1)^2$
19. $g(h(x))$ $4x - 1$
20. $f(h(x))$ $16x^2$
21. $g(f(x))$ $x^2 - 1$
22. $g(g(x))$ $x - 2$
23. $f(f(x))$ x^4
24. $h(f(x))$ $4x^2$
25. $h(h(x))$ $16x$

B

26. A person's bowling average is defined as follows. Bowling average $= \left[\frac{P}{n}\right]$ where P = total number of pins, and n = total number of games bowled. Find the bowling average.
a. 547 pins in 3 games 182
b. 4621 pins in 27 games 171

27. Draw the graph of the postage step function described in the introduction to this lesson. What is the domain and the range of this function?

28. The **signum function, sg,** is defined as follows: $sg(x) = -1$ when $x < 0$, $sg(x) = 0$ when $x = 0$, and $sg(x) = 1$ when $x > 0$. Draw a graph of the signum function.

Suppose $f(x) = |x|$ and $g(x) = 2x$.

29. Find $f(g(-5))$. 10
30. Find $g(f(-6))$. 12
31. Find $f(g(-18))$. 36

The composite of two functions f and g is sometimes represented by $f \circ g$. Thus $(f \circ g)(x) = f(g(x))$. Suppose $f(x) = -x$ and $g(x) = 7x$.

32. Find $(f \circ g)(-3)$. 21 **33.** Find $(f \circ g)(7)$. -49 **34.** Find $(g \circ f)(0)$. 0

Suppose $f(x) = -x^2$, $g(x) = x - 3$ and $h(x) = -2x$. Find the following.

35. $f(g(h(1)))$ -25 **36.** $g(h(f(0)))$ -3 **37.** $h(g(f(4)))$ 38 **38.** $h(h(h(2)))$ -16

Suppose $f(x) = 5x$, $g(x) = 2x - 1$ and $h(x) = x + 5$. Find expressions for the following.

39. $f(g(h(x)))$ $10x + 45$ **40.** $g(g(h(x)))$ $4x + 17$ **41.** $h(g(f(x)))$ $10x + 4$ **42.** $f(g(f(x)))$ $50x - 5$

43. The temperature in degrees Kelvin is the number of degrees Celsius plus 273. The temperature in degrees Fahrenheit is $\frac{9}{5}$ times the number of degrees Celsius, plus 32.
a. Write a function for degrees Kelvin in terms of degrees Fahrenheit. $K(F) = \frac{5}{9}F + 255\frac{2}{9}$
b. Find the Kelvin temperature for $-13°F$. 248 K

44. ***Critical Thinking*** The graph of a function is the reflection of $f(x) = |x|$ across the x-axis. Write an equation that defines this function. $f(x) = -|x|$

Challenge

45. Graph $|x| - |y| = 1$.

46. Graph the relation $\{(x, y) \mid |x| \leq 1 \text{ and } |y| \leq 2\}$.

47. Determine whether the relation $\{(x, y) \mid xy = 0\}$ is a function. No

48. Graph the equation $[y] = [x]$. Is this the graph of a function? No

49. $f(x) = 2x + 7$ and $g(x) = 3x + b$. Find b such that $f(g(x)) = g(f(x))$. 14

50. $f(x) = ax + b$. Find an expression for $f(f(x))$. $a^2x + ab + b$

Mixed Review

For each pair of points, find the equation of the line containing them.

51. (1, 3) and (6, 13) **52.** (−1, −1) and (3, 3) **53.** (0, 0) and (2, −3)

Write each expression without negative exponents. **54.** 5^{-4} **55.** $(2w)^{-3}$

56. m^2n^{-9}

Solve. **57.** $0.8a = -2.4$ **58.** $1.02 + c = -0.85$ **59.** $|3x - 5| = 19$

60. Valerie's mother loaned her $8700 interest-free. Valerie was to pay all but 25% of the money in equal monthly payments over 3 years and the remainder at the end of the loan. How much is her monthly payment?

WRITING TO LEARN

Suppose a friend called asking how to graph a function that rounds a number to the nearest ten. Describe your instructions. Answers may vary.

ADDITIONAL ANSWERS

Exercises

For Exercises 1–9, see Teacher's Answer Section.

27. 

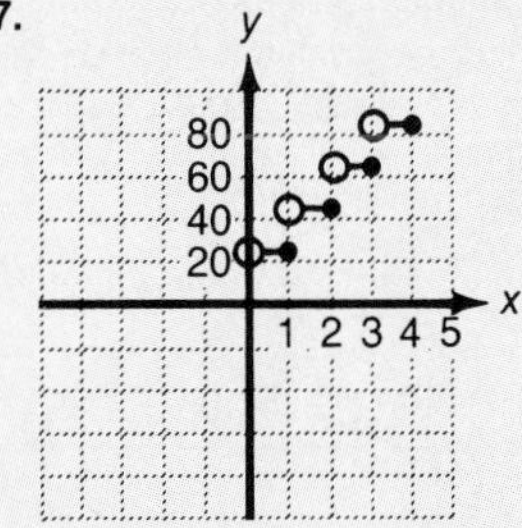

Domain: $\{x \mid x > 0\}$
Range: $\{y \mid y = 25 + 20n$, n a whole number$\}$

28.

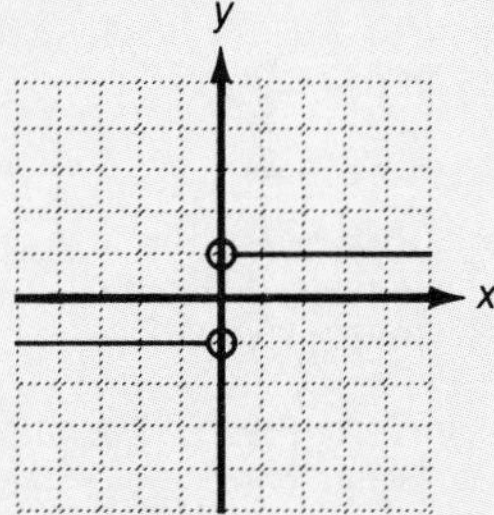

For graphs of Exercises 45–48, see Teacher's Answer Section.

Mixed Review

51. $y = 2x + 1$ **52.** $y = x$
53. $y = -\frac{3}{2}x$ **54.** $\frac{1}{5^4}$
55. $\frac{1}{(2w)^3}$ **56.** $\frac{m^2}{n^9}$
57. -3 **58.** -1.87
59. $8, -\frac{14}{3}$ **60.** $181.25

3-10

FIRST FIVE MINUTES

1. An island will be divided by four landowners into four pieces. How can this be done so that each piece shares borders with the other three?
   Answers may vary. (Draw a Diagram)
2. Find x so that $3^x = 729$.
   6 (Guess, Check, Revise)

Make an Organized List

The key to a successful list is organization. It may be necessary to try several different ways of organizing data before finding the pattern that leads to a solution. Here we emphasize the use of organized lists for counting. Later, we will use an organized list in the form of a table to look for a pattern.

Key Questions

- If a letter could be used twice in the same license plate, would there be more or fewer choices?
  More
- How many choices would there be if the license plates consisted of only 3 letters, without repetitions?
  6

Chalkboard Example

1. There are five finalists in a tennis tournament. Each finalist will play all the other finalists. The player who wins the most matches wins the tournament. How many matches will be played?
   Label the players A, B, C, D, and E and make an organized list.
   A plays B, AC, AD, and AE
   B plays A is the same as A plays B, so B's other matches will be BC, BD, and BE.
   The remaining matches are CD, CE, and DE.
   There are 10 matches in all.

3-10 Problem Solving: Strategies

Make an Organized List

Objective: Solve problems using the strategy *Make an Organized List* and other strategies.

PROBLEM-SOLVING GUIDELINES
■ UNDERSTAND the problem
■ Develop and carry out a PLAN
■ Find the ANSWER and CHECK

Some problems can be solved by listing information from the problem in a systematic or organized way. This strategy for solving problems is called Make an Organized List.

EXAMPLE

A taxicab company was told that their license plates would consist of three letters followed by two numbers. The letters would be A, B, and C, and the numbers would be 3 and 5. No letter could be used twice in the same license plate, but a number could be used twice. How many choices did this company have for license plates?

We can solve this problem by *making an organized list.* First we can list the ways the letters can be arranged. There are 6 ways this could be done.

ABC	BAC	CAB
ACB	BCA	CBA

Next we can list the ways the numbers can be arranged. There are 4 ways.

33	53
35	55

Now we can list the ways the letters and numbers can be combined.

ABC33	BAC33	CAB33
ABC35	BAC35	CAB35
ABC53	BAC53	CAB53
ABC55	BAC55	CAB55
ACB33	BCA33	CBA33
ACB35	BCA35	CBA35
ACB53	BCA53	CBA53
ACB55	BCA55	CBA55

There are 24 choices for license plates. Notice that the list above was organized by first listing all possibilities with ABC in the license plate, then with BAC, and so on. Organizing the lists helps you know that you have listed all possibilities.

Problem-Solving Strategies		
Write an Equation	Draw a Diagram	Guess, Check, Revise
Make an Organized List	Make a Table	Look for a Pattern
Use Logical Reasoning	Simplify the Problem	Work Backward

3-10 PROBLEMS

Solve using one or more of the strategies presented.

1. A radio announcer had $48 to buy tapes. The $9.50 tapes were on sale for $6 and the $8.25 tapes were on sale for $4. In how many different ways could the announcer spend all of her money buying the tapes on sale?
2. The cost of a rectangular carpet for a certain room will be $442. Carpeting is sold with whole-number dimensions only, and then trimmed to fit the room. The cost is $2 per square foot. What are the dimensions of the carpet?
3. A designer had a poster board 36″ high by 48″ wide. She wanted to use 2″ high letters with 1″ of space between each line of words. She also wanted a 2″ border around the edge of the entire poster. How many lines of words can she get on this poster?
4. A basketball series between two teams is determined when one team wins three games. In how many ways could a team win the series?
5. At a banquet in a Chinese restaurant, 65 dishes were served. Every 2 guests shared a dish of rice between them; every 3 guests shared a dish of noodles; and every 4 guests shared a dish of meat. How many people were at the banquet?
6. Suppose you had an $8\frac{1}{2}''$ by 11″ sheet of paper. How could you use that paper to measure a line segment 6″ long?

7. Theo always carries lots of change in quarters, nickels, dimes and pennies. Sonia needed change for a dollar. It turned out that Theo had the most change he could possibly have without having change for a dollar. How much did Theo have in change?
8. Avram forgot his four-digit autoteller code. He knew that the four numbers were 2, 3, 5, and 8, but he could not remember the order. How many possible codes were there?
9. Three machines produce three pairs of headphones in three hours. How many pairs of headphones would nine machines produce in nine hours?

Hints for Problems

1. Make a list showing the prices for different numbers of each type of tape.
2. First find the area of the floor. Then look for two whole numbers whose product is the area.
3. Draw a diagram showing each dimension.
4. Find the number of ways with no losses, then 1 loss, then 2 consecutive losses, then 2 losses separated by a win, and so on.
5. Guess how many people were at the banquet.
6. Draw a diagram showing different lengths that can be made with the sheet of paper.
7. Guess, check, and revise.
8. Make an organized list of the possible codes.
9. Figure out how many pairs of headphones one machine makes in one hour.

ANSWERS

1.

$6 tapes	$4 tapes
8	0
6	3
4	6
2	9
0	12

The announcer could spend all of the money in 5 ways.

2. The dimensions of the floor are 13 ft by 17 ft.
3. There can be 11 rows of letters on the poster.
4. There are 10 ways to win 3 out of 5 games.
5. There could be 60 people at the party. (Note: You can show that there could also be 59 people at the party. Since 2, 3, and 4 divide evenly into 60, each bowl of each type would be used with no extra dishes. For 59 people, 65 dishes would still be needed, but there would be extra dishes.
6. Two $8\frac{1}{2}''$ segments is 17″, which is 6″ longer than an 11″ segment.
7. $1.19 (3 quarters, 4 dimes, 4 pennies, or 1 quarter, 9 dimes, 4 pennies)
8. 24
9. 27

Problem Solving: Application

You may want to have students make a graph of the daily mileages that would result in equal charges by the two companies. The graph will be the linear function Miles = 50 × days. For any number of days. Penguin will be cheaper for less than 50 miles per day, Drive-Far will be cheaper for more than 50 miles per day.

Hint for Problem

2. Find the driving distance for which the two companies charge the same: $30 + 0.1d = 15 + 0.15d$. Then for any greater distance per day, Buckle-Up is a better choice.

ANSWERS

1. Rent a Roadster
2. Buckle-Up
3. Rent a Roadster
4. 320
5. No situation

Problem Solving: Application

Comparative Shopping

Whether you are buying or renting, you can save money by doing some comparative shopping. Consider car rentals. The rental fee may be a function of the number of days the car is rented, the number of miles driven, the amount of gasoline used, and the type of car rented.

EXAMPLE

Suppose you have a choice between the following companies for renting a particular car. You can assume that the gasoline costs will be equal.

Drive-Far Rent-A-Car	\$25/day and \$0.10/mile
Penguin Rent-A-Car	\$10/day and \$0.40/mile

You need to consider your driving plans. If you'll be driving far, you may want to choose the lower mileage rate. If you plan to keep the car a long time, you may want to choose the lower daily rate. You can use equations to help make the decision. Compare the charges, assuming you need to rent a car for two days and drive it 60 miles.

Drive-Far: $2(\$25) + 60(\$0.10) = \$56$

Penguin: $2(\$10) + 60(\$0.40) = \$44$

In this case, Penguin is cheaper.

What if you planned to drive 300 miles in two days?

Drive-Far: $2(\$25) + 300(\$0.10) = \$80$

Penguin: $2(\$10) + 300(\$0.40) = \$140$

For this driving distance, Drive-Far is cheaper.

Problems

Choose which company you would use in each situation. Explain your decision.

Buckle-Up Car Rentals	\$30/day and \$0.10/mile
Rent-A-Roadster Car Rentals	\$14/day and \$0.15/mile

1. You need to rent a car for 3 days and drive 375 miles.
2. You need to rent a car for 3 days and drive 1200 miles.
3. You need to rent a car for 12 days and drive 3000 miles.
4. At what amount of mileage per day does one company become a better choice than the other?
5. Swift Car Rentals has a rate of \$25/day + \$0.20/mile, but the first 100 miles are free. For which situation in Problems 1–3 would Swift be cheapest?

Chapter 3 Summary and Review

3-1

A relation from set A to set B is any set of ordered pairs in the Cartesian product $A \times B$.

1. Consider sets A and B, where $A = \{a, b, c\}$ and $B = \{1, 2\}$. List the set of ordered pairs in $A \times B$.
2. Consider the relation $C \times C$, where $C = \{-2, -1, 0, 1\}$. Find the set of ordered pairs determined by the relation $>$.
3. List the domain and the range of the relation $\{(1, 2), (-1, 4), (0, 5), (2, -4), (-6, 5), (2, 1)\}$.

3-2

If an equation has two variables, its solutions are ordered pairs. Each ordered pair, when substituted for the variables, produces a true equation.

4. Which of these ordered pairs $(-3, -3)$, $(0, 3)$, $(-1, 2)$ is a solution to the equation $y = 3 - 2x$?
5. Graph $y = -2x - 2$.
6. Graph $y = x^2 - 1$.

3-3

A function is a relation in which no two ordered pairs have the same first coordinate and different second coordinates.

Which of the following are graphs of functions?

7.

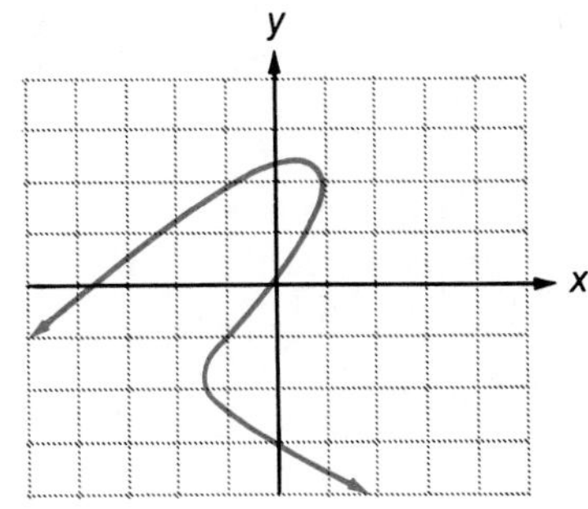

8.

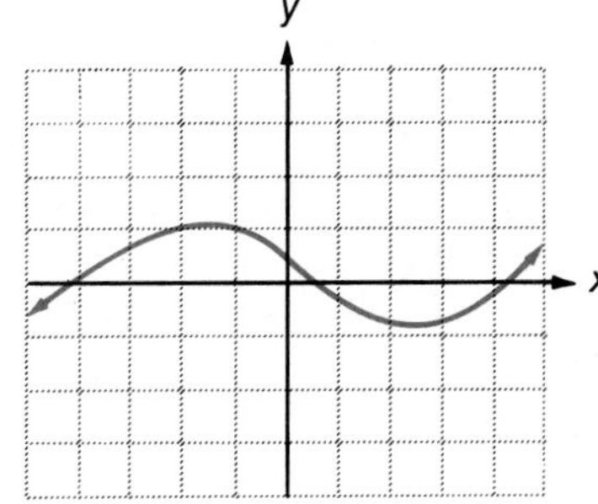

3-4

An equation is linear if the variables occur to the first power only, its graph is a straight line, and there are no variables in a denominator.

Which of these are linear equations?

9. $x - 5y = 8$
10. $3xy + y^2 = 0$
11. $2x = 5y - 9$
12. $y^2 - 7 = 9y$

ANSWERS

1. $\{(a, 1), (a, 2), (b, 1), (b, 2), (c, 1), (c, 2)\}$
2. $\{(1, 0), (1, -1), (1, -2), (0, -1), (0, -2), (-1, -2)\}$
3. Domain $\{-6, -1, 0, 1, 2\}$; range $\{-4, 1, 2, 4, 5\}$
4. $(0, 3)$
5.

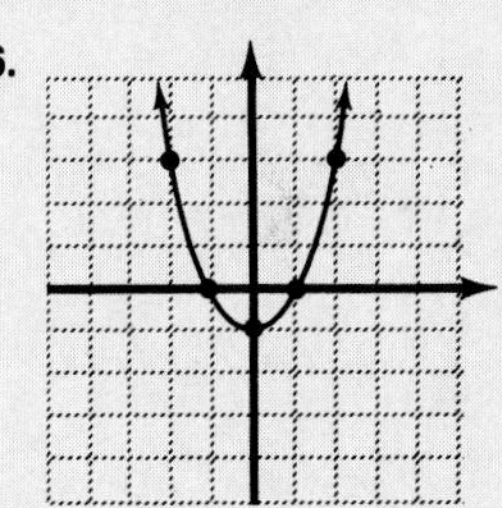

6.

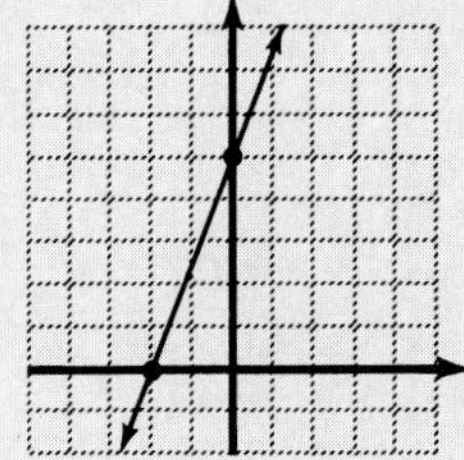

7. No
8. Yes
9. Yes
10. No
11. Yes
12. No
13.

14.

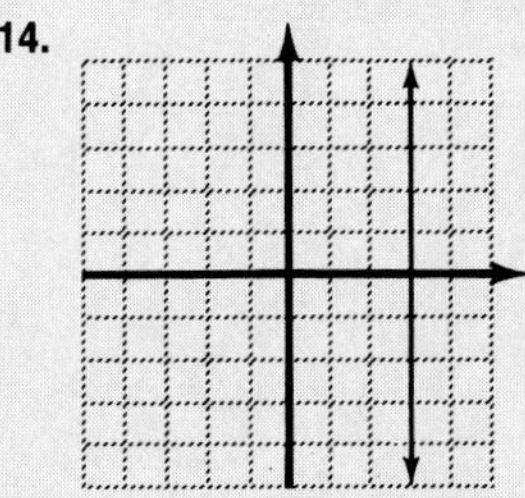

The **y-intercept** is the y-coordinate of the point where the graph crosses the y-axis. The **x-intercept** is the x-coordinate of the point where the graph crosses the x-axis.

13. Graph $-5x + 2y = 10$. **14.** Graph $x = 3$. **15.** Graph $y = -2$.

3-5

For a line containing, (x_1, y_1) and (x_2, y_2), the **slope** $m = \frac{\text{change in } y}{\text{change in } x}$, or $\frac{y_2 - y_1}{x_2 - x_1}$.

16. Find the slope of the line containing $(8, 2)$ and $(-4, -3)$.

A line containing a point (x_1, y_1) with slope m, has an equation $(y - y_1) = m(x - x_1)$.

17. Find the equation of the line containing $(-4, 2)$ with $m = \frac{1}{2}$.

3-6

A line containing (x_1, y_1) and (x_2, y_2) has an equation $y - y_1 = \frac{y_2 - y_1}{x_2 - x_1}(x - x_1)$.

18. Find the equation of the line containing $(8, 2)$ and $(-4, -3)$.

The **slope-intercept equation** is $y = mx + b$ where m is the slope and b is the y-intercept.

19. Find the slope and y-intercept of $-5x + 2y = -4$.

The **standard form** for a linear equation is $Ax + By + C = 0$. Its slope is $-\frac{A}{B}$.

20. Find the standard form and the slope of $5x + 2y - 7 = 5y - 11$.

3-7

If two nonvertical lines are **parallel**, then they have the same slope. If two nonvertical lines are **perpendicular**, then the product of their slopes is -1.

21. Find an equation of the line containing $(-3, 7)$ that is
a. parallel to the line $5x + 3y = 8$. **b.** perpendicular to the line $5x + 3y = 8$.

3-8

A **linear function** is a function f given by $f(x) = mx + b$.

In 1920 the record for the 200-m dash was 20.8 seconds. In 1945 it was 20.1 seconds. Let r represent the record in the 200-m dash and t the number of years since 1920.

22. Fit a linear function to the data points. **23.** Predict the record in 1994.

24. When would you predict that the record will be 18.5 seconds?

3-9

Two special functions are the **absolute value** and **greatest integer** functions.

25. Graph $y = |x - 2|$. **26.** Graph $y = [x] - 1$.

To find the **composition** $f(g(x))$, first find $g(x)$. Then substitute the value of $g(x)$ into $f(x)$.

If $f(x) = 2x$, $g(x) = x^2 - 1$, and $h(x) = x + 1$,

27. find $f(g(3))$. **28.** find $h(g(f(2)))$. **29.** find an expression for $f(g(h(x)))$.

See also Problem 3, Computer-Assisted Problem Solving, page 840.

15.

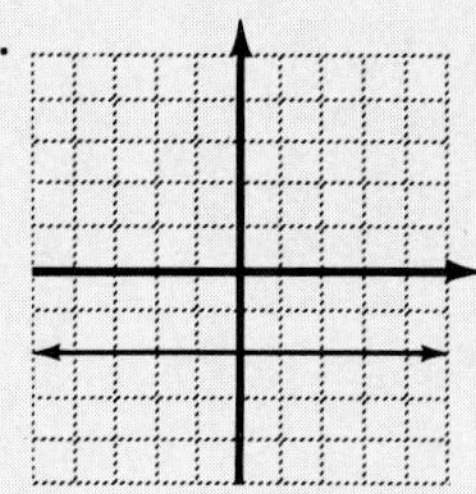

16. $\frac{5}{12}$

17. $y = \frac{1}{2}x + 4$

18. $y = \frac{5}{12}x - \frac{4}{3}$

19. $m = \frac{5}{2}; b = -2$

20. $5x - 3y + 4 = 0; m = \frac{5}{3}$

21. a. $y = -\frac{5}{3}x + 2$

b. $y = \frac{3}{5}x + \frac{44}{5}$

22. $R = -\frac{7}{250} \cdot t + 20.8$

23. 18.728 sec

24. 2002

25.

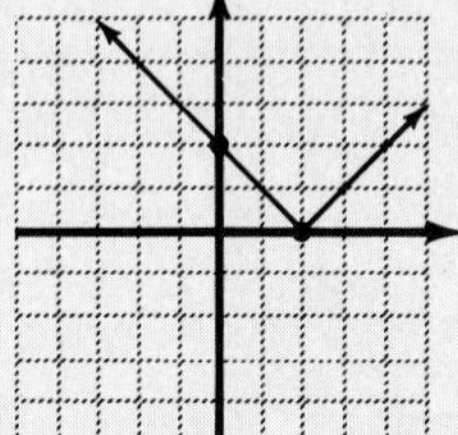

26.

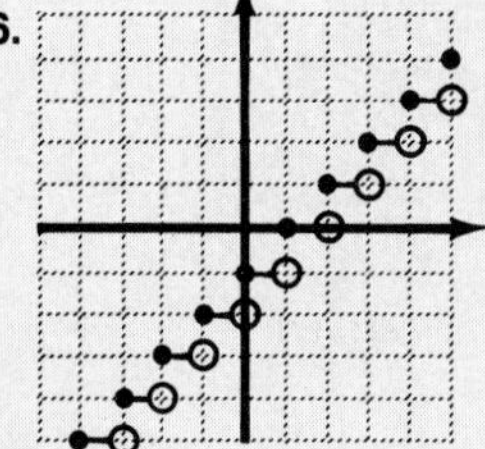

27. 16

28. 16

29. $2x^2 + 4x$

Chapter 3 Test

1. $A = \{-1, 1, 3, 7\}$ and $B = \{p, q\}$. List all ordered pairs in $A \times B$.
2. Consider the set $\{-4, -2, 0, 2\}$. Find the set of ordered pairs determined by the relation $\leq$ (is less than or equal to).
3. List the domain and the range of the relation $\{(-1, 4), (2, 3), (-2, -3), (1, -2)\}$.
4. Consider the set $\{-10, -5, 0, 5, 10\}$. Find the set indicated by $\{x \mid -7 < x < 5\}$.
5. Which of $(-2, 5)$, $(-2, 0)$, $(3, -1)$, and $(0, -1)$ is a solution to $y = 2x - 7$?
6. Graph $y = -3x + 1$.
7. Graph $y = 2x^2 + 1$.

Which of the following are graphs of functions?

8.

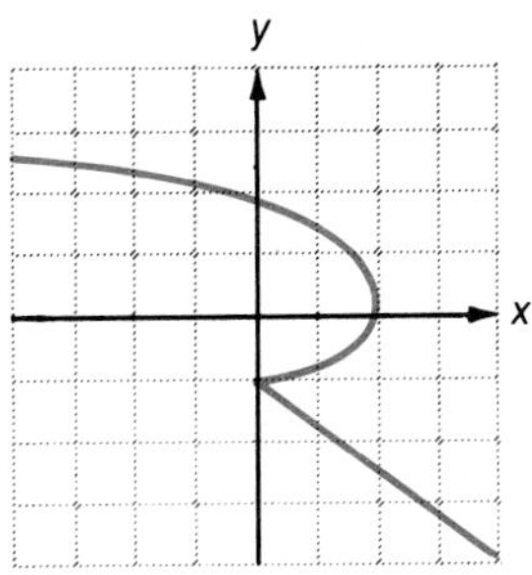

9.

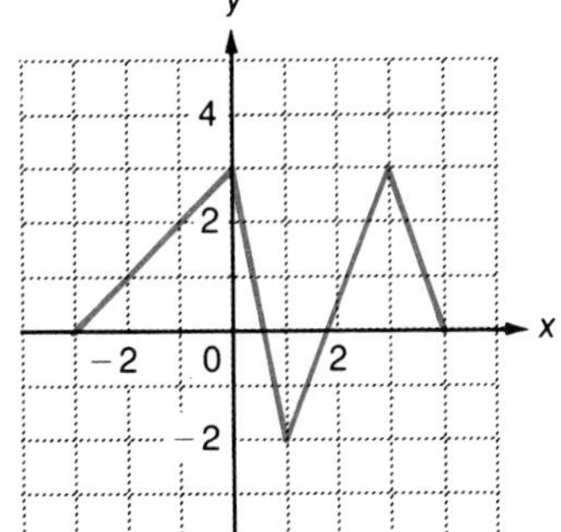

Which of these are linear equations?

10. $xy = 5$
11. $\frac{x}{y} = 4$
12. $2x = y$
13. $x = 7$
14. Graph $6x - 4y = 12$ using intercepts.
15. Graph $x = -4$.
16. Graph $y = 3$.
17. Find the slope of the line containing $(-3, 4)$ and $(5, -2)$.
18. Find the equation of the line containing $(-2, -3)$ with $m = -\frac{3}{4}$.
19. Find the equation of the line containing $(-3, -6)$ and $(2, -5)$.
20. Find the slope and y-intercept of the equation $-3x + 5y - 6 = 0$.
21. Find the standard form and the slope for $y = -\frac{3}{5}x - \frac{8}{5}$.

Find an equation of the line containing $(4, -3)$ that is

22. parallel to the line $6x - 4y = 1$.
23. perpendicular to the line $6x - 4y = 1$.
24. If you rent a car for one day and drive it 100 miles, the cost is \$40. If you drive it 150 miles, the cost is \$48.50.
    a. Fit a linear function to the data points.
    b. How much does it cost to rent the car for one day if you drive 200 miles?
    c. How far can you drive in one day for \$91?
25. Graph $y = |x| + 3$.
26. Graph $y = |x - 1|$.

If $f(x) = -2x + 1$, $g(x) = x^2$, and $h(x) = 2 - x$, find

27. $h(-2)$.
28. $g(f(2))$.
29. $f(h(g(-1)))$.
30. an expression for $g(h(f(x)))$.

ANSWERS

1. $\{(-1, p), (-1, q), (1, p), (1, q), (3, p), (3, q), (7, p), (7, q)\}$
2. $\{(-4, -4), (-4, -2), (-4, 0), (-4, 2), (-2, -2), (-2, 0), (-2, 2), (0, 0), (0, 2), (2, 2)\}$
3. Domain $\{-2, -1, 1, 2\}$; range $\{-3, -2, 3, 4\}$
4. $\{-5, 0\}$
5. $(3, -1)$

For Exercises 6–7, see Teacher's Answer Section.

8. No
9. Yes
10. No
11. No
12. Yes
13. Yes

For Exercises 14–16, see Teacher's Answer Section.

17. $-\frac{3}{4}$
18. $y = -\frac{3}{4}x - \frac{9}{2}$
19. $y = \frac{1}{5}x - \frac{27}{5}$
20. $m = \frac{3}{5}$, y-intercept $= \frac{6}{5}$
21. $3x + 5y + 8 = 0$, $m = -\frac{3}{5}$
22. $y = \frac{3}{2}x - 9$
23. $y = -\frac{2}{3}x - \frac{1}{3}$
24. a. $y = \frac{17}{100}x + 23$
    b. \$57.00
    c. 400 mi

For Exercises 25–26, see Teacher's Answer Section.

27. 4
28. 9
29. -1
30. $4x^2 + 4x + 1$ or $(2x + 1)^2$

Test Item Analysis

Item	Lesson
1–4	3-1
5–7	3-2
8,9	3-3
10–16	3-4
17,18	3-5
19–21	3-6
22,23	3-7
24	3-8
25–30	3-9

CHAPTER 4

Systems of Equations and Problem Solving

Chapter Overview

Chapter 4 covers systems of linear equations and inequalities in two and three variables. Systems of equations are solved by progressively more sophisticated techniques; by graphing, substitution, and finally by linear combinations. Three-variable systems are solved by the triangularization method. Systems are examined for consistency and dependency. Systems of inequalities are graphed, and a lesson on linear programming is included. The chapter concludes with the first of several strategies for college entrance exams, using shortcut methods to solve certain systems.

The first three lessons of Chapter 13, introducing matrices and Cramer's rule, may be covered at this time.

Objectives

4-1 ▪ Solve a system of equations in two variables graphically.
4-2 ▪ Solve a system of equations in two variables by the substitution method.
▪ Solve a system of equations in two variables by linear combinations.
4-3 ▪ Solve problems by translating to systems of equations in two variables.
4-4 ▪ Solve a system of equations in three variables by linear combinations.
4-5 ▪ Solve problems by translating to a system of three equations in three variables.
4-6 ▪ Determine whether a system of equations is consistent or inconsistent.
▪ Determine whether a system of equations is dependent.
4-7 ▪ Graph linear inequalities.
▪ Graph systems of inequalities in two variables in the plane, finding vertices, if they exist.
4-8 ▪ Solve problems using linear programming.

TEACHING CHAPTER 4

Cooperative Learning Opportunities

The **Try This** activities that follow the examples can be used for cooperative learning in pairs. In some places, such as Example 1 in Lessons 4-1 and 4-2, which review skills from Algebra 1, you can assign the **Try This** in place of your explanation of the example. In each case, there are two exercises. Have each student in a pair do one of the exercises. Then ask them to review each other's work.

In working to solve three equations in three unknowns, students often make careless errors. Cooperative pairs can help combat this problem. In example 2 of Lesson 4-4, have students work together on just one of the exercises. Going over each step together should help them catch errors in simple arithmetic or manipulation. Ask them to check their answers in the equations.

The **Try This** activities for systems of inequalities in Lesson 4-7 can be done by pairs with individuals again working separately and then checking their graphs and finding mistakes.

Multicultural Note: *Seki Kowa*

The only thing a mathematician likes better than solving an equation is finding a general solution for a class of equations. Seki Kowa was the greatest Japanese mathematician of the 17th century. He solved many problems that had been previously posed as unsolvable. He invented a method for using determinants to solve systems of linear equations. Some of your students may be interested in a preview of determinants and want to use them as the basis for a computer program to solve equations.

The standard system is: $a_1 + b_1 = c_1$
$a_2 + b_2 = c_2$

The value of the determinant from the coefficients is: $D = a_1b_2 - a_2b_1$
Values of x and y are found as follows

$$x = \frac{c_1b_2 - b_1c_2}{D} \qquad y = \frac{a_1c_2 - c_1a_2}{D}$$

For more information, see page 151 of **Multiculturalism in Mathematics, Science, and Technology**.

Alternative Assessment and Communication Ideas

Explaining an algorithm in words can help a student achieve a more solid understanding of the procedure and also place the method more firmly in the memory. There are several procedures in Lesson 4-4 that can be used as the basis for an alternative assessment.

In Lesson 4-2, page 165, the steps for using linear combinations can serve as the basis for a written or oral presentation on solving a system of linear equations. Ask students to give a reason for each step and to supply an example.

In Lesson 4-4, page 176, the algorithm for solving a system of three linear equations can be used in a similar way. Point out that it does not matter which equations you first work with nor is the order in which solutions are found important. Ask students to rephrase the algorithm to make it more general.

Finally, students might write a paragraph explaining the meaning of the words: consistent, inconsistent, and dependent systems.

Investigations and Projects

The geometric interpretations of an equation in three variables are mentioned at several places in the chapter. It is very difficult to construct the actual plane for a particular equation but some students may be interested in doing a project on the relationships among planes. The lesson **Enrichment** on page 185 and the **Connections** activity on page 187 could together form the basis for such a project.

After students do both of the activities mentioned ask them to try devising equations that would result in the different configurations. Suggest that students can get started on this activity by considering the equation for planes that are parallel to one or other of the coordinate planes. For example, the equation, $y = 2$, describes a plane parallel to the xy-plane and 2 units above it.

A second project would be for a group of students to research the various applications of linear programming and how computers are used to find solutions.

MANAGING CHAPTER 4

Lesson	PACING CHART (DAYS) Algebra	Algebra w/Finite	Algebra w/Trig	Compre-hensive	Opening Activity	Cooperative Activity	Seat or Group Work
4-1	1	1	1	1	First Five Minutes 4-1: **TE** p.160 or ***FFM Transparency Masters*** p.13	Critical Thinking: **SE** p.161 ✂ Manipulative Activity 4: ***Enrichment*** p.45	Try This a–b
4-2	1	1	1	1	First Five Minutes 4-2: **TE** p.162 or ***FFM Transparency Masters*** p.13	Critical Thinking: **SE** p.167	Try This a–g
4-3	2	2	2	1	First Five Minutes 4-3: **TE** p.168 or ***FFM Transparency Masters*** p.13	Critical Thinking: **SE** p.173 Critical Thinking 4: ***Enrichment*** p.25	Try This a–c
4-4	1	1	1	1	First Five Minutes 4-4: **TE** p.174 or ***FFM Transparency Masters*** p.14	Explore: **SE** p.174 Critical Thinking: **SE** p.179	Try This a–c
4-5	1	1	1	1	First Five Minutes 4-5: **TE** p.180 or ***FFM Transparency Masters*** p.14	Critical Thinking: **SE** p.182	Try This a
4-6	1	1	1	1	First Five Minutes 4-6: **TE** p.183 or ***FFM Transparency Masters*** p.14	Critical Thinking: **SE** p.187 Connections: **SE** p.187	Try This a–h
4-7	2	2	2	1	First Five Minutes 4-7: **TE** p.188 or ***FFM Transparency Masters*** p.15	Critical Thinking: **SE** p.192	Try This a–j
4-8	1	1	1	1	First Five Minutes 4-8: **TE** p.193 or ***FFM Transparency Masters*** p.15	Critical Thinking: **SE** p.195 Problem Solving: **SE** pp.196–197	Try This a
Review	1	1	1	1			
Cum. Review	1	1	1	1			
Test	1	1	1	1			

FFM: First Five Minutes SPMR: Skills Practice Mixed Review

MANAGING CHAPTER 4

Enrichment	Review/Assess	Reteach	Technology	Lesson
Writing to Learn: **SE** p.161 ✂ Manipulative Activity 4: ***Enrichment*** p.45	Lesson Quiz: **TE** p.161	Skills Practice 9, #1–5: ***SPMR*** p.21	Worksheet 4: ***TI-81 Activities*** pp.17–20 Worksheet 4: ***Master Grapher*** pp.25–28, pp.159–162, or pp.295–298	**4-1**
Cramer's Rule: **SE** p.166 Problem for Programmers: **SE** p.167	Lesson Quiz: **TE** p.166	Skills Practice 9, #6–17: ***SPMR*** p.21	Worksheet 5: ***TI-81 Activities*** pp.21–23 Worksheet 5: ***Master Grapher*** pp.29–31, pp.163–165, or pp.299–301 Calculator Worksheet 6: ***Technology*** p.8; Problem for Programmers: **SE** p.167	**4-2**
Critical Thinking 4: ***Enrichment*** p.25	Lesson Quiz: **TE** p.171 Quiz 7: ***Assessment*** p.15	Skills Practice 9, #18–23: ***SPMR*** p.21 Problem Bank 5: ***Problem Bank*** p.26		**4-3**
Bonus Topic 3: ***Enrichment*** p.4	Lesson Quiz: **TE** p.177	Skills Practice 10, #1–8: ***SPMR*** p.22	Spreadsheet Activity 2: ***Technology*** pp.48–50	**4-4**
BASIC Computer Project 3: ***Technology*** p.83	Lesson Quiz: **TE** p.181 Mixed Review 7: ***SPMR*** p.71	Skills Practice 10, #9–12: ***SPMR*** p.22 Problem Bank 6: ***Problem Bank*** p.27	BASIC Computer Project 3: ***Technology*** p.83	**4-5**
Lesson Enrichment: **TE** p.185 Connections: **SE** p.187	Lesson Quiz: **TE** p.186 Quiz 8: ***Assessment*** p.16	Skills Practice 11, #1–9: ***SPMR*** p.23		**4-6**
Bonus Topic 4: ***Enrichment*** p.5	Lesson Quiz: **TE** p.191	Skills Practice 11, #10–24: ***SPMR*** p.23		**4-7**
Problem Solving: **SE** pp.196–197 Problem 4: Computer Assisted Problem Solving, **SE** p.841	Lesson Quiz: **TE** p.194 Mixed Review 8: ***SPMR*** p.72	Skills Practice 11, #25: ***SPMR*** p.23 Problem Bank 7: ***Problem Bank*** p.28	Problem 4: Computer Assisted Problem Solving, **SE** p.841	**4-8**
	Summary and Review: **SE** pp.198–199; Test: **SE** p.200			**Review**
	Cumulative Review: **SE** pp.201–203			**Cum. Review**
	Chapter 4 Test: ***Assessment*** pp.65–70(reg.), pp.163–164 (adv.)			**Test**

The solution to the problem posed on the facing page can be found on page 194.

Ready for Systems of Equations and Problem Solving?

1-1 Find the additive inverse of each number.

1. -8 8 **2.** 7 -7 **3.** $\frac{3}{4}$ $-\frac{3}{4}$ **4.** 0 0

1-1 Add.

5. $-\frac{3}{4} + \frac{1}{6}$ $-\frac{7}{12}$ **6.** $\frac{4}{5} + \left(-\frac{4}{5}\right)$ 0 **7.** $-8.6 + (-3.4)$ -12

1-1 Subtract.

8. $8 - (-2)$ 10 **9.** $-\frac{2}{3} - \frac{4}{5}$ $-\frac{22}{15}$ **10.** $-3.2 - (-8.1)$ 4.9

3-4 Graph. For Exercises 11-16, see Teacher's Answer Section.

11. $y - 3x = 2$ **12.** $2y = 3x + 2$ **13.** $\frac{1}{2}x = 4y - 3$

14. $4y - 4 = 2x$ **15.** $2y + 4 = 3x$ **16.** $y = -1$

2-5 Solve.

17. $3y - 1 > y - 3$ $y > -1$ **18.** $2x - 3 > 5$ $x > 4$

19. $|x + 2| \leq 6$ $x \leq 4$ and $x \geq -8$ **20.** $-7 \leq 2x - 7 < 7$ $0 \leq x$ and $x < 7$

3-7 Determine whether the lines are parallel.

21. $\frac{1}{2}x - 5y = 3$ and $-2x + 10y = 1$ No

CHAPTER 4

Systems of Equations and Problem Solving

Wheels Inc. makes mopeds and bicycles. Experience shows they must produce at least 10 mopeds. The factory can produce at most 60 mopeds and 120 bicycles per month. If the profit on a moped is \$134, the profit on a bicycle is \$20, and they can make at most 160 units combined, how many of each should Wheels Inc. make per month to maximize profit?

4-1

FIRST FIVE MINUTES

For each equation, determine whether the indicated pair (x, y) is a solution of the equation.

1. $2x + y = 5$; (1,3)
   $2(1) + (3) = 5$
   The pair is a solution.
2. $4x - 3y = 14$; (5,2)
   $4(5) - 3(2) = 14$
   The pair is a solution.

Emphasize the need for accurate graphing. Without graph paper and a straightedge, it will be difficult to read the solution from the graph. In addition, all numbers read from the graph should not be considered solutions until they have been checked.

Key Question

Have the following system and graph put on the board or an overhead projector.

$$y = \frac{1}{10}x + 1$$

$$y = \frac{1}{12}x + 2$$

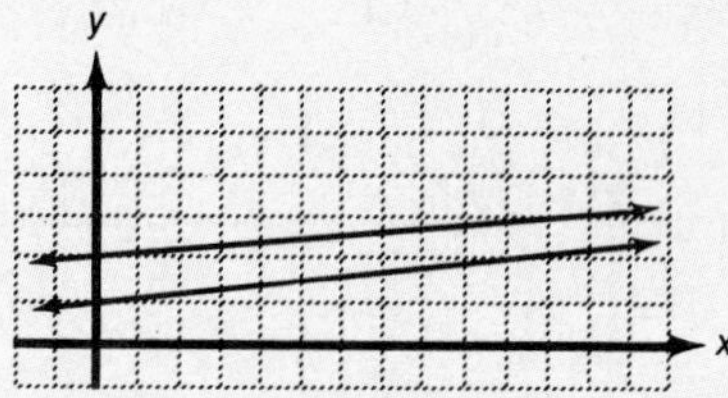

- Does a solution exist?
  Yes; the lines will eventually intersect since they are not parallel.

Chalkboard Example (T4)

1. Solve graphically.
   $2x + 3y = 12$
   $x - y = 1$

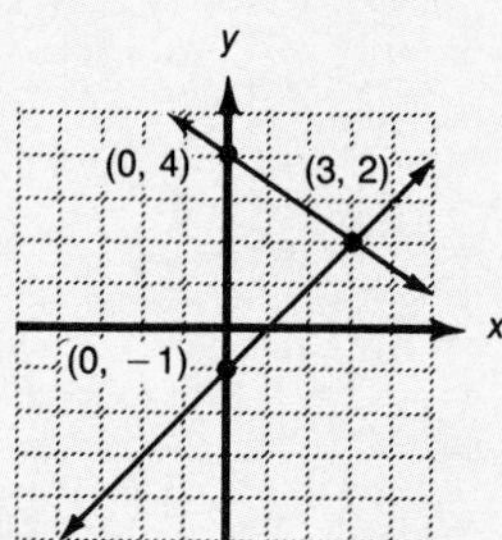

The intersection appears to be the point (3, 2). Substituting
$2(3) + 3(2) = 12$
$(3) - (2) = 1$
The pair is a solution.

4-1 Systems of Equations in Two Variables

Objective: Solve a system of equations in two variables graphically.

Master Grapher Worksheet 4, *Finding Solutions to Systems of Equations*, can be used for lesson closure.

A set of two or more equations with the same variables is called a **system of equations.** The solution set of a system consists of all ordered pairs that make all of the equations in the system true.

The only solution of the following system is the ordered pair (4, 7). If a system has only one solution it is the **unique** solution.

$$x + y = 11$$
$$3x - y = 5$$

(4, 7) is a solution of both equations.

One way to find solutions of a system is to graph the equations and look for points of intersection.

EXAMPLE 1 Solve graphically.

$$y - x = 1$$
$$y + x = 3$$

The graph shows the solution sets of $y - x = 1$ and $y + x = 3$. Their intersection appears to be the single ordered pair (1, 2). We check by substituting.

$y - x = 1$		$y + x = 3$	
$2 - 1$	1	$2 + 1$	3
1	1 ✓	3	3 ✓

Since both are true, (1, 2) is the solution.

Try This Solve graphically.

a. $x + y = 11$
$3x - y = 5$ (4, 7)

b. $2x - y = 7$
$-x + 2y = -5$ (3, −1)

The graphs of two linear equations can be two intersecting lines. They can also be two parallel lines or the same line. We will discuss the latter two possibilities in Lesson 4-6.

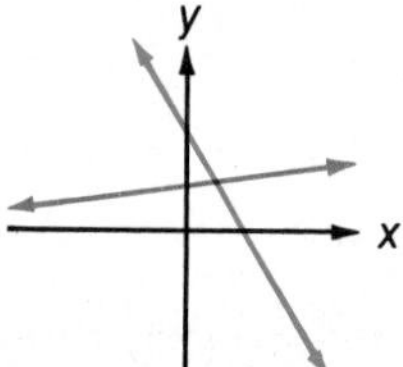

Two intersecting lines
Unique solution

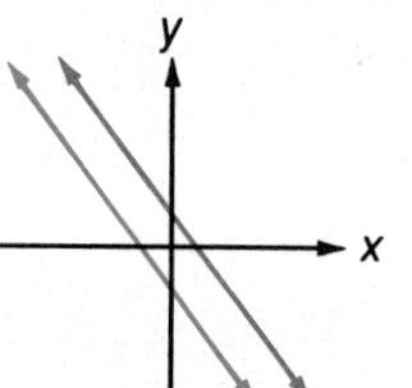

Parallel lines
No solution

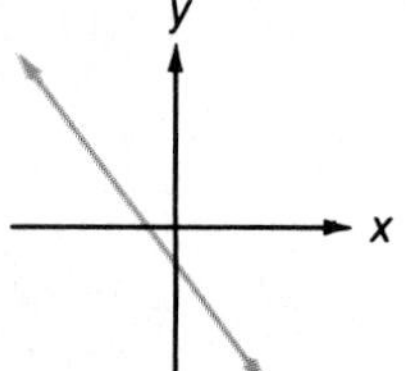

Same line
Infinitely many solutions

4-1 EXERCISES

A

Solve graphically.

1. $x + y = 4$
   $x - y = 2$ (3, 1)
2. $x - y = 3$
   $x + y = 5$ (4, 1)
3. $2x - y = 4$
   $5x - y = 13$ (3, 2)
4. $3x + y = 5$
   $x - 2y = 4$ (2, −1)
5. $4x - y = 9$
   $x - 3y = 16$ (1, −5)
6. $2y = 6 - x$
   $3x - 2y = 6$ $\left(3, \frac{3}{2}\right)$
7. $a = 1 + b$
   $b = -2a + 5$ (2, 1)
8. $x = y - 1$
   $2x = 3y$ (−3, −2)
9. $2u + v = 3$
   $2u = v + 7$ $\left(\frac{5}{2}, -2\right)$
10. $2b + a = 11$
    $a - b = 5$ (7, 2)
11. $y = -\frac{1}{3}x - 1$
    $4x - 3y = 18$ (3, −2)
12. $y = -\frac{1}{4}x + 1$
    $2y = x - 4$ (4, 0)

B

Solve graphically.

13. $3x - y = -5$
    $y - 3x = -2$ No solution
14. $y = -3x + 5$
    $4y + 12x = 20$ Infinitely many solutions; any point on line $y = -3x + 5$
15. ***Critical Thinking*** Write systems of equations with the following solutions.
    a. (5, 1) **b.** (−7, 3) **c.** no solution **d.** infinitely many solutions

Challenge

Solve graphically. (Hint: Make a table of values.)

16. $x - y = 0$
    $y = x^2$ (1, 1) or (0, 0)
17. $x - y = 0$
    $y = |x|$ $\{(x, y) | x = y \text{ and } x \geq 0\}$
18. A system of linear equations has solutions (1, −1) and (−2, 3).
    a. Can you find another solution? (4, −5) is one
    b. How many solutions must exist? Infinitely many solutions

Mixed Review

Consider the function $f(x) = 2x^2 - x$ and find the following function values.

19. $f(3)$ **20.** $f(0)$ **21.** $f(-1)$ **22.** $f(1)$ **23.** $f(-3)$ **24.** $f(2)$

Find the slope and y-intercept of the line. **25.** $6x + 3y - 12 = 0$

Solve. **26.** $-9 < 3t < 6$ **27.** $|5a - 1| > 9$ **28.** $3.2(1.5 + m) = 19.2$

WRITING TO LEARN

Write a paragraph in which you explain how we can think of a system of equations as a conjunction of sentences. Include an example in your paragraph.

LESSON QUIZ

Solve graphically.

1. $3x + 2y = 12$
   $8x - 4y = 4$
   (2, 3)
2. $5x - 3y = 12$
   $2x + 2y = 8$
   (3, 1)

Assignment Guide

Algebra: 1–12 e/o, MR

Alg w/Finite or Trig: 1–14 e/o, 15, MR

Comprehensive: 1–14 e/o, 15–18, MR

ADDITIONAL ANSWERS

Exercises

For graphs see Teacher's Answer Section.

15. Answers may vary.
a. $x + y = 6$
$x - y = 4$
b. $x + 2y = -1$
$x + 3y = 2$
c. $x + y = 3$
$x + y = 1$
d. $x + y = 3$
$2x + 2y = 6$

Mixed Review

19. 15 **20.** 0
21. 3 **22.** 1
23. 21 **24.** 6
25. $m = -2, b = 4$
26. $-3 < t < 2$
27. $\left\{a \,|\, a > 2 \text{ or } a < -\frac{8}{5}\right\}$
28. 4.5

Writing to Learn

Answers may vary.

4-2

FIRST FIVE MINUTES

1. Solve by graphing.
$3x - 6y = -6$
$5x + 5y = 20$
The solution is (2, 2).

The Substitution Method

Emphasize that the possible solution must be checked in both equations. Also remind students that if one equation is solved for y, then the substitution must be made in the other equation.

Key Question

Consider the system

$$x + y = 4$$
$$19x - 32y = 113$$

- Rewrite the second equation substituting for x.
$19(4 - y) - 32y = 113$

Chalkboard Example

1. Use the substitution method to solve the system.
$6x + y = 7$
$y = 3x + 1$
$6x + (3x + 1) = 7$
$9x + 1 = 7$
$9x = 6$
$x = \frac{2}{3}$
Substituting in the second equation yields y
$y = 3\left(\frac{2}{3}\right) + 1$
$y = 3$
Check $\left(\frac{2}{3}, 3\right)$ in both equations.

$6x + y = 7$	
$6\left(\frac{2}{3}\right) + 3$	7
$4 + 3$	7
7	7✓

$y = 3x + 1$	
3	$3\left(\frac{2}{3}\right) + 1$
3	$2 + 1$
3	3✓

The pair $\left(\frac{2}{3}, 3\right)$ satisfies both equations, hence it is a solution of the system.

4-2 Solving Systems of Equations

Master Grapher Worksheet 5, *Finding Non-Integer Solutions to Systems of Equations*, can be used as a lesson opener.

Graphing may not be an efficient or accurate method of solving a system of equations in two variables. We now consider more efficient methods.

The Substitution Method

Objective: Solve a system of equations in two variables by the substitution method.

The substitution method is a useful technique for solving systems in which a variable has a coefficient of 1.

EXAMPLE 1 Use the substitution method to solve this system.

$$2x + y = 6$$
$$3x + 4y = 4$$

We solve the first equation for y because its y-term has a coefficient of 1.

$$y = 6 - 2x$$

Thus y and $6 - 2x$ are equivalent. We can substitute $6 - 2x$ for y in the second equation.

$$3x + 4y = 4$$
$$3x + 4(6 - 2x) = 4 \quad \text{Substituting } 6 - 2x \text{ for } y$$

This gives us an equation in one variable. We can then solve for x.

$$3x + 24 - 8x = 4 \quad \text{Using the distributive property}$$
$$-5x = -20$$
$$x = 4$$

Now we can substitute 4 for x in either equation and solve for y.

$$2x + y = 6 \quad \text{Choosing the first equation}$$
$$2 \cdot 4 + y = 6$$
$$y = -2$$

We obtain $(4, -2)$. This checks, so it is the solution of the system.

Try This Use the substitution method to solve these systems.

a. $2y + x = 1$
$3y - 2x = 12$ $(-3, 2)$

b. $5x + 3y = 6$
$x - y = -1$ $\left(\frac{3}{8}, \frac{11}{8}\right)$

Linear Combinations

Objective: Solve a system of equations in two variables by linear combinations.

If all variables have coefficients other than 1, we can use the multiplication and addition properties to find a combination of the linear equations that will eliminate a variable. This is called the method of **linear combinations.**

EXAMPLE 2 Use linear combinations to solve this system.

$$3x - 4y = -1$$
$$-3x + 2y = 0$$

The first equation tells us that $3x - 4y$ and -1 are equivalent expressions. We can use the addition property to add the same quantity to both sides of the second equation. Thus we can add $3x - 4y$ to the left side and -1 to the right side of the second equation.

$$-3x + 2y + (3x - 4y) = 0 + 1(-1) \quad \text{Using the addition property}$$

When we do this, we have actually added one multiple of the first equation to one multiple of the second equation. It is usually easier to add equations in column form.

$$\begin{array}{r} 3x - 4y = -1 \\ -3x + 2y = 0 \\ \hline -2y = -1 \end{array} \quad \text{Adding}$$

We can solve this equation easily, finding $y = \frac{1}{2}$. Next, we substitute $\frac{1}{2}$ for y in either of the original equations.

$$-3x + 2y = 0$$
$$-3x + 2\left(\frac{1}{2}\right) = 0 \quad \text{Substituting } \tfrac{1}{2} \text{ for } y \text{ in the second equation}$$
$$-3x + 1 = 0$$

Solving for x, we find $x = \frac{1}{3}$. Substitution will show that $\left(\frac{1}{3}, \frac{1}{2}\right)$ checks. The solution of the system is $\left(\frac{1}{3}, \frac{1}{2}\right)$.

Using this method we try to get an equation with only one variable, or *to eliminate* a variable. This method is thus also known as the **method of elimination.**

Note in Example 2 that a term in one equation and a term in the other were additive inverses of each other, thus their sum was 0. That enabled us to eliminate a variable.

We may need to multiply an equation by a constant in order to make two terms additive inverses of each other.

Key Questions

What "multiplying" constants would you use in each of the following systems?

- $x + 5y = 3$
  $2x + 7y = 3$
  Multiply the first equation by -2.
- $5x - 3y = 2$
  $7x + 12y = 6$
  Multiply the first equation by 4.
- $2x + 13y = 4$
  $3x + 11y = 5$
  Multiply the first equation by 3 and the second equation by -2, or the first by -3 and the second by 2.

Linear Combinations

Emphasize that multiplying both sides of an equation by a nonzero constant yields an equivalent equation with the same solutions as the original equation.

Point out that both linear combinations and the substitution method will always work, but one is usually easier than the other. For example, when the coefficients are fractions, it is usually easier to use the substitution method.

When students become proficient adding linear combinations of equations, they may use subtraction where appropriate. Subtracting an equation is equivalent to multiplying it by -1 and adding.

Avoiding Common Errors

In this lesson, some students will forget to multiply the right side of the equation when multiplying the left side (even though they have been using the multiplication property for some time). Remind them that this is not a special case and that the multiplication property is to be used as it has been all along (i.e., they are to multiply *both* sides of the equation).

Chalkboard Examples

1. Use linear combinations to solve the system.
   $5x + 2y = 30$
   $3x - 2y = 2$
   Addition yields
   $8x + 0 = 32$
   $x = 4$
   Substitution in the first equation gives
   $5(4) + 2y = 30$
   $2y = 10$
   $y = 5$
   The pair (4, 5) is a solution of the system.
2. Use linear combinations to solve the system.
   $4x + 5y = 23$
   $2x + 3y = 13$
   Multiply both sides of the second equation by -2 to get the equivalent system
   $4x + 5y = 23$
   $-4x - 6y = -26$
   Adding the two equations yields
   $0 - y = -3$
   $y = 3$
   Substitution for y in the first equation yields
   $4x + 5(3) = 23$
   $4x = 8$
   $x = 2$
   The solution is (2, 3).
3. Use linear combinations to solve the system.
   $4x + 3y = 19$
   $5x + 7y = 40$
   Multiply each equation to make the coefficients of the x-terms additive inverses of each other.
   $5(4x + 3y) = 5 \cdot 19$
   $-4(5x + 7y) = -4 \cdot 40$
   We get the equivalent system
   $20x + 15y = 95$
   $-20x - 28y = -160$
   Adding yields
   $-13y = -65$
   $y = 5$
   Substitute for y in the first equation to get
   $4x + 3(5) = 19$
   $4x = 4$
   $x = 1$
   The solution is (1, 5).

EXAMPLE 3 Use linear combinations to solve this system.

$$3x + 3y = 15$$
$$2x + 6y = 22$$

If we add the equations, no variables will be eliminated. We could eliminate the y-variable, however, if the $3y$ in the first equation were $-6y$. Therefore we multiply both sides of the first equation by -2 and then add.

$$\begin{aligned} -2(3x + 3y) &= -2(15) &\rightarrow\quad -6x - 6y &= -30 \\ 2x + 6y &= 22 &\rightarrow\quad 2x + 6y &= 22 \\ &&-4x \quad &= -8 &&\text{Adding} \\ &&x \quad &= 2 &&\text{Solving for } x \end{aligned}$$

Substitute 2 for x in either of the original equations.

$$\begin{aligned} 2x + 6y &= 22 \\ 2(2) + 6y &= 22 && \text{Substituting 2 for } x \text{ in the second equation} \\ 4 + 6y &= 22 \\ y &= 3 && \text{Solving for } y \end{aligned}$$

Substitution will show that (2, 3) checks. The solution of the system is (2, 3).

Try This Use linear combinations to solve these systems.

c. $5x + 3y = 17$, $-5x + 2y = 3$ (1, 4)

d. $6x + 2y = -16$, $-12x - 5y = 31$ (−3, 1)

Often we need to use linear combinations of both equations in order to make two terms additive inverses of each other.

EXAMPLE 4 Use linear combinations to solve this system.

$$5x + 4y = 11$$
$$3x - 5y = -23$$

We can multiply both sides of the first equation by -3 and both sides of the second equation by 5, in order to make the x-terms additive inverses of each other. Then we add and solve for y.

$$\begin{aligned} -3(5x + 4y) &= -3(11) &\rightarrow\quad -15x - 12y &= -33 \\ 5(3x - 5y) &= 5(-23) &\rightarrow\quad 15x - 25y &= -115 \\ &&-37y &= -148 &&\text{Adding} \\ &&y &= 4 &&\text{Solving for } y \end{aligned}$$

When we substitute 4 for y in either of the original equations, we find $x = -1$. The ordered pair $(-1, 4)$ checks, and is the solution of the system.

EXAMPLE 5 Use linear combinations to solve this system.

$$-0.3x + 0.5y = -0.1$$
$$0.01x - 0.4y = -0.38$$

We multiply the first equation by 10 and the second by 100 to clear the decimals.

$$10(-0.3x + 0.5y) = 10(-0.1) \rightarrow -3x + 5y = -1$$
$$100(0.01x - 0.4y) = 100(-0.38) \rightarrow x - 40y = -38$$

Solving this system, we obtain (2, 1) as a solution.

EXAMPLE 6 Use linear combinations to solve this system.

$$\frac{1}{2}x + \frac{2}{3}y = 1$$
$$\frac{3}{4}x - \frac{1}{3}y = 2$$

To clear fractions, we multiply both sides of the first equation by 6 and the second by 12.

$$6\left(\frac{1}{2}x + \frac{2}{3}y\right) = 6(1) \rightarrow 3x + 4y = 6$$
$$12\left(\frac{3}{4}y - \frac{1}{3}y\right) = 12(2) \rightarrow 9x - 4y = 24$$

Solving this system, we obtain $\left(\frac{5}{2}, -\frac{3}{8}\right)$ as a solution.

Try This Use linear combinations to solve these systems.

e. $3x + 5y = 30$
$5x + 3y = 34$
(5, 3)

f. $0.2x + 0.3y = 0.1$
$0.03x - 0.01y = 0.07$
(2, −1)

g. $\frac{3}{5}x + \frac{2}{3}y = 14$
$\frac{3}{4}x - \frac{1}{3}y = 14$
(20, 3)

We summarize the steps for using linear combinations for systems of two equations.

Steps for Using Linear Combinations

1. Write both equations in the form $Ax + By = C$.
2. Clear any decimals or fractions.
3. Choose a variable to eliminate.
4. Make the chosen variable's terms additive inverses by multiplying one or both equations by a number.
5. Eliminate the variable by adding the equations.
6. Substitute to solve for the remaining variable.

---

4. Use linear combinations to solve the system.
$0.2x - 0.5y = 0.2$
$0.3x + 0.7y = 3.2$
Multiply both equations by 10 to clear the decimals.
$2x - 5y = 2$
$3x + 7y = 32$
Multiply the first equation by 3 and the second equation by −2.
$6x - 15y = 6$
$-6x - 14y = -64$
Add.
$0 - 29y = -58$
$y = 2$
Substitute for y.
$2x - 5(2) = 2$
$2x = 12$
$x = 6$
The solution is (6, 2).

Cramer's rule will be taught using matrices and determinants in Chapter 13.

LESSON QUIZ

1. Use the substitution method to solve the system.
   $2x - 5y = 4$
   $y = 2x - 12$
   The solution is (7, 2).
2. Use linear combinations to solve the system.
   $6x - 2y = 20$
   $3x + 4y = 50$
   The solution is (6, 8).
3. Use linear combinations to solve the system.
   $\frac{4}{5}x - y = 1$
   $x + \frac{2}{3}y = 7$
   The solution is (5, 3).

> ***Assignment Guide***
> Algebra: 1–22 e/o, MR
>
> Alg w/Finite or Trig: 1–25 e/o, 26, MR
>
> Comprehensive: 1–25 e/o, 26–28, MR

ADDITIONAL ANSWERS

1. (2, −2)
2. (2, −7)
3. (−2, 1)
4. (4, −1)
5. (1, 2)
6. (2, 7)
7. (3, 0)
8. (10, 2)
9. (−1, 2)
10. $\left(\frac{1}{2}, -5\right)$
11. (−3, 2)
12. (4, 5)
13. (6, 2)
14. (1, 3)
15. (3, −3)
16. (2, 3)

Cramer's Rule for Two Equations

Gabriel Cramer (1704–1752), a Swiss physicist, developed an algorithm to solve systems of linear equations. The general system of two equations,

$ax + by = c$

$dx + ey = f$ can be solved for x and y: $x = \dfrac{ce - bf}{ae - bd}$ $y = \dfrac{af - cd}{ae - bd}$

Since the denominators are the same, $ae - bd$, it is helpful to find this value first and store the result.

Solve. $5x - 2y = 10$
$-8x + 0.4y = 40$

The denominator is $ae - bd$,

5 [×] 0.4 [−] 2 [+/−] [×] 8 [+/−] [=] **−14** [STO]

Solving for x,

10 [×] 0.4 [−] 2 [+/−] [×] 40 [=] 84 [/] [RCL] [=] **−6**

Use this method to verify that $y = -20$, and the solution is thus $(-6, -20)$.

Solve these systems using the algorithm shown.

a. $0.2x + 1.2y = 3.1$; $2x + y = 9$ (3.5, 2)
b. $-4.05x + 10y = -66.2$; $2x - 36.5 = 5.7y$ (4, −5)
c. $x + 0.35y = 3.6$; $y + 0.22x = 4.484$ (2.2, 4)

For additional calculator practice, see Calculator Worksheet 6.

4-2 EXERCISES

Use the substitution method to solve these systems.

1. $5m + n = 8$; $3m - 4n = 14$
2. $4x + y = 1$; $x - 2y = 16$
3. $4x + 12y = 4$; $5x - y = -11$
4. $3b - a = -7$; $5a + 6b = 14$

Use **linear combinations** to solve these systems. Clear decimals or fractions as needed.

5. $x + 3y = 7$; $-x + 4y = 7$
6. $x + y = 9$; $2x - y = -3$
7. $2x + y = 6$; $x - y = 3$
8. $x - 2y = 6$; $-x + 3y = -4$
9. $9x + 3y = -3$; $2x - 3y = -8$
10. $6x - 3y = 18$; $6x + 3y = -12$
11. $5x + 3y = -9$; $2x - 5y = -16$
12. $3x + 2y = 22$; $9x - 8y = -4$
13. $5r - 3s = 24$; $3r + 5s = 28$
14. $5x - 7y = -16$; $2x + 8y = 26$
15. $0.3x + 0.2y = 0.3$; $0.2x + 0.3y = -0.3$
16. $0.7x - 0.3y = 0.5$; $-0.4x + 0.7y = 1.3$

17. $5x - 9y = 7$
$7y - 3x = -5$

18. $a - 2b = 16$
$b + 3 = 3a$

19. $3(a - b) = 15$
$4a = b + 1$

20. $1.3x - 0.2y = 12$
$0.4x + 17y = 89$

21. $x - \frac{1}{10}y = 100$
$y - \frac{1}{10}x = -100$

22. $\frac{1}{8}x + \frac{3}{5}y = \frac{19}{2}$
$-\frac{3}{10}x - \frac{7}{20}y = -1$

B

Each of the following is a system of equations that is *not* linear. Each is *linear in form* because an appropriate substitution (say u for $\frac{1}{x}$ and v for $\frac{1}{y}$) yields a linear system.

Solve for the new variable, and then solve for the original variable.

23. $\frac{1}{x} - \frac{3}{y} = 2$
$\frac{6}{x} + \frac{5}{y} = -34$

24. $\frac{2}{x} + \frac{1}{y} = 0$
$\frac{5}{x} + \frac{2}{y} = -5$

25. $3|x| + 5|y| = 30$
$5|x| + 3|y| = 34$

26. ***Critical Thinking*** Compare System A and System B shown below by graphing on the same set of axes. What is true of the two systems?

A: $2x - y = 10$ B: $x = 3$
$x + 2y = -1$ $y = -2$

Describe what happens when you solve System B by linear combinations.

Challenge

27. For $y = mx + b$, two solutions are $(1, 2)$ and $(-3, 4)$. Find m and b. $-\frac{1}{2}, \frac{5}{2}$

28. For $y = ax^2 + c$, two solutions are $(0, 3)$ and $(-2, 3)$. Find a and c. 0, 3

Mixed Review

Write each equation in standard form. 29. $2x + 6 = y$ 30. $y = -7$

State whether or not the graphs of the following equations are linear.

31. $y = \frac{3}{x} + 2$ 32. $y = (x + 2)^2$ 33. $y = 3xy + 1$ 34. $y + x = 2x + 1$

35. Hideko invested \$5000 in two funds. After one year, fund A earned 10% interest and fund B earned 8% interest. She received at least \$435 interest from her investments. What is the most she could have invested in the B fund?

Problem for Programmers

Write a program to solve systems of two linear equations.
(Hint: Use Cramer's rule shown in the calculator box on page 166.)
Test your program using Exercises 1–26.

17. $\left(\frac{1}{2}, -\frac{1}{2}\right)$
18. $(-2, -9)$
19. $\left(-\frac{4}{3}, -\frac{19}{3}\right)$
20. $(10, 5)$
21. $(90.91, -90.91)$
22. $(-20, 20)$
23. $\left(-\frac{1}{4}, -\frac{1}{2}\right)$
24. $\left(-\frac{1}{5}, \frac{1}{10}\right)$
25. $\{(5, 3), (5, -3), (-5, -3), (-5, 3)\}$
26. Both lines in each set are perpendicular. System B cannot be solved by linear combinations.

Mixed Review

29. $2x - y + 6 = 0$
30. $0x + y + 7 = 0$
31. Not linear
32. Not linear
33. Not linear
34. Linear
35. \$3250

4-3

FIRST FIVE MINUTES

1. Solve the system.

$$3x + 5y = 26$$
$$y = 2x - 13$$
$$3x + 5(2x - 13) = 26$$
$$3x + 10x - 65 = 26$$
$$13x = 91$$
$$x = 7$$

Substitute to calculate y.

$$y = 2(7) - 13 = 1$$

The solution is (7, 1).

2. Solve the system.

$$4x - 3y = 13$$
$$2x - 2y = 4$$

Multiply the second equation by -2.

$$4x - 3y = 13$$
$$-4x + 4y = -8$$

Add.

$$y = 5$$

Substitute for y.

$$4x - 3(5) = 13$$
$$4x = 28$$
$$x = 7$$

The solution is (7, 5).

It is easier to translate problems into equations when more than one variable is allowed. Remind students that if they use two different variables, they must find a system of two equations in order to have a unique solution.

Point out that there is more than one way to set up the problems and more than one way to solve the problems. In Example 2, we could let x represent the liters in solution B and y represent the liters in solution A. In this case the solution to the system would be (18, 42), which is a different solution than (42, 18). However, when the answer is stated clearly, we have the same answer, "The owner should use 42 L of solution A and 18 L of solution B."

4-3 Problem Solving: Using a System of Two Equations

Objective: Solve problems by translating to systems of equations in two variables.

A delivery truck arrives at the Roberts' store with 8 small boxes and 5 large boxes. The total charge for the boxes, without tax or delivery charges, is \$184. A large box costs \$3.00 more than a small box. What is the cost of each size box?

PROBLEM-SOLVING GUIDELINES
■ UNDERSTAND the problem
■ Develop and carry out a PLAN
■ Find the ANSWER and CHECK

To solve the problems, we often translate to a system of equations in two variables. In this case the system becomes the mathematical model of the situation.

EXAMPLE 1

We can solve the problem above using the Problem-Solving Guidelines.

■ UNDERSTAND the problem

Question: What is the cost of each size box? — Clarifying the question

Data: 8 small boxes plus 5 large boxes cost \$184. A large box costs \$3.00 more than a small box. — Finding the relationships

■ Develop and carry out a PLAN

There are two statements in the problem. Translate each to an equation.

Let x represent the cost of a small box.
Let y represent the cost of a large box.

8 times the cost of a small box plus 5 times the cost of a large box is \$184.

$$8x \quad + \quad 5y \quad = \quad 184$$

Translating statement 1

The cost of a large box is \$3.00 more than the cost of a small box.

$$y \quad = \quad 3 \quad + \quad x$$

Translating statement 2

We now have a system of equations.

$$8x + 5y = 184$$
$$y = 3 + x$$

Substituting $3 + x$ for y in the first equation, we get $8x + 5(3 + x) = 184$. Solving for x, we find that $x = 13$. Since $y = 3 + x$, $y = 16$.

Find the ANSWER and CHECK

8 times \$13 (\$104) plus 5 times \$16 (\$80) is \$184. \$16 is \$3 more than \$13. Both conditions are satisfied. — Checking in the original problem

A large box costs \$16, a small box costs \$13. — Stating the answer clearly

Try This

a. One number is four times another number and their sum is 175. Find the numbers.
35, 140

EXAMPLE 2

Solution A is 2% alcohol. Solution B is 6% alcohol. A service station owner wants to mix the two to get 60 liters of solution that is 3.2% alcohol. How many liters of each should the owner use?

UNDERSTAND the problem

Question: How many liters of each solution are needed for the mixture to be 3.2% alcohol? — Clarifying the question

Data: Solution A is 2% alcohol. Solution B is 6% alcohol. 60 L of mixture are needed. — Identifying the given data

Develop and carry out a PLAN

Organize the information in a *table*.

	Amount of solution	Percent of alcohol	Amount of alcohol in solution
A	x liters	2%	$2\%x$ or $0.02x$
B	y liters	6%	$6\%y$ or $0.06y$
Mixture	60 liters	3.2%	0.032×60, or 1.92 liters

If we add x and y in the first column, we get 60, the total amount of solution. This gives us one equation, $x + y = 60$.

We multiply each amount by the percent of alcohol to find the amount of alcohol in each solution and in the mixture. If we add the amounts in the third column, we get 1.92. This gives us a second equation, $0.02x + 0.06y = 1.92$.

We now have a system of equations.

$$x + y = 60$$
$$0.02x + 0.06y = 1.92$$

We clear the second equation of decimals.

$$x + y = 60 \rightarrow x + y = 60$$
$$100(0.02x) + 100(0.06y) = 100(1.92) \rightarrow 2x + 6y = 192$$ Multiplying by 100

The solution of the system is (42, 18).

Key Questions

What are some other ways in which the examples could be set up or worked?
Answers may vary.

- Example 1
  The variable x could represent the cost of the small box and $x + 3$ the cost of the large box, and one equation could be used.
  Students could try guessing and checking their answers.
- Example 3
  The variable t could represent the time of the slow train and $t - 2$ the time for the fast train.

Chalkboard Examples

1. Twice a first number, added to a second number, equals eleven. Twice the second number, added to the first number, equals 10. What are the numbers?
   Let x be the first number and y be the second number.
   $2x + y = 11$
   $x + 2y = 10$
   Multiply the second equation by -2.
   $2x + y = 11$
   $-2x - 4y = -20$
   Add.
   $-3y = -9$
   $y = 3$
   Substitute for y.
   $x + 2(3) = 10$
   $x = 4$
   The first number is 4, the second number is 3.
   Since twice the first number, $2 \cdot 4$, added to the second number, 3, equals 11, the answer checks.

2. Heavy cream, which is 30 percent butterfat, and low-fat milk, which is 2 percent butterfat, are added together to make 100 gallons of regular milk, which is 4 percent butterfat. How much cream and low-fat milk should be used?
Let x be the gallons of cream used. Let y be the gallons of milk used. The amount of butterfat required is 4 percent of 100 gallons, or 4 gallons. The fat furnished by the cream is $0.30x$.
The fat furnished by the milk is $0.02y$.
The total fat from both cream and milk is
$0.30x + 0.02y = 4$, or $30x + 2y = 400$
The total milk equals 100.
$x + y = 100$
The required system is
$30x + 2y = 400$
$x + y = 100$
Multiply the second equation by -2.
$-2x - 2y = -200$
Add to the first equation.
$28x = 200$
$x = \frac{50}{7}$
Substitute for x.
$\left(\frac{50}{7}\right) + y = 100$
$y = 100 - \frac{50}{7}$
$y = \frac{650}{7}$
The solution is $\frac{50}{7} \approx 7.14$ gallons of cream, and $\frac{650}{7} \approx 92.86$ gallons of low-fat milk.

3. Pearl starts walking at a rate of 3 miles per hour. Four hours later, John hops on his bicycle and travels at a rate of 15 miles per hour to catch her. How long will it take him to catch her?
Let t be John's time in hours. The time traveled by Pearl is 4 hours longer, or $t + 4$.
The distances traveled will be equal when they meet. The distance traveled by Pearl is $3(t + 4)$.
The distance traveled by John is $15t$.
Hence, $3(t + 4) = 15t$
$3t + 12 = 15t$
$12 = 12t$
$t = 1$ hour

■ **Find the ANSWER and CHECK**

Total number of liters of mixture

Checking in the original problem

$$x + y = 42 + 18 = 60 \text{ L}$$

Total amount of alcohol

$$2\% \times 42 + 6\% \times 18 = 0.02 \times 42 + 0.06 \times 18 = 1.92 \text{ L}$$

Percent of alcohol in mixture

The numbers check in the problem.

$$\frac{1.92}{60} = 0.032, \text{ or } 3.2\%$$

The owner should use 42 L of 2% solution and 18 L of 6% solution.

This is reasonable, since more of solution A than B is needed. (3.2% is closer to 2% than to 6%).

Try This

b. A gardener has two solutions containing weedkiller and water. One is 5% weedkiller and the other is 15% weedkiller. The gardener needs 100 L of a solution that is 12% weedkiller. How much of each solution should she use? 30 L of 5%, 70 L of 15%

EXAMPLE 3

A train leaves Sioux City traveling east at 30 km/h. Two hours later, another train leaves Sioux City traveling in the same direction on a parallel track at 45 km/h. How far from Sioux City will the faster train catch the slower one?

To translate motion problems, we use the definition of speed.

$$\text{rate of speed} = \frac{\text{distance}}{\text{time}} \left(r = \frac{d}{t}\right)$$

or the equivalent equation $d = rt$.

To solve this problem, we first *draw a diagram.*

Sioux City — 30 km/h
$t + 2$ hours — d kilometers
Sioux City — 45 km/h
t hours — d kilometers
Trains meet here

From the drawing we see that the distances are the same. Both distances can be represented by d. Let t represent the time for the faster train. Then the time for the slower train will be $t + 2$. We can organize the information in a table.

	Distance (km)	Rate (km/h)	Time (hrs)
Slow train	d	30	$t + 2$
Fast train	d	45	t

Using $d = rt$ in each row of the table, we get an equation. Thus we get a system of two equations.

$$d = 30(t + 2)$$
$$d = 45t$$

We solve using substitution.

$$45t = 30(t + 2) \quad \text{Substituting } 45t \text{ for } d \text{ in the first equation}$$
$$45t = 30t + 60$$
$$15t = 60$$
$$t = 4$$

Thus the time for the faster train should be 4 hours, and for the slower train 6 hours. The faster train would travel $45 \cdot 4$, or 180 km in 4 hours. The slower train would travel $30 \cdot 6$, or 180 km in 6 hours.

The faster train will catch the slower train 180 km from Sioux City.

Try This

c. A freight train leaves Tyler, traveling east at 35 km/h. One hour later a passenger train leaves Tyler, also traveling east on a parallel track at 40 km/h. How far from Tyler will the passenger train catch the freight train? 280 km

4-3 EXERCISES

A

1. The sum of a certain number and a second number is -42. The first number minus the second is 52. Find the numbers. 5, -47
2. The sum of two numbers is -63. The first number minus the second is -41. Find the numbers. -52, -11
3. The difference between two numbers is 16. Three times the larger number is nine times the smaller. What are the numbers? 24, 8
4. The difference between two numbers is 11. Twice the smaller number plus three times the larger number is 123. What are the numbers? 29, 18
5. Soybean meal is 16% protein and corn meal is 9% protein. How many pounds of each should be mixed together to get a 350-lb mixture that is 12% protein? 150 lb soybean meal, 200 lb corn meal
6. A chemist has one solution that is 25% acid and a second that is 50% acid. How many liters of each should be mixed to get 10 L of a solution that is 40% acid? 4 L of 25% solution, 6 L of 50% solution
7. One canned juice drink is 15% orange juice and another is 5% orange juice. How many liters of each should be mixed together to get a 10 L solution that is 10% orange juice? 5 L of each

LESSON QUIZ

1. The sum of two numbers is 31 and their difference is 19. Find the numbers.
   The numbers are 25 and 6.
2. In one day, a business sold 22 aglets. The large aglets sell for $0.20. The small aglets sell for $0.10. The total income for the day was $3.20. How many of each were sold?
   The company sold 10 large and 12 small aglets.

Assignments Guide

Algebra: Day 1: 1 – 13, MR
Day 2: 14 – 26

Alg w/Finite or Trig: Day 1: 1 – 16, MR
Day 2: 17 – 32

Comprehensive: 1–26 m3, 27–31 e/o, 32–34, MR

8. Antifreeze A is 18% alcohol. Antifreeze B is 10% alcohol. How many liters of each should be mixed to get 20 L of a mixture that is 15% alcohol? $12\frac{1}{2}$ L of A, $7\frac{1}{2}$ L of B

9. Two investments were made totaling $8800. For a certain year these investments yielded $1326 in simple interest. Part of the $8800 was invested at 14% and part at 16%. Find the amount invested at each rate. $4100 at 14%, $4700 at 16%

10. Two investments were made totaling $15,000. For a certain year these investments yielded $1432 in simple interest. Part of the $15,000 was invested at 9% and part at 10%. Find the amount invested at each rate. $6800 at 9%, $8200 at 10%

11. A total of $1150 was invested, part of it at 12% and part at 11%. The total yield was $133.75. How much was invested at each rate? $725 at 12%, $425 at 11%

12. A total of $27,000 was invested, part of it at 10% and part at 12%. The total yield was $2990. How much was invested at each rate? $12,500 at 10%, $14,500 at 12%

13. A train leaves a station and travels north at 75 km/h. Two hours later a second train leaves on a parallel track and travels north at 125 km/h. How far from the station will they meet? 375 km

14. Two cars leave town traveling in opposite directions. One travels at 80 km/h and the other at 96 km/h. In how many hours will they be 528 km apart? 3

15. Two motorcycles travel toward each other from Chicago and Indianapolis, which are about 350 km apart, at rates of 110 and 90 km/h. They started at the same time. In how many hours will they meet? $1\frac{3}{4}$

16. Two planes travel toward each other from cities that are 780 km apart, at rates of 190 and 200 km/h. They started at the same time. In how many hours will they meet? 2

17. One day a store sold 30 sweatshirts. White ones cost $9.95, and yellow ones cost $10.50. In all, $310.60 worth of sweatshirts were sold. How many of each color were sold? 8 white, 22 yellow

18. One week a business sold 40 scarves. White ones cost $4.95, and printed ones cost $7.95. In all, $282 worth of scarves were sold. How many of each kind were sold? 12 white, 28 printed

19. One day a store sold 45 pens, one kind at $8.50 and another kind at $9.75. In all, $398.75 was taken in. How many of each kind were sold? 13 at $9.75, 32 at $8.50

20. At a club play, 117 tickets were sold. Adult tickets cost $1.25, and children's tickets cost $0.75. In all, $129.75 was taken in. How many of each kind of ticket were sold? 84 adult, 33 children

21. Carlos is 8 years older than his sister Maria. Four years ago Maria was two thirds as old as Carlos. How old are they now? Maria 20, Carlos 28

22. Paula is 12 years older than her brother Bob. Four years from now Bob will be two thirds as old as Paula. How old are they now? Paula 32, Bob 20

23. The perimeter of a rectangular field is 628 m. The length of the field exceeds its width by 6 m. Find the dimensions. $l = 160$ m, $w = 154$ m

24. The perimeter of a lot is 190 m. The width is one fourth the length. Find the dimensions. $l = 76$ m, $w = 19$ m

25. The perimeter of a rectangle is 86 cm. The length is 19 cm greater than the width. Find the length and the width. $l = 31$ cm, $w = 12$ cm

26. The perimeter of a rectangle is 384 m. The length is 82 m greater than the width. Find the length and the width. $l = 137$ m, $w = 55$ m

B

27. Mr. Irwin and Mr. Lippi are mathematics teachers. They have a total of 46 years of teaching. Two years ago Mr. Irwin had taught 2.5 times as many years as Mr. Lippi. How long has each taught? Irwin, 32 yrs; Lippi, 14 years

28. Nancy jogs and walks to school each day. She averages 4 km/h walking and 8 km/h jogging. The distance from home to school is 6 km, and she makes the trip in 1 hour. How far does she jog in a trip? 4 km

29. The tens digit of a two-digit positive integer is 2 more than three times the ones digit. If the digits are interchanged, the new number is 13 less than half the given number. Find the given integer. (Hint: Let x = tens-place digit and y = ones-place digit, then $10x + y$ is the number.) 82

30. A limited edition of a book published by a historical society was offered for sale to its members. The cost was one book for \$12 or two books for \$20. The society sold 880 books, and the total amount of money taken in was \$9840. How many members ordered two books? 180

31. The measure of one of two supplementary angles is 8° more than three times the other. Find the measure of the larger of the two angles. 137°

32. ***Critical Thinking*** Write a problem that can be solved using the system

$$x + 2y = 25$$
$$2x + y = 20$$
Answers may vary.

Challenge

33. An automobile radiator contains 16 liters of antifreeze and water. This mixture is 30% antifreeze. How much of this mixture should be drained and replaced with pure antifreeze so that there will be 50% antifreeze? $4\frac{4}{7}$ L

34. A train leaves Union Station for Central Station, 216 km away, at 9 a.m. One hour later, a train leaves Central Station for Union Station. They meet at noon. If the second train had started at 9 a.m., and the first train at 10:30 a.m., they would still have met at noon. Find the speed of each train. First train: 36 km/h; second train: 54 km/h

Mixed Review

Simplify. **35.** $|m^4|$ **36.** $|-3t|$ **37.** $|w^7|$ **38.** $|m^5n^4|$ **39.** $|75a^3|$

Find the slope of the line containing each pair of points. **40.** $(-5, 2)$ and $(3, 2)$

41. $(1.9, 2.4)$ and $(1.1, 3.2)$ **42.** $(2, -3)$ and $(-2, 5)$

Write an equation of the line containing the given point and parallel to the given line.

43. $(2, 1)$; $x + y = 1$

Suppose $f(x) = 2x - 1$ and $g(x) = \frac{1}{2}x + 1$

44. Find $f(g(1))$. **45.** Find an expression for $f(g(x))$.

46. Find $g(f(1))$. **47.** Find an expression for $g(f(x))$.

ADDITIONAL ANSWERS

Mixed Review

35. m^4
36. $3|t|$
37. $w^6|w|$
38. $m^4n^4|m|$
39. $75a^2|a|$
40. 0
41. -1
42. -2
43. $y = -x + 3$
44. 2
45. $x + 1$
46. $\frac{3}{2}$
47. $x + \frac{1}{2}$

4-4

FIRST FIVE MINUTES

Solve the systems.

1. $2x + 4y = 34$
   $2x + 3y = 31$
   (11, 3)
2. $3x - 2y = 11$
   $4x - 3y = 13$
   (7, 5)

Explore

Students should recognize that the graph of an equation with one variable on a number line is a point and that the graph of an equation with two variables on a coordinate plane is a line. From this, they can generalize that an equation in three variables must be graphed in three dimensions, and that it will be represented by a plane.

Explain that just as a system of equations with two variables must have two equations to have a unique solution, a system of equations with three variables must have three equations to have a unique solution.

If a solution exists, the solution to a system of three equations in three variables is either a plane, a line, or a point, the unique solution we are usually looking for. Many 3-dimensional systems have no solutions.

In this lesson, the circled numbers refer to the current version of the equation, not the original equation.

Key Questions

- How many equations must you have to solve a system of two variables?
  Two
- Is there always a unique solution to a system of equations?
  No
- What is the graph of a linear equation in three variables?
  A plane
- If an ordered triple makes two out of three equations true in a system of equations, is it a solution of the system?
  No, it must make all three true.

4-4 Systems of Equations in Three Variables

Objective: Solve a system of equations in three variables by linear combinations.

Explore

Some basic geometric figures represent the graphs of algebraic equations.

On a number line, what geometric figure represents the equation $3x = 6$?

On a coordinate plane, what geometric figure represents the equation $3x + y = 6$?

Now suppose you have an equation with three variables, such as $3x + y + 2z = 6$. What kind of coordinate system would be used to graph it? What geometric figure would represent the graph?

A solution of a linear equation in three variables is an ordered triple (x, y, z) that makes the equation true. For instance, $\left(\frac{3}{2}, -4, 3\right)$ is a solution of the equation $4x - 2y - 3z = 5$. Thus, a solution of a system of equations in three variables is an ordered triple (x, y, z) that makes all of the equations in the system true. To show that $\left(\frac{3}{2}, -4, 3\right)$ is a solution of the following system, we substitute into all three equations, using alphabetical order. (Verify this on your own.)

$$4x - 2y - 3z = 5$$
$$-8x - y + z = -5$$
$$2x + y + 2z = 5$$

The graph of a linear equation in two variables is a line. The graph of a linear equation in three variables is a plane. Thus, if a system of equations in three variables has a unique solution it is a point common to all of the planes.

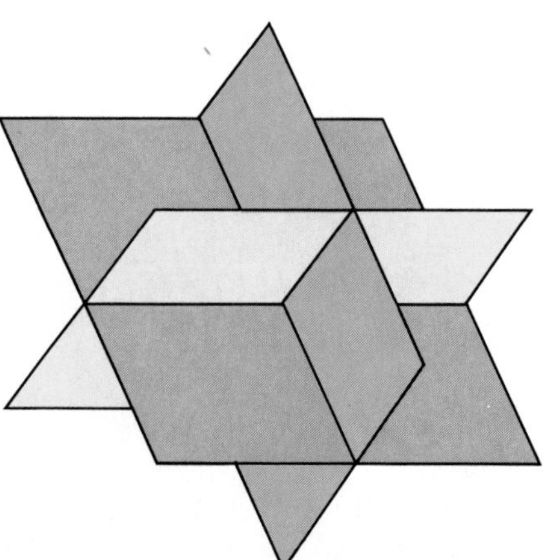

Graphical methods for solving linear equations in three variables are unsatisfactory because a three-dimensional coordinate system is required. Linear combinations followed by substitution is an effective method for solving systems of equations.

EXAMPLE 1 Solve.

$$x + y + z = 4 \quad ①$$
$$x - 2y - z = 1 \quad ②$$
$$2x - y - 2z = -1 \quad ③$$

These numbers indicate the equations in the first, second, and third positions, respectively.

We begin by multiplying ① by -1, and adding it to ② to eliminate x from the second equation. Equations ① and ③ are unchanged by this step.

$$-x - y - z = -4 \quad \text{Multiplying ① by } -1$$
$$x - 2y - z = 1 \quad ②$$
$$-3y - 2z = -3 \quad \text{Adding}$$

$$x + y + z = 4 \quad ①$$
$$-3y - 2z = -3 \quad ②$$
$$2x - y - 2z = -1 \quad ③$$

To eliminate x from the third equation, we multiply ① by -2 and add it to ③.

$$-2x - 2y - 2z = -8 \quad \text{Multiplying ① by } -2$$
$$2x - y - 2z = -1 \quad ③$$
$$-3y - 4z = -9 \quad \text{Adding}$$

$$x + y + z = 4 \quad ①$$
$$-3y - 2z = -3 \quad ②$$
$$-3y - 4z = -9 \quad ③$$

Next we eliminate y from the third equation by multiplying ② by -1 and adding the result to ③.

$$3y + 2z = 3 \quad \text{Multiplying ② by } -1$$
$$-3y - 4z = -9 \quad ③$$
$$-2z = -6 \quad \text{Adding}$$

$$x + y + z = 4 \quad ①$$
$$-3y - 2z = -3 \quad ②$$
$$-2z = -6 \quad ③$$

Since the third equation can be easily solved for z, we can use substitution to easily solve for the three variables.

First we solve ③ for z.

$$-2z = -6$$
$$z = 3$$

Next we substitute 3 for z in ② and solve for y.

$$-3y - 2z = -3 \quad ②$$
$$-3y - 2(3) = -3$$
$$-3y - 6 = -3$$
$$-3y = 3$$
$$y = -1$$

Chalkboard Examples

1. Solve.

$x - 3y + z = 2$ (1)
$2x + y - z = 5$ (2)
$x + 4y + 3z = 13$ (3)

Multiply (1) by -2 and add to (2).
Multiply (1) by -1 and add to (3).
The new system is

$x - 3y + z = 2$ (1)
$7y - 3z = 1$ (2)
$7y + 2z = 11$ (3)

Multiply (2) by -1 and add to (3).
The new system is

$x - 3y + z = 2$ (1)
$7y - 3z = 1$ (2)
$5z = 10$ (3)

Solve for z.
$z = 2$
Substitute in (2).
$7y - 3(2) = 1$
Solve for y.
$7y = 7$
$y = 1$
Substitute for y and z in (1).
$x - 3(1) + (2) = 2$
Solve for x.
$x = 3.$
The solution is the ordered triple (3, 1, 2).
The solution checks in the original system.

2. Solve.

$x + 2y + 3z = 6$ (1)
$3x + 7y + 11z = 22$ (2)
$5x + 12y + 48z = 125$ (3)

Multiply (1) by -3 and add to (2).
Multiply (1) by -5 and add to (3).
The new system is

$x + 2y + 3z = 6$ (1)
$y + 2z = 4$ (2)
$2y + 33z = 95$ (3)

Multiply (2) by -2 and add to (3).
The new system is

$x + 2y + 3z = 6$ (1)
$y + 2z = 4$ (2)
$29z = 87$ (3)

Solve for z.
$z = 3$
Substitute in (2).
$y + 2(3) = 4$
Solve for y.
$y = -2$
Substitute in (1).
$x + 2(-2) + 3(3) = 6$
Solve for x.
$x = 1$
The solution is $(1, -2, 3)$.

Finally we substitute -1 for y and 3 for z in ①, and solve for x.

$$x + y + z = 4 \quad ①$$
$$x + (-1) + 3 = 4$$
$$x + 2 = 4$$
$$x = 2$$

The solution is $(2, -1, 3)$. To be sure computational errors have not been made, check by substituting 2 for x, -1 for y, and 3 for z in the three original equations. If the ordered triple makes all three equations true, then it is a solution.

The algorithm we are using to solve systems of three equations is shown below. It can easily be extended to systems of more than three equations.

Triangularization Algorithm for Solving Systems of Linear Equations

For a system of three equations in three variables, our goal is to obtain an equivalent system of equations in the following **triangular form.**

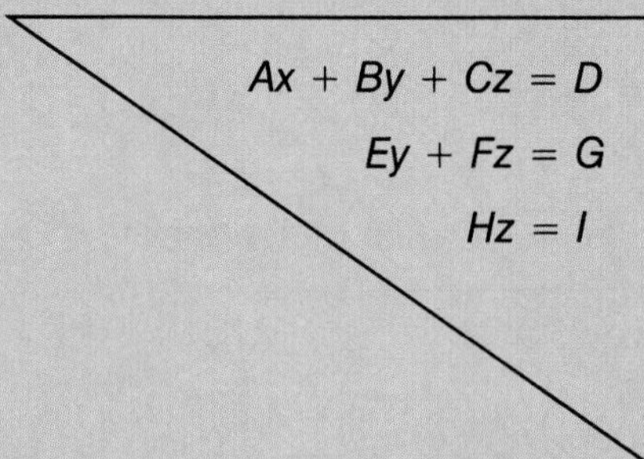

1. Use linear combinations to eliminate x-terms from the second and third equations.
2. Use linear combinations to eliminate the y-term from the third equation. The system will now be in triangular form.
3. Solve the third equation for z, substitute z in the second equation to find y, and then substitute y and z in the first equation to find x.

EXAMPLE 2 Solve.

$$2x - 4y + 7z = 24 \quad ①$$
$$4x + 2y - 3z = 4 \quad ②$$
$$3x + 3y - z = 4 \quad ③$$

We begin by multiplying ③ by 2 to make each x-coefficient a multiple of the first.

$$2x - 4y + 7z = 24 \quad ①$$
$$4x + 2y - 3z = 4 \quad ②$$
$$6x + 6y - 2z = 8 \quad 2③$$

Next we multiply ① by -2 and add it to ② to eliminate the x-coefficient in ②.

$$\begin{aligned} 2x - 4y + 7z &= 24 \quad ① \\ 10y - 17z &= -44 \quad -2① + ② \\ 6x + 6y - 2z &= 8 \quad ③ \end{aligned}$$

We also multiply ① by -3 and add it to ③.

$$\begin{aligned} 2x - 4y + 7z &= 24 \quad ① \\ 10y - 17z &= -44 \quad ② \\ 18y - 23z &= -64 \quad -3① + ③ \end{aligned}$$

Now we multiply the new ③ by -5 to make the y-coefficient a multiple of the y-coefficient in the new ②.

$$\begin{aligned} 2x - 4y + 7z &= 24 \quad ① \\ 10y - 17z &= -44 \quad ② \\ -90y + 115z &= 320 \quad -5③ \end{aligned}$$

Next we multiply ② by 9 and add it to ③.

$$\begin{aligned} 2x - 4y + 7z &= 24 \quad ① \\ 10y - 17z &= -44 \quad ② \\ -38z &= -76 \quad 9② + ③ \end{aligned}$$ The system is in triangular form.

We can now solve ③ for z.

$$\begin{aligned} -38z &= -76 \\ z &= 2 \end{aligned}$$

Next we substitute 2 for z in ②, and solve for y.

$$\begin{aligned} 10y - 17(2) &= -44 \quad \text{Substituting in } 10y - 17z = -44 \\ 10y - 34 &= -44 \\ y &= -1 \end{aligned}$$

Finally we substitute -1 for y and 2 for z in ①.

$$\begin{aligned} 2x - 4(-1) + 7(2) &= 24 \quad \text{Substituting in } 2x - 4y + 7z = 24 \\ 2x + 4 + 14 &= 24 \\ x &= 3 \end{aligned}$$

The solution is $(3, -1, 2)$.

Try This Solve these systems.

a. $x + 2y - z = 5$
$2x - 4y + z = 0$
$3x + 2y + 2z = 3$ $\left(2, \frac{1}{2}, -2\right)$

b. $x + y + z = 2$
$x - 2y - z = 2$
$3x + 2y + z = 2$ $(1, -2, 3)$

c. $x + y - z = 2$
$x - y - 2z = 2$
$2x + 3y + z = 9$ $(5, -1, 2)$

LESSON QUIZ

Solve.

1. $x + 2y + z = 5$ (1)
$x - 2y - z = 5$ (2)
$3x + y - 2z = 10$ (3)
$(5, -1, 2)$
2. $x + y + z = 15$ (1)
$x + 2y + 3z = 34$ (2)
$x + 3y + 4z = 49$ (3)
$(3, 5, 7)$

Assignment Guide
Algebra: 1–18 e/o, MR

Alg w/Finite or Trig: 1–26 e/o, 27, MR

Comprehensive: 1–18 m3, 19–26 e/o, 27–30, MR

4-4 EXERCISES

A

Solve these systems.

1. $x + y + z = 6$
$2x - y + 3z = 9$
$-x + 2y + 2z = 9$ (1, 2, 3)

2. $2x - y + z = 10$
$4x + 2y - 3z = 10$
$x - 3y + 2z = 8$ (4, 0, 2)

3. $2x - y - 3z = -1$
$2x - y + z = -9$
$x + 2y - 4z = 17$ (−1, 5, −2)

4. $x - y + z = 6$
$2x + 3y + 2z = 2$
$3x + 5y + 4z = 4$ (2, −2, 2)

5. $2x - 3y + z = 5$
$x + 3y + 8z = 22$
$3x - y + 2z = 12$ (3, 1, 2)

6. $6x - 4y + 5z = 31$
$5x + 2y + 2z = 13$
$x + y + z = 2$ (3, −2, 1)

7. $3a - 2b + 7c = 13$
$a + 8b - 6c = -47$
$7a - 9b - 9c = -3$ (−3, −4, 2)

8. $x + y + z = 0$
$2x + 3y + 2z = -3$
$-x + 2y - 3z = -1$ (7, −3, −4)

9. $2x + 3y + z = 17$
$x - 3y + 2z = -8$
$5x - 2y + 3z = 5$ (2, 4, 1)

10. $2x + y - 3z = -4$
$4x - 2y + z = 9$
$3x + 5y - 2z = 5$ (2, 1, 3)

11. $2x + y + z = -2$
$2x - y + 3z = 6$
$3x - 5y + 4z = 7$ (−3, 0, 4)

12. $2x + y + 2z = 11$
$3x + 2y + 2z = 8$
$x + 4y + 3z = 0$ (2, −5, 6)

13. $x - y + z = 4$
$5x + 2y - 3z = 2$
$3x - 7y + 4z = 8$ (2, 2, 4)

14. $2x + y + 2z = 3$
$x + 6y + 3z = 4$
$3x - 2y + z = 0$ (−2, −1, 4)

15. $4x - y - z = 4$
$2x + y + z = -1$
$6x - 3y - 2z = 3$ $\left(\frac{1}{2}, 4, -6\right)$

16. $a + 2b + c = 1$
$7a + 3b - c = -2$
$a + 5b + 3c = 2$ (3, −5, 8)

17. $2r + 3s + 12t = 4$
$4r - 6s + 6t = 1$
$r + s + t = 1$ $\left(\frac{1}{2}, \frac{1}{3}, \frac{1}{6}\right)$

18. $10x + 6y + z = 7$
$5x - 9y - 2z = 3$
$15x - 12y + 2z = -5$ $\left(\frac{3}{5}, \frac{2}{3}, -3\right)$

B

Solve these systems.

19. $4a + 9b = 8$
$8a + 6c = -1$
$6b + 6c = -1$ $\left(\frac{1}{2}, \frac{2}{3}, -\frac{5}{6}\right)$

20. $3p + 2r = 11$
$q - 7r = 4$
$p - 6q = 1$ $\left(4, \frac{1}{2}, -\frac{1}{2}\right)$

21. $\frac{x+2}{3} - \frac{y+4}{2} + \frac{z+1}{6} = 0$
$\frac{x-4}{3} + \frac{y+1}{4} - \frac{z-2}{2} = -1$
$\frac{x+1}{2} + \frac{y}{2} + \frac{z-1}{4} = \frac{3}{4}$ (1, −1, 2)

22. $0.2x + 0.3y + 1.1z = 1.6$
$0.5x - 0.2y + 0.4z = 0.7$
$-1.2x + y - 0.7z = -0.9$
(1, 1, 1)

23. $w + x + y + z = 2$
$w + 2x + 2y + 4z = 1$
$w - x + y + z = 6$
$w - 3x - y + z = 2$ (1, −2, 4, −1)

24. $w + x - y + z = 0$
$w - 2x - 2y - z = -5$
$w - 3x - y + z = 4$
$2w - x - y + 3z = 7$ (−3, −1, 0, 4)

Solve. (Hint: Let u represent $\frac{1}{x}$, v represent $\frac{1}{y}$, and w represent $\frac{1}{z}$.) Solve for u, v, and w first.

25. $\frac{2}{x} - \frac{1}{y} - \frac{3}{z} = -1$
$\frac{2}{x} - \frac{1}{y} + \frac{1}{z} = -9$
$\frac{1}{x} + \frac{2}{y} - \frac{4}{z} = 17$ $\left(-1, \frac{1}{5}, -\frac{1}{2}\right)$

26. $\frac{2}{x} + \frac{2}{y} - \frac{3}{z} = 3$
$\frac{1}{x} - \frac{2}{y} - \frac{3}{z} = 9$
$\frac{7}{x} - \frac{2}{y} + \frac{9}{z} = -39$ $\left(-\frac{1}{2}, -1, -\frac{1}{3}\right)$

27. ***Critical Thinking*** Determine whether the following statement is true or false: For any ordered triple (x, y, z) there is a unique system of three equations in three variables that has (x, y, z) as a solution. If it is true, tell why. If it is false, give a counterexample.

Challenge

28. Determine a, b, and c if $(2, 3, -4)$ is a solution of the system.

$ax + by + cz = -11$
$bx - cy + az = -19$
$ax + cy - bz = 9$ $a = 2; b = -1; c = 3$

In each case three solutions of an equation are given. Find the equation using a system of equations.

29. $Ax + By + Cz = 12$; $\left(1, \frac{3}{4}, 3\right)$, $\left(\frac{4}{3}, 1, 2\right)$, and $(2, 1, 1)$ $3x + 4y + 2z = 12$

30. $z = b - mx - ny$; $(1, 1, 2)$, $(3, -1, 6)$, and $\left(\frac{3}{2}, 1, 1\right)$ $z = 8 - 2x - 4y$

Mixed Review

Write an equation of the line containing the given point and perpendicular to the given line. 31. $(5, 1)$; $y - 3x = 2$

Find the domain of each of the following functions. 32. $f(x) = -9x - 42$

33. $f(x) = \frac{3}{x} + \frac{1}{2}$ 34. $f(x) = \frac{4}{x + 5}$

Write each equation in both standard form and slope-intercept form.

35. $4y = 2x - 8$ 36. $x = 3y + 5$

37. To store material at one warehouse for six weeks costs $42. For thirteen weeks it costs $73.50.
 a. Fit a linear function to the data.
 b. How much would it cost to store the material for 26 weeks?

ADDITIONAL ANSWERS

Exercises

27. False. Answers may vary. Example: if $(x, y, z) = (1, 2, 3)$,
$x + y + z = 6$ $2x + 2y + z = 9$
$2x + y + z = 7$ $3x + 2y + z = 10$
$3x + y + z = 8$ $3x + y + 2z = 11$

Mixed Review

31. $y = -\frac{1}{3}x + \frac{8}{3}$
32. R
33. $\{x \mid x \neq 0\}$
34. $\{x \mid x \neq -5\}$
35. $-2x + 4y + 8 = 0$; $y = \frac{1}{2}x - 2$
36. $x - 3y - 5 = 0$; $y = \frac{1}{3}x - \frac{5}{3}$
37. a. $c = 4.5d + 15$
 b. $132

4-5

FIRST FIVE MINUTES

1. Solve and check.

$$\begin{aligned} x - y + z &= 3 && (1)\\ -x - y + 2z &= 3 && (2)\\ x + y - z &= 1 && (3)\end{aligned}$$

(2, 3, 4)

Remind students that if they are going to use three variables to set up a problem, they must find three equations in order to find a unique solution.

You may want to complete the solution of the system of equations in Example 1.

$$\begin{aligned} x + y + z &= 222 && (1)\\ x + y \quad &= 159 && (2)\\ y + z &= 147 && (3)\end{aligned}$$

Add -1 times (1) to (2). The new system is

$$\begin{aligned} x + y + z &= 222 && (1)\\ -z &= -63 && (2)\\ y + z &= 147 && (3)\end{aligned}$$

Hence $z = 63$. Substitute in (3) to get $y = 84$. Substitute in (1) to get $x = 75$. The solution is (75, 84, 63).

Key Questions

- Suppose that in the Example you also know that when machines A and C work and B does not, they produce 138 suitcases per day. Will this change the answer?
  No, $75 + 63 = 138$
- What would it mean if you knew that machines A and C produced 150 suitcases per day?
  There is no solution. The data must be incorrect.

Chalkboard Example

1. In professional hockey, a win counts as 2 points, a tie as 1 point and a loss as 0 points. A team has played 62 games, has 83 points, and has 7 more losses than ties. Find the number of wins, ties and losses for the team.

$$\begin{aligned} w + t + l &= 62 && (1)\\ 2w + t \quad &= 83 && (2)\\ -t + l &= 7 && (3)\end{aligned}$$

(37, 9, 16)
The team won 37 games, tied 9 games, and lost 16 games.

4-5 Problem Solving: Using a System of Three Equations

Objective: Solve problems by translating to a system of three equations in three variables.

PROBLEM-SOLVING GUIDELINES
■ UNDERSTAND the problem
■ Develop and carry out a PLAN
■ Find the ANSWER and CHECK

Some problems can be solved by first translating to a system of three equations. Thus, the system of three equations becomes a mathematical model of the problem.

EXAMPLE

In a factory there are three machines, A, B, and C. When all three are running, they produce 222 suitcases per day. If A and B work, but C does not, they produce 159 suitcases per day. If B and C work, but A does not, they produce 147 suitcases per day. What is the daily production of each machine?

Let us use x, y, and z for the number of suitcases produced daily by the machines A, B, and C, respectively. There are three statements.

When all three are running, they produce 222 suitcases per day.

$$x + y + z = 222$$

When A and B work, they produce 159 suitcases per day.

$$x + y = 159$$

When B and C work, they produce 147 suitcases per day.

$$y + z = 147$$

We now have a system of three equations.

$$\begin{aligned} x + y + z &= 222\\ x + y &= 159\\ y + z &= 147\end{aligned}$$

We solve and get $x = 75$, $y = 84$, $z = 63$. These numbers check, so the answer to the problem is that A produces 75 suitcases per day, B produces 84 suitcases per day, and C produces 63 suitcases per day.

Try This

a. There are three machines, A, B, and C, in a factory. When all three work, they produce 287 bolts per hour. When only A and C work, they produce 197 bolts per hour. When A and B work, they produce 202 bolts per hour. How many bolts per hour can each machine produce alone? A: 112, B: 90, C: 85

4-5 EXERCISES

A

1. The sum of three numbers is 105. The third is 11 less than ten times the second. Twice the first is 7 more than three times the second. Find the numbers. 17, 9, 79
2. The sum of three numbers is 57. The second is 3 more than the first. The third is 6 more than the first. Find the numbers. 16, 19, 22
3. The sum of three numbers is 5. The first number minus the second plus the third is 1. The first minus the third is 3 more than the second. Find the numbers. 4, 2, −1
4. The sum of three numbers is 26. Twice the first minus the second is 2 less than the third. The third is the second minus three times the first. Find the numbers. 8, 21, −3
5. In triangle ABC, the measure of angle B is 2° more than three times the measure of angle A. The measure of angle C is 8° more than the measure of angle A. Find the angle measures. A = 34°, B = 104°, C = 42°
6. In triangle PQR, the measure of angle Q is three times the measure of angle P. The measure of angle R is 30° greater than the measure of angle P. Find the angle measures. P = 30°, Q = 90°, R = 60°
7. In triangle TUV, the measure of angle U is twice the measure of angle T. The measure of angle V is 80° more than that of angle T. Find the angle measures. T = 25°, U = 50°, V = 105°
8. In triangle FGH, the measure of angle G is three times that of angle F. The measure of angle H is 20° more than that of angle F. Find the angle measures. F = 32°, G = 96°, H = 52°
9. Gina sells magazines part time. On Thursday, Friday, and Saturday, she sold $66 worth. On Thursday she sold $3 more than on Friday. On Saturday she sold $6 more than on Thursday. How much did she take in each day? $21 on Thur., $18 on Fri., $27 on Sat.
10. Pat picked strawberries on three days. He picked a total of 87 quarts. On Tuesday he picked 15 quarts more than on Monday. On Wednesday he picked 3 quarts fewer than on Tuesday. How many quarts did he pick each day? 20 on Mon., 35 on Tues., 32 on Wed.
11. Kristin has a total of 225 on three tests. The sum of the scores on the first and second tests exceeds her third score by 61. Her first score exceeds her second by 6. Find the three scores. First score: 74.5, second score: 68.5, third score: 82
12. In a factory there are three polishing machines, A, B, and C. When all three of them are working, 5700 lenses can be polished in one week. When only A and B are working, 3400 lenses can be polished in one week. When only B and C are working, 4200 lenses can be polished in one week. How many lenses can be polished in a week by each machine? A: 1500, B: 1900, C: 2300
13. Sawmills A, B, and C can produce 7400 board feet of lumber per day. A and B together can produce 4700 board feet, while B and C together can produce 5200 board feet. How many board feet can each mill produce by itself? A: 2200, B: 2500, C: 2700
14. When pumps A, B, and C are running together, they can pump 3700 gallons per hour. When only A and B are running, 2200 gallons per hour can be pumped. When only A and C are running, 2400 gallons per hour can be pumped. What is the pumping capacity of each pump? A: 900 gal/hr; B: 1300 gal/hr; C: 1500 gal/hr

LESSON QUIZ

1. The sum of three numbers is 6. The difference of the first two numbers, plus the third number, equals 2. The sum of the first two numbers, minus the third, equals 0. Find the numbers.

$x + y + z = 6$ (1)

$x - y + z = 2$ (2)

$x + y - z = 0$ (3)

The solution is (1, 2, 3).

Assignment Guide

Algebra: 1–15 e/o, MR

Alg w/Finite or Trig: 1–17 e/o, 18, MR

Comprehensive: 1–17 e/o, 18–20, MR

ADDITIONAL ANSWERS

Mixed Review

21. 25
22. 11
23. 8
24. 4
25. 6
26. Parallel
27. Not parallel
28. A linear function does not fit the data.

15. Todd, Don, and Carla can weld 37 linear feet per hour when working together. Todd and Don together can weld 22 linear feet per hour, while Todd and Carla together can weld 25 linear feet per hour. How many linear feet per hour can each weld alone? Todd 10; Don 12; Carla 15

B

16. Tammy's age is the sum of the ages of Carmen and Dennis. Carmen's age is 2 more than the sum of the ages of Dennis and Mark. Dennis's age is four times Mark's age. The sum of all four ages is 42. How old is Tammy? 20

17. Find a three-digit positive integer such that the sum of all three digits is 14, the tens digit is 2 more than the ones digit, and if the digits are reversed the number is unchanged. 464

18. ***Critical Thinking*** Abe gives Rafer as many raffle tickets as Rafer already had and Jorge as many as Jorge already had. Then Rafer gives Abe and Jorge as many tickets as each of them has. Similarly, Jorge gives Abe and Rafer as many tickets as each of them has. They each end up with 40 tickets. How many tickets did Rafer have originally? 35

Challenge

19. At a county fair, adults' tickets sold for \$5.50, senior citizens' tickets sold for \$4.00, and children's tickets sold for \$1.50. On the opening day, the number of children's and senior citizens' tickets sold was 30 more than half the number of adults' tickets sold. The number of senior citizens' tickets sold was 5 more than four times the number of children's tickets. How many of each type of ticket were sold if the total receipts from the ticket sales were \$14,970? Adults': 2050; senior citizens': 845; children's: 210

20. A bicyclist averages one speed uphill, one speed on level ground, and one speed downhill. She estimates the following mileage for her three previous rides:

Miles uphill	Miles level	Miles downhill	Total time
2	15	5	1.5 hours
6	9	1	1.4 hours
8	3	8	1.6 hours

What were her average speeds uphill, on level ground, and downhill?
8 mi/h, 15 mi/h, and 20 mi/h

Mixed Review

Consider $f(x) = x^2$, $g(x) = (x + 2)$, $h(x) = 2x$. Find each of the following.

21. $f(g(3))$ **22.** $g(f(3))$ **23.** $h(g(2))$ **24.** $f(h(-1))$ **25.** $g(h(2))$

Determine whether the graphs of each pair of equations are parallel.

26. $y = 9 - 4x$ and $2y - 9 + 8x = 0$ **27.** $3y + 4 = 2x$ and $4y + 8 = 6x$

28. During an experiment, the number of cells in a sample doubled each minute. There were 4 cells after 1 min, 8 cells after 2 min, and so on. If a linear function fits the data, determine the function and predict the number of cells after 10 minutes.

4-6 Consistent and Dependent Systems

Consistent Systems

Objective: Determine whether a system of equations is consistent or inconsistent.

Some systems of equations have no solution. Some systems may have more than one solution. We now consider such systems.

Consistent and Inconsistent Systems

If a system of equations has at least one solution, we say that it is **consistent.** If a system does not have a solution, we say that it is **inconsistent.**

EXAMPLE 1 Determine whether this system is consistent or inconsistent.

$$x - 3y = 1 \quad ①$$
$$-2x + 6y = 5 \quad ②$$

We attempt to find a solution. We multiply ① by 2 and add it to ②.

$$x - 3y = 1 \quad ①$$
$$0 = 7 \quad 2① + ②$$

The last equation says that $0 \cdot x + 0 \cdot y = 7$. There are no numbers x and y for which this is true, so there is no solution. The system is inconsistent.

We can also consider the problem graphically. The slope-intercept forms of the original equations are

$$y = \frac{1}{3}x - \frac{1}{3} \quad ①$$
$$y = \frac{1}{3}x + \frac{5}{6} \quad ②$$

We can see that the lines are parallel. They have no point of intersection, so the system is inconsistent.

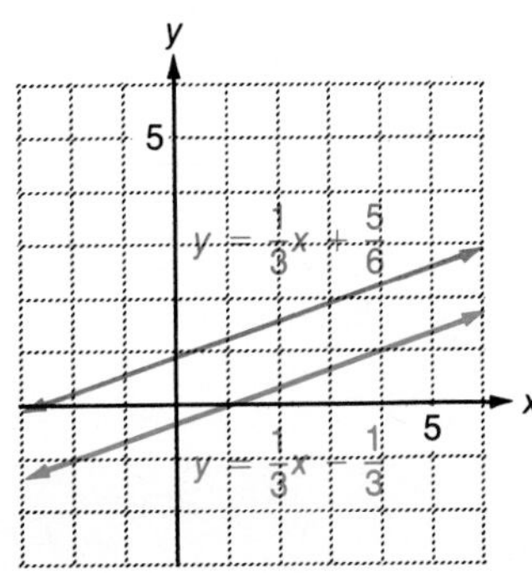

If when solving a system of equations we arrive at an obviously false equation, such as $0 = 7$, then the system is inconsistent.

4-6

FIRST FIVE MINUTES

1. Graph the system.
   $x + y = 2$
   $2x + 2y = 6$
   Two parallel lines, each with slope -1
2. Graph the system.
   $2x + 3y = 12$
   $4x + 6y = 24$
   Both equations graph the line $2x + 3y = 12$.

Consistent Systems

Point out that if a system of two linear equations is inconsistent (has no solution), the graphs of the two equations are parallel lines. The converse is also true. There are many ways in which a system of more than two equations can be inconsistent. You may want to make 3-dimensional models (or have students make models—see *Enrichment* in Lesson 4-4) to demonstrate the ways.

Key Questions

- If a system of equations is consistent, must it have a solution?
  Yes
- Can a system of equations be both consistent and inconsistent?
  No

Chalkboard Examples

Determine whether these systems are consistent or inconsistent.

1. $x - y = 2$ (1)
   $x + y = 4$ (2)
   $2x = 6$
   $x = 3$
   Substituting for x in equation (1),
   $x - y = 2$
   $3 - y = 2$
   $y = 1$
   There is a solution; the system is consistent.
2. $2x + y = 4$ (1)
   $4x + 2y = 16$ (2)
   $-4x - 2y = -8$ $-2(1)$
   $4x + 2y = 16$
   $0 = 8$
   This is a false statement. No replacement for x and y will make it true. The system is inconsistent.

3. $x + y + z = 1$ (1)
$2x + 2y + 2z = 3$ (2)
$3x + 4y + 5z = 5$ (3)
$-2x - 2y - 2z = -2$ -2(1)
$2x + 2y + 2z = 3$ (2)
$0 = 1$
This is a false statement. No replacement for x, y and z will make it true. The system is inconsistent.

Dependent Systems

Point out that a system of two linear equations in two variables is dependent (has many solutions) if the graphs of the two equations are the same line. A system of three linear equations in three variables is dependent if the graphs are all the same plane or if all three graphs intersect in a line.

Key Questions

- Can a system of equations be both consistent and dependent?
  Yes
- Can a system of equations be both consistent and not dependent?
  Yes
- Can a system of equations be both inconsistent and dependent?
  No
- Can a system of equations be both inconsistent and not dependent?
  Yes

Chalkboard Examples

Determine whether these systems are dependent.

1. $4x - 5y = 2$ (1)
$8x - 10y = 6$ (2)
$-8x + 10y = -4$ -2(1)
$8x - 10y = 6$
$0 = 2$
This statement is false. There are no solutions. The system is inconsistent and therefore not dependent.

Try This Determine whether these systems are consistent or inconsistent.

a. $3x - y = 2$
$6x - 2y = 3$ Inconsistent

b. $x + 4y = 2$
$2x - y = 1$ Consistent

EXAMPLE 2 Determine whether this system is consistent or inconsistent.

$$x + 2y + z = 1 \quad ①$$
$$-x - y + 2z = 0 \quad ②$$
$$y + 3z = 4 \quad ③$$

We attempt to find a solution. We add equation ① to ②.

$$x + 2y + z = 1 \quad ①$$
$$y + 3z = 1 \quad ① + ②$$
$$y + 3z = 4 \quad ③$$

We multiply our new second equation by -1 and add it to ③.

$$x + 2y + z = 1$$
$$y + 3z = 1$$
$$0 = 3 \quad -1② + ③$$

The system is inconsistent.

Try This Determine whether these systems are consistent or inconsistent.

c. $x + 2y + z = 1$
$3x + 3y + z = 2$
$2x + y = 2$ Inconsistent

d. $x + z = 1$
$y + z = 1$
$x + y = 1$ Consistent

Dependent Systems

Objective: Determine whether a system of equations is dependent.

Consider this system.

$$5x + 2y = 3$$
$$10x + 4y = 6$$

If we multiply the first equation by 2, we get the second equation. The graphs of the equations are the same line. Thus the system will have infinitely many solutions. We call the system dependent.

Dependent Systems

If a system of linear equations has infinitely many solutions, we say the system is **dependent.**

EXAMPLE 3 Determine whether this system is dependent.

$$2x + 3y = 1 \quad ①$$
$$4x + 6y = 2 \quad ②$$

We attempt to solve. We multiply ① by -2 and add it to ②.

$$2x + 3y = 1$$
$$0 = 0 \quad -2① + ②$$

The last equation says that $0 \cdot x + 0 \cdot y = 0$. This is true for all numbers x and y. The system is dependent.

We can also consider the problem graphically. The slope-intercept forms of the equations are

$$y = -\frac{2}{3}x + \frac{1}{3} \quad ①$$

$$y = -\frac{2}{3}x + \frac{1}{3} \quad ②$$

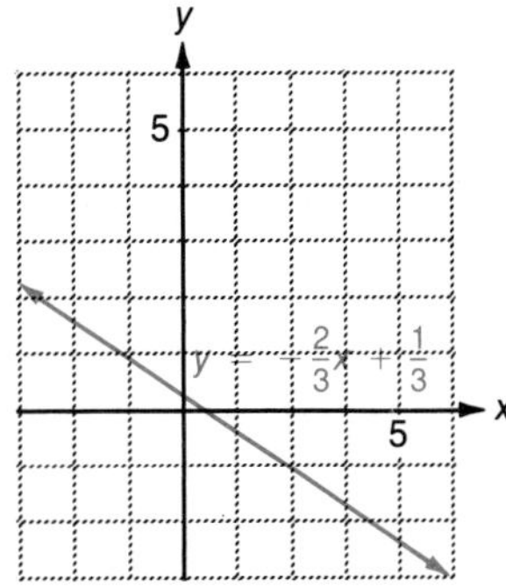

The slope-intercept equations of the lines are the same. This tells us that the graphs are the same. This system of equations has infinitely many solutions. Each point on the line $y = -\frac{2}{3}x + \frac{1}{3}$ has coordinates that constitute a solution. The system is dependent.

Try This Determine whether these systems are dependent.

e. $3x - 2y = 1$
$-6x + 4y = -2$ Dependent

f. $x - y = 2$
$x + y = 4$ Not dependent

EXAMPLE 4 Determine whether this system is dependent.

$$x + 2y + z = 1 \ ①$$
$$x - y + z = 1 \ ②$$
$$2x + y + 2z = 2 \ ③$$

We attempt to solve. We multiply ① by -1 and add it to ②.

$$x + 2y + z = 1$$
$$-3y = 0 \quad -1① + ②$$
$$2x + y + 2z = 2$$

We then multiply ① by -2 and add it to ③.

$$x + 2y + z = 1$$
$$-3y = 0$$
$$-3y = 0 \quad -2① + ③$$

2. $x + y + z = 1$ (1)
$x + 2y + 2z = 3$ (2)
$2x + 3y + 3z = 4$ (3)

$-x - y - z = -1$ -1(1)
$x + 2y + 2z = 3$ (2)
$y + z = 2$ (2)

$-2x - 2y - 2z = -2$ -2(1)
$2x + 3y + 3z = 4$ (3)
$y + z = 2$ (3)

$-y - z = -2$ -1(2)
$y + z = 2$ (3)
$0 = 0$

This is a true statement. This system has an infinite number of solutions. Thus the system is dependent.

LESSON ENRICHMENT

Have students create models using index cards demonstrating the various ways in which 3 planes can intersect (or not intersect). For each model, is the system consistent or inconsistent? Is it dependent or independent?

Consistent Independent

Consistent Dependent

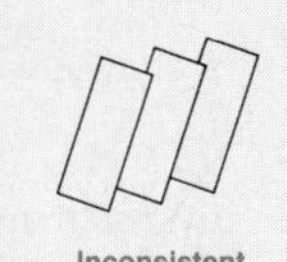
Inconsistent Independent

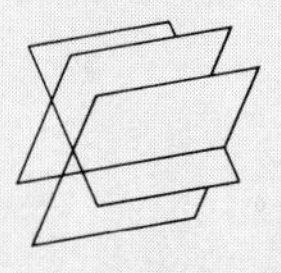
Inconsistent Independent

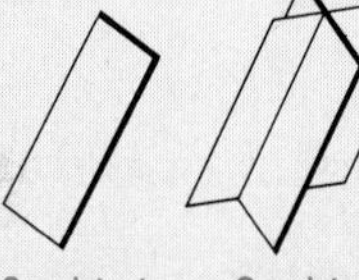
Consistent Dependent

Consistent Dependent

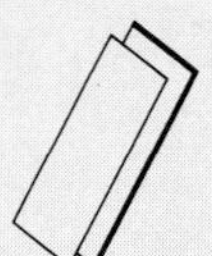
Inconsistent Independent

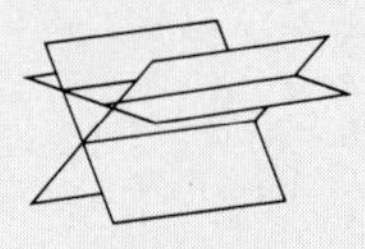
Inconsistent Independent

LESSON QUIZ

- Determine whether this system is consistent or inconsisent.

$x + y = 1$ (1)
$2x + 2y = 3$ (2)

Add -2 times (1) to (2) to get
$0 = 1$
The system is inconsistent.

- Determine whether the system is dependent.

$x - 3y = 2$ (1)
$3x - 9y = 6$ (2)

Add -3 times (1) to (2) to get
$0 = 0$
The system is dependent.

- Determine whether the system is dependent.

$x + y = 1$ (1)
$-x + z = 1$ (2)
$y + z = 2$ (3)

Add (1) to (2) to get
$y + z = 2$
This is identical to (3); the system is dependent.

Assignment Guide
Algebra: 1–20, MR

Alg w/Finite or Trig: 1–28 e/o, 29, MR

Comprehensive: 1–28 e/o, 29, 30–33 e/o, MR

ADDITIONAL ANSWERS

Exercises

1. Inconsistent
2. Inconsistent
3. Consistent
4. Consistent
5. Consistent
6. Consistent
7. Inconsistent
8. Inconsistent
9. Consistent
10. Consistent
11. Dependent
12. Dependent
13. Not dependent
14. Not dependent
15. Dependent
16. Dependent
17. Not dependent
18. Not dependent
19. Dependent
20. Dependent

Since the last two equations are identical, the system of three equations is equivalent to the following system of two equations.

$$\begin{aligned} x + 2y + z &= 1 \\ -3y \quad &= 0 \end{aligned}$$

The system is dependent.

In solving a system, how do we know it is dependent? If, at some stage, we find that two of the equations are identical, or we obtain an obviously true equation such as $0 = 0$, then we can eliminate an equation. If we then have fewer equations than variables, the system is dependent. Be sure to check whether any inconsistent equations remain, however. An inconsistent system cannot be dependent, since it has no solution.

Try This Determine whether these systems are dependent.

g. $x + y + 2z = 1$
$x - y + z = 1$
$2x + 3z = 2$ Dependent

h. $x + y + 2z = 1$
$x - y + z = 1$
$x + 2y + z = 2$ Not dependent

4-6 EXERCISES

A

Determine whether these systems are consistent or inconsistent.

1. $x + 2y = 6$
$2x = 8 - 4y$

2. $y - 2x = 1$
$2x - 3 = y$

3. $y - x = 4$
$x + 2y = 2$

4. $y + x = 5$
$y = x - 3$

5. $x - 3 = y$
$2x - 2y = 6$

6. $3y = x - 2$
$3x = 6 + 9y$

7. $x + z = 0$
$x + y + 2z = 3$
$y + z = 2$

8. $x + y = 0$
$x + y = 1$
$2x + y + z = 2$

9. $x + z = 0$
$x + y = 1$
$y + z = 1$

10. $x - y = 0$
$y - z = 0$
$x - z = 0$

Determine whether these systems are dependent.

11. $x - 3 = y$
$2x - 2y = 6$

12. $3y = x - 2$
$3x = 6 + 9y$

13. $y - x = 4$
$x + 2y = 2$

14. $y + x = 5$
$y = x - 3$

15. $2x + 3y = 1$
$x + 1.5y = 0.5$

16. $15x + 6y = 20$
$7.5x - 10 = -3y$

17. $x + z = 0$
$x + y = 1$
$y + z = 1$

18. $2x + y = 1$
$x + 2y + z = 0$
$x + z = 1$

19. $x + y + z = 1$
$-x + 2y + z = 2$
$2x - y = -1$

20. $x - y = 0$
$y - z = 0$
$x - z = 0$

B

Solve. If a system has more than one solution, list three of them.

21. $9x - 3y = 15$
$6x - 2y = 10$ (0, −5), (1, −2), (−1, −8)

22. $2s - 3t = 9$
$4s - 6t = 9$ No solution

23. $x + 2y - z = -8$
$2x - y + z = 4$
$8x + y + z = 2$ No solution

24. $2x + y + z = 0$
$x + y - z = 0$
$x + 2y + 2z = 0$ (0, 0, 0)

25. $2x + 4y + 8z = 5$
$x + 2y + 4z = 13$
$4x + 8y + 16z = 10$ No solution

26. $x + y + z = 4$
$5x + 5y + 5z = 15$
$2x + 2y + 2z = 6$ No solution

27. Classify each of the systems in Exercises 21, 23, and 25 as consistent and dependent, consistent and not dependent, or inconsistent.

28. Classify each of the systems in Exercises 22, 24, and 26 as consistent and dependent, consistent and not dependent, or inconsistent.

29. ***Critical Thinking*** Suppose when we graph a system of three equations in x and y in the coordinate plane, the lines form a triangle. How many solutions does the system have? Is the system consistent? Dependent? Explain.

Challenge

Determine the constant k such that each system is dependent.

30. $6x - 9y = -3$
$-4x + 6y = k$ 2

31. $8x - 16y = 20$
$10x - 20y = k$ 25

Consider the following dependent systems. For each system, find an ordered pair in terms of y that describes the solution set of the system.

32. $2x + 3y = 1$
$4x + 6y = 2$ $\left(\frac{1-3y}{2}, y\right)$

33. $-6x + 4y = 10$
$3x - 2y = -5$ $\left(\frac{2y-5}{3}, y\right)$

Mixed Review

Find the domain of each function. **34.** $f(x) = \frac{1}{2x - 4}$ **35.** $f(x) = \frac{1}{x(x - 1)}$

Find the slope and y-intercept of each line. **36.** $3x - 4y + 11 = 0$
37. $9y + 6x = 15$ **38.** $y = 4$ **39.** $2y = 5x + 11$ **40.** $3y = -6x + 9$

Solve. **41.** $11 - 35m = -59$ **42.** $t + 4.2t = 156$ **43.** $-16 = 3c + 2$

CONNECTIONS: GEOMETRY

The graph of an equation $ax + by + cz = d$ is a plane. Three equations in x, y, and z represent planes in space. Just as two lines on a plane may be parallel, intersect at one point, or coincide, three planes in space also may be related in several possible ways. What are the possible ways three planes may be related in space?

27. 21: Consistent and dependent
23: Inconsistent
25: Inconsistent

28. 22: Inconsistent
24: Consistent and not dependent
26: Inconsistent

29. There is no solution. Each vertex satisfies 2 equations, but not the third. The system is inconsistent. It is not dependent.

Mixed Review

34. $\{x \mid x \neq 2\}$
35. $\{x \mid x \neq 1 \text{ and } x \neq 0\}$
36. $m = \frac{3}{4}, b = \frac{11}{4}$
37. $m = -\frac{2}{3}, b = \frac{5}{3}$
38. $m = 0, b = 4$
39. $m = \frac{5}{2}, b = \frac{11}{2}$
40. $m = -2, b = 3$
41. 2
42. 30
43. −6

Connections: Geometry

Students may wish to use the models they made in Lesson Enrichment 4-6.
1) All intersect at 1 point. 2) All intersect in 1 line. 3) The three planes are parallel. 4) Two planes are parallel; the third intersects each of the others in a line. 5) The three planes coincide. 6) Two planes coincide; the third intersects them in a line. 7) Two planes coincide; the third is parallel to them. 8) Each plane intersects with each one of the others, forming a 3-d triangle.

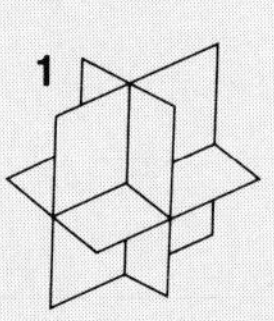

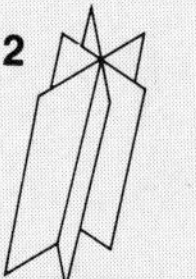

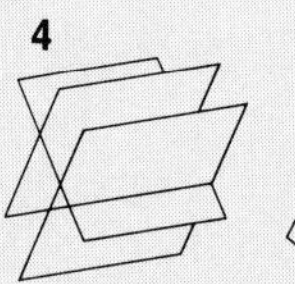

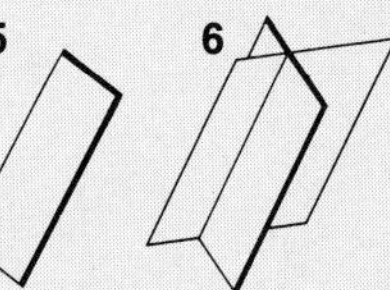

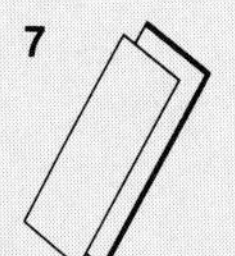

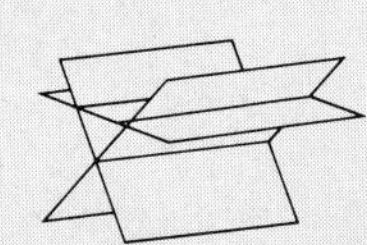

4-7

FIRST FIVE MINUTES

1. Graph the points on the line that satisfy the inequality $3 < x$.

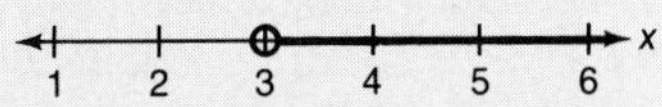

2. Does (3, 1) satisfy the equality $2x + 3y = 5$?
No, $2(3) + 3(1) > 5$.
3. Shade the area underneath the line $x + y = 2$, above the x-axis and to the right of the y-axis.

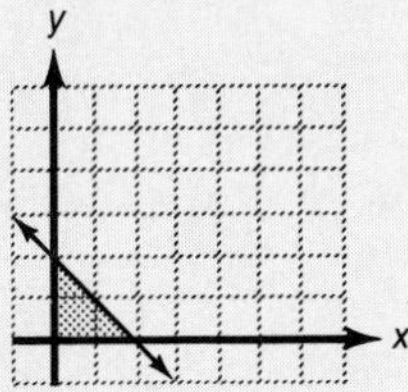

Linear Inequalities

Point out that a line separates the coordinate plane into two regions called half-planes. The graph of any linear inequality in two variables is a half-plane or a half-plane along with the line, the boundary of the half-plane.

Key Questions

- If the coordinates of a point below the line make the inequality false, do you shade the area above or below the line?
Above
- What is an easy point to test?
The origin
- If you solve for y and the equation is $y < 3x - 4$, do you shade above or below the line?
Below
- Does $x + y < 1$ contain as many solutions as $x + y < 1000$?
Yes, each has an infinite number of solutions.

4-7 Systems of Inequalities

Linear Inequalities

Objective: Graph linear inequalities.

An inequality in two variables is a **linear inequality.**

A solution of an inequality in two variables is an ordered pair of numbers that makes the inequality true. To show that an ordered pair (x, y) is a solution of a linear inequality, we substitute in the inequality in alphabetical order.

To determine whether $(-3, 2)$ is a solution of $5x - 4y \leq 13$ replace x by -3 and y by 2.

$$\begin{aligned} 5x - 4y &\leq 13 \\ 5(-3) - 4(2) &\leq 13 \\ -15 - 8 &\leq 13 \\ -23 &< 13 \end{aligned}$$

Since -23 is less than 13, the ordered pair $(-3, 2)$ makes the inequality true and is a solution.

The graphs of linear inequalities in two variables can be used to solve many problems, particularly those concerned with maximizing or minimizing quantities.

To graph a linear inequality, we first graph the corresponding linear equation.

EXAMPLE 1 Graph $y < x$.

We first graph the equation $y = x$. This line marks the **boundary** of points that satisfy the inequality and points that do not. We draw this line dashed, since the points on the line are not in the solution set of $y < x$.

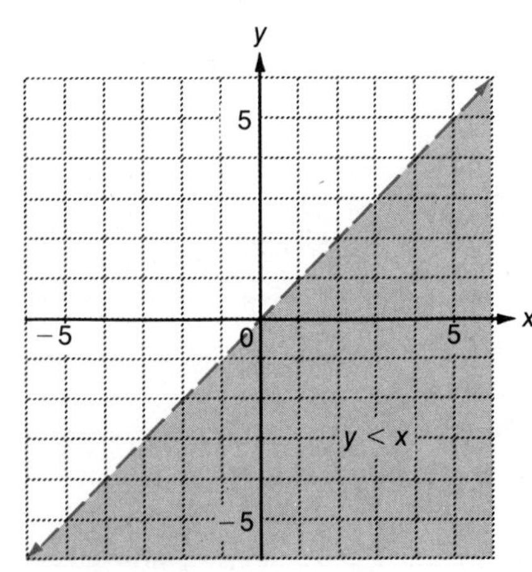

For any point above the line, y is greater than x, or $y > x$. For any point below the line, y is less than x, or $y < x$. Thus the graph is the **half-plane** below the boundary line $y = x$. We show this by shading the lower half-plane.

The graph of any linear inequality in two variables is either a half-plane or a half-plane together with its boundary (the line).

EXAMPLE 2 Graph $6x - 2y \leq 12$.

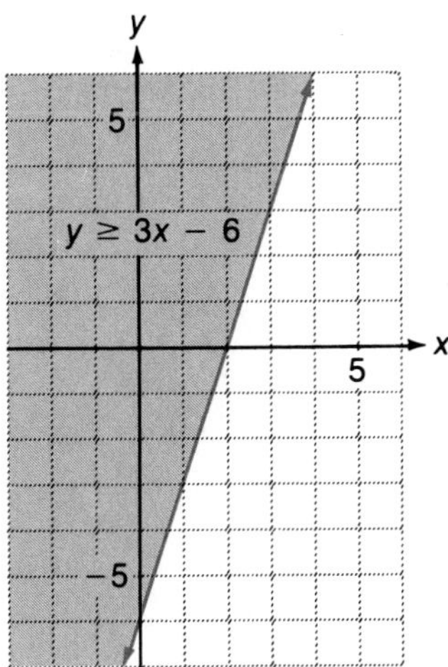

Method 1. Solve for y.

$$y \geq 3x - 6$$

Graph the line $y = 3x - 6$. Since $y = 3x - 6$ is part of the solution, we draw the line solid this time. For any point above the line, the value of y is greater than $3x - 6$. Hence the graph of the inequality is the half-plane above the line, together with the line or boundary.

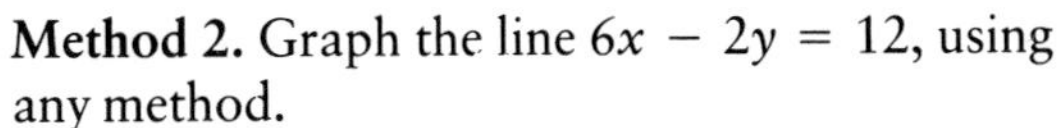

Method 2. Graph the line $6x - 2y = 12$, using any method.
This time we will use the intercept method. The intercepts are at $(0, -6)$ and $(2, 0)$. We plot them and draw the line.

To determine which half-plane is the solution, we test a point. The origin is an easy point to use if the line doesn't contain the origin. We try $(0, 0)$.

$$6 \cdot 0 - 2 \cdot 0 \leq 12$$
$$0 \leq 12$$

This gives us a true sentence. Hence $(0, 0)$ is a solution. We graph the half-plane containing $(0, 0)$.

Try This Graph. See Selected Answers.

a. $y > -2x$ **b.** $2x + y \geq 2$ **c.** $3x - y < -3$

EXAMPLE 3 Graph $-1 < y \leq 2$.

This is a conjunction of two inequalities.

$$-1 < y \text{ and } y \leq 2$$

It will be true for any y that is both greater than -1 and less than or equal to 2. Since our inequality is a conjunction, the graph is the intersection of the graphs of the two inequalities.

y
5
−1 < y ≤ 2
0
5
x

Try This Graph. See Selected Answers.

d. $-4 \leq x < 1$ **e.** $1 \leq y \leq 2\frac{1}{2}$

Chalkboard Examples (T5)

1. Graph $3x - 2y \geq 6$.
   Graph the line $3x - 2y = 6$. The solution set is on one side of this line. The point (0, 0) is not a solution, hence the points below the line are the required solutions.

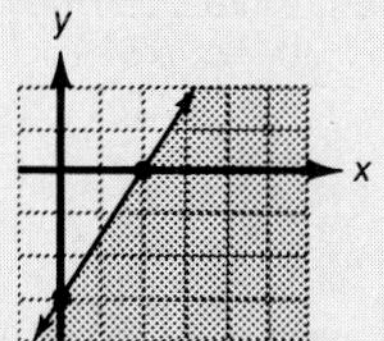

2. Graph $3x - 2y \geq -6$.
   Graph the line $3x - 2y = -6$. The solution set is on one side of this line. The point (0, 0) is a solution, hence the points on the same side as (0,0) are the required solutions.

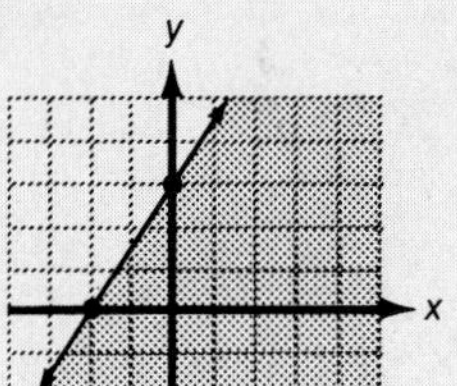

Systems of Inequalities

You may want to use colored chalk for graphs of systems of inequalities. Students may want to use colored pencils. As an alternative, you may want to show students how to use hatch marks going in different directions for each inequality. See Chalkboard Example 1.

Chalkboard Examples (T6)

1. Graph the system of inequalities.
   $2x + 3y \leq 6$
   $4x + y \leq 4$
   The solution set is the intersection of the individual solution sets.

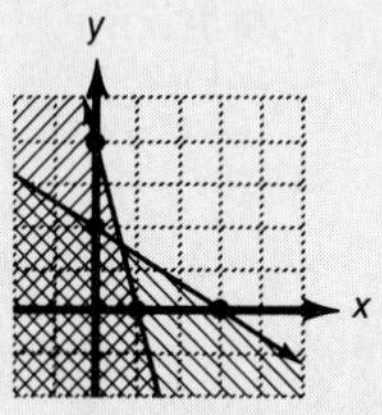

2. Graph the system of inequalities.
   $2x + 3y \leq 6$
   $x + 5y \leq 5$
   $x \geq 0$
   $y \geq 0$

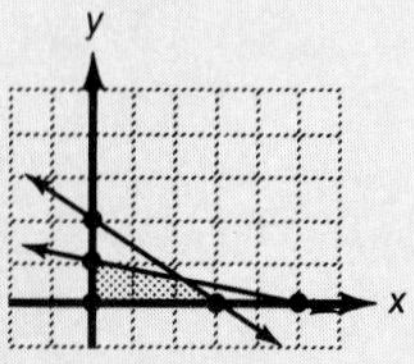

There are four vertices belonging to the solution set. The vertex formed by the intersection of the lines $2x + 3y = 6$ and $x + 5y = 5$ is $\left(\frac{15}{7}, \frac{4}{7}\right)$.
The vertex formed by the lines $x = 0$ and $y = 0$ is (0, 0).
The vertex formed by the lines $x = 0$ and $x + 5y = 5$ is (0, 1).
The vertex formed by the lines $y = 0$ and $2x + 3y = 6$ is (3, 0).

Systems of Inequalities

Objective: Graph systems of inequalities in two variables in the plane, finding vertices, if they exist.

To graph the solution set of a system, or conjunction, of inequalities, graph the inequalities separately on the same axes and find their intersection.

EXAMPLE 4 Graph this system of inequalities.

$$2x + y > 5$$
$$3x - y > 2$$

Consider the graph of each inequality separately.

Graph $2x + y > 5$.

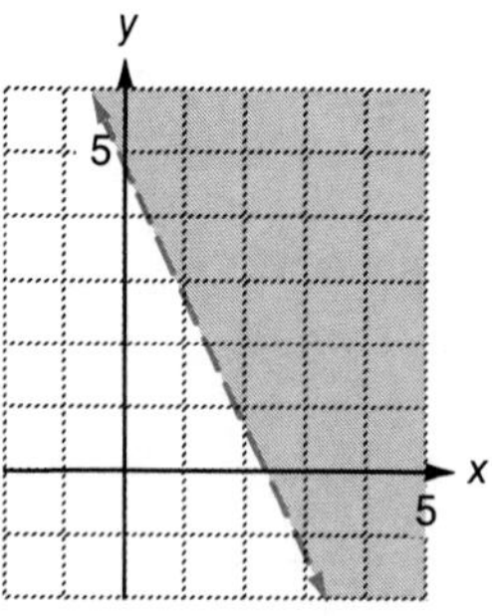

Graph $3x - y > 2$.

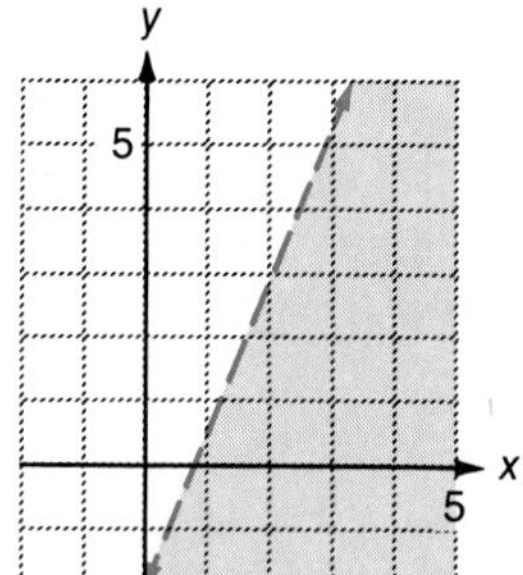

The intersection of the individual graphs is the graph of the system.

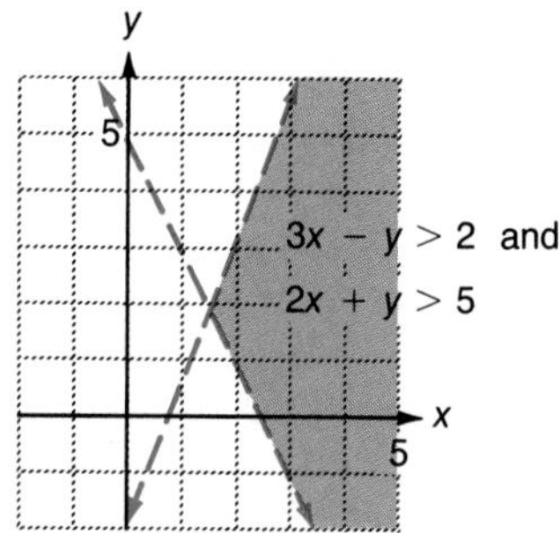

Try This Graph these systems of inequalities. See Selected Answers.

f. $y \geq 4$
$x - 2y \leq 3$

g. $x + y < 2$
$x - y \geq -3$

h. $x - 2y \geq 4$
$2x + 3y \leq 3$

A system of linear inequalities may have a graph that consists of a polygon and its interior. Some problems can be solved by finding the coordinates of the vertices.

EXAMPLE 5

Graph the inequalities. Find the coordinates of any vertices formed.

$$2x + y \geq 2$$
$$4x + 3y \leq 12$$
$$\frac{1}{2} \leq x \leq 2$$
$$y \geq 0$$

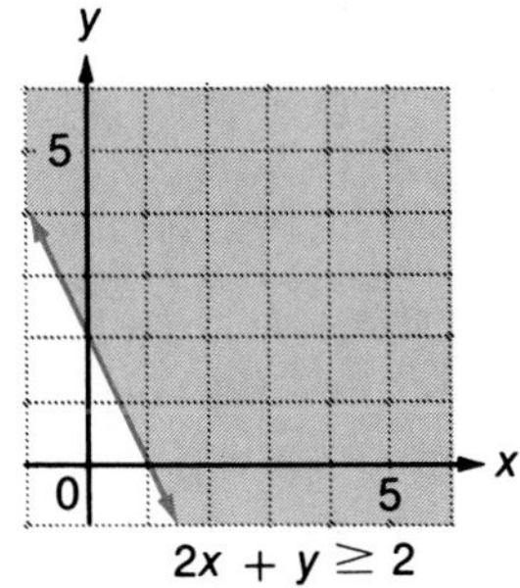

$2x + y \geq 2$

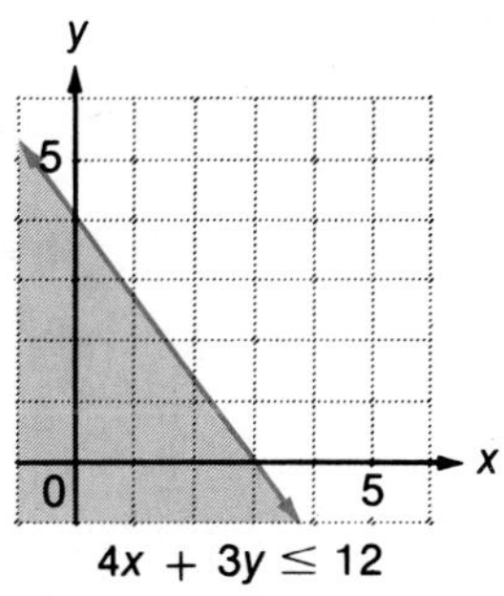

$4x + 3y \leq 12$

The separate graphs are shown at the right, and the graph of the intersection, which is the graph of the system, is shown below.

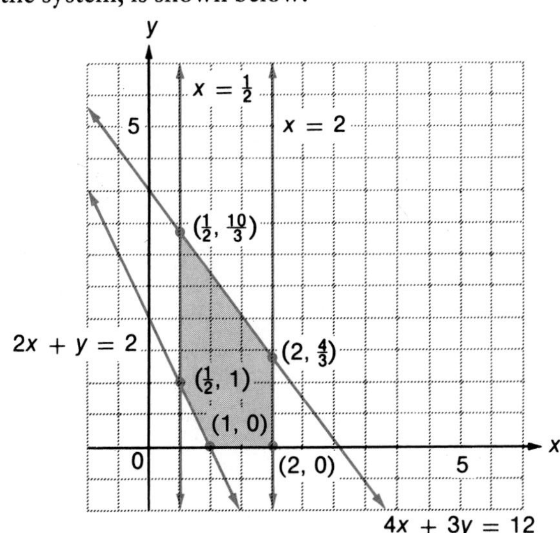

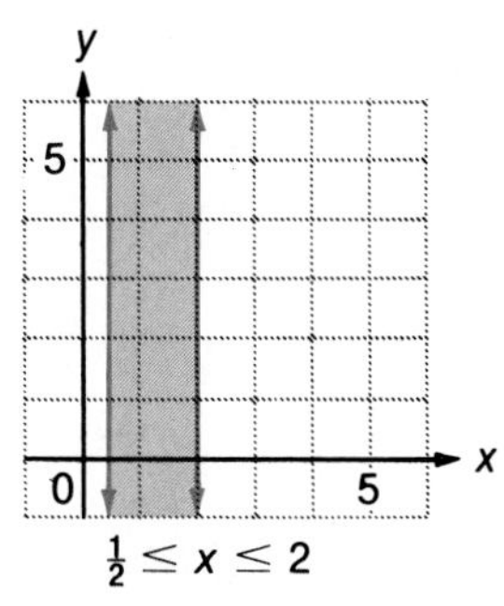

$\frac{1}{2} \leq x \leq 2$

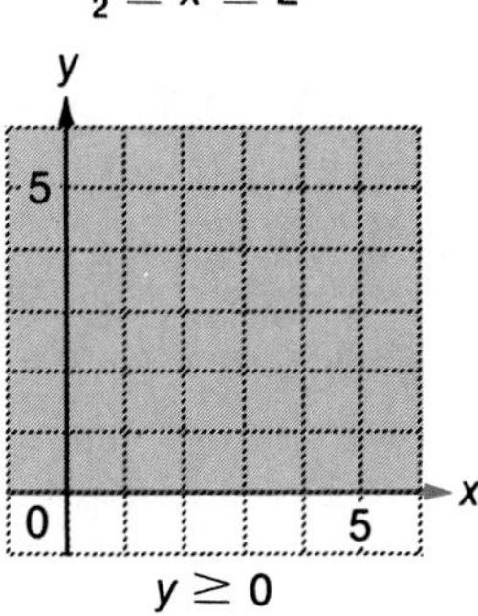

$y \geq 0$

We find the vertices $\left(\frac{1}{2}, 1\right)$ and (2, 0) by solving these systems, respectively.

$$2x + y = 2 \qquad x = 2$$
$$\text{and}$$
$$x = \frac{1}{2} \qquad y = 0$$

The vertices $\left(2, \frac{4}{3}\right)$ and $\left(\frac{1}{2}, \frac{10}{3}\right)$ were found by solving, respectively, the following two systems.

$$x = 2 \qquad x = \frac{1}{2}$$
$$\text{and}$$
$$4x + 3y = 12 \qquad 4x + 3y = 12$$

Try This Graph. Find the coordinates of any vertices formed. See Selected Answers.

i. $x + y \geq 1$ $\left(-\frac{1}{2}, \frac{3}{2}\right)$
$y - x \geq 2$

j. $5x + 6y \leq 30$ (0, 0), (0, 3), (4, 0), (2, 3), $\left(4, \frac{5}{3}\right)$
$0 \leq y \leq 3$
$0 \leq x \leq 4$

LESSON QUIZ

1. Graph $4x + 2y \leq 8$.

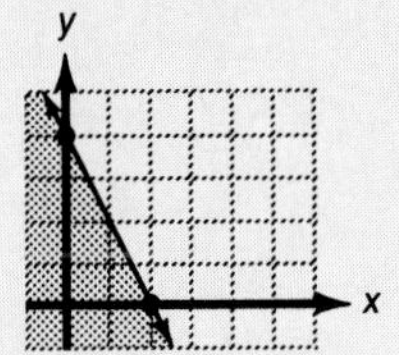

2. Graph.
$5x + 4y \leq 20$
$3x + 6y \leq 18$

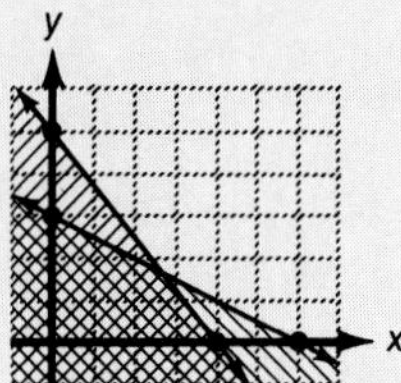

Assignment Guide
Algebra: Day 1: 1–21
Day 2: 22–39, MR

Alg w/Finite or Trig: Day 1: 1–21, MR
Day 2: 22–46

Comprehensive: 1–45 e/o, 46, 47, MR

ADDITIONAL ANSWERS

Exercises

For graphs, see Teacher's Answer Section

37. (0, 0), (0, −3), (−4, −6), (−12, 0)

38. (0, 0), (0, 4), $\left(\frac{40}{11}, \frac{24}{11}\right)$, (5, 0)

39. $\left(1, \frac{9}{4}\right), \left(1, \frac{25}{6}\right), \left(3, \frac{3}{4}\right), \left(3, \frac{5}{2}\right)$

46. Answers may vary.
a. $0 \le x \le 3$
$0 \le y \le 3$
b. $y \le -x + 4$
$x \ge 0$
$y \ge 0$
c. $y \le x$
$y \ge x - 5$
$0 \le y \le 5$
d. $0 \le y \le 2$
$y \le x$
$y \ge -x + 10$

47. Yes, for example
$y > 2x + 1$
$y < 2x + 1$

Mixed Review

48. $y = 3x - 11$
49. $y = -2x + 4$
50. $y = \frac{1}{2}x - \frac{7}{2}$
51. $y = \frac{4}{5}x - \frac{22}{5}$
52. $y = -\frac{2}{3}x$
53. −6
54. 13
55. −0.225

4-7 EXERCISES

A

Graph.

1. $y > 2x$ **2.** $y < 3x$ **3.** $y < x + 1$ **4.** $y \le x - 3$
5. $y > x - 2$ **6.** $y \ge x + 4$ **7.** $x + y < 4$ **8.** $x - y \ge 3$
9. $3x + 4y \le 12$ **10.** $2x + 3y < 6$ **11.** $2y - 3x > 6$ **12.** $2y - x \le 4$
13. $3x - 2 \le 5x + y$ **14.** $2x - 2y \ge 8 + 2y$ **15.** $x < -4$
16. $y \ge 5$ **17.** $x > -2$ **18.** $-4 < y < -1$
19. $-2 < y < 3$ **20.** $-3 \le x \le 3$ **21.** $-4 \le x \le 4$

Graph these systems of inequalities.

22. $y < x$, $y > -x + 3$
23. $y > x$, $y < -x + 1$
24. $y \ge x$, $y < -x + 4$
25. $y \le x$, $y < -x + 2$
26. $y \ge -2$, $x > 1$
27. $y \le -2$, $x > 2$
28. $x < 3$, $y \ge -3x + 2$
29. $x > -2$, $y \le -2x + 3$
30. $y \ge -2$, $y \ge x + 3$
31. $y \le 4$, $y \ge -x + 2$
32. $x + y \le 1$, $x - y \ge 2$
33. $x + y < 3$, $x - y < 4$
34. $y - 2x > 1$, $y - 2x < 3$
35. $y + 3x > 0$, $y + 3x < 2$
36. $2y - x \le 2$, $y - 3x \ge -1$

Graph. Find the coordinates of any vertices formed.

37. $4y - 3x \ge -12$, $4y + 3x \ge -36$, $y \le 0$, $x \le 0$
38. $8x + 5y \le 40$, $x + 2y \le 8$, $x \ge 0$, $y \ge 0$
39. $3x + 4y \ge 12$, $5x + 6y \le 30$, $1 \le x \le 3$

B

Graph.

40. $y \ge |x|$ **41.** $y > |x| + 3$ **42.** $|x + y| \le 1$
43. $|x| + |y| \le 1$ **44.** $|x| > |y|$ **45.** $|x + y| \ge 2$

46. ***Critical Thinking*** Write a system of inequalities in two variables whose graphs will be the following geometric figures.

a. a square and its interior **b.** a triangle and its interior
c. a parallelogram and its interior **d.** a trapezoid and its interior

Challenge

47. Can a system of linear inequalities be inconsistent? If so, give an example.

Mixed Review

Write an equation of the line containing the point (3, −2) with the given slope.

48. 3 **49.** −2 **50.** $\frac{1}{2}$ **51.** $\frac{4}{5}$ **52.** $-\frac{2}{3}$

Solve. **53.** $3m + 13 = 1 + m$ **54.** $4(4 - t) = 3(1 - t)$ **55.** $-3.6 = 16a$

4-8 Problem Solving: Using Linear Programming

Objective: Solve problems using linear programming.

Mathematical models can be created to find optimal results based upon certain limits, or constraints. For example, a model may be created to maximize profits or minimize costs, given production limits, time constraints, or a specific allocation of resources. A field of mathematics where systems of linear inequalities are the basis of the model is called linear programming.

EXAMPLE 1

You are taking a test in which items of type A are worth 10 points and items of type B are worth 15 points. It takes 3 minutes to answer each item of type A and 6 minutes for each item of type B. The total time allowed is 60 minutes, and you may not answer more than 16 questions. Assuming all of your answers are correct, how many items of each type should you answer to get the highest score?

An application of mathematics called linear programming provides the answer.

Let x = the number of items of type A, and y = the number of items of type B

The total score T is given by $T = 10x + 15y$. The set of ordered pairs (x, y) for which this equation makes sense is determined by the following constraints.

Total number of questions allowed, not more than 16: $x + y \leq 16$

Time, not more than 60 minutes: $3x + 6y \leq 60$

Number of items of type A, nonnegative: $x \geq 0$

Number of items of type B, nonnegative: $y \geq 0$

We now graph the system of inequalities and determine the vertices, if any are formed.

The graph consists of a polygon and its interior. Under this condition, T has a maximum value and a minimum value, and they occur at the vertices of the polygon. All we need to do is find the vertices and substitute the coordinates in $T = 10x + 15y$.

Vertices: (x, y)	Score: $T = 10x + 15y$	
(0,0)	0	Minimum
(16, 0)	160	
(12, 4)	180	Maximum
(0, 10)	150	

The maximum score is 180. To achieve this score, you would answer 12 of type A and 4 of type B.

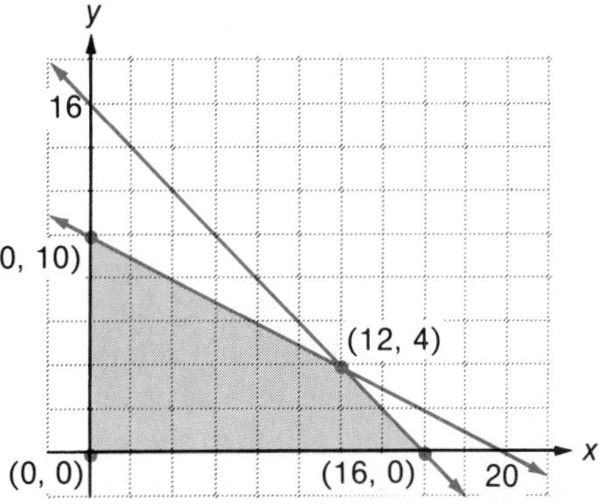

4-8

FIRST FIVE MINUTES

1. Graph the system of inequalities and find the vertices.

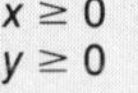

$x + y \leq 3$
$x \geq 0$
$y \geq 0$

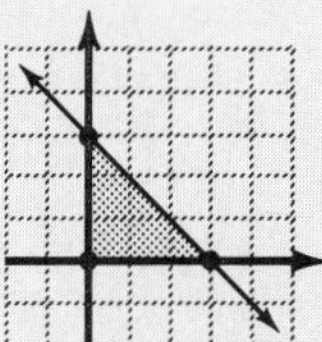

The vertices are (0, 0), (0, 3), (3, 0).

Emphasize that the power of linear programming is that the solutions are at the vertices. Note that more than one vertex may give the same result.

Chalkboard Example

1. Mrs. Wood's Biscuit Factory makes two types of biscuits, Biscuit Jumbos and Mini Mint Biscuits.
   (a) The oven can cook at most 200 biscuits per day.
   (b) Jumbos each require 2 ounces of flour. Minis each require 1 ounce of flour. There are 300 ounces of flour available.
   (c) The income from Jumbos is 10 cents each. The income from Minis is 8 cents each. How many of each type should be baked to earn the greatest amount?

The solution will be a pair of numbers, the number of Jumbos per day and the number of Minis per day.
Let j be the number of Jumbos per day.
Let m be the number of Minis per day.
Paragraph (a) is
$j + m \leq 200$ (1)
Paragraph (b) is
$2j + m \leq 300$ (2)
A hidden assumption is that the number of biscuits cannot be negative, hence
$j \geq 0$ (3)
$m \geq 0$ (4)
Paragraph (c) gives the income I.
$I = 10j + 8m$ (5)
Graph the system.

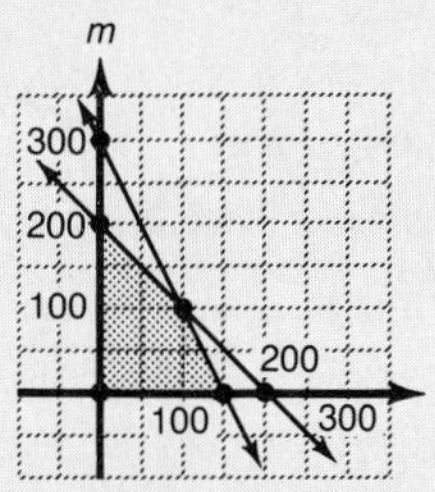

The maximum income will occur at a vertex. The vertices and their incomes are

(1) and (2) at $(j, m) = (100, 100)$, $I = 1800$
(1) and (3) at $(j, m) = (0, 200)$, $I = 1600$
(2) and (4) at $(j, m) = (150, 0)$, $I = 1500$
(3) and (4) at $(j, m) = (0, 0)$, $I = 0$

The maximum income occurs when 100 Jumbos and 100 Minis are baked.

LESSON QUIZ

1. Write the following constraints as a system of inequalities, but do not solve.
   There are 12 gallons of gas available to be distributed between the car and the scooter. The car's tank can hold at most 10 gallons. The scooter can hold at most 3 gallons. The car can go 20 miles on each gallon, and the scooter can go 100 miles on each gallon. How much should each vehicle get to achieve the greatest total miles?
   Let c be the amount, in gallons, allocated to the car.
   Let s be the amount, in gallons, allocated to the scooter.
   $c + s \le 12$
   $c \le 10$
   $s \le 3$
   $c \ge 0$
   $s \ge 0$
   Let M be the total miles.
   $M = 20c + 100s$
   We want to make M as large as possible.

The following is the main theorem used to solve linear programming problems.

Theorem 4-1

Suppose a quantity F is given by a linear equation $F = ax + by + c$, and that the set of ordered pairs (x, y) for which the equation makes sense can be described by a system of linear inequalities. If the graph of this system consists of a polygon and its interior, then F has a maximum and a minimum value that occur at the vertices.

EXAMPLE 2

Wheels Inc. makes mopeds and bicycles. Experience shows they must produce at least 10 mopeds. The factory can produce at most 60 mopeds and 120 bicycles per month. If the profit on a moped is \$134, the profit on a bicycle is \$20, and they can make at most 160 units combined, how many of each should Wheels Inc. make per month to maximize profit?

Let x = the number of mopeds to be produced
y = the number of bicycles to be produced

The profit $134x + 20y$ is subject to the constraints $10 \le x \le 60$, $0 \le y \le 120$, and $x + y \le 160$.

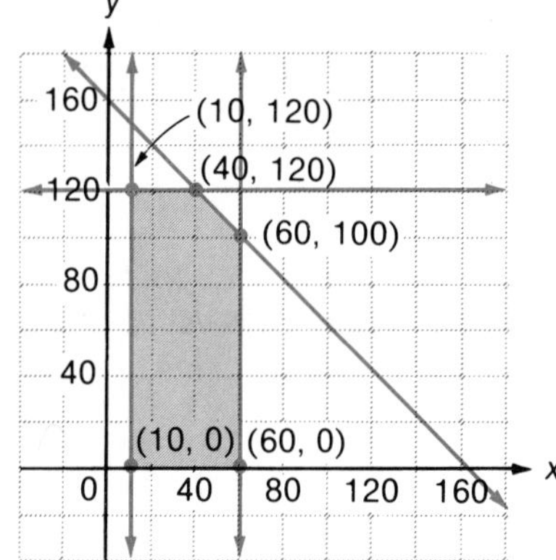

Vertices: (x, y)	Profit: $P = 134x + 20y$	
(10, 0)	1340	
(60, 0)	8040	
(60, 100)	10,040	Maximum
(40,120)	7760	
(10, 120)	3740	

Wheels Inc. will make a maximum profit of \$10,040 with 60 mopeds and 100 bicycles.

Try This

a. A snack bar cooks and sells hamburgers and hot dogs during football games. To stay in business, it must sell at least 10 hamburgers but cannot cook more than 40. It must also sell at least 30 hot dogs but cannot cook more than 70. The snack bar cannot cook more than 90 items total. The profit on a hamburger is 33¢ and on a hot dog it is 21¢. How many of each item should it sell to make the maximum profit?
40 hamburgers, 50 hot dogs

4-8 EXERCISES

A

1. You are about to take a test that contains questions of type A worth 4 points and of type B worth 7 points. You must answer at least 5 of type A and 3 of type B, but time restricts answering more than 10 of either type. In total, you can answer no more than 18. How many of each type of question must you answer, assuming all of your answers are correct, to maximize your score? What is the maximum score?
2. You are about to take a test that contains questions of type A worth 10 points and of type B worth 25 points. You must answer at least 3 of type A, but time restricts answering more than 12. You must answer at least 4 questions of type B, but time restricts answering more than 15. In total, you can answer no more than 20. How many of each type of question must you answer, assuming all of your answers are correct, to maximize your score? What is the maximum score?
3. A man plans to invest up to \$22,000 in bank X or bank Y, or both. He will invest at least \$2000, but no more than \$14,000, in bank X. He will invest no more than \$15,000 in bank Y. Bank X pays 6% simple interest, and bank Y pays $6\frac{1}{2}\%$. How much should he invest in each to maximize income? What is the maximum income?
4. Ms. Sugimoto plans to invest up to \$40,000 in corporate or municipal bonds, or both. She does not want to invest less than \$6000 or more than \$22,000 in corporate bonds. She also does not want to invest more than \$30,000 in municipal bonds. Corporate bonds earn 8% simple interest, and municipal bonds earn $7\frac{1}{2}\%$. How much should she invest in each to maximize income? What is the maximum income?

B

5. It takes a tailoring firm 2 hours of cutting and 4 hours of sewing to make a knit suit. To make a worsted suit it takes 4 hours of cutting and 2 hours of sewing. At most, 20 hours per day are available for cutting, and, at most, 16 hours per day are available for sewing. The profit on a knit suit is \$34 and on a worsted suit \$31. How many of each kind of suit should be made to maximize profit? What is the maximum profit?
6. ***Critical Thinking*** Suppose the profit on a bicycle and a moped were each \$100 in Example 2. How many of each should be produced? What is the maximum profit?

Challenge

7. An airline will provide accommodations for a minimum of 2000 first-class, 1500 tourist, and 2400 economy-class passengers. Airplane P-1 costs \$12,000 per mile to operate and can accommodate 40 first-class, 40 tourist, and 120 economy-class passengers. Airplane P-2 costs \$10,000 per mile to operate and can accommodate 80 first-class, 30 tourist, and 40 economy-class passengers. How many of each type of airplane should be used to minimize the operating cost?

Mixed Review

Solve. **8.** $19(c + 3) = 76$ **9.** $14 < 3r + 2$ **10.** $-4c + 2c > -18$

Assignment Guide
Algebra: 1 – 4, MR

Alg w/Finite or Trig: 1–6, MR

Comprehensive: 1–7, MR

ANSWERS

Exercises

1. You must correctly answer 8 questions of type A and 10 of type B to maximize your score. The maximum score is 102.
2. You must correctly answer 5 questions of type A and 15 of type B to maximize your score. The maximum score is 425.
3. \$7000 should be invested at bank X and \$15,000 at bank Y to maximize his income at \$1395.
4. \$22,000 should be invested in corporate bonds and \$18,000 in municipal bonds to maximize her income at \$3110.
5. 2 knit suits; 4 worsted suits; maximum profit is \$192.
6. The profit for (40, 120) or (60, 100) is \$16,000. Since the number produced must be an integer, the number of mopeds can be any integer from 40 to 60; the number of bicycles is 160 minus the number of mopeds.
7. 30 P-1 and 10 P-2 airplanes should be used to minimize the cost at \$460,000.

Mixed Review

8. 1
9. $r > 4$
10. $c < 9$

Problem Solving: College Entrance Exams

All of the strategies for solving problems are useful on pre-college tests. The strategies for college entrance exams are extensions of the other strategies presented throughout the text.

These questions are posed in the format that is found on many standardized tests. If students are familiar with this format prior to taking a standardized test, they can be more relaxed and perform at their best level.

Before solving, students should determine whether it would be easier to use substitution, linear combinations, or one of the variations presented here.

Caution is advised when using shortcut methods.
For example, if $2x + 3y = 5$ and $4x + 6y = 8$, then $12x + 18y =$
A. 26 B. 30 C. 24 D. 18 E. No solution

Adding the equations and multiplying by 2 gives $12x + 18y = 26$. But multiplying $2x + 3y = 5$ by 6 gives $12x + 18y = 30$, and multiplying $4x + 6y = 8$ by 3 gives $12x + 18y = 24$. The system is inconsistent, so there is no solution.

Problem Solving: College Entrance Exams

Systems of Equations

Some items on college entrance exams can be solved using the methods you learned in this chapter for solving systems of equations. Some items on these tests, however, can be solved more quickly using other methods.

EXAMPLE 1

If $3x + 2y = 17$ and $2x + y = 7$, then $\frac{5x + 3y}{2} =$

(A) 10 **(B)** 12 **(C)** 17 **(D)** 20 **(E)** 34

While linear combinations could be used to solve for x and y, this problem can be more easily solved by adding the two equations together and dividing by 2.

$$\begin{array}{r} 3x + 2y = 17 \\ 2x + y = 7 \\ \hline 5x + 3y = 24 \end{array}$$

Dividing by 2,

$$\frac{5x + 3y}{2} = 12$$

The answer is 12, choice B.

Another variation involves subtracting equations.

EXAMPLE 2

If $6x + 4y = 14$ and $3x + y = 8$, then $x + y =$

(A) 5 **(B)** 4 **(C)** 3 **(D)** 2 **(E)** 1

Subtracting equations results in the answer directly.

$$\begin{array}{r} 6x + 4y = 14 \\ -(3x + y = 8) \\ \hline 3x + 3y = 6 \end{array}$$

Multiplying by $\frac{1}{3}$,

$$\frac{1}{3}(3x + 3y) = \frac{1}{3}(6)$$

$$x + y = 2$$

The answer is 2, choice D.

Before solving, determine whether it would be easier to use substitution, linear combinations, or one of these variations.

EXAMPLE 3

If $8x - 7y = 14$ and $6x + 9y = -11$, then $7x + y =$

(A) $\frac{3}{2}$ **(B)** 3 **(C)** $\frac{49}{114}$ **(D)** 0 **(E)** $-\frac{2}{15}$

Adding the equations,

$$\begin{array}{r} 8x - 7y = \quad 14 \\ 6x + 9y = -11 \\ \hline 14x + 2y = \quad 3 \end{array}$$

Multiplying by $\frac{1}{2}$,

$$7x + y = \frac{3}{2}$$

The answer is $\frac{3}{2}$, choice A.

Problems

1. If $x + 2y = 6$ and $3x + y = 3$, then $8x + 6y =$
   (A) 18 **(B)** 9 **(C)** 20 **(D)** 3 **(E)** 24
2. If $5x - 3y = 6$ and $x = \frac{4y}{5}$ then $y =$
   (A) $\frac{4}{5}$ **(B)** $\frac{8}{5}$ **(C)** 6 **(D)** $\frac{8}{3}$ **(E)** 8
3. If $3x + 3y = 7$ and $x + 4y = 3$, then $\frac{4x + 7y}{5} =$
   (A) 10 **(B)** 2 **(C)** 5 **(D)** 4 **(E)** 3
4. If $x + 4y = 5$ and $4x + 3y = 4$, then $10x + 14y =$
   (A) 8 **(B)** 9 **(C)** 16 **(D)** 18 **(E)** 20
5. If $x + y = 3$ and $x - y = 2$, then $6x =$
   (A) 15 **(B)** 14 **(C)** 30 **(D)** 12 **(E)** 5
6. If $4x - 3y = 10$ and $x = \frac{7y}{4}$, then $2y =$
   (A) 2 **(B)** 10 **(C)** 4 **(D)** 5 **(E)** $\frac{5}{2}$
7. If $x + 2y = 3$ and $2x + y = 1$, then $9x + 9y =$
   (A) 4 **(B)** 9 **(C)** 27 **(D)** 36 **(E)** 12
8. If $5x + 3y = 8$ and $3x + y = 4$, then $4x + 2y =$
   (A) 5 **(B)** 4 **(C)** 3 **(D)** 6 **(E)** 12
9. If $3x + 5y = 44$ and $2x - 5y = -29$, then $5x + 5y =$
   (A) 15 **(B)** 75 **(C)** 30 **(D)** 10 **(E)** 50
10. If $ax + by = c$ and $ax - by = d$, then $2x =$
    (A) $\frac{c + d}{b}$ **(B)** $\frac{c - d}{a}$ **(C)** $\frac{c + d}{a}$ **(D)** $\frac{a}{c + d}$ **(E)** $\frac{2(c + d)}{a}$

ANSWERS

1. (A)
2. (C)
3. (B)
4. (D)
5. (A)
6. (D)
7. (E)
8. (D)
9. (E)
10. (C)

ANSWERS

1. (0, 1)
2. (3, 3)
3. $(-5, -1)$
4. (2, 4)
5. (5, 2)
6. $(-6, 2)$
7. $\left(\frac{7}{5}, \frac{10}{3}\right)$
8. $\left(\frac{1}{3}, \frac{1}{2}\right)$
9. Carol's speed = 51 km/h
   Ellie's speed = 68 km/h
10. $(1, -2, 3)$
11. $\left(2, -2, \frac{1}{2}\right)$

Chapter 4 Summary and Review

4-1

One way to solve a system of equations is to graph the equations and find points of intersection.

Solve graphically.

1. $-2x + y = 1$
$3x + y = 1$

2. $x = y$
$3x + y = 12$

4-2

The substitution method is a useful technique for solving systems in which a variable has a coefficient of 1.

Solve using the substitution method.

3. $2x - y = -9$
$3x - 8y = -7$

4. $x + y = 6$
$y = x + 2$

5. $y = 7 - x$
$2x - y = 8$

If all the variables have coefficients other than 1, linear combinations may be easier to use than the substitution method.

Solve using linear combinations.

6. $2x + 7y = 2$
$3x + 5y = -8$

7. $5x + 3y = 17$
$-5x + 3y = 3$

8. $-3a + 2b = 0$
$3a - 4b = -1$

4-3

Translating to a system of equations will often help when solving some problems.

9. On a recent trip, Ellie drove 264 km in the same length of time that Carol took to drive 198 km. Ellie's speed was 17 km/h greater than Carol's speed. Find the rate of each.

4-4

A solution of a system of equations in three variables is an ordered triple that makes all three equations true.

Solve.

10. $2x - y + z = 7$
$x + 2y + 2z = 3$
$7x - 3y - 3z = 4$

11. $2a + b - 4c = 0$
$a - b + 2c = 5$
$3a + 2b + 2c = 3$

4-5

Some problems can be best solved by translating to a system of three equations.

Solve.

12. Three assemblers, A, B, and C can produce 86 circuit boards per hour. A and B together can produce 59 circuit boards per hour, while A and C together can produce 58 circuit boards per hour. How many circuit boards can each assembler produce in one hour?

4-6

If a system of linear equations has at least one solution, we say that it is consistent. If a system does not have a solution, we say that it is inconsistent. If a consistent system of linear equations has infinitely many solutions, we say the system is dependent.

Which system is inconsistent? Which is dependent?

13. $2x - y = 4$
 $2x - y = 6$

14. $x - 2y = 3$
 $4x - 8y = 12$

4-7

The solution set of an inequality in two variables is the set of all ordered pairs that make the inequality true.

Graph.

15. $y > x + 2$

16. $3x - 5y \leq 15$

Graph these systems of inequalities.

17. $y \geq 2x$
 $y < -x + 3$

18. $y \leq 3$
 $x \geq -5$

4-8

If the graph of a system of inequalities consists of a polygon and its interior, a linear function has a maximum and a minimum value satisfying the system. These occur at the vertices.

19. A woman wants to invest $60,000 in mutual funds and municipal bonds. She does not want to invest more than 50%, or less than 20%, of her money in mutual funds. The minimum investment for municipal bonds is $10,000, and they are only guaranteed up to $40,000, so she will not invest more than $40,000 in municipal bonds. The mutual funds should produce a return of 10%, and the municipal bonds a return of 12%. How much should she invest in each to maximize her income? What is her maximum income?

See also Problem 4, Computer-Assisted Problem Solving, page 841.

12. A = 31, B = 28, C = 27
13. Inconsistent
14. Dependent

15.

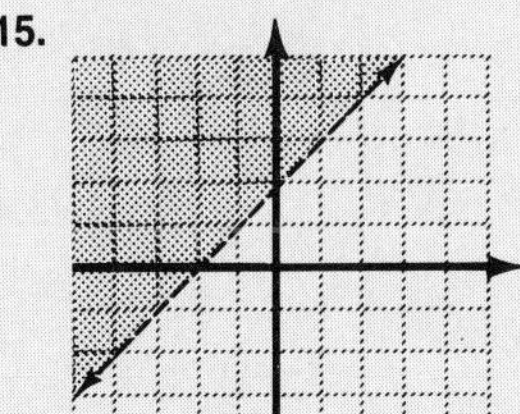

16.

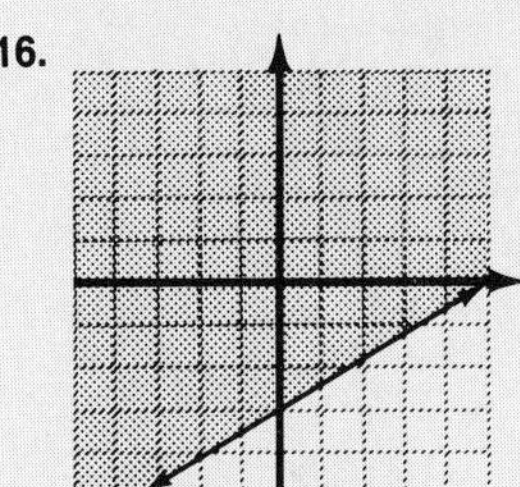

17.

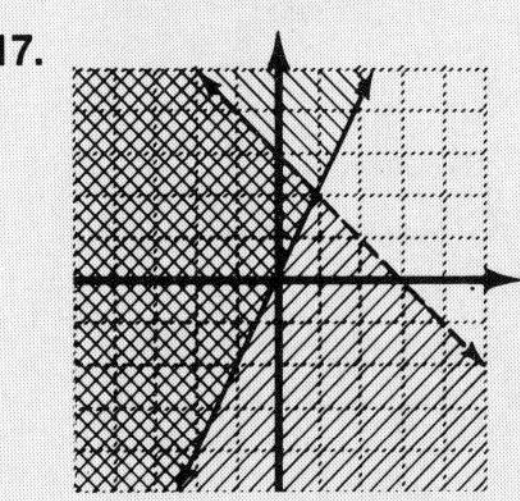

18.

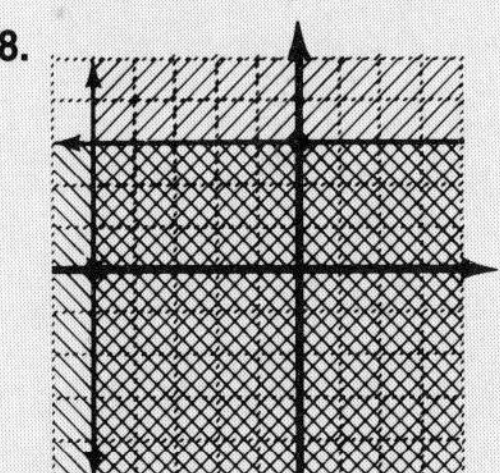

19. $40,000 in municipal bonds, $20,000 in mutual funds; $6800 maximum income

ANSWERS

1. (3, −1)
2. (6, 2)
3. (3, 2)
4. (−1, 3)
5. (6, 0)
6. (−3, −5)
7. 87 m by 216 m
8. (2, 3, −1)
9. A: 1200, B: 1700, C: 1350
10. Inconsistent
11. 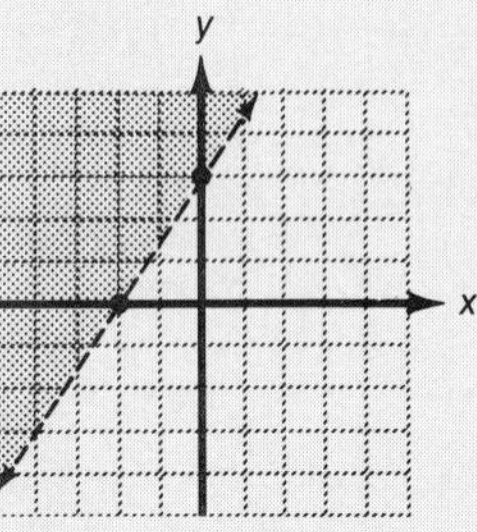

12. 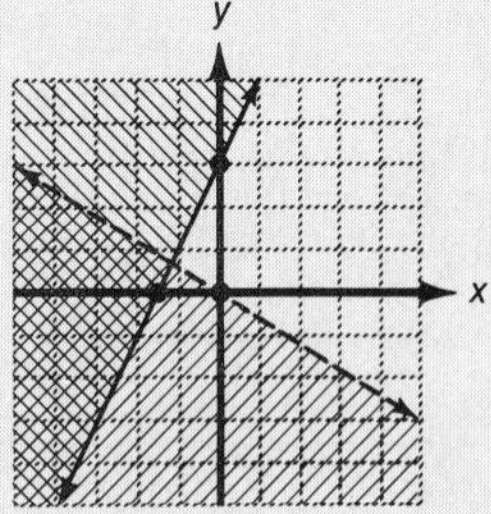

13. 10 oz of raisins, 6 oz of sunflower seeds

Test Item Analysis

Item	Lesson
1–2	4-1
3–6	4-2
7	4-3
8	4-4
9	4-5
10	4-6
11, 12	4-7
13	4-8

Chapter 4 Test

Solve graphically.

1. $x + y = 2$
$x - y = 4$

2. $x = 3y$
$2x - 3y = 6$

Solve using the substitution method.

3. $2x - 3y = 0$
$x + y = 5$

4. $2x = y - 5$
$5x + 3y = 4$

Solve using linear combinations.

5. $x - 5y = 6$
$3x + 4y = 18$

6. $4x - 7y = 23$
$6x + 3y = -33$

7. Solve.

The perimeter of a rectangular field is 606 m. The length is 42 m more than twice the width. Find the dimensions.

8. Solve.

$$x + y - 3z = 8$$
$$2x - 3y + z = -6$$
$$3x + 4y - 2z = 20$$

9. Solve.

When three printers, A, B, and C, are working together, they produce 4250 pages per hour. When only A and B are running, they produce 2900 pages per hour. When only B and C are running, they produce 3050 pages per hour. How many pages can each printer produce in one hour?

10. Is this system of equations inconsistent? Is it dependent?

$$x = 3y + 4$$
$$6y = 2x - 6$$

11. Graph $2y > 3x + 6$.

12. Graph this system of inequalities.

$$y \geq 2x + 3$$
$$3x + 5y < 0$$

13. Solve.

A company produces a 16-oz jar of sunflower seeds and raisins. The jar cannot have more than 10 oz of raisins and cannot have more than 12 oz of sunflower seeds. Each ounce of raisins costs 3¢ to package, while each ounce of sunflower seeds costs 5¢ to package. In order to make a satisfactory profit, the cost of packaging the mixture should be at most 60¢ per jar. Find the number of ounces of each to put into the mixture in order to maximize profit.

Chapters 1 – 4 Cumulative Review

1-1 Subtract.

1. $-\frac{11}{13} - \frac{4}{5}$ **2.** $-18.9 - (-7.7)$ **3.** $17 - \left(-\frac{4}{31}\right)$

1-2 Multiply.

4. $-5\left(-\frac{3}{7}\right)$ **5.** $-2.3(-5.5)$ **6.** $-\frac{7}{8}\left(\frac{2}{3}\right)$

1-3 Evaluate each expression for $x = -1$ and $y = 4$.

7. $-(2x - y - 6)$ **8.** $2|y - 8| - |x|$ **9.** $-3|x + y|$

1-4 Simplify.

10. $3x - 2(5y - 4x)$ **11.** $8y - [2y - (5y - 7)]$ **12.** $xy - (3x + xy - 5y)$

1-5 Solve.

13. $6x - 7 = 23$ **14.** $-5y - 11 = -1$

1-6

15. A swim club requires a $120 membership, plus $4 each swim. How much would a person pay to swim 35 times?

1-7 Simplify.

16. $(5y)^3$ **17.** $(-3x)^4$ **18.** $\left(-\frac{1}{2}\right)^5$

1-8 Simplify.

19. $(2x^2y)(-5x^{-5}y^6)$ **20.** $-\frac{28x^{-3}y^2}{4x^5y^{-3}}$ **21.** $(8x^3)^{-2}$

1-9 Convert to scientific notation.

22. 676,000 **23.** 0.0015 **24.** 10.09

2-1 Solve.

25. $3(x - 5) = 18x$ **26.** $\frac{1}{8}x + \frac{3}{2} = \frac{1}{3} - \frac{1}{6}x$ **27.** $(x - 7)(2x + 1) = 0$

2-2

28. Monthly credit card interest is charged at a rate of 1.5%. After one month, total purchases plus interest is $46.69. How much were the purchases?

ANSWERS

1. $-\frac{107}{65}$
2. -11.2
3. $17\frac{4}{31}$
4. $\frac{15}{7}$
5. 12.65
6. $-\frac{7}{12}$
7. 12
8. 7
9. -9
10. $11x - 10y$
11. $11y - 7$
12. $5y - 3x$
13. 5
14. -2
15. $260
16. $125y^3$
17. $81x^4$
18. $-\frac{1}{32}$
19. $-10x^{-3}y^7$
20. $-7x^{-8}y^5$
21. $\frac{1}{64}x^{-6}$
22. 6.76×10^5
23. 1.5×10^{-3}
24. 1.009×10^1
25. -1
26. -4
27. $7, -\frac{1}{2}$
28. $46.00

29. $\frac{e}{c^2}$
30. $\frac{fg^2}{m}$
31. $x > 7$
32. $y \geq -18$
33. $x < \frac{12}{5}$
34. 9, 11, 13
35. $-1 < x < \frac{5}{4}$

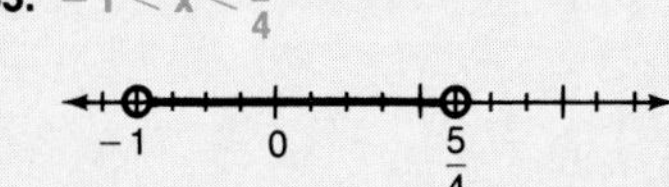

36. $x < -1$ or $x > 7$

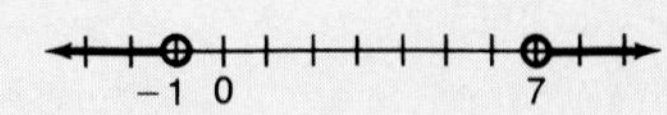

37. $-\frac{1}{2} < x < \frac{1}{2}$
38. $4 < y < 24$
39. $x \leq 4$ or $x \geq 10$
40. $\{(-3, 1), (-3, 2), (-2, 1), (-2, 2), (-1, 1), (-1, 2)\}$
41. $\{(-1, -1), (-1, 0), (-1, 1), (-1, 2), (-1, 3), (0, 0), (0, 1), (0, 2), (0, 3), (1, 1), (1, 2), (1, 3), (2, 2), (2, 3), (3, 3)\}$

42.

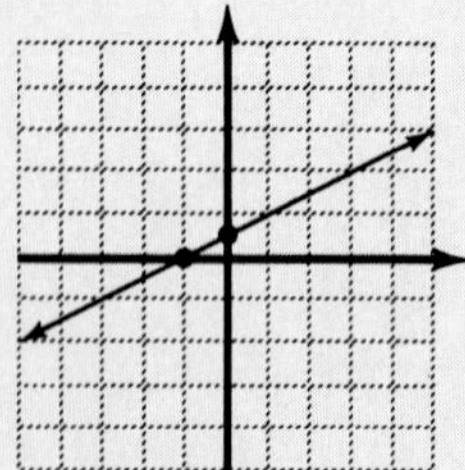

43.

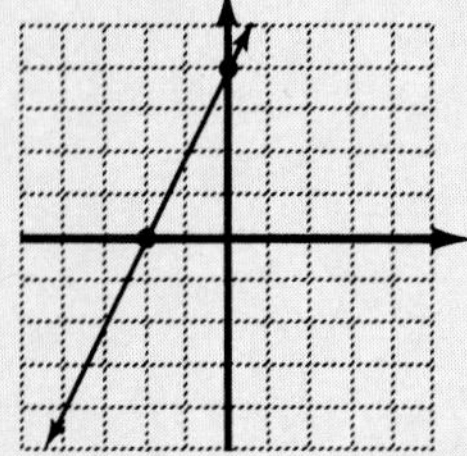

44. $\{x \mid x \neq -3\}$
45. R

46.

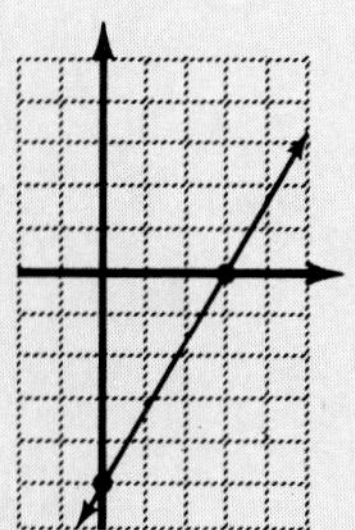

2-3 Solve for the given letter.

29. $e = mc^2$, for m **30.** $f = m\frac{M}{g^2}$, for M

2-4 Solve.

31. $3x - 8 > 2x - 1$ **32.** $-\frac{2}{3}y \leq 12$ **33.** $-3 + 7x < 2x + 9$

2-5

34. The sum of three consecutive odd integers is greater than 30. What are the least possible values for the integers?

2-6 Solve and graph.

35. $-3 < 4x + 1 < 6$ **36.** $2x + 1 < -1$ or $x - 3 > 4$

2-7 Solve.

37. $|x| < \frac{1}{2}$ **38.** $|14 - y| < 10$ **39.** $|-x + 7| \geq 3$

3-1 Consider the relation $A \times A$, where $A = \{-3, -2, -1, 0, 1, 2, 3\}$. Find the sets indicated by the following relations.

40. $\{(x, y) \mid -3 \leq x < 0 \text{ and } 0 < y < 3\}$ **41.** $\{(x, y) \mid -2 < x \leq y\}$

3-2 Graph.

42. $-x + 2y = 1$ **43.** $2x - y = -4$

3-3 What is the domain of each function?

44. $f(x) = \frac{x - 2}{x + 3}$ **45.** $f(x) = -x^2 + \frac{x}{2}$

3-4 Graph using intercepts.

46. $5x - 3y = 15$ **47.** $-2x + 7y = 14$

3-5 Find an equation of each line. Write in standard form.

48. Line with slope $-\frac{1}{2}$ and containing $(-8, 0)$
49. Line containing $(-2, -1)$ and $(-3, 7)$

3-6 Find the slope and y-intercept.

50. $y = -4$ **51.** $5y - 3x + 8 = 0$

3-7 Write an equation of the line containing $(2, -3)$

52. parallel to $2y + x = 5$.
53. perpendicular to $2y + x = 5$.

3-8

54. The world land-speed record has been increasing linearly since 1898. In 1898 the record was 39.2 mi/h. In 1970 the record was 622.3 mi/h. Predict the record for the year 2000.

3-9

55. Suppose $f(x) = 1 + 3x$ and $g(x) = 2 - x^2$. Find $f(g(-3))$.

4-1 – 4-2 Solve each system

56. by graphing.
$3x - y = 6$
$x = \frac{1}{2}y + 3$

57. by substitution.
$2y + x = -8$
$4x - 3y = 1$

58. by addition.
$3x - 4y = 7$
$-12x + 4y = 20$

4-3

59. Judy bought $3\frac{1}{2}$ lb of rice and 4 lb of sunflower seeds for \$4.90. Margarite bought 2 lb of rice and $\frac{1}{2}$ lb of sunflower seeds for a total of \$1.05. What is the per pound price for each item?

4-4 Solve.

60. $2x - y - z = -11$
$x + 2y - 3z = -13$
$-x - y + 4z = 22$

61. $3x + y - 2z = 1$
$x - y - z = -6$
$-x + y - 3z = 10$

4-5

62. Virgil needs to buy 4 tablecloths. He picks one cotton, one linen, and one vinyl tablecloth, but he still needs a fourth. If the fourth is cotton, the total cost will be \$120. If it is linen, the total cost will be \$155, and if it is vinyl, the total cost will be \$105. Find the price of each kind of tablecloth.

4-6 Which system is inconsistent? Which is dependent?

63. $4x - 6y = 12$
$-6x + 9y = 18$

64. $-8x - 9y = -12$
$-2x - \frac{9}{4}y = -3$

4-7 Graph.

65. $-3x + y > 1$

66. $y > x - 1$
$2x + y < 5$

4-8

67. A glassmaker makes windows and doors. The profit per window is \$3 and per door is \$5. Each day he has enough glass to make no more than 4 windows, or no more than 6 doors. His daily allotment of 18 sheets of glass would be used up by producing 2 windows and 3 doors. How many of each should he produce daily to maximize profits?

47.
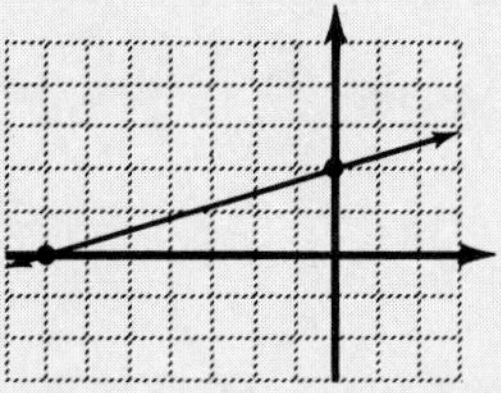

48. $x + 2y + 8 = 0$
49. $8x + y + 17 = 0$
50. Slope = 0, y-intercept = -4
51. Slope = $\frac{3}{5}$, y-intercept = $-\frac{8}{5}$
52. $2y + x = -4$
53. $2x - y = 7$
54. 865.3 mi/h
55. -20
56. $(0, -6)$
57. $(-2, -3)$
58. $(-3, -4)$
59. Rice \$0.28/lb, seeds \$0.98/lb
60. $(-1, 3, 6)$
61. $(-2, 5, -1)$
62. Vinyl \$10, cotton \$25, linen \$60
63. Inconsistent
64. Dependent

65.
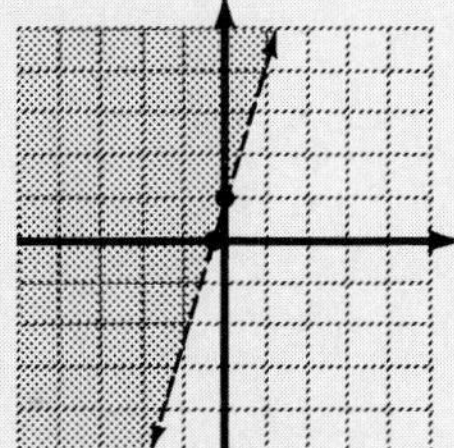

66.
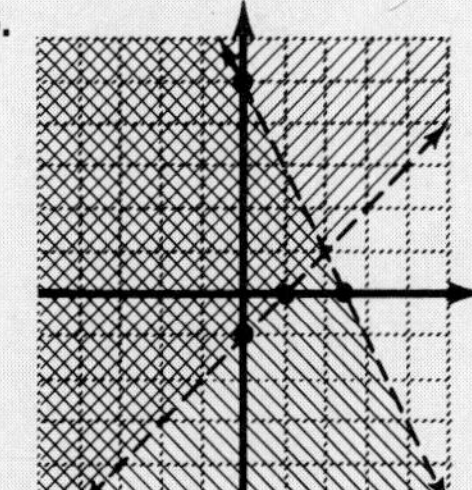

67. 0 windows, 6 doors

CHAPTER 5

Polynomials and Polynomial Equations

Chapter Overview

Chapter 5 reviews the basic operations involving polynomials, extending them to include polynomial functions, factoring by grouping, and factoring sums and differences of cubes. The principle of zero products is used to solve polynomial equations. Problem-solving lessons involve solving problems that require translation to polynomial equations, and strategies using factoring for college entrance exam questions.

Objectives

5-1
- Evaluate polynomial functions.
- Simplify polynomials by collecting like terms.

5-2
- Add polynomials.
- Find the additive inverse of a polynomial.
- Subtract polynomials.

5-3
- Multiply any two polynomials.
- Multiply two binomials using the FOIL method.
- Square a binomial.
- Multiply the sum and difference of the same two terms.
- Cube a binomial.

5-4
- Factor polynomials with a common factor.
- Identify and factor trinomial squares.
- Factor differences of two squares.
- Factor a polynomial of four or more terms by grouping.

5-5
- Factor sums or differences of two cubes.
- Factor trinomials of the type $x^2 + bx + c$.
- Factor trinomials of the type $ax^2 + bx + c$.

5-6
- Factor polynomials using any of the methods learned previously.

5-7
- Solve equations by factoring and using the principle of zero products.

5-8
- Solve problems by translating to equations and solving them by factoring.

TEACHING CHAPTER 5

Cooperative Learning Opportunities

It will be helpful if before each cooperative learning session you explain one or two of the rules. In the cooperative learning for this chapter it is likely that students will want to confer with you. A good rule is that only one person from each group, as designated, is to speak with the teacher. The question must be from the whole group, though, not just 1 individual. This prevents confusion and also helps hold the groups together.

Students are apt to forget that multiplication and factoring of polynomials are reverse operations. To reinforce this connection assign groups of three to do some of the exercises in Lesson 5-4.

Students in groups of 3 should follow these steps as roles. Student A factors the given expression. Student B multiplies out the factors obtained by student A. This should be done carefully because student A may have made a mistake. Student C checks the work done by the first two students and writes the general form for the factoring.

Multicultural Note: *David Blackwell*

David Blackwell (born 1919) is a noted professor of statistics at the University of California, Berkeley. He graduated from high school in Centralia, Illinois, at age 16 and then entered the University of Illinois intending to earn a bachelor's degree so that he could teach elementary school. But, he had discovered that mathematics was a beautiful subject full of ideas. Within six years he had not only received his baccalaureate degree, but his Ph.D. in mathematics as well, and he had become the first African-American to receive a fellowship to the Institute for Advanced Study at Princeton.

Professor Blackwell has made contributions to Bayesian Statistics, game theory, set theory, information theory, probability, and dynamic programming. He is one of the pioneers in the study of duels. He says, "Basically, I'm not interested in doing research and I never have been. I'm interested in *understanding*, which is quite a different thing."

Alternative Assessment and Communication Ideas

While some students are quick to grasp mathematical symbols, others can profit from the use of concrete manipulatives. Still others will be aided by verbal experiences. Chapter 5 allows you to try all three approaches. The use of algebra tiles is mentioned several times in Chapter 5. It is quite easy to become proficient using tiles and some students can find them a helpful aid to understanding. You can use them to assess the progress of students who may be making careless mistakes in manipulation. Setting up the tiles correctly will tell you that students are making definite progress.

The **Writing to Learn** activity on page 228 asks students to explain an algorithm in words. This approach can also be used for multiplying sums and difference, page 216, and factoring trinomial squares, page 220. Some students will not need this verbalization, preferring to simply learn the mathematics. But others will find their understanding enhanced by verbal descriptions.

Investigations and Projects

Products of polynomials with rather complicated results, such as those contained in the **Challenge Exercises** on page 218, can be almost impossible to check by factoring. But these products can be checked by substituting arbitrary numbers for the variables and then determining the value of the expressions in factored form and as products. You will not want to recommend that this be done long hand. But using a scientific calculator, entries can be made in a form identical with what is written out.

As a project, perhaps for extra credit, have students do Exercises 51, 52, and 53 on page 218 and check by substituting. In Exercise 51, for example, if $a = 2$, $b = 3$, $c = 4$, and $d = 5$, then -28 is obtained. The **Challenge Exercises** on pages 223, 228, and 231 can be checked using the same method.

Have students doing the project, check 10 problems using the substitution method and write out the results. Some of these might be used as a bulletin board display.

MANAGING CHAPTER 5

Lesson	PACING CHART (DAYS) Algebra	Algebra w/Finite	Algebra w/Trig	Comprehensive	Opening Activity	Cooperative Activity	Seat or Group Work
5-1	1	1	1	0.5	First Five Minutes 5-1: **TE** p.206 or ***FFM Transparency Masters*** p.15	Critical Thinking: **SE** p.209 Strategy Problem Bank 4: ***Problem Bank*** p.5	Try This a–d
5-2	1	1	1	0.5	First Five Minutes 5-2: **TE** p.210 or ***FFM Transparency Masters*** p.16	Critical Thinking: **SE** p.213 Looking for Errors 4: ***Enrichment*** p.65	Try This a–f
5-3	1	1	1	0.5	First Five Minutes 5-3: **TE** p.214 or ***FFM Transparency Masters*** p.16	Critical Thinking: **SE** p.218	Try This a–o
5-4	1	1	1	0.5	First Five Minutes 5-4: **TE** p.219 or ***FFM Transparency Masters*** p.16	Critical Thinking: **SE** p.223 ✂ Manipulative Activity 5: ***Enrichment*** p.46	Try This a–s
5-5	2	1	1	0.5	First Five Minutes 5-5: **TE** p.224 or ***FFM Transparency Masters*** p.17	Explore: **SE** p.224 Critical Thinking: **SE** p.228	Try This a–l
5-6	2	1	1	0.5	First Five Minutes 5-6: **TE** p.229 or ***FFM Transparency Masters*** p.17	Critical Thinking: **SE** p.231	Try This a–i
5-7	1	1	1	1	First Five Minutes 5-7: **TE** p.232 or ***FFM Transparency Masters*** p.17	Critical Thinking: **SE** p.233 Looking for Errors 5: ***Enrichment*** p.66	Try This a–f
5-8	2	2	2	2	First Five Minutes 5-8: **TE** p.234 or ***FFM Transparency Masters*** p.18	Critical Thinking: **SE** p.236 Problem Solving: **SE** pp.237–238	Try This a–b
Review	1	1	1	1			
Test	1	1	1	1			

FFM: First Five Minutes SPMR: Skills Practice Mixed Review

MANAGING CHAPTER 5

Enrichment	Review/Assess	Reteach	Technology	Lesson
Critical Thinking 5: ***Enrichment*** p.26	Lesson Quiz: **TE** p.207	Skills Practice 12, #1–8: ***SPMR*** p.24	Calculator Worksheet 7: ***Technology*** p.9	**5-1**
Looking for Errors 4: ***Enrichment*** p.65	Lesson Quiz: **TE** p.211	Skills Practice 12, #9–17: ***SPMR*** p.24	Problem for Programmers: **SE** p.213	**5-2**
BASIC Computer Project 4: ***Technology*** p.84	Lesson Quiz: **TE** p.217 Quiz 9: ***Assessment*** p.17	Skills Practice 12, #18–29: ***SPMR*** p.24	BASIC Computer Project 4: ***Technology*** p.84	**5-3**
✂ Manipulative Activity 5: ***Enrichment*** p.46	Lesson Quiz: **TE** p.222	Skills Practice 13, #1–22: ***SPMR*** p.25	BASIC Computer Project 5: ***Technology*** p.85	**5-4**
Writing to Learn: **SE** p.228	Lesson Quiz: **TE** p.226 Mixed Review 9: ***SPMR*** p.73	Skills Practice 13, #23–42: ***SPMR*** p.25	Calculator Worksheet 8: ***Technology*** p.10	**5-5**
College Entrance Exam 2, Section I: ***Problem Bank*** pp.55–58	Lesson Quiz: **TE** p.230	Skills Practice 14, #1–18: ***SPMR*** p.26		**5-6**
Looking for Errors 5: ***Enrichment*** p.66	Lesson Quiz: **TE** p.232 Quiz 10: ***Assessment*** p.18	Skills Practice 14, #19–36: ***SPMR*** p.26		**5-7**
Problem Solving: **SE** pp.237–238 Problem 5: Computer Assisted Problem Solving, **SE** p.842	Lesson Quiz: **TE** p.235 Mixed Review 10: ***SPMR*** p.74	Skills Practice 14, #37–38: ***SPMR*** p.26 Problem Bank 8: ***Problem Bank*** p.29	Problem 5: Computer Assisted Problem Solving, **SE** p.842	**5-8**
	Summary and Review: **SE** pp.239–240 Test: **SE** p.241			**Review**
	Chapter 5 Test: ***Assessment*** pp.71–76(reg.), pp.165–166 (adv.)			**Test**

The solution to the problem posed on the facing page can be found on page 208.

Ready for Polynomials and Polynomial Equations?

1-3

1. Evaluate $xy - xz$ for $x = -2, y = 4, z = 3$. -2

1-4 Factor.

2. $5x + 5y$ $5(x + y)$

3. $10x + 15y - 5$ $5(2x + 3y - 1)$

1-4 Multiply.

4. $3(y - 2)$ $3y - 6$

5. $4(x + 12)$ $4x + 48$

6. $c(t + s - f)$ $ct + cs - cf$

1-4 Collect like terms.

7. $3y + 2y$ $5y$

8. $a + 4a$ $5a$

9. $b - 4b + 3b$ 0

1-4 Remove parentheses and simplify.

10. $3x - (2x + 4)$ $x - 4$

11. $7y - 2 - (8y - 4)$ $-y + 2$

1-8 Multiply and simplify.

12. $3^{-2} \cdot 3^5$ 3^3

13. $(4a^7b^{-2})(2a^2b^3)$ $8a^9b$

14. $(8x^{-3}y^4)(3x^{-9}y^{-2})$ $24x^{-12}y^2$

1-8 Simplify.

15. $(3a)^2$ $9a^2$

16. $(-2y)^3$ $-8y^3$

17. $(2^{-3})^4$ 2^{-12}

18. $(x^{-2})^{-4}$ x^8

2-1 Solve.

19. $(x - 3)(x + 5) = 0$ $3, -5$

20. $3x(2x + 10) = 0$ $0, -5$

CHAPTER

5 Polynomials and Polynomial Equations

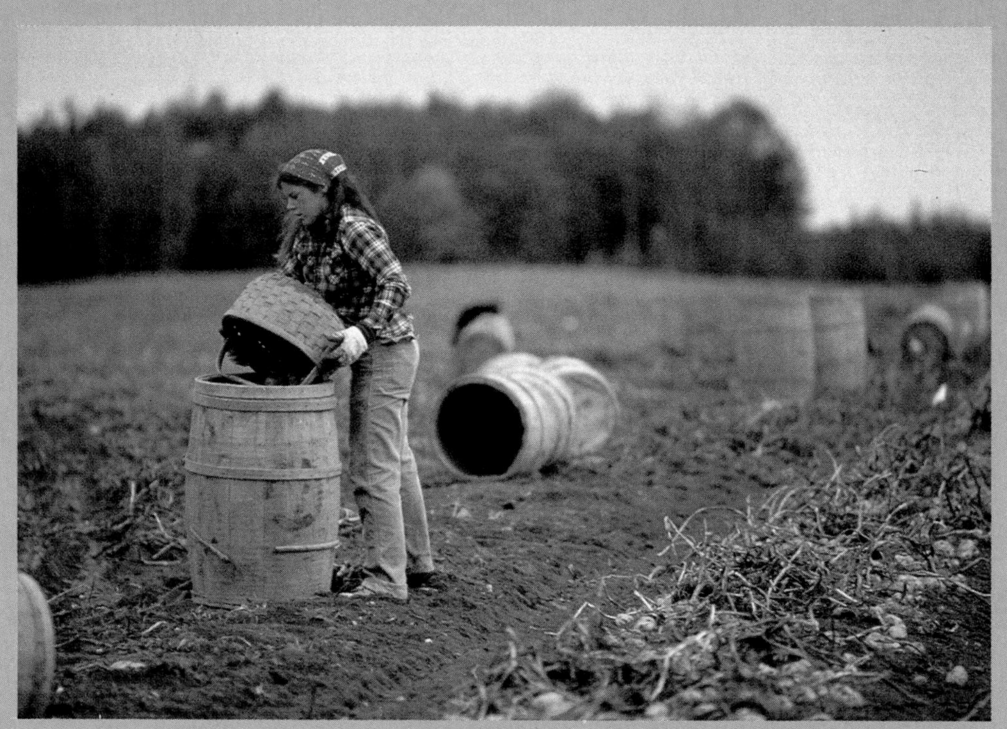

The polynomial $0.524hD^2 + 0.262hd^2$ *can be used to find the approximate volume of a barrel given its height* h, *its outside diameter* D, *and its inside diameter* d.

What is the volume of a barrel that is 48 inches high, with an outside diameter of 24 inches and an inside diameter of 18 inches?

5-1

FIRST FIVE MINUTES

Simplify.

1. x^2x^3
   x^5
2. $(x^3y^2)(x^4y^5)$
   x^7y^7
3. $(x^0y)(x^1y^0)$
   $(1 \cdot y)(x \cdot 1) = xy$

Polynomial Functions

Review that a function is a set of ordered pairs with a special property. For a given first coordinate, there is only one second coordinate.

Stress that $P(x)$ denotes the unique second coordinate that corresponds to the first coordinate x. $P(x)$ does not mean P times x.

Key Questions

- Is 1 a polynomial?
  Yes, $1 = 1x^0$
- Is the set of ordered pairs $\{(1, 2), (2, 3)\}$ a function? Why or why not?
  Yes, each first coordinate is assigned only one second coordinate.
- Is the set of ordered pairs $\{(1, 2), (1, 3)\}$ a function? Why or why not?
  No, 1 is assigned to two different numbers, 2 and 3.

Chalkboard Example

1. For the polynomial
   $P(x) = 1 - x^2$
   find the function values.
   a. $P(0)$
      $P(0) = 1 - 0^2 = 1$
   b. $P(1)$
      $P(1) = 1 - 1^2 = 0$
   c. $P(-1)$
      $P(-1) = 1 - (-1)^2 = 0$

5-1 Polynomials and Functions

The polynomial $0.524hD^2 + 0.262hd^2$ can be used to find the approximate volume of a barrel given its height h, its outer diameter D, and its inner diameter d.

In this chapter we will discuss polynomials. Here is a quick review of terms related to polynomials that you may recall from first-year algebra.

Polynomial Functions

Objective: Evaluate polynomial functions.

Expressions like these are polynomials in one variable.

$$5x^2 \qquad 8a \qquad 2 \qquad -7x + 5 \qquad 2y^2 + 5y - 3 \qquad 5a^4 - 3a^2 + \frac{1}{4}a - 8$$

Expressions like these are polynomials in several variables.

$$5x - xy^2 + 7y + 2 \qquad 9xy^2z - 4x^3z + (-14x^4y^2) + 9 \qquad 15x^3y^2$$

The polynomial $5x^3y - 7xy^2 + 2$ has three terms, $5x^3y$, $-7xy^2$, and 2.

The coefficients of the terms are 5, -7, and 2. The degree of a term is the sum of the exponents of the variables in that term. The degree of $-7xy^2$ is 3 since the exponents are 1 and 2. The degree of a polynomial is the highest degree of its terms.

A polynomial with a single term is a monomial. A polynomial with two terms is a binomial, and one with three terms is a trinomial. Polynomials are usually arranged in order of increasing or decreasing powers of one variable (ascending or descending order). We now give a precise definition of a polynomial in one variable.

Definition

A **polynomial in x** is any expression of the form

$$a_nx^n + a_{n-1}x^{n-1} + \cdots + a_1x + a_0$$

where n is a nonnegative integer and the coefficients $a_0, \ldots, a_n$ are real numbers.

A polynomial function is a function that can be defined by a polynomial. For instance, $P(x) = 5x^7 + 3x^5 - 4x^2 - 5$ defines a polynomial function. To find values of a polynomial function, we substitute into the polynomial expression.

EXAMPLE 1

For the polynomial function $P(x) = 2x^2 - 3x + 4$, find the following function values.

$$P(x) = 2x^2 - 3x + 4$$

(a) $P(0) = 2 \cdot 0^2 - 3 \cdot 0 + 4$ Substituting
$= 4$

(b) $P(-10) = 2 \cdot (-10)^2 - 3(-10) + 4$
$= 200 + 30 + 4$
$= 234$

Try This

a. For $P(x) = 2x^3 - 3x^2 + 5$, find the following function values.

(1) $P(0)$ 5 **(2)** $P(4)$ 85 **(3)** $P(-2)$ −23

Collecting Like Terms

Objective: Simplify polynomials by collecting like terms.

If two terms of a polynomial have the same variables raised to the same powers, the terms are called similar or like terms. Like terms can be "combined" or "collected" using the distributive property.

EXAMPLES Collect like terms.

2. $3x^2 - 4y + 2x^2 = 3x^2 + 2x^2 - 4y$ Rearranging terms
$= (3 + 2)x^2 - 4y$ Using the distributive property
$= 5x^2 - 4y$

3. $3x^2y - 5xy^2 - 3x^2y - xy^2 = -6xy^2$

In Example 3, we collected like terms mentally, first recognizing that the two x^2y terms were additive inverses, and then collecting the two xy^2 terms.

Try This Collect like terms.

b. $5x^2 + 3x^4 - 2x^2 - x^4$ $3x^2 + 2x^4$

c. $5x^3y^2 - 2x^2y^3 + 4x^3y^2$ $9x^3y^2 - 2x^2y^3$

d. $3xy^2 - 4x^2y + 4xy^2 + 2x^2y + 3x^2 - y^2 + 2x^2y$ $7xy^2 + 3x^2 - y^2$

Collecting Like Terms

Point out that arranging terms in descending or ascending order will aid in collecting like terms.

Chalkboard Examples

Collect like terms.

1. $3 + 4x + y + 5 + 3y$
   $8 + 4x + 4y$
2. $3x + 2x^2 + 4x + 5x^2$
   $7x + 7x^2$
3. $4x^2y + xy + 5xy + 3x^2y$
   $7x^2y + 6xy$

LESSON QUIZ

Find the function values for the polynomial $P(x) = 1 + x + x^2$.

1. $P(2)$ 7
2. $P(-2)$ 3

Collect like terms.

3. $2xy^2 - 4x + 4y - 3xy^2 + x$
   $-xy^2 - 3x + 4y$
4. $1 + 2x^2y + 3xy + 4x^2y + 5xy$
   $1 + 6x^2y + 8xy$

Assignment Guide
Algebra: 1–16 e/o, MR

Alg w/Finite or Trig: 1–32 e/o, 33, MR

Comprehensive: 1–32 m4, 33, 34–40 e/o, MR, assign w. 5-2

ADDITIONAL ANSWERS

Exercises

9. $a + 6$
10. $7x + 14$
11. $-6a^2b - 2b^2$
12. $-8x^3 - 3x^2y^2$

21. $-3x^2 - 6ax + 6x - 3a^2 + 6a - 4$
22. $24x^2 + 40x + 3$
23. $55x^5 - 59x^4 + 14x^3 + 12x^2 + 18x + 175$
24. $-29x^5 + 15x^4 - 86x^3 + 68x^2 - 50x - 25$
25. $29x^5 - 15x^4 + 86x^3 - 68x^2 + 50x + 25$
26. $178x^5 - 199x^4 + 6x^3 + 76x^2 + 38x + 600$
27. 160
28. 9.5¢ per km, 11¢ per km

5-1 EXERCISES

A

For each polynomial function, find the specified function values.

1. $P(x) = 4x^2 - 3x + 2$
Find $P(4)$ and $P(0)$. 54, 2
2. $Q(x) = -5x^3 + 7x^2 - 12$
Find $Q(3)$ and $Q(-1)$. -84, 0
3. $P(y) = 8y^3 - 12y - 5$
Find $P(-2)$ and $P\left(\frac{1}{3}\right)$. $-45, -\frac{235}{27}$
4. $Q(y) = 9y^3 + 8y^2 - 4y - 9$
Find $Q(-3)$ and $Q(-1)$. $-168, -6$

Collect like terms.

5. $6x^2 - 7x^2 + 3x^2$ $2x^2$
6. $-2y^2 - 7y^2 + 5y^2$ $-4y^2$
7. $5x - 4y - 2x + 5y$ $3x + y$
8. $4a - 9b - 6a + 3b$ $-2a - 6b$
9. $5a + 7 - 4 + 2a - 6a + 3$
10. $9x + 12 - 8 - 7x + 5x + 10$
11. $3a^2b + 4b^2 - 9a^2b - 6b^2$
12. $5x^2y^2 + 4x^3 - 8x^2y^2 - 12x^3$
13. $8x^2 - 3xy + 12y^2 + x^2 - y^2 + 5xy + 4y^2$ $9x^2 + 2xy + 15y^2$
14. $a^2 - 2ab + b^2 + 9a^2 + 5ab - 4b^2 + a^2$ $11a^2 + 3ab - 3b^2$
15. $4x^2y - 3y + 2xy^2 - 5x^2y + 7y + 7xy^2$ $-x^2y + 9xy^2 + 4y$
16. $3xy^2 + 4xy - 7xy^2 + 7xy + x^2y$ $x^2y + 11xy - 4xy^2$

B

For each polynomial function find the specified function value.

17. $P(x) = -4x^3 + 2x^2 - 7x + 5$
Find $P(a)$. $-4a^3 + 2a^2 - 7a + 5$
18. $Q(x) = 6x^3 - 12x^2 - 8x - 3$
Find $Q(-b)$. $-6b^3 - 12b^2 + 8b - 3$
19. $P(x) = x^3 - 4x^2 + 3x - 7$
Find $P(2a)$. $8a^3 - 16a^2 + 6a - 7$
20. $Q(x) = -7x^3 + 10x^2 + 6$
Find $Q\left(\frac{c}{2}\right)$. $-\frac{7}{8}c^3 + \frac{10}{4}c^2 + 6$
21. $P(x) = -3x^2 + 6x - 4$
Find $P(x + a)$.
22. $Q(x) = 6x^2 + 8x - 11$
Find $Q(2x + 1)$.

For the polynomial functions $P(x)$ and $Q(x)$, find each of the following.

$$P(x) = 13x^5 - 22x^4 - 36x^3 + 40x^2 - 16x + 75$$
$$Q(x) = 42x^5 - 37x^4 + 50x^3 - 28x^2 + 34x + 100$$

23. $P(x) + Q(x)$
24. $P(x) - Q(x)$
25. $Q(x) - P(x)$
26. $4[P(x)] + 3[Q(x)]$
27. Evaluate $f(x, y) = 3xy^2 - 2x^2y$ for $x = 5$ and $y = -2$.
28. The cost, in cents per kilometer, of operating an automobile at speed s is approximated by the polynomial function $C(s) = 0.002s^2 - 0.21s + 15$. How much does it cost to operate the automobile at 50 km/h? 80 km/h?
29. The polynomial $0.524hD^2 + 0.262hd^2$ gives the approximate volume of certain barrels where d is the inside diameter, D is the outside diameter, and h is the height. Find the approximate volume of a barrel that is 48 inches high, has an inside diameter of 18 inches, and an outside diameter of 24 inches. 18,562.2 in.^{3} or 10.7 ft^3

30. The polynomial $\pi(R^2 - r^2)$ gives the area of a ring with inner radius r and outer radius R. Find the area of a ring with outer radius 20 cm and inner radius 15 cm. $175\pi \approx 549.8 \text{ cm}^2$

31. The polynomial $0.49W + 0.45P - 6.36R + 8.7$ gives an estimate of the percent of body fat of a man, where W is the waist circumference in centimeters, P is the skin fold above the pectoral muscle in millimeters, and R is the wrist diameter in centimeters. Find the percent of body fat for Frank Scavone. $W = 83.9$ cm, $P = 6.0$ mm, and $R = 7.1$ cm. 7.36%

32. The polynomial $0.041h - 0.018A - 2.69$ gives the lung capacity in liters for a woman, where h is the height in centimeters and A is the age in years. Find the lung capacity for Delia Jackson. $h = 139.8$ cm, $A = 41$ years. 2.304 L

33. ***Critical Thinking*** Write a trinomial in x and y of degree 6 in which all of the coefficients are negative even numbers. Answers may vary.

Challenge

Find the value for a so that each term has degree n.

34. $x^n y^a$ 0 35. $x^{(n-2)}y^a$ 2 36. $x^a y^{\frac{n}{2}}$ $\frac{n}{2}$ 37. $x^5 y^a z^a$ $\frac{n-5}{2}$

38. Using only the variables x, y, and z, how many different terms of degree 3 can you write? 10; x^3, y^3, z^3, x^2y, x^2z, xy^2, y^2z, xz^2, yz^2, and xyz

39. Express the area of this box as a polynomial. The box is rectangular with an open top and dimensions as shown. $x^2 + 4hx$ square units

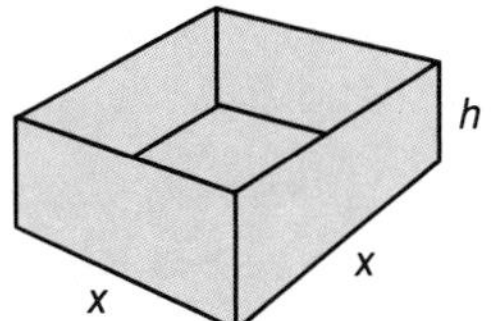

40. A box with an open top is to be made from a piece of cardboard 12 inches square. Corners are cut out and the sides are folded up. Express the volume of the box as a polynomial. $6x^2 - \frac{1}{2}x^3$

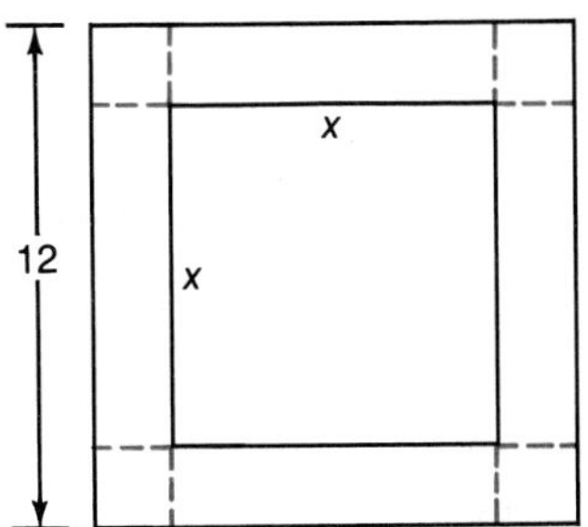

Mixed Review

Factor. 41. $6m^2 + 3m$ 42. $21n - 36m$ 43. $17 + 51c$ 44. $2ab + 4ac$

For each pair of points, find an equation of the line containing them.

45. $(1, -2)$ and $(-1, 4)$ 46. $(-2, -1)$ and $(6, 3)$ 47. $(0, 2)$ and $(-2, 0)$

Solve. 48. $2(m + 66) = 12$ 49. $4(1 - t) = 6$ 50. $11a + 2 = 6a + 12$

Mixed Review

41. $3m(2m + 1)$
42. $3(7n - 12m)$
43. $17(1 + 3c)$
44. $2a(b + 2c)$
45. $y = -3x + 1$
46. $y = \frac{1}{2}x$
47. $y = x + 2$
48. -60
49. -0.5
50. 2

5-2

FIRST FIVE MINUTES

1. $P(x) = 3x^2 - 9x + 4$
   Find $P(-1)$.
   16
2. $P(x) = x^3 - x^2 + x - 1$
   Find $P(2)$.
   5
3. Collect like terms.
   $2x^3y + 4xy^4 + 5x^3y + xy^4$
   $7x^3y + 5xy^4$

Addition

Encourage students to simply write the answers instead of using columns, except in the case of complicated problems.

Key Questions

- Is it possible to add two polynomials that have no like terms?
  Yes
- Suppose a two-term polynomial and a three-term polynomial were added. What is the maximum number of terms that can be in the sum?
  5
  What is the minimum number of terms that can be in the sum?
  1

Chalkboard Examples

1. Add.
   $2x^3 + 3x$ and $6x^3 + 4x + 1$
   $$\begin{array}{r} 2x^3 + 3x \\ 6x^3 + 4x + 1 \\ \hline 8x^3 + 7x + 1 \end{array}$$
2. Add.
   $3x^4 + 5x^3 + 2x + 7$ and $4x^4 + 3x^2 + 2$
   $$\begin{array}{rrrrr} 3x^4 & + 5x^3 & & + 2x & + 7 \\ 4x^4 & & + 3x^2 & & + 2 \\ \hline 7x^4 & + 5x^3 & + 3x^2 & + 2x & + 9 \end{array}$$
3. Add.
   $2x^2y^3 + 4xy + 3xy^2$ and $4x^2y^3 + 5xy^2 + 3xy$
   $$\begin{array}{r} 2x^2y^3 + 4xy + 3xy^2 \\ 4x^2y^3 + 3xy + 5xy^2 \\ \hline 6x^2y^3 + 7xy + 8xy^2 \end{array}$$

5-2 Addition and Subtraction of Polynomials

Addition

Objective: Add polynomials.

The sum of two polynomials can be found by writing a plus sign between them and then collecting like terms.

EXAMPLE 1 Add $-3x^3 + 2x - 4$ and $4x^3 + 3x^2 + 2$.

The use of columns is often helpful. Write the polynomials one under the other, writing like terms under one another and leaving spaces for missing terms.

$$\begin{array}{rrrrr} & -3x^3 & & + 2x & - 4 \\ + & 4x^3 & + 3x^2 & & + 2 \\ \hline & x^3 & + 3x^2 & + 2x & - 2 \end{array}$$

EXAMPLE 2 Add $4ax^2 + 4bx - 5$ and $3ax^2 + 5bx + 8$.

$$\begin{array}{r} 4ax^2 + 4bx - 5 \\ + \; 3ax^2 + 5bx + 8 \\ \hline 7ax^2 + 9bx + 3 \end{array}$$

Addition of polynomials can also be done mentally.

EXAMPLE 3 Add.

$$(13x^3y + 3x^2y - 5y) + (x^3y + 4x^2y - 3xy + 3y)$$
$$= 14x^3y + 7x^2y - 3xy - 2y$$

EXAMPLE 4 Add.

$$\left(\frac{5}{6}dx^8 + \frac{2}{3}dx^4\right) + \left(-\frac{2}{3}dx^4 + \frac{1}{5}d\right)$$
$$= \frac{5}{6}dx^8 + \frac{1}{5}d$$

Try This Add.

a. $3x^3 + 4x^2 - 7x - 2$ and $-7x^3 - 2x^2 + 3x + \frac{1}{2}$ $-4x^3 + 2x^2 - 4x - \frac{3}{2}$

b. $5p^2q^4 - 2p^2q^2 - 3q + (-6pq^2 + 3p^2q^2 + 5)$ $5p^2q^4 + p^2q^2 - 6pq^2 - 3q + 5$

Additive Inverses

Objective: Find the additive inverse of a polynomial.

The sum of a polynomial and its additive inverse is 0. The additive inverse of a polynomial can be found by replacing each term by its additive inverse.

EXAMPLE 5 Find the additive inverse of $7xy^2 - 6xy - 4y + 3$.

The additive inverse of $7xy^2 - 6xy - 4y + 3$ can be written as $-(7xy^2 - 6xy - 4y + 3)$.

$$-(7xy^2 - 6xy - 4y + 3)$$
$$= -7xy^2 + 6xy + 4y - 3 \quad \text{Replacing each term by its additive inverse}$$

Try This Find the additive inverse.

c. $5x^2t^2 - 4xy^2t - 3xt + 6x - 5$ $\quad -5x^2t^2 + 4xy^2t + 3xt - 6x + 5$

d. $-3x^2y + 5xy - 7x + 4y + 2$ $\quad 3x^2y - 5xy + 7x - 4y - 2$

Subtraction

Objective: Subtract polynomials.

Using Theorem 1-1, we can subtract by adding an inverse. Thus to subtract one polynomial from another, we add its additive inverse. We change the sign of each term of the polynomial to be subtracted and then add.

EXAMPLE 6 Subtract.

$$(-9x^5 - x^3 + 2x^2 + 4) - (2x^5 - x^4 + 4x^3 - 3x^2)$$
$$= (-9x^5 - x^3 + 2x^2 + 4) + [-(2x^5 - x^4 + 4x^3 - 3x^2)] \quad \text{Adding the inverse}$$
$$= (-9x^5 - x^3 + 2x^2 + 4) + [-2x^5 + x^4 - 4x^3 + 3x^2]$$
$$= -11x^5 + x^4 - 5x^3 + 5x^2 + 4$$

EXAMPLE 7 Subtract the second polynomial from the first.

$$\begin{array}{r} 4x^2y - 6x^3y^2 \qquad\qquad + x^2y^2 - 5y) \\ -\ (4x^2y + x^3y^2 + 3x^2y^3 \qquad\qquad + 6y) \\ \hline -7x^3y^2 - 3x^2y^3 + x^2y^2 - 11y \end{array} \quad \text{Mentally changing signs and adding}$$

Try This Subtract.

e. $(5xy^4 - 7xy^2 + 4x^2 - 3) - (-3xy^4 + 2xy^2 - 2y + 4)$ $\quad 8xy^4 - 9xy^2 + 4x^2 + 2y - 7$

f.
$$\begin{array}{r} 5x^2y - 7x^3y^2 \qquad\qquad - x^2y^2 + 4y \\ -(-2x^2y + 2x^3y^2 - 5x^2y^3 \qquad\qquad - 5y) \end{array}$$
$7x^2y - 9x^3y^2 + 5x^2y^3 - x^2y^2 + 9y$

Additive Inverses

You may wish to show that

$-(7xy^2 - 6xy - 4y + 3)$
$= -1(7xy^2 - 6xy - 4y + 3)$
$= -7xy^2 + 6xy + 4y - 3.$

Chalkboard Examples

1. Find the additive inverse of $5x^3y + 2xy^4 + 7$.
   $-(5x^3y + 2xy^4 + 7)$
   $= -5x^3y - 2xy^4 - 7$
2. Find the additive inverse of $-3xy + 5xy^2 - 6x^3y^2$.
   $-(-3xy + 5xy^2 - 6x^3y^2)$
   $= 3xy - 5xy^2 + 6x^3y^2$

Subtraction

Encourage students to do subtraction mentally.

Chalkboard Examples

1. Subtract.
   $(5x + 7xy + 6x^2y)$
   $-(2x + 3xy + 4x^2y)$

   $(5x + 7xy + 6x^2y)$
   $+(-2x - 3xy - 4x^2y)$
   $= 3x + 4xy + 2x^2y$
2. Subtract.
   $$\begin{array}{r} (4xy^2 - 6x^2y^2 + 5x^3y^2) \\ -(2xy^2 + 4x^2y^2 - 8x^3y^2) \\ \hline 2xy^2 - 10x^2y^2 + 13x^3y^2 \end{array}$$

LESSON QUIZ

1. Add $5x^5 - 3x^3 + 7x - 1$ and $4x^5 + 3x^3 - 6x^2 + 5$.
   $9x^5 - 6x^2 + 7x + 4$
2. Find the additive inverse.
   $7x^3y^2 - 5x^2y^3 + 6xy^4$
   $-7x^3y^2 + 5x^2y^3 - 6xy^4$
3. Subtract.
   $(7x^2y^4 - 3xy + 7)$
   $-(5x^2y^4 + 2xy - 4)$
   $2x^2y^4 - 5xy + 11$

Assignment Guide
Algebra: 1–23 e/o, MR

Alg w/Finite or Trig: 1–31 e/o, 32, MR

Comprehensive: 1 – 31 m4, 32 – 35, MR, assign w. 5-1

ADDITIONAL ANSWERS

Exercises

1. $3x^3 - x^2 + 7x$
2. $-9x^3 + 10x^2 - 8x - 18$
3. $3x^2y - 5xy^2 + 7xy + 2$
4. $2x^2y - 7xy^2 + 8xy + 5$
5. $3x + 2y - 2z - 3$
6. $7x^2 + 12xy - 2x - y - 9$
7. $9.46y^4 + 2.5y^3 - 11.8y - 3.1$
8. $\frac{1}{2}x^5 - \frac{3}{10}x^3 - \frac{1}{4}x^2 + \frac{2}{3}x - 19$
9. $\frac{3}{4}x^3 + \frac{1}{4}x^2 + \frac{1}{16}x + \frac{23}{24}$
10. $-5x^3 + 7x^2 - 3x + 6$
11. $4y^4 - 7y^2 + 2y + 1$
12. $6x^2y - 2xy^2 + 5y^3 - 10$
13. $-20x^4y^4 + 12x^3y^3 - 5x^2y^2 + 3xy - 19$
14. $-2x^2 + 6x - 2$
15. $-2x^3 - 6x^2 - x + 11$
16. $-2x^2 + 6x - 2$
17. $-4x^2 - 5y^2 + 3$
18. $-4a^2 + 8ab - 5b^2$
19. $6x^4 - 8x^2 + 9x - 4$
20. $3x^4 - 9x^3 + 7x - x^3y$
21. $0.06y^4 + 0.032y^3 - 0.94y^2 + 0.93$
22. $x^4 - x^2 - 1$
23. $-\frac{4}{9}y^3 + \frac{4}{9}y^2 + \frac{26}{27}y + \frac{4}{9}$
24. $8x^{2a} + 7x^a + 7$
25. $47x^{4a} + 40x^{3a} + 30x^{2a} + x^a + 4$

5-2 EXERCISES

A

Add.

1. $5x^3 + 7x - 8$ and $-2x^3 - x^2 + 8$
2. $-9x^3 + 3x^2 - 6x$ and $7x^2 - 2x - 18$
3. $5x^2y - 2xy^2 + 3xy - 5$ and $-2x^2y - 3xy^2 + 4xy + 7$
4. $6x^2y - 3xy^2 + 5xy - 3$ and $-4x^2y - 4xy^2 + 3xy + 8$
5. $2x + 3y + z - 7$ and $4x - 2y - z + 8$ and $-3x + y - 2z - 4$
6. $2x^2 + 12xy - 11$ and $6x^2 - 2x + 4$ and $-x^2 - y - 2$
7. $1.23y^4 - 2.25y^3 - 3.4y - 5.2 + (8.23y^4 + 4.75y^3 - 8.4y + 2.1)$
8. $\frac{1}{3}x^5 - \frac{1}{5}x^3 - \frac{1}{2}x^2 - 8 + \left(\frac{1}{6}x^5 - \frac{1}{10}x^3 + \frac{1}{4}x^2 + \frac{2}{3}x - 11\right)$
9. $\frac{3}{4}x^3 + \frac{1}{8}x - \frac{1}{24} + \left(\frac{1}{4}x^2 - \frac{1}{16}x + 1\right)$

Find the additive inverse.

10. $5x^3 - 7x^2 + 3x - 6$
11. $-4y^4 + 7y^2 - 2y - 1$
12. $-6x^2y + 2xy^2 - 5y^3 + 10$
13. $20x^4y^4 - 12x^3y^3 + 5x^2y^2 - 3xy + 19$

Subtract.

14. $-x^3 + 3x^2 - 2x + 2$
    $-(-x^3 + 5x^2 - 8x + 4)$
15. $-2x^3 - 7x + 8$
    $-(6x^2 - 6x - 3)$
16. $3x^2 - 2x - x^3 + 2$
    $-(5x^2 - 8x - x^3 + 4)$
17. $5x^2 + 4xy - 3y^2 + 2$
    $-(9x^2 + 4xy + 2y^2 - 1)$
18. $5a^2 + 4ab - 3b^2 - (9a^2 - 4ab + 2b^2)$
19. $8x^4 - (2x^4 + 8x^2 - 9x + 4)$
20. $-5x^3 - (-3x^4 + 4x^3 - 7x + x^3y)$
21. $(0.09y^4 - 0.052y^3 + 0.93) - (0.03y^4 - 0.084y^3 + 0.94y^2)$
22. $\left(\frac{5}{8}x^4 - \frac{1}{4}x^2 - \frac{1}{2}\right) - \left(-\frac{3}{8}x^4 + \frac{3}{4}x^2 + \frac{1}{2}\right)$
23. $\left(\frac{4}{9}y^2 - \frac{10}{27}y + \frac{1}{3}\right) - \left(\frac{4}{9}y^3 - \frac{4}{3}y - \frac{1}{9}\right)$

B

Add.

24. $(2x^{2a} + 4x^a + 3) + (6x^{2a} + 3x^a + 4)$
25. $(47x^{4a} + 3x^{3a} + 22x^{2a} + x^a + 1) + (37x^{3a} + 8x^{2a} + 3)$

Add or subtract.

26. $(3x^{6a} - 5x^{5a} + 4x^{3a} + 8) - (2x^{6a} + 4x^{4a} + 3x^{3a} + 2x^{2a})$

27. $(2x^{5b} + 4x^{4b} + 3x^{3b} + 8) - (x^{5b} + 2x^{3b} + 6x^{2b} + 9x^{b} + 8)$

28. $(3x^2y + 5x^2z + 2y^2z - xyz) + (-5xy^2 - 11x^2z + 7xyz + z^2y)$

29. $(12x^3y^2z - 4x^2y^2z^2 + 16xy^2z^3 - 7x^3y^2z + 2xyz)$
$+ (-12x^3yz + 4x^2y^2z - 16xy^2z^3 - xyz^2 - 9)$

30. $(8ab^2c - 10ab^2 + 2ac + 15b^2c - 11ab^2c)$
$- (-2ab + ab^2c - 9b^2c - 10ab^2)$

31. $(17 - 24pq^2 + 4p^2q + p^2qr + 8pq^2r)$
$- (6q^2p + 8q^2pr + 4qp^2 - 7qp^2r - 3pqr)$

32. ***Critical Thinking*** Find two polynomials whose difference is $9x^3y^2 - 3x^2y^2 + 8xy^2 - 3xy$.

Challenge

33. Suppose $f(x) = 2x^2 + 3x + 5$ and $g(x) = 6x^2 - 9x - 11$. Find $f(2)$, $g(2)$, and $f(2) + g(2)$. Now find $h(x) = f(x) + g(x)$. Find $h(2)$. What do you observe?

34. Suppose $f(x)$ and $g(x)$ are defined as in Exercise 32. Find $f(3)$, $g(3)$, and $f(3) - g(3)$. Now find $p(x) = f(x) - g(x)$. Find $p(3)$. What do you observe?

35. For Exercise 30, suppose $a = b$ and $b = 2c$. Find the result in terms of a.

Mixed Review

Evaluate for $a = -2$. **36.** $(3 - a)(a + 5)$ **37.** $(4a)^a$ **38.** $9a - (3a)^2$

Write each equation in standard form. **39.** $6 - 4y = 2x$ **40.** $2(x - y) = 4$

Solve. **41.** $5x + 6 = 12 + 8x$ **42.** $7a + 11a = 162$ **43.** $25 = 4(m - 3) - 3$

44. 272 adults entered the amusement park one day. 183 paid the regular \$9 adult admission price, the rest had discount coupons. A total of \$2136.50 was collected on adult tickets at the admissions gate. How much was a discount coupon worth?

45. Senior citizens at a local restaurant receive a 25% discount. Sunday brunch costs \$9.88 per person. Last Sunday, the restaurant collected \$2324.27 from 247 customers. How many customers were senior citizens?

Problem for Programmers

Write a program to both add and subtract any two polynomials in one variable of degree 4 or less. The solutions should omit missing terms.

Test your program on Exercises 1, 2, 14, and 15 in Lesson 5-2.

Challenge: Display the results in polynomial form with raised exponents, write terms with negative coefficients as subtractions, and omit coefficients of 1 before variables.

26. $x^{6a} - 5x^{5a} - 4x^{4a} + x^{3a} - 2x^{2a} + 8$
27. $x^{5b} + 4x^{4b} + x^{3b} - 6x^{2b} - 9x^{b}$
28. $3x^2y - 6x^2z + 2y^2z + 6xyz - 5xy^2 + z^2y$
29. $5x^3y^2z - 4x^2y^2z^2 + 2xyz - 12x^3yz + 4x^2y^2z - xyz^2 - 9$
30. $-4ab^2c + 2ac + 24b^2c + 2ab$
31. $17 - 30pq^2 + 8p^2qr + 3pqr$
32. Answers may vary.
33. $f(2) = 19, g(2) = -5,$
$f(2) + g(2) = 14;$
$h(x) = 8x^2 - 6x - 6,$
$h(2) = 14 = f(2) + g(2)$
34. $f(3) = 32, g(3) = 16,$
$f(3) - g(3) = 16;$
$p(x) = -4x^2 + 12x + 16,$
$p(3) = 16 = f(3) - g(3)$
35. $-2a^4 + 12a^3 + 3a^2$

Mixed Review

36. 15
37. $\frac{1}{64}$
38. -54
39. $-2x - 4y + 6 = 0$ or $2x + 4y - 6 = 0$
40. $2x - 2y - 4 = 0$ or $-2x + 2y + 4 = 0$
41. -2
42. 9
43. 10
44. \$3.50
45. 47

5-3

FIRST FIVE MINUTES

1. Simplify.
   $5x^2y + 7x^3y^2 - 2x^2y + x^3y^2$
   $3x^2y + 8x^3y^2$
2. Multiply.
   $3(5x + 4)$
   $15x + 12$
3. Simplify.
   $(3x^4y^2)(2x^3y^6)$
   $6x^7y^8$

Multiplication of Any Two Polynomials

Remind students of the rules for multiplying monomials before beginning polynomial multiplication.

Key Question

- If a two-term polynomial and a three-term polynomial are multiplied, how many terms will the product have before like terms are collected?
  6

Chalkboard Example

1. Multiply.
   $2a^2 - ab + b^2$ and $a - 2b$

$$\begin{array}{rrrr} 2a^2 & - ab & + b^2 & \\ & a & - 2b & \\ \hline 2a^3 & - a^2b & + ab^2 & \\ & - 4a^2b & + 2ab^2 & - 2b^3 \\ \hline 2a^3 & - 5a^2b & + 3ab^2 & - 2b^3 \end{array}$$

Products of Two Binomials

The general rule for multiplying two polynomials together is to multiply every term in the first polynomial by every term in the second polynomial. The objective is to do this in an orderly way so that nothing gets lost. The FOIL method is simply one way of organizing this process.

Chalkboard Examples

Multiply.

1. $(3x + 2y)(5x + y)$
   $15x^2 + 13xy + 2y^2$
2. $(2xy + 3x)(4x - 1)$
   $8x^2y - 2xy + 12x^2 - 3x$
3. $(3x + xy)(2x^2y - 4x)$
   $6x^3y - 12x^2 + 2x^3y^2 - 4x^2y$

5-3 Multiplication of Polynomials

Multiplication of Any Two Polynomials

Objective: Multiply any two polynomials.

Multiplication of polynomials is based on the distributive property. To multiply two polynomials, we multiply each term of one polynomial by each term of the other and then add the results.

EXAMPLE 1 Multiply.

$$\begin{array}{rrrrl} & 4x^4y & - 7x^2y & + 3y & \\ \times & & - 3x^2y & + 2y & \\ \hline -12x^6y^2 & + 21x^4y^2 & - 9x^2y^2 & & \text{Multiplying by } -3x^2y \\ & 8x^4y^2 & - 14x^2y^2 & + 6y^2 & \text{Multiplying by } 2y\text{, aligning like terms} \\ \hline -12x^6y^2 & + 29x^4y^2 & - 23x^2y^2 & + 6y^2 & \text{Adding} \end{array}$$

Try This Multiply.

a. $3x^2y - 2xy + 3y$ and $xy + 2y$ $3x^3y^2 + 4x^2y^2 - xy^2 + 6y^2$

b. $p^2q + 2pq + 2q$ and $2p^2q - pq + q$ $2p^4q^2 + 3p^3q^2 + 3p^2q^2 + 2q^2$

Products of Two Binomials

Objective: Multiply two binomials using the FOIL method.

We can find a product of two binomials mentally. The procedure can be simplified as follows.

Multiplying Binomials

Multiply the First terms, then the Outside terms, then the Inside terms, then the Last terms. We abbreviate this as **FOIL**.

F O I L

$$(A + B)(C + D) = AC + AD + BC + BD$$

(1 = First, 2 = Outside, 3 = Inside, 4 = Last)

EXAMPLES Multiply.

2. $(3xy + 2x)(x^2 + 2xy^2) = 3x^3y + 6x^2y^3 + 2x^3 + 4x^2y^2$ (F O I L; arrows 1, 2, 3, 4)

3. $(2x + 3y)(x - 4y) = 2x^2 - 5xy - 12y^2$

Try This Multiply.

c. $(2xy + 3x)(x^2 - 2)$ $2x^3y - 4xy + 3x^3 - 6x$

d. $(3x - 2y)(5x + 3y)$ $15x^2 - xy - 6y^2$

e. $(2x + 20)(3y - 20)$ $6xy - 40x + 60y - 400$

Squares of Binomials

Objective: Square a binomial.

Note the following.

$$(A + B)^2 = (A + B)(A + B)$$
$$= A^2 + AB + AB + B^2 \quad \text{Using FOIL}$$
$$= A^2 + 2AB + B^2$$

Squaring Binomials

$$(A + B)^2 = A^2 + 2AB + B^2 \qquad (A - B)^2 = A^2 - 2AB + B^2$$

The square of a binomial is the square of the first expression, plus or minus twice the product of the expressions, plus the square of the second expression.

EXAMPLES Multiply.

$$(A - B)^2 = A^2 - 2\,A\,B + B^2$$

4. $(y - 5)^2 = y^2 - 2(y)(5) + 5^2$
$= y^2 - 10y + 25$

$$(A + B)^2 = A^2 + 2\,A\,B + B^2$$

5. $(2x + 3y)^2 = (2x)^2 + 2\,(2x)\,(3y) + (3y)^2$ $A = 2x, B = 3y$
$= 4x^2 + 12xy + 9y^2$

6. $(a^2b^3 + a^3b^2)^2 = (a^2b^3)^2 + 2(a^2b^3)(a^3b^2) + (a^3b^2)^2$
$= a^4b^6 + 2a^5b^5 + a^6b^4$

Try This Multiply.

f. $(4x - 5y)^2$ $16x^2 - 40xy + 25y^2$

g. $(2y^2 + 6x^2y)^2$ $4y^4 + 24x^2y^3 + 36x^4y^2$

Squares of Binomials

You may want to encourage students to recite the rules while they use them. This will aid in their understanding and retention.

Some students may find that algebra tiles or binomial grids help them visualize binomial products. Using algebra tiles for Example 4 would give the following.

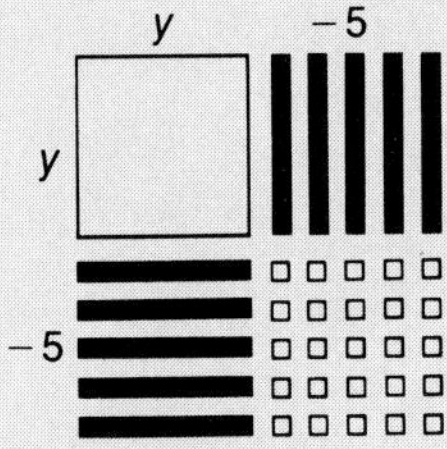

Chalkboard Examples

Multiply.

1. $(x - 3)^2$
$x^2 - 6x + 9$
2. $(3x + 4y)^2$
$9x^2 + 24xy + 16y^2$
3. $(2x^2 - 3xy)^2$
$4x^4 - 12x^3y + 9x^2y^2$

Products of Sums and Differences

Students can make the following model out of paper. By cutting along the lines and fitting the two pieces together, they can show concretely that $a^2 - b^2 = (a + b)(a - b)$.

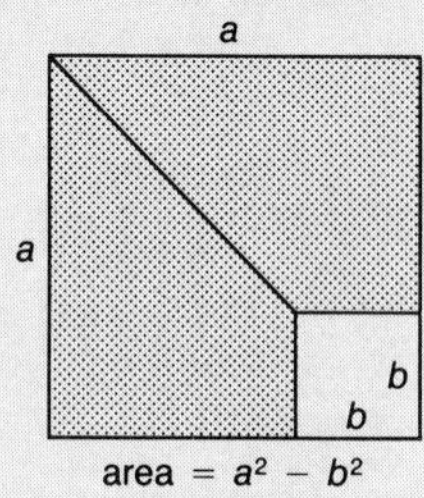

area $= a^2 - b^2$

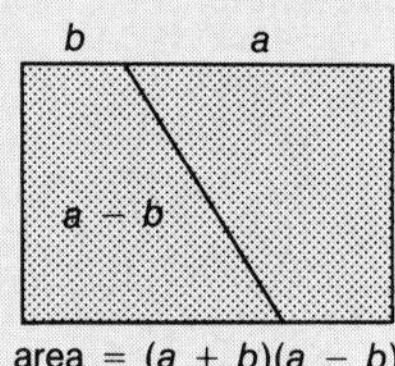

area $= (a + b)(a - b)$

Chalkboard Examples

Multiply.

1. $(x + y)(x - y)$
   $x^2 - y^2$
2. $(3xy - 4)(3xy + 4)$
   $9x^2y^2 - 16$
3. $(2x + 1 + y)(2x + 1 - y)$
   $((2x + 1) + y)((2x + 1) - y)$
   $(2x + 1)^2 - y^2$
   $= 4x^2 + 4x + 1 - y^2$

Cubing a Binomial

Remind students that if they do not remember the special product formulas, it is an easy task to derive them by multiplying.

Chalkboard Examples

Multiply.

1. $(a + b)^3$
   $a^3 + 3a^2b + 3ab^2 + b^3$
2. $(x - 1)^3$
   $x^3 + 3x^2(-1) + 3x(-1)^2 + (-1)^3$
   $= x^3 - 3x^2 + 3x - 1$
3. $(2x + 3y)^3$
   $(2x)^3 + 3(2x)^2(3y) + 3(2x)(3y)^2 + (3y)^3$
   $= 8x^3 + 36x^2y + 54xy^2 + 27y^3$

Products of Sums and Differences

Objective: Multiply the sum and difference of the same two terms.

We can use FOIL when finding the product of a sum and a difference of the same two terms. Note the following.

$$\begin{aligned}(A + B)(A - B) &= A^2 - AB + AB - B^2 \quad \text{Using FOIL} \\ &= A^2 - B^2\end{aligned}$$

Multiplying Sums and Differences

$$(A + B)(A - B) = A^2 - B^2$$

The product of the sum and difference of two expressions is the square of the first expression minus the square of the second.

EXAMPLES Multiply.

$$(A + B)(A - B) = A^2 - B^2$$

7. $(y + 5)(y - 5) = y^2 - 5^2$
$= y^2 - 25$

8. $(3xy^2 + 4y)(-3xy^2 + 4y) = (4y + 3xy^2)(4y - 3xy^2)$ Using the commutative property
$= (4y)^2 - (3xy^2)^2$
$= 16y^2 - 9x^2y^4$

9. $(5y + 4 + 3x)(5y + 4 - 3x) = (5y + 4)^2 - (3x)^2$
$= 25y^2 + 40y + 16 - 9x^2$

Try This Multiply.

h. $(4x + 7)(4x - 7)$ $16x^2 - 49$

i. $(5x^2y + 2y)(5x^2y - 2y)$ $25x^4y^2 - 4y^2$

j. $(2x + 3 + 5y)(2x + 3 - 5y)$ $4x^2 + 12x + 9 - 25y^2$

k. $(-2x^3y^2 + 5t)(2x^3y^2 + 5t)$ $25t^2 - 4x^6y^4$

Cubing a Binomial

Objective: Cube a binomial.

The following multiplication gives another useful pattern.

$$\begin{aligned}(A + B)^3 &= (A + B)(A + B)^2 \\ &= (A + B)(A^2 + 2AB + B^2) \quad \text{Squaring a binomial} \\ &= (A + B)A^2 + (A + B)2AB + (A + B)B^2 \quad \text{Using the distributive property} \\ &= A^3 + A^2B + 2A^2B + 2AB^2 + AB^2 + B^3 \quad \text{Using the distributive property} \\ &= A^3 + 3A^2B + 3AB^2 + B^3 \quad \text{Collecting like terms}\end{aligned}$$

Cubing Binomials

$$(A + B)^3 = A^3 + 3A^2B + 3AB^2 + B^3$$

EXAMPLES Multiply.

$$(A + B)^3 = A^3 + 3A^2B + 3AB^2 + B^3$$

10. $(x + 2)^3 = x^3 + 3(x)^2(2) + 3(x)(2)^2 + 2^3$
$= x^3 + 6x^2 + 12x + 8$

11. $(x - 2)^3 = [x + (-2)]^3$ Writing in the form $(A + B)^3$
$= x^3 + 3(x)^2(-2) + 3(x)(-2)^2 + (-2)^3$
$= x^3 - 6x^2 + 12x - 8$

12. $(5m^2 - 4n^3)^3 = (5m^2)^3 + 3(5m^2)^2(-4n^3) + 3(5m^2)(-4n^3)^2 + (-4n^3)^3$
$= 125m^6 - 300m^4n^3 + 240m^2n^6 - 64n^9$

Note in Examples 11 and 12 that a separate formula for $(A - B)^3$ does not need to be memorized. We can think of $(A - B)^3$ as $[A + (-B)]^3$.

Try This Multiply. See Additional Answers.

l. $(x + 1)^3$ **m.** $(x - 1)^3$ **n.** $(t^2 + 3b)^3$ **o.** $(2a^3 - 5b^2)^3$

5-3 EXERCISES

A

Multiply.

1. $2x^2 + 4x + 16$ and $3x - 4$
2. $3y^2 - 3y + 9$ and $2y + 3$
3. $4a^2b - 2ab + 3b^2$ and $ab - 2b + 1$
4. $2x^2 + y^2 - 2xy$ and $x^2 - 2y^2 - xy$
5. $(a - b)(a^2 + ab + b^2)$
6. $(t + 1)(t^2 - t + 1)$
7. $(2x + 3y)(2x + y)$
8. $(2a - 3b)(2a - b)$
9. $\left(4x^2 - \frac{1}{2}y\right)\left(3x + \frac{1}{4}y\right)$
10. $\left(2y^3 + \frac{1}{5}x\right)\left(3y - \frac{1}{4}x\right)$
11. $(2x^2 - y^2)(2x - 2y)$
12. $(3y^2 - 2)(3y - x)$
13. $(2x + 3y)^2$
14. $(5x + 2y)^2$
15. $(2x^2 - 3y)^2$
16. $(4x^2 - 5y)^2$
17. $(2x^3 + 3y^2)^2$
18. $(5x^3 + 2y^2)^2$
19. $(3x - 2y)(3x + 2y)$
20. $(3x + 5y)(3x - 5y)$
21. $(x^2 + yz)(x^2 - yz)$
22. $(2x^2 + 5y)(2x^2 - 5y)$
23. $(3x^2 - 2)(3x^2 + 2)$
24. $(5x^2 - 3)(5x^2 + 3)$
25. $(y + 5)^3$
26. $(t - 7)^3$
27. $(m^2 - 2n)^3$
28. $(2f + 3d)^3$

LESSON QUIZ

Multiply.

1. $x^2 - 1$ and $3x^2 + 2x + 1$
   $3x^4 + 2x^3 - 2x^2 - 2x - 1$
2. $(2x + 4y)^2$
   $4x^2 + 16xy + 16y^2$
3. $(2x + 1)(2x - 1)$
   $4x^2 - 1$
4. $(a + 2)^3$
   $a^3 + 6a^2 + 12a + 8$

Assignment Guide

Algebra: 1 – 28 e/o, MR

Alg w/Finite or Trig: 1–43 e/o, 44, MR

Comprehensive: 1–43 m4, 44, 45–53 e/o, MR, assign w. 5-4

ADDITIONAL ANSWERS

Try This

l. $x^3 + 3x^2 + 3x + 1$
m. $x^3 - 3x^2 + 3x - 1$
n. $t^6 + 9t^4b + 27t^2b^2 + 27b^3$
o. $8a^9 - 60a^6b^2 + 150a^3b^4 - 125b^6$

Exercises

1. $6x^3 + 4x^2 + 32x - 64$
2. $6y^3 + 3y^2 + 9y + 27$
3. $4a^3b^2 - 10a^2b^2 + 3ab^3 + 4ab^2 - 6b^3 + 4a^2b - 2ab + 3b^2$
4. $2x^4 - x^2y^2 - 4x^3y - 2y^4 + 3xy^3$
5. $a^3 - b^3$
6. $t^3 + 1$
7. $4x^2 + 8xy + 3y^2$
8. $4a^2 - 8ab + 3b^2$
9. $12x^3 + x^2y - \frac{3}{2}xy - \frac{1}{8}y^2$
10. $6y^4 - \frac{1}{2}xy^3 + \frac{3}{5}xy - \frac{1}{20}x^2$
11. $4x^3 - 4x^2y - 2xy^2 + 2y^3$
12. $9y^3 - 3y^2x - 6y + 2x$
13. $4x^2 + 12xy + 9y^2$
14. $25x^2 + 20xy + 4y^2$
15. $4x^4 - 12x^2y + 9y^2$
16. $16x^4 - 40x^2y + 25y^2$
17. $4x^6 + 12x^3y^2 + 9y^4$
18. $25x^6 + 20x^3y^2 + 4y^4$
19. $9x^2 - 4y^2$
20. $9x^2 - 25y^2$
21. $x^4 - y^2z^2$
22. $4x^4 - 25y^2$
23. $9x^4 - 4$
24. $25x^4 - 9$
25. $y^3 + 15y^2 + 75y + 125$
26. $t^3 - 21t^2 + 147t - 343$
27. $m^6 - 6m^4n + 12m^2n^2 - 8n^3$
28. $8f^3 + 36f^2d + 54fd^2 + 27d^3$

29. $\frac{1}{4}x^4 - \frac{3}{5}x^2y + \frac{9}{25}y^2$
30. $\frac{1}{16}x^4 - \frac{1}{3}x^2y + \frac{4}{9}y^2$
31. $0.25x^2 + 0.70xy^2 + 0.49y^4$
32. $0.09x^2 + 0.48xy^2 + 0.64y^4$
33. $4x^2 + 12xy + 9y^2 - 16$
34. $x^4 + 6x^2y + 9y^2 - y^4$
35. $x^4 - 1$
36. $y^4 - 16$
37. $16x^4 - y^4$
38. $625x^4 - y^4$
39. $16x^4 - 32x^3 + 16x^2$
40. $9x^6 - \frac{30}{11}x^3 + \frac{25}{121}$
41. $x^{4a} - y^{4b}$
42. $x^{a^2 - b^2}$
43. a. \$1368.90 b. \$1367.63
c. \$1360.49
d. $b=2, A(r)=1000(r^2 + 2r + 1)$
$b=3, A(r)=1000(r^3 + 3r^2 + 3r + 1)$
$b=4, A(r)=1000(r^4 + 4r^3 + 6r^2 + 4r + 1)$
45. $16x^4 - 32x^3 + 16x^2$
46. $-a^4 - 2a^3b + 25a^2 + 2ab^3 - 25b^2 + b^4$
47. $x^6 - 1$
48. $x^3 + y^3 + 3y^2 + 3y + 1$
49. $y^6 - 3y^4 + 3y^2 - 1$
50. $r^8 - 2r^4s^4 + s^8$
51. $a^2 + 2ac + c^2 - b^2 - 2bd - d^2$
52. $16x^4 + 4x^2y^2 + y^4$
53. $y^{3+3n}z^{n+3} - 4y^4z^{3n}$

Mixed Review

54. x^3y^2
55. $(2c)^{-3}$
56. $xy^5b^2a^{-2}$
57. m^{-1}
58. t
59. $-8x^{3+a}y^8$
60. 1.5×10^{-1}
61. $3y^2|y|$
62. $-3(c + 1)$
63. \$1600 + \$0.18 per mile

B

Multiply.

29. $\left(\frac{1}{2}x^2 - \frac{3}{5}y\right)^2$
30. $\left(\frac{1}{4}x^2 - \frac{2}{3}y\right)^2$
31. $(0.5x + 0.7y^2)^2$
32. $(0.3x + 0.8y^2)^2$
33. $(2x + 3y + 4)(2x + 3y - 4)$
34. $(x^2 + 3y + y^2)(x^2 + 3y - y^2)$
35. $(x + 1)(x - 1)(x^2 + 1)$
36. $(y - 2)(y + 2)(y^2 + 4)$
37. $(2x + y)(2x - y)(4x^2 + y^2)$
38. $(5x + y)(5x - y)(25x^2 + y^2)$
39. $[4x(x - 1)]^2$
40. $\left(3x^3 - \frac{5}{11}\right)^2$
41. $(x^a + y^b)(x^a - y^b)(x^{2a} + y^{2b})$
42. $(x^{a-b})^{a+b}$
43. The amount to which \$1000 will grow in b years, when the interest rate (r), compounded annually, is given by the polynomial function A.

$$A(r) = \$1000(1 + r)^b$$

a. Find the amount to which \$1000 will grow in 2 years at 17%.
b. Find the amount to which \$1000 will grow in 3 years at 11%.
c. Find the amount to which \$1000 will grow in 4 years at 8%.
d. Find expanded forms of $A(r)$ for $b = 2, 3$, and 4 years.

44. ***Critical Thinking*** The cube of a certain binomial is $8y^3 - 36y^2 + 54y - 27$. Find the binomial. $2y - 3$

Challenge

Multiply.

45. $[(2x - 1)^2 - 1]^2$
46. $[(a + b)(a - b)][5 - (a + b)][5 + (a + b)]$
47. $(x - 1)(x^2 + x + 1)(x^3 + 1)$
48. $[x + y + 1][x^2 - x(y + 1) + (y + 1)^2]$
49. $(y - 1)^3(y + 1)^3$
50. $(r^2 + s^2)^2(r^2 + 2rs + s^2)(r^2 - 2rs + s^2)$
51. $(a - b + c - d)(a + b + c + d)$
52. $(4x^2 + 2xy + y^2)(4x^2 - 2xy + y^2)$
53. $y^3z^n(y^{3n}z^3 - 4yz^{2n})$

Mixed Review

Simplify. 54. $\frac{x^3}{y^{-2}}$ 55. $\frac{1}{8c^3}$ 56. $\frac{xy^5}{a^2b^{-2}}$

57. $m^{-4} \cdot m^3$ 58. $t^2 \cdot t^{-1}$ 59. $(4x^3y^2)(-2x^ay^6)$

60. $(2.5 \times 10^4)(6 \times 10^{-6})$ 61. $|3y^3|$ 62. $3c + 9 + (-6c) - 12$

63. Vicki estimated the cost of operating her car for a year. If she drives 5000 miles, it will cost her \$2500. If she drives 15,000 miles, it will cost her \$4300. Fit a linear function to the data.

5-4 Factoring

Terms with Common Factors

Objective: Factor polynomials with a common factor.

Factoring is the reverse of multiplying. To factor an expression means to write it as an equivalent expression that is a product. When factoring a polynomial, first look for common factors.

EXAMPLE 1 Factor out a common factor.

$$4y^2 - 8 = 4 \cdot y^2 - 4 \cdot 2 \quad \text{4 is a common factor.}$$
$$= 4(y^2 - 2)$$

In some cases there is more than one common factor. In Example 2 below, 5 is a common factor, and x^3 is also a common factor.

EXAMPLES Factor out a common factor.

2. $5x^4 - 20x^3 = 5x^3(x - 4)$
3. $12x^2y - 20x^3y = 4x^2y(3 - 5x)$
4. $10p^6q^2 - 4p^5q^3 + 2p^4q^4 = 2p^4q^2(5p^2 - 2pq + q^2)$

We usually try to factor out all common factors. When we do this we say we have factored the greatest common factor.

Try This Factor out a common factor.

a. $3x^2 - 6x$ $3x(x - 2)$

b. $P + Prt$ $P(1 + rt)$

c. $9y^4 - 15y^3 + 3y^2$ $3y^2(3y^2 - 5y + 1)$

d. $6x^2y - 21x^3y^2 + 3x^2y^3$ $3x^2y(2 - 7xy + y^2)$

Factoring Trinomial Squares

Objective: Identify and factor trinomial squares.

Squares of binomials are also called trinomial squares. They have the form $A^2 + 2AB + B^2$ or $A^2 - 2AB + B^2$. Here are some examples of trinomial squares.

$x^2 + 6x + 9$ This is the square of $x + 3$.

$y^2 - 22y + 121$ This is the square of $y - 11$.

We must first be able to recognize a trinomial square.

5-4

FIRST FIVE MINUTES

1. Multiply $(x + 2)(x + 3)$.
   $x^2 + 5x + 6$
2. Multiply $(2x - 1)(2x + 1)$.
   $4x^2 - 1$
3. Write 105 as the product of prime factors.
   $3 \cdot 5 \cdot 7$

Terms with Common Factors

Point out that the instruction "factor out a common factor" means "factor out *all* the common factors."

Key Question

- Do all polynomials have common factors?
  No, 1 is a trivial factor.

Chalkboard Examples

Factor out a common factor.

1. $3x^2 + 12$
   $3x^2 + 3 \cdot 4 = 3(x^2 + 4)$
2. $7y^3 + 14y^2$
   $7y^2(y + 2)$
3. $6u^2v^3 + 21uv^2$
   $3uv^2(2uv + 7)$
4. $9x^3y^2 - 6x^2y^3 + 3x^3y^3$
   $3x^2y^2(3x - 2y + xy)$

Factoring Trinomial Squares

Emphasize that factoring is the reverse of multiplication. Show this by factoring a polynomial and then multiplying the factors to obtain the original polynomial.

Key Questions

- Is $x^2 + 2x - 1$ a trinomial square?
  No
- Is $4 + 4y + y^2$ a trinomial square?
  Yes

Chalkboard Examples

Factor, if possible.

1. $x^2 - 8x + 16$
   $(x - 4)^2$
2. $x^2 + 8x - 16$
   Not a trinomial square

Identifying Trinomial Squares

For a trinomial to be square, three conditions must be true.

1. Two of the terms must be squares (A^2 and B^2).
2. There must be no minus sign before A^2 or B^2.
3. If we multiply A and B (the square roots of A^2 and B^2) and double the result, we get the remaining term $2 \cdot A \cdot B$, or its additive inverse, $-2 \cdot A \cdot B$.

To factor trinomial squares, we use the following equations.

Factoring Trinomial Squares

$$A^2 + 2AB + B^2 = (A + B)^2$$
$$A^2 - 2AB + B^2 = (A - B)^2$$

EXAMPLES Factor as a trinomial square, if possible.

5. $x^2 - 10x + 25 = (x - 5)^2$

6. $16y^2 + 49 + 56y = 16y^2 + 56y + 49$ Rearranging terms
$= (4y + 7)^2$

7. $-20xy + 4y^2 + 25x^2 = 4y^2 - 20xy + 25x^2$ Rearranging terms
$= (2y - 5x)^2$

8. $36y^2 + 42y + 49$ Not a trinomial square, since $2AB$ is $2 \cdot 6y \cdot 7$, or $84y$

Try This Factor as a trinomial square, if possible.

e. $x^2 + 14x + 49$ $(x + 7)^2$

f. $9y^2 + 25 - 30y$ $(3y - 5)^2$

g. $72xy + 16x^2 + 81y^2$ $(9y + 4x)^2$

h. $100x^2 + 10xy + y^2$ Not a trinomial square

Trinomial squares also occur in higher-degree polynomials.

EXAMPLES Factor.

9. $25x^4 + 70x^2y^3 + 49y^6 = (5x^2 + 7y^3)^2$

10. $-4y^2 - 144y^8 + 48y^5 = -4y^2(1 - 12y^3 + 36y^6)$ Removing a common factor first
$= -4y^2(1 - 6y^3)^2$

Try This Factor.

i. $16x^4 - 40x^2y^3 + 25y^6$ $(4x^2 - 5y^3)^2$

j. $24a^2b^2 - 8a^4 - 18b^4 - 2(2a^2 - 3b^2)^2$ $-4(2a^2 - 3b^2)^2$

k. $-12x^4y^2 + 60x^2y^5 - 75y^8$ $-3y^2(2x^2 - 5y^3)^2$

Differences of Squares

Objective: Factor differences of two squares.

To factor a difference of squares, we reverse the procedure for multiplying a sum and difference of two expressions.

Factoring Differences of Squares

$$A^2 - B^2 = (A + B)(A - B)$$

To factor the difference of two squares, write the square root of the first expression *plus* the square root of the second, times the square root of the first *minus* the square root of the second.

EXAMPLE 11 Factor $x^2 - 9$.

$$x^2 - 9 = x^2 - 3^2$$
$$= (x + 3)(x - 3)$$

EXAMPLE 12 Factor $25y^6 - 49x^2$.

$$A^2 \quad - \quad B^2 \quad = \quad (A \; + \; B) \; (A \; - \; B)$$
$$(5y^3)^2 - (7x)^2 = (5y^3 + 7x)(5y^3 - 7x)$$

Try This Factor.

l. $y^2 - 4$ $(y + 2)(y - 2)$

m. $49x^4 - 25y^{10}$ $(7x^2 + 5y^5)(7x^2 - 5y^5)$

n. $36x^4 - 16y^6$ $(6x^2 + 4y^3)(6x^2 - 4y^3)$

A difference of two squares can have more than two terms.

EXAMPLE 13 Factor.

$$x^2 + 6x + 9 - 25y^2 = (x^2 + 6x + 9) - 25y^2$$
$$= (x + 3)^2 - (5y)^2$$

This is now a difference of two squares, one of which is a square of a binomial. When we factor, we get

$$(x + 3 + 5y)(x + 3 - 5y)$$

Try This Factor.

o. $x^2 + 2x + 1 - p^2$ $(x + 1 + p)(x + 1 - p)$

p. $64 - (x^2 + 8x + 16)$ $(12 + x)(4 - x)$

Differences of Squares

Avoiding Common Errors

Many students will try to factor $(a + b)^2$ into $(a + b)(a - b)$. Point out that $(a + b)^2$ is completely factored already. $(a + b)^2 = (a + b)(a + b)$

Chalkboard Examples

Factor.

1. $x^2 - 25$
   $x^2 - 5^2 = (x + 5)(x - 5)$
2. $9x^2 - 16y^2$
   $(3x)^2 - (4y)^2$
   $= (3x + 4y)(3x - 4y)$
3. $x^2 + 2x + 1 - y^2$
   $(x + 1)^2 - y^2$
   $= (x + 1 + y)(x + 1 - y)$

Factoring by Grouping

Note that factoring by grouping is used to factor a polynomial with four terms only if a true proportion can be set up among the four coefficients. For example, in Example 14,

$\frac{4}{-3} = \frac{20}{-15}$, or $\frac{4}{20} = \frac{-3}{-15}$

Chalkboard Examples

Factor.

1. $x^2 + 3x + 2x + 6$
   $x(x + 3) + 2(x + 3)$
   $= (x + 2)(x + 3)$
2. $ac + ad + bc + bd$
   $a(c + d) + b(c + d)$
   $= (a + b)(c + d)$

LESSON QUIZ

Factor.

1. $x^3 + 3x$
   $x(x^2 + 3)$
2. $4x^2 + 6xy + 8xy^2$
   $2x(2x + 3y + 4y^2)$
3. $4a^2 - 12ab + 9b^2$
   $(2a - 3b)^2$
4. $ax - 3a + bx - 3b$
   $(a + b)(x - 3)$
5. $c^2 - 8c + 16 - d^2$
   $(c - 4 + d)(c - 4 - d)$

Assignment Guide

Algebra: 1 – 63 e/o, MR

Alg w/Finite or Trig: 1–63 m3, 64–69 e/o, 70, MR

Comprehensive: 1–69 m4, 70, 71–81 e/o, MR, assign w. 5-3

ADDITIONAL ANSWERS

Exercises

1. $y(y - 5)$
2. $2a(2a + 1)$
3. $3y(2y + 1)$
4. $y^2(y + 9)$
5. $x^2(x + 8)$
6. $3(y^2 - y - 3)$
7. $5(x^2 - x + 3)$
8. $3x^2(2 - x^2)$
9. $4y^2(2 + y^2)$
10. $2a(2b - 3c + 6d)$
11. $2x(4y + 5z - 7w)$
12. $4xy(x - 3y)$
13. $5x^2y^2(y + 3x)$
14. $x^2(x^4 + x^3 - x + 1)$
15. $y(y^3 - y^2 + y + 1)$
16. $12x(2x^2 - 3x + 6)$
17. $5(2a^4 + 3a^2 - 5a - 6)$
18. $(y - 3)^2$

Factoring by Grouping

Objective: Factor a polynomial of four or more terms by grouping.

Sometimes an expression of four or more terms can be grouped in such a way that common factors can be found. The common factor may itself be a binomial.

In the following expression, we note that 4 is a factor of the last two terms and y is a factor of the first two terms.

$$\begin{aligned} y^2 + 3y + 4y + 12 &= (y^2 + 3y) + (4y + 12) \\ &= y(y + 3) + 4(y + 3) \quad \text{Factoring out } y \text{ and } 4 \\ &= (y + 4)(y + 3) \quad \text{Factoring out } y + 3 \end{aligned}$$

EXAMPLES Factor.

14. $$\begin{aligned} 4x^2 - 3x + 20x - 15 &= x(4x - 3) + 5(4x - 3) \quad \text{Factoring out } x \text{ and } 5 \\ &= (x + 5)(4x - 3) \quad \text{Factoring out } 4x - 3 \end{aligned}$$

15. $$\begin{aligned} ax^2 + ay - bx^2 - by &= ax^2 + ay + (-bx^2 - by) \\ &= a(x^2 + y) - b(x^2 + y) \quad \text{Factoring out } a \text{ and } -b \\ &= (a - b)(x^2 + y) \quad \text{Factoring out } x^2 + y \end{aligned}$$

Try This Factor.

q. $x^2 + 5x + 4x + 20$ $(x + 4)(x + 5)$
r. $5y^2 + 2y + 10y + 4$ $(5y + 2)(y + 2)$
s. $px + py - qx - qy$ $(p - q)(x + y)$

5-4 EXERCISES

A

Factor.

1. $y^2 - 5y$
2. $4a^2 + 2a$
3. $6y^2 + 3y$
4. $y^3 + 9y^2$
5. $x^3 + 8x^2$
6. $3y^2 - 3y - 9$
7. $5x^2 - 5x + 15$
8. $6x^2 - 3x^4$
9. $8y^2 + 4y^4$
10. $4ab - 6ac + 12ad$
11. $8xy + 10xz - 14xw$
12. $4x^2y - 12xy^2$
13. $5x^2y^3 + 15x^3y^2$
14. $x^6 + x^5 - x^3 + x^2$
15. $y^4 - y^3 + y^2 + y$
16. $24x^3 - 36x^2 + 72x$
17. $10a^4 + 15a^2 - 25a - 30$
18. $y^2 - 6y + 9$
19. $x^2 - 8x + 16$
20. $x^2 + 14x + 49$
21. $x^2 + 16x + 64$
22. $x^2 + 1 + 2x$
23. $x^2 + 1 - 2x$
24. $a^2 + 4a + 4$
25. $a^2 - 4a + 4$
26. $y^2 + 36 - 12y$
27. $y^2 + 36 + 12y$
28. $-18y^2 + y^3 + 81y$
29. $24a^2 + a^3 + 144a$
30. $12a^2 + 36a + 27$
31. $20y^2 + 100y + 125$
32. $2x^2 - 40x + 200$
33. $32x^2 + 48x + 18$
34. $1 - 8d + 16d^2$
35. $64 + 25y^2 - 80y$

36. $x^2 - 16$ 37. $y^2 - 9$ 38. $9x^2 - 25$ 39. $4a^2 - 49$

40. $4x^2 - 25$ 41. $100y^2 - 81$ 42. $6x^2 - 6y^2$ 43. $8x^2 - 8y^2$

44. $3x^8 - 3y^8$ 45. $5x^4 - 5y^4$ 46. $4xy^4 - 4xz^4$ 47. $9a^4 - a^2b^2$

48. $a^2 + 2ab + b^2 - 9$ 49. $x^2 - 2xy + y^2 - 25$

50. $r^2 - 2r + 1 - 4s^2$ 51. $c^2 + 4cd + 4d^2 - 9p^2$

52. $2m^2 + 4mn + 2n^2 - 50b^2$ 53. $12x^2 + 12x + 3 - 3y^2$

54. $9 - (a^2 + 2ab + b^2)$ 55. $16 - (x^2 - 2xy + y^2)$

56. $ac + ad + bc + bd$ 57. $xy + xz + wy + wz$

58. $b^3 - b^2 + 2b - 2$ 59. $y^3 - y^2 + 3y - 3$

60. $y^2 - 8y - y + 8$ 61. $t^2 + 6t - 2t - 12$

62. $2y^4 + 6y^2 + 5y^2 + 15$ 63. $2xy - x^2y - 6 + 3x$

B

Factor.

64. $\frac{4}{7}x^6 - \frac{6}{7}x^4 + \frac{1}{7}x^2 - \frac{3}{7}x$ 65. $4y^{4a} + 12y^{2a} + 10y^{2a} + 30$

66. $0.25 - y^2$ 67. $0.04x^2 - 0.09y^2$

68. $\frac{1}{25} - x^2$ 69. $\frac{1}{36}y^4 - \frac{1}{81}x^2$

70. ***Critical Thinking*** Find two binomials whose product is a binomial; a trinomial; a four-term polynomial. Answers may vary.

Challenge

Factor. Assume variables in exponents represent positive integers.

71. $a^{16} - 1$ 72. $x^{2a} - y^2$ 73. $y^{32} - 1$

74. $x^2 + ax + bx + ab$ 75. $\frac{1}{4}p^2 - \frac{2}{5}p + \frac{4}{25}$

76. $bdx^2 + adx + bcx + ac$ 77. $-225x + x^3$

78. $\frac{4}{27}r^2 + \frac{5}{9}rs + \frac{1}{12}s^2 - \frac{1}{3}rs$ 79. $9^4x^8 - 16^2y^{16}$

80. $4x^{a+b} + 7x^{a-b}$ (assume $a > b$) 81. $7y^{2a+b} - 5y^{a+b} + 3y^{a+2b}$

Mixed Review

Consider the function $f(x) = -3x + 1$ and find the function values.

82. $f(0)$ 83. $f(-2)$ 84. $f(3)$ 85. $f(-9)$ 86. $f(4)$

Find the slope and y-intercept. 87. $y = -5x + 6$

88. $y = 3x - 1$ 89. $3y = -6x + 9$ 90. $2y = x$

Solve. 91. $-15 - c = 4c$ 92. $14 + a = 3a + 2$ 93. $9m + 4m + 6 = 32$

19. $(x - 4)^2$ 20. $(x + 7)^2$
21. $(x + 8)^2$ 22. $(x + 1)^2$
23. $(x - 1)^2$ 24. $(a + 2)^2$
25. $(a - 2)^2$ 26. $(y - 6)^2$
27. $(y + 6)^2$ 28. $y(y - 9)^2$
29. $a(a + 12)^2$ 30. $3(2a + 3)^2$
31. $5(2y + 5)^2$ 32. $2(x - 10)^2$
33. $2(4x + 3)^2$ 34. $(1 - 4d)^2$
35. $(5y - 8)^2$
36. $(x + 4)(x - 4)$
37. $(y + 3)(y - 3)$
38. $(3x + 5)(3x - 5)$
39. $(2a + 7)(2a - 7)$
40. $(2x + 5)(2x - 5)$
41. $(10y + 9)(10y - 9)$
42. $6(x + y)(x - y)$
43. $8(x + y)(x - y)$
44. $3(x^4 + y^4)(x^2 + y^2)(x + y)(x - y)$
45. $5(x^2 + y^2)(x + y)(x - y)$
46. $4x(y^2 + z^2)(y + z)(y - z)$
47. $a^2(3a + b)(3a - b)$
48. $(a + b + 3)(a + b - 3)$
49. $(x - y - 5)(x - y + 5)$
50. $(r - 1 - 2s)(r - 1 + 2s)$
51. $(c + 2d - 3p)(c + 2d + 3p)$
52. $2(m + n - 5b)(m + n + 5b)$
53. $3(2x + 1 - y)(2x + 1 + y)$
54. $(3 - a - b)(3 + a + b)$
55. $(4 - x + y)(4 + x - y)$
56. $(a + b)(c + d)$
57. $(x + w)(y + z)$
58. $(b^2 + 2)(b - 1)$
59. $(y^2 + 3)(y - 1)$
60. $(y - 1)(y - 8)$
61. $(t - 2)(t + 6)$
62. $(2y^2 + 5)(y^2 + 3)$
63. $(xy - 3)(2 - x)$
64. $\frac{1}{7}x(4x^5 - 6x^3 + x - 3)$
65. $2(2y^{2a} + 5)(y^{2a} + 3)$
66. $(0.5 + y)(0.5 - y)$
67. $(0.2x + 0.3y)(0.2x - 0.3y)$
68. $\left(\frac{1}{5} + x\right)\left(\frac{1}{5} - x\right)$
69. $\left(\frac{1}{6}y^2 + \frac{1}{9}x\right)\left(\frac{1}{6}y^2 - \frac{1}{9}x\right)$

For Exercises 71–81, see Teacher's Answer Section.

Mixed Review

82. 1 83. 7
84. -8 85. 28
86. -11 87. $m = -5, b = 6$
88. $m = 3, b = -1$
89. $m = -2, b = 3$
90. $m = \frac{1}{2}, b = 0$
91. -3
92. 6
93. 2

5-5

FIRST FIVE MINUTES

1. Factor.
   $25c^2 - 16d^2$
   $(5c + 4d)(5c - 4d)$
2. Multiply.
   $(x + 3)(x + 4)$
   $x^2 + 7x + 12$
3. Multiply.
   $(x - 5)(x + 4)$
   $x^2 - x - 20$

EXPLORE

You may wish to have students use their calculators to verify these products.

Factoring Sums or Differences of Two Cubes

Point out that there are some polynomials that are both a difference of cubes and a difference of squares. For example,

$$x^6 - y^6 = (x^2)^3 - (y^2)^3$$
$$= (x^3)^2 - (y^3)^2$$

You may want to have students verify this.

Key Questions

- Calculate $(3 - 5)(9 + 15 + 25)$.
  $(-2)(49) = -98$
- Calculate $3^3 - 5^3$.
  $3^3 - 5^3 = 27 - 125 = -98$
- Calculate $6^3 + 4^3$ mentally, using the equation for the sum of two cubes.
  $(6 + 4)(6^2 - 6 \cdot 4 + 4^2) = 10(36 - 24 + 16) = 10 \cdot 28 = 280$

Chalkboard Example

1. Factor $y^3 - 8$.
   $A = y, B = 2$
   $(y - 2)(y^2 + 2y + 4)$

5-5 More Factoring

Explore

Compute and compare.

$(4 + 5)(4^2 - 4 \cdot 5 + 5^2)$ and $4^3 + 5^3$ $\quad$ $(7 - 3)(7^2 + 7 \cdot 3 + 3^2)$ and $7^3 - 3^3$

$(3x + 2)[(3x)^2 - 3 \cdot 2 + 2^2]$ and $(3x)^3 + 2^3$ $\quad$ $(2y - 9)[(2y)^2 + (2y) \cdot 9 + 9^2]$ and $(2y)^3 - 9^3$

Look for patterns in the factors above.
How can the pattern be used to factor a sum or difference of two cubes?

Factoring Sums or Differences of Two Cubes

Objective: Factor sums or differences of two cubes.

Factoring Sums or Differences of Two Cubes

$$A^3 + B^3 = (A + B)(A^2 - AB + B^2)$$
$$A^3 - B^3 = (A - B)(A^2 + AB + B^2)$$

EXAMPLE 1 Factor.

$$x^3 + 125 = x^3 + 5^3$$

In one set of parentheses we write the cube root of the first term, which is x. Then we write the cube root of the second term, which is 5. This gives us the expression $x + 5$.

$$(x + 5)(\qquad\qquad)$$

To get the next factor, we do the following.

1. Square the first term: x^2.
2. Multiply the terms and then change the sign: $-5x$.
3. Square the second term: 25.

$$(x + 5)(x^2 - 5x + 25)$$

Note that we cannot factor $x^2 - 5x + 25$. A polynomial that cannot be factored is called a prime polynomial. The factors $x + 5$ and $x^2 - 5x + 25$ are prime factors, since neither can be factored.

Try This Factor.

a. $1000x^3 + 1$ $(10x + 1)(100x^2 - 10x + 1)$ $\quad$ **b.** $y^3 + 64x^3$ $(y + 4x)(y^2 - 4xy + 16x^2)$

We can treat a difference of cubes as a sum in order to factor sums and differences of cubes using the same method.

EXAMPLE 2 Factor.

$$x^3 - 27y^3 = x^3 + (-3y)^3 \qquad A \text{ is } x,\ B \text{ is } -3y.$$
$$(A + B)(A^2 - AB + B^2)$$
$$= (x - 3y)(x^2 + 3xy + 9y^2)$$

Try This Factor.

c. $x^3 - 8$ $(x - 2)(x^2 + 2x + 4)$ **d.** $-8x^3 + 27y^3$ $(3y - 2x)(9y^2 + 6xy + 4x^2)$

Factoring Trinomials of the Type $x^2 + bx + c$

Objective: Factor trinomials of the type $x^2 + bx + c$.

Consider this product.

$$\begin{aligned} & \quad\ \ \text{F} \quad \text{O} \quad \text{I} \quad \text{L} \\ (x + 3)(x + 5) &= x^2 + 5x + 3x + 15 \\ &= x^2 + 8x + 15 \end{aligned}$$

Note that the coefficient 8 is the sum of 3 and 5, and that the constant term 15 is the product of 3 and 5.

In general, $(x + A)(x + B) = x^2 + (A + B)x + AB$. To factor we can use this equation in reverse.

$$x^2 + (A + B)x + AB = (x + A)(x + B)$$

EXAMPLE 3 Factor $x^2 - 3x - 10$.

We look for pairs of integers whose product is -10 and whose sum is -3.

Pairs of factors	Sum of factors
$-2,\ 5$	3
$2,\ -5$	-3
$10,\ -1$	9
$-10,\ 1$	-9

The desired integers are 2 and -5.

$$x^2 - 3x - 10 = (x + 2)(x - 5)$$

We can check by multiplying.

$$\begin{aligned} (x + 2)(x - 5) &= x^2 - 5x + 2x - 10 \\ &= x^2 - 3x - 10 \end{aligned}$$

Try This Factor.

e. $x^2 + 5x - 14$ $(x + 7)(x - 2)$ **f.** $x^2 + 21 - 10x$ $(x - 7)(x - 3)$

g. $y^2 - y - 2$ $(y - 2)(y + 1)$ **h.** $y^2 + 18y + 32$ $(y + 16)(y + 2)$

Factoring Trinomials of the Type $x^2 + bx + c$

You may want students to "guess and check" the correct factors rather than make a table and then exhaust the possibilities.

Stress that multiplication serves as a quick check.

Key Questions

- What pairs of factors would you check in order to factor $x^2 - 16x + 63$?
  -1 and -63, -3 and -21, -7 and -9
- In the trinomial $x^2 + bx + c$, if c is negative, will the factors have the same sign or opposite signs?
  Opposite signs
- In the trinomial $x^2 + bx + c$, if c is positive, will the factors have the same sign or opposite signs?
  The same sign

Chalkboard Example

Factor.

1. $x^2 + 14x + 45$
   The pairs of factors are
   1, 45
   5, 9
   3, 15
   Only 5 and 9 have the correct sum of 14.
   $(x + 5)(x + 9)$

Factoring Trinomials of the Type $ax^2 + bx + c$

Emphasize that all common factors should be factored out before attempting to factor the polynomial.

Note that in Example 4 we ignored the negative pairs -6 and -1, and -2 and -3, when we looked for pairs of numbers whose product is 6.

It should be noted that although we usually use positive pairs, the negative factors also lead to a factorization.

$(6x^2 + 17x + 7)$

$= (-2x - 1)(-3x - 7)$

See Exercise 106 for a further consideration of this topic.

Chalkboard Example

1. Factor $8x^2 - 2x - 15$.
   The factors of 8 are 1, 8; 2, 4.
   The factors of -15 are $-1, 15; -3, 5; 1, -15; 3, -5$.
   By substituting and multiplying, we find $8x^2 - 2x - 15 = (2x - 3)(4x + 5)$

LESSON QUIZ

Factor.

1. $x^2 + 9x + 20$
   $(x + 4)(x + 5)$
2. $10ax^2 + 20ax + 10a$
   $10a(x + 1)^2$
3. $6a^2 - ab - 2b^2$
   $(2a + b)(3a - 2b)$
4. $x^3 - 1$
   $(x - 1)(x^2 + x + 1)$

Assignment Guide

Algebra: Day 1: 1–36 e/o, MR
Day 2: 37–72 e/o

Alg w/Finite or Trig: 1–72 m4, 73–92 e/o, 93, MR

Comprehensive: 1–92 m4, 93, 94–106 m4, MR, assign w. 5-6

Factoring Trinomials of the Type $ax^2 + bx + c$

Objective: Factor trinomials of the type $ax^2 + bx + c$.

In the trinomial $ax^2 + bx + c$, the x^2 term has a coefficient other than 1.

$$\begin{aligned} & \quad\quad\quad\;\; \text{F} \quad\;\; \text{O} \quad\;\; \text{I} \quad\; \text{L} \\ (2x + 3)(5x + 4) &= 10x^2 + 8x + 15x + 12 \\ &= 10x^2 + 23x + 12 \end{aligned}$$

Factoring Trinomials

To factor $ax^2 + bx + c$ we look for binomials

$$(\_\_\_\_x + \_\_\_\_)(\_\_\_\_x + \_\_\_\_)$$

where products of numbers in the blanks are as follows.

1. The numbers in the *first* blanks have the product a.
2. The product of the numbers in the *outside* blanks and the product of the numbers in the *inside* blanks have a sum of b.
3. The numbers in the *last* blanks have the product c.

EXAMPLE 4 Factor $12x^2 + 34x + 14$.

We first note that the number 2 is a common factor, so we factor it out.

$$2(6x^2 + 17x + 7)$$

Now we consider $6x^2 + 17x + 7$. We first look for pairs of numbers whose product is 6. The positive numbers are 6, 1 and 2, 3. We then have these possibilities.

$$(6x + \_\_\_\_)(x + \_\_\_\_) \text{ or } (2x + \_\_\_\_)(3x + \_\_\_\_)$$

Next we look for pairs of numbers whose product is 7. The pairs are 7, 1 and $-7, -1$. By substituting and multiplying we find that

$$12x^2 + 34x + 14 = 2(2x + 1)(3x + 7)$$

EXAMPLE 5 Factor $x^2y^2 + 5xy + 4$.

In this case, we treat xy as if it were a single variable.

$$\begin{aligned} x^2y^2 + 5xy + 4 &= (xy)^2 + (4 + 1)xy + 4 \cdot 1 \\ &= (xy + 4)(xy + 1) \end{aligned}$$

Try This Factor.

i. $3x^2 + 5x + 2$ $(3x + 2)(x + 1)$

j. $4x^2 - 3 + 4x$ $(2x + 3)(2x - 1)$

k. $24y^2 - 46y + 10$ $2(4y - 1)(3y - 5)$

l. $2x^4y^6 - 3x^2y^3 - 20$ $(2x^2y^3 + 5)(x^2y^3 - 4)$

5-5 EXERCISES

A

Factor.

1. $x^3 + 8$ **2.** $c^3 + 27$ **3.** $y^3 - 64$

4. $z^3 - 1$ **5.** $w^3 + 1$ **6.** $x^3 + 125$

7. $8a^3 + 1$ **8.** $27x^3 + 1$ **9.** $y^3 - 8$

10. $p^3 - 27$ **11.** $8 - 27b^3$ **12.** $64 - 125x^3$

13. $64y^3 + 1$ **14.** $125x^3 + 1$ **15.** $343x^3 + 27$

16. $27y^3 + 64$ **17.** $a^3 - b^3$ **18.** $x^3 - y^3$

19. $a^3 + \frac{1}{8}b^3$ **20.** $b^3 + \frac{1}{27}a^3$ **21.** $8x^3 - 27y^3$

22. $x^2 + 9x + 20$ **23.** $y^2 + 8y + 15$ **24.** $y^2 - 8y + 16$

25. $a^2 - 10a + 25$ **26.** $x^2 - 27 - 6x$ **27.** $t^2 - 15 - 2t$

28. $m^2 - 3m - 28$ **29.** $x^2 - 2x - 8$ **30.** $14x + x^2 + 45$

31. $12y + y^2 + 32$ **32.** $y^2 + 2y - 63$ **33.** $x^2 + 3x - 40$

34. $t^2 - 11t + 28$ **35.** $y^2 - 14y + 45$ **36.** $3x + x^2 - 10$

37. $x + x^2 - 6$ **38.** $x^2 + 5x + 6$ **39.** $y^2 + 8y + 7$

40. $32 + 4y - y^2$ **41.** $56 + x - x^2$ **42.** $15 + t^2 + 8t$

43. $3b^2 + 8b + 4$ **44.** $9x^2 + 15x + 4$ **45.** $6y^2 - y - 2$

46. $3a^2 - a - 4$ **47.** $-7a + 6a^2 - 10$ **48.** $-35z + 12z^2 - 3$

49. $9a^2 + 6a - 8$ **50.** $4t^2 + 4t - 15$ **51.** $3x^2 - 16x - 12$

52. $6x^2 - 5x - 25$ **53.** $6x^2 - 15 - x$ **54.** $10y^2 - 12 - 7y$

55. $3a^2 - 10a + 8$ **56.** $12a^2 - 7a + 1$ **57.** $35y^2 + 34y + 8$

58. $9a^2 + 18a + 8$ **59.** $2t + 5t^2 - 3$ **60.** $4x + 15x^2 - 3$

61. $8x^2 - 16 - 28x$ **62.** $18x^2 - 24 - 6x$ **63.** $3x^3 - 5x^2 - 2x$

64. $18y^3 - 3y^2 - 10y$ **65.** $24x^2 - 2 - 47x$ **66.** $15y^2 - 10 - 19y$

67. $21x^2 + 37x + 12$ **68.** $10y^2 + 23y + 12$ **69.** $17x + 40x^2 - 12$

70. $2y + 24y^2 - 15$ **71.** $12a^2 - 17a + 6$ **72.** $20a^2 - 23a + 6$

B

Factor.

73. $x^4 + 11x^2 - 80$ **74.** $y^4 + 5y^2 - 84$ **75.** $x^2 - \frac{4}{25} + \frac{3}{5}x$

76. $y^2 - \frac{8}{49} + \frac{2}{7}y$ **77.** $y^2 + 0.4y - 0.05$ **78.** $t^2 + 0.6t - 0.27$

79. $2x^2 + xy - 6y^2$ **80.** $2m^2 + mn - 10n^2$ **81.** $-6xy + 8x^2 - 9y^2$

82. $-7ts + 2t^2 - 4s^2$ **83.** $7a^2b^2 + 6 + 13ab$ **84.** $9x^2y^2 - 4 + 5xy$

85. $rs^3 + 64r$ **86.** $ab^3 + 125a$ **87.** $5x^3 - 40z^3$

88. $2y^3 - 54z^3$ **89.** $x^3 + 0.001$ **90.** $y^3 + 0.125$

91. $64x^6 - 8t^6$ **92.** $125c^6 - 8d^6$

ADDITIONAL ANSWERS

1. $(x + 2)(x^2 - 2x + 4)$
2. $(c + 3)(c^2 - 3c + 9)$
3. $(y - 4)(y^2 + 4y + 16)$
4. $(z - 1)(z^2 + z + 1)$
5. $(w + 1)(w^2 - w + 1)$
6. $(x + 5)(x^2 - 5x + 25)$
7. $(2a + 1)(4a^2 - 2a + 1)$
8. $(3x + 1)(9x^2 - 3x + 1)$
9. $(y - 2)(y^2 + 2y + 4)$
10. $(p - 3)(p^2 + 3p + 9)$
11. $(2 - 3b)(4 + 6b + 9b^2)$
12. $(4 - 5x)(16 + 20x + 25x^2)$
13. $(4y + 1)(16y^2 - 4y + 1)$
14. $(5x + 1)(25x^2 - 5x + 1)$
15. $(7x + 3)(49x^2 - 21x + 9)$
16. $(3y + 4)(9y^2 - 12y + 16)$
17. $(a - b)(a^2 + ab + b^2)$
18. $(x - y)(x^2 + xy + y^2)$
19. $\left(a + \frac{1}{2}b\right)\left(a^2 - \frac{1}{2}ab + \frac{1}{4}b^2\right)$
20. $\left(b + \frac{1}{3}a\right)\left(b^2 - \frac{1}{3}ab + \frac{1}{3}a^2\right)$
21. $(2x - 3y)(4x^2 + 6xy + 9y^2)$
22. $(x + 5)(x + 4)$
23. $(y + 5)(y + 3)$
24. $(y - 4)^2$
25. $(a - 5)^2$
26. $(x - 9)(x + 3)$
27. $(t - 5)(t + 3)$
28. $(m - 7)(m + 4)$
29. $(x - 4)(x + 2)$
30. $(x + 9)(x + 5)$
31. $(y + 8)(y + 4)$
32. $(y + 9)(y - 7)$
33. $(x + 8)(x - 5)$
34. $(t - 7)(t - 4)$
35. $(y - 5)(y - 9)$
36. $(x + 5)(x - 2)$
37. $(x + 3)(x - 2)$
38. $(x + 2)(x + 3)$
39. $(y + 7)(y + 1)$
40. $(8 - y)(4 + y)$
41. $(8 - x)(7 + x)$
42. $(t + 5)(t + 3)$
43. $(3b + 2)(b + 2)$
44. $(3x + 1)(3x + 4)$
45. $(3y - 2)(2y + 1)$
46. $(3a - 4)(a + 1)$
47. $(6a + 5)(a - 2)$
48. $(12z + 1)(z - 3)$
49. $(3a + 4)(3a - 2)$
50. $(2t + 5)(2t - 3)$
51. $(3x + 2)(x - 6)$
52. $(3x + 5)(2x - 5)$
53. $(3x - 5)(2x + 3)$
54. $(5y + 4)(2y - 3)$
55. $(3a - 4)(a - 2)$
56. $(4a - 1)(3a - 1)$
57. $(5y + 2)(7y + 4)$

58. $(3a + 2)(3a + 4)$
59. $(5t - 3)(t + 1)$
60. $(5x + 3)(3x - 1)$
61. $4(2x + 1)(x - 4)$
62. $6(3x - 4)(x + 1)$
63. $x(3x + 1)(x - 2)$
64. $y(6y - 5)(3y + 2)$
65. $(24x + 1)(x - 2)$
66. $(5y + 2)(3y - 5)$
67. $(7x + 3)(3x + 4)$
68. $(5y + 4)(2y + 3)$
69. $(5x + 4)(8x - 3)$
70. $(6y + 5)(4y - 3)$
71. $(4a - 3)(3a - 2)$
72. $(4a - 3)(5a - 2)$
73. $(x^2 + 16)(x^2 - 5)$
74. $(y^2 + 12)(y^2 - 7)$
75. $\left(x + \frac{4}{5}\right)\left(x - \frac{1}{5}\right)$
76. $\left(y + \frac{4}{7}\right)\left(y - \frac{2}{7}\right)$
77. $(y - 0.1)(y + 0.5)$
78. $(t + 0.9)(t - 0.3)$
79. $(2x - 3y)(x + 2y)$
80. $(2m + 5n)(m - 2n)$
81. $(2x - 3y)(4x + 3y)$
82. $(2t + s)(t - 4s)$
83. $(7ab + 6)(ab + 1)$
84. $(9xy - 4)(xy + 1)$
85. $r(s + 4)(s^2 - 4s + 16)$
86. $a(b + 5)(b^2 - 5b + 25)$
87. $5(x - 2z)(x^2 + 2xz + 4z^2)$
88. $2(y - 3z)(y^2 + 3yz + 9z^2)$
89. $(x + 0.1)(x^2 - 0.1x + 0.01)$
90. $(y + 0.5)(y^2 - 0.5y + 0.25)$
91. $8(2x^2 - t^2)(4x^4 + 2x^2t^2 + t^4)$
92. $(5c^2 - 2d^2)(25c^4 + 10c^2d^2 + 4d^4)$
93. The cube has volume a^3, the missing piece has volume b^3, so the figure has volume $a^3 - b^3$. The large piece has volume $(a - b)a^2$, the piece below it $(a - b)ab$, the small piece $(a - b)b^2$. Adding the three gives $(a - b)(a^2 + ab + b^2)$. Thus $a^3 - b^3 = (a - b)(a^2 + ab + b^2)$.

For Exercises 94–106, see Teacher's Answer Section.

Mixed Review

107. $(2, 8, -1)$
108. $(1, -3, 5)$
109. $y = -2x + 3$
110. $y = -x + 1$
111. $y = 2x + 4$
112. 2×10^{-1}
113. $285

93. ***Critical Thinking*** Use the model to verify that $a^3 - b^3 = (a - b)(a^2 + ab + b^2)$.

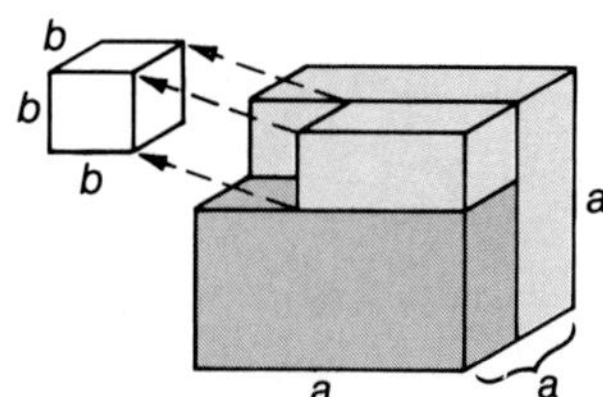

Challenge

Factor. Assume variables in exponents represent positive integers.

94. $3x^2 + 12x - 495$
95. $x^{6a} + y^{3b}$
96. $4y^3 - 96y^2 + 576y$
97. $3xy^2 - 150xy + 1875x$
98. $a^3x^3 - b^3y^3$
99. $12x^2 - 72xy + 108y^2$
100. $15t^3 - 60t^2 - 315t$
101. $216x + 78x^2 + 6x^3$
102. $x^{2a} + 5x^a - 24$
103. $\frac{8}{27}x^3 + \frac{1}{64}y^3$
104. $4x^{2a} - 4x^a - 3$
105. $\frac{1}{16}x^{3a} + \frac{1}{2}y^{6a}z^{9b}$

106. Factor $8x^2 - 10x - 3$. Then show why it is unnecessary to find the negative factors of 8.

Mixed Review

Solve these systems.

107. $x - y - z = -5$
$3y + 2z = 22$
$3x - 2y - 3z = -7$

108. $4a = 2c - 6$
$3a + 3b + c = -1$
$2(a - b) = c + 3$

Write an equation of the line containing the given point and perpendicular to the given line. **109.** $(0, 3)$; $2x - 4y = 12$

Find the equation of the line containing the given point with the indicated slope.

110. $(3, -2)$; $m = -1$ **111.** $(0, 4)$; $m = 2$

112. Estimate. $\dfrac{(3.7 \times 10^{-7})(4.1 \times 10^4)}{7.7 \times 10^{-2}}$

113. Yetta has dental insurance that pays 80% of all fees during the year after the first $75 deductible. Yetta's insurance company paid $168 of her dental fees this year. How much were her dental fees altogether?

WRITING TO LEARN

In your own words, write a step-by-step set of instructions that tells how to factor the sum or difference of two cubes.

Answers may vary. For formulas see page 224.

5-6 Factoring: A General Strategy

Objective: Factor polynomials using any of the methods learned previously.

The following guidelines summarize the factoring procedures we have studied so far.

Guidelines for Factoring

A. Always look first for a common factor.

B. Consider the number of terms.

Two terms

Try factoring as a difference of two squares, or a sum or difference of two cubes.

Three terms

Is it a trinomial square? If so, factor as a square of a binomial. If not, test the factors of the terms.

More than three terms

1. Try grouping.
2. Try differences of squares again.

C. Factor completely. Make sure that each remaining factor is prime.

EXAMPLES Factor.

1. $10a^2x - 40b^2x$

A. We look first for a common factor: $10x(a^2 - 4b^2)$.

B. The factor $a^2 - 4b^2$ has only two terms. It is a difference of squares. We factor it: $10x(a + 2b)(a - 2b)$.

C. Have we factored completely? Yes, because each factor with more than one term is prime.

2. $x^6 - y^6$

A. We look for a common factor. There isn't one.

B. There are only two terms. It is a difference of squares: $(x^3)^2 - (y^3)^2$. We factor it: $(x^3 + y^3)(x^3 - y^3)$.

One factor is a sum of two cubes, and the other factor is a difference of two cubes. We factor them.

$$(x + y)(x^2 - xy + y^2)(x - y)(x^2 + xy + y^2)$$

C. We have factored completely because each factor is prime.

5-6

FIRST FIVE MINUTES

Factor.

1. $3x^3 + 6x^2$
   $3x^2(x + 2)$
2. $a^2 - b^2$
   $(a + b)(a - b)$
3. $u^3 - v^3$
   $(u - v)(u^2 + uv + v^2)$
4. $x^2 + 8x + 16$
   $(x + 4)^2$

This lesson serves as an excellent review of factoring. However, its purpose is to diagnose students' abilities in selecting the correct method of factoring.

Key Questions

- If a polynomial is a candidate for factorization as a difference of squares, how many terms does it have?
  2
- How many terms does a trinomial square have?
  3

Chalkboard Examples

Factor.

1. $5ux^2 - 20uy^2$
   $= 5u(x^2 - 4y^2)$
   $= 5u(x + 2y)(x - 2y)$
2. $x^6 + y^6$
   $= (x^2)^3 + (y^2)^3$
   $= (x^2 + y^2)[(x^2)^2 - x^2y^2 + (y^2)^2]$
   $= (x^2 + y^2)(x^4 - x^2y^2 + y^4)$
3. $12x^2y^3 - 27x^2y$
   $= 3x^2y(4y^2 - 9)$
   $= 3x^2y(2y - 3)(2y + 3)$
4. $8au^2 + 24au + 18a$
   $= 2a(4u^2 + 12u + 9)$
   $= 2a(2u + 3)^2$
5. $2a^2 - 18a + 36$
   $= 2(a^2 - 9a + 18)$
   $= 2(a - 3)(a - 6)$
6. $5ac + 5ad + 5bc + 5bd$
   $= 5(ac + ad + bc + bd)$
   $= 5(a(c + d) + b(c + d))$
   $= 5(a + b)(c + d)$
7. $x^2 + 2x + 1 - y^2 - 2y - 1$
   $= (x + 1)^2 - (y + 1)^2$
   $= [(x + 1) + (y + 1)]\cdot$
   $[(x + 1) - (y + 1)]$
   $= (x + y + 2)(x - y)$
8. $ax^3 - ay^3 - bx^3 + by^3$
   $= a(x^3 - y^3) - b(x^3 - y^3)$
   $= (a - b)(x^3 - y^3)$
   $= (a - b)(x - y)(x^2 + xy + y^2)$

LESSON QUIZ

Factor completely.

1. $a^2 - 64$
   $(a - 8)(a + 8)$
2. $x^2 + 81 - 18x$
   $(x - 9)^2$
3. $2xy^2 - 8x^3$
   $2x(y + 2x)(y - 2x)$
4. $24x^3 + 3y^3$
   $3(2x + y)(4x^2 - 2xy + y^2)$
5. $3ef - 6fg + 4de - 8dg$
   $(3f + 4d)(e - 2g)$
6. $10m^2 - 7mn - 12n^2$
   $(2m - 3n)(5m + 4n)$

Assignment Guide

Algebra: Day 1: 1 – 20 e/o, MR
Day 2: 21 – 41 e/o

Alg w/Finite or Trig: 1–41 m3, 42–47 e/o, 48, MR

Comprehensive: 1–47 m4, 48, 49–53 e/o, MR, assign w. 5-5

ADDITIONAL ANSWERS

Try This

a. $2(1 + 4x^2)(1 + 2x)(1 - 2x)$
b. $7(a + 1)(a - 1)(a^2 - a + 1)(a^2 + a + 1)$
c. $(3 + x)(4 + x)$
d. $(c - d + t + 4)(c - d - t - 4)$
e. $5(y^4 + 4x^6)$
f. $3(2x + 3)(x - 2)$
g. $(a + b)(a - b)^2$
h. $3(x + 3a)^2$
i. $(a + b - c)(a + b + c)$

3. $10x^6 + 40y^2$

$$10x^6 + 40y^2 = 10(x^6 + 4y^2) \quad \text{Removing the largest common factor}$$

In the parentheses there are two terms, a sum of squares, that cannot be factored.

4. $2x^2 + 50a^2 - 20ax$

$$\begin{aligned} 2x^2 + 50a^2 - 20ax &= 2(x^2 - 10ax + 25a^2) \\ &= 2(x - 5a)^2 \end{aligned}$$

Removing the common factor and arranging; the trinomial is a square.

No factor with more than one term is factorable.

5. $6x^2 - 20x - 16$

$$6x^2 - 20x - 16 = 2(3x^2 - 10x - 8) \quad \text{Removing the largest common factor}$$

The trinomial is not a square. We factor by testing factors of 3 and -8.

$$= 2(x - 4)(3x + 2)$$

We cannot factor further.

6. $y^2 - 9a^2 + 12y + 36$

There is no common factor (other than 1 or -1). There are four terms. Grouping to remove a common binomial factor is not possible. We try grouping as a difference of squares.

$$\begin{aligned} y^2 - 9a^2 + 12y + 36 &= (y^2 + 12y + 36) - 9a^2 && \text{Grouping} \\ &= (y + 6)^2 - 9a^2 && \text{Factoring a trinomial square} \\ &= (y + 6 + 3a)(y + 6 - 3a) && \text{Factoring the difference of squares} \end{aligned}$$

Each factor is prime, so we have factored completely.

7. $x^3 - xy^2 + x^2y - y^3$

There is no common factor (other than 1 or -1). There are four terms. We try grouping to remove a common binomial factor.

$$\begin{aligned} x^3 - xy^2 + x^2y - y^3 &= x(x^2 - y^2) + y(x^2 - y^2) && \text{Factoring two grouped binomials} \\ &= (x + y)(x^2 - y^2) \\ &= (x + y)(x + y)(x - y) && \text{Factoring the difference of squares} \\ &= (x + y)^2(x - y) && \text{Simplifying} \end{aligned}$$

Each factor is prime, so we have factored completely.

Try This Factor completely. See Additional Answers.

a. $2 - 32x^4$ **b.** $7a^6 - 7$ **c.** $3x + 12 + 4x + x^2$
d. $c^2 - 2cd + d^2 - t^2 - 8t - 16$ **e.** $5y^4 + 20x^6$
f. $6x^2 - 3x - 18$ **g.** $a^3 - ab^2 - a^2b + b^3$
h. $3x^2 + 18ax + 27a^2$ **i.** $a^2 + 2ab + b^2 - c^2$

5-6 EXERCISES

A

Factor completely. Remember to look first for a common factor.

1. $x^2 - 144$ **2.** $2x^2 + 11x + 12$ **3.** $3x^4 - 12$

4. $2xy^2 - 50x$ **5.** $a^2 + 25 + 10a$ **6.** $p^2 + 64 + 16p$

7. $2x^2 - 10x - 132$ **8.** $3y^2 - 15y - 252$ **9.** $9x^2 - 25y^2$

10. $16a^2 - 81b^2$ **11.** $4c^2 - 4cd + d^2$ **12.** $70b^2 - 3ab - a^2$

13. $-7x^2 + 2x^3 + 4x - 14$ **14.** $9m^2 + 3m^3 + 8m + 24$

15. $4x^2 - 27x + 45$ **16.** $3y^2 + 15y - 42$

17. $8m^3 + m^6 - 20$ **18.** $-37x^2 + x^4 + 36$

19. $ac + cd - ab - bd$ **20.** $xw - yw + xz - yz$

21. $m^6 - 1$ **22.** $64t^6 - 1$ **23.** $x^2 + 6x - y^2 + 9$

24. $t^2 + 10t - p^2 + 25$ **25.** $36y^2 - 35 + 12y$ **26.** $2b - 28a^2b + 10ab$

27. $a^8 - b^8$ **28.** $2x^4 - 32$ **29.** $8p^3 + 27q^3$

30. $125x^3 + 64y^3$ **31.** $64p^3 - 1$ **32.** $8y^3 - 125$

33. $a^3b - 16ab^3$ **34.** $x^3y - 25xy^3$ **35.** $-23xy + 20x^2y^2 + 6$

36. $42ab + 27a^2b^2 + 8$ **37.** $2x^3 + 6x^2 - 8x - 24$ **38.** $3x^3 + 6x^2 - 27x - 54$

39. $250x^3 - 128y^3$ **40.** $27a^3 - 343b^3$ **41.** $16x^3 + 54y^3$

B

Factor.

42. $(x - p)^2 - p^2$ **43.** $30y^4 - 97xy^2 + 60x^2$

44. $5c^{100} - 80d^{100}$ **45.** $3a^2 + 3b^2 - 3c^2 - 3d^2 + 6ab - 6cd$

46. $8(a - 3)^2 - 64(a - 3) + 128$ **47.** $-16 + 17(5 - y^2) - (5 - y^2)^2$

48. ***Critical Thinking*** Factor $x^6 - y^6$ by factoring first as a difference of cubes. How can you use the result of multiplying $(x^2 + xy + y^2)$ by $(x^2 - xy + y^2)$ to help you do this?

Challenge

Factor.

49. $x^6 - 2x^5 + x^4 - x^2 + 2x - 1$ **50.** $(y - 1)^4 - (y - 1)^2$

51. $27x^{6s} + 64y^{3t}$ **52.** $c^{2w+1} + 2c^{w+1} + c$ **53.** $24x^{2a} - 6$

Mixed Review

Find an equation of the line containing each pair of points.

54. $(1, 3)$ and $(4, 9)$ **55.** $(-2, 1)$ and $(1, -5)$ **56.** $(3, 11)$ and $(-2, -9)$

Consider the polynomial function $P(x) = 3x^3 - 4x^2 + 2x - 1$.

Find the specified function values. **57.** $P(1)$ **58.** $P(-1)$ **59.** $P(0)$ **60.** $P(m)$

Exercises

1. $(x + 12)(x - 12)$
2. $(2x + 3)(x + 4)$
3. $3(x^2 + 2)(x^2 - 2)$
4. $2x(y + 5)(y - 5)$
5. $(a + 5)^2$
6. $(p + 8)^2$
7. $2(x - 11)(x + 6)$
8. $3(y - 12)(y + 7)$
9. $(3x + 5y)(3x - 5y)$
10. $(4a + 9b)(4a - 9b)$
11. $(2c - d)^2$
12. $(10b + a)(7b - a)$
13. $(x^2 + 2)(2x - 7)$
14. $(3m^2 + 8)(m + 3)$
15. $(4x - 15)(x - 3)$
16. $3(y + 7)(y - 2)$
17. $(m^3 + 10)(m^3 - 2)$
18. $(x + 6)(x - 6)(x + 1)(x - 1)$
19. $(c - b)(a + d)$
20. $(w + z)(x - y)$
21. $(m + 1)(m^2 - m + 1)(m - 1)(m^2 + m + 1)$
22. $(2t + 1)(4t^2 - 2t + 1)(2t - 1)(4t^2 + 2t + 1)$
23. $(x + y + 3)(x - y + 3)$
24. $(t + p + 5)(t - p + 5)$
25. $(6y - 5)(6y + 7)$
26. $-2b(7a + 1)(2a - 1)$
27. $(a^4 + b^4)(a^2 + b^2)(a + b)(a - b)$
28. $2(x^2 + 4)(x + 2)(x - 2)$
29. $(2p + 3q)(4p^2 - 6pq + 9q^2)$
30. $(5x + 4y)(25x^2 - 20xy + 16y^2)$
31. $(4p - 1)(16p^2 + 4p + 1)$
32. $(2y - 5)(4y^2 + 10y + 25)$
33. $ab(a + 4b)(a - 4b)$
34. $xy(x + 5y)(x - 5y)$
35. $(4xy - 3)(5xy - 2)$
36. $(3ab + 4)(9ab + 2)$
37. $2(x + 2)(x - 2)(x + 3)$
38. $3(x + 3)(x - 3)(x + 2)$
39. $2(5x - 4y)(25x^2 + 20xy + 16y^2)$
40. $(3a - 7b)(9a^2 + 21ab + 49b^2)$
41. $2(2x + 3y)(4x^2 - 6xy + 9y^2)$
42. $x(x - 2p)$
43. $(5y^2 - 12x)(6y^2 - 5x)$
44. $5(c^{50} + 4d^{50})(c^{25} + 2d^{25})(c^{25} - 2d^{25})$
45. $3(a + b + c + d)(a + b - c - d)$
46. $8(a - 7)^2$
47. $(y^2 + 11)(2 - y)(2 + y)$
For Exercises 48–53, see Teacher's Answer Section.

Mixed Review

54. $y = 2x + 1$
55. $y = -2x - 3$
56. $y = 4x - 1$
57. 0
58. -10
59. -1
60. $3m^3 - 4m^2 + 2m - 1$

5-7

FIRST FIVE MINUTES

1. Factor $x^2 - 5x + 6$.
   $(x - 2)(x - 3)$
2. Factor $2x^2 - 4x$.
   $2x(x - 2)$
3. Factor $8x^2 - 24x + 18$.
   $2(4x^2 - 12x + 9)$
   $= 2(2x - 3)^2$
4. Solve $3(x - 5) = 0$.
   $x - 5 = 0$
   $x = 5$

After solving Example 1, substitute 7 and -4 into $(x - 7)(x + 4) = 0$ as an illustration of the principle of zero products.

Key Questions

- What are the solutions of $x(x - 1) = 0$?
  $x = 0$ or $x = 1$
- How many solutions does $(3)(x + 1)(x - 1) = 0$ have?
  2

Chalkboard Examples

1. Solve $x^2 - 5x + 6 = 0$.
   Factor.
   $(x - 2)(x - 3) = 0$
   $x = 2$ or $x = 3$
2. Solve $4x^2 - 9 = 0$.
   Factor.
   $(2x - 3)(2x + 3) = 0$
   $2x - 3 = 0$, or
   $2x + 3 = 0$
   $x = \frac{3}{2}$ or $x = -\frac{3}{2}$
3. Solve $3x^2 - 36x + 105 = 0$.
   Factor.
   $3(x^2 - 12x + 35) = 0$
   $3(x - 5)(x - 7) = 0$
   $x - 5 = 0$ or $x - 7 = 0$
   $x = 5$ or $x = 7$

LESSON QUIZ

Solve.

1. $2x^2 - 2x = 0$
   $x = 0$ or $x = 1$
2. $x^2 - 9x + 18 = 0$
   $x = 3$ or $x = 6$
3. $5x^2 + 20x + 20 = 0$
   $x = -2$

5-7 Solving Equations by Factoring

Objective: Solve equations by factoring and using the principle of zero products.

Theorem 2-1, the principle of zero products, states that a product is 0 if and only if at least one of the factors is 0. To use this principle in solving equations, we make sure that 0 is on one side of the equation and then factor the other side.

EXAMPLE 1 Solve $x^2 - 3x - 28 = 0$.

First we factor the polynomial.

$$x^2 - 3x - 28 = 0$$
$$(x - 7)(x + 4) = 0 \quad \text{Factoring}$$

We now have two factors whose product is 0. By the principle of zero products, one of the factors must be zero.

$$x - 7 = 0 \text{ or } x + 4 = 0 \quad \text{Using the principle of zero products}$$
$$x = 7 \text{ or } x = -4$$

Check:

$x^2 - 3x - 28$	$= 0$
$7^2 - 3(7) - 28$	0
$49 - 21 - 28$	0
0	0 ✓

$x^2 - 3x - 28$	$= 0$
$(-4)^2 - 3(-4) - 28$	0
$16 + 12 - 28$	0
0	0 ✓

The solutions are 7 and -4.

Try This Solve.

a. $x^2 + 8 - 6x = 0$ 2, 4 **b.** $12y^2 - 3y = 9$ 1, $-\frac{3}{4}$ **c.** $25 + x^2 = -10x$ -5

Here are some other examples of polynomial equations and their solutions.

EXAMPLES Solve.

	Factored	Using zero products	Solution
2. $5b^2 - 10b = 0$	$5b(b - 2) = 0$	$b = 0$ or $b - 2 = 0$	0, 2
3. $x^2 - 6x + 9 = 0$	$(x - 3)(x - 3) = 0$	$x - 3 = 0$ or $x - 3 = 0$	3
4. $x^3 + 4x^2 - 9x = 36$	$(x + 3)(x - 3)(x + 4) = 0$	$x + 3 = 0$ or $x - 3 = 0$ or $x + 4 = 0$	$-3, 3, -4$

Try This Solve.

d. $8b^2 - 16b = 0$ 0, 2 **e.** $9x^2 + 27x = 0$ 0, -3 **f.** $x^3 + 3 = x + 3x^2$ 3, 1, -1

5-7 EXERCISES

A

Solve.

1. $x^2 + 3x - 28 = 0$
2. $y^2 - 4y - 45 = 0$
3. $y^2 - 8y + 16 = 0$
4. $r^2 - 2r + 1 = 0$
5. $x^2 - 12x + 36 = 0$
6. $y^2 + 16y + 64 = 0$
7. $9x + x^2 + 20 = 0$
8. $8y + y^2 + 15 = 0$
9. $x^2 + 8x = 0$
10. $t^2 + 9t = 0$
11. $x^2 - 9 = 0$
12. $p^2 - 16 = 0$
13. $z^2 = 36$
14. $y^2 = 81$
15. $x^2 + 14x + 45 = 0$
16. $y^2 + 12y + 32 = 0$
17. $y^2 + 2y = 63$
18. $a^2 + 3a = 40$
19. $p^2 - 11p = -28$
20. $x^2 - 14x = -45$
21. $32 + 4x - x^2 = 0$
22. $27 + 12t + t^2 = 0$
23. $3b^2 + 8b + 4 = 0$
24. $9y^2 + 15y + 4 = 0$
25. $8y^2 - 10y + 3 = 0$
26. $4x^2 + 11x + 6 = 0$
27. $6z - z^2 = 0$
28. $8y - y^2 = 0$
29. $12z^2 + z = 6$
30. $6x^2 - 7x = 10$
31. $5x^2 - 20 = 0$
32. $6y^2 - 54 = 0$
33. $2x^2 - 15x = -7$
34. $x^2 - 9x = -8$
35. $21r^2 + r - 10 = 0$
36. $12a^2 - 5a - 28 = 0$
37. $15y^2 = 3y$
38. $18x^2 = 9x$
39. $100x^2 = 81$

B

Solve.

40. $x^2 - \frac{1}{25} = 0$
41. $y^2 - \frac{1}{64} = 0$
42. $16x^3 = x$
43. $9x^3 = x$
44. $x(x + 8) = 16(x - 1)$
45. $m(m + 9) = 4(2m + 5)$
46. $(a - 5)^2 = 36$
47. $(x - 6)^2 = 81$
48. $(x + 1)^3 = (x - 1)^3 + 26$
49. $(x - 2)^3 = x^3 - 2$
50. ***Critical Thinking*** Find two different equations whose solutions are 5 and -8.

Challenge

Solve for x.

51. $x^2 + 2ax - 3x - 6a = 0$
52. $2x^2 - 5bx + 4cx - 10bc = 0$
53. $x^3 + ax^2 - a^2x - a^3 = 0$
54. $x^2 + 10x + 25 - 9a^2 = 0$

Mixed Review

Solve these systems.

55. $3x + 5y = 2$, $x = 3y - 4$
56. $6x - y = 17$, $2x + y = -1$
57. $2x - y = 0$, $y + x = 3$
58. The average male grows from a height of 20 inches at birth to 51 inches at age 8. How tall would a male be at age 60 if growth continued at this rate?

Assignment Guide

Algebra: 1–39 e/o, MR

Alg w/Finite or Trig: 1–39 m3, 40–49 e/o, 50, MR

Comprehensive: 1–49 m3, 50, 51–54 e/o, MR

ADDITIONAL ANSWERS

Exercises

1. $-7, 4$ **2.** $9, -5$
3. 4 **4.** 1
5. 6 **6.** -8
7. $-5, -4$ **8.** $-5, -3$
9. $0, -8$ **10.** $0, -9$
11. $-3, 3$ **12.** $-4, 4$
13. $-6, 6$ **14.** $-9, 9$
15. $-5, -9$ **16.** $-8, -4$
17. $-9, 7$ **18.** $-8, 5$
19. $7, 4$ **20.** $9, 5$
21. $8, -4$ **22.** $-9, -3$
23. $-\frac{2}{3}, -2$ **24.** $-\frac{4}{3}, -\frac{1}{3}$
25. $\frac{3}{4}, \frac{1}{2}$ **26.** $-\frac{3}{4}, -2$
27. $0, 6$ **28.** $0, 8$
29. $-\frac{3}{4}, \frac{2}{3}$ **30.** $-\frac{5}{6}, 2$
31. $-2, 2$ **32.** $-3, 3$
33. $\frac{1}{2}, 7$ **34.** $8, 1$
35. $-\frac{5}{7}, \frac{2}{3}$ **36.** $-\frac{7}{4}, -\frac{4}{3}$
37. $0, \frac{1}{5}$ **38.** $0, \frac{1}{2}$
39. $-\frac{9}{10}, \frac{9}{10}$ **40.** $-\frac{1}{5}, \frac{1}{5}$
41. $-\frac{1}{8}, \frac{1}{8}$ **42.** $0, \frac{1}{4}, -\frac{1}{4}$
43. $0, \frac{1}{3}, -\frac{1}{3}$ **44.** 4
45. $-5, 4$ **46.** $-1, 11$
47. $-3, 15$ **48.** $2, -2$
49. 1
50. Answers may vary.
51. $-2a, 3$ **52.** $\frac{5}{2}b, -2c$
53. $a, -a$ **54.** $3a - 5, -3a - 5$

Mixed Review

55. $(-1, 1)$ **56.** $(2, -5)$
57. $(1, 2)$
58. 252.5 in., or 21 ft ½ in.

5-8

FIRST FIVE MINUTES

Solve.

1. $x^2 - 11x + 18 = 0$
   $(x - 2)(x - 9) = 0$
   $x = 2$ or $x = 9$
2. $4x^2 - 4x = 0$
   $4x(x - 1) = 0$
   $x = 0$ or $x = 1$
3. $x^2 - 20x + 100 = 0$
   $(x - 10)^2 = 0$
   $x = 10$

Point out that problems sometimes ask for "a number," and the solution provides us with more than one number, as in Example 1.

Avoiding Common Errors

Students will sometimes translate an expression such as "the length times the length minus 2" as $l^2 - 2$. The correct translation is $l(l - 2)$.

Chalkboard Examples

1. The square of a number equals twice the number minus 1. Find the number.
   Let x be the number.
   $$x^2 = 2x - 1$$
   $$x^2 - 2x + 1 = 0$$
   $$(x - 1)^2 = 0$$
   $$x = 1$$
2. A square region with an area of 1 square unit is cut from a square piece of cardboard. The remaining cardboard has area equal to 3 square units. What is the length of a side of the large square?
   Let x be the length of a side of the large square.
   $$x^2 - 1 = 3$$
   $$x^2 - 4 = 0$$
   $$(x - 2)(x + 2) = 0$$
   $$x = 2 \text{ or } x = -2$$
   There are two solutions to this equation. Since the length of a side of a square, however, must be a positive length, the only acceptable answer is $x = 2$. The length of the side of the large square is 2 units.

5-8 Problem Solving: Using Equations

Objective: Solve problems by translating to equations and solving them by factoring.

The Schroeders are remodeling their square living room by tearing down one wall and extending the room by 3 meters. The room will then be rectangular with an area of 180 m². What are the current dimensions of the living room?

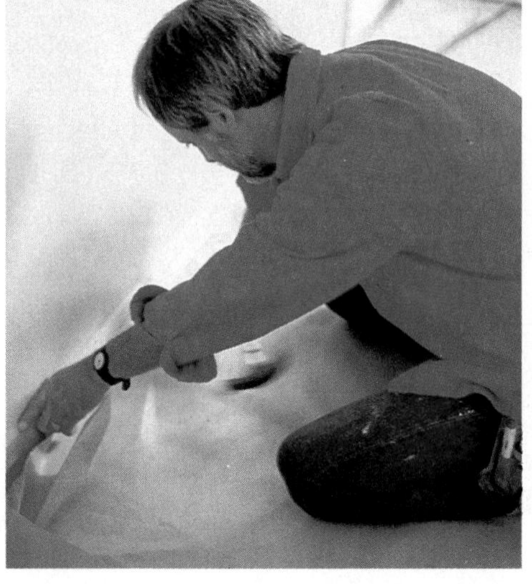

PROBLEM-SOLVING GUIDELINES
■ UNDERSTAND the problem
■ Develop and carry out a PLAN
■ Find the ANSWER and CHECK

EXAMPLE

Solve the problem stated above.

We can *draw a diagram* of the situation and use the Problem-Solving Guidelines to help solve the problem.

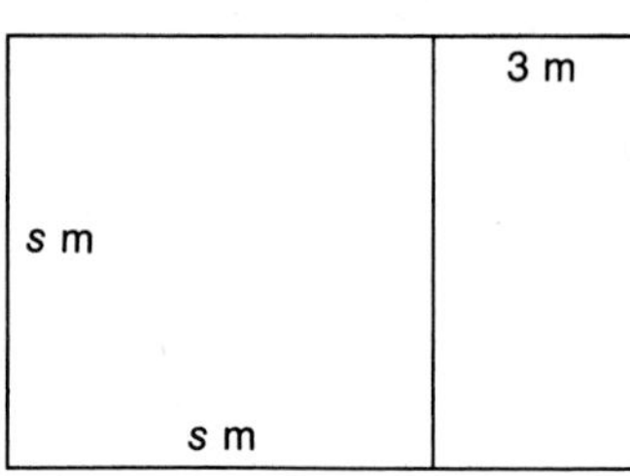

■ **UNDERSTAND the problem**

Question: What are the current dimensions of the living room? — Clarifying the question

Data: Increasing one side of the square room will give the room an area of 180 m². — Identifying the data

■ **Develop and carry out a PLAN**

Reword and translate to an equation.

The length of a side (s) times the length plus 3 is 180.

$$s \cdot (s + 3) = 180$$

Solve the equation.

$s(s + 3) = 180$

$s^2 + 3s - 180 = 0$ Adding −180 to both sides so that 0 is on one side

$(s + 15)(s - 12) = 0$ Factoring

$s = -15$ or $s = 12$ Using the principle of zero products

■ **Find the ANSWER and CHECK**

The solutions of the equation are -15 and 12. The solution -15 is not reasonable since the length of the room cannot be negative. Thus the length is 12 m. Since the room is square, the dimensions of the room are 12 m by 12 m.

Try This

a. The square of a number minus twice the number is 48. Find the number. 8 or −6

b. The width of a rectangle is 5 cm less than the length. The area is 24 cm^2. Find the dimensions. Length is 8 cm; width is 3 cm.

5-8 EXERCISES

A

Solve these problems.

1. Four times the square of a number is 21 more than eight times the number. What is the number? $\frac{7}{2}$ or $-\frac{3}{2}$
2. Four times the square of a number is 45 more than eight times the number. What is the number? $\frac{9}{2}$ or $-\frac{5}{2}$
3. The square of a number plus the number is 132. What is the number? −12 or 11
4. The square of a number plus the number is 156. What is the number? −13 or 12
5. The length of the top of a table is 5 ft greater than the width. Find the length and width if the area is 84 ft^2.
6. The length of the top of a workbench is 4 ft greater than the width. The area is 96 ft^2. Find the length and the width.
7. Sam Stratton is planning a garden 25 m longer than it is wide. The garden will have an area of 7500 m^2. What will its dimensions be?
8. A flower bed is to be 3 m longer than it is wide. The flower bed will have an area of 108 m^2. What will its dimensions be?
9. The sum of the squares of two consecutive odd positive integers is 202. Find the integers. 9 and 11
10. The sum of the squares of two consecutive odd positive integers is 394. Find the integers. 13 and 15

LESSON QUIZ

1. Find the length of a side of a square whose area is twice the length of its side.
   $x = 0$ or $x = 2$
   The answer $x = 0$ is a trivial solution. The solution $x = 2$ is the required solution.

Assignment Guide

Algebra: 1–17 e/o, MR

Alg w/Finite or Trig: 1–19 e/o, 20, MR

Comprehensive: 1–19 e/o, 20–23, MR

ADDITIONAL ANSWERS

Exercises

5. Length is 12 ft; width is 7 ft
6. Length is 12 ft; width is 8 ft
7. Length is 100 m; width is 75 m
8. Length is 12 m; width is 9 m

16. 11, 12, and 13; −2, −1, and 0
17. 9, 10, and 11; 3, 4, and 5
18. (3, 14) or (14, 3)
19. Length is 28 cm; width is 14 cm
20. 15 m by 12 m
21. Width is 30 in., length is 40 in.; depth is 20 in.
22. 12 m
23. 54 cm^2

Mixed Review

24. $9x^2y + 2xy^2 - xy - 15$
25. $8x^6 - 12x^4 + 6x^2 - 1$
26. $y(y + 7)$
27. $(x + 2)(x - 2)$
28. $4y(4y + 1)$
29. $2y(2y - 1)$
30. 8
31. −6
32. −12

11. If the sides of a square are lengthened by 4 cm, the area becomes 49 cm^2. Find the length of a side of the original square. 3 cm
12. If the sides of a square are lengthened by 6 m, the area becomes 144 m^2. Find the length of a side of the original square. 6 m
13. The base of a triangle is 9 cm greater than the height. The area is 56 cm^2. Find the height and base. Height is 7 cm; base is 16 cm.
14. The base of a triangle is 5 cm less than the height. The area is 18 cm^2. Find the height and base. Height is 9 cm; base is 4 cm.
15. Three consecutive even integers are such that the square of the third is 76 more than the square of the second. Find the three integers. 16, 18, and 20
16. Find three consecutive integers such that the product of the first and third minus the second is one more than 10 times the third.
17. Find three consecutive integers such that four times the square of the third, less three times the square of the first, minus 41, is twice the square of the second.

B

18. Find a and b, such that $a + b = 17$ and $a^2 + b^2 = 205$.
19. A rectangular piece of tin is twice as long as it is wide. Squares 2 cm on a side are cut out of each corner, and the ends are turned up to make a box whose volume is 480 cm^3. What are the dimensions of the piece of tin?

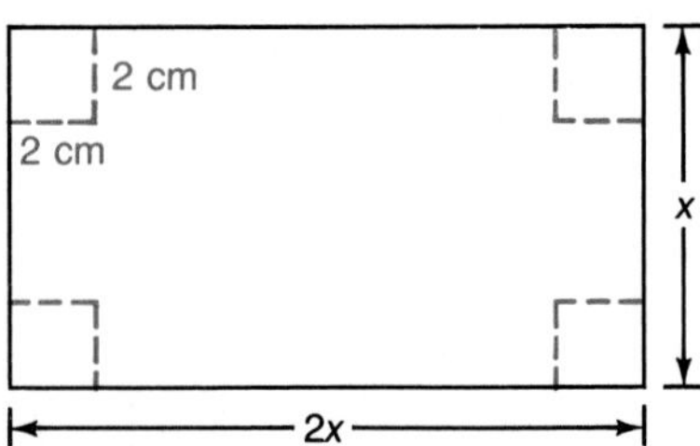

20. *Critical Thinking* Suppose the Schroeders' room in the Example is rectangular with an area of 180 m^2, but it will be square after the wall is torn down. What are the dimensions?

Challenge

21. The top and base of a fish tank are rectangles whose length is 10 in. more than the width. If the depth and the width of the tank total 50 in. and the combined area of the top and base is 400 in^2 less than the total area of the four sides, what are the dimensions of the tank?
22. A rectangular swimming pool with dimensions of 11 m and 8 m is built in a rectangular back yard. The area of the back yard is 1120 m^2. If the strip of yard surrounding the pool is of uniform width, how wide is the strip?
23. The hypotenuse of a right triangle is 3 cm longer than one of its legs and 6 cm longer than its other leg. What is the area of the triangle?

Mixed Review

Simplify. **24.** $(5x^2y + 3xy - 6) + (4x^2y + 2xy^2 - 4xy - 9)$ **25.** $(2x^2 - 1)^3$

Factor. **26.** $y^2 + 7y$ **27.** $x^2 - 4$ **28.** $16y^2 + 4y$ **29.** $4y^2 - 2y$

Solve. **30.** $3a - 5 = 19$ **31.** $-16 = 3x + 2$ **32.** $-6 = 0.75y + 3$

Problem Solving: College Entrance Exams

Factoring

Some problems on college entrance exams can be solved using the skills you have learned related to *factoring*. Test items, however, will usually not tell you that factoring is a good approach to solving the problem. Your job is to look at a problem and decide whether factoring might be helpful in finding the solution. The reason for including these types of problems on exams is to determine whether you can apply algebraic skills to situations without being told to do so. Here are three factoring situations that are often encountered on college entrance exams.

$$a^2 - b^2 = (a - b)(a + b)$$
$$a^2 + 2ab + b^2 = (a + b)^2$$
$$a^2 - 2ab + b^2 = (a - b)^2$$

EXAMPLE 1

$0.85^2 - 0.75^2 =$

(A) 1.6 **(B)** 0.16 **(C)** 0.10 **(D)** 0.01 **(E)** 0.001

Here we factor and we can do the arithmetic mentally.

$$\begin{aligned} 0.85^2 - 0.75^2 &= (0.85 + 0.75)(0.85 - 0.75) \\ &= (1.60)(0.1) \\ &= 0.16 \end{aligned}$$

The arithmetic is simpler this way than directly squaring both numbers and subtracting. The answer is choice B.

EXAMPLE 2

If $x^2 - 9 = (15)(21)$, then x could be

(A) 16 **(B)** 17 **(C)** 18 **(D)** 19 **(E)** 20

Here we can factor $x^2 - 9 = (x - 3)(x + 3)$ and place the factors under $(15)(21)$.

$$\begin{aligned} x^2 - 9 = \quad &(15) \cdot (21) \\ &(x - 3)(x + 3) \end{aligned}$$

By inspection $x = 18$, so the answer is choice C.

EXAMPLE 3

If $x = 236.81$, then $\dfrac{x^2 + x - 12}{x + 4}$ rounded to the nearest whole number is

(A) 100 **(B)** 204 **(C)** 234 **(D)** 264 **(E)** 267

This problem appears to involve complicated mathematics. We can factor before we substitute, however.

Problem Solving: College Entrance Exams

Shortcut methods must always be examined for their exceptions. In Example 3, if we had $x = -4$ and factored first, we would get $(x - 3) = -4 - 3 = -7$ as the solution. But -4 would give the original expression a denominator of 0, thus there would be no solution.

For Problem 6, substitution is used

$(a - b)^2 = a^2 - 2ab + b^2 = 10$

$ab = 2$, so $2ab = 4$

thus $a^2 - 4 + b^2 = 10$,

$a^2 + b^2 = 14$

The answer is choice A.

ANSWERS
1. (D)
2. (E)
3. (B)
4. (C)
5. (C)
6. (A)
7. (B)
8. (B)
9. (C)

$$\frac{x^2 + x - 12}{x + 4} = \frac{(x - 3)(x + 4)}{x + 4}$$
$$= x - 3 = 236.81 - 3 \approx 234$$

The answer is choice C.

EXAMPLE 4

$(59)^2 - 2(59)(49) + (49)^2 =$

(A) 10 **(B)** 71 **(C)** 100 **(D)** 108 **(E)** 1247

Here we recognize that this problem can be simplified to the form $(a - b)^2$, and instead of doing all of the arithmetic we can simplify first.

$$a^2 \quad - \quad 2ab \quad + \quad b^2 \quad = \quad (a - b)^2$$
$$(59)^2 - 2(59)(49) + (49)^2 = (59 - 49)^2 = 10^2 = 100$$

The answer is choice C.

Problems

1. If $(r - 3)\left(\frac{1}{r}\right) = 0$, what is r?

(A) 0 **(B)** 1 **(C)** 2 **(D)** 3 **(E)** Any nonzero integer

2. If $x - y = 7$ and $x + y = 5$, then $x^2 - y^2 =$

(A) 12 **(B)** 21 **(C)** 49 **(D)** 25 **(E)** 35

3. $0.53^2 - 0.47^2 =$

(A) 0.6 **(B)** 0.06 **(C)** 0.006 **(D)** 0.36 **(E)** 0.036

4. $(13)^2 - 2(13)(23) + (23)^2 =$

(A) 1,296 **(B)** 698 **(C)** 100 **(D)** 46 **(E)** -100

5. If $x^2 - 16 = (12)(20)$, then x could be

(A) 14 **(B)** 15 **(C)** 16 **(D)** 17 **(E)** 18

6. If $ab = 2$ and $(a - b)^2 = 10$, then $a^2 + b^2 =$

(A) 14 **(B)** 18 **(C)** 6 **(D)** 8 **(E)** 12

7. If $m = 5$ and $n = 4$, then $\frac{m^2 - n^2}{m - n} =$

(A) 1 **(B)** 9 **(C)** 16 **(D)** 25 **(E)** 81

8. If $x + y = r$ and $x - y = \frac{1}{r}$, $(r \neq 0)$, then $x^2 - y^2 =$

(A) r **(B)** 1 **(C)** $\frac{1}{r}$ **(D)** $1 - \frac{1}{r}$ **(E)** Undefined

9. If $x^2 - y^2 = 60$ and $x + y = 10$, then $x - y =$

(A) 50 **(B)** $\frac{1}{6}$ **(C)** 6 **(D)** 9 **(E)** 10

Chapter 5 Summary and Review

5-1

To find values of a polynomial function, substitute into the polynomial expression.

For each polynomial function, find the specified function value.

1. $P(x) = -3x^2 + 2x - 1$; $P(2)$

2. $P(y) = 2y^3 - 2y^2 - y - 33$; $P(-3)$

If two terms have the same variables raised to the same powers, the terms are similar or like terms and can be "combined" or "collected."

Collect like terms.

3. $2a + 7 - 3 + 9a + 3 - 7a$

4. $-3x^2y - 2xy + 5xy - 7xy^2$

5-2

The sum of two polynomials can be found by writing a plus sign between them and then collecting like terms. To subtract one polynomial from another, find the additive inverse of the second polynomial and then add it to the first polynomial.

Add.

5. $5x^2 - 8x^3 + 3x - 2$ and $4x^3 + 5x^2 + 9 - x$

6. $5a^4 + 7a^3 + 6a^2 - 7$ and $3a^4 - 5a^2 + 2 - a^3$

7. $p^3 - 5q^2 + 2pq$ and $3pq^3 - p^3 - 6$ and $4pq^2 + 5p^3 - pq + 6$

Find the additive inverse.

8. $x^5 - x^3 - 2x^2 + 18x - 1$

9. $-4y^4 - 16x^3y^3 + 13xy^2$

Subtract.

10. $(8y^2 + 3y + 6) - (-5y^2 + 4y - 3)$

11. $(8p - 5q + 7r) - (2p + 5q - 4r)$

12. $(8x^2 - 3xy - 7y^2) - (4x^2 - 6xy - 8y^2)$

13. $(15a - 5c + 4b) - (8b + 4c + 5a)$

5-3

To multiply any two polynomials, multiply each term of one by every term of the other and then add the results.

Multiply.

14. $(-8x^2y)(4xy^2)$

15. $(3xy + 4y)(x^2 - 2)$

16. $(3x - 2y + 5z)(-3x + 4z)$

17. $(5y^3 + 3y - 6)(6y^3 - 4y + 7)$

18. $(a - b)(a^2 + ab + b^2)$

19. $(-3x^2y^3 + 2t)(3x^2y^3 + 2t)$

20. $(7x - 5y)^2$

21. $(2x + 1)^3$

ANSWERS

1. -9
2. -102
3. $4a + 7$
4. $-3x^2y + 3xy - 7xy^2$
5. $-4x^3 + 10x^2 + 2x + 7$
6. $8a^4 + 6a^3 + a^2 - 5$
7. $5p^3 + pq + 4pq^2 + 3pq^3 - 5q^2$
8. $-x^5 + x^3 + 2x^2 - 18x + 1$
9. $4y^4 + 16x^3y^3 - 13xy^2$
10. $13y^2 - y + 9$
11. $6p - 10q + 11r$
12. $4x^2 + 3xy + y^2$
13. $10a - 4b - 9c$
14. $-32x^3y^3$
15. $3x^3y + 4x^2y - 6xy - 8y$
16. $-9x^2 + 6xy - 3xz - 8yz + 20z^2$
17. $30y^6 - 2y^4 - y^3 - 12y^2 + 45y - 42$
18. $a^3 - b^3$
19. $-9x^4y^6 + 4t^2$
20. $49x^2 - 70xy + 25y^2$
21. $8x^3 + 12x^2 + 6x + 1$

22. $8y(3x^2 - 5y)$
23. $7t^2(4t^2 - 5t + 2)$
24. $(7y - 9)(7y + 9)$
25. $(3y - 8)(3y + 8)$
26. $xy(4x - y)$
27. $9(x + y)(x - y)$
28. $(x - y - 3)(x - y + 3)$
29. $(y - 2 - 2x)(y - 2 + 2x)$
30. $(2a - 1)(4a^2 + 2a + 1)$
31. $(5x - 2y)^2$
32. $(x + y^2)(x^2 - xy^2 + y^4)$
33. $(a - 4)(a - 6)$
34. $(ab + 3)(ab + 4)$
35. $(9 + x)(8 - x)$
36. $(2y + 1)(y - 2)$
37. $(4x - 3)(2x - 3)$
38. $(x + 9)(x - 9)$
39. $3(x + 3)(x - 3)$
40. $2(2x + 5)^2$
41. $4(y + 7)(y - 2)$
42. $y(x + 4y)(x - 4y)$
43. $(2x - 3y)(4x^2 + 6xy + 9y^2)$
44. $5(x + 2)(x + 3)(x - 3)$
45. $(w + y)(k - t)$
46. 0, 8
47. $-\frac{1}{2}, -4$
48. $-3, -4$
49. 9 cm by 6 cm

5-4 – 5-6

When factoring, always look first for a common factor. Then consider the number of terms. For two terms, try factoring as a difference of two squares or a sum or difference of two cubes. For three terms, is it a trinomial square? If so, factor as a square of a binomial. If not, test the factors of the terms. For more than three terms, try grouping, or try differences of squares again. Factor completely, making sure that each remaining factor is prime.

5-4

Factor.

22. $24x^2y - 40y^2$
23. $28t^4 - 35t^3 + 14t^2$
24. $49y^2 - 81$
25. $9y^2 - 64$
26. $4x^2y - xy^2$
27. $9x^2 - 9y^2$
28. $x^2 - 2xy + y^2 - 9$
29. $y^2 - 4y + 4 - 4x^2$

5-5

Factor.

30. $8a^3 - 1$
31. $25x^2 - 20xy + 4y^2$
32. $x^3 + y^6$
33. $a^2 - 10a + 24$
34. $a^2b^2 + 7ab + 12$
35. $72 - x - x^2$
36. $2y^2 - 3y - 2$
37. $8x^2 + 9 - 18x$

5-6

Factor.

38. $x^2 - 81$
39. $3x^2 - 27$
40. $8x^2 + 50 + 40x$
41. $4y^2 + 20y - 56$
42. $x^2y - 16y^3$
43. $8x^3 - 27y^3$
44. $5x^3 + 10x^2 - 45x - 90$
45. $kw - tw + ky - ty$

5-7

A product is zero if and only if one of the factors is 0. This is the principle of zero products.

Solve.

46. $x^2 - 8x = 0$
47. $2x^2 + 9x = -4$

5-8

Factoring can be used effectively when solving many problems.

48. The square of a number plus seven times the number is -12. Find the number.
49. The length of a rectangle is 3 cm more than the width, and the area is 54 cm^2. Find its dimensions.

See also Problem 5, Computer-Assisted Problem Solving, page 842.

Chapter 5 Test

For each polynomial function, find the specified function value.

1. $Q(x) = 3x^3 - x + 3$
   Find $Q(0)$ and $Q(-2)$.

2. $H(y) = -2y^4 + y^3 + 3y^2 - y - 6$
   Find $H(2)$ and $H(-2)$.

Collect like terms.

3. $3x - 5 - 3 - 3x + 5 - 1$

4. $-3xy - 2x^2 + y^2 - xy + 3x^2$

Add.

5. $3x^2 - 4x^3 + 2x - 1$ and $5x^3 + 4x^2 + 3 - x$
6. $4y^2 - 3xy + 4x^2 + 7x^3$ and $5x^3 - 3x^2 - 2xy + 5y^2$
7. $-3x^2 - 2x - 6x^3$ and $x^3 - 7 + 2x^2 + 2x$
8. $x^2 - 3x - 2$ and $3x^2 - 2x + 5$ and $-2x^3 - 5x - 3$

Find the additive inverse.

9. $-3x^5 - x^3 + 2x^2 - 28x + 2$

10. $-4xy^4 + x^3y^3 - 23xy^2 + 16x^2$

Subtract.

11. $(7x^2 + 2x + 4) - (-2x^2 + 2x - 2)$
12. $(5r^2 - 2rs - 6s^2) - (3r^2 - 4rs - 7s^2)$
13. $(3x^4 - 2x^2 - 4) - (3x^3 - 2x^2 + 4)$
14. $(x^3 - x^2 + x - 1) - (-x^3 - x^2 + x - 1)$

Multiply.

15. $(14x^2y)(3xy^2)$
16. $(-3x^2y^2)(-2xy)(-x^2y)$
17. $(-4x + 3z)(2x - 3y + 4z)$
18. $(3x - 5)(3x + 5)$
19. $(x - 2)(x^2 + 2x + 4)$
20. $(5x + 2y)^2$
21. $(7x - 2y)(3x + y)$
22. $(9x - 5y)(2x - 7y)$
23. $(2x^2 - 3)^2$
24. $(y^2 - 3y + 9)(y + 3)$

Factor.

25. $9t - 27$
26. $16x^2 - 81$
27. $9x^2 + 24x + 16$
28. $3y^3 - 27y$
29. $x^2y^2 - 2xy - 15$
30. $6x^2 + 11x - 10$
31. $36 - 16x - x^2$
32. $y^6 - z^6$
33. $64p^3 - 125q^3$
34. $x^2 - 6x + 9 - a^2 + 2a - 1$
35. $x^3 + 4x^2 - 8x - 32$
36. $2a^2 + 4ab^2 - ab - 2b^3$

Solve.

37. $x^2 - 21 = 4x$
38. $y^2 - 9y = 0$
39. $2x^2 + 75 = 25x$
40. $x^3 + 2x^2 = 9x + 18$
41. The square of a number plus nine times the number is -8. Find the number.
42. The length of a rectangle is 5 cm more than the width, and the area is 84 cm^2. Find its dimensions.

ANSWERS

1. 3, −19
2. −20, −32
3. −4
4. $x^2 + y^2 - 4xy$
5. $x^3 + 7x^2 + x + 2$
6. $9y^2 - 5xy + x^2 + 12x^3$
7. $-5x^3 - x^2 - 7$
8. $-2x^3 + 4x^2 - 10x$
9. $3x^5 + x^3 - 2x^2 + 28x - 2$
10. $-4xy^4 - x^3y^3 + 23xy^2 - 16x^2$
11. $9x^2 + 6$
12. $2r^2 + 2rs + s^2$
13. $3x^4 - 3x^3 - 8$
14. $2x^3$
15. $42x^3y^3$
16. $-6x^5y^4$
17. $-8x^2 + 12xy - 10xz - 9yz + 12z^2$
18. $9x^2 - 25$
19. $x^3 - 8$
20. $25x^2 + 20xy + 4y^2$
21. $21x^2 + xy - 2y^2$
22. $18x^2 - 73xy + 35y^2$
23. $4x^4 - 12x^2 + 9$
24. $y^3 + 27$
25. $9(t - 3)$
26. $(4x - 9)(4x + 9)$
27. $(3x + 4)^2$
28. $3y(y + 3)(y - 3)$
29. $(xy - 5)(xy + 3)$
30. $(3x - 2)(2x + 5)$
31. $(2 - x)(18 + x)$
32. $(y + z)(y - z)(y^2 - yz + z^2)(y^2 + yz + z^2)$
33. $(4p - 5q)(16p^2 + 20pq + 25q^2)$
34. $(x + a - 4)(x - a - 2)$
35. $(x^2 - 8)(x + 4)$
36. $(2a - b)(a + 2b^2)$
37. 7, −3
38. 0, 9
39. $\frac{15}{2}$, 5
40. 3, −3, −2
41. −1, −8
42. 12 cm, 7 cm

Test Item Analysis

Item	Lesson
1–4	5-1
5–14	5-2
15–24	5-3
25–28	5-4
29–31	5-5
32, 33, 34	5-5, 5-6
35–40	5-7
41, 42	5-8

CHAPTER 6

Rational Expressions and Equations

Chapter Overview

Chapter 6 covers operations with rational expressions and equations, division of polynomials, rational formulas, complex rational expressions, and direct and inverse variation. Synthetic division is used for division with special divisors. There are problem-solving lessons for rational equations and variation, and a strategy lesson requiring the strategies *Make a Table* and *Look for a Pattern.*

Objectives

6-1
- Multiply by 1 to obtain equivalent rational expressions.
- Simplify rational expressions.
- Multiply and simplify rational expressions.
- Divide and simplify rational expressions.

6-2
- Add or subtract rational expressions when the denominators are the same.
- Add or subtract rational expressions when denominators are different.
- Graph and analyze rational functions.

6-3
- Simplify complex rational expressions.

6-4
- Divide a polynomial by a monomial.
- Divide two polynomials when the divisor is not a monomial.

6-5
- Use synthetic division to find the quotient of certain polynomials.

6-6
- Solve rational equations.

6-7
- Solve work problems using rational equations.
- Solve motion problems using rational equations.

6-8
- Solve rational formulas for a specified variable.
- Solve problems involving the use of a formula.

6-9
- Find the constant of variation and an equation of variation for direct variation problems.
- Find the constant of variation and an equation of variation for inverse variation problems.
- Solve problems using direct variation and inverse variation.

6-10
- Solve problems using the strategies *Make a Table, Look for a Pattern,* and other strategies.

TEACHING CHAPTER 6

Cooperative Learning Opportunities

Some students are likely to get bogged down when working with rational expressions and the division of polynomials. Group work can help them remain involved and on track.

For this activity there are no assigned roles but the following rules will help: (1) All students must participate. (2) There is no talking to those in other groups. (3) All members of a group must agree on a solution.

During the final 10 or 15 minutes of a class, assign students in groups of three to begin the homework together. This activity may be particularly useful in Lessons 6-3 through 6-6. Students should talk quietly, only to those in their group, and agree on answers.

You might ask students to draw a double rule on their papers to indicate how much of the homework they did during class. You can then check whether they did as well with the rest of the assignment. This will tell you whether they were learning or simply copying as they did the group work.

Multicultural Note: *Maria Agnesi*

Maria Gaetana Agnesi was brilliant in many ways. As a child she used to give oral presentations at social gatherings in her home. The topics for these talks included logic, mechanics, chemistry, botany, zoology, mineralogy and mathematics. She later devoted herself to mathematics and wrote one of the earliest and most complete textbooks on calculus.

Agnesi worked on the equation $x^2y = a^2(a - y)$ and its bell-shaped curve is named the *versiera of Agnesi*. Because of a mistaken translation from Italian, it is also known as *the witch of Agnesi*. Students can plot points and graph this equation using these steps.
(1) Let $a = 2$
(2) Solve the equation for y.
(3) Complete the table.

x	−3	−2	−1	0	1	2	3
y							

(4) Use the points to draw the graph. **Ans: $(-3, \frac{8}{13})$, $(-2, 1)$, $(-1, \frac{8}{5})$, $(0, 2)$, $(1, \frac{8}{5})$, $(2, 1)$, $(3, \frac{8}{13})$; The graph is a bell shaped curve symmetric around the *y*-axis.**

For more information, see page 9 of **Multiculturalism in Mathematics, Science, and Technology**.

Alternative Assessment and Communication Ideas

It is important for you, as teacher, to know whether students are comfortable with the procedures involved in simplifying rational expressions and the division of polynomials. One way to go about this kind of assessment is to have students tell honestly how they thought they did on a quiz.

If, for example, a one-problem quiz is worth 15 points, you might offer 2 points of additional credit for a student who correctly analyzes his or her work. Ask them to score according to the following categories.
(1) Done correctly, score 15 points.
(2) Used the method correctly but feel that I made a careless error, score 12.
(3) Was confused and unable to use the method successfully, score between 7 and 10.
(4) Did not know what to do, score 2 to 6. In analyzing their work students will also be taking a more objective look at themselves and this might remove certain mental blocks.

Investigations and Projects

The graphing calculator activity referred to on page 255 and located on page 855 will make an excellent project. Work with rational functions demonstrates the power and efficiency of the graphing calculator. It is difficult and time-consuming to graph these functions by hand. With the calculator it is easy to do these graphs but mathematical understanding is required to find asymptotes, intercepts, and in general to explain the behavior of the function.

A second project relates to formulas. Students with an interest in science can be asked to locate some not so common formulas in physics and chemistry texts, business math books, and anywhere else they can think of looking. As part of their report students should present the formula, write clear explanations, solve for different variables in the formula, and prepare an oral report for the class. They might also collect photographs or illustrations showing situations in which the formula is applied, and prepare a poster for display on the bulletin board.

MANAGING CHAPTER 6

Lesson	PACING CHART (DAYS) Algebra	Algebra w/Finite	Algebra w/Trig	Compre-hensive	Opening Activity	Cooperative Activity	Seat or Group Work
6-1	1	1	1	1	First Five Minutes 6-1: **TE** p.244 or ***FFM Transparency Masters*** p.18	Critical Thinking: **SE** p.248 Connections: **SE** p.249	Try This a–p
6-2	2	1	1	0.5	First Five Minutes 6-2: **TE** p.250 or ***FFM Transparency Masters*** p.18	Critical Thinking: **SE** p.254	Try This a–k
6-3	1	1	1	1	First Five Minutes 6-3: **TE** p.256 or ***FFM Transparency Masters*** p.19	Critical Thinking: **SE** p.258 Strategy Problem Bank 5: ***Problem Bank*** p.6	Try This a–f
6-4	1	1	1	0.5	First Five Minutes 6-4: **TE** p.259 or ***FFM Transparency Masters*** p.19	Critical Thinking: **SE** p.262	Try This a–j
6-5	1	1	1	1	First Five Minutes 6-5: **TE** p.263 or ***FFM Transparency Masters*** p.20	Critical Thinking: **SE** p.265	Try This a–d
6-6	2	1	1	1	First Five Minutes 6-6: **TE** p.266 or ***FFM Transparency Masters*** p.20	Critical Thinking: **SE** p.269	Try This a–j
6-7	1	1	1	1	First Five Minutes 6-7: **TE** p.270 or ***FFM Transparency Masters*** p.20	Critical Thinking: **SE** p.274	Try This a–c
6-8	1	1	1	1	First Five Minutes 6-8: **TE** p.276 or ***FFM Transparency Masters*** p.20	Critical Thinking: **SE** p.278 ✂ Manipulative Activity 6: ***Enrichment*** p.47	Try This a–b
6-9	1	1	1	1	First Five Minutes 6-9: **TE** p.279 or ***FFM Transparency Masters*** p.21	Critical Thinking: **SE** p.284 Looking for Errors 6: ***Enrichment*** p.67	Try This a–d
6-10	1	1	1	0.5	First Five Minutes 6-10: **TE** p.285 or ***FFM Transparency Masters*** p.21	Strategy Problem Bank 6: ***Problem Bank*** p.7	Problem 1: **SE** p.286
Review	1	1	1	0.5			
Test	1	1	1	1			
Cum. Review	1	0	0	0			
Mid-year Test	1	0	0	0			

FFM: First Five Minutes SPMR: Skills Practice Mixed Review

MANAGING CHAPTER 6

Enrichment	Review/Assess	Reteach	Technology	Lesson
Connections: **SE** p.249	Lesson Quiz: **TE** p.247	Skills Practice 15, #1–11: ***SPMR*** p.27		**6-1**
Math Point: **TE** p.251 TI-81 Investigation 1: **SE** pp.855–857	Lesson Quiz: **TE** p.252	Skills Practice 15, #12–19: ***SPMR*** p.27	Wkst 6: ***TI-81 Activities*** pp.25–27; Wkst 6: ***Master Grapher*** pp.32–34, pp.166–168, or pp.302–304; TI-81 Investigation 1: **SE** pp.855–857	**6-2**
Critical Thinking 6: ***Enrichment*** p.27	Lesson Quiz: **TE** p.257 Quiz II: ***Assessment*** p.19	Skills Practice 15, #20–25: ***SPMR*** p.27		**6-3**
Bonus Topic 5: ***Enrichment*** p.6	Lesson Quiz: **TE** p.261	Skills Practice 16, #1–10: ***SPMR*** p.28		**6-4**
Spreadsheet Activity 3: ***Technology*** pp.51–52	Lesson Quiz: **TE** p.264 Mixed Review 11: ***SPMR*** p.75	Skills Practice 16, #11–18: ***SPMR*** p.28	Calculator 9: ***Technology*** p.11; Spreadsheet Activity 3: ***Technology*** pp.51–52	**6-5**
Worksheet 7: ***TI-81 Activities*** pp.29–31	Lesson Quiz: **TE** p.268	Skills Practice 16, #19–26: ***SPMR*** p.28	Worksheet 7: ***TI-81 Activities*** pp.29–31; Worksheet 7: ***Master Grapher*** pp.35–37, pp.169–171, or pp.305–307	**6-6**
Teacher Demo 1: ***Master Grapher*** pp.5–6(Apple II) pp.139–140(IBM) or pp. 275–276(Mac)	Lesson Quiz: **TE** p.273 Quiz 12: ***Assessment*** p.20	Problem Bank 9: ***Problem Bank*** p.30	Problem for Programmers: **SE** p.275	**6-7**
✂ Manipulative Activity 6: ***Enrichment*** p.47	Lesson Quiz: **TE** p.277	Skills Practice 17, #1–9: ***SPMR*** p.29 Problem Bank 10: ***Problem Bank*** p.31	Calculator Worksheet 10: ***Technology*** p.12	**6-8**
Looking for Errors 6: ***Enrichment*** p.67	Lesson Quiz: **TE** p.282	Skills Practice 17, #10–15: ***SPMR*** p.29 Problem Bank 11: ***Problem Bank*** p.32		**6-9**
Problem 6: Computer Assisted Problem Solving, **SE** pp.842–843	Mixed Review 12: ***SPMR*** p.76	Strategy Problem Bank 6: ***Problem Bank*** p.7	Problem 6: Computer Assisted Problem Solving, **SE** pp.842–843	**6-10**
	Summary and Review: **SE** pp.287–288; Test: **SE** p.289			**Review**
	Chapter 6 Test: ***Assessment*** pp.77–82(reg.), pp.167–168 (adv.); Assessing Strategies 4: ***Assessment*** pp.201–202			**Test**
	Cumulative Review: **SE** pp.377–381			**Cum. Review**
	Mid-year Test: ***Assessment*** pp.215–218 or pp.219–226			**Mid-year Test**

The solution to the problem posed on the facing page can be found on page 275.

Ready for Rational Expressions and Equations?

1-2 Add or subtract.

1. $\frac{2}{7} + \left(-\frac{7}{9}\right)$ $-\frac{31}{63}$

2. $\frac{5}{3} - \left(-\frac{3}{5}\right)$ $\frac{34}{15}$

1-2 Multiply.

3. $7 \cdot \left(-\frac{2}{3}\right)$ $-\frac{14}{3}$

4. $-\frac{3}{8} \cdot \left(-\frac{4}{7}\right)$ $\frac{3}{14}$

1-2 Divide.

5. $\frac{2}{3} \div \frac{3}{4}$ $\frac{8}{9}$

6. $-\frac{7}{3} \div \frac{1}{2}$ $-\frac{14}{3}$

7. $\frac{3}{4} \div \left(-\frac{1}{4}\right)$ -3

1-3

8. Evaluate $xy - xz$ for $x = 3$, $y = -2$, $z = 4$. -18

1-4 Factor.

9. $4x + 4y$ $4(x + y)$

10. $3y + 6$ $3(y + 2)$

11. $cx - cr + cw$ $c(x - r + w)$

1-8 Simplify.

12. $(7x^3y^{-2})(2x^{-2}y^4)$ $14xy^2$

13. $\frac{10x^5y^2}{2xy^4}$ $\frac{5x^4}{y^2}$

14. $(2x^2y^{-4}z^3)^4$ $16x^8y^{-16}z^{12}$

2-2

15. Solve $8 - 3(a - 1) = 2 + 4(3 - a)$. 3

2-4

16. Solve $E = mc^2$, for m. $m = \frac{E}{c^2}$

CHAPTER

6 Rational Expressions and Equations

An airplane leaves Los Angeles for Honolulu, 2574 miles away, traveling with a 50 mi/h tail wind. What is the point of no return *for the plane?*

6-1

FIRST FIVE MINUTES

1. Multiply $(x + 2)(x + 3)$.
   $x^2 + 5x + 6$
2. Factor $x^2 + 7x + 12$.
   $(x + 3)(x + 4)$
3. Simplify $\frac{5}{7}\left(\frac{14}{30} + \frac{7}{5}\right)$.
   $= \frac{5}{7}\cdot\frac{14}{30} + \frac{5}{7}\cdot\frac{7}{5}$
   $= \frac{1}{3} + 1 = \frac{4}{3}$

Multiplying by 1

Emphasize the similarity between rational numbers and rational expressions. A rational number is the ratio of two integers, while a rational expression is the ratio of two polynomials.

Key Questions

- What does $\frac{5}{7}\cdot\frac{3}{2}$ equal?
  $\frac{5\cdot 3}{7\cdot 2} = \frac{15}{14}$
- What does $\frac{4}{9}\cdot\frac{7}{7}$ equal?
  $\frac{4}{9}$

Chalkboard Examples

Multiply to obtain equivalent expressions.

1. $\frac{x-1}{x+1}\cdot\frac{x+2}{x+2}$
   $\frac{(x-1)(x+2)}{(x+1)(x+2)}$
   $= \frac{x^2 + x - 2}{x^2 + 3x + 2}$
2. $\frac{2x+1}{x}\cdot\frac{x+1}{x+1}$
   $\frac{(2x+1)(x+1)}{x(x+1)}$
   $= \frac{2x^2 + 3x + 1}{x^2 + x}$

6-1 Multiplying and Simplifying

A rational expression is a quotient of two polynomials.

$\frac{a}{b}$ means $a \div b$, and $\frac{x^2 + 7xy - 4}{x^3 - y^3}$ means $(x^2 + 7xy - 4) \div (x^3 - y^3)$.

Since a rational expression indicates division, we cannot replace the variables in a denominator with numbers that make the denominator zero.

Multiplying by 1

Objective: Multiply by 1 to obtain equivalent rational expressions.

To multiply rational expressions, we multiply numerators and denominators.

Theorem 6-1

Multiplication of Rational Expressions

For any rational expressions $\frac{a}{b}$ and $\frac{c}{d}$, where b and d are nonzero, $\frac{a}{b}\cdot\frac{c}{d} = \frac{a\cdot c}{b\cdot d}$.

Any rational expression with the same numerator and denominator is equivalent to 1.

$\frac{y+5}{y+5}$, $\frac{4x^2 - 5}{4x^2 - 5}$, $\frac{-1}{-1}$ Each represents the number 1 for all acceptable replacements.

Any number multiplied by 1 is that same number, so we can multiply by 1 to get equivalent expressions.

EXAMPLE 1 Multiply $\frac{x+y}{5}$ by 1, using $\frac{x-y}{x-y}$ for 1.

$$\frac{x+y}{5}\cdot\frac{x-y}{x-y} = \frac{(x+y)(x-y)}{5(x-y)} \quad \text{Multiplying}$$
$$= \frac{x^2 - y^2}{5x - 5y}$$

The expressions $\frac{x+y}{5}$ and $\frac{x^2 - y^2}{5x - 5y}$ are equivalent. They represent the same number for all replacements, except those that make a denominator zero.

Try This Multiply.

a. $\frac{3x + 2y}{5x + 4y}\cdot\frac{x}{x}$ $\frac{3x^2 + 2xy}{5x^2 + 4xy}$ **b.** $\frac{2x^2 - y}{3x + 4}\cdot\frac{3x + 2}{3x + 2}$ $\frac{6x^3 + 4x^2 - 3xy - 2y}{9x^2 + 18x + 8}$ **c.** $\frac{2a - 5}{a - b}\cdot\frac{-1}{-1}$ $\frac{5 - 2a}{b - a}$

Simplifying Rational Expressions

Objective: Simplify rational expressions.

We can simplify a rational expression by reversing the procedure of multiplying by 1. First we factor both the numerator and denominator, then we remove a factor of 1.

EXAMPLES Simplify.

2. $\frac{5x^2}{x} = \frac{5x \cdot x}{1 \cdot x}$ Factoring numerator and denominator

$= \frac{5x}{1} \cdot \frac{x}{x}$ Factoring the rational expression

$= 5x$ Simplifying

3. $\frac{4a + 8}{2} = \frac{2 \cdot 2a + 2 \cdot 4}{2 \cdot 1} = \frac{2(2a + 4)}{2 \cdot 1} = \frac{2}{2} \cdot \frac{2a + 4}{1} = 2a + 4$

Try This Simplify.

d. $\frac{7x^2}{x}$ $7x$ **e.** $\frac{6a + 9}{3}$ $2a + 3$ **f.** $\frac{20y^2 + 32y}{4y}$ $5y + 8$

EXAMPLES Simplify.

4. $\frac{x^2 - 1}{2x^2 - x - 1} = \frac{(x - 1)(x + 1)}{(2x + 1)(x - 1)}$ Factoring numerator and denominator

$= \frac{x - 1}{x - 1} \cdot \frac{x + 1}{2x + 1}$ Factoring the rational expression

$= 1 \cdot \frac{x + 1}{2x + 1}$

$= \frac{x + 1}{2x + 1}$ Simplifying

5. $\frac{9x^2 + 6xy - 3y^2}{12x^2 - 12y^2} = \frac{3(x + y)(3x - y)}{12(x + y)(x - y)}$ Factoring

$= \frac{3(x + y)}{3(x + y)} \cdot \frac{3x - y}{4(x - y)}$

$= \frac{3x - y}{4(x - y)}$ Simplifying

After removing all possible factors of 1, we usually leave the numerator and denominator in factored form.

Try This Simplify.

g. $\frac{6x^2 + 4x}{2x^2 + 4x}$ $\frac{3x + 2}{x + 2}$ **h.** $\frac{y^2 + 3y + 2}{y^2 - 1}$ $\frac{y + 2}{y - 1}$ **i.** $\frac{10x^2 - 25xy + 15y^2}{7x^2 + 7xy - 14y^2}$ $\frac{5(2x - 3y)}{7(x + 2y)}$

Simplifying Rational Expressions

Show students that factoring is the opposite of multiplication.

Point out that in Example 2 the expressions $\frac{5x^2}{x}$ and $5x$ are equivalent only for acceptable replacements. When $x = 0$, the first expression is undefined, and the expressions are *not* equivalent. Such exceptions will not be noted in this chapter, but when students simplify rational expressions they should be aware that some unacceptable replacements may exist.

Chalkboard Examples

Simplify.

1. $\frac{3a^3}{a}$

$\frac{3a^2 \cdot a}{1 \cdot a}$

$= 3a^2$

2. $\frac{7x + 21}{7}$

$\frac{7(x + 3)}{7}$

$= x + 3$

3. $\frac{x^2 + 5x + 4}{x^2 + 2x + 1}$

$\frac{(x + 1)(x + 4)}{(x + 1)^2}$

$= \frac{x + 4}{x + 1}$

4. $\frac{4x^2 + 12x + 8}{x^2 + 5x + 6}$

$\frac{4(x + 1)(x + 2)}{(x + 2)(x + 3)}$

$= \frac{4(x + 1)}{x + 3}$

Multiplying and Simplifying

Point out the analogy between multiplication of rational expressions and the multiplication of rational numbers. In general, students should use arithmetic rules as a guideline for algebraic rules.

Chalkboard Examples

Multiply and simplify.

1. $\frac{x^2+6x+8}{x^2+4x+3} \cdot \frac{x+3}{x+2}$

$\frac{(x+2)(x+4)}{(x+1)(x+3)} \cdot \frac{x+3}{x+2}$

$= \frac{x+4}{x+1}$

2. $\frac{uv+7u^2}{6u+6v} \cdot \frac{3u^2+6uv+3v^2}{7u^2+uv}$

$\frac{u(v+7u)}{2 \cdot 3(u+v)} \cdot \frac{3(u+v)^2}{u(7u+v)}$

$= \frac{u+v}{2}$

Dividing and Simplifying

Point out that Theorem 6-3 is identical to the rule for arithmetic division.

Avoiding Common Errors

Students often improperly "cancel" individual terms of an expression. For example, $\frac{x^2+1}{x+1}$ cannot be simplified. However, many students will cancel terms to obtain x. Stress that common factors, not terms, can be reduced or "cancelled."

Multiplying and Simplifying

Objective: Multiply and simplify rational expressions.

We can simplify products of rational expressions by first factoring numerators and denominators, then removing factors of 1.

EXAMPLES Multiply and simplify.

6. $\frac{x+2}{x-2} \cdot \frac{x^2-4}{x^2+x-2} = \frac{(x+2)(x^2-4)}{(x-2)(x^2+x-2)}$ Multiplying numerators and denominators

$= \frac{(x+2)(x-2)(x+2)}{(x-2)(x+2)(x-1)}$ Factoring numerator and denominator

$= \frac{(x+2)(x-2)}{(x+2)(x-2)} \cdot \frac{x+2}{x-1}$

$= \frac{x+2}{x-1}$ Simplifying

7. $\frac{a^3-b^3}{a^2-b^2} \cdot \frac{a^2+2ab+b^2}{a^2+ab+b^2} = \frac{(a^3-b^3)(a^2+2ab+b^2)}{(a^2-b^2)(a^2+ab+b^2)}$

$= \frac{(a-b)(a^2+ab+b^2)(a+b)(a+b)}{(a-b)(a+b)(a^2+ab+b^2)}$

$= \frac{(a-b)(a^2+ab+b^2)(a+b)}{(a-b)(a^2+ab+b^2)(a+b)} \cdot \frac{a+b}{1}$

$= \frac{a+b}{1}$

$= a+b$

Try This Multiply and simplify.

j. $\frac{(x-y)^2}{x+y} \cdot \frac{3x+3y}{x^2-y^2}$ $\frac{3(x-y)}{x+y}$

k. $\frac{a^3+b^3}{a^2-b^2} \cdot \frac{a^2-2ab+b^2}{a^2-ab+b^2}$ $a-b$

Dividing and Simplifying

Objective: Divide and simplify rational expressions.

Two expressions are reciprocals of each other if their product is 1. The reciprocal of a fraction $\frac{a}{b}$ is the fraction $\frac{b}{a}$. This is also true for rational expressions.

Theorem 6-2

Reciprocals of Rational Expressions

For any rational expression $\frac{a}{b}$ that is nonzero, its reciprocal is $\frac{b}{a}$.

EXAMPLES Find the reciprocal.

8. $\frac{x + 2y}{3x^2y + 7}$ The reciprocal of $\frac{x + 2y}{3x^2y + 7}$ is $\frac{3x^2y + 7}{x + 2y}$.

9. $y - 8$ The reciprocal of $y - 8$ is $\frac{1}{y - 8}$.

10. $\frac{1}{x^2 + 3}$ The reciprocal of $\frac{1}{x^2 + 3}$ is $x^2 + 3$.

Try This Find the reciprocal.

l. $\frac{x + 3}{x - 5}$ $\frac{x - 5}{x + 3}$ m. $x + 7$ $\frac{1}{x + 7}$ n. $\frac{1}{y^3 - 9}$ $y^3 - 9$

Recall that we can always divide by multiplying by the reciprocal. This is also true for rational expressions.

Theorem 6-3

Division of Rational Expressions

For any rational expressions $\frac{a}{b}$ and $\frac{c}{d}$ for which $\frac{c}{d}$ is nonzero,

$$\frac{a}{b} \div \frac{c}{d} = \frac{a}{b} \cdot \frac{d}{c}$$

(We can divide by multiplying by the reciprocal.)

EXAMPLES Divide and simplify.

11. $\frac{x - 2}{x + 1} \div \frac{x + 5}{x - 3} = \frac{x - 2}{x + 1} \cdot \frac{x - 3}{x + 5}$ Multiplying by the reciprocal

$= \frac{(x - 2)(x - 3)}{(x + 1)(x + 5)}$ Multiplying numerators and denominators

12. $\frac{a^2 - 1}{a + 1} \div \frac{a^2 - 2a + 1}{a + 1} = \frac{a^2 - 1}{a + 1} \cdot \frac{a + 1}{a^2 - 2a + 1}$ Multiplying by the reciprocal

$= \frac{(a + 1)(a - 1)}{a + 1} \cdot \frac{a + 1}{(a - 1)(a - 1)}$ Factoring numerators and denominators

$= \frac{(a + 1)(a - 1)}{(a + 1)(a - 1)} \cdot \frac{a + 1}{a - 1}$

$= \frac{a + 1}{a - 1}$ Simplifying

Try This Divide and simplify.

o. $\frac{x^2 + 7x + 10}{2x - 4} \div \frac{x^2 - 3x - 10}{x - 2}$ $\frac{(x + 5)}{2(x - 5)}$ p. $\frac{a^2 - b^2}{ab} \div \frac{a^2 - 2ab + b^2}{2a^2b^2}$ $\frac{2ab(a + b)}{(a - b)}$

Chalkboard Examples

Find the reciprocal.

1. $\frac{x + y}{z}$

$\frac{z}{x + y}$

2. $3a + b$

$\frac{1}{3a + b}$

3. $\frac{1}{3 + y^2}$

$3 + y^2$

Divide and simplify.

4. $\frac{x + 6}{x + 1} \div \frac{x + 3}{x + 2}$

$\frac{x + 6}{x + 1} \cdot \frac{x + 2}{x + 3}$

$= \frac{x^2 + 8x + 12}{x^2 + 4x + 3}$

5. $\frac{y^2 + 4x + 4}{y^2 + 6x + 9} \div \frac{y + 2}{y + 3}$

$\frac{y^2 + 4x + 4}{y^2 + 6x + 9} \cdot \frac{y + 3}{y + 2}$

$= \frac{(y + 2)^2(y + 3)}{(y + 3)^2(y + 2)}$

$= \frac{y + 2}{y + 3}$

LESSON QUIZ

1. Simplify.

$\frac{u^2 - 1}{u^2 - 2u + 1}$

$\frac{u + 1}{u - 1}$

2. Multiply and simplify.

$\frac{x + 3}{x + 2} \cdot \frac{x^2 + 4x + 4}{x^2 - 9}$

$\frac{x + 2}{x - 3}$

3. Divide and simplify.

$\frac{x^2 - 25}{x + 4} \div \frac{x^2 + 10x + 25}{3x + 12}$

$\frac{3(x - 5)}{x + 5}$

Assignment Guide
Algebra: 1–32 e/o, MR

Alg w/Finite or Trig: 1–38 e/o, 39, MR

Comprehensive: 1–38 m3, 39–44, MR

ANSWERS

Exercises

1. $\frac{3x(x+1)}{3x(x+3)}$
2. $\frac{(4-y^2)\cdot(-1)}{(6-y)\cdot(-1)}$
3. $\frac{(t-3)(t+3)}{(t+2)(t+3)}$
4. $\frac{(p-4)(p+5)}{(p-5)(p+5)}$

23. 3
24. $6x^2$
25. $\frac{(y-3)(y+2)}{y}$
26. $\frac{(x+2)(x+4)}{x}$
27. $\frac{2a+1}{a+2}$
28. $\frac{5x+2}{x-3}$
29. $\frac{(x+4)(x+2)}{3(x-5)}$
30. $\frac{(y+6)(y+3)}{3(y-4)}$
31. $\frac{x^2+4x+16}{(x+4)^2}$
32. $\frac{4y^2-6y+9}{(4y-1)(2y-3)}$

6-1 EXERCISES

A

Multiply to obtain equivalent expressions. Do not simplify.

1. $\frac{3x}{3x}\cdot\frac{x+1}{x+3}$ **2.** $\frac{4-y^2}{6-y}\cdot\frac{-1}{-1}$ **3.** $\frac{t-3}{t+2}\cdot\frac{t+3}{t+3}$ **4.** $\frac{p-4}{p-5}\cdot\frac{p+5}{p+5}$

Simplify.

5. $\frac{3a-6}{3}$ $a-2$ **6.** $\frac{4y-12}{4y+12}$ $\frac{y-3}{y+3}$ **7.** $\frac{8x+16}{8x-16}$ $\frac{x+2}{x-2}$ **8.** $\frac{t^2-16}{t^2-8t+16}$ $\frac{t+4}{t-4}$

9. $\frac{p^2-25}{p^2+10p+25}$ $\frac{p-5}{p+5}$ **10.** $\frac{x^2+7x-8}{4x^2-8x+4}$ $\frac{x+8}{4(x-1)}$ **11.** $\frac{y^2+4y-12}{3y^2-12y+12}$ $\frac{y+6}{3(y-2)}$

12. $\frac{x^4-4x^2}{x^3+2x^2}$ $x-2$ **13.** $\frac{a^3-b^3}{a^2-b^2}$ $\frac{a^2+ab+b^2}{a+b}$ **14.** $\frac{x^3+y^3}{x^2-y^2}$ $\frac{x^2-xy+y^2}{x-y}$

Multiply and simplify.

15. $\frac{x^2-16}{x^2}\cdot\frac{x^2-4x}{x^2-x-12}$ $\frac{(x+4)(x-4)}{x(x+3)}$ **16.** $\frac{y^2+10y+25}{y^2-9}\cdot\frac{y+3}{y+5}$ $\frac{y+5}{y-3}$

17. $\frac{y^2-16}{2y+6}\cdot\frac{y+3}{y-4}$ $\frac{y+4}{2}$ **18.** $\frac{m^2-n^2}{4m+4n}\cdot\frac{m+n}{m-n}$ $\frac{m+n}{4}$

19. $\frac{x^2-2x-35}{2x^3-3x^2}\cdot\frac{4x^3-9x}{7x-49}$ $\frac{(x+5)(2x+3)}{7x}$ **20.** $\frac{y^2-10y+9}{y^2-1}\cdot\frac{y+4}{y^2-5y-36}$ $\frac{1}{y+1}$

21. $\frac{x^2-y^2}{x^3-y^3}\cdot\frac{x^2+xy+y^2}{x^2+2xy+y^2}$ $\frac{1}{x+y}$ **22.** $\frac{4x^2-9y^2}{8x^3-27y^3}\cdot\frac{4x^2+6xy+9y^2}{4x^2+12xy+9y^2}$ $\frac{1}{2x+3y}$

Divide and simplify.

23. $\frac{3y+15}{y}\div\frac{y+5}{y}$ **24.** $\frac{6x+12}{x}\div\frac{x+2}{x^3}$ **25.** $\frac{y^2-9}{y}\div\frac{y+3}{y+2}$

26. $\frac{x^2-4}{x}\div\frac{x-2}{x+4}$ **27.** $\frac{4a^2-1}{a^2-4}\div\frac{2a-1}{a-2}$ **28.** $\frac{25x^2-4}{x^2-9}\div\frac{5x-2}{x+3}$

29. $\frac{x^2-16}{x^2-10x+25}\div\frac{3x-12}{x^2-3x-10}$ **30.** $\frac{y^2-36}{y^2-8y+16}\div\frac{3y-18}{y^2-y-12}$

31. $\frac{x^3-64}{x^3+64}\div\frac{x^2-16}{x^2-4x+16}$ **32.** $\frac{8y^3+27}{64y^3-1}\div\frac{4y^2-9}{16y^2+4y+1}$

B

33. $\frac{x(x+1)-2(x+3)}{(x+1)(x+2)(x+3)}$ $\frac{x-3}{(x+1)(x+3)}$ **34.** $\frac{2x-5(x+2)-(x-2)}{x^2-4}$ $\frac{-4}{x-2}$

35. $\frac{m^2-t^2}{m^2+t^2+m+t+2mt}$ $\frac{m-t}{m+t+1}$ **36.** $\frac{a^3-2a^2+2a-4}{a^3-2a^2-3a+6}$ $\frac{a^2+2}{a^2-3}$

37. $\frac{x^3+x^2-y^3-y^2}{x^2-2xy+y^2}$ $\frac{x^2+xy+y^2+x+y}{x-y}$ **38.** $\frac{u^6+v^6+2u^3v^3}{u^3-v^3+u^2v-uv^2}$ $\frac{(u^2-uv+v^2)^2}{(u-v)}$

39. ***Critical Thinking*** Write three different rational expressions that, when simplified, are equivalent to $\frac{x+3}{x-1}$. Answers may vary.

Challenge

Simplify.

40. $\dfrac{x^5 - x^3 + x^2 - 1 - (x^3 - 1)(x + 1)^2}{(x^2 - 1)^2}$ $\dfrac{-2x}{x-1}$

Prove the following theorems.

41. Theorem 6-1 **42.** Theorem 6-2 **43.** Theorem 6-3

44. For any rational expressions a and b, $(ab)^{-1} = a^{-1}b^{-1}$.
Prove this theorem by showing that the product of $a^{-1}b^{-1}ab$ is 1.

Mixed Review

Arrange in decreasing degrees of x. **45.** $2xy^2 + 4x^3y^3 - x^7 + x^4 - \frac{1}{2}$

Factor. **46.** $81x^4 - 16$ **47.** $x^2 - 4x + 4 - y^2$ **48.** $ab - bc + 2ad - 2cd$

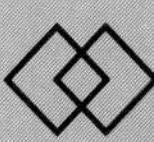

Connections: Calculus

The slope of a linear function does not change. For any two points, the slope is the same. For a curve, the slope is constantly changing. The slope is a function of x, and is the slope of the line tangent to $f(x)$ at any point on the curve.

We can find the **slope function,** $f'(x)$, by first finding the slope of a line through any two points P and Q of $f(x)$ that are h units apart on the x-axis, $(x, f(x))$, and $(x + h, f(x + h))$.

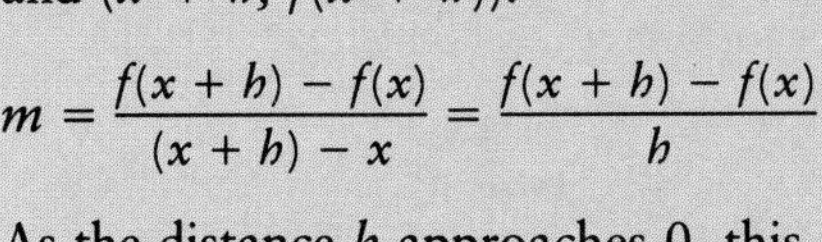

$$m = \frac{f(x + h) - f(x)}{(x + h) - x} = \frac{f(x + h) - f(x)}{h}$$

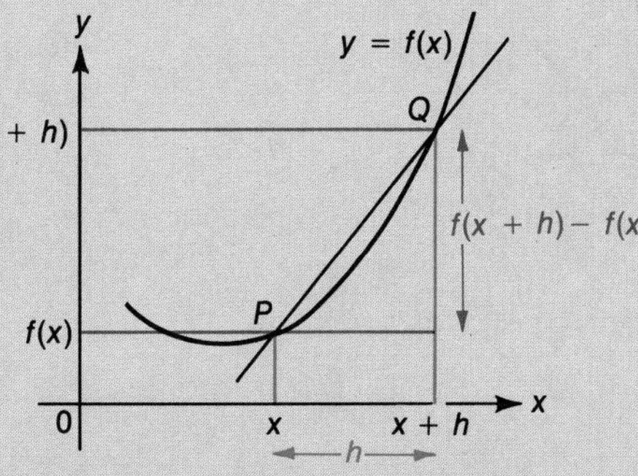

As the distance h approaches 0, this expression approaches the slope of the tangent line at P.

Example: Find the slope function $f'(x)$ for $f(x) = x^2$.

$$m = \frac{f(x + h) - f(x)}{h} = \frac{(x + h)^2 - x^2}{h} = \frac{x^2 + 2hx + h^2 - x^2}{h} = \frac{2hx + h^2}{h} = 2x + h$$

When h approaches 0, $2x + h$ approaches $2x$. Thus the slope function of $f(x) = x^2$ is given by $f'(x) = 2x$. So when $x = 0$, the slope of $f(x)$ is 0; when x is 5, the slope is 10; and so on.

Find the slope function $f'(x)$.

a. $f(x) = x^3$ **b.** $f(x) = x^4$ **c.** $f(x) = x^5$ **d.** $f(x) = \dfrac{1}{x}$

41. $\frac{a}{b} \cdot \frac{c}{d} = (ab^{-1})(cd^{-1}) = (ac)(b^{-1}d^{-1})$
$= (ac)(bd)^{-1} = \frac{ac}{bd}$

42. $\frac{a}{b} \cdot \frac{b}{a} = \frac{a \cdot b}{b \cdot a} = \frac{a \cdot b}{a \cdot b} = 1$; thus the reciprocal of $\frac{a}{b}$ is $\frac{b}{a}$.

43. $\frac{a}{b} \div \frac{c}{d}$ is that number which when multiplied by $\frac{c}{d}$ gives $\frac{a}{b}$. We assert that $\frac{a}{b} \cdot \frac{d}{c}$ is that number by multiplying it by $\frac{c}{d}$.
$\left(\frac{a}{b} \cdot \frac{d}{c}\right) \cdot \frac{c}{d} = \frac{a}{b} \cdot \left(\frac{d}{c} \cdot \frac{c}{d}\right) = \frac{a}{b} \cdot 1 = \frac{a}{b}$

44. $(a^{-1}b^{-1})(ab) = (aa^{-1})(bb^{-1})$
$= 1 \cdot 1 = 1$, using associative and commutative properties and property of multiplicative inverses. Thus, $(ab)^{-1} = a^{-1}b^{-1}$.

Mixed Review

45. $-x^7 + x^4 + 4x^3y^3 + 2xy^2 - \frac{1}{2}$
46. $(9x^2 + 4)(3x + 2)(3x - 2)$
47. $(x - 2 + y)(x - 2 - y)$
48. $(b + 2d)(a - c)$

Connections: Calculus

Note that when $h = 0$, $\frac{f(x + h) - f(x)}{h} = \frac{0}{0}$, which is undefined. This is why we say that h *approaches* 0. Note that we can use the same method to find the slope of a line:

$f(x) = -3x + 4$

$m = \dfrac{-3(x + h) + 4 - (-3x + 4)}{h}$

$= \dfrac{-3x - 3h + 4 + 3x - 4}{h}$

$= \dfrac{-3h}{h} = -3$

Answers
a. $f'(x) = 3x^2$
b. $f'(x) = 4x^3$
c. $f'(x) = 5x^4$
d. $f'(x) = -\frac{1}{x^2}$

6-2

FIRST FIVE MINUTES

Add.

1. $\frac{3}{7} + \frac{5}{7}$

   $\frac{8}{7}$

2. $\frac{4}{3} + \frac{7}{2}$

   $\frac{8}{6} + \frac{21}{6} = \frac{29}{6}$

Addition with Like Denominators

You may want to review the rules for adding and subtracting fractions. Emphasize that this section will use the old rules for fractions in a new way.

Key Questions

- $\frac{3}{8} + \frac{7}{8} = ?$

  $\frac{5}{4}$

- $2a + 5a = ?$

  $7a$

- $\frac{1}{2}x + \frac{1}{2}y = ?$

  $\frac{1}{2}(x + y)$

Chalkboard Examples

Add.

1. $\frac{5}{x} + \frac{3}{x}$

   $\frac{8}{x}$

2. $\frac{3}{x+1} + \frac{8}{x+1}$

   $\frac{11}{x+1}$

3. Subtract.

   $\frac{4x+3}{x+1} - \frac{2x+1}{x+1}$

   $\frac{4x+3-(2x+1)}{x+1}$

   $= \frac{4x+3-2x-1}{x+1}$

   $= \frac{2x+2}{x+1} = \frac{2(x+1)}{(x+1)} = 2$

6-2 Addition and Subtraction

 *Master Grapher* Worksheet 6, *Graphing Rational Expressions*, can be used for lesson closure.

TI-81 Investigation 1 (page 855) can be used with this lesson.

Addition with Like Denominators

Objective: Add or subtract rational expressions when the denominators are the same.

When we add or subtract rational expressions with the same denominator, we add or subtract the numerators and keep the same denominator.

Theorem 6-4

Addition of Rational Expressions

For any rational expressions $\frac{a}{c}$ and $\frac{b}{c}$ for which c is nonzero,

$$\frac{a}{c} + \frac{b}{c} = \frac{a+b}{c} \quad \text{and} \quad \frac{a}{c} - \frac{b}{c} = \frac{a-b}{c}$$

EXAMPLE 1 Add.

$$\frac{3+x}{x} + \frac{4}{x} = \frac{3+x+4}{x} = \frac{7+x}{x} \quad \text{Adding numerators}$$

Example 1 shows that $\frac{3+x}{x} + \frac{4}{x}$ and $\frac{7+x}{x}$ are equivalent expressions. This means that both expressions represent the same number for all replacements except 0.

EXAMPLE 2 Subtract.

$$\frac{4x+5}{x+3} - \frac{x-2}{x+3} = \frac{4x+5-(x-2)}{x+3} \quad \text{Subtracting numerators}$$

$$= \frac{4x+5-x+2}{x+3} = \frac{3x+7}{x+3}$$

Try This Add or subtract.

a. $\frac{5+y}{y} + \frac{7}{y}$ $\frac{12+y}{y}$

b. $\frac{2x^2+5x-9}{x-5} + \frac{x^2-19x+4}{x-5}$ $3x+1$

c. $\frac{a}{b+2} - \frac{b}{b+2}$ $\frac{a-b}{b+2}$

d. $\frac{4y+7}{x^2+y^2} - \frac{3y-5}{x^2+y^2}$ $\frac{y+12}{x^2+y^2}$

When one denominator is the additive inverse of the other, we first multiply one expression by $\frac{-1}{-1}$. This will give us a common denominator.

EXAMPLE 3 Add.

$$\frac{9}{2a} + \frac{a^3}{-2a} = \frac{9}{2a} + \frac{-1}{-1} \cdot \frac{a^3}{-2a} \quad \text{Multiplying by } \frac{-1}{-1}$$

$$= \frac{9}{2a} + \frac{-a^3}{2a} = \frac{9 - a^3}{2a} \quad \text{Adding numerators}$$

Try This Add or subtract.

e. $\frac{3x^2 + 4}{x - 5} + \frac{x^2 - 7}{5 - x}$ $\frac{2x^2 + 11}{x - 5}$

f. $\frac{4x^2}{2x - y} - \frac{7x^2}{y - 2x}$ $\frac{11x^2}{2x - y}$

Addition with Unlike Denominators

Objective: Add or subtract rational expressions when denominators are different.

When we add or subtract rational expressions with different denominators that are not additive inverses of each other, we must first find the least common denominator or LCD. The LCD is the least common multiple (LCM) of the denominators.

To find the LCM of two or more algebraic expressions, we first factor each expression. Then we use each factor the greatest number of times it occurs in any of the factorizations.

To find the LCM of $x^2 - y^2$, $x^3 + y^3$, and $x^2 - 2xy + y^2$ we first factor.

$$x^2 - y^2 = (x + y)(x - y)$$
$$x^3 + y^3 = (x + y)(x^2 - xy + y^2)$$
$$x^2 - 2xy + y^2 = (x + y)(x + y)$$

The LCM is $(x - y)(x + y)(x + y)(x^2 - xy + y^2)$.

In finding LCMs, if factors that are additive inverses occur, we do not use them both. Fot example, if $(a - b)$ occurs in one factorization and $(b - a)$ occurs in another, we do not use them both, since $b - a = -(a - b)$.

EXAMPLE 4 Add.

$$\frac{7a}{8} + \frac{5b}{12a}$$

First find the LCD.

$$8 = 2 \cdot 2 \cdot 2$$
$$12a = 2 \cdot 2 \cdot 3 \cdot a \quad \text{The LCD is } 2^3 \cdot 3 \cdot a\text{, or } 24a.$$

Now we multiply each expression by 1. For each expression we choose a ratio equivalent to 1 that will give us the least common denominator.

Addition with Unlike Denominators

Remind students that prime numbers have only the trivial factors, 1 and the number itself. Numbers with nontrivial factors are called composite numbers.

Math Point

A *perfect number* is one that is the sum of its factors. For example, $6 = 1 + 2 + 3$ and $28 = 1 + 2 + 4 + 7 + 14$. The next perfect number is 496. There are about 18 known perfect numbers, all of which are even.

Key Questions

- Is 17 prime or composite?
  Prime
- What is the prime factorization of 105?
  $3 \cdot 5 \cdot 7$
- What is the LCM of $x^2 - 4$ and $x^2 + 5x + 6$?
  $x^2 - 4 = (x + 2)(x - 2)$
  $x^2 + 5x + 6 = (x + 2)(x + 3)$
  The LCM is $(x + 2)(x - 2)(x + 3)$.

Chalkboard Examples

Add or subtract.

1. $\frac{3}{2x} + \frac{5}{x}$

$\frac{3}{2x} + \frac{10}{2x}$

$= \frac{3 + 10}{2x} = \frac{13}{2x}$

2. $\frac{-3z}{1 - z} - \frac{2z + 1}{z - 1}$

$\frac{-1}{-1} \cdot \frac{-3z}{1 - z} - \frac{2z + 1}{z - 1}$

$= \frac{3z - (2z + 1)}{z - 1}$

$= \frac{3z - 2z - 1}{z - 1}$

$= \frac{z - 1}{z - 1}$

$= 1$

3. $\frac{6}{5} + \frac{3}{x}$

$\frac{6}{5} \cdot \frac{x}{x} + \frac{5}{5} \cdot \frac{3}{x}$

$= \frac{6x + 15}{5x}$

4. $\frac{3x}{x + 2} + \frac{2}{x + 3}$

$\frac{3x}{(x + 2)} \cdot \frac{(x + 3)}{(x + 3)} + \frac{2}{(x + 3)} \cdot \frac{(x + 2)}{(x + 2)}$

$= \frac{3x^2 + 11x + 4}{(x + 2)(x + 3)}$

5. $\frac{4}{x} - \frac{1}{(x + 1)}$

$\frac{4}{x} \cdot \frac{(x + 1)}{(x + 1)} - \frac{1}{(x + 1)} \cdot \frac{x}{x}$

$= \frac{4x + 4 - x}{x(x + 1)}$

$= \frac{3x + 4}{x(x + 1)}$

LESSON QUIZ

1. Add.

$\frac{5}{x + 3} + \frac{x}{x + 3}$

$\frac{x + 5}{x + 3}$

2. Add.

$\frac{5x}{x + 7} + \frac{7}{x}$

$\frac{5x^2 + 7x + 49}{x(x + 7)}$

3. Subtract.

$\frac{3x}{x + 5} - \frac{9}{x + 1}$

$\frac{3x^2 - 6x - 45}{(x + 5)(x + 1)}$

$$\frac{7a}{8} \cdot \frac{3a}{3a} + \frac{5b}{12a} \cdot \frac{2}{2} = \frac{21a^2}{24a} + \frac{10b}{24a} \quad \text{Multiplying each factor by 1}$$

$$= \frac{21a^2 + 10b}{24a}$$

Multiplying by $\frac{3a}{3a}$ in the first term gave us a denominator of $24a$.
Multiplying by $\frac{2}{2}$ in the second term also gave us a denominator of $24a$.

EXAMPLE 5 Add.

$$\frac{1}{2x} + \frac{5x}{x^2 - 1} + \frac{3}{x + 1}$$

We first factor the denominators and find the LCD.

$$2x = 2 \cdot x$$

$$x^2 - 1 = (x - 1)(x + 1) \quad \text{The LCD is } 2x(x - 1)(x + 1).$$

$$x + 1 = x + 1$$

Now we multiply by 1 to get the LCM in each denominator. Then we add and simplify. We leave the result in factored form.

$$\frac{1}{2x} \cdot \frac{(x - 1)(x + 1)}{(x - 1)(x + 1)} + \frac{5x}{(x - 1)(x + 1)} \cdot \frac{2x}{2x} + \frac{3}{x + 1} \cdot \frac{2x(x - 1)}{2x(x - 1)} \quad \text{Multiplying by 1}$$

$$= \frac{(x - 1)(x + 1)}{2x(x - 1)(x + 1)} + \frac{10x^2}{2x(x - 1)(x + 1)} + \frac{6x(x - 1)}{2x(x - 1)(x + 1)} \quad \text{Multiplying in the numerator}$$

$$= \frac{x^2 - 1}{2x(x - 1)(x + 1)} + \frac{10x^2}{2x(x - 1)(x + 1)} + \frac{6x^2 - 6x}{2x(x - 1)(x + 1)}$$

$$= \frac{17x^2 - 6x - 1}{2x(x - 1)(x + 1)}$$

EXAMPLE 6 Subtract.

$$\frac{2y + 1}{y^2 - 7y + 6} - \frac{y + 3}{y^2 - 5y - 6} = \frac{2y + 1}{(y - 6)(y - 1)} - \frac{y + 3}{(y - 6)(y + 1)} \quad \text{The LCD is } (y - 6)(y - 1)(y + 1).$$

$$= \frac{2y + 1}{(y - 6)(y - 1)} \cdot \frac{y + 1}{y + 1} - \frac{y + 3}{(y - 6)(y + 1)} \cdot \frac{y - 1}{y - 1}$$

$$= \frac{(2y + 1)(y + 1) - (y + 3)(y - 1)}{(y - 6)(y - 1)(y + 1)}$$

$$= \frac{2y^2 + 3y + 1 - (y^2 + 2y - 3)}{(y - 6)(y - 1)(y + 1)}$$

$$= \frac{2y^2 + 3y + 1 - y^2 - 2y + 3}{(y - 6)(y - 1)(y + 1)}$$

$$= \frac{y^2 + y + 4}{(y - 6)(y - 1)(y + 1)}$$

Try This Add or subtract. See Additional Answers.

g. $\frac{3x}{7} + \frac{4y}{3x}$ **h.** $\frac{4y - 5}{y^2 - 7y + 12} - \frac{y + 7}{y^2 + 2y - 15}$ **i.** $\frac{a}{a + 3} - \frac{a - 4}{a}$

EXAMPLE 7 Calculate.

$$\frac{2x}{x^2 - 4} + \frac{5}{2 - x} - \frac{1}{x + 2}$$

$$= \frac{2x}{(x - 2)(x + 2)} + \frac{-5}{x - 2} - \frac{1}{x + 2} \quad \text{Factoring and multiplying by } \frac{-1}{-1}$$

$$= \frac{2x}{(x - 2)(x + 2)} + \frac{-5}{x - 2} \cdot \frac{x + 2}{x + 2} - \frac{1}{x + 2} \cdot \frac{x - 2}{x - 2} \quad \text{The LCD is } (x - 2)(x + 2).$$

$$= \frac{2x - 5(x + 2) - (x - 2)}{(x - 2)(x + 2)} = \frac{2x - 5x - 10 - x + 2}{(x - 2)(x + 2)}$$

$$= \frac{-4x - 8}{(x - 2)(x + 2)} = \frac{-4(x + 2)}{(x - 2)(x + 2)}$$

$$= \frac{-4}{x - 2}$$

Try This Calculate. See Additional Answers.

j. $\frac{8x}{x^2 - 1} + \frac{2}{1 - x} - \frac{4}{x + 1}$ **k.** $\frac{7y}{y^2 - y} + \frac{8}{2 - y} - \frac{3}{y + 2}$

6-2 EXERCISES

A

Add or subtract.

1. $\frac{3y}{x} + \frac{5y}{x}$ $\frac{8y}{x}$
2. $\frac{-8x}{3y} + \frac{6x}{3y}$ $\frac{-2x}{3y}$
3. $\frac{-9y}{x + y} + \frac{16y}{x + y}$ $\frac{7y}{x + y}$
4. $\frac{3a^2}{a - b} + \frac{-4a^2}{a - b}$ $\frac{-a^2}{a - b}$
5. $\frac{25xy}{x^2 + y^2} - \frac{16xy}{x^2 + y^2}$ $\frac{9xy}{x^2 + y^2}$
6. $\frac{37a^2b}{a^2 - b} - \frac{42a^2b}{a^2 - b}$ $\frac{-5a^2b}{a^2 - b}$
7. $\frac{a - 3b}{a + b} + \frac{a + 5b}{a + b}$ 2
8. $\frac{x - 5y}{x + y} + \frac{x + 7y}{x + y}$ 2
9. $\frac{4y + 3}{y - 2} - \frac{y - 2}{y - 2}$ $\frac{3y + 5}{y - 2}$
10. $\frac{3t + 2}{t - 4} - \frac{t - 4}{t - 4}$ $\frac{2t + 6}{t - 4}$
11. $\frac{a^2}{a - b} + \frac{b^2}{b - a}$ $a + b$
12. $\frac{r^2}{r - s} + \frac{s^2}{s - r}$ $r + s$
13. $\frac{3}{x} + \frac{8}{-x}$ $\frac{11}{x}$
14. $\frac{2}{a} - \frac{5}{-a}$ $\frac{7}{a}$
15. $\frac{2x - 10}{x^2 - 25} - \frac{5 - x}{25 - x^2}$ $\frac{1}{x + 5}$
16. $\frac{y - 9}{y^2 - 16} - \frac{7 - y}{16 - y^2}$ $\frac{-2}{y^2 - 16}$

Assignment Guide

Algebra: Day 1: 1–19 e/o, MR
Day 2: 20–38 e/o

Alg w/Finite or Trig: 1–38 m3, 39–43 e/o, 44, MR

Comprehensive: 1–38 m4, 39–43 e/o, 44, 45–51 e/o, MR, assign w. 6-3

ADDITIONAL ANSWERS

Try This

g. $\frac{9x^2 + 28y}{21x}$

h. $\frac{3y^2 + 12y + 3}{(y - 4)(y - 3)(y + 5)}$

i. $\frac{a + 12}{a(a + 3)}$

j. $\frac{2}{x - 1}$

k. $\frac{4y^2 - y + 18}{(y - 1)(2 - y)(y + 2)}$

Exercises

17. $\frac{x + y}{x - y}$

18. $\frac{a^2 + 7ab + b^2}{a^2 - b^2}$

19. $\frac{3x - 4}{(x - 2)(x - 1)}$

20. $\frac{3y^2 + 7y + 14}{(2y - 5)(y + 2)(y - 1)}$

21. $\frac{8x + 1}{x^2 - 1}$

22. $\frac{4y + 17}{y^2 - 4}$

23. $\frac{2x - 14}{15x + 75}$

24. $\frac{y - 34}{20y + 40}$

25. $\frac{-a^2 + 7ab - b^2}{a^2 - b^2}$

26. $\frac{-x^2 + 4xy - y^2}{x^2 - y^2}$

27. $\frac{y}{(y - 2)(y - 3)}$

28. $\frac{2x^2 + 21x}{(x - 2)(x - 4)(x + 3)}$

29. $\frac{3y - 10}{y^2 - y - 20}$

30. $\frac{11y - 3}{(y + 3)^2(y - 3)}$

31. $\frac{3y^2 - 3y - 29}{(y - 3)(y + 8)(y - 4)}$

32. $\frac{5y^2 - 11y - 6}{(y - 2)(y - 5)(y - 3)}$

33. $\frac{2x^2 - 13x + 7}{(x + 3)(x - 1)(x - 3)}$

34. $\frac{2p^2 + 7p + 10}{(p - 4)(p + 6)(p + 4)}$

35. 0

36. $\frac{-y}{y^2 + 2y - 3}$

37. $\frac{-3x^2 - 3x - 4}{x^2 - 1}$

38. $\frac{-14y^2 - 3y + 3}{4y^2 - 1}$

44. Answers may vary. Example: $\frac{2xy}{(x - y)^2}, \frac{3x^2y}{x + y}, \frac{1}{x^2 + xy + y^2}$

45. $\frac{x - 4}{x - 5}$

46. $\frac{x + 4}{x + 5}$

47. $\frac{x^2 - 30}{x^2 - 11}$

Add or subtract.

17. $\frac{4xy}{x^2 - y^2} + \frac{x - y}{x + y}$

18. $\frac{5ab}{a^2 - b^2} + \frac{a + b}{a - b}$

19. $\frac{9x + 2}{3x^2 - 2x - 8} + \frac{7}{3x^2 + x - 4}$

20. $\frac{3y + 2}{2y^2 - y - 10} + \frac{8}{2y^2 - 7y + 5}$

21. $\frac{4}{x + 1} + \frac{x + 2}{x^2 - 1} + \frac{3}{x - 1}$

22. $\frac{-2}{y + 2} + \frac{5}{y - 2} + \frac{y + 3}{y^2 - 4}$

23. $\frac{x - 1}{3x + 15} - \frac{x + 3}{5x + 25}$

24. $\frac{y - 2}{4y + 8} - \frac{y + 6}{5y + 10}$

25. $\frac{5ab}{a^2 - b^2} - \frac{a - b}{a + b}$

26. $\frac{6xy}{x^2 - y^2} - \frac{x + y}{x - y}$

27. $\frac{3y}{y^2 - 7y + 10} - \frac{2y}{y^2 - 8y + 15}$

28. $\frac{5x}{x^2 - 6x + 8} - \frac{3x}{x^2 - x - 12}$

29. $\frac{y}{y^2 - y - 20} + \frac{2}{y + 4}$

30. $\frac{6}{y^2 + 6y + 9} + \frac{5}{y^2 - 9}$

31. $\frac{3y + 2}{y^2 + 5y - 24} + \frac{7}{y^2 + 4y - 32}$

32. $\frac{3y + 2}{y^2 - 7y + 10} + \frac{2y}{y^2 - 8y + 15}$

33. $\frac{3x - 1}{x^2 + 2x - 3} - \frac{x + 4}{x^2 - 9}$

34. $\frac{3p - 2}{p^2 + 2p - 24} - \frac{p - 3}{p^2 - 16}$

35. $\frac{1}{x + 1} - \frac{x}{x - 2} + \frac{x^2 + 2}{x^2 - x - 2}$

36. $\frac{2}{y + 3} - \frac{y}{y - 1} + \frac{y^2 + 2}{y^2 + 2y - 3}$

37. $\frac{4x}{x^2 - 1} + \frac{3x}{1 - x} - \frac{4}{x - 1}$

38. $\frac{5y}{1 - 2y} - \frac{2y}{2y + 1} + \frac{3}{4y^2 - 1}$

B

Perform the indicated operations and simplify. Write without negative exponents.

39. $2x^{-2} + 3x^{-2}y^{-2} - 7xy^{-1}$ $\frac{2y^2 + 3 - 7x^3y}{x^2y^2}$

40. $5(x - 3)^{-1} + 4(x + 3)^{-1} - 2(x + 3)^{-2}$ $\frac{9x^2 + 28x + 15}{(x - 3)(x + 3)^2}$

41. $4(y - 1)(2y - 5)^{-1} + 5(2y + 3)(5 - 2y)^{-1} + (y - 4)(2y - 5)^{-1}$ $\frac{5y + 23}{5 - 2y}$

Simplify each of the following, using $A = x + y$ and $B = x - y$.

42. $\frac{A + B}{A - B} - \frac{A - B}{A + B}$ $\frac{x^2 - y^2}{xy}$

43. $\left(\frac{1}{A} + \frac{x}{B}\right) \div \left(\frac{1}{B} - \frac{x}{A}\right)$ $\frac{x - y + x^2 + xy}{x + y - x^2 + xy}$

44. ***Critical Thinking*** Find three rational expressions whose LCD is $(x - y)(x - y)(x + y)(x^2 + xy + y^2)$.

Challenge

Consider the following polynomial functions.

$$g(x) = x^2 - 16, h(x) = x^2 + x - 20, d(x) = x^2 - 25$$

Find a simplified expression for each *rational function* given below.

45. $R(x) = \frac{h(x)}{d(x)}$

46. $R(x) = \frac{g(x)}{h(x)}$

47. $R(x) = \frac{d(d(x))}{h(g(x))}$

48. Prove the first part of Theorem 6-4.

49. Prove the second part of Theorem 6-4.

Find the LCM.

50. $x^8 - x^4, x^5 - x^2, x^5 - x^3, x^5 + x^2$ $x^4(x^2+1)(x^2-1)(x^2+x+1)(x^2-x+1)$

51. The LCM of two expressions is $8a^4b^7$. One of the expressions is $2a^3b^7$. List all the possibilities for the other expression. $8a^4, 8a^4b, 8a^4b^2, 8a^4b^3, 8a^4b^4, 8a^4b^5, 8a^4b^6, 8a^4b^7$

Mixed Review

Solve each system of equations.

52. $x + \frac{1}{3}y = 19$
$-\frac{1}{2}x - 4y = -67$

53. $0.25x + 1.25y = 0.84$
$6x + 30y = 20.16$

54. $x - y + z = 6$
$2x + y - z = 0$
$3x - 2y - 4z = -2$

Solve. **55.** $2x^2 - 24x + 22 = 0$ **56.** $256x^4 = 16$ **57.** $2x^3 = 6x^2 + 8x$

Graphing Rational Functions

 TI-81 Investigation 1 (page 855) can be used with this lesson.

Functions can be defined by rational expressions. Consider the function $f(x) = \frac{1}{x-2}$. We can see that this function is not defined when $x = 2$. (Why?) It is interesting to see how the graph of this function behaves when the value of x is close to 2. We first make a table of values and then graph.

Exercises

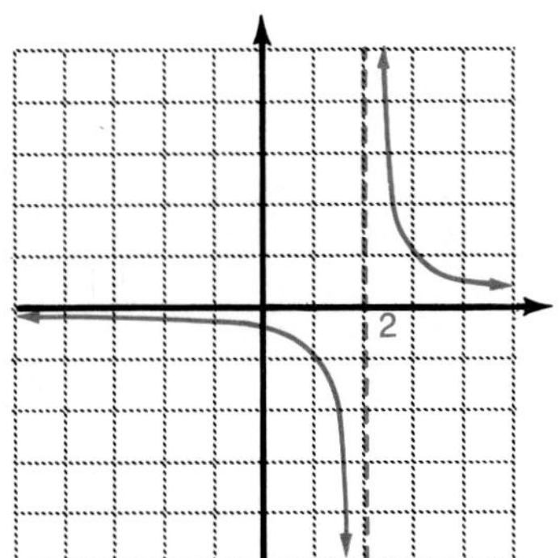

1. What happens to $f(x)$ as x approaches 2?

2. Will the graph of this function ever cross the x-axis? Why or why not?

3. Graph these rational functions. Use your calculator to make a table of values. Observe what happens to $f(x)$ as x approaches any unacceptable value.

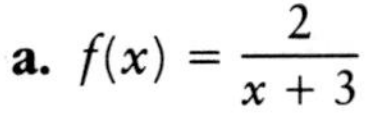

a. $f(x) = \frac{2}{x+3}$ **b.** $f(x) = \frac{1}{x+3}$

4. Graph $f(x) = \frac{x+1}{x^2 - x - 2}$. (Hint: Factor the denominator first. Compare the graph of this rational function with the graph at the right.)

---

48. $\frac{a}{c} + \frac{b}{c} = ac^{-1} + bc^{-1}$
$= (a + b)c^{-1} = \frac{a+b}{c}$

49. $\frac{a}{c} - \frac{b}{c} = ac^{-1} - bc^{-1}$
$= (a - b)c^{-1} = \frac{a-b}{c}$

Mixed Review

52. (14, 15)
53. Dependent; $25x + 125y = 84$
54. $\left(2, -\frac{4}{3}, \frac{8}{3}\right)$ **55.** 1, 11
56. $-\frac{1}{2}, \frac{1}{2}$ **57.** 0, −1, 4

Graphing Rational Functions

You may wish to define the term "asymptote." A line is an asymptote to a curve if the curve approaches the line but never meets it. In the example, the lines $x = 2$ and $y = 0$ are both asymptotes to the curve.

1. As x approaches 2 from the positive side, $f(x)$ becomes larger. As x approaches 2 from the negative side, $f(x)$ becomes smaller.
2. No; there is no value of x for which $f(x) = 0$.
3. a.

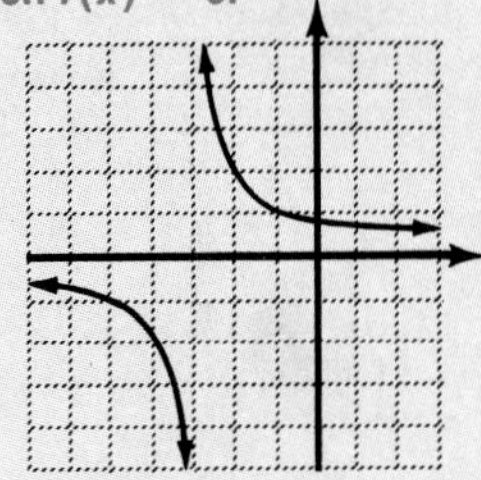

b.

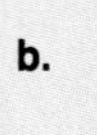
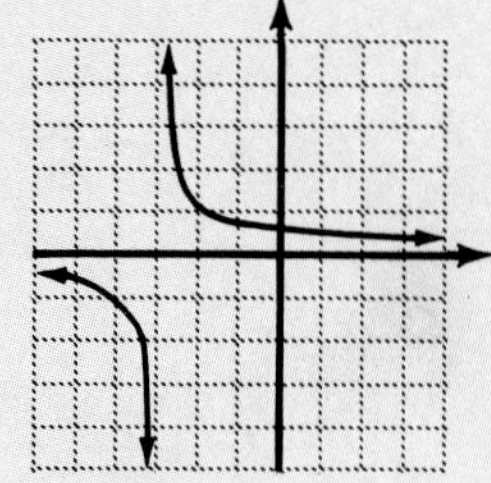

4.

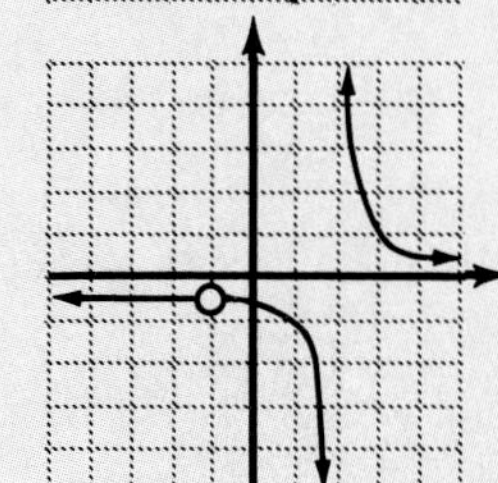

6-3

FIRST FIVE MINUTES

Simplify.

1. $\dfrac{1}{\frac{1}{2}+\frac{3}{4}}$

$\dfrac{1}{\frac{2}{4}+\frac{3}{4}}$

$=\dfrac{1}{\frac{5}{4}}=\dfrac{4}{5}$

2. $\dfrac{\frac{2}{3}}{\frac{4}{9}}$

$\dfrac{2}{3}\cdot\dfrac{9}{4}=\dfrac{3}{2}$

Remind students of the definition of *rational expression:* the ratio of polynomial expressions. Point out that expressions such as x^{-1} and a^{-3} are rational expressions, since they can be represented as the ratios $\frac{1}{x}$ and $\frac{1}{a^3}$.

Key Questions

- Is the number 2 a rational expression? Yes, rational numbers, like $\frac{2}{1}$, are rational expressions.
- Is $\sqrt{x}$ a rational expression? No, it is not a polynomial or a ratio of polynomials.
- Is x^{-2} a rational expression? Yes, it can be written in the equivalent form $\frac{1}{x^2}$.

6-3 Complex Rational Expressions

Objective: Simplify complex rational expressions.

A **complex rational expression** is one that has a rational expression either in its numerator, its denominator, or both. Here are some examples of complex rational expressions.

$$\frac{x}{x-\frac{1}{3}},\quad \frac{2x-\frac{4x}{3y}}{\frac{5x^2+2x}{6y^2}},\quad \frac{a^{-1}+b^{-1}}{a^{-3}b^{-3}},\quad \frac{\frac{5}{x}}{\frac{x}{y}}$$

Complex rational expressions can be simplified. One method is to find the LCD of *all* denominators appearing in the expression, then multiply both the numerator and denominator by the LCD.

EXAMPLE 1 Simplify $\dfrac{1+\frac{1}{x}}{1-\frac{1}{x^2}}$.

$$\frac{1+\frac{1}{x}}{1-\frac{1}{x^2}}=\frac{x^2}{x^2}\cdot\frac{\left(1+\frac{1}{x}\right)}{\left(1-\frac{1}{x^2}\right)}$$ The LCD is x^2.

$$=\frac{x^2+\frac{x^2}{x}}{x^2-\frac{x^2}{x^2}}$$ Using the distributive property

$$=\frac{x^2+x}{x^2-1}$$ Simplifying

$$=\frac{x(x+1)}{(x-1)(x+1)}$$ Factoring the numerator and denominator

$$=\frac{(x+1)}{(x+1)}\cdot\frac{x}{(x-1)}$$ Factoring the rational expression

$$=\frac{x}{x-1}$$ Simplifying

Try This Simplify.

a. $\dfrac{y+\frac{1}{2}}{y-\frac{1}{7}}$ $\dfrac{14y+7}{14y-2}$

b. $\dfrac{1-\frac{1}{x}}{1-\frac{1}{x^2}}$ $\dfrac{x}{x+1}$

Another method for simplifying complex rational expressions is to simplify the numerator and denominator separately, then treat the result as a division.

EXAMPLE 2 Simplify $\dfrac{\dfrac{x^2-9}{x^2+5x+4}}{\dfrac{x^2+6x+9}{x^2-1}}$

$$\frac{\frac{x^2-9}{x^2+5x+4}}{\frac{x^2+6x+9}{x^2-1}} = \frac{\frac{(x+3)(x-3)}{(x+1)(x+4)}}{\frac{(x+3)(x+3)}{(x+1)(x-1)}} \quad \text{Factoring numerators and denominators}$$

$$= \frac{(x+3)(x-3)}{(x+1)(x+4)} \cdot \frac{(x+1)(x-1)}{(x+3)(x+3)} \quad \text{Using Theorem 6-3 (multiplying by the reciprocal)}$$

$$= \frac{(x+3)(x+1)}{(x+3)(x+1)} \cdot \frac{(x-3)(x-1)}{(x+4)(x+3)} \quad \text{Factoring the rational expression}$$

$$= \frac{(x-3)(x-1)}{(x+4)(x+3)} \quad \text{Simplifying}$$

Try This Simplify.

c. $\dfrac{\dfrac{c^2-1}{4c+4}}{\dfrac{c-1}{c+1}}$ $\frac{c+1}{4}$

d. $\dfrac{\dfrac{a^3+b^3}{a^2-b^2}}{\dfrac{a^2-ab+b^2}{a^2-2ab+b^2}}$ $a-b$

When simplifying rational expressions that have negative integers as exponents, first rename the expression to remove the negative exponents and then simplify the new complex rational expression.

EXAMPLE 3 Simplify $\dfrac{1-3a^{-1}}{1-2a^{-1}-3a^{-2}}$.

$$\frac{1-3a^{-1}}{1-2a^{-1}-3a^{-2}} = \frac{1-\frac{3}{a}}{1-\frac{2}{a}-\frac{3}{a^2}} \quad \text{Writing without negative exponents}$$

The denominators are a and a^2, so the LCD is a^2.

$$= \frac{a^2}{a^2} \cdot \frac{\left(1-\frac{3}{a}\right)}{\left(1-\frac{2}{a}-\frac{3}{a^2}\right)} = \frac{a^2-3a}{a^2-2a-3}$$

$$= \frac{a(a-3)}{(a+1)(a-3)} = \frac{a}{a+1}$$

Try This Simplify.

e. $\dfrac{x^{-1}+y^{-1}}{x^{-1}+3y^{-1}}$ $\frac{y+x}{y+3x}$

f. $\dfrac{(x-2)^{-2}(x+2)}{\dfrac{1}{(x^2+x-2)^{-1}(x^2-4)}}$ $\frac{x+2}{(x-2)(x-1)}$

Chalkboard Examples

Simplify.

1. $\dfrac{2-\frac{3}{a}}{5+\frac{1}{a}}$

Multiply by $\frac{a}{a}$ to clear fractions.

$\frac{a}{a} \cdot \dfrac{2-\frac{3}{a}}{5+\frac{1}{a}}$

$= \dfrac{a\left(2-\frac{3}{a}\right)}{a\left(5+\frac{1}{a}\right)}$

$= \dfrac{2a-3}{5a+1}$

2. $\dfrac{1+2x^{-1}}{3+x^{-1}}$

$\dfrac{1+\frac{2}{x}}{3+\frac{1}{x}}$

Multiply numerator and denominator by x to clear the fractions.

$\dfrac{x\left(1+\frac{2}{x}\right)}{x\left(3+\frac{1}{x}\right)}$

$= \dfrac{x+2}{3x+1}$

LESSON QUIZ

Simplify.

1. $\dfrac{x-\frac{1}{x}}{1-\frac{1}{x}}$

$x+1$

2. $\dfrac{1}{\frac{1}{x}+\frac{1}{y}}$

$\dfrac{xy}{x+y}$

Assignment Guide
Algebra: 1–20 e/o, MR

Alg w/Finite or Trig: 1–24 e/o, 25, MR

Comprehensive: Day 1: 1–15 m3, MR, assign w. 6-2
Day 2: 16–24 m3, 25–28, assign w. 6-4

ADDITIONAL ANSWERS

Exercises

1. $\frac{1+4x}{1-3x}$ 2. $\frac{1+7y}{1-5y}$
3. $\frac{(x+1)(x-1)}{x^2+1}$ 4. $\frac{y^2+1}{(y+1)(y-1)}$
5. $\frac{3y+4x}{4y-3x}$ 6. $\frac{2z+5y}{z-4y}$
7. $\frac{x+y}{x}$ 8. $\frac{a-b}{a}$
9. $\frac{a^2(b-3)}{b^2(a-1)}$ 10. $\frac{3}{3x+2}$
11. $\frac{1}{a-b}$ 12. $\frac{-1}{x+y}$
13. $\frac{1+x^2}{x}$ 14. $\frac{1+y^4}{y(1+y^2)}$
15. $\frac{y-3}{y+5}$
16. $\frac{(x-4)(x-7)}{(x-5)(x+6)}$
17. $\frac{1+x}{1-x}$
18. $\frac{x^3(x+y)}{y(x-y)(x^2+xy-y^2)}$

Mixed Review

29. −6 or 7 30. $22,000

6-3 EXERCISES

A

Simplify.

1. $\dfrac{\frac{1}{x}+4}{\frac{1}{x}-3}$ 2. $\dfrac{\frac{1}{y}+7}{\frac{1}{y}-5}$ 3. $\dfrac{x-\frac{1}{x}}{x+\frac{1}{x}}$ 4. $\dfrac{y+\frac{1}{y}}{y-\frac{1}{y}}$ 5. $\dfrac{\frac{3}{x}+\frac{4}{y}}{\frac{4}{x}-\frac{3}{y}}$

6. $\dfrac{\frac{2}{y}+\frac{5}{z}}{\frac{1}{y}-\frac{4}{z}}$ 7. $\dfrac{\frac{x^2-y^2}{xy}}{\frac{x-y}{y}}$ 8. $\dfrac{\frac{a^2-b^2}{ab}}{\frac{a+b}{b}}$ 9. $\dfrac{a-\frac{3a}{b}}{b-\frac{b}{a}}$ 10. $\dfrac{1-\frac{2}{3x}}{x-\frac{4}{9x}}$

11. $\dfrac{\frac{1}{a}+\frac{1}{b}}{\frac{a^2-b^2}{ab}}$ 12. $\dfrac{\frac{1}{x}-\frac{1}{y}}{\frac{x^2-y^2}{xy}}$ 13. $\dfrac{x^{-3}-x}{x^{-2}-1}$ 14. $\dfrac{y^{-3}+y}{y^{-2}+1}$ 15. $\dfrac{\frac{y^2-y-6}{y^2-5y-14}}{\frac{y^2+6y+5}{y^2-6y-7}}$

16. $\dfrac{\frac{x^2-x-12}{x^2-2x-15}}{\frac{x^2+8x+12}{x^2-5x-14}}$ 17. $\dfrac{\frac{x}{1-x}+\frac{1+x}{x}}{\frac{1-x}{x}+\frac{x}{1+x}}$ 18. $\dfrac{\frac{y}{x-y}+\frac{x+y}{y}}{\frac{x-y}{x}+\frac{y}{x+y}}$

19. $\dfrac{5x^{-1}-5y^{-1}+10x^{-1}y^{-1}}{6y^{-1}+12x^{-1}y^{-1}}$ $\frac{5(y-x+2)}{6(x+2)}$ 20. $\dfrac{\frac{4}{x-5}+\frac{2}{x+2}}{\frac{2x}{x^2-3x-10}+\frac{3}{x-5}}$ $\frac{6x-2}{5x+6}$

B

Find the reciprocal.

21. $\frac{1}{x}+1$ $\frac{x}{x+1}$ 22. $x^2-\frac{1}{x}$ $\frac{x}{x^3-1}$ 23. $\dfrac{1-\frac{1}{a}}{a-1}$ a 24. $\frac{a^3+b^3}{a+b}$ $\frac{1}{a^2-ab+b^2}$

25. ***Critical Thinking*** Find a complex rational expression whose reciprocal is $x+1$. Answers may vary.

Challenge

26. Simplify $1+\cfrac{1}{1+\cfrac{1}{1+\cfrac{1}{1+\cfrac{1}{x}}}}$. $\frac{5x+3}{3x+2}$

27. For $f(x)=\frac{1}{1-x}$, find $f(f(x))$ and $f(f(fx)))$. $\frac{x-1}{x}$, x

28. Find and simplify $\frac{f(x+h)-f(x)}{h}$ for the rational function $f(x)=\frac{x}{1+x}$. $\frac{1}{(1+x)(1+x+}$

Mixed Review

29. The sum of a number and its square is 42 more than twice the number. What is the number?

30. Jeremy received a 14% raise, bringing his salary to $25,080. What was Jeremy's salary before he received the raise?

6-4 Division of Polynomials

Dividing Polynomials by Monomials

Objective: Divide a polynomial by a monomial.

Remember that rational expressions indicate division. In some cases, it is useful to carry out that division. Division by a monomial can be done by first writing a rational expression.

EXAMPLE 1 Divide $12x^3 + 8x^2 + x + 4$ by $4x$.

$$\frac{12x^3 + 8x^2 + x + 4}{4x}$$ Writing a rational expression

$$= \frac{12x^3}{4x} + \frac{8x^2}{4x} + \frac{x}{4x} + \frac{4}{4x}$$ Using Theorem 6-4

$$= 3x^2 + 2x + \frac{1}{4} + \frac{1}{x}$$ Simplifying each rational expression

Try This Divide.

a. $\frac{x^3 + 16x^2 + 6x}{2x}$ $\frac{x^2}{2} + 8x + 3$ **b.** $(12x^3 + 3x^2 + 6x) \div 3x$ $4x^2 + x + 2$

c. $(4x^7 + 3x^6 + 6x^5 + 12x^4 + 2x^3 + x^2 + 2x) \div 2x$ $2x^6 + \frac{3}{2}x^5 + 3x^4 + 6x^3 + x^2 + \frac{1}{2}x + 1$

EXAMPLE 2 Divide $(8x^4 - 3x^3 + 5x^2)$ by x^2.

$$\frac{8x^4 - 3x^3 + 5x^2}{x^2} = \frac{8x^4}{x^2} - \frac{3x^3}{x^2} + \frac{5x^2}{x^2}$$

$$= 8x^2 - 3x + 5$$

Dividing a Polynomial by a Monomial

To divide a polynomial by a monomial, divide each term by the monomial.

Try This Divide.

d. $(15y^5 - 6y^4 + 18y^3) \div 3y^2$ $5y^3 - 2y^2 + 6y$ **e.** $(x^4 + 10x^3 + 16x^2) \div 2x^2$ $\frac{x^2}{2} + 5x + 8$

f. $\frac{16y^4 + 4y^3 + 2y^2}{4y}$ $4y^3 + y^2 + \frac{1}{2}y$

6-4

FIRST FIVE MINUTES

Simplify.

1. $\frac{1 + \frac{1}{a}}{1 + \frac{2}{a}}$ $\frac{a+1}{a+2}$

2. $\frac{1}{1 + \frac{1}{2x}}$ $\frac{2x}{2x+1}$

Dividing Polynomials by Monomials

Remind students that polynomials have all the properties of rational numbers. They can be added, subtracted, multiplied and divided.

Emphasize that the denominator divides each term of the numerator.

Encourage students to do as many steps as they can mentally.

Key Questions

- If you divide a 3-term polynomial by a monomial, how many terms will the answer have? 3
- If you divide a polynomial by a monomial, will the answer always be a polynomial? No, it may have negative exponents.

Chalkboard Examples

1. Divide $8x^2 + 4x + 12$ by $4x$.

$\frac{8x^2 + 4x + 12}{4x}$

$= \frac{8x^2}{4x} + \frac{4x}{4x} + \frac{12}{4x}$

$= 2x + 1 + \frac{3}{x}$

2. Divide $6x^3 + 2x^2 + 8x$ by $2x$.

$\frac{6x^3 + 2x^2 + 8x}{2x}$

$= \frac{6x^3}{2x} + \frac{2x^2}{2x} + \frac{8x}{2x}$

$= 3x^2 + x + 4$

Dividing Two Polynomials

Students should use zero coefficients as place holders until they are comfortable with spaces.

Stress that the remainder is a rational expression.

Chalkboard Examples

1. Divide $2x^2 + 3x + 5$ by $x + 1$.

$$\begin{array}{r} 2x + 1 \\ x + 1\overline{)2x^2 + 3x + 5} \\ \underline{2x^2 + 2x} \\ x + 5 \\ \underline{x + 1} \\ 4 \end{array}$$

The quotient is $2x + 1$ with remainder 4.

2. Divide $x^4 + x^3 + x^2 + 2x + 1$ by $x + 1$.

$$\begin{array}{r} x^3 + \quad x + 1 \\ x + 1\overline{)x^4 + x^3 + x^2 + 2x + 1} \\ \underline{x^4 + x^3} \\ x^2 + 2x \\ \underline{x^2 + x} \\ x + 1 \\ \underline{x + 1} \\ 0 \end{array}$$

The quotient is $x^3 + x + 1$.

3. Divide $x^3 + x + 3$ by $x + 1$.

$$\begin{array}{r} x^2 - x + 2 \\ x + 1\overline{)x^3 \quad + x + 3} \\ \underline{x^3 + x^2} \\ -x^2 + x + 3 \\ \underline{-x^2 - x} \\ 2x + 3 \\ \underline{2x + 2} \\ 1 \end{array}$$

The quotient is $x^2 - x + 2$ with remainder 1.

Dividing Two Polynomials

Objective: Divide two polynomials when the divisor is not a monomial.

When the divisor is not a monomial, we use a procedure very much like long division.

EXAMPLE 3 Divide $x^2 + 5x + 8$ by $x + 3$.

$$\begin{array}{r} x \\ x + 3\overline{)x^2 + 5x + 8} \\ \underline{x^2 + 3x} \\ 2x \end{array}$$

Dividing the first term of the dividend by the first term of the divisor: $\frac{x^2}{x} = x$

Multiplying the divisor by x

Subtracting

We now "bring down" 8, the next term of the dividend.

$$\begin{array}{r} x + 2 \\ x + 3\overline{)x^2 + 5x + 8} \\ \underline{x^2 + 3x} \\ 2x + 8 \\ \underline{2x + 6} \\ 2 \end{array}$$

Dividing the first term by the first term of the divisor: $\frac{2x}{x} = 2$

Multiplying the divisor by 2

Subtracting

The quotient is $x + 2$, the remainder is 2. To check, we multiply the quotient by the divisor and add the remainder to see if we get the dividend.

$$\underbrace{(x + 2)}_{\text{Quotient}} \cdot \underbrace{(x + 3)}_{\text{Divisor}} + \underbrace{2}_{\text{Remainder}} = \underbrace{(x^2 + 5x + 6) + 2}_{\text{Dividend}} = x^2 + 5x + 8$$

The answer checks.

Try This Divide and check.

g. $x - 2\overline{)x^2 + 3x - 10}$ $x + 5$

Always remember to arrange polynomials in descending order and to leave space for missing terms in the dividend (or write them with 0 coefficients).

EXAMPLE 4 Divide $(125y^3 - 8)$ by $(5y - 2)$.

$$\begin{array}{r} 25y^2 + 10y + 4 \\ 5y - 2\overline{)125y^3 + 0y^2 + 0y - 8} \\ \underline{125y^3 - 50y^2} \\ 50y^2 + 0y \\ \underline{50y^2 - 20y} \\ 20y - 8 \\ \underline{20y - 8} \\ 0 \end{array}$$

Writing zero coefficients for missing terms

The quotient is $25y^2 + 10y + 4$.

EXAMPLE 5 Divide $(x^4 - 9x^2 - 5)$ by $(x - 2)$.

$$
\begin{array}{r}
x^3 + 2x^2 - 5x - 10 \\
x - 2 \,\overline{) \; x^4 + 0x^3 - 9x^2 + 0x - 5} \\
\underline{x^4 - 2x^3} \qquad\qquad\qquad \\
2x^3 - 9x^2 \qquad\qquad \\
\underline{2x^3 - 4x^2} \qquad\qquad \\
-5x^2 \qquad\qquad \\
\underline{-5x^2 + 10x} \qquad \\
-10x - 5 \\
\underline{-10x + 20} \\
-25
\end{array}
$$

The first subtraction is $x^4 - (x^4 - 2x^3)$.

The second subtraction is $(2x^3 - 9x^2) - (2x^3 - 4x^2)$.

The quotient is $x^3 + 2x^2 - 5x - 10$, the remainder is -25.

This can be written as $x^3 + 2x^2 - 5x - 10$, R -25, or

$$x^3 + 2x^2 - 5x - 10 - \frac{25}{x - 2}$$ This expression is the remainder over the divisor.

Try This Divide and check.

h. $(9y^4 + 14y^2 - 8) \div (3y + 2)$ $3y^3 - 2y^2 + 6y - 4$

i. $(y^3 - 11y^2 + 6) \div (y - 3)$ $y^2 - 8y - 24, R - 66$

When dividing, we continue until the degree of the remainder is less than the degree of the divisor. The answer can be written as a quotient and remainder, or as a polynomial plus a rational expression.

EXAMPLE 6 Divide $(x^3 + 9x^2 - 5)$ by $(x^2 - 1)$.

$$
\begin{array}{r}
x + 9 \qquad\qquad \\
x^2 - 1 \,\overline{) \; x^3 + 9x^2 \qquad - 5} \\
\underline{x^3 \qquad\quad - x} \quad\;\; \\
9x^2 + x - 5 \\
\underline{9x^2 \qquad - 9} \\
x + 4
\end{array}
$$

Leaving space for the missing term

The degree of the remainder is less than the degree of the divisor, so we are finished.

The quotient is $x + 9$, R $x + 4$, or

$$x + 9 + \frac{x + 4}{x^2 - 1}$$

Checking,

$$(x + 9)(x^2 - 1) + x + 4 = x^3 - x + 9x^2 - 9 + x + 4$$
$$= x^3 + 9x^2 - 5$$ The answer checks.

Try This Divide and check.

j. $(y^3 - 11y^2 + 6) \div (y^2 - 3)$ $y - 11 + \frac{3y - 27}{y^2 - 3}$

LESSON QUIZ

1. Divide $x^4 - x^3 + x^2 - x$ by $x - 1$.
   The quotient is $x^3 + x$, or $x(x^2 + 1)$.
2. Divide $x^4 - x^2 + x$ by $x^2 - x + 1$.
   The quotient is $x^2 + x - 1$ with remainder $-x + 1$.

Assignment Guide
Algebra: 1–30 e/o, MR

Alg w/Finite or Trig: 1–34 e/o, 35, MR

Comprehensive: 1–30 m4, 31–34 e/o, 35–37, MR, assign w. 6-3

ADDITIONAL ANSWERS

Exercises

5. $y^3 - 2y^2 + 3y$
6. $12a^2 + 14a - 10$
7. $-6x^5 + 3x^3 + 2x$
8. $-6y^5 + 9y^2 + 1$
9. $1 - ab^2 - a^3b$
10. $x - xy - x^2$
11. $-2pq + 3p - 4q$
12. $4z - 2y^2z^3 + 3y^4z^2$
13. $x + 7$
14. $y - 4$
15. $a - 12$, R: 32
16. $y - 5$, R: -50
17. $y - 5$
18. $a + 9$
19. $y^2 - 2y - 1$, R: -8
20. $x^2 - 2x - 2$, R: -13
21. $a^2 + 4a + 15$, R: 72
22. $x^2 - 2x + 3$
23. $4x^2 - 6x + 9$
24. $16y^2 + 8y + 4$
25. $x^2 + 6$
26. $y^2 + 2$, R: -48
27. $4x^2 - 1$, R: $-2x + 1$
28. $y^3 - y^2 - 1$, R: 4
29. $2y^2 + 2y - 1 + \frac{8}{5y - 2}$
30. $3x^2 - x + 4 + \frac{10}{2x - 3}$
35. Answers may vary. Example: $5x^3 + 28x^2 + 27x + 67$, $x + 5$

Mixed Review

38. $4n^8m^{-13}$
39. 1
40. $\frac{9m^2n^4}{16}$
41. $\frac{n^9}{8m^6}$
42. 1040
43. 0.000634
44. $(y + 6)^2$
45. $4(2x + y)^2$
46. $x(x - 7)$

6-4 EXERCISES

A

Divide.

1. $\frac{30x^8 - 15x^6 + 40x^4}{5x^4}$ $6x^4 - 3x^2 + 8$
2. $\frac{24y^6 + 18y^5 - 36y^2}{6y^2}$ $4y^4 + 3y^3 - 6$
3. $\frac{-14a^3 + 28a^2 - 21a}{7a}$ $-2a^2 + 4a - 3$
4. $\frac{-32x^4 - 24x^3 - 12x^2}{4x}$ $-8x^3 - 6x^2 - 3x$
5. $(9y^4 - 18y^3 + 27y^2) \div 9y$
6. $(24a^3 + 28a^2 - 20a) \div 2a$
7. $(36x^6 - 18x^4 - 12x^2) \div (-6x)$
8. $(18y^7 - 27y^4 - 3y^2) \div (-3y^2)$
9. $(a^2b - a^3b^3 - a^5b^2) \div a^2b$
10. $(x^3y^2 - x^3y^3 - x^4y^2) \div x^2y^2$
11. $(6p^2q^2 - 9p^2q + 12pq^2) \div (-3pq)$
12. $(16y^4z^2 - 8y^6z^4 + 12y^8z^3) \div 4y^4z$

Divide and check.

13. $(x^2 + 10x + 21) \div (x + 3)$
14. $(y^2 - 8y + 16) \div (y - 4)$
15. $(a^2 - 8a - 16) \div (a + 4)$
16. $(y^2 - 10y - 25) \div (y - 5)$
17. $(y^2 - 25) \div (y + 5)$
18. $(a^2 - 81) \div (a - 9)$
19. $(y^3 - 4y^2 + 3y - 6) \div (y - 2)$
20. $(x^3 - 5x^2 + 4x - 7) \div (x - 3)$
21. $(a^3 - a + 12) \div (a - 4)$
22. $(x^3 - x + 6) \div (x + 2)$
23. $(8x^3 + 27) \div (2x + 3)$
24. $(64y^3 - 8) \div (4y - 2)$
25. $(x^4 - x^2 - 42) \div (x^2 - 7)$
26. $(y^4 - y^2 - 54) \div (y^2 - 3)$
27. $(8x^4 - 6x^2 - 2x + 2) \div (2x^2 - 1)$
28. $(y^4 - y^2 - y + 3) \div (y + 1)$
29. $(10y^3 + 6y^2 - 9y + 10) \div (5y - 2)$
30. $(6x^3 - 11x^2 + 11x - 2) \div (2x - 3)$

B

Divide.

31. $(x^4 - x^3y + x^2y^2 + 2x^2y - 2xy^2 + 2y^3) \div (x^2 - xy + y^2)$ $x^2 + 2y$
32. $(4a^3b + 5a^2b^2 + a^4 + 2ab^3) \div (a^2 + 2b^2 + 3ab)$ $a^2 + ab$
33. $(x^4 - y^4) \div (x - y)$ $x^3 + x^2y + xy^2 + y^3$
34. $(a^7 + b^7) \div (a + b)$ $a^6 - a^5b + a^4b^2 - a^3b^3 + a^2b^4 - ab^5 + b^6$
35. ***Critical Thinking*** When two rational expressions are divided, the quotient is $5x^2 + 3x + 12 + \frac{7}{x + 5}$. What are the two polynomials?

Challenge

36. Find k so that $x^3 - kx^2 + 3x + 7k$ divided by $x + 2$ has remainder 0. $\frac{14}{3}$
37. When $x^2 - 3x + 2k$ is divided by $x + 2$, the remainder is 7. Find the value of k. $-\frac{3}{2}$

Mixed Review

Simplify. 38. $\frac{-16n^5m^{-7}}{-4n^{-3}m^6}$ 39. $\frac{25w^2}{(-5w)^2}$ 40. $\left(\frac{3m^2n^3}{4mn}\right)^2$ 41. $\left(\frac{n^3}{2m^2}\right)^3$

Convert to decimal notation. 42. 1.04×10^3 43. 6.34×10^{-4}

Factor. 44. $y^2 + 12y + 36$ 45. $16x^2 + 16xy + 4y^2$ 46. $x^2 - 7x$

6-5 Synthetic Division

Objective: Use synthetic division to find the quotient of certain polynomials.

An **algorithm** is a systematic procedure for doing a certain computation. The division algorithm of the preceding section can be shortened in certain cases. If the divisor is a linear polynomial of the form $x - a$, then the shorter procedure will work.

EXAMPLE 1 Divide $4x^3 + x + 7$ by $x - 2$.

To streamline division, we can arrange the work so that duplicate writing is avoided. Note that we can divide using only the coefficients. Compare B to A.

A.

$$\begin{array}{r|l} & 4x^2 + 8x + 17 \\ \hline x - 2 & 4x^3 + 0x^2 + x + 7 \\ & 4x^3 - 8x^2 \\ \hline & 8x^2 + x \\ & 8x^2 - 16x \\ \hline & 17x + 7 \\ & 17x - 34 \\ \hline \text{Remainder} & 41 \end{array}$$

B.

$$\begin{array}{r|l} & 4 \quad 8 \quad 17 \\ \hline 1 - 2 & 4 + 0 + 1 + 7 \\ & 4 - 8 \\ \hline & 8 + 1 \\ & 8 - 16 \\ \hline & 17 + 7 \\ & 17 - 34 \\ \hline & 41 \end{array}$$

Note also that when we subtract, we add an additive inverse. We can accomplish this by using the additive inverse of -2 in the divisor.

The following algorithm, called **synthetic division,** uses addition rather than subtraction and also avoids repeating numbers.

C. Synthetic Division

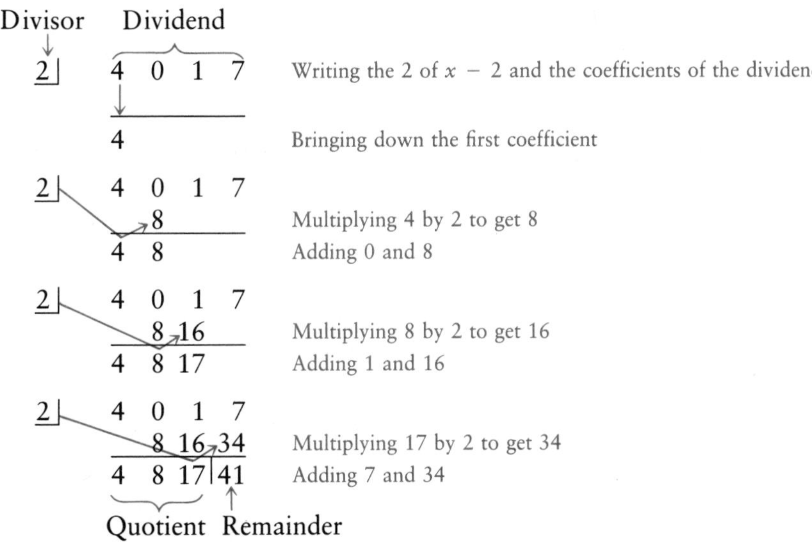

Writing the 2 of $x - 2$ and the coefficients of the dividend

Bringing down the first coefficient

Multiplying 4 by 2 to get 8
Adding 0 and 8

Multiplying 8 by 2 to get 16
Adding 1 and 16

Multiplying 17 by 2 to get 34
Adding 7 and 34

6-5

FIRST FIVE MINUTES

1. Divide $x^4 + 4x^3 + 6x^2 + 4x + 1$ by $x + 1$.

$$\begin{array}{r|l} & x^3 + 3x^2 + 3x + 1 \\ \hline x + 1 & x^4 + 4x^3 + 6x^2 + 4x + 1 \\ & x^4 + x^3 \\ \hline & 3x^3 + 6x^2 \\ & 3x^3 + 3x^2 \\ \hline & 3x^2 + 4x \\ & 3x^2 + 3x \\ \hline & x + 1 \\ & x + 1 \\ \hline & 0 \end{array}$$

The quotient is $x^3 + 3x^2 + 3x + 1$.

Emphasize that the divisor must be of the form $x - a$ for this algorithm to work. The constant a is used at the upper left corner of the work array. A divisor like $x + 3$ can be put into the proper form as $x - (-3)$.

Key Questions

- How would you write $5x^3 - 2x + 5$ as the dividend for synthetic division?
  $5 + 0 - 2 + 5$
- How would you write $x + 4$ as the divisor?
  -4

Chalkboard Examples

Use synthetic division to find the quotient and remainder.

1. $2x^3 - 7x^2 - 11x - 20$ divided by $x - 5$

$$\begin{array}{r|rrrr} 5 & 2 & -7 & -11 & -20 \\ & & & & \\ \hline & 2 & & & \end{array}$$

$$\begin{array}{r|rrrr} 5 & 2 & -7 & -11 & -20 \\ & & 10 & & \\ \hline & 2 & & & \end{array}$$

$$\begin{array}{r|rrrr} 5 & 2 & -7 & -11 & -20 \\ & & 10 & 15 & \\ \hline & 2 & 3 & & \end{array}$$

$$\begin{array}{r|rrr|r} 5 & 2 & -7 & -11 & -20 \\ & & 10 & 15 & 20 \\ \hline & 2 & 3 & 4 & 0 \end{array}$$

The quotient is $2x^2 + 3x + 4$ with remainder 0.

2. $2x^3 + 5x^2 + 5x + 6$ divided by $x + 2$

Rewrite $x + 2$ as $x - (-2)$.

−2	2	5	5	6
		−4	−2	−6
	2	1	3	0

The quotient is $2x^2 + x + 3$ with remainder 0.

3. $(2x^4 - 30x^2 - 2x - 1)$ by $(x - 4)$

4	2	0	−30	−2	−1
		8	32	8	24
	2	8	2	6	23

The quotient is $2x^3 + 8x^2 + 2x + 6$ with remainder 23.

4. $(x^5 + x^4 + x^3 + x^2 + x + 1)$ by $(x + 1)$

−1	1	1	1	1	1	1
		−1	0	−1	0	−1
	1	0	1	0	1	0

The quotient is $x^4 + x^2 + 1$ with remainder 0.

LESSON QUIZ

Use synthetic division to find the quotient and remainder.

1. $(x^4 - 8x^3 + 24x^2 - 32x + 16) \div (x - 2)$
   The quotient is $x^3 - 6x^2 + 12x - 8$ with remainder 0.
2. $x^4 + 3x^3 + 5x^2 + 4x + 1$ by $x + 1$
   The quotient is $1x^3 + 2x^2 + 3x + 1$ with remainder 0.

The last number, 41, is the remainder. The other numbers are the coefficients of the quotient, with that of the term of highest degree first.

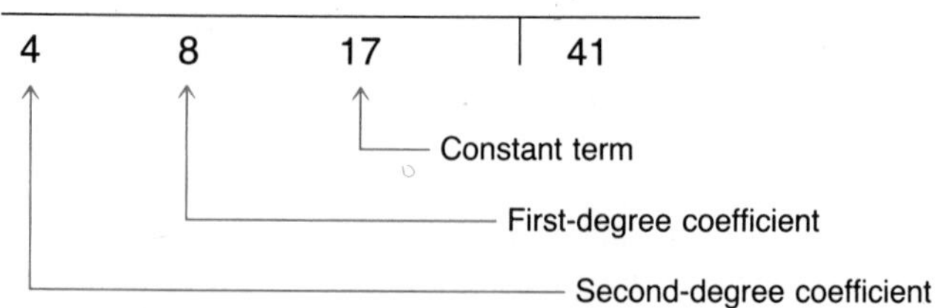

The quotient is $4x^2 + 8x + 17$, the remainder is 41.

Remember that for this method to work, the divisor *must* be in the form $x - a$.

EXAMPLE 2 Use synthetic division to find the quotient and remainder.

$$(x^3 + 6x^2 - x - 30) \div (x - 2)$$

2	1	6	−1	−30	Writing the 2 of $x - 2$ and the coefficients of the dividend
		2	16	30	
	1	8	15	0	Using synthetic division

The quotient is $x^2 + 8x + 15$, the remainder is 0.

Try This Use synthetic division to find the quotient and remainder.

a. $(x^3 + 5x^2 - 9x - 45) \div (x - 3)$ Q: $x^2 + 8x + 15$, R: 0

b. $(8x^2 - 12x + 4) \div (x - 3)$ Q: $8x + 12$, R: 40

EXAMPLES Use synthetic division to find the quotient and remainder.

3. $(2x^3 + 7x^2 - 5) \div (x + 3)$

There is no first degree x-term in the dividend, so we must write a 0 for that coefficient. To write the divisor $x + 3$ as a difference, we write $x - (-3)$.

−3	2	7	0	−5	Note: We must write 0's for missing terms.
		−6	−3	9	
	2	1	−3	4	

The quotient is $2x^2 + 1x - 3$, the remainder is 4.

4. $$\frac{8x^5 - 6x^3 + x - 8}{x + 2}$$

−2	8	0	−6	0	1	−8
		−16	32	−52	104	−210
	8	−16	26	−52	105	−218

The quotient is $8x^4 - 16x^3 + 26x^2 - 52x + 105$, the remainder is -218.

Try This Use synthetic division to find the quotient and the remainder.

c. $(x^3 - 2x^2 + 5x - 4) \div (x + 2)$ Q: $x^2 - 4x + 13$, R: -30

d. $(y^3 + 1) \div (y + 1)$ Q: $y^2 - y + 1$, R: 0

6-5 EXERCISES

A

Use synthetic division to find the quotient and remainder.

1. $(x^3 - 2x^2 + 2x + 5) \div (x - 1)$
2. $(x^3 - 2x^2 + 2x + 5) \div (x + 1)$
3. $(a^2 + 11a - 19) \div (a + 4)$
4. $(a^2 + 11a - 19) \div (a - 4)$
5. $(x^3 - 7x^2 - 13x + 3) \div (x - 2)$
6. $(x^3 - 7x^2 - 13x + 10) \div (x + 2)$
7. $(3x^3 + 7x^2 - 4x + 3) \div (x + 3)$
8. $(3x^3 + 7x^2 - 4x + 3) \div (x - 3)$
9. $(y^3 - 3y + 10) \div (y - 2)$
10. $(x^3 - 2x^2 + 8) \div (x + 2)$
11. $(3x^4 - 25x^2 - 18) \div (x - 3)$
12. $(6y^4 + 15y^3 + 6) \div (y + 3)$
13. $(x^3 - 27) \div (x - 3)$
14. $(y^3 + 27) \div (y + 3)$
15. $(y^4 + 1) \div (y - 1)$
16. $(x^5 - 32) \div (x - 2)$
17. $(5x^2 - 7x) \div (x - 3)$
18. $(9x^3 - 15x^2 + 4x) \div (x - 3)$
19. $(3x^4 - 5x^2 + 10) \div (x - 7)$
20. $(x^4 + 5x) \div (x + 5)$
21. $(4x^3 - 4x^2 + 4x - 9) \div (x - 4)$
22. $(-7x^3 + 6x^2 + 50) \div (x + 7)$

B

Use synthetic division and a calculator to find the quotient and remainder.

23. $(3x^4 - 24x^2 - 13) \div (x - 2.41)$
24. $(5x^5 + 11x^3 + 217) \div (x + 17.07)$

25. ***Critical Thinking*** $P(x) = 8x^5 - 3x^4 + 7x - 4$.
  a Find the remainder using synthetic division. $P(x) \div (x - 2)$; $P(x) \div (x + 4)$.
  b. Find $P(2)$; $P(-4)$.
  c. Compare the answers and the algorithms.

Challenge

26. Devise a procedure to use synthetic division when the divisor is a linear polynomial $ax + b$ with a leading coefficient different from 1. Use the procedure to divide $12x^4 - 30x^2 + 30x - 12$ by $6x + 12$. $2x^3 - 4x^2 + 3x - 1$

27. Use synthetic division to divide $7x^9 - 15x^6 - 3x^3 + 10$ by $x^3 - 3$. Q: $7x^6 + 6x^3 + 15$, R:55

Mixed Review

Give the domain of each of the following functions. **28.** $f(x) = x^2$

29. $f(x) = \frac{7}{x + 3}$ **30.** $f(x) = \frac{2}{x + 2x}$ **31.** $f(x) = \frac{6}{x(x + 3)}$ **32.** $f(x) = \frac{1}{2 + x^2}$

Factor. **33.** $8x^2 - 8xy + 2y^2$ **34.** $9y^2 - x^2 - 2x - 1$ **35.** $27x^3 - 1$

Assignment Guide
Algebra: 1 – 22 e/o, MR

Alg w/Finite or Trig: 1–24 e/o, 25, MR

Comprehensive: 1–24 e/o, 25–27, MR

ADDITIONAL ANSWERS

Exercises

1. Q: $x^2 - x + 1$, R: 6
2. Q: $x^2 - 3x + 5$, R: 0
3. Q: $a + 7$, R: -47
4. Q: $a + 15$, R: 41
5. Q: $x^2 - 5x - 23$, R: -43
6. Q: $x^2 - 9x + 5$, R: 0
7. Q: $3x^2 - 2x + 2$, R: -3
8. Q: $3x^2 + 16x + 44$, R: 135
9. Q: $y^2 + 2y + 1$, R: 12
10. Q: $x^2 - 4x + 8$, R: -8
11. Q: $3x^3 + 9x^2 + 2x + 6$, R: 0
12. Q: $6y^3 - 3y^2 + 9y - 27$, R: 87
13. Q: $x^2 + 3x + 9$, R: 0
14. Q: $y^2 - 3y + 9$, R: 0
15. Q: $y^3 + y^2 + y + 1$, R: 2
16. Q: $x^4 + 2x^3 + 4x^2 + 8x + 16$, R: 0
17. Q: $5x + 8$, R: 24
18. Q: $9x^2 + 12x + 40$, R: 120
19. Q: $3x^3 + 21x^2 + 142x + 994$, R: 6968
20. Q: $x^3 - 5x^2 + 25x - 120$, R: 600
21. Q: $4x^2 + 12x + 52$, R: 199
22. Q: $-7x^2 + 55x - 385$, R: 2745

23. Q: $3x^3 + 7.23x^2 - 6.58x - 15.85$ R: -51.19
24. Q: $5x^4 - 85.35x^3 + 1467.9245x^2 - 25057.471x + 427731.03$ R: $-7{,}301{,}151.7$
25. **a.** 218; -8992
b. 218; -8992
c. The answers are equal; the algorithms are equivalent.

Mixed Review

28. R
29. $\{x \mid x \neq -3\}$
30. $\{x \mid x \neq 0\}$
31. $\{x \mid x \neq 0, x \neq -3\}$
32. R
33. $2(2x - y)^2$
34. $(3y - x - 1)(3y + x + 1)$
35. $(3x - 1)(9x^2 + 3x + 1)$

6-6

FIRST FIVE MINUTES

1. Use synthetic division to find the quotient and remainder.
$(3x^3 - 7x^2 - 5x - 3) \div (x - 3)$
The quotient is $3x^2 + 2x + 1$ with remainder 0.

2. Solve for x where $\frac{x}{3} = \frac{1}{2} - x$.
Multiply through by 6 to clear the fractions.
$2x = 3 - 6x$
$8x = 3$
$x = \frac{3}{8}$

Point out that we are trying to clear the equation of all fractions before solving.

Remind students that division by 0 is not defined. An expression like $\frac{1}{x-2}$ makes sense only if $x - 2$ is not 0, that is, only if x is not equal to 2.

Key Questions

- What LCD would clear $\frac{2}{5} + \frac{3}{4} = \frac{6}{x^2}$?
$20x^2$
- Is 0 a possible solution of $-1 + 1 = \frac{3}{x}$?
No, $\frac{3}{0}$ has no meaning.

Chalkboard Examples

1. Solve $\frac{1}{x} = \frac{2}{3}$.
Multiply through by $3x$ to clear the fractions.
$3x \cdot \frac{1}{x} = 3x \cdot \frac{2}{3}$
$3 = 2x$
$\frac{3}{2} = x$
$\frac{3}{2}$ checks; the solution is $\frac{3}{2}$.

2. Solve $\frac{2}{x} = \frac{3}{x-4}$.
Multiply through by $x(x - 4)$ to clear the fractions.
$2(x - 4) = 3x$
$2x - 8 = 3x$
$-8 = x$
-8 checks in the original equation. The solution is -8.

6-6 Solving Rational Equations

Objective: Solve rational equations.

Master Grapher Worksheet 7, *Solving Rational Equations*, can be used for lesson closure.

A **rational equation** is an equation that contains one or more rational expressions. These are rational equations.

$$\frac{2}{3} + \frac{5}{6} = \frac{1}{x}, \qquad \frac{x-1}{x-5} = \frac{4}{x-5}$$

To solve a rational equation, we multiply both sides by the LCD to clear fractions.

EXAMPLE 1 Solve $\frac{2}{3} - \frac{5}{6} = \frac{1}{x}$.

The LCD is $6x$.

$$\begin{aligned}
6x\left(\frac{2}{3} - \frac{5}{6}\right) &= 6x\left(\frac{1}{x}\right) && \text{Multiplying by the LCD} \\
6x\left(\frac{2}{3}\right) - 6x\left(\frac{5}{6}\right) &= 6x\left(\frac{1}{x}\right) && \text{Multiplying to remove parentheses} \\
4x - 5x &= 6 && \text{Simplifying} \\
-x &= 6 \\
x &= -6
\end{aligned}$$

Check:

$\frac{2}{3} - \frac{5}{6}$	$= \frac{1}{x}$
$\frac{2}{3} - \frac{5}{6}$	$\frac{1}{-6}$
$\frac{4}{6} - \frac{5}{6}$	$-\frac{1}{6}$
$-\frac{1}{6}$	$-\frac{1}{6}$ ✓

When clearing fractions, be sure to multiply every term in the equation by the LCD. This yields an equation without rational expressions, which can be solved directly.

Try This Solve.

a. $\frac{2}{3} + \frac{5}{6} = \frac{1}{x}$ $\frac{2}{3}$

b. $\frac{1}{8} - \frac{2}{5} = \frac{3}{x}$ $-\frac{120}{11}$

When we multiply both sides of an equation by an expression containing a variable, we may not get an equivalent equation. The new equation may have solutions that the original one does not. Thus we must *always* check possible solutions in the *original* equation.

EXAMPLE 2 Solve $\frac{x-1}{x-5} = \frac{4}{x-5}$.

The LCD is $x - 5$. We multiply by $x - 5$ to clear fractions.

$$(x-5)\cdot\frac{x-1}{x-5} = (x-5)\cdot\frac{4}{x-5}$$
$$x - 1 = 4$$
$$x = 5$$

Check: $\frac{x-1}{x-5} = \frac{4}{x-5}$

$\frac{5-1}{5-5}$	$\frac{4}{5-5}$
$\frac{4}{0}$	$\frac{4}{0}$

5 is not a solution of the original equation because it results in division by 0. Since 5 is the only possible solution, the equation has no solution.

Try This Solve.

c. $\frac{y-2}{5} - \frac{y-5}{4} = -2$ $y = 57$

d. $\frac{x-7}{x-9} = \frac{2}{x-9}$ No solution

EXAMPLE 3 Solve $\frac{x^2}{x-2} = \frac{4}{x-2}$.

The LCD is $x - 2$. We multiply by $x - 2$.

$$(x-2)\cdot\frac{x^2}{x-2} = (x-2)\cdot\frac{4}{x-2}$$
$$x^2 = 4$$
$$x^2 - 4 = 0$$
$$(x+2)(x-2) = 0$$
$$x = -2 \text{ or } x = 2$$ Using the principle of zero products

Check: For -2: $\frac{x^2}{x-2} = \frac{4}{x-2}$

$\frac{(-2)^2}{-2-2}$	$\frac{4}{-2-2}$
$\frac{4}{-4}$	$\frac{4}{-4}$
-1	-1 ✓

For 2: $\frac{x^2}{x-2} = \frac{4}{x-2}$

$\frac{2^2}{2-2}$	$\frac{4}{2-2}$
$\frac{4}{0}$	$\frac{4}{0}$

The number -2 is a solution, but 2 is not since it results in division by 0.

3. Solve $\frac{x}{x-3} = \frac{5}{x-3}$.
   Multiply through by $x - 3$.
   $x = 5$
   5 checks; the solution is 5.
4. Solve $x + \frac{3}{x} = 4$.
   Multiply through by x to clear the fractions.
   $x^2 + 3 = 4x$
   $x^2 - 4x + 3 = 0$
   $(x-1)(x-3) = 0$
   $x = 1$ or $x = 3$
   Both 1 and 3 check in the original equation. The solutions are 1 and 3.
5. Solve.
   $\frac{1}{x-1} + \frac{1}{x-2} = \frac{1}{(x-1)(x-2)}$
   Multiply through by $(x-1)(x-2)$ to clear the fractions.
   $x - 2 + x - 1 = 1$
   $2x = 4$
   $x = 2$
   2 is not acceptable since it would cause division by 0. There is no solution.

LESSON QUIZ

1. Solve.

$\frac{2}{x} + \frac{1}{5x} = 1$

$x = \frac{11}{5}$

2. Solve.

$\frac{x}{x+5} + \frac{1}{x} = \frac{7}{x(x+5)}$

$x = 1$ or $x = -2$

EXAMPLE 4 Solve $x + \frac{6}{x} = 5$.

The LCD is x. We multiply both sides by x.

$$x\left(x + \frac{6}{x}\right) = 5 \cdot x \quad \text{Multiplying both sides by } x$$

$$x^2 + x \cdot \frac{6}{x} = 5x$$

$$x^2 + 6 = 5x \quad \text{Simplifying}$$

$$x^2 - 5x + 6 = 0 \quad \text{Using the addition principle}$$

$$(x - 3)(x - 2) = 0 \quad \text{Factoring}$$

$$x = 3 \text{ or } x = 2 \quad \text{Using the principle of zero products}$$

Check:

$x + \frac{6}{x} = 5$	
$3 + \frac{6}{3}$	5
5	5 ✓

$x + \frac{6}{x} = 5$	
$2 + \frac{6}{2}$	5
5	5 ✓

The solutions are 2 and 3.

Try This Solve.

e. $\frac{x^2}{x+3} = \frac{9}{x+3}$ 3

f. $x - \frac{12}{x} = 1$ $-3, 4$

g. $1 + \frac{1}{x} = 2x$ $1, -\frac{1}{2}$

h. $2 - \frac{1}{x^2} = \frac{1}{x}$ $1, -\frac{1}{2}$

EXAMPLE 5 Solve $\frac{2}{x+5} + \frac{1}{x-5} = \frac{16}{x^2 - 25}$.

The LCD is $(x + 5)(x - 5)$. We multiply both sides of the equation by $(x + 5)(x - 5)$.

$$(x+5)(x-5) \cdot \left[\frac{2}{x+5} + \frac{1}{x-5}\right] = (x+5)(x-5) \cdot \frac{16}{x^2 - 25}$$

$$(x+5)(x-5) \cdot \frac{2}{x+5} + (x+5)(x-5) \cdot \frac{1}{x-5} = (x+5)(x-5) \cdot \frac{16}{x^2-25}$$

$$2(x - 5) + (x + 5) = 16$$

$$2x - 10 + x + 5 = 16$$

$$x = 7$$

This checks in the original equation, so the solution is 7.

Try This Solve.

i. $\frac{2}{x-1} = \frac{3}{x+2}$ $x = 7$

j. $\frac{2}{x^2 - 9} + \frac{5}{x-3} = \frac{3}{x+3}$ $x = -13$

6-6 EXERCISES

A

Solve.

1. $\frac{2}{5} + \frac{7}{8} = \frac{y}{20}$ $\frac{51}{2}$
2. $\frac{1}{3} - \frac{5}{6} = \frac{1}{x}$ -2
3. $\frac{5}{8} - \frac{2}{5} = \frac{1}{y}$ $\frac{40}{9}$
4. $\frac{x}{3} - \frac{x}{4} = 12$ 144
5. $y + \frac{5}{y} = -6$ $-5, -1$
6. $\frac{y+2}{4} - \frac{y-1}{5} = 15$ 286
7. $\frac{x+1}{3} - \frac{x-1}{2} = 1$ -1
8. $\frac{4}{3y} - \frac{3}{y} = \frac{10}{3}$ $-\frac{1}{2}$
9. $\frac{x-3}{x+2} = \frac{1}{5}$ $\frac{17}{4}$
10. $\frac{y-5}{y+1} = \frac{3}{5}$ 14
11. $\frac{y-1}{y-3} = \frac{2}{y-3}$ No solution
12. $\frac{3}{y+1} = \frac{2}{y-3}$ 11
13. $\frac{x+1}{x} = \frac{3}{2}$ 2
14. $\frac{y+2}{y} = \frac{5}{3}$ 3
15. $\frac{2}{x} - \frac{3}{x} + \frac{4}{x} = 5$ $\frac{3}{5}$
16. $\frac{4}{y} - \frac{6}{y} + \frac{8}{y} = 8$ $\frac{3}{4}$
17. $\frac{1}{2} + \frac{2}{x} = \frac{1}{3} + \frac{3}{x}$ 6
18. $-\frac{1}{3} - \frac{5}{4y} = \frac{3}{4} - \frac{1}{6y}$ -1
19. $\frac{60}{x} - \frac{60}{x-5} = \frac{2}{x}$ -145
20. $\frac{50}{y} - \frac{50}{y-2} = \frac{4}{y}$ -23
21. $\frac{7}{5x-2} = \frac{5}{4x}$ $-\frac{10}{3}$
22. $\frac{1}{2t} - \frac{2}{5t} = \frac{1}{10t} - 3$ No solution
23. $\frac{x}{x-2} + \frac{x}{x^2-4} = \frac{x+3}{x+2}$ -3
24. $\frac{3}{y-2} + \frac{2y}{4-y^2} = \frac{5}{y+2}$ 4
25. $\frac{a}{2a-6} - \frac{3}{a^2-6a+9} = \frac{a-2}{3a-9}$ $-6, 5$
26. $\frac{2}{x+4} + \frac{2x-1}{x^2+2x-8} = \frac{1}{x-2}$ 3
27. $\frac{2x+3}{x-1} = \frac{10}{x^2-1} + \frac{2x-3}{x+1}$ No solution

B

Equations that are true for all acceptable replacements of the variables are *identities*. Determine which equations are identities.

28. $\frac{x^2+6x-16}{x-2} = x + 8$ Yes
29. $\frac{x^3+8}{x^2-4} = \frac{x^2-2x+4}{x-2}$ Yes
30. ***Critical Thinking*** Write a rational equation that cannot have 2 or -7 as solutions.

Challenge

Solve.

31. $\frac{x^3+8}{x+2} = x^2 - 2x + 4$ All real numbers except -2
32. $\frac{(x-3)^2}{x-3} = x - 3$ All real numbers except 3
33. $\frac{x+3}{x+2} - \frac{x+4}{x+3} = \frac{x+5}{x+4} - \frac{x+6}{x+5}$ $-\frac{7}{2}$
34. $\left(\frac{y+3}{y-1}\right)^2 - 2 = \frac{y+3}{y-1}$ $5, -1$

Mixed Review

Simplify. 35. $\frac{25y^2}{10y}$ 36. $\frac{6x+12}{6}$ 37. $\frac{3x+9}{3x-9}$ 38. $\frac{x^2-y^2}{x^3-y^3}$

Evaluate for $a = 2.5$, $b = 3$. 39. $2(a-b)$ 40. $b(b^2-a)$ 41. $(a+b)(a-b)$

Assignment Guide

Algebra: Day 1: 1–12, MR
Day 2: 13–27

Alg w/Finite or Trig: 1–29 e/o, 30, MR

Comprehensive: 1–29 e/o, 30, 31–34 e/o, MR

ADDITIONAL ANSWERS

Exercises

30. Answers may vary. Example: $\frac{x-2}{x^2+5x-14} = \frac{1}{(x+7)}$

Mixed Review

35. $2.5y$
36. $x + 2$
37. $\frac{x+3}{x-3}$
38. $\frac{x+y}{x^2+xy+y^2}$
39. -1
40. 19.5
41. -2.75

6-7

FIRST FIVE MINUTES

1. Solve $\frac{2}{x-1} + x = 4$.

   Multiply through by $x - 1$.

   $2 + x(x - 1) = 4(x - 1)$
   $2 + x^2 - x = 4x - 4$
   $x^2 - 5x + 6 = 0$
   $(x - 2)(x - 3) = 0$
   $x = 2$ or $x = 3$

2. If a computer's printer can print 12 pages in 3 minutes, how many pages can it print in 1 minute?

   $\frac{12}{3} = 4$ pages in 1 minute

Work Problems

Remind students of familiar measures of rate such as miles per hour, pages per week, etc.

Point out that the word "rate" often applies to situations that change with time and that the word "per" followed by a time unit indicates a rate.

Key Questions

- What are some examples of rates?
  gallons per minute
  kilowatts per hour
  commercials per hour, etc.
- If a job can be done in 3 hours, how much of it can be completed in 1 hour?
  $\frac{1}{3}$

Chalkboard Examples

1. Sally can type one page in 10 minutes. Tim can type one page in 15 minutes. How long will it take them, working together, to type 100 pages?

   Let t be the time, in minutes, that it takes them to finish 100 pages. Sally types one page every 10 minutes. Tim types one page every 15 minutes.

   $$\frac{1}{10} + \frac{1}{15} = \frac{100}{t}$$
   $$30t\left(\frac{1}{10} + \frac{1}{15}\right) = 30t \cdot \frac{100}{t}$$
   $$3t + 2t = 3000$$
   $$5t = 3000$$
   $$t = 600$$

   The time required is 600 minutes or 10 hours.

6-7 Problem Solving: Using Rational Equations

Work Problems

Objective: Solve work problems using rational equations.

Tom knows that he can mow a golf course lawn in 4 hours. He also knows that Perry takes 5 hours to mow the same lawn. Tom must complete the job in $2\frac{1}{2}$ hours. Can he and Perry get the job done in time? How long will it take them to complete the job together?

Solving Work Problems

If a job can be done in t hours, then $\frac{1}{t}$ of it can be done in one hour.

(The above condition holds for any unit of time.)

EXAMPLE 1

Tom can mow a lawn in 4 hours. Perry can mow the same lawn in 5 hours. How long would it take both of them, working together with two lawn mowers, to mow the lawn?

UNDERSTAND the problem

Question: How long will it take the two of them to mow the lawn together? — *Clarifying the question*

Data: Tom takes 4 hours to mow the lawn. Perry takes 5 hours to mow the lawn. — *Identifying the data*

Develop and carry out a PLAN

Let t represent the total number of hours it takes them working together. Then they can mow $\frac{1}{t}$ of it in 1 hour.

We can now translate to an equation.

$$\frac{1}{4} + \frac{1}{5} = \frac{1}{t}$$ *Translating to an equation*

We solve the equation.

$$20t\left(\frac{1}{4} + \frac{1}{5}\right) = 20t\left(\frac{1}{t}\right)$$ Multiplying on both sides by the LCD to clear fractions

$$\frac{20t}{4} + \frac{20t}{5} = \frac{20t}{t}$$

$$5t + 4t = 20$$

$$9t = 20$$

$$t = \frac{20}{9}, \text{ or } 2\tfrac{2}{9} \text{ hours}$$

■ **Find the ANSWER and CHECK**

Tom can do the entire job in 4 hours, so he can do *just over half* in $2\frac{2}{9}$ hours. Perry can do the entire job in 5 hours, so he can do *just under half* the job in $2\frac{2}{9}$ hours. It is reasonable that they can finish the job in $2\frac{2}{9}$ hours.

It will take them $2\frac{2}{9}$ hours together, so they will finish in time.

Try This

a. Carlos can do a typing job in 6 hours. Lynn can do the same job in 4 hours. How long would it take them to do the job working together with two typewriters? $2\frac{2}{5}$h

---

EXAMPLE 2

At a factory, smokestack A pollutes the air twice as fast as smokestack B. When the stacks operate together, they yield a certain amount of pollution in 15 hours. Find the time it would take each to yield that same amount of pollution operating alone.

Let x represent the number of hours it takes A to yield the pollution. Then $2x$ is the number of hours it takes B to yield the same amount of pollution.

$\frac{1}{x}$ is the fraction of the pollution produced by A in 1 hour.

$\frac{1}{2x}$ is the fraction of the pollution produced by B in 1 hour.

Together the stacks yield $\frac{1}{x} + \frac{1}{2x}$ of the total pollution in 1 hour. They also yield $\frac{1}{15}$ of it in 1 hour. We now have an equation.

$$\frac{1}{x} + \frac{1}{2x} = \frac{1}{15}$$ This is the translation.

Solving for x we get $x = 22\frac{1}{2}$ hours for smokestack A, and $2x$ or 45 hours for smokestack B. This checks.

Try This

b. Two pipes carry water to the same tank. Pipe A can fill the tank three times as fast as pipe B. Together they can fill the tank in 24 hours. Find the time it takes each pipe to fill the tank. A, 32 hours; B, 96 hours

---

2. A swimming pool has 2 input pipes, A and B. Pipe A can fill the pool in 2 days. Pipe B can fill the pool in 3 days. How long will it take to fill the pool using both pipes?
Let t be the time, in days, that it takes to fill the pool using both pipes. Pipe A can fill $\frac{1}{2}$ of a pool in one day. Pipe B can fill $\frac{1}{3}$ of a pool in one day. The total filled by both A and B is one pool.
$\frac{1}{2} + \frac{1}{3} = \frac{1}{t}$
$3t + 2t = 6$
$5t = 6$
$t = \frac{6}{5}$ days

3. Gerome's new tractor plows four times as fast as Luke's old one. Working together they can plow Luke's field in 4 hours. How long would it take Luke to plow his field working alone?
Let x be the number of hours it takes Gerome to plow the field. Then 4x is the number of hours it takes Luke.
$\frac{1}{x}$ is the fraction of the field Gerome plows in 1 hour.
$\frac{1}{4x}$ is the fraction Luke plows in 1 hour.
Together they plow $\frac{1}{x} + \frac{1}{4x}$ in 1 hour. They also plow $\frac{1}{4}$ of the field in 1 hour.
$\frac{1}{x} + \frac{1}{4x} = \frac{1}{4}$
$\frac{4}{4x} + \frac{1}{4x} = \frac{x}{4x}$
$x = 5$
It takes Gerome 5 hours to plow the field, so it takes Luke 20 hours.

Motion Problems

You may wish to have students show the steps in solving the resulting proportion in Example 3.

Note that the exercises in this section include several different types of motion problems. You may wish to use the Chalkboard Examples to demonstrate some types of problems not included in the student text.

Chalkboard Examples

1. It takes two hours to drive between the towns of Potter and Germantown. It takes 8 hours to make the trip by bicycle. How long will it take for a car and a bicycle to meet, starting at opposite towns at the same time?
   Let t be the time, in hours, for the car and the bicycle to meet. The car can cover $\frac{1}{2}$ the trip in one hour. The bicycle can cover $\frac{1}{8}$ of the trip in one hour. The total distance covered must equal one whole trip.
   $\frac{1}{2} + \frac{1}{8} = \frac{1}{t}$
   $4t + t = 8$
   $5t = 8$
   $t = \frac{8}{5}$ hours
2. Two canoeists paddle 10 km upstream in 5 hours. They make the return trip in only 1 hour. Assuming that the canoeists paddle at a constant rate, what is the speed of the current?
   Let r = rate of canoe in still water.
   Let c = speed of the current.
   Using $r = \frac{d}{t}$, the rate upstream is
   $r - c = \frac{10}{5}$
   $r - c = 2$
   The rate downstream is
   $r + c = \frac{10}{1}$
   $r + c = 10$
   Adding the equations we get
   $2r = 12$
   $r = 6$
   Substituting 6 for r in the first equation we get
   $6 - c = 2$
   $c = 4$ km/h
   The current has a speed of 4 km/h.

Motion Problems

Objective: Solve motion problems using rational equations.

Recall from Chapter 4 the equation for the rate of speed, $r = \frac{d}{t}$. From this we can easily obtain rational equations for time and for distance.

$$t = \frac{d}{r} \text{ and } d = rt$$

We can use these equations to solve motion problems.

EXAMPLE 3

An airplane flies 1062 km with the wind. In the same amount of time it can fly 738 km against the wind. The speed of the plane in still air is 200 km/h. Find the speed of the wind.

UNDERSTAND the problem

Question: What is the speed of the wind? — Clarifying the problem

Data: An airplane has a speed of 200 km/h. The airplane flies 1062 km with the wind. The airplane can only fly 738 km against the wind in the same time. — Identifying the data

Develop and carry out a PLAN

First *draw a diagram.* Let r represent the speed of the wind and organize the facts in a *chart.*

1062 km → t hours
$200 + r$ (The wind increases the speed.)

t hours ← 738 km
$200 - r$ (The wind decreases the speed.)

	Distance	Rate	Time
With wind	1062	$200 + r$	t
Against wind	738	$200 - r$	t

The times are the same, so we write the equations in the form $t = \frac{d}{r}$.

$$t = \frac{1062}{200 + r} \text{ and } t = \frac{738}{200 - r}$$ This is the translation.

Using substitution, we obtain $\frac{1062}{200 + r} = \frac{738}{200 - r}$.

Solving for r, we get 36.

Find the ANSWER and CHECK

The number 36 checks in the equation. A 36 km/h wind also makes sense in the problem. With the wind, the plane has a speed of 236 km/h. If it travels 1062 km, it must fly for 4.5 hours. Against the wind, the plane travels at 164 km/h. It will travel 738 km, also in 4.5 hours.

Thus the speed of the wind is 36 km/h. Stating the answer clearly

Try This

c. A boat travels 246 mi downstream in the same time it takes to travel 180 mi upstream. The speed of the current in the stream is 5.5 mi/h. Find the speed of the boat in still water. 35.5 mi/h

6-7 EXERCISES

A

1. Antonio, an experienced shipping clerk, can fill a certain order in 5 hours. Brian, a new clerk, needs 9 hours to do the same job. Working together, how long would it take them to fill the order? $3\frac{3}{14}$ hours
2. Leslie can paint a room in 4 hours. Fran can paint the same room in 3 hours. Working together, how long would it take them to paint the room? $1\frac{5}{7}$ hours
3. Sheila can frame in a room in 5 hours. David can do the same job in 4 hours. Working together, how long would it take them to frame in a room? $2\frac{2}{9}$ hours
4. Andrew can complete a plumbing job in 6 hours. Vivian can do the same job in 4 hours. Working together, how long would it take them to complete the job? $2\frac{2}{5}$ hours
5. A swimming pool can be filled using either a pipe, a hose, or both. Using the pipe alone it takes 12 hours. Using both it takes $8\frac{4}{7}$ hours. How long does it take using the hose alone? 30 hours
6. A tank can be filled using pipes A, B, or both. It takes pipe A, working alone, 18 hours to fill the tank. It takes both pipes, working together, 9.9 hours to fill the tank. How long does it take pipe B, working alone, to fill the tank? 22 hours
7. Ally can clear a lot in 5.5 hours. Her partner can do the same job in 7.5 hours. How long would it take them to clear the lot working together? 3.173 hours
8. One printing press can print an order of booklets in 4.5 hours. Another press can do the same job in 5.5 hours. How long would it take if both presses are used? 2.475 hours
9. The speed of a stream is 3 km/h. A boat travels 4 km upstream in the same time it takes to travel 10 km downstream. What is the speed of the boat in still water? 7 km/h
10. The speed of a stream is 4 km/h. A boat travels 6 km upstream in the same time it takes to travel 12 km downstream. What is the speed of the boat in still water? 12 km/h

LESSON QUIZ

1. A water tank is filled by pipes from 2 wells. The first pipe can fill the tank in 4 days. The second pipe can fill the tank in 6 days. How long will it take to fill the tank using both pipes?
   $\frac{12}{5}$ days
2. A boat travels 6 miles upstream in the same amount of time it can travel 10 miles downstream. In still water the speed of the boat is 5 mi/h. What is the speed of the current?
   1.25 mi/h

Assignment Guide
Algebra: 1–22 e/o, MR

Alg w/Finite or Trig: 1–27 e/o, 28, MR

Comprehensive: 1–22 m3, 23–27 e/o, 28, 29–32 e/o, MR

ADDITIONAL ANSWERS

Exercises

11. Train A, 46 km/h
Train B, 58 km/h
12. Train X, 80 km/h
Train Y, 66 km/h

11. The speed of train A is 12 km/h slower than the speed of train B. Train A travels 230 km in the same time it takes train B to travel 290 km. Find the speed of each.
12. The speed of train X is 14 km/h faster than the speed of train Y. Train X travels 400 km in the same time it takes train Y to travel 330 km. Find the speed of each.
13. Manuel has a boat that can move at a speed of 15 km/h in still water. He rides 140 km downstream in a river in the same time it takes to ride 35 km upstream. What is the speed of the river? 9 km/h
14. A paddleboat can move at a speed of 2 km/h in still water. The boat is paddled 4 km downstream in a river in the same time it takes to go 1 km upstream. What is the speed of the river? $1\frac{1}{5}$ km/h
15. Jennifer Chin has just enough money to rent a canoe for $1\frac{1}{2}$ hours. How far out on a lake can she paddle and return on time if she paddles out at 2 km/h and back at 4 km/h? 2 km
16. Kelly has just enough money to rent a canoe for $2\frac{1}{2}$ hours. How far out on the lake can she paddle and return on time if she paddles out at 3 km/h and back at 2 km/h? 3 km
17. One car travels 25 km/h faster than another. While one travels 300 km the other travels 450 km. Find their speeds. 50 km/h and 75 km/h
18. One car travels 30 km/h faster than another. While one travels 450 km the other travels 600 km. Find their speeds. 90 km/h and 120 km/h
19. The reciprocal of 5 plus the reciprocal of 7 is the reciprocal of what number? $\frac{35}{12}$
20. The reciprocal of 3 plus the reciprocal of 6 is the reciprocal of what number? 2
21. The sum of a number and 6 times its reciprocal is -5. Find the number. $-3, -2$
22. The sum of a number and 21 times its reciprocal is -10. Find the number. $-3, -7$

B

23. In a rational numeral the numerator is 3 more than the denominator. If 2 is added to both numerator and denominator, the result is $\frac{3}{2}$. Find the original numeral. $\frac{7}{4}$
24. In a rational numeral the denominator is 8 more than the numerator. If 5 is subtracted from both numerator and denominator, the result is $\frac{1}{2}$. Find the original numeral. $\frac{13}{21}$

Average speed is defined as a total distance divided by total time.

25. Wayne drove 3 hours on a freeway at 55 mi/h and then drove 10 miles in the city at 35 mi/h. What was his average speed? 53.26 mi/h
26. For the first 100 miles of a 200 mile trip, Deborah drove at a speed of 40 mi/h. For the second half of the trip, she drove at a speed of 60 mi/h. What was the average speed for the entire trip? (It was not 50 mi/h.) 48 mi/h
27. Donna drove half the distance of a trip at 40 mi/h. At what speed would she have to drive for the rest of the distance so that the average speed for the entire trip would be 45 mi/h? $51\frac{3}{7}$ mi/h
28. ***Critical Thinking*** Trucks A, B, and C, working together, can move a load of sand in t hours. When working alone, it takes truck A one extra hour to move the sand; B, six extra hours; and C, t extra hours. Find t. $\frac{2}{3}$ hr or 40 min

Challenge

29. At what time after 4:00 will the minute hand and the hour hand of a clock first be in the same position? $4{:}21\frac{9}{11}$
30. At what time after 10:30 will the hands of a clock first be perpendicular? $10{:}38\frac{2}{11}$
31. An employee drove to work on Monday at 45 mi/h and arrived one minute early. The employee drove to work on Tuesday, leaving home at the same time driving 40 mi/h and arriving one minute late.
    a. How far does the employee live from work? 12 mi
    b. At what speed would the employee need to drive to arrive five minutes early? 60 mi/h
32. The *point of no return* for an airplane, flying over water from point A on land to point B on land, is that distance into the trip for which it takes just as much time to go on to B as it does to return to A. The distance, in statute miles, from Los Angeles to Honolulu is 2574 miles. A plane leaves Los Angeles at a speed, in still air, of 400 mi/h. There is a 50 mi/h tail wind.
    a. Find the point of no return.
    b. After traveling 1187 miles, the pilot of the plane determines that it is necessary to make an emergency landing. Would it require less time to continue to Honolulu or to return to Los Angeles?

Mixed Review

Simplify. **33.** $\dfrac{\frac{1}{x}+2}{\frac{1}{x}-5}$ **34.** $\dfrac{y-\frac{2}{y}}{y+\frac{2}{y}}$ **35.** $\dfrac{\frac{3}{x}+\frac{2}{y}}{\frac{2}{x}-\frac{3}{y}}$

Factor. **36.** $8x^2 + 12x - 8$ **37.** $2x^2 + x - 3$ **38.** $x^3 + 27$

Solve. **39.** $x^2 + 3x + 2 = 0$ **40.** $y^2 + 12y + 36 = 0$ **41.** $6 = 0.8m$

Problem for Programmers

Write a program to determine the number of hours it will take a given number of people to do a job, given the amount of time it would take each person to do the job alone. The program should allow the user to first enter the number of people, then for each person, enter the number of hours it would take that person to do the job. Test your program on Exercises 1–4 in Lesson 6-7.

Challenge: Expand the program so that it will find how long it would take one of the people working alone, if the time it would take each of the others, and *all* of them together, are input. The program should determine whether the solution is possible.

ADDITIONAL ANSWERS

Exercises

32. a. $1126\frac{1}{8}$ from Los Angeles
    b. Continue to Honolulu

Mixed Review

33. $\frac{1 + 2x}{1 - 5x}$
34. $\frac{y^2 - 2}{y^2 + 2}$
35. $\frac{3y + 2x}{2y - 3x}$
36. $4(x + 2)(2x - 1)$
37. $(2x + 3)(x - 1)$
38. $(x + 3)(x^2 - 3x + 9)$
39. $-1, -2$
40. -6
41. 7.5

6-8

FIRST FIVE MINUTES

1. John can walk from town A to town B in 5 hours. Juana can walk the same distance in 4 hours. If they start at the same time, at opposite towns, how long will it take them to meet?
   Let t be the time it takes for them to meet. John walks $\frac{1}{5}$ of the trip in one hour. Juana walks $\frac{1}{4}$ of the trip in one hour.
   $\frac{1}{5} + \frac{1}{4} = \frac{1}{t}$
   $4t + 5t = 20$
   $9t = 20$
   $t = \frac{20}{9} \approx 2$ h 13 min

Solving Rational Formulas

In this lesson, the techniques of algebra are used to manipulate equations into new forms, rather than solving for a numeric solution. Some students may be confused by the change in goals.

Emphasize that the goal in this section will be to solve an equation for one variable in terms of the other variables. We may later use this new equation to find numeric solutions.

Chalkboard Example

1. The volume V of a pyramid with a square base of length L and altitude H is given by
   $V = \frac{1}{3}L^2H$
   Solve for H in terms of L and V.
   $3V = L^2H$
   $\frac{3V}{L^2} = H$
   $H = \frac{3V}{L^2}$

Problem Solving: Solving Formulas

Point out that it is most efficient to solve for the unknown variable before substituting the values of the known variables. If known variables are substituted before solving, expressions may become complex and difficult to manipulate.

6-8 Formulas

Solving Rational Formulas

Objective: Solve rational formulas for a specified variable.

The formula for calculating a pitcher's earned run average (ERA) is $A = \frac{9R}{I}$ where A is the ERA, R is the number of earned runs, and I is the number of innings pitched. If we know the ERA and the number of earned runs we can find the number of innings pitched by solving the formula for I. To solve a rational formula for a specific letter we can use the same techniques as we use to solve rational equations.

EXAMPLE 1 Solve the formula $A = \frac{9R}{I}$ for I.

$$I \cdot A = I \cdot \frac{9R}{I} \quad \text{Clearing fractions}$$
$$I \cdot A = 9R$$
$$I = \frac{9R}{A}$$

From the formula solved for I, you can calculate the number of innings a pitcher pitched if you know the pitcher's ERA and the number of earned runs the pitcher gave up.

Try This

a. The formula $\frac{PV}{T} = k$ relates the pressure, volume, and temperature of a gas. Solve it for T. $T = \frac{PV}{k}$

Problem Solving: Solving Formulas

Objective: Solve problems involving the use of a formula.

It may be necessary to look up a formula or a definition to understand a problem fully. You may then need to solve a formula for a certain variable.

EXAMPLE 2

Two electrical resistors are connected in parallel. The resistance of one of them is 6 ohms and the resistance of the combination is 3.75 ohms. What is the resistance of the other resistor?

UNDERSTAND the problem

In a book on electricity or physics, we find that resistors in parallel are diagrammed like this:

Using a reference to find missing information

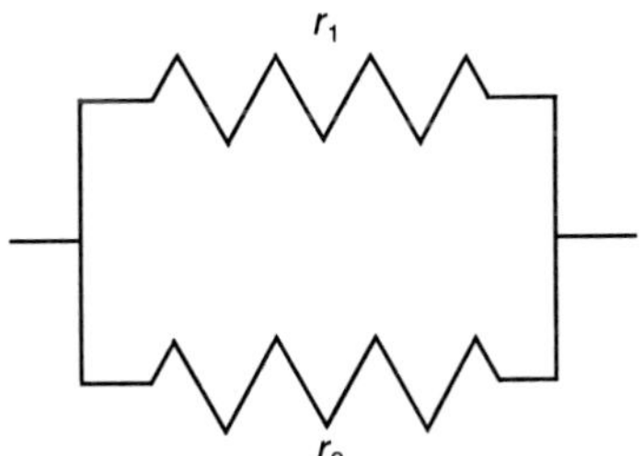

The rule for finding the resistance of a combination is given by the formula $\frac{1}{R} = \frac{1}{r_1} + \frac{1}{r_2}$, where r_1 and r_2 are the resistances of the individual resistors, and R is the resistance of the combination. In this problem we know $R = 3.75$ ohms and $r_1 = 6$ ohms. We want to find r_2.

Develop and carry out a PLAN

We solve the formula for the unknown resistance r_2.

$$\frac{1}{R} = \frac{1}{r_1} + \frac{1}{r_2}$$

$$Rr_1r_2\left(\frac{1}{R}\right) = Rr_1r_2\left(\frac{1}{r_1} + \frac{1}{r_2}\right)$$ Multiplying by Rr_1r_2

$$r_1r_2 = Rr_2 + Rr_1$$ Simplifying

$$r_1r_2 - Rr_2 = Rr_1$$ Adding $-Rr_2$ to both sides

$$r_2(r_1 - R) = Rr_1$$

$$r_2 = \frac{Rr_1}{r_1 - R}$$

We now substitute into the formula.

$$r_2 = \frac{3.75(6)}{6 - 3.75} = \frac{22.5}{2.25} = 10$$

Find the ANSWER and CHECK

The resistor has a resistance of 10 ohms.

10 ohms checks in the original formula.

Try This

b. The formula $\frac{1}{p} + \frac{1}{q} = \frac{1}{f}$ applies to a lens. The distance from an object to the lens and from the image to the lens are represented, respectively, by p and q. The focal length of the lens is represented by f. Find the focal length of a lens that forms an image 15 cm from the lens when an object is placed 10 cm from the lens. 6 cm

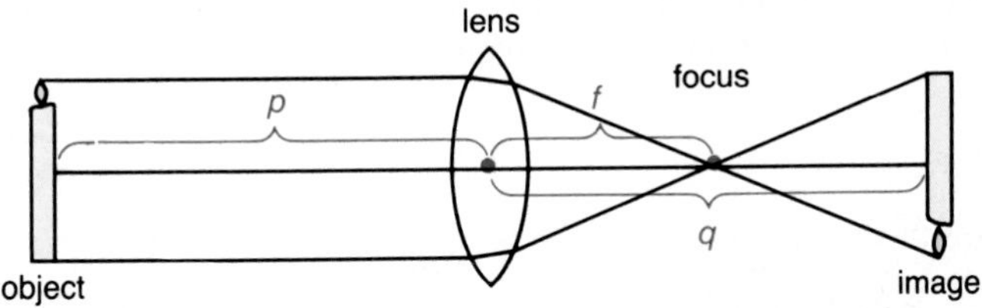

Chalkboard Example

1. If an initial amount P is invested at annual interest rate R, then the amount F after one year is given by the formula
   $F = P(1 + R)$
   If an amount of \$120 is invested and grows to \$138 after one year, what is the interest rate?
   $\frac{F}{P} = 1 + R$
   $\frac{F}{P} - 1 = R$
   Substitute for F and P.
   $R = \frac{138}{120} - 1$
   $= 15\%$

LESSON QUIZ

1. Solve $\frac{1}{f} = \frac{1}{a} + \frac{1}{b}$, for a.
   $a = \frac{bf}{b - f}$
2. Solve $d = \frac{a}{b(c - 1)}$, for c.
   $c = \frac{db + a}{db}$
3. A rectangular swimming pool holds 1500 m³ of water. If the depth of the pool is 1.5 m and the width is 20 m, what is the length of the pool?
   50 m

Assignment Guide
Algebra: 1 – 22 e/o, MR

Alg w/Finite or Trig: 1–23 e/o, 24, MR

Comprehensive: 1–23 e/o, 24, 25, MR

ADDITIONAL ANSWERS

Exercises

1. $d_1 = \frac{d_2W_1}{W_2}$ 2. $W_2 = \frac{d_2W_1}{d_1}$
3. $t = \frac{2S}{v_1 + v_2}$ 4. $v_1 = \frac{2S - v_2t}{t}$
5. $r_2 = \frac{Rr_1}{r_1 - R}$ 6. $R = \frac{r_1r_2}{r_2 + r_1}$
7. $s = \frac{Rg}{g - R}$ 8. $g = \frac{Rs}{s - R}$
9. $r = \frac{2V - IR}{2I}$ 10. $R = \frac{2V - 2Ir}{I}$
11. $r = \frac{nE - IR}{In}$ 12. $n = \frac{IR}{E - Ir}$
13. $H = m(t_1 - t_2)S$
14. $t_1 = \frac{H + Smt_2}{Sm}$
15. $e = \frac{Er}{R + r}$
16. $r = \frac{eR}{E - e}$
17. $a = \frac{S - Sr}{1 - r^n}$
18. $r = \frac{S - a}{S}$

Mixed Review

26. $24x^3y^2$
27. $42ab$
28. $-4, 3$
29. $-7, -3$
30. $5, -5$

6-8 EXERCISES

A

Solve each formula for the given letter.

1. $\frac{W_1}{W_2} = \frac{d_1}{d_2}; d_1$
2. $\frac{W_1}{W_2} = \frac{d_1}{d_2}; W_2$
3. $S = \frac{1}{2}v_1t + \frac{1}{2}v_2t; t$
4. $S = \frac{1}{2}v_1t + \frac{1}{2}v_2t; v_1$
5. $\frac{1}{R} = \frac{1}{r_1} + \frac{1}{r_2}; r_2$
6. $\frac{1}{R} = \frac{1}{r_1} + \frac{1}{r_2}; R$
7. $R = \frac{gs}{g + s}; s$
8. $R = \frac{gs}{g + s}; g$
9. $I = \frac{2V}{R + 2r}; r$
10. $I = \frac{2V}{R + 2r}; R$
11. $I = \frac{nE}{R + nr}; r$
12. $I = \frac{nE}{R + nr}; n$
13. $S = \frac{H}{m(t_1 - t_2)}; H$
14. $S = \frac{H}{m(t_1 - t_2)}; t_1$
15. $\frac{E}{e} = \frac{R + r}{r}; e$
16. $\frac{E}{e} = \frac{R + r}{r}; r$
17. $S = \frac{a - ar^n}{1 - r}; a$
18. $S = \frac{a}{1 - r}; r$
19. Two resistors are connected in parallel. Their resistances are 8 ohms and 15 ohms. What is the resistance of the combination? $\frac{120}{23}$ ohms
20. A resistor has a resistance of 30 ohms. What size resistor should be put with it, in parallel, to obtain a resistance of 3 ohms? $\frac{10}{3}$ ohms
21. A lens with a focal length of 8 cm forms an image of an object that is 24 cm away from it. How far from the lens is the image? 12 cm
22. A pitcher's earned run average is 2.40, and he has pitched 45 innings. How many earned runs were given up? 12 runs

B

23. Pam can do a certain job in a hours working alone. Elaine, working alone, can do the same job in b hours. Working together, it takes them t hours to do the job.
 a. Find a formula for t. $t = \frac{ab}{b + a}$ **b.** Solve the formula for a. $a = \frac{tb}{b - t}$
 c. Solve the formula for b. $b = \frac{ta}{a - t}$
24. ***Critical Thinking*** The harmonic mean of two numbers, a and b, is a number M, such that the reciprocal of M is the average of the reciprocals of a and b. Find a formula for the harmonic mean. $M = \frac{2ab}{a + b}$

Challenge

25. In a physics book, find the formula for *centripetal force*. Solve the formula for r. Find the length of a string fastened to a 5-kg mass being spun at a speed of 3 meters per second (m/s) and that has a centripetal force of 22.5 newtons acting upon it. $F = \frac{mv^2}{r}$; $r = \frac{mv^2}{F}$; $r = 2$ meters

Mixed Review

Find the least common multiple. **26.** $24xy, 6x^3, 8y^2$ **27.** $3a, 6b, 7a$

Solve. **28.** $x^2 + x - 12 = 0$ **29.** $x^2 + 10x + 21 = 0$ **30.** $x^2 - 25 = 0$

6-9 Variation and Problem Solving

Direct Variation

Objective: Find the constant of variation and an equation of variation for direct variation problems.

A plumber earns \$35 per hour. In 2 hours \$70 is earned. In 3 hours \$105 is earned, and so on. This pattern results in a set of ordered pairs of numbers, all having the same ratio.

$$(1, 35), (2, 70), (3, 105), (4, 140), \ldots$$

The ratio of earnings to time is $\frac{35}{1}$ in every case.

Whenever a situation results in pairs of numbers in which the ratio is constant, we say that there is direct variation. Here the earnings vary directly with the time, t.

$$\frac{E}{t} = 35 \text{ (a constant), or } E = 35t$$

Note that the constant 35 is positive. Note also that when one quantity increases, so does the other. When one decreases, so does the other.

Definition

Whenever a situation translates to a linear function $f(x) = kx$, or $y = kx$, where k is a positive constant, we say that there is **direct variation**, or that y **varies directly** with x. The number k is the **constant of variation.**

EXAMPLE 1

Find the constant of variation and an equation of variation where y varies directly with x, and where $y = 32$ when $x = 2$.

We know that (2, 32) is a solution of $y = kx$.

$32 = k \cdot 2$ Substituting

$\frac{32}{2} = k$, or $k = 16$ Solving for k

The constant of variation is 16. The equation of variation is $y = 16x$.

Try This

a. Find the constant of variation and an equation of variation where y varies directly with x, and $y = 8$ when $x = 20$. $k = 0.4, y = 0.4x$

6-9

FIRST FIVE MINUTES

1. Solve for n where
$m = \frac{1 + n}{a}$.
$am = 1 + n$
$am - 1 = n$
$n = am - 1$

2. Solve $u = \frac{vw}{v - w}$, for v.
$u(v - w) = vw$
$uv - uw = vw$
$uv - vw = uw$
$v(u - w) = uw$
$v = \frac{uw}{u - w}$

Direct Variation

Give students examples of some common situations in which one quantity varies directly as another. For example, the cost of gas for a car trip varies directly with the length of the trip.

Emphasize that in a relationship of direct variation, one quantity increases or decreases when the other quantity increases or decreases, respectively.

Key Questions

Assume $F = ma$.

- Does m vary directly as F?
  Yes, $m = \frac{1}{a} \cdot F$.
- Does m vary directly as a?
  No, $m = \frac{F}{a}$.

Chalkboard Example

1. The length of a spring varies directly as the force applied to it. When the spring is stretched 4 inches, the force is 8 pounds. Find the constant of variation and the equation of variation.
Let L be the length of stretch, in inches.
Let F be the force in pounds.
$L = kF$, k constant
$L = 4, F = 8$
The values satisfy the equation.
$4 = k \cdot 8$
$k = \frac{1}{2}$
The equation of variation is
$L = \frac{1}{2}F$

Inverse Variation

Give students examples of some common situations in which one quantity varies inversely as another. For example, the time for a trip varies inversely with the speed. Also, when we speak of 80 "man hours" or "person hours", 80 is the constant k in the equation of inverse variation.

Emphasize the difference between direct variation and inverse variation.

Key Questions

Assume $\frac{P}{T} = k$.

- Does P vary inversely with k? No
- Does P vary inversely with T? No
- Does k vary inversely with T? Yes

Chalkboard Example

1. The voltage V, in volts, in an electrical circuit varies inversely as the resistance R, in ohms. The voltage in the circuit is 12 volts when the resistance is 240 ohms. Find the equation of variation.
   The equation must be of the form $V = \frac{k}{R}$
   The values $V = 12$ and $R = 240$ satisfy the equation.
   $12 = \frac{k}{240}$
   $k = 12 \cdot 240$
   $k = 2880$
   The equation of variation is $V = \frac{2880}{R}$

Inverse Variation

Objective: Find the constant of variation and an equation of variation for inverse variation problems.

A bus is traveling a distance of 20 km. At a speed of 20 km/h it will take 1 hour. At 40 km/h it will take $\frac{1}{2}$ hour. At 60 km/h it will take $\frac{1}{3}$ hour, and so on. This pattern results in a set of ordered pairs of numbers, all having the same product.

$$(20, 1), \left(40, \frac{1}{2}\right), \left(60, \frac{1}{3}\right), \left(80, \frac{1}{4}\right), \ldots$$

Whenever a situation results in pairs of numbers whose product is constant, we say that there is inverse variation. Here the time varies inversely with the speed.

$$rt = 20 \text{ (a constant), or } t = \frac{20}{r}$$

Note that the constant, 20, is positive. Note also that when one quantity increases, the other decreases.

Definition

Whenever a situation translates to a rational function $f(x) = \frac{k}{x}$, or $y = \frac{k}{x}$, where k is a positive constant, we say that there is **inverse variation,** or that **y varies inversely** with x. The number k is the constant of variation.

EXAMPLE 2

Find the constant of variation and an equation of variation where y varies inversely with x, and $y = 32$ when $x = 0.2$.

We know that $(0.2, 32)$ is a solution of $y = \frac{k}{x}$.

$$32 = \frac{k}{0.2} \quad \text{Substituting}$$
$$(0.2)32 = k \quad \text{Solving}$$
$$6.4 = k$$

The constant of variation is 6.4. The equation of variation is $y = \frac{6.4}{x}$.

Try This

b. Find the constant of variation and an equation of variation where y varies inversely with x, $y = 0.012$ when $x = 50$. $k = 0.6, y = \frac{0.6}{x}$

Problem Solving: Using Variation

Objective: Solve problems using direct variation and inverse variation.

PROBLEM-SOLVING GUIDELINES
■ UNDERSTAND the problem
■ Develop and carry out a PLAN
■ Find the ANSWER and CHECK

Equations of direct and inverse variation can serve as mathematical models of many situations. We can then use the Problem-Solving Guidelines to solve problems related to them.

EXAMPLE 3

The volume of water produced from melting snow varies directly with the volume of snow. Meteorologists have found that 150 cm^3 of snow will melt to 16.8 cm^3 of water. Suppose 200 cm^3 of snow melts. Predict the resulting volume of water.

■ **UNDERSTAND the problem**

Question: Into how many cm^3 of water will 200 cm^3 of snow melt? — Clarifying the question

Data: 150 cm^3 of snow will melt to 16.8 cm^3 of water. — Identifying the data
The volume of snow varies directly with the volume of water produced when snow melts.

■ **Develop and carry out a PLAN**

First find the constant of variation using the data, and then find an equation of variation.

$W = kS$ — W is the volume of water, S the volume of snow.

$16.8 = k \cdot 150$ — Substituting

$\frac{16.8}{150} = k$ — Solving for k

$0.112 = k$ — This is the constant of variation.

The equation of variation is $W = 0.112S$.

Next use the equation to predict how many cm^3 of water will result from melting 200 cm^3 of snow.

$$W = 0.112S$$
$$W = 0.112(200) = 22.4$$

■ **Find the ANSWER and CHECK**

22.4 cm^3 of water is reasonable, since it is about $\frac{1}{9}$ the volume of snow, just as 16.8 is about $\frac{1}{9}$ of 150. Thus 200 cm^3 of snow will melt to 22.4 cm^3 of water. — Stating the answer clearly

Problem Solving: Using Variation

Chalkboard Examples

1. The cost c, in cents, of lighting a 100-watt light bulb varies directly as the time t, in hours, that the light is on. The cost of using the light for 1000 hours is 15 cents. Write the equation of variation. Determine the cost of using the light for 2400 hours.
   The equation of variation is of the form $c = kt$.
   The values $c = 15$, $t = 1000$ satisfy the equation.
   $15 = k \cdot 1000$
   $k = \frac{15}{1000}$
   $k = \frac{3}{200}$
   The equation of variation is
   $c = \frac{3}{200}t$
   To find the cost of 2400 hours, substitute for t.
   $c = \frac{3}{200} \cdot 2400$
   $c = 36$
   The cost is 36 cents.
2. The time t required to harvest the potato crop varies inversely as the number n of people on the job. It takes 8 hours for 10 people to do the job. How long will it take for 36 people to do the job?
   The equation of variation must be of the form $t = \frac{k}{n}$, where k is a constant.
   The equation is satisfied by $t = 8$, $n = 10$.
   $8 = \frac{k}{10}$
   $k = 8 \cdot 10$
   $k = 80$
   The equation of variation is
   $t = \frac{80}{n}$
   When $n = 36$,
   $t = \frac{80}{36}$
   $t = 2\frac{2}{9}$
   It will take the 36 people $2\frac{2}{9}$ hours to do the job.

LESSON QUIZ

1. Find the variation constant and the equation of variation where y varies directly as x, and $y = 2$ when $x = 7$.

   $k = \frac{2}{7}$

   The equation of variation is

   $y = \frac{2}{7}x$

2. Find the variation constant and the equation of variation where y varies inversely as x, and $y = 6$ when $x = 5$.

   $k = 30$

   The equation of variation is

   $y = \frac{30}{x}$

3. The income I earned by a theatre varies directly as the number n of persons attending. The theatre receives $2250 when 500 persons attend. How much does the theatre receive when 200 persons attend?

   The equation of variation is

   $I = \frac{9}{2}n$

   When $n = 200$,

   $I = \frac{9}{2}(200)$

   $I = 900$ dollars

Try This

c. Ohm's law states that the voltage in an electric circuit varies directly as the number of amperes of electric current in the circuit. If the voltage is 10 volts when the current is 3 amperes, what is the voltage when the current is 15 amperes? 50 volts

---

EXAMPLE 4

The time (t) required to do a job varies inversely with the number of people (P) who work on the job. It takes 4 hours for 12 people to erect some football bleachers. Predict how long it would take for 3 people to do the same job.

■ UNDERSTAND the problem

Question: How long would it take 3 people to erect the bleachers? — Clarifying the question

Data: It takes 4 hours for 12 people to do the job. The time required varies inversely with the number of people. — Identifying the data

■ Develop and carry out a PLAN

First find the constant of variation using the data, and then find an equation of variation.

$$t = \frac{k}{P}$$

$$4 = \frac{k}{12} \quad \text{Substituting}$$

$$48 = k \quad \text{Solving for } k\text{, the constant of variation}$$

The equation of variation is $t = \frac{48}{P}$. Next use the equation to find the time it would take 3 people to do the job.

$$t = \frac{48}{P}$$

$$t = \frac{48}{3} = 16$$

■ Find the ANSWER and CHECK

The time is reasonable since it would take 3 people four times as long as it takes 12 people.
It would take 3 people 16 hours.

Try This

d. The time (t) required to drive a fixed distance varies inversely as the speed (r). It takes 5 hours at 60 km/h to drive a fixed distance. How long would it take to drive that same distance at 40 km/h? $7\frac{1}{2}$ hours

---

6-9 EXERCISES

Assignment Guide
Algebra: 1–28 e/o, MR

Alg w/Finite or Trig: 1–30 e/o, 31, MR

Comprehensive: 1–30 e/o, 31–33, MR

A

Find the constant of variation and an equation of variation, where y varies directly as x.

1. $y = 24$ when $x = 3$ $k = 8, y = 8x$
2. $y = 5$ when $x = 12$ $k = \frac{5}{12}, y = \frac{5}{12}x$
3. $y = 16$ when $x = 1$ $k = 16, y = 16x$
4. $y = 2$ when $x = 5$ $k = \frac{2}{5}, y = \frac{2}{5}x$
5. $y = 15$ when $x = 3$ $k = 5, y = 5x$
6. $y = 1$ when $x = 2$ $k = \frac{1}{2}, y = \frac{1}{2}x$
7. $y = 1$ when $x = 1$ $k = 1, y = x$
8. $y = 0.6$ when $x = 0.4$ $k = \frac{3}{2}, y = \frac{3}{2}x$

Find the constant of variation and an equation of variation, where y varies inversely as x.

9. $y = 6$ when $x = 10$ $k = 60, y = \frac{60}{x}$
10. $y = 16$ when $x = 4$ $k = 64, y = \frac{64}{x}$
11. $y = 12$ when $x = 3$ $k = 36, y = \frac{36}{x}$
12. $y = 9$ when $x = 5$ $k = 45, y = \frac{45}{x}$
13. $y = 27$ when $x = \frac{1}{3}$ $k = 9, y = \frac{9}{x}$
14. $y = 81$ when $x = \frac{1}{9}$ $k = 9, y = \frac{9}{x}$
15. The electric current (I), in amperes, in a circuit varies directly as the voltage (V). When 12 volts are applied, the current is 4 amperes. Predict the current when 18 volts are applied. 6 amperes
16. Hooke's law states that the distance (d) a spring is stretched by a hanging object varies directly as the weight (w) of the object. The distance is 40 cm when the weight is 3 kg. Predict the distance when the weight is 5 kg. $66\frac{2}{3}$cm
17. The current (I) in an electrical conductor varies inversely as the resistance (R) of the conductor. The current is $\frac{1}{2}$ ampere when the resistance is 240 ohms. What is the current when the resistance is 540 ohms? $\frac{2}{9}$ ampere
18. The time (t) required to empty a tank varies inversely as the rate (r) of pumping. A pump can empty a tank in 45 minutes at the rate of 600 kiloliters per minute. How long will it take the pump to empty the tank at the rate of 1000 kL/m? 27 minutes
19. The number (N) of plastic straws produced by a machine varies directly as the amount of time (t) the machine is operating. The machine produces 20,000 straws in 8 hours. How many straws can it produce in 50 hours? 125,000
20. The time (T) required to do a job varies inversely as the number of people (P) working. It takes 5 hours for 7 bricklayers to complete a certain job. How long would it take 10 bricklayers to complete the job? 3.5 hours
21. The volume (V) of a gas varies inversely as the pressure (P) upon it. The volume of a gas is 200 cm^3 under a pressure of 32 kg/cm^2. Predict its volume under a pressure of 40 kg/cm^2. 160 cm^3
22. The weight (M) of an object on the moon varies directly as its weight (E) on earth. A person who weighs 95 kg on earth weighs 15.2 kg on the moon. How much would a 105-kg person weigh on the moon? 16.8 kg
23. The amount of pollution (A) entering the atmosphere varies directly as the number of people (N) living in an area. 60,000 people result in 42,600 tons of pollutants entering the atmosphere. Predict how many tons enter the atmosphere in a city with a population of 750,000. 532,500 tons

ADDITIONAL ANSWERS

Exercises

29. 2074
30. 100 oz
31. a. Inverse variation
    b. Direct variation
    c. Neither
32. $P = kQ$, so $Q = \frac{1}{k}P$, and $\frac{1}{k}$ becomes the constant of variation
33. $A = \frac{k}{B}$, so $B = \frac{k}{A}$, and $\frac{1}{A} = \frac{B}{k} = \frac{1}{k} \cdot B$

Mixed Review

34. $-8x^5y^{-1}$
35. $40x^{2+a}y^2$
36. 1.87×10^7
37. $7a^3b$
38. $8v$
39. 2×10^{-2}
40. $(x - 3)(x^2 + 3x + 9)$
41. $4(2x - 3)(2x + 3)$
42. $3x^2(2x^2 - x + 6)$

24. The time (t) required to drive a fixed distance varies inversely as the speed (r). It takes 5 hours at 80 km/h to drive a fixed distance. How long would it take to drive the fixed distance at 60 km/h? $6\frac{2}{3}$ hours
25. The weight (M) of an object on Mars varies directly as its weight (E) on Earth. A person who weighs 95 kg on Earth weighs 38 kg on Mars. How much would a 100-kg person weigh on Mars? 40 kg
26. The number (N) of aluminum cans used each year varies directly as the number of people using the cans. 250 people use 60,000 cans in one year. Predict the number of cans used each year in a city with a population of 850,000. 204,000,000
27. The wavelength (W) of a radio wave varies inversely as its frequency (F). A wave with a frequency of 1200 kilohertz per second has a length of 300 meters. Predict the length of a wave with a frequency of 800 kilohertz per second. 450 m
28. The number of kilograms of water (W) in a human body varies directly as the total weight. A person weighing 96 kg contains 64 kg of water. How many kilograms of water are in a person weighing 75 kg? 50 kg

B

29. To determine the number of deer in a forest, a conservationist catches 612 deer, tags them, and releases them. Later, 244 deer are caught, 72 of which are tagged. Predict how many deer are in the forest.
30. It is known that it takes 60 oz of grass seed to seed 3000 ft^2 of lawn. At this rate, how much would be needed for 5000 ft^2 of lawn?
31. ***Critical Thinking*** Consider these graphs of variation functions. Describe each as a graph of direct variation, inverse variation, or neither. Tell how you made your decision about each graph.

a. 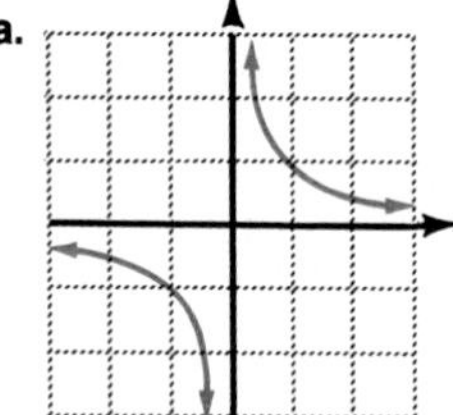

b. 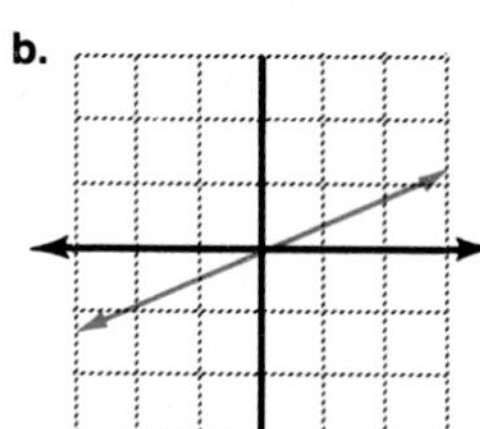

c. 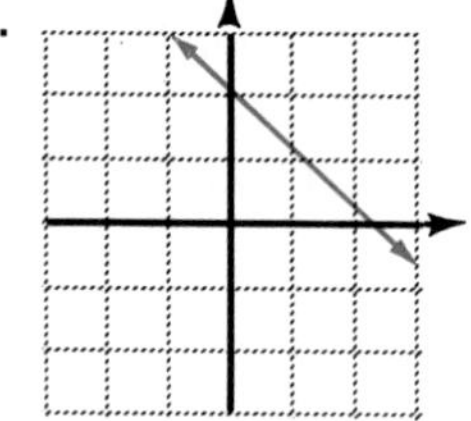

Challenge

32. Show that if P varies directly as Q, then Q varies directly as P.
33. Show that if A varies inversely as B, then B varies inversely as A and $\frac{1}{A}$ varies directly as B.

Mixed Review

Simplify. **34.** $(-4x^2y^{-3})(2x^3y^2)$ **35.** $(-5x^2y^5)(-8x^ay^{-3})$

36. $(3.4 \times 10^{10})(5.5 \times 10^{-4})$ **37.** $\frac{21a^5b^3}{3a^2b^2}$ **38.** $\frac{64w^{-2}v^2}{8w^{-2}v}$ **39.** $4.6 \times \frac{10^5}{2.3} \times 10^{-7}$

Factor. **40.** $x^3 - 27$ **41.** $16x^2 - 36$ **42.** $6x^4 - 3x^3 + 18x^2$

6-10 Problem Solving: Strategies

Make a Table, Look for a Pattern

Objective: Solve problems using the strategies *Make a Table, Look for a Pattern,* and other strategies.

The problem-solving strategies called Make a Table and Look for a Pattern are helpful when solving problems involving numerical relationships. When data are organized in a table, numerical patterns are easier to recognize.

EXAMPLE 1

How many steps would there be if 55 blocks were used?

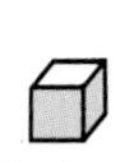
1 step

2 steps

3 steps

You can *make a table* showing the number of steps and the number of blocks used.

Number of steps	0	1	2	3	4	5	6	7	8	9	10
Number of blocks	0	1	3	6	10						

+1 +2 +3 +4

You can use this pattern to extend the table to 55 blocks for 10 steps. Notice another pattern in the number of blocks.

Number of Steps	Number of Blocks
1	1
2	$1 + 2 = 3$
3	$1 + 2 + 3 = 6$
4	$1 + 2 + 3 + 4 = 10$
10	$1 + 2 + 3 + 4 + \ldots + 10 = 55$

Note the following for when there are 5 steps.

$$\begin{array}{r l} 1 + 2 + 3 + 4 + 5 & \text{The number of blocks for 5 steps} \\ + \underline{5 + 4 + 3 + 2 + 1} & \textit{Also} \text{ the number of blocks for 5 steps} \\ 6 + 6 + 6 + 6 + 6 = 5(6) & \end{array}$$

The sum $5(6)$ represents *twice* the number of blocks for 5 steps, so $\frac{5(6)}{2}$ blocks are used for 5 steps. For n steps, $\frac{n(n + 1)}{2}$ blocks are used.

6-10

FIRST FIVE MINUTES

1. What three whole numbers have a sum of 15 and a product of 105?
   3, 5, 7 (Try factoring 105. Make an organized list.)
2. A sealed box contains hardbound and softbound books. The hardbound books weigh 3 lb each and the softbound books weigh 2 lb each. The contents of the box weigh 15 lb. What are the possible quantities of each kind of book?
   1 hardbound and 6 softbound or 3 hardbound and 3 softbound (Make an organized list.)

Make a Table, Look for a Pattern

Point out that the Make a Table, Look for a Pattern strategies can be used any time a problem involves a sequence of numbers that are related to each other by some kind of pattern.

Key Questions

- If there are 28 blocks when there are 7 steps, how many blocks are there when there are 8 steps?
  $28 + 8 = 36$ blocks
- If there are 325 blocks when there are 25 steps, how many blocks are there when there are 26 steps?
  $325 + 26 = 341$ blocks

Chalkboard Example

1. The figure below has 3 triangles in its base and contains 9 small triangles. How many small triangles would it contain if it had 15 triangles in the base?

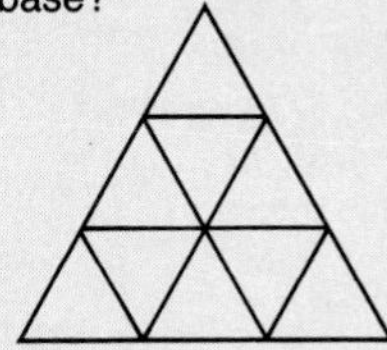

Make a table

Base	1	2	3	4	5
Total	1	4	9	16	25

The total number of triangles is the square of the number in the base. When there are 15 triangles in the base, there will be 15^2 or 225 small triangles altogether.

Hints for Problems

1. Make a table showing the height of each array and the total number of dots.
2. Write an equation. Note that one sheet is made up of two pages.
3. Make a table showing the multiples of 3 and 5 pounds.
4. Make a table showing the number of cells for each two-hour period.
5. Make a table for each person, writing the number of days worked and the total earnings.
6. Make an organized list showing the number of digits used for the project numbers.
7. Make an organized list showing the possible numbers of touchdowns, field goals, and extra points. Begin with the greatest number of touchdowns.

ANSWERS

1. There are 10 (10 + 1) = 10 × 11 = 110 dots.
2. 11 sheets were torn out of the book.
3. One can buy one 3 lb and nine 5 lb bags, or six of each, or eleven 3 lb bags and three 5 lb bags, or sixteen 3 lb bags .
4. There would be 4096 cells of each type after 24 hours.
5. One worked 10 days and the other worked 15 days.
6. Each participant had to pay about $0.67 for the stickers.
7. They could have scored 34 points 7 different ways.

Problem-Solving Strategies		
Write an Equation	Draw a Diagram	Guess, Check, Revise
Make an Organized List	Make a Table	Look for a Pattern
Use Logical Reasoning	Simplify the Problem	Work Backward

6-10 PROBLEMS

Solve using one or more of the strategies.

1. Find the total number of dots in B_{10}.

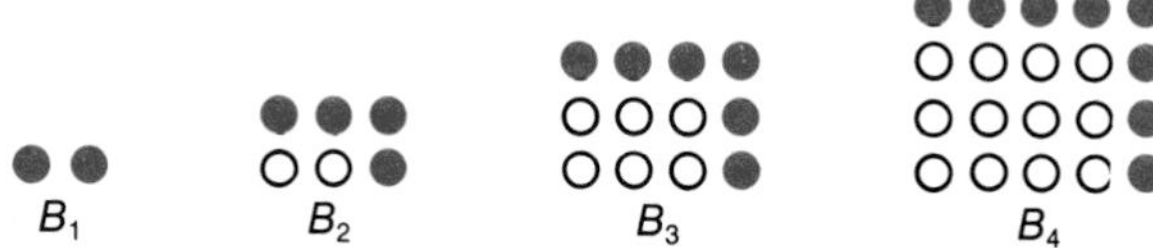

2. Some pages were torn out of a book by mistake. The person repairing the book noticed that the number on one of the facing pages was 11 more than twice the number on the other facing page, and the difference of the page numbers was 23. How many sheets of paper were torn out of this book?

3. Grass seed was sold in 3 lb and 5 lb bags. An order came in for exactly 48 lb of this grass seed. How many bags of each size could be sent to fill this order?

4. A biologist has a mixture made up of two types of cells, type A and type B. Every 2 hours each B cell produces one A cell and one B cell. Type A cells do not produce additional cells. Assume there was one cell of each type to start. How many cells of each type would accumulate after 1 day?

5. A waiter earned an average of $15 a day in tips working at a restaurant. His friend earned an average of $10 a day in tips working at another restaurant. At the end of the first pay period, the one earning less had worked 5 more days than the other, and they had both earned the same amount in tips. How many days did each work?

6. Each piece of art in an art show had to be assigned its own number. The art projects had to be numbered consecutively starting at 1. The person responsible for doing this had to place on the display table a sticker for each digit in the number given each piece of art. Each digit sticker cost 25¢. A total of 882 stickers were used and none were wasted. The total cost of the stickers had to be shared equally by the people who entered projects. How much did each person pay for stickers?

7. A football team scored 34 points in its last victory. All the points were scored on touchdowns (6 points), extra points after touchdowns (1 point), and field goals (3 points). In how many ways could the points have been scored?

Chapter 6 Summary and Review

6-1

To multiply two rational expressions, multiply the numerators and denominators. To simplify rational expressions, first factor the numerator and denominator. To divide two rational expressions, multiply by the reciprocal.

Multiply.

1. $\frac{y}{y} \cdot \frac{4y - 3}{2y + 5}$

2. $\frac{4x - 3}{x + 5} \cdot \frac{x^2 - 1}{x^2 - 1}$

Simplify.

3. $\frac{3a^2 - 3b^2}{4a^2 + 8ab + 4b^2}$

4. $\frac{3x^2 - 4x - 4}{4x^2 - 3x - 10}$

5. $\frac{x^3 - 64}{8x^3 + 1} \cdot \frac{4x^2 - 1}{x^2 + 4x + 16}$

6. $\frac{6y^2}{y^2 - 9} \div \frac{3y^2}{2y^2 + 7y + 3}$

6-2

To add or subtract rational expressions, first find the least common denominator.

Add or subtract. Simplify if possible.

7. $\frac{a + 9}{a + 3} + \frac{12 - 5a}{a + 3}$

8. $\frac{y + 2}{y - 3} + \frac{y}{3 - y}$

9. $\frac{7}{x^2 - 81} - \frac{x - 4}{3x^2 - 25x - 18}$

10. $\frac{1}{3y} + \frac{4y}{y^2 - 1} + \frac{7}{y - 1}$

6-3

To simplify a complex rational expression, simplify the numerator and denominator separately and divide, or multiply the numerator and denominator by the LCD.

Simplify.

11. $\frac{\frac{1}{a} + \frac{1}{b}}{\frac{1}{a} - \frac{1}{b}}$

12. $\frac{\frac{x^2 - 16}{x^2 - 6x + 9}}{\frac{x^2 - 3x - 4}{x^2 - 2x - 3}}$

13. $\frac{a^{-1} - b^{-1}}{a^{-2} - b^{-2}}$

6-4

To divide a polynomial by a monomial, divide each term by the monomial. When the divisor is not a monomial, use a procedure similar to long division in arithmetic. Be sure to account for missing terms in the dividend.

Divide and check.

14. $(10y^4 - 8y^3 + 12y^2) \div 2y^2$

15. $(2x - 3)\overline{)4x^4 - 5x^2 + 2x - 10}$

ANSWERS

1. $\frac{4y^2 - 3y}{2y^2 + 5y}$
2. $\frac{4x^3 - 3x^2 - 4x + 3}{x^3 + 5x^2 - x - 5}$
3. $\frac{3(a - b)}{4(a + b)}$
4. $\frac{3x + 2}{4x + 5}$
5. $\frac{(x - 4)(2x - 1)}{4x^2 - 2x + 1}$
6. $\frac{2(2y + 1)}{y - 3}$
7. $\frac{-4a + 21}{a + 3}$
8. $\frac{2}{y - 3}$
9. $\frac{-x^2 + 16x + 50}{(x + 9)(x - 9)(3x + 2)}$
10. $\frac{34y^2 + 21y - 1}{3y(y - 1)(y + 1)}$
11. $\frac{b + a}{b - a}$
12. $\frac{x + 4}{x - 3}$
13. $\frac{ab}{b + a}$
14. $5y^2 - 4y + 6$
15. $2x^3 + 3x^2 + 2x + 4 + \frac{2}{2x - 3}$

16. Q: $x^3 - x^2 - 2x - 6$, R: -8
17. Q: $3x^2 + 2x - 2$, R: -1
18. 3
19. 5, -3
20. 3
21. 30 km/h and 20 km/h
22. $13\frac{7}{11}$ h
23. 84 mi/h
24. $p = \frac{mn}{T - Rn}$
25. $q = \frac{fp}{p - f}$
26. $y = 4.5x$
27. 168.75 kg
28. $y = \frac{288}{x}$
29. 40 days

6-5

Synthetic division is an algorithm that simplifies polynomial division.

Divide.

16. $(x^4 - 3x^3 - 2x + 4) \div (x - 2)$ **17.** $(3x^3 + 5x^2 - 3) \div (x + 1)$

6-6

To solve a rational equation, first multiply both sides by the LCD of all the denominators, then solve the resulting equation.

Solve.

18. $\frac{x^2}{x + 3} = \frac{9}{x + 3}$ **19.** $\frac{15}{y} - \frac{15}{y - 2} = -2$ **20.** $\frac{2}{y + 4} + \frac{2y - 1}{y^2 + 2y - 8} = \frac{1}{y - 2}$

6-7

Work and motion problems can be solved using rational expressions and the Problem-Solving Guidelines.

21. One car travels 90 km in the same time that a car going 10 km/h slower travels 60 km. Find the speed of each.

22. Sue can paint a chair in 3 hours. Jerry can paint the same size chair in $2\frac{1}{2}$ hours. Working together, how long would it take them to paint 10 chairs?

23. An airplane flies 560 miles against the wind. In the same amount of time, it can fly 840 miles with the wind. The speed of the plane in still air is 420 miles per hour. Find the speed of the wind.

6-8

To solve rational formulas, use the same techniques used to solve rational equations.

24. Solve $T = Rn + \frac{mn}{p}$, for p. **25.** Solve $\frac{1}{p} + \frac{1}{q} = \frac{1}{f}$, for q.

6-9

If $y = kx$, then y is said to vary directly with x, and k is called the constant of variation.

26. Find the equation of direct variation, where y varies directly as x, and $y = 36$ when $x = 8$.

27. The weight (M) of an object on the moon varies directly as its weight (E) on Earth. A person who weighs 75 kg on Earth would weigh 12 kg on the moon. How much would a person who weighs 27 kg on the moon weigh on Earth?

If $y = \frac{k}{x}$, then y is said to vary inversely with x.

28. Find the equation of inverse variation, where y varies inversely as x, and $y = 36$ when $x = 8$.

29. The time required to build a house varies inversely as the number of workers. It takes 8 workers 25 days to build a house. How long would it take 5 workers?

See also Problem 6, Computer-Assisted Problem Solving, page 842.

Chapter 6 Test

Multiply.

1. $\frac{y+1}{2y-3} \cdot \frac{y^2}{y^2}$

Simplify.

2. $\frac{5x^2 + 38x + 21}{3x^2 + 22x + 7}$

3. $\frac{y^3 + 27}{9y} \cdot \frac{3y}{y+3}$

4. $\frac{8t^5}{t^2 - 25} \div \frac{4t^2}{7t^2 - 34t - 5}$

Add or subtract. Simplify if possible.

5. $\frac{t+9}{t-5} + \frac{2t}{5-t}$

6. $\frac{4}{5x-15} + \frac{x+8}{4x^2 - 11x - 3}$

7. $\frac{8}{y^2 - 64} - \frac{y-5}{2y^2 - 15y - 8}$

8. $\frac{1}{2x} + \frac{4x}{x^2 - 1} - \frac{2}{x+1}$

Simplify.

9. $\dfrac{\dfrac{b^2 + 3b - 10}{b^2 - 5b + 6}}{\dfrac{b^2 - 25}{b^2 - 4b - 5}}$

10. $\frac{(3a)^{-1} - 4}{(2a)^{-1} - 1}$

Divide.

11. $(-6x^3 + 4x^2 - 10x) \div -2x$

12. $3x - 1\overline{)15x^4 - 5x^3 + 3x^2 - 4x + 2}$

Use synthetic division to find the quotient and remainder.

13. $(x^4 - 2x^3 + 3x^2 - x + 2) \div (x - 2)$

14. $(2x^4 - x^3 - 2x^2 - 2x - 3) \div (x + 1)$

Solve.

15. $\frac{x}{x-1} = \frac{7}{1-x}$

16. $\frac{12}{x-1} - \frac{8}{x} = 2$

17. Kaya can ride her bike 3 mi/h faster than Josh can ride his bike. If Kaya and Josh ride their bikes at the same time, Kaya will travel 60 mi and Josh will travel 12 mi less. How fast can Josh and Kaya ride their bikes?

18. Chan can mow a lawn in 4 hours. When Tao helps him, they can mow the lawn in $2\frac{1}{2}$ hours. How long would it take Tao to mow the lawn?

19. Solve $\frac{E}{e} = \frac{T+r}{r}$, for T.

20. Find the equation of direct variation where y varies directly as x, and $y = 5$ when $x = 16$.

21. Find the equation of inverse variation where y varies inversely as x, and $y = 5$ when $x = 16$.

22. The time (t) required to make a car varies inversely with the number of people (p) working on it. Twelve auto workers can produce a new car in 18 working hours. How long would it take if there were only 8 auto workers?

23. The time (t) required to drive a car at a fixed speed varies directly as the distance (d). It takes 8 hours to drive 380 mi at a fixed speed. How long would it take to drive 475 mi at that same fixed speed?

ANSWERS

1. $\frac{y^3 + y^2}{2y^3 - 3y^2}$
2. $\frac{5x+3}{3x+1}$
3. $\frac{y^2 - 3y + 9}{3}$
4. $\frac{2t^3(7t+1)}{t+5}$
5. $\frac{-t+9}{t-5}$
6. $\frac{21x+44}{5(x-3)(4x+1)}$
7. $\frac{-(y-16)(y+3)}{(y+8)(y-8)(2y+1)}$
8. $\frac{5x-1}{2x(x-1)}$
9. $\frac{b+1}{b-3}$
10. $\frac{2(1-12a)}{3(1-2a)}$
11. $3x^2 - 2x + 5$
12. $5x^3 + x - 1 + \frac{1}{3x-1}$
13. Q: $x^3 + 3x + 5$, R: 12
14. Q: $2x^3 - 3x^2 + x - 3$, R: 0
15. -7
16. $-1, 4$
17. 15 mi/h
12 mi/h
18. $6\frac{2}{3}$ h
19. $T = \frac{Er}{e} - r$
20. $y = \frac{5}{16}x$
21. $y = \frac{80}{x}$
22. 27 h
23. 10 h

Test Item Analysis

Item	Lesson
1–4	6-1
5–8	6-2
9, 10	6-3
11, 12	6-4
13, 14	6-5
15, 16	6-6
17, 18	6-7
19	6-8
20–23	6-9

CHAPTER 7

Powers, Roots, and Complex Numbers

Chapter Overview

Chapter 7's coverage of roots begins with operations using square roots and moves into higher roots and rational exponents. Powers of roots and rationalizing denominators precede equations with radicals and problem solving.

Consideration of the existence of the square root of -1 develops the complex-number system from the real-number system by the inclusion of imaginary numbers. Operations are performed using complex numbers, and complex numbers are considered as roots of equations. The chapter concludes with a college entrance exam strategy lesson involving averages.

Objectives

7-1 ■ Find principal square roots of numbers.
■ Find odd and even k-th roots.
7-2 ■ Multiply radical expressions.
■ Simplify radical expressions by factoring.
■ Multiply and simplify radical expressions.
7-3 ■ Find roots of quotients.
■ Divide radical expressions.
■ Add or subtract radical expressions.
7-4 ■ Multiply radical expressions.
■ Rationalize denominators of radical expressions.
7-5 ■ Calculate expressions of the form $\sqrt[k]{a^m}$ in two ways.
■ Write expressions with rational exponents as radical expressions and vice versa.
■ Simplify expressions containing negative rational exponents.
■ Use rational exponents to simplify radical expressions.
7-6 ■ Solve radical equations.
■ Solve problems with radicals.
7-7 ■ Express the square root of negative numbers and their products in terms of i.
■ Add or subtract complex numbers.
7-8 ■ Graph complex numbers in a plane.
■ Find absolute values of complex numbers.
7-9 ■ Solve equations with complex numbers.
■ Multiply complex numbers.
■ Find conjugates of complex numbers.
■ Divide and find reciprocals of complex numbers.
7-10 ■ Determine whether a complex number is a solution of an equation.
■ Find an equation that has given complex numbers as solutions.
■ Solve first-degree equations that have complex numbers as solutions.
■ Verify one square root of a complex number and find the other square root.

TEACHING CHAPTER 7

Cooperative Learning Opportunities

When assigning cooperative groups, you may have to mention from time to time that while students in a group should try to work well together, you are not assigning them to groups on the basis of friendship. It will be useful for students to learn that productive working relationships are different from friendship.

Paired checking can be useful in exercises for which checking is an essential part of the solution process, such as solving radical equations.

For Lesson 7-6, assign pairs to do the **Try This** or the first few A Exercises. This could be done as a cooperative quiz. Since a student may rush through the check of his or her own problem, have them exchange papers after finding possible solutions. The partner then checks the possible numbers and identifies the solution(s). If two problems are assigned, you will collect only two papers, one for each problem, and the pair of students will receive the same grade.

Multicultural Note: *Babylonian Square Roots*

Ancient Babylonia also known as Mesopotamia was an active civilization in the years around 2,000 B.C. Babylonia was situated between the Tigris and Euphrates rivers in present-day Iraq.

The arithmetic of Babylonia was based, in part, on the number 60. The use of 60 in measuring time is so imbedded in our thinking that we can forget it is an invention and not in the nature of things.

The Babylonians found square roots using the "guess and average" method. Although we now use calculators to find square roots, the "guess and average" method is a useful numerical experience. To find the square root of 17, for example, you might start with 4. You know that this is not the square root but it is close.

The average of 4 and $\frac{17}{4}$ is 4.125, and $4.125^2 = 17.02$. So after only one averaging we have a close approximation. This process can, of course, be continued to find a square root of any desired degree of accuracy.

Alternative Assessment and Communication Ideas

The theorems and definitions of chapter 7 contain a number of subtleties that students can miss. A useful alternative assessment is for students to give reasons or explanations, either for an entire statement or for a condition given as part of the statement. Students might write up these reasons as part of a portfolio, or you might use them in a bulletin board display. The following are some examples.

Definition on page 292: Why is the radical sign defined to represent the principal, nonnegative, square root? **Ans: We want it to be unambiguous.**

Theorem 7-3 on page 295: Can either *A* or *B* result in a negative number? **Ans: Yes, *B***

Theorem 7-4 on page 297: Why is the theorem stated for, "nonnegative numbers *a* and *b*?" **(Ans: If $k = 2$ and *a* is odd, the radical is undefined.)**

Investigations and Projects

Quaternions belong to advanced mathematics but basic definitions are straight forward and the manipulations may interest some students. Of special interest is the lack of commutativity.

Quaternions are like complex numbers except that in addition to i, we have j and k.

Products are defined as: $ij = k$, $ji = -k$; $jk = i$, $kj = -i$; $ki = j$, $ik = -j$. $i^2 = j^2 = k^2 = -1$

If $p = (2 + i + 2j + k)$ and $q = (1 + 2i + j + k)$, multiplying and collecting like terms gives

$$pq = -3 + 6i + 5j + 2k.$$

But, $qp = -3 + 4i + 4j + 6k$

The above are arrived at through the usual computation. There are 16 products that must then be simplified and combined. Have students verify the results. Have students do other manipulations and write them up in a short paper. What is the multiplicative identity element? **(Ans: 1)**

MANAGING CHAPTER 7

Lesson	PACING CHART (DAYS) Algebra	Algebra w/Finite	Algebra w/Trig	Compre-hensive	Opening Activity	Cooperative Activity	Seat or Group Work
7-1	1	1	1	1	First Five Minutes 7-1: **TE** p.292 or ***FFM Transparency Masters*** p.21	Critical Thinking: **SE** p.296 ✂ Manipulative Activity 7: ***Enrichment*** p.48	Try This a–z
7-2	1	1	1	1	First Five Minutes 7-2: **TE** p.297 or ***FFM Transparency Masters*** p.22	Explore: **SE** p.297 Critical Thinking: **SE** p.299 Critical Thinking 7: ***Enrichment*** p.28	Try This a–p
7-3	1	1	1	1	First Five Minutes 7-3: **TE** p.300 or ***FFM Transparency Masters*** p.22	Critical Thinking: **SE** p.304	Try This a–n
7-4	2	1	1	1	First Five Minutes 7-4: **TE** p.305 or ***FFM Transparency Masters*** p.22	Critical Thinking: **SE** p.309	Try This a–o
7-5	2	2	2	2	First Five Minutes 7-5: **TE** p.310 or ***FFM Transparency Masters*** p.23	Explore: **SE** p.310 Critical Thinking: **SE** p.316	Try This a–z
7-6	1	1	1	1	First Five Minutes 7-6: **TE** p.317 or ***FFM Transparency Masters*** p.23	Critical Thinking: **SE** p.320	Try This a–e
7-7	1	1	1	1	First Five Minutes 7-7: **TE** p.321 or ***FFM Transparency Masters*** p.24	Critical Thinking: **SE** p.323	Try This a–i
7-8	1	1	1	1	First Five Minutes 7-8: **TE** p.324 or ***FFM Transparency Masters*** p.24	Critical Thinking: **SE** p.325 Looking for Errors 7: ***Enrichment*** p.68	Try This a–h
7-9	1	1	1	1	First Five Minutes 7-9: **TE** p.326 or ***FFM Transparency Masters*** p.24	Critical Thinking: **SE** p.329 Looking for Errors: **SE** p.329	Try This a–n
7-10	2	2	2	1	First Five Minutes 7-10: **TE** p.330 or ***FFM Transparency Masters*** p.25	Critical Thinking: **SE** p.333 Problem Solving: **SE** pp.334–335	Try This a–f
Review	1	1	1	1			
Test	1	1	1	1			
Cum. Review	0	1	1	0			
Mid-year Test	0	1	1	0			

FFM: First Five Minutes SPMR: Skills Practice Mixed Review

MANAGING CHAPTER 7

Enrichment	Review/Assess	Reteach	Technology	Lesson
Math Point: **TE** p.294 ✂ Manipulative Activity 7: ***Enrichment*** p.48	Lesson Quiz: **TE** p.295	Skills Practice 18, #1–15: ***SPMR*** p.30	Worksheet 8: ***TI-81 Activities*** pp.33–36; Worksheet 8: ***Master Grapher*** pp.38–41, pp.172–175, or pp.308–311	**7-1**
Critical Thinking 7: ***Enrichment*** p.28	Lesson Quiz: **TE** p.299	Skills Practice 18, #16–31: ***SPMR*** p.30		**7-2**
College Entrance Exam 2, Section II: ***Problem Bank*** pp.59–62	Lesson Quiz: **TE** p.302	Skills Practice 18, #32–49: ***SPMR*** p.30	Problem for Programmers: **SE** p.304	**7-3**
Bonus Topic 6: ***Enrichment*** p.7	Lesson Quiz: **TE** p.307 Quiz 13: ***Assessment*** p.21	Skills Practice 19, #1–12: ***SPMR*** p.31		**7-4**
Bonus Topic 7: ***Enrichment*** p.8	Lesson Quiz: **TE** p.314	Skills Practice 19, #13–24: ***SPMR*** p.31		**7-5**
Using a Calculator: **SE** p.320	Lesson Quiz: **TE** p.319 Mixed Review 13: ***SPMR*** p.77	Skills Practice 19, #25–32: ***SPMR*** p.31	Worksheet 9: ***TI-81 Activities*** pp.37–39; Worksheet 9: ***Master Grapher*** pp.42–44, pp.176–178, or pp.312–314; Calculator Worksheet 11: ***Technology*** p.13; Using a Calculator: **SE** p.320	**7-6**
Math Point: **TE** p.321	Lesson Quiz: **TE** p.322	Skills Practice 20, #1–20: ***SPMR*** p.32	BASIC Computer Project 6: ***Technology*** p.86	**7-7**
Looking for Errors 7: ***Enrichment*** p.68	Lesson Quiz: **TE** p.325 Quiz 14: ***Assessment*** p.22	Skills Practice 20, #21–23: ***SPMR*** p.32		**7-8**
Math Point: **TE** p.327 Looking for Errors: **SE** p.329	Lesson Quiz: **TE** p.328	Skills Practice 20, #24–34: ***SPMR*** p.32	Spreadsheet Activity 4: ***Technology*** pp.53–55	**7-9**
Math Point: **TE** p.332 Problem Solving: **SE** pp.334–335	Lesson Quiz: **TE** p.322 Mixed Review 14: ***SPMR*** p.78	Skills Practice 20, #35–40: ***SPMR*** p.32	Problem 7: Computer Assisted Problem Solving, **SE** pp.843–844	**7-10**
	Summary and Review: **SE** pp.336–338; Test: **SE** p.339			**Review**
	Chapter 7 Test: ***Assessment*** pp.83–88 or pp.169–170			**Test**
	Cumulative Review: **SE** pp.377–381			**Cum. Review**
	Mid-year Test: ***Assessment*** pp.215–218 or pp.219–226			**Mid-year Test**

The solution to the problem posed on the facing page can be found on p. 318.

Ready for Powers, Roots, and Complex Numbers?

1-1 Simplify.

1. $|-8|$ 8 **2.** $|0|$ 0 **3.** $|\sqrt{3}|$ $\sqrt{3}$

1-8 Simplify.

4. $y^7 \cdot y^3$ y^{10} **5.** $8^3 \cdot 8^{-2}$ 8 **6.** $(3x^2y^{-4})(4x^3y^2)$ $12x^5y^{-2}$

7. $\frac{4^8}{4^2}$ 4^6 **8.** $\frac{3^{-4}}{3^{-6}}$ 3^2 **9.** $\frac{32x^3y^{10}}{4x^4y^4}$ $8x^{-1}y^6$

1-8 Simplify.

10. $(4^2)^4$ 4^8 **11.** $(a^{-3})^{-4}$ a^{12} **12.** $(4xy^{-3})^3$ $64x^3y^{-9}$ **13.** $(10x^3y^{-2}z^{-4})^2$ $100x^6y^{-4}z^{-8}$

2-1 Solve.

14. $2(8 - 3x) = 3 - 5(x - 1)$ 8 **15.** $9x + 7 - 2x = -12 - 4x + 5$ $-\frac{14}{11}$

16. $(x - 5)(x + 3) = 0$ 5, −3 **17.** $(x + 5)(x - 7) = 0$ −5, 7

5-3 Multiply.

18. $(2 - 3y)(1 + 4y)$ $2 + 5y - 12y^2$ **19.** $(3x + 8)^2$ $9x^2 + 48x + 64$ **20.** $(2x - 3)(2x + 3)$ $4x^2 - 9$

5-4–5-6 Factor.

21. $x^2 - 1$ $(x + 1)(x - 1)$ **22.** $16x^4 - 40x^2y^4 + 25y^8$ $(4x^2 - 5y^4)^2$

23. $-27x^2 + 36x - 12$ $-3(3x - 2)^2$ **24.** $x^2 - 13x + 36$ $(x - 4)(x - 9)$

CHAPTER

7

Powers, Roots, and Complex Numbers

The formula $V = 1.2\sqrt{h}$ *is a radical equation that approximates the distance (V) in miles that a person can see to the horizon from a height of h feet. How high is a person who can see 72 miles to the horizon?*

7-1

FIRST FIVE MINUTES

1. Factor 121.
   $121 = 11^2$
2. Factor $x^2 + 20x + 100$.
   $(x + 10)^2$
3. Solve for x where $4x^2 = 9$.
   $x = \frac{3}{2}$ or $x = -\frac{3}{2}$

Square Roots

Emphasize that the symbol $\sqrt{\ }$ represents "principal square root" even though it is often read "square root." All nonnegative numbers have two square roots but only one principal square root.

Emphasize that $\sqrt{(-5)^2}$ is 5, *not* -5. The principal real root is a nonnegative number. Point out that $\sqrt{(-5)^2} = \sqrt{25} = \sqrt{(5)^2} = 5$. Thus when $x = -5$, $\sqrt{x^2} = -x$, and when $x = 5$, $\sqrt{x^2} = x$. The rule $\sqrt{x^2} = |x|$ covers both cases.

Key Questions

- How many principal square roots does -2 have?
  0
- What is the greatest number of principal square roots a number can have?
  1
- Does $\sqrt{(-x)^2} = \sqrt{(x)^2}$?
  Yes
- For what values of x does $\sqrt{x} = \sqrt{(-x)}$?
  $x = 0$

7-1 Radical Expressions

Master Grapher Worksheet 8, *Graphs of Radical Expressions*, can be used for lesson closure.

Square Roots

Objective: Find principal square roots of numbers.

A square root of a number a is a number c such that $c^2 = a$.

25 has a square root of 5 because $5^2 = 25$.

25 has a square root of -5 because $(-5)^2 = 25$.

-16 does not have a real-number square root because there is no real number c such that $c^2 = -16$.

Later in this chapter we shall see that there is a number system in which negative numbers do have square roots.

Theorem 7-1

Every positive real number has two real-number square roots. The number 0 has just one square root, 0 itself. Negative numbers do not have real-number square roots.

EXAMPLE 1 Find the two square roots of 64.

The square roots are 8 and -8 because $8^2 = 64$ and $(-8)^2 = 64$.

Try This Find the square roots of each number.

a. 9 3, −3 **b.** 36 6, −6 **c.** 121 11, −11

Definition

The **principal square root** of a nonnegative number is its nonnegative square root. The symbol $\sqrt{a}$ represents the principal square root of a. The negative square root of a is written $-\sqrt{a}$.

EXAMPLES Simplify. Remember, $\sqrt{\ }$ indicates the principal square root.

2. $\sqrt{25} = 5$ **3.** $-\sqrt{64} = -8$ **4.** $\sqrt{\frac{25}{64}} = \frac{5}{8}$ **5.** $\sqrt{0.0049} = 0.07$

Try This Simplify.

d. $\sqrt{1}$ 1 **e.** $-\sqrt{36}$ -6 **f.** $\sqrt{\frac{81}{100}}$ $\frac{9}{10}$ **g.** $-\sqrt{0.0064}$ -0.08

These are radical expressions.

$$\sqrt{5}, \quad \sqrt{a}, \quad -\sqrt{5x}, \quad \sqrt{\frac{y^2+7}{\sqrt{x}}}$$

Definition

The symbol $\sqrt{}$ is a **radical sign.** An expression written with a radical sign is a **radical expression.** The expression written under the radical sign is the **radicand.**

In the expression $\sqrt{a^2}$, the radicand is a perfect square.

Suppose $a = 5$. Then we have $\sqrt{5^2}$, which is $\sqrt{25}$, or 5.

Suppose $a = -5$. Then we have $\sqrt{(-5)^2}$, which is $\sqrt{25}$, or 5.

Suppose $a = 0$. Then we have $\sqrt{0^2}$, which is $\sqrt{0}$, or 0.

The symbol $\sqrt{a^2}$ does not represent a negative number. It represents the principal square root of a^2. Note that if $a \geq 0$, then $\sqrt{a^2} = a$. If $a < 0$, $\sqrt{a^2} = -a$. In all cases the radical expression $\sqrt{a^2}$ represents the absolute value of a.

Theorem 7-2

For any real number a, $\sqrt{a^2} = |a|$. The principal (nonnegative) square root of a^2 is the absolute value of a.

EXAMPLES

6. $\sqrt{(-16)^2} = |-16| = 16$
7. $\sqrt{(3b)^2} = |3b| = 3|b|$
8. $\sqrt{(x-1)^2} = |x-1|$
9. $\sqrt{x^2+8x+16} = \sqrt{(x+4)^2} = |x+4|$

Try This Find the following. Assume that variables represent any real number.

h. $\sqrt{(-24)^2}$ 24 **i.** $\sqrt{(5y)^2}$ $5|y|$

j. $\sqrt{16y^2}$ $4|y|$ **k.** $\sqrt{(x+7)^2}$ $|x+7|$

Chalkboard Examples

1. Find two square roots for each of the following numbers.
   a. 100 b. 1 c. 5^2
   a. 10, -10; b. 1, -1; c. 5, -5

Simplify.

2. $\sqrt{1}$
   1
3. $-\sqrt{4}$
   -2
4. $\sqrt{0.01}$
   0.1
5. $\sqrt{(-17)^2}$
   17
6. $\sqrt{(2x)^2}$
   $|2x| = 2|x|$
7. $\sqrt{(-x)^2}$
   $|x|$
8. $\sqrt{x^2+10x+25}$
   $\sqrt{(x+5)^2} = |x+5|$

Odd and Even k-th Roots

Point out that the terms "square" and "cube" are derived from the processes we use to find the areas of squares and the volumes of cubes.

Explain that the symbol $\sqrt{\ }$ is equivalent to $\sqrt[2]{\ }$

Point out the distinction between even roots and odd roots. There are pairs of even roots for nonnegative numbers, and no even roots for negative numbers; there are single odd roots for nonnegative and negative numbers.

Math Point
The symbol $\sqrt{\ }$ for square root was introduced in 1525 by Christoff Rudolff in his influential algebra book *The Unknown*. This was one of the earliest printed books to use decimal notation.

Key Questions

- What is $\sqrt[3]{(-27)}$?
  -3
- Can you think of a number greater than one that has a whole number square root and a whole number cube root?
  64, 729, or any number that is the sixth power of a positive integer

Chalkboard Examples

Simplify.

1. $\sqrt[3]{-1}$
   -1
2. $\sqrt[3]{x^3}$
   x
3. $\sqrt[3]{\frac{8}{27}}$
   $\frac{2}{3}$
4. $\sqrt[3]{27x^3}$
   $3x$
5. $\sqrt[5]{100000}$
   $\sqrt[5]{10^5} = 10$
6. $\sqrt[5]{32}$
   $\sqrt[5]{2^5} = 2$
7. $\sqrt[7]{-1}$
   $\sqrt[7]{(-1)^7} = -1$
8. $-\sqrt[5]{-100000}$
   $-\sqrt[5]{(-10)^5} = -(-10) = 10$

Odd and Even k-th Roots

Objective: Find odd and even k-th roots.

The number c is the cube root of a if $c^3 = a$.

2 is the cube root of 8 because $2^3 = 2 \cdot 2 \cdot 2 = 8$.

-4 is the cube root of -64 because $(-4)^3 = (-4)(-4)(-4) = -64$.

Every real number has *exactly one* cube root in the system of real numbers. The symbol $\sqrt[3]{a}$ represents the cube root of a.

EXAMPLES Simplify.

10. $\sqrt[3]{8} = 2$ **11.** $\sqrt[3]{-27} = -3$ **12.** $\sqrt[3]{-\frac{216}{125}} = -\frac{6}{5}$ **13.** $\sqrt[3]{-8y^3} = -2y$

No absolute value signs are needed when finding cube roots because a real number has just one cube root. The cube root of a positive number is positive. The cube root of a negative number is negative.

Try This Simplify.

l. $\sqrt[3]{-64}$ -4 **m.** $\sqrt[3]{27y^3}$ $3y$ **n.** $\sqrt[3]{-\frac{343}{64}}$ $-\frac{7}{4}$

There are also 4th roots, 5th roots, 6th roots, and so on. If $\sqrt[4]{a} = c$, then we know $c^4 = a$.

Similarly, if $\sqrt[9]{a} = c$, then $c^9 = a$.

EXAMPLES Rewrite using exponential notation.

14. $c = \sqrt[7]{b} \rightarrow c^7 = b$ **15.** $y = \sqrt[6]{100} \rightarrow y^6 = 100$ **16.** $t = \sqrt[11]{22} \rightarrow t^{11} = 22$

Try This Rewrite using exponential notation.

o. $b = \sqrt[5]{a}$ $b^5 = a$ **p.** $c = \sqrt[12]{63}$ $c^{12} = 63$ **q.** $\sqrt[9]{16a} = n$ $n^9 = 16a$

The number k in $\sqrt[k]{\ }$ is called the index. If k is an odd number, we say that we are finding an odd root.

When finding any odd root of a number, there is just one answer. If the number is positive, the root is positive. If the number is negative, the root is negative. Absolute value signs are never needed when finding odd roots.

EXAMPLES Find the following.

17. $\sqrt[5]{-32} = -2$ **18.** $-\sqrt[5]{32} = -2$ **19.** $\sqrt[7]{x^7} = x$ **20.** $\sqrt[9]{(x-1)^9} = x - 1$

Try This Find the following.

r. $\sqrt[5]{-243}$ -3 **s.** $-\sqrt[5]{243}$ -3 **t.** $\sqrt[5]{-32x^5}$ $-2x$ **u.** $\sqrt[7]{(3x+2)^7}$ $3x + 2$

When the index k in $\sqrt[k]{\ }$ is an even number, we say that we are finding an even root. Every positive real number has two k-th roots when k is even. One of those roots is positive and one is negative. Negative numbers do not have real-number k-th roots when k is even. When finding even k-th roots, absolute value signs are sometimes necessary.

EXAMPLES Find the following.

21. $\sqrt[4]{16} = 2$ **22.** $-\sqrt[4]{16} = -2$ **23.** $\sqrt[4]{-16}$ No real root

24. $\sqrt[4]{81x^4} = 3|x|$ **25.** $\sqrt[6]{(y+7)^6} = |y + 7|$

Theorem 7-3

For any real number a, the following statements are true.

A. $\sqrt[k]{a^k} = |a|$ when k is even.

B. $\sqrt[k]{a^k} = a$ when k is odd.

We use absolute value when k is even unless a is nonnegative. We do not use absolute value when k is odd.

Try This Find the following.

v. $\sqrt[4]{81}$ 3 **w.** $-\sqrt[4]{81}$ -3 **x.** $\sqrt[4]{-81}$ No real root **y.** $\sqrt[4]{16(x-2)^4}$ $2|x-2|$ **z.** $\sqrt[8]{(x+3)^8}$ $|x+3|$

7-1 EXERCISES

A

Find the square roots of each number.

1. 16 $4, -4$ **2.** 225 $15, -15$ **3.** 144 $12, -12$ **4.** 9 $3, -3$ **5.** 400 $20, -20$ **6.** 81 $9, -9$

Find the following.

7. $-\sqrt{\frac{49}{36}}$ $-\frac{7}{6}$ **8.** $-\sqrt{\frac{361}{9}}$ $-\frac{19}{3}$ **9.** $\sqrt{196}$ 14 **10.** $-\sqrt{\frac{16}{81}}$ $-\frac{4}{9}$

11. $\sqrt{\frac{81}{144}}$ $\frac{3}{4}$ **12.** $\sqrt{0.09}$ 0.3 **13.** $-\sqrt{0.0049}$ -0.07 **14.** $\sqrt{0.0144}$ 0.12

9. $\sqrt[7]{x^{14}}$
$\sqrt[7]{(x^2)^7} = x^2$
10. $\sqrt[7]{(a+1)^7}$
$a + 1$
11. $\sqrt[6]{64}$
$\sqrt[6]{2^6} = 2$
12. $\sqrt{-64}$
No real number
13. $-\sqrt[4]{256}$
$-\sqrt[4]{4^4} = -4$
14. $\sqrt[6]{2^6x^6}$
$|2x| = 2|x|$
15. $\sqrt[4]{(x-1)^8}$
$\sqrt[4]{[(x-1)^2]^4} = (x-1)^2$

LESSON QUIZ

1. Find the square roots of 169.
$13, -13$
2. Simplify $-\sqrt{0.04}$.
-0.2
3. Simplify $\sqrt{x^2 + 18x + 81}$.
$\sqrt{(x+9)^2} = |x + 9|$
4. Simplify $\sqrt[3]{64}$.
4
5. Simplify $\sqrt[4]{16t^4}$.
$2|t|$

Assignment Guide
Algebra: 1–50 e/o, MR

Alg w/Finite or Trig: 1–50 m3, 51–57 e/o, 58, MR

Comprehensive: 1–57 m3, 58–61, MR

ADDITIONAL ANSWERS

Exercises

15. $4|x|$
16. $6|b|$
17. $5|t|$
18. $7|c|$
19. $|a + 1|$
20. $|5 - b|$
21. $|x - 2|$
22. $|2x + 7|$
23. 3
24. -4
25. $-4x$
26. $-5y$
27. 10
28. $-4xy^2$
29. $0.7(x + 1)$
30. $0.2(y - 2)$
31. $p^4 = 10$
32. $k^8 = 56$
33. $r^{28} = 500h$
34. $a^x = y$

52. $\{x \mid x \geq 0\}$
53. All real numbers
54. $\{x \mid x \geq -4\}$
55. $\left\{x \mid x \leq \frac{4}{3}\right\}$
56. $\{x \mid x = 0\}$
57. All real numbers
58. Answers may vary. Some examples are 1 and 1, 16 and 1024, 81 and 59,049. Note that $\sqrt{x^4} = \sqrt[5]{x^{10}}$.
59. $\left\{x \mid x \geq 0 \text{ and } x \neq \frac{5}{2}\right\}$
60. $\{x \mid x \geq -3 \text{ and } x \neq 2 \text{ and } x \neq -1\}$
61. $\{x \mid x > 0\}$

Mixed Review

62. $\frac{22}{5}$
63. 4, -1
64. 6
65. 3 or -2
66. Soph. 641, jr. 1067, sr. 1708

15. $\sqrt{16x^2}$ **16.** $\sqrt{(-6b)^2}$ **17.** $\sqrt{25t^2}$ **18.** $\sqrt{(-7c)^2}$

19. $\sqrt{(a + 1)^2}$ **20.** $\sqrt{(5 - b)^2}$ **21.** $\sqrt{x^2 - 4x + 4}$ **22.** $\sqrt{4x^2 + 28x + 49}$

23. $\sqrt[3]{27}$ **24.** $-\sqrt[3]{64}$ **25.** $\sqrt[3]{-64x^3}$ **26.** $\sqrt[3]{-125y^3}$

27. $-\sqrt[3]{-1000}$ **28.** $\sqrt[3]{-64x^3y^6}$ **29.** $\sqrt[3]{0.343(x + 1)^3}$ **30.** $\sqrt[3]{0.008(y - 2)^3}$

Rewrite using exponential notation.

31. $p = \sqrt[4]{10}$ **32.** $\sqrt[8]{56} = k$ **33.** $r = \sqrt[28]{500h}$ **34.** $a = \sqrt[x]{y}$

Simplify.

35. $\sqrt[4]{625}$ 5 **36.** $-\sqrt[4]{256}$ -4 **37.** $\sqrt[5]{-1}$ -1 **38.** $-\sqrt[5]{-32}$ 2

39. $\sqrt[5]{-\frac{32}{243}}$ $-\frac{2}{3}$ **40.** $\sqrt[5]{-\frac{1}{32}}$ $-\frac{1}{2}$ **41.** $\sqrt[6]{x^6}$ $|x|$ **42.** $\sqrt[8]{y^8}$ $|y|$

43. $\sqrt[4]{(5a)^4}$ $5|a|$ **44.** $\sqrt[4]{(7b)^4}$ $7|b|$ **45.** $\sqrt[10]{(-6)^{10}}$ 6 **46.** $\sqrt[12]{(-10)^{12}}$ 10

47. $\sqrt[7]{y^7}$ y **48.** $\sqrt[3]{(-6)^3}$ -6 **49.** $\sqrt[5]{(x - 2)^5}$ $x - 2$ **50.** $\sqrt[9]{(2xy)^9}$ $2xy$

B

51. A parking lot has attendants to park the cars. The number (N) of temporary stalls needed for waiting cars before attendants can get to them is given by $N = 2.5\sqrt{A}$ where A is the number of arrivals during peak hours. Find the number of spaces needed for the given average number of arrivals during peak hours.

a. 25 13 **b.** 36 15 **c.** 49 18 **d.** 64 20

Find the domain of each function.

52. $f(x) = \sqrt{x}$ **53.** $f(x) = \sqrt[3]{x}$ **54.** $f(x) = \sqrt{2x + 8}$

55. $f(x) = \sqrt{4 - 3x}$ **56.** $f(x) = \sqrt{-3x^2}$ **57.** $f(x) = \sqrt{x^2 + 1}$

58. ***Critical Thinking*** Find several pairs of numbers such that the square root of the first is the same as the fifth root of the second.

Challenge

Find the domain of each function.

59. $f(x) = \dfrac{\sqrt{x}}{2x^2 - 3x - 5}$ **60.** $f(x) = \dfrac{\sqrt{x + 3}}{x^2 - x - 2}$ **61.** $f(x) = \dfrac{\sqrt{x + 1}}{x + |x|}$

Mixed Review

Solve. **62.** $\frac{1}{3} + \frac{2}{5} = \frac{x}{6}$ **63.** $y - \frac{4}{y} = 3$ **64.** $\frac{2}{x - 2} = \frac{5}{x + 4}$

65. The square of a number minus the number is 6. Find the number.

66. Ervin ran for 3416 yards during his three years playing college football. During his senior year, he ran for as many yards as in his sophomore and junior years combined. He also ran for 426 more yards in his junior year than in his sophomore year. How many yards did he gain each year?

7-2 Multiplying and Simplifying

Explore

Simplify and compare your answers.

$\sqrt{4} \cdot \sqrt{25}$ and $\sqrt{4 \cdot 25}$ $\quad$ $\sqrt[3]{27} \cdot \sqrt[3]{8}$ and $\sqrt[3]{27 \cdot 8}$

Multiplying

Objective: Multiply radical expressions.

The results of the exploratory activity suggest the following theorem.

Theorem 7-4

For any nonnegative numbers a and b, and any natural-number index k,

$$\sqrt[k]{a} \cdot \sqrt[k]{b} = \sqrt[k]{ab}$$

EXAMPLES Multiply.

1. $\sqrt{x+2}\sqrt{x-2} = \sqrt{(x+2)(x-2)} = \sqrt{x^2-4}$ Using Theorem 7-4

2. $\sqrt[3]{4}\sqrt[3]{5} = \sqrt[3]{4 \cdot 5} = \sqrt[3]{20}$

3. $\sqrt[4]{\frac{y}{5}}\sqrt[4]{\frac{7}{x}} = \sqrt[4]{\frac{y}{5} \cdot \frac{7}{x}} = \sqrt[4]{\frac{7y}{5x}}$

Try This Multiply.

a. $\sqrt{19}\sqrt{7}$ $\sqrt{133}$

b. $\sqrt{x+2y}\sqrt{x-2y}$ $\sqrt{x^2-4y^2}$

c. $\sqrt[4]{403}\sqrt[4]{7}$ $\sqrt[4]{2821}$

d. $\sqrt[3]{8x}\sqrt[3]{x^4+5}$ $\sqrt[3]{8x^5+40x}$

Simplifying by Factoring

Objective: Simplify radical expressions by factoring.

Reversing the equation of Theorem 7-4, we have $\sqrt[k]{ab} = \sqrt[k]{a} \cdot \sqrt[k]{b}$. This shows a way to factor and thus simplify radical expressions.

Consider $\sqrt{20}$. The number 20 has 4 as a factor, which is a perfect square.

$\sqrt{20} = \sqrt{4 \cdot 5}$ Factoring the radicand (4 is a perfect square)

$= \sqrt{4} \cdot \sqrt{5}$ Factoring into two radicals

$= 2\sqrt{5}$ Finding the square root of 4

7-2

FIRST FIVE MINUTES

Simplify.

1. $(\sqrt{x+3})^2$ $x+3$
2. $\sqrt{(x+3)^2}$ $|x+3|$
3. $(\sqrt[3]{y-2})^3$ $y-2$

EXPLORE

$\sqrt{4} \cdot \sqrt{25} = \sqrt{4 \cdot 25} = 10$ and $\sqrt[3]{27} \cdot \sqrt[3]{8} = \sqrt[3]{27 \cdot 8} = 6$. From this students should be able to deduce Theorem 7-4.

Multiplying

Note that if k is an odd index, then $\sqrt[k]{a} \cdot \sqrt[k]{b} = \sqrt[k]{ab}$ for *all* real numbers a and b.

You may want to point out to students the analogy between the property of exponents $a^k b^k = (ab)^k$ and Theorem 7-4.

Key Questions

- Does $\sqrt[5]{3} = \sqrt[3]{5}$? No
- Does $\sqrt{x} \cdot \sqrt{y} = \sqrt{y} \cdot \sqrt{x}$? Yes

Chalkboard Examples

Multiply and simplify.

1. $\sqrt{a+b} \cdot \sqrt{a-b}$
   $\sqrt{(a+b)(a-b)}$
   $= \sqrt{a^2-b^2}$
2. $\sqrt[3]{3^2} \cdot \sqrt[3]{3}$
   $\sqrt[3]{3^2 \cdot 3} = \sqrt[3]{3^3} = 3$
3. $\sqrt[5]{\frac{4}{7}} \cdot \sqrt[5]{\frac{7}{4}}$
   $\sqrt[5]{\frac{4}{7} \cdot \frac{7}{4}} = \sqrt[5]{1} = 1$

Simplifying by Factoring

Key Questions

- Before simplifying $\sqrt{x^4}$, what assumptions must be made, if any?
  None
- Before simplifying a fourth root of a number, what assumptions must be made, if any?
  x is nonnegative.
- Before simplifying a third root of a number, what assumptions must be made, if any?
  None

Chalkboard Examples

Simplify by factoring.

1. $\sqrt{8}$
$= \sqrt{4 \cdot 2}$
$= 2\sqrt{2}$
2. $\sqrt[4]{162}$
$= \sqrt[4]{81 \cdot 2}$
$= 3\sqrt[4]{2}$
3. $\sqrt{3x^2 + 18x + 27}$
$= \sqrt{3(x+3)^2}$
$= \sqrt{3}\,|x+3|$
4. $\sqrt{6} \cdot \sqrt{12}$
$= \sqrt{6 \cdot 12}$
$= \sqrt{2^2\, 3^2\, 2}$
$= 6\sqrt{2}$
5. $5\sqrt[4]{12} \cdot 7\sqrt[4]{108}$
$= 35\sqrt[4]{12 \cdot 108}$
$= 35\sqrt[4]{3 \cdot 2^2 \cdot 3^3 \cdot 2^2}$
$= 35\sqrt[4]{2^4 \cdot 3^4}$
$= 35 \cdot 2 \cdot 3$
$= 210$

To simplify a radical expression by factoring, look for factors of the radicand that are perfect k-th powers, where k is the index. Remove those factors by finding the k-th root.

EXAMPLES Simplify by factoring.

4. $\sqrt{50} = \sqrt{25 \cdot 2} = \sqrt{25} \cdot \sqrt{2} = 5\sqrt{2}$ Finding a perfect-square factor

5. $\sqrt[3]{32} = \sqrt[3]{8 \cdot 4} = \sqrt[3]{8} \cdot \sqrt[3]{4} = 2\sqrt[3]{4}$ Finding a perfect-cube factor

Try This Simplify by factoring.

e. $\sqrt{32}$ $4\sqrt{2}$ **f.** $\sqrt[3]{80}$ $2\sqrt[3]{10}$

EXAMPLE 6 Simplify by factoring.

$$\begin{aligned}\sqrt{2x^2 - 4x + 2} &= \sqrt{2(x-1)^2} \\ &= \sqrt{(x-1)^2} \cdot \sqrt{2} \\ &= |x-1| \cdot \sqrt{2}\end{aligned}$$

Try This Simplify by factoring.

g. $\sqrt{300}$ $10\sqrt{3}$ **h.** $\sqrt{3x^2 + 12x + 12}$ $|x+2|\sqrt{3}$ **i.** $\sqrt{12ab^3c^2}$ $2|bc|\sqrt{3ab}$

j. $\sqrt[3]{16}$ $2\sqrt[3]{2}$ **k.** $\sqrt[4]{81x^4y^8}$ $3|x|y^2$ **l.** $\sqrt[3]{(a+b)^4}$ $(a+b)\sqrt[3]{a+b}$

Multiplying and Simplifying

Remind students to use absolute value signs when simplifying radical expressions. It may help them to remember the following rule: any expression that is simplified from an even root to an odd power requires an absolute value sign (unless the expression is known to be nonnegative).

It may be difficult to find factors that are perfect third or higher powers. Suggest that students factor the number into primes and then combine products of the desired power.

Chalkboard Example

Simplify.

1. $\sqrt[5]{16a^3} \cdot \sqrt[5]{4a^4}$
$= \sqrt[5]{2^6 \cdot a^7}$
$= \sqrt[5]{2^5a^5 \cdot 2a^2}$
$= 2a\sqrt[5]{2a^2}$

Multiplying and Simplifying

Objective: Multiply and simplify radical expressions.

After we multiply, we can often simplify by factoring.

EXAMPLES Multiply and simplify.

7. $\sqrt{15}\sqrt{6} = \sqrt{15 \cdot 6} = \sqrt{90} = \sqrt{9 \cdot 10} = 3\sqrt{10}$

8. $3\sqrt[3]{25} \cdot 2\sqrt[3]{5} = 6 \cdot \sqrt[3]{25 \cdot 5}$ Multiplying radicands
$= 6\sqrt[3]{125}$
$= 6 \cdot 5$, or 30

9. $\sqrt[3]{18y^3}\sqrt[3]{4x^2} = \sqrt[3]{18y^3 \cdot 4x^2}$
$= \sqrt[3]{2 \cdot 3^2 \cdot y^3 \cdot 2^2 \cdot x^2}$ Factoring the radicand
$= \sqrt[3]{2^3 \cdot y^3 \cdot 3^2 \cdot x^2}$ Using the commutative and associative properties
$= 2y\sqrt[3]{9x^2}$ Simplifying

Try This Multiply and then simplify by factoring.

m. $\sqrt{3}\sqrt{6}$ $3\sqrt{2}$ **n.** $\sqrt{18y}\sqrt{14y}$ $6|y|\sqrt{7}$ **o.** $\sqrt[3]{3x^2y}\sqrt[3]{36x}$ $3x\sqrt[3]{4y}$ **p.** $\sqrt{7a}\sqrt{21b}$ $7\sqrt{3ab}$

7-2 EXERCISES

A

Multiply.

1. $\sqrt{3}\sqrt{2}$ $\sqrt{6}$
2. $\sqrt{5}\sqrt{7}$ $\sqrt{35}$
3. $\sqrt[3]{2}\sqrt[3]{5}$ $\sqrt[3]{10}$
4. $\sqrt[3]{7}\sqrt[3]{2}$ $\sqrt[3]{14}$
5. $\sqrt[4]{8}\sqrt[4]{9}$ $\sqrt[4]{72}$
6. $\sqrt[4]{6}\sqrt[4]{3}$ $\sqrt[4]{18}$
7. $\sqrt{3a}\sqrt{10b}$ $\sqrt{30ab}$
8. $\sqrt{2x}\sqrt{13y}$ $\sqrt{26xy}$
9. $\sqrt[5]{9t^2}\sqrt[5]{2t}$ $\sqrt[5]{18t^3}$
10. $\sqrt[5]{8y^3}\sqrt[5]{10y}$
11. $\sqrt{x-a}\sqrt{x+a}$
12. $\sqrt{y-b}\sqrt{y+b}$
13. $\sqrt[3]{0.3x}\sqrt[3]{0.2x}$
14. $\sqrt[3]{0.7y}\sqrt[3]{0.3y}$
15. $\sqrt[4]{x-1}\sqrt[4]{x^2+x+1}$
16. $\sqrt[5]{x-2}\sqrt[5]{(x-2)^2}$
17. $\sqrt{\frac{6}{x}}\sqrt{\frac{y}{5}}$

Simplify by factoring.

18. $\sqrt{24}$
19. $\sqrt{20}$
20. $\sqrt{180x^4}$
21. $\sqrt{175y^6}$
22. $\sqrt[3]{54x^8}$
23. $\sqrt[3]{40y^3}$
24. $\sqrt[3]{80x^8}$
25. $\sqrt[3]{108m^5}$
26. $\sqrt[4]{32}$
27. $\sqrt[4]{80}$
28. $\sqrt[4]{162c^4d^6}$
29. $\sqrt[4]{243x^8y^{10}}$
30. $\sqrt[3]{(x+y)^4}$
31. $\sqrt[5]{64x^6y^9}$
32. $\sqrt[6]{(a+b)^7}$
33. $\sqrt[9]{512x^3y^{12}}$

Multiply and simplify by factoring.

34. $\sqrt{3}\sqrt{6}$
35. $\sqrt{5}\sqrt{10}$
36. $\sqrt{2}\sqrt{32}$
37. $\sqrt{6}\sqrt{8}$
38. $\sqrt{18}\sqrt{14}$
39. $\sqrt{45}\sqrt{60}$
40. $\sqrt[3]{3}\sqrt[3]{18}$
41. $\sqrt{5b^3}\sqrt{10c^4}$
42. $\sqrt{2x^3y}\sqrt{12xy}$
43. $\sqrt[3]{y^4}\sqrt[3]{16y^5}$
44. $\sqrt[3]{5^2t^4}\sqrt[3]{5^4t^6}$
45. $\sqrt[3]{(b+3)^4}\sqrt[3]{(b+3)^2}$
46. $\sqrt[3]{(x+y)^3}\sqrt[3]{(x+y)^5}$

B

The speed that a car was traveling can be estimated by measuring its skid marks. The formula $r = 2\sqrt{5L}$ can be used, where r is the speed in mi/h and L is the length of the skid marks in feet. Estimate the speed of a car that left skid marks of

47. 20 ft 20 mi/h
48. 70 ft 37.4 mi/h
49. 156.8 ft 56 mi/h
50. ***Critical Thinking*** Find two radical expressions whose simplified product is $5\sqrt{10}$.

Challenge

Here is a formula for finding *windchill temperature,* when T is actual temperature given in degrees Celsius and v is the wind speed in m/s. Find the windchill temperature for the given actual temperatures and wind speeds.

$$T_w = 33 - (10.45 + 10\sqrt{v} - v)(33 - T) \div 22$$

51. $T = 7°\text{C}$, $v = 8$ m/s
52. $T = 0°\text{C}$, $v = 12$ m/s
53. $T = -23°\text{C}$, $v = 15$ m/s

Mixed Review

Factor.
54. $4x^2 + 6x + 2$
55. $3y^2 - 14y - 5$
56. $9a^2 - 3a$

Divide.
57. $(x^2 + 10x + 21) \div (x + 3)$
58. $(3y^2 - 13y - 12) \div (y - 5)$

LESSON QUIZ

1. Multiply and simplify.
   $\sqrt[3]{3a} \cdot \sqrt[3]{9a^2}$ $3a$
2. Multiply and simplify.
   $\sqrt{3(x-1)} \cdot \sqrt{x-1}$ $\sqrt{3}|x-1|$
3. Simplify by factoring.
   $\sqrt{75a^3}$ $5|a|\sqrt{3a}$
4. Multiply and simplify.
   $\sqrt{2a^2b} \cdot \sqrt{4ab^3}$ $2|a|b^2\sqrt{2a}$

Assignment Guide

Algebra: 1–46 e/o, MR

Alg w/Finite or Trig: 1–49 e/o, 50, MR

Comprehensive: 1–49 e/o, 50–53, MR

ADDITIONAL ANSWERS

Exercises

10. $\sqrt[5]{80y^4}$
11. $\sqrt{x^2 - a^2}$
12. $\sqrt{y^2 - b^2}$
13. $\sqrt[3]{0.06x^2}$
14. $\sqrt[3]{0.21y^2}$
15. $\sqrt[4]{x^3 - 1}$
16. $\sqrt[5]{(x-2)^3}$
17. $\sqrt{\frac{6y}{5x}}$
18. $2\sqrt{6}$
19. $2\sqrt{5}$
20. $6x^2\sqrt{5}$
21. $5|y^3|\sqrt{7}$
22. $3x^2\sqrt[3]{2x^2}$
23. $2y\sqrt[3]{5}$
24. $2x^2\sqrt[3]{10x^2}$
25. $3m\sqrt[3]{4m^2}$
26. $2\sqrt[4]{2}$
27. $2\sqrt[4]{5}$
28. $3|cd|\sqrt[4]{2d^2}$
29. $3x^2y^2\sqrt[4]{3y^2}$
30. $(x+y)\sqrt[3]{x+y}$
31. $2xy\sqrt[5]{2xy^4}$
32. $|a+b|\sqrt[6]{a+b}$
33. $2y\sqrt[9]{x^3y^3}$
34. $3\sqrt{2}$
35. $5\sqrt{2}$
36. 8
37. $4\sqrt{3}$
38. $6\sqrt{7}$
39. $30\sqrt{3}$
40. $3\sqrt[3]{2}$
41. $5|b|c^2\sqrt{2b}$
42. $2x^2|y|\sqrt{6}$
43. $2y^3\sqrt[3]{2}$
44. $25t^3\sqrt[3]{t}$
45. $(b+3)^2$
46. $(x+y)^2\sqrt[3]{(x+y)^2}$
50. Answers may vary. Examples are $\sqrt{125} \cdot \sqrt{2}$, $\sqrt{25} \cdot \sqrt{10}$, and $\sqrt{50} \cdot \sqrt{5}$.
51. $-3.3°\text{C}$
52. $-16.6°\text{C}$
53. $-54.0°\text{C}$

Mixed Review

54. $2(2x+1)(x+1)$
55. $(3y+1)(y-5)$
56. $3a(3a-1)$
57. $x + 7$
58. $3y + 2$, R: -2

7-3

FIRST FIVE MINUTES

Simplify.

1. $\sqrt{3} \cdot \sqrt{12}$
   6
2. $\sqrt{27a^3}$
   $3a\sqrt{3a}$
3. $\sqrt{x^2 + 14x + 49}$
   $|x + 7|$

Roots of Quotients

You may want to point out the analogy between the properties of exponents,

$\left(\frac{a}{b}\right)^k = \frac{a^k}{b^k}$,

and Theorem 7-5,

$\sqrt[k]{\frac{a}{b}} = \frac{\sqrt[k]{a}}{\sqrt[k]{b}}$

Chalkboard Examples

Simplify.

1. $\sqrt{\frac{4}{9}}$
   $\frac{2}{3}$
2. $\sqrt[4]{\frac{16}{x^4}}$
   $\frac{2}{|x|}$
3. $\sqrt{\frac{8x}{4y^2}}$
   $\frac{\sqrt{2^2 \cdot 2x}}{\sqrt{2^2y^2}} = \frac{2\sqrt{2x}}{2|y|} = \frac{\sqrt{2x}}{|y|}$
4. $\sqrt[5]{\frac{32a^5}{243b^5}}$
   $\frac{\sqrt[5]{2^5a^5}}{\sqrt[5]{3^5b^5}} = \frac{2a}{3b}$

7-3 Operations with Radical Expressions

The *period* of a pendulum is the time it takes to complete one cycle, swinging side to side and back. If a pendulum consists of a ball on a string, the period *(T)* is given by the following formula.

$$T = 2\pi\sqrt{\frac{L}{980}}$$

T is in seconds and L is the length of the pendulum in centimeters.

Roots of Quotients

Objective: Find roots of quotients.

Consider the following.

$$\sqrt{\frac{16}{9}} = \frac{4}{3} \text{ and } \frac{\sqrt{16}}{\sqrt{9}} = \frac{4}{3}$$

$$\sqrt[3]{\frac{27}{8}} = \frac{3}{2} \text{ and } \frac{\sqrt[3]{27}}{\sqrt[3]{8}} = \frac{3}{2}$$

These examples suggest the following theorem.

Theorem 7-5

For any natural-number index k and any real numbers a and b, $(b \neq 0)$, where $\sqrt[k]{a}$ and $\sqrt[k]{b}$ are real numbers, $\sqrt[k]{\frac{a}{b}} = \frac{\sqrt[k]{a}}{\sqrt[k]{b}}$.

From Theorem 7-5, we have the following rule.

Finding *k*-th Roots

To find the k-th root of a quotient, find the k-th roots of the numerator and denominator separately.

EXAMPLES Simplify by finding roots of the numerator and denominator.

1. $\sqrt[3]{\frac{27}{125}} = \frac{\sqrt[3]{27}}{\sqrt[3]{125}} = \frac{3}{5}$ Finding the cube root of the numerator and denominator

2. $\sqrt{\dfrac{25}{y^2}} = \dfrac{\sqrt{25}}{\sqrt{y^2}} = \dfrac{5}{|y|}$ Finding the square root of the numerator and denominator

3. $\sqrt{\dfrac{16x^3}{y^4}} = \dfrac{\sqrt{16x^3}}{\sqrt{y^4}} = \dfrac{\sqrt{16x^2 \cdot x}}{\sqrt{y^4}} = \dfrac{4|x|\sqrt{x}}{y^2}$

4. $\sqrt[3]{\dfrac{27y^5}{343x^3}} = \dfrac{\sqrt[3]{27y^5}}{\sqrt[3]{343x^3}} = \dfrac{\sqrt[3]{27y^3 \cdot y^2}}{\sqrt[3]{343x^3}} = \dfrac{\sqrt[3]{27y^3} \cdot \sqrt[3]{y^2}}{\sqrt[3]{343x^3}} = \dfrac{3y\sqrt[3]{y^2}}{7x}$

Try This Simplify by finding roots of the numerator and denominator.

a. $\sqrt{\dfrac{25}{36}}$ $\frac{5}{6}$ **b.** $\sqrt[3]{\dfrac{1000}{27}}$ $\frac{10}{3}$ **c.** $\sqrt{\dfrac{x^2}{100}}$ $\frac{|x|}{10}$ **d.** $\sqrt{\dfrac{4a^3}{b^4}}$ $\frac{2|a|\sqrt{a}}{b^2}$

Dividing Radical Expressions

Objective: Divide radical expressions.

Reversing the equation of Theorem 7-5, we have

$$\frac{\sqrt[k]{a}}{\sqrt[k]{b}} = \sqrt[k]{\frac{a}{b}}$$

This gives us a rule for dividing radical expressions.

Dividing Radical Expressions

To divide radical expressions with the same index, divide the radicands.

After dividing radicands, we can sometimes simplify.

EXAMPLES Divide. Then simplify by finding roots, if possible.

5. $\dfrac{\sqrt{80}}{\sqrt{5}} = \sqrt{\dfrac{80}{5}}$ Dividing radicands
$= \sqrt{16}$
$= 4$

6. $\dfrac{5\sqrt[3]{32}}{\sqrt[3]{2}} = 5\sqrt[3]{\dfrac{32}{2}}$ Dividing radicands
$= 5\sqrt[3]{16}$
$= 5\sqrt[3]{8 \cdot 2}$ Finding a perfect cube factor
$= 5\sqrt[3]{8}\sqrt[3]{2}$ Factoring
$= 5 \cdot 2\sqrt[3]{2} = 10\sqrt[3]{2}$ Simplifying

7. $\dfrac{\sqrt[4]{32a^5b^3}}{\sqrt[4]{2b^{-1}}} = \sqrt[4]{\dfrac{32a^5b^3}{2b^{-1}}} = \sqrt[4]{16a^5b^4} = \sqrt[4]{16a^4b^4 \cdot a} = \sqrt[4]{16a^4b^4}\sqrt[4]{a} = 2|ab|\sqrt[4]{a}$

Dividing Radical Expressions

Chalkboard Examples

Divide and simplify.

1. $\dfrac{\sqrt{200}}{\sqrt{2}}$
$\sqrt{\dfrac{200}{2}} = \sqrt{100} = 10$

2. $\dfrac{7\sqrt[3]{81}}{\sqrt[3]{3}}$
$7\sqrt[3]{\dfrac{81}{3}} = 7\sqrt[3]{27} = 7 \cdot 3 = 21$

3. $\dfrac{\sqrt[5]{64a^2b^6}}{\sqrt[5]{2a^7b}}$
$\sqrt[5]{\dfrac{64a^2b^6}{2a^7b}} = \sqrt[5]{\dfrac{32b^5}{a^5}} = \dfrac{2b}{a}$

Addition and Subtraction

Note that there is often more than one correct form for an answer. The answer for Example 13 could be written $\sqrt[3]{2y}(10y + 7)$ or $(7 + 10y)\sqrt[3]{2y}$. When students compare their answers with those in the Selected Answer section, they should understand that even if their answer doesn't match exactly, it may still be correct.

Chalkboard Examples

Add or subtract. Simplify if possible.

1. $5\sqrt{3} + 4\sqrt{3}$
   $= (5 + 4)\sqrt{3}$
   $= 9\sqrt{3}$
2. $2\sqrt[3]{7} + 3\sqrt[3]{7} - \sqrt[3]{7}$
   $= (2 + 3 - 1)\sqrt[3]{7}$
   $= 4\sqrt[3]{7}$
3. $-3\sqrt[4]{2x} + 8\sqrt[4]{2x} + 4\sqrt[4]{2x}$
   $= (-3 + 8 + 4)\sqrt[4]{2x}$
   $= 9\sqrt[4]{2x}$
4. $5\sqrt{12} + 2\sqrt{3}$
   $= 5\sqrt{2^2 \cdot 3} + 2\sqrt{3}$
   $= 10\sqrt{3} + 2\sqrt{3}$
   $= 12\sqrt{3}$
5. $7\sqrt[3]{6} + 5\sqrt[3]{35}$
   No simplification possible
6. $3\sqrt[4]{32x^5} + 5\sqrt[4]{2x}$
   $= 3\sqrt[4]{2^4 \cdot 2x^4x} + 5\sqrt[4]{2x}$
   $= 3 \cdot 2|x|\sqrt[4]{2x} + 5\sqrt[4]{2x}$
   $= (6|x| + 5)\sqrt[4]{2x}$

LESSON QUIZ

1. Simplify.
   $\sqrt{\frac{25x^2}{121y^2}}$
   $\frac{5|x|}{11|y|}$
2. Divide and simplify.
   $\frac{\sqrt{45x^3}}{\sqrt{5x}}$
   $3|x|$
3. Add or subtract and simplify by collecting like radical terms.
   $3\sqrt{28} + 5\sqrt{7}$
   $11\sqrt{7}$
4. Add or subtract and simplify by collecting like radicals.
   $8\sqrt{12x^3} + 3x\sqrt{75x}$
   $31x\sqrt{3x}$

Try This Divide. Then simplify by finding roots, if possible.

e. $\frac{\sqrt{75}}{\sqrt{3}}$ 5 **f.** $\frac{14\sqrt{128xy}}{2\sqrt{2}}$ $56\sqrt{xy}$ **g.** $\frac{4\sqrt[3]{250}}{7\sqrt[3]{2}}$ $\frac{20}{7}$ **h.** $\frac{\sqrt[3]{8a^3b}}{\sqrt[3]{27b^{-2}}}$ $\frac{2ab}{3}$

Addition and Subtraction

Objective: Add or subtract radical expressions.

Any two real numbers can be added. For example, the sum of 7 and $\sqrt{3}$ can be expressed as $7 + \sqrt{3}$. We cannot simplify this sum. However, when we have like radical terms (radical terms having the same index and radicand), we can use the distributive property to simplify, then collect like radical terms.

EXAMPLES Add or subtract. Simplify by collecting like radical terms, if possible.

8. $6\sqrt{7} + 4\sqrt{7} = (6 + 4)\sqrt{7}$ Using the distributive property
$= 10\sqrt{7}$

9. $8\sqrt[3]{2} - 7x\sqrt[3]{2} + 5\sqrt[3]{2} = (8 - 7x + 5)\sqrt[3]{2}$ Factoring out $\sqrt[3]{2}$
$= (13 - 7x)\sqrt[3]{2}$

10. $6\sqrt[5]{4x} + 4\sqrt[5]{4x} - \sqrt[3]{4x} = (6 + 4)\sqrt[5]{4x} - \sqrt[3]{4x}$
$= 10\sqrt[5]{4x} - \sqrt[3]{4x}$

Try This Add or subtract. Simplify by collecting like radical terms, if possible.

i. $5\sqrt{2} + 8\sqrt{2}$ $13\sqrt{2}$ **j.** $7\sqrt[4]{5x} + 3\sqrt[4]{5x} - \sqrt{7}$ $10\sqrt[4]{5x} - \sqrt{7}$

Sometimes we need to factor in order to have like radical terms.

EXAMPLES Add or subtract. Simplify by collecting like radical terms, if possible.

11. $3\sqrt{8} - 5\sqrt{2} = 3\sqrt{4 \cdot 2} - 5\sqrt{2}$ Factoring 8
$= 3\sqrt{4} \cdot \sqrt{2} - 5\sqrt{2}$ Factoring $\sqrt{4 \cdot 2}$ into 2 radicals
$= 3 \cdot 2\sqrt{2} - 5\sqrt{2}$ Finding the square root of 4
$= 6\sqrt{2} - 5\sqrt{2}$
$= \sqrt{2}$ Collecting like radical terms

12. $5\sqrt{2} - 4\sqrt{3}$ No simplification possible

13. $5\sqrt[3]{16y^4} + 7\sqrt[3]{2y} = 5\sqrt[3]{8y^3 \cdot 2y} + 7\sqrt[3]{2y}$ Factoring the first radical
$= 5\sqrt[3]{2^3y^3} \cdot \sqrt[3]{2y} + 7\sqrt[3]{2y}$
$= 5 \cdot 2y \cdot \sqrt[3]{2y} + 7\sqrt[3]{2y}$ Finding the cube root
$= 10y\sqrt[3]{2y} + 7\sqrt[3]{2y}$
$= (10y + 7)\sqrt[3]{2y}$ Collecting like radical terms

Try This Add or subtract. Simplify by collecting like radical terms, if possible.

k. $7\sqrt{45} - 2\sqrt{5}$ $19\sqrt{5}$

l. $3\sqrt[3]{y^5} + 4\sqrt[3]{y^2} + \sqrt[3]{8y^6}$ $(3y+4)\sqrt[3]{y^2} + 2y^2$

m. $\sqrt{25x - 25} - \sqrt{9x - 9}$ $2\sqrt{x-1}$

n. $\sqrt[3]{54} - \sqrt{54}$ $3(\sqrt[3]{2} - \sqrt{6})$

7-3 EXERCISES

A

Simplify by finding roots of the numerator and denominator.

1. $\sqrt{\frac{16}{25}}$ **2.** $\sqrt{\frac{100}{81}}$ **3.** $\sqrt[3]{\frac{64}{27}}$ **4.** $\sqrt[3]{\frac{343}{512}}$ **5.** $\sqrt{\frac{49}{y^2}}$

6. $\sqrt{\frac{121}{x^2}}$ **7.** $\sqrt{\frac{25y^3}{x^4}}$ **8.** $\sqrt{\frac{36a^5}{b^6}}$ **9.** $\sqrt[3]{\frac{8x^5}{27y^3}}$ **10.** $\sqrt[3]{\frac{64x^7}{216y^6}}$

Divide. Then simplify by finding roots, if possible.

11. $\frac{\sqrt{21a}}{\sqrt{3a}}$ **12.** $\frac{\sqrt{28y}}{\sqrt{4y}}$ **13.** $\frac{\sqrt[3]{54}}{\sqrt[3]{2}}$ **14.** $\frac{\sqrt[3]{40}}{\sqrt[3]{5}}$

15. $\frac{\sqrt{40xy^3}}{\sqrt{8x}}$ **16.** $\frac{\sqrt{56ab^3}}{\sqrt{7a}}$ **17.** $\frac{\sqrt[3]{96a^4b^2}}{\sqrt[3]{12a^2b}}$ **18.** $\frac{\sqrt[3]{189x^5y^7}}{\sqrt[3]{7x^2y^2}}$

19. $\frac{\sqrt{72xy}}{2\sqrt{2}}$ **20.** $\frac{\sqrt{75ab}}{3\sqrt{3}}$ **21.** $\frac{\sqrt{x^3 - y^3}}{\sqrt{x - y}}$ **22.** $\frac{\sqrt{r^3 + s^3}}{\sqrt{r + s}}$

Add or subtract. Simplify by collecting like radical terms, if possible.

23. $6\sqrt{3} + 2\sqrt{3}$ $8\sqrt{3}$

24. $8\sqrt{5} + 9\sqrt{5}$ $17\sqrt{5}$

25. $9\sqrt[3]{5} - 6\sqrt[3]{5}$ $3\sqrt[3]{5}$

26. $14\sqrt[5]{2} - 6\sqrt[5]{2}$ $8\sqrt[5]{2}$

27. $4\sqrt[3]{y} + 9\sqrt[3]{y}$ $13\sqrt[3]{y}$

28. $6\sqrt[4]{t} - 3\sqrt[4]{t}$ $3\sqrt[4]{t}$

29. $8\sqrt{2} - 6\sqrt{2} + 5\sqrt{2}$ $7\sqrt{2}$

30. $2\sqrt{6} + 8\sqrt{6} - 3\sqrt{6}$ $7\sqrt{6}$

31. $4\sqrt[3]{5} - \sqrt{3} + 2\sqrt[3]{5} + \sqrt{3}$ $6\sqrt[3]{5}$

32. $5\sqrt{7} - 8\sqrt[4]{11} + \sqrt{7} + 9\sqrt[4]{11}$ $6\sqrt{7} + \sqrt[4]{11}$

33. $6\sqrt{8} + 11\sqrt{2}$ $23\sqrt{2}$

34. $2\sqrt{12} + 5\sqrt{3}$ $9\sqrt{3}$

35. $8\sqrt{27} - 3\sqrt{3}$ $21\sqrt{3}$

36. $9\sqrt{50} - 4\sqrt{2}$ $41\sqrt{2}$

37. $8\sqrt{45} + 7\sqrt{20}$ $38\sqrt{5}$

38. $9\sqrt{12} + 16\sqrt{27}$ $66\sqrt{3}$

39. $18\sqrt{72} + 2\sqrt{98}$ $122\sqrt{2}$

40. $12\sqrt{45} - 8\sqrt{80}$ $4\sqrt{5}$

41. $3\sqrt[3]{16} + \sqrt[3]{54}$ $9\sqrt[3]{2}$

42. $\sqrt[3]{27} - 5\sqrt[3]{8}$ -7

43. $5\sqrt[3]{32} - 2\sqrt[3]{108}$ $4\sqrt[3]{4}$

44. $9\sqrt[3]{40} - 7\sqrt[3]{135}$ $-3\sqrt[3]{5}$

45. $2\sqrt{128} - \sqrt{18} + 4\sqrt{32}$ $29\sqrt{2}$

46. $5\sqrt{50} - 2\sqrt{18} + 9\sqrt{32}$ $55\sqrt{2}$

47. $\sqrt{5a} + 2\sqrt{45a^3}$ $(1 + 6|a|)\sqrt{5a}$

48. $4\sqrt{3x^3} - \sqrt{12x}$ $(4|x| - 2)\sqrt{3x}$

49. $\sqrt[3]{24x} - \sqrt[3]{3x^4}$ $(2 - x)\sqrt[3]{3x}$

50. $\sqrt[3]{54x} - \sqrt[3]{2x^4}$ $(3 - x)\sqrt[3]{2x}$

51. $2\sqrt[3]{125a^4} - 5\sqrt[3]{8a}$ $10(a - 1)\sqrt[3]{a}$

52. $9\sqrt[3]{16x^5y} - 2\sqrt[3]{128x^2y}$ $2(9x - 4)\sqrt[3]{2x^2y}$

53. $\sqrt{8y - 8} + \sqrt{2y - 2}$ $3\sqrt{2y - 2}$

54. $\sqrt{12t + 12} + \sqrt{3t + 3}$ $3\sqrt{3t + 3}$

55. $\sqrt{x^3 - x^2} + \sqrt{9x - 9}$ $(|x| + 3)\sqrt{x - 1}$

56. $\sqrt{4x - 4} - \sqrt{x^3 - x^2}$ $(2 - |x|)\sqrt{x - 1}$

Assignment Guide
Algebra: 1–56 e/o, MR

Alg w/Finite or Trig: 1–56 m3, 57–62, MR

Comprehensive: 1–56 m3, 57–61 e/o, 62–65, MR

ADDITIONAL ANSWERS

Exercises

1. $\frac{4}{5}$
2. $\frac{10}{9}$
3. $\frac{4}{3}$
4. $\frac{7}{8}$
5. $\frac{7}{|y|}$
6. $\frac{11}{|x|}$
7. $\frac{5|y|\sqrt{y}}{x^2}$
8. $\frac{6a^2\sqrt{a}}{|b^3|}$
9. $\frac{2x\sqrt[3]{x^2}}{3y}$
10. $\frac{2x^2\sqrt[3]{x}}{3y^2}$
11. $\sqrt{7}$
12. $\sqrt{7}$
13. 3
14. 2
15. $|y|\sqrt{5y}$
16. $2|b|\sqrt{2b}$
17. $2\sqrt[3]{a^2b}$
18. $3xy\sqrt[3]{y^2}$
19. $3\sqrt{xy}$
20. $\frac{5\sqrt{ab}}{3}$
21. $\sqrt{x^2 + xy + y^2}$
22. $\sqrt{r^2 - rs + s^2}$

Mixed Review

66. $y = \frac{1}{2}x$
67. $y = -2x$
68. $y = \frac{4}{7}x$
69. 2×10^{-7}
70. 1.4×10^{-1}
71. 3.5×10^{3}
72. 4, −2
73. 7, −3
74. $\frac{5}{2}, -\frac{5}{2}$
75. a. $f(x) = 2 + 1.5x$
b. $18.50
76. 4 L of A, 8 L of B

B

Use the formula at the beginning of the lesson to find the period of a pendulum for each length given. Use 3.14 for π.

57. 65 cm 1.62 sec **58.** 98 cm 1.99 sec **59.** 120 cm 2.20 sec

60. What conditions must be satisfied for the following equation to be true?
$\sqrt{a} + \sqrt{b} = \sqrt{a + b}$ $a \geq 0$ and $b = 0$, or $a = 0$ and $b \geq 0$

61. What conditions must be satisfied for the following equation to be true?
$\sqrt[3]{a} + \sqrt[3]{b} = \sqrt[3]{a + b}$ $a = -b$ or $a = 0$ or $b = 0$

62. ***Critical Thinking*** Find three different pairs of radical expressions whose sum is $2\sqrt{7}$. Answers may vary.

Challenge

Simplify.

63. $\frac{2}{3}\sqrt{4\frac{1}{2}} + \frac{3}{2}\sqrt[3]{16} + \frac{1}{4}\sqrt{72}$ $\frac{5}{2}\sqrt{2} + 3\sqrt[3]{2}$ **64.** $x\sqrt[3]{2y} - \sqrt[3]{16x^3y} + \frac{x}{3}\sqrt[3]{54y}$ 0

65. Without using a calculator, determine which is larger, $5\sqrt[3]{2}$ or $2\sqrt[3]{31}$. $5\sqrt[3]{2}$

Mixed Review

Find the variation constant and an equation of variation where y varies directly as x and the following are true.

66. $y = 3$ when $x = 6$ **67.** $y = -4$ when $x = 2$ **68.** $y = 4$ when $x = 7$

Simplify. **69.** $\frac{5.2 \times 10^{-3}}{2.6 \times 10^{4}}$ **70.** $\frac{3.78 \times 10^{7}}{2.7 \times 10^{8}}$ **71.** $\frac{5.95 \times 10^{8}}{1.7 \times 10^{5}}$

Solve. **72.** $x^2 - 2x = 8$ **73.** $y^2 - 4y = 21$ **74.** $4a^2 = 25$

75. Six yards of fabric cost $11.00, and 15 yards cost $24.50.
a. Fit a linear function to the data points.
b. Use the function to find the cost of 11 yards of fabric.

76. Canned juice A contains 70% apple juice; canned juice B contains 55% apple juice. How many liters of each should be mixed together to get 12 liters of juice that contains 60% apple juice?

Problem for Programmers

Write a program to simplify principle k-th roots of integers. The program should recognize whether the root exists, whether the simplification contains a radical, and whether simplification is possible. Test your program using Try This j and Exercises 18 and 26 in Lesson 7-2.

7-4 More Operations with Radical Expressions

Multiplying

Objective: Multiply radical expressions.

To multiply radical expressions in which some factors contain more than one term, we use the same procedures as for multiplying polynomials.

EXAMPLES Multiply.

1. $\sqrt[3]{y}(\sqrt[3]{y^2} + \sqrt[3]{2}) = \sqrt[3]{y} \cdot \sqrt[3]{y^2} + \sqrt[3]{y} \cdot \sqrt[3]{2}$ Using the distributive property

$= \sqrt[3]{y^3} + \sqrt[3]{2y}$ Multiplying radicals

$= y + \sqrt[3]{2y}$ Simplifying $\sqrt[3]{y^3}$

2. $(4\sqrt{3} + \sqrt{2})(\sqrt{3} - 5\sqrt{2}) = \overset{F}{4(\sqrt{3})^2} - \overset{O}{20\sqrt{3} \cdot \sqrt{2}} + \overset{I}{\sqrt{2} \cdot \sqrt{3}} - \overset{L}{5(\sqrt{2})^2}$

$= 4 \cdot 3 - 20\sqrt{6} + \sqrt{6} - 5 \cdot 2$

$= 12 - 20\sqrt{6} + \sqrt{6} - 10$

$= 2 - 19\sqrt{6}$

3. $(\sqrt{5} + \sqrt{7})(\sqrt{5} - \sqrt{7}) = (\sqrt{5})^2 - (\sqrt{7})^2$ Multiplying as the sum and difference of two expressions

$= 5 - 7$

$= -2$

Try This Multiply.

a. $\sqrt{2}(5\sqrt{3} + 3\sqrt{7})$ $5\sqrt{6} + 3\sqrt{14}$ **b.** $(\sqrt{a} + 2\sqrt{3})(3\sqrt{b} - 4\sqrt{3})$ $3\sqrt{ab} - 4\sqrt{3a} + 6\sqrt{3b} - 24$

c. $(2\sqrt{5} - y)^2$ $20 - 4y\sqrt{5} + y^2$ **d.** $(8 - 5\sqrt{x})(8 + 5\sqrt{x})$ $64 - 25|x|$

Rationalizing Denominators

Objective: Rationalize denominators of radical expressions.

When calculating with radical expressions, it is standard to write the result without radicals in the denominator. This is called rationalizing the denominator. When rationalizing a denominator, we multiply by 1 to make the denominator a perfect power.

EXAMPLE 4 Rationalize the denominator.

$\sqrt[3]{\frac{7}{9}} = \sqrt[3]{\frac{7}{3 \cdot 3} \cdot \frac{3}{3}}$ Multiplying the radicand by 1 to make the denominator a perfect cube

$= \sqrt[3]{\frac{21}{3 \cdot 3 \cdot 3}} = \frac{\sqrt[3]{21}}{\sqrt[3]{3^3}} = \frac{\sqrt[3]{21}}{3}$

7-4

FIRST FIVE MINUTES

Simplify.

1. $\frac{\sqrt{20}}{\sqrt{5}}$

$\frac{\sqrt{4 \cdot 5}}{\sqrt{5}} = 2$

2. $5\sqrt{7} + 6\sqrt{7}$

$(5 + 6)\sqrt{7} = 11\sqrt{7}$

3. $2\sqrt{3x} + 4\sqrt{12x^3}$

$= 2\sqrt{3x} + 4\sqrt{4x^2 3x}$

$= 2\sqrt{3x} + 4 \cdot 2|x|\sqrt{3x}$

$= (2 + 8|x|)\sqrt{3x}$

Multiplying

Remind students that an expression like $3\sqrt[5]{7}$ represents a single real number. It has all the properties of a real number and can be manipulated using the properties of algebra.

Chalkboard Examples

Multiply.

1. $\sqrt{3}(\sqrt{2} + \sqrt{3})$

$= \sqrt{3} \cdot \sqrt{2} + \sqrt{3} \cdot \sqrt{3}$

$= \sqrt{6} + 3$

2. $(\sqrt{2} + 1)(\sqrt{2} - 1)$

$= (\sqrt{2})^2 - 1$

$= 2 - 1$

$= 1$

3. $(\sqrt{3} + \sqrt{2})^2$

$= (\sqrt{3})^2 + 2\sqrt{3} \cdot \sqrt{2} + (\sqrt{2})^2$

$= 3 + 2\sqrt{6} + 2$

$= 5 + 2\sqrt{6}$

Rationalizing Denominators

Chalkboard Examples

Rationalize the denominator.

1. $\sqrt{\frac{1}{2}}$

$\frac{\sqrt{1} \cdot \sqrt{2}}{\sqrt{2} \cdot \sqrt{2}} = \frac{\sqrt{2}}{2}$

2. $\frac{3}{\sqrt{5}}$

$\frac{3 \cdot \sqrt{5}}{\sqrt{5} \cdot \sqrt{5}}$

$= \frac{3\sqrt{5}}{5}$

3. $\frac{1}{\sqrt[4]{2x}}$

$\frac{1 \cdot \sqrt[4]{8x^3}}{\sqrt[4]{2x}\sqrt[4]{8x^3}}$

$= \frac{\sqrt[4]{8x^3}}{\sqrt[4]{16x^4}} = \frac{\sqrt[4]{8x^3}}{2|x|}$

4. $\frac{2}{3 + \sqrt{2}}$

$\frac{2(3 - \sqrt{2})}{(3 + \sqrt{2})(3 - \sqrt{2})}$

$= \frac{2(3 - \sqrt{2})}{9 - 2}$

$= \frac{2(3 - \sqrt{2})}{7}$

5. $\frac{5}{\sqrt{3} - \sqrt{7}}$

$\frac{5(\sqrt{3} + \sqrt{7})}{(\sqrt{3} - \sqrt{7})(\sqrt{3} + \sqrt{7})}$

$= \frac{5(\sqrt{3} + \sqrt{7})}{3 - 7}$

$= \frac{5(\sqrt{3} + \sqrt{7})}{-4}$

Try This Rationalize the denominator.

e. $\sqrt{\frac{2}{3}}$ $\frac{\sqrt{6}}{3}$ **f.** $\sqrt{\frac{10}{7}}$ $\frac{\sqrt{70}}{7}$ **g.** $\sqrt[3]{\frac{3}{6}}$ $\frac{\sqrt[3]{4}}{2}$

In Example 4, we multiplied by 1 inside the radical sign. We can also multiply by 1 outside the radical sign.

EXAMPLE 5 Rationalize the denominator.

$$\sqrt{\frac{2a}{5b}} = \frac{\sqrt{2a}}{\sqrt{5b}} \quad \text{Converting to a quotient of radicals}$$

$$= \frac{\sqrt{2a}}{\sqrt{5b}} \cdot \frac{\sqrt{5b}}{\sqrt{5b}} \quad \text{Multiplying by 1}$$

$$= \frac{\sqrt{10ab}}{\sqrt{25b^2}} \quad \text{The radicand in the denominator is a perfect square.}$$

$$= \frac{\sqrt{10ab}}{5|b|} \quad \text{Finding the square root of } 25b^2$$

Try This Rationalize the denominator.

h. $\sqrt{\frac{4a}{3b}}$ $\frac{2\sqrt{3ab}}{3|b|}$ **i.** $\frac{\sqrt{4x^5}}{\sqrt{3y^3}}$ $\frac{2x^2\sqrt{3xy}}{3y^2}$

EXAMPLE 6 Rationalize the denominator.

$$\frac{\sqrt[3]{a}}{\sqrt[3]{9x}}$$

To choose the symbol for 1, we look at the radicand $9x$. This is $3 \cdot 3 \cdot x$. To make it a cube we need another 3 and two more x's. Thus we multiply by $\frac{\sqrt[3]{3x^2}}{\sqrt[3]{3x^2}}$.

$$\frac{\sqrt[3]{a}}{\sqrt[3]{9x}} = \frac{\sqrt[3]{a}}{\sqrt[3]{9x}} \cdot \frac{\sqrt[3]{3x^2}}{\sqrt[3]{3x^2}} \quad \text{Multiplying by 1}$$

$$= \frac{\sqrt[3]{3ax^2}}{\sqrt[3]{27x^3}}$$

$$= \frac{\sqrt[3]{3ax^2}}{3x} \quad \text{Simplifying}$$

Try This Rationalize the denominator.

j. $\frac{\sqrt[3]{7}}{\sqrt[3]{2}}$ $\frac{\sqrt[3]{28}}{2}$ **k.** $\sqrt[7]{\frac{3x^5}{2y}}$ $\frac{\sqrt[7]{192y^6x^5}}{2|y|}$

When the denominator to be rationalized has two terms, we choose a symbol for 1 as illustrated below.

Expression	Symbol for 1	Expression	Symbol for 1
$\frac{3}{2+\sqrt{7}}$	$\frac{2-\sqrt{7}}{2-\sqrt{7}}$	$\frac{4+\sqrt{3}}{\sqrt{3}-\sqrt{11}}$	$\frac{\sqrt{3}+\sqrt{11}}{\sqrt{3}+\sqrt{11}}$

Multiplying by such symbols for 1 produces a difference of two squares in the denominator. Expressions such as $2 + \sqrt{7}$ and $2 - \sqrt{7}$ are conjugates of each other.

EXAMPLE 7 Rationalize the denominator.

$$\frac{3}{2+\sqrt{7}} = \frac{3}{2+\sqrt{7}} \cdot \frac{2-\sqrt{7}}{2-\sqrt{7}}$$ Using the conjugate of the denominator to multiply by 1

$$= \frac{3(2-\sqrt{7})}{(2+\sqrt{7})(2-\sqrt{7})}$$ Multiplying numerators and denominators

$$= \frac{3(2-\sqrt{7})}{(2)^2-(\sqrt{7})^2}$$ Multiplying as the sum and difference of two expressions

$$= \frac{3(2-\sqrt{7})}{4-7}$$ Simplifying

$$= \frac{3(2-\sqrt{7})}{-3}$$

$$= -2+\sqrt{7}$$

EXAMPLE 8 Rationalize the denominator.

$$\frac{4+\sqrt{2}}{\sqrt{5}-\sqrt{2}} = \frac{4+\sqrt{2}}{\sqrt{5}-\sqrt{2}} \cdot \frac{\sqrt{5}+\sqrt{2}}{\sqrt{5}+\sqrt{2}}$$ Using the conjugate of the denominator to multiply by 1

$$= \frac{(4+\sqrt{2})(\sqrt{5}+\sqrt{2})}{(\sqrt{5}-\sqrt{2})(\sqrt{5}+\sqrt{2})}$$ Multiplying numerators and denominators

$$= \frac{4\sqrt{5}+4\sqrt{2}+\sqrt{2}\sqrt{5}+(\sqrt{2})^2}{(\sqrt{5})^2-(\sqrt{2})^2}$$ Using FOIL

$$= \frac{4\sqrt{5}+4\sqrt{2}+\sqrt{10}+2}{5-2}$$ Squaring in the denominator

$$= \frac{4\sqrt{5}+4\sqrt{2}+\sqrt{10}+2}{3}$$

Try This Rationalize the denominator.

l. $\frac{5}{1-\sqrt{2}}$ $-5(1+\sqrt{2})$

m. $\frac{1}{\sqrt{2}+\sqrt{3}}$ $-\sqrt{2}+\sqrt{3}$

n. $\frac{\sqrt{5}+1}{\sqrt{3}-1}$ $\frac{\sqrt{15}+\sqrt{3}+\sqrt{5}+1}{2}$

o. $\frac{2\sqrt{3}-3}{3\sqrt{3}-3}$ $\frac{3-\sqrt{3}}{6}$

LESSON QUIZ

1. Multiply and simplify.
   $\sqrt{7}(4-2\sqrt{7})$
   $4\sqrt{7}-14$
2. Multiply and simplify.
   $(\sqrt{5}+\sqrt{11})(\sqrt{5}-\sqrt{11})$
   -6
3. Rationalize the denominator.
   $\frac{1}{5\sqrt{7}}$
   $\frac{\sqrt{7}}{35}$
4. Rationalize the denominator.
   $\frac{5}{\sqrt{2}+\sqrt{x}}$
   $= \frac{5(\sqrt{2}-\sqrt{x})}{2-x}$

Assignment Guide

Algebra: Day 1: 1 – 30 e/o
Day 2: 31 – 57 e/o, MR

Alg w/Finite or Trig: 1–57 m3, 58–68 e/o, 69, MR

Comprehensive: 1–68 m3, 69, 70–73 e/o, MR

ADDITIONAL ANSWERS

Exercises

23. $|a| + \sqrt{3a} + \sqrt{2a} + \sqrt{6}$
24. $2 - 3\sqrt{x} + |x|$
25. $2\sqrt[3]{9} - 3\sqrt[3]{6} - 2\sqrt[3]{4}$
26. $6\sqrt[4]{63} - 9\sqrt[4]{42} + 2\sqrt[4]{54} - 3\sqrt[4]{36}$

46. $\frac{7(9 - \sqrt{10})}{71}$
47. $-2\sqrt{7}(\sqrt{5} + \sqrt{3})$
48. $\frac{3\sqrt{2}(\sqrt{3} + \sqrt{5})}{2}$
49. $-\frac{\sqrt{15} + 20 - 6\sqrt{2} - 8\sqrt{30}}{77}$
50. $-\frac{3\sqrt{2} + 2\sqrt{42} - 3\sqrt{15} - 6\sqrt{35}}{25}$
51. $\frac{x - 2\sqrt{xy} + y}{x - y}$
52. $\frac{a + 2\sqrt{ab} + b}{a - b}$
53. $\frac{3\sqrt{6} + 4}{2}$
54. $\frac{4\sqrt{6} + 9}{3}$
55. $\frac{4\sqrt{ab} - 12b}{a - 9b}$
56. $\frac{3\sqrt{c} + 2\sqrt{cd} + 12\sqrt{d} + 8d}{c - 16d}$
57. $\frac{x + 8\sqrt{xy} + 15y}{x - 25y}$

7-4 EXERCISES

A

Multiply.

1. $\sqrt{6}(2 - 3\sqrt{6})$ $2\sqrt{6} - 18$
2. $\sqrt{3}(4 + \sqrt{3})$ $4\sqrt{3} + 3$
3. $\sqrt{2}(\sqrt{3} - \sqrt{5})$ $\sqrt{6} - \sqrt{10}$
4. $\sqrt{5}(\sqrt{5} - \sqrt{2})$ $5 - \sqrt{10}$
5. $\sqrt{3}(2\sqrt{5} - 3\sqrt{4})$ $2\sqrt{15} - 6\sqrt{3}$
6. $\sqrt{2}(3\sqrt{10} - 2\sqrt{2})$ $6\sqrt{5} - 4$
7. $\sqrt[3]{2}(\sqrt[3]{4} - 2\sqrt[3]{32})$ -6
8. $\sqrt[3]{3}(\sqrt[3]{9} - 4\sqrt[3]{21})$ $3 - 4\sqrt[3]{63}$
9. $\sqrt[3]{a}(\sqrt[3]{2a^2} + \sqrt[3]{16a^2})$ $3a\sqrt[3]{2}$
10. $\sqrt[3]{x}(\sqrt[3]{3x^2} - \sqrt[3]{81x^2})$ $-2x\sqrt[3]{3}$
11. $(\sqrt{3} - \sqrt{2})(\sqrt{3} + \sqrt{2})$ 1
12. $(\sqrt{5} + \sqrt{6})(\sqrt{5} - \sqrt{6})$ -1
13. $(\sqrt{8} + 2\sqrt{5})(\sqrt{8} - 2\sqrt{5})$ -12
14. $(\sqrt{18} + 3\sqrt{7})(\sqrt{18} - 3\sqrt{7})$ -45
15. $(\sqrt{a} + \sqrt{b})(\sqrt{a} - \sqrt{b})$ $a - b$
16. $(\sqrt{x} - \sqrt{y})(\sqrt{x} + \sqrt{y})$ $x - y$
17. $(3 - \sqrt{5})(2 + \sqrt{5})$ $1 + \sqrt{5}$
18. $(2 + \sqrt{6})(4 - \sqrt{6})$ $2 + 2\sqrt{6}$
19. $(\sqrt{3} + 1)(2\sqrt{3} + 1)$ $7 + 3\sqrt{3}$
20. $(4\sqrt{3} + 5)(\sqrt{3} - 2)$ $2 - 3\sqrt{3}$
21. $(2\sqrt{7} - 4\sqrt{2})(3\sqrt{7} + 6\sqrt{2})$ -6
22. $(4\sqrt{5} + 3\sqrt{3})(3\sqrt{5} - 4\sqrt{3})$ $24 - 7\sqrt{15}$
23. $(\sqrt{a} + \sqrt{2})(\sqrt{a} + \sqrt{3})$
24. $(2 - \sqrt{x})(1 - \sqrt{x})$
25. $(2\sqrt[3]{3} + \sqrt[3]{2})(\sqrt[3]{3} - 2\sqrt[3]{2})$
26. $(3\sqrt[4]{7} + \sqrt[4]{6})(2\sqrt[4]{9} - 3\sqrt[4]{6})$
27. $(2 + \sqrt{3})^2$ $7 + 4\sqrt{3}$
28. $(\sqrt{5} + 1)^2$ $6 + 2\sqrt{5}$
29. $(3\sqrt{2} - \sqrt{3})^2$ $21 - 6\sqrt{6}$
30. $(5\sqrt{3} + 3\sqrt{5})^2$ $120 + 30\sqrt{15}$

Rationalize the denominator.

31. $\sqrt{\frac{6}{5}}$ $\frac{\sqrt{30}}{5}$
32. $\sqrt{\frac{11}{6}}$ $\frac{\sqrt{66}}{6}$
33. $\sqrt{\frac{10}{7}}$ $\frac{\sqrt{70}}{7}$
34. $\sqrt{\frac{22}{3}}$ $\frac{\sqrt{66}}{3}$
35. $\frac{6\sqrt{5}}{5\sqrt{3}}$ $\frac{2\sqrt{15}}{5}$
36. $\frac{2\sqrt{3}}{5\sqrt{2}}$ $\frac{\sqrt{6}}{5}$
37. $\sqrt[3]{\frac{16}{9}}$ $\frac{2\sqrt[3]{6}}{3}$
38. $\sqrt[3]{\frac{3}{9}}$ $\frac{\sqrt[3]{9}}{3}$
39. $\frac{\sqrt[3]{3a}}{\sqrt[3]{5c}}$ $\frac{\sqrt[3]{75ac^2}}{5c}$
40. $\frac{\sqrt[3]{7x}}{\sqrt[3]{3y}}$ $\frac{\sqrt[3]{63xy^2}}{3y}$
41. $\frac{\sqrt[3]{2y^4}}{\sqrt[3]{6x^4}}$ $\frac{y\sqrt[3]{9yx^2}}{3x^2}$
42. $\frac{\sqrt[3]{3a^4}}{\sqrt[3]{7b^2}}$ $\frac{a\sqrt[3]{147ab}}{7b}$
43. $\frac{1}{\sqrt[3]{xy}}$ $\frac{\sqrt[3]{x^2y^2}}{xy}$
44. $\frac{1}{\sqrt[3]{ab}}$ $\frac{\sqrt[3]{a^2b^2}}{ab}$
45. $\frac{5}{8 - \sqrt{6}}$ $\frac{5(8 + \sqrt{6})}{58}$
46. $\frac{7}{9 + \sqrt{10}}$
47. $\frac{-4\sqrt{7}}{\sqrt{5} - \sqrt{3}}$
48. $\frac{-3\sqrt{2}}{\sqrt{3} - \sqrt{5}}$
49. $\frac{\sqrt{5} - 2\sqrt{6}}{\sqrt{3} - 4\sqrt{5}}$
50. $\frac{\sqrt{6} - 3\sqrt{5}}{\sqrt{3} - 2\sqrt{7}}$
51. $\frac{\sqrt{x} - \sqrt{y}}{\sqrt{x} + \sqrt{y}}$
52. $\frac{\sqrt{a} + \sqrt{b}}{\sqrt{a} - \sqrt{b}}$
53. $\frac{5\sqrt{3} - 3\sqrt{2}}{3\sqrt{2} - 2\sqrt{3}}$
54. $\frac{7\sqrt{2} + 4\sqrt{3}}{4\sqrt{3} - 3\sqrt{2}}$
55. $\frac{4\sqrt{b}}{\sqrt{a} + 3\sqrt{b}}$
56. $\frac{3 + 2\sqrt{d}}{\sqrt{c} - 4\sqrt{d}}$
57. $\frac{\sqrt{x} + 3\sqrt{y}}{\sqrt{x} - 5\sqrt{y}}$

B

Rationalize the numerator.

58. $\frac{\sqrt{7}}{\sqrt{3}}$ $\frac{7}{\sqrt{21}}$

59. $\sqrt{\frac{14}{21}}$ $\frac{2}{\sqrt{6}}$

60. $\frac{4\sqrt{13}}{3\sqrt{7}}$ $\frac{52}{3\sqrt{91}}$

61. $\frac{\sqrt[3]{7}}{\sqrt[3]{2}}$ $\frac{7}{\sqrt[3]{98}}$

62. $\sqrt{\frac{7x}{3y}}$ $\frac{7|x|}{\sqrt{21xy}}$

63. $\frac{\sqrt[3]{5y^4}}{\sqrt[3]{6x^5}}$ $\frac{5y^2}{x\sqrt[3]{150x^2y^2}}$

64. $\frac{\sqrt{3} + 5}{8}$

65. $\frac{\sqrt{3} - 5}{\sqrt{2} + 5}$

66. $\frac{\sqrt{5} - \sqrt{2}}{\sqrt{2} + \sqrt{3}}$

Multiply.

67. $(\sqrt{x + 3} - 3)(\sqrt{x + 3} + 3)$

68. $(\sqrt{x + h} - \sqrt{x})(\sqrt{x + h} + \sqrt{x})$

69. ***Critical Thinking*** Find two different pairs of conjugates whose product is 8.

Challenge

Simplify.

70. $\frac{\sqrt[3]{c^3 + 3c^2d + 3cd^2 + d^3}}{\sqrt{c^2 - d^2} \cdot \sqrt{c^2 - d^2}}$

71. $\frac{1 + \sqrt{y}}{\sqrt{x} + \sqrt{xy}} \cdot \frac{1 - \sqrt{y}}{1 - y} \cdot \frac{x - xy}{\sqrt{x} - \sqrt{xy}}$

72. $\frac{\sqrt{x}}{\sqrt{x} - \sqrt{x + 1}}$

73. $\frac{\sqrt{p - 4q}}{\sqrt{3q^2 + 4pq + p^2}} \cdot \frac{\sqrt{p + 3q}}{\sqrt{p^2 + 6pq + 8q^2}} \div \frac{1}{\sqrt{p^2 + 3pq + 2q^2}}$

Mixed Review

Find the variation constant and an equation of variation where y varies inversely as x and the following are true.

74. $y = -4$ when $x = 2$

75. $y = 4$ when $x = 7$

Factor. 76. $2x^2 + 4x + 2$

77. $9y^2 - x^2 - 2x - 1$

78. $8y^3 - 27$

Suppose $f(x) = x^2 + 1$ and $g(x) = \frac{1}{2}x - 3$. **79.** Find $f(g(10))$ **80.** Find $g(f(10))$

81. Find an expression for $f(g(x))$ **82.** Find an expression for $g(f(x))$

83. The sum of the squares of two consecutive even integers is 52. Find the integers.

84. The Looksnice Painting Company charges $125 plus $85 per room to paint interiors. Find the cost of painting a six-room house.

85. A telethon raised $1250 so far. That is about 2.5% of its goal. Find the amount the telethon is trying to raise.

64. $\frac{-11}{4(\sqrt{3} - 5)}$

65. $\frac{-22}{\sqrt{6} + 5\sqrt{2} + 5\sqrt{3} + 25}$

66. $\frac{3}{\sqrt{10} + 2 + \sqrt{15} + \sqrt{6}}$

67. $x - 6$

68. h

69. Answers may vary. Ex: $(\sqrt{15} + \sqrt{7})(\sqrt{15} - \sqrt{7})$; $(\sqrt{10} + \sqrt{2})(\sqrt{10} - \sqrt{2})$

70. $\frac{1}{c - d}$

71. 1

72. $-x - \sqrt{x^2 + x}$

73. $\frac{\sqrt{p^2 - 16q^2}}{p + 4q}$

Mixed Review

74. $y = -\frac{8}{x}$

75. $y = \frac{28}{x}$

76. $2(x + 1)^2$

77. $(3y - x - 1)(3y + x + 1)$

78. $(2y - 3)(4y^2 + 6y + 9)$

79. 5

80. 47.5

81. $\frac{1}{4}x^2 - 3x + 10$

82. $\frac{1}{2}x^2 - \frac{5}{2}$

83. 4, 6, and −6, −4

84. $635

85. $50,000

7-5

FIRST FIVE MINUTES

1. Multiply and simplify.
   $\sqrt{13}(2 + 3\sqrt{13})$
   $= 2\sqrt{13} + 3\sqrt{13} \cdot \sqrt{13}$
   $= 2\sqrt{13} + 3 \cdot 13$
   $= 2\sqrt{13} + 39$
2. Rationalize the denominator.
   $\frac{1}{\sqrt{5}}$
   $\frac{1 \cdot \sqrt{5}}{\sqrt{5} \cdot \sqrt{5}} = \frac{\sqrt{5}}{5}$
3. Rationalize the denominator.
   $\frac{5}{1 + \sqrt{2}}$
   $\frac{5 \cdot (1 - \sqrt{2})}{(1 + \sqrt{2})(1 - \sqrt{2})}$
   $= \frac{5 \cdot (1 - \sqrt{2})}{1 - 2} = \frac{5(1 - \sqrt{2})}{-1}$
   $= -5(1 - \sqrt{2})$

Combinations of Powers and Roots

You may want to point out the analogy between the property of exponents,

$a^{mk} = (a^m)^k = (a^k)^m,$

and Theorem 7-6,

$\sqrt[k]{a^m} = (\sqrt[k]{a})^m$

Key Question

- What is an equivalent expression for $\sqrt[3]{x^5}$?
  $(\sqrt[3]{x})^5$

Chalkboard Examples

1. $\sqrt[3]{64^2}$
   $(\sqrt[3]{64})^2 = 4^2 = 16$
   or $\sqrt[3]{4096} = 16$
2. $\sqrt[4]{81^3}$
   $(\sqrt[4]{81})^3 = 3^3 = 27$
   or $\sqrt[4]{81^3} = \sqrt[4]{531{,}441} = 27$
3. $\sqrt[3]{(8x^3)^2}$
   $(\sqrt[3]{8x^3})^2 = (2x)^2 = 4x^2$
   or $\sqrt[3]{(8x^3)^2} = \sqrt[3]{64x^6} = 4x^2$

7-5 Rational Numbers as Exponents

Explore

Simplify and compare your answers.

$\sqrt[3]{8^2}$ and $(\sqrt[3]{8})^2$ 4 $\sqrt{4^2}$ and $(\sqrt{4})^2$ 4

Combinations of Powers and Roots

Objective: Calculate expressions of the form $\sqrt[k]{a^m}$ in two ways.

The results of the exploratory activity suggest the following theorem.

Theorem 7-6

For any nonnegative number a, any natural-number index k, and any integer m,

$$\sqrt[k]{a^m} = (\sqrt[k]{a})^m$$

We can raise to a power and then take a root, or we can take a root and then raise to a power. One method of simplifying may be easier than the other.

EXAMPLES Simplify as shown. Then use Theorem 7-6 to simplify another way.

1. $\sqrt[3]{27^2} = \sqrt[3]{729} = 9$
$(\sqrt[3]{27})^2 = (3)^2 = 9$

2. $\sqrt[3]{2^6} = \sqrt[3]{64} = 4$
$(\sqrt[3]{2})^6 = \sqrt[3]{2} \cdot \sqrt[3]{2} \cdot \sqrt[3]{2} \cdot \sqrt[3]{2} \cdot \sqrt[3]{2} \cdot \sqrt[3]{2} = 2 \cdot 2 = 4$

3. $(\sqrt{5x})^3 = \sqrt{5x} \cdot \sqrt{5x} \cdot \sqrt{5x}$
$= \sqrt{5^3x^3}$
$= \sqrt{5^2x^2}\,\sqrt{5x} = 5|x|\sqrt{5x}$
$\sqrt{(5x)^3} = \sqrt{125x^3}$
$= \sqrt{25x^2} \cdot \sqrt{5x} = 5|x|\sqrt{5x}$

Try This Simplify as shown. Then use Theorem 7-6 to simplify another way.

a. $\sqrt[3]{8^2}$ $\sqrt[3]{8^2} = 4$ $(\sqrt[3]{8})^2 = 4$

b. $(\sqrt{6y})^3$ $(\sqrt{6y})^3 = 6|y|\sqrt{6y}$ $\sqrt{(6y)^3} = 6|y|\sqrt{6y}$

Rational Exponents

Objective: Write expressions with rational exponents as radical expressions and vice versa.

To extend the idea of an exponent to include rational exponents, consider $a^{\frac{1}{2}} \cdot a^{\frac{1}{2}}$. If the usual properties of exponents are to hold, then $a^{\frac{1}{2}} \cdot a^{\frac{1}{2}}$ should equal a^1, or a. We also know that $\sqrt{a} \cdot \sqrt{a} = a$. Thus $a^{\frac{1}{2}}$ should be defined as $\sqrt{a}$. Similarly, $a^{\frac{1}{3}} \cdot a^{\frac{1}{3}} \cdot a^{\frac{1}{3}} = a^1$, or a. Thus $a^{\frac{1}{3}}$ should be defined as $\sqrt[3]{a}$.

Definition

For any nonnegative number a and any natural-number index k, $a^{\frac{1}{k}}$ means $\sqrt[k]{a}$ (the nonnegative k-th root of a).

When working with rational exponents, we will assume that variables in the base are nonnegative.

EXAMPLES Write without rational exponents.

4. $x^{\frac{1}{2}} = \sqrt{x}$ 5. $27^{\frac{1}{3}} = \sqrt[3]{27}$, or 3 6. $(abc)^{\frac{1}{5}} = \sqrt[5]{abc}$

Radical expressions can also be rewritten with rational exponents.

EXAMPLES Write with rational exponents.

7. $\sqrt[5]{7xy} = (7xy)^{\frac{1}{5}}$ 8. $\sqrt[7]{\frac{x^3y}{9}} = \left(\frac{x^3y}{9}\right)^{\frac{1}{7}}$

Try This Write without rational exponents.

c. $y^{\frac{1}{4}}$ $\sqrt[4]{y}$ **d.** $(3a)^{\frac{1}{2}}$ $\sqrt{3a}$ **e.** $16^{\frac{1}{4}}$ $\sqrt[4]{16}$, or 2

Write with rational exponents.

f. $\sqrt[4]{a^3b^2c}$ $(a^3b^2c)^{\frac{1}{4}}$ **g.** $\sqrt[5]{\frac{x^2y}{16}}$ $\left(\frac{x^2y}{16}\right)^{\frac{1}{5}}$

How should we define $a^{\frac{2}{3}}$? If the usual properties of exponents are to hold, we have $a^{\frac{2}{3}} = (a^{\frac{1}{3}})^2$, or $(\sqrt[3]{a})^2$, or $\sqrt[3]{a^2}$.

Definition

For any natural numbers m and k, and any nonnegative number a, $a^{\frac{m}{k}}$ means $\sqrt[k]{a^m}$.

Thus $a^{\frac{m}{k}}$ represents the principal k-th root of a^m. Since by Theorem 7-6 we know that $\sqrt[k]{a^m} = (\sqrt[k]{a})^m$, it follows that $a^{\frac{m}{k}}$ also represents $(\sqrt[k]{a})^m$.

Rational Exponents

Key Questions

- What is the number whose product with itself is 7?
  $\sqrt{7}$ or $-\sqrt{7}$
- What is $9^{1/2}$?
  3

Chalkboard Examples

Write without rational exponents.

1. $7^{1/2}$
   $\sqrt{7}$
2. $x^{1/3}$
   $\sqrt[3]{x}$
3. $8^{1/3}$
   $\sqrt[3]{8} = 2$

Write with rational exponents.

4. $\sqrt[3]{11}$
   $11^{1/3}$
5. $\sqrt[5]{3x}$
   $(3x)^{1/5}$

Negative Rational Exponents

Key Questions

- What fraction is equivalent to 3^{-1}?
  $\frac{1}{3}$
- Is $2^{-3} < 0$ since the exponent is negative?
  No

Chalkboard Examples

Rewrite with positive exponents.

1. $8^{-1/3}$
   $\frac{1}{8^{1/3}} = \frac{1}{2}$
2. $16^{-3/4}$
   $\frac{1}{16^{3/4}} = \frac{1}{(16^{1/4})^3}$
   $= \frac{1}{2^3} = \frac{1}{8}$

Simplify.

3. $2^{4/5} \cdot 2^{6/5}$
   $2^{4/5 + 6/5} = 2^{10/5} = 2^2 = 4$
4. $\frac{5^{4/3}}{5^{1/3}}$
   $5^{4/3 - 1/3} = 5^{3/3} = 5^1 = 5$
5. $(9^{4/3})^{3/8}$
   $9^{4/3 \cdot 3/8} = 9^{1/2} = 3$

EXAMPLES Write without rational exponents.

9. $(27)^{\frac{2}{3}} = (\sqrt[3]{27})^2$, or $(27)^{\frac{2}{3}} = \sqrt[3]{27^2}$
$= (3)^2 \qquad = \sqrt[3]{729}$
$= 9 \qquad = 9$

10. $4^{\frac{3}{2}} = (\sqrt[2]{4})^3$, or $4^{\frac{3}{2}} = \sqrt[2]{4^3}$
$= 2^3 \qquad = \sqrt{64}$
$= 8 \qquad = 8$

EXAMPLES Write with rational exponents.

11. $\sqrt[3]{8^4} = 8^{\frac{4}{3}}$

12. $(\sqrt[4]{7xy})^5 = (7xy)^{\frac{5}{4}}$

Try This Write without rational exponents.

h. $x^{\frac{3}{2}}$ $x\sqrt{x}$

i. $8^{\frac{2}{3}}$ 4

Write with rational exponents.

j. $(\sqrt[3]{7abc})^4$ $(7abc)^{\frac{4}{3}}$

k. $\sqrt[5]{6^7}$ $6^{\frac{7}{5}}$

l. $\sqrt[4]{x^2y^3}$ $(x^2y^3)^{\frac{1}{4}}$, or $x^{\frac{1}{2}}y^{\frac{3}{4}}$

Negative Rational Exponents

Objective: Simplify expressions containing negative rational exponents.

Negative rational exponents have a meaning similar to that of negative integer exponents. Changing the sign of an exponent amounts to finding a reciprocal.

Definition

For any rational number $\frac{m}{n}$ and any positive real number a, $a^{-\frac{m}{n}}$ means $\frac{1}{a^{\frac{m}{n}}}$.

$a^{\frac{m}{n}}$ and $a^{-\frac{m}{n}}$ are reciprocals.

EXAMPLES Rewrite with positive exponents.

13. $4^{-\frac{1}{2}} = \frac{1}{4^{\frac{1}{2}}}$ $\quad 4^{-\frac{1}{2}}$ is the reciprocal of $4^{\frac{1}{2}}$.

Since $4^{\frac{1}{2}} = \sqrt{4} = 2$, the answer simplifies to $\frac{1}{2}$.

14. $(5xy)^{-\frac{4}{5}} = \frac{1}{(5xy)^{\frac{4}{5}}}$ $\quad (5xy)^{-\frac{4}{5}}$ is the reciprocal of $(5xy)^{\frac{4}{5}}$.

Try This Rewrite with positive exponents.

m. $5^{-\frac{1}{4}}$ $\frac{1}{5^{\frac{1}{4}}}$

n. $(3xy)^{-\frac{7}{8}}$ $\frac{1}{(3xy)^{\frac{7}{8}}}$

The properties of exponents that hold for integer exponents also hold for rational exponents.

EXAMPLES Use the properties of exponents to simplify.

15. $3^{\frac{1}{5}} \cdot 3^{\frac{3}{5}} = 3^{\frac{1}{5}+\frac{3}{5}} = 3^{\frac{4}{5}}$ Adding exponents

16. $\frac{7^{\frac{1}{4}}}{7^{\frac{1}{2}}} = 7^{\frac{1}{4}-\frac{1}{2}} = 7^{\frac{1}{4}-\frac{2}{4}} = 7^{-\frac{1}{4}}$ Subtracting exponents

17. $(7.2^{\frac{2}{3}})^{\frac{3}{4}} = 7.2^{\frac{2}{3}\cdot\frac{3}{4}} = 7.2^{\frac{6}{12}} = 7.2^{\frac{1}{2}}$ Multiplying exponents

Try This Use the properties of exponents to simplify.

o. $7^{\frac{1}{3}} \cdot 7^{\frac{3}{5}}$ $7^{\frac{14}{15}}$ **p.** $\frac{5^{\frac{7}{6}}}{5^{\frac{5}{6}}}$ $5^{\frac{1}{3}}$ **q.** $(9^{\frac{3}{5}})^{\frac{2}{3}}$ $9^{\frac{2}{5}}$

Simplifying Radical Expressions

Objective: Use rational exponents to simplify radical expressions.

Rational exponents can be used to simplify some radical expressions. The procedure is as follows.

1. Convert radical expressions to exponential expressions.
2. Use the properties of exponents to simplify.
3. Convert back to radical notation when appropriate.

EXAMPLES Use rational exponents to simplify.

18. $\sqrt[6]{x^3} = x^{\frac{3}{6}}$ Converting to an exponential expression

$= x^{\frac{1}{2}}$ Simplifying the exponent

$= \sqrt{x}$ Converting back to radical notation

19. $\sqrt[6]{4} = 4^{\frac{1}{6}}$

$= (2^2)^{\frac{1}{6}}$

$= 2^{\frac{2}{6}}$

$= 2^{\frac{1}{3}}$

$= \sqrt[3]{2}$

Try This Use rational exponents to simplify.

r. $\sqrt[4]{a^2}$ $\sqrt{a}$ **s.** $\sqrt[4]{x^4}$ x **t.** $\sqrt[6]{8}$ $\sqrt{2}$

Simplifying Radical Expressions

Chalkboard Examples

Use rational exponents to simplify.

1. $\sqrt[4]{25^2}$
   $25^{2/4} = 25^{1/2} = 5$
2. $\sqrt[8]{a^4}$
   $a^{4/8} = a^{1/2} = \sqrt{a}$
3. $\sqrt[6]{2^{12}a^6}$
   $(2^{12}a^6)^{1/6}$
   $= (2^{12})^{1/6}(a^6)^{1/6}$
   $= 2^{12/6}a^{6/6} = 2^2a$
   $= 4a$

Write as a single radical expression.

4. $\sqrt{10} \cdot \sqrt[4]{3}$
   $10^{1/2} \cdot 3^{1/4}$
   $10^{2/4} \cdot 3^{1/4}$
   $= (10^2)^{1/4} \cdot 3^{1/4}$
   $= (100 \cdot 3)^{1/4} = \sqrt[4]{300}$
5. $\frac{\sqrt[3]{x^2}}{\sqrt{x}}$
   $\frac{(x^2)^{1/3}}{x^{1/2}} = x^{2/3} \cdot x^{-1/2}$
   $= x^{2/3-1/2} = x^{1/6} = \sqrt[6]{x}$
6. $\sqrt[3]{a+1} \cdot \sqrt[4]{(a+1)^3}$
   $(a+1)^{1/3}(a+1)^{3/4}$
   $= (a+1)^{1/3+3/4}$
   $= (a+1)^{13/12}$
   $= \sqrt[12]{(a+1)^{13}}$
7. $x^{1/3}y^{-1/4}$
   $x^{4/12}y^{-3/12}$
   $= (x^4)^{1/12}(y^{-3})^{1/12}$
   $= \left(\frac{x^4}{y^3}\right)^{\frac{1}{12}}$
   $= \sqrt[12]{\frac{x^4}{y^3}}$

LESSON QUIZ

1. Simplify $\sqrt{9^3}$.
   $(\sqrt{9})^3 = 3^3 = 27$
2. Simplify $27^{2/3}$.
   $(27^{1/3})^2 = 3^2 = 9$
3. Rewrite without rational exponents.
   $5^{2/3}$
   $\sqrt[3]{5^2}$ or $(\sqrt[3]{5})^2$
4. Rewrite using rational exponents.
   $\sqrt[3]{x^7}$
   $(\sqrt[3]{x})^7 = x^{7/3}$
5. Simplify $9^{-1/2}$.
   $\frac{1}{9^{1/2}} = \frac{1}{3}$
6. Simplify using rational exponents.
   $\frac{7^{5/3}}{(\sqrt[3]{7})^2}$
   $7^{5/3} \cdot 7^{-2/3} = 7^{5/3 - 2/3}$
   $= 7^{3/3}$
   $= 7$

EXAMPLE 20 Use rational exponents to simplify.

$$\begin{aligned}\sqrt[8]{a^2b^4} &= (a^2b^4)^{\frac{1}{8}}\\ &= a^{\frac{2}{8}} \cdot b^{\frac{4}{8}}\\ &= a^{\frac{1}{4}} \cdot b^{\frac{2}{4}}\\ &= (ab^2)^{\frac{1}{4}}\\ &= \sqrt[4]{ab^2}\end{aligned}$$

Try This Use rational exponents to simplify.

u. $\sqrt[4]{x^4y^{12}}$ xy^3

v. $\sqrt[12]{x^3y^6}$ $\sqrt[4]{xy^2}$

We can use properties of rational exponents to write a single radical expression for a product or quotient.

EXAMPLES Write as a single radical expression.

21. $$\begin{aligned}\sqrt[3]{5} \cdot \sqrt{2} &= 5^{\frac{1}{3}} \cdot 2^{\frac{1}{2}}\\ &= 5^{\frac{2}{6}}2^{\frac{3}{6}}\\ &= (5^2 \cdot 2^3)^{\frac{1}{6}}\\ &= \sqrt[6]{5^2 \cdot 2^3}\\ &= \sqrt[6]{200}\end{aligned}$$

22. $$\begin{aligned}\sqrt{x-2} \cdot \sqrt[4]{3y} &= (x-2)^{\frac{1}{2}}(3y)^{\frac{1}{4}}\\ &= (x-2)^{\frac{2}{4}}(3y)^{\frac{1}{4}}\\ &= [(x-2)^2(3y)]^{\frac{1}{4}}\\ &= \sqrt[4]{(x^2-4x+4) \cdot 3y}\\ &= \sqrt[4]{3x^2y - 12xy + 12y}\end{aligned}$$

23. $$\begin{aligned}\frac{\sqrt[4]{(x+y)^3}}{\sqrt{x+y}} &= \frac{(x+y)^{\frac{3}{4}}}{(x+y)^{\frac{1}{2}}}\\ &= (x+y)^{\frac{3}{4}-\frac{1}{2}}\\ &= (x+y)^{\frac{1}{4}}\\ &= \sqrt[4]{x+y}\end{aligned}$$

Try This Write as a single radical expression.

w. $\sqrt[4]{7} \cdot \sqrt{3}$ $\sqrt[4]{63}$

x. $\frac{\sqrt[4]{(a-b)^5}}{a-b}$ $\sqrt[4]{a-b}$

EXAMPLE 24 Write as a single radical expression.

$$\begin{aligned}a^{\frac{1}{2}}b^{-\frac{1}{2}}c^{\frac{5}{6}} &= a^{\frac{3}{6}}b^{-\frac{3}{6}}c^{\frac{5}{6}} && \text{Rewriting exponents with a common denominator}\\ &= (a^3b^{-3}c^5)^{\frac{1}{6}} && \text{Using the properties of exponents}\\ &= \sqrt[6]{a^3b^{-3}c^5} && \text{Converting to radical notation}\end{aligned}$$

Try This Write as a single radical expression.

y. $x^{-\frac{2}{3}}y^{\frac{1}{2}}z^{\frac{5}{6}}$ $\sqrt[6]{x^{-4}y^3z^5}$

z. $\frac{a^{\frac{1}{2}}b^{\frac{3}{8}}}{a^{\frac{1}{4}}b^{\frac{1}{8}}}$ $\sqrt[4]{ab}$

We have now seen four different methods of simplifying radical expressions.

Simplifying Radical Expressions

1. **Simplifying by factoring** Factor the radicand, looking for factors that are perfect powers.
2. **Rationalizing denominators** Multiply the radical expression by 1 to make the denominator a perfect power. Then simplify the expression.
3. **Collecting like radical terms** Use the distributive laws to collect terms with the same radicand and index.
4. **Using rational exponents** Convert to exponential notation and use the properties of exponents to simplify. Then convert back to radical notation.

7-5 EXERCISES

A

Simplify as shown. Then use Theorem 7-6 to simplify another way.

1. $\sqrt{(6a)^3}$ **2.** $\sqrt{(7y)^3}$ **3.** $(\sqrt[3]{16b^2})^2$ **4.** $(\sqrt[3]{25r^2})^2$

5. $\sqrt{(18a^2b)^3}$ **6.** $\sqrt{(12x^2y)^3}$ **7.** $(\sqrt[3]{12c^2d})^2$ **8.** $(\sqrt[3]{9x^2y})^2$

Write without rational exponents.

9. $x^{\frac{1}{4}}$ **10.** $y^{\frac{1}{5}}$ **11.** $(8)^{\frac{1}{3}}$ **12.** $(16)^{\frac{1}{2}}$ **13.** $(a^2b^2)^{\frac{1}{5}}$

14. $(x^3y^3)^{\frac{1}{4}}$ **15.** $a^{\frac{2}{3}}$ **16.** $b^{\frac{3}{2}}$ **17.** $16^{\frac{3}{4}}$ **18.** $4^{\frac{7}{2}}$

19. $(a^5t^3)^{\frac{1}{2}}$ **20.** $m^{\frac{5}{6}}$ **21.** $y^{\frac{7}{2}}$ **22.** $32^{\frac{3}{5}}$ **23.** $(m^3n^5)^{\frac{1}{4}}$

Write with rational exponents.

24. $\sqrt[3]{20}$ **25.** $\sqrt[3]{19}$ **26.** $\sqrt{17}$ **27.** $\sqrt{6}$

28. $\sqrt[4]{cd}$ **29.** $\sqrt[5]{xy}$ **30.** $\sqrt[5]{xy^2z}$ **31.** $\sqrt[7]{x^3y^2z^2}$

32. $(\sqrt{3mn})^3$ **33.** $(\sqrt[3]{7xy})^4$ **34.** $(\sqrt[7]{8x^2y})^5$ **35.** $(\sqrt[6]{2a^5b})^7$

36. $(\sqrt[4]{16xy})^5$ **37.** $(\sqrt[6]{12ab})^3$ **38.** $(\sqrt[8]{2x^4y^6})^3$ **39.** $(\sqrt[7]{3a^4b^3})^4$

Write with positive exponents.

40. $x^{-\frac{1}{3}}$ **41.** $y^{-\frac{1}{4}}$ **42.** $(2rs)^{-\frac{3}{4}}$ **43.** $(5xy)^{-\frac{5}{6}}$

44. $\left(\frac{1}{10}\right)^{-\frac{2}{3}}$ **45.** $\left(\frac{1}{8}\right)^{-\frac{3}{4}}$ **46.** $\frac{1}{x^{-\frac{2}{3}}}$ **47.** $\frac{1}{x^{-\frac{5}{6}}}$

Use the properties of exponents to simplify.

48. $5^{\frac{3}{4}} \cdot 5^{\frac{1}{8}}$ **49.** $11^{\frac{2}{3}} \cdot 11^{\frac{1}{2}}$ **50.** $\frac{7^{\frac{5}{8}}}{7^{\frac{3}{8}}}$ **51.** $\frac{9^{\frac{9}{11}}}{9^{\frac{7}{11}}}$

52. $\frac{8.3^{\frac{3}{4}}}{8.3^{\frac{2}{5}}}$ **53.** $\frac{3.9^{\frac{3}{5}}}{3.9^{\frac{1}{4}}}$ **54.** $(10^{\frac{3}{5}})^{\frac{2}{5}}$ **55.** $(5^{\frac{5}{4}})^{\frac{3}{7}}$

Assignment Guide

Algebra: Day 1: 1 – 39 e/o, MR
Day 2: 40 – 75 e/o

Alg w/Finite or Trig: Day 1: 1 – 47 e/o, MR
Day 2: 48 – 86 e/o, 87

Comprehensive: Day 1: 1 – 47 e/o, MR
Day 2: 48–86 e/o, 87–91

ADDITIONAL ANSWERS

Exercises

1. $6a\sqrt{6a}$
2. $7y\sqrt{7y}$
3. $4b\sqrt[3]{4b}$
4. $5r\sqrt[3]{5r}$
5. $54a^3b\sqrt{2b}$
6. $24x^3y\sqrt{3y}$
7. $2c\sqrt[3]{18cd^2}$
8. $3x\sqrt[3]{3xy^2}$
9. $\sqrt[4]{x}$
10. $\sqrt[5]{y}$
11. 2
12. 4
13. $\sqrt[5]{a^2b^2}$
14. $\sqrt[4]{x^3y^3}$
15. $\sqrt[3]{a^2}$
16. $b\sqrt{b}$
17. 8
18. 128
19. $\sqrt{a^5t^3}$
20. $\sqrt[6]{m^5}$
21. $\sqrt[2]{y^7}$
22. 8
23. $\sqrt[4]{m^3n^5}$
24. $20^{1/3}$
25. $19^{1/3}$
26. $17^{1/2}$
27. $6^{1/2}$
28. $(cd)^{1/4}$
29. $(xy)^{1/5}$
30. $(xy^2z)^{1/5}$
31. $(x^3y^2z^2)^{1/7}$
32. $(3mn)^{3/2}$
33. $(7xy)^{4/3}$
34. $(8x^2y)^{5/7}$
35. $(2a^5b)^{7/6}$
36. $(16xy)^{5/4}$ or $32(xy)^{5/4}$
37. $(12ab)^{1/2}$ or $2(3ab)^{1/2}$
38. $(2x^4y^6)^{3/8}$
39. $(3a^4b^3)^{4/7}$
40. $\frac{1}{x^{1/3}}$
41. $\frac{1}{y^{1/4}}$
42. $\frac{1}{(2rs)^{3/4}}$
43. $\frac{1}{(5xy)^{5/6}}$
44. $10^{2/3}$
45. $8^{3/4}$
46. $x^{2/3}$
47. $x^{5/6}$
48. $5^{7/8}$
49. $11^{7/6}$
50. $7^{1/4}$
51. $9^{2/11}$
52. $8.3^{7/20}$
53. $3.9^{7/20}$
54. $10^{6/25}$
55. $5^{15/28}$

56. $\sqrt[3]{a^2}$
57. $\sqrt[3]{y}$
58. $2y^2$
59. x^2y^3
60. $2c^2d^3$
61. $2x^3y^4$
62. $\frac{m^2n^4}{2}$
63. $\frac{x^3y^4}{2}$
64. $\sqrt[4]{r^2s}$
65. $3ab^3$
66. $\sqrt{2ts}$
67. $3x^2y^2$
68. $\sqrt[6]{x^5 - 4x^4 + 4x^3}$
69. $\sqrt[4]{3xy^2 + 24xy + 48x}$
70. $\sqrt[6]{a + b}$
71. $\sqrt[12]{(x + y)^{-1}}$
72. $\sqrt[12]{a^8b^9}$
73. $\sqrt[12]{x^4y^3z^2}$
74. $\sqrt[4]{st^4}$
75. $\sqrt[5]{xy^5}$
76. $\frac{\sqrt{xy}}{xy}$
77. $\sqrt{(a^2 - b^2)}$
78. $x + y$
79. $\frac{\sqrt{a - b}}{(a - b)^2}$
80. $\sqrt{x^2 - y^2}$
81. $\frac{1}{a + 2b}$
82. $x^{1/20}$
83. $a^{2/15}$
84. $(c + 1)^{2/3}$
85. $(x + 6)^{1/2}$
86. $[(x + y)^{1/2} + (x - y)^{1/2}](x^2 - y^2)^{-1/2}$
87. Answers may vary. Should include the idea that $a^{\frac{m}{n}} \cdot a^{-\frac{m}{n}} = 1$

Mixed Review

92. Yes
93. No
94. No
95. $4x^3 + 3x^2$
96. $6x^{10}$

Write an exponential expression. Then simplify, if possible. Write radical notation for the answer, if appropriate.

56. $\sqrt[6]{a^4}$ **57.** $\sqrt[6]{y^2}$ **58.** $\sqrt[3]{8y^6}$ **59.** $\sqrt{x^4y^6}$

60. $\sqrt[5]{32c^{10}d^{15}}$ **61.** $\sqrt[4]{16x^{12}y^{16}}$ **62.** $\sqrt[6]{\frac{m^{12}n^{24}}{64}}$ **63.** $\sqrt[5]{\frac{x^{15}y^{20}}{32}}$

64. $\sqrt[8]{r^4s^2}$ **65.** $\sqrt[3]{27a^3b^9}$ **66.** $\sqrt[12]{64t^6s^6}$ **67.** $\sqrt[4]{81x^8y^8}$

Write as a single radical expression.

68. $\sqrt{x}\sqrt[3]{x - 2}$ **69.** $\sqrt[4]{3x}\sqrt{y + 4}$ **70.** $\frac{\sqrt[3]{(a + b)^2}}{\sqrt{(a + b)}}$ **71.** $\frac{\sqrt[3]{(x + y)^2}}{\sqrt[4]{(x + y)^3}}$

72. $a^{\frac{2}{3}} \cdot b^{\frac{3}{4}}$ **73.** $x^{\frac{1}{3}} \cdot y^{\frac{1}{4}} \cdot z^{\frac{1}{6}}$ **74.** $\frac{s^{\frac{7}{12}} \cdot t^{\frac{5}{6}}}{s^{\frac{1}{3}} \cdot t^{-\frac{1}{6}}}$ **75.** $\frac{x^{\frac{8}{15}} \cdot y^{\frac{4}{5}}}{x^{\frac{1}{3}} \cdot y^{-\frac{1}{5}}}$

B

Simplify. Write without rational exponents.

76. $\frac{1}{x^{\frac{1}{2}}} \cdot \frac{1}{y^{\frac{1}{2}}}$ **77.** $\frac{(a + b)^{\frac{1}{2}}}{(a - b)^{-\frac{1}{2}}}$

78. $(x^2 + 2xy + y^2)^{\frac{1}{3}}(x + y)^{\frac{1}{3}}$ **79.** $(a^3 - 3a^2b + 3ab^2 - b^3)^{-\frac{1}{2}}$

80. $(x + y)^{\frac{1}{2}}(x - y)^{\frac{1}{2}}$ **81.** $\left(\frac{1}{a^{-2}} + 4ab + \frac{4}{b^{-2}}\right)^{-\frac{1}{2}}$

Simplify. Write with rational exponents.

82. $\sqrt[5]{\sqrt[4]{x}}$ **83.** $\sqrt[5]{\sqrt[3]{a^2}}$ **84.** $\sqrt[3]{c^2 + 2c + 1}$

85. $\frac{\sqrt{x^2 + 7x + 6}}{\sqrt{x + 1}}$ **86.** $\frac{1}{\sqrt{x + y}} + \frac{1}{\sqrt{x - y}}$

87. ***Critical Thinking*** Write a convincing argument that $a^{\frac{m}{n}}$ and $a^{-\frac{m}{n}}$ are reciprocals.

Challenge

The optimal length (L) of the letters of a message printed on pavement is given by the following formula, where d is the distance of a car from the lettering and h is the height of the eye above the surface of the road. Find L, given the values of d and h.

$$L = \frac{(0.00252)d^{2.27}}{h}$$

h
d
L

88. $h = 1$ m, $d = 60$ m 27.4 m **89.** $h = 0.9906$ m, $d = 75$ m 45.9 m

90. $h = 2.4$ m, $d = 80$ m 21.9 m **91.** $h = 1.1$ m, $d = 100$ m 79.4 m

Mixed Review

Determine whether these systems are dependent.

92. $3x + y = 5$; $2y = 10 - 6x$ **93.** $2y = x - 3$; $x = 2y - 3$ **94.** $2x + 4y = 6$; $-2y = 3 - x$

Simplify. **95.** $x^2 + x^3 + 2x^2 + 3x^3$ **96.** $x^2 \cdot x^3 \cdot 2x^2 \cdot 3x^3$

7-6 Solving Radical Equations

Master Grapher Worksheet 9, *Solving Radical Equations*, can be used for lesson closure.

The formula $V = 1.2\sqrt{h}$ is a radical equation that can be used to approximate the distance (V) in miles that a person can see to the horizon from a height of h feet.

The Principle of Powers

Objective: Solve radical equations.

Suppose the equation $a = b$ is true. When we square both sides we still get a true equation, $a^2 = b^2$.

Theorem 7-7

The Principle of Powers

For any natural number n, if $a = b$ is true, then $a^n = b^n$ is true.

EXAMPLES Solve.

1. $\sqrt{x} - 3 = 4$

$\sqrt{x} = 7$ Adding 3 to both sides

$x = 7^2$, or 49 Squaring both sides

Check: $\sqrt{x} - 3 = 4$

$\sqrt{49} - 3$	4
$7 - 3$	4
4	4 ✓

The solution is 49.

2. $\sqrt{x} = -3$

$(\sqrt{x})^2 = (-3)^2$ Using the principle of powers

$x = 9$

Check: $\sqrt{x} = -3$

$\sqrt{9}$	-3
3	-3

The number 9 does not check because the principal square root of a number is never negative. Hence the equation has no solution.

Try This Solve.

a. $\sqrt{x} - 7 = 3$ 100 **b.** $3 - \sqrt{x} = 12$ No solution

To solve a radical equation, first isolate a radical term on one side of the equation.

7-6

FIRST FIVE MINUTES

Simplify.

1. $25^{3/2}$ $(25^{1/2})^3 = 5^3 = 125$
2. $\sqrt[3]{8^2}$ $(\sqrt[3]{8})^2 = 2^2 = 4$
3. $(3a^2)^4$ $3^4(a^2)^4 = 81a^8$
4. $(8x^3)^{1/3}$ $8^{1/3}(x^3)^{1/3} = 2x$
5. $\sqrt[3]{a^2} \cdot \sqrt[3]{8a}$ $\sqrt[3]{a^2 \cdot 8a} = \sqrt[3]{8a^3} = 2a$

The Principle of Powers

Remind students that equivalent equations have the same solution sets. In Example 1 in the text, $\sqrt{x} - 3 = 4$ implies that $x = 49$, and, conversely, $x = 49$ implies that $\sqrt{x} - 3 = 4$. The converse is true, the equations are equivalent, and the equations have the same solution sets.

Key Questions

- If $a = b$, does $a^2 = b^2$? Yes
- If $a^2 = b^2$, does $a = b$? No; let $a = 3$, $b = -3$.

Chalkboard Examples

1. Solve.

$\sqrt{a} + 2 = 7$

$\sqrt{a} = 5$

$(\sqrt{a})^2 = 5^2$

$a = 25$

Check: $\sqrt{a} + 2 = 7$

$\sqrt{25} + 2$	7
$5 + 2$	7
7	7 ✓

The solution is 25.

2. $3\sqrt{x} = 2\sqrt{x} - 1$
$3\sqrt{x} - 2\sqrt{x} = -1$
$\sqrt{x} = -1$
$x = 1$
Check: $3\sqrt{x} = 2\sqrt{x} - 1$

$3\sqrt{1}$	$2\sqrt{1} - 1$
$3 \cdot 1$	$2 \cdot 1 - 1$
3	1

There is no real solution.

3. $x - 5 = \sqrt{18 - 2x}$
$(x - 5)^2 = 18 - 2x$
$x^2 - 10x + 25 = 18 - 2x$
$x^2 - 8x + 7 = 0$
$(x - 1)(x - 7) = 0$
$x = 1$ or $x = 7$
1 does not check in the original equation; 7 does check in the original equation. The solution is 7.

4. $\sqrt{3x + 3} + \sqrt{x + 2} = 5$
$\sqrt{3x + 3} = 5 - \sqrt{x + 2}$
$(\sqrt{3x + 3})^2 = (5 - \sqrt{x + 2})^2$
$3x + 3 = 25 - 10\sqrt{x + 2} + x + 2$
$10\sqrt{x + 2} = 24 - 2x$
$5\sqrt{x + 2} = 12 - x$
$(5\sqrt{x + 2})^2 = (12 - x)^2$
$25(x + 2) = 144 - 24x + x^2$
$25x + 50 = 144 - 24x + x^2$
$0 = 94 - 49x + x^2$
$0 = (x - 2)(x - 47)$
$x = 2$ or $x = 47$
2 checks in the original equation; 47 does not check. The solution is 2.

EXAMPLE 3 Solve $x = \sqrt{x + 7} + 5$.

$$x - 5 = \sqrt{x + 7}$$ Isolating the radical

$$(x - 5)^2 = (\sqrt{x + 7})^2$$ Using the principle of powers; squaring both sides

$$x^2 - 10x + 25 = x + 7$$

$$x^2 - 11x + 18 = 0$$

$$(x - 9)(x - 2) = 0$$ Factoring

$$x = 9 \text{ or } x = 2$$ Using the principle of zero products

Check: $x - 5 = \sqrt{x + 7}$

$9 - 5$	$\sqrt{9 + 7}$
4	$\sqrt{16}$
4	4 ✓

Check: $x - 5 = \sqrt{x + 7}$

$2 - 5$	$\sqrt{2 + 7}$
-3	$\sqrt{9}$
-3	3

Since 9 checks but 2 does not, the solution is 9.

Note that 2 is a solution to the equation that resulted from squaring both sides. It is not a solution of the *original* equation. Such numbers are extraneous roots.

A radical term may remain after squaring both sides. The same procedures may be used again when this occurs.

EXAMPLE 4 Solve.

$$\sqrt{2x - 5} = 1 + \sqrt{x - 3}$$

$$(\sqrt{2x - 5})^2 = (1 + \sqrt{x - 3})^2$$ One radical is already isolated; squaring both sides

$$2x - 5 = 1 + 2\sqrt{x - 3} + (x - 3)$$

$$x - 3 = 2\sqrt{x - 3}$$ Isolating the remaining radical

$$(x - 3)^2 = (2\sqrt{x - 3})^2$$ Squaring both sides again

$$x^2 - 6x + 9 = 4(x - 3)$$

$$x^2 - 10x + 21 = 0$$

$$x = 7 \text{ or } x = 3$$ 7 and 3 check and are the solutions

Try This Solve.

c. $\sqrt{x} - \sqrt{x - 5} = 1$ 9

d. $\sqrt{3x + 1} = 1 + \sqrt{x + 4}$ 5

Problem Solving

Objective: Solve problems with radicals.

EXAMPLE 5

The formula $V = 1.2\sqrt{h}$ is a radical equation that approximates the distance (V) in miles that a person can see to the horizon from a height of h feet. Find a formula to approximate height. How high is a person who can see 72 miles to the horizon?

$$V = 1.2\sqrt{h}$$

$$V^2 = (1.2\sqrt{h})^2 \quad \text{Squaring both sides}$$

$$V^2 = 1.44h$$

$$\frac{V^2}{1.44} = h \quad \text{Solving for } h$$

Substituting 72 for V, $h = \frac{72^2}{1.44} = \frac{5184}{1.44} = 3600$

The person is at a height of 3600 feet.

Try This See Additional Answers.

e. The formula $S = \pi r\sqrt{r^2 + h^2}$ gives the surface area of a cone, given its radius and height. Solve the formula for h. What is h when $S = 15\pi$ and $r = 3$?

7-6 EXERCISES

A

Solve.

1. $\sqrt{2x - 3} = 1$ 2
2. $\sqrt{x + 3} = 6$ 33
3. $\sqrt{y + 1} - 5 = 8$ 168
4. $\sqrt{x - 2} - 7 = -4$ 11
5. $\sqrt[3]{x + 5} = 2$ 3
6. $\sqrt[3]{x - 2} = 3$ 29
7. $\sqrt[4]{y - 3} = 2$ 19
8. $\sqrt[4]{x + 3} = 3$ 78
9. $\sqrt{3y + 1} = 9$ $\frac{80}{3}$
10. $\sqrt{2y + 1} = 13$ 84
11. $3\sqrt{x} = 6$ 4
12. $8\sqrt{y} = 2$ $\frac{1}{16}$
13. $\sqrt[3]{x} = -3$ −27
14. $\sqrt[3]{y} = -4$ −64
15. $\sqrt{y + 3} - 20 = 0$ 397
16. $\sqrt{x + 4} - 11 = 0$ 117
17. $\sqrt{x + 2} = -4$ No solution
18. $\sqrt{y - 3} = -2$ No solution
19. $8 = \frac{1}{\sqrt{x}}$ $\frac{1}{64}$
20. $3 = \frac{1}{\sqrt{y}}$ $\frac{1}{9}$
21. $\sqrt[3]{6x + 9} + 8 = 5$ −6
22. $\sqrt[3]{3y + 6} + 2 = 3$ $-\frac{5}{3}$
23. $\sqrt{3y + 1} = \sqrt{2y + 6}$ 5
24. $\sqrt{5x - 3} = \sqrt{2x + 3}$ 2
25. $2\sqrt{1 - x} = \sqrt{5}$ $-\frac{1}{4}$
26. $2\sqrt{2y - 3} = \sqrt{4y}$ 3
27. $2\sqrt{t - 1} = \sqrt{3t - 1}$ 3
28. $\sqrt{y + 10} = 3\sqrt{2y + 3}$ −1
29. $\sqrt{y - 5} + \sqrt{y} = 5$ 9
30. $\sqrt{x - 9} + \sqrt{x} = 1$ No solution
31. $3 + \sqrt{z - 6} = \sqrt{z + 9}$ 7
32. $\sqrt{4x - 3} = 2 + \sqrt{2x - 5}$ 7, 3
33. $\sqrt{20 - x} + 8 = \sqrt{9 - x} + 11$ $\frac{80}{9}$
34. $4 + \sqrt{10 - x} = 6 + \sqrt{4 - x}$ $\frac{15}{4}$
35. $\sqrt{x + 2} + \sqrt{3x + 4} = 2$ −1
36. $\sqrt{6x + 7} - \sqrt{3x + 3} = 1$ $\frac{1}{3}$, −1
37. $\sqrt{4y + 1} - \sqrt{y - 2} = 3$ 6, 2
38. $\sqrt{y + 15} - \sqrt{2y + 7} = 1$ 1
39. $\sqrt{3x - 5} + \sqrt{2x + 3} + 1 = 0$ No solution
40. $\sqrt{2m - 3} = \sqrt{m + 7} - 2$ 2

41. The formula $v = \sqrt{2gs}$ represents the velocity (v) of an object that has fallen a distance of s feet, where g is acceleration due to gravity. Solve the formula for s, and find s for a falling object with velocity $32g$. $s = \frac{v^2}{2g}$; $512g$

Problem Solving

Chalkboard Example

1. The formula $V = \frac{4}{3}\pi r^3$ gives the volume of a sphere. Find the radius of a sphere with volume 905 cm³.
Solve for r.

$$r^3 = V \cdot \frac{3}{4\pi}$$

$$r = \sqrt[3]{\frac{3V}{4\pi}}$$

Substitute 905 for V.

$$r = \sqrt[3]{\frac{3 \cdot 905}{4 \cdot 3.14}}$$

$$r \approx \sqrt[3]{216}$$

$$r \approx 6 \text{ cm}$$

LESSON QUIZ

Solve.

1. $\sqrt{3x + 4} = 5$

$$3x + 4 = 25$$
$$3x = 21$$
$$x = 7$$

2. $x - 2 = \sqrt{2x - 1}$

$$(x - 2)^2 = 2x - 1$$
$$x^2 - 4x + 4 = 2x - 1$$
$$x^2 - 6x + 5 = 0$$
$$(x - 1)(x - 5) = 0$$
$$x = 1 \text{ or } x = 5$$

1 does not check; 5 checks.
The solution is 5.

3. $\sqrt{x + 7} - \sqrt{x - 1} = 2$

$$\sqrt{x + 7} = \sqrt{x - 1} + 2$$
$$(\sqrt{x + 7})^2 = (\sqrt{x - 1} + 2)^2$$
$$x + 7 = x - 1 + 4\sqrt{x - 1} + 4$$
$$4 = 4\sqrt{x - 1}$$
$$1 = \sqrt{x - 1}$$
$$1 = x - 1$$
$$2 = x$$

2 checks. The solution is 2.

Assignment Guide

Algebra: 1–42 e/o, MR

Alg w/Finite or Trig: 1–42 m3, 43–49 e/o, 50, MR

Comprehensive: 1–49 m3, 50–53, MR

ADDITIONAL ANSWERS

Try This

e. $h = \frac{1}{\pi r}\sqrt{s^2 - \pi^2 r^4}$

$h = 4$

Exercises

42. $Q = \frac{10^4 \times R^2}{3.334276}3.334276 \approx 2999.15R^2$; 6748.09 coulombs

50. Use a calculator to estimate, or solve the equation $x = \sqrt{6 + x}$. The solution is 3.

51. Let $a = b$.
$a^n = a \cdot a^{n-1}$
Substituting b for a, $a^n = b \cdot a^{n-1}$. Continuing to factor an a out of the right side and substituting b, $a^n = b \cdot a^{n-1} = b^2 \cdot a^{n-2} = \ldots b^{n-1} \cdot a = b^n$. So if $a = b$, $a^n = b^n$.

52. $y = 2$

53. No solution

Mixed Review

54. 6

55. $2|y|\sqrt{3}$

56. $(y - 5)\sqrt[3]{y - 5}$

57. 4

42. The radius of a Van de Graaff generator that can collect a maximum charge of Q coulombs on its surface is given by $R = 1.826 \times 10^{-2}\sqrt{Q}$. Solve the formula for Q, and find Q for a generator with a radius of 1.5 m.

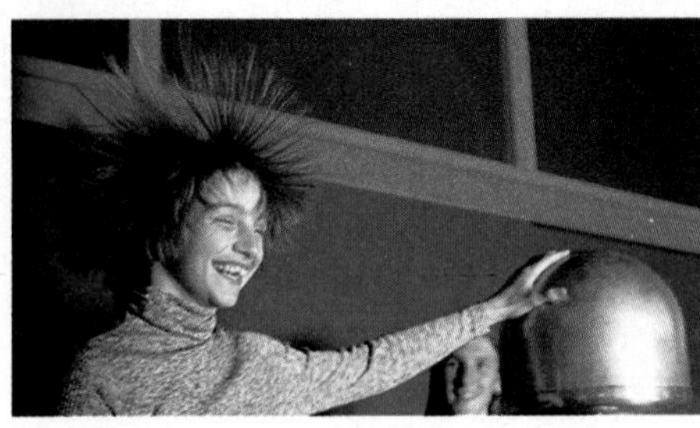

B

Solve.

43. $x^{\frac{1}{3}} + 5 = 7$ 8 **44.** $(x - 5)^{\frac{1}{5}} - 3 = 7$ $5 + 10^5$ **45.** $(x - 5)^{\frac{2}{3}} = 2$ $5 \pm 2\sqrt{2}$

46. $\frac{x + \sqrt{x + 1}}{x - \sqrt{x + 1}} = \frac{5}{11}$ $-\frac{8}{9}$ **47.** $\sqrt{x + 2} - \sqrt{x - 2} = \sqrt{2x}$ 2

48. $2\sqrt{x + 3} = \sqrt{x} + \sqrt{x + 8}$ 1 **49.** $\sqrt[3]{2x - 1} = \sqrt[6]{x + 1}$ $\frac{5}{4}$

50. ***Critical Thinking*** Consider the equation $x = \sqrt{6 + \sqrt{6 + \sqrt{6 + \sqrt{6 + \ldots}}}}$ where the radicals continue infinitely. Design a plan for estimating or finding the solution.

Challenge

51. Prove Theorem 7-7.

Solve.

52. $\sqrt{y + \sqrt{2y}} = 2$ **53.** $\sqrt{\sqrt{x + 25}} - \sqrt{x} = 5$

Mixed Review

Simplify. **54.** $\sqrt[3]{216}$ **55.** $\sqrt{12y^2}$ **56.** $\sqrt[3]{(y - 5)^2}$ **57.** $\sqrt{2} \cdot \sqrt{8}$

Using a Calculator: Finding Roots

If your calculator has an $\sqrt[x]{y}$ key, you can find the k-th root of a number.

To find $\sqrt[9]{0.01}$, press:

0.01 $\sqrt[x]{y}$ 9 = → 0.5994843

You can also find k-th roots using rational exponents and the y^x key.

To find $\sqrt[5]{83}$, recall that $\sqrt[5]{83} = 83^{\frac{1}{5}}$. Press:

83 y^x (1 ÷ 5) = → 2.4200014

For additional calculator practice, see Calculator Worksheet 11.

7-7 Imaginary and Complex Numbers

Imaginary Numbers

Objective: Express the square root of negative numbers and their products in terms of i.

In the set of real numbers, negative numbers do not have square roots. An equation like $x^2 = -1$ has no solution. Imaginary numbers were invented so that negative numbers would have square roots and certain equations would have solutions. These numbers were devised using an imaginary unit named i and the agreement that $i^2 = -1$, or $i = \sqrt{-1}$.

We assume that i acts like a real number in other respects. Square roots of all negative numbers can then be expressed as a product of i and a real number.

EXAMPLES Express these numbers in terms of i.

1. $\sqrt{-5} = \sqrt{-1 \cdot 5}$ Factoring the radicand

$= \sqrt{-1}\sqrt{5}$ Using Theorem 7-5

$= i\sqrt{5}$, or $\sqrt{5}i$ Using the definition of i

2. $-\sqrt{-7} = -\sqrt{-1 \cdot 7} = -\sqrt{-1}\sqrt{7} = -i\sqrt{7}$

3. $\sqrt{-99} = \sqrt{-1 \cdot 9 \cdot 11} = i\sqrt{9}\sqrt{11} = 3i\sqrt{11}$

Try This Express these numbers in terms of i.

a. $\sqrt{-7}$ $i\sqrt{7}$ **b.** $-\sqrt{-36}$ $-6i$ **c.** $\sqrt{-160}$ $4i\sqrt{10}$

Definition

The **imaginary numbers** consist of all numbers bi, where b is a real number and i is the imaginary unit, with the property that $i^2 = -1$.

The first four powers of i establish an important pattern and should be memorized.

Powers of *i*

$i^1 = i$ $i^2 = -1$ $i^3 = -i$ $i^4 = 1$

7-7

FIRST FIVE MINUTES

Solve.

1. $\sqrt{x+1} = 5$
   $x + 1 = 25$
   $x = 24$
   24 checks. The solution is 24.
2. $x - 1 = \sqrt{2x+6}$
   $x^2 - 2x + 1 = 2x + 6$
   $x^2 - 4x - 5 = 0$
   $(x+1)(x-5) = 0$
   $x = -1$ or $x = 5$
   -1 does not check; 5 checks. The solution is 5.
3. $x^2 = -1$
   There is no real solution.

Imaginary Numbers

You may want to review the different sets of numbers: natural numbers, whole numbers, integers, rational numbers, irrational numbers, and real numbers.

Point out that i precedes the radical sign in this book, to emphasize that it is not placed under the radical sign.

Some students may benefit from seeing the derivation of powers of i.

$i^1 = i$

$i^2 = (\sqrt{-1})^2 = -1$

$i^3 = i^2 \cdot i = -1 \cdot i = -i$

$i^4 = i^2 \cdot i^2 = -1 \cdot -1 = 1$

or $i^4 = i \cdot i^3 = i(-i) = -i^2 = 1$

Math Point
Imaginary numbers have many important applications, particularly in engineering and electronics.

Avoiding Common Errors

Many students forget that $\sqrt{a} \cdot \sqrt{b} = \sqrt{ab}$ is true only for nonnegative a and b. For instance, students may incorrectly solve Example 6 as follows.

$-\sqrt{-3} \cdot \sqrt{-7}$

$= -\sqrt{-3 \cdot -7}$

$= -\sqrt{21}$

Key Questions

- What powers of i equal 1?
  4, 8, . . . , $4n$
- What does i^{37} equal?
  i

To multiply imaginary numbers or an imaginary number by a real number, it is important first to express the imaginary numbers in terms of i.

EXAMPLES Multiply.

4. $47i \cdot 2 = 94i$

5. $\sqrt{-5} \cdot 2i = i\sqrt{5} \cdot 2i = 2i^2\sqrt{5} = -2\sqrt{5}$

6. $-\sqrt{-3} \cdot \sqrt{-7} = -i\sqrt{3} \cdot i\sqrt{7} = -i^2\sqrt{21} = -(-1)\sqrt{21} = \sqrt{21}$

Try This Multiply.

d. $6i \cdot 3i$ -18 **e.** $\sqrt{-3} \cdot 3i$ $-3\sqrt{3}$ **f.** $\sqrt{-3} \cdot \sqrt{-6}$ $-3\sqrt{2}$

Complex Numbers

Objective: Add or subtract complex numbers.

To construct a complete number system, we shall define sums of real and imaginary numbers. We call these complex numbers.

Definition

The **complex numbers** consist of all sums $a + bi$, where a and b are real numbers and i is the imaginary unit. The real part is a, and the imaginary part is bi.

Every real number a is a complex number because $a = a + 0 \cdot i$. Thus the complex numbers are an extension of the real number system. All imaginary numbers bi are also complex because $bi = 0 + bi$. We show these relationships with the following diagram.

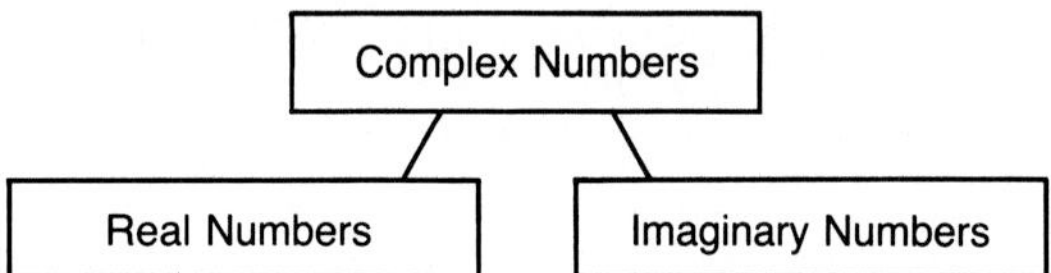

We assume that i acts like a real number, obeying the commutative, associative, and distributive properties. Thus to add or subtract complex numbers, we can treat i as we would treat a variable. We combine like terms.

EXAMPLES Add or subtract.

7. $7i + 9i = (7 + 9)i = 16i$

8. $(-5 + 6i) + (2 - 11i) = -5 + 2 + 6i - 11i = -3 - 5i$

9. $(2 + 3i) - (4 + 2i) = 2 + 3i - 4 - 2i = -2 + i$

Try This Add or subtract.

g. $(-2 + 3i) + (2 - 3i)$ 0 **h.** $3i - 4i$ $-i$ **i.** $(-4 + 10i) - (-2 + 3i)$ $-2 + 7i$

Chalkboard Examples

Express these numbers in terms of i.

1. $\sqrt{-4}$
   $\sqrt{-4} = \sqrt{4(-1)} = 2\sqrt{-1} = 2i$
2. $-\sqrt{-3}$
   $-\sqrt{3(-1)} = -\sqrt{3} \cdot \sqrt{-1}$
   $= -i\sqrt{3}$
3. $\sqrt{-12}$
   $\sqrt{4 \cdot 3 \cdot (-1)} = 2i\sqrt{3}$

Multiply.

4. $3 \cdot 2i$
   $6i$
5. $\sqrt{2} \cdot i\sqrt{10}$
   $i\sqrt{20} = i\sqrt{4 \cdot 5} = 2i\sqrt{5}$
6. $\sqrt{-2} \cdot \sqrt{-3}$
   $i\sqrt{2} \cdot i\sqrt{3} = i^2\sqrt{6} = -\sqrt{6}$

Complex Numbers

Emphasize that in the expression $a + bi$, bi is the imaginary part but b is a real number. In $3 - 2i$, for example, b is -2, not $-2i$.

Chalkboard Examples

Add.

1. $3i + 4i$
   $7i$
2. $(2i + 1) + (5i + 3)$
   $7i + 4$

Subtract.

3. $9i - 2i$
   $7i$
4. $(6i + 4) - (2i + 1)$
   $4i + 3$
5. $(-4i - 3) - (2i + 5)$
   $-6i - 8$

LESSON QUIZ

1. Express $\sqrt{-7}$ in terms of i.
   $i\sqrt{7}$
2. Multiply $12i \cdot 3i$.
   $36i^2 = -36$
3. Add.
   $(8i + 4) + (i + 3)$
   $9i + 7$
4. Subtract.
   $(7i + 8) - (3i + 2)$
   $4i + 6$
5. Subtract.
   $(-6i + 6) - (-2i - 2)$
   $-4i + 8$

7-7 EXERCISES

A

Express these numbers in terms of i.

1. $\sqrt{-2}$ $i\sqrt{2}$ **2.** $\sqrt{-3}$ $i\sqrt{3}$ **3.** $\sqrt{-36}$ $6i$ **4.** $\sqrt{-25}$ $5i$

5. $-\sqrt{-9}$ $-3i$ **6.** $-\sqrt{-16}$ $-4i$ **7.** $\sqrt{-128}$ $8i\sqrt{2}$ **8.** $\sqrt{-12}$ $2i\sqrt{3}$

9. $\sqrt{-\frac{9}{16}}$ $\frac{3}{4}i$ **10.** $\sqrt{-\frac{25}{4}}$ $\frac{5}{2}i$ **11.** $-\sqrt{-80}$ $-4i\sqrt{5}$ **12.** $-\sqrt{-75}$ $-5i\sqrt{3}$

Multiply.

13. $23i \cdot 4$ $92i$ **14.** $-12i \cdot (-3)$ $36i$ **15.** $\sqrt{-3} \cdot 4i$ $-4\sqrt{3}$

16. $\sqrt{-5} \cdot 6i$ $-6\sqrt{5}$ **17.** $\sqrt{-2}\sqrt{-3}$ $-\sqrt{6}$ **18.** $\sqrt{-5}\sqrt{-3}$ $-\sqrt{15}$

19. $-\sqrt{-2}\sqrt{-18}$ 6 **20.** $-\sqrt{-3}\sqrt{-15}$ $3\sqrt{5}$ **21.** $\sqrt{-3}\sqrt{-15}$ $-3\sqrt{5}$

22. $\sqrt{-10}\sqrt{-2}$ $-2\sqrt{5}$ **23.** $-\sqrt{-10}(-\sqrt{-10})$ -10 **24.** $-\sqrt{-7}(-\sqrt{-7})$ -7

Add or subtract.

25. $-7i + 10i$ $3i$ **26.** $4i + (-10i)$ $-6i$

27. $(3 + 2i) + (5 - i)$ $8 + i$ **28.** $(-2 + 3i) + (7 + 8i)$ $5 + 11i$

29. $(4 - 3i) + (5 - 2i)$ $9 - 5i$ **30.** $2i - (4 - 3i)$ $-4 + 5i$

31. $3i - (5 - 2i)$ $-5 + 5i$ **32.** $(3 - i) - (5 + 2i)$ $-2 - 3i$

33. $(-2 + 8i) - (7 + 3i)$ $-9 + 5i$ **34.** $(4 - 2i) - (5 - 3i)$ $-1 + i$

B

Simplify. (Hint: $i^{31} = i^{28} \cdot i^3 = (i^4)^7 \cdot i^3$)

35. i^{13} i **36.** i^{20} 1 **37.** i^{18} -1 **38.** i^{27} $-i$

39. i^{99} $-i$ **40.** $i^{71} - i^{49}$ $-2i$ **41.** $i^{68} - i^{72} + i^{76} - i^{80}$ 0

42. ***Critical Thinking*** Write a formula for all powers of i that are equal to 1, to -1.

Challenge

Simplify.

43. i^{-1} **44.** i^{-2} **45.** i^{-3} **46.** i^{-4} **47.** i^{-99} **48.** i^{-27}

For any integer n, find i^{4n+a} when a takes on the following values.

49. 3 **50.** 2 **51.** 1 **52.** 0 **53.** -1 **54.** -2 **55.** -3

Mixed Review

Simplify. **56.** $\sqrt[3]{7} \cdot \sqrt[3]{5}$ **57.** $\sqrt{m+n} \cdot \sqrt{m-n}$ **58.** $\sqrt[4]{112m^5n^2}$

Divide. **59.** $\frac{x^2 + x - 6}{x^2 + 3x - 10}$ **60.** $\frac{y^2 - 5y + 4}{y - 4}$ **61.** $\frac{x^2 - 4}{4x^2 + 13x + 3} \div \frac{x + 2}{x + 3}$

Solve. **62.** $x + \frac{8}{x} = 6$ **63.** $\frac{x + 2}{3x + 1} = \frac{2x - 3}{2x}$ **64.** $3x - \frac{2}{x} = 1$

Assignment Guide
Algebra: 1–34 e/o, MR

Alg w/Finite or Trig: 1–41 e/o, 42, MR

Comprehensive: 1–41 m3, 42, 43–55 e/o, MR

ADDITIONAL ANSWERS

Exercises

42. $i^{4k} = 1$ and $i^{4k-2} = -1$ for $k = 1, 2, 3, \ldots$
43. $-i$
44. -1
45. i
46. 1
47. i
48. i
49. $-i$
50. -1
51. i
52. 1
53. $-i$
54. -1
55. i

Mixed Review

56. $\sqrt[3]{35}$
57. $\sqrt{m^2 - n^2}$
58. $2|m|\sqrt[4]{7mn^2}$
59. $\frac{(x + 3)}{(x + 5)}$
60. $y - 1$
61. $\frac{x - 2}{4x + 1}$
62. 4, 2
63. $3, -\frac{1}{4}$
64. $1, -\frac{2}{3}$

7-8

FIRST FIVE MINUTES

1. Write using i.
   $-\sqrt{-11}$
   $-\sqrt{11(-1)} = -i\sqrt{11}$
2. Multiply.
   $i\sqrt{3} \cdot i\sqrt{7}$
   $i^2\sqrt{21} = -\sqrt{21}$
3. Add.
   $(6i - 2) + (2i + 7)$
   $8i + 5$
4. Subtract.
   $(8i - 2) - (3i + 4)$
   $5i - 6$

Graphing Complex Numbers

Emphasize that complex numbers do not have order. For example, it does not make sense to ask if $i > 1$. Complex numbers are two dimensional, and they are plotted on a two-dimensional coordinate system.

Chalkboard Examples

1. Graph.
   A: $2 + 0i$
   B: $2 + 5i$
   C: $3i$
   D: $-4 - 2i$

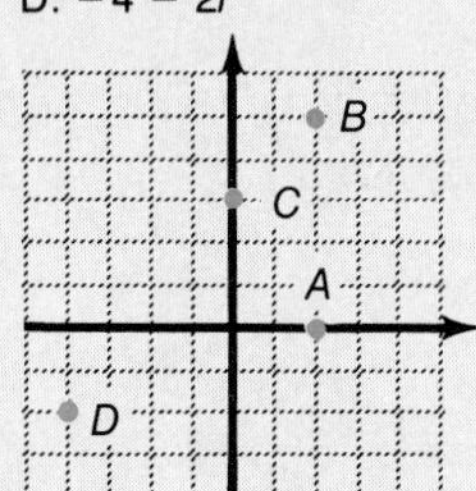

Absolute Value

Emphasize that the absolute value of a real number is its distance from the origin. You may want to point out the similarity among the distance formula, the Pythagorean theorem, and the absolute value of a complex number. All describe a relationship of the hypotenuse within a right triangle.

7-8 Complex Numbers and Graphing

Graphing Complex Numbers

Objective: Graph complex numbers in a plane.

The real numbers are graphed on a line. We graph a complex number, $a + bi$, in the same way we graph ordered pairs of real numbers, (a, b). In place of an x-axis we have a real axis, and in place of a y-axis we have an imaginary axis.

EXAMPLE 1 Graph.

A: $3 + 2i$
B: $-4 + 5i$
C: $-5 - 4i$
D: i (or $0 + i$)
E: 5 (or $5 + 0i$)

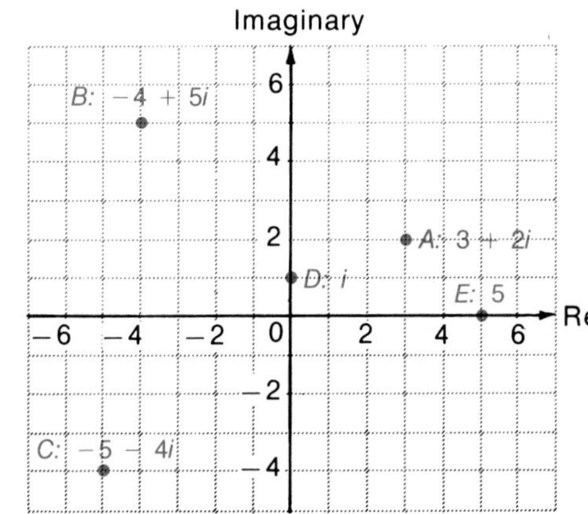

Horizontal distance corresponds to the real part of a complex number. Vertical distance corresponds to the imaginary part.

Try This Graph. See Selected Answers.

a. $5 - 3i$ **b.** $-3 + 4i$ **c.** $-5 - 2i$ **d.** $-5i$ **e.** -5

Absolute Value

Objective: Find absolute values of complex numbers.

We know the absolute value of a real number can be thought of as its distance from 0. We can think of the absolute value of a complex number in a similar manner.

From the graph at the right, we see that the length of the segment drawn from the origin to $a + bi$ is $\sqrt{a^2 + b^2}$. Note that this quantity is a real number. It is called the absolute value of $a + bi$ and is denoted $|a + bi|$.

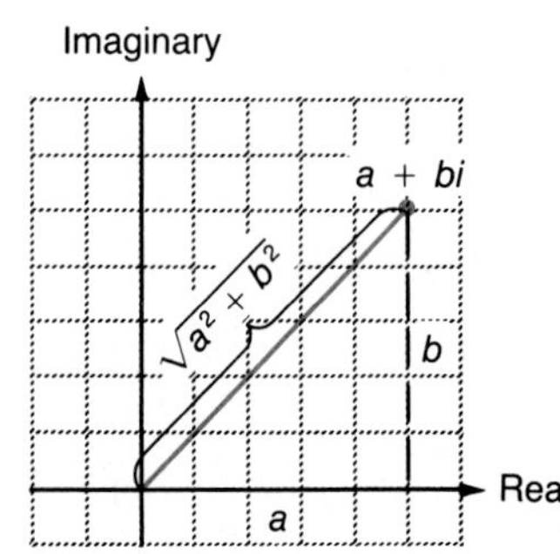

Definition

The **absolute value** of a complex number $a + bi$ is denoted $|a + bi|$ and is defined as $\sqrt{a^2 + b^2}$.

EXAMPLE 2 Find $|-3 + 4i|$.

$$|-3 + 4i| = \sqrt{(-3)^2 + 4^2} = \sqrt{9 + 16} = \sqrt{25} = 5$$

Try This Find the absolute values.

f. $|4 - 3i|$ 5 **g.** $|-12 - 5i|$ 13 **h.** $|1 + i|$ $\sqrt{2}$

7-8 EXERCISES

A

Graph.

1. $3 + 2i, 2 - 5i, -4 - 2i$
2. $3 - 4i, -5 + 3i, -2 - 3i$
3. $-4 + 2i, -3 - 4i, 2 - 3i$
4. $-5 + 4i, 3 - 2i, -5 + 5i$
5. $-2 - 5i, 5 + 3i, -3 - 4i$
6. $2 + 2i, -3 - 3i, 2 - 3i$

Find the absolute values.

7. $|-4 - 3i|$ 5 **8.** $|-3 - 4i|$ 5 **9.** $|8 + 15i|$ 17 **10.** $|7 - 24i|$ 25
11. $|1 - 3i|$ $\sqrt{10}$ **12.** $|-2 + i|$ $\sqrt{5}$ **13.** $|3i|$ 3 **14.** $|-2i|$ 2
15. $|c - di|$ $\sqrt{c^2 + d^2}$ **16.** $|-c + di|$ $\sqrt{c^2 + d^2}$ **17.** $|4c + 2i|$ $2\sqrt{4c^2 + 1}$ **18.** $|-4p - 3qi|$ $\sqrt{16p^2 + 9q^2}$

B

19. Graph.

a. $\{a + bi \mid a \leq 3 \text{ and } b \leq 2\}$ **b.** $\{a + bi \mid |a + bi| \leq 3\}$
c. $\{a + bi \mid a = 3 \text{ and } |b| \geq 2\}$

20. Let $G = \{a + bi \mid |a + bi| \leq 4\}$. Which of these numbers are in G? b and d

a. $3 + 3i$ **b.** $3i$ **c.** $-4 + 3i$ **d.** i^5 **e.** $2 - 4i$ **f.** $6 + 2i$

21. ***Critical Thinking*** What happens to the absolute value of a complex number $a + bi$ if it is multiplied by i? Describe what happens to its graph.

Challenge

22. Show that for any complex number z, $|z| = |-z|$. (Hint: Let $z = a + bi$.)

Mixed Review

Simplify. **23.** $\sqrt{27}$ **24.** $\sqrt{45m^2}$ **25.** $\sqrt[3]{16a^3}$ **26.** $\sqrt[8]{(-2)^8}$

Factor. **27.** $a^3 + 27$ **28.** $m^3 - 8$ **29.** $x^3 - 12x^2 + 48x - 64$

Chalkboard Example

1. Find $|8 + 15i|$.
$\sqrt{8^2 + 15^2} = \sqrt{64 + 225}$
$= \sqrt{289} = 17$

LESSON QUIZ

1. Graph.
A: $3 + 4i$
B: $2 - 3i$
C: $-i$

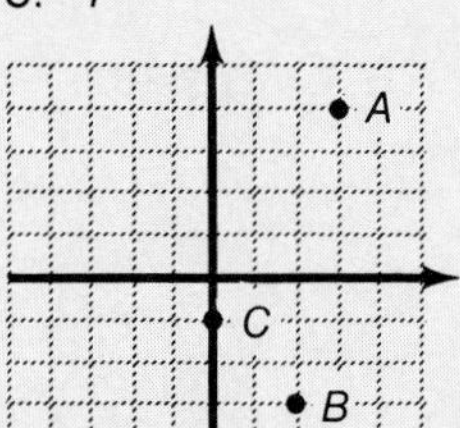

2. Calculate $|6 - 8i|$.
$\sqrt{6^2 + (-8)^2} = \sqrt{36 + 64}$
$= \sqrt{100} = 10$
3. Calculate $|5i|$.
$|0 + 5i| = \sqrt{0 + 25} = 5$

Assignment Guide
Algebra: 1 – 18 e/o, MR

Alg w/Finite or Trig: 1–20 e/o, 21, MR

Comprehensive: 1–20 e/o, 21, 22, MR

ADDITIONAL ANSWERS

Exercises

1–6, 19. See Teacher's Answer Section.

21. The absolute value does not change. The coordinates of the graph change from (a, b) to $(-b, a)$. (The point is rotated 90°.)

22. Let $z = a + bi$. Then $|z| = \sqrt{a^2 + b^2}$. $-z = -a - bi$. $|-z| = \sqrt{(-a)^2 + (-b)^2} = \sqrt{a^2 + b^2}$, so $|z| = |-z|$.

Mixed Review

23. $3\sqrt{3}$
24. $3|m|\sqrt{5}$
25. $2a\sqrt[3]{2}$
26. 2
27. $(a + 3)(a^2 - 3a + 9)$
28. $(m - 2)(m^2 + 2m + 4)$
29. $(x - 4)^3$

7-9

FIRST FIVE MINUTES

1. Add $(3 + 5i) + (3 - 5i)$.
   6
2. Simplify i^5.
   $i^4 i = 1i = i$
3. Calculate $|-3 + 4i|$.
   $\sqrt{(-3)^2 + 4^2} = \sqrt{25} = 5$

Equality for Complex Numbers

Key Questions

- Does $3 + 2i = 2i + 3$?
  Yes
- Does $-1 + i = 1 - i$? If not, which is greater?
  No; neither

Chalkboard Example

1. Solve for x and y.
   $5x + 6i = 10 + 2yi$
   $5x = 10$ and $6 = 2y$
   $x = 2$ and $y = 3$

Multiplying

Chalkboard Examples

Simplify.

1. $5i \cdot 2i$
   $10i^2 = -10$
2. $(2 + 5i) \cdot (3 + 4i)$
   $6 + 8i + 15i + 20i^2$
   $= 6 + 8i + 15i + 20(-1)$
   $= -14 + 23i$
3. $(1 + i) \cdot (1 - i)$
   $1 - i^2$
   $= 1 - (-1)$
   $= 2$

7-9 More About Complex Numbers

Equality for Complex Numbers

Objective: Solve equations with complex numbers.

Equality for complex numbers is the same as equality for real numbers. A sentence $a + bi = c + di$ says that $a + bi$ and $c + di$ represent the same number. For this to be true, a and c must be the same and b and d must be the same. Thus $a + bi = c + di$ when $a = c$ and $b = d$.

EXAMPLE 1 Solve for x and y.

Suppose that $3x + yi = 5x + 1 + 2i$. Find x and y.

We equate the real parts. We equate the imaginary parts.

$3x = 5x + 1$ $\qquad$ $yi = 2i$

$x = -\frac{1}{2}$ Solving $\qquad$ $y = 2$ Solving

Check:

$3x + yi$	$= 5x + 1 + 2i$
$3\left(-\frac{1}{2}\right) + (2)i$	$5\left(-\frac{1}{2}\right) + 1 + 2i$
$-\frac{3}{2} + 2i$	$-\frac{5}{2} + 1 + 2i$
$-\frac{3}{2} + 2i$	$-\frac{3}{2} + 2i$ ✓

Try This Solve for x and y.

a. Suppose $3x + 1 + (y + 2)i = 2x + 2yi$. $x = -1, y = 2$

Multiplying

Objective: Multiply complex numbers.

We multiply complex numbers as we would multiply monomials or binomials, treating the imaginary parts as like terms. Remember that $i^2 = -1$.

EXAMPLES Multiply.

2. $3i \cdot 4i = (3 \cdot 4)i^2$
$= 12(-1)$
$= -12$

3. $(7i)^2 = 7^2 i^2$
$= 49(-1)$
$= -49$

4. $(4 + 3i) \cdot (7 + 2i) = 28 + 8i + 21i + 6i^2$
$= 28 + (8i + 21i) + 6(-1)$ Since $i^2 = -1$
$= 28 + 29i - 6$
$= 22 + 29i$

Try This Multiply.

b. $5i \cdot 6i$ -30 **c.** $(10i)^2$ -100 **d.** $(-2 - 3i)(6 + 5i)$ $3 - 28i$

Complex Conjugates

Objective: Find conjugates of complex numbers.

Definition

The **conjugate** of $a + bi$ is $a - bi$, and the conjugate of $a - bi$ is $a + bi$.

EXAMPLES Find the conjugate of each number.

5. $3 + 4i$ The conjugate of $3 + 4i$ is $3 - 4i$.

6. $-4 - 7i$ The conjugate of $-4 - 7i$ is $-4 + 7i$.

7. $5i$ The conjugate of $5i$ is $-5i$, since $0 - 5i$ is the conjugate of $0 + 5i$.

8. 6 The conjugate of 6 is 6, since $6 - 0i$ is the conjugate of $6 + 0i$.

Try This Find the conjugate of each number.

e. $6 + 3i$ $6 - 3i$ **f.** $-9 - 5i$ $-9 + 5i$ **g.** $-7i$ $7i$ **h.** -8 -8

The product $(A + B)(A - B) = A^2 - B^2$ applies to complex numbers.

Theorem 7-8

The product of a nonzero complex number $a + bi$ and its conjugate $a - bi$ is the positive real number $a^2 + b^2$.

EXAMPLES Multiply.

9. $(5 + 7i)(5 - 7i) = 5^2 - (7i)^2$
$= 25 - (49i^2)$
$= 25 + 49$
$= 74$

10. $(a + bi)(a - bi) = a^2 - (bi)^2$
$= a^2 - b^2i^2$
$= a^2 + b^2$

Try This Multiply.

i. $(7 - 2i)(7 + 2i)$ 53 **j.** $(-3 + i)(-3 - i)$ 10 **k.** $(3p - 2qi)(3p + 2qi)$ $9p^2 + 4q^2$

Complex Conjugates

Point out that conjugates mirror each other across the real axis.

After working Example 10, you may want to point out that complex numbers enable us to factor a sum of squares. For example,

$x^2 + 49 = (x + 7i)(x - 7i)$

Math Point

The importance and necessity of complex numbers was recognized around 1550, when Jerome Cardan published a method for solving cubic equations such as $x^3 = 15x + 4$.

Two hundred and fifty years later, around 1800, Wessel, Argand, and Gauss all independently discovered that imaginary numbers could be viewed as points or arrows in the plane. A few years later, Sir William Rowan Hamilton found a way to define the imaginary number system as pairs of ordinary numbers, without referring to $\sqrt{-1}$. This took the final mystery out of imaginary numbers.

Chalkboard Examples

Find the conjugate.

1. $7 + 5i$
   $7 - 5i$
2. $3 - 8i$
   $3 + 8i$
3. i
   $-i$
4. 7
   7

Multiply.

5. $(4 + 2i)(4 - 2i)$
   $16 - (2i)^2$
   $= 16 - 4(-1)$
   $= 20$
6. $(x + yi)(x - yi)$
   $x^2 - y^2i^2 = x^2 + y^2$

Division and Reciprocals

As a comparison, you may want to rewrite Example 11 as

$$\frac{-5 + 9\sqrt{-1}}{1 - \sqrt{-1}}$$

and then solve by rationalizing the denominator.

Chalkboard Examples

Divide.

1. $\frac{2}{i}$

$\frac{2i}{i \cdot i} = \frac{2i}{-1} = -2i$

2. $\frac{1 + 2i}{3 + 4i}$

$\frac{(1 + 2i)(3 - 4i)}{(3 + 4i)(3 - 4i)}$

$= \frac{11 + 2i}{25} = \frac{11}{25} + \frac{2i}{25}$

3. Find the reciprocal of $3 - 4i$.

$\frac{1}{3 - 4i} = \frac{3 + 4i}{(3 - 4i)(3 + 4i)}$

$= \frac{3 + 4i}{25} = \frac{3}{25} + \frac{4i}{25}$

LESSON QUIZ

1. Solve for x and y.
   $4x + 2yi = 8 + 6i$
   $x = 2$ and $y = 3$
2. Multiply.
   $(2 + 4i)(3 + 5i)$
   $-14 + 22i$
3. Find the conjugate of $7 - 2i$.
   $7 + 2i$
4. Multiply.
   $(4 + 2i)(4 - 2i)$
   20
5. Divide $\frac{2 + 3i}{1 - i}$.
   $-\frac{1}{2} + \frac{5i}{2}$

Division and Reciprocals

Objective: Divide and find reciprocals of complex numbers.

To divide complex numbers, we multiply by 1 using the same techniques as when rationalizing a denominator with two terms. In choosing a symbol for 1, we use the conjugate of the divisor.

EXAMPLES Divide.

11.
$$\frac{-5 + 9i}{1 - i} = \frac{-5 + 9i}{1 - i} \cdot \frac{1 + i}{1 + i} = \frac{-14 + 4i}{1 - i^2} = \frac{-14 + 4i}{2} = -7 + 2i$$

12.
$$\frac{2 - 3i}{3 + 5i} = \frac{2 - 3i}{3 + 5i} \cdot \frac{3 - 5i}{3 - 5i} = \frac{-9 - 19i}{9 - 25i^2} = \frac{-9 - 19i}{34} = -\frac{9}{34} - \frac{19}{34}i$$

Try This Divide.

l. $\frac{6 + 2i}{1 - 3i}$ $2i$

m. $\frac{2 + 3i}{-1 + 4i}$ $\frac{10}{17} - \frac{11}{17}i$

The reciprocal of a number $c + di$ is, of course, that number by which we multiply $c + di$ to get 1. By definition of division this is $\frac{1}{c + di}$. To express $\frac{1}{c + di}$ in the form $a + bi$, we can divide.

EXAMPLE 13 Find the reciprocal of $2 - 3i$ and express it in the form $a + bi$.

The reciprocal of $2 - 3i$ is $\frac{1}{2 - 3i}$.

$$\frac{1}{2 - 3i} = \frac{1}{2 - 3i} \cdot \frac{2 + 3i}{2 + 3i} = \frac{2 + 3i}{2^2 - 3^2 i^2} = \frac{2 + 3i}{4 + 9} = \frac{2}{13} + \frac{3}{13}i$$

Try This

n. Find the reciprocal of $3 + 4i$ and express it in the form $a + bi$. $\frac{3}{25} - \frac{4}{25}i$

7-9 EXERCISES

A

Solve for x and y.

1. $4x + 7i = -6 + yi$ **2.** $8 + 8yi = 4x - 2i$ **3.** $-5x - yi = 10 + 8i$

Multiply.

4. $7i \cdot 9i$ **5.** $3i \cdot i$ **6.** $(9i)^2$ **7.** $(-5i)^2$

8. $(3 + 2i)(1 + i)$ **9.** $(4 + 3i)(2 + i)$ **10.** $(5 - 2i)^2$ **11.** $(-2 + 2i)^2$

Find the conjugate of each number.

12. $-4 + 8i$ **13.** $7 - i$ **14.** $\sqrt{2} - \frac{1}{2}i$ **15.** $-m + ni$

Multiply or divide.

16. $(1 - i)(1 + i)$ **17.** $(6 + 3i)(6 - 3i)$ **18.** $(3 - i\sqrt{2})(3 + i\sqrt{2})$

19. $\frac{3 + 2i}{2 + i}$ **20.** $\frac{8 - 3i}{-2 + 7i}$ **21.** $\frac{5 - 10i}{-3 + 4i}$ **22.** $\frac{\sqrt{2} + i}{\sqrt{2} - i}$

Find the reciprocal of each number and express it in the form $a + bi$.

23. i **24.** $-i$ **25.** $2 - 4i$ **26.** $-3 - 5i$ **27.** $-4 + 7i$

B

Express in the form $a + bi$.

28. i^{-3} i **29.** i^2 -1 **30.** $\frac{1 - i}{(1 + i)^2}$ $-\frac{1}{2} - \frac{1}{2}i$ **31.** $\frac{1 + i}{(1 - i)^2}$ $-\frac{1}{2} + \frac{1}{2}i$

32. Let $z = a + bi$. Find a general expression for $\frac{1}{z}$. $\frac{a}{a^2 + b^2} - \frac{b}{a^2 + b^2}i$

33. Show that $\sqrt{a \cdot b} = \sqrt{a} \cdot \sqrt{b}$ does not hold for all real numbers.

34. ***Critical Thinking*** Find the complex number whose reciprocal is $5 + 6i$. $\frac{5}{61} - \frac{6}{61}i$

Challenge

Simplify to the form $a + bi$.

35. $(1 + \sqrt{-3})^{-2}$ **36.** $(\sqrt{-2} + 2\sqrt{-6})^2$ **37.** $(1 + i)^{-3}(2 - i)^{-2}$

Mixed Review

Rationalize the denominator. **38.** $\sqrt{\frac{9}{2}}$ **39.** $\frac{3\sqrt{3}}{2\sqrt{5}}$ **40.** $\frac{\sqrt{m} - \sqrt{n}}{\sqrt{m} + \sqrt{n}}$

41. Find an equation of the line containing $(2, 3)$ and $(-1, -6)$.

LOOKING FOR ERRORS

Mario said, "The product of a complex number and its conjugate is the square of its absolute value." Evaluate his statement. It is correct.

Assignment Guide

Algebra: 1–27 e/o, MR

Alg w/Finite or Trig: 1–33 e/o, 34, MR

Comprehensive: 1–33 m3, 34–37, MR

ADDITIONAL ANSWERS

Exercises

1. $x = -\frac{3}{2}, y = 7$

2. $x = 2, y = -\frac{1}{4}$

3. $x = -2, y = -8$

4. -63 **5.** -3

6. -81 **7.** -25

8. $1 + 5i$ **9.** $5 + 10i$

10. $21 - 20i$ **11.** $-8i$

12. $-4 - 8i$ **13.** $7 + i$

14. $\sqrt{2} + \frac{1}{2}i$ **15.** $-m - ni$

16. 2 **17.** 45

18. 11 **19.** $\frac{8}{5} + \frac{1}{5}i$

20. $-\frac{37}{53} - \frac{50}{53}i$ **21.** $-\frac{11}{5} + \frac{2}{5}i$

22. $\frac{1}{3} + \frac{2}{3}i\sqrt{2}$ **23.** $-i$

24. i **25.** $\frac{1}{10} + \frac{1}{5}i$

26. $-\frac{3}{34} + \frac{5}{34}i$ **27.** $-\frac{4}{65} - \frac{7}{65}i$

33. For example, $\sqrt{-1}\sqrt{-1} = i^2 = -1$, but $\sqrt{(-1)(-1)} = \sqrt{1} = 1$.

35. $-\frac{1}{8} - \frac{\sqrt{3}}{8}i$

36. $-26 - 8\sqrt{3}$

37. $\frac{1}{100} - \frac{7}{100}i$

Mixed Review

38. $\frac{3\sqrt{2}}{2}$

39. $\frac{3\sqrt{15}}{10}$

40. $\frac{m + n - 2\sqrt{mn}}{m - n}$

41. $y = 3x - 3$

7-10

FIRST FIVE MINUTES

1. Solve for x and y.
   $4 + 5yi = 2x + 15i$
   $4 = 2x$ and $5y = 15$
   $x = 2$ and $y = 3$
2. Multiply.
   $(5 + 2i)(3 + 4i)$
   $15 + 20i + 6i + 8(-1)$
   $= 7 + 26i$
3. Divide $\frac{1 - 2i}{2 - i}$.
   $\frac{(1 - 2i)(2 + i)}{(2 - i)(2 + i)}$
   $= \frac{4 - 3i}{5} = \frac{4}{5} - \frac{3}{5}i$

Complex Numbers as Solutions of Equations

Key Question

- How do you determine if $a + bi$ is a solution of an equation?
  Substitute $a + bi$ for the variable.

Chalkboard Example

1. Determine whether $2 + i$ is a solution of $x^2 - 4x + 5 = 0$.
   $(2 + i)^2 - 4(2 + i) + 5$
   $= 4 + 4i - 1 - 8 - 4i + 5$
   $= 0$
   $2 + i$ is a solution.

Writing Equations with Given Solutions

Chalkboard Example

1. Find the equation having $1 + 2i$ and $1 - 2i$ as solutions.
   $[x - (1 + 2i)]\,[x - (1 - 2i)] = 0$
   $[(x - 1) - 2i]\,[(x - 1) + 2i] = 0$
   $(x - 1)^2 - (2i)^2 = 0$
   $x^2 - 2x + 1 + 4 = 0$
   $x^2 - 2x + 5 = 0$

7-10 Solutions of Equations

Complex Numbers as Solutions of Equations

Objective: Determine whether a complex number is a solution of an equation.

EXAMPLE 1 Determine whether $1 + i\sqrt{7}$ is a solution of $x^2 - 2x + 8 = 0$.

$x^2 - 2x + 8 = 0$	
$(1 + i\sqrt{7})^2 - 2(1 + i\sqrt{7}) + 8$	0
$1 + 2(i\sqrt{7}) + (i\sqrt{7})^2 - 2 - 2i\sqrt{7} + 8$	0
$1 + 2i\sqrt{7} - 7 - 2 - 2i\sqrt{7} + 8$	0
0	0 ✓

$1 + i\sqrt{7}$ is a solution.

Try This

a. Determine whether $1 - i$ is a solution of $x^2 + 2x + 1 = 0$. No (See Additional Answers.)

Writing Equations with Given Solutions

Objective: Find an equation that has given complex numbers as solutions.

The principle of zero products for real numbers also holds for complex numbers, thus we can find equations having given solutions.

EXAMPLE 2 Find an equation having $4 + 3i$ and $4 - 3i$ as solutions.

$$x = 4 + 3i \text{ or } x = 4 - 3i$$
$$x - (4 + 3i) = 0 \text{ or } x - (4 - 3i) = 0$$
$$[x - (4 + 3i)][x - (4 - 3i)] = 0 \quad \text{Using the principle of zero products}$$
$$[x - 4 - 3i][x - 4 + 3i] = 0$$
$$(x - 4)^2 - (3i)^2 = 0 \quad \text{Multiplying as the sum and difference of two expressions}$$
$$x^2 - 8x + 16 - 9i^2 = 0$$
$$x^2 - 8x + 16 + 9 = 0$$
$$x^2 - 8x + 25 = 0 \quad \text{Simplifying}$$

Try This Find an equation having the given numbers as solutions.

b. $1 + i, 1 - i$ $x^2 - 2x + 2 = 0$ **c.** $2 - 3i, 2 + 3i$ $x^2 - 4x + 13 = 0$

Solving Equations

Objective: Solve first-degree equations that have complex numbers as solutions.

First-degree equations in complex numbers are solved very much like first-degree equations in real numbers.

EXAMPLE 3 Solve $3ix + 4 - 5i = (1 + i)x + 2i$.

We begin by getting all x terms to one side of the equation.

$$3ix - (1 + i)x = -4 + 7i \quad \text{Adding } -(1 + i)x \text{ and } -(-4 - 5i) \text{ to both sides}$$

$$(-1 + 2i)x = -4 + 7i \quad \text{Simplifying}$$

$$x = \frac{-4 + 7i}{-1 + 2i} \quad \text{Dividing}$$

$$x = \frac{-4 + 7i}{-1 + 2i} \cdot \frac{-1 - 2i}{-1 - 2i} \quad \text{Multiplying by 1}$$

$$x = \frac{18 + i}{5}$$

$$x = \frac{18}{5} + \frac{1}{5}i$$

Try This Solve.

d. $3 - 4i + 2ix = 3i - (1 - i)x$ $2 + 5i$

Linear equations always have solutions. Complex numbers were invented so that certain other equations would have solutions. How many solutions, if any, does a polynomial equation have? The answer depends upon a very important theorem.

Theorem 7-9

Every polynomial with complex coefficients and of degree n (where $n > 1$) can be factored into n linear factors.

The factors of a polynomial are not always easy to find, but they exist.

EXAMPLE 4 Show that $(x + i)(x - i)$ is a factorization of $x^2 + 1$.

$(x + i)(x - i)$ Multiplying

$= x^2 - ix + ix - i^2$

$= x^2 + 1$

Try This

e. Show that $(x + 2i)(x - 2i)$ is a factorization of $x^2 + 4$. $(x + 2i)(x - 2i) = x^2 + 2ix - 2ix - 4i^2$
$= x^2 + 4$

Solving Equations

Theorem 7-9 is a consequent of the Fundamental Theorem of Algebra, which will be discussed in more detail in Chapter 11.

Key Questions

- If a polynomial equation is of degree n, must it have n solutions?
  No, $x^2 - 2x + 1 = 0$ has only 1 solution.
- If a polynomial equation is of degree n, must it have n linear factors?
  Yes

Chalkboard Examples

1. Solve.
   $(3 + 4i)x = 1 + i$
   $x = \frac{1 + i}{3 + 4i}$
   $= \frac{(1 + i)(3 - 4i)}{(3 + 4i)(3 - 4i)}$
   $= \frac{7 - i}{25} = \frac{7}{25} - \frac{1}{25}i$
2. Show that $[x - (2 + 3i)][x - (2 - 3i)]$ is a factorization of $x^2 - 4x + 13$.
   $[(x - (2 + 3i)][x - (2 - 3i)]$
   $= ((x - 2) - 3i)((x - 2) + 3i)$
   $= x^2 - 4x + 4 + 9$
   $= x^2 - 4x + 13$

Square Roots of Complex Numbers

Math Point
Niels Henrik Abel proved in 1824 that there is no formula, using ordinary algebraic operations, for finding the solutions or the factorizations of a polynomial of degree five or higher. Abel was 19 years old when he made this revolutionary discovery.

Chalkboard Example

1. Show that $3 - i$ is a square root of $8 - 6i$. Find the other root.
$(3 - i)^2 = 9 - 6i - 1$
$= 8 - 6i$
The other square root is the additive inverse of $3 - i$, or $-3 + i$.

LESSON QUIZ

1. Determine whether $3 + 2i$ is a solution of $x^2 - 6x + 13 = 0$.
$3 + 2i$ is a solution.
2. Write an equation having $1 + 3i$ and $1 - 3i$ as solutions.
$x^2 - 2x + 10 = 0$
3. Solve.
$(5 + 2i)x = 1 + 3i$
$= \frac{11}{29} + \frac{13}{29}i$

We can now answer the question about solutions of polynomial equations.

Theorem 7-10

Every polynomial equation of degree n ($n \geq 1$) with complex coefficients has at least one solution and at most n solutions in the system of complex numbers.

Proof of Theorem 7-10

Consider a polynomial equation of degree n, $P(x) = 0$. The polynomial $P(x)$ is either of degree 1, in which case there is a solution, or, by Theorem 7-9, it can be factored into n linear factors. We then have

$$(x - a_1)(x - a_2) \ldots (x - a_n) = 0$$

By the principle of zero products, we have

$$x = a_1 \text{ or } x = a_2 \text{ or } x = a_3 \text{ or} \ldots \text{or } x = a_n$$

Thus the equation has solutions $a_1, a_2, \ldots, a_n$. Some of these may be the same. Therefore, there is at least one solution, and there are not more than n solutions.

Square Roots of Complex Numbers

Objective: Verify one square root of a complex number, and find the other square root.

Theorem 7-9 can be used to show that all complex numbers have square roots.

Theorem 7-11

Every nonzero complex number has two square roots. They are additive inverses of each other. Zero has just one square root.

EXAMPLE 5 Show that $1 + i$ is a square root of $2i$. Find the other square root.

We square $(1 + i)$ to show that we get $2i$.

$$(1 + i)^2 = 1 + 2i + i^2 = 1 + 2i - 1 = 2i$$

By Theorem 7-11, the other square root of $2i$ is the additive inverse of $1 + i$, so it is $-1 - i$.

Try This

f. Show that $(-1 + i)$ is a square root of $-2i$. Then find the other square root.
$(-1 + i)^2 = 1 - 2i + i^2 = 1 - 2i - 1 = -2i, 1 - i$

7-10 EXERCISES

A

Determine whether the given numbers are solutions of the equation.

1. $2i, -2i; x^2 + 4 = 0$ Yes, yes
2. $4i, -4i; x^2 + 16 = 0$ Yes, yes
3. $i\sqrt{2}, -i\sqrt{3}; x^2 + 3 = 0$ No, yes
4. $i\sqrt{3}, -i\sqrt{2}; x^2 + 2 = 0$ No, yes
5. $-1 + i, -1 - i; z^2 + 2z + 2 = 0$ Yes, yes
6. $2 - i, 2 + i; z^2 - 4z + 5 = 0$ Yes, yes

Find an equation having the specified numbers as solutions.

7. $5i, -5i$
8. $7i, -7i$
9. $2 + 3i, 2 - 3i$
10. $4 + 3i, 4 - 3i$
11. $i\sqrt{3}, -i\sqrt{3}$
12. $2 - i\sqrt{2}, 2 + i\sqrt{2}$
13. $6 + i\sqrt{6}, 6 - i\sqrt{6}$
14. $1 - i\sqrt{8}, 1 + i\sqrt{8}$
15. $3 - i\sqrt{17}, 3 + i\sqrt{17}$

Solve.

16. $(3 + i)x + i = 5i$ $\frac{2}{5} + \frac{6}{5}i$
17. $(2 + i)x - i = 5 + i$ $\frac{12}{5} - \frac{1}{5}i$
18. $2ix + 5 - 4i = (2 + 3i)x - 2i$ $\frac{8}{5} - \frac{9}{5}i$
19. $5ix + 3 + 2i = (3 - 2i)x + 3i$ $\frac{8}{29} + \frac{9}{29}i$
20. $(1 + 2i)x + 3 - 2i = 4 - 5i + 3ix$ $2 - i$
21. $(5 + i)x + 1 - 3i = (2 - 3i)x + 2 - i$ $\frac{11}{25} + \frac{2}{25}i$
22. $(5 - i)x + 2 - 3i = (3 - 2i)x + 3 - i$ $\frac{4}{5} + \frac{3}{5}i$
23. Show that $(2x + i)(2x - i)$ is a factorization of $4x^2 + 1$.
24. Show that $(2x + 2i)(2x - 2i)$ is a factorization of $4x^2 + 4$.
25. Show that $(2 + i)$ is a square root of $3 + 4i$. Then find the other square root.
26. Show that $(2 - i)$ is a square root of $3 - 4i$. Then find the other square root.

B

Find an equation having the specified numbers as solutions.

27. $5, i$
28. $1, 3i, -3i$
29. $2, 1 + i, i$
30. $i, 2i, -i$
31. ***Critical Thinking*** $3 + 5i$ is a square root of a certain complex number. Find the number. $-16 + 30i$

Challenge

32. Show that $(a + bi)^2 = (a + b)(a - b) + 2abi$.
33. Find the square roots of $3 - 4i$. (Hint: Use the result of Exercise 32.)

Mixed Review

Convert to standard notation. **34.** 5.023×10^{-5} **35.** 4.441×10^6

Simplify.

36. $\dfrac{\frac{2}{x} + 3}{\frac{2}{x} - 5}$
37. $\dfrac{m - \frac{3}{m}}{m + \frac{3}{m}}$
38. $\dfrac{\frac{2}{x} + \frac{5}{y}}{\frac{5}{x} - \frac{2}{y}}$
39. $\dfrac{3c + \frac{2}{c}}{3c - \frac{2}{c}}$

Assignment Guide
Algebra: 1–26 e/o, MR

Alg w/Finite or Trig: 1–30 e/o, 31, MR

Comprehensive: 1–30 e/o, 31–33, MR

ADDITIONAL ANSWERS

Try This

a. $(1 - i)^2 + 2(1 - i) + 1$
$= 1 - 2i + i^2 + 2 - 2i + 1$
$= 3 - 4i$; therefore $(1 - i)$ is not a solution of $x^2 + 2x + 1 = 0$.

Exercises

7. $x^2 + 25 = 0$
8. $x^2 + 49 = 0$
9. $x^2 - 4x + 13 = 0$
10. $x^2 - 8x + 25 = 0$
11. $x^2 + 3 = 0$
12. $x^2 - 4x + 6 = 0$
13. $x^2 - 12x + 42 = 0$
14. $x^2 - 2x + 9 = 0$
15. $x^2 - 6x + 26 = 0$

23. $(2x + i)(2x - i)$
$= 4x^2 - 2ix + 2ix - i^2$
$= 4x^2 + 1$
24. $(2x + 2i)(2x - 2i)$
$= 4x^2 - 4ix + 4ix - 4i^2$
$= 4x^2 + 4$
25. $(2 + i)^2 = 4 + 4i + i^2 = 3 + 4i$, $-2 - i$
26. $(2 - i)^2 = 4 - 4i + i^2 = 3 - 4i$, $-2 + i$
27. $x^2 - ix - 5x + 5i = 0$
28. $x^3 - x^2 + 9x - 9 = 0$
29. $x^3 - 2ix^2 - 3x^2 + 5ix + x - 2i + 2 = 0$
30. $x^3 - 2ix^2 + x - 2i = 0$
32. $(a + bi)^2 = a^2 + 2abi - b^2$
$= (a^2 - b^2) + 2abi$
$= (a + b)(a - b) + 2abi$
33. $2 - i, -2 + i$

Mixed Review

34. 0.00005023
35. 4,441,000
36. $\frac{2 + 3x}{2 - 5x}$
37. $\frac{m^2 - 3}{m^2 + 3}$
38. $\frac{2y + 5x}{5y - 2x}$
39. $\frac{3c^2 + 2}{3c^2 - 2}$

Problem Solving: College Entrance Exams

Chalkboard Example

The average of three numbers is k. One number is $\frac{2}{3}k$. The average of the other two numbers is

(A) $\frac{1}{6}k$ (B) $\frac{1}{3}k$ (C) $\frac{7}{3}k$

(D) $\frac{7}{6}k$ (E) $\frac{7}{18}k$

The correct answer is choice D. The sum of the three numbers is $3k$. The average of two other numbers is $\frac{3k - \frac{2}{3}k}{2}$, which reduces to $\frac{7}{6}k$.

Students who neglect to divide by 2 will choose C. Students who mistake k for the sum of the numbers will choose A $\left(\frac{1}{3}k \text{ divided by } 2\right)$ or E $\left(2\frac{1}{3}k \text{ over 3, divided by } 2\right)$.

Students who choose B will have made both errors.

Problem Solving: College Entrance Exams

Averages

College entrance exams often require that the average, or mean, of a set of numbers be found. These test items usually do not tell you to find the average. Many of these problems can be solved using the *Guess, Check, Revise* strategy. Most are solved more efficiently, however, using the definition of average and the equation-solving techniques you have learned.

EXAMPLE 1

Tony's scores on five tests are 60, 80, 55, 75, and 65. What must his score be on the next test to raise his average to 70?

(A) 70 (B) 75 (C) 80 (D) 85 (E) 90

Since we know the average we want is 70, and the number of tests is 6, we can write the following equation.

$$70 = \frac{\text{(sum of the 6 numbers)}}{6}$$

$$70 \cdot 6 = \text{sum of the 6 numbers}$$

$$420 = \text{sum of the 6 numbers}$$

The sum of the 5 test scores is $60 + 80 + 55 + 75 + 65 = 335$.
Thus he needs $420 - 335 = 85$ points on the last test to get an average of 70. The correct answer is (D).

Example 2 involves a weighted average because the groups are of different sizes.

EXAMPLE 2

If the average of three numbers is 5, and the average of seven other numbers is 15, then the average of all the numbers is

(A) 8 (B) 10 (C) 9.6 (D) 12 (E) 13

Using the formula for average, we know that the following are true.

$$5 = \frac{\text{the first sum}}{3} \rightarrow \text{the first sum} = 3 \cdot 5 = 15$$

$$15 = \frac{\text{the second sum}}{7} \rightarrow \text{the second sum} = 7 \cdot 15 = 105$$

To find the mean for all numbers, we divide the *total sum* by 10, the total number of numbers.

$$\begin{aligned} \text{total sum} &= \text{the first sum} + \text{the second sum} \\ &= 15 + 105 \\ &= 120 \end{aligned}$$

$$\text{Average} = \frac{120}{10} = 12, \text{ so the correct answer is (D).}$$

Problems

1. If Nick's first three test grades are 79, 85, and 90, what grade does he need on the next test to average 85?

   (A) 87 (B) 86 (C) 85 (D) 84 (E) 83

2. If Esperanza's first two test grades are 80 and 71, what grade must she make on her third test for the average of the three to be 70?

   (A) 59 (B) 58 (C) 57 (D) 56 (E) 55

3. The average of three numbers is greater than 50. If two of them are 47 and 48, then the third number could be

   (A) 56 (B) 55 (C) 54 (D) 53 (E) either **A** or **B**

4. In an algebra class there are 20 boys and 15 girls. If the 20 boys have an average score of 50 and the 15 girls have an average score of 57, then what is the average score for all 35 students?

   (A) 55 (B) 54 (C) 53 (D) 53.2 (E) Cannot be determined

5. If the average of three numbers is between 8 and 12, then the sum of the three numbers could be any one of the following except

   (A) $20\frac{1}{2}$ (B) $24\frac{1}{2}$ (C) 26 (D) 28 (E) 35

6. The average of two numbers is A, and one number is N. The other number is

   (A) $2N$ (B) $2A - 2$ (C) $2A$ (D) $A - N$ (E) $2A - N$

7. If two students averaged 75 on a test and three other students averaged 90, find the average of all five students.

   (A) 85 (B) 84 (C) 83 (D) 82 (E) 81

8. If the average of the first 5 numbers on a list is equal to the average of the first 4 numbers on the list, then the fifth number must be equal to

   (A) the average of the first 4 numbers.
   (B) zero
   (C) a negative number.
   (D) a number greater than the average of the first 4 numbers.
   (E) a number less than the average of the first 4 numbers.

9. The average of five positive numbers is 26. If three of the numbers are 25, 28, and 22, which of the following could *not* be one of the other two numbers?

   (A) 8 (B) 30 (C) 36 (D) 43 (E) 56

10. A class of 30 students took a test that was scored from 0 to 60. Exactly 10 students received scores less than or equal to 30. If A is the class average score, what is the greatest possible value of A?

    (A) 30 (B) 40 (C) 48 (D) 50 (E) 52

11. The average of M numbers is A, and the average of N numbers is B. What is the average of all the numbers?

    (A) $A + B$ (B) $\frac{A + B}{2}$ (C) $\frac{AM + BN}{2}$ (D) $\frac{AM + BN}{M + N}$ (E) $\frac{AM + BN}{A + B}$

ANSWERS

1. (B)
2. (A)
3. (A)
4. (C)
5. (A)
6. (E)
7. (B)
8. (A)
9. (E)
10. (D)
11. (D)

ANSWERS

1. 36
2. $4|x|$
3. $-\frac{2x}{3}$
4. -3
5. $2|x|$
6. $6|x|\sqrt{6}$
7. $a^2b^2\sqrt[3]{b}$
8. $2cd^2\sqrt[3]{6cd}$
9. $2\sqrt[3]{2}$
10. $\frac{2|a|}{b^4}\sqrt{3ab}$
11. $\frac{x^2\sqrt{5}}{2}$
12. $12\sqrt{2}$
13. $-\sqrt[3]{3}$
14. $(5y-2)\sqrt{3y}$
15. 1
16. $58 + 12\sqrt{6}$
17. $2\sqrt[3]{4} + 7\sqrt[3]{6} + 3\sqrt[3]{9}$

Chapter 7 Summary and Review

7-1

A **k-th root** of a number a is a number c such that $c^k = a$. When k is even, every positive real number has two roots, one positive and one negative. When k is odd, every real number has one root that has the same sign as the number.

Simplify.

1. $\sqrt{(-36)^2}$ **2.** $\sqrt{16x^2}$ **3.** $\sqrt[3]{\frac{-8x^3}{27}}$

4. $\sqrt[5]{-243}$ **5.** $\sqrt[4]{(-2x)^4}$

7-2

For any nonnegative real numbers a and b, and any index k,

$$\sqrt[k]{a}\cdot\sqrt[k]{b} = \sqrt[k]{ab}$$

To simplify a **radical expression,** find the k-th root of factors that are perfect k-th powers. Assume variables represent nonnegative numbers.

Multiply and simplify.

6. $\sqrt{18x}\cdot\sqrt{12x}$ **7.** $\sqrt[3]{a^2b}\cdot\sqrt[3]{a^4b^6}$ **8.** $\sqrt[3]{3c^2d^5}\cdot\sqrt[3]{16c^2d^2}$

7-3

For any nonnegative number a, any positive number b, and any index k,

$$\sqrt[k]{\frac{a}{b}} = \frac{\sqrt[k]{a}}{\sqrt[k]{b}}$$

Divide and simplify.

9. $\frac{\sqrt[3]{32}}{\sqrt[3]{2}}$ **10.** $\sqrt{\frac{12a^3}{b^7}}$ **11.** $\frac{\sqrt{40x^7}}{\sqrt{32x^3}}$

Like radical terms can be combined.

$$a\sqrt[k]{x} + b\sqrt[k]{x} = (a+b)\sqrt[k]{x}$$

Add or subtract.

12. $2\sqrt{32} - \sqrt{50} + \sqrt{162}$ **13.** $\sqrt[3]{24} - \sqrt[3]{81}$ **14.** $5\sqrt{3y^3} - \sqrt{12y}$

7-4

To multiply radical expressions with more than one term, use the FOIL method for multiplying polynomials.

Multiply and simplify.

15. $(7 - 4\sqrt{3})(7 + 4\sqrt{3})$ **16.** $(3\sqrt{6} + 2)^2$

17. $(2\sqrt[3]{2} + \sqrt[3]{3})(\sqrt[3]{2} + 3\sqrt[3]{3})$

When rationalizing a denominator, multiply both the numerator and denominator by an expression for 1 that will make the denominator rational.

Rationalize the denominator.

18. $\dfrac{\sqrt{8}}{\sqrt{3}}$ **19.** $\dfrac{6}{3 - \sqrt{17}}$ **20.** $\dfrac{\sqrt{3} + 5}{7 + \sqrt{3}}$

7-5

For any nonnegative number a, any natural-number index k, and any integer m,

$$\sqrt[k]{a^m} = (\sqrt[k]{a})^m$$

Simplify.

21. $(\sqrt[3]{16})^2$ **22.** $(\sqrt{3x})^3$ **23.** $\sqrt{(a^3b^2)^2}$ **24.** $\sqrt[3]{\left(\dfrac{3}{a^2}\right)^3}$

For any natural number m, integer k, and any nonnegative number a,

$$a^{\frac{m}{k}} \text{ means } \sqrt[k]{a^m}$$

Write without rational exponents.

25. $x^{\frac{2}{3}}$ **26.** $27^{\frac{1}{3}}$ **27.** $32^{\frac{2}{5}}$ **28.** $(8x)^{\frac{5}{2}}$

Write with rational exponents.

29. $\sqrt[3]{15}$ **30.** $\sqrt[2]{32}$ **31.** $\sqrt[3]{x^3y^4z^5}$ **32.** $\sqrt[4]{8x^3y^2}$

For any rational number $\frac{m}{n}$ and any positive real number a, $a^{-\frac{m}{n}}$ means $\dfrac{1}{a^{\frac{m}{n}}}$.

Rewrite with positive exponents.

33. $x^{-\frac{1}{2}}$ **34.** $\dfrac{1}{x^{-4}}$ **35.** $\left(\dfrac{1}{16}\right)^{-\frac{1}{2}}$ **36.** $\dfrac{1}{8^{-\frac{2}{3}}}$

Use rational exponents to write in simplest radical form.

37. $\sqrt[4]{x^2}$ **38.** $\sqrt[3]{16y^6}$ **39.** $\sqrt[4]{\dfrac{x^{-8}y^{12}}{16}}$ **40.** $\sqrt[10]{\dfrac{64x^6}{y^8z^{-4}}}$

7-6

For any natural number n, if an equation $a = b$ is true, then the equation $a^n = b^n$ is true. To solve an equation containing radical signs, isolate a radical term, then use the principle of powers. If a radical term remains, repeat this procedure. Always check your solutions.

Solve.

41. $\sqrt{5 - 3x} - 6 = 0$ **42.** $\sqrt{7 - 4x} - \sqrt{3 - 2x} = 1$

Solve the formula for the given variable.

43. $T = 4\pi\sqrt{\dfrac{L}{g}}$; L **44.** $\sqrt{\dfrac{E}{m}} = c$; E **45.** $A = \sqrt{\dfrac{w_1}{w_2}}$; w_2

18. $\dfrac{2\sqrt{6}}{3}$
19. $\dfrac{9 + 3\sqrt{17}}{-4}$
20. $\dfrac{\sqrt{3} + 16}{23}$
21. $4\sqrt[3]{4}$
22. $3x\sqrt{3x}$
23. $|a^3|b^2$
24. $\dfrac{3}{a^2}$
25. $\sqrt[3]{x^2}$
26. 3
27. 4
28. $2^7x^2\sqrt{2x}$
29. $15^{1/3}$
30. $2^{5/2}$
31. $x^1y^{4/3}z^{5/3}$
32. $2^{3/4}x^{3/4}y^{1/2}$
33. $\dfrac{1}{x^{1/2}}$
34. x^4
35. 4
36. 4
37. $\sqrt{x}$
38. $2y^2\sqrt[3]{2}$
39. $\dfrac{|y^3|}{2x^2}$
40. $\sqrt[5]{\dfrac{8x^3z^2}{y^4}}$ or $\dfrac{\sqrt[5]{8x^3z^2y}}{\cdot y}$
41. $-\dfrac{31}{3}$
42. $-\dfrac{1}{2}, \dfrac{3}{2}$
43. $L = \dfrac{gT^2}{16\pi^2}$
44. $E = mc^2$
45. $w_2 = \dfrac{w_1}{A^2}$

46. $7i$
47. $-5i$
48. $-6\sqrt{6}$
49. $2 - i$
50. $1 - 4i$
51.

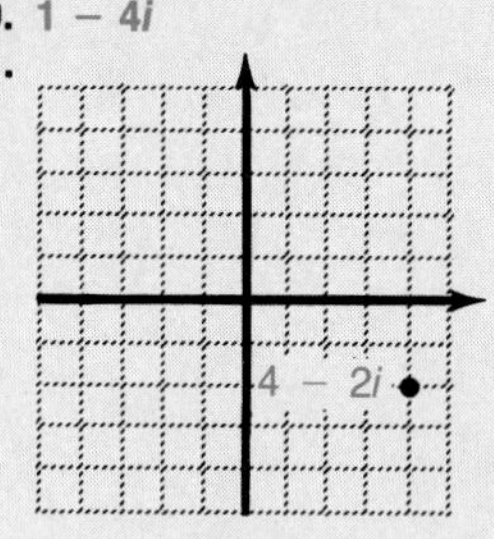

52.

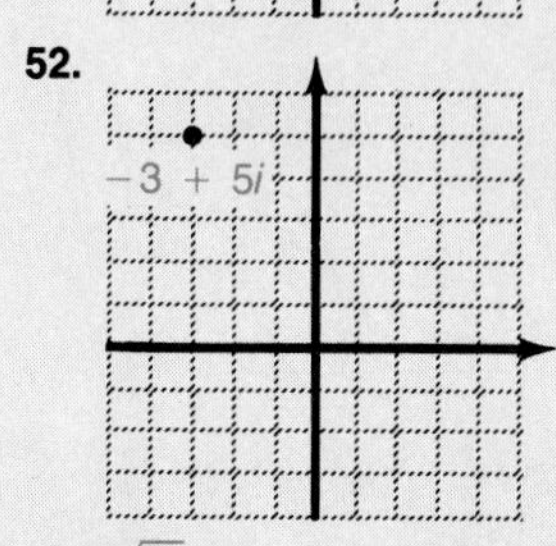

53. $\sqrt{34}$
54. 5
55. $14 + 2i$
56. $12 - 5i$
57. 13
58. 40
59. $\frac{8 - i}{5}$
60. $\frac{3 - 4i}{5}$
61. $\frac{1}{10} - \frac{1}{5}i$
62. $\frac{1}{2} + \frac{1}{2}i$
63. $-\frac{16}{13} - \frac{11}{13}i$

7-7

Remember that the imaginary number $i = \sqrt{-1}$, and $i^1 = i, i^2 = -1, i^3 = -i, i^4 = 1$.

Express these numbers in terms of i.

46. $\sqrt{-49}$ **47.** $-\sqrt{-25}$

Simplify.

48. $\sqrt{-6} \cdot 6i$ **49.** $(6 + 2i) + (-4 - 3i)$ **50.** $(3 - 5i) - (2 - i)$

7-8

To graph a complex number $a + bi$, replace the x-axis with a real axis and replace the y-axis with an imaginary axis.

Graph.

51. $4 - 2i$ **52.** $-3 + 5i$

The absolute value of a complex number $a + bi$ is denoted by $|a + bi|$ and is defined as $\sqrt{a^2 + b^2}$.

Find the absolute values.

53. $|5 - 3i|$ **54.** $|-4 + 3i|$

7-9

Multiply complex numbers as you would multiply monomials or binomials, treating real and imaginary parts as unlike terms.

Multiply and simplify.

55. $(2 - 2i)(3 + 4i)$ **56.** $(2 - 3i)(3 + 2i)$

57. $(3 - 2i)(3 + 2i)$ **58.** $(2 + 6i)(2 - 6i)$

To divide complex numbers, rationalize the denominator by multiplying both numerator and denominator by the conjugate of the denominator.

59. $\frac{3 - 2i}{2 - i}$ **60.** $\frac{4 - 2i}{4 + 2i}$

The reciprocal of $c + di$ is $\frac{1}{c + di}$.

Find the reciprocal and express it in the form $a + bi$.

61. $2 + 4i$ **62.** $1 - i$

7-10

First-degree equations in complex numbers are solved very much like first-degree equations for real numbers.

Solve.

63. $2ix - 5 + 3i = (2 - i)x + i$

See also Problem 7, Computer-Assisted Problem Solving, page 843.

Chapter 7 Test

Simplify. Assume variables represent any real number.

1. $-\sqrt{121}$ -11
2. $\sqrt[3]{-0.027}$ -0.3

Simplify.

3. $\sqrt{x^2 - 10x + 25}$ $|x - 5|$
4. $\sqrt{49y^2}$ $7|y|$
5. $\sqrt[3]{-y^3}$ $-y$
6. $\sqrt[8]{x^8}$ $|x|$
7. $\sqrt{20}\sqrt{18}$ $6\sqrt{10}$
8. $\sqrt[3]{x^2y^4}\sqrt[3]{x^5y^2}$ $x^2y^2\sqrt[3]{x}$
9. $\sqrt{12x^5}\sqrt{6x^2y}$ $6x^3\sqrt{2xy}$
10. $\dfrac{\sqrt{8x^2}}{\sqrt{2x}}$ $2\sqrt{x}$
11. $\dfrac{\sqrt[3]{750}}{\sqrt[3]{3}}$ $5\sqrt[3]{2}$
12. $\sqrt[4]{\dfrac{64x^5y^7}{36xy^2}}$ $\dfrac{2|xy|\sqrt[4]{9y}}{3}$

Add or subtract.

13. $\sqrt{27} + \sqrt{108}$ $9\sqrt{3}$
14. $\sqrt[3]{40} - \sqrt[3]{135}$ $-\sqrt[3]{5}$

Multiply.

15. $(8 + 5\sqrt{6})(8 - 5\sqrt{6})$ -86
16. $(2\sqrt{7} - 3\sqrt{5})(\sqrt{7} - \sqrt{5})$ $29 - 5\sqrt{35}$

Rationalize the denominator.

17. $\dfrac{\sqrt{5}}{\sqrt{7}}$
18. $\dfrac{\sqrt{3} + 7}{8 - \sqrt{5}}$

Simplify. Assume variables represent nonnegative numbers.

19. $\sqrt[3]{9a^2b^4}$
20. $\sqrt[3]{\dfrac{n^{24}}{a^8}}$
21. $\sqrt[4]{81x^8y^8}$

Write in simplest radical form with positive exponents.

22. $x^{-\frac{2}{3}}$ $\dfrac{\sqrt[3]{x}}{x}$
23. $\sqrt[3]{\dfrac{81x^8y^{-3}}{z^2}}$ $\dfrac{3x^2}{yz}\sqrt[3]{3x^2z}$
24. $\sqrt[4]{9x^6}$ $x\sqrt{3x}$

Solve.

25. $x - 5 = \sqrt{x + 7}$ 9
26. $\sqrt{2x - 5} = 1 + \sqrt{x - 3}$ 7, 3
27. Solve $c = \sqrt{a^2 + b^2}$ for b. Find b if $a = 5$ and $c = 13$.

Add or subtract.

28. $(3 + 2i) + (2 - 3i)$ $5 - i$
29. $(9 - 4i) - (3 + 2i)$ $6 - 6i$
30. Graph $2 + 3i$.
31. Find $|4 + 2i|$.

Multiply or divide.

32. $(1 + 2i)(2i - 1)$
33. $(2 + 5i)(2 - 5i)$
34. $\dfrac{1 - 3i}{2 + i}$
35. Find the reciprocal of $1 + 2i$ and express it in the form $a + bi$.
36. Solve $-5ix + 8i - 4 = (7 + i)x + 10i$.

ADDITIONAL ANSWERS

17. $\dfrac{\sqrt{35}}{7}$

18. $\dfrac{8\sqrt{3} + \sqrt{15} + 56 + 7\sqrt{5}}{59}$

19. $b\sqrt[3]{9a^2b}$

20. $\dfrac{n^8\sqrt[3]{a}}{a^3}$

21. $3x^2y^2$

27. $b = \sqrt{c^2 - a^2}, b = 12$

30.

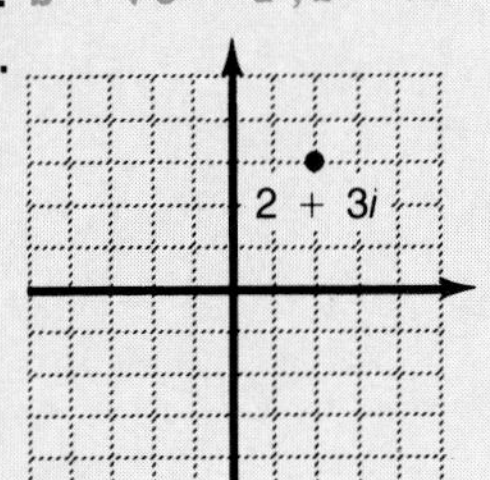

31. $2\sqrt{5}$

32. -5

33. 29

34. $-\frac{1}{5} - \frac{7}{5}i$

35. $\frac{1}{5} - \frac{2i}{5}$

36. $-\frac{8}{17} + \frac{2}{17}i$

Test Item Analysis

Item	Lesson
1–6	7-1
7–9	7-2
10–14	7-3
15–18	7-4
19–24	7-5
25–27	7-6
28, 29	7-7
30, 31	7-8
32–35	7-9
36	7-10

CHAPTER **8**

Quadratic Equations

Chapter Overview

Chapter 8 is the study of quadratic equations. Completing the square is used as a technique for solving quadratic equations, leading to the general solution of a quadratic equation in standard form—the quadratic formula. The discriminant is used to quickly determine the nature of solutions, and properties of solutions are used to find equations. Formulas and quadratic variation are studied, and a problem-solving lesson involving quadratic equations and variation is included. The problem-solving strategy lesson discussing the strategy *Use Logical Reasoning* concludes the material.

Objectives

8-1 ■ Solve equations of the type $ax^2 + bx + c = 0$.
■ Solve a quadratic equation by completing the square.
8-2 ■ Solve problems by translating to quadratic equations.
8-3 ■ Solve quadratic equations using the quadratic formula.
■ Find approximate values for solutions to quadratic equations.
8-4 ■ Determine the nature of the solutions of a quadratic equation with real coefficients.
■ Find and use sums and products of solutions of quadratic equations.
■ Find a quadratic equation given its solutions.
8-5 ■ Solve equations that are reducible to quadratic form.
8-6 ■ Solve second-degree formulas for a given letter.
■ Solve problems using quadratic equations.
8-7 ■ Find an equation of direct quadratic variation.
■ Find equations of inverse and joint quadratic variation.
■ Solve problems involving quadratic variation and proportion.
8-8 ■ Solve problems using the strategy *Use Logical Reasoning*, and other strategies.

TEACHING CHAPTER 8

Cooperative Learning Opportunities

For the **Try This** Exercises after the examples in Lesson 8-2, assign groups of three with the following roles: (1) reads the problem, draws a figure and sets up a plan; (2) does the computation needed; (3) checks the solution to be sure it answers the original question. Have students change roles for each problem.

Less structured groups of three might be used to try to reconstruct the proof of the quadratic formula. This is not easy but with a reminder that the idea is to complete the square, students may find that each one in a group remembers part of the procedure and together they can set up the entire derivation.

The problem solving in Lesson 8-8 can also be done in a group setting. In this case you might ask one person to be keeper of the chart and the others to reason toward the conclusions.

Multicultural Note: *Al-Khowarizmi*

Al-Khowarizmi, a ninth century Arab mathematician, wrote an algebra book that became famous throughout the world. The Arabic title for this book was *Al-jabr w'al muqabalah*. The spelling of *al-jabr* eventually changed to algebra, thus giving us the word algebra. The al-jabr book showed how to use both algebraic and geometric methods to solve quadratic equations. Al-Khowarizmi's method of completing the square is virtually the same as what we use. The geometric approach is quite different.

Suppose a square of unknown side is extended 8 units in one direction forming a rectangle whose area is 33 square units. How can you find the side of the original square? The extension of the original square is 8 units by x units. This extension is evenly divided and two pieces can be placed on each side of the square. By filling in the corners we can obtain an area for both squares.

For more information see page 15 of **Multiculturalism in Mathematics, Science, and Technology**.

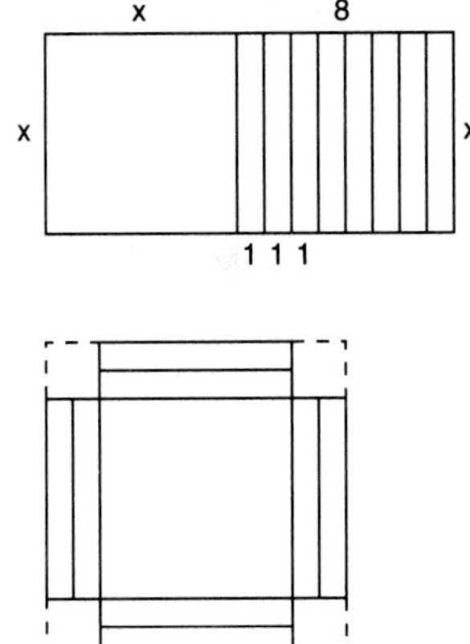

Alternative Assessment and Communication Ideas

The scientific calculator may be used for several methods of alternative assessment in Chapter 8. Students can enter a program for the quadratic formula and use it to solve equations.

The calculator may also be used effectively to check the real number solutions of quadratic equations. For example, checking the solution to Exercise 1 on page 352 can be done quickly with a calculator. Using the TI-81 to calculate the value on the left of the equal sign gives 1 E–12, which is very close to 0. But calculating only the first two terms of the quadratic gives –4, which proves the solution.

The **Writing to Learn** activity on page 365 provides an opportunity for contact with science. This activity can be extended to involve several equations—on motion or measurement—and a report comparing how the equations are used and what scientific results are obtained.

Investigations and Projects

The exploration of complex numbers completes the number system. You can involve students in a project about the different subsets of numbers.

A set of numbers is closed under a particular operation if, whenever two numbers from the set are combined using the operation, the answer is also in the set of numbers. The positive integers are closed under addition but are not closed under subtraction.

Ask students to do a report analyzing closure of different sets of numbers under different operations. To help them get started suggest that they consider: the natural numbers using division; the integers using subtraction; the rational numbers using multiplication; the rational numbers using division; the real numbers using addition; the real numbers taking square roots; imaginary numbers using multiplication; complex numbers using square roots.

MANAGING CHAPTER 8

Lesson	PACING CHART (DAYS) Algebra	Algebra w/Finite	Algebra w/Trig	Comprehensive	Opening Activity	Cooperative Activity	Seat or Group Work
8-1	2	1	1	1	First Five Minutes 8-1: **TE** p.342 or ***FFM Transparency Masters*** p.25	Critical Thinking: **SE** p.346 Strategy Problem Bank 7: ***Problem Bank*** p.8	Try This a–n
8-2	1	1	1	1	First Five Minutes 8-2: **TE** p.347 or ***FFM Transparency Masters*** p.25	Critical Thinking: **SE** p.349	Try This a–b
8-3	2	1	1	1	First Five Minutes 8-3: **TE** p.350 or ***FFM Transparency Masters*** p.25	Critical Thinking: **SE** p.353	Try This a–e
8-4	2	1	1	1	First Five Minutes 8-4: **TE** p.354 or ***FFM Transparency Masters*** p.26	Critical Thinking: **SE** p.358 Critical Thinking 8: ***Enrichment*** p.29	Try This a–l
8-5	1	1	1	1	First Five Minutes 8-5: **TE** p.359 or ***FFM Transparency Masters*** p.26	Critical Thinking: **SE** p.361 Looking for Errors 8: ***Enrichment*** p.69	Try This a–f
8-6	2	2	2	1	First Five Minutes 8-6: **TE** p.362 or ***FFM Transparency Masters*** p.26	Critical Thinking: **SE** p.365	Try This a–c
8-7	1	1	1	1	First Five Minutes 8-7: **TE** p.366 or ***FFM Transparency Masters*** p.26	Critical Thinking: **SE** p.371	Try This a–e
8-8	1	1	1	0.5	First Five Minutes 8-8: **TE** p.372 or ***FFM Transparency Masters*** p.27	Strategy Problem Bank 8: ***Problem Bank*** p.9	Problem 2: **SE** p.373
Review	1	1	1	0.5			
Test	1	1	1	1			

FFM: First Five Minutes SPMR: Skills Practice Mixed Review

MANAGING CHAPTER 8

Enrichment	Review/Assess	Reteach	Technology	Lesson
✂ Manipulative Activity 8: ***Enrichment*** p.49	Lesson Quiz: **TE** p.345	Skills Practice 21, #1–23: ***SPMR*** p.33		**8-1**
Pythagorean Theorem Proof: **TE** p.347	Lesson Quiz: **TE** p.349 Quiz 15: ***Assessment*** p.23	Skills Practice 21, #24–26 ***SPMR*** p.33 Problem Bank 12: ***Problem Bank*** p.33		**8-2**
Math Point: **TE** p.351 Lesson Enrichment: **TE** p.352	Lesson Quiz: **TE** p.352	Skills Practice 21, #27–36 ***SPMR*** p.33	Calculator Worksheet 12: ***Technology*** p.14 Problem for Programmers: **SE** p.353	**8-3**
Critical Thinking 8: ***Enrichment*** p.29	Lesson Quiz: **TE** p.356	Skills Practice 22, #1–26 ***SPMR*** p.34	Worksheet 10: ***TI-81 Activities*** pp.41–44; Worksheet 10: ***Master Grapher*** pp.45–48, pp.179–182, or pp.315–318 Calculator Worksheet 13: ***Technology*** p.15	**8-4**
Looking for Errors 8: ***Enrichment*** p.69	Lesson Quiz: **TE** p.360 Quiz 16: ***Assessment*** p.24	Skills Practice 22, #27–40 ***SPMR*** p.34	Worksheet 11: ***TI-81 Activities*** pp.45–47; Worksheet 11: ***Master Grapher*** pp.49–51, pp.183–185, or pp.319–321	**8-5**
Writing to Learn: **SE** p.365	Lesson Quiz: **TE** p.363 Mixed Review 15: ***SPMR*** p.79	Skills Practice 23, #1–10 ***SPMR*** p.35 Problem Bank 13: ***Problem Bank*** p.34	BASIC Computer Project 7: ***Technology*** p.87	**8-6**
Bonus Topic 8: ***Enrichment*** p.9	Lesson Quiz: **TE** p.370	Skills Practice 23, #11–16 ***SPMR*** p.35 Problem Bank 14: ***Problem Bank*** p.35	Calculator Worksheet 14: ***Technology*** p.16	**8-7**
Problem 8: Computer Assisted Problem Solving, p.844	Mixed Review 16: ***SPMR*** p.80	Strategy Problem Bank 8: ***Problem Bank*** p.9	Problem 8: Computer Assisted Problem Solving, **SE** p.844	**8-8**
	Summary and Review: **SE** pp.374–375 Test: **SE** p.376			**Review**
	Chapter 8 Test: ***Assessment*** pp.89–94(reg.), pp.171–172 (adv.); Assessing Strategies 5: ***Assessment*** pp.203–204			**Test**

The solution to the problem posed on the facing page can be found on p. 368.

Ready for Quadratic Equations?

5-5 Solve.

1. $x^2 - 5x - 14 = 0$ 7, −2

2. $4x^2 - 8x = 0$ 0, 2

3. $x^2 + 10x + 25 = 0$ −5

4. $x^2 - 9 = 0$ 3, −3

6-9 Find the constant of variation and an equation of variation.

5. y varies directly as x, and $y = 8$ when $x = 20$ $\frac{2}{5}$; $y = \frac{2}{5}x$

6. y varies inversely as x, and $y = 20$ when $x = 8$ 160; $y = \frac{160}{x}$

7-4 Rationalize the denominator.

7. $\sqrt{\frac{8}{7}}$ $\frac{2\sqrt{14}}{7}$

8. $\frac{1}{2\sqrt{2}}$ $\frac{\sqrt{2}}{4}$

9. $\frac{1}{3 - \sqrt{3}}$ $\frac{3 + \sqrt{3}}{6}$

7-7 Express in terms of i.

10. $\sqrt{-7}$ $i\sqrt{7}$

11. $\sqrt{-20}$ $2i\sqrt{5}$

CHAPTER

Quadratic Equations 8

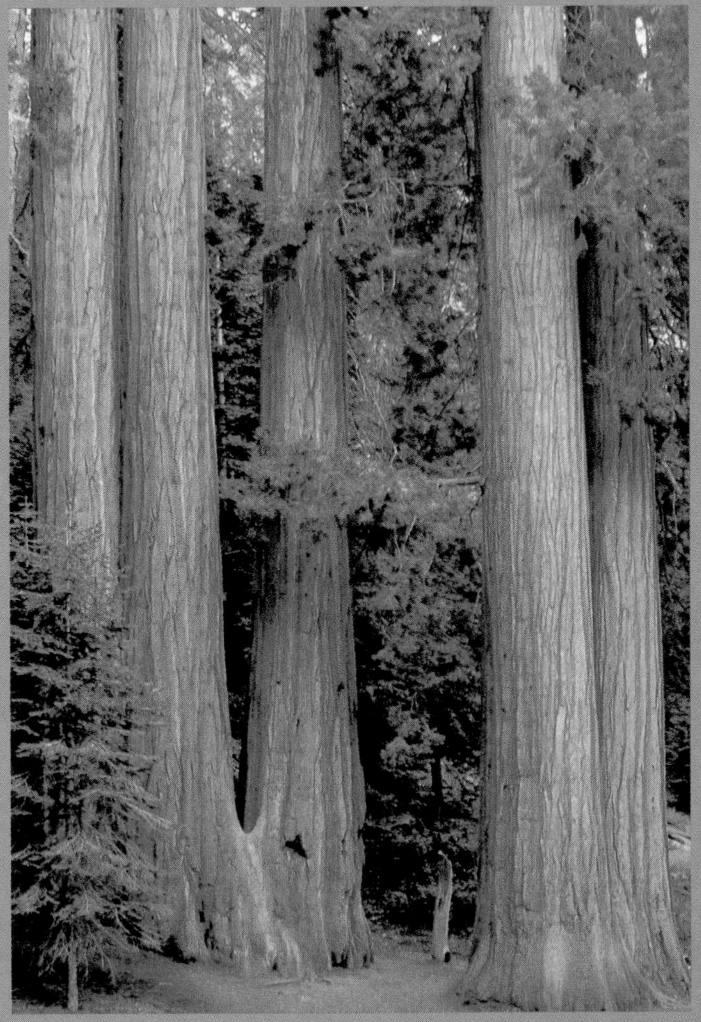

The volume (V) *of wood in a tree varies jointly as the height* (h) *and the square of the girth* (g), *the distance around the tree. The volume of a tree is 216 m^3 for a height of 30 m and a girth of 1.5 m. What is the height of a tree whose volume is 960 m^3 and girth is 2 m?*

8-1

FIRST FIVE MINUTES

1. Simplify i^5.
   i
2. Multiply $(5 + 2i)(3 + 7i)$.
   $(15 - 14) + (35 + 6)i$
   $= 1 + 41i$
3. Divide $\frac{3 + 5i}{6 + 8i}$.
   $\frac{3 + 5i}{6 + 8i} \cdot \frac{6 - 8i}{6 - 8i}$
   $= \frac{58 + 6i}{100} = \frac{29}{50} + \frac{3}{50}i$

Equations of the Type $ax^2 + bx + c = 0$

Remind the students that the complex numbers include the real numbers.

In example 1, explain to students that $3x^2 + 5x = 0$ is indeed in standard form, and that $c = 0$. You may also want to point out that when $c = 0$, the solutions are always in the form $0, -\frac{b}{a}$.

Key Questions

- What are a, b, and c for the quadratic equation $7x + 5x^2 = 9$?
  $a = 5, b = 7, c = -9$
- What is an example of a quadratic equation with only one solution?
  Any trinomial square;
  $x^2 - 10x + 25 = 0$ is one possible answer.

Chalkboard Examples

Solve.

1. $2x^2 + 7x = 0$
   $x(2x + 7) = 0$
   $x = 0$ or $2x + 7 = 0$
   $x = 0$ or $x = -\frac{7}{2}$
2. $5x^2 - 7 = 0$
   $5x^2 = 7$
   $x^2 = \frac{7}{5}$
   $x = \pm\sqrt{\frac{7}{5}} = \pm\frac{\sqrt{35}}{5}$
3. $2x^2 + 3 = 0$
   $x^2 = -\frac{3}{2}$
   $x = \pm\sqrt{-\frac{3}{2}}$
   $x = \pm i\sqrt{\frac{3}{2}} = \pm i\frac{\sqrt{6}}{2}$

8-1 Introduction to Quadratic Equations

The second-degree or quadratic equation $16t^2 + v_0t - h = 0$ relates the time t an object is in the air to the initial velocity v_0 and the height h of the object.

Definition

An equation of the type $ax^2 + bx + c = 0$, where a, b, and c are constants and $a \neq 0$, is called the **standard form** of a quadratic equation.

Equations of the Type $ax^2 + bx + c = 0$

Objective: Solve equations of the type $ax^2 + bx + c = 0$.

Every quadratic polynomial $ax^2 + bx + c$ with complex coefficients can be factored into two linear factors.

EXAMPLE 1 Solve $3x^2 + 5x = 0$.

This is an equation of the type $ax^2 + bx + c = 0$, where $c = 0$. Quadratic equations in standard form where $c = 0$ can be easily solved by factoring.

$$x(3x + 5) = 0 \quad \text{Factoring}$$
$$x = 0 \text{ or } 3x + 5 = 0 \quad \text{Using the principle of zero products}$$
$$x = 0 \text{ or } x = -\frac{5}{3}$$

These numbers check, so the solutions are 0 and $-\frac{5}{3}$.

A quadratic equation of this type will always have 0 as one solution.

Sometimes it helps to find standard form before factoring.

EXAMPLE 2 Solve $(x - 1)(x + 1) = 5(x - 1)$.

$$x^2 - 1 = 5x - 5 \quad \text{Multiplying}$$
$$x^2 - 5x + 4 = 0 \quad \text{Finding standard form}$$
$$(x - 4)(x - 1) = 0 \quad \text{Factoring}$$
$$x = 4 \text{ or } x = 1 \quad \text{Using the principle of zero products}$$

These numbers check, so the solutions are 4 and 1.

Try This Solve.

a. $5x^2 + 8x = 0$ $0, -\frac{8}{5}$ **b.** $14x^2 + 2 = 11x$ $\frac{2}{7}, \frac{1}{2}$ **c.** $(x + 2)(x - 2) = 2 - x$ $-3, 2$

Consider any quadratic equation in standard form $ax^2 + bx + c = 0$, where $b = 0$, that is, an equation of the form $ax^2 + c = 0$. We can use the multiplication and addition principles to obtain an equation of the form $x^2 = k$, where $x = \sqrt{k}$ or $x = -\sqrt{k}$.

EXAMPLE 3 Solve $3x^2 - 6 = 0$.

$3x^2 = 6$ Using the addition property

$x^2 = 2$ Multiplying both sides by $\frac{1}{3}$

$x = \sqrt{2}$ or $x = -\sqrt{2}$

We can abbreviate this as $x = \pm\sqrt{2}$.

Sometimes we get solutions that are complex numbers.

EXAMPLE 4 Solve $4x^2 + 9 = 0$.

$4x^2 = -9$ Adding -9 to both sides

$x^2 = -\frac{9}{4}$ Multiplying both sides by $\frac{1}{4}$

$x = \sqrt{-\frac{9}{4}}$ or $x = -\sqrt{-\frac{9}{4}}$ Finding square roots

$x = \frac{3}{2}i$ or $x = -\frac{3}{2}i$

$x = \pm\frac{3}{2}i$

Try This Solve.

d. $7x^2 - 5 = 0$ $\pm\frac{\sqrt{35}}{7}$ **e.** $2x^2 + 1 = 0$ $\pm\frac{\sqrt{2}}{2}i$ **f.** $49x^2 + 4 = 0$ $\pm\frac{2}{7}i$

Solving Quadratic Equations by Completing the Square

Objective: Solve a quadratic equation by completing the square.

The trinomial $x^2 + 10x + 25$ is the square of a binomial, because $x^2 + 10x + 25 = (x + 5)^2$. Given the first two terms of a trinomial, we can find the third term that will make it a square. This process is called completing the square.

EXAMPLE 5 Complete the square for $x^2 + 12x$.

What must be added to $x^2 + 12x$ to make it a trinomial square? We take half the coefficient of x and square it.

$x^2 + 12x$

↓

Half of 12 is 6, and $6^2 = 36$. We add 36.

$x^2 + 12x + 36$ is a trinomial square. It is equal to $(x + 6)^2$.

Solving Quadratic Equations by Completing the Square

The following diagram may serve as a useful illustration of completing the square.

This is how we would complete the square for $x^2 + 12x$.

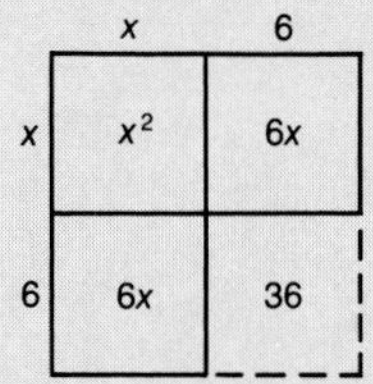

You may wish to show completing the square for a leading coefficient other than 1.

Point out that an alternate form for the answer to Example 7 is $1 \pm \sqrt{6}$, which is read, "one plus or minus the square root of six."

Chalkboard Examples

1. What must be added to $x^2 + 8x$ to make it a perfect trinomial square?
   Half of 8 is 4. Add $4^2 = 16$ to get $x^2 + 8x + 16$, which factors into $(x + 4)^2$.

Solve by completing the square.

2. $x^2 + 10x + 23 = 0$
   $x^2 + 10x = -23$
   $x^2 + 10x + 25 = -23 + 25$
   $(x + 5)^2 = 2$
   $x + 5 = \pm\sqrt{2}$
   $x = -5 + \sqrt{2}$ or $x = -5 - \sqrt{2}$
3. $9x^2 - 9x + 2 = 0$
   $x^2 - x = -\frac{2}{9}$
   $x^2 - x + \frac{1}{4} = -\frac{2}{9} + \frac{1}{4}$
   $\left(x - \frac{1}{2}\right)^2 = \frac{1}{36}$
   $x - \frac{1}{2} = \pm\frac{1}{6}$
   $x = \frac{1}{2} \pm \frac{1}{6}$
   $x = \frac{2}{3}$ or $x = \frac{1}{3}$

LESSON ENRICHMENT

Solve $(3 + 4i)x^2 = 3 - 4i$.

$$x^2 = \frac{3 - 4i}{3 + 4i}$$
$$= \frac{(3 - 4i)(3 - 4i)}{(3 + 4i)(3 - 4i)}$$
$$= \frac{(3 - 4i)^2}{25}$$
$$x = \pm\frac{3 - 4i}{5}$$
$$x = \frac{3}{5} - \frac{4}{5}i \text{ or}$$
$$x = -\frac{3}{5} + \frac{4}{5}i$$

EXAMPLE 6 Complete the square for $y^2 + \frac{3}{4}y$.

Half of $\frac{3}{4}$ (the coefficient of y) is $\frac{1}{2} \cdot \frac{3}{4} = \frac{3}{8}$.

$$\left(\frac{3}{8}\right)^2 = \frac{9}{64}$$

Thus $y^2 + \frac{3}{4}y + \frac{9}{64}$ is a trinomial square. It is $(y + \frac{3}{8})^2$.

Try This Complete the square.

g. $x^2 + 14x$ $x^2 + 14x + 49$

h. $y^2 - 11y$ $y^2 - 11y + \frac{121}{4}$

i. $x^2 - \frac{2}{5}x$ $x^2 - \frac{2}{5}x + \frac{1}{25}$

j. $x^2 + 2ax$ $x^2 + 2ax + a^2$

We can solve quadratic equations of the form $ax^2 + bx + c = 0$ by completing the square.

EXAMPLE 7 Solve by completing the square.

$$x^2 - 2x - 5 = 0$$
$$x^2 - 2x = 5 \quad \text{Adding 5 to both sides}$$
$$x^2 - 2x + 1 = 5 + 1 \quad \text{Adding 1 to complete the square, } \left(\frac{-2}{2}\right)^2 = 1$$
$$(x - 1)^2 = 6$$
$$x - 1 = \sqrt{6} \text{ or } x - 1 = -\sqrt{6}$$
$$x = 1 + \sqrt{6} \text{ or } x = 1 - \sqrt{6}$$

Check:

$x^2 - 2x - 5$	$= 0$
$(1 + \sqrt{6})^2 - 2(1 + \sqrt{6}) - 5$	0
$1 + 2\sqrt{6} + 6 - 2 - 2\sqrt{6} - 5$	0
0	0 ✓

$x^2 - 2x - 5$	$= 0$
$(1 - \sqrt{6})^2 - 2(1 - \sqrt{6}) - 5$	0
$1 - 2\sqrt{6} + 6 - 2 + 2\sqrt{6} - 5$	0
0	0 ✓

The numbers check, so they are the solutions. The solutions can be abbreviated as $x = 1 \pm \sqrt{6}$.

Try This Solve by completing the square.

k. $x^2 + x - 1 = 0$ $\frac{-1 \pm \sqrt{5}}{2}$

l. $x^2 - \frac{1}{2}x - \frac{1}{2} = 0$ $-\frac{1}{2}, 1$

For many quadratic equations the leading coefficient is not 1, but we can use the multiplication principle to make it 1.

EXAMPLE 8 Solve by completing the square.

$$4x^2 + 12x - 7 = 0$$
$$x^2 + 3x - \frac{7}{4} = 0 \quad \text{Multiplying both sides by } \frac{1}{4}$$

$$x^2 + 3x = \frac{7}{4}$$

$$x^2 + 3x + \frac{9}{4} = \frac{7}{4} + \frac{9}{4} \quad \text{Adding } \tfrac{9}{4} \text{ to complete the square}$$

$$\left(x + \frac{3}{2}\right)^2 = 4$$

$$x + \frac{3}{2} = 2 \text{ or } x + \frac{3}{2} = -2$$

$$x = \frac{1}{2} \text{ or } x = -\frac{7}{2}$$

Try This Solve by completing the square.

m. $8x^2 - x - 1 = 0$ $\frac{1 \pm \sqrt{33}}{16}$ **n.** $9x^2 + 9x - 10 = 0$ $\frac{2}{3}, -\frac{5}{3}$

8-1 EXERCISES

A

Solve.

1. $7x^2 - 3x = 0$ $0, \frac{3}{7}$ **2.** $14x^2 + 9x = 0$ $0, -\frac{9}{14}$ **3.** $19x^2 + 8x = 0$ $0, -\frac{8}{19}$

4. $x^2 + 8x + 15 = 0$ $-5, -3$ **5.** $x^2 + 9x + 14 = 0$ $-7, -2$

6. $6x^2 - x - 2 = 0$ $\frac{2}{3}, -\frac{1}{2}$ **7.** $2x^2 + 13x + 15 = 0$ $-\frac{3}{2}, -5$

8. $9t^2 + 15t + 4 = 0$ $-\frac{4}{3}, -\frac{1}{3}$ **9.** $3y^2 + 10y - 8 = 0$ $\frac{2}{3}, -4$

10. $6x^2 + 4x = 10$ $-\frac{5}{3}, 1$ **11.** $3x^2 + 7x = 20$ $\frac{5}{3}, -4$

12. $2x(4x - 5) = 3$ $-\frac{1}{4}, \frac{3}{2}$ **13.** $t(2t + 9) = -7$ $-\frac{7}{2}, -1$

14. $(p - 3)(p - 4) = 42$ $10, -3$ **15.** $16(t - 1) = t(t + 8)$ 4

16. $4x(x - 2) - 5x(x - 1) = 2$ **17.** $14(x - 4) - (x + 2) = (x + 2)(x - 4)$

Solve.

18. $4x^2 = 20$ **19.** $3x^2 = 21$ **20.** $10x^2 = 0$

21. $9x^2 = 0$ **22.** $2x^2 - 3 = 0$ **23.** $3x^2 - 7 = 0$

24. $-3x^2 + 5 = 0$ **25.** $-2x^2 + 1 = 0$ **26.** $25x^2 + 4 = 0$

27. $9x^2 + 16 = 0$ **28.** $3x^2 + 1 = 0$ **29.** $5x^2 + 1 = 0$

30. $x^2 + 5 = 0$ **31.** $x^2 + 6 = 0$ **32.** $2x^2 + 14 = 0$

33. $3x^2 + 15 = 0$ **34.** $\frac{4}{9}x^2 - 1 = 0$ **35.** $\frac{16}{25}x^2 - 1 = 0$

Complete the square.

36. $x^2 + 8x$ **37.** $y^2 - 20y$ **38.** $a^2 - 7a$

39. $y^2 - \frac{1}{5}y$ **40.** $x^2 + \frac{1}{2}x$ **41.** $x^2 - 2.6kx$

LESSON QUIZ

Solve.

1. $x^2 + 3x = 0$
   $x(x + 3) = 0$
   $x = 0$ or $x = -3$
2. $x^2 - 7 = 0$
   $x = \pm\sqrt{7}$
3. $x^2 - 9x + 20 = 0$
   $(x - 4)(x - 5) = 0$
   $x = 4$ or $x = 5$
4. $x^2 + 2x - 5 = 0$
   $x = -1 \pm \sqrt{6}$

Assignment Guide

Algebra: Day 1: 1–17, MR
Day 2: 18–52 e/o

Alg w/Finite or Trig: 1–59 m3, 60, MR

Comprehensive: 1–59 m3, 60–63, MR

ADDITIONAL ANSWERS

Exercises

16. $-2, -1$
17. $10, 5$
18. $\pm\sqrt{5}$
19. $\pm\sqrt{7}$
20. 0
21. 0
22. $\pm\frac{\sqrt{6}}{2}$
23. $\pm\frac{\sqrt{21}}{3}$
24. $\pm\frac{\sqrt{15}}{3}$
25. $\pm\frac{\sqrt{2}}{2}$
26. $\pm\frac{2}{5}i$
27. $\pm\frac{4}{3}i$
28. $\pm\frac{i\sqrt{3}}{3}$
29. $\pm\frac{i\sqrt{5}}{5}$
30. $\pm i\sqrt{5}$
31. $\pm i\sqrt{6}$
32. $\pm i\sqrt{7}$
33. $\pm i\sqrt{5}$
34. $\pm\frac{3}{2}$
35. $\pm\frac{5}{4}$

36. $x^2 + 8x + 16$
37. $y^2 - 20y + 100$
38. $a^2 - 7a + \frac{49}{4}$
39. $y^2 - \frac{1}{5}y + \frac{1}{100}$
40. $x^2 + \frac{1}{2}x + \frac{1}{16}$
41. $x^2 - 2.6kx + 1.69k^2$
42. 1, 2
43. −3, −4
44. $\frac{-1 \pm i\sqrt{3}}{2}$ or $-\frac{1}{2} \pm \frac{i\sqrt{3}}{2}$
45. $2 \pm \sqrt{3}$
46. $-3 \pm 2\sqrt{3}$
47. $\frac{-1 \pm \sqrt{69}}{2}$
48. $\frac{5 \pm \sqrt{77}}{2}$
49. $\frac{5 \pm \sqrt{145}}{6}$
50. $1, -\frac{9}{2}$

Mixed Review

64. $(m + 4)^2$
65. $2a^3\sqrt{15}$
66. $4m^2n^4\sqrt{3m}$
67. $\sqrt{2} - 4\sqrt{10}$
68. $m - n$
69. $7 - \sqrt{21} + \sqrt{14} - \sqrt{6}$
70.

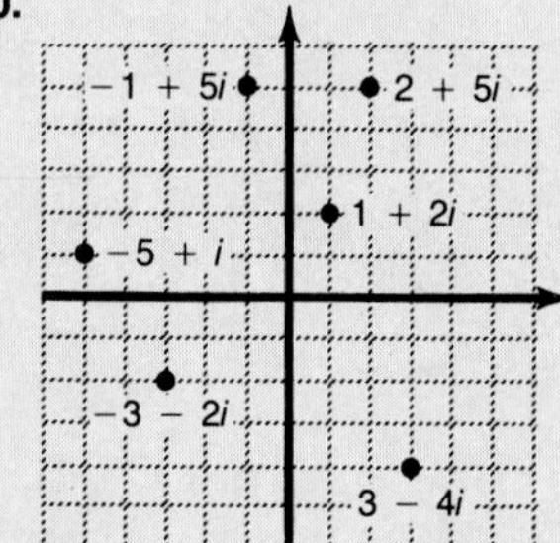

71. 13
72. 5
73. 4
74. $412.09

Solve by completing the square.

42. $x^2 - 3x + 2 = 0$ **43.** $y^2 + 7y + 12 = 0$ **44.** $x^2 + x + 1 = 0$
45. $x^2 - 4x + 1 = 0$ **46.** $y^2 + 6y - 3 = 0$ **47.** $y^2 + y - 17 = 0$
48. $x^2 - 5x - 13 = 0$ **49.** $3x^2 - 5x - 10 = 0$ **50.** $2y^2 + 7y - 9 = 0$

51. $\frac{1}{2}y^2 - 3y + 9 = 0$ $3 \pm 3i$ **52.** $2d^2 + 2d + 4 = 0$ $-\frac{1}{2} \pm \frac{\sqrt{7}}{2}i$

B

Solve.

53. $(3x^2 - 7x - 20)(2x - 5) = 0$ $-\frac{5}{3}, 4, \frac{5}{2}$

54. $x(2x^2 + 9x - 56)(3x + 10) = 0$ $-8, -\frac{10}{3}, 0, \frac{7}{2}$

Solve for x.

55. $ax^2 - b = 0$ $\pm\sqrt{\frac{b}{a}}$ or $\frac{\sqrt{ab}}{a}$ **56.** $ax^2 - bx = 0$ $0, \frac{b}{a}$

57. $\left(x - \frac{1}{3}\right)\left(x - \frac{1}{3}\right) + \left(x - \frac{1}{3}\right)\left(x + \frac{2}{9}\right) = 0$ $\frac{1}{18}, \frac{1}{3}$

Solve by completing the square.

58. $\frac{1}{2}(1 + m)(1 - m) = 10m$ $-10 \pm \sqrt{101}$ **59.** $a^2 - 2\sqrt{3}\,a + 2 = 0$ $\sqrt{3} \pm 1$

60. ***Critical Thinking*** Show the geometrical representation of completing the square for $x^2 + ax$ by providing the missing labels. What is the resulting binomial square? ◇ $\left(x + \frac{a}{2}\right)^2$

x ? $\frac{a}{2}$
x | x^2 | ? $\frac{ax}{2}$
$\frac{a}{2}$? | ? $\frac{ax}{2}$ | ? $\frac{a^2}{4}$

Challenge

Solve for x.

61. $ax^n + bx^{n-1} = 0$ $0, -\frac{b}{a}$ **62.** $ax^n + b = 0$ $\sqrt[n]{-\frac{b}{a}}$

63. How do the solutions of $ax^2 + h = 0$ compare to the solutions of $ax^2 = h$, where a and h are positive? The solutions to $ax^2 = h$ are $\pm\sqrt{\frac{h}{a}}$; the solutions to $ax^2 + h = 0$ are $\pm i\sqrt{\frac{h}{a}}$.

Mixed Review

Multiply. **64.** $\sqrt[5]{(m + 4)^6} \cdot \sqrt[5]{(m + 4)^4}$ **65.** $\sqrt{6a} \cdot \sqrt{10a^5}$

66. $\sqrt{6m^3n^5} \cdot \sqrt{8m^2n^3}$ **67.** $\sqrt{2}\,(1 - 4\sqrt{5})$ **68.** $(\sqrt{m} + \sqrt{n})(\sqrt{m} - \sqrt{n})$

69. $(\sqrt{7} + \sqrt{2})(\sqrt{7} - \sqrt{3})$

Graph. **70.** $2 + 5i$; $3 - 4i$; $-1 + 5i$; $-3 - 2i$; $-5 + i$; $1 + 2i$

Find the absolute value. **71.** $|12 + 5i|$ **72.** $|4 - 3i|$ **73.** $|4i|$

74. Linessa's credit card interest was 1.5% per month, compounded monthly. She paid $400 for an item with her credit card. Assuming she made no payments, how much did she owe after two months?

8-2 Problem Solving: Using Quadratic Equations

Objective: Solve problems by translating to quadratic equations.

PROBLEM-SOLVING GUIDELINES
■ UNDERSTAND the problem
■ Develop and carry out a PLAN
■ Find the ANSWER and CHECK

For some problems a quadratic equation will serve as a mathematical model. Problem-solving strategies such as *write an equation, draw a diagram,* and others may be used together, as with a linear model.

EXAMPLE 1

A rectangular lawn is 60 m by 80 m. Part of the lawn is torn up to install a pool, leaving a strip of lawn of uniform width around the pool. The area of the pool is $\frac{1}{6}$ of the old lawn area. How wide is the strip of lawn?

■ UNDERSTAND the problem

Question: Find the width of the strip of lawn. — Clarifying the question

Data: The lawn is 60 m by 80 m. — Identifying the important data

The pool is $\frac{1}{6}$ of the total area.

■ Develop and carry out a PLAN

First *draw a diagram.* — Letting x stand for the width of the strip of lawn

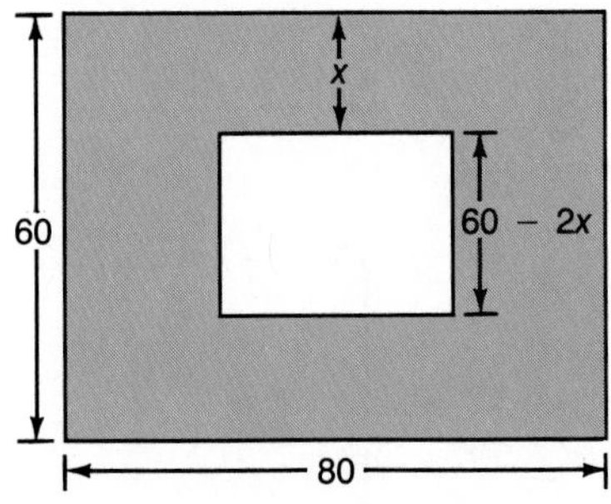

$$\text{Total area} = 60 \cdot 80$$
$$\text{Area of pool} = (60 - 2x)(80 - 2x)$$

The area of the pool is $\frac{1}{6}$ the original area of the lawn.

Therefore,

$$(60 - 2x)(80 - 2x) = \frac{1}{6} \cdot 60 \cdot 80$$

$$4800 - 160x - 120x + 4x^2 = 800$$ — Solving the equation

$$4x^2 - 280x + 4000 = 0$$
$$x^2 - 70x + 1000 = 0$$
$$(x - 20)(x - 50) = 0$$
$$x = 20 \text{ or } x = 50$$

8-2

FIRST FIVE MINUTES

Solve.

1. $3x^2 + 6x = 0$
   $3x(x + 2) = 0$
   $x = 0$ or $x = -2$
2. $x^2 + 10x + 23 = 0$
   $x^2 + 10x + 25 = 2$
   $(x + 5)^2 = 2$
   $x + 5 = \pm\sqrt{2}$
   $x = -5 \pm \sqrt{2}$

Emphasize the importance of naming unknown quantities and specifying the units of measurement.

You may want to show students the following proof of the Pythagorean theorem.

Assume we have a square with sides of length $a + b$. As shown in the figure below, we draw four right triangles with legs a and b.

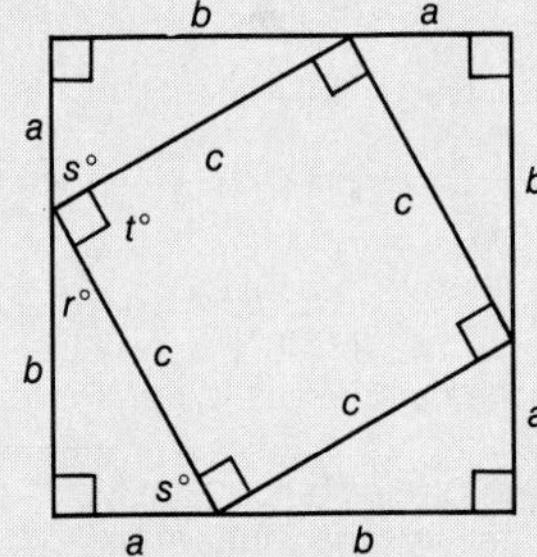

1. By the SAS postulate, the four right triangles are congruent.
2. Since corresponding parts of congruent triangles are congruent, we know that the hypotenuse of each triangle is of the same length, which we will call c.
3. Since the acute angles of a right triangle are complementary, we know that $r + s = 90$. Using the notation of the figure, we also know that $r + s + t = 180$. Therefore, $t = 90$ and the quadrilateral inside the square is also a square.
4. The area of the large square, $(a + b)^2$, minus the area of the four right triangles, $4\left(\frac{1}{2}ab\right)$, equals the area of the small square, c^2.

$$(a + b)^2 - 4\left(\frac{1}{2}ab\right) = c^2$$
$$a^2 + 2ab + b^2 - 2ab = c^2$$
$$a^2 + b^2 = c^2$$

Key Questions

- If the sides of a field are given in miles, what will the unit of measurement be for the area of the field?
  Square miles
- If the legs of a right triangle are of lengths 5 and 12, what is the length of the hypotenuse?
  13

Chalkboard Examples

1. Thomas, having mowed a large rectangular plot of grass, estimates the area to be 400 square feet. Elva walks around the plot and estimates the perimeter to be 100 feet. Find the approximate dimensions of the plot.
   Let x and y be the lengths of the sides in feet.
   The area is
   $xy = 400.$ (1)
   The perimeter is
   $2x + 2y = 100.$ (2)
   Solve (2) for y.
   $y = 50 - x$
   Substitute in (1).
   $x(50 - x) = 400$
   $x^2 - 50x + 400 = 0$
   $(x - 10)(x - 40) = 0$
   The plot is 10′ by 40′.
2. A ladder is two feet longer than the height of a certain wall. When the top of the ladder is placed against the top of the wall, the distance from the base of the ladder to the wall is exactly equal to the height of the wall. How high is the wall?
   Let x be the height of the wall, in feet.
   By the Pythagorean theorem,
   $x^2 + x^2 = (x + 2)^2$
   $2x^2 = x^2 + 4x + 4$
   $x^2 - 4x = 4$
   Complete the square.
   $x^2 - 4x + 4 = 8$
   $(x - 2)^2 = 8$
   $x - 2 = \pm\sqrt{8}$
   $x = 2 \pm 2\sqrt{2}$
   $x = 2(1 \pm \sqrt{2})$
   $2(1 - \sqrt{2})$ is not acceptable since it is negative. The wall is $2(1 + \sqrt{2})$ feet (≈4.83 ft).

Find the ANSWER and CHECK

We see that 50 cannot be a solution because when x is 50, $60 - 2x$, which is the width of the pool, is -40. But the width of the pool cannot be negative.

A 20 meter wide strip checks in the problem. Since the width must be smaller than 60, it is a reasonable answer.

Try This

a. An open box is to be made from a 10 cm by 20 cm rectangular piece of cardboard by cutting a square from each corner. The area of the bottom of the box is 96 cm^2. What is the length of the sides of the squares that are cut from the corners? 2 cm

---

The following theorem is helpful for solving problems involving quadratic equations.

Theorem 8-1

The Pythagorean Theorem

In any right triangle, if a and b are the lengths of the legs and c is the length of the hypotenuse, then $a^2 + b^2 = c^2$.

EXAMPLE 2

Bicyclists A and B leave the same point P at the same time at right angles. B travels 7 km/h faster than A. After 3 hours they are 39 km apart. Find the speed of each.

We first make a *drawing*, letting r be the speed of A and $r + 7$ be the speed of B. Since they both travel 3 hours, their distances from P are $3r$ and $3(r + 7)$, respectively.

$$[3(r + 7)]^2 + (3r)^2 = 39^2 \quad \text{Using the Pythagorean theorem}$$
$$9(r + 7)^2 + 9r^2 = 1521$$
$$(r + 7)^2 + r^2 = 169 \quad \text{Multiplying by } \tfrac{1}{9}$$
$$r^2 + 14r + 49 + r^2 = 169$$
$$2r^2 + 14r + 49 = 169$$

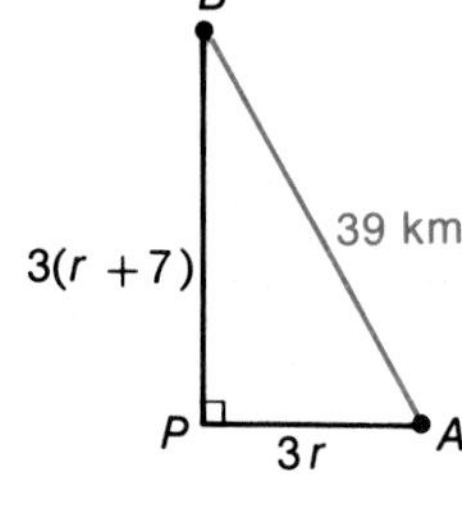

$$2r^2 + 14r - 120 = 0 \quad \text{Finding standard form}$$
$$r^2 + 7r - 60 = 0 \quad \text{Multiplying by } \tfrac{1}{2}$$
$$(r + 12)(r - 5) = 0 \quad r = -12 \text{ or } r = 5$$

The solutions of the equation are -12 and 5. Since speed cannot be negative, -12 is not a solution. The speed of A is 5 km/h and the speed of B is 12 km/h.

Try This

b. Runners A and B leave the same point P at right angles. A runs 4 km/h faster than B. After 2 hours they are 40 km apart. Find the speed of each. *A*: 16 km/h; *B*: 12 km/h

---

8-2 EXERCISES

A

1. A picture frame measures 14 cm by 20 cm. 160 cm^2 of picture shows inside the frame. Find the width of the frame. 2 cm
2. A picture frame measures 12 cm by 20 cm. 84 cm^2 of picture shows inside the frame. Find the width of the frame. 3 cm

Find the length and width. Assume the shapes are rectangular.

3. The width of a dock is 4 m less than the length. The area is 12 m^2. Length 6 m; width 2 m
4. The width of a photo is 5cm less than the length. The area is 24 cm^2. Length 8 cm; width 3 cm
5. The length of a swimming pool is twice the width. The area is 288 m^2. Length 24 m; width 12 m
6. The length of a park is twice the width. The area is 338 km^2. Length 26 km; width 13 km
7. The hypotenuse of a right triangle is 26 m long. One leg is 14 m longer than the other. Find the lengths of the legs. 24 m and 10 m
8. The hypotenuse of a right triangle is 25 km long. The length of one leg is 17 km less than the other. Find the lengths of the legs. 24 km and 7 km
9. Boats A and B leave the same point at the same time at right angles. B travels 7 km/h slower than A. After 4 hours they are 68 km apart. Find the speed of each boat. A: 15 km/h; B: 8 km/h

B

10. Find three consecutive integers such that the square of the first plus the product of the other two is 46. 4, 5, and 6
11. A bicyclist travels 280 km at a certain speed. If the speed had been increased 5 km/h, the trip could have been made in 1 hour less time. Find the actual speed. 35 km/h
12. Airplane A travels 2800 km at a certain speed. Airplane B travels 2000 km at a speed that is 50 km/h faster than Plane A in 3 hours less time. Find the speed of each. A: 350 km/h; B: 400 km/h
13. ***Critical Thinking*** Write a consecutive integer problem that can be solved by using a quadratic equation. Answers may vary.

Challenge

14. Find three consecutive integers such that the sum of their squares is 149. 6, 7, 8, or −8, −7, −6
15. Two open boxes are made by cutting squares from each corner of a 20″ by 15″ piece of cardboard, and from an 18″ by 18″ piece. The same size squares are cut from the corners of both pieces, and the flaps created are folded up. Is it possible for the boxes to have equal volumes? If so, find the length of a side of the square. Not possible. The length of a side must be 0 or 12. If $s = 0$, no box can be made. If $s = 12$, all side lengths would be negative.

Mixed Review

Solve. **16.** $\sqrt[3]{x+3} = 2$ **17.** $\sqrt{2x-1} - 3 = 0$ **18.** $\sqrt[4]{x} - 2 = 0$

Solve. **19.** $\frac{x}{4} - \frac{x}{5} = 5$ **20.** $\frac{(x+2)}{2} - \frac{(x-2)}{4} = 3$ **21.** $\frac{5x}{8} - \frac{15}{6} = \frac{x}{2}$

LESSON QUIZ

1. A rectangular garden plot has an area of 200 square yards and a perimeter of 60 yards. Find the dimensions of the rectangle.
   10 yards by 20 yards

Assignment Guide

Algebra: 1–9 e/o, MR

Alg w/Finite or Trig: 1–12 e/o, 13, MR

Comprehensive: 1–12 e/o, 13–15, MR

ADDITIONAL ANSWERS

Mixed Review

16. 5
17. 5
18. 16
19. 100
20. 6
21. 20

8-3

FIRST FIVE MINUTES

1. Solve $3x^2 - 7 = 0$.

$x^2 = \frac{7}{3}$

$x = \pm\sqrt{\frac{7}{3}} = \pm\frac{\sqrt{21}}{3}$

2. Solve $x^2 + 6x - 1 = 0$.

Complete the square.

$x^2 + 6x + 9 = 1 + 9$

$(x + 3)^2 = 10$

$x + 3 = \pm\sqrt{10}$

$x = -3 \pm \sqrt{10}$

Solving Equations Using the Quadratic Formula

Before introducing the quadratic formula, point out that some quadratic equations can be solved by factoring and some by finding the square roots. However, all quadratic equations can be solved by completing the square. A formula was derived based on the procedure used for completing a square. We call this formula the *quadratic formula* since it allows us (and computers) to solve all quadratic equations.

Demonstrate how to read the formula, "*x* equals inverse *b* plus or minus the square root of *b* squared minus four *ac*, all divided by 2*a*." Encourage students to memorize this formula.

You may wish to have students write complex solutions in the form $a \pm bi$. For example, the solution to Example 2 would be written $-\frac{1}{2} \pm \frac{\sqrt{3}}{2}i$.

Key Questions

- What are *a*, *b*, and *c* in the equation $5x + 3x^2 + 1 = 0$?
  $a = 3, b = 5, c = 1$
- If $b^2 = 4ac$, how many solutions will the quadratic formula give?
  1
- Why is it unnecessary to state that $a \neq 0$ in the quadratic formula?
  If $a = 0$, the equation is not quadratic.

8-3 The Quadratic Formula

Solving Equations Using the Quadratic Formula

Objective: Solve quadratic equations using the quadratic formula.

Some quadratic equations cannot be solved by factoring. Here is a formula for finding the solutions of any quadratic equation.

Theorem 8-2

The Quadratic Formula

The solutions of any quadratic equation with complex coefficients, $ax^2 + bx + c = 0$, are given by the **quadratic formula.**

$$x = \frac{-b \pm \sqrt{b^2 - 4ac}}{2a}$$

EXAMPLE 1 Solve $3x^2 + 5x = -1$.

First find the standard form and determine *a, b,* and *c*.

$$3x^2 + 5x + 1 = 0$$

$$a = 3, b = 5, c = 1$$

Then use the quadratic formula.

$$x = \frac{-b \pm \sqrt{b^2 - 4ac}}{2a}$$

$$x = \frac{-(5) \pm \sqrt{(5)^2 - 4 \cdot 3 \cdot 1}}{2 \cdot 3} \quad \text{Substituting}$$

$$x = \frac{-5 \pm \sqrt{25 - 12}}{6} = \frac{-5 \pm \sqrt{13}}{6}$$

The solutions are $\frac{-5 + \sqrt{13}}{6}$ and $\frac{-5 - \sqrt{13}}{6}$.

When using the quadratic formula, the solutions obtained are always solutions of the original equation unless a computational error has been made.

Try This Solve using the quadratic formula.

a. $3x^2 + 2x = 7$ $\frac{-1 \pm \sqrt{22}}{3}$ **b.** $5x^2 + 3x = 9$ $\frac{-3 \pm 3\sqrt{21}}{10}$

When the expression under the radical sign is negative, we obtain complex solutions.

EXAMPLE 2 Solve $x^2 + x + 1 = 0$.

$$a = 1, b = 1, c = 1$$
$$x = \frac{-b \pm \sqrt{b^2 - 4ac}}{2a}$$
$$x = \frac{-1 \pm \sqrt{1^2 - 4 \cdot 1 \cdot 1}}{2 \cdot 1} \quad \text{Substituting}$$
$$x = \frac{-1 \pm \sqrt{1 - 4}}{2}$$
$$x = \frac{-1 \pm \sqrt{-3}}{2}$$
$$x = \frac{-1 \pm i\sqrt{3}}{2}$$

The solutions are $\frac{-1 + i\sqrt{3}}{2}$ and $\frac{-1 - i\sqrt{3}}{2}$.

Try This Solve.

c. $x^2 - x + 2 = 0$ $\frac{1 \pm i\sqrt{7}}{2}$ **d.** $3x^2 + 2x + 2 = 0$ $\frac{-1 \pm i\sqrt{5}}{3}$

Approximating Solutions

Objective: Find approximate values for solutions to quadratic equations.

A calculator or square root table can be used to find rational-number approximations to the exact solutions given by the formula.

EXAMPLE 3 Approximate the solutions of the equation in Example 1. Use a calculator or Table 1.

$$\frac{-5 + \sqrt{13}}{6} \approx \frac{-5 + 3.6055513}{6} \quad \text{Using a calculator to find } \sqrt{13}$$
$$\approx \frac{-1.3944488}{6}$$
$$\approx -0.23 \quad \text{Rounding to the nearest hundredth}$$
$$\frac{-5 - \sqrt{13}}{6} \approx \frac{-5 + 3.6055513}{6}$$
$$\approx \frac{-8.6055513}{6}$$
$$\approx -1.43 \quad \text{Rounding to the nearest hundredth}$$

Try This

e. Approximate the solutions to $3x^2 + 2x = 7$. Round to the nearest hundredth. 1.23, −1.90

Chalkboard Examples

1. Solve $5x^2 + 6x + 1 = 0$.
$$x = \frac{-6 \pm \sqrt{6^2 - 4 \cdot 5 \cdot 1}}{2 \cdot 5}$$
$$= \frac{-6 \pm 4}{10}$$
$$x = \frac{-1}{5} \text{ or } x = -1$$

2. Solve $5x^2 + 6x + 2 = 0$.
$$x = \frac{-6 \pm \sqrt{6^2 - 4 \cdot 5 \cdot 2}}{2 \cdot 5}$$
$$x = \frac{-6 \pm \sqrt{-4}}{2 \cdot 5}$$
$$x = \frac{-3}{5} + \frac{1}{5}i \text{ or}$$
$$x = \frac{-3}{5} - \frac{1}{5}i$$

Approximating Solutions

Point out that because of rounding, Table 1 and calculators lead to different answers.

Math Point

The following is an alternate proof to Theorem 8-2.

Consider the quadratic equation $ax^2 + bx + c = 0$. The coefficients can be any complex numbers, but a cannot equal 0.

Multiply both sides by $4a$.
$$4a^2x^2 + 4abx + 4ac = 0$$
Add b^2 to both sides.
$$4a^2x^2 + 4abx + b^2 + 4ac = b^2$$
Rearrange, factor, and solve for x.
$$4a^2x^2 + 4abx + b^2 = b^2 - 4ac$$
Factor the left side.
$$(2ax + b)^2 = b^2 - 4ac$$
$$2ax + b = \pm\sqrt{b^2 - 4ac}$$
$$x = \frac{-b \pm \sqrt{b^2 - 4ac}}{2a}$$

Chalkboard Example

1. Use a calculator or Table 1 to find the value of the expression
$$\frac{-3 + \sqrt{7}}{5}$$
Round the answer to two decimal places.
−0.07

LESSON ENRICHMENT

Have students verify the quadratic formula by substituting $x = \frac{-b + \sqrt{b^2 - 4ac}}{2a}$ into the equation $ax^2 + bx + c = 0$.

LESSON QUIZ

Solve.

1. $9x^2 - 9x + 2 = 0$

   $x = \frac{1}{3}$ or $x = \frac{2}{3}$

2. $2x^2 + 5x + 1 = 0$

   $x = \frac{-5 \pm \sqrt{17}}{4}$

3. $2x^2 + 3x + 4 = 0$

   $x = \frac{-3 \pm i\sqrt{23}}{4}$

Assignment Guide

Algebra: Day 1: 1–18, MR
Day 2: 19–40

Alg w/Finite or Trig: 1–47 e/o, 48, MR

Comprehensive: 1–47 e/o, 48–51, MR

Proof of Theorem 8-2

Consider any quadratic equation in the form $ax^2 + bx + c = 0$, $(a > 0)$.

Let's solve by completing the square.

$$x^2 + \frac{b}{a}x + \frac{c}{a} = 0 \qquad \text{Multiplying by } \tfrac{1}{a}$$

$$x^2 + \frac{b}{a}x = -\frac{c}{a} \qquad \text{Adding } -\tfrac{c}{a}$$

Half of $\frac{b}{a}$ is $\frac{b}{2a}$. The square is $\frac{b^2}{4a^2}$. We complete the square.

$$x^2 + \frac{b}{a}x + \frac{b^2}{4a^2} = -\frac{c}{a} + \frac{b^2}{4a^2} \qquad \text{Adding } \tfrac{b^2}{4a^2} \text{ to both sides}$$

$$\left(x + \frac{b}{2a}\right)^2 = -\frac{4ac}{4a^2} + \frac{b^2}{4a^2} \qquad \text{The LCD is } 4a^2.$$

$$\left(x + \frac{b}{2a}\right)^2 = \frac{b^2 - 4ac}{4a^2}$$

$$x + \frac{b}{2a} = \sqrt{\frac{b^2 - 4ac}{4a^2}} \text{ or } x + \frac{b}{2a} = -\sqrt{\frac{b^2 - 4ac}{4a^2}}$$

$$x + \frac{b}{2a} = \frac{\sqrt{b^2 - 4ac}}{2a} \text{ or } x + \frac{b}{2a} = -\frac{\sqrt{b^2 - 4ac}}{2a} \qquad \text{Since } a > 0, |a| = a.$$

$$x = -\frac{b}{2a} + \frac{\sqrt{b^2 - 4ac}}{2a} \text{ or } x = -\frac{b}{2a} - \frac{\sqrt{b^2 - 4ac}}{2a}$$

The solutions are given by $x = \frac{-b \pm \sqrt{b^2 - 4ac}}{2a}$

8-3 EXERCISES

A

Solve.

1. $x^2 + 6x + 4 = 0$ $-3 \pm \sqrt{5}$

2. $x^2 - 6x - 4 = 0$ $3 \pm \sqrt{13}$

3. $x^2 + 4x - 5 = 0$ $1, -5$

4. $x^2 - 2x - 15 = 0$ $5, -3$

5. $y^2 + 7y = 30$ $3, -10$

6. $y^2 - 7y = 30$ $-3, 10$

7. $2t^2 - 3t - 2 = 0$ $2, -\frac{1}{2}$

8. $5m^2 + 3m - 2 = 0$ $\frac{2}{5}, -1$

9. $3p^2 = -8p - 5$ $-1, -\frac{5}{3}$

10. $3u^2 = 18u - 6$ $3 \pm \sqrt{7}$

11. $x^2 - x + 1 = 0$ $\frac{1 \pm i\sqrt{3}}{2}$

12. $x^2 + x + 2 = 0$ $\frac{-1 \pm i\sqrt{7}}{2}$

13. $1 + \frac{2}{x} + \frac{5}{x^2} = 0$ $-1 \pm 2i$

14. $1 + \frac{5}{x^2} = \frac{2}{x}$ $1 \pm 2i$

15. $x^2 - 2x + 5 = 0$ $1 \pm 2i$

16. $x^2 - 4x + 5 = 0$ $2 \pm i$

17. $x^2 + 13 = 4x$ $2 \pm 3i$

18. $x^2 + 13 = 6x$ $3 \pm 2i$

19. $z^2 + 5 = 0$ $\pm i\sqrt{5}$ 20. $t^2 + 3 = 0$ $\pm i\sqrt{3}$ 21. $r^2 + 3r = 8$ $\frac{-3 \pm \sqrt{41}}{2}$

22. $h^2 + 4 = 6h$ $3 \pm \sqrt{5}$ 23. $2x^2 = 5$ $\pm\frac{\sqrt{10}}{2}$ 24. $3x^2 = 2$ $\pm\frac{\sqrt{6}}{3}$

25. $3x + x(x - 2) = 0$ $0, -1$ 26. $4x + x(x - 3) = 0$ $0, -1$

27. $5x^2 + 2x + 1 = 0$ $\frac{-1 \pm 2i}{5}$ 28. $3x^2 + x + 2 = 0$ $\frac{-1 \pm i\sqrt{23}}{6}$

29. $(2t - 3)^2 + 17t = 15$ $\frac{3}{4}, -2$ 30. $2y^2 - (y + 2)(y - 3) = 12$ $2, -3$

31. $(x - 2)^2 + (x + 1)^2 = 0$ $\frac{1 \pm 3i}{2}$ 32. $(x + 3)^2 + (x - 1)^2 = 0$ $-1 \pm 2i$

33. $x + \frac{1}{x} = \frac{13}{6}$ $\frac{3}{2}, \frac{2}{3}$ 34. $\frac{3}{x} + \frac{x}{3} = \frac{5}{2}$ $6, \frac{3}{2}$

Approximate solutions to the nearest hundredth.

35. $x^2 + 4x - 7 = 0$ 36. $x^2 + 6x + 4 = 0$ 37. $x^2 - 6x + 4 = 0$

38. $x^2 - 4x + 1 = 0$ 39. $2x^2 - 3x - 7 = 0$ 40. $3x^2 - 3x - 2 = 0$

B

Solve.

41. $x^2 + x - \sqrt{2} = 0$ 42. $x^2 - x - \sqrt{3} = 0$ 43. $\sqrt{2}x^2 + 5x + \sqrt{2} = 0$

44. $x^2 + \sqrt{5}x - \sqrt{3} = 0$ 45. $x^2 + 3x + i = 0$ 46. $ix^2 - 2x + 1 = 0$

47. A boat travels 2 km upstream and 2 km downstream. The total time of the trip is 1 hour. The speed of the stream is 2 km/h. What is the speed of the boat in still water?

48. ***Critical Thinking*** Write a quadratic equation whose solutions are not real numbers. Answers may vary.

Challenge

49. Solve $3x^2 + xy + 4y^2 - 9 = 0$ for x in terms of y.

50. One solution of $kx^2 + 3x - k = 0$ is -2. Find the other solution.

51. Prove that the solutions of $ax^2 + bx + c = 0$ are the reciprocals of the solutions of $cx^2 + bx + a = 0$.

Mixed Review

Divide and simplify. 52. $\frac{\sqrt{35x}}{\sqrt{7x}}$ 53. $\frac{\sqrt[3]{216}}{\sqrt[3]{8}}$ 54. $\frac{\sqrt{42x^2y^2}}{\sqrt{7x}}$

Find the reciprocal of each number and express it in the form $a + bi$. 55. i

56. $1 - 3i$ 57. $3 + i$ 58. $3 - 4i$

Solve. 59. $2x - 19 + 4i = 5ix$ 60. $x^2 + 9 = 0$ 61. $x^2 - 9 = 0$

Problem for Programmers

Write a program that will approximate the real solutions for any equation of the form $ax^2 + bx + c = 0$. Test your program using Exercises 1–4 and 35–40 in Lesson 8-3.

Challenge: Modify the program to find all complex solutions, writing the solutions in the form $a + bi$.

ADDITIONAL ANSWERS

Exercises

35. 1.32, −5.32
36. −0.76, −5.24
37. 5.24, 0.76
38. 3.73, 0.27
39. 2.77, −1.27
40. 1.46, −0.46
41. $\frac{-1 \pm \sqrt{1 + 4\sqrt{2}}}{2}$
42. $\frac{1 \pm \sqrt{1 + 4\sqrt{3}}}{2}$
43. $\frac{-5\sqrt{2} \pm \sqrt{34}}{4}$
44. $\frac{-\sqrt{5} \pm \sqrt{5 + 4\sqrt{3}}}{2}$
45. $\frac{-3 \pm \sqrt{9 - 4i}}{2}$
46. $\frac{1 \pm \sqrt{1 - i}}{i}$
47. 4.8 km/h
49. $x = \frac{-y \pm \sqrt{-47y^2 + 108}}{6}$
50. $\frac{1}{2}$
51. The solutions of $cx^2 + bx + a = 0$ are $\frac{-b \pm \sqrt{b^2 - 4ac}}{2c}$. The reciprocals of these are $\frac{2c}{-b \pm \sqrt{b^2 - 4ac}}$. Multiply $\frac{2c}{-b + \sqrt{b^2 - 4ac}}$ by $\frac{-b - \sqrt{b^2 - 4ac}}{-b - \sqrt{b^2 - 4ac}}$ and multiply $\frac{2c}{-b - \sqrt{b^2 - 4ac}}$ by $\frac{-b + \sqrt{b^2 - 4ac}}{-b + \sqrt{b^2 - 4ac}}$. The results are $\frac{-b - \sqrt{b^2 - 4ac}}{2a}$ and $\frac{-b + \sqrt{b^2 - 4ac}}{2a}$, which are the solutions to $ax^2 + bx + c = 0$.

Mixed Review

52. $\sqrt{5}$ 53. 3
54. $|y|\sqrt{6x}$ 55. $-i$
56. $\frac{1 + 3i}{10}$ 57. $\frac{3 - i}{10}$
58. $\frac{3 + 4i}{25}$ 59. $2 + 3i$
60. $3i, -3i$ 61. $3, -3$

8-4

FIRST FIVE MINUTES

Solve using the quadratic formula.

1. $3x^2 + 7x + 2 = 0$

$$x = \frac{-7 \pm \sqrt{49 - 4 \cdot 3 \cdot 2}}{2 \cdot 3}$$
$$= \frac{-7 \pm \sqrt{25}}{6}$$
$$x = -\frac{1}{3} \text{ or } x = -2$$

2. $3x^2 + 7x + 5 = 0$

$$x = \frac{-7 \pm \sqrt{49 - 4 \cdot 3 \cdot 5}}{2 \cdot 3}$$
$$= \frac{-7 \pm \sqrt{-11}}{6}$$
$$= \frac{-7 \pm i\sqrt{11}}{6}$$

The Discriminant

Write the quadratic formula on the chalkboard. Point out that the expression under the square root sign determines whether there is a real solution or not. This expression allows us to distinguish, or *discriminate,* between the possible types of solutions to the corresponding quadratic equation.

Key Questions

- How many real square roots does $4^2 - 4 \cdot 1 \cdot 2$ have? 2
- How many real square roots does $4^2 - 4 \cdot 2 \cdot 2$ have? 1
- How many real square roots does $4^2 - 4 \cdot 4 \cdot 2$ have? None

Chalkboard Examples

Use the discriminant to determine the nature of the solutions.

1. $8x^2 + 9x + 1 = 0.$
   The discriminant is $9^2 - 4 \cdot 8 \cdot 1 = 81 - 32 = 49.$
   There are two real roots.
2. $4x^2 - 12x + 9 = 0$
   $(-12)^2 - 4 \cdot 4 \cdot 9 = 0$
   There is one real root.
3. $6x^2 + 2x + 5 = 0$
   $2^2 - 4 \cdot 6 \cdot 5 = -116$
   There are two nonreal solutions.

8-4 Solutions of Quadratic Equations

Master Grapher Worksheet 10, *Solutions of Quadratic Equations*, can be used as a lesson opener.

The quadratic formula can be used when the coefficients are any complex numbers. Now we restrict our attention to equations with real-number coefficients.

The Discriminant

Objective: Determine the nature of the solutions of a quadratic equation with real coefficients.

The expression $b^2 - 4ac$ in the quadratic formula is called the **discriminant**. From this number we can determine the nature of the solutions of a quadratic equation.

Theorem 8-3

An equation $ax^2 + bx + c = 0$, with $a \neq 0$ and all coefficients real numbers, has

A. exactly one real-number solution if $b^2 - 4ac = 0$.
B. two real number solutions if $b^2 - 4ac > 0$.
C. two complex but not real-number solutions that are conjugates of each other if $b^2 - 4ac < 0$.

EXAMPLE 1 Determine the nature of the solutions of $9x^2 - 12x + 4 = 0$.

$$a = 9, b = -12, \text{ and } c = 4$$

We compute the discriminant.

$$b^2 - 4ac = (-12)^2 - 4 \cdot 9 \cdot 4 = 144 - 144 = 0$$

By Theorem 8-3, there is just one solution and it is a real number.

EXAMPLE 2 Determine the nature of the solutions of $x^2 + 5x + 8 = 0$.

$$a = 1, b = 5, \text{ and } c = 8$$

We compute the discriminant.

$$b^2 - 4ac = 5^2 - 4 \cdot 1 \cdot 8 = 25 - 32 = -7$$

Since the discriminant is negative, there are two nonreal solutions that are complex conjugates of each other.

EXAMPLE 3 Determine the nature of the solutions of $x^2 + 5x + 6 = 0$.

$$a = 1, b = 5, \text{ and } c = 6$$
$$b^2 - 4ac = 5^2 - 4 \cdot 1 \cdot 6 = 1$$

Since the discriminant is positive, there are two solutions and they are real numbers.

Try This Determine the nature of the solutions of each equation.

a. $x^2 + 5x - 3 = 0$ Two real **b.** $9x^2 - 6x + 1 = 0$ One real **c.** $3x^2 - 2x + 1 = 0$ Two nonreal

Sums and Products of Solutions

Objective: Find and use sums and products of solutions of quadratic equations.

Theorem 8-4

For the equation $ax^2 + bx + c = 0$, the sum of the solutions is $-\frac{b}{a}$, and the product of the solutions is $\frac{c}{a}$.

Note that if we express $ax^2 + bx + c = 0$ in the equivalent form

$$x^2 + \frac{b}{a}x + \frac{c}{a} = 0$$

then the sum of the solutions is the additive inverse of the coefficient of the x-term, and the product of the solutions is the constant term.

We can find the sum and product of the solutions without solving the equation.

EXAMPLE 4 Find the sum and product of the solutions of $2x^2 = 6x + 5$.

Let x_1 and x_2 represent the solutions.

Since $2x^2 - 6x - 5 = 0$, we have $a = 2$, $b = -6$, and $c = -5$.

$$x_1 + x_2 = -\frac{b}{a} = -\left(\frac{-6}{2}\right) = 3 \qquad x_1 \cdot x_2 = \frac{c}{a} = \frac{-5}{2}$$

Try This Find the sum and product of the solutions.

d. $3x^2 + 4 = 12x$ Sum $= 4$; product $= \frac{4}{3}$ **e.** $x^2 + \sqrt{2}x - 4 = 0$ Sum $= -\sqrt{2}$; product $= -4$

EXAMPLE 5 Find a quadratic equation for which the sum of the solutions is $-\frac{4}{5}$, and the product of the solutions is $\frac{2}{3}$.

$$x^2 - \left(-\frac{b}{a}\right)x + \frac{c}{a} = 0$$

$$x^2 - \left(-\frac{4}{5}\right)x + \frac{2}{3} = 0$$

$$x^2 + \frac{4}{5}x + \frac{2}{3} = 0$$

We usually write the equation with integer coefficients.

$$15x^2 + 12x + 10 = 0$$ Multiplying by 15, the LCD

Sums and Products of Solutions

You may want to read a list of quadratic equations as a quick drill. Have students give you the sum and product of the solutions.

Chalkboard Examples

Find, without solving, the sum and product of the solutions.

1. $4x^2 - 3x + 2 = 0$
   The sum of the solutions is $\frac{3}{4}$.
   The product of the solutions is $\frac{2}{4} = \frac{1}{2}$.
2. Find a quadratic equation for which the sum of the solutions is -2 and the product of the solutions is 6.
   $x^2 + 2x + 6 = 0$

Writing Equations from Solutions

Chalkboard Examples

1. Find a quadratic equation whose solutions are 5 and 7.
   $x = 5$ or $x = 7$
   $x - 5 = 0$ or $x - 7 = 0$
   $(x - 5)(x - 7) = 0$
   $x^2 - 12x + 35 = 0$
2. Find a quadratic equation whose solutions are $\frac{2}{3}$ and $\frac{1}{5}$.
   $\left(x - \frac{2}{3}\right)\left(x - \frac{1}{5}\right) = 0$
   $x^2 - \left(\frac{2}{3} + \frac{1}{5}\right)x + \frac{2}{15} = 0$
   $x^2 - \frac{13}{15}x + \frac{2}{15} = 0$
   $15x^2 - 13x + 2 = 0$

LESSON QUIZ

1. Use the discriminant to determine the nature of the solutions of $3x^2 + 4x + 1 = 0$.
   There are two real solutions.
2. Find the sum and product of the solutions without solving. $5x^2 + 2x + 1 = 0$
   The sum is $-\frac{2}{5}$.
   The product is $\frac{1}{5}$.
3. Find a quadratic equation for which the sum of the roots is 4 and the product of the roots is 7.
   $x^2 - 4x + 7 = 0$
4. Find a quadratic equation whose solutions are $\frac{1}{2}$ and $\frac{1}{3}$.
   $x^2 - \frac{5}{6}x + \frac{1}{6} = 0$ or
   $6x^2 - 5x + 1 = 0$

Try This

f. Find a quadratic equation for which the sum of the solutions is 3 and the product is $-\frac{1}{4}$. $4x^2 - 12x - 1 = 0$

Writing Equations from Solutions

Objective: Find a quadratic equation given its solutions.

We can use the principle of zero products to write a quadratic equation whose solutions are known.

EXAMPLE 6 Find a quadratic equation whose solutions are 3 and $-\frac{2}{5}$.

$$x = 3 \text{ or } x = -\frac{2}{5}$$

$$x - 3 = 0 \text{ or } x + \frac{2}{5} = 0$$

$$(x - 3)\left(x + \frac{2}{5}\right) = 0 \quad \text{Multiplying}$$

$$x^2 - \frac{13}{5}x - \frac{6}{5} = 0$$

$$5x^2 - 13x - 6 = 0 \quad \text{Multiplying by 5, the LCD}$$

When radicals are involved, it is sometimes easier to use the properties of the sum and product.

EXAMPLE 7 Find the quadratic equation whose solutions are $2 + \sqrt{5}$ and $2 - \sqrt{5}$.

Let the solutions be x_1 and x_2.

$$x_1 + x_2 = (2 + \sqrt{5}) + (2 - \sqrt{5}) \quad \text{Finding the sum of the solutions; } -\frac{b}{a}$$

$$= 4$$

$$x_1 \cdot x_2 = (2 + \sqrt{5}) \cdot (2 - \sqrt{5}) \quad \text{Finding the product of the solutions; } \frac{c}{a}$$

$$= 4 - 5 = -1$$

$$x^2 - \left(-\frac{b}{a}\right)x + \frac{c}{a} = 0 \quad \text{Using Theorem 8-4}$$

$$x^2 - (4)x + (-1) = 0 \quad \text{Substituting}$$

$$x^2 - 4x - 1 = 0 \quad \text{Simplifying}$$

Try This

Find a quadratic equation whose solutions are the following.

g. $-4, \frac{5}{3}$ $3x^2 + 7x - 20 = 0$
h. $-7, 8$ $x^2 - x - 56 = 0$
i. m, n $x^2 - (m + n)x + mn = 0$
j. $8, -9$ $x^2 + x - 72 = 0$
k. $3 + \sqrt{2}, 3 - \sqrt{2}$ $x^2 - 6x + 7 = 0$
l. $\frac{2 + \sqrt{5}}{2}, \frac{2 - \sqrt{5}}{2}$ $4x^2 - 8x - 1 = 0$

8-4 EXERCISES

A

Determine the nature of the solutions of each equation.

1. $x^2 - 6x + 9 = 0$
2. $x^2 + 10x + 25 = 0$
3. $x^2 + 7 = 0$
4. $x^2 + 2 = 0$
5. $x^2 - 2 = 0$
6. $x^2 - 5 = 0$
7. $4x^2 - 12x + 9 = 0$
8. $4x^2 + 8x - 5 = 0$
9. $x^2 - 2x + 4 = 0$
10. $x^2 + 3x + 4 = 0$
11. $9t^2 - 3t = 0$
12. $4m^2 + 7m = 0$
13. $y^2 = \frac{1}{2}y + \frac{3}{5}$
14. $y^2 + \frac{9}{4} = 4y$
15. $4x^2 - 4\sqrt{3}x + 3 = 0$

Find the sum and product of the solutions.

16. $x^2 + 7x + 8 = 0$
17. $x^2 - 2x + 10 = 0$
18. $x^2 - x + 1 = 0$
19. $x^2 + x - 1 = 0$
20. $8 - 2x^2 + 4x = 0$
21. $4 + x + 2x^2 = 0$
22. $m^2 = 25$
23. $t^2 = 49$
24. $(2 + 3x)^2 = 7x$
25. $2x - 1 = (1 - 5x)^2$
26. $5(t - 3)^2 = 4(t + 3)^2$
27. $3(y + 4)^2 = 2(y + 5)^2$

Find a quadratic equation for which the sum and product of the solutions are as given.

28. Sum $= -5$; product $= \frac{1}{2}$
29. Sum $= -\pi$; product $= \frac{1}{4}$
30. Sum $= \sqrt{3}$; product $= 8$
31. Sum $= 5$; product $= -\sqrt{2}$

Find a quadratic equation whose solution or solutions are the following.

32. $-11, 9$
33. $-4, 4$
34. 7 (only solution)
35. -5 (only solution)
36. $-\frac{2}{5}, \frac{6}{5}$
37. $-\frac{1}{4}, -\frac{1}{2}$
38. $\frac{c}{2}, \frac{d}{2}$
39. $\frac{k}{3}, \frac{m}{4}$
40. $\sqrt{2}, 3\sqrt{2}$
41. $-\sqrt{3}, 2\sqrt{3}$
42. $\pi, -2\pi$
43. $-3\pi, 4\pi$

Use the sum and product properties to write a quadratic equation whose solutions are the following.

44. $4, 3$ $x^2 - 7x + 12 = 0$
45. $5, 6$ $x^2 - 11x + 30 = 0$
46. $-2, \frac{5}{4}$ $4x^2 + 3x - 10 = 0$
47. $-6, \frac{1}{4}$ $4x^2 + 23x - 6 = 0$
48. $1 + \sqrt{2}, 1 - \sqrt{2}$ $x^2 - 2x - 1 = 0$
49. $2 + \sqrt{3}, 2 - \sqrt{3}$ $x^2 - 4x + 1 = 0$
50. $\frac{2 + \sqrt{3}}{2}, \frac{2 - \sqrt{3}}{2}$ $4x^2 - 8x + 1 = 0$
51. $\frac{1 + \sqrt{13}}{2}, \frac{1 - \sqrt{13}}{2}$ $x^2 - x - 3 = 0$
52. $\frac{m}{n}, -\frac{n}{m}$ $mnx^2 - (m^2 - n^2)x - mn = 0$
53. $\frac{g}{h}, -\frac{h}{g}$ $ghx^2 - (g^2 - h^2)x - gh = 0$
54. $2 - 5i, 2 + 5i$ $x^2 - 4x + 29 = 0$
55. $4 + 3i, 4 - 3i$ $x^2 - 8x + 25 = 0$

Assignment Guide

Algebra: Day 1: 1 – 27
Day 2: 28 – 55 e/o, MR

Alg w/Finite or Trig: 1–55 m3, 56–65 e/o, 66, MR

Comprehensive: 1–65 m3, 66, 67–72 e/o, MR

ADDITIONAL ANSWERS

Exercises

1. One real
2. One real
3. Two nonreal
4. Two nonreal
5. Two real
6. Two real
7. One real
8. Two real
9. Two nonreal
10. Two nonreal
11. Two real
12. Two real
13. Two real
14. Two real
15. One real
16. Sum $= -7$; product $= 8$
17. Sum $= 2$; product $= 10$
18. Sum $= 1$; product $= 1$
19. Sum $= -1$; product $= -1$
20. Sum $= 2$; product $= -4$
21. Sum $= -\frac{1}{2}$; product $= 2$
22. Sum $= 0$; product $= -25$
23. Sum $= 0$; product $= -49$
24. Sum $= -\frac{5}{9}$; product $= \frac{4}{9}$
25. Sum $= \frac{12}{25}$; product $= \frac{2}{25}$
26. Sum $= 54$; product $= 9$
27. Sum $= -4$; product $= -2$
28. $2x^2 + 10x + 1 = 0$
29. $4x^2 + 4\pi x + 1 = 0$
30. $x^2 - \sqrt{3}x + 8 = 0$
31. $x^2 - 5x - \sqrt{2} = 0$
32. $x^2 + 2x - 99 = 0$
33. $x^2 - 16 = 0$
34. $x^2 - 14x + 49 = 0$
35. $x^2 + 10x + 25 = 0$
36. $25x^2 - 20x - 12 = 0$
37. $8x^2 + 6x + 1 = 0$
38. $4x^2 - 2(c + d)x + cd = 0$
39. $12x^2 - (4k + 3m)x + km = 0$
40. $x^2 - 4\sqrt{2}x + 6 = 0$
41. $x^2 - \sqrt{3}x - 6 = 0$
42. $x^2 + \pi x - 2\pi^2 = 0$
43. $x^2 - \pi x - 12\pi^2 = 0$

56. a. $k < \frac{9}{4}$ b. $k = \frac{9}{4}$ c. $k > \frac{9}{4}$

57. a. $k < \frac{1}{4}$ b. $k = \frac{1}{4}$ c. $k > \frac{1}{4}$

58. a. $k < 4$ b. $k = 4$ c. $k > 4$

59. a. $k < 1$ b. $k = 1$ c. $k > 1$

60. a. $k < \frac{5}{4}$ b. $k = \frac{5}{4}$ c. $k > \frac{5}{4}$

61. a. $k > \frac{11}{3}$ b. $k = \frac{11}{3}$ c. $k < \frac{11}{3}$

66. Solving for x yields $x = \frac{-b \pm \sqrt{b^2 + 4c}}{2}$. This is equivalent to the quadratic formula for $x^2 + bx - c = 0$.

67. Given $a^2 x + bx + c = 0$, $a \neq 0$, $a, b, c \in$ rationals, $b^2 - 4ac > 0$ and $b^2 - 4ac = d^2$ where d is rational
$$x = \frac{-b \pm \sqrt{b^2 - 4ac}}{2a} = \frac{-b \pm d}{2a}.$$
By the closure properties in rationals both $\frac{-b + d}{2a}$ and $\frac{-b - d}{2a}$ are rational.

68. a. Two rational solutions b. Two real (nonrational) solutions

69–70. See Teacher's Answer Section

71. $h = -36, k = 15$

72. $b^2 \geq 0$; $4ac$ must be negative since a and c have opposite signs. So $b^2 - 4ac$ must be positive, thus $\sqrt{b^2 - 4ac}$ is real and nonzero, and the solutions are real and unequal.

Mixed Review

73. $(5x + 2)(3x + 1)$

74. $(2y + 3)(y - 1)$

75. $a(a + 1)(a - 1)$

76. $\sqrt{2}, -\sqrt{2}$

77. 2, 0

78. $0, -\frac{1}{3}, \frac{1}{3}$

79. 4, 6

80. 4, 3

81. 5, −5

B

Find the value of k for **a.** two real-number solutions **b.** one real-number solution **c.** two complex-conjugate solutions.

56. $x^2 + 3x + k = 0$ **57.** $x^2 + x + k = 0$ **58.** $kx^2 - 4x + 1 = 0$

59. $x^2 - x + 3x + k = 0$ **60.** $x^2 + x = 1 - k$ **61.** $3x^2 + 4x = k - 5$

For each equation, one solution is given. Find the other solution, and then find the value of k.

62. $kx^2 - 17x + 33 = 0$; 3 $\frac{11}{2}, k = 2$ **63.** $kx^2 - 2x + k = 0$; -3 $-\frac{1}{3}, k = -\frac{3}{5}$

64. $x^2 - kx - 25 = 0$; -5 $5, k = 0$

65. Find k if $kx^2 - 4x + (2k - 1) = 0$ and the product of the solution is 3. -1

66. ***Critical Thinking*** Al-Khowarizmi, the Arabic mathematician (c. 825), used a "completing the square" method to solve quadratics of the form $x^2 + bx = c$. The unshaded portion represents $x^2 + bx$. To "complete the square" he added the area of the four small shaded squares, each with area $\frac{b^2}{16}$. This gives an area for the large square of $x^2 + bx + \frac{b^2}{4}$. Thus $x^2 + bx + \frac{b^2}{4} = c + \frac{b^2}{4}$. Solve this equation for x. Then evaluate Al-Khowarizmi's solution.

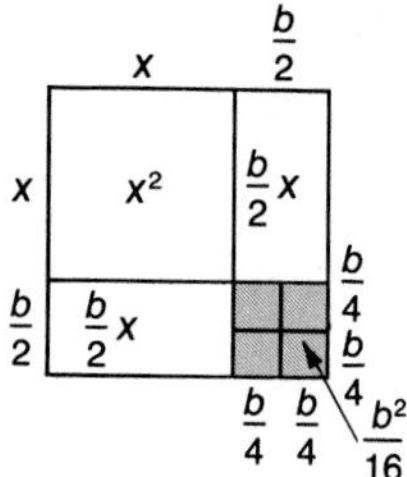

Challenge

Suppose in a quadratic equation $ax^2 + bx + c = 0$, and a, b, and c are integers.

67. Prove that the quadratic equation has two rational-number solutions if the discriminant is positive and a perfect square.

68. Use the result of Exercise 67 to determine whether each equation has rational solutions.

a. $6x^2 + 5x + 1 = 0$ **b.** $x^2 + 4x - 2 = 0$

69. Prove that the solutions of $ax^2 + bx + c = 0$ and $ax^2 - bx + c = 0$ are additive inverses of each other.

70. Prove Theorem 8-3. (Hint: Use the quadratic formula.)

71. Find h and k if $3x^2 - hx + 4k = 0$, the sum of the solutions is -12, and the product of the solutions is 20.

72. Prove that if the coefficients of $ax^2 + bx + c = 0$ are real, and if a and c have opposite signs, then the solutions are real and unequal.

Mixed Review

Factor. **73.** $15x^2 + 11x + 2$ **74.** $2y^2 + y - 3$ **75.** $a^3 - a$

Solve. **76.** $4y^2 - 1 = 7$ **77.** $9c^2 - 18c = 0$ **78.** $\frac{1}{2}x^3 - \frac{1}{18}x = 0$

79. $(a - 8)(a - 2) = -8$ **80.** $m(m - 5) = 2(m - 6)$ **81.** $3x^2 = 75$

8-5 Equations Reducible to Quadratic Form

Objective: Solve equations that are reducible to quadratic form.

Master Grapher Worksheet 11, *Solutions to Equations Reducible to Quadratic Form*, can be used as a lesson opener.

The following problem was found in the writings of the Hindu mathematician Mahavira (c. 850).

> One fourth of a herd of camels was seen in the forest, twice the square root of the number of camels in the herd had gone to the mountain slope, and three times five camels were found to remain on the bank of a river. What is the numerical measure of that herd of camels?

The equation $\frac{1}{4}x + 2\sqrt{x} + 15 = x$, which models Mahavira's situation, is not quadratic. However, after a substitution for x, we get a quadratic equation. Such equations are said to be reducible to quadratic form. To solve such equations, we first make a substitution and solve for the new variable. Then we substitute back the original variable and solve again.

EXAMPLE 1 Solve $x^4 - 9x^2 + 8 = 0$.

Let $u = x^2$. Then we solve the equation found by substituting u for x^2.

$$u^2 - 9u + 8 = 0$$
$$(u - 8)(u - 1) = 0$$
$$u - 8 = 0 \text{ or } u - 1 = 0$$
$$u = 8 \text{ or } u = 1$$

Now we substitute x^2 for u and solve these equations.

$$x^2 = 8 \text{ or } x^2 = 1$$
$$x = \pm\sqrt{8} \text{ or } x = \pm 1$$
$$x = \pm 2\sqrt{2} \text{ or } x = \pm 1$$

These four numbers check. The solutions are $1, -1, 2\sqrt{2}$, and $-2\sqrt{2}$.

EXAMPLE 2 Solve $x - 3\sqrt{x} - 4 = 0$.

Let $u = \sqrt{x}$. Then we solve the equation found by substituting u for $\sqrt{x}$.

$$u^2 - 3u - 4 = 0$$
$$(u - 4)(u + 1) = 0$$
$$u = 4 \text{ or } u = -1$$
$$\sqrt{x} = 4 \text{ or } \sqrt{x} = -1 \quad \text{Substituting } \sqrt{x} \text{ for } u$$

Squaring the first equation we get $x = 16$. The second equation has no solution since principal square roots are never negative. The number 16 checks and is the only solution.

8-5

FIRST FIVE MINUTES

1. Find the solution to $2x^2 + 3x + 1 = 0$.
   $x = \frac{-3 \pm \sqrt{9 - 4\cdot 2\cdot 1}}{4}$
   $x = \frac{-3 \pm 1}{4}$
   $x = -1$ or $x = -\frac{1}{2}$
2. Find a quadratic equation given that the sum of its roots is 7 and the product of its roots is 1.
   $x^2 - 7x + 1 = 0$
3. Find the quadratic equation whose solutions are $\frac{1}{7}$ and $\frac{1}{4}$.
   $x^2 - \left(\frac{1}{7} + \frac{1}{4}\right)x + \frac{1}{28} = 0$
   $x^2 - \frac{11}{28}x + \frac{1}{28} = 0$
   $28x^2 - 11x + 1 = 0$

You may want to rewrite the equation in Example 1,
$x^4 - 9x^2 + 8 = 0$, as
$(x^2)^2 - 9(x^2) + 8 = 0$
before replacing x^2 with u.

Remind students that any number can be expressed as the square of another number.

Key Questions

- What number squared equals x^6?
  $\pm x^3$
- What number squared equals $\sqrt{x}$?
  $\pm\sqrt[4]{x}$
- What number squared equals $x^{1/3}$?
  $\pm x^{1/6}$

Chalkboard Examples

Solve.

1. $x^6 + 6x^3 + 9 = 0$
   $(x^3)^2 + 6x^3 + 9 = 0$
   Let $u = x^3$.
   $u^2 + 6u + 9 = 0$
   $(u + 3)^2 = 0$
   $u = -3$
   $x^3 = -3$
   $x = -\sqrt[3]{3}$

2. $x - 6\sqrt{x} + 8 = 0$
Let $u = \sqrt{x}$.
$u^2 - 6u + 8 = 0$
$(u - 2)(u - 4) = 0$
$u = 2$ or $u = 4$
$\sqrt{x} = 2$ or $\sqrt{x} = 4$
$x = 4$ or $x = 16$

3. $(2x - 1)^2 - 4(2x - 1) + 3 = 0$
Let $u = 2x - 1$.
$u^2 - 4u + 3 = 0$
$(u - 1)(u - 3) = 0$
$u = 1$ or $u = 3$
$2x - 1 = 1$ or $2x - 1 = 3$
$x = 1$ or $x = 2$

4. $x^{2/3} - 3x^{1/3} + 2 = 0$
Let $u = x^{1/3}$.
$u^2 - 3u + 2 = 0$
$(u - 1)(u - 2) = 0$
$u = 1$ or $u = 2$
$x^{1/3} = 1$ or $x^{1/3} = 2$
$x = 1$ or $x = 8$

LESSON QUIZ

1. Solve $x^4 - 5x^2 + 4 = 0$.
   $x = \pm 1$ or $x = \pm 2$
2. Solve $x - 3x^{1/2} + 2 = 0$.
   $x = 1$ or $x = 4$

Try This Solve.

a. $x^4 - 10x^2 + 9 = 0$ $\pm 3, \pm 1$ **b.** $x^4 - 4 = 0$ $\pm\sqrt{2}, \pm\sqrt{2}i$ **c.** $x + 3\sqrt{x} - 10 = 0$ 4

EXAMPLE 3 Solve $(x^2 - 1)^2 - (x^2 - 1) - 2 = 0$.

Let $u = x^2 - 1$.

$u^2 - u - 2 = 0$ Substituting u for $x^2 - 1$

$(u - 2)(u + 1) = 0$ Factoring

$u = 2$ or $u = -1$ Using the principle of zero products

Now we substitute $x^2 - 1$ for u and solve these equations.

$x^2 - 1 = 2$ or $x^2 - 1 = -1$

$x^2 = 3$ or $x^2 = 0$

$x = \pm\sqrt{3}$ or $x = 0$

The numbers $\sqrt{3}$, $-\sqrt{3}$, and 0 check. They are the solutions.

Try This Solve.

d. $(x^2 - x)^2 - 14(x^2 - x) + 24 = 0$ 4, 2, −1, −3

EXAMPLE 4 Solve $t^{\frac{2}{5}} - t^{\frac{1}{5}} - 2 = 0$.

Let $u = t^{\frac{1}{5}}$. Then solve the equation found by substituting u for $t^{\frac{1}{5}}$.

$u^2 - u - 2 = 0$

$(u - 2)(u + 1) = 0$ Factoring

$u = 2$ or $u = -1$

Now we substitute $t^{\frac{1}{5}}$ for u and solve these equations.

$t^{\frac{1}{5}} = 2$ or $t^{\frac{1}{5}} = -1$

$t = 32$ or $t = -1$ Principle of powers; raising to the 5th power

Check:

$t^{\frac{2}{5}} - t^{\frac{1}{5}} - 2$	$= 0$
$32^{\frac{2}{5}} - 32^{\frac{1}{5}} - 2$	0
$4 - 2 - 2$	0
0	0 ✓

$t^{\frac{2}{5}} - t^{\frac{1}{5}} - 2$	$= 0$
$(-1)^{\frac{2}{5}} - (-1)^{\frac{1}{5}} - 2$	0
$1 - (-1) - 2$	0
0	0 ✓

The numbers 32 and -1 check and are the solutions.

Try This Solve.

e. $t^{\frac{2}{3}} - 3t^{\frac{1}{3}} - 10 = 0$ 125, −8

f. $\sqrt[7]{y^2} + 4\sqrt[7]{y} + 4 = 0$ −128

8-5 EXERCISES

A

Solve.

1. $x - 10\sqrt{x} + 9 = 0$
2. $2x - 9\sqrt{x} + 4 = 0$
3. $x^4 - 10x^2 + 25 = 0$
4. $x^4 - 3x^2 + 2 = 0$
5. $(x^2 - 6x)^2 - 2(x^2 - 6x) - 35 = 0$
6. $(1 + \sqrt{x})^2 + (1 + \sqrt{x}) - 6 = 0$
7. $(y^2 - 5y)^2 - 2(y^2 - 5y) - 24 = 0$
8. $(2t^2 + t)^2 - 4(2t^2 + t) + 3 = 0$
9. $w^4 - 4w^2 - 12 = 0$ $\pm\sqrt{6}, \pm i\sqrt{2}$
10. $t^4 - 5t^2 - 36 = 0$ $\pm 3, \pm 2i$
11. $x^{-2} - x^{-1} - 6 = 0$ $\frac{1}{3}, -\frac{1}{2}$
12. $4x^{-2} - x^{-1} - 5 = 0$ $\frac{4}{5}, -1$
13. $2x^{-2} + x^{-1} - 1 = 0$ $2, -1$
14. $m^{-2} + 9m^{-1} - 10 = 0$ $-\frac{1}{10}, 1$
15. $t^{\frac{2}{3}} + t^{\frac{1}{3}} - 6 = 0$ $-27, 8$
16. $w^{\frac{2}{3}} - 2w^{\frac{1}{3}} - 8 = 0$ $64, -8$
17. $z^{\frac{1}{2}} - z^{\frac{1}{4}} - 2 = 0$ 16
18. $m^{\frac{1}{3}} - m^{\frac{1}{6}} - 6 = 0$ 729
19. $\sqrt{x^2} + 5\sqrt{x} - 36 = 0$ $x = 16$
20. $\sqrt[5]{t^2} + 5\sqrt[5]{t} + 6 = 0$ $t = -32$ or $t = -243$

B

Solve.

21. $\left(\frac{x^2 - 1}{x}\right)^2 - \left(\frac{x^2 - 1}{x}\right) - 2 = 0$
22. $\left(\frac{x^2 - 2}{x}\right)^2 - 7\left(\frac{x^2 - 2}{x}\right) - 18 = 0$
23. $\left(\frac{x^2 + 1}{x}\right)^2 - 8\left(\frac{x^2 + 1}{x}\right) + 15 = 0$
24. $\frac{x}{x - 1} - 6\sqrt{\frac{x}{x - 1}} - 40 = 0$
25. $\left(\frac{x + 1}{x - 1}\right)^2 + \left(\frac{x + 1}{x - 1}\right) - 2 = 0$
26. $5\left(\frac{x + 2}{x - 2}\right)^2 - 3\left(\frac{x + 2}{x - 2}\right) - 2 = 0$
27. ***Critical Thinking*** Solve Mahavira's problem from the introduction, page 359. (How many camels were in the herd?) 36 camels

Challenge

Solve.

28. $9x^{\frac{3}{2}} - 8 = x^3$ $1, 4$
29. $\sqrt[3]{2x + 3} = \sqrt[6]{2x + 3}$ $-\frac{3}{2}, -1$
30. $\sqrt{x - 3} - \sqrt[4]{x - 3} = 2$ 19
31. $a^3 - 26a^{\frac{3}{2}} - 27 = 0$ 9
32. $x^8 - 20x^4 + 64 = 0$
33. $x^8 + 20x^4 + 64 = 0$

Mixed Review

Rationalize the denominator. **34.** $\sqrt{\frac{15}{7}}$ **35.** $\frac{1}{\sqrt{ab}}$ **36.** $\frac{2\sqrt{5} - 3\sqrt{2}}{3\sqrt{2} - 2\sqrt{5}}$

Find an equation having the specified numbers as solutions. **37.** $4i, -4i$ **38.** $7i, -7i$ **39.** $2 - 5i, 2 + 5i$

Solve. **40.** $x^2 - 5x - 6 = 0$ **41.** $2y^2 - y - 15 = 0$ **42.** $(a - 1)(a - 3) = 15$ **43.** $c(c - 2) = 3(c + 8)$ **44.** $4m^2 = 9$

Assignment Guide

Algebra: 1 – 20 e/o, MR

Alg w/Finite or Trig: 1–26 e/o, 27, MR

Comprehensive: 1–20 m3, 21–26 e/o, 27, 28–33 e/o, MR

ADDITIONAL ANSWERS

Exercises

1. 81, 1
2. $\frac{1}{4}$, 16
3. $\pm\sqrt{5}$
4. $\pm\sqrt{2}, \pm 1$
5. 7, −1, 5, 1
6. 1
7. 4, 1, 6, −1
8. $-\frac{3}{2}, 1, \frac{1}{2}, -1$
21. $1 \pm \sqrt{2}, \frac{-1 \pm \sqrt{5}}{2}$
22. $\frac{9 \pm \sqrt{89}}{2}, -1 \pm \sqrt{3}$
23. $\frac{5 \pm \sqrt{21}}{2}, \frac{3 \pm \sqrt{5}}{2}$
24. $\frac{100}{99}$
25. $\frac{1}{3}$
26. $-\frac{6}{7}$
32. $\pm 2i, \pm 2, \pm i\sqrt{2}, \pm\sqrt{2}$
33. $1 \pm i, -1 \pm i, \sqrt{2} \pm i\sqrt{2}, -\sqrt{2} \pm i\sqrt{2}$

Mixed Review

34. $\frac{\sqrt{105}}{7}$
35. $\frac{\sqrt{ab}}{ab}$
36. −1
37. $x^2 = -16$
38. $x^2 + 49 = 0$
39. $x^2 - 4x + 29 = 0$
40. 6, −1
41. $-\frac{5}{2}, 3$
42. −2, 6
43. 8, −3
44. $\pm\frac{3}{2}$

8-6

FIRST FIVE MINUTES

1. Solve $x^6 - 7x^3 + 10 = 0$.
   Let $u = x^3$.
   $u^2 - 7u + 10 = 0$
   $(u - 2)(u - 5) = 0$
   $u = 2$ or $u = 5$
   $x^3 = 2$ or $x^3 = 5$
   $x = \sqrt[3]{2}$ or $x = \sqrt[3]{5}$
2. Solve $x - 4\sqrt{x} + 4 = 0$.
   Let $u = \sqrt{x}$.
   $u^2 - 4u + 4 = 0$
   $(u - 2)^2 = 0$
   $u = 2$
   $\sqrt{x} = 2$
   $x = 4$

Solving Formulas

Point out that in most formulas the variables represent measurable, nonnegative quantities, so we do not need absolute value signs when taking principal square roots.

Remind students that the operations of squaring and taking square roots are inverse operations; that is, performing one after the other gives the original expression. Remind them that if the same operation is applied to both sides of a true equation, then the result is a true equation.

In Example 1 explain that the discriminant will always be nonnegative because if $h = 0$, $t = \frac{v_0 - v_0}{32} = 0$. If $h > 0$, $t > 0$.

Chalkboard Examples

1. Solve $m = (ab)^{1/2}$, for a.
   Square both sides.
   $m^2 = [(ab)^{1/2}]^2$
   $m^2 = ab$
   $\frac{m^2}{b} = a$
2. Solve $f = \frac{m}{d^2}$, for d.
   $fd^2 = m$
   $d^2 = \frac{m}{f}$
   $d = \pm\sqrt{\frac{m}{f}}$

8-6 Formulas and Problem Solving

The height of an object that has been fired upward with initial velocity v_0 at any given time t is given by the formula $h = v_0t - 16t^2$, where h is in feet, t is in seconds, and v_0 is in ft/s.

How long has an object been in the air, given it is at height h and was fired with initial velocity v_0. In other words, can we determine t if we know h and v_0?

Solving Formulas

Objective: Solve second-degree formulas for a given letter.

EXAMPLE 1 Solve $h = v_0t - 16t^2$ for t, the time an object is in the air, given h, the height of the object, and v_0, the initial velocity.

$$16t^2 - v_0t + h = 0 \quad \text{Finding standard form}$$

$$a = 16, b = -v_0, c = h$$

$$t = \frac{-b \pm \sqrt{b^2 - 4ac}}{2a}$$

$$t = \frac{v_0 \pm \sqrt{(-v_0)^2 - 4 \cdot 16 \cdot h}}{2 \cdot 16} \quad \text{Substituting into the quadratic formula}$$

$$t = \frac{v_0 \pm \sqrt{v_0^2 - 64h}}{32}$$

$$t = \frac{v_0 + \sqrt{v_0^2 - 64h}}{32} \text{ or } t = \frac{v_0 - \sqrt{v_0^2 - 64h}}{32}$$

Since h is nonnegative, both of these give nonnegative values for t.

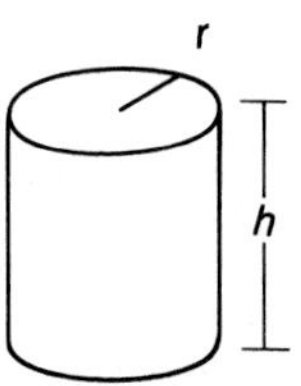

Try This Solve for the indicated letter.

a. $V = \pi r^2h$; r **b.** $2\pi r^2 + 2\pi rh = 1$; r

a. $r = \sqrt{\frac{V}{\pi h}}$ b. $r = \frac{-\pi h + \sqrt{\pi^2h^2 + 2\pi}}{2\pi}$

Problem Solving: Quadratic Equations

Objective: Solve problems using quadratic equations.

When an object is dropped or thrown downward, the distance in meters that it falls in t seconds is given by $s = 4.9t^2 + v_0 t$. In this formula v_0 is the initial velocity.

EXAMPLE 2

(a) An object is dropped from the top of the Gateway Arch in St. Louis, which is 195 meters high. How long does it take to reach the ground?

Since the object was dropped, its initial velocity was 0. Thus we substitute 0 for v_0 and 195 for s, and then solve for t.

$$195 = 4.9t^2 + 0 \cdot t$$
$$195 = 4.9t^2$$
$$t^2 \approx 39.8$$
$$t \approx \sqrt{39.8}$$ Finding the positive square root because t cannot be negative
$$t \approx 6.31$$

Therefore, it takes about 6.31 seconds to reach the ground.

(b) An object is thrown downward from the top of the arch at an initial velocity of 16 meters per second (m/s). How long does it take to reach the ground?

We substitute 195 for s and 16 for v_0 and solve for t.

$$195 = 4.9t^2 + 16t$$
$$0 = 4.9t^2 + 16t - 195$$

By the quadratic formula we obtain $t \approx -8.15$ or $t \approx 4.88$. The negative answer is meaningless in this problem, so the answer is 4.88 seconds.

(c) How far will an object fall in 3 seconds if it is thrown downward from the top of the arch at an initial velocity of 16 m/s?

We substitute 16 for v_0 and 3 for t and solve for s.

$$s = 4.9t^2 + v_0 t$$
$$= 4.9(3)^2 + 16 \cdot 3 = 92.1$$

Thus the object falls 92.1 meters in 3 seconds.

Try This

c. An object is dropped from the top of the Statue of Liberty, which is 92 meters high.

(1) How long does it take to reach the ground? 4.33 sec

(2) An object is thrown downward from the top of the statue at an initial velocity of 40 m/s. How long does it take to reach the ground? 1.87 sec

(3) How far will an object fall in 1 second, thrown downward from the top of the statue at an initial velocity of 40 m/s? 44.9 m

Problem Solving: Quadratic Equations

Chalkboard Example

1. When an object is thrown, the height h in feet is given by the formula $h = -16t^2 + v_0 t + h_0$, where v_0 is the initial velocity and h_0 is the initial height. If a stone is thrown upward from a height of 8.25 feet with an initial velocity of 64 feet per second, how long does it take for the stone to fall to ground level?
   The initial height is $h_0 = 8.25$. The initial velocity is $v_0 = 64$.
   The formula for the height h is $h = -16t^2 + 64t + 8.25$.
   The height at ground level is $h = 0$.
   Solve for t.
   $0 = -16t^2 + 64t + 8.25$
   The quadratic formula yields
   $$t = \frac{-64 \pm \sqrt{4096 - 4(-16)(8.25)}}{2 \cdot (-16)}$$
   $$= \frac{-64 \pm \sqrt{4624}}{-32}$$
   $$= \frac{-64 \pm 68}{-32}$$
   The positive solution is
   $t = \frac{33}{8} = 4.125$ seconds.

LESSON QUIZ

1. Solve for z.
   $d = \sqrt{x^2 + y^2 + z^2}$
   $\pm\sqrt{d^2 - x^2 - y^2} = z$
2. Solve for g.
   $a = \frac{2}{g^2}$
   $g = \pm\sqrt{\frac{2}{a}}$
3. Use the formula $s = 4.9t^2 + v_0 t$. A stone is dropped from a bridge that is 9.8 meters high. How long will it take for the stone to hit the water?
   $\sqrt{2}$ seconds

Assignment Guide
Algebra: Day 1: 1–16 e/o
Day 2: 17–23 e/o, MR

Alg w/Finite or Trig: Day 1: 1–16 e/o, 24–27
Day 2: 17–23 e/o, 28–30, MR

Comprehensive: 1–29 m3, 30–32, MR

ADDITIONAL ANSWERS

Exercises

1. $s = \frac{\sqrt{P}}{2}$
2. $r = \sqrt{\frac{A}{\pi}}$
3. $r = \sqrt{\frac{Gm_1m_2}{F}}$
4. $t = \sqrt{\frac{Qab}{K}}$
5. $r = \sqrt{x^2 + y^2}$
6. $h = \sqrt{a^2 + b^2}$
7. $z = \sqrt{d^2 - x^2 - y^2}$
8. $b = \sqrt{t^2 - a^2 - c^2}$
9. $t = \frac{v_0 \pm \sqrt{v_0^2 - 19.6h}}{9.8}$
10. $r = \frac{-\pi s \pm \sqrt{\pi^2 s^2 + 4\pi A}}{2\pi}$
11. $t = \sqrt{\frac{2S}{g}}$
12. $V = \sqrt{2gh}$
13. $r = \frac{-\pi h \pm \sqrt{\pi^2 h^2 + \pi A}}{\pi}$
14. $t = \sqrt{\frac{h - 2v_0}{10}}$
15. $t = \frac{\pi \pm \sqrt{\pi^2 - 12k\sqrt{2}}}{2\sqrt{2}}$
16. $t = \frac{0.2 \pm \sqrt{0.04 + 16\pi\sqrt{3}}}{2\sqrt{3}}$

8-6 EXERCISES

A

Solve for the indicated letter.

1. $P = 4s^2; s$

2. $A = \pi r^2; r$

3. $F = \frac{Gm_1m_2}{r^2}; r$

4. $K = \frac{Qab}{t^2}; t$

5. $x^2 + y^2 = r^2; r$

6. $a^2 + b^2 = h^2; h$

7. $x^2 + y^2 + z^2 = d^2; z$

8. $a^2 + b^2 + c^2 = t^2; b$

9. $h = v_0 t - 4.9t^2; t$

10. $A = \pi rs + \pi r^2; r$

11. $S = \frac{1}{2}gt^2; t$

12. $h = \frac{V^2}{2g}; V$

13. $A = \pi r^2 + 2\pi rh; r$

14. $h = 2v_0 + 10t^2; t$

15. $t^2\sqrt{2} + 3k = \pi t; t$

16. $t^2\sqrt{3} - 4\pi = 0.2t; t$

Solve. Use the formula $s = 4.9t^2 + v_0 t$.

17. An object is dropped from an airplane from a height of 75 m.
a. How long does it take to reach the ground? 3.91 s
b. If the object has an initial velocity of 30 m/s, how long does it take to reach the ground? How far will it fall in 2 seconds? 1.91 s, 79.6 m

18. An object is dropped from an airplane from a height of 500 m.
a. How long does it take to reach the ground? 10.10 s
b. If the object has an initial velocity of 12 m/s, how long does it take to reach the ground? How far will it fall in 5 seconds? 8.95 s, 182.5 m

19. An amount of money P is invested at interest rate r. In t years it will grow to the amount A given by $A = P(1 + r)^t$, where interest is compounded annually. For the following situations, find the interest rate if interest is compounded annually.
a. \$2560 grows to \$3610 in 2 years. 18.75%
b. \$1000 grows to \$1210 in 2 years. 10%
c. \$8000 grows to \$9856.80 in 2 years. (Use a calculator.) 11%
d. \$1000 grows to \$1271.26 in 2 years. (Use a calculator.) 12.75%

20. A ladder 10 ft long leans against a wall. The bottom of the ladder is 6 ft from the wall. How much would the lower end of the ladder have to be pulled away so that the top end would be pulled down the same amount? 2 ft

21. A ladder 13 ft long leans against a wall. The bottom of the ladder is 5 ft from the wall. How much would the lower end of the ladder have to be pulled away so that the top end would be pulled down the same amount? 7 ft

22. Trains A and B leave the same city at the same time, headed east and north respectively. Train B travels 5 mi/h faster than train A. After 2 hours they are 50 miles apart. Find the speed of each train. A: 15 mi/h; B: 20 mi/h

23. Trains A and B leave the same city at the same time, headed west and south respectively. Train A travels 14 km/h faster than train B. After 5 hours they are 130 km apart. Find the speed of each train. A: 24 km/h; B: 10 km/h

B

24. The diagonal of a square is 1.341 cm longer than a side. Use a calculator to find the length of the side. 3.237 cm

25. The hypotenuse of a right triangle is 8.312 cm long. The sum of the lengths of the legs is 10.23 cm. Use a calculator to find the lengths of the legs. 2.2199 cm; 8.0101 cm

Solve for the indicated letter.

26. $m = \dfrac{m_0}{\sqrt{1 - \dfrac{v^2}{c^2}}}$; v

27. $T = \sqrt{\dfrac{a^2 + b^2}{a^2}}$; a

For Exercises 28 and 29 use the formula $T = cN$, where T is the total cost, c is the cost per item or cost per person, and N is the number of items or number of persons.

28. A group of students share equally in the \$140 cost of a boat. At the last minute 3 students drop out, and this raises the share of each remaining student \$15. How many students were in the group at the outset? 7

29. An investor had purchased a group of lots for \$8400. All but 4 of them were later sold, also for a total of \$8400. The selling price for each lot was \$350 greater than the cost. How many lots were originally purchased? 12

30. ***Critical Thinking*** Solve the formula for a falling object, $s = 4.9t^2 + v_0 t$, for time. Explain why there is only one solution.

Challenge

31. A rectangle of 12-cm² area is inscribed in the right triangle ABC as shown in the drawing. What are its dimensions? 3 cm × 4 cm

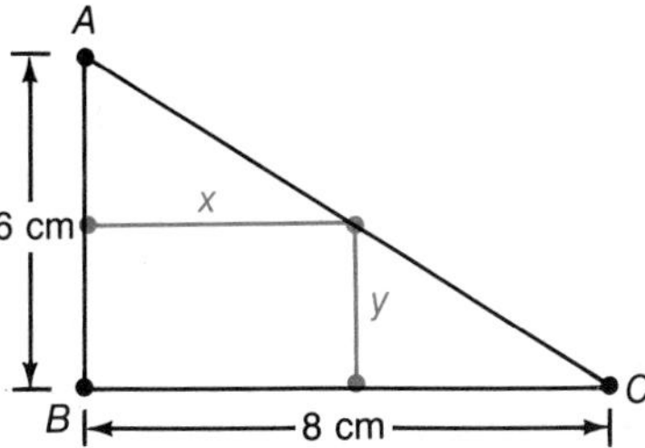

32. The world record for free-fall to earth without a parachute by a woman is 175 ft, and is held by Kitty O'Neill. Approximately how long did the fall take? 3.3 sec

Mixed Review

Simplify. **33.** i^3 **34.** $(5i)^2$ **35.** $(-6i)^2$ **36.** $(1 + i)^2$ **37.** $(1 + i)^3$

Solve. **38.** $8x^2 - 6x + 1 = 0$ **39.** $y(y - 7) = 12(y - 5)$ **40.** $5m^2 = 0$

41. $3a^2 + 12a = 0.$ **42.** $2c^2 = 4.$ **43.** $6x^2 = 25$ **44.** $x^2 - 4x + 7 = 0$

45. $y^2 + 4y + 8 = 0$ **46.** $6a^2 - a - 15 = 0$

Graph. **47.** $y = |x - 1|$ **48.** $x - y = 3$

WRITING TO LEARN

Use a reference book to find a science formula that is quadratic. Write a description of the formula telling what each letter represents. Answers may vary.

26. $v = \dfrac{c\sqrt{m^2 - m_0^2}}{m}$

27. $a = \dfrac{b}{\sqrt{T^2 - 1}}$

30. $t = \dfrac{-v_0 + \sqrt{v_0^2 + 19.6s}}{9.8}$

There is only one solution because the negative square root would give a negative answer for time.

Mixed Review

33. $-i$
34. -25
35. -36
36. $2i$
37. $-2 + 2i$
38. $\frac{1}{2}, \frac{1}{4}$
39. 4, 15
40. 0
41. 0, -4
42. $\sqrt{2}, -\sqrt{2}$
43. $\frac{5\sqrt{6}}{6}, \frac{-5\sqrt{6}}{6}$
44. $2 \pm i\sqrt{3}$
45. $-2 \pm 2i$
46. $\frac{5}{3}, -\frac{3}{2}$

47.

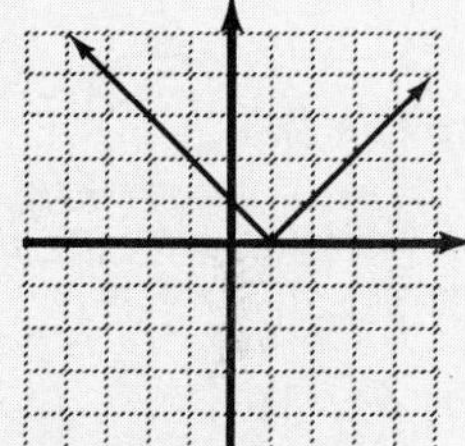

48.

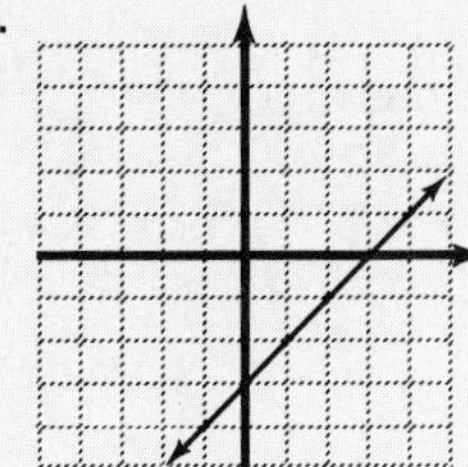

8-7

FIRST FIVE MINUTES

1. Solve for x.

$\sqrt{x^2 + y^2} = d$

$x^2 + y^2 = d^2$

$x^2 = d^2 - y^2$

$x = \pm\sqrt{d^2 - y^2}$

2. Solve for m.

$a = \frac{1}{m^2 + n^2}$

$a(m^2 + n^2) = 1$

$am^2 + an^2 = 1$

$am^2 = 1 - an^2$

$m^2 = \frac{1 - an^2}{a}$

$m = \pm\sqrt{\frac{1 - an^2}{a}}$

Direct Variation

Key Questions

- If $\frac{y}{k} = x^2$, does y vary directly as the square of x? Yes
- If $y \cdot x^2 = k$, does y vary directly as the square of x? No

Chalkboard Example

1. Find an equation of variation where y varies directly as the square of x, and $y = 2$ when $x = 3$.

$y = kx^2$

$(2) = k(3)^2$

$\frac{2}{9} = k$

$y = \frac{2}{9}x^2$

8-7 Quadratic Variation and Applications

The relationship between the height and girth of a tree and the volume of wood it produces can be modeled using a quadratic variation function.

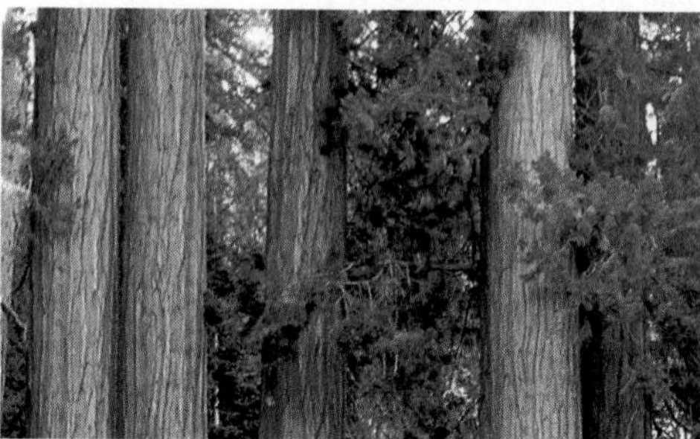

Direct Variation

Objective: Find an equation of direct quadratic variation.

Definition

Direct Quadratic Variation

y **varies directly** as the square of x if there is some positive number k such that $y = kx^2$.

Consider the equation for the area of a circle, $a = \pi r^2$. It shows that the area varies directly as the square of the radius and π is the constant of variation.

EXAMPLE 1 Find an equation of variation where y varies directly as the square of x, and $y = 12$ when $x = 2$.

We write an equation of variation and find k.

$$y = kx^2$$

$$12 = k \cdot 2^2 \quad \text{Substituting}$$

$$3 = k \quad \text{Solving for } k$$

Now we write an equation.

$$y = 3x^2 \quad \text{Substituting for } k \text{ in the original equation}$$

Try This

a. Find an equation of variation where y varies directly as the square of x, and $y = 175$ when $x = 5$. $y = 7x^2$

Inverse and Joint Variation

Objective: Find equations of inverse and joint quadratic variation.

Definition

Inverse Quadratic Variation

y **varies inversely** as the square of x if there is some positive number k such that $y = \frac{k}{x^2}$.

The law of gravity states that the weight (W) of an object varies inversely as the square of the distance (d) from the center of the earth.

$$W = \frac{k}{d^2}$$

EXAMPLE 2 Find an equation of variation where W varies inversely as the square of d, and $W = 3$ when $d = 5$.

$W = \frac{k}{d^2}$ Definition of inverse quadratic variation

$3 = \frac{k}{5^2}$ Solving for k

$75 = k$

$W = \frac{75}{d^2}$ Substituting for k in the original equation

Try This

b. Find an equation of variation where y varies inversely as the square of x, and $y = \frac{1}{4}$ when $x = 6$. $y = \frac{9}{x^2}$

Consider the equation for the area A of a triangle with height h and base b.

$$A = \frac{1}{2}bh$$

We say that the area varies jointly as the height and the base.

Definition

Joint Variation

y **varies jointly** as x and z if there is some positive number k such that $y = kxz$.

Inverse and Joint Variation

Key Questions

- If y varies inversely as the square of x, does x vary directly with the square of y?
  No
- If $y = xz$, what is the constant of variation?
  1

Chalkboard Examples

1. Find the equation of variation where y varies inversely as the square of x, and $y = 2$ when $x = 3$.

   $y = \frac{k}{x^2}$

   $(2) = \frac{k}{(3)^2}$

   $18 = k$

   $y = \frac{18}{x^2}$

2. Find an equation where y varies jointly as x and z, and $y = 2$ when $x = 3$ and $z = 4$.

   $y = kxz$

   $(2) = k(3)(4)$

   $k = \frac{1}{6}$

   $y = \frac{1}{6}xz$

3. Find an equation of variation where y varies directly as x and inversely as the square of z, and $y = 8$ when $x = 2$ and $z = 5$.

   $y = \frac{kx}{z^2}$

   $(8) = \frac{k(2)}{(5)^2}$

   $k = 100$

   $y = \frac{100x}{z^2}$

Problem Solving: Variation and Proportion

Chalkboard Examples

1. The current I in an electrical circuit varies directly as the voltage E and inversely as the resistance R. The current is 2 amperes when the voltage is 8 volts and the resistance is 4 ohms. Find the equation of variation. Find the current when the voltage is 10 volts and the resistance is 20 ohms.

$$I = \frac{kE}{R}$$
$$(2) = \frac{k(8)}{(4)}$$
$$k = 1$$
$$I = \frac{E}{R}$$

When $E = 10$ and $R = 20$, $I = \frac{10}{20} = 0.5$ amperes.

2. The intensity I of the light from a lamp varies directly as the wattage W of the lamp and inversely as the square of the distance D from the lamp. The intensity is 10 units when a 100-watt bulb is used at a distance of 20 feet. What is the intensity if a 75-watt bulb is used at 25 feet?

$$I = \frac{kW}{D^2}$$
$$(10) = \frac{k(100)}{(20)^2}$$
$$k = 40$$
$$I = \frac{40W}{D^2}$$

When $W = 75$ and $D = 25$,

$$I = \frac{40(75)}{(25)^2}$$
$$I = 4.8$$

EXAMPLE 3 Find an equation of variation where y varies jointly as x and z, and $y = 42$ when $x = 2$ and $z = 3$.

$$y = kxz$$
$$42 = k \cdot 2 \cdot 3$$
$$7 = k \qquad \text{Solving for } k$$

Substituting for k in the original equation we have $y = 7xz$.

Try This

c. Find an equation of variation where y varies jointly as x and z, and $y = 65$ when $x = 10$ and $z = 13$. $y = \frac{1}{2}xz$

The following equation asserts that y varies jointly as x and the cube of z, and inversely as w. Note that all these values are factors. There is no addition in the equation.

$$y = k \cdot \frac{xz^3}{w}$$

EXAMPLE 4 Find an equation of variation where y varies jointly as x and z and inversely as the square of w, and $y = 105$ when $x = 3$, $z = 20$, and $w = 2$.

$$y = k \cdot \frac{xz}{w^2}$$
$$105 = k \cdot \frac{3 \cdot 20}{2^2}$$
$$7 = k$$

Thus $y = 7 \cdot \frac{xz}{w^2}$.

Try This

d. Find an equation of variation where y varies jointly as x and the square of z and inversely as w, and $y = 80$ when $x = 4$, $z = 10$, and $w = 25$. $y = \frac{5xz^2}{w}$

Problem Solving: Variation and Proportion

Objective: Solve problems involving quadratic variation and proportion.

Many problem situations can be described with equations of variation.

EXAMPLE 5

The volume (V) of wood in a tree varies jointly as the height (h) and the square of the girth (g), the distance around the tree. The volume of a tree is 216 m^3 for a height of 30 m and a girth of 1.5 m. What is the height of a tree whose volume is 960 m^3 and girth is 2 m?

First find k using the first set of data. Then solve for h using the second set of data.

$$V = khg^2$$
$$216 = k \cdot 30 \cdot 1.5^2$$
$$3.2 = k \quad \text{Solving for } k$$

Then

$$960 = 3.2 \cdot h \cdot 2^2 \quad \text{Using 3.2 for } k \text{ to solve for } h$$
$$75 = h$$

The height of the tree is 75 m.

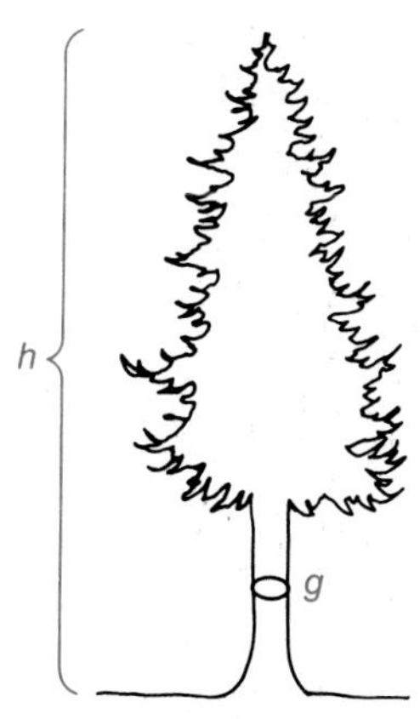

Proportions can be used to solve variation problems. In Example 5, the volumes of the two trees are proportional.

EXAMPLE 6

Use a proportion to solve the problem in Example 5.

Let h_1 represent the height of the first tree and h_2 the height of the second tree.

$$\frac{V_1}{V_2} = \frac{k \cdot h_1 \cdot g_1^2}{k \cdot h_2 \cdot g_2^2}$$
$$= \frac{h_1 g_1^2}{h_2 g_2^2} \quad \frac{k}{k} = 1$$

Now we can solve directly for the unknown height (h_2) without first finding the constant of variation.

$$\frac{216}{960} = \frac{30 \cdot 1.5^2}{h_2 \cdot 2^2}$$
$$h_2 = \frac{960 \cdot 67.5}{4 \cdot 216}$$
$$h_2 = 75 \text{ m}$$

EXAMPLE 7

The intensity (I) of a TV signal varies inversely as the square of the distance (d) from the transmitter. The intensity is 23 watts per square meter (W/m^2) at a distance of 2 km. What is the intensity at a distance of 6 km?

We use the proportion.

$$\frac{I_1}{I_2} = \frac{d_2^2}{d_1^2} \quad I_1 = \frac{k}{d_1^2},\ I_2 = \frac{k}{d_2^2}$$
$$\frac{I_2}{23} = \frac{2^2}{6^2}$$
$$I_2 = \frac{4 \cdot 23}{36}$$
$$I_2 = 2.56 \text{ W/m}^2 \quad \text{Rounding to the nearest hundredth}$$

3. The force of attraction F between two magnets varies inversely as the square of the distance D between them. The force is 5 newtons when the magnets are 2 centimeters apart. What is the force when the magnets are 5 centimeters apart?

$$F = \frac{k}{D^2}$$
$$(5) = \frac{k}{(2)^2}$$
$$k = 20$$
$$F = \frac{20}{D^2}$$

Substituting, $D = 5$,

$$F = \frac{4}{5}$$

LESSON QUIZ

Find the equation of variation.

1. y varies inversely as the square of x, and $y = 2$ when $x = 5$.

   $y = \frac{50}{x^2}$

2. y varies directly as x and inversely as the square of z, and $y = 6$ when $x = 2$ and $z = 3$.

   $y = \frac{27x}{z^2}$

3. y varies jointly as x and z, and $y = 4$ when $x = 1$ and $z = 2$.

   $y = 2xz$

Assignment Guide

Algebra: 1 – 16 e/o, MR

Alg w/Finite or Trig: 1–21 e/o, 22, MR

Comprehensive: 1–16 m3, 17–21 e/o, 22, 23, MR

Try This

e. The distance(s) that an object falls when dropped from some point above the ground varies directly as the square of the time (t) it falls. If the object falls 19.6 m in 2 seconds, how far will the object fall in 10 seconds? 490 m

8-7 EXERCISES

A

Find an equation of variation where

1. y varies inversely as the square of x, and $y = 6$ when $x = 3$. $y = \frac{54}{x^2}$
2. y varies directly as the square of x, and $y = 0.6$ when $x = 0.4$. $y = 3.75x^2$
3. y varies inversely as the square of x, and $y = 0.4$ when $x = 0.8$. $y = \frac{0.256}{x^2}$
4. y varies directly as the square of x, and $y = 0.15$ when $x = 0.1$. $y = 15x^2$
5. y varies directly as the square of x, and $y = 6$ when $x = 3$. $y = \frac{2}{3}x^2$
6. y varies inversely as the square of x, and $y = 0.15$ when $x = 0.1$. $y = \frac{0.0015}{x^2}$
7. y varies jointly as x and z, and $y = 56$ when $x = 7$ and $z = 8$. $y = xz$
8. y varies directly as x and inversely as z, and $y = 4$ when $x = 12$ and $z = 15$. $y = \frac{5x}{z}$
9. y varies directly as x and inversely as the square of z, and $y = 105$ when $x = 14$ and $z = 5$. $y = 187.5\frac{x}{z^2}$
10. y varies jointly as x and z and inversely as w, and $y = \frac{3}{2}$ when $x = 2$, $z = 3$, and $w = 4$. $y = \frac{xz}{w}$
11. y varies jointly as x and z and inversely as the product of w and p, and $y = \frac{3}{28}$ when $x = 3$, $z = 10$, $w = 7$, and $p = 8$. $y = \frac{xz}{5wp}$
12. y varies jointly as x and z and inversely as the square of w, and $y = \frac{12}{5}$ when $x = 16$, $z = 3$, and $w = 5$. $y = \frac{5xz}{4w^2}$
13. The stopping distance (d) of a car after the brakes are applied varies directly as the square of the speed (r). A car traveling 60 km/h can stop in 80 m. How many meters will it take the same car to stop when it is traveling 90 km/h? 180 m
14. The area of a cube varies directly as the square of the length of a side. A cube has an area 168.54 m^2 when the length of a side is 5.3 m. What will the area be when the length of a side is 10.2 m? ◇ 624.24 m^2
15. The weight (W) of an object varies inversely as the square of the distance (d) from the center of the earth. At sea level (6400 km from the center of the earth) an astronaut weighs 100 kg. Find the astronaut's weight in a spacecraft 200 km above the surface of the earth. (Assume the spacecraft is not in motion.) 94.03 kg
16. The intensity of light (I) from a light bulb varies inversely as the square of the distance (d) from the bulb. Suppose I is 90 W/m^2 when the distance is 5 m. Find the intensity at a distance of 10 m. 22.5 W/m^2

B

17. Show that if p varies directly as q, then q varies directly as p.

18. Show that if u varies inversely as v, then v varies inversely as u, and $\frac{1}{u}$ varies directly as v.

19. The area of a circle varies directly as the square of the length of its diameter. What is the variation constant?

20. P varies directly as the square of t. How does t vary in relationship to P?

21. In Example 7, why is the equation not appropriate when the distance is 0 km from a transmitter whose initial signal is 316,000 W/m^2?

22. ***Critical Thinking***

a. Suppose y varies directly as the square of x. Predict what happens to y when x is doubled; when x is multiplied by n.

b. Suppose y varies inversely as the square of x. Predict what happens to y when x is tripled; when x is multiplied by n.

Challenge

23. It has been determined that the average number of daily phone calls (N) between two cities is directly proportional to the populations (P_1 and P_2) of the cities, and inversely proportional to the square of the distance (d) between the cities. That is, $N = \frac{kP_1P_2}{d^2}$. Use a calculator to find solutions to these problems.

a. The population of Indianapolis is about 690,000, and the population of Cincinnati is about 360,000. The distance between the cities is 174 km. The average number of daily phone calls between the two cities is 8205. Find the value (k) and write the equation of variation.

b. The population of Detroit is about 1,100,000, and it is 446 km from Indianapolis. Find the average number of daily phone calls between them.

c. The average number of daily phone calls between Indianapolis and New York City is 3514, and the population of New York City is about 6,700,000. Find the distance between Indianapolis and New York City.

d. Why is this model not appropriate for adjoining cities?

Mixed Review

Determine the nature of the solution of each equation. **24.** $x^2 - 10x + 25 = 0$
25. $y^2 + y + 1 = 0$ **26.** $a^2 - 121 = 0$

Without solving, find the sum and product of the solutions. **27.** $m^2 + 5m - 2 = 0$
28. $2x^2 + 6x = 0$ **29.** $2y^2 + 8y - 3 = 0$

Solve. **30.** $c^2 + 6c - 5 = 0$ **31.** $3m^2 - 10m + 3 = 0$

Find the conjugate of each number. **32.** $a - bi$ **33.** $-x + yi$

ADDITIONAL ANSWERS

Exercises

17. If p varies directly as q, then $p = kq$. Thus $q = \frac{1}{k}p$, so q varies directly as p.

18. $u = \frac{k}{v}$, so $v = \frac{k}{u}$ and $\frac{1}{u} = \frac{1}{k} \cdot v$

19. $\frac{\pi}{4}$

20. t varies directly as $\sqrt{p}$.

21. Division by zero is undefined.

22. a. y is multiplied by 4; y is multiplied by n^2.
b. y is divided by 9; y is divided by n^2.

23. a. $k = 0.001$
$N = \frac{P_1P_2}{1000d^2}$
b. $N = 3816$
c. $d = 1147$ km
d. $d = 0$, and division by zero is undefined

Mixed Review

24. 1 real
25. 2 nonreal
26. 2 real
27. Sum = -5; product = -2
28. Sum = -3; product = 0
29. Sum = -4; product = $-\frac{3}{2}$
30. $-3 \pm \sqrt{14}$
31. $3, \frac{1}{3}$
32. $a + bi$
33. $-x - yi$

8-8

FIRST FIVE MINUTES

1. Lines are drawn connecting each corner of a cube to every other corner. How many lines are drawn?
   28 lines: 12 edges, 12 diagonals of the faces, and 4 diagonals of the cube. (Draw a diagram)
2. How many different sets of positive integers have elements that total five?
   7 sets: {5}, {1, 4}, {2, 3}, {1, 1, 3}, {1, 2, 2}, {1, 1, 1, 2}, {1, 1, 1, 1, 1} (Make an Organized List)

Use Logical Reasoning

Explain that sometimes a problem requires us to match two groups of things, given certain facts about them. The strategy *Use Logical Reasoning* helps organize the matching process. With the table we can describe any of the possible ways to match the two groups. The strategy consists of carefully recording the information and making further conclusions by ruling out possibilities. Note that when not enough information is given, or when contradictory information is given, there may not be a unique solution.

Key Questions

- What does statement (a) tell you? **Ong is not the vice-president.**
- What does the combination of statements (a) and (e) tell you? **Gray is not the vice-president.**
- What does the combination of statements (a) and (f) tell you? **Vasquez is not the vice-president.**
- Who must be the vice-president? **Martin**

8-8 Problem Solving: Strategies

Use Logical Reasoning

Objective: Solve problems using the strategy *Use Logical Reasoning,* and other strategies.

Some problems must be solved by understanding the given relationships among the facts and using known facts and relationships to make conclusions. The problem-solving strategy called Use Logical Reasoning is a name for this process.

PROBLEM-SOLVING GUIDELINES
■ UNDERSTAND the problem
■ Develop and carry out a PLAN
■ Find the ANSWER and CHECK

We can use the Problem-Solving Guidelines at the left to help us solve problems where our plan involves the strategy *Use Logical Reasoning.*

EXAMPLE

A news service released facts about four officials in an election (president, vice-president, secretary-general, and chief of staff). The last names of those elected, not necessarily in order are Ong, Vasquez, Martin, and Gray. Which person was elected to which office?

(a) Ong and the vice-president once shared the same office and were best friends.
(b) Gray and the chief of staff will continue to vacation together each year.
(c) Vasquez is the president's best source of information; the president does not consult with Gray, however.
(d) Martin has announced that she will run for president for the first time in the next election.
(e) Ong and Gray have never been friends and never shared an office.
(f) Vasquez has always had an office of his own.

You can solve this problem by recording the given information in a *chart* and making conclusions based on it. The charts below show the reasoning you might go through.

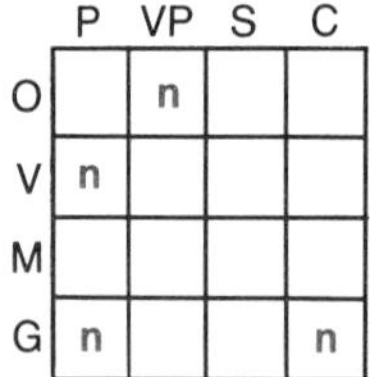

	P	VP	S	C
O		n		
V	n			
M				
G	n			n

The first three statements allow us to write NO (n) in these cells.

	P	VP	S	C
O	(y)	n	n	n
V	n			
M	n			
G	n			n

(d) Martin is not president, so Ong must be. Ong can hold no other office.

	P	VP	S	C
O	(y)	n	n	n
V	n		n	
M	n		n	
G	n	n	(y)	n

(a) and (e) show that Gray is not vice-president. Gray must be secretary-general, since no one else can.

	P	VP	S	C
O	(y)	n	n	n
V	n	n	n	(y)
M	n	(y)	n	n
G	n	n	(y)	n

(a) and (f) show that Vasquez is not vice-president. Vasquez must be chief of staff. Martin must be vice-president.

The offices and those elected are: president, Ong; vice-president, Martin; secretary-general, Gray; chief of staff, Vasquez.

Problem-Solving Strategies		
Write an Equation	Draw a Diagram	Guess, Check, Revise
Make an Organized List	Make a Table	Look for a Pattern
Use Logical Reasoning	Simplify the Problem	Work Backward

8-8 PROBLEMS

Solve using one or more of the strategies.

1. An automobile factory needs to select other companies as suppliers for 3 different parts. The factory contacted a number of companies and found that some companies produce 1 needed item, others produce 2 needed items, and others produce 3 needed items. Thirty-five companies produce part A, 24 produce part B, and 27 produce part C. Of these companies, 12 produce both parts A and B, 19 produce parts B and C, and 13 produce parts A and C. Nine produce all 3 parts. What was the total number of companies contacted?

2. Adele accidentally hit the button on her clock radio that makes it go on and off repeatedly. The buzzer came on at exactly 7:00 a.m. Then it went on and off at regular intervals. At 7:09 a.m. the buzzer was off, at 7:17 a.m. it was on, and at 7:58 a.m. it was on. Was the buzzer on or off at 9:00 a.m.?

3. Six friends graduated from the same college with teaching degrees in mathematics. They all took jobs teaching in different states. The states were Indiana, Illinois, Florida, Hawaii, California, and New York. The friends names, in no particular order, were Tracy, Sally, Juan, Herb, Rick and Terry. Sally didn't get a job in Illinois, and Tracy didn't get to move to California. Herb got the job he wanted in New York, and Terry got the job she wanted in Florida. Juan hoped to get a job in Hawaii but did not. Sally turned down a job in Indiana just after Juan took a job in California, and Rick took a job in Indiana. In which state did each person get a job?

4. A rapidly expanding factory had to hire a large number of employees during the year. There were 220 employees at the beginning of the year. The plan was to hire 1 employee at the beginning of the first month. Then, at the beginning of each following month, 4 more employees would be hired than had been hired in the previous month, until the company expanded to 340 employees. Under this plan, how many months did it take to hire the needed number of employees?

5. It takes four regular triangles with sides of length 1, to make a regular triangle with sides of length 2. How many regular triangles with sides of length 1 does it take to make a regular triangle with sides of length 10?

Chalkboard Example

1. Hye-Won is planning her class schedule. She will take math, English, Spanish, history, and drama. English is offered only in the morning 3 periods; math is offered only in the afternoon. History is offered 3rd and 4th period. Spanish is offered 1st and 4th period, and drama is offered only 5th period. When should she take each class?
   Make a chart. First eliminate the periods in which each class is not offered.

	1	2	3	4	5
Eng.				X	X
Math	X	X	X		
Span.		X	X		X
Hist.	X	X			X
Drama	X	X	X	X	

   Hye-Won must take drama 5th period. Then she can only take math 4th period. She must then take Spanish 1st period and history 3rd period. She is left with English 2nd period.

Hints for Problems

1. The 9 suppliers that produce all 3 parts are included in the 12 suppliers that produce parts A and B. Try drawing a picture.
2. Try guessing the time interval the buzzer was on or off.
3. Make a table showing the people and the states they are from.
4. Make a table showing the months, the number of employees hired, and the total number of employees after each month.
5. Draw a picture. Extend the triangle. Then make a table and look for a pattern.

ANSWERS

1. **There were 51 companies contacted.**
2. **The interval is 7 min. The buzzer will be off at 9 a.m.**
3. **Tracy: Illinois; Sally: Hawaii; Juan: California; Herb: New York; Rick: Indiana; Terry: Florida**
4. **It took 8 months to hire the 120 employees needed.**
5. **$10^2 = 100$**

ANSWERS

1. $0, -\frac{6}{7}$
2. $0, 3$
3. $\frac{2}{3}, -4$
4. $\frac{3}{4}, 6$
5. $\pm\frac{i\sqrt{2}}{2}$
6. $\pm\frac{2}{3}$
7. $x^2 + 16x + 64$
8. $x^2 - 9x + \frac{81}{4}$
9. $-2 \pm \sqrt{10}$
10. $-\frac{3}{2}, \frac{5}{2}$
11. 25 m, 20 m, 15 m
12. $-2 \pm \sqrt{11}$
13. $\frac{-3 \pm \sqrt{29}}{2}$
14. $-1 \pm i\sqrt{3}$
15. $\frac{-1 \pm i\sqrt{15}}{2}$
16. 7.3, 0.7

Chapter 8 Summary and Review

8-1

Some quadratic equations of the type $ax^2 + bx + c = 0$ can be solved easily by factoring.

Solve.

1. $7x^2 + 6x = 0$
2. $7x^2 - 21x = 0$
3. $3x^2 + 10x - 8 = 0$
4. $4x^2 - 27x + 18 = 0$

Equations of the type $ax^2 + c = 0$ can be changed to the form $x^2 = k$, where $x = \pm\sqrt{k}$.

Solve.

5. $4x^2 + 2 = 0$
6. $9x^2 - 4 = 0$

To complete the square, take half the coefficient of the x-term and square it.

Complete the square.

7. $x^2 + 16x$
8. $x^2 - 9x$

Solve by completing the square.

9. $x^2 + 4x - 6 = 0$

When the leading coefficient is not 1, we can use the multiplication property to make it 1.

Solve by completing the square.

10. $4x^2 - 4x - 15 = 0$

8-2

The Problem-Solving Guidelines and the methods of solving quadratic equations can be used to solve some problems.

11. One leg of a right triangle is 10 m less than the hypotenuse, and the other leg is 5 m less than the hypotenuse. Find the length of all three sides of the triangle.

8-3

The quadratic formula $x = \frac{-b \pm \sqrt{b^2 - 4ac}}{2a}$ can be used to find the solutions of any quadratic equation.

Solve.

12. $x^2 + 4x - 7 = 0$
13. $x^2 + 3x - 5 = 0$
14. $x^2 + 2x + 4 = 0$
15. $x^2 + x + 4 = 0$

A calculator or a square root table can be used to find rational number approximations to the exact solutions given by the formula.

16. Approximate solutions of $x^2 - 8x + 5 = 0$ to the nearest tenth.

8-4

An equation $ax^2 + bx + c = 0$ with $a \neq 0$ and all coefficients real numbers, has exactly one real-number solution if the discriminant $b^2 - 4ac = 0$, two real-number solutions if $b^2 - 4ac > 0$, and two complex nonreal solutions that are conjugates if $b^2 - 4ac < 0$.

17. Find the discriminant and the nature of the solutions of $4y^2 + 5y + 1 = 0$.

For $ax^2 + bx + c = 0$, the solutions have a sum of $-\frac{b}{a}$ and a product of $\frac{c}{a}$.

18. Find the sum and product of the solutions of $5y^2 - 4y + 2 = 0$.

19. Find a quadratic equation for which the sum of the solutions is $-\frac{1}{2}$ and the product of the solutions is $\frac{3}{5}$.

If the solutions of a quadratic equation are j and k, then $(x - j)(x - k) = 0$ is an equation that can be changed to the standard form of a quadratic equation.

20. Write a quadratic equation in standard form whose solutions are -3 and $-\frac{1}{2}$.

8-5

Substitute for the variables to solve an equation that is quadratic in form.

21. Solve $y^4 - 2y^2 + 1 = 0$ 22. Solve $(x^2 + 1)^2 - 15(x^2 + 1) + 50 = 0$

8-6

A formula containing a second-degree term may require finding the square root of both sides when solving for a specified variable.

23. Solve $A^2 + a^2 = 1$ for A. 24. Solve $S = at + \frac{1}{2}gt^2$ for t.

25. From a height of 200 m, an object is thrown downward at an initial velocity of 20 m/s. How long does it take to reach the ground? Use $s = 4.9t^2 + v_0t$.

8-7

y varies directly as the square of x if there is some positive number k such that $y = kx^2$.

Find an equation of variation in which

26. y varies directly as the square of x, and $y = 2$ when $x = 3$.

27. y varies directly as the square of x, and $y = 0.1$ when $x = 0.2$.

y varies inversely as the square of x if there is some positive number k such that $y = \frac{k}{x^2}$.

Find an equation of variation in which

28. y varies inversely as the square of x, and $y = 0.5$ when $x = 2$.

29. y varies inversely as the square of x, and $y = -0.1$ when $x = 10$.

Many problem situations can be described with equations of variation, and can be solved by using proportions.

30. The surface area of a sphere varies directly as the square of its radius. If the surface area of a sphere is 1257 m^2 when the radius is 10 m, what is the area when the radius is 3m?

See also Problem 8, Computer-Assisted Problem Solving, page 844.

17. Discriminant = 9
There are two real roots.
18. Sum = $\frac{4}{5}$; product = $\frac{2}{5}$
19. $10x^2 + 5x + 6 = 0$
20. $2x^2 + 7x + 3 = 0$
21. ± 1
22. $\pm 3, \pm 2$
23. $A = \sqrt{1 - a^2}$
24. $t = \frac{-a \pm \sqrt{a^2 + 2gS}}{g}$
25. 4.67 s
26. $y = \frac{2}{9}x^2$
27. $y = \frac{5}{2}x^2$
28. $y = \frac{2}{x^2}$
29. $y = \frac{-10}{x^2}$
30. 113.13 m^2

ANSWERS

1. 0, 5
2. 0, $\frac{6}{5}$
3. 1, 5
4. $\pm\frac{3}{4}$
5. $\frac{2}{5}$, -3
6. $\pm i\sqrt{5}$
7. $x^2 - \frac{1}{4}x + \frac{1}{64}$
8. $y^2 + 2.5y + 1.5625$
9. $-2 \pm \sqrt{15}$
10. $\frac{-2 \pm \sqrt{26}}{2}$
11. Eric travels 12 mi/h; Hilary travels 16 mi/h.
12. $\frac{-2 \pm \sqrt{3}}{2}$
13. $\frac{3 \pm \sqrt{17}}{4}$
14. $\frac{-1 \pm \sqrt{5}}{2}$
15. $\frac{-1 \pm i\sqrt{17}}{2}$
16. 2.3, 0.2
17. Discriminant = 1 There are two real, unequal solutions.
18. $-\frac{4}{3}$, $-\frac{7}{6}$
19. $6x^2 - 4x + 5 = 0$
20. $x^2 - 6x + 7 = 0$
21. $\pm 1, \pm 2$
22. $\pm 2, \pm 3$
23. $\frac{-1 \pm i\sqrt{23}}{2}$
24. 1
25. $A = \sqrt{4 - a^2}$
26. 158.4 m
27. $y = \frac{7}{4}x^2$
28. $y = \frac{3}{x^2}$
29. $y = \frac{2tr}{w^2}$
30. 122.5 m

Test Item Analysis

Item	Lesson
1–10	8-1
11	8-2
12–16	8-3
17–19	8-4
20	8-5
21–23	8-3
25, 26	8-6
27–29	8-7
30	8-6

Chapter 8 Test

Solve.

1. $3x^2 - 15x = 0$
2. $5x^2 - 6x = 0$
3. $x^2 - 6x + 5 = 0$
4. $16x^2 - 9 = 0$
5. $5x^2 + 13x - 6 = 0$
6. $3x^2 + 15 = 0$

Complete the square.

7. $x^2 - \frac{1}{4}x$
8. $y^2 + 2.5y$

Solve by completing the square.

9. $x^2 + 4x - 11 = 0$
10. $2x^2 + 4x - 11 = 0$
11. Bicyclists Hilary and Eric leave the same point Q at the same time at right angles. Hilary travels four mi/h faster than Eric. After 4 hours they are 80 miles apart. Find the speed of each.

Solve.

12. $4x^2 + 8x + 1 = 0$
13. $2x^2 - 3x - 1 = 0$
14. $x^2 + x - 1 = 0$
15. $2x^2 + 2x + 9 = 0$
16. Approximate solutions of $2x^2 - 5x + 1 = 0$ to the nearest tenth.
17. Find the discriminant and determine the nature of the solutions of $2x^2 - 5x + 3 = 0$.
18. Without solving, find the sum and product of the solutions of $6y^2 + 8y - 7 = 0$.
19. Find a quadratic equation for which the sum of the solutions is $\frac{2}{3}$ and the product of the solutions is $\frac{5}{6}$.
20. Write an equation in standard form whose solutions are $3 + \sqrt{2}$ and $3 - \sqrt{2}$.

Solve.

21. $x^4 - 5x^2 + 4 = 0$
22. $y^4 - 13y^2 + 36 = 0$
23. $x^2 + x + 6 = 0$
24. $x - 2x^{\frac{1}{2}} + 1 = 0$
25. Solve $A^2 + a^2 = 4$, for A
26. How far will an object fall in 4 seconds, thrown downward with an initial velocity of 20 m/s? Round the answer to the nearest hundredth. Use $s = 4.9t^2 + v_0t$.

Find an equation of variation where

27. y varies directly as the square of x, and $y = 7$ when $x = 2$.
28. y varies inversely as the square of x, and $y = \frac{1}{3}$ when $x = 3$.
29. y varies jointly as t and r and inversely as the square of w, and $y = 2$ when $t = 4$, $r = 9$, and $w = 6$.

Solve.

30. The distance (s) that an object falls when dropped from a point above the ground varies directly as the square of the time (t) it falls. If the object falls 44.1 m in 3 seconds, how far will it fall in 5 seconds?

Chapters 1 – 8 Cumulative Review

1-4 Simplify.

1. $5x - 3 - (2 - 3x)$

2. $-3[y - 3(4y - 2) - (5 - y)]$

1-5 Solve.

3. $5x - 3 = 7 - x$

4. $3y - 20 - y = 6 - 3y - 6$

1-6 Solve.

5. A baby sitter charges \$1.75 per hour. She also charges the parents another \$1.00 per evening for each child. How much would she charge to baby-sit 4 children for 3 hours?

1-8 Write without negative exponents.

6. 9^{-2}

7. $\frac{-3x^{-2}y^3}{z^{-4}}$

1-9 Multiply. Write the answer in scientific notation.

8. $(3.6 \times 10^5)(2.5 \times 10^3)$

9. $(7.2 \times 10^{-8})(4.5 \times 10^5)$

2-2 Solve.

10. The sum of three consecutive odd integers equals 240 more than the third integer. Find all three integers.

2-4 Solve, then graph.

11. $-3x \geq -15$

12. $3y - 9 < 6 + 6y$

2-5 Solve.

13. A car rents for \$18.75 per day, plus 25¢ per mile. If you rent the car for one week, what is the greatest number of miles you can drive and still keep the cost of renting the car under \$200 for the week?

2-7 Solve and graph.

14. $|x - 3| \leq 6$

15. $|2x - 5| \geq 7$

3-1 List the domain and range for the following relation.

16. $\{(3, 2), (3, -2), (0, 0)\}$

3-3 $g(x) = -2x^2 + 3x + 1$

17. Find $g(0)$.

18. Find $g(-2)$.

ANSWERS

1. $8x - 5$
2. $30y - 3$
3. $\frac{5}{3}$
4. 4
5. \$9.25
6. $\frac{1}{81}$
7. $-\frac{3y^3z^4}{x^2}$
8. 9×10^8
9. 3.24×10^{-2}
10. 119, 121, 123
11. $x \leq 5$

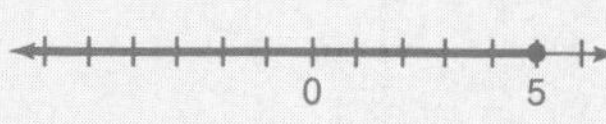

12. $y > -5$

13. Less than 275 mi
14. $-3 \leq x \leq 9$

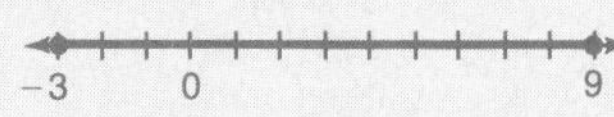

15. $x \geq 6$ or $x \leq -1$

16. Domain $\{0, 3\}$; range $\{-2, 0, 2\}$
17. 1
18. -13

19.

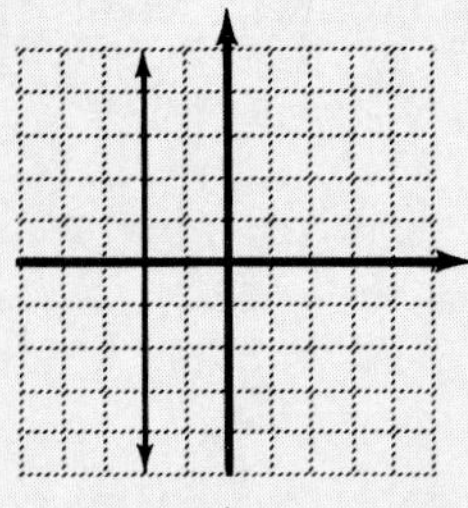

20.

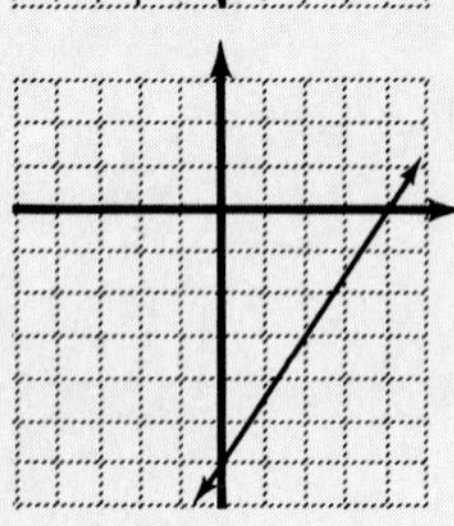

21. $y = -\frac{5}{4}x - \frac{5}{2}$

22. $y = 2x + 3$

23. $m = \frac{3}{4}, b = -3$

24. $2x - 3y + 9 = 0$

25. $y = -\frac{4}{5}x - \frac{17}{5}$

26. $y = \frac{5}{4}x - \frac{15}{2}$

27. $y = \frac{25}{7}x + \frac{10}{7}$

28. Approximately 91¢

29. 52

30. $-12x^2 + 4$

31. $\left(-\frac{1}{3}, -\frac{19}{3}\right)$

32. $(1, -2)$

33. $6, -4$

34. $(0, 3, -2)$

35. $(-2, 1, 4)$

36.

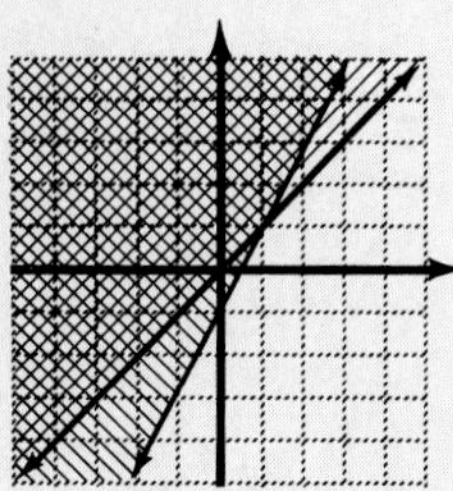

3-4 Graph.

19. $x = -2$

20. $3x - 2y = 12$

3-5

21. Find an equation of the line containing $(2, -5)$ and having slope $-\frac{5}{4}$.

3-6

22. Write the equation in slope-intercept form of the line containing $(-4, -5)$ and $(-2, -1)$.

23. Find the slope and y-intercept of $3x - 4y = 12$.

24. Write $y = \frac{2}{3}x + 3$ in standard form.

3-7 Find an equation in slope-intercept form of the line containing $(2, -5)$ and

25. parallel to the line $4x + 5y = 8$.

26. perpendicular to the line $4x + 5y = 8$.

3-8 The cost of an 8-oz can of tomato sauce is 30 cents, and the cost of a 15-oz can is 55 cents.

27. Fit a linear function to the data points.

28. Use the function to determine the cost of a 25-oz can.

3-9 $f(x) = 3x - 2$, $g(x) = 2x^2$, and $h(x) = -2x$

29. Find $f(g(-3))$.

30. Find $h(f(g(x)))$.

4-2 Solve each system.

31. $-3x + 3y = -18$
$4x - y = 5$

32. $2x - 3y = 8$
$5x + 2y = 1$

4-3

33. The difference between two numbers is 10. When eight times the smaller number is added to 40, the result is ten less than three times the larger number. Find both numbers.

4-4 Solve.

34. $2x + y - z = 5$
$y - 2z = 7$
$2y + 3z = 0$

35. $5x + 3y + 2z = 1$
$2x - y + z = -1$
$-2x + 2y - z = 2$

4-7 Graph this system of inequalities.

36. $y \geq x$
$y > 2x - 1$

5-1 Collect like terms.

37. $3x - 2y - 5y - 3x$

38. $2x^2 - 3x - 4x + 5x^2 + x$

5-2 Add or subtract.

39. $(3x^2 + 5x - 2) + (-3x^2 - x)$

40. $(-2x^2 + x - 3) - (5x^2 - 3x - 3)$

5-3 Multiply.

41. $(x^2 - 3y)^2$

42. $(3x - 2y - 1)(3x + 2y + 1)$

5-4 – 5-6 Factor.

43. $24x^3 - 84x^2 + 72x$

44. $36y^2 - 100$

45. $x^2 - 2xy + y^2 - 36$

46. $z^3 - 27$

47. $-3y + 12y^3 - 12y^5$

48. $5x^2 - 9x - 2$

49. $2x^2 - 4xy + 2y^2 - 18t^2$

50. $x^2 - 2xy + y^2 - r^2 + 8r - 16$

5-7 Solve.

51. $4x^2 + 11x + 6 = 0$

52. $3x^2 + 36x = 0$

5-8

53. Peter's pool table is 1 ft longer than twice its width. The area of the pool table is 15 ft². Find the dimensions of the pool table.

6-1 – 6-3 Simplify.

54. $\dfrac{3x^2 + xy - 2y^2}{x^2 - y^2}$

55. $\dfrac{8x^3 - 27}{64x^3 + 1} \div \dfrac{4x^2 - 12x + 9}{16x^2 + 8x + 1}$

56. $\dfrac{x - 1}{x - 2} - \dfrac{x + 1}{x + 2} + \dfrac{x - 6}{x^2 - 4}$

57. $\dfrac{\dfrac{1}{x} + \dfrac{1}{y}}{\dfrac{x^2 - y^2}{xy}}$

6-4 Divide.

58. $\dfrac{18xy^2 - 6x^2y + 9x^3y^3}{3x^2y}$

59. $(4x - 3)\overline{)64x^3 - 27}$

60. $(y^3 - y + 6) \div (y + 2)$

6-5 Use synthetic division to find the quotient and remainder.

61. $(x^3 - 2x^2 - 4x - 6) \div (x - 2)$

62. $(y^4 - 1) \div (y + 1)$

6-6 Solve.

63. $-\dfrac{1}{3} - \dfrac{5}{4x} = \dfrac{3}{4} - \dfrac{1}{6x}$

64. $\dfrac{x}{2x - 6} - \dfrac{3}{x^2 - 6x + 9} = \dfrac{x - 2}{3x - 9}$

37. $-7y$
38. $7x^2 - 6x$
39. $4x - 2$
40. $-7x^2 + 4x$
41. $x^4 - 6x^2y + 9y^2$
42. $9x^2 - 4y^2 - 4y - 1$
43. $12x(2x - 3)(x - 2)$
44. $4(3y + 5)(3y - 5)$
45. $(x - y + 6)(x - y - 6)$
46. $(z - 3)(z^2 + 3z + 9)$
47. $-3y(2y^2 - 1)(2y^2 - 1)$
48. $(x - 2)(5x + 1)$
49. $2(x - y + 3t)(x - y - 3t)$
50. $(x - y + r - 4)(x - y - r + 4)$
51. $-2, -\frac{3}{4}$
52. $0, -12$
53. $2\frac{1}{2}$ ft by 6 ft
54. $\frac{3x - 2y}{x - y}$
55. $\frac{(4x + 1)(4x^2 + 6x + 9)}{(2x - 3)(16x^2 - 4x + 1)}$
56. $\frac{3}{x + 2}$
57. $\frac{1}{x - y}$
58. $\frac{6y}{x} - 2 + 3xy^2$
59. $16x^2 + 12x + 9$
60. $y^2 - 2y + 3$
61. Q: $x^2 - 4$; R: -14
62. Q: $y^3 - y^2 + y - 1$, R: 0
63. -1
64. $-6, 5$

65. $13\frac{5}{7}h$

66. Train A travels 40 mi/h; train B travels 50 mi/h.

67. $y_2 = \frac{x_2 y_1}{x_1}$

68. $k_1 = \frac{3T}{t} - k_2$

69. 1166

70. $25|t|$

71. 2

72. $2x^2|y|$

73. $2x^2\sqrt[3]{3x}$

74. $\frac{|a|}{6}\sqrt{30a}$

75. $\sqrt{x^2 - xy + y^2}$

76. $3\sqrt[3]{4} - 3\sqrt{3}$

77. $x\sqrt[3]{3} + \sqrt[3]{12x^2}$

78. 4

79. $\frac{2x}{y^{1/4}}$

80. 28

81. 6, 2

82. $-5\sqrt{3}$

83. $9 - 8i$

84.

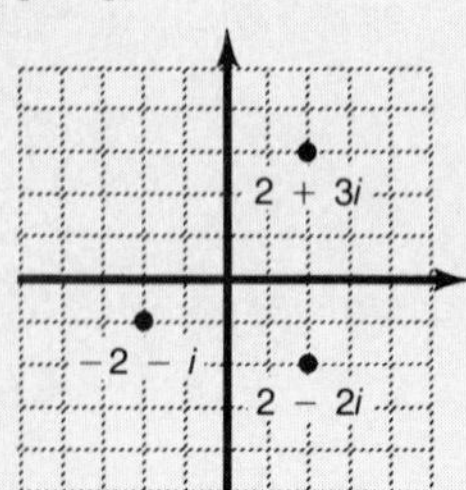

85. $\sqrt{13}$

86. 5

87. 89

88. 7

89. $\frac{i}{-2}$

90. $\frac{\sqrt{5}(2 + i)}{5}$

6-7

65. Nigel can paint a room in 8 hours, while Phil can paint the same room in 6 hours. How long would it take them together to paint 4 rooms of that same size?

66. Train A travels 10 mi/h slower than train B. Train A travels 400 miles in the same time that train B travels 500 miles. Find the speed of each train.

6-8 Solve each equation for the given variable.

67. $\frac{x_1}{y_1} = \frac{x_2}{y_2}$ for y_2

68. $T = \frac{(k_1 + k_2)t}{3}$ for k_1

6-9

69. The number (N) of pizzas produced at a pizza parlor varies directly as the amount of time (t) the store is open. If the pizza parlor produces 350 pizzas in 15 hours, how many pizzas can it produce in 50 hours?

7-1 – 7-4 Simplify.

70. $\sqrt{(-25t)^2}$

71. $-\sqrt[5]{-32}$

72. $\sqrt[4]{16x^8y^4}$

73. $\sqrt[3]{12x^3}\sqrt[3]{2x^4}$

74. $\frac{\sqrt{60a^8}}{\sqrt{72a^5}}$

75. $\frac{\sqrt{y^3 + x^3}}{\sqrt{y + x}}$

76. $\sqrt[3]{108} - 2\sqrt{75} + \sqrt{147}$

77. $\sqrt[3]{x}\left(\sqrt[3]{3x^2} + \sqrt[3]{12x}\right)$

7-5 Rewrite with positive exponents.

78. $\left(\frac{1}{8}\right)^{-\frac{2}{3}}$

79. $2x(y)^{-\frac{1}{4}}$

7-6 Solve.

80. $\sqrt{5x + 4} = 12$

81. $\sqrt{4x + 1} - \sqrt{x - 2} = 3$

7-7 Simplify.

82. $\sqrt{-3} \cdot 5i$

83. $(8 - 5i) - (-1 + 3i)$

7-8 Graph.

84. $2 + 3i, -2 - i, 2 - 2i$

Find the following absolute values.

85. $|3 - 2i|$

86. $|-3 + 4i|$

7-9 Multiply.

87. $(8 - 5i)(8 + 5i)$

88. $(2 - i\sqrt{3})(2 + i\sqrt{3})$

Divide.

89. $2 \div 4i$

90. $\frac{\sqrt{2} + i}{\sqrt{2} - i}$

7-10 Find an equation having the specified numbers as solutions.

91. $2i, -2i$

92. $3 + 4i, 3 - 4i$

Solve.

93. $x + 2ix - 1 = 2i + 3ix - 5i$

8-1 Solve.

94. $9x^2 - 15x + 4 = 0$

95. $4x^2 = 20$

Complete the square.

96. $x^2 + 14x$

97. $y^2 - \frac{1}{3}y$

Solve by completing the square.

98. $2x^2 - 7x = 15$

8-2

99. The length of a swimming pool is 10 m less than twice its width. The area of the swimming pool is 1000 m^2. Find the dimensions of the pool.

8-3 Solve.

100. $x^2 - 3x + 5 = 0$

101. $4x^2 - 2x + 5 = 0$

8-4 Find the discriminant and determine the number and nature of the solutions.

102. $x^2 + 3x + 5 = 0$

103. $10 - 2x^2 - 6x = 0$

104. Find an equation in which the sum of the solutions is -4 and the product of the solutions is $\frac{1}{4}$.

8-5 Solve.

105. $y - 5\sqrt{y} + 4 = 0$

106. $x^4 - 3x^2 - 18 = 0$

107. $x^{-2} - x^{-1} - 6 = 0$

8-6 Solve for the indicated variable.

108. $T = \frac{1}{3}gt^2$ for t

109. $\sqrt{\frac{x + 2}{y^2}} = k$ for y

Use the formula $s = 4.9t^2 + v_0t$

110. An object is thrown from an airplane at an initial velocity (v_0) of 30 m/sec. If the object takes 5 seconds to hit the ground, what was the height (s) of the airplane?

8-7

111. Find an equation of variation when x varies jointly as y and inversely as the square of z, and $y = 50$ when $x = 20$ and $z = 60$.

112. The intensity of light (I) from a light bulb varies inversely as the square of the distance (d) from the bulb. Suppose I is 160 W/m^2 when the distance is 4 m. Find the intensity at a distance of 12 m.

91. $x^2 + 4 = 0$
92. $x^2 - 6x + 25 = 0$
93. $-i + 2$
94. $\frac{4}{3}, \frac{1}{3}$
95. $\pm\sqrt{5}$
96. $x^2 + 14x + 49$
97. $y^2 - \frac{1}{3}y + \frac{1}{36}$
98. $-\frac{3}{2}, 5$
99. 25 m by 40 m
100. $\frac{3 \pm i\sqrt{11}}{2}$
101. $\frac{1 \pm i\sqrt{19}}{4}$
102. Discriminant = -11
There are two complex roots.
103. Discriminant = 116
There are two irrational roots.
104. $4x^2 + 16x + 1 = 0$
105. 16, 1
106. $\pm\sqrt{6}, \pm i\sqrt{3}$
107. $\frac{1}{3}, -\frac{1}{2}$
108. $t = \pm\sqrt{\frac{3T}{g}}$
109. $y = \pm\frac{\sqrt{x + 2}}{k}$
110. 272.5 m
111. $xz^2 = 1440y$
112. $\frac{160}{9}$ w/m^2

CHAPTER 9

Quadratic Functions and Transformations

Chapter Overview

Chapter 9 develops quadratic functions for graphing, developing a standard form and examining symmetry, translation, and stretching and shrinking of graphs. Maximum or minimum values are determined, and the relationship between x-intercepts and roots is examined. Quadratic functions are fit to graphs and data points using a system of equations. Problem-solving lessons for quadratic functions and strategies for college entrance exams are included.

Objectives

9-1
- Test the equation of a relation for symmetry with respect to an axis.
- Test the equation of a relation for symmetry with respect to the origin.
- Determine whether a function is even or odd.

9-2
- Sketch a graph that is a vertical translation of a given graph.
- Sketch a graph that is a horizontal translation of a given graph.

9-3
- Sketch a graph that is a vertical stretching or shrinking of a given graph.
- Sketch a graph that is a horizontal stretching or shrinking of a given graph.

9-4
- Graph a function $f(x) = a(x - h)^2$, and determine its characteristics.

9-5
- Graph a function $f(x) = a(x - h)^2 + k$, and determine its characteristics.
- Determine the characteristics of a function $f(x) = a(x - h)^2 + k$.

9-6
- Find standard form for a quadratic function, and then find the vertex, line of symmetry, and maximum or minimum value for the quadratic function defined.
- Solve maximum and minimum value problems that involve quadratic functions.

9-7
- Find the x-intercepts of the graph of a quadratic function, if they exist.

9-8
- Find quadratic functions given a graph or three data points.
- Solve problems using quadratic functions.

TEACHING CHAPTER 9

Cooperative Learning Opportunities

One of your goals in pursuing cooperative learning activities is to give students the experience of working productively with a variety of students. Thus, it generally helps to reassign groups regularly.

With the time pressure to cover the topics in algebra and trigonometry, it is easy to skip the mixed review exercises. But skills not maintained may not be available when needed. Although it may appear to be wasting time, constant review is really a time saver.

Groups with three or four students working together, with no assigned roles, can be asked to do a mixed review. Using this approach, students should not feel as frustrated by the need to constantly look back and to check their memory and the accuracy of their work. Rather, they will depend on one another's expertise and should be able to move quickly and easily through a review.

Multicultural Note: *Winifred Edgerton Merrill*

In 1883, Winifred Edgerton graduated from Wellesley and applied to the graduate program at Columbia University—which had had no female students, undergraduate or graduate. Conditions of her admission were that she dust the astronomical equipment and "comport herself so as not to disturb the men students." 1886 Edgerton became the first woman to receive a Ph.D. in mathematics from an American university. The title of her dissertation was, "The Unification of the Several Systems of Mathematical Co-ordinates." After her marriage in 1888, Winifred Edgerton Merrill became one of the founders of Barnard College.

Edgerton Merrill said that her effort to bring together different topics and branches of mathematics exemplified a life-long "search for co-ordinating elements in life-experience." Under her portrait in Columbia's Philosophy Hall is the inscription, "She Opened the Door."

Alternative Assessment and Communication Ideas

The **Writing to Learn** activity on page 390 can be expanded to form the basis of an alternative assessment for the chapter. There are a number of mathematical terms in the chapter with an intuitive meaning that will aid the understanding but which must then be followed by a mathematical definition that will remove vagueness and ambiguity.

Have students prepare a journal of terms used in the chapter. For each term, they should write their own understanding of the word followed by the mathematical definition; then an example with both an equation and a graph. Finally, they should write about how the use of the term is helpful but why it also could be misunderstood if it were not given a more exact definition.

If students have trouble getting started you could supply them with the following list: symmetry, transformation, stretching, shrinking, vertex, function, maximum, minimum, intercept.

Investigations and Projects

Chapter 9 brings into focus and interrelates many previously covered topics. In particular, Lesson 9-5 consolidates the geometric and algebraic interpretations of the parabola.

After completing Lesson 9-7, you can use the general form of the quadratic as the basis for a project. Have students assign values to *a*, *h*, and *k*. Then have them vary one while keeping the other two fixed. Ask them to do this for each of the values. They should show how the graph is affected and use previously learned vocabulary to describe the symmetry, transformations, and intercepts. Suggest that students prepare a poster of their results for a bulletin board display. This activity will strengthen students' understanding of the mathematical concepts and also help them see the importance of the general form.

Another project would be for students to research further applications of the quadratic function and where possible find equations. These would include parabolic reflectors, telescopic equipment, and suspension bridges.

MANAGING CHAPTER 9

Lesson	PACING CHART (DAYS) Algebra	Algebra w/Finite	Algebra w/Trig	Compre-hensive	Opening Activity	Cooperative Activity	Seat or Group Work
9-1	2	1	1	1	First Five Minutes 9-1: **TE** p.384 or ***FFM Transparency Masters*** p.27	Critical Thinking: **SE** p.390	Try This a–i
9-2	1	1	1	1	First Five Minutes 9-2: **TE** p.391 or ***FFM Transparency Masters*** p.27	Critical Thinking: **SE** p.394 Critical Thinking 9: ***Enrichment*** p.30	Try This a–d
9-3	1	1	1	1	First Five Minutes 9-3: **TE** p.395 or ***FFM Transparency Masters*** p.27	Critical Thinking: **SE** p.399	Try This a–f
9-4	1	1	1	1	First Five Minutes 9-4: **TE** p.400 or ***FFM Transparency Masters*** p.28	Explore: **SE** p.400 Critical Thinking: **SE** p.402	Try This a–b
9-5	1	1	1	1	First Five Minutes 9-5: **TE** p.404 or ***FFM Transparency Masters*** p.28	Explore: **SE** p.404 Critical Thinking: **SE** p.407	Try This a–f
9-6	2	1	1	1	First Five Minutes 9-6: **TE** p.408 or ***FFM Transparency Masters*** p.28	Critical Thinking: **SE** p.411	Try This a–d
9-7	1	1	1	1	First Five Minutes 9-7: **TE** p.412 or ***FFM Transparency Masters*** p.29	Critical Thinking: **SE** p.413 Looking for Errors 9: ***Enrichment*** p.70	Try This a–c
9-8	3	2	2	1	First Five Minutes 9-8: **TE** p.414 or ***FFM Transparency Masters*** p.29	Critical Thinking: **SE** p.419 Problem Solving: **SE** pp.420–423; ✂ Manipulative Activity 9: ***Enrichment*** p.50	Try This a–d
Review	1	1	1	1			
Test	1	1	1	1			
Cum. Review	0	0	0	1			
Mid-year Test	0	0	0	1			

 FFM: First Five Minutes SPMR: Skills Practice Mixed Review

MANAGING CHAPTER 9

Enrichment	Review/Assess	Reteach	Technology	Lesson
Writing to Learn: **SE** p.390	Lesson Quiz: **TE** p.388	Skills Practice 24, #1–19: ***SPMR*** p.36	Worksheet 12: ***TI-81 Activities*** pp.49–52; Worksheet 12: ***Master Grapher*** pp.52–55, pp.186–189, or pp.322–325	**9-1**
Critical Thinking 9: ***Enrichment*** p.30	Lesson Quiz: **TE** p.392	Skills Practice 24, #20–25: ***SPMR*** p.36	Worksheet 13: ***TI-81 Activities*** pp.53–56; Worksheet 13: ***Master Grapher*** pp.56–59, pp.190–193, or pp.326–329	**9-2**
Worksheet 14: ***Master Grapher*** pp.60–64(Apple II), pp.194–198(IBM), or pp.330–334(Mac)	Lesson Quiz: **TE** p.398 Quiz 17: ***Assessment*** p.25	Skills Practice 24, #26–37: ***SPMR*** p.36	Worksheet 14: ***TI-81 Activities*** pp.57–61; Worksheet 14: ***Master Grapher*** pp.60–64, pp.194–198, or pp.330–334	**9-3**
Activity: **SE** p.403	Lesson Quiz: **TE** p.401 Mixed Review 17: ***SPMR*** p.81	Skills Practice 25, #1–12: ***SPMR*** p.37	Worksheet 15: ***TI-81 Activities*** pp.63–66; Worksheet 15: ***Master Grapher*** pp.65–68, pp.199–202, or pp.335–338	**9-4**
College Entrance Exam 3, Section I: ***Problem Bank*** pp.63–66	Lesson Quiz: **TE** p.405	Skills Practice 25, #13–30: ***SPMR*** p.37	Problem for Programmers: **SE** p.407	**9-5**
College Entrance Exam 3, Section II: ***Problem Bank*** pp.67–70	Lesson Quiz: **TE** p.409 Quiz 18: ***Assessment*** p.26	Problem Bank 15: ***Problem Bank*** p.36	Calculator Worksheet 15: ***Technology*** p.17	**9-6**
Bonus Topic 9: ***Enrichment*** p.10	Lesson Quiz: **TE** p.412	Skills Practice 26, #1–11: ***SPMR*** p.38	BASIC Computer Project 8: ***Technology*** p.88	**9-7**
Problem Solving: **SE** pp.420–421 Problem 9: Computer Assisted Problem Solving, **SE** p.845 ✂ Manipulative Activity 9: ***Enrichment*** p.50	Lesson Quiz: **TE** p.417 Mixed Review 18: ***SPMR*** p.82	Skills Practice 26, #12–16: ***SPMR*** p.38 Problem Bank 16: ***Problem Bank*** p.37	Problem 9: Computer Assisted Problem Solving, **SE** p.845	**9-8**
	Summary and Review: **SE** pp.424–426; Test: **SE** pp.426–427			**Review**
	Chapter 9 Test: ***Assessment*** pp.95–100(reg.), pp.173–174 (adv.)			**Test**
	Cumulative Review: **SE** pp.377–381, pp.563–565			**Cum. Review**
	Mid-year Test: ***Assessment*** pp.227–230(adv.)			**Mid-year Test**

The solution to the problem posed on the facing page can be found on p. 415.

Ready for Quadratic Functions and Transformations?

3-2 Graph.

1. $2y = \frac{1}{3}x - 1$ Line containing (3, 0) and (−3, −1) **2.** $y = -2x + 3$ Line containing (0, 3) and (1, 1)

3-3 Tell whether or not each graph is the graph of a function.

3. No

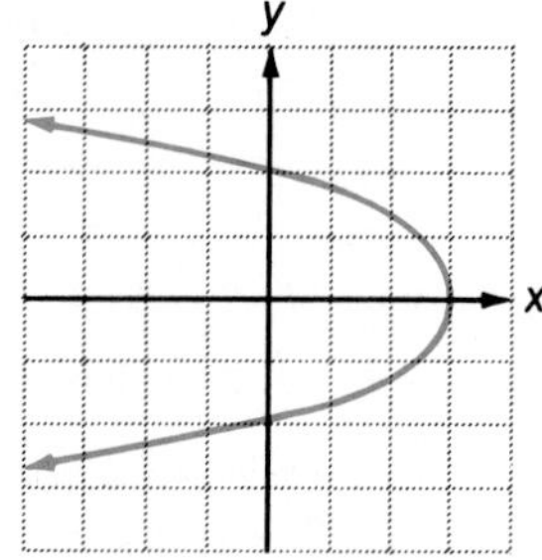

4. Yes

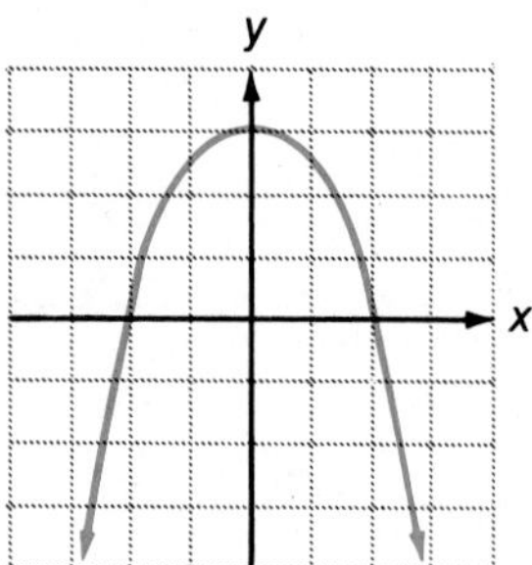

3-4 Find the x- and y-intercepts of each.

5. $2x - 5y = 10$ 5, −2

6. $3x + y = 6$ 2, 6

7. $-4x + 3y = 12$ −3, 4

8. $-x + 2y = 4$ −4, 2

9. $3x + 5y = 10$ $\frac{10}{3}$, 2

10. $x - 7y = 4$ 4, $-\frac{4}{7}$

8-1 Solve by completing the square.

11. $x^2 - \frac{2}{3}x - \frac{1}{3} = 0$ $-\frac{1}{3}$, 1

12. $x^2 + 2x - 6 = 0$ $-1 \pm \sqrt{7}$

CHAPTER

9

Quadratic Functions and Transformations

A pizza shop lists the following prices for pizzas.

Diameter in cm	Price
20	\$ 6.00
30	\$ 8.50
40	\$11.50

What price should be given to a 35-cm pizza?

9-1

FIRST FIVE MINUTES

1. Evaluate.
   $f(x) = x^2$ and $g(x) = x^3$ at $x = 2$ and $x = -2$
   $f(2) = f(-2) = 4$
   $g(2) = 8, g(-2) = -8$
2. Evaluate.
   $f(x) = x^4$ and $g(x) = x^5$ at $x = a$ and $x = -a$
   $f(a) = f(-a) = a^4$
   $g(a) = a^5, g(-a) = -a^5$

Symmetry with Respect to the Axes

Point out examples of *symmetric* objects. For example, a sphere is symmetric about any line containing the center of the sphere.

Before introducing Theorem 9-2, remind students that equivalent equations have the same solutions.

Avoiding Common Errors

Emphasize that replacement of x by $-x$ is used to test for symmetry with respect to the y-axis. Replacement of y by $-y$ is used to test for symmetry with respect to the x-axis.

Key Questions

- Where is the line of symmetry for a circle?
  Any line through the center
- Which capital letters have an axis of symmetry?
  A, B, C, D, E, H, I, K, M, O, T, U, V, W, X, Y
- What is the axis of symmetry for (2, 0) and (−2, 0)?
  y-axis

9-1 Symmetry

Master Grapher Worksheet 12, *Symmetry*, can be used as a lesson opener.

In this chapter we consider how changes in the equation $y = f(x)$ affect the graph of the function it defines. Then we use this information to graph quadratic functions $f(x) = ax^2 + bx + c$, where $a \neq 0$.

Symmetry with Respect to the Axes

Objective: Test the equation of a relation for symmetry with respect to an axis.

Many examples of line symmetry can be found in nature. A leaf, a butterfly, or a kitten's face all exhibit line symmetry. The idea of line symmetry can be described precisely in mathematical language.

Definition

Two points, P and P_1, are **symmetric with respect to a line** l when they are the same distance from l, measured along a perpendicular to l. Line l is known as a **line** or **axis of symmetry.** P_1 is said to be the **image** of P. A figure, or set of points, is symmetric with respect to a line when the image of each point in the set is also in the set.

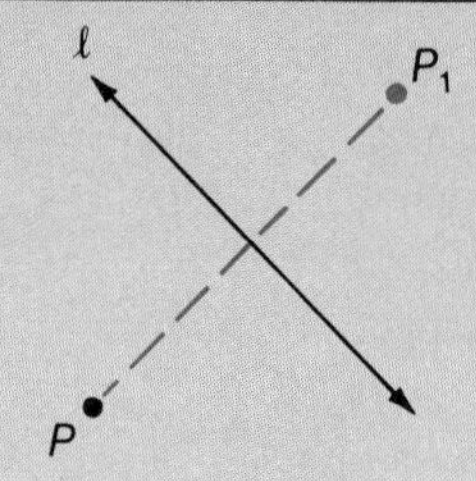

Two points symmetric with respect to a line are called reflections of each other across the line. The line is known as a line of symmetry.

The figure at the right is symmetric with respect to line l. Imagine picking this figure up and flipping it over line l. Points P and P_1 would be interchanged. Points Q and Q_1 would be interchanged. These are pairs of symmetric points. The entire figure would look exactly as it did before flipping.

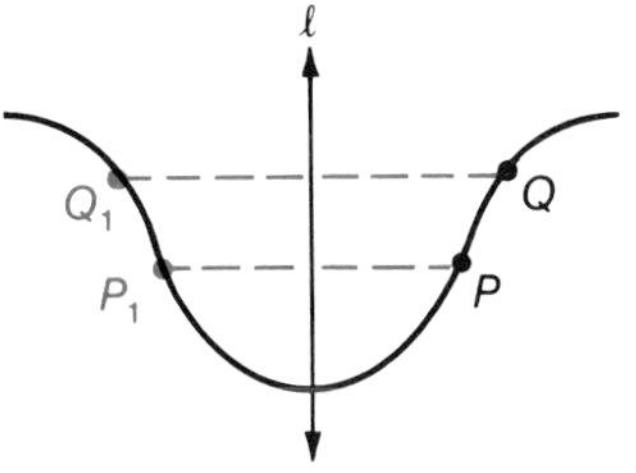

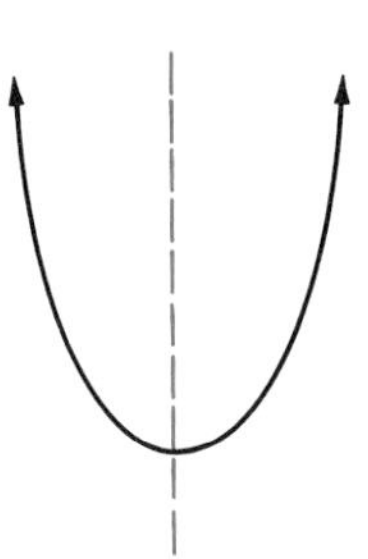

Symmetric with respect to the line

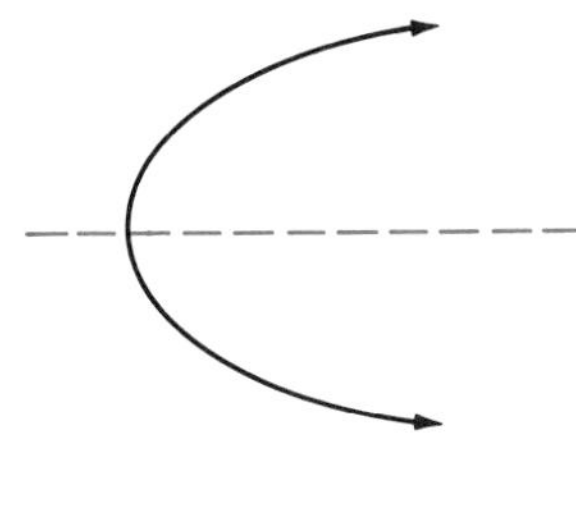

Symmetric with respect to the line

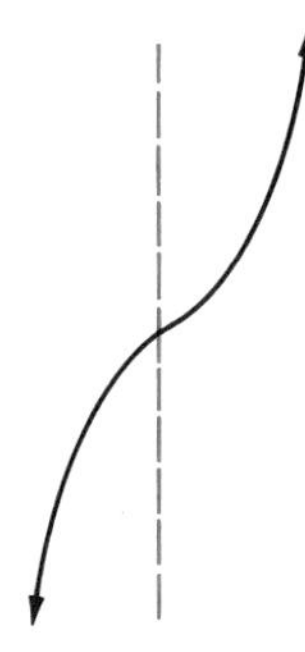

Not symmetric with respect to the line

The figure at the right is not symmetric with respect to the vertical line shown, or with respect to a horizontal line. It is symmetric in other respects, as we will see later.

There are types of symmetry in which the x-axis or the y-axis is a line of symmetry.

Theorem 9-1

Two points are symmetric with respect to the x-axis if and only if their y-coordinates are additive inverses and they have the same x-coordinate.

Two points are symmetric with respect to the y-axis if and only if their x-coordinates are additive inverses and they have the same y-coordinate.

The relation defined by $y = x^2$ contains (2, 4) and (−2, 4). The first coordinates, 2 and −2, are additive inverses of each other. The second coordinates are the same. For every point (x, y) of the relation, there is another point $(-x, y)$. So the relation $y = x^2$ is symmetric with respect to the y-axis.

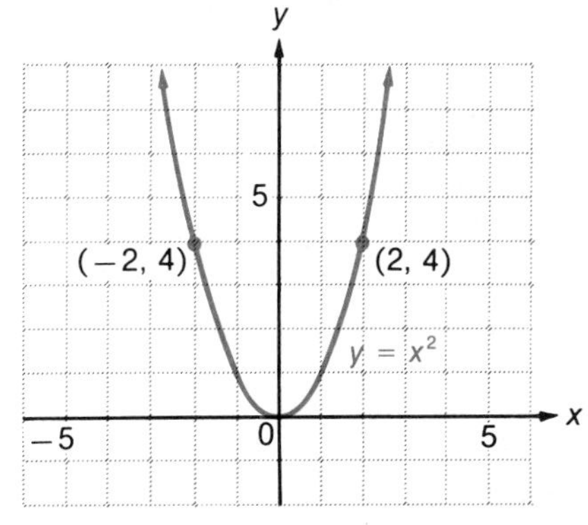

Chalkboard Examples

1. Test $x^3 = y^2 + 3$ for symmetry with respect to the axes.
   Replace x by $-x$. The equation becomes
   $(-x)^3 = y^2 + 3$
   $-x^3 = y^2 + 3$
   The original equation is not symmetric with respect to the x-axis.
   Replace y by $-y$ to obtain
   $x^3 = (-y)^2 + 3$
   $x^3 = y^2 + 3$
   The original equation is symmetric with respect to the y-axis.
2. Test $x^2 - y^2 = 1$ for symmetry with respect to the axes.
   Replace x by $-x$. The equation becomes
   $(-x)^2 - y^2 = 1$
   $x^2 - y^2 = 1$
   The original equation is symmetric with respect to the y-axis.
   Replace y by $-y$ to obtain
   $x^2 - (-y)^2 = 1$.
   The original equation is symmetric with respect to the x-axis.

Symmetry with Respect to the Origin

This symmetry can be demonstrated by having two students move so that a fixed point is midway between them at all times.

Key Question

- Which capital letters are symmetric with respect to a point?
  H, I, N, O, S, X, Z

Chalkboard Examples

1. Test $\frac{y^3}{6x} = 10$ for symmetry with respect to the origin.
   Replace x by $-x$ and y by $-y$. The transformed equation is
   $\frac{(-y)^3}{6(-x)} = 10$
   $\frac{-y^3}{-6x} = 10$
   $\frac{y^3}{6x} = 10$
   The original equation is symmetric with respect to the origin.
2. Test $x^2 + y^3 = 1$ for symmetry with respect to the origin.
   Replace x by $-x$ and y by $-y$. The transformed equation is
   $(-x)^2 + (-y)^3 = 1$
   $x^2 - y^3 = 1$
   This is not equivalent to the original equation. The equation is not symmetric with respect to the origin.

We now have a means of testing a relation for symmetry with respect to the x- and y-axes when the relation is defined by an equation.

Theorem 9-2

When a relation is defined by an equation,

A. its graph is symmetric with respect to the y-axis if and only if replacing x by $-x$ produces an equivalent equation.

B. its graph is symmetric with respect to the x-axis if and only if replacing y by $-y$ produces an equivalent equation.

EXAMPLE 1 Test $y = x^2 + 2$ for symmetry with respect to the axes.

To test for symmetry with respect to the y-axis, we replace x by $-x$ and obtain $y = (-x)^2 + 2$. This is equivalent to $y = x^2 + 2$. Therefore, the graph is symmetric with respect to the y-axis.

To test for symmetry with respect to the x-axis, we replace y by $-y$ and obtain $-y = x^2 + 2$, or $y = -x^2 - 2$. This is not equivalent to $y = x^2 + 2$. Therefore, the graph is not symmetric with respect to the x-axis.

Try This Test for symmetry with respect to the axes.

a. $y = x^2 + 3$ Symmetric with respect to the y-axis **b.** $x^2 + y^2 = 2$ Symmetric with respect to both axes

Symmetry with Respect to the Origin

Objective: Test the equation of a relation for symmetry with respect to the origin.

We can find examples of point symmetry in the real world. The bloom of a flower or a pinwheel exhibit point symmetry. The idea of point symmetry can also be defined precisely in mathematical language.

Definition

Two points, P and P_1, are **symmetric with respect to a point** Q when they are the same distance from Q, and all three points are on a line. P_1 is said to be the *image* of P. A figure or set of points is symmetric with respect to a point when the image of each point in the set is also in the set.

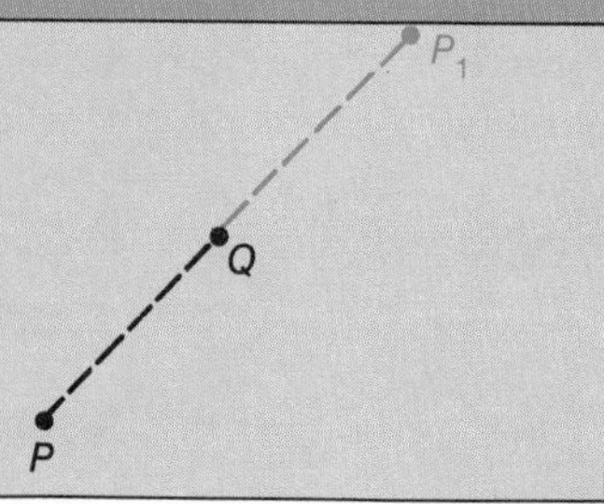

The figure below is symmetric with respect to the origin. Imagine sticking a pin in this figure at the origin and then rotating the figure 180°. Points P and P_1 would be interchanged. Points Q and Q_1 would be interchanged. These are pairs of symmetric points. The entire figure would look exactly as it did before rotating. This means that the image of each point of the figure is also on the figure.

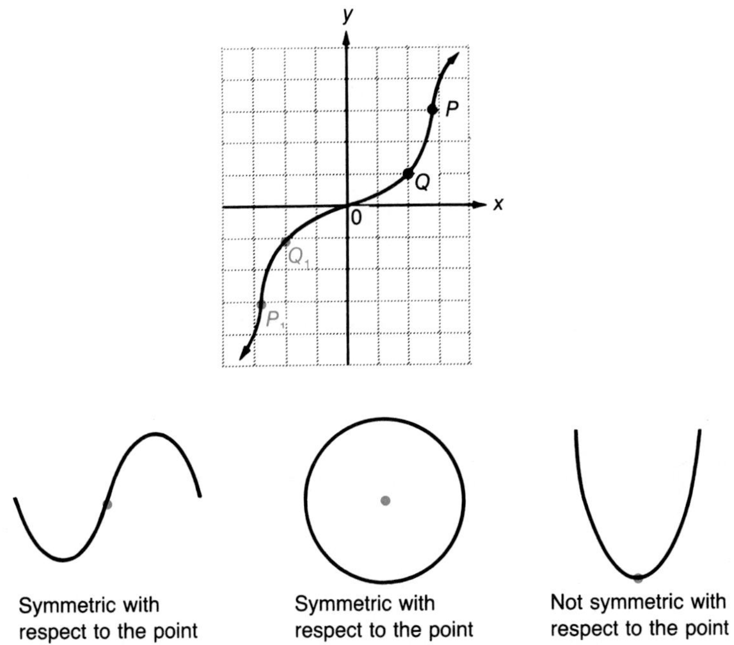

Symmetry with respect to the origin is a special kind of point symmetry.

Theorem 9-3

Two points are symmetric with respect to the origin if and only if both their x- and y-coordinates are additive inverses of each other.

The point symmetric to $(3, -5)$ with respect to the origin is $(-3, 5)$.

Theorem 9-4

A graph of a relation defined by an equation is symmetric with respect to the origin if and only if replacing x by $-x$ and replacing y by $-y$ produces an equivalent equation.

This gives us a means for testing a relation for symmetry with respect to the origin when it is defined by an equation.

Even and Odd Functions

Examples of even and odd functions can be obtained from power functions $f(x) = x^n$, where n is an integer. After substituting several values of n, students should realize the following generalizations.
$f(x) = x^n$ is an even function when n is even.
$f(x) = x^n$ is an odd function when n is odd.

Chalkboard Example

1. Determine whether $f(x) = x^3$ is even, odd or neither.
   $f(-x) = (-x)^3 = -x^3 = -f(x)$
   The function is odd.

LESSON ENRICHMENT

Suppose you have a graph of a curve. How can you plot the curve that is symmetric to the original curve

1. with respect to the x-axis?
   For every point (x, y) in the curve, plot $(x, -y)$.
2. with respect to the y-axis?
   For every (x, y), plot $(-x, y)$.
3. with respect to the origin?
   For every (x, y), plot $(-x, -y)$.
4. Is there any function whose graph is symmetric with respect to the x-axis?
   Only $x = 0$

LESSON QUIZ

Determine whether the following are symmetric with respect to the x-axis, the y-axis, the origin, or none of these.

1. $y = x^4 + 3$
   The equation is symmetric with respect to the y-axis.
2. $2x + y^2 = 1$
   The equation is symmetric with respect to the x-axis.
3. $y = x$
   The equation is symmetric with respect to the origin.
4. Is the function $f(x) = 1 - x^2$ even, odd or neither?
   The function is even.

EXAMPLE 2 Test $x^2 = y^2 + 2$ for symmetry with respect to the origin.

We replace x by $-x$ and y by $-y$. We obtain $(-x)^2 = (-y)^2 + 2$, which is equivalent to $x^2 = y^2 + 2$, the original equation. Therefore the graph is symmetric with respect to the origin.

Try This Test each relation for symmetry with respect to the origin.

c. $y^2 + x^2 = 16$ Yes **d.** $y = x^3$ Yes

e. $y = x^2$ No **f.** $\frac{1}{2}y^2 + x = \frac{3}{4}$ No

Even and Odd Functions

Objective: Determine whether a function is even or odd.

Function whose graphs are symmetric with respect to the y-axis are called even functions. If $y = f(x)$ defines an even function, then, by Theorem 9-1, $y = f(-x)$ will define the same function.

Definition

A function is an **even function** when $f(x) = f(-x)$ for all x in the domain of f.

Functions whose graphs are symmetric with respect to the origin are called odd functions. If $y = f(x)$ defines an odd function, then, by Theorem 9-4, $-y = f(-x)$.

Definition

A function is an **odd function** when $-f(x) = f(-x)$ for all x in the domain of f.

EXAMPLE 3 Determine whether $f(x) = x^2 + 1$ is even, odd, or neither.

$$f(x) = x^2 + 1 \qquad \begin{aligned} f(-x) &= (-x)^2 + 1 \\ &= x^2 + 1 \end{aligned} \qquad \begin{aligned} -f(x) &= -(x^2 + 1) \\ &= -x^2 - 1 \end{aligned}$$

Compare $f(x)$ and $f(-x)$. They are the same for all x in the domain, so f is an even function.

Compare $f(x)$ and $-f(x)$. They are *not* the same for all x in the domain. The function is not an odd function.

Try This Determine whether each function is even, odd, or neither.

g. $f(x) = x^4 - x^6$ Even **h.** $f(x) = 3x^2 + 3x^5$ Neither **i.** $f(x) = x^3 + x$ Odd

9-1 EXERCISES

Assignment Guide
Algebra: Day 1: 1–24 e/o, MR
Day 2: 25–44 e/o

Alg w/Finite or Trig: 1–47 e/o, 48, MR

Comprehensive: 1–36 m3, 37–47 e/o, 48, 49–54 e/o, MR

A

Test for symmetry with respect to the axes.

1. $3y = x^2 + 4$ y-axis

2. $5y = 2x^2 - 3$ y-axis

3. $2x^4 + 3 = y^2$ Both axes

4. $3y^2 = 2x^4 - 5$ Both axes

5. $2x - 5 = 3y$ Neither axis

6. $5y = 4x + 5$ Neither axis

7. $y^3 = 2x^2$ y-axis

8. $3y^3 = 4x^2$ y-axis

9. $2y^2 = 5x^2 + 12$ Both axes

10. $3x^2 - 2y^2 = 7$ Both axes

11. $3y^3 = 4x^3 + 2$ Neither axis

12. $x^3 - 4y^3 = 12$ Neither axis

Test for symmetry with respect to the origin.

13. $3x^2 - 2y^2 = 3$ Yes

14. $5y^2 = -7x^2 + 4$ Yes

15. $3x + 3y = 0$ Yes

16. $7x = -7y$ Yes

17. $5x - 5y = 0$ Yes

18. $3x = 3y$ Yes

19. $3x = \frac{5}{y}$ Yes

20. $3y = \frac{7}{x}$ Yes

21. $3x^2 + 4x = 2y$ No

22. $5y = 7x^2 - 2x$ No

23. $y = |2x|$ No

24. $3x = |y|$ No

Determine whether each function is even, odd, or neither.

25. $f(x) = 2x^2 + 4x$ Neither

26. $f(x) = -3x^3 + 2x$ Odd

27. $f(x) = 3x^4 - 4x^2$ Even

28. $f(x) = 4x$ Odd

29. $f(x) = |3x|$ Even

30. $f(x) = x^{24}$ Even

31. $f(x) = x + \frac{1}{x}$ Odd

32. $f(x) = x - |x|$ Neither

33. $f(x) = \sqrt{x}$ Neither

34. $f(x) = \sqrt[3]{x}$ Odd

35. $f(x) = 7$ Even

36. $f(x) = 0$ Even and odd

For each function, tell whether it is even, odd, or neither.

37. Even

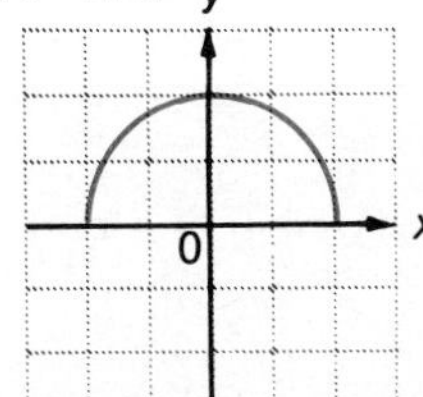

38. Even

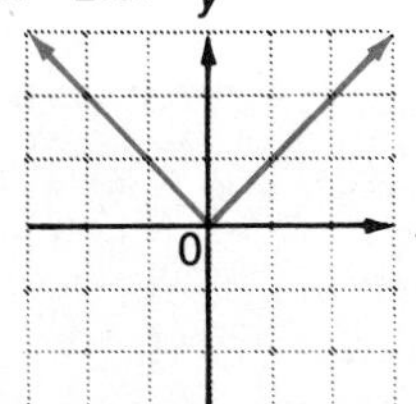

39. Even

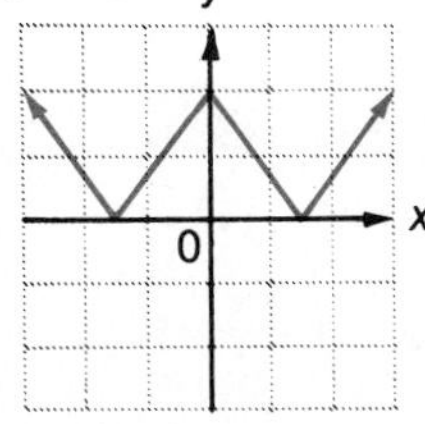

ADDITIONAL ANSWERS

Exercises

45.

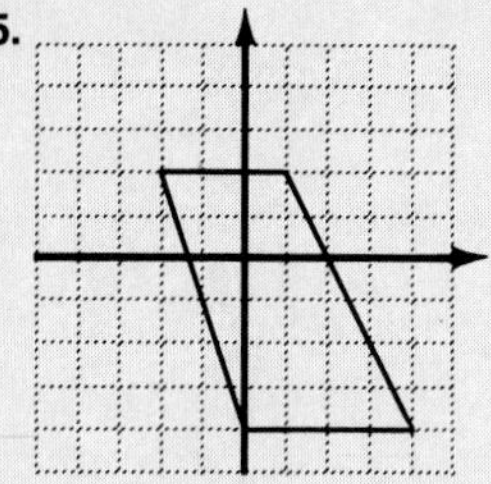

46.

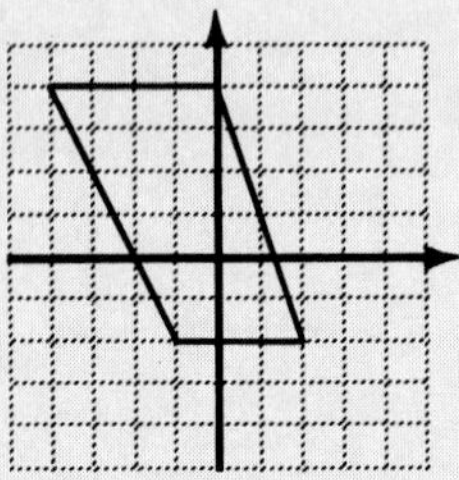

47.

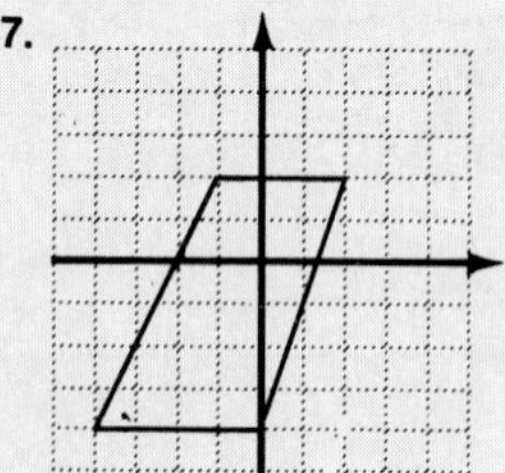

Mixed Review

55. $4\sqrt{15}$
56. 8
57. $4\sqrt{5}$
58. 6
59. $-4, -\frac{3}{2}$
60. $\frac{5}{3}, \frac{2}{3}$
61. $-5, 6$
62. $x^2 - 10x + 24 = 0$
63. $x^2 + 4x = 0$
64. $x^2 - 6x + 6 = 0$
65. $x^2 - 6x + 13 = 0$

40. Even

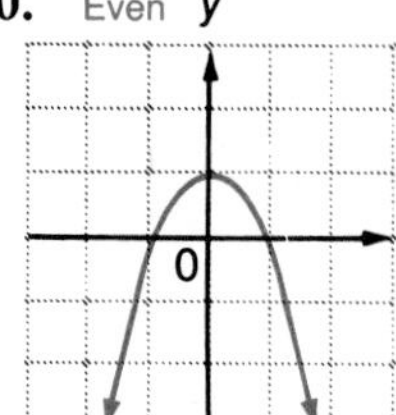

41. Odd

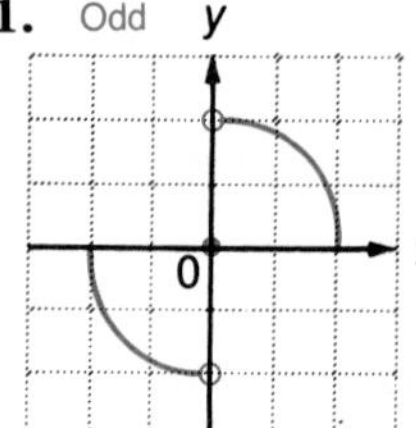

42. Neither

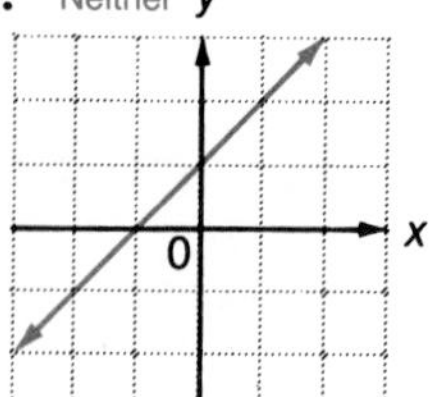

43. Odd

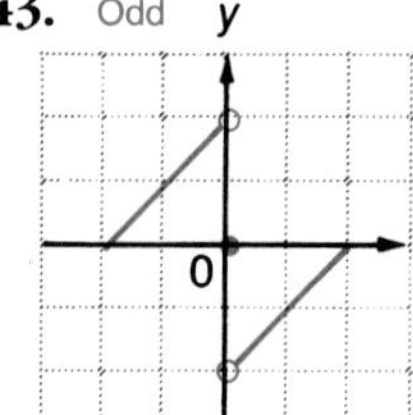

44. Neither

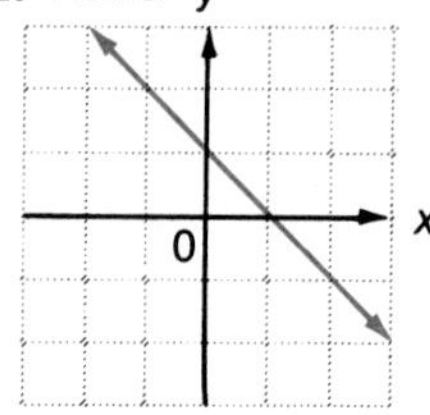

B

On a coordinate grid draw the quadrilateral with vertices (0, 4), (4, 4), (−2, −2), and (1, −2).

45. Graph the reflection across the x-axis. **46.** Graph the reflection across the y-axis.

47. Graph the figure formed by reflecting each point through the origin.

48. ***Critical Thinking*** Find a function that is both odd and even. (Hint: There is only one.) $f(x) = 0$

Challenge

Test for symmetry with respect to the axes.

49. $y = |x|$ y-axis **50.** $|x| = |y|$ Both axes **51.** $|y| = |x| + 1$ Both axes

52. $y = |x| - 3$ y-axis **53.** $|x| + |y| = 3$ Both axes **54.** $|x| - |y| = 5$ Both axes

Mixed Review

Simplify. **55.** $\sqrt{12}\sqrt{20}$ **56.** $\sqrt[3]{512}$ **57.** $\sqrt{80}$ **58.** $\sqrt{3}\sqrt{12}$

Find, without solving, the sum and product of the solutions.

59. $2x^2 + 8x - 3 = 0$ **60.** $3x^2 - 5x + 2 = 0$ **61.** $x^2 + 5x + 6 = 0$

Find a quadratic equation whose solutions are the following. **62.** 6, 4

63. 0, −4 **64.** $3 + \sqrt{3}, 3 - \sqrt{3}$ **65.** $3 + 2i, 3 - 2i$

WRITING TO LEARN

Keep a **learning log** for this chapter. In your log include notes on new ideas, old ideas, and new techniques or skills that you have learned.

9-2 Transformations

Master Grapher Worksheet 13, *Translating Graphs of Functions*, can be used for lesson closure.

An alteration of a relation is called a **transformation**. If such an alteration results in moving the graph of the relation without changing its size or shape and without rotating it, the transformation is called a **translation**.

Vertical Translations

Objective: Sketch a graph that is a vertical translation of a given graph.

Consider the following relations and their graphs.

$$y = x^2$$
$$y = x^2 + 1$$

The graphs have the same shape except that $y = x^2 + 1$ is moved up a distance of 1 unit.

Consider any equation $y = f(x)$. Add a constant k to produce $y = f(x) + k$. This changes each function value by the same amount k but produces no change in the shape of the graph. If k is positive, the graph is moved, or translated, upward. If k is negative, the graph is translated downward.

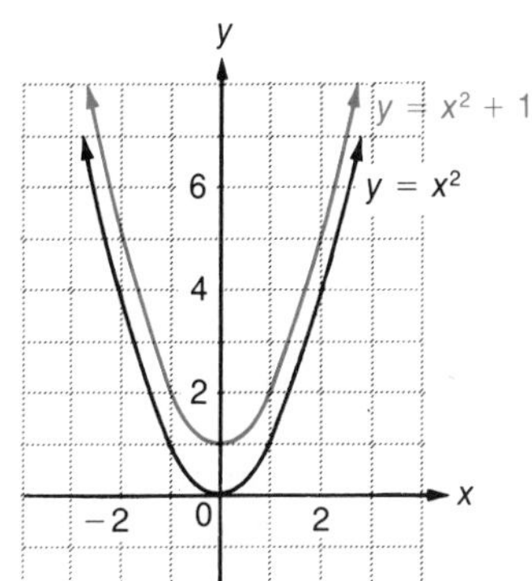

The equation $y = x^2 + 1$ can be rewritten as $y - 1 = x^2$.

Thus the transformation above is equivalent to replacing y by $y - 1$ in the original equation.

Theorem 9-5

In an equation of a relation, replacing y by $y - k$, where k is a constant, translates the graph vertically a distance of $|k|$. If k is positive, the translation is upward. If k is negative, the translation is downward.

Replacing y by $(y + 3)$ in an equation is the same as replacing it by $y - (-3)$. In this case the constant k is -3, and the translation is downward. If we replace y by $y - 5$, the constant k is 5, and the translation is upward.

9-2

FIRST FIVE MINUTES

Tell whether the following are symmetric with respect to the x-axis, the y-axis, the origin, or none of these.

1. $y = x^2$
   Symmetric with respect to the y-axis
2. $x^2 + y^4 = 2$
   Symmetric with respect to the x-axis, the y-axis, and the origin
3. $x + 2y = 3$
   None of these

Vertical Translations

Relations other than functions can be translated. Theorems 9-5 and 9-6 hold for any relation. A relation may be translated both horizontally and vertically.

Avoiding Common Errors

Remind students that replacing y by $y - 3$ in an equation translates the graph in the y direction by $+3$. We can think of the graph moving $+3$, or the coordinate axes moving -3. Most people find it easier to think of the figure as moving and the coordinate system as remaining fixed.

Key Questions

- How many vertical units apart are the graphs of $y = x$ and $y = x - 2$?
  2
- How many vertical units apart are the graphs of $y = x - 2$ and $y + 2 = x$?
  0

Chalkboard Example (*T7*)

1. Sketch the graph of $y - 3 = |x|$ by translating the graph of $y = |x|$.
   The graph of $y - 3 = |x|$ is the graph of $y = |x|$, translated up three units.

Horizontal Translations

Key Question

- What function is translated three units to the right of $y = |x|$? $y = |x - 3|$

Chalkboard Example (*T8*)

1. Use the graph of $y = |x|$ to graph $y = |x - 3|$.
   The graph of $y = |x - 3|$ is the graph of $y = |x|$ translated by +3 to the right.

LESSON QUIZ

Use the graph of $y = |x|$ to graph the following.

1. $y = |x| + 1$
   The graph is shifted up by 1 unit.

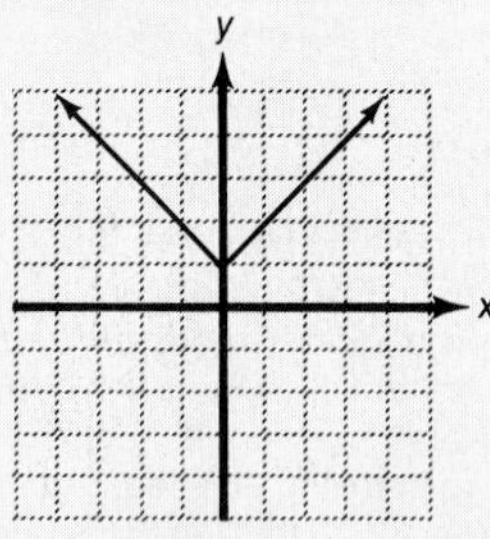

2. $y = |x - 1|$
   The graph is translated to the right by +1.

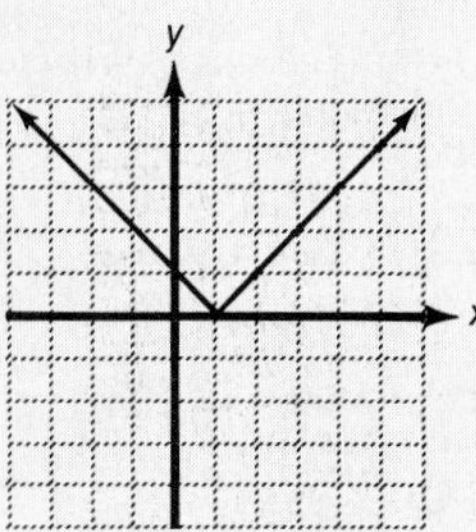

3. $y - 2 = |x - 3|$
   The graph is shifted up 2 units and right by 3 units.

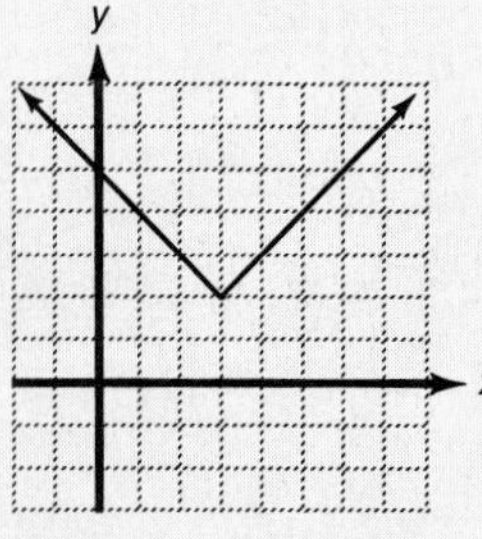

EXAMPLE 1 Consider the graph of $y = |x|$. Sketch the graph of $y = |x| - 2$ by translating.

The graphs of $y = |x|$ and $y = |x| - 2$ are shown below. Note that $y = |x| - 2$ is equivalent to $y + 2 = |x|$ or $y - (-2) = |x|$. Thus the new equation can be obtained by replacing y by $y - (-2)$. Therefore, by Theorem 9-5, the translation is downward two units.

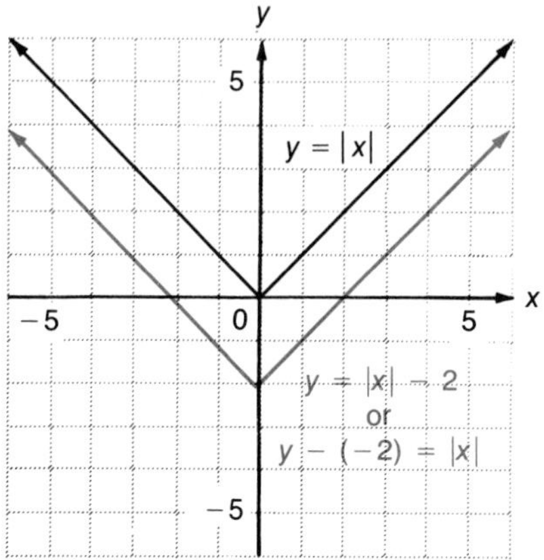

Try This Consider the graph of $y = |x|$ as shown in Example 1. Sketch the graphs of the following by translating. See Additional Answers.

a. $y = -1 + |x|$ **b.** $y = 4 + |x|$

Horizontal Translations

Objective: Sketch a graph that is a horizontal translation of a given graph.

Translations can also be horizontal. If we replace x by $x - h$ everywhere it occurs in an equation, we translate a distance of $|h|$ horizontally.

Theorem 9-6

In an equation of a relation, replacing x by $x - h$, where h is a constant, translates the graph horizontally a distance of $|h|$. If h is positive, the translation is to the right. If h is negative, the translation is to the left.

EXAMPLE 2 Consider the graph of $y = |x|$. Sketch the graph of $y = |x + 2|$ by translating.

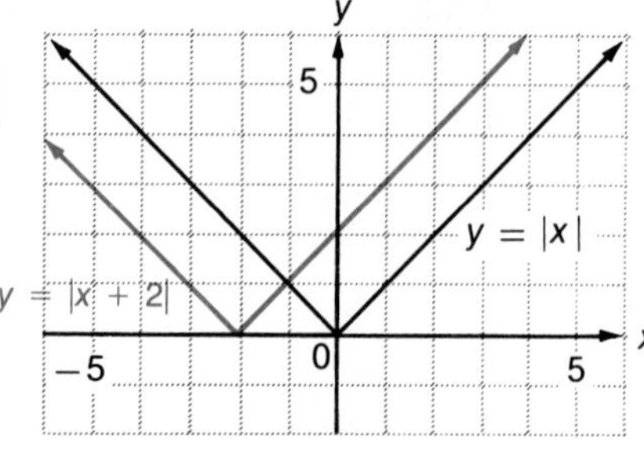

Here we note that x is replaced by $x + 2$, or $x - (-2)$. Thus $h = -2$, and by Theorem 9-6 the translated graph will be moved two units to the left.

Try This Consider the graph of $y = |x|$ as shown in Example 2. Sketch the graphs of the following by translating. See Additional Answers.

c. $y = |x + 3|$ **d.** $y = |x - 1|$

Assignment Guide
Algebra: 1 – 19 e/o, MR
Alg w/Finite or Trig: 1–19 m3, 20–29 e/o, 30, MR
Comprehensive: 1–19 m4, 20–29 e/o, 30–33, MR

9-2 EXERCISES

A

Consider the graph of $y = |x|$.

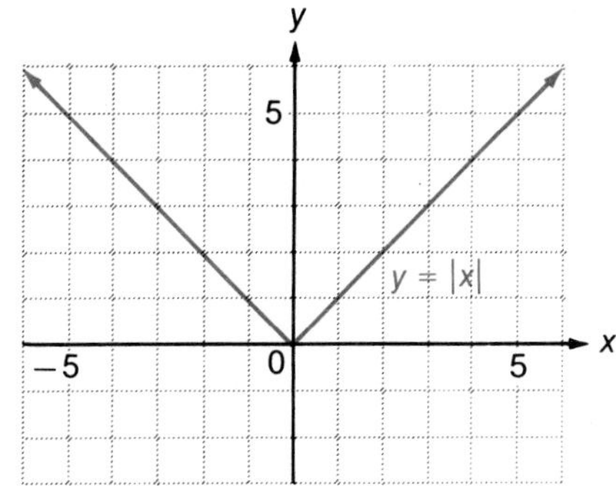

Sketch graphs of the following by translating. For graphs of Exercises 5 – 27, See Teacher's Answer Section.

1. $y = |x| + 2$ **2.** $y = |x| + 3$

3. $y = |x| - 2$ **4.** $y = |x| - 3$

5. $y = |x| + 5$ **6.** $y = |x| + 6$

7. $y = |x| - 4$ **8.** $y = |x| - 5$

9. $y = |x| + \frac{1}{2}$ **10.** $y = |x| + \frac{3}{4}$

Consider the graph of $y = |x|$. Sketch graphs of the following by translating.

11. $y = |x - 3|$ **12.** $y = |x - 2|$ **13.** $y = |x + 2|$

14. $y = |x + 4|$ **15.** $y = |x - 4|$ **16.** $y = |x - 5|$

17. $y = |x + 5|$ **18.** $y = |x + 6|$ **19.** $y = \left|x - \frac{1}{2}\right|$

B

Sketch each graph.

20. $y = |x + 3| - 5$ **21.** $y = |x - 1| - 2$

22. $y = |x + 1| + 1$ **23.** $y = |x - 6| + 6$

Sketch each graph.

24. $(x - 1)^2 + y^2 = 1$ **25.** $x^2 + (y + 2)^2 = 1$

26. $(x + 2)^2 + (y - 1)^2 = 1$ **27.** $(x + 1)^2 + (y + 1)^2 = 1$

ADDITIONAL ANSWERS

Try This

a.

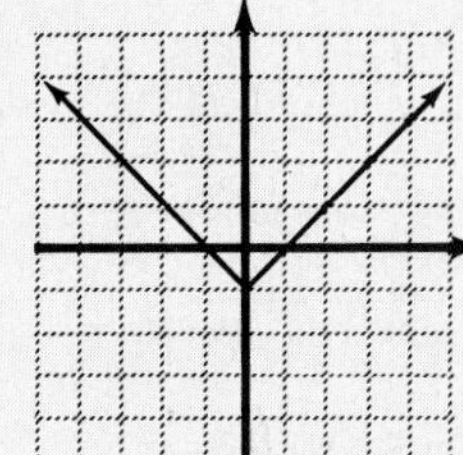

b.

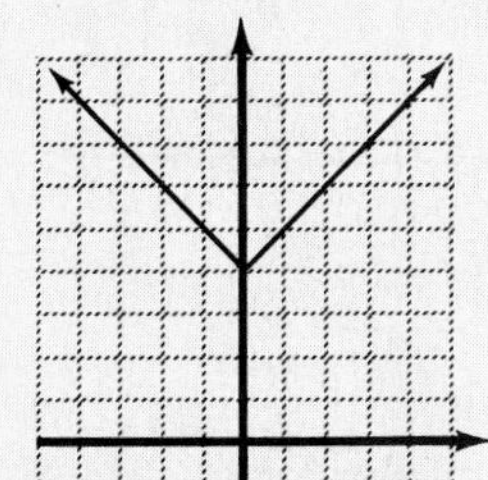

c.

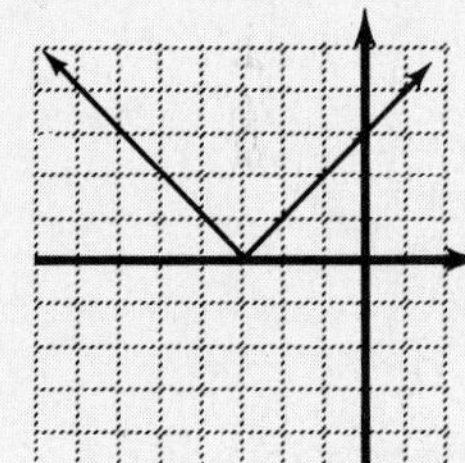

d.

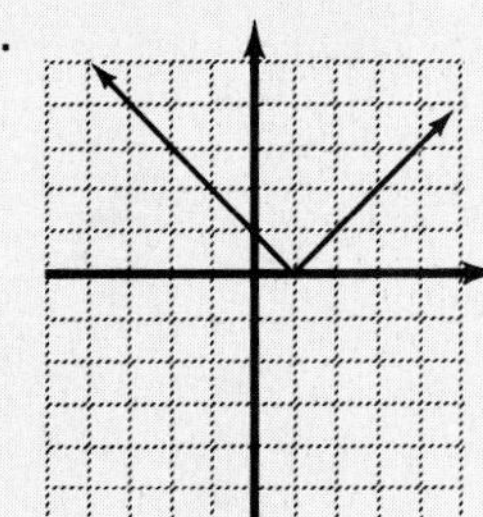

Exercises

1.

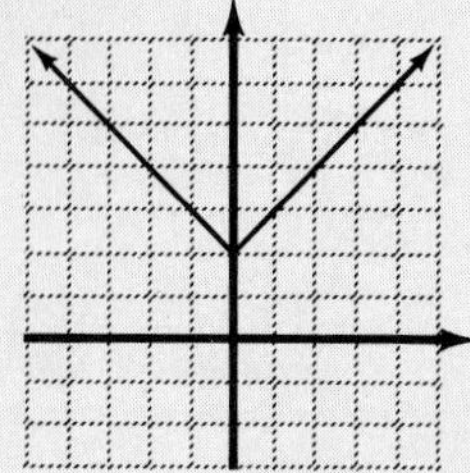

2.

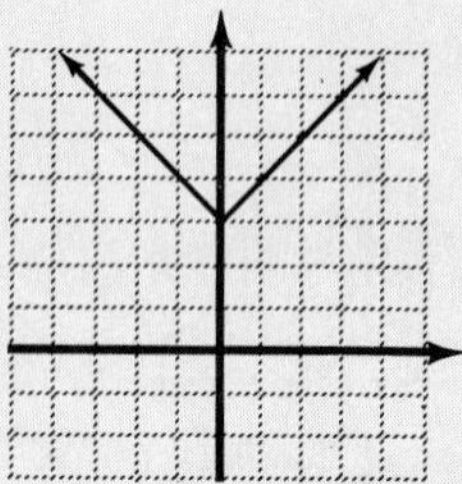

3.

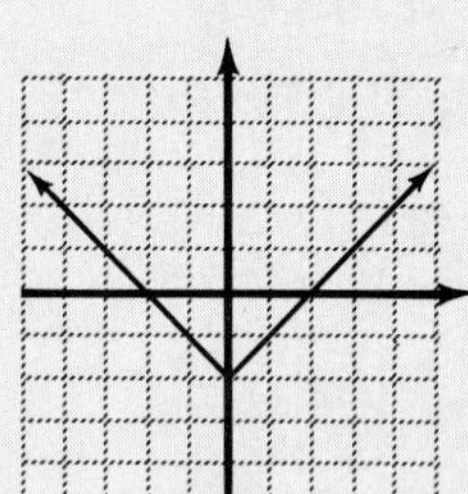

4.

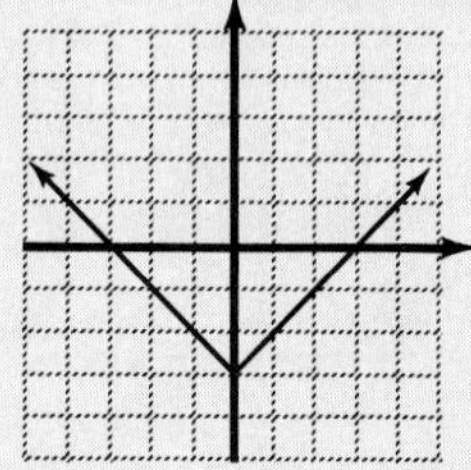

30. The graph of the relation is translated upward 6 units and 4 units to the left.

Mixed Review

34. $3x^2 - x + 9 = 0$
35. $x^2 + 3x + 2 = 0$
36. -49
37. 26
38. 6
39. $\sqrt{m^2 + n^2}$
40. $\sqrt{n^2 + m^2}$
41. 3
42. $\pm 4, \pm 2$
43. $0, \pm 3$
44. $y = 2x^2$

A circle centered at the origin with radius of length 1 has an equation $x^2 + y^2 = 1$.

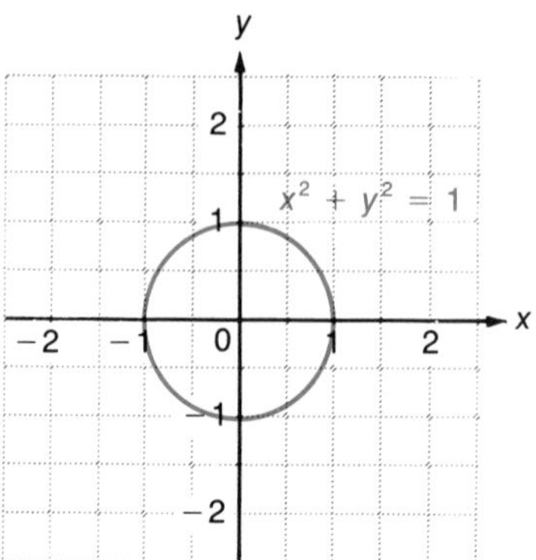

28. Consider the circle $x^2 + y^2 = 1$ centered at the origin. If we replace x by $x - 2$ and y by $y + 3$, what are the coordinates of the center of the translated circle? (2, −3)

29. Consider a circle centered at (2, 4). What are the coordinates of the center of the translated circle if we replace x with $x - 3$ and y with $y + 5$ in the equation of the circle? (5, −1)

30. ***Critical Thinking*** In the equation of a relation, y is replaced by $y - 6$ and x is replaced by $x + 4$. Describe what happens to the graph of the relation.

Challenge

Consider the graph of $|x| + |y| = 1$.

For graphs of Exercises 31–33, see Teacher's Answer Section.

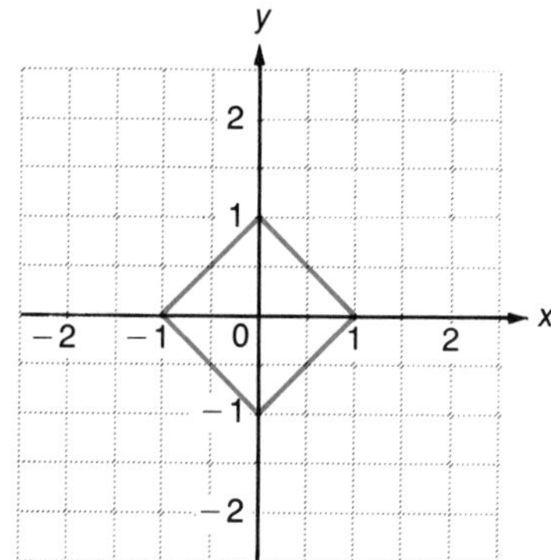

31. Sketch the graph of $|x| + |y + 3| = 1$.

32. Sketch the graph of $|x - 4| + |y| = 1$.

33. Sketch the graph of $|x - 2| + |y + 4| = 1$.

Mixed Review

Find a quadratic equation for which the sum and product of the solutions are the following.

34. Sum, $\frac{1}{3}$; product, 3 **35.** Sum, -3; product, 2

Multiply. **36.** $(-7i)^2$ **37.** $(5 + i)(5 - i)$ **38.** $(\sqrt{5} + i)(\sqrt{5} - i)$

Find the absolute value. **39.** $|m - ni|$ **40.** $|n + mi|$ **41.** $|3i|$

Solve. **42.** $x^4 - 20x^2 + 64 = 0$ **43.** $x^4 - 9x^2 = 0$

44. Find an equation of variation where y varies directly as the square of x, and $y = 18$ when $x = 3$.

9-3 Stretching and Shrinking

Master Grapher Worksheet 14, *Stretching and Shrinking*, can be used for lesson closure.

Vertical Stretchings and Shrinkings

Objective: Sketch a graph that is a vertical stretching or shrinking of a given graph.

Compare the graphs of $y = f(x)$, $y = 2f(x)$, and $y = \frac{1}{2}f(x)$. The graph of $y = 2f(x)$ looks like that of $y = f(x)$, but is stretched vertically. The graph of $y = \frac{1}{2}f(x)$ is flattened, or shrunk, vertically.

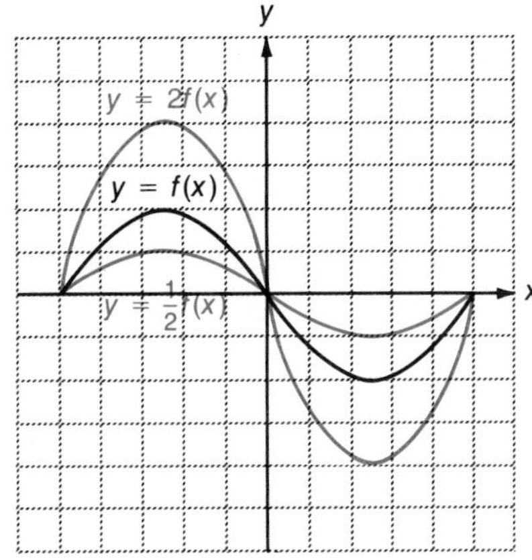

Consider any equation $y = f(x)$. If we multiply $f(x)$ by 2, then every function value is doubled. This has the effect of stretching the graph away from the horizontal axis. This is true for any constant greater than 1.

Multiplying $f(x)$ by $\frac{1}{2}$ will halve every function value, thus shrinking the graph toward the the horizontal axis. This is true for any constant between 0 and 1.

Now compare the graphs of $y = f(x)$, $y = -2f(x)$, and $y = -\frac{1}{2}f(x)$.

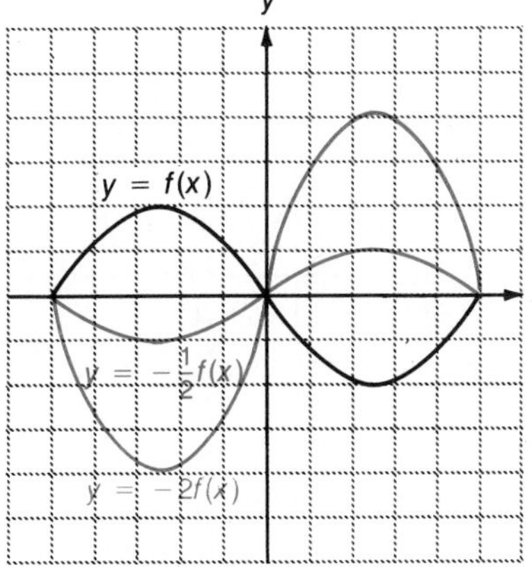

When we multiply by a negative constant, the graph is reflected across the x-axis, and is also being stretched or shrunk. Note that multiplying $f(x)$ by -1 has the effect of replacing y by $-y$, and that we obtain a reflection without stretching or shrinking.

Consider $y = f(x)$. Multiply $f(x)$ by a constant c. We then have

$$y = c \cdot f(x)$$

This is equivalent to $\frac{y}{c} = f(x)$.

Thus in an equation of any relation, dividing y by 2 will stretch the graph in the y-direction. Similarly, dividing y by $\frac{1}{2}$ will shrink the graph in the y-direction.

9-3

FIRST FIVE MINUTES

1. Use the graph of $y = |x|$ to sketch the graph of $y = |x| + 5$.
   The graph is shifted up 5 units.

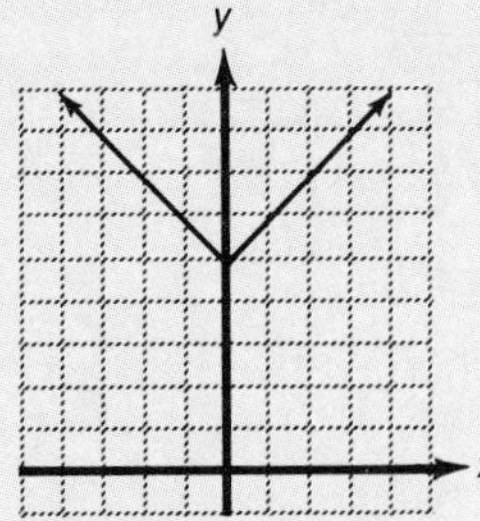

2. Use the graph of $y = |x|$ to sketch the graph of $y = |x - 5|$.
   The graph is shifted right by 5 units.

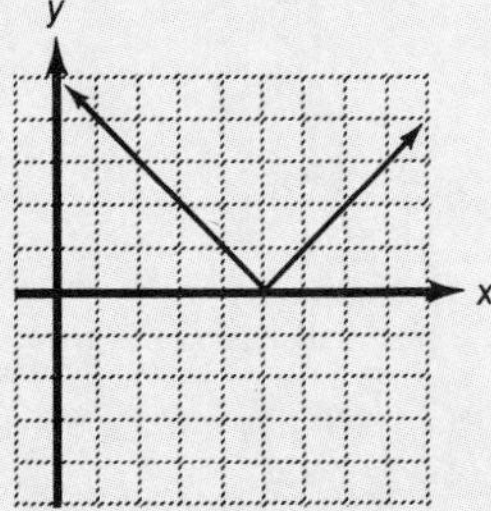

Vertical Stretchings and Shrinkings

Point out that the amount of stretching or shrinking is proportional to c. If c is 4, then each point on the graph becomes four times as far from the x-axis.

Remind students that replacing y by $\frac{y}{3}$ stretches the graph; the y-values are tripled. Replacing y by $3y$ shrinks the graph; the y-values are $\frac{1}{3}$ of their original values.

Key Questions

- If the highest point on the graph of the function $y = f(x)$ is 3 units above the x-axis, what is the highest point on the graph of the function $y = 2f(x)$?
  6 units above the x-axis
- If the lowest point on the graph of the function $y = f(x)$ is 1 unit above the x-axis, what is the lowest point on the graph of the function $y = 5f(x)$?
  5 units above the x-axis

Chalkboard Examples (*T9, T10*)

1. The graph of $y = f(x)$ is shown below. Sketch the graph of $y = \frac{1}{2}f(x)$.

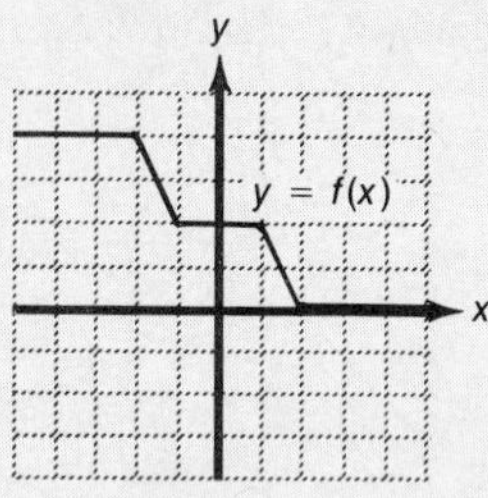

The equation is equivalent to

$\frac{y}{\frac{1}{2}} = f(x)$

The graph is shrunk by $\frac{1}{2}$ in the y direction.

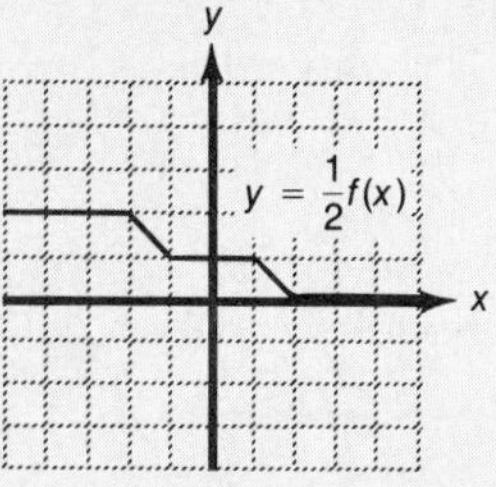

2. Below is the graph of $y = f(x)$. Sketch the graph of $y = -2f(x)$.

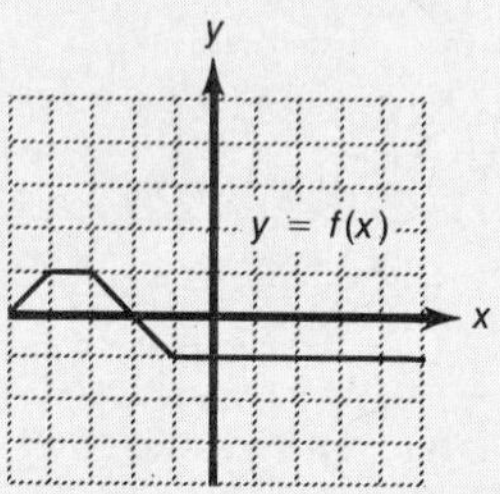

The equation is equivalent to

$\frac{y}{-2} = f(x)$

The equation is stretched in the y direction and is reflected across the x-axis.

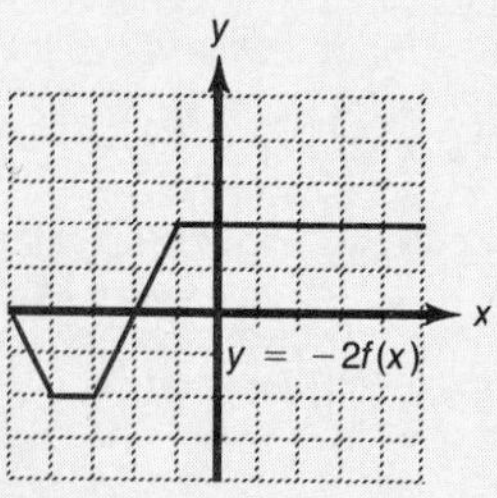

Theorem 9-7

In an equation of a relation, dividing y by a constant c does the following to the graph.

A. If $|c| > 1$, the graph is stretched vertically.

B. If $|c| < 1$, the graph is shrunk vertically.

C. If c is negative, the graph is also reflected across the x-axis.

EXAMPLE 1 Here is a graph of $y = f(x)$. Sketch a graph of $y = 2f(x)$.

$y = 2f(x)$ is equivalent to $\frac{y}{2} = f(x)$. By Theorem 9-7 the graph is stretched vertically. Every function value is doubled.

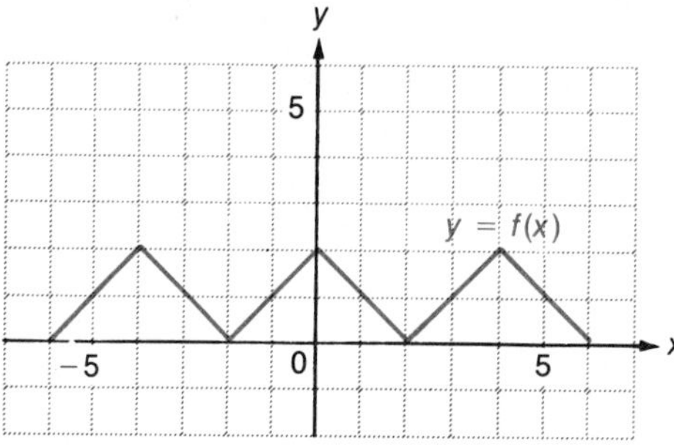

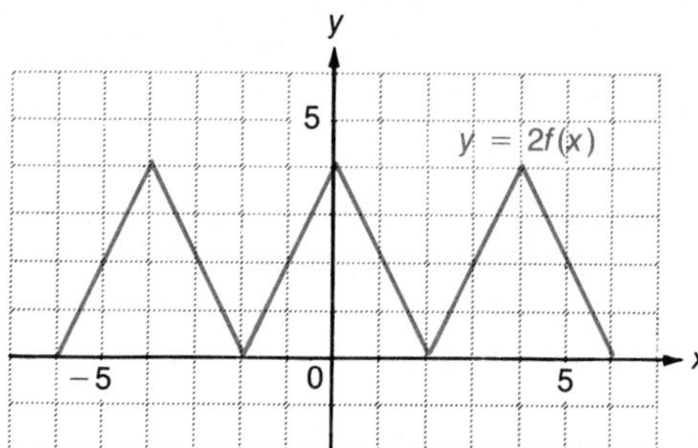

EXAMPLE 2 Here is a graph of $y = g(x)$. Sketch a graph of $y = -\frac{1}{2}g(x)$.

$y = -\frac{1}{2}g(x)$ is equivalent to $\frac{y}{-\frac{1}{2}} = g(x)$. By Theorem 9-7 the graph is shrunk in the y-direction and also reflected across the x-axis. We halve each function value and change its sign.

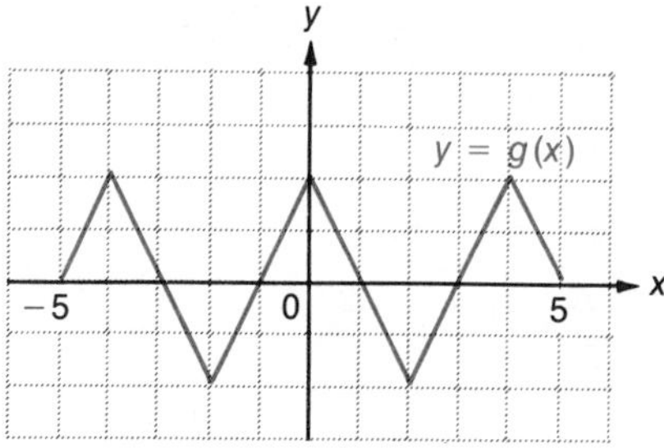

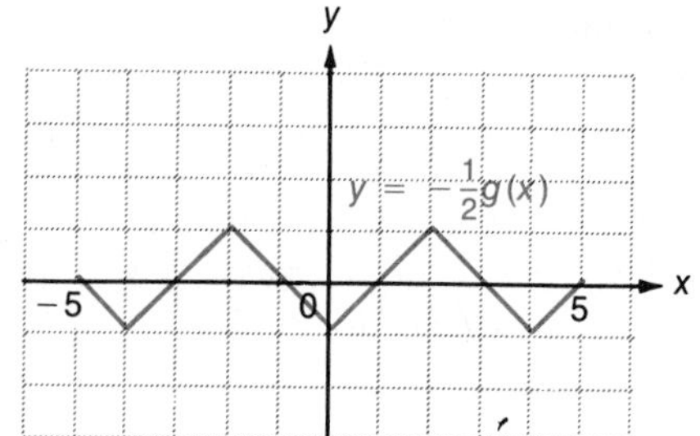

Try This Here is a graph of $y = f(x)$. Sketch these graphs. See Additional Answers.

a. $y = 3f(x)$ **b.** $y = \frac{1}{2}f(x)$ **c.** $y = -\frac{1}{2}f(x)$

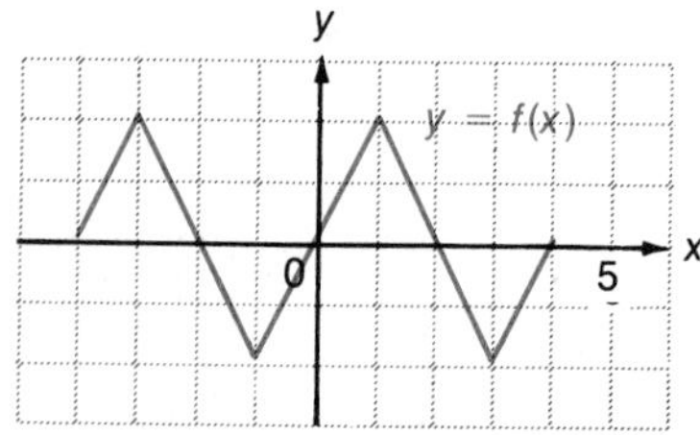

Horizontal Stretchings and Shrinkings

Objective: Sketch a graph that is a horizontal stretching or shrinking of a given graph.

If we divide y by a constant, a graph is stretched or shrunk vertically. If we divide x by a constant, a graph is stretched or shrunk horizontally.

Theorem 9-8

In an equation of a relation, dividing x wherever it occurs by a constant d does the following to the graph.

A. If $|d| > 1$, the graph is stretched horizontally.

B. If $|d| < 1$, the graph is shrunk horizontally.

C. If d is negative, the graph is also reflected across the y-axis.

Note that if $d = -1$, this has the effect of replacing x by $-x$, and we obtain a reflection without stretching or shrinking.

EXAMPLE 3

Here is a graph of $y = f(x)$.

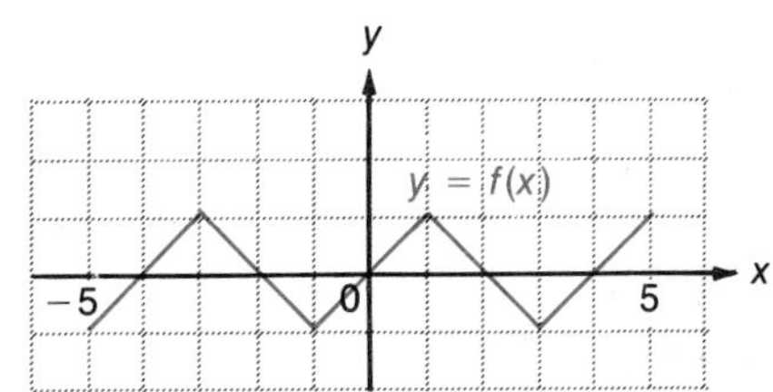

Sketch a graph of each of the following.

(a) $y = f(2x)$

$= f\left(\frac{x}{\frac{1}{2}}\right)$

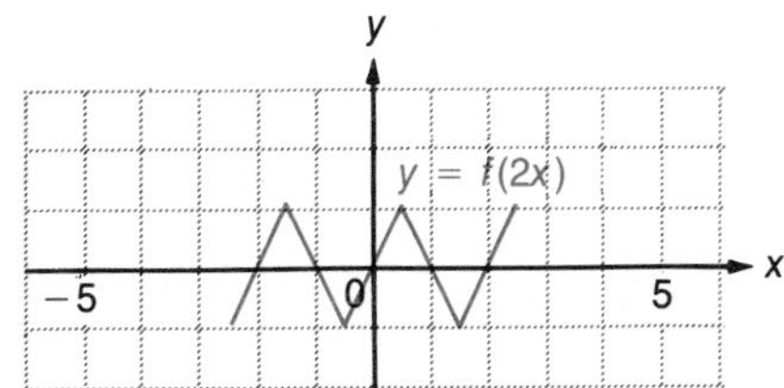

By Theorem 9-8 the graph will be shrunk. Each x-coordinate will be halved.

(b) $y = f\left(\frac{1}{2}x\right)$

$= f\left(\frac{x}{2}\right)$

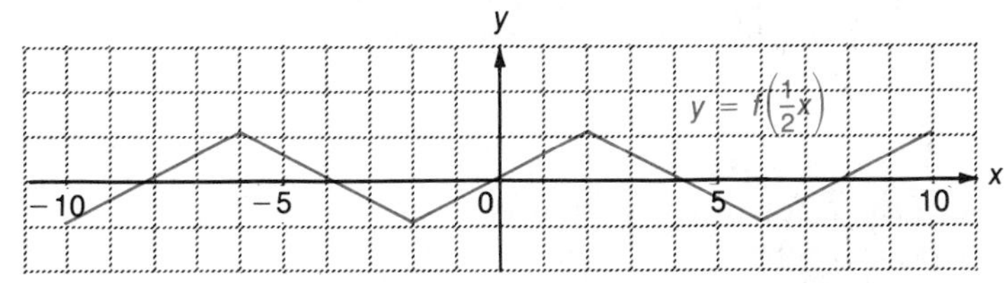

The graph will be stretched. Each x-coordinate will be doubled.

Horizontal Stretchings and Shrinkings

Emphasize the parallel between Theorem 9-7 and Theorem 9-8.

Have students look at the graphs in Example 3(b) and (c). Point out that the two can be thought of as reflections of each other across the y-axis or as translations of each other.

Chalkboard Example (*T11*)

1. Below is the graph of $y = f(x)$. Sketch the graph of each of the following.

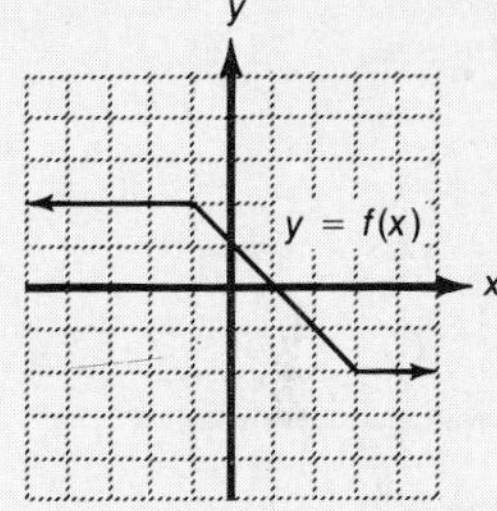

a. $y = f(-x)$
The graph will be reflected across the y-axis.

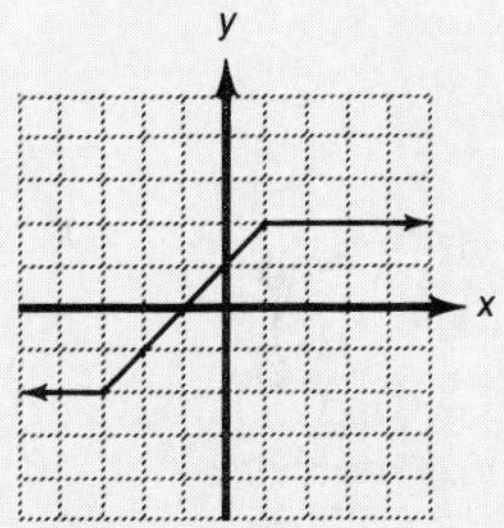

b. $y = f\left(\frac{x}{3}\right)$
The graph will be stretched in the x-direction; each x-coordinate will be tripled.

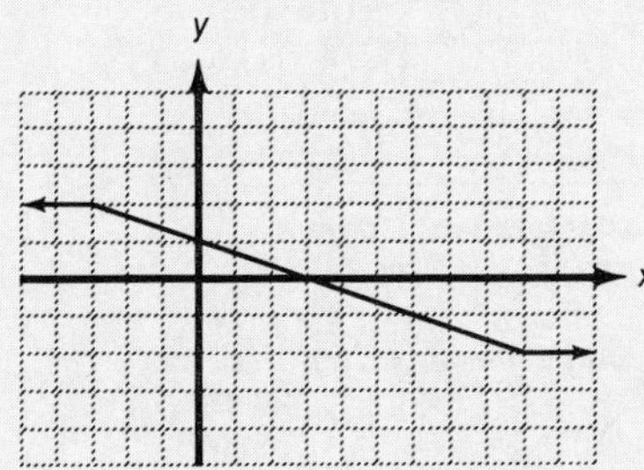

LESSON QUIZ

1. Below is the graph of $y = f(x)$. Sketch the graph of the following.

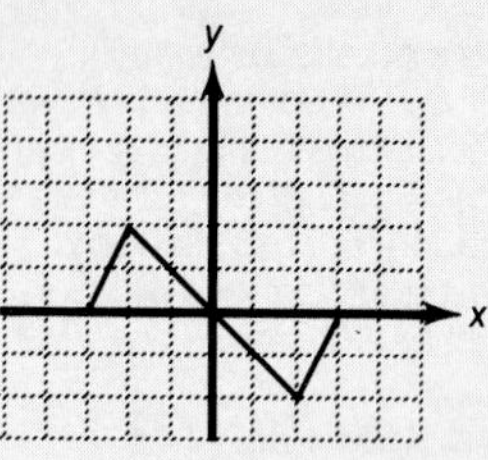

a. $y = f(4x)$
The graph is shrunk in the x-direction; each x-coordinate is multiplied by $\frac{1}{4}$.

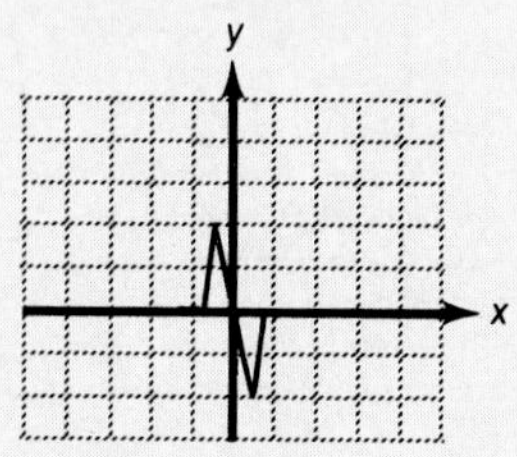

b. $y = 4f(x)$
The graph is stretched in the y-direction; each y-coordinate is multiplied by 4.

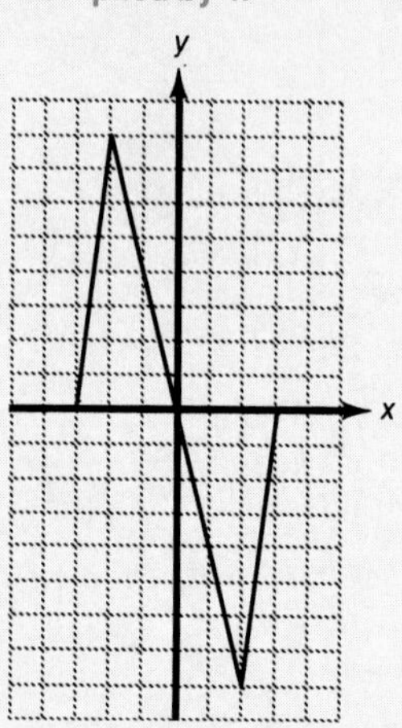

Assignment Guide
Algebra: 1 – 27 e/o, MR

Alg w/Finite or Trig: 1–27 m3, 28–37 e/o, 38, MR

Comprehensive: 1–37 m3, 38, 39–44 e/o, MR

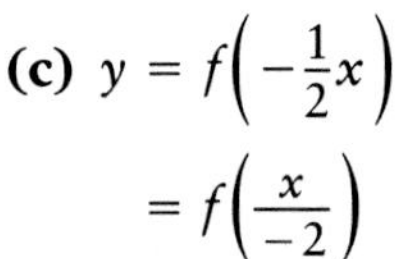

(c) $y = f\left(-\frac{1}{2}x\right)$

$= f\left(\frac{x}{-2}\right)$

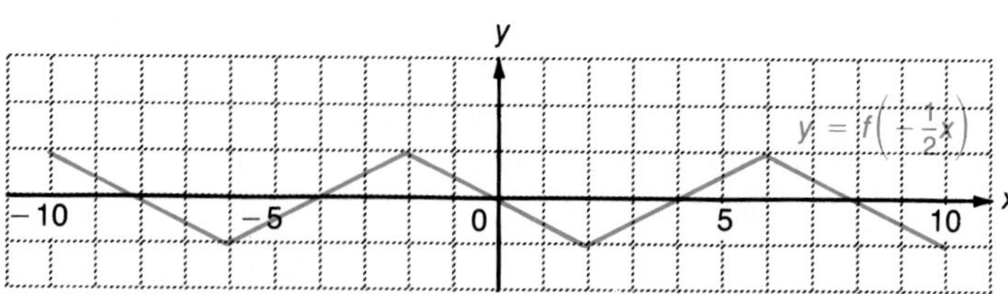

Try This Here is a graph of $y = f(x)$.

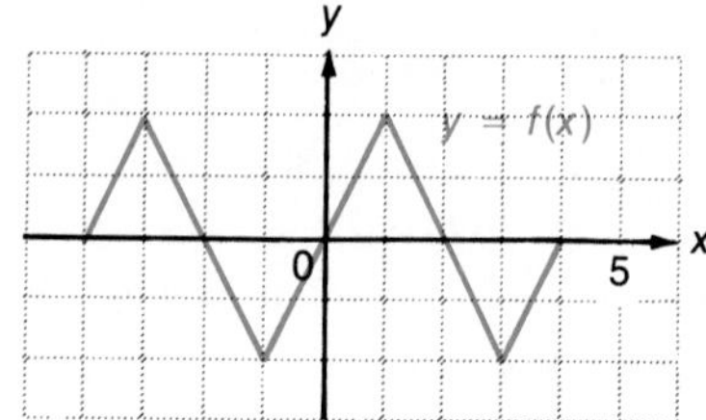

Sketch these graphs.

d. $y = -f(2x)$ **e.** $y = f\left(\frac{1}{2}x\right)$ **f.** $y = f\left(-\frac{1}{2}x\right)$

For graphs of Try This d–f, see Selected Answers.

9-3 EXERCISES

A

Here is a graph of $y = |x|$. Sketch these graphs.

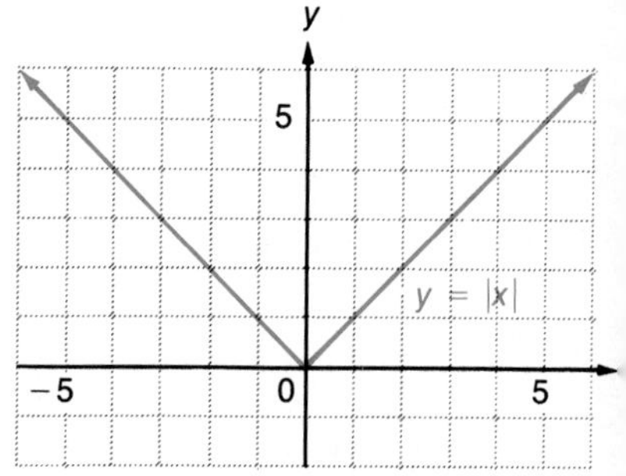

1. $y = 4|x|$ **2.** $y = 3|x|$ **3.** $y = 5|x|$

4. $y = 6|x|$ **5.** $y = \frac{1}{4}|x|$ **6.** $y = \frac{1}{3}|x|$

7. $y = -3|x|$ **8.** $y = -4|x|$ **9.** $y = -\frac{1}{4}|x|$

Here is a graph of $y = f(x)$. Sketch these graphs.

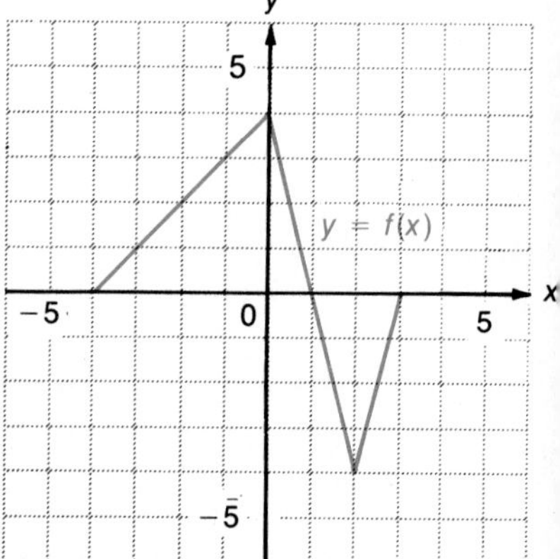

10. $y = 3f(x)$ **11.** $y = 2f(x)$ **12.** $y = -2f(x)$

13. $y = -3f(x)$ **14.** $y = 4f(x)$ **15.** $y = 5f(x)$

16. $y = \frac{1}{2}f(x)$ **17.** $y = \frac{1}{3}f(x)$ **18.** $y = -\frac{1}{2}f(x)$

Consider the graph of $y = |x|$ above.
Sketch these graphs.

19. $y = |2x|$ **20.** $y = |3x|$ **21.** $y = \left|\frac{1}{2}x\right|$

Consider the graph of $y = f(x)$. Sketch these graphs.

22. $y = f(3x)$ **23.** $y = f(2x)$ **24.** $y = f\left(\frac{1}{2}x\right)$

25. $y = f\left(\frac{1}{3}x\right)$ **26.** $y = f(-2x)$ **27.** $y = f(-3x)$

B

For Exercises 28 – 37, sketch graphs by transforming the graph of $y = f(x)$.

28. $y = 2 + f(x)$ **29.** $y + 1 = f(x)$

30. $y = f(x - 1)$ **31.** $y = f(x + 2)$

32. $\frac{y}{-2} = f(x)$ **33.** $y = \frac{1}{3}f(x)$

34. $y = 3f(x)$ **35.** $y = -\frac{1}{2}f(x)$

36. $y = f(x - 2) + 3$ **37.** $y = -3f(x - 2)$

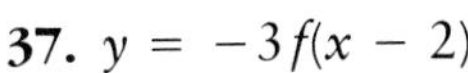

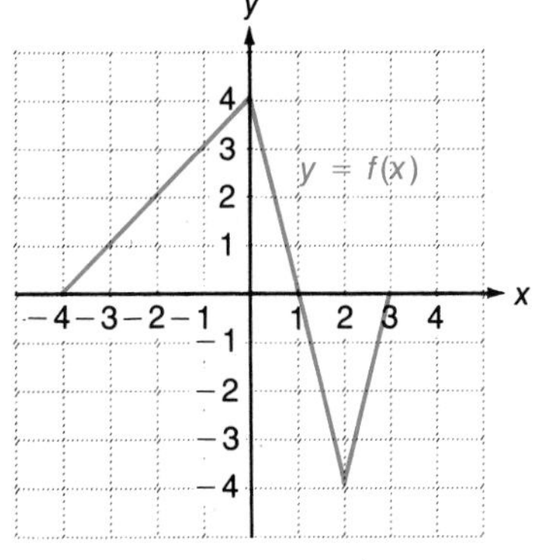

38. ***Critical Thinking*** In the equation of a relation, y is divided by $-\frac{1}{4}$ and x is divided by -5. Describe what happens to the graph of the relation.

Challenge

For Exercises 39–44, sketch graphs by transforming the graph of $y = f(x)$.

39. $y = 2 \cdot f(x + 1) - 2$

40. $y = \frac{1}{2}f(x + 2) - 1$

41. $y = -2f(x + 1) - 1$

42. $y = 3f(x + 2) + 1$

43. $y = \frac{5}{2}f(x - 3) - 2$

44. $y = -\frac{1}{2}f(x + 2) - 3$

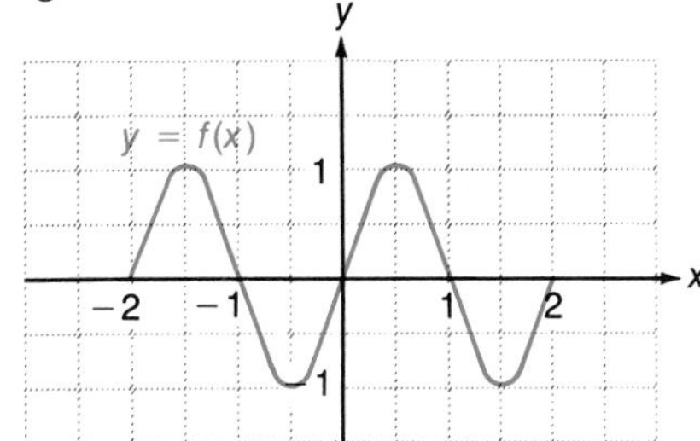

Mixed Review

Determine whether the given numbers are solutions of the equation.

45. $3i, -3i; x^2 + 9 = 0$ **46.** $i\sqrt{3}, -i\sqrt{5}; x^2 + 5 = 0$

Find a quadratic equation whose solutions are the following. **47.** $\frac{1}{3}, \frac{1}{2}$ **48.** $4, \frac{1}{3}$

Solve. **49.** $-4x - 10i = 2ix$ **50.** $x^4 - 10x^2 + 9 = 0$ **51.** $x - 2\sqrt{x} + 1 = 0$

52. $x^2 - 7x + 12 = 0$ **53.** $(x + 6)(x - 1) = 18$ **54.** $x^2 - 8x = 0$

ADDITIONAL ANSWERS

Try This

a.

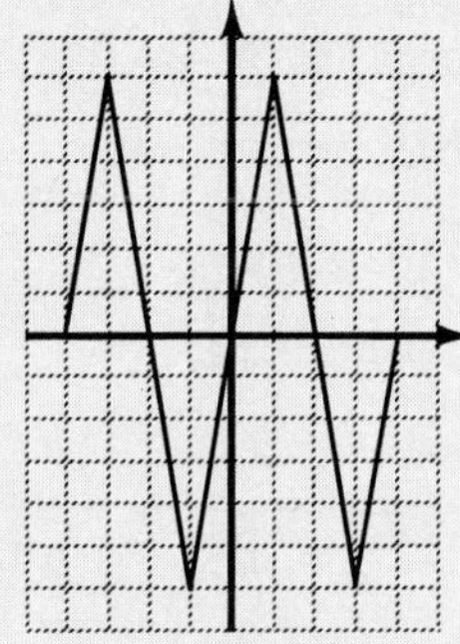

b.

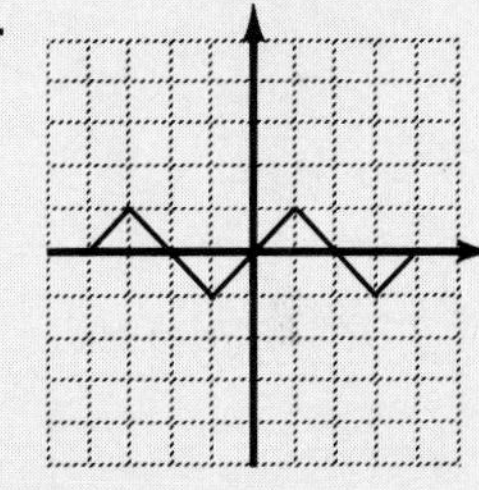

c.

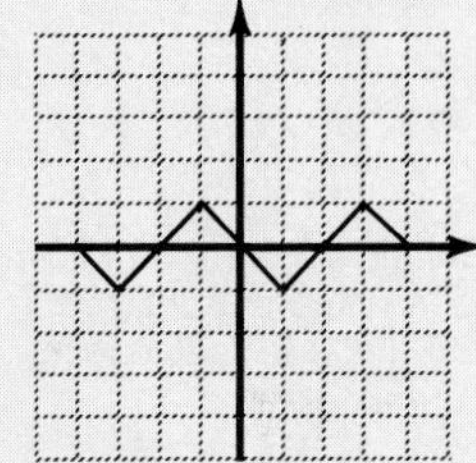

Exercises

For Exercises 1-44 see Teacher's Answer Section.

Mixed Review

45. Yes, yes
46. No, yes
47. $6x^2 - 5x + 1 = 0$
48. $3x^2 - 13x + 4 = 0$
49. $-1 - 2i$
50. $\pm 3, \pm 1$
51. 1
52. 3, 4
53. 3, −8
54. 0, 8

FIRST FIVE MINUTES

Here is the graph of $y = f(x)$.

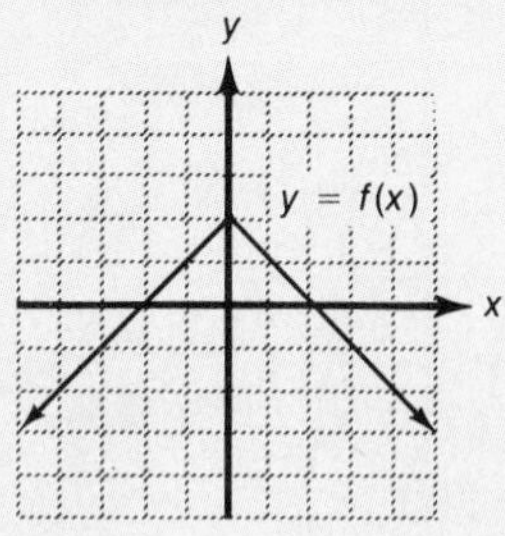

1. Sketch the graph of $y = 2f(x)$.

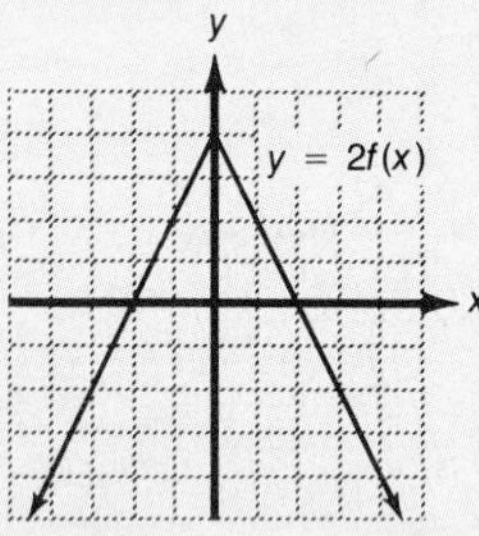

EXPLORE

Students should notice that as $|a|$ increases, the graph becomes narrower; that if $a > 0$ the graph opens upward; and if $a < 0$ the graph opens downward; and that h indicates the y-coordinate of the vertex.

Graphs of $f(x) = ax^2$ and $f(x) = a(x - h)^2$

Point out that parabolas occur often in the physical world. A ball thrown in the air follows a parabolic path, unless it is thrown straight up. Solar panels are shaped parabolically as well.

Point out that $f(x) = x^2$ and $f(x) = ax^2$ have the same axis of symmetry and the same vertex.

Key Questions

- What is the vertex and line of symmetry of $f(x) = 3(x + 2)^2$? $(-2, 0)$; $x = -2$
- Is $f(x) = x^3 - x^2$ a quadratic function? No

9-4 Graphs of Quadratic Functions

Master Grapher Worksheet 15, *Graphs of Quadratic Functions*, can be used for lesson closure.

Explore

Graph the equations $y = x^2$, $y = 2x^2$, and $y = -2x^2$. Use the same set of axes.

Study the graphs that you have drawn. In graphs of equations of the form $y = ax^2$, what effect does changing the value of a have on the graph?

Now graph the equations $y = (x - 3)^2$, $y = 2(x - 3)^2$, and $y = -2(x - 3)^2$. Use a new set of axes.

Again, study the graphs that you have drawn. In graphs of equations of the form $y = a(x - h)^2$, what effect does h have on the graph?

Graphs of $f(x) = ax^2$ and $f(x) = a(x - h)^2$

Objective: Graph a function $f(x) = a(x - h)^2$, and determine its characteristics.

Definition

A **quadratic function** is a function that can be described as

$$f(x) = ax^2 + bx + c, \text{ where } a \neq 0.$$

Graphs of quadratic functions are called parabolas.

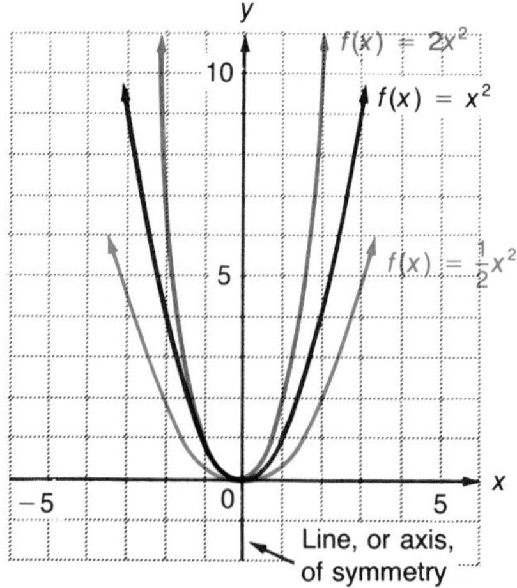

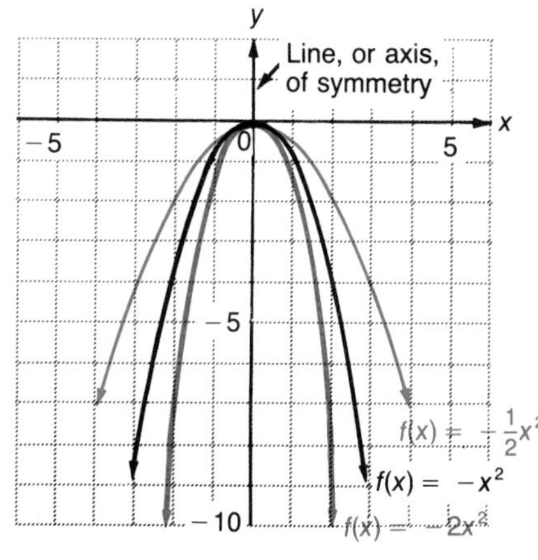

Consider the graph of $f(x) = x^2$ on page 400. The function is even because $f(x) = f(-x)$ for all x. Thus the y-axis is a line of symmetry. The point (0, 0), where the graph crosses the line of symmetry, is called the **vertex** of the parabola.

Next consider $f(x) = ax^2$. By Theorem 9-7 we know the following about its graph.

Compared with the graph of $f(x) = x^2$,

1. if $|a| > 1$, the graph is stretched vertically.
2. if $|a| < 1$, the graph is shrunk vertically.
3. if $a < 0$, the graph is reflected across the x-axis.

EXAMPLE 1

(a) Graph $f(x) = 3x^2$.
(b) What is the line of symmetry?
(c) What is the vertex?

The line of symmetry is the y-axis.
The vertex is (0, 0).

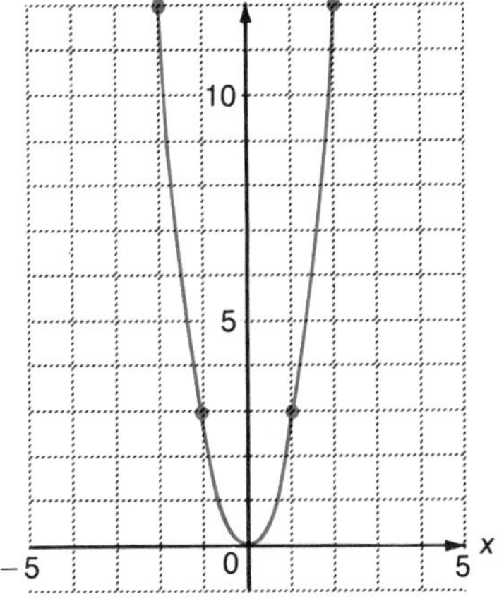

Try This

a. **(1)** Graph $f(x) = -\frac{1}{4}x^2$. See Additional Answers.

(2) What is the line of symmetry? y-axis ($x = 0$)

(3) What is the vertex? (0, 0)

In $f(x) = ax^2$, let us replace x by $x - h$. By Theorem 9-6, if h is positive, the graph will be translated to the right. If h is negative, the translation will be to the left. The line, or axis, of symmetry and the vertex will also be translated the same way. Thus for $f(x) = a(x - h)^2$, the axis of symmetry is $x = h$ and the vertex is $(h, 0)$.

Compare the graph of $f(x) = 2(x + 3)^2$ to the graph of $f(x) = 2x^2$.

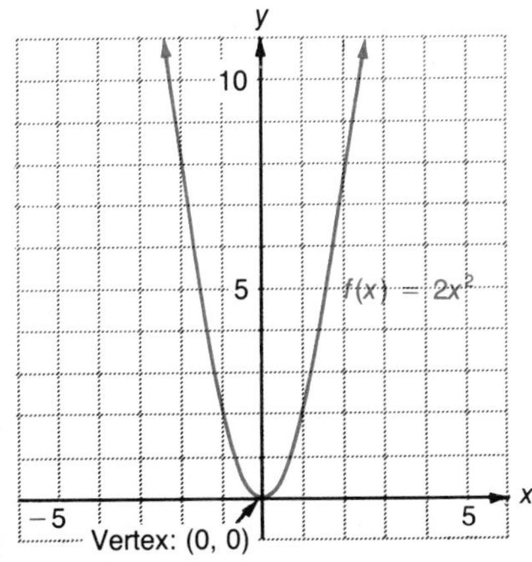

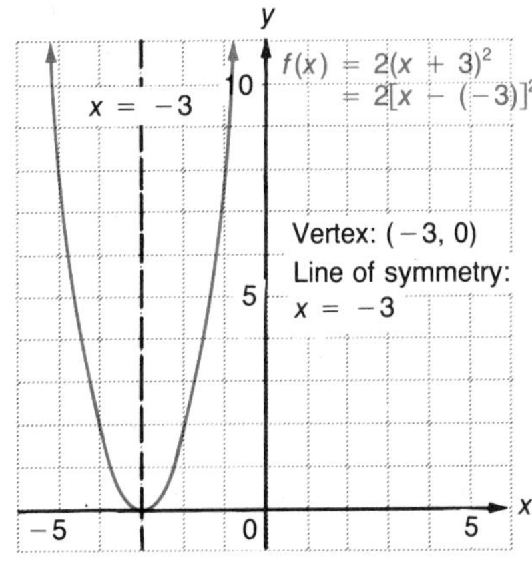

Chalkboard Examples (*T12, T13*)

1. Graph $f(x) = -2x^2$. Find the line of symmetry and the vertex.
   The line of symmetry is the y-axis. The vertex is (0, 0).

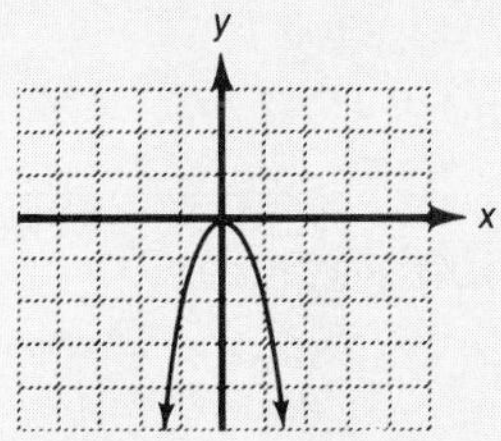

2. Graph $f(x) = (x - 3)^2$. Find the line of symmetry and the vertex.
   The line of symmetry is the line $x = 3$. The vertex is (3, 0).

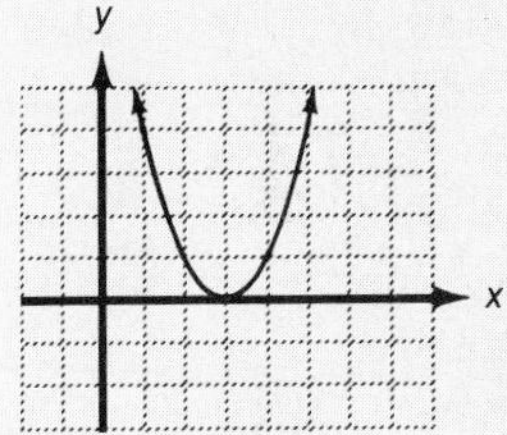

LESSON QUIZ

1. Graph $f(x) = -3x^2$. Find the line of symmetry and the vertex.
   The line of symmetry is $x = 0$, the y-axis. The vertex is (0, 0).

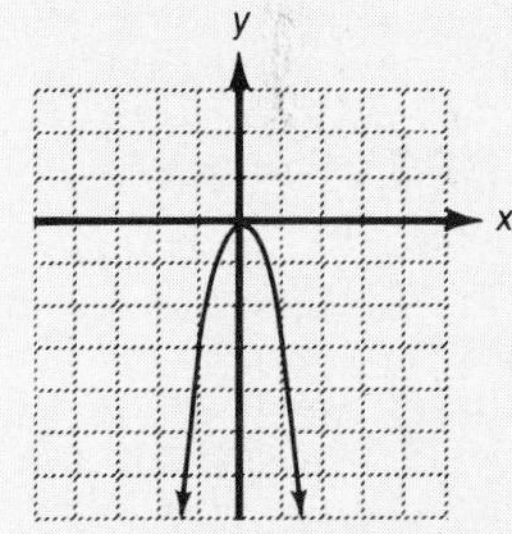

2. Graph $f(x) = -(x - 2)^2$. Find the line of symmetry and the vertex.
   The line of symmetry is the line $x = 2$. The vertex is (2, 0).

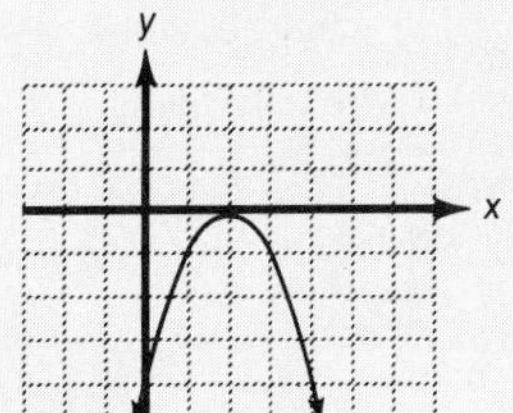

Assignment Guide
Algebra: 1 – 20 e/o, MR

Alg w/Finite or Trig: 1–20 m3, 21–28 e/o, 29, MR

Comprehensive: 1–28 m3, 29–33, MR

ADDITIONAL ANSWERS

Try This

a.

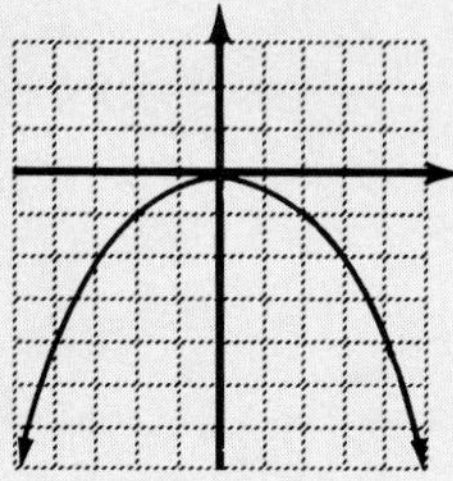

b.

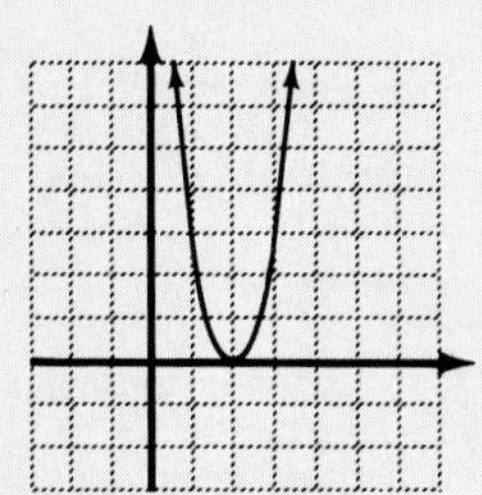

Exercises

1. Vertex: (0, 0), Line of sym: $x = 0$
2. Vertex: (0, 0), Line of sym: $x = 0$
3. Vertex: (0, 0), Line of sym: $x = 0$
4. Vertex: (0, 0), Line of sym: $x = 0$
5. Vertex: (0, 0), Line of sym: $x = 0$
6. Vertex: (0, 0), Line of sym: $x = 0$
7. Vertex: (0, 0), Line of sym: $x = 0$
8. Vertex: (0, 0), Line of sym: $x = 0$
9. Vertex: (7, 0), Line of sym: $x = 7$
10. Vertex: (−4, 0), Line of sym: $x = -4$
11. Vertex: (2, 0), Line of sym: $x = 2$
12. Vertex: (3, 0), Line of sym: $x = 3$
13. Vertex: (7, 0), Line of sym: $x = 7$
14. Vertex: (−9, 0), Line of sym: $x = -9$
15. Vertex: (−7, 0), Line of sym: $x = -7$
16. Vertex: (1, 0), Line of sym: $x = 1$
17. Vertex: (2, 0), Line of sym: $x = 2$
18. Vertex: $(-\frac{1}{2}, 0)$, Line of sym: $x = -\frac{1}{2}$
19. Vertex: (−1, 0), Line of sym: $x = -1$
20. Vertex: (2, 0), Line of sym: $x = 2$

EXAMPLE 2

(a) Graph $f(x) = -2(x - 1)^2$.
(b) What is the line of symmetry?
(c) What is the vertex?

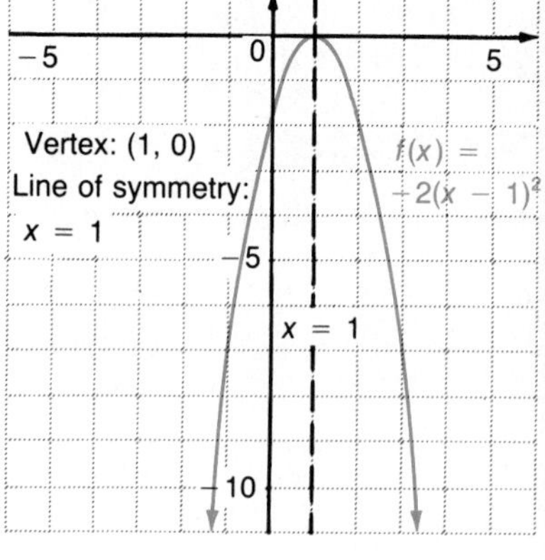

We obtain the line of symmetry from the equation $x - 1 = 0$; the line of symmetry is $x = 1$.

The vertex is (1, 0).

Try This

b. **(1)** Graph $f(x) = 3(x - 2)^2$. See Additional Answers.
(2) What is the line of symmetry? $x = 2$
(3) What is the vertex? (2, 0)

9-4 EXERCISES

A

Graph the function, find the vertex, and find the line of symmetry. For graphs of Exercises 1–28, see Teacher's Answer Section.

1. $f(x) = x^2$ **2.** $f(x) = -x^2$ **3.** $f(x) = -4x^2$ **4.** $f(x) = 2x^2$

5. $f(x) = \frac{1}{2}x^2$ **6.** $f(x) = \frac{1}{4}x^2$ **7.** $f(x) = -\frac{1}{5}x^2$ **8.** $f(x) = \frac{1}{3}x^2$

9. $f(x) = (x - 7)^2$ **10.** $f(x) = -(x + 4)^2$ **11.** $f(x) = -(x - 2)^2$

12. $f(x) = 2(x - 3)^2$ **13.** $f(x) = -4(x - 7)^2$ **14.** $f(x) = -2(x + 9)^2$

15. $f(x) = 2(x + 7)^2$ **16.** $f(x) = 3(x - 1)^2$ **17.** $f(x) = -4(x - 2)^2$

18. $f(x) = -2\left(x + \frac{1}{2}\right)^2$ **19.** $f(x) = \frac{1}{2}(x + 1)^2$ **20.** $f(x) = \frac{1}{3}(x - 2)^2$

B

Graph these quadratic inequalities.

21. $y \le x^2$ **22.** $y > x^2$ **23.** $y > 2x^2$

24. $y \le 2x^2$ **25.** $y < -x^2$ **26.** $y \ge -x^2$

27. $y < -\frac{1}{3}x^2$ **28.** $y \le 3(x + 4)^2$

29. ***Critical Thinking*** What does a quadratic function described by $y = ax^2$ have in common with a linear function described by $y = mx$? Both go through the origin.

Challenge

30. Describe the range of the quadratic function whose graph opens upward and whose vertex is (h, k).

31. Consider $y = mx^2$ and $y = nx^2$. Describe the relationship between m and n if
    a. the graph of $y = mx^2$ is wider than the graph of $y = nx^2$.
    b. the graphs of $y = mx^2$ and $y = nx^2$ open in opposite directions.

32. Consider the equation $f(x) = 2(x - 1)^4$.
    a. Is there a vertex? If so, what is it?
    b. Is there a line of symmetry? If so, what is it?
    c. Is there a point of symmetry? If so, what is it?

33. Consider the equation $f(x) = 2(x - 1)^3$.
    a. Is there a vertex? If so, what is it?
    b. Is there a line of symmetry? If so, what is it?
    c. Is there a point of symmetry? If so, what is it?

Mixed Review

Determine the nature of the solutions of each equation. **34.** $x^2 + 6x + 9 = 0$
35. $x^2 - 3x + 9 = 0$ **36.** $x^2 - 81 = 0$

Solve. **37.** $x^2 + 6x + 4 = 0$ **38.** $x^4 - 25x^2 = 0$ **39.** $2x + 3\sqrt{x} - 2 = 0$

ACTIVITY

1. Cut out a sheet of waxed paper about 5″ by 5″.
2. Draw a line and a point on the waxed paper as shown.

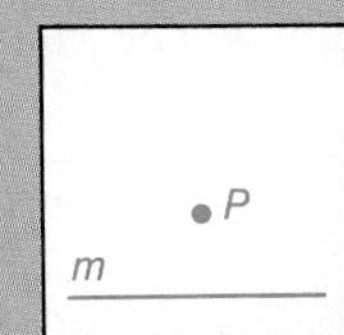

3. Fold and crease the paper so that point P is against line m. Repeat at least 50 times.

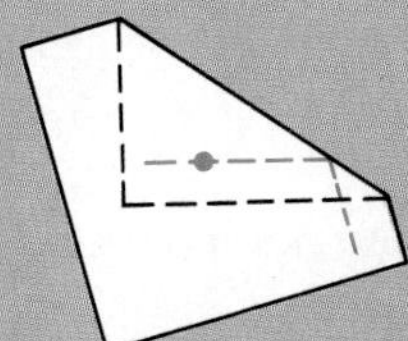

4. What figure seems to be formed by the creases? a parabola

30. $\{y \mid y \geq k\}$
31. a. $|n| > |m|$
    b. m is negative and n is positive, or n is negative and m is positive.
32. a. Yes, (1, 0)
    b. Yes, $x = 1$
    c. No
33. a. No
    b. No
    c. Yes, (1, 0)

Mixed Review

34. 1 real
35. 2 nonreal
36. 2 real
37. $-3 \pm \sqrt{5}$
38. $0, \pm 5$
39. $\frac{1}{4}$

9-5

FIRST FIVE MINUTES

1. Graph $f(x) = 2(x - 1)^2$.

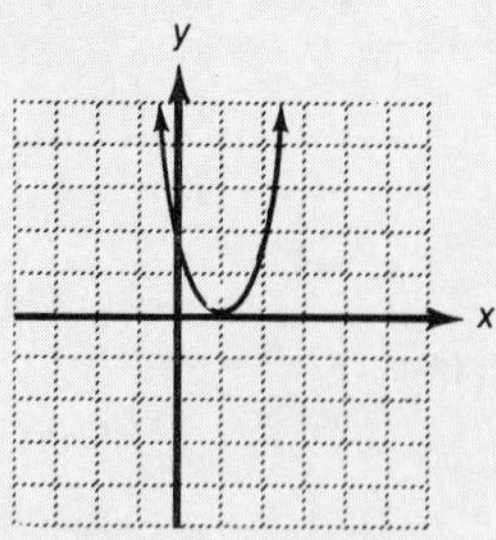

EXPLORE

By examining their graphs, students should be able to deduce some of the guidelines for graphing quadratic functions given below.

Graphs of $f(x) = a(x - h)^2 + k$

Remind students that the graph of any function can be translated, stretched, and shrunk by the proper replacement of x and y in the original equation.

Explain to students that if $a = 0$, the graph would be the horizontal line $y = k$.

Key Questions

- If the equation $f(x) = x^2$ is transformed to $f(x) = (x - 2)^2$, how is the graph transformed?
  It is shifted right 2 units.
- If the equation $f(x) = x^2$ is transformed to $f(x) = 3x^2$, which is then transformed to $f(x) = 3(x - 2)^2$, how is the original graph transformed?
  The original graph is stretched by a multiple of 3 in the y-direction and then moved 2 units to the right.

9-5 Graphs of $f(x) = a(x - h)^2 + k$

Explore

Graph these equations.

$$y = (x - 2)^2$$
$$y = (x - 2)^2 + 4$$
$$y = (x - 2)^2 - 3$$

Study your graphs. What are the coordinates of the vertex of each graph? Predict the coordinates of the vertex of the function $y = (x - 20)^2 + 40$.

In graphs of equations of the form $y = (x - h)^2 + k$, what effect does k have on the graph?

Graphs of $f(x) = a(x - h)^2 + k$

Objective: Graph a function $f(x) = a(x - h)^2 + k$, and determine its characteristics.

In $f(x) = a(x - h)^2$, let us replace $f(x)$ by $f(x) - k$.

$$f(x) - k = a(x - h)^2$$

Adding k on both sides gives $f(x) = a(x - h)^2 + k$.

By Theorem 9-5 we know that the graph will be translated upward if k is positive and downward if k is negative.

The vertex will be translated the same way. The line of symmetry will not be affected.

Guidelines for Graphing Quadratic Functions $f(x) = a(x - h)^2 + k$

When graphing quadratic functions in the form $f(x) = a(x - h)^2 + k$,

1. the line of symmetry is $x - h = 0$, or $x = h$.
2. the vertex is (h, k).
3. if $a > 0$, then (h, k) is the lowest point of the graph, and k is the **minimum value** of the function.
4. if $a < 0$, then (h, k) is the highest point of the graph, and k is the **maximum value** of the function.

EXAMPLE 1

(a) Graph $f(x) = 2(x + 3)^2 - 2$.
(b) What is the vertex?
(c) What is the line of symmetry?
(d) Is there a minimum or maximum value? If so, what is it?

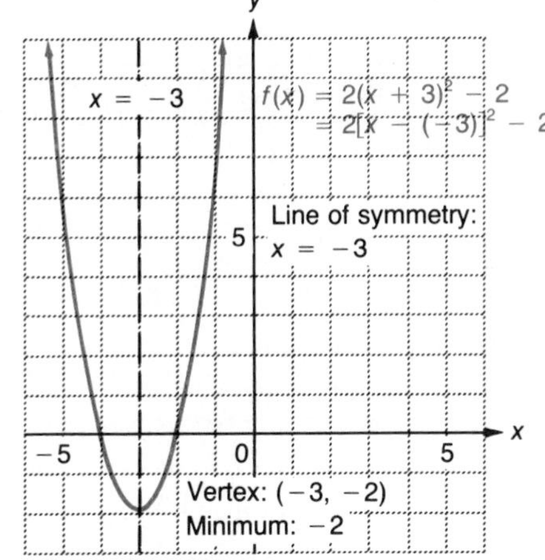

Try This For each of the following graph the function, find the vertex, find the line of symmetry, and find the minimum or maximum value. See Additional Answers.

a. $f(x) = 3(x - 2)^2 + 4$

b. $f(x) = -3(x + 2)^2 - 1$

Analyzing $f(x) = a(x - h)^2 + k$ without Graphing

Objective: Determine the characteristics of a function $f(x) = a(x - h)^2 + k$.

EXAMPLES Without graphing, find the vertex, find the line of symmetry, and find the minimum or maximum value.

2. $f(x) = 3\left(x - \frac{1}{4}\right)^2 - 2$

It is best to break a complex question into its components. We make a chart.

(a) What is the vertex?	$\left(\frac{1}{4}, -2\right)$
(b) What is the line of symmetry?	$x - \frac{1}{4} = 0$ or $x = \frac{1}{4}$
(c) Is there a minimum or maximum value?	Minimum. The graph extends upward since $3 > 0$.
(d) What is the minimum or maximum value?	The minimum value is -2.

Chalkboard Example (*T14*)

1. Graph $f(x) = -2(x - 1)^2 + 3$. Find the vertex, line of symmetry, and minimum or maximum value.
The vertex is (1, 3). The line of symmetry is $x = 1$. There is a maximum at (1, 3).

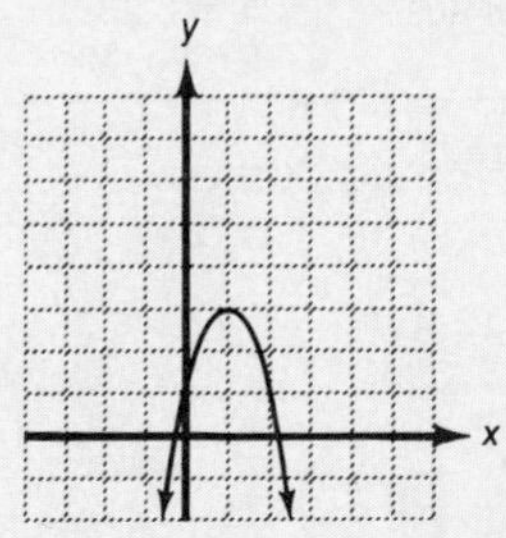

Analyzing $f(x) = a(x - h)^2 + k$ without Graphing

Chalkboard Examples

Without graphing, find the vertex, line of symmetry, and minimum or maximum value.

1. $f(x) = \frac{1}{2}(x - 5)^2 - 3$
The vertex is (5, −3). The line of symmetry is $x = 5$. The minimum value is at $f(5) = -3$.
2. $h(x) = -5(x - 6)^2 + 7$
The vertex is (6, 7). The line of symmetry is $x = 6$. The maximum value is $h(6) = 7$.

LESSON QUIZ

1. Graph $f(x) = 4(x - 1)^2 + 2$.

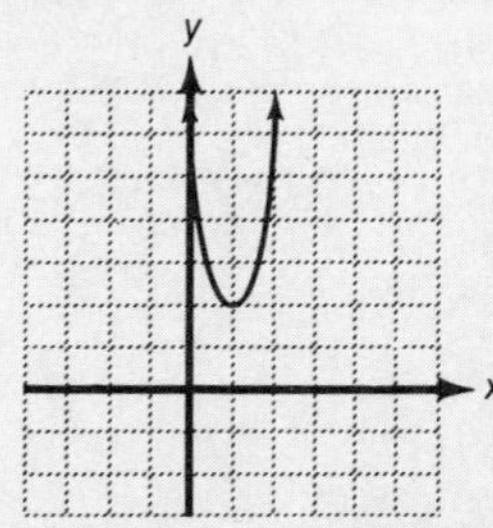

2. Without graphing, find the vertex, line of symmetry, and maximum or minimum value.
$f(x) = -(x + 1)^2 + 5$.
The vertex is (−1, 5). The line of symmetry is $x = -1$. The maximum value is $f(-1) = 5$.

Assignment Guide
Algebra: 1 – 16 e/o, MR

Alg w/Finite or Trig: 1–16 m3, 17–25 e/o, 26, MR

Comprehensive: 1–25 m3, 26, 27–32 e/o, MR

ADDITIONAL ANSWERS

Try This

a. Vertex: (2, 4)
Line of symmetry: x = 2
Minimum: 4

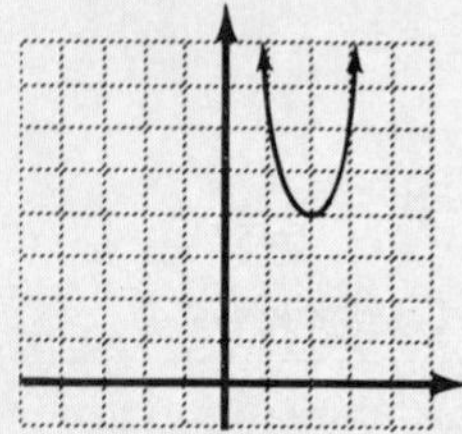

b. Vertex: (−2, −1)
Line of symmetry: x = −2
Maximum: −1

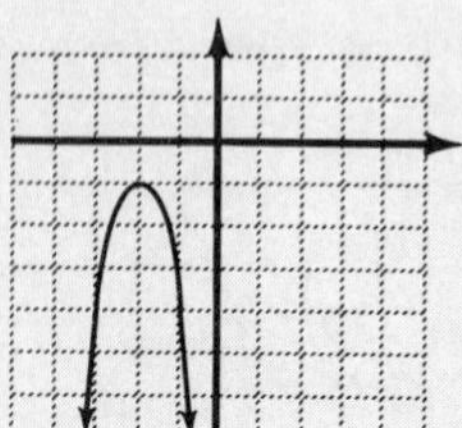

c. Vertex: (5, 40)
Line of symmetry: x = 5
Minimum: 40

d. Vertex: (5, 0)
Line of symmetry: x = 5
Maximum: 0

e. Vertex: $\left(-\frac{3}{4}, -6\right)$
Line of symmetry: $x = -\frac{3}{4}$
Minimum: −6

f. Vertex: (−9, 3)
Line of symmetry: x = −9
Maximum: 3

Exercises

9. (9, 5); x = 9; min. = 5
10. (−5, −8); x = −5; min. = −8
11. $\left(-\frac{1}{4}; -13\right)$; $x = -\frac{1}{4}$; min. = −13

3. $g(x) = -4(x + 5)^2 + 7$
$= -4[x - (-5)]^2 + 7$

(a) What is the vertex?	$(-5, 7)$
(b) What is the line of symmetry?	$x = -5$
(c) Is there a minimum or maximum value?	Maximum. The graph extends downward since $-4 < 0$.
(d) What is the minimum or maximum value?	The maximum value is 7.

Try This Without graphing, find the vertex, find the line of symmetry, and find the minimum or maximum value. See Additional Answers.

c. $f(x) = (x - 5)^2 + 40$

d. $f(x) = -3(x - 5)^2$

e. $f(x) = 2\left(x + \frac{3}{4}\right)^2 - 6$

f. $f(x) = -\frac{1}{4}(x + 9)^2 + 3$

9-5 EXERCISES

A

For each of the following graph the function, find the vertex, find the line of symmetry, and find the minimum or maximum value. For Exercises 1–8, see Teacher's Answer Section.

1. $f(x) = (x - 3)^2 + 1$

2. $f(x) = (x + 2)^2 - 3$

3. $f(x) = (x + 1)^2 - 2$

4. $f(x) = (x - 1)^2 + 2$

5. $f(x) = 2(x - 1)^2 - 3$

6. $f(x) = 2(x + 1)^2 + 4$

7. $f(x) = -3(x + 4)^2 + 1$

8. $f(x) = -2(x - 5)^2 - 3$

Without graphing, find the vertex, find the line of symmetry, and find the minimum or maximum value.

9. $f(x) = 8(x - 9)^2 + 5$

10. $f(x) = 10(x + 5)^2 - 8$

11. $f(x) = 5\left(x + \frac{1}{4}\right)^2 - 13$

12. $f(x) = 6\left(x - \frac{1}{4}\right)^2 + 19$

13. $f(x) = -7(x - 10)^2 - 20$

14. $f(x) = -9(x + 12)^2 + 23$

15. $f(x) = \sqrt{2}(x + 4.58)^2 + 65\pi$

16. $f(x) = 4\pi(x - 38.2)^2 - \sqrt{34}$

B

Write the equation of the parabola that is a translation of $f(x) = 2x^2$ and has a minimum or maximum value at the given point.

17. Maximum (0, 4)

18. Minimum (2, 0)

19. Minimum (6, 0)

20. Maximum (0, 3)   21. Maximum (3, 8)   22. Minimum (−2, 3)

23. Minimum (−3, 5)   24. Maximum (−4, −3)   25. Minimum (2, −3)

26. ***Critical Thinking*** Suppose that y and x are interchanged in a quadratic function $y = a(x - h)^2 + k$. What happens to the graph?

Challenge

Write the equation of the parabola.

27. The parabola has a minimum value at the same point as $f(x) = 3(x - 4)^2$, but for all x in the domain of $f(x)$ the function values are doubled. $g(x) = 6(x - 4)^2$

28. The parabola is a translation of $f(x) = -\frac{1}{2}(x - 2)^2 + 4$ and has a maximum value at the same point as $g(x) = -2(x - 1)^2 - 6$. $h(x) = -\frac{1}{2}(x - 1)^2 - 6$

29. The parabola has a maximum value at (2, 5) and contains (1, 2). $f(x) = -3(x - 2)^2 + 5$

30. The parabola has a minimum value at (−2, −6) and contains (1, 0). $f(x) = \frac{2}{3}(x + 2)^2 - 6$

31. The parabola is a reflection of $f(x) = 2(x - 5)^2 + 3$ across the line $y = -4$. $g(x) = -2(x - 5)^2 - 11$

32. To graph on the Apple II computer's hi-res screen, it is necessary to translate to a coordinate system where the point (0, 0) is in the upper left corner, and the point (140, 80) is in the center of the screen. You want to graph using this screen, but you want (0, 0) to graph in the center and (−14, 16) in the upper left corner.
    a. Write functions that will translate x and y values to the Apple's coordinate system. (Hint: Fit linear functions to the data.) $f(x) = 10x + 140$, $g(y) = -5y + 80$
    b. Suppose you want to graph $y = x^2$. Find the Apple's coordinates for the points (−2, 4), (0, 0), and (2, 4). (120, 60), (140, 80), and (160, 60)

Mixed Review

Solve for the indicated letter. **33.** $a^2 + b^2 = c^2$, for c **34.** $A = \pi r^2$, for r

35. $E = mc^2$, for c **36.** $\frac{1}{R_1} + \frac{1}{R_2} = \frac{1}{t}$, for t

37. Find an equation of variation where y varies jointly as x and z, and $y = 24$ when $x = 4$ and $z = 3$.

Problem for Programmers

Write a program that will take any values input for a, h, and k for the equation $f(x) = a(x - h)^2 + k$ and determine whether the function has a maximum or a minimum value, find the line of symmetry, and find the vertex.

12. $\left(\frac{1}{4}, 19\right)$; $x = \frac{1}{4}$; min. = 19
13. (10, −20); x = 10; max. = −20
14. (−12, 23); x = −12; max. = 23
15. (−4.58, 65π); x = −4.58; min. = 65π
16. $(38.2, -\sqrt{34})$; x = 38.2; min. = $-\sqrt{34}$
17. $f(x) = -2x^2 + 4$
18. $f(x) = 2(x - 2)^2$
19. $f(x) = 2(x - 6)^2$
20. $f(x) = -2x^2 + 3$
21. $f(x) = -2(x - 3)^2 + 8$
22. $f(x) = 2(x + 2)^2 + 3$
23. $f(x) = 2(x + 3)^2 + 5$
24. $f(x) = -2(x + 4)^2 - 3$
25. $f(x) = 2(x - 2)^2 - 3$
26. The graph is a parabola with a line of symmetry $y = h$ and vertex (k, h).

Mixed Review

33. $c = \pm\sqrt{a^2 + b^2}$ **34.** $r = \pm\frac{\sqrt{A\pi}}{\pi}$
35. $c = \pm\frac{\sqrt{Em}}{m}$ **36.** $t = \frac{R_1R_2}{R_1 + R_2}$
37. $y = 2xz$

FIRST FIVE MINUTES

Find the vertex, line of symmetry, and minimum or maximum of each of the following functions.

1. $f(x) = 7(x - 4)^2 - 5$
   The vertex is $(4, -5)$. The line of symmetry is $x = 4$. The minimum is at $(4, -5)$.
2. $g(x) = -6(x + 2)^2 + 8$
   The vertex is $(-2, 8)$. The line of symmetry is $x = -2$. The maximum is at $(-2, 8)$.

Standard Form for Quadratic Functions

Emphasize that the standard form for a quadratic function,

$f(x) = a(x - h)^2 + k,$

is not the same as the standard form for a quadratic equation, $ax^2 + bx + c = 0$.

Key Questions

- Is $f(x) = 4x^2 - 6x + 9$ in standard form?
  No
- Is $f(x) = 4(x - 1)^2 + 5$ in standard form?
  Yes

Chalkboard Example

1. For $f(x) = 3x^2 + 12x + 1$,
   a. find the standard form for the function.
   b. find the vertex, line of symmetry, and the maximum or minimum value.
   $= 3(x^2 + 4x) + 1$
   $= 3(x^2 + 4x + 4 - 4) + 1$
   $= 3(x^2 + 4x + 4) - 12 + 1$
   $= 3(x + 2)^2 - 11$
   The vertex is $(-2, -11)$. The line of symmetry is $x = -2$. The minimum occurs at $f(-2) = -11$.

9-6 Standard Form for Quadratic Functions

Standard Form for Quadratic Functions

Objective: Find standard form and characteristics for a quadratic function.

Consider a quadratic function described by $f(x) = ax^2 + bx + c, a \neq 0$. By completing the square we can rewrite it as $f(x) = a(x - h)^2 + k$. A quadratic function is in standard form when written as $f(x) = a(x - h)^2 + k$.

EXAMPLE 1 For $f(x) = x^2 - 6x + 4$,

(a) find standard form for the function.

$$\begin{aligned} f(x) &= x^2 - 6x + 4 \\ &= (x^2 - 6x) + 4 \quad \text{Writing with parentheses} \end{aligned}$$

We complete the square inside the parentheses. We take half of the x-coefficient and square it to get 9. Then we add $9 - 9$ inside the parentheses. Since $9 - 9 = 0$, we have not changed the expression inside the parentheses.

$$\begin{aligned} f(x) &= (x^2 - 6x + 9 - 9) + 4 \\ &= (x^2 - 6x + 9) + (-9 + 4) \quad \text{Using the associative property for addition} \\ &= 1 \cdot (x - 3)^2 - 5 \end{aligned}$$

(b) find the vertex, line of symmetry, and the maximum or minimum value.

Using the standard form for the quadratic function, we find $a = 1, h = 3$, and $k = -5$. The vertex is $(3, -5)$. The line of symmetry is $x = 3$. Since the coefficient 1 is positive, there is a minimum function value. It is -5.

Try This

a. For $f(x) = x^2 - 4x + 7$,
  (1) find standard form for the function. $f(x) = (x - 2)^2 + 3$
  (2) find the vertex, line of symmetry, and the maximum or minimum value. $(2, 3), x = 2$, minimum $= 3$

EXAMPLE 2 For $f(x) = -2x^2 + 10x - 7$,

(a) find standard form for the function.

We first factor the expression $-2x^2 + 10x$. We factor -2 from the first two terms. This makes the coefficient of x^2 inside the parentheses 1.

$$f(x) = -2(x^2 - 5x) - 7$$

We take half of the x-coefficient and square it to get $\frac{25}{4}$. Then we add $\frac{25}{4} - \frac{25}{4}$ inside the parentheses.

$$\begin{aligned} f(x) &= -2\left(x^2 - 5x + \frac{25}{4} - \frac{25}{4}\right) - 7 \\ &= -2\left(x^2 - 5x + \frac{25}{4}\right) + 2\left(\frac{25}{4}\right) - 7 \quad \text{Multiplying by } -2 \text{, using the distributive property, and rearranging terms} \\ &= -2\left(x - \frac{5}{2}\right)^2 + \frac{11}{2} \end{aligned}$$

(b) find the vertex, line of symmetry, and the maximum or minimum value. The vertex is $\left(\frac{5}{2}, \frac{11}{2}\right)$. The line of symmetry is $x = \frac{5}{2}$. The coefficient -2 is negative, so there is a maximum function value. It is $\frac{11}{2}$.

Try This

b. For $f(x) = -4x^2 + 12x - 5$,

(1) find standard form for the function. $f(x) = -4\left(x - \frac{3}{2}\right)^2 + 4$

(2) find the vertex, line of symmetry, and the maximum or minimum value. $\left(\frac{3}{2}, 4\right)$, $x = \frac{3}{2}$, maximum $= 4$

Problem Solving: Maximum and Minimum Values

Objective: Solve maximum and minimum value problems that involve quadratic functions.

Maximum and minimum value problems are concerned with finding the largest or smallest value. Some maximum or minimum problems involve quadratic functions. To solve such a problem, we translate by finding the appropriate function. Then we find the maximum or minimum value of that function.

EXAMPLE 3

What are the dimensions of the largest rectangular pen that can be enclosed with 64 meters of fence?

We make a *drawing* and label it. The perimeter must be 64 m, so we have

$$2w + 2l = 64.$$

We wish to find the maximum area.

$$A = lw$$

$l = 32 - w$

w

Solving $2w + 2l = 64$ for l, we get $l = 32 - w$. We substitute for l in the area formula.

$$A = (32 - w)w = -w^2 + 32w$$

Then we complete the square.

$$A = -(w - 16)^2 + 256$$

The maximum function value is 256. It occurs when $w = 16$. Thus the dimensions are 16 m by 16 m.

Problem Solving: Maximum and Minimum Values

Chalkboard Example

1. One hundred feet of fencing is available to make a rectangular dog pen against an existing wall. What are the dimensions of the pen that will yield the maximum area?

Let x denote the length of fence at each end of the pen. Let y denote the remaining side parallel to the wall.

$2x + y = 100$ (1)

The area A is given by

$A = xy$ (2)

Solving (1) for y yields

$y = 100 - 2x$

Substituting for y in (2) yields

$$\begin{aligned} A &= x(100 - 2x) \\ &= 100x - 2x^2 \\ &= -2(x^2 - 50x) \\ &= -2(x^2 - 50x + 25^2 - 25^2) \\ &= -2(x - 25)^2 + 2 \cdot 25^2 \\ &= -2(x - 25)^2 + 1250 \end{aligned}$$

The maximum occurs at $f(25) = 1250$.

Solving for y when $x = 25$,

$2(25) + y = 100$

$y = 50$

The dimensions are 25 ft by 50 ft.

LESSON QUIZ

1. Find the standard form for the function $f(x) = x^2 - 12x + 40$. Find the vertex, line of symmetry, and the minimum or maximum value.
   $f(x) = (x - 6)^2 + 4$
   The vertex is (6, 4). The line of symmetry is $x = 6$. The minimum occurs at $f(6) = 4$.
2. What is the minimum product of two numbers whose difference is 8?
   -16; the numbers are 4 and -4.

Assignment Guide
Algebra: Day 1: 1 – 12
Day 2: 13 – 20, MR
Alg w/Finite or Trig: 1–12 m3, 13–28 e/o, 29, MR
Comprehensive: 1–28 m3, 29, 30–35 e/o, MR

ADDITIONAL ANSWERS

Exercises

1. $f(x) = (x - 1)^2 - 4$
Vertex: $(1, -4)$
Line of symmetry: $x = 1$
Minimum: -4
2. $f(x) = (x + 1)^2 - 6$
Vertex: $(-1, -6)$
Line of symmetry: $x = -1$
Minimum: -6
3. $f(x) = -(x - 2)^2 + 10$
Vertex: $(2, 10)$
Line of symmetry: $x = 2$
Maximum: 10
4. $f(x) = -(x + 2)^2 + 7$
Vertex: $(-2, 7)$
Line of symmetry: $x = -2$
Maximum: 7
5. $f(x) = \left(x + \frac{3}{2}\right)^2 - \frac{49}{4}$
Vertex: $\left(-\frac{3}{2}, -\frac{49}{4}\right)$
Line of symmetry: $x = -\frac{3}{2}$
Minimum: $-\frac{49}{4}$
6. $f(x) = \left(x + \frac{5}{2}\right)^2 - \frac{9}{4}$
Vertex: $\left(-\frac{5}{2}, -\frac{9}{4}\right)$
Line of symmetry: $x = -\frac{5}{2}$
Minimum: $-\frac{9}{4}$
7. $f(x) = \left(x - \frac{9}{2}\right)^2 - \frac{81}{4}$
Vertex: $\left(\frac{9}{2}, -\frac{81}{4}\right)$
Line of symmetry: $x = \frac{9}{2}$
Minimum: $-\frac{81}{4}$

Try This

c. What is the maximum product of two numbers whose sum is 30? 225

d. What are the dimensions of the largest rectangular pen that can be enclosed with 100 meters of fence? 25 m by 25 m

9-6 EXERCISES

A

For each function find standard form, the vertex, line of symmetry, and the maximum or minimum value.

1. $f(x) = x^2 - 2x - 3$

2. $f(x) = x^2 + 2x - 5$

3. $f(x) = -x^2 + 4x + 6$

4. $f(x) = -x^2 - 4x + 3$

5. $f(x) = x^2 + 3x - 10$

6. $f(x) = x^2 + 5x + 4$

7. $f(x) = x^2 - 9x$

8. $f(x) = x^2 + x$

9. $f(x) = 3x^2 - 24x + 50$

10. $f(x) = 4x^2 + 8x - 3$

11. $f(x) = \frac{3}{4}x^2 + 9x$

12. $f(x) = -2x^2 + 2x + 1$

Solve.

13. A rancher is fencing off a rectangular area with a fixed perimeter of 76 m. What dimensions would yield the maximum area? What is the maximum area? 19 m by 19 m; 361 m^2

14. A carpenter is building a rectangular room with a fixed perimeter of 68 m. What dimensions would yield the maximum area? What is the maximum area? 17 m by 17 m; 289 m^2

15. What is the maximum product of two numbers whose sum is 22? What numbers yield this product? 121; 11 and 11

16. What is the maximum product of two numbers whose sum is 45? What numbers yield this product? 506.25; 22.5 and 22.5

17. What is the minimum product of two numbers whose difference is 4? What are the numbers? -4; 2 and -2

18. What is the minimum product of two numbers whose difference is 6? What are the numbers? -9; 3 and -3

19. What is the minimum product of two numbers whose difference is 5? What are the numbers? $-\frac{25}{4}$; $\frac{5}{2}$ and $-\frac{5}{2}$

20. What is the minimum product of two numbers whose difference is 7? What are the numbers? $-\frac{49}{4}$; $\frac{7}{2}$ and $-\frac{7}{2}$

B

21. Find an equation in standard form for $f(x) = 3x^2 + mx + m^2$.

Graph.

22. $f(x) = |x^2 - 1|$

23. $f(x) = |3 - 2x - x^2|$

Use a calculator to find the maximum or minimum value for each function.

24. $f(x) = 2.31x^2 - 3.135x - 5.89$ **25.** $f(x) = -18.8x^2 + 7.92x + 6.18$

26. What is the minimum product of two numbers whose difference is 4.932? What are the numbers?

27. What is the maximum product of two numbers whose sum is 21.355? What are the numbers?

28. Find the vertex and line of symmetry for the function $f(x) = ax^2 + bx + c$.

29. ***Critical Thinking*** Apply the technique of completing the square to $f(x) = ax^2 + bx + c$. Find a formula for (h, k) in terms of a, b, and c.

Challenge

30. An orange grower finds that she gets an average yield of 40 bushels per tree when she plants 20 trees on an acre of ground. Each time she adds a tree to an acre, the yield per tree decreases by 1 bushel, due to congestion. How many trees per acre should she plant for maximum yield? 30

31. When a theater owner charges \$2 for admission, an average of 100 people attend. For each 10¢ increase in admission price, the average number decreases by 1. What should he charge to make the most money? \$6

32. Find the dimensions and area of the largest rectangle that can be inscribed as shown in a right triangle ABC, whose sides have lengths of 9 cm, 12 cm, and 15 cm. 6 cm by 4.5 cm; 27 cm²

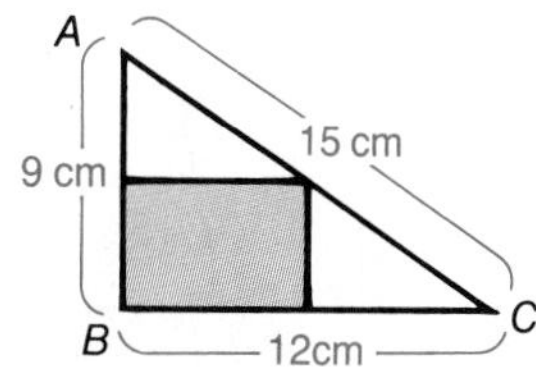

33. A farmer wants to build a rectangular fence near a river, and he will use 120 ft of fencing. The side next to the river will not be fenced. What is the area of the largest region that can be enclosed? 1800 ft²

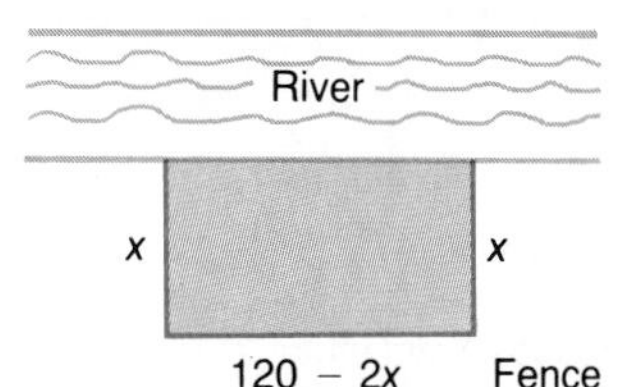

34. The sum of the base and the height of a triangle is 38 cm. Find the dimensions for which the area is a maximum, and find the maximum area. 19 cm by 19 cm; 180.5 cm²

35. The perimeter of rectangle $RSTV$ is 44 ft. Find the least value of the diagonal RT. $11\sqrt{2}$ ft

Mixed Review

Test for symmetry with respect to the axes. **36.** $y = 2x^4 + 1$ **37.** $y^2 = 2x^4 + 1$

38. $y = 2x^3 + 1$ **39.** $y^2 = 2x^5 + 1$

Solve. **40.** $\sqrt{x + 2} = x$ **41.** $\sqrt{x^5} = 32$ **42.** $\sqrt[3]{r - 2} = 1$

Multiply. **43.** $-8i(-2)$ **44.** $\sqrt{-3}\sqrt{-7}$ **45.** $-\sqrt{-50}\sqrt{-2}$

Write using scientific notation. **46.** 0.07112 **47.** 34,095,600

8. $f(x) = \left(x + \frac{1}{2}\right)^2 - \frac{1}{4}$
Vertex: $\left(-\frac{1}{2}, -\frac{1}{4}\right)$
Line of symmetry: $x = -\frac{1}{2}$
Minimum: $-\frac{1}{4}$

9. $f(x) = 3(x - 4)^2 + 2$
Vertex: (4, 2)
Line of symmetry: $x = 4$
Minimum: 2

10. $f(x) = 4(x + 1)^2 - 7$
Vertex: (−1, −7)
Line of symmetry: $x = -1$
Minimum: −7

11. $f(x) = \frac{3}{4}(x + 6)^2 - 27$
Vertex: (−6, −27)
Line of symmetry: $x = -6$
Minimum: −27

12. $f(x) = -2\left(x - \frac{1}{2}\right)^2 + \frac{3}{2}$
Vertex: $\left(\frac{1}{2}, \frac{3}{2}\right)$
Line of symmetry: $x = \frac{1}{2}$
Maximum: $\frac{3}{2}$

21. $f(x) = 3\left[x - \left(-\frac{m}{6}\right)\right]^2 + \frac{11m^2}{12}$

For Exercises 22,23, see Teacher's Answer Section

24. Minimum: −6.95
25. Maximum: 7.014
26. Minimum: −6.081; ± 2.466
27. Maximum: 114.009; both ±10.6775
28. Vertex: $\left(-\frac{b}{2a}, c - \frac{b^2}{4a}\right)$
Line of symmetry: $x = -\frac{b}{2a}$
29. $h = -\frac{b}{2a}$ $k = \frac{4ac - b^2}{4a}$

Mixed Review

36. y-axis
37. Both
38. Neither
39. x-axis
40. 2
41. 4
42. 3
43. $16i$
44. $-\sqrt{21}$
45. 10
46. 7.112×10^{-2}
47. 3.40956×10^7

9-7

FIRST FIVE MINUTES

1. Write in standard form.
   $f(x) = x^2 - 8x + 10$
   $f(x) = x^2 - 8x + 16 - 6$
   $f(x) = (x - 4)^2 - 6$
2. Find the solutions of the equation $(x - 2)(x - 5) = 0$.
   By inspection, $x = 2$ and $x = 5$ are solutions.

Point out that the number of x-intercepts can be found from the graph of an equation but their exact values are best determined through algebraic techniques.

Key Questions

- How many x-intercepts does the graph of $f(x) = x^2 + x + 1$ have?
  0
- How many x-intercepts does the graph of $f(x) = 2x^2 + 3x + 1$ have?
  2
- How many x-intercepts does the graph of $f(x) = 2x^2 + 4x + 2$ have?
  1

Chalkboard Example

1. Find the x-intercepts of the graph of $f(x) = x^2 + 3x + 2$.
   Solve $0 = x^2 + 3x + 2$.
   $0 = (x + 1)(x + 2)$
   The intercepts are -1 and -2.

LESSON QUIZ

Find the x-intercepts.

1. $f(x) = x^2 - 5x + 6$
   2, 3
2. $f(x) = 4x^2 + 2x + 1$
   There is no x-intercept.
3. $f(x) = x^2 + 6x + 9$
   -3

9-7 Graphs and x-intercepts

Objective: Find the x-intercepts of the graph of a quadratic function, if they exist.

The x-coordinates of the points where a graph crosses the x-axis are its **x-intercepts.** These are the points at which $y = 0$.

To find the x-intercepts of a quadratic function $f(x) = ax^2 + bx + c$, we solve the equation $0 = ax^2 + bx + c$.

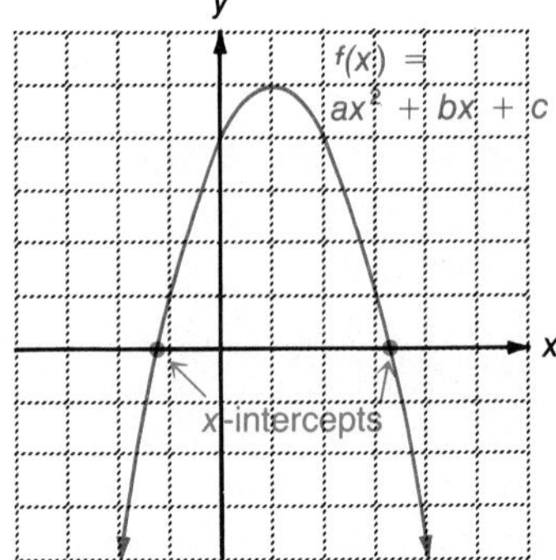

Recall that the discriminant $b^2 - 4ac$ tells us how many real-number solutions the equation $0 = ax^2 + bx + c$ has. Thus it also indicates how many x-intercepts there are. Compare.

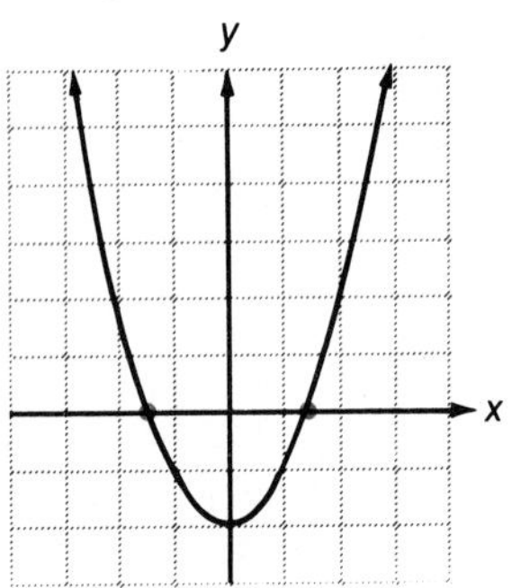

$y = ax^2 + bx + c$
$b^2 - 4ac > 0$
Two real solutions
Two x-intercepts

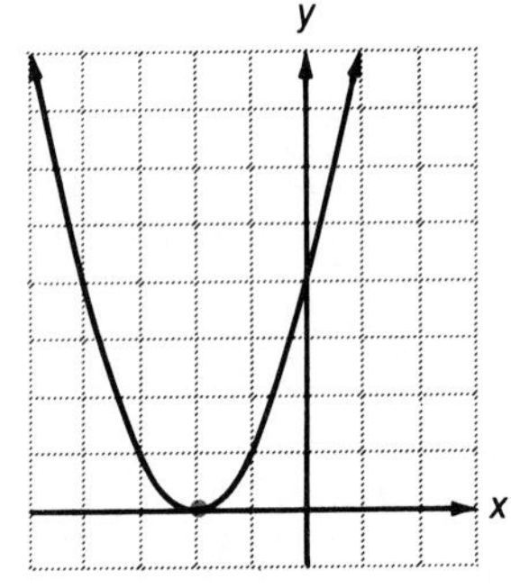

$y = ax^2 + bx + c$
$b^2 - 4ac = 0$
One real solution
One x-intercept

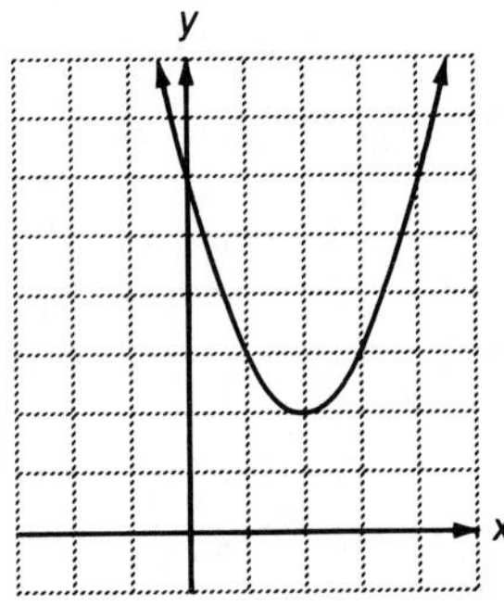

$y = ax^2 + bx + c$
$b^2 - 4ac < 0$
No real solutions
No x-intercepts

EXAMPLE Find the x-intercepts of the graph of $f(x) = x^2 - 2x - 2$.

We solve the equation $0 = x^2 - 2x - 2$.

We can use the quadratic formula

$$x = \frac{2 \pm \sqrt{4 + 8}}{2} = \frac{2 \pm 2\sqrt{3}}{2} = 1 \pm \sqrt{3}$$

Thus the x-intercepts are $1 + \sqrt{3}$ and $1 - \sqrt{3}$, and these occur at $(1 + \sqrt{3}, 0)$ and $(1 - \sqrt{3}, 0)$.

Try This Find the x-intercepts, if they exist.

a. $f(x) = x^2 - 2x - 5$ $1 + \sqrt{6}, 1 - \sqrt{6}$ **b.** $f(x) = x^2 + 8x + 16$ -4
c. $f(x) = -2x^2 - 4x - 3$ None

9-7 EXERCISES

A

Find the x-intercepts.

1. $f(x) = x^2 - 4x + 1$ $2 + \sqrt{3}, 2 - \sqrt{3}$
2. $f(x) = x^2 + 6x + 10$ None
3. $f(x) = -x^2 + 2x + 3$ $3, -1$
4. $f(x) = x^2 + 2x - 5$ $-1 - \sqrt{6}, -1 + \sqrt{6}$
5. $f(x) = x^2 - 3x - 4$ $4, -1$
6. $f(x) = x^2 - 8x + 5$ $4 + \sqrt{11}, 4 - \sqrt{11}$
7. $f(x) = -x^2 + 3x + 4$ $4, -1$
8. $f(x) = 2x^2 - 4x + 6$ None
9. $f(x) = 2x^2 + 4x - 1$ $\frac{-2 \pm \sqrt{6}}{2}$
10. $f(x) = x^2 - x + 2$ None
11. $f(x) = x^2 - x + 1$ None
12. $f(x) = 4x^2 + 12x + 9$ $-\frac{3}{2}$
13. $f(x) = -x^2 - 3x - 3$ None
14. $f(x) = -5x^2 + 6x - 5$ None
15. $f(x) = 3x^2 - 6x + 1$ $\frac{3 \pm \sqrt{6}}{3}$
16. $f(x) = x^2 - 4x + 4$ 2

B

17. Graph the function $f(x) = x^2 - x - 6$. Use your graph to approximate solutions to the following equations.
    a. $x^2 - x - 6 = 2$ **b.** $x^2 - x - 6 = -3$
18. Graph the function $f(x) = \frac{x^2}{8} + \frac{x}{4} - \frac{3}{8}$. Use your graph to approximate solutions to the following equations.
    a. $\frac{x^2}{8} + \frac{x}{4} - \frac{3}{8} = 0$ **b.** $\frac{x^2}{8} + \frac{x}{4} - \frac{3}{8} = 1$ **c.** $\frac{x^2}{8} + \frac{x}{4} - \frac{3}{8} = 2$
19. ***Critical Thinking*** Write an equation for a quadratic function that has x-intercepts of $(-3, 0)$ and $(5, 0)$.

Challenge

Find the x-intercepts.

20. $f(x) = x^4 - 10$
21. $f(x) = x^4 - 3x^2 + 9$

Mixed Review

Test for symmetry with respect to the origin. **22.** $y + x = 1$ **23.** $y - x^2 = 4$ **24.** $4y = 3x - 7$ **25.** $x^2 + y^2 = 3$

For each function graph the function, find the vertex, and find the line of symmetry. **26.** $f(x) = x^2$ **27.** $f(x) = -2(x + 3)^2$

Graph the following relations. **28.** $y = |x|$ **29.** $y = |x + 4|$

30. The distance s that an object falls when dropped from some point above the ground varies directly as the square of the time t it falls. The object falls 19.6 meters in 2 seconds.
    a. Find the equation of variation.
    b. How far will the object fall in 15 seconds?
    c. How long will it take for the object to fall 122.5 meters?

Assignment Guide
Algebra: 1 – 16 e/o, MR

Alg w/Finite or Trig: 1–18 e/o, 19, MR

Comprehensive: 1–18 m3, 19–21, MR, assign w. Application

ADDITIONAL ANSWERS

Exercises

For Exercises 17 – 18, answers may vary.

17. a. 3.4, −2.4
b. 2.3, −1.3

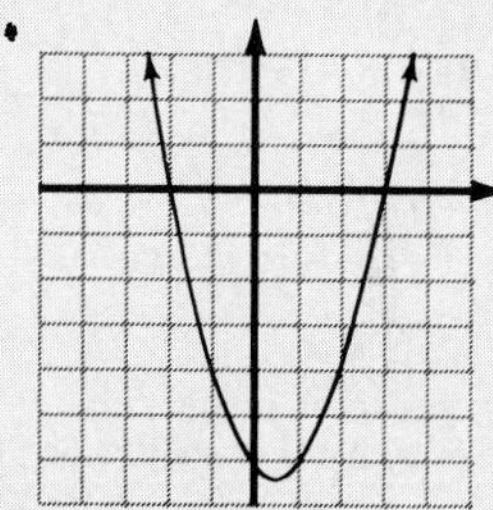

18. a. 1, −3
b. 2.5, −4.5
c. 3.5, −5.5

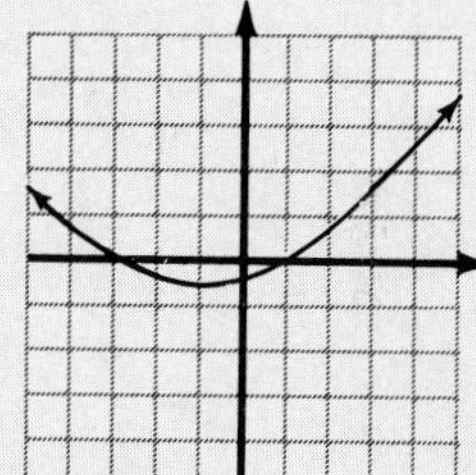

19. $f(x) = x^2 - 2x - 15$
20. $\sqrt[4]{10}, -\sqrt[4]{10}$
21. None

Mixed Review

22. No **23.** No
24. No **25.** Yes

For graphs of Exercises 26, 27, see Teacher's Answer Section.

26. Vertex: (0, 0)
Line of symmetry: y-axis
27. Vertex: (−3, 0)
Line of symmetry: $x = -3$

For Exercises 28, 29, see Teacher's Answer Section

30. a. $s = 4.9\,t^2$
b. 1102.5 m
c. 5 s

9-8

FIRST FIVE MINUTES

Find the x-intercepts.

1. $f(x) = x^2 + 7x + 10$
   $0 = (x + 2)(x + 5)$
   $-2, -5$
2. $f(x) = x^2 + x + 3$
   The discriminant is less than 0. There is no x-intercept.
3. $f(x) = x^2 + x - 1$
   $x = \frac{-1 \pm \sqrt{1^2 - (-4)}}{2 \cdot 1}$
   $x = \frac{-1 \pm \sqrt{5}}{2}$

Fitting Quadratic Functions to Data

Key Questions

- If $f(x) = ax^2 + bx + c$ and $f(0) = 5$, what is c?
  $c = 5$
- Can you name three points that cannot be fit by a quadratic function?
  Any three collinear points, such as (1, 0), (2, 0), (3, 0)

Chalkboard Example

1. Find the quadratic function that fits the points (0, 0), (1, 0), (−1, 1).
   Substitute the three data points into
   $f(x) = ax^2 + bx + c$
   $0 = c$
   $0 = a + b + c$
   $1 = a - b + c$
   Solving this system, $a = \frac{1}{2}$, $b = -\frac{1}{2}$, $c = 0$.

Problem Solving: Quadratic Functions

In Example 2, point out that the function $f(x) = 0.0025x^2 + 0.125x + 2.5$ always gives a price of at least \$2.50, even when the diameter equals 0. In other words, \$2.50 is the fixed cost of making the pizza.

Emphasize that the graph in Example 3 is not the path of the rocket. The horizontal axis is time, not horizontal distance. The rocket is fired directly upward.

9-8 Mathematical Modeling: Using Quadratic Functions

Fitting Quadratic Functions

Objective: Find quadratic functions given a graph or three data points.

We can find a quadratic function that fits a curve if we know three data points.

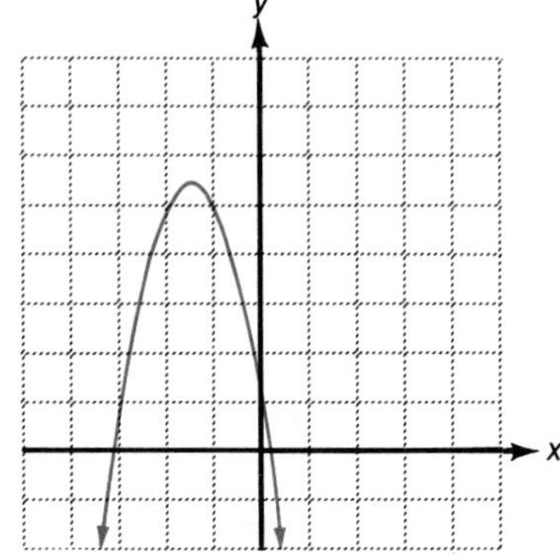

EXAMPLE 1 Find the quadratic function that fits the curve.

Three data points on the graph are $(-2, 5)$, $(-1, 5)$, and $(0, 1)$. We substitute the three data points in $f(x) = ax^2 + bx + c$.

$$5 = a(-2)^2 + b(-2) + c$$
$$5 = a(-1)^2 + b(-1) + c$$
$$1 = a(0)^2 + b(0) + c$$

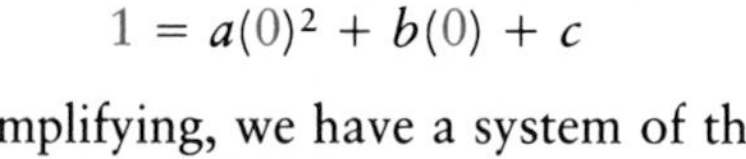

Simplifying, we have a system of three equations with three unknowns.

$$5 = 4a - 2b + c$$
$$5 = a - b + c$$
$$1 = c$$

Solving this system, we obtain $a = -2$, $b = -6$, and $c = 1$. These are the coefficients of the quadratic function $f(x) = ax^2 + bx + c$.

Thus the quadratic function is $f(x) = -2x^2 - 6x + 1$.

Try This

a. Find the quadratic equation that fits the curve. $f(x) = x^2 - 2x + 1$

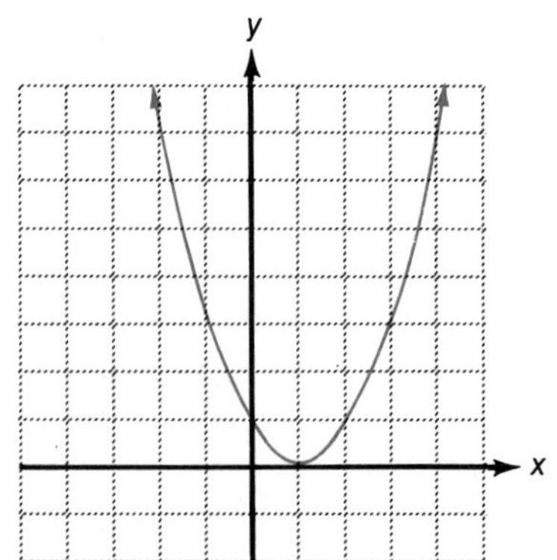

b. Find the quadratic function that fits the data points $(1, 6)$, $(-2, 3)$, and $(3, 18)$. $f(x) = x^2 + 2x + 3$

Problem Solving: Quadratic Functions

Objective: Solve problems using quadratic functions.

Often, problems generate nonlinear data points that can be fit by quadratic functions. We can combine our knowledge of quadratic functions and problem-solving techniques to solve them.

EXAMPLE 2

A pizza shop lists the following prices for pizzas.

Diameter in cm	Price
20	\$ 6.00
30	\$ 8.50
40	\$11.50

What price should be given to a 35-cm pizza?

UNDERSTAND the problem

Question: What is the price of a 35-cm pizza?
Data: A 20-cm pizza costs \$6.00, a 30-cm pizza costs \$8.50, and a 40-cm pizza costs \$11.50.

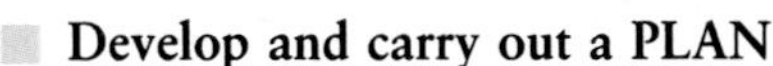

Develop and carry out a PLAN

The area of a circular region is given by the formula $A = \pi r^2$, or $A = \frac{\pi d^2}{4}$. Thus the area of a pizza is a quadratic function of the diameter. Since the price should be related to the area, it should be a quadratic function of the diameter.

We can fit a quadratic function to the data points (20, 6), (30, 8.5), and (40, 11.5). Then we can use the function to find the price of a 35-cm pizza.

Use the data points in $f(x) = ax^2 + bx + c$, where x is the diameter of a pizza and $f(x)$ represents the price.

$$6 = a \cdot 20^2 + b \cdot 20 + c$$
$$8.5 = a \cdot 30^2 + b \cdot 30 + c \qquad \text{Fitting a function to the data points}$$
$$11.5 = a \cdot 40^2 + b \cdot 40 + c$$

Simplifying, we get the following system.

$$6 = 400a + 20b + c$$
$$8.5 = 900a + 30b + c$$
$$11.5 = 1600a + 40b + c$$

We solve this system, obtaining $a = 0.0025$, $b = 0.125$, and $c = 2.5$

Thus the function $f(x) = 0.0025x^2 + 0.125x + 2.5$ is a mathematical model of the situation.

To find the price of a 35-cm pizza, we find $f(35)$.

$$f(35) = 0.0025(35)^2 + 0.125(35) + 2.5 = \$9.94$$

Chalkboard Examples

1. A ball thrown in the air follows a parabolic path. The height h is a quadratic function of the time t of the form $h(t) = at^2 + bt + c$. The path of the ball goes through the points (0, 6), (1, 22), and (2, 6). Find the equation for the height as a function of time. Find the time the ball hits the ground.

   Substituting the data points yields the system
   $c = 6$ (1)
   $a + b + c = 22$ (2)
   $4a + 2b + c = 6$ (3)
   Substituting for c yields
   $a + b = 16$ (2)
   $4a + 2b = 0$ (3)
   $a = -16, b = 32, c = 6$
   $h(t) = -16t^2 + 32t + 6$
   The ball hits the ground when $h(t) = 0$.
   $-16t^2 + 32t + 6 = 0$
   The quadratic equation gives $t \approx 2.17$ seconds as the time the ball hits the ground.

2. A solar heating device requires a parabolic reflector to focus sunlight on a pipe filled with water. The design requires that the parabolic cross section go through the points (−1, 2), (0, 0), and (1, 1). Find the quadratic function $f(x)$ which contains these data points.

   Substituting the data points in the equation $f(x) = ax^2 + bx + c$ yields the system
   $a - b + c = 2$ (1)
   $c = 0$ (2)
   $a + b + c = 1$ (3)
   Solving the system yields
   $a = \frac{3}{2}$
   $b = -\frac{1}{2}$
   $c = 0$
   The equation is
   $f(x) = \frac{3}{2}x^2 - \frac{1}{2}x$

■ **Find the ANSWER and CHECK**

A 35-cm pizza should cost \$9.94. The answer is reasonable, since the price for the 35-cm pizza falls between the prices of a 30-cm and a 40-cm pizza.

Stating the answer clearly

Try This

c. The following table shows the accident records for a city. It has values that a quadratic function will fit.

Age of drivers	Number of accidents in a year
20	250
40	150
60	200

(1) Assuming that a quadratic function will describe the situation, find the number of accidents as a function of age. $f(x) = 0.1875x^2 - 16.25x + 500$

(2) Use the function to calculate the total number of accidents in which 16-year-olds might be involved. 288

A physics theory shows that when an object such as a ball is thrown upward with an initial velocity v_0, its approximate height is given by a quadratic function.

$$s = -4.9t^2 + v_0 t + h$$

In the formula, h is the starting height in meters and s is the actual height in meters, t seconds after the object is thrown.

EXAMPLE 3

A model rocket is fired upward. At the end of the burn it has an upward velocity of 49 m/sec and is 155 m high.

(a) Find its maximum height and when it is attained.

We will start counting time at the end of the burn. Thus $v_0 = 49$ and $h = 155$. We will graph the appropriate function, and we begin by completing the square.

$$\begin{aligned} s &= -4.9t^2 + 49t + 155 \\ &= -4.9\left(t^2 - \frac{49}{4.9}t\right) + 155 \\ &= -4.9(t^2 - 10t) + 155 \\ &= -4.9(t^2 - 10t + 25 - 25) + 155 && \text{Simplifying} \\ &= -4.9(t^2 - 10t + 25) + (-4.9)(-25) + 155 && \text{Completing the square} \\ &= -4.9(t - 5)^2 + 122.5 + 155 \\ &= -4.9(t - 5)^2 + 277.5 \end{aligned}$$

The vertex of the graph is the point (5, 277.5). The graph is shown below. The maximum height reached is 277.5 m and it is attained 5 seconds after the end of the burn.

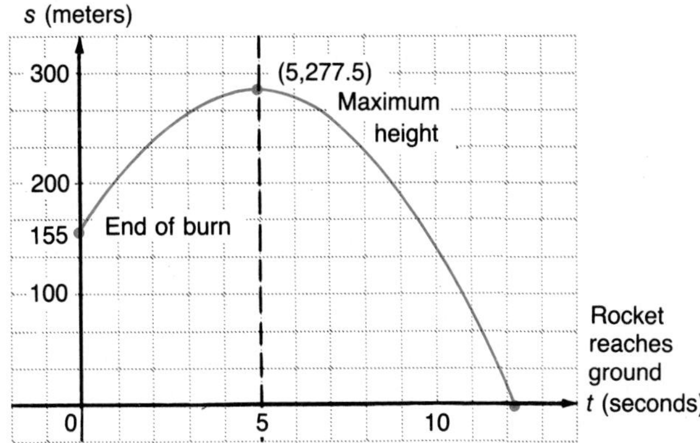

(b) Find when it reaches the ground.

To find when the rocket reaches the ground, we set $s = 0$ in our equation and solve for t.

$$-4.9(t - 5)^2 + 277.5 = 0$$
$$4.9(t - 5)^2 = 277.5$$
$$(t - 5)^2 = \frac{277.5}{4.9}$$
$$t - 5 = \pm\sqrt{\frac{277.5}{4.9}}$$
$$t - 5 \approx \pm 7.525$$
$$t \approx 12.525 \qquad \text{t must be nonnegative.}$$

We can use a calculator to check 12.525 seconds. Note that this is an approximation for time, so we will probably not find that the height s is *exactly* 0 meters for this value.

$$s = -4.9t^2 + v_0t + h$$
$$\approx -4.9(12.525)^2 + 49(12.525) + 155 \qquad \text{Substituting for t, v_0, and h}$$
$$\approx -4.9(156.87563) + 613.725 + 155$$
$$\approx 0.034413$$

Our value for s is close to zero, so our approximation is reasonable. The rocket will reach the ground about 12.525 seconds after the end of the burn.

Try This

d. A ball is thrown upward from the top of a cliff 12 meters high, at a velocity of 2.8 m/sec. Find

(1) its maximum height and when it is attained. Maximum height = 12.4 m in 0.286 sec

(2) when it reaches the ground. 1.876 sec

LESSON QUIZ

1. Find the quadratic equation that fits the points (−1, 2), (0, 1), (1, 3).
   $f(x) = \frac{3}{2}x^2 + \frac{1}{2}x + 1$

Assignment Guide
Algebra: Day 1: 1 – 5, MR
Day 2: 6 – 10, assign w. Application
Alg w/Finite or Trig: 1–14 e/o, 15, MR, assign w. Application
Comprehensive: 1–14 m3, 15–18, MR

ADDITIONAL ANSWERS

Exercises

1. $f(x) = 2x^2 + 3x - 1$
2. $f(x) = 3x^2 - x + 2$
3. $f(x) = -3x^2 + 13x - 5$
4. $f(x) = x^2 - 5x$

15. Answers may vary. Answer should include the idea that the points lie on a straight line. The function can be written as $f(x) = 5$, which has no equivalent quadratic function.

17. 300 m^2
18. 4800 yd^2

9-8 EXERCISES

A

Find the quadratic function that fits each set of data points.

1. (1, 4), (−1, −2), (2, 13)
2. (1, 4), (−1, 6), (−2, 16)
3. 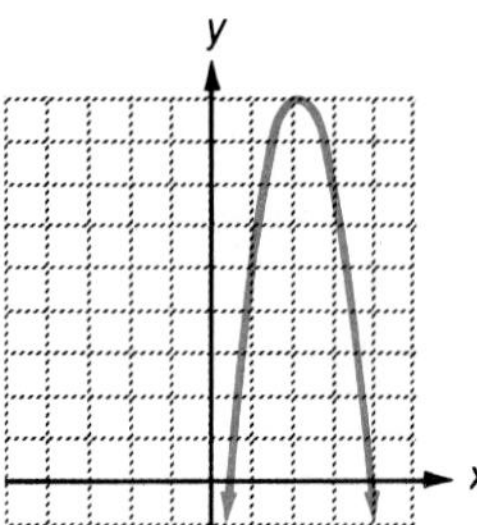

4. 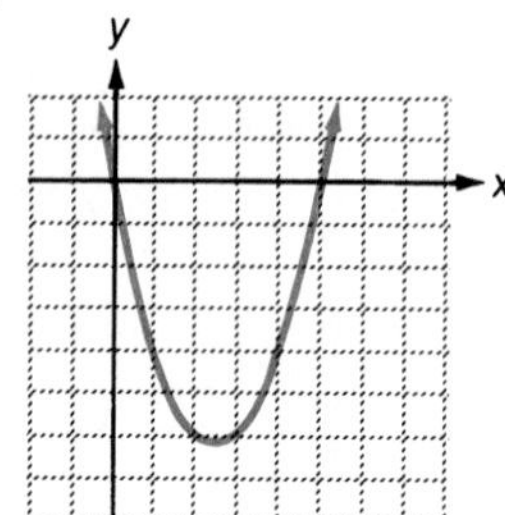

5. A business earns \$38 in the first day, \$66 in the second day, and \$86 in the third day. The manager plots the points (1, 38), (2, 66), and (3, 86).
   a. Find a quadratic function that fits the data. $-4x^2 + 40x + 2$
   b. Using the function, predict the earnings for the fourth day. \$98

6. A business earns \$1000 in the first month, \$2000 in the second month, and \$8000 in the third month. The manager plots the points (1, 1000), (2, 2000), and (3, 8000).
   a. Find a quadratic function that fits the data. $2500x^2 - 6500x + 5000$
   b. Using the function, predict the earnings for the fourth month. \$19,000

7. a. Find a quadratic function that fits the following data. $0.0875r^2 - 10.5r + 436.25$

Travel speed in km/h	Number of daytime accidents
50	130
70	130
90	200

   b. Use the function to calculate the number of daytime accidents which occur at 60 km/h. 121.25

8. a. Find a quadratic function that fits the following data. $0.1875r^2 - 18r + 670$

Travel speed in km/h	Number of nighttime accidents
40	250
60	265
80	430

   b. Use the function to calculate the number of nighttime accidents which occur at 90 km/h. 568.75

9. A rocket is fired upward. At the end of the burn it has an upward velocity of 245 m/sec and is 14.7 m high. Find
   a. its maximum height and when it is attained. 3077 m at 25 sec
   b. when it reaches the ground. 50.1 sec

10. A rocket is fired upward. At the end of the burn it has an upward velocity of 147 m/sec and is 73.5 m high. Find
   a. its maximum height and when it is attained. 1176 m at 15 sec
   b. when it reaches the ground. 30.5 sec

B

11. Use the quadratic function you found in Exercise 7 to find the number of daytime accidents for 80 km/h. Then find another travel speed that has the same number of accidents. 156.25, 40 km/h

12. Use the quadratic function you found in Exercise 8 to find the number of nighttime accidents for 70 km/h. Then find another travel speed that has the same number of accidents. 328.75, 26 km/h

13. The wattage of an electrical circuit is given by the equation $W = VI - RI^2$, where V is voltage, R is resistance in ohms, and I is current in amperes.
    a. Find the current that produces the maximum wattage for a 120-volt circuit with a resistance of 12 ohms. 5 amperes
    b. Find the maximum wattage produced by the circuit. 300 watts

14. A rocket is fired upward from a mine shaft. At the end of the burn it has an upward velocity of 196 m/sec and is 29.4 m below ground level. Find
    a. its maximum height and when it is attained. 1931 m at 20 s
    b. when it first reaches ground level. 0.15 s
    c. when it falls to earth. 39.9 s

15. ***Critical Thinking*** Write a convincing argument that there is no quadratic function that will fit the data points (2, 5), (−8, 5), and (10, 5).

Challenge

16. Let $y = (x - p)^2 + (x - q)^2$ where p and q are constants. For what value of x is y a minimum? $\frac{p+q}{2}$

17. A farmer wants to enclose two adjacent rectangular regions next to a river, one for sheep and one for cattle. No fencing will be used next to the river, but 60 m of fencing will be used. What is the area of the largest region that can be enclosed?

18. A city council is planning to use 200 yd of fencing to enclose a park for physically handicapped citizens. The park will be adjacent to the community center and will have two rectangular areas connected by a bridge crossing a creek that is 10 yd from the building. The area next to the community center can have a length no greater than the length of the building, which is 75 yd, but the area across the creek may have any dimensions. No fencing will be used next to the creek. What is the total area of the largest park they may enclose? Be sure to use a drawing.

Mixed Review

Test for symmetry with respect to the x-axis and the y-axis.

19. $y^3 = 2x^5 + 1$ 20. $y^2 = 2x^3 + 1$ 21. $y = x^2$ 22. $x^2 + y^2 = 1$

For each of the following functions graph the function, find the vertex, and find the line of symmetry. 23. $f(x) = 3x^2$ 24. $f(x) = (x - 2)^2$ 25. $f(x) = 3(x + 1)^2$

Solve. 26. $x - 16\sqrt{x} + 64 = 0$ 27. $x^4 - 5x^2 - 36 = 0$

28. Find an equation of variation where y varies jointly as x and inversely as z, and $y = 6$ when $x = 16$ and $z = 8$.

Mixed Review

19. Neither
20. x-axis
21. y-axis
22. Both
23. Vertex: (0, 0)
    Line of symmetry: y-axis

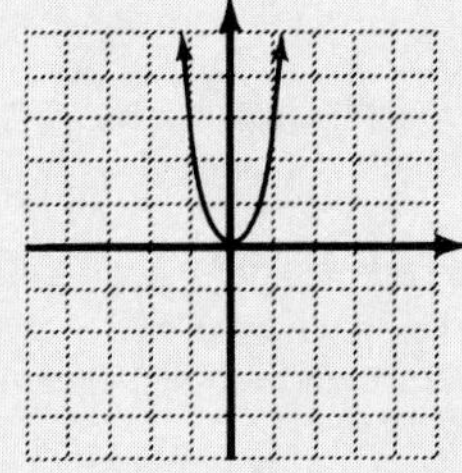

24. Vertex: (2, 0)
    Line of symmetry: $x = 2$

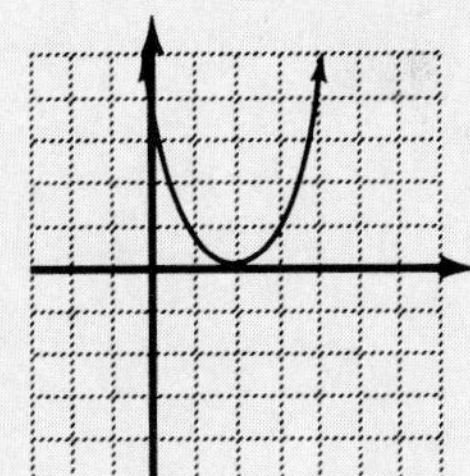

25. Vertex: (−1, 0)
    Line of symmetry: $x = -1$

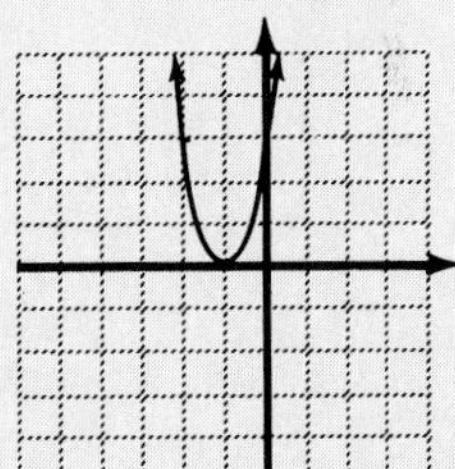

26. 64
27. $\pm 3, \pm 2i$
28. $y = \frac{3x}{z}$

Problem Solving: College Entrance Exams

When choices are listed as in Problem 2 (II only, II and III only, etc.), use logical reasoning to eliminate possibilities. Here is how the problem might be considered.

1. Find any of I, II, or III that you are sure about. Since the sum of two odd numbers is even, $a + b$ is a multiple of 2, so II must be true. Cross off any choices that don't include II (choice D).
2. 1 and 5 are odd integers, but $\frac{1+5}{2}$ is not even, so I must be false. Cross off any choices that include I (choice *C* and *E*).
3. The difference between two odd numbers is even, so the answer is choice *B*.

Problem Solving: College Entrance Exams

Odd and Even Problems

Another type of problem found on college entrance exams is the "odd and even" problem. Here you are told that a given variable represents an odd or an even number, and you are asked to make a decision about one or more expressions involving that variable.

EXAMPLE 1

If n is odd, then which of the following could be even?

(A) $3n + 4$ **(B)** $5n + 2$ **(C)** $3n + 9$ **(D)** $6n + 3$ **(E)** $2n + 3$

A problem like this could be solved using the facts below.

odd + odd = even	odd × odd = odd
odd + even = odd	odd × even = even
even + odd = odd	even × odd = even
even + even = even	even × even = even

It is better, however, to develop specific shortcuts and strategies to arrive at answers quickly and easily.

Using the strategy *Look for a Pattern,* we discover that since the facts above are true for all integers, they are true for particular odds and evens. Therefore, a good beginning strategy is

if an unknown number is odd, use 1

if an unknown number is even, use 0 or 2

Applying the strategy to the example above, since n is odd, we will let $n = 1$. Then the problem could be solved as shown

(A) $3n + 4 = 3(1) + 4 = 7$

(B) $5n + 2 = 5(1) + 2 = 7$

(C) $3n + 9 = 3(1) + 9 = 12$

(D) $6n + 3 = 6(1) + 3 = 9$

(E) $2n + 3 = 2(1) + 3 = 5$

The answer is **C** because the other four answers are odd and only 12 is even.

EXAMPLE 2

If x is a nonnegative integer, which of the following *must* be an odd integer?

(A) $x^3 + 2$ **(B)** $5x + 4$ **(C)** $4x + 2$ **(D)** $2x^2 + 1$ **(E)** $x^2 + x + 6$

Applying our strategy here means that since x can be either odd or even, we will check each answer for both cases. As soon as an answer becomes "even" we can go on to the next answer.

(A) $x^3 + 2 = (0)^3 + 2 = 2$

(B) $5x + 4 = 5(0) + 4 = 4$

(C) $4x + 2 = 4(0) + 2 = 2$

(D) $2x^2 + 1 = 2(0)^2 + 1 = 1$
$2x^2 + 1 = 2(1)^2 + 1 = 3$

At this point, we know **D** is correct because both answers are odd. To confirm our strategy, let's try **E**.

(E) $x^2 + x + 6 = (1)^2 + 1 + 6 = 8$

Problems

1. If a is an odd integer and b is an even integer, which of the following *could* be an odd integer?

(A) $2a + b$ **(B)** $4a - b$ **(C)** $a + 3b$ **(D)** $b \times b$ **(E)** $\frac{a}{2} + \frac{b}{2}$

2. If a and b are nonnegative odd integers, which of the following *must* be true?

I. $\frac{a + b}{2}$ is even.
II. $a + b$ is a multiple of 2.
III. $a - b$ is even.

(A) II only **(B)** II and III only **(C)** I and II only
(D) I and III only **(E)** I, II, and III

3. For any integer n, which of the following represents three consecutive odd integers?

(A) $n + 3, n + 5, n + 7$
(B) $n, n + 1, n + 2$
(C) $n, 3n, 5n$
(D) $2n, 2n + 2, 2n + 4$
(E) $2n + 1, 2n + 3, 2n + 5$

4. For what whole number w is the sum of w, $w + 1$, and $w + 2$ even?
(A) for all odd numbers w **(B)** for no w **(C)** for all w
(D) for all even numbers w **(E)** for some w, but for none of the sets above

5. If $3x + y = 18$ and x is an even positive integer, which of the following *must* be true?
I. y is an odd integer.
II. y is an even integer.
III. y is a multiple of 6.
(A) I only **(B)** II only **(C)** III only
(D) I and III only **(E)** II and III only

6. If $5x - 1$ is an even integer, which of the following represents the next consecutive even integer?

(A) $6x + 1$ **(B)** $5x$ **(C)** $6x - 1$ **(D)** $5x + 1$ **(E)** $6x$

ANSWERS
1. (C)
2. (B)
3. (E)
4. (A)
5. (E)
6. (D)

Problem Solving: Application

Note that we need to have the equation for P in terms of s alone to answer the question "what price s will bring the most profit?" We could solve for P in terms of d, but that would be more complicated and would not lead to a direct answer.

Some students will have difficulty completing the square in a relation because it will look unfamiliar. The relation could be written as the function $P(s) = -20s^2 + 7000s - 300{,}000$.

Problem Solving: Application

Merchandising

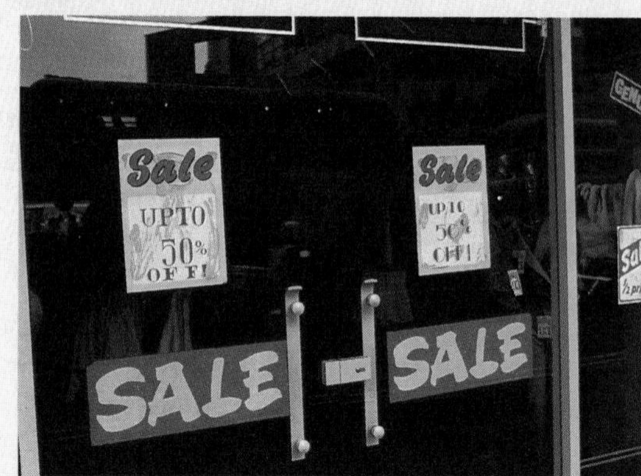

When merchandising experts set a selling price for a new product, their goal is to maximize profits. They begin by estimating the demand for the product at various selling prices. Generally, the demand for a given product will decrease as the selling price increases.

EXAMPLE

The following chart shows the estimated demand for a bicycle, given some possible selling prices.

Selling Price	Estimated Yearly Demand
50	5,000
100	4,000
150	3,000
300	0

Determine the selling price that maximizes yearly profits, the demand at that price, and the maximum profit.

Suppose it costs \$50 to make one bicycle. This means the company cannot consider any selling price less than \$50. If we plot the data points given above, we will find that they lie on a straight line. The equation of the line is $d = -20s + 6000$, where d is the demand and s is the selling price. We find a selling price s that maximizes yearly profits.

Let P represent yearly profits. Then

$$\begin{aligned} P &= (\text{Gross receipts}) - (\text{Production costs}) \\ &= s \cdot d - 50d \\ &= d(s-50) \\ &= (-20s + 6000)(s - 50) \quad \text{Substituting } -20s + 6000 \text{ for } d \\ &= -20s^2 + 7000s - 300{,}000 \end{aligned}$$

This is a quadratic function whose graph opens downward and thus has a maximum value.

We complete the square to find the maximum value.

$$\begin{aligned} P &= -20(s^2 - 350s) - 300{,}000 \\ &= -20[s^2 - 350s + (175)^2] - 300{,}000 + 20(175)^2 \\ &= -20(s - 175)^2 - 300{,}000 + 612{,}500 \\ &= -20(s - 175)^2 + 312{,}500 \end{aligned}$$

This means that profit P will be maximized for a selling price s of \$175. The maximum profit is thus \$312,500. The demand is $-20(175) + 6000$, or 2500 bicycles.

Checking,

$$\begin{aligned} P &= s \cdot d - 50d \\ &= 175(2500) - 50(2500) \\ &= 125(2500) \\ &= 312{,}500 \end{aligned}$$

Problems

1. For a new printer, the marketing experts have estimated the following:

Selling Price	Estimated Yearly Demand
\$100	7000
\$300	5000
\$600	2000
\$800	0

The production cost per item is \$40. Determine a selling price that maximizes the yearly profits, the demand at that price, and the maximum profit.

2. The production cost for the printer in problem 1 rises to \$60. What selling price will now maximize profits? What will the demand be, and what will the maximum profit be?

3. Sciact Corporation's marketing experts have estimated the demand for a new product as follows:

Selling Price	Estimated Yearly Demand
\$20	825
\$40	525
\$60	225

The production cost per item is \$75. Determine a selling price that maximizes the yearly profits, the demand at that price, and the maximum profit. What other decisions should be made about the product?

ANSWERS

1. $d = -10s + 8000$
   $P = d(s - 40)$
   $= (-10s + 8000)(s - 40)$
   $= -10s^2 + 8000s + 400s - 320{,}000$
   $= -10s^2 + 8400s - 320{,}000$
   $= -10(s^2 - 840s + 32{,}000)$
   $s = 420$ $d = 3800$ $P = 1{,}444{,}000$
2. \$430, 3700, \$1,369,000
3. The selling price is \$75. At this price, demand is 0, so the expected profit is 0. The product should not be marketed unless demand rises or costs are reduced.

1. Both
2. x-axis
3. Neither
4. y-axis
5. Neither
6. y-axis
7. No
8. Yes
9. No
10. No
11. Yes
12. No

13.

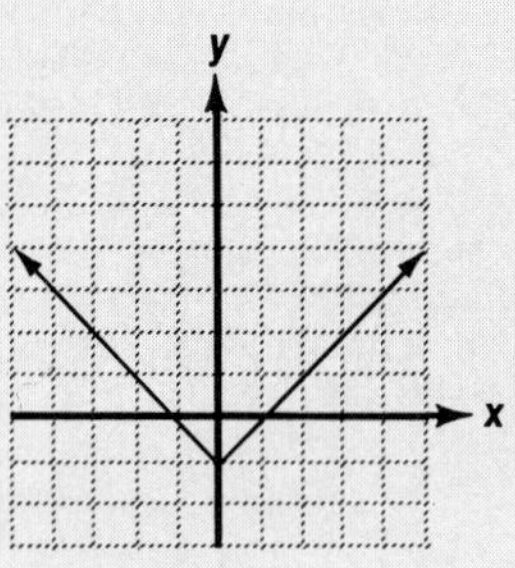

14.

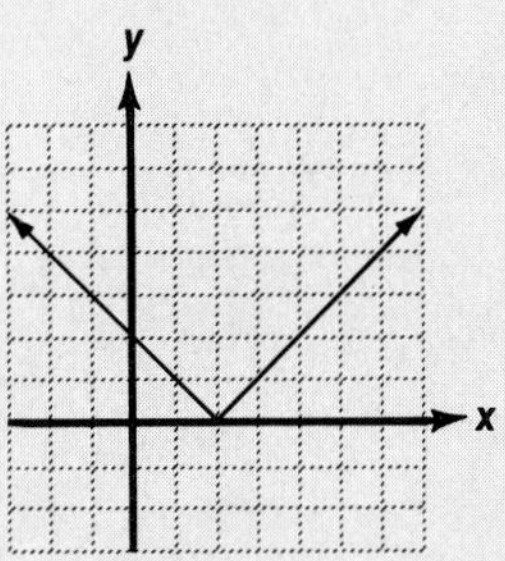

15.

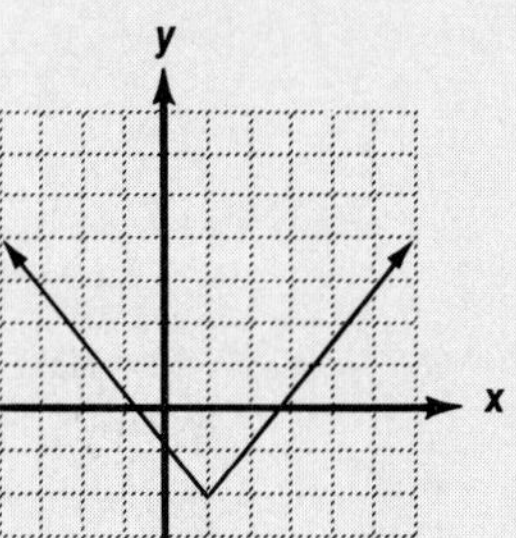

16.

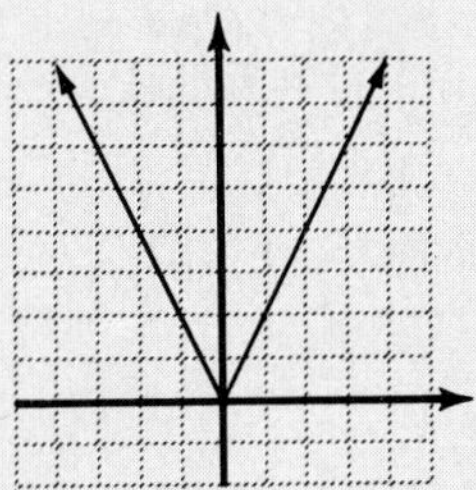

Chapter 9 Summary and Review

9-1

A graph is symmetric with respect to the y-axis if and only if replacing x with $-x$ produces an equivalent equation.

A graph is symmetric with respect to the x-axis if and only if replacing y with $-y$ produces an equivalent equation.

Test for symmetry with respect to the x-axis and the y-axis.

1. $x^2 + y^2 = 4$ **2.** $x = 3$ **3.** $x^3 = y^3 - y$

4. $x^2 = y + 3$ **5.** $x - y = 1$ **6.** $3 - x^2 = y$

A graph of a relation defined by an equation is symmetric with respect to the origin if and only if replacing x with $-x$ and replacing y with $-y$ produce an equivalent equation.

Test for symmetry with respect to the origin.

7. $x + y = 3$ **8.** $y = x^3$ **9.** $x = 2$

10. $y = -4$ **11.** $x^2 - y^2 = 1$ **12.** $1 - y^3 = x$

9-2

In an equation of a relation, replacing y with $y - k$, where k is a constant, translates the graph vertically a distance of $|k|$. If k is positive, the translation is upward. If k is negative, the translation is downward.

In an equation of a relation, replacing x with $x - h$, where h is a constant, translates the graph horizontally a distance of $|h|$. If h is positive, the translation is to the right. If h is negative, the translation is to the left.

Consider the graph of $y = |x|$.

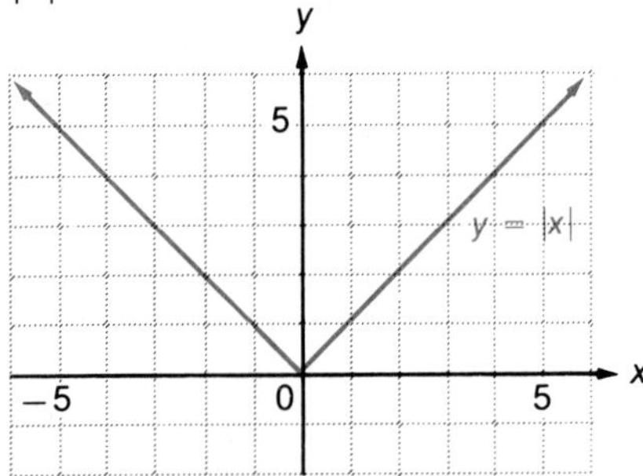

Sketch graphs of the following by translating.

13. $y = |x| - 1$ **14.** $y = |x - 2|$ **15.** $y + 2 = |x - 1|$

9-3

In an equation of a relation, dividing y by a constant c changes the graph in these ways.

If $|c| > 1$, the graph is stretched vertically.
If $|c| < 1$, the graph is shrunk vertically.
If $c < 0$, the graph is reflected across the x-axis.

In an equation of a relation, dividing x by a constant d changes the graph in these ways.

If $|d| > 1$, the graph is stretched horizontally.
If $|d| < 1$, the graph is shrunk horizontally.
If $d < 0$, the graph is reflected across the y-axis.

Consider the graph of $y = |x|$ above. Sketch graphs of the following by stretching or shrinking.

16. $y = 2|x|$ **17.** $y = |2x|$ **18.** $y = -|x|$

19. Sketch $y - 2 = \frac{1}{3}|x + 1|$ by transforming $y = |x|$.

9-4

If a quadratic function is written in the form $f(x) = a(x - h)^2$, then the axis of symmetry is $x = h$ and the vertex is $(h, 0)$.

For each function graph the function, find the vertex, and find the line of symmetry.

20. $f(x) = -2x^2$ **21.** $f(x) = \frac{1}{4}x^2$

22. $f(x) = -2(x + 1)^2$ **23.** $f(x) = 3(x - 2)^2$

9-5

For the quadratic function $f(x) = a(x - h)^2 + k$, the line of symmetry is $x = h$, and the vertex is (h, k). If $a > 0$, there is a minimum value k. If $a < 0$, there is a maximum value k.

For each function graph the function, find the vertex, line of symmetry, and find the minimum or maximum value.

24. $f(x) = -2(x + 1)^2 - 2$

25. $f(x) = \frac{1}{2}(x - 1)^2 + 5$

26. $f(x) = -3(x + 2)^2 + 1$

9-6

Completing the square is useful in changing a quadratic function to standard form $f(x) = a(x - h)^2 + k$.

For each function find standard form.

27. $f(x) = x^2 - 8x + 5$

17. Graph same as 16.

18.

19.

For graphs of exercises 20–26, see Teacher's Answer Section.

20. Vertex: (0, 0)
Line of symmetry: $x = 0$
21. Vertex: (0, 0)
Line of symmetry: $x = 0$
22. Vertex: (−1, 0)
Line of symmetry: $x = -1$
23. Vertex: (2, 0)
Line of symmetry: $x = 2$
24. Vertex: (−1, −2)
Line of symmetry: $x = -1$
Maximum: −2
25. Vertex: (1, 5)
Line of symmetry: $x = 1$
Minimum: 5
26. Vertex: (−2, 1)
Line of symmetry: $x = -2$
Maximum: 1
27. $(x - 4)^2 - 11$
28. $-\frac{1}{2}(x - 6)^2 + 2$
29. $-2(x + 1)^2 + 5$
30. 256; 16 and 16
31. −16; 4 and −4
32. $\frac{-2 \pm \sqrt{10}}{2}$
33. $-1 \pm \sqrt{5}$
34. 3, 1
35. $f(x) = -2x^2 - 4x + 3$
36. $f(x) = 3x^2 - 6x + 5$
37. $f(x) = -x^2 + 8x - 8$
38. **a.** $f(x) = -0.005x^2 + 0.2x + 7$
b. 1 ft

Answers

1. y-axis
2. Both
3. Both
4. x-axis
5. Neither
6. x-axis
7. No
8. Yes
9. No

10.

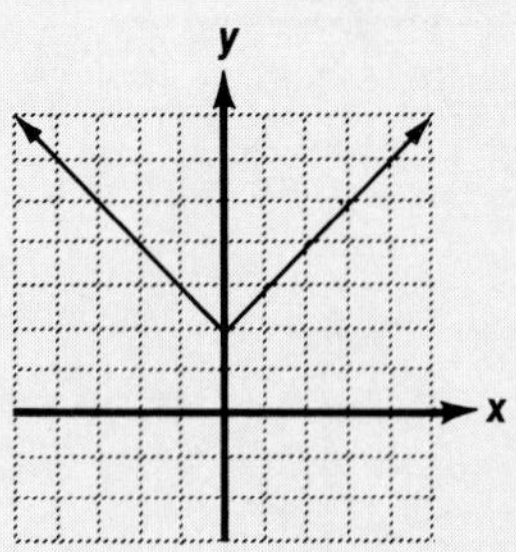

11.

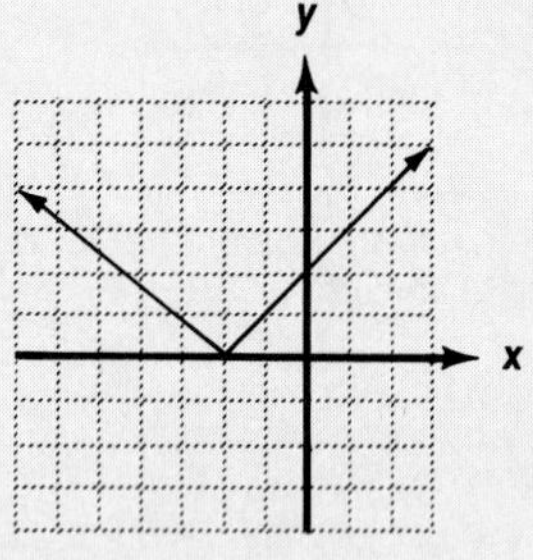

12. Vertex: (0, 0)
Line of symmetry: $x = 0$

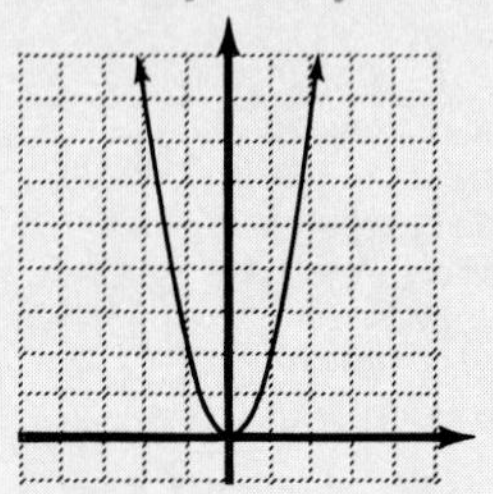

13. Vertex: (5, 0)
Line of symmetry: $x = 5$

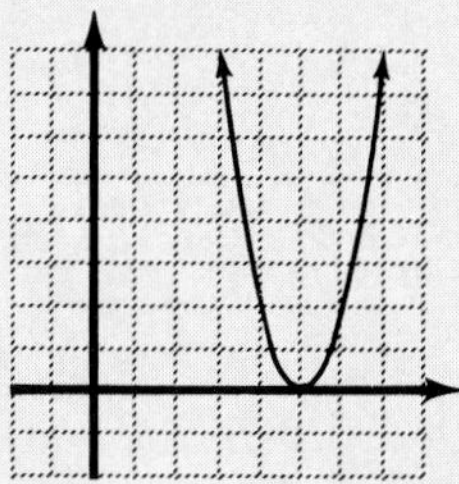

28. $f(x) = -\frac{1}{2}x^2 + 6x - 16$

29. $f(x) = -2x^2 - 4x + 3$

The vertex will be either the minimum or maximum value of the graph of a function.

30. What is the maximum product of two numbers whose sum is 32? What numbers yield this product?

31. What is the minimum product of two numbers whose difference is 8? What are the numbers?

9-7

To find the **x-intercepts** of a quadratic function $f(x) = ax^2 + bx + c$, solve the equation $0 = ax^2 + bx + c$.

Find the x-intercepts, if they exist.

32. $f(x) = -2x^2 - 4x + 3$

33. $f(x) = -x^2 - 2x + 4$

34. $f(x) = x^2 - 4x + 3$

9-8

A quadratic function that fits three **data points** can be found by substituting three times (using the three data points) into $f(x) = ax^2 + bx + c$, thereby creating a system of three equations with three unknowns.

Find the quadratic function that fits each set of data points.

35. $(1, -3), (-1, 5), (2, -13)$

36. $(1, 2), (0, 5), (-1, 14)$

37. $(3, 7), (4, 8), (5, 7)$

38. A baseball is released from a height of 7 feet, thrown towards the catcher. After it travels 20 ft, its height is 9 ft; after it travels 40 ft, its height is 7 ft.
a. Fit a quadratic function to the data.
b. Predict the height of the baseball after it travels 60ft.

See also Problem 9, Computer-Assisted Problem Solving, page 845.

Chapter 9 Test

Test for symmetry with respect to the x-axis and the y-axis.

1. $y = 4$

2. $y^2 = x^2 + 8$

3. $x^2 + y^2 = 9$

4. $x = 5$

5. $x^5 = y^5 - y$

6. $x^7 = y^4$

Test for symmetry with respect to the origin.

7. $x + y = 7$

8. $y = 2x^3$

9. $x = 4$

Consider the graph of $y = |x|$.

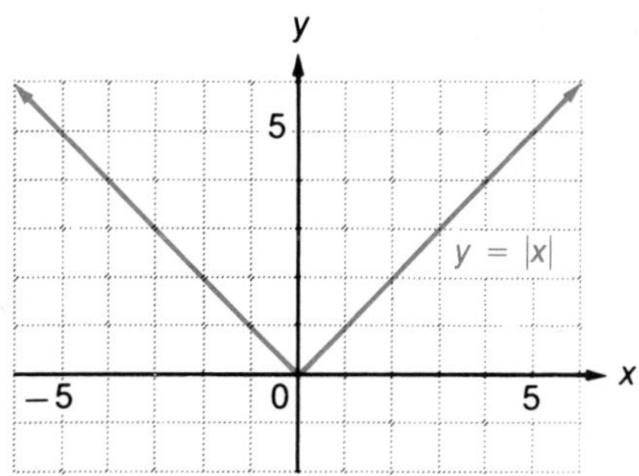

Sketch graphs of the following by translating.

10. $y = |x| + 2$ **11.** $y = |x + 3|$

For each function graph the function, find the vertex, and find the line of symmetry.

12. $f(x) = 2x^2$

13. $f(x) = 2(x - 5)^2$

For each of the following graph the function, find the vertex, find the line of symmetry, and find the maximum or minimum value.

14. $f(x) = 2(x - 5)^2 - 4$

15. $f(x) = -3(x + 1)^2 - 2$

For each function, find standard form and then find the vertex, line of symmetry, and the maximum or minimum value.

16. $f(x) = -x^2 - 6x + 7$

17. $f(x) = 2x^2 - 10x - 7$

18. What is the maximum product of two numbers whose sum is 40? What numbers yield this product?

Find the x-intercepts, if they exist.

19. $f(x) = 2x^2 - 5x + 8$

20. $f(x) = -x^2 - 2x + 2$

21. While Keisha was making popcorn, she found 90 kernels popped during the 3rd minute, 180 during the 5th minute, and 30 during the 7th minute.
  a. Find a quadratic function that fits the data.
  b. Using the function, calculate the number of kernels that popped during the 4th minute.

22. A ball is thrown upward from a rooftop 27 meters high at a velocity of 9.8 m/sec. Find
  a. its maximum height and when it is attained.
  b. when it reaches the ground.

Challenge

23. The sum of the lengths of the base and the height of a triangle is 24 cm. Find the dimensions for which the area is a maximum, and find the maximum area.

14. Vertex: $(5, -4)$
Line of symmetry: $x = 5$
Minimum: -4

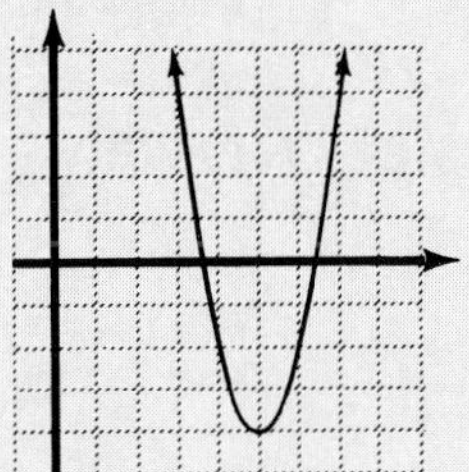

15. Vertex: $(-1, -2)$
Line of symmetry: $x = -1$
Maximum: -2

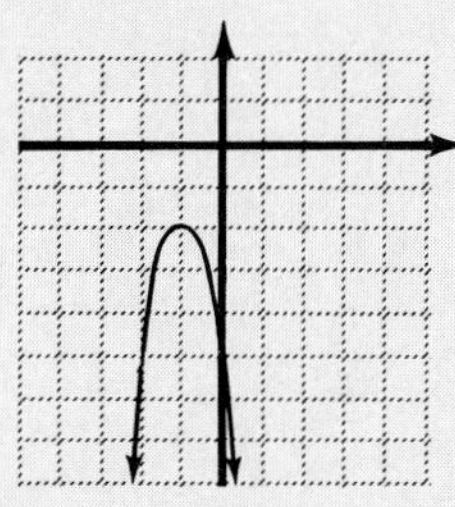

16. $f(x) = -(x + 3)^2 + 16$
Vertex: $(-3, 16)$
Line of symmetry: $x = -3$
Maximum: 16

17. $f(x) = 2\left(x - \frac{5}{2}\right)^2 - \frac{39}{2}$
Vertex: $\left(\frac{5}{2}, -\frac{39}{2}\right)$
Line of symmetry: $x = \frac{5}{2}$
Minimum: $-\frac{39}{2}$

18. 400; 20 and 20

19. None

20. $-1 + \sqrt{3}, -1 - \sqrt{3}$

21. a. $f(t) = -30t^2 + 285t - 495$
b. 165

22. a. 31.9m at 1 sec
b. 3.55 sec

23. $b = h = 12$ cm, 72 cm^2

Test Item Analysis

Item	Lesson
1–9	9-1
10, 11	9-2
12, 13	9-4
14, 15	9-5
16–18	9-6
19, 20	9-7
21–23	9-8

CHAPTER 10 Equations of Second Degree

Chapter Overview

Chapter 10 relates second-degree equations to conic sections. The distance formula is used to develop the equation for a circle. Equations for circles, ellipses, hyperbolas, and parabolas are studied and graphed; standard forms are found by completing the square. Components of each shape, such as the center, foci, vertices, line of symmetry, directrix, and asymptotes, are detailed. Criteria are presented for recognizing the shape of a figure by its given equation. Equations of conics are then determined from their graphs. Systems of second-degree equations are solved both by graphing and algebraically. Problem solving for second-degree equations and the strategy *Simplify the Problem* are included.

Objectives

10-1
- Use the distance formula to find the distance between any two points in a plane.
- Find the coordinates of the midpoint of a segment, given the coordinates of the endpoints.

10-2
- Find the equation of a circle, given the coordinates of the center and the radius.
- Find the coordinates of the center and the radius of a circle, given its equation.
- Find the coordinates of the center and the radius of a circle by first completing the square.

10-3
- Find the vertices and foci, and draw a graph of an ellipse given its equation.
- Find the center, vertices, and foci, and draw a graph of an ellipse by first completing the square.

10-4
- Find the vertices, foci, and asymptotes, and draw a graph of a hyperbola given its equation.
- Find standard form and graph a hyperbola by first completing the square.
- Graph a hyperbola that has an equation of the form $xy = c$.

10-5
- Find the vertex, focus, and directrix, and draw a graph of a parabola, given its equation.
- Find the equation of a parabola, given certain characteristics.
- Find the vertex, focus, and directrix, and graph a parabola by first completing the square.

10-6
- Recognize equations of circles, ellipses, hyperbolas, and parabolas.
- Determine a second-degree equation from its graph.
- Solve systems of second-degree equations graphically.

10-7
- Solve systems having a first-degree and a second-degree equation algebraically.
- Solve systems of second-degree equations algebraically.

10-8
- Solve problems that translate to a system of second-degree equations.

10-9
- Solve problems using the strategy *Simplify the Problem,* and other strategies.

TEACHING CHAPTER 10

Cooperative Learning Opportunities

Cooperative learning groups should help foster students' sense of responsibility. One way to achieve this is to give an open-ended assignment that requires several group meetings with student activity between meetings.

After completing Lessons 10-1 through 10-5, assign students to groups of four with the following roles: (1) discussion leader, responsible for group progress; (2) recorder, responsible for writing down findings and conclusions; (3) materials manager, responsible for the use of special materials, computer, and calculators; (4) timekeeper, keeps track of time and lets the group know if it seems to be slowing down.

The groups should meet three times. At the first meeting they identify a specific application or a historical development in conics that they wish to pursue. The group assigns individual tasks to be accomplished before the next meeting. At the next meeting, the group reviews its data and plans a report. Tasks are again assigned. At the last meeting the group finalizes its report.

Multicultural Note: *Conic Sections Through the Centuries*

Euclid and others of his time discussed conic sections. Appolonius was the first to describe the double cone as the surface generated by a line, indefinite in length, passing through a point and moving around the circumference of a circle. His work, *Conic Sections*, contained 487 propositions in eight books. Several were preserved in Arabic and contributed to the European revival in science and mathematics based on Arabic translation and achievements.

In 17th century Europe, the study of the movement of astronomical bodies, the design of lenses, the motion of projectiles, and the paths of ships all resulted in a renewed interest in conic sections. The conic sections began to be considered not as static slices of a cone or geometric constructions, but as curves in a plane. Coordinate geometry furthered the algebra of conic sections.

In our own day the applications of conic sections have contributed to advances in transportation, communication, medicine, astronomy, and optics.

Alternative Assessment and Communication Ideas

Many students succeed reasonably well in their day to day classroom learning but do not retain very much of what they study. Research has shown that integrated knowledge is more likely to remain in the mind and be available in the future. The conic sections are naturally connected and an alternative assessment can help establish this in students' minds.

Have students answer the following as a take-home paper. Ask for examples of equations and graphs in each case.

(1) How is an ellipse like a circle?
(2) In what way does an ellipse have a center?
(3) How is the center of an ellipse different from the center of a circle?
(4) What in an ellipse corresponds to the radius of a circle?
(5) Devise a formula for the area of an ellipse.
(6) How is a hyperbola similar to an ellipse?
(7) How is a hyperbola different from an ellipse?

Investigations and Projects

Several proofs are given in the early lessons of Chapter 10. They can provide the start for a project on coordinate proofs. Suggest several propositions and show students how to get started. You might also refer them to *Addison-Wesley Geometry* for some ideas. After they have begun, some students may want to investigate theorems of their own.

You can build the activities around the distance formula, which is used in the proofs in the chapter and also plays a role in the development of conic sections. Proof of the following might be used as a start.

(1) Diagonals of a square have the same length.
(2) Diagonals of a square bisect each other.
(3) Diagonals of a square are perpendicular.
(4) Diagonals of a rhombus bisect each other.
(5) The length of a median of a trapezoid is half the length of sum of the basis.
(6) Segments joining the midpoints of opposite sides of a quadrilateral bisect each other.

MANAGING CHAPTER 10

Lesson	PACING CHART (DAYS) Algebra	Algebra w/Finite	Algebra w/Trig	Comprehensive	Opening Activity	Cooperative Activity	Seat or Group Work
10-1	1	1	1	1	First Five Minutes 10-1: **TE** p.430 or ***FFM Transparency Masters*** p.29	Critical Thinking: **SE** p.432	Try This a–d
10-2	1	1	1	1	First Five Minutes 10-2: **TE** p.433 or ***FFM Transparency Masters*** p.30	Explore: **SE** p.433 Critical Thinking: **SE** p.437	Try This a–g
10-3	1	1	1	1	First Five Minutes 10-3: **TE** p.438 or ***FFM Transparency Masters*** p.30	Critical Thinking: **SE** p.443 ✂ Manipulative Activity 10: ***Enrichment*** p.51	Try This a–i
10-4	1	1	1	1	First Five Minutes 10-4: **TE** p.445 or ***FFM Transparency Masters*** p.30	Critical Thinking: **SE** p.450 Strategy Problem Bank 9: ***Problem Bank*** p.10	Try This a–h
10-5	2	1	1	1	First Five Minutes 10-5: **TE** p.452 or ***FFM Transparency Masters*** p.31	Critical Thinking: **SE** p.457	Try This a–i
10-6	2	1	1	1	First Five Minutes 10-6: **TE** p.458 or ***FFM Transparency Masters*** p.31	Critical Thinking: **SE** p.463	Try This a–k
10-7	2	1	1	1	First Five Minutes 10-7: **TE** p.464 or ***FFM Transparency Masters*** p.31	Critical Thinking: **SE** p.467 Looking for Errors 10: ***Enrichment*** p.71	Try This a–h
10-8	1	1	1	0.5	First Five Minutes 10-8: **TE** p.469 or ***FFM Transparency Masters*** p.32	Critical Thinking: **SE** p.471	Try This a–c
10-9	1	1	1	0.5	First Five Minutes 10-9: **TE** p.472 or ***FFM Transparency Masters*** p.32	Problem Solving: **SE** p.474 Strategy Problem Bank 10: ***Problem Bank*** p.11	Problem 1: **SE** p.473
Review	1	1	1	1			
Test	1	1	1	1			

FFM: First Five Minutes SPMR: Skills Practice Mixed Review

MANAGING CHAPTER 10

Enrichment	Review/Assess	Reteach	Technology	Lesson
Critical Thinking 10: ***Enrichment*** p.31	Lesson Quiz: **TE** p. 431	Skills Practice 27, #1–10: ***SPMR*** p.39	Calculator Worksheet 16: ***Technology*** p.18	**10-1**
Looking for Errors 9: ***Enrichment*** p.70	Lesson Quiz: **TE** p.436 Quiz 19: ***Assessment*** p.27	Skills Practice 27, #11–20: ***SPMR*** p.39	Worksheet 16: ***Master Grapher*** pp.69–70, pp.203–204, or pp.339–340	**10-2**
✂ Manipulative Activity 10: ***Enrichment*** p.51	Lesson Quiz: **TE** p.442	Skills Practice 27, #21–28: ***SPMR*** p.39	Worksheet 17: ***Master Grapher*** pp.71–74, pp.205–208, or pp.341–344	**10-3**
Math Point: **TE** p.445 Activity: **SE** p.451	Lesson Quiz: **TE** p.449	Strategy Problem Bank 9: ***Problem Bank*** p.10	Worksheet 18: ***Master Grapher*** pp.75–77, pp.209–211, or pp.345–347	**10-4**
Bonus Topic 10: ***Enrichment*** p.11	Lesson Quiz: **TE** p.455 Quiz 20: ***Assessment*** p.28	Skills Practice 28, #1–25: ***SPMR*** p.40	Worksheet 19: ***Master Grapher*** pp.78–81, pp.212–215, or pp.348–351	**10-5**
Spreadsheet Activity 5: ***Technology*** pp.56–58	Lesson Quiz: **TE** p.461 Mixed Review 19: ***SPMR*** p.83	Skills Practice 29, #1–13: ***SPMR*** p.41	Worksheet 20: ***Master Grapher*** pp.82–85, pp.216–219, or pp.352–355; Spreadsheet Activity 5: ***Technology*** pp.56–58	**10-6**
Looking for Errors 10: ***Enrichment*** p.71	Lesson Quiz: **TE** p.466	Skills Practice 29, #14–19: ***SPMR*** p.41	Worksheet 21: ***Master Grapher*** pp.86–89, pp.220–223, or pp.356–359; Problem for Programmers: **SE** p.468	**10-7**
BASIC Computer Project 9: ***Technology*** p.89	Lesson Quiz: **TE** p.470	Problem Bank 17: ***Problem Bank*** p.38	BASIC Computer Project 9: ***Technology*** p.89	**10-8**
Problem 10: Computer Assisted Problem Solving, **SE** pp.845–846	Mixed Review 20: ***SPMR*** p.84	Strategy Problem Bank 10: ***Problem Bank*** p.11	Problem 10: Computer Assisted Problem Solving, **SE** pp.845–846 BASIC Computer Project 10: ***Technology*** p.90	**10-9**
	Summary and Review: **SE** pp.475–477; Test: **SE** p.477			**Review**
	Chapter 10 Test: ***Assessment*** pp.101–106(reg.), pp.175–176 (adv.); Assessing Strategies 6: ***Assessment*** pp.205–206			**Test**

The solution to the problem posed on the facing page can be found on page 457.

Ready for Equations of Second Degree?

7-1, 7-2 Simplify.

1. $\sqrt{169}$ 13

2. $\sqrt{48}$ $4\sqrt{3}$

8-1 Complete the square.

3. $x^2 - 4x$ $x^2 - 4x + 4$

4. $x^2 + 3x$ $x^2 + 3x + \frac{9}{4}$

3-2, 9-4 Graph.

5. $y = 3x - 1$

6. $y = 3x^2$

4-2 Solve.

7. $6x + 3y = -12$
$2x - y = 6$ $\left(\frac{1}{2}, -5\right)$

8. $3x - 5y = 44$
$y = 4x - 2$ $(-2, -10)$

5-7, 8-1, 8-3 Solve.

9. $x^2 - 9x + 14 = 0$ 2, 7

10. $x^2 = 5$ $\sqrt{5}, -\sqrt{5}$

5.

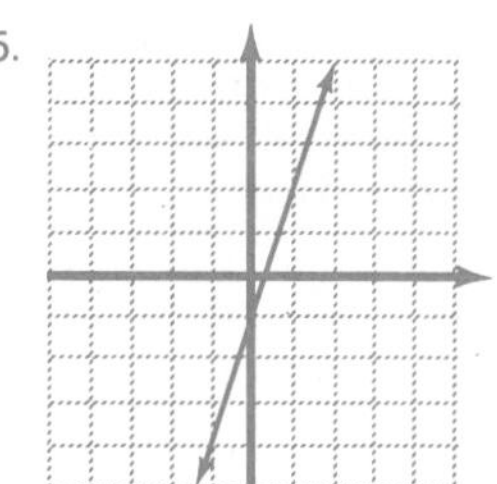

6.

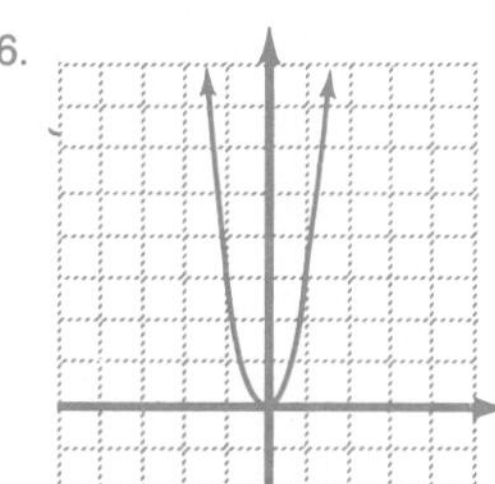

CHAPTER

10

Equations of Second Degree

The cables of a suspension bridge are 50 ft above the roadbed at the towers of the bridge and 10 ft above it in the center of the bridge. The roadbed is 200 ft long. Vertical cables are to be spaced every 20 ft along the bridge. Calculate the lengths of these vertical cables.

10-1

FIRST FIVE MINUTES

The Pythagorean theorem states that if a right triangle has legs of lengths *a* and *b* and a hypotenuse of length *c*, then $a^2 + b^2 = c^2$.

1. Find the length of the hypotenuse of a right triangle with sides of lengths 3 and 4.
   $c^2 = 3^2 + 4^2 = 25$
   $c = 5$
2. If a beetle is 6 feet away from the base of an eight-foot tree, how far is the beetle from the top of the tree?
   $c^2 = 6^2 + 8^2 = 100$
   $c = 10$ feet

Finding Distances

Point out to students that x_1 is read "*x* sub 1."

The proof of Theorem 10-1 is based on the Pythagorean theorem. The negative square root of d^2 is ignored because distance is nonnegative. The theorem is proved for two points on a horizontal or vertical line in Exercise 25.

Key Questions

A first point is at (2, 3) and a second point is at (7, 11).

- What is x_1?
  2
- What is y_2?
  11
- What is $y_2 - y_1$?
  8
- What is $(x_1 - x_2)^2$?
  25
- Which is larger, $(x_1 - x_2)^2$ or $(x_2 - x_1)^2$?
  They are equal.

Chalkboard Example

1. Find the distance between (7, 8) and (3, 5).
   $d = \sqrt{(7 - 3)^2 + (8 - 5)^2}$
   $= \sqrt{25} = 5$
2. Find the distance between (−5, 5) and (−3, −1).
   $d = \sqrt{(-5 - (-3))^2 + (5 - (-1))^2}$
   $= \sqrt{40}$
   $= 2\sqrt{10}$

10-1 Coordinate Geometry

Finding Distances

Objective: Use the distance formula to find the distance between any two points in the plane.

The **distance formula** can be used to find the distance between two points when we know the coordinates of the points.

Theorem 10-1

The Distance Formula

The distance between any two points (x_1, y_1) and (x_2, y_2), is given by

$$d = \sqrt{(x_1 - x_2)^2 + (y_1 - y_2)^2}$$

Proof of Theorem 10-1

We prove this theorem for the case where the points are not on a horizontal or vertical line.

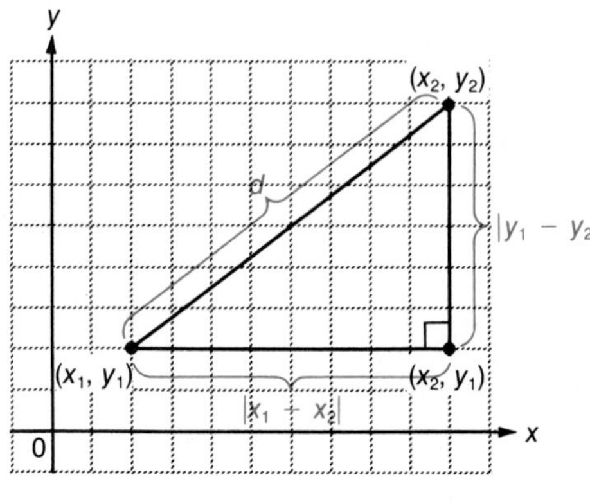

Consider any two points (x_1, y_1) and (x_2, y_2) not on a horizontal or vertical line. These points are vertices of a right triangle as shown. The other vertex is (x_2, y_1). The legs of the triangle have lengths $|x_1 - x_2|$, and $|y_1 - y_2|$. By the Pythagorean theorem, $d^2 = |x_1 - x_2|^2 + |y_1 - y_2|^2$. Since squares of numbers are never negative, $d^2 = (x_1 - x_2)^2 + (y_1 - y_2)^2$. Finding the principal square root, we have $d = \sqrt{(x_1 - x_2)^2 + (y_1 - y_2)^2}$.

EXAMPLE 1 Find the distance between the points (8, 7) and (3, −5).

We substitute the coordinates into the distance formula.

$$\begin{aligned} d &= \sqrt{(8 - 3)^2 + [7 - (-5)]^2} \\ &= \sqrt{25 + 144} \\ &= \sqrt{169} \\ &= 13 \end{aligned}$$

Try This Find the distance between the points.

a. $(-5, 3)$ and $(2, -7)$ $\sqrt{149}$ **b.** $(3, 3)$ and $(-3, -3)$ $6\sqrt{2}$

Midpoints of Segments

Objective: Find the coordinates of the midpoint of a segment, given the coordinates of the endpoints.

The coordinates of the midpoint of a segment can be found by averaging the coordinates of the endpoints. We can use the distance formula to verify a formula for finding the coordinates of the midpoint of a segment when the coordinates of the endpoints are known.

Theorem 10-2

The Midpoint Formula

If the coordinates of the endpoints of a segment are (x_1, y_1) and (x_2, y_2), then the coordinates of the midpoint are

$$\left(\frac{x_1 + x_2}{2}, \frac{y_1 + y_2}{2}\right)$$

EXAMPLE 2 Find the coordinates of the midpoint of the segment with endpoints $(-3, 5)$ and $(4, -7)$.

Using the midpoint formula, we get $\left(\frac{-3 + 4}{2}, \frac{5 + (-7)}{2}\right)$, or $\left(\frac{1}{2}, -1\right)$.

Try This Find the coordinates of the midpoints of the segments having the following endpoints.

c. $(-2, 1)$ and $(5, -6)$ $\left(\frac{3}{2}, -\frac{5}{2}\right)$ **d.** $(9, -6)$ and $(9, -4)$ $(9, -5)$

10-1 EXERCISES

A

Find the distance between the points.

1. $(-3, -2)$ and $(1, 1)$ **2.** $(5, 9)$ and $(-1, 6)$ **3.** $(0, -7)$ and $(3, -4)$
4. $(2, 2)$ and $(-2, -2)$ **5.** $(9, 5)$ and $(6, 1)$ **6.** $(1, 10)$ and $(7, 2)$
7. $(5, 6)$ and $(5, -2)$ **8.** $(5, 6)$ and $(0, 6)$ **9.** $(a, -3)$ and $(2a, 5)$
10. $(5, 2k)$ and $(-3, k)$ **11.** $(0, 0)$ and (a, b) **12.** $(\sqrt{2}, \sqrt{3})$ and $(0, 0)$
13. $(\sqrt{a}, \sqrt{b})$ and $(-\sqrt{a}, \sqrt{b})$ **14.** $(c - d, c + d)$ and $(c + d, d - c)$

Find the coordinates of the midpoint of the segments having the following endpoints.

15. $(-4, 7)$ and $(3, -9)$ $\left(-\frac{1}{2}, -1\right)$ **16.** $(4, 5)$ and $(6, -7)$ $(5, -1)$

Midpoints of Segments

Point out that the distances from the midpoint to each endpoint are equal. Have students verify this for Example 2.

Note that the proof of Theorem 10-2 is given as Exercise 26.

Chalkboard Example

1. Find the midpoint of the segment with endpoints (1, 6) and (5, 8).
$\left(\frac{(1 + 5)}{2}, \frac{(6 + 8)}{2}\right) = (3, 7)$

LESSON QUIZ

1. Find the distance between (8, 12) and (2, 4).
10
2. Find the midpoint of the segment with endpoints (2, 5) and (4, 7).
(3, 6)
3. Find an expression for the distance from the point (a, b) to the point (c, h).
$d = \sqrt{(a - c)^2 + (b - h)^2}$

Assignment Guide

Algebra: 1–22 e/o, MR

Alg w/Finite or Trig: 1–22 m3, 23–29 e/o, 30, MR

Comprehensive: 1–29 m3, 30–33, MR

ADDITIONAL ANSWERS

Exercises

1. 5
2. $3\sqrt{5}$
3. $3\sqrt{2}$
4. $4\sqrt{2}$
5. 5
6. 10
7. 8
8. 5
9. $\sqrt{a^2 + 64}$
10. $\sqrt{64 + k^2}$
11. $\sqrt{a^2 + b^2}$
12. $\sqrt{5}$
13. $2\sqrt{a}$
14. $2\sqrt{d^2 + c^2}$

Exercises

17. $\left(-\frac{7}{2}, -\frac{15}{2}\right)$ 18. $\left(\frac{5}{2}, \frac{5}{2}\right)$

19. (4, 4)   20. $\left(\frac{1}{2}, 0\right)$

21. $(a, 0)$ 22. $(0, d)$

For Exercises 25–27, see Teacher's Answer Section.

30. a. $2x_m - x_1, 2y_m - y_1)$
b. $(-17, 13)$

31. The vertices are $O(0, 0)$, $H(0, h)$, and $B(b, 0)$. Then $P = \left(\frac{b}{2}, \frac{h}{2}\right)$. Use the distance formula to find the distances between P and H, P and B, and P and O.

32. The vertices are $O(0, 0)$, $A(a, b)$, $B(c, d)$, and $C(k, 0)$. The midpoints are $M_1\left(\frac{a}{2}, \frac{b}{2}\right)$, $M_2\left(\frac{a+c}{2}, \frac{b+d}{2}\right)$, $M_3\left(\frac{c+k}{2}, \frac{d}{2}\right)$, and $M_4\left(\frac{k}{2}, 0\right)$. Find the slopes of $\overline{M_1M_2}$, $\overline{M_2M_3}$, $\overline{M_3M_4}$, $\overline{M_4M_1}$, and compare. Also, find the lengths of the segments and compare. The opposite sides of a parallelogram are parallel and have equal lengths.

33. The distance between (a, b) and (c, d) is $\sqrt{(a-c)^2 + (b-d)^2}$.
a. The distance between (a, d) and (c, b) is $\sqrt{(a-c)^2 + (d-b)^2}$.
b. The distance between (b, a) and (d, c) is $\sqrt{(b-d)^2 + (a-c)^2}$.
c. The distance between (b, c) and (d, a) is $\sqrt{(b-d)^2 + (c-a)^2}$. Since $(a-c)^2 = (c-a)^2$ and $(b-d)^2 = (d-b)^2$, the distances are all the same.

Mixed Review

34. 5, −8   35. −6, 0
36. −3, −2   37. No
38. Yes   39. No
40. No
41. $x^2 - 6x + 9$
42. $y^2 + 14y + 49$
43. $x^2 + 3x + \frac{9}{4}$
44. $y^2 - 9y + \frac{81}{4}$
45. $m^2 + 7.4m + 13.69$
46. $a^2 - 3.2a + 2.56$
47. $c^2 - c + \frac{1}{4}$

17. $(2, -5)$ and $(-9, -10)$ **18.** $(8, -4)$ and $(-3, 9)$ **19.** $(2, 2)$ and $(6, 6)$
20. $(-2, 0)$ and $(3, 0)$ **21.** (a, b) and $(a, -b)$ **22.** $(-c, d)$ and (c, d)

B

The converse of the Pythagorean theorem is true. That is, if the sides of a triangle have lengths a, b, and c, and $a^2 + b^2 = c^2$, then the triangle is a right triangle. Determine whether the points whose coordinates are given are vertices of a right triangle.

23. $(9, 6), (-1, 2), (1, -3)$ Yes **24.** $(-8, -5), (6, 1), (-4, 5)$ Yes

25. Prove that the distance formula, Theorem 10-1, holds when two points are on either a vertical or a horizontal line.

26. Prove the midpoint formula, Theorem 10-2.

27. Prove that the diagonals of a rectangle bisect each other. (Hint: Locate the rectangle on the x- and y-axes of a graph as shown.)

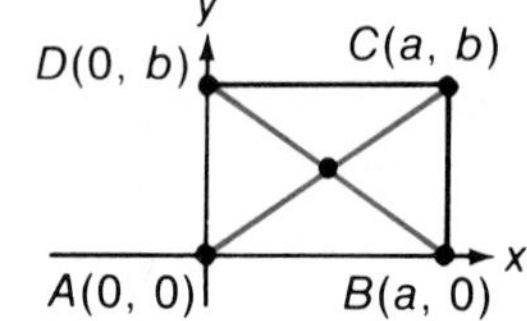

28. Find the point on the x-axis that is equidistant from the points whose coordinates are $(1, 3)$ and $(8, 4)$. (5, 0)

29. Find the point on the y-axis that is equidistant from the points whose coordinates are $(-2, 0)$ and $(4, 6)$. (0, 4)

30. ***Critical Thinking*** A segment has an endpoint at (x_1, y_1) and a midpoint at (x_m, y_m).
a. What are the coordinates of the other endpoint?
b. Find the other endpoint for a segment with an endpoint $(3, -7)$ and midpoint $(-7, 3)$.

Challenge

31. Consider any right triangle with base b and height h, situated as shown. Show that the midpoint of the hypotenuse P is equidistant from the three vertices of the triangle.

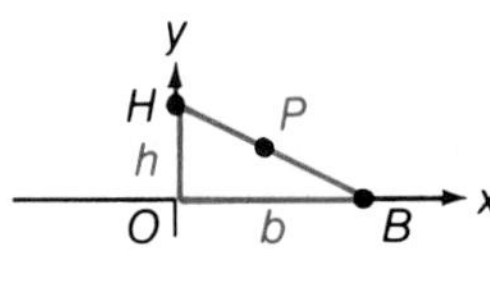

32. Consider any quadrilateral situated as shown. Show that the segments joining the midpoints of the sides, in order as shown, form a parallelogram.

33. Show that the distance between points with coordinates (a, b) and (c, d) is the same as the distance between points with the following coordinates.
a. (a, d) and (c, b) **b.** (b, a) and (d, c) **c.** (b, c) and (d, a)

Mixed Review

Solve. **34.** $x(x + 7) = 4(x + 10)$ **35.** $4y^2 + 24y = 0$ **36.** $m^2 + 5m + 6 = 0$

Test for symmetry with respect to the origin. **37.** $y = |x| + 1$ **38.** $5y^4 - 2x^2 = 1$
39. $x - y = 9$ **40.** $3n^2 - 4m = n$

Complete the square. **41.** $x^2 - 6x$ **42.** $y^2 + 14y$ **43.** $x^2 + 3x$
44. $y^2 - 9y$ **45.** $m^2 + 7.4m$ **46.** $a^2 - 3.2a$ **47.** $c^2 - c$

10-2 Conic Sections: Circles

Master Grapher Worksheet 16, *Conic Sections: Circles*, can be used for lesson closure.

Explore

Graph each equation.

$x^2 + y^2 = 16$ Circle $x^2 + 4y^2 = 16$ Ellipse $x^2 - y^2 = 16$ Hyperbola $x^2 + y = 16$ Parabola

Study and contrast the graphs. For each successive graph, explain why it might differ from the first graph.

The nonempty intersection of any plane with a cone is called a **conic section**. Some conic sections are shown below.

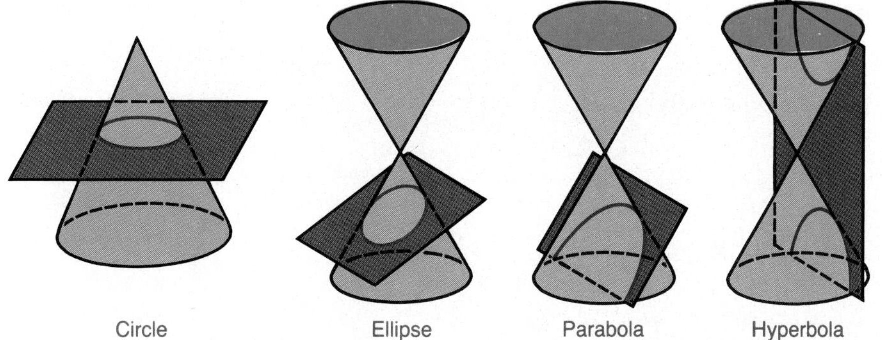

Circle   Ellipse   Parabola   Hyperbola

In this chapter we will study certain equations of second degree and their graphs. Graphs of most such equations are conic sections.

Equations of Circles

Objective: Find the equation of a circle, given the coordinates of the center and the radius.

Some equations of second degree have graphs that are circles. A circle is defined as follows.

Definition

A **circle** is the set of all points in a plane that are at a constant distance from a fixed point in that plane. The fixed point is the **center** of the circle.

10-2

FIRST FIVE MINUTES

1. Find the distance between (4, 8) and (16, 13).
   $d = 13$
2. Find the distance between $(-2, 3)$ and $(1, -1)$.
   $d = 5$
3. Find the midpoint of the segment with endpoints (3, 7) and (5, 9).
   (4, 8)

EXPLORE

For the ellipse, students should note that the coefficients of the variables are not equal. For the hyperbola, they should note that the difference rather than the sum of x^2 and y^2 is used. For the parabola, they should note that the variables are given with different powers.

Equations of Circles

Emphasize that the center of a circle is not part of the circle. Likewise, (0, 0) does not satisfy $x^2 + y^2 = r^2$.

Remind students that replacing x by $x - h$ and y by $y - k$ in an equation yields an equation whose graph is the same as the original equation, but shifted right by h and shifted up by k.

In Example 1, you may want to have students find any two points on the circle by substituting a value for x and then solving for y.

The proof of Theorem 10-4 is analogous to that of Theorem 10-3, with (h, k) used as the center rather than (0, 0).

Avoiding Common Errors

Emphasize that the right-hand term in the equation is the radius *squared*. Students often forget to take the square root to get the radius.

Key Questions

- If (3, 4) is a point on a circle with radius 5, how far is it from the center?
  5
- Can $(3, -1)$ be on a circle centered at the origin with radius 6?
  No

Chalkboard Examples

1. Find the equation of the circle with center at (0, 0) and radius 3.
   $x^2 + y^2 = 3^2$
   $x^2 + y^2 = 9$
2. Find the equation of the circle with center at (2, 3) and radius 6.
   $(x - 2)^2 + (y - 3)^2 = 36$

We first consider an equation for a circle centered at the origin.

Theorem 10-3

The equation (in standard form) of the circle centered at the origin with radius r is $x^2 + y^2 = r^2$.

Proof of Theorem 10-3

We must prove that a point (x, y) is on the circle centered at the origin with radius r if and only if $x^2 + y^2 = r^2$. To prove a sentence, *P if and only if Q*, we must prove *If P, then Q*, and *If Q, then P*. Thus there are two parts to the proof.

1. Assume (x, y) is on the circle. Then it is a distance r from (0, 0). By the distance formula, we get the following.

   $$r = \sqrt{(x - 0)^2 + (y - 0)^2}$$
   $$r^2 = x^2 + y^2$$

   We have now shown that if (x, y) is on the circle, then $x^2 + y^2 = r^2$.

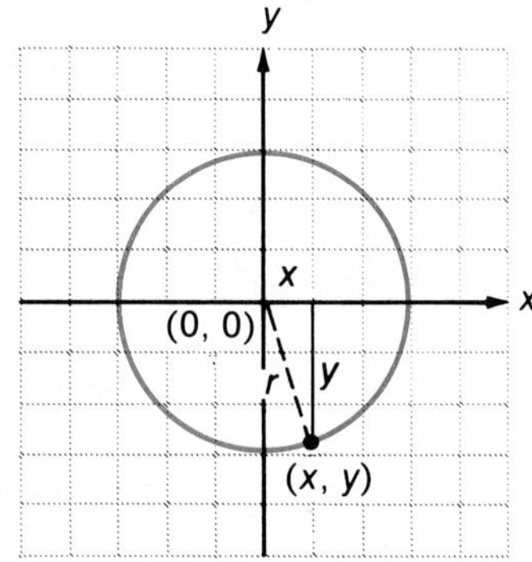

2. Now assume $x^2 + y^2 = r^2$ is true for a point (x, y). This can be expressed as

   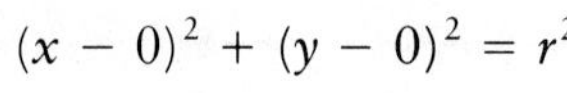

   $$(x - 0)^2 + (y - 0)^2 = r^2$$

   Finding the principal square root we have

   $$\sqrt{(x - 0)^2 + (y - 0)^2} = r$$

   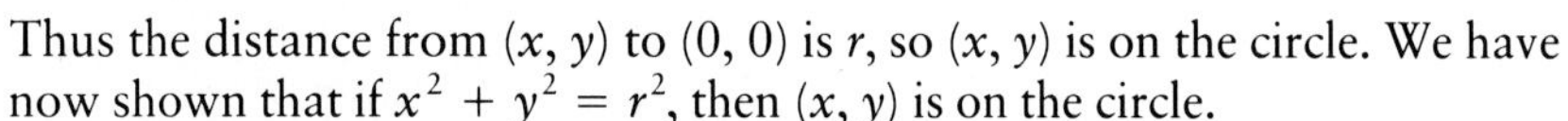

   Thus the distance from (x, y) to (0, 0) is r, so (x, y) is on the circle. We have now shown that if $x^2 + y^2 = r^2$, then (x, y) is on the circle.

Thus the two parts of the proof together show that the equation $x^2 + y^2 = r^2$ gives *all* the points of the circle, *and no others*.

EXAMPLE 1 Find an equation of a circle with center at (0, 0) and radius $\sqrt{5}$.

$x^2 + y^2 = r^2$ Standard form for a circle centered at the origin

$x^2 + y^2 = (\sqrt{5})^2$ Substituting $\sqrt{5}$ for r

$x^2 + y^2 = 5$

Consider an equation for a circle with its center anywhere in the coordinate plane.

Theorem 10-4

The equation (in standard form) of a circle with center (h, k) and radius r is $(x - h)^2 + (y - k)^2 = r^2$.

EXAMPLE 2 Find an equation of a circle with center at $(-1, 3)$ and radius $\sqrt{2}$.

$[x - (-1)]^2 + (y - 3)^2 = (\sqrt{2})^2$ Standard form

$(x + 1)^2 + (y - 3)^2 = 2$ Simplifying

Try This Find an equation of a circle with center and radius as given.
See Additional Answers.

a. Center: $(0, 0)$; radius: $\sqrt{6}$

b. Center: $(-3, 7)$; radius: 5

c. Center: $(5, -2)$: radius: $\sqrt{3}$

d. Center: $(-2, -6)$; radius: $2\sqrt{7}$

Finding the Center and Radius

Objective: Find the coordinates of the center and the radius of a circle, given its equation.

EXAMPLE 3 Find the center and radius of $(x - 2)^2 + (y + 3)^2 = 16$. Then graph the circle.

We first write standard form,
$(x - 2)^2 + [y - (-3)]^2 = 4^2$.
The center is $(2, -3)$ and the radius is 4.
We then draw the graph using a compass.

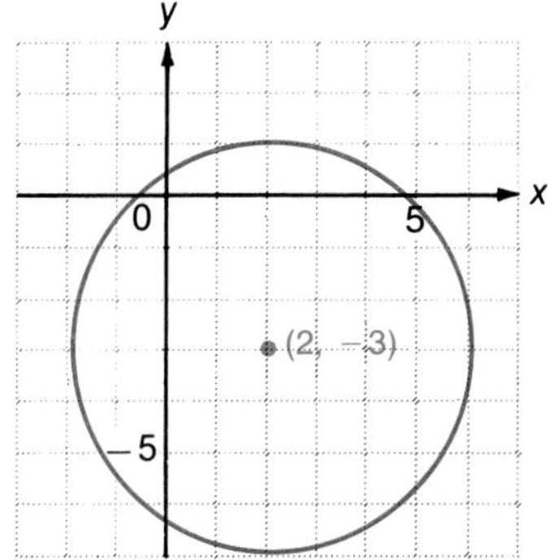

Try This

e. Find the center and radius of $(x + 1)^2 + (y - 3)^2 = 4$. Then graph the circle.
$(-1, 3)$, 2 For graph, see Selected Answers.

Finding Standard Form by Completing the Square

Objective: Find the coordinates of the center and the radius of a circle by first completing the square.

Completing the square allows us to find the standard form for the equation of a circle.

EXAMPLE 4 Find the center and radius of $x^2 + y^2 + 8x - 2y + 15 = 0$.

We complete the squares to obtain standard form.

Finding the Center and Radius

Point out that the left side of an equation of a circle in standard form equals zero when the coordinates of the center are substituted. Since the right side cannot be zero, the center cannot be on the circle.

Chalkboard Example

1. Find the center and radius of the circle.
$(x - 7)^2 + (y - 3)^2 = 25$
Write the equation in standard form.
$(x - 7)^2 + (y - 3)^2 = 5^2$
The center is (7, 3). The radius is 5.

Finding Standard Form by Completing the Square

You may want to review completing the square before beginning this section.

Note that equations such as $(x + 4)^2 + (y - 1)^2 = 2$ will be regarded as standard form from now on; it is understood that the equation could be written as $[x - (-4)]^2 + (y - 1)^2 = (\sqrt{2})^2$.

Key Questions

- What term should be added to make $x^2 + 2x$ a perfect square?
1
- What term should be added to make $x^2 + 10x$ a perfect square?
25

Chalkboard Example

1. Find the radius and center of the circle.
$x^2 + 2x + y^2 + 10y = 23$
Complete the squares by adding 1 and 25 to both sides.
$x^2 + 2x + 1 + y^2 + 10y + 25 = 49$
$(x + 1)^2 + (y + 5)^2 = 7^2$
The center is $(-1, -5)$.
The radius is 7.

LESSON QUIZ

1. Find an equation for the circle with center (5, 9) and radius 7.
   $(x - 5)^2 + (y - 9)^2 = 49$
2. Find the center and radius of the circle.
   $(x + 2)^2 + (y - 5)^2 = 64$
   The center is $(-2, 5)$.
   The radius is 8.
3. Find the center and radius of the circle.
   $x^2 + 6x + y^2 - 8y = 0$
   The center is $(-3, 4)$.
   The radius is 5.

Assignment Guide
Algebra: 1–18 e/o, MR

Alg w/Finite or Trig: 1–18 m3, 19–27 e/o, 28, MR

Comprehensive: 1–27 m3, 28, 29–34 e/o, MR

ADDITIONAL ANSWERS

Try This

a. $x^2 + y^2 = 6$
b. $(x + 3)^2 + (y - 7)^2 = 25$
c. $(x - 5)^2 + (y + 2)^2 = 3$
d. $(x + 2)^2 + (y + 6)^2 = 28$

Exercises

For graphs of Exercises 5–12, see Teacher's Answer Section.

5. $(-1, -3), 2$
6. $(2, -3), 1$
7. $(8, -3), 2\sqrt{10}$
8. $(-5, 1), 5\sqrt{3}$
9. $(0, 0), \sqrt{2}$
10. $(0, 0), \sqrt{3}$
11. $(5, 0), \frac{1}{2}$
12. $(0, 1), \frac{1}{5}$

$$(x^2 + 8x \quad\quad) + (y^2 - 2y \quad\quad) = -15$$
$$(x^2 + 8x + 16) + (y^2 - 2y \quad\quad) = -15 + 16 \qquad \text{Completing the square for } x^2 + 8x$$
$$(x^2 + 8x + 16) + (y^2 - 2y + 1) = -15 + 16 + 1 \qquad \text{Completing the square for } y^2 - 2y$$
$$(x + 4)^2 + (y - 1)^2 = 2 \qquad \text{Simplifying}$$

In standard form, the equation is $(x - (-4))^2 + (y - 1)^2 = (\sqrt{2})^2$. The center is $(-4, 1)$, the radius is $\sqrt{2}$.

Try This

f. Find the center and radius of the circle $x^2 + y^2 - 14x + 4y - 11 = 0$. $(7, -2), 8$

g. Find the center and radius of the circle $x^2 + y^2 - 12x - 8y + 27 = 0$. $(6, 4), 5$

10-2 EXERCISES

A

Find an equation of a circle with center and radius as given.

1. Center: (0, 0); radius: 7 $x^2 + y^2 = 49$

2. Center: (0, 0); radius: π $x^2 + y^2 = \pi^2$

3. Center: $(-2, 7)$; radius: $\sqrt{5}$ $(x + 2)^2 + (y - 7)^2 = 5$

4. Center: (5, 6); radius: $2\sqrt{3}$ $(x - 5)^2 + (y - 6)^2 = 12$

Find the center and radius of each circle. Then graph the circle.

5. $(x + 1)^2 + (y + 3)^2 = 4$

6. $(x - 2)^2 + (y + 3)^2 = 1$

7. $(x - 8)^2 + (y + 3)^2 = 40$

8. $(x + 5)^2 + (y - 1)^2 = 75$

9. $x^2 + y^2 = 2$

10. $x^2 + y^2 = 3$

11. $(x - 5)^2 + y^2 = \frac{1}{4}$

12. $x^2 + (y - 1)^2 = \frac{1}{25}$

Find the center and radius of each circle.

13. $x^2 + y^2 + 8x - 6y - 15 = 0$

14. $x^2 + y^2 + 6x - 4y - 15 = 0$

15. $x^2 + y^2 - 8x + 2y + 13 = 0$

16. $x^2 + y^2 + 6x + 4y + 12 = 0$

17. $x^2 + y^2 - 4x = 0$

18. $x^2 + y^2 + 10y - 75 = 0$

B

Find an equation of a circle satisfying the given conditions.

19. Center (0, 0), containing $(-3, 4)$ $x^2 + y^2 = 25$

20. Center $(3, -2)$, containing $(11, -2)$ $(x - 3)^2 + (y + 2)^2 = 64$

21. Center (2, 4), tangent (touching at one point) to the x-axis $(x - 2)^2 + (y - 4)^2 = 16$

22. Center $(-3, -2)$, tangent to the y-axis $(x + 3)^2 + (y + 2)^2 = 9$

23. For the circle with center (1, 2) and radius 9, find the x- and y-intercepts. $1 \pm \sqrt{77}, 2 \pm 4$

24. Find an equation of a circle such that the endpoints of a diameter are $(5, -3)$ and $(-3, 7)$. $(x - 1)^2 + (y - 2)^2 = 41$

25. For the circle with equation $(x - 2)^2 + (y + 3)^2 = 9$, find the x- and y-intercepts. 2, $-3 \pm \sqrt{5}$

26. A unit circle is a circle with radius of 1.

Determine whether each of the following points lies on the unit circle $x^2 + y^2 = 1$.

a. $(0, -1)$ Yes **b.** $\left(\frac{\sqrt{3}}{2}, -\frac{1}{2}\right)$ Yes

c. $(\sqrt{2} + \sqrt{3}, 0)$ No **d.** $\left(\frac{\pi}{4}, \frac{4}{\pi}\right)$ No

27. What is the graph of $x^2 + y^2 = r^2$ when $r = 0$? The origin

28. ***Critical Thinking***

a. Graph $x^2 + y^2 = 4$. Is this relation a function?

b. Graph $y = \sqrt{4 - x^2}$. Find the domain and range. Is this relation a function?

c. Graph $y = -\sqrt{4 - x^2}$. Find the domain and range. Is this relation a function?

d. Solve $x^2 + y^2 = r^2$ for y. Is the result a function?

e. How can a computer program graph $x^2 + y^2 = r^2$ if it can only graph functions?

Challenge

29. Prove that $\angle ABC$ is a right angle. Assume point B is on the circle whose radius is a and whose center is at the origin.

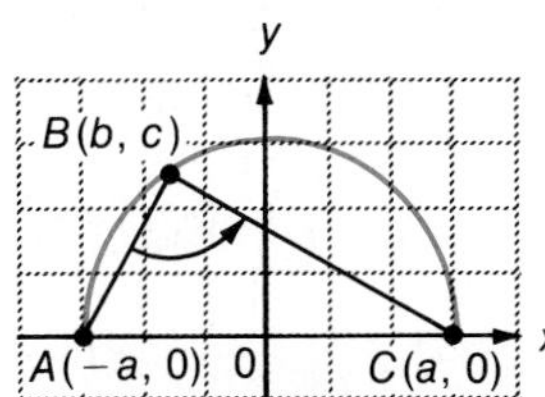

30. Write the equation for a circle that has area 25π and contains the points (2, 2) and (2,10). $(x + 1)^2 + (y - 6)^2 = 25$ or $(x - 5)^2 + (y - 6)^2 = 25$

Graph these inequalities.

31. $x^2 + y^2 \le 16$ 32. $x^2 + y^2 > 25$ 33. $(x + 1)^2 + (y - 3)^2 \le 16$

34. Prove Theorem 10-4.

Mixed Review

Test for symmetry with respect to the axes. 35. $3y^2 = 5x + 1$ 36. $y^2 - x^2 = 1$

37. $y^3 = 5x^2 - 7$

Find the x-intercepts. 38. $f(x) = 4x^2 - 2x + 1$ 39. $f(x) = x^2 - 6x + 5$

Find the quadratic function that fits each set of data points.

40. $(1, -2), (-1, 8), (2, -1)$ 41. $(1, -4), (2, -4), (-1, 8)$

Solve. 42. $x(2x - 7) + 30 = (x + 9)(x - 2)$ 43. $8x^2 - 14x - 15 = 0$

44. $2 + \sqrt{x} = x$ 45. $2\sqrt{x} = x - 3$ 46. $4\sqrt{x} = x - 12$ 47. $x^4 - 8x^2 = 0$

48. A parking garage was 84% full. After 37 cars enter and 23 cars leave the garage, it is 91% full. How many cars does the garage hold?

13. $(-4, 3), 2\sqrt{10}$
14. $(-3, 2), 2\sqrt{7}$
15. $(4, -1), 2$
16. $(-3, -2), 1$
17. $(2, 0), 2$
18. $(0, -5), 10$

For graphs of Exercises 28 and 31–33, see Teacher's Answer Section.

28. a. No
b. Domain: $\{x \mid -2 \le x \le 2\}$ Range: $\{y \mid 0 \le y \le 2\}$ Yes, it is a function.
c. Domain: $\{x \mid -2 \le x \le 2\}$ Range: $\{y \mid -2 \le y \le 0\}$ Yes, it is a function.
d. $y \pm \sqrt{r^2 - x^2}$; no
e. It should graph $y = \sqrt{r^2 - x^2}$ and then $y = -\sqrt{r^2 - x^2}$.

29. From the equation of a circle we have $b^2 + c^2 = a^2$; $c^2 = a^2 - b^2$; the slope of $\overline{AB}$ is $\frac{c}{b + a}$ and the slope of $\overline{BC}$ is $\frac{c}{b - a}$; since $\frac{c}{b + a} \cdot \frac{c}{b - a} = \frac{c^2}{b^2 - a^2} = \frac{a^2 - b^2}{b^2 - a^2} = -1$, $\overline{AB}$ and $\overline{BC}$ are perpendicular and angle ABC is a right angle.

34. If (x, y) is any point on the circle, its distance to the center, (h, k), is $\sqrt{(x - h)^2 + (y - k)^2}$, which must equal r. Thus $\sqrt{(x - h)^2 + (y - k)^2} = r$, so $(x - h)^2 + (y - k)^2 = r^2$.

Now assume that $(x - h)^2 + (y - k)^2 = r^2$ is true for (x, y). Finding the principal square root, $\sqrt{(x - h)^2 + (y - k)^2} = r$, so the distance from (x, y) to (h, k) is r. Thus (x, y) is on the circle.

Mixed Review

35. x-axis
36. Both
37. y-axis
38. None
39. (5, 0), (1, 0)
40. $f(x) = 2x^2 - 5x + 1$
41. $f(x) = 2x^2 - 6x$
42. 6, 8
43. $\frac{5}{2}, -\frac{3}{4}$
44. 4
45. 9
46. 36
47. $2\sqrt{2}, 0, -2\sqrt{2}$
48. 200

10-3

FIRST FIVE MINUTES

1. Find the equation of the circle with center at (9, 2) and radius 2.
   $(x - 9)^2 + (y - 2)^2 = 4$
2. Find the center and radius of the circle.
   $(x - 10)^2 + (y + 3)^2 = 100$
   The center is (10, −3).
   The radius is 10.
3. Find the center and radius of the circle.
   $x^2 + 12x + y^2 + 4y = 9$
   $x^2 + 12x + 36 + y^2 + 4y + 4 = 49$
   $(x + 6)^2 + (y + 2)^2 = 7^2$
   The center is (−6, −2).
   The radius is 7.

Equations of Ellipses

An ellipse can be drawn on the chalkboard using string, two large paper clips, and masking tape. Cut a piece of string about one yard long. Bend the center of each paper clip upward, and tie an end of the string onto each as shown.

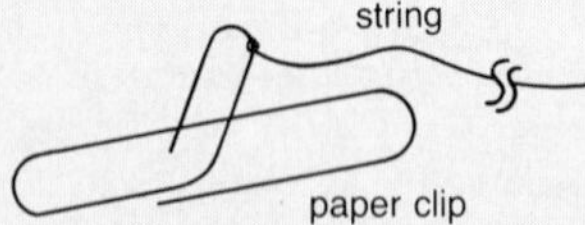

Tape the paper clips to the chalkboard, leaving plenty of slack in the string. Pull the chalk taut against the string from underneath and draw the top of the ellipse, then draw the bottom of the ellipse by pushing against the string from above.

Emphasize that the ellipse has a major axis of length $2a$, and a minor axis of length $2b$.

You may want to show students the following proof that $r_1 + r_2$ = length of major axis.

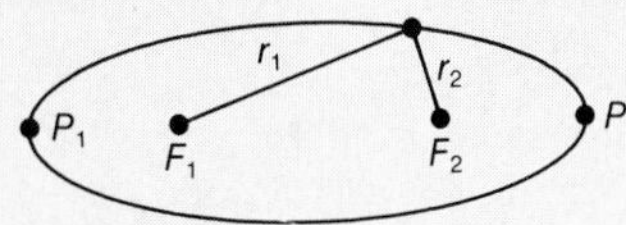

$r_1 + r_2$
$= F_1P_2 + F_2P_2$
$= F_1P_2 + F_1P_1 \quad (F_2P_2 = F_1P_1)$
= length of major axis

In Theorem 10-5, $c^2 = a^2 - b^2$ regardless of the order relation between a and b.

Point out that the vertices of an ellipse centered at (0, 0) are $(\pm a, 0)$ and $(0, \pm b)$ if the ellipse is horizontal and $(\pm b, 0)$ and $(0, \pm a)$ if vertical.

10-3 Ellipses

Master Grapher Worksheet 17, *Conic Sections: Ellipses*, can be used for lesson closure.

An interesting attraction found in museums is the whispering gallery. It is elliptical. Persons with their heads at the foci can whisper and hear each other clearly, while persons at other positions cannot hear them. This happens because sound waves emanating from one focus are reflected to the other focus, being concentrated there.

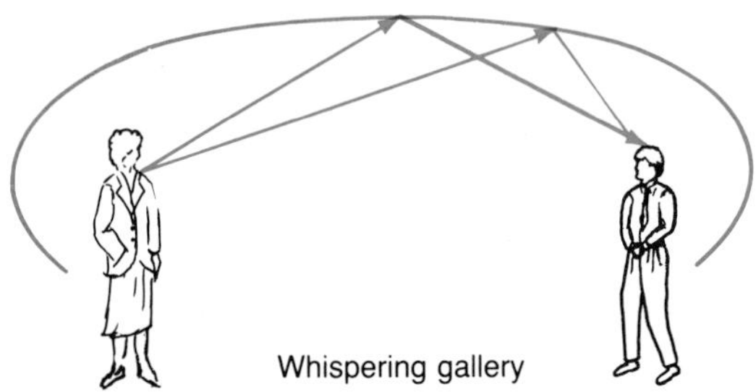

Whispering gallery

Equations of Ellipses

Objective: Find the vertices and the foci, and draw a graph of an ellipse, given its equation.

Some equations of second degree have graphs that are **ellipses.**

Definition

An ellipse is the set of all points P in a plane such that the sum of the distances from P to two fixed points F_1 and F_2 is constant. Each fixed point is called a **focus** (plural: **foci**) of the ellipse. r_1 and r_2 are called **focal radii.**

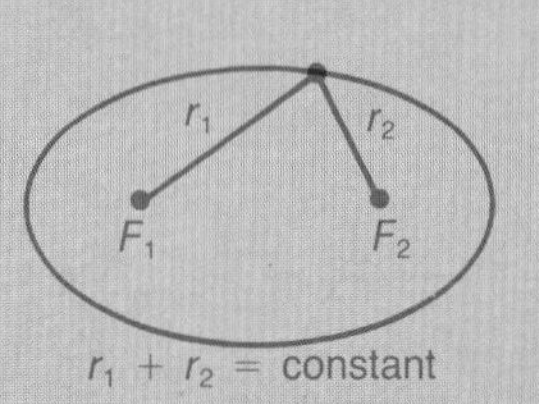

$r_1 + r_2$ = constant

Ellipses have many other applications. Earth satellites travel around the earth in elliptical orbits. The planets of the solar system travel around the sun in elliptical orbits with the sun located at one focus.

An ellipse has two axes of symmetry. The larger axis is the **major axis,** and the shorter axis is the **minor axis.** The axes are perpendicular at the midpoint of each axis, the **center** of the ellipse. The foci lie on the major axis. The ellipse intersects the major and minor axes at the **vertices.**

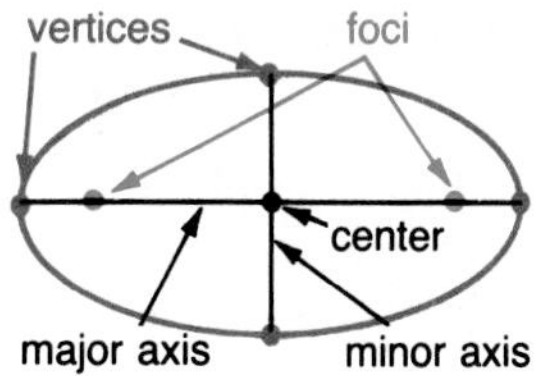

We first consider an equation of an ellipse whose center is at the origin with foci on either the x- or y-axes.

For foci on the x-axis, the ellipse is horizontal.

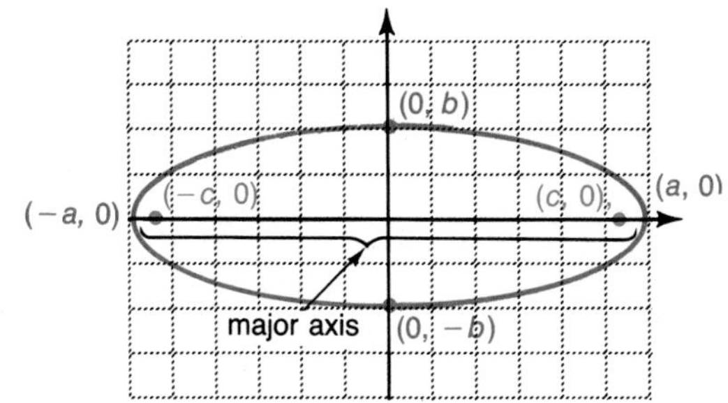

For foci on the y-axis, the ellipse is vertical.

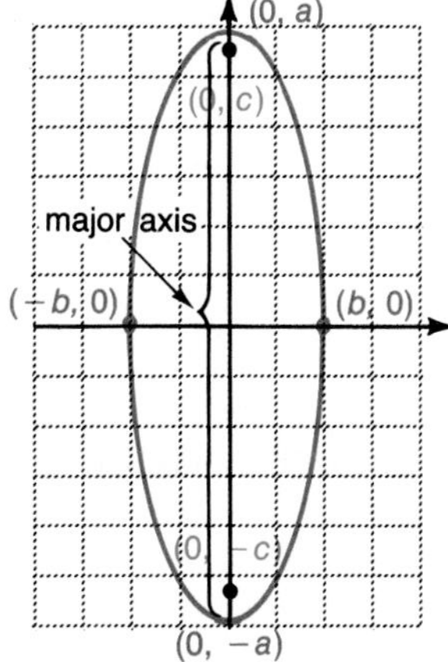

The sum of the focal radii is constant and is equal to the length of the major axis.

In the graph at the right, $r_1 + r_2 = 2a$.

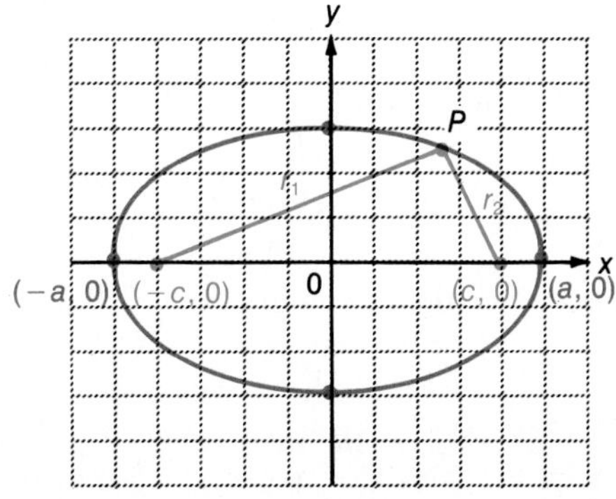

Theorem 10-5

The equation, in standard form, of an ellipse centered at the origin with foci on an axis c units from the origin is

$$\frac{x^2}{a^2} + \frac{y^2}{b^2} = 1, \text{ (major axis horizontal) or } \frac{x^2}{b^2} + \frac{y^2}{a^2} = 1, \text{ (major axis vertical)}$$

where $c^2 = a^2 - b^2$.

Key Questions

- Why does the path of the chalk satisfy the definition of an ellipse?
  The sum of the distance from the chalk to each of the fixed points equals the length of the string, which has a constant length.
- What is the length of the major axis if a equals 4 and b equals 3?
  8

Chalkboard Examples (*T15*)

1. Find the vertices and foci, and draw the graph of the ellipse $4x^2 + 9y^2 = 36$.
   Divide by 36 and put into standard form.
   $\frac{x^2}{9} + \frac{y^2}{4} = 1$
   $\frac{x^2}{3^2} + \frac{y^2}{2^2} = 1$
   The vertices are $(\pm 3, 0)$ and $(0, \pm 2)$.
   $c = \sqrt{9-4} = \sqrt{5}$
   The foci are $(\sqrt{5}, 0)$ and $(-\sqrt{5}, 0)$.

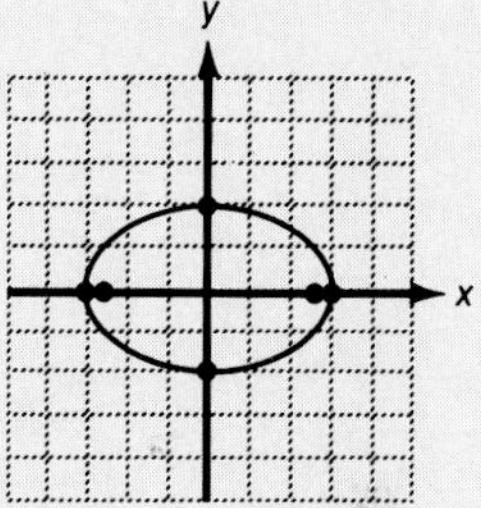

2. Find the vertices and foci, and draw a graph of the ellipse.
   $4x^2 + 9y^2 = 1$
   Put into standard form.
   $\frac{x^2}{\left(\frac{1}{2}\right)^2} + \frac{y^2}{\left(\frac{1}{3}\right)^2} = 1$
   The vertices are $\left(\pm\frac{1}{2}, 0\right)$ and $\left(0, \pm\frac{1}{3}\right)$.
   $c = \sqrt{\frac{1}{4} - \frac{1}{9}} = \frac{1}{6}\sqrt{5}$
   The foci are $\left(\pm\frac{1}{6}\sqrt{5}, 0\right)$.

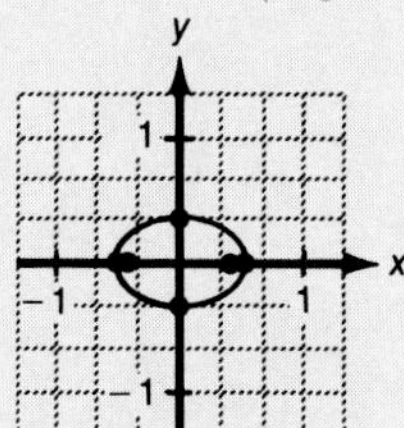

EXAMPLE 1 For the ellipse $x^2 + 16y^2 = 16$, find the vertices and foci, and draw a graph.

We first multiply by $\frac{1}{16}$ to find standard form.

$$\frac{x^2}{16} + \frac{y^2}{1} = 1, \text{ or } \frac{x^2}{4^2} + \frac{y^2}{1^2} = 1$$

Since the denominator for x^2 is larger, the foci are on the x-axis, and the ellipse is horizontal. Thus $a = 4$ and $b = 1$. The vertices on the major axis are $(-4, 0)$ and $(4, 0)$. The other vertices are $(0, -1)$ and $(0, 1)$.

$c^2 = a^2 - b^2$, so $c^2 = 16 - 1$, $c = \sqrt{15}$, and the foci are $(-\sqrt{15}, 0)$ and $(\sqrt{15}, 0)$.

To graph, we plot the vertices and draw a smooth curve.

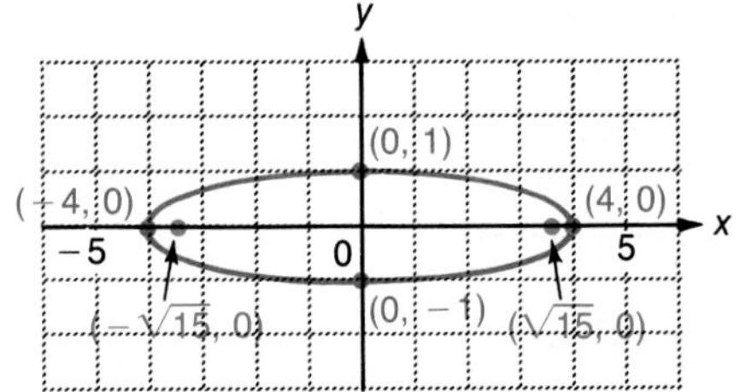

Try This For each ellipse find the vertices and foci, and draw a graph.
See Additional Answers.

a. $x^2 + 9y^2 = 9$ **b.** $9x^2 + 25y^2 = 225$ **c.** $2x^2 + 4y^2 = 8$

EXAMPLE 2 For the ellipse $9x^2 + 2y^2 = 18$, find the vertices and foci, and draw a graph.

(a) We first multiply by $\frac{1}{18}$ to find standard form.

$$\frac{x^2}{2} + \frac{y^2}{9} = 1, \text{ or } \frac{x^2}{(\sqrt{2})^2} + \frac{y^2}{3^2} = 1$$

(b) Since the denominator for y^2 is larger, the foci are on the y-axis, and the ellipse is vertical. Thus $a = 3$ and $b = \sqrt{2}$. The vertices on the major axis are $(0, -3)$ and $(0, 3)$. The other vertices are $(-\sqrt{2}, 0)$ and $(\sqrt{2}, 0)$.
$c^2 = a^2 - b^2$, so $c^2 = 9 - 2$, $c = \sqrt{7}$, and the foci are $(0, -\sqrt{7})$ and $(0, \sqrt{7})$.

(c) The graph is at the right.

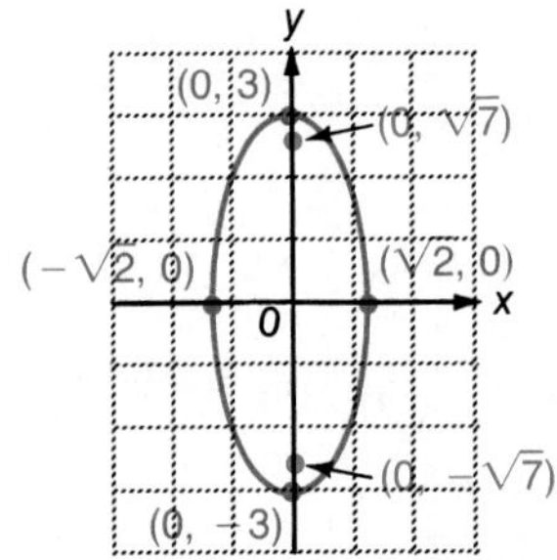

Try This For each ellipse find the center, vertices, and foci, and draw a graph.
See Additional Answers.

d. $9x^2 + y^2 = 9$ **e.** $25x^2 + 9y^2 = 225$ **f.** $4x^2 + 2y^2 = 8$ **g.** $x^2 + 3y^2 = 48$

Complete the Square to Find Standard Form

Objective: Find the center, vertices, and foci, and graph an ellipse by first completing the square.

If the center of an ellipse is not at the origin but at some point (h, k), then the standard form of the equation is as follows.

Theorem 10-6

The equation, in standard form, of an ellipse centered at (h, k) with foci c units from (h, k) is

$$\frac{(x-h)^2}{a^2}+\frac{(y-k)^2}{b^2}=1, \left(\begin{matrix}\text{major axis}\\ \text{horizontal}\end{matrix}\right) \text{ or } \frac{(x-h)^2}{b^2}+\frac{(y-k)^2}{a^2}=1, \left(\begin{matrix}\text{major axis}\\ \text{vertical}\end{matrix}\right)$$

where $c^2 = a^2 - b^2$.

EXAMPLE 3 For the ellipse $16x^2 + 4y^2 + 96x - 8y + 84 = 0$, find the center, vertices, and foci, and draw a graph.

(a) We first complete the square to get standard form.

$$16(x^2 + 6x \qquad) + 4(y^2 - 2y \qquad) = -84$$

$$16(x^2 + 6x + 9) + 4(y^2 - 2y + 1) = -84 + 16 \cdot 9 + 4 \cdot 1 \quad \text{Using the addition principle}$$

$$16(x^2 + 6x + 9) + 4(y^2 - 2y + 1) = -84 + 144 + 4$$

$$16(x + 3)^2 + 4(y - 1)^2 = 64$$

$$\frac{16(x + 3)^2}{64} + \frac{4(y - 1)^2}{64} = 1 \quad \text{Dividing to make the right side 1}$$

$$\frac{(x + 3)^2}{4} + \frac{(y - 1)^2}{16} = 1$$

$$\frac{(x + 3)^2}{2^2} + \frac{(y - 1)^2}{4^2} = 1$$

The center is $(-3, 1)$, $a = 4$, and $b = 2$. The major axis is vertical.

(b) The vertices of $\frac{x^2}{2^2} + \frac{y^2}{4^2} = 1$ are $(2, 0)$, $(-2, 0)$, $(0, 4)$ and $(0, -4)$. Since $c^2 = 16 - 4 = 12$, $c = 2\sqrt{3}$, and its foci are $(0, 2\sqrt{3})$ and $(0, -2\sqrt{3})$. This ellipse is centered at the origin. Thus we need to translate the ellipse so that the center is at $(-3, 1)$.

(c) The vertices and foci of the translated ellipse are found by translation in the same way that the center has been translated. Thus the vertices are

$(-3 + 2, 1)$, $(-3 - 2, 1)$, $(-3, 1 + 4)$, and $(-3, 1 - 4)$, or,

$(-1, 1)$, $(-5, 1)$, $(-3, 5)$, and $(-3, -3)$.

The foci are $(-3, 1 + 2\sqrt{3})$ and $(-3, 1 - 2\sqrt{3})$.

Complete the Square to Find Standard Form

Remind students of the translation principle. Replacing x by $x - h$ and y by $y - k$ yields an equation whose graph is the original graph shifted right by h and up by k.

Key Question

- Where is the center of the ellipse?
  $\frac{(x - 3)^2}{5^2} + \frac{(y - 2)^2}{4^2} = 1$
  The center is at (3, 2).

Chalkboard Example

1. Find the center, vertices and foci, and graph the ellipse.
   $4x^2 - 24x + 16y^2 = 28$
   Complete the square.
   $4(x^2 - 6x) + 16y^2 = 28$
   $4(x^2 - 6x + 9) + 16y^2 = 64$
   $4(x - 3)^2 + 16y^2 = 64$
   $\frac{(x - 3)^2}{4^2} + \frac{y^2}{2^2} = 1$
   The center is (3, 0).
   The vertices are (7, 0), (−1, 0), (3, 2), (3, −2).
   $\sqrt{16 - 4} = 2\sqrt{3}$
   The foci are $(3 \pm 2\sqrt{3}, 0)$.

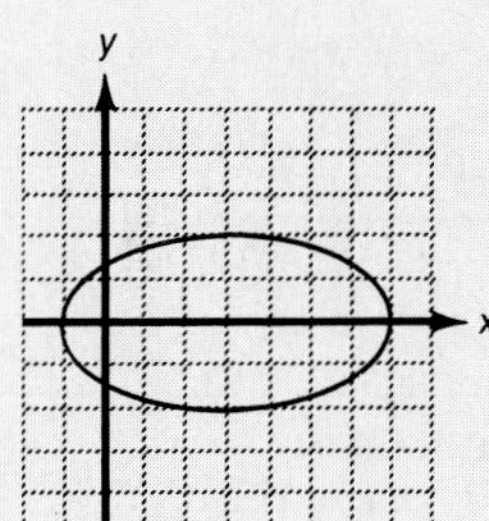

LESSON QUIZ

1. Find the vertices and foci, and draw the graph of the ellipse.

   $\frac{x^2}{25} + \frac{y^2}{9} = 1$

   The vertices are $(\pm 5, 0)$, $(0, \pm 3)$.
   The foci are $(\pm 4, 0)$.

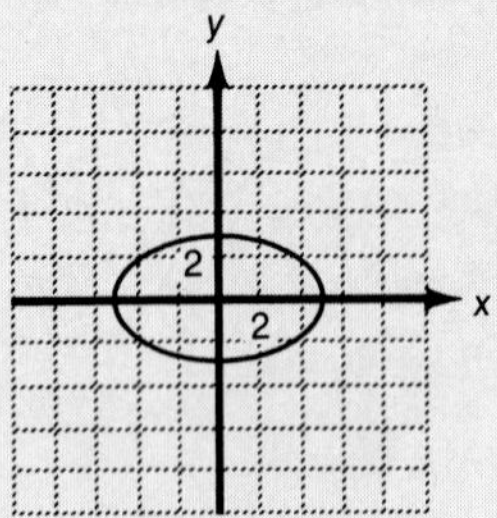

2. Find the center, vertices and foci, and draw the graph of the ellipse.

   $\frac{(x - 7)^2}{36} + \frac{(y - 9)^2}{25} = 1$

   The center is $(7, 9)$.
   The vertices are $(7 \pm 6, 9)$, $(7, 9 \pm 5)$.
   The foci are $(7 \pm \sqrt{11}, 9)$.

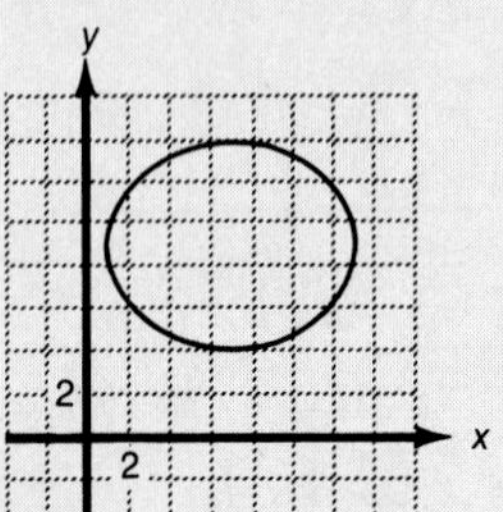

Assignment Guide

Algebra: 1–18 e/o, MR

Alg w/Finite or Trig: 1–18 m3, 19–30 e/o, 31, MR

Comprehensive: 1–30 m3, 31–34, 35–39 e/o, MR

ADDITIONAL ANSWERS

Try This

For graphs of Try This *a–i*, see Selected Answers.

a. Vertices: $(\pm 3, 0)$, $(0, \pm 1)$; foci $(\pm 2\sqrt{2}, 0)$

b. Vertices: $(\pm 5, 0)$, $(0, \pm 3)$; foci: $(\pm 4, 0)$

(d) The graph is as follows.

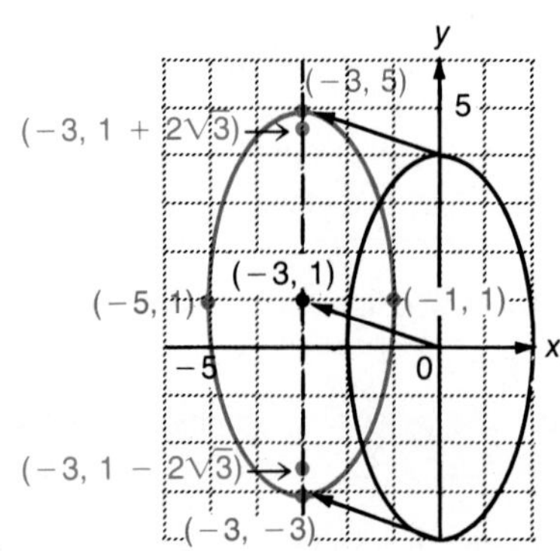

Try This For each ellipse find the center, vertices and foci, and draw a graph. See Additional Answers.

h. $25x^2 + 9y^2 + 150x - 36y + 260 = 0$

i. $9x^2 + 25y^2 - 36x + 150y + 260 = 0$

10-3 EXERCISES

A

For each ellipse find the vertices and foci, and draw a graph.

1. $\frac{x^2}{4} + \frac{y^2}{1} = 1$

2. $\frac{x^2}{1} + \frac{y^2}{4} = 1$

3. $16x^2 + 9y^2 = 144$

4. $9x^2 + 16y^2 = 144$

5. $2x^2 + 3y^2 = 6$

6. $5x^2 + 7y^2 = 35$

7. $4x^2 + 9y^2 = 1$

8. $25x^2 + 16y^2 = 1$

For each ellipse find the center, vertices and foci, and draw a graph.

9. $\frac{(x - 1)^2}{4} + \frac{(y - 2)^2}{1} = 1$

10. $\frac{(x - 1)^2}{1} + \frac{(y - 2)^2}{4} = 1$

11. $\frac{(x + 3)^2}{25} + \frac{(y - 2)^2}{16} = 1$

12. $\frac{(x - 2)^2}{25} + \frac{(y + 3)^2}{16} = 1$

13. $3(x + 2)^2 + 4(y - 1)^2 = 192$

14. $4(x - 5)^2 + 3(y - 5)^2 = 192$

15. $4x^2 + 9y^2 - 16x + 18y - 11 = 0$

16. $x^2 + 2y^2 - 10x + 8y + 29 = 0$

17. $4x^2 + y^2 - 8x - 2y + 1 = 0$

18. $9x^2 + 4y^2 + 54x - 8y + 49 = 0$

B

For each ellipse approximate the center and vertices. Use a calculator.

19. $\pi x^2 + \pi^2 y^2 - 5\pi x + 6\pi y - \pi^2 = 0$

20. $\pi^2 x^2 + \pi y^2 + \pi^3 x - \pi^2 y + \frac{5}{4}\pi = 0$

Find equations of the ellipses with the following vertices. (Hint: Graph the vertices.)

21. (2, 0), (−2, 0), (0, 3), (0, −3)

22. (1, 0), (−1, 0), (0, 4), (0, −4)

23. (1, 1), (5, 1), (3, 6), (3, −4)

24. (−1, −1), (−1, 5), (−3, 2), (1, 2)

Find equations of the ellipses satisfying the given conditions.

25. Center at (−2, 3) with major axis of length 8 and parallel to the y-axis, minor axis of length 2 $(x + 2)^2 + \frac{(y - 3)^2}{16} = 1$

26. Vertices (3, 0) and (−3, 0), and containing the point $\left(2, \frac{22}{3}\right)$ $\frac{x^2}{9} + \frac{y^2}{\frac{484}{5}} = 1$

27. **a.** Graph $9x^2 + y^2 = 9$. Is this relation a function? No

b. Solve $9x^2 + y^2 = 9$ for y. $y = \pm 3\sqrt{1 - x^2}$

c. Graph $y = 3\sqrt{1 - x^2}$ and determine whether it is a graph of a function. Find the domain and range. Yes; domain $\{x \mid -1 \le x \le 1\}$; range $\{y \mid 0 \le y \le 3\}$

d. Graph $y = -3\sqrt{1 - x^2}$ and determine whether it is a graph of a function. Find the domain and range. Yes; domain $\{x \mid -1 \le x \le 1\}$; range $\{y \mid -3 \le y \le 0\}$

28. Draw a large-scale precise graph of $\frac{x^2}{25} + \frac{y^2}{16} = 1$ by calculating and plotting a large number of points. Use a calculator to find the points.

29. The maximum distance from the earth to the sun is 9.3×10^7 miles. The minimum distance is 9.1×10^7 miles. The sun is at one focus of the elliptical orbit. Find the distance from the sun to the other focus. 2.0×10^6 miles

30. Find F_1P, F_2P, a, and b for this figure. $F_1P = 40$ $F_2P = 30$ $a = 35$ $b = 10\sqrt{6}$

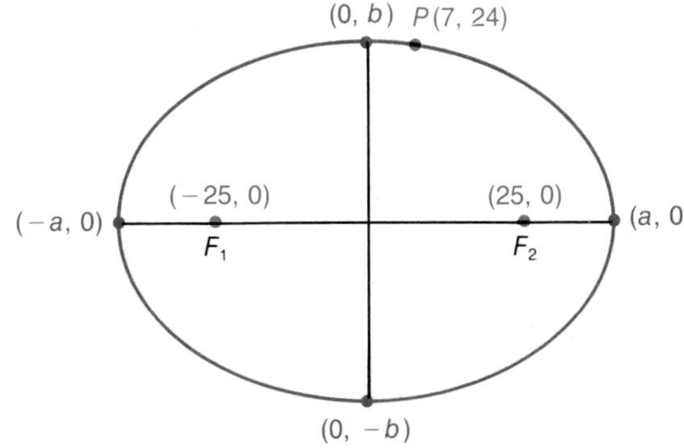

31. ***Critical Thinking*** Describe the graph of $\frac{x^2}{a^2} + \frac{y^2}{b^2} = 1$, where $a^2 = b^2$.

Challenge

32. An ellipse has foci F_1 $(-c, 0)$ and F_2 $(c, 0)$. $P(x, y)$ is a point on the ellipse and $F_1P + F_2P$ is the given constant distance. Let $F_1P + F_2P = 2a$. Use the distance formula to derive the standard form equation of the ellipse as given in Theorem 10-5. (Hint: $F_1P = \sqrt{(x + c)^2 + y^2}$)

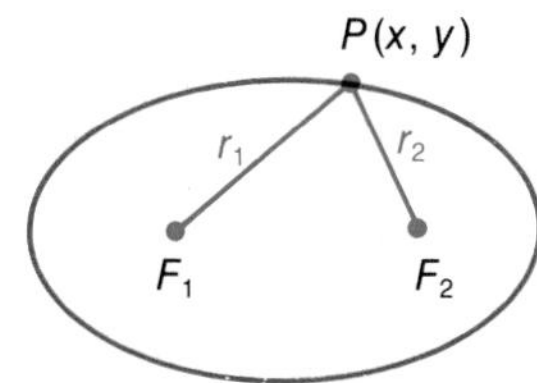

c. Vertices: $(\pm 2, 0)$, $(0, \pm\sqrt{2})$; foci: $(\pm\sqrt{2}, 0)$

d. Center: (0, 0); vertices: $(\pm 1, 0)$, $(0, \pm 3)$; foci: $(0, \pm 2\sqrt{2})$

e. Center: (0, 0); vertices: $(\pm 3, 0)$, $(0, \pm 5)$; foci: $(0, \pm 4)$

f. Center: (0, 0); vertices: $(\pm\sqrt{2}, 0)$, $(0, \pm 2)$; foci: $(0, \pm\sqrt{2})$

g. Center: (0, 0); vertices: $(\pm 4\sqrt{3}, 0)$, $(0, \pm 4)$; foci: $(\pm 4\sqrt{2}, 0)$

h. Center: (−3, 2); vertices: $\left(-3\frac{1}{5}, 2\right)$, $\left(-3, 2\frac{1}{3}\right)$, $\left(-3, 1\frac{2}{3}\right)$, $\left(-2\frac{4}{5}, 2\right)$; foci: $\left(-3, 2\frac{4}{15}\right)$, $\left(-3, 1\frac{11}{15}\right)$

i. Center: (2, −3); vertices: $\left(2\frac{1}{3}, -3\right)$, $\left(2, -3\frac{1}{5}\right)$, $\left(2, -2\frac{4}{5}\right)$, $\left(1\frac{2}{3}, -3\right)$, foci: $\left(2\frac{4}{15}, -3\right)$, $\left(1\frac{11}{15}, -3\right)$

Exercises

For graphs of Exercises 1–18, see Teacher's Answer Section.

1. Vertices: $(\pm 2, 0)$, $(0, \pm 1)$; foci: $(\pm\sqrt{3}, 0)$

2. Vertices: $(\pm 1, 0)$, $(0, \pm 2)$; foci: $(0, \pm\sqrt{3})$

3. Vertices: $(\pm 3, 0)$, $(0, \pm 4)$; foci: $(0, \pm\sqrt{7})$

4. Vertices: $(\pm 4, 0)$, $(0, \pm 3)$; foci: $(\pm\sqrt{7}, 0)$

5. Vertices: $(\pm\sqrt{3}, 0)$, $(0, \pm\sqrt{2})$; foci: $(\pm 1, 0)$

6. Vertices: $(\pm\sqrt{7}, 0)$, $(0, \pm\sqrt{5})$; foci: $(\pm\sqrt{2}, 0)$

7. Vertices: $\left(\pm\frac{1}{2}, 0\right)$, $\left(0, \pm\frac{1}{3}\right)$; foci: $\left(\pm\frac{\sqrt{5}}{6}, 0\right)$

8. Vertices: $\left(\pm\frac{1}{5}, 0\right)$, $\left(0, \pm\frac{1}{4}\right)$; foci: $\left(0, \pm\frac{3}{20}\right)$

9. Center: (1, 2); vertices: (−1, 2), (3, 2), (1, 1), (1, 3); foci: $(1 \pm \sqrt{3}, 2)$

10. Center: (1, 2); vertices: (0, 2), (2, 2), (1, 0), (1, 4); foci: $(1, 2 \pm \sqrt{3})$

11. Center: (−3, 2); vertices: (−8, 2), (2, 2), (−3, −2), (−3, 6); foci: (−6, 2), (0, 2)

12. Center: (2, −3); vertices: (−3, −3), (7, −3), (2, −7), (2, 1); foci: (−1, −3), (5, −3)

13. Center: (−2, 1); vertices: (−10, 1), (6, 1), $(-2, 1 \pm 4\sqrt{3})$; foci: (−6, 1), (2, 1)

14. Center: (5, 5); vertices: $(5 \pm 4\sqrt{3}, 5)$, (5, 13), (5, −3); foci: (5, 9), (5, 1)

15. Center: (2, −1); vertices: (−1, −1), (5, −1), (2, −3), (2, 1); foci: $(2 \pm \sqrt{5}, -1)$
16. Center: (5, −2); vertices: (3, −2), (7, −2), $(5, -2 \pm \sqrt{2})$; foci: $(5 \pm \sqrt{2}, -2)$
17. Center: (1, 1); vertices: (0, 1), (2, 1), (1, −1), (1, 3); foci: $(1, 1 \pm \sqrt{3})$
18. Center: (−3, 1); vertices: (−5, 1), (−1, 1), (−3, −2), (−3, 4); foci: $(-3, 1 \pm \sqrt{5})$
19. Center (2.5, −0.95); vertices (6, −0.95), (−1, 0.95), (2.5, 1.02), (2.5, −2.93)
20. Center (−1.57, 1.57); vertices (0.12, 1.57), (−3.26, 1.57), (−1.57, 4.57), (−1.57, −1.42)
21. $\frac{x^2}{4} + \frac{y^2}{9} = 1$ 22. $x^2 + \frac{y^2}{16} = 1$
23. $\frac{(x-3)^2}{4} + \frac{(y-1)^2}{25} = 1$
24. $\frac{(x+1)^2}{4} + \frac{(y-2)^2}{9} = 1$

For graphs of Exercises 27 and 28 see Teacher's Answer Section.

31. A circle with radius a centered at the origin

For Exercises 32 and 37–39, see Teacher's Answer Section.

Mixed Review

40. $f(x) = (x - 1.5)^2 + 1.75$
Vertex: (1.5, 1.75)
Line of symmetry: x = 1.5
Minimum: 1.75
41. $f(x) = (x + 2.5)^2 - 7.25$
Vertex: (−2.5, −7.25)
Line of symmetry: x = −2.5
Minimum: −7.25
42. $f(x) = -(x - 1)^2 - 4$
Vertex: (1, −4)
Line of symmetry: x = 1
Maximum: −4
43. $\left(-1 + \frac{\sqrt{6}}{2}, 0\right), \left(-1 - \frac{\sqrt{6}}{2}, 0\right)$
44. (−3, 0), (4, 0)
45. $\sqrt{34}$
46. $3\sqrt{2}$
47. $f(x) = 3x^2 + 2x - 4$
48. $f(x) = 3x^2 - 9x - 16$
49. $n < 70$

33. The eccentricity (e) of an ellipse is $\frac{c}{a}$. What is the range for the eccentricity of an ellipse? $0 < e < 1$

34. What happens to the shape of an ellipse as the eccentricity gets closer to 1? What would be true if $e = 1$? The ellipse becomes a line.

35. The unit square on the left is transformed to the rectangle on the right by a stretch or shrink in the x-direction and a stretch or shrink in the y-direction.

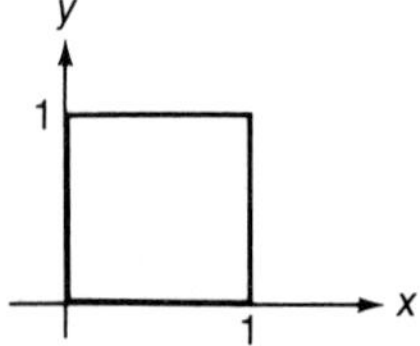

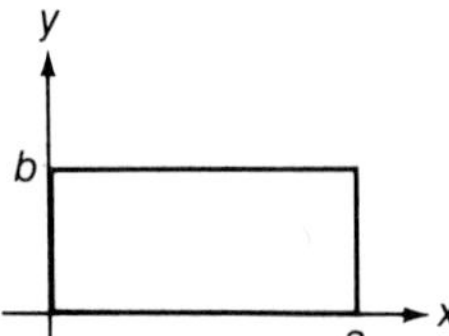

a. Use the above result to develop a formula for the area of the ellipse $\frac{x^2}{a^2} + \frac{y^2}{b^2} = 1$. (Hint: The area of the circle $x^2 + y^2 = r^2$ is $\pi \cdot r \cdot r$.) $A = \pi ab$

b. Use the result of **a** to find the area of the ellipse $\frac{x^2}{16} + \frac{y^2}{25} = 1$. 20π

c. Use the result of **a** to find the area of the ellipse $\frac{x^2}{4} + \frac{y^2}{3} = 1$. $2\pi\sqrt{3}$

36. Kidney stones can be treated using a lithotripter. An electrode at one focus of an elliptical reflector sends high-energy shock waves to crush the kidney stone at the other focus. How far must the electrode be placed from the kidney stone? 16 cm

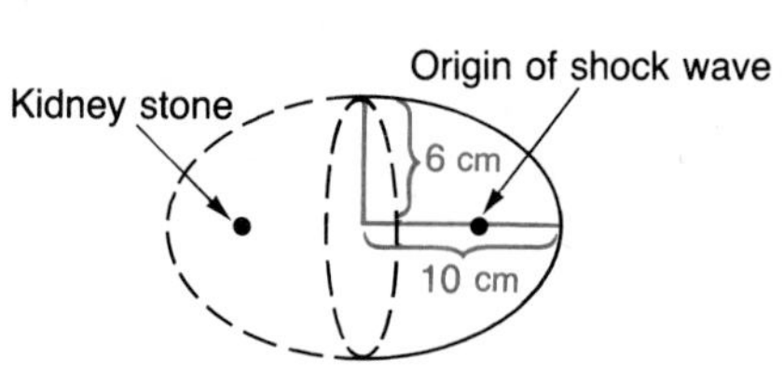

Graph these inequalities.

37. $\frac{x^2}{9} + \frac{y^2}{4} \le 1$ **38.** $\frac{x^2}{9} + \frac{y^2}{25} > 1$ **39.** $\frac{(x-1)^2}{2} + \frac{(y-3)^2}{9} < 1$

Mixed Review

Find the standard form for each quadratic equation and then find the vertex, the line of symmetry, and the maximum or minimum value.

40. $f(x) = x^2 - 3x + 4$ **41.** $f(x) = x^2 + 5x - 1$ **42.** $f(x) = -x^2 + 2x - 5$

Find the x-intercepts. **43.** $f(x) = 2x^2 + 4x - 1$ **44.** $f(x) = 2x^2 - 2x - 24$

Find the distance between the points. **45.** (4, 5) and (7, 10)

46. (−5, −2) and (−2, 1)

Find the quadratic function that fits each set of points. **47.** (1, 1), (−1, −3), (2, 12)

48. (1, −22), (−2, 14), (−1, −4)

49. A computer programmer can be paid in two ways.
Plan A: \$315 plus \$28.00 per hour
Plan B: straight \$32.50 per hour
Suppose the job takes n hours. For what values of n is plan A better for the programmer than plan B?

10-4 Hyperbolas

Master Grapher Worksheet 18, *Conic Sections: Hyperbolas*, can be used for lesson closure.

Hyperbolas have many applications. A jet breaking the sound barrier creates a sonic boom whose wave front has the shape of a cone. The cone intersects the ground in one branch of a hyperbola. Some comets travel in hyperbolic orbits.

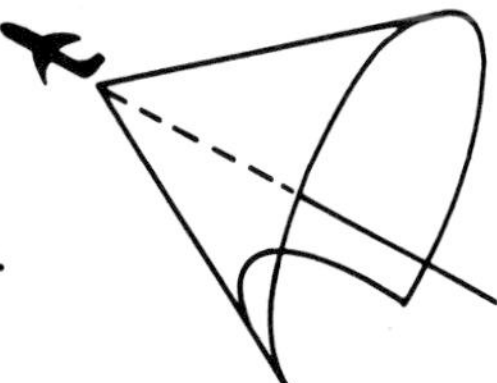

Equations of Hyperbolas

Objective: Find the vertices, foci, and asymptotes, and draw a graph of a hyperbola, given its equation.

Some equations of second degree have graphs that are hyperbolas.

Definition

A **hyperbola** is the set of all points P in a plane such that the absolute value of the difference of the distances from P to two fixed points, F_1 and F_2, is constant. The fixed points F_1 and F_2 are the **foci.** The midpoint of the segment F_1F_2 is the center. r_1 and r_2 are the **focal radii.**

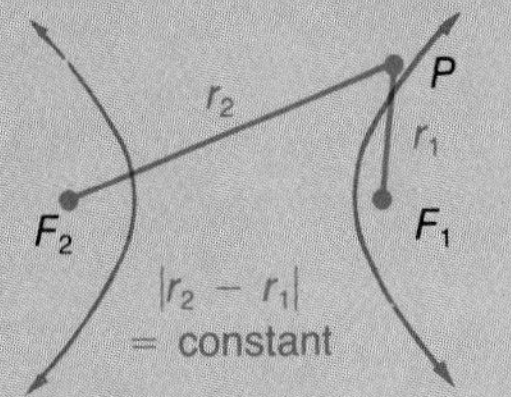

Theorem 10-7

The equation, in standard form, of a hyperbola centered at the origin with foci on an axis c units from the origin is

$$\frac{x^2}{a^2} - \frac{y^2}{b^2} = 1, \text{(foci on the } x\text{-axis)} \quad \text{or} \quad \frac{y^2}{a^2} - \frac{x^2}{b^2} = 1, \text{(foci on the } y\text{-axis)}$$

where $c^2 = a^2 + b^2$.

The two parts of the hyperbola are branches. Points $(a, 0)$ and $(-a, 0)$ are the vertices, and the line segment joining them is the transverse axis. The line segment from $(0, b)$ to $(0, -b)$ is the conjugate axis.

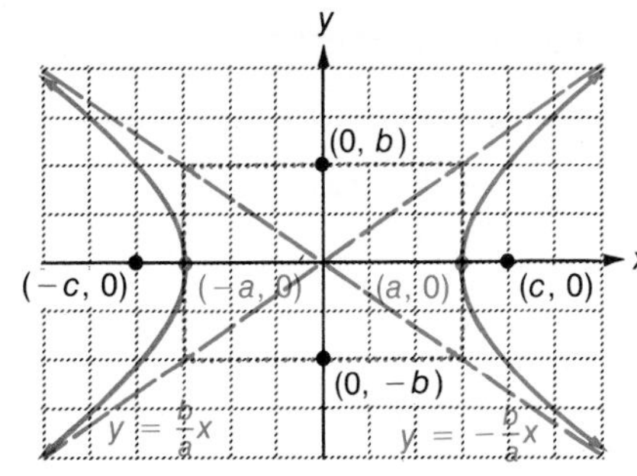

By looking at the equation, we can see that the hyperbola is symmetric with respect to the origin, and that the x-axis and y-axis are lines of symmetry.

The constant distance, $|r_2 - r_1|$, is $2a$.

10-4

FIRST FIVE MINUTES

1. Find the center and vertices of the ellipse.
   $$\frac{x^2}{49} + \frac{y^2}{16} = 1$$
   The center is (0, 0).
   The vertices are $(\pm 7, 0)$, $(0, \pm 4)$.
2. Find the center and vertices of the ellipse.
   $$\frac{(x-2)^2}{100} + \frac{(y-5)^2}{9} = 1$$
   The center is (2, 5).
   The vertices are $(2 \pm 10, 5)$ and $(2, 5 \pm 3)$.

Equations of Hyperbolas

Remind students that the hyperbola is a conic section, and emphasize that one branch of a hyperbola is not a parabola.

When introducing asymptotes, give $y = \frac{1}{x}$ as an example.

Emphasize that $c^2 = a^2 + b^2$, regardless of which axis the foci are on.

Math Point
The discovery of the conic sections is attributed by historians to the ancient Greek mathematician Menaechmus who lived around 300 B.C. Along with Aristotle, Menaechmus was a teacher of Alexander the Great.

Key Questions

- What determines the shape of a hyperbola?
  The position of the two foci and the constant difference
- How would you describe the hyperbola for which the difference constant is 0?
  If the difference constant is 0, then the points on the hyperbola are equally distant from each focus. The points lie on a straight line.

Chalkboard Examples (*T16, T17*)

1. Find the vertices, foci, and asymptotes, and draw the graph of the hyperbola.
   $\frac{x^2}{3^2} - \frac{y^2}{4^2} = 1$
   The vertices are $(-3, 0)$ and $(3, 0)$.
   $c = \sqrt{9 + 16} = 5$
   The foci are $(-5, 0)$ and $(5, 0)$.
   The asymptotes are the lines $y = \frac{4}{3}x$ and $y = -\frac{4}{3}x$.

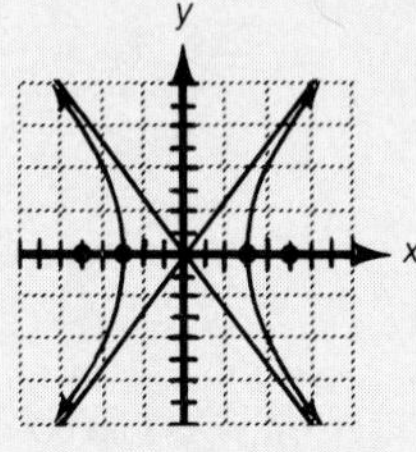

2. Find the vertices, foci, and asymptotes, and draw the graph of the hyperbola.
   $36x^2 - 9y^2 = 324$
   Multiply by $\frac{1}{324}$ and find the standard form.
   $\frac{x^2}{3^2} - \frac{y^2}{6^2} = 1$
   $a = 3$ and $b = 6$
   The vertices are $(-3, 0)$ and $(3, 0)$.
   $c = \sqrt{9 + 36} = \sqrt{45} = 3\sqrt{5}$
   The foci are $(-3\sqrt{5}, 0)$ and $(3\sqrt{5}, 0)$.
   The asymptotes are $y = 2x$ and $y = -2x$.

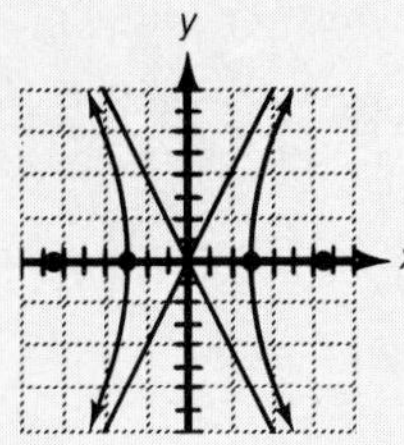

Notice that the branches of the hyperbola approach the lines $y = \frac{b}{a}x$ and $y = -\frac{b}{a}x$ as $|x|$ increases. These lines are called **asymptotes**. A line is an asymptote to a curve if the distance between a point on the curve and the line approaches zero as the point moves farther from the vertices.

EXAMPLE 1 For the hyperbola $9x^2 - 16y^2 = 144$, find the vertices, the foci, and the asymptotes. Then draw a graph.

(a) We first multiply by $\frac{1}{144}$ to find the standard form.

$$\frac{x^2}{16} - \frac{y^2}{9} = 1$$

Thus $a = 4$ and $b = 3$. The vertices are $(4, 0)$ and $(-4, 0)$. Since $c^2 = a^2 + b^2$, $c = \sqrt{a^2 + b^2} = \sqrt{4^2 + 3^2} = 5$. Thus the foci are $(5, 0)$ and $(-5, 0)$. The asymptotes are $y = \frac{3}{4}x$ and $y = -\frac{3}{4}x$.

(b) To graph the hyperbola it is helpful to first graph the asymptotes. An easy way to do this is to draw the rectangle formed by the lines $y = 3$, $y = -3$, $x = 4$ and $x = -4$. By extending the diagonals, we have the asymptotes. Then we draw the branches of the hyperbola outward from the vertices toward the asymptotes.

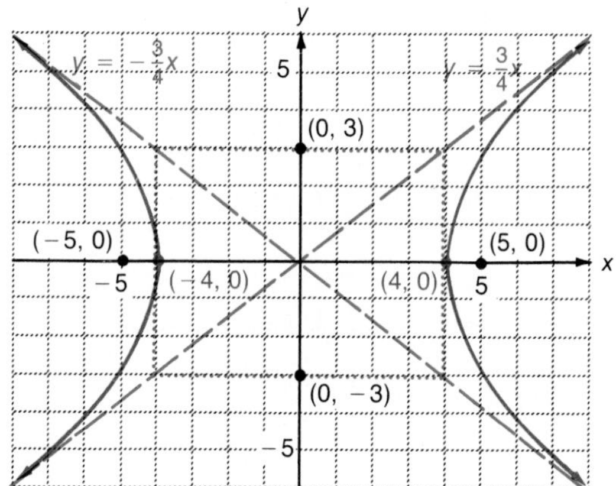

Try This For each hyperbola find the vertices, foci, and asymptotes. Then graph.
See Additional Answers.

a. $4x^2 - 9y^2 = 36$ **b.** $x^2 - y^2 = 16$

The foci of a hyperbola can be on the y-axis. The slopes of the asymptotes are $\pm\frac{a}{b}$.

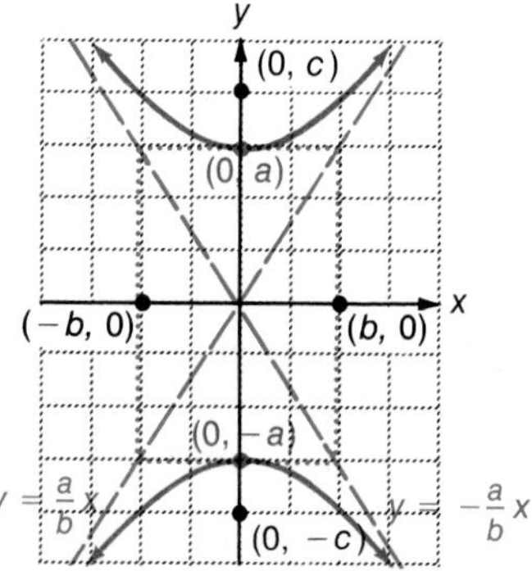

EXAMPLE 2 For the hyperbola $25y^2 - 16x^2 = 400$, find the vertices, foci, and asymptotes. Then draw a graph.

(a) We first multiply by $\frac{1}{400}$ to find the standard form.

$$\frac{y^2}{16} - \frac{x^2}{25} = 1$$

This is the equation of a hyperbola with foci and vertices on the y-axis.

From the equation, $a = 4$ and $b = 5$. The vertices are $(0, 4)$ and $(0, -4)$. Since $c = \sqrt{4^2 + 5^2} = \sqrt{41}$, the foci are $(0, \sqrt{41})$ and $(0, -\sqrt{41})$. The asymptotes are $y = \frac{4}{5}x$ and $y = -\frac{4}{5}x$.

(b) The graph is as shown.

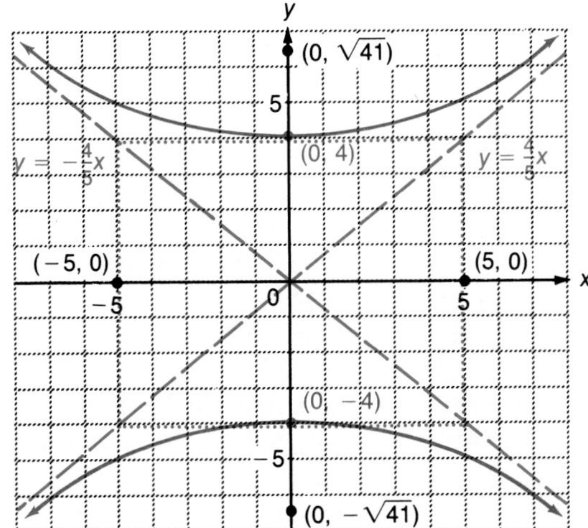

Try This For each hyperbola find the vertices, foci, and asymptotes. Then draw a graph. See Additional Answers.

c. $9y^2 - 25x^2 = 225$

d. $y^2 - x^2 = 25$

Finding Standard Form by Completing the Square

Objective: Find standard form and graph a hyperbola by first completing the square.

If the center of a hyperbola is not at the origin but at some point (h, k), then the standard form for the equation is as follows.

Finding Standard Form by Completing the Square

Chalkboard Example (*T18*)

1. Find the center, vertices, foci, and asymptotes, and draw the graph of the hyperbola.
   $25x^2 - 50x - 4y^2 + 24y = 111$
   Complete the square and put into standard form.
   $25(x^2 - 2x) - 4(y^2 - 6y) = 111$
   $25(x^2 - 2x + 1) - 4(y^2 - 6y + 9)$
   $= 111 + 25 - 36$
   $25(x - 1)^2 - 4(y - 3)^2 = 100$
   Divide by 100 to get
   $\frac{(x - 1)^2}{2^2} - \frac{(y - 3)^2}{5^2} = 1$
   We see that the center is (1, 3).
   $a = 2$ and $b = 5$
   The vertices are $(1 \pm 2, 3)$.
   $c = \sqrt{4 + 25} = \sqrt{29}$
   The foci are $(1 \pm \sqrt{29}, 3)$.
   The asymptotes are
   $y - 3 = \frac{5}{2}(x - 1)$, and
   $y - 3 = -\frac{5}{2}(x - 1)$.

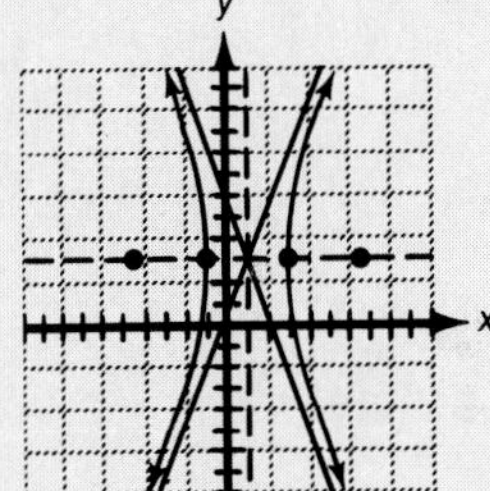

Theorem 10-8

The equation, in standard form, of a hyperbola centered at (h, k) with foci c units from (h, k) is

$$\frac{(x-h)^2}{a^2}-\frac{(y-k)^2}{b^2}=1, \left(\begin{matrix}\text{foci}\\ \text{horizontal}\end{matrix}\right) \text{ or } \frac{(y-k)^2}{a^2}-\frac{(x-h)^2}{b^2}=1, \left(\begin{matrix}\text{foci}\\ \text{vertical}\end{matrix}\right)$$

where $c^2 = a^2 + b^2$.

EXAMPLE 3 For the hyperbola $4x^2 - y^2 + 24x + 4y + 28 = 0$, find the center, vertices, foci, and asymptotes, and draw a graph.

(a) First we complete the square to find standard form.

$$4(x^2 + 6x \qquad) - (y^2 - 4y \qquad) = -28$$
$$4(x^2 + 6x + 9) - (y^2 - 4y + 4) = -28 + 4 \cdot 9 - 1 \cdot 4$$
$$4(x + 3)^2 - (y - 2)^2 = 4$$
$$\frac{(x + 3)^2}{1} - \frac{(y - 2)^2}{4} = 1$$

The center is $(-3, 2)$.

(b) Consider $\frac{x^2}{1} - \frac{y^2}{4} = 1$. We have $a = 1$ and $b = 2$. The vertices of this hyperbola are $(1, 0)$ and $(-1, 0)$. Also, $c = \sqrt{1^2 + 2^2} = \sqrt{5}$, so the foci are $(\sqrt{5}, 0)$ and $(-\sqrt{5}, 0)$. The asymptotes are $y = 2x$ and $y = -2x$.

(c) The vertices, foci, and asymptotes of the translated hyperbola are found in the same way by which the center has been translated. The vertices are $(-3 + 1, 2)$, $(-3 - 1, 2)$, or $(-2, 2)$, $(-4, 2)$. The foci are $(-3 + \sqrt{5}, 2)$ and $(-3 - \sqrt{5}, 2)$. The asymptotes are $y - 2 = 2(x + 3)$ and $y - 2 = -2(x + 3)$.

(d) The graph is as follows.

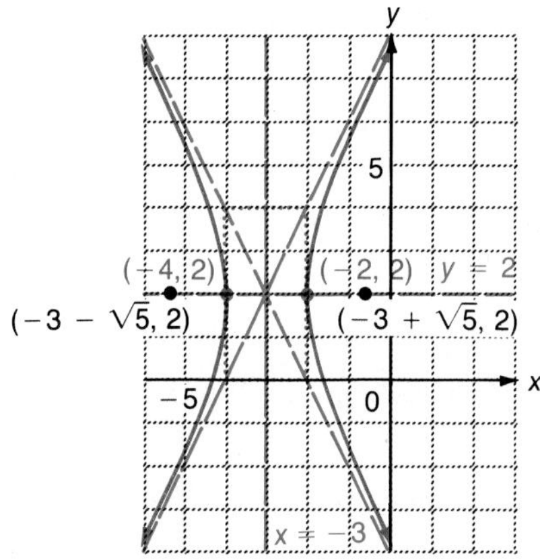

Try This For each hyperbola find the center, vertices, foci, and asymptotes. Then draw a graph. See Additional Answers.

e. $4x^2 - 25y^2 - 8x - 100y - 196 = 0$

f. $\frac{(y-2)^2}{9} - \frac{(x+1)^2}{16} = 1$

Asymptotes on the Coordinate Axes

Objective: Graph a hyperbola that has an equation of the form $xy = c$.

If a hyperbola has its center at the origin and its axes at 45° to the coordinate axes, it has a simple equation. The coordinate axes are its asymptotes. Such hyperbolas are known as equilateral or rectangular hyperbolas.

Theorem 10-9

The equation of a hyperbola with asymptotes on the axes is $xy = c$, where $c \neq 0$.

If c is positive, the branches of the hyperbola lie in the first and third quadrants. If c is negative, the branches lie in the second and fourth quadrants. In either case, the asymptotes are the x-axis and the y-axis.

EXAMPLE 4 Graph $xy = 4$ and $xy = -4$.

x	y
1	4
−1	−4
4	1
−4	−1

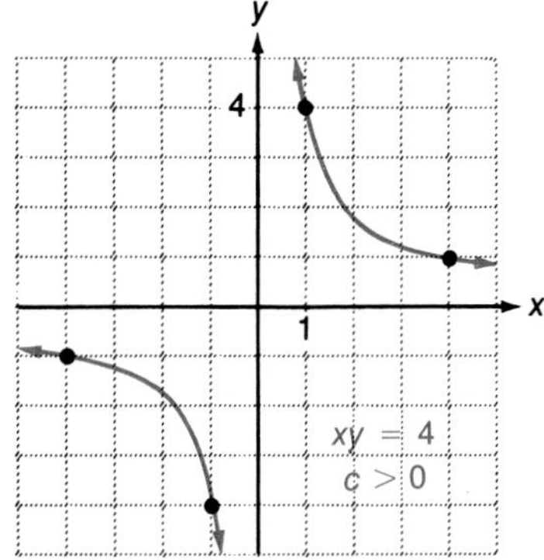

x	y
1	−4
−1	4
4	−1
−4	1

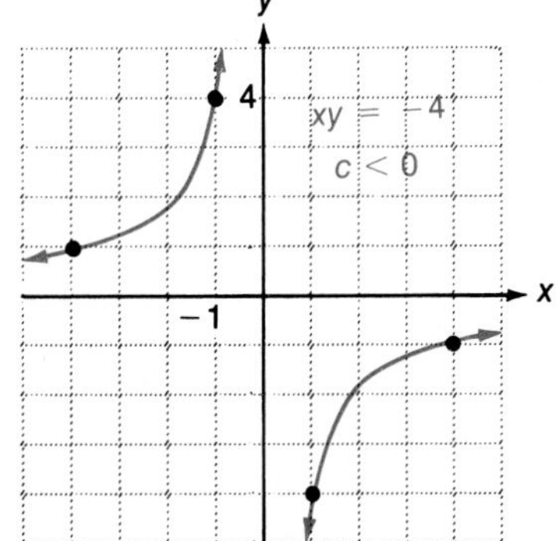

Asymptotes on the Coordinate Axes

Point out that the equation $xy = c$ is equivalent to the equation $y = \frac{c}{x}$, which is an equation of inverse variation.

Chalkboard Example (*T19*)

1. Graph $xy = -\frac{1}{2}$

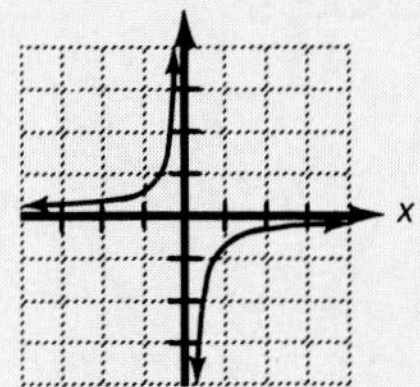

LESSON QUIZ

Find the center, vertices, foci, and asymptotes, and graph each hyperbola.

1. $\frac{x^2}{16} - \frac{y^2}{25} = 1$

   The center is (0, 0).
   The vertices are $(\pm 4, 0)$.
   The foci are $(\pm\sqrt{41}, 0)$.
   The asymptotes are $y = \pm\frac{5}{4}x$.

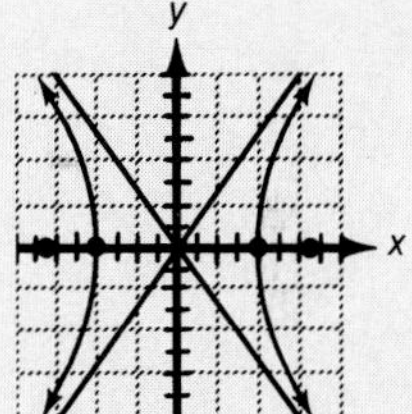

2. $\frac{(x-1)^2}{16} - \frac{(y-2)^2}{\left(\frac{1}{4}\right)} = 1$

The center is (1, 2). The vertices are $(1 \pm 4, 2)$. The foci are $1 \pm \frac{\sqrt{65}}{2}, 2)$.
The asymptotes are $y - 2 = \pm\frac{1}{8}(x - 1)$.

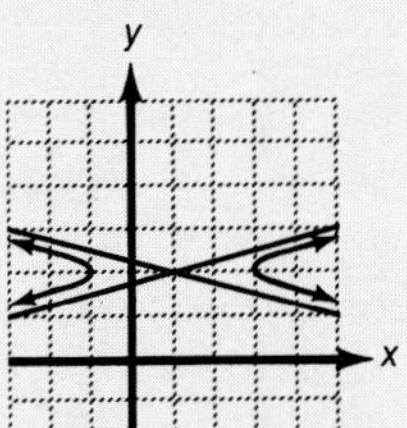

Assignment Guide
Algebra: 1–21 e/o, MR

Alg w/Finite or Trig: 1–21 m3, 22–24, MR

Comprehensive: 1–21 m3, 22–24, 25–32 e/o, MR

ADDITIONAL ANSWERS

Try This

For graphs of Try This *a–f*, see Selected Answers.

a. Vertices: $(-3, 0), (3, 0)$; foci: $(-\sqrt{13}, 0), (\sqrt{13}, 0)$; asymptotes: $y = -\frac{2}{3}x, y = \frac{2}{3}x$

b. Vertices: $(-4, 0), (4, 0)$; foci: $(-4\sqrt{2}, 0), (4\sqrt{2}, 0)$; asymptotes: $y = x, y = -x$

c. Vertices: $(0, -5), (0, 5)$; foci: $(0, -\sqrt{34}), (0, \sqrt{34})$; asymptotes: $y = -\frac{5}{3}x, y = \frac{5}{3}x$

d. Vertices: $(0, 5), (0, -5)$; foci: $(0, -5\sqrt{2}), (0, 5\sqrt{2})$; asymptotes: $y = x, y = -x$

e. Center: $(1, -2)$; vertices: $(-4, -2), (6, -2)$; foci: $(1 \pm \sqrt{29}, -2)$; asymptotes: $y + 2 = \pm\frac{2}{5}(x - 1)$

f. Center: $(-1, 2)$; vertices: $(-1, -1), (-1, 5)$; foci: $(-1, -3), (-1, 7)$; asymptotes: $y - 2 = \pm\frac{3}{4}(x + 1)$

Exercises

For graphs of Exercises 1–21, see Answer Section.

1. Center: $(0, 0)$; foci: $(\pm\sqrt{10}, 0)$; vertices: $(\pm 3, 0)$; asym: $y = \pm\frac{1}{3}x$
2. Center: $(0, 0)$; foci: $(\pm\sqrt{10}, 0)$; vertices: $(\pm 1, 0)$; asym: $y = \pm 3x$
3. Center: $(0, 0)$; foci: $(0, \pm 2\sqrt{5})$; vertices: $(0, \pm 4)$; asym: $y = \pm 2x$
4. Center: $(0, 0)$; foci: $(\pm\sqrt{5}, 0)$; vertices: $(\pm 2, 0)$; asym: $y = \pm\frac{1}{2}x$
5. Center: $(0, 0)$; foci: $\pm\sqrt{5}, 0)$; vertices: $(\pm 1, 0)$; asym: $y = \pm 2x$
6. Center: $(0, 0)$; foci: $(0, \pm\sqrt{5})$; vertices: $(0, \pm 1)$; asym: $y = \pm\frac{1}{2}x$

Try This See Selected Answers.

g. Graph $xy = 3$. **h.** Graph $xy = -12$.

10-4 EXERCISES

A

For each hyperbola find the center, vertices, foci, and asymptotes. Then draw a graph.

1. $\frac{x^2}{9} - \frac{y^2}{1} = 1$ **2.** $\frac{x^2}{1} - \frac{y^2}{9} = 1$ **3.** $\frac{y^2}{16} - \frac{x^2}{4} = 1$

4. $x^2 - 4y^2 = 4$ **5.** $4x^2 - y^2 = 4$ **6.** $4y^2 - x^2 = 4$

7. $y^2 - 4x^2 = 4$ **8.** $x^2 - y^2 = 2$ **9.** $x^2 - y^2 = 3$

For each hyperbola find the center, vertices, foci, and asymptotes. Then draw a graph.

10. $\frac{(x-2)^2}{1} - \frac{(y+5)^2}{9} = 1$ **11.** $\frac{(y+3)^2}{4} - \frac{(x+1)^2}{16} = 1$

12. $\frac{(x-2)^2}{9} - \frac{(y+5)^2}{1} = 1$ **13.** $\frac{(y+3)^2}{25} - \frac{(x+1)^2}{16} = 1$

14. $x^2 - y^2 - 2x - 4y - 4 = 0$ **15.** $4x^2 - y^2 + 8x - 4y - 4 = 0$

16. $36x^2 - y^2 - 24x + 6y - 41 = 0$ **17.** $9x^2 - 4y^2 + 54x + 8y + 41 = 0$

Graph.

18. $xy = 1$ **19.** $xy = -1$ **20.** $xy = -8$ **21.** $xy = 3$

B

Find equations of the hyperbolas satisfying the given conditions.

22. vertices at $(1, 0)$ and $(-1, 0)$, and foci at $(2, 0)$ and $(-2, 0)$ $\frac{x^2}{1} - \frac{y^2}{3} = 1$

23. asymptotes $y = \frac{3}{2}x$ and $y = -\frac{3}{2}x$, and one vertex $(2, 0)$ $\frac{x^2}{4} - \frac{y^2}{9} = 1$

24. ***Critical Thinking*** Contrast the graphs of $\frac{x^2}{9} - \frac{y^2}{4} = 1$ and $\frac{x^2}{4} - \frac{y^2}{9} = 1$. Write a general statement about the graphs of $\frac{x^2}{a^2} - \frac{y^2}{b^2} = 1$ and $\frac{x^2}{b^2} - \frac{y^2}{a^2} = 1$.

Challenge

25. A hyperbola has foci $F_1\ (c, 0)$ and $F_2\ (-c, 0)$ on the x-axis. Let $P(x, y)$ be any point in the first quadrant, and $PF_2 - PF_1 = 2a$. Use the distance formula to derive the standard form equation of the hyperbola as given in Theorem 10-8. (Hint: $PF_2 = \sqrt{(x + c)^2 + y^2}$)

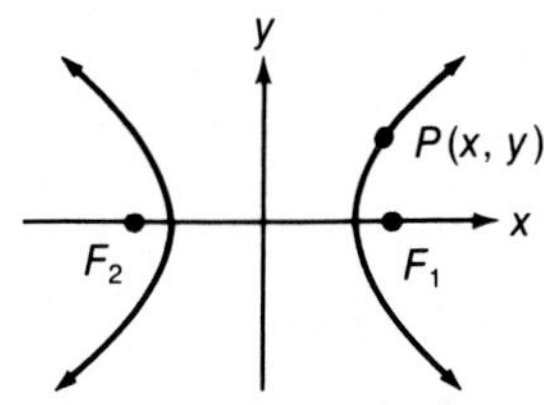

26. Solve the equation $\frac{x^2}{16} = \frac{y^2}{9} = 1$ for y^2. What happens to this equation as $|x|$ gets larger? What are the equations for the asymptotes of this graph?

27. The eccentricity (e) of a hyperbola is $\frac{c}{a}$. What is the range of e for any hyperbola? $e > 1$

28. Hyperbolas of the form $\frac{x^2}{a^2} - \frac{y^2}{b^2} = 1$ and $\frac{y^2}{a^2} - \frac{x^2}{b^2} = 1$ are conjugate hyperbolas. Graph a pair of conjugate hyperbolas on the same coordinate axes. What do you observe? They have the same asymptotes.

29. What happens to the graph of $xy = k$ as $|k|$ gets smaller? The graph gets closer to the coordinate axes.

Graph these inequalities.

30. $\frac{x^2}{25} - \frac{y^2}{16} < 1$ **31.** $\frac{y^2}{36} - \frac{x^2}{25} \geq 1$ **32.** $\frac{(y+4)^2}{1} - \frac{(x+2)^2}{4} \geq 1$

Mixed Review

Find the coordinates of the midpoint of the segment having the following endpoints.
33. (2, 7), (4, 5) **34.** (−1, 6), (4, −2) **35.** (3, 0), (9, 0)

Find the distance between the points. **36.** (1, −2) and (13, −7)
37. (2, 6) and (−4, 14) **38.** (−1, 6) and (−4, 10) **39.** (−7, 2) and (−2, 2)

Test for symmetry with respect to the axes. **40.** $5y^4 = -4x^2 - 1$ **41.** $y = x^3 + 2$

Determine whether the graphs are perpendicular. **42.** $y = 2x - 3$ and $x = 2y - 3$

43. $y = \frac{1}{3}x + 2$ and $y = -3x + 2$ **44.** $x = y - 10$ and $y - x = 5$

45. The surface area of a cube varies directly as the square of the length of one side. A cube has a surface area of 168.54 m² when the length of one side is 5.3 m. What will the surface area be when the length of one side is 4.8 m?

ACTIVITY

1. Cut three sheets of waxed paper about 5″ × 5″.
2. Draw a circle and a point P on each as shown below.

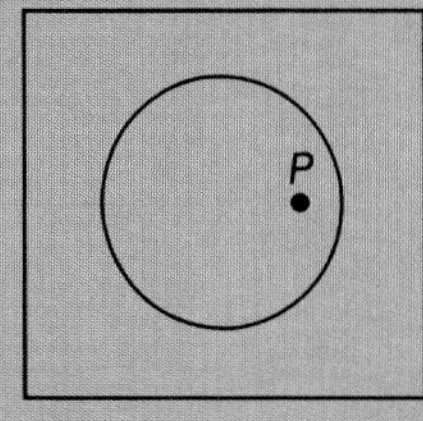

Ellipse

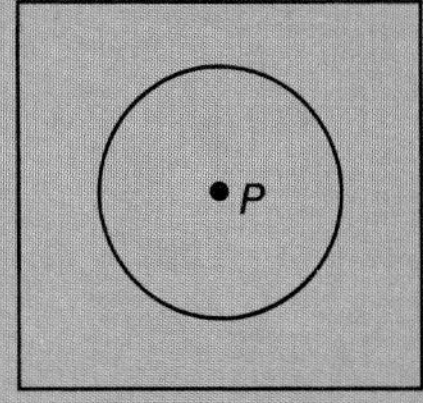

Circle

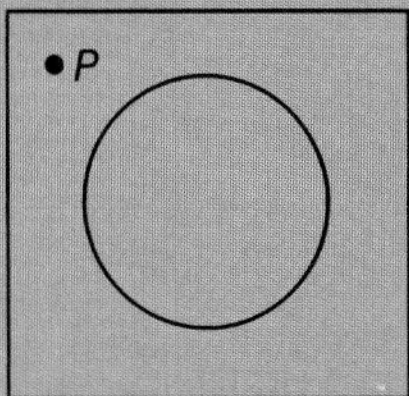

Hyperbola

3. Fold and crease each piece of paper so that the point P is against the circle. Repeat at least 50 times from a variety of positions.
4. What types of figures seem to be formed by the creases?

7. Center: (0, 0); foci: (0, $\pm\sqrt{5}$); vertices: (0, ±2); asym: $y = \pm 2x$
8. Center: (0, 0); foci: (±2, 0); vertices: ($\pm\sqrt{2}$, 0); asym: $y = \pm x$
9. Center: (0, 0); foci: ($\pm\sqrt{6}$, 0); vertices: ($\pm\sqrt{3}$, 0); asym: $y = \pm x$
10. Center: (2, −5); foci: ($2 \pm \sqrt{10}$, −5); vertices: (3, −5) and (1, −5); asym: $y = 3x - 11$ and $-3x + 1$
11. Center: (−1, −3); foci: (−1, $-3 \pm 2\sqrt{5}$); vertices: (−1, −1) and (−1 −5); asym: $y = \frac{1}{2}x - \frac{5}{2}$ and $y = -\frac{1}{2}x - \frac{7}{2}$
12. Center: (2, −5); foci: ($2 \pm \sqrt{10}$, −5); vertices: (5, −5) and (−1, −5); asym: $y = \frac{1}{3}x - \frac{17}{3}$ and $y = -\frac{1}{3}x - \frac{13}{3}$
13. Center: (−1, −3); foci: (−1, $-3 \pm \sqrt{41}$); vertices: (−1, −8) and (−1, 2); asym: $y = \frac{5}{4}x - \frac{7}{4}$ and $y = -\frac{5}{4}x - \frac{17}{4}$
14. Center: (1, −2); foci: ($1 \pm \sqrt{2}$, −2); vertices: (2, −2) and (0, −2); asym: $y = x - 3$ and $y = -x - 1$
15. Center: (−1, −2); foci: ($-1 \pm \sqrt{5}$, −2); vertices: (−2, −2) and (0, −2); asym: $y = 2x$ and $y = -2x - 4$
16. Center: $\left(\frac{1}{3}, 3\right)$; foci: $\left(\frac{1}{3} \pm \sqrt{37}, 3\right)$; vertices: $\left(-\frac{2}{3}, 3\right)$ and $\left(\frac{4}{3}, 3\right)$; asym: $y = 6x + 1$ and $y = -6x + 5$
17. Center: (−3, 1); foci: ($-3 \pm \sqrt{13}$, 1); vertices: (−1, 1) and (−5, 1); asym: $y = \frac{3}{2}x + \frac{11}{2}$ and $y = -\frac{3}{2}x - \frac{7}{2}$

For Exercises 18–21, 24–26, and 30–32, see Teacher's Answer Section.

Mixed Review

33. (3, 6) **34.** $\left(\frac{3}{2}, 2\right)$
35. (6, 0) **36.** 13
37. 10 **38.** 5
39. 5 **40.** Both
41. Neither **42.** No
43. Yes **44.** No
45. 138.24m^2

10-5

FIRST FIVE MINUTES

Find the center, vertices, and foci of the following hyperbolas.

1. $\frac{x^2}{1} - \frac{y^2}{4} = 1$

   The center is (0, 0). The vertices are $(\pm 1, 0)$.
   The foci are $(\pm\sqrt{5}, 0)$.

2. $\frac{(x-10)^2}{64} - \frac{(y-2)^2}{81} = 1$

   The center is (10, 2).
   The vertices are $(10 \pm 8, 2)$.
   The foci are $(10 \pm \sqrt{145}, 2)$.

Equations of Parabolas

The parabola was introduced as the graph of a second-degree polynomial in the previous chapter. In this section, the parabola is given a geometrical definition.

Point out that both a thrown ball and water from a hose follow a parabolic path.

Key Questions

- What geometric factors determine the shape of a parabola?
  The directrix line and the focus point
- What is the shape of a parabola whose focus is very near the directrix?
  The parabola will appear very long and narrow, like a needle.
- What is the shape of a parabola whose focus is very far from the directrix?
  The parabola will appear short and wide, like a shallow bowl.

10-5 Parabolas

Master Grapher Worksheet 19, *Conic Sections: Parabolas*, can be used for lesson closure.

When a plane intersects a cone parallel to an element of the cone, a parabola is formed. Cross sections of a headlight are parabolas with the bulb located at the focus. All light from the focus is reflected outward, parallel to the axis of symmetry.

Radar and radio antennas may have cross sections that are parabolas. Incoming radio waves are reflected and concentrated at the focus. Some comets have parabolic orbits.

Cables hung from suspension bridges form parabolas. When a cable supports only its own weight, it does not form a parabola, but rather a curve called a catenary.

Equations of Parabolas

Objective: Find the vertex, focus, and directrix, and draw a graph of a parabola, given its equation.

Some equations of second degree have graphs that are parabolas.

Definition

A **parabola** is a set of all points P in a plane equidistant from a fixed line and a fixed point in the plane. The fixed line is called the **directrix** and the fixed point is called the **focus**.

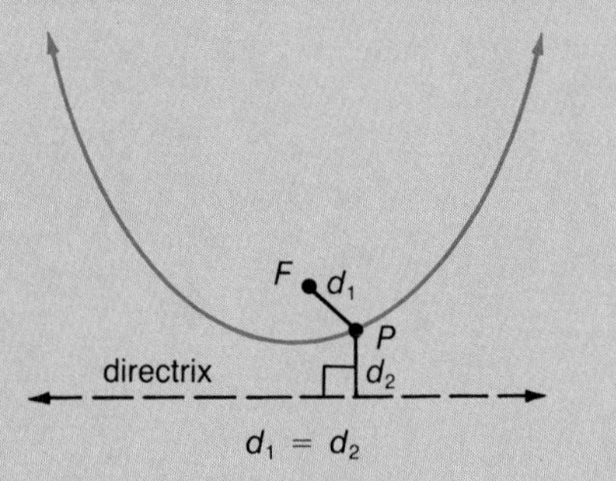

Theorem 10-10

A parabola with focus at $(0, p)$ and vertex at $(0, 0)$ has directrix $y = -p$.

We first obtain an equation of a parabola with focus on the y-axis, directrix parallel to the x-axis with equation $y = -p$, and vertex at the origin.

Consider the point P with coordinates (x, y). We know from the definition of a parabola that $FP = PD$. Using the distance formula we have
$FP = \sqrt{(x - 0)^2 + (y - p)^2}$.
The distance $PD = y + p$.
Thus $\sqrt{(x - 0)^2 + (y - p)^2} = y + p$.
Squaring both sides we have

$$x^2 + (y - p)^2 = y^2 + 2py + p^2$$

$$x^2 + y^2 - 2py + p^2 = y^2 + 2py + p^2$$

This yields $x^2 = 4py$.

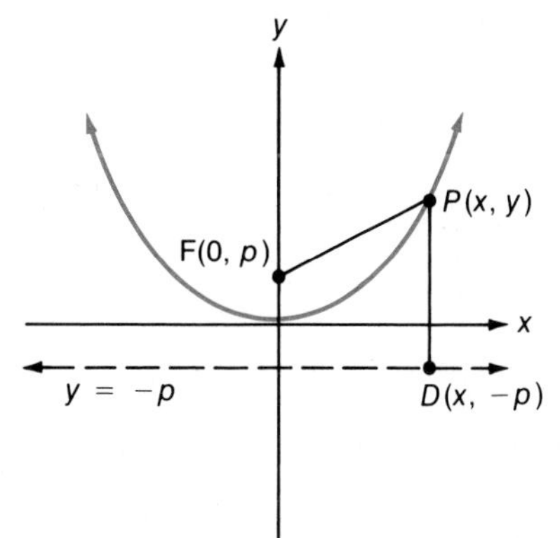

Theorem 10-11

The equation (in standard form) of a parabola with focus at $(0, p)$, directrix $y = -p$, vertex $(0, 0)$, and y-axis as the only line of symmetry is $x^2 = 4py$.

EXAMPLE 1 For the parabola $x^2 = y$, find the vertex, focus, and directrix. Then draw a graph.

The equation is in the form $x^2 = 4py$.

Since the coefficient of y is 1, $4p = 1$, so $p = \frac{1}{4}$.

Thus the focus is $\left(0, \frac{1}{4}\right)$ and the directrix is $y = -\frac{1}{4}$. The vertex is $(0, 0)$.

If $p > 0$, the graph opens upward. If $p < 0$, the graph opens downward and the focus and directrix exchange sides of the x-axis.

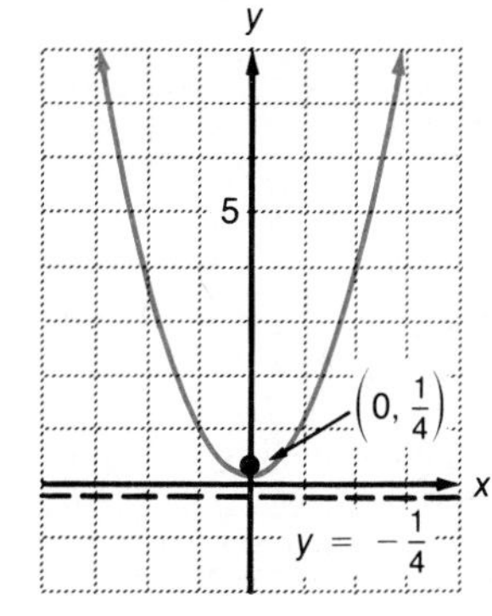

Try This For each parabola, find the vertex, focus, and directrix. Then draw a graph. See Additional Answers.

a. $x^2 = 8y$ Vertex (0, 0); focus (0, 2); directrix $y = -2$

b. $y = -\dfrac{x^2}{2}$ Vertex (0, 0); focus $\left(0, -\frac{1}{2}\right)$; directrix $y = \frac{1}{2}$

Theorem 10-12

The equation (in standard form) of a parabola with focus $(p, 0)$, directrix $x = -p$, vertex $(0, 0)$, and x-axis as the line of symmetry is $y^2 = 4px$.

Chalkboard Examples (*T20*)

1. Find the vertex, focus, and directrix, and draw the graph of the parabola $8y = x^2$.
   The vertex is (0, 0).
   $4p = 8$
   $p = 2$
   The focus is (0, 2).
   The directrix is $y = -2$.

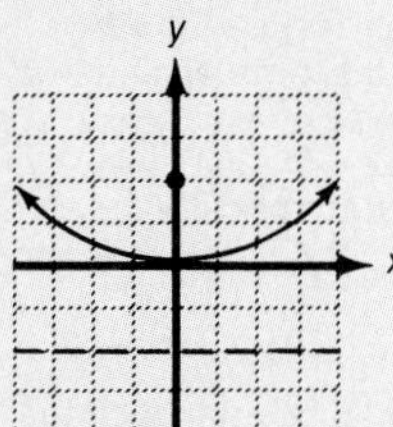

2. Find the vertex, focus, and directrix, and draw a graph of the parabola $8x = y^2$.
   The line of symmetry is the x-axis.
   The center is (0, 0)
   $4p = 8$
   $p = 2$
   The focus is (2, 0).
   The directrix is $x = -2$.

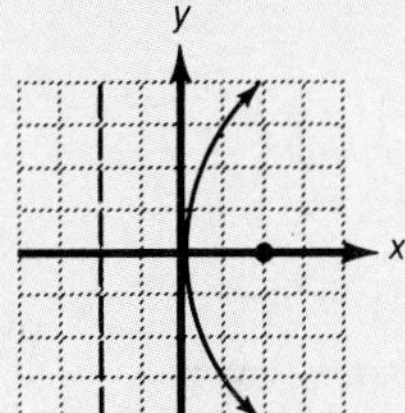

Finding Standard Form by Completing the Square

Emphasize the generality of the translation rule. For any equation in x and y, if x is replaced by $x - h$, and y is replaced by $y - k$, then the graph of the new equation is the original graph shifted h units in the x-direction and k units in the y-direction.

Chalkboard Examples

1. Put the parabola $x^2 - 6x - 4y + 29 = 0$ into standard form, find the vertex, focus, and directrix, and graph the parabola.
   $x^2 - 6x = 4y - 29$
   Complete the square.
   $x^2 - 6x + 9 = 4y - 20$
   $(x - 3)^2 = 4(y - 5)$
   The vertex is (3, 5).
   $4p = 4, p = 1$
   The focus is (3, 5 + 1) = (3, 6).
   The directrix is $y = 5 - 1$, or $y = 4$.

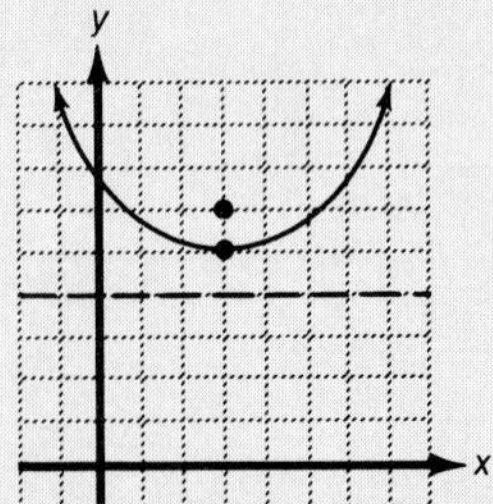

2. Put the parabola $8x - y^2 + 12y - 60 = 0$ into standard form. Find the vertex, focus, and directrix, and graph the parabola.
   $8x - 60 = y^2 - 12y$
   Complete the square.
   $8x - 60 + 36 = y^2 - 12x + 36$
   $8(x - 3) = (y - 6)^2$
   The vertex is (3, 6).
   $4p = 8, p = 2$
   The focus is (3 + 2, 6) = (5, 6).
   The directrix is $x = 3 - 2$, or $x = 1$.

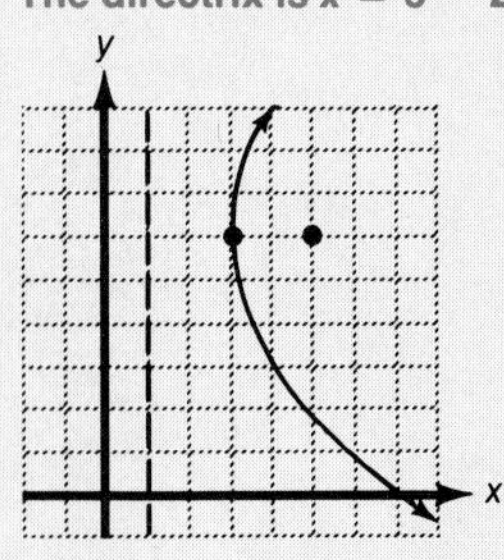

EXAMPLE 2 For the parabola $y^2 = -12x$, find the vertex, focus, and directrix. Then draw a graph.

The equation is in the form $y^2 = 4px$.

Since the coefficient of x is -12, $4p = -12$, so $p = -3$.

Thus the focus is $(-3, 0)$ and the directrix is $x = -(-3) = 3$. The vertex is $(0, 0)$.

We find two other points on the graph by substituting -3 for x. Choosing -3 for x will give us a perfect square for y^2. This yields $(-3, 6)$ and $(-3, -6)$.

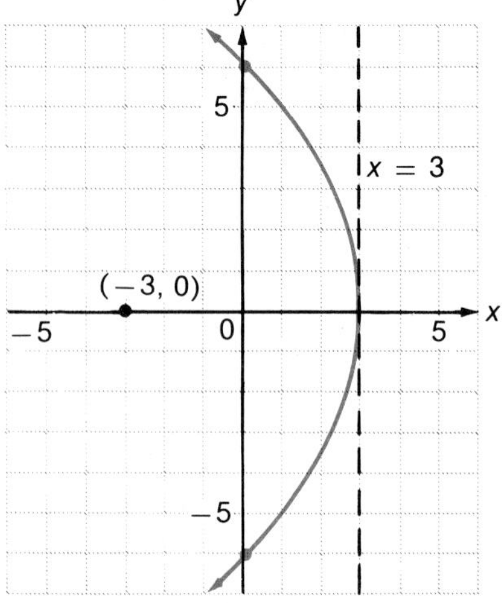

Try This For each parabola find the vertex, focus, and directrix. Then draw a graph.

For graphs, see Selected Answers.

c. $y^2 = 2x$ Vertex (0, 0); focus $\left(\frac{1}{2}, 0\right)$; directrix $x = -\frac{1}{2}$ **d.** $x = -\frac{y^2}{4}$ Vertex (0, 0); focus $(-1, 0)$; directrix $x = 1$

Finding Standard Form by Completing the Square

Objective: Find the vertex, focus, and directrix, and graph a parabola by first completing the square.

Theorem 10-13

If a parabola is translated so that its vertex is (h, k) and its axis of symmetry is parallel to the y-axis, it has an equation of $(x - h)^2 = 4p(y - k)$, where the focus is $(h, k + p)$ and the directrix is $y = k - p$.

If a parabola is translated so that its vertex is (h, k) and its axis of symmetry is parallel to the x-axis, it has an equation of $(y - k)^2 = 4p(x - h)$, where the focus is $(h + p, k)$, and the directrix is $x = h - p$.

EXAMPLE 3 For the parabola $x^2 + 6x + 4y + 5 = 0$, find the vertex, focus, and directrix. Then draw a graph.

First, we complete the square.

$$\begin{aligned} x^2 + 6x &= -4y - 5 \\ x^2 + 6x + 9 &= -4y - 5 + 9 \\ x^2 + 6x + 9 &= -4y + 4 \\ (x + 3)^2 &= -4y + 4 \\ &= 4(-1)(y - 1) \end{aligned}$$

Vertex $(-3, 1)$; focus $(-3, 1 + (-1))$ or $(-3, 0)$; directrix $y = 2$

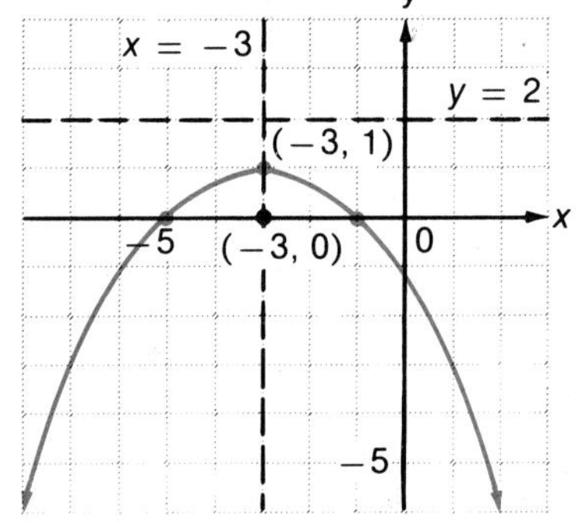

EXAMPLE 4 For the parabola $y^2 + 6y - 8x - 31 = 0$, find the vertex, focus, and directrix. Then draw a graph.

We complete the square.

$$
\begin{aligned}
y^2 + 6y &= 8x + 31 \\
y^2 + 6y + 9 &= 8x + 31 + 9 \\
y^2 + 6y + 9 &= 8x + 40 \\
(y + 3)^2 &= 8x + 40 \\
&= 8(x + 5) \\
&= 4(2)(x + 5)
\end{aligned}
$$

Vertex $(-5, -3)$; focus $(-5 + 2, -3)$ or $(-3, -3)$; directrix $x = -5 - 2 = -7$

Try This For each parabola find the vertex, focus and directrix. Then graph.
See Additional Answers.

e. $x^2 + 2x - 8y - 3 = 0$ **f.** $y^2 + 2y + 4x - 7 = 0$

Finding Equations of Parabolas

Objective: Find the equation of a parabola, given certain characteristics.

EXAMPLE 5 Find the equation of a parabola with focus (3, 9) and directrix $y = -1$.

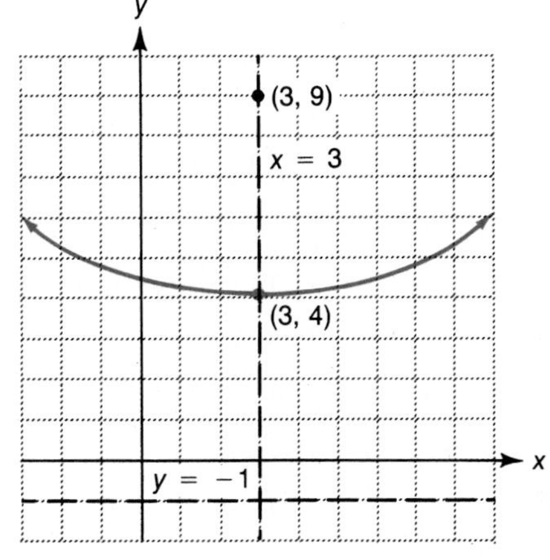

Since the directrix is a horizontal line below the focus, the parabola opens upward. The line of symmetry is $x = 3$. The vertex is the midpoint between $(3, -1)$ and $(3, 9)$, so the vertex is $(3, 4)$. The focus is 5 units in the positive direction (up) from the vertex, so $p = 5$.

Substituting in $(x - h)^2 = 4p(y - k)$, we have $(x - 3)^2 = 4(5)(y - 4)$, or $(x - 3)^2 = 20(y - 4)$.

EXAMPLE 6 Find the equation of a parabola with focus (3, 9) and vertex (5, 9).

Since the focus is to the left of the vertex, the parabola opens to the left. The line of symmetry is $y = 9$. The focus is 2 units in the negative direction (left) from the vertex, so $p = -2$. The directrix is thus 2 units in the positive direction (right) from the vertex, or $x = 7$.

Substituting in $(y - k)^2 = 4p(x - h)$, we have $(y - 9)^2 = 4(-2)(x - 5)$, or $(y - 9)^2 = -8(x - 5)$.

Finding Equations of Parabolas

Chalkboard Examples

1. Find the equation of a parabola with focus $(1, -1)$ and directrix $x = -3$.
Since the directrix is a vertical line to the left of the focus, the parabola opens to the right. The line of symmetry is $y = -1$. The vertex is the midpoint between $(1, -1)$ and $(-3, -1)$, so the vertex is $(-1, -1)$. The focus is 2 units to the right of the vertex, so $p = 2$. Substituting in $(y - k)^2 = 4p(x - h)$, we have $(y - (-1))^2 = 4(2)(x - (-1))$, or $(y + 1)^2 = 8(x + 1)$.
2. Find the equation of a parabola with focus (2, 0) and vertex (2, 4).
Since the vertex is above the focus, the parabola opens downward. The line of symmetry is $x = 2$. The focus is 4 units in the negative direction from the vertex so $p = -4$. The directrix is thus 4 units in the positive direction from the vertex, or $y = 8$. Substituting in $(x - h)^2 = 4p(y - k)$, we have $(x - 2)^2 = -16(y - 4)$.

LESSON QUIZ

2. Find the equation of the parabola with focus (0, 5) and directrix $y = -5$.
$20y = x^2$
3. Find the vertex, focus, and directrix, and graph.
$x^2 - 4x - 8y + 12 = 0$
The vertex is (2, 1).
The focus is (2, 3).
The directrix is $y = -1$.

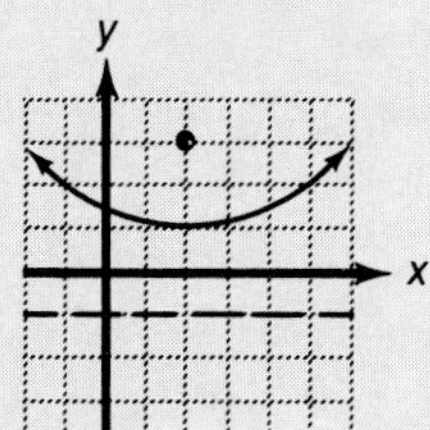

Assignment Guide	
Algebra:	Day 1: 1–10, MR Day 2: 11–24
Alg w/Finite or Trig:	1–35 e/o, 36, MR assign w. Application
Comprehensive:	1–24 m3, 25–35 e/o, 36, 37–40 e/o, MR

ADDITIONAL ANSWERS

Try This

a.

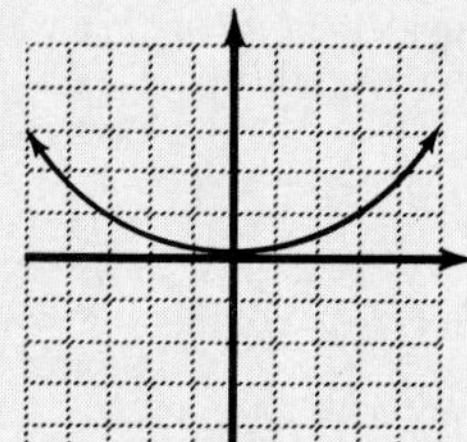

b.

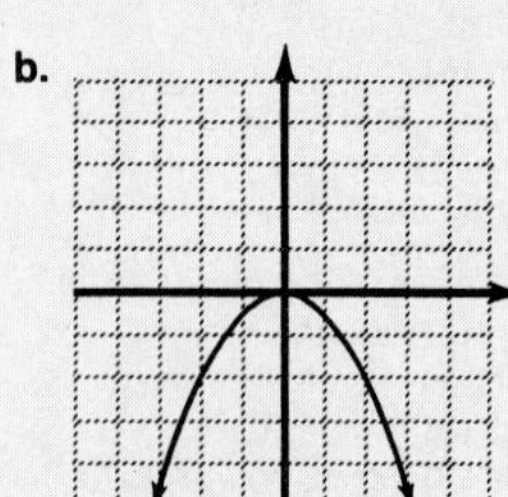

For graphs of Try This c–f, see Selected Answers.

e. Vertex: $\left(-1, -\frac{1}{2}\right)$; focus: $\left(-1, \frac{3}{2}\right)$; directrix: $y = -\frac{5}{2}$

f. Vertex: $(2, -1)$: focus: $(1, -1)$; directrix: $x = 3$

Exercises

For all graphs, see Teacher's Answer Section.

9. $V(-2, 1)$; $F\left(-2, -\frac{1}{2}\right)$; $y = \frac{5}{2}$
10. $V(-2, 3)$; $F(-7, 3)$; $x = 3$
11. $V(-1, -3)$; $F\left(-1, -\frac{7}{2}\right)$; $y = -\frac{5}{2}$
12. $V(7, -3)$; $F\left(7\frac{1}{4}, -3\right)$; $x = 6\frac{3}{4}$
13. $V(0, -2)$; $F\left(0, -\frac{7}{4}\right)$; $y = -\frac{9}{4}$

Try This Find the equation of the parabola satisfying the given conditions.

g. Focus $(0, 3)$, vertex $(0, 0)$ $x^2 = 12y$

h. Focus $(-4, 2)$, directrix $x = -6$ $(y - 2)^2 = 4(x + 5)$

i. Focus $(-4, 2)$, vertex $(-4, 5)$ $(x + 4)^2 = -12(y - 5)$

10-5 EXERCISES

A

For each parabola find the vertex, focus, and directrix. Then draw a graph.

1. $x^2 = 8y$ $V(0, 0)$; $F(0, 2)$; $y = -2$

2. $x^2 = 16y$ $V(0, 0)$; $F(0, 4)$; $y = -4$

3. $y^2 = -6x$ $V(0, 0)$; $F\left(-\frac{3}{2}, 0\right)$; $x = \frac{3}{2}$

4. $y^2 = -2x$ $V(0, 0)$; $F\left(-\frac{1}{2}, 0\right)$; $x = \frac{1}{2}$

5. $x^2 - 4y = 0$ $V(0, 0)$; $F(0, 1)$; $y = -1$

6. $y^2 + 4x = 0$ $V(0, 0)$; $F(-1, 0)$; $x = 1$

7. $y = 2x^2$ $V(0, 0)$; $F\left(0, \frac{1}{8}\right)$; $y = -\frac{1}{8}$

8. $y = \frac{1}{2}x^2$ $V(0, 0)$; $F\left(0, \frac{1}{2}\right)$; $y = -\frac{1}{2}$

Find the vertex, focus, and directrix. Then draw a graph.

9. $(x + 2)^2 = -6(y - 1)$

10. $(y - 3)^2 = -20(x + 2)$

11. $x^2 + 2x + 2y + 7 = 0$

12. $y^2 + 6y - x + 16 = 0$

13. $x^2 - y - 2 = 0$

14. $x^2 - 4x - 2y = 0$

15. $y = x^2 + 4x + 3$

16. $y = x^2 + 6x + 10$

17. $4y^2 - 4y - 4x + 24 = 0$

18. $4y^2 + 4y - 4x - 16 = 0$

Find an equation of a parabola satisfying the given conditions.

19. Focus $(4, 0)$; directrix $x = -4$

20. Focus $\left(0, \frac{1}{4}\right)$; vertex $(0, 0)$

21. Focus $(-\sqrt{2}, 0)$; vertex $(0, 0)$

22. Focus $(0, -\pi)$; directrix $y = \pi$

23. Focus $(0, 3\sqrt{3})$; directrix $y = -3\sqrt{3}$

24. Focus $(\sqrt{2} - 2, 0)$; directrix $x = 0$

25. Focus $(3, 2)$; directrix $x = -4$

26. Focus $(-2, 3)$; directrix $y = -3$

27. Focus $(3, 4)$; vertex $(3, 7)$

28. Focus $(-2, -1)$; vertex $(0, -1)$

B

For each parabola find the vertex, focus, and directrix. Use a calculator.

29. $x^2 = 8056.25y$

30. $y^2 = -7645.88x$

Graph each of the following, using the same set of axes.

31. $x^2 - y^2 = 0, x^2 - y^2 = 1$
$x^2 + y^2 = 1, \quad y = x^2$

32. $x^2 - 4y^2 = 0, x^2 - 4y^2 = 1$
$x^2 + 4y^2 = 1, x = 4y^2$

33. Find equations of the following parabola: line of symmetry parallel to the y-axis, vertex $(-1, 2)$, and containing $(-3, 1)$. $(x + 1)^2 = -4(y - 2)$

34. a. Graph $(y - 3)^2 = -20(x + 1)$. Is this relation a function? No

b. In general, is $(y - k)^2 = 4p(x - h)$ a function? No, unless $p = 0$

35. The cables of a suspension bridge are 50 ft above the roadbed at the towers of the bridge and 10 ft above it in the center of the bridge. The roadbed is 200 ft long. Vertical cables are to be spaced every 20 ft along the bridge. Calculate the lengths of these vertical cables.
10 ft, 11.6 ft, 16.4 ft, 24.4 ft, 35.6 ft, 50 ft

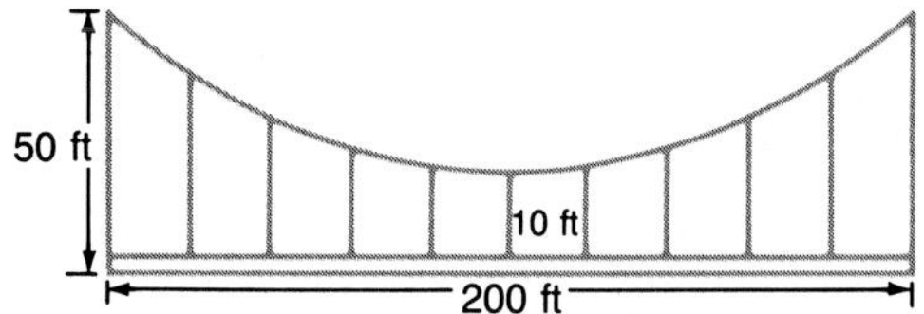

36. ***Critical Thinking*** Write an equation in standard form for a parabola with vertex at $(-3, 1)$ that opens **a**) up, **b**) left, **c**) down, **d**) right.

Challenge

37. In the figure to the right, the segment PP' is perpendicular to the axis of symmetry of the parabola and contains F, the focus. The lines OP and OP' are tangent to the parabola at P and P', and intersect at the same point that the axis of symmetry intersects the directrix.

a. Prove that $\angle POF$ has a measure of 45°. (Hint: Use the definition of a parabola.)

b. Suppose that the segment PP' is the hypotenuse of a right triangle. Explain how you can find the vertex of the parabola. Suppose that the vertex is three units from the segment. How long is the segment?

Graph these inequalities.

38. $y > 3x^2$ **39.** $x^2 \geq 25y$ **40.** $(x + 2)^2 > -6(y - 2)$

Mixed Review

Find the vertex, line of symmetry, and minimum or maximum value.

41. $f(x) = 5(x - 3)^2 + 11$ **42.** $f(x) = -2(x - 13.5)^2 + 1.6$

Complete the square. **43.** $y^2 - 8y$ **44.** $m^2 + 5m$ **45.** $a^2 - 0.2a$

Find the distance between the points. **46.** $(\sqrt{m}, \sqrt{n})$ and $(\sqrt{m}, -\sqrt{n})$

Solve. **47.** $3x^2 + 13x + 12 = 0$ **48.** $2x^2 - 3x - 9 = 0$ **49.** $10x^2 + x = 2$

50. $\frac{3}{5}x^2 + x + \frac{2}{5} = 0$ **51.** $\frac{6}{13}x^2 + x = \frac{5}{13}$

14. $V(2, -2); F\left(2, -\frac{3}{2}\right); y = -\frac{5}{2}$
15. $V(-2, -1); F\left(-2, -\frac{3}{4}\right); y = -\frac{5}{4}$
16. $V(-3, 1); F\left(-3, \frac{5}{4}\right); y = \frac{3}{4}$
17. $V\left(\frac{23}{4}, \frac{1}{2}\right); F\left(6, \frac{1}{2}\right); x = \frac{11}{2}$
18. $V\left(-\frac{17}{4}, -\frac{1}{2}\right); F\left(-4, -\frac{1}{2}\right); x = -\frac{9}{2}$
19. $y^2 = 16x$
20. $x^2 = y$
21. $y^2 = -4\sqrt{2}x$
22. $x^2 = -4\pi y$
23. $x^2 = 12\sqrt{3}y$
24. $y^2 = (2\sqrt{2} - 4)(x + 2 - \sqrt{2})$
25. $(y - 2)^2 = 14\left(x + \frac{1}{2}\right)$
26. $(x + 2)^2 = 12y$
27. $(x - 3)^2 = -12(y - 7)$
28. $(y + 1)^2 = -8x$
29. Vertex: (0, 0)
Focus: (0, 2014.0625)
Directrix:
$y = -2014.0625$
30. Vertex: (0, 0)
Focus: (−1911.47, 0)
Directrix: $x = 1911.47$

36. Answers may vary. Examples:
a. $(x + 3)^2 = 4(y - 1)$
b. $(y - 1)^2 = -4(x + 3)$
c. $(x + 3)^2 = -4(y - 1)$
d. $(y - 1)^2 = 4(x + 3)$
37. See Teacher's Answer Section.

Mixed Review

41. Vertex: (3, 11). Min: 11
Line of symmetry: $x = 3$
42. Vertex: (13.5, 1.6). Max: 1.6
Line of symmetry: $x = 13.5$
43. $y^2 - 8y + 16$
44. $m^2 + 5m + \frac{25}{4}$
45. $a^2 - 0.2a + 0.01$
46. $2\sqrt{n}$ **47.** $-\frac{4}{3}, -3$
48. $-\frac{3}{2}, 3$ **49.** $\frac{2}{5}, -\frac{1}{2}$
50. $-\frac{2}{3}, -1$ **51.** $-\frac{5}{2}, \frac{1}{3}$

10-6

FIRST FIVE MINUTES

1. Find the vertex, focus and directrix of the parabola.
$x^2 - 2x - 6y + 13 = 0$
$x^2 - 2x = 6y - 13$
Complete the square.
$x^2 - 2x + 1 = 6y - 12$
$(x - 1)^2 = 6(y - 2)$
The vertex is (1, 2).
$4p = 6, p = \frac{3}{2}$
The focus is $\left(1, \frac{7}{2}\right)$.
The directrix is $y = \frac{1}{2}$.

Recognizing Conics

Remind students of the standard equations for the conic sections.

$\frac{x^2}{a^2} + \frac{y^2}{b^2} = 1$	Ellipse
$x^2 + y^2 = r^2$	Circle
$\frac{x^2}{a^2} - \frac{y^2}{b^2} = 1$	Hyperbola
$4py = x^2$	Parabola

Chalkboard Examples

Tell in each case which conic is defined by the equation.

1. $3x^2 + 3y^2 + 2x - 3 = 0$
$A = B$; the equation may define a circle. Complete the square to check.
$3x^2 + 2x + 3y^2 = 3$
$3\left(x^2 + \frac{2}{3}x\right) + 3y^2 = 3$
$3\left(x + \frac{1}{3}\right)^2 + 3y^2 = 3 + \frac{1}{9}$
The right side of the equation is positive, so the equation describes a circle.
2. $2x^2 + 5y^2 + 4x + 7y + 12 = 0$
A and B have the same sign but are unequal. Completing the square,
$2(x + 1)^2 + 5\left(y + \frac{7}{10}\right)^2$
$= -10 + \frac{49}{25}$
The right side of the equation is negative; no solution exists.
3. $5x^2 + 4x + 6y + 3 = 0$
There is no y^2 term. The equation defines a parabola.

10-6 Second-Degree Equations and Systems

Master Grapher Worksheet 20, *Quadratic-Linear Systems*, can be used as a lesson opener.

Recognizing Conics

Objective: Recognize equations of circles, ellipses, hyperbolas, and parabolas.

It is important to be able to look at a second-degree equation and determine whether it is the equation of a circle, ellipse, hyperbola, or parabola. Following are some key points which will help in the recognition of the conics.

Recognizing Conics

Consider the second-degree equation $Ax^2 + By^2 + Cx + Dy + E = 0$.
1. If $A = B$, the equation may define a circle.
2. If A and B have the same sign and $A \neq B$, the equation may define an ellipse.
3. If A and B have different signs, the equation defines a hyperbola.
4. If either A or B is 0, the equation defines a parabola.

Equations representing closed figures (circles or ellipses) must be checked to determine whether real solutions exist. For example, the equation $x^2 + y^2 = -1$ has no real solutions since x^2 and y^2 are nonnegative.

EXAMPLES Tell which conic is defined by each equation.

1. $3x^2 - 4y^2 + 2y - 5 = 0$
A and B have different signs. Thus the equation defines a hyperbola.

2. $6x^2 + 17x - 9y - 7 = 0$
There is no y^2 term, so $B = 0$. The equation defines a parabola.

3. $2x^2 + 2y^2 - 3x + \frac{1}{2} = 0$

$A = B$. The equation may define a circle. We can complete the square to check.

$$2x^2 - 3x + 2y^2 = -\frac{1}{2} \qquad \text{Rearranging}$$
$$2\left(x^2 - \frac{3}{2}x + \frac{9}{16}\right) + 2y^2 = -\frac{1}{2} + \frac{9}{8}$$
$$2\left(x^2 - \frac{3}{2}x + \frac{9}{16}\right) + 2y^2 = \frac{5}{8}$$

After completing the square, the right side of the equation is positive, so real solutions exist. The equation defines a circle.

Try This Tell which conic is defined by each equation.

a. $4x^2 + 9y^2 + 16x - 54y - 61 = 0$ Ellipse **b.** $-3x^2 - 3y^2 + 7y + 9 = 0$ Circle

c. $5y^2 - 3x + 9 = 0$ Parabola **d.** $2x^2 - 4y^2 - 5x + 8y + 19 = 0$ Hyperbola

Finding Second-Degree Equations from Graphs

Objective: Determine a second-degree equation from its graph.

Geometric models can be represented algebraically to help solve some problems.

EXAMPLE 4 Determine the equation represented by the graph.

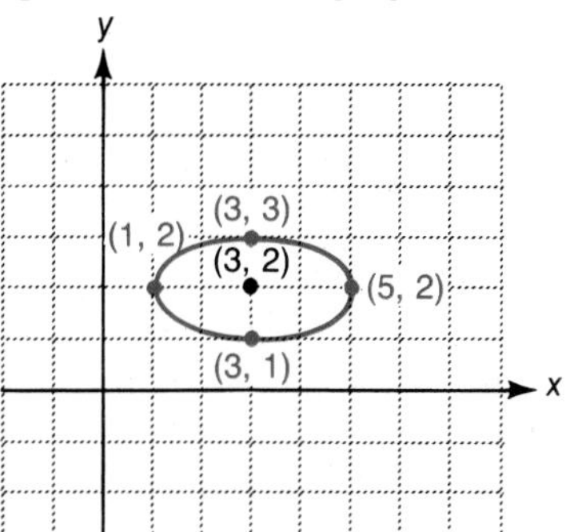

The graph shown is an ellipse. To solve this problem we can start by locating the vertices and the center.

The vertices are at (1, 2), (5, 2), (3, 1), and (3, 3). Thus, the center is at the midpoint of the segment from (1, 2) to (5, 2), which is (3, 2).

The length of the major axis, $2a$, is 4. So $a = 2$. The length of the minor axis, $2b$, is 2. So $b = 1$.

Since the equation of an ellipse is $\frac{(x-h)^2}{a^2} + \frac{(y-k)^2}{b^2} = 1$, we substitute and have $\frac{(x-3)^2}{4} + \frac{(y-2)^2}{1} = 1$, as the equation of the ellipse shown.

EXAMPLE 5 Determine the equation represented by the graph.

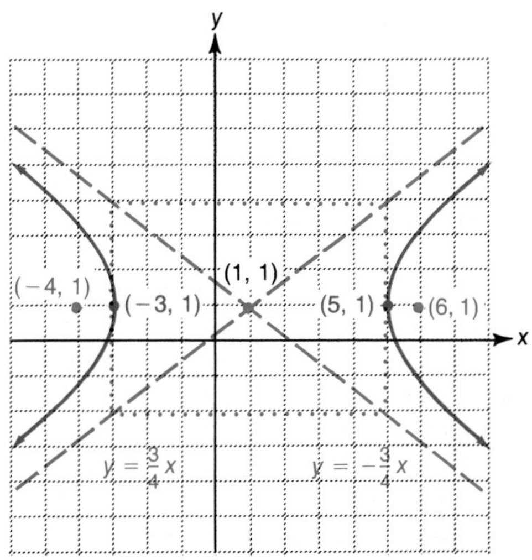

The graph shown is a hyperbola. The vertices are (5, 1) and (−3, 1). So the center is (1, 1). The foci are (6, 1) and (−4, 1). This graph has been translated 1 unit to the right and 1 unit upward. For the untranslated graph, $c^2 = a^2 + b^2$. So we have

$$5^2 = 4^2 + b^2$$
$$25 = 16 + b^2$$
$$9 = b^2$$

Thus, the equation is $\frac{(x-1)^2}{16} - \frac{(y-1)^2}{9} = 1$.

Finding Second-Degree Equations from Graphs

Chalkboard Examples

Determine the equation represented by the graph.

1.

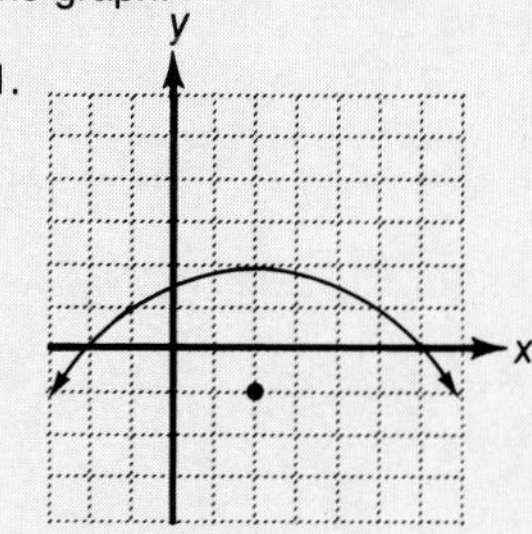

The graph shown is a parabola. The vertex is (2, 1) and the focus is (2, −1). Since the focus is $(h, k + p)$ where (h, k) is the vertex, $p = -2$. Substituting into the equation $(x - h)^2 = 4p(y - k)$, the equation of the parabola is $(x - 2)^2 = -8(y - 2)$.

2.

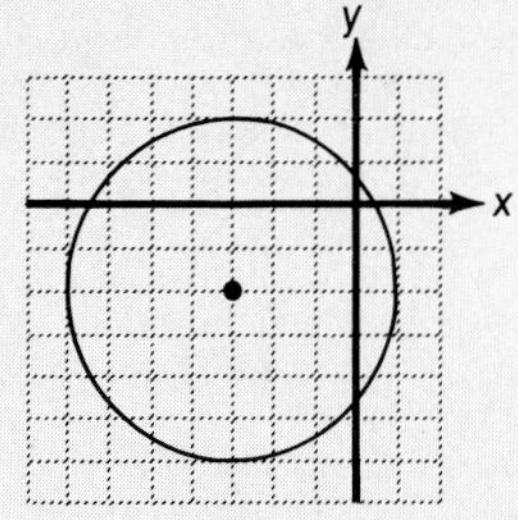

The graph shown is a circle. The center is (−3, −2) and a point on the circle is (1, −1). The distance between these points is $\sqrt{-(3-1)^2 + (-2-(-1))^2}$ or $\sqrt{17}$. Substituting into the equation $(x - h)^2 + (y - k)^2 = r^2$, the equation of the circle is $(x + 3)^2 + (y + 2)^2 = 17$.

Solving Systems Graphically

Point out that our sense of geometry can make algebra easier. For example, the system

$$x^2 + y^2 = 16$$
$$7x + 2y = 14$$

has at most two solutions, because a circle and a line intersect in at most two points.

Point out that solving graphically will not always give exact solutions. For example, have students graphically solve

$$y = x^2$$
$$x^2 + y^2 = 1$$

It is impossible to "estimate" the solutions.

$$\left(\pm\sqrt{-\frac{1}{2} + \frac{\sqrt{5}}{2}}, -\frac{1}{2} + \frac{\sqrt{5}}{2}\right)$$

Key Questions

- What is the possible number of points of intersection for two different circles? 2, 1, or 0
- What is the possible number of points of intersection for a circle and an ellipse? 4, 3, 2, 1, or 0
- What is the possible number of points of intersection for a circle and a parabola? 4, 3, 2, 1, or 0

Chalkboard Examples (*T21, T22*)

1. Solve the system graphically.
   $x^2 + y^2 = 9$
   $x + y = 5$

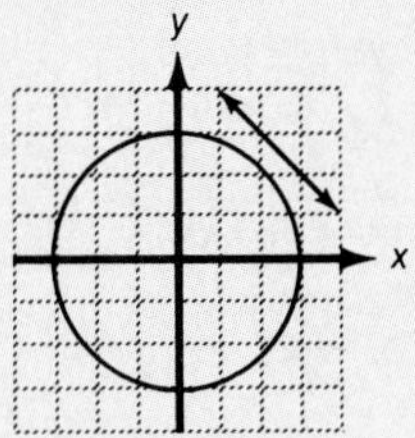

The circle and the line do not intersect. There is no solution to the system.

Try This Determine the equation represented by the graph.

e.

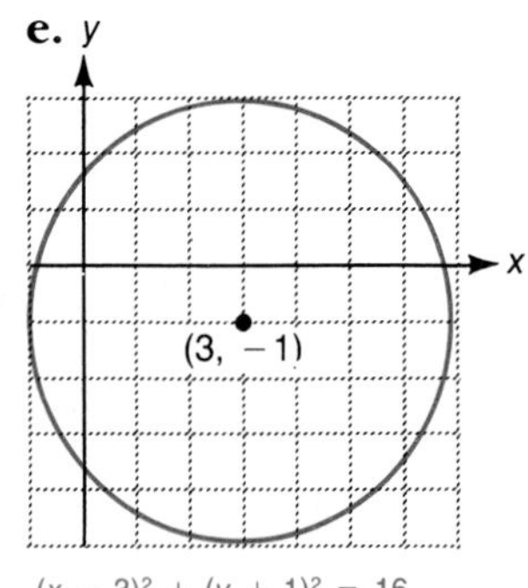

$(x - 3)^2 + (y + 1)^2 = 16$

f.

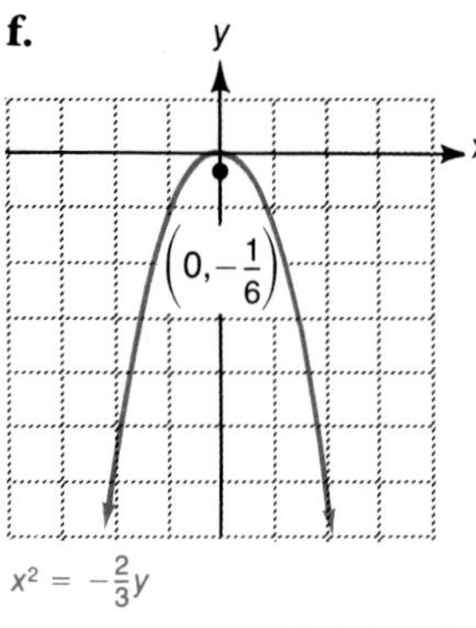

$x^2 = -\frac{2}{3}y$

g.

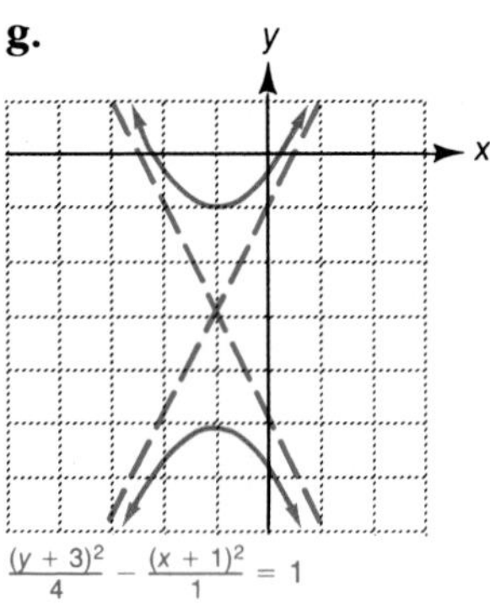

$\frac{(y + 3)^2}{4} - \frac{(x + 1)^2}{1} = 1$

Solving Systems Graphically

Objective: Solve second-degree systems graphically.

When we studied systems of linear equations, we solved them both graphically and algebraically. Here we study systems in which one equation is of first degree and one is of second degree. We will use graphical and then algebraic methods of solving. Recall that a solution is an ordered pair that satisfies all the equations in the system.

We consider a system of equations, an equation of a circle, and an equation of a line. Let us think about the possible ways in which a circle and a line can intersect. The three possibilities are shown in the figure at the right. For L_1 there is no point of intersection, hence the system of equations has no real solution. For L_2 there is one point of intersection, hence one real solution. For L_3 there are two points of intersection, hence two real solutions.

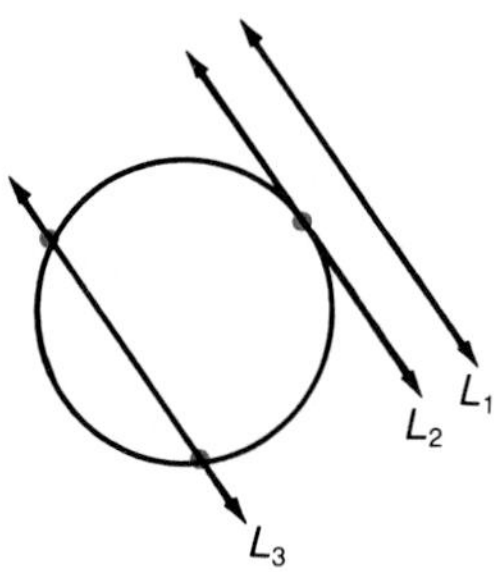

EXAMPLE 6 Solve graphically.

$$x^2 + y^2 = 25$$
$$3x - 4y = 0$$

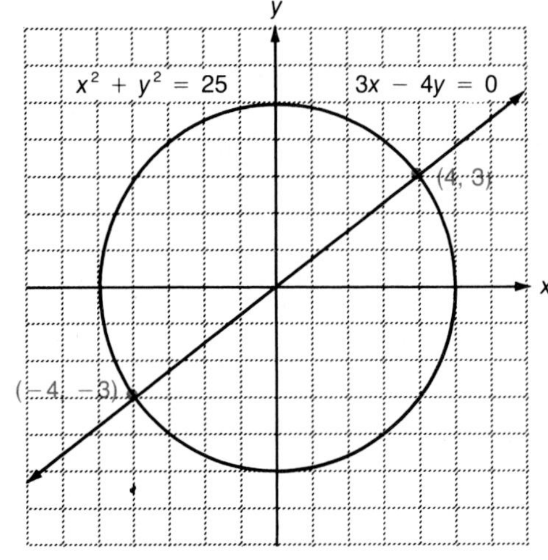

We graph the two equations, using the same axes. The first is the graph of a circle. The points of intersection have coordinates that must satisfy both equations. The solutions appear to be $(4, 3)$ and $(-4, -3)$. These points each check in the system, so the solutions are $(4, 3)$ and $(-4, -3)$.

The following figures show ways in which a circle and a hyperbola can intersect.

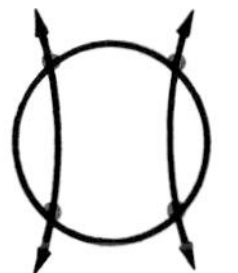
4 real solutions

3 real solutions

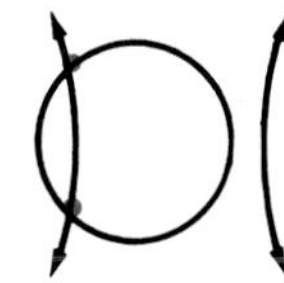
2 real solutions

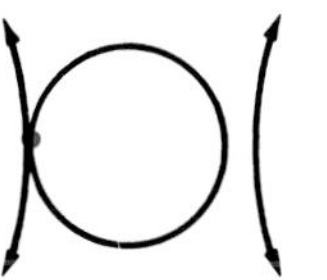
2 real solutions

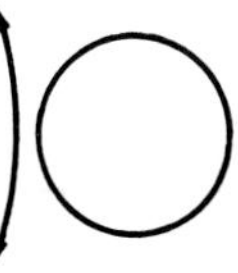
1 real solution

0 real solutions

EXAMPLE 7 Solve this system graphically.

$$x^2 + y^2 = 25$$
$$\frac{x^2}{25} - \frac{y^2}{25} = 1$$

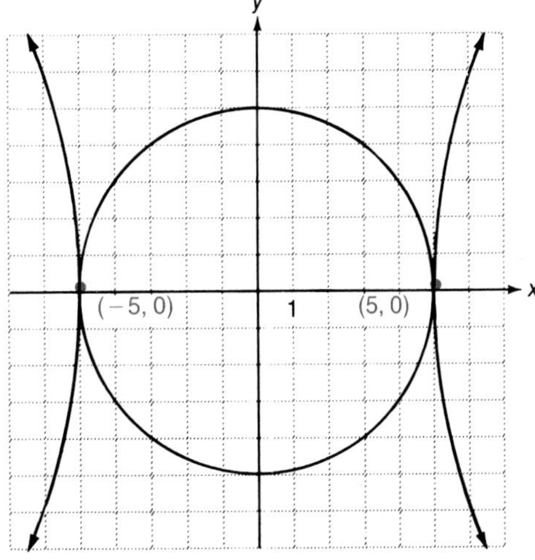

We graph the two equations using the same axes. The first equation is a circle and the second a hyperbola. The points of intersection have coordinates that must satisfy both equations; the solutions appear to be $(5, 0)$ and $(-5, 0)$.

Check: Since $(5)^2 = 25$ and $(-5)^2 = 25$, we can do both checks at once.

$x^2 + y^2 = 25$	
$(\pm 5)^2 + 0^2$	25
$25 + 0$	25
25	25 ✓

$\frac{x^2}{25} - \frac{y^2}{25} = 1$	
$\frac{(\pm 5)^2}{25} - \frac{0^2}{25}$	1
$1 - 0$	1
1	1 ✓

The solutions are $(5, 0)$ and $(-5, 0)$. This can be confirmed using computer graphing techniques.

Try This Solve these systems graphically. See Additional Answers.

h. $x^2 + y^2 = 25$
$y - x = -1$
$(4, 3), (-3, -4)$

i. $y = x^2 - 2x - 1$
$y = x + 3$
$(4, 7), (-1, 2)$

j. $x^2 + y^2 = 4$
$\frac{x^2}{4} - \frac{y^2}{4} = 1$ $(\pm 2, 0)$

k. $x^2 + y^2 = 16$
$\frac{x^2}{16} + \frac{y^2}{9} = 1$ $(\pm 4, 0)$

2. Solve this system graphically.
$x^2 + y^2 = 13$
$y = x^2 - 1$
The circle has radius $\sqrt{13}$. The parabola is symmetric with respect to the y-axis. The vertex is $(0, -1)$. The two intersection points are $(-2, 3)$ and $(2, 3)$.

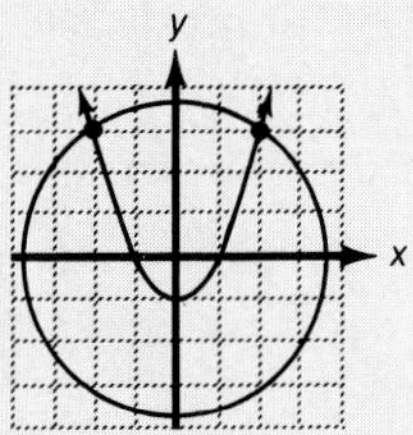

LESSON QUIZ

Identify the conics defined by each equation.

1. $x^2 - y^2 = 1$
Hyperbola
2. $3x^2 + 5y^2 + 2y - 7 = 0$
Ellipse

Solve graphically.

3. $x^2 + y^2 - 10 = 0$ (1)
$x - y = 2$ (2)
$(3, 1)$ or $(-1, -3)$

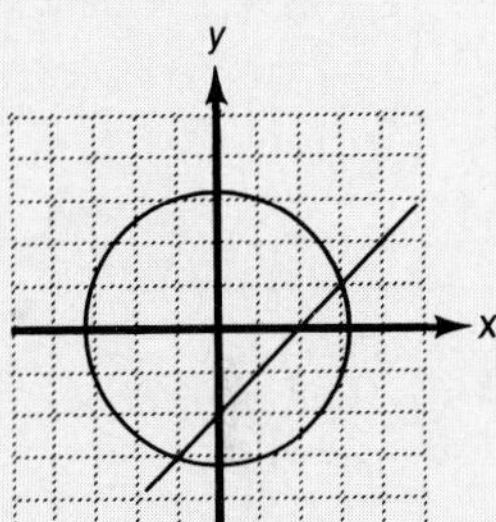

4. $x^2 + 3 = y^2$ (1)
$y = 2x^2$ (2)
$(1, 2)$ or $(-1, 2)$

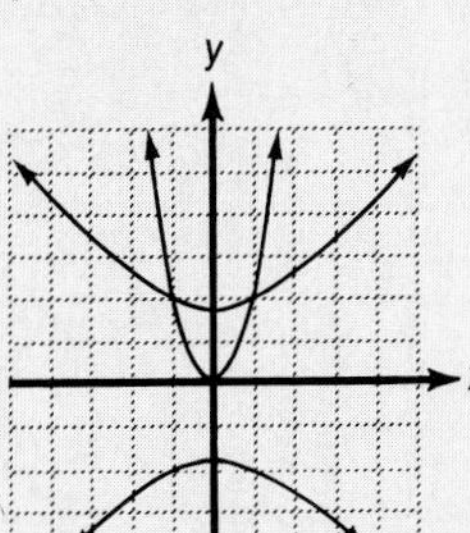

Assignment Guide
Algebra: Day 1: 1–19
Day 2: 20–35 e/o, MR

Alg w/Finite or Trig: 1–40 e/o, 41, MR

Comprehensive: 1–35 m3, 36–40 e/o, 41–43, MR

ADDITIONAL ANSWERS

Try This

h.

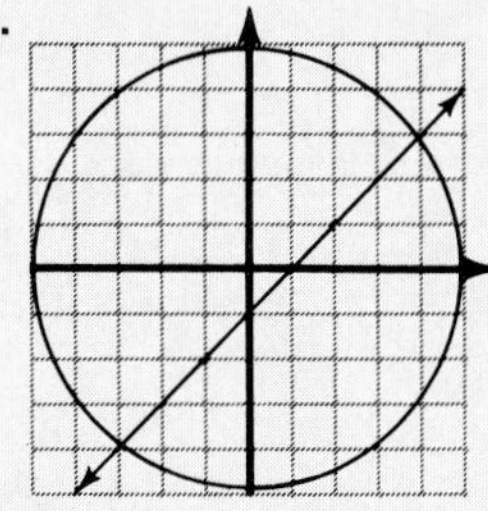

i.

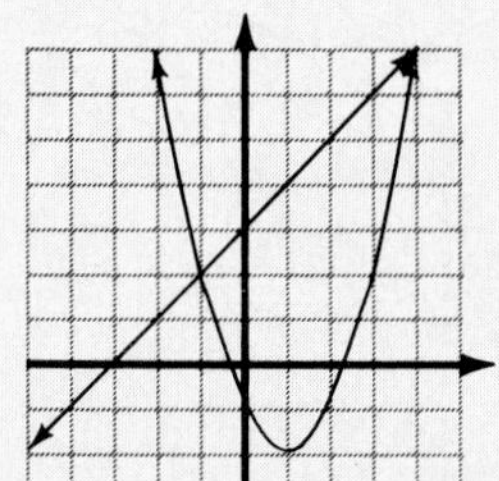

j.

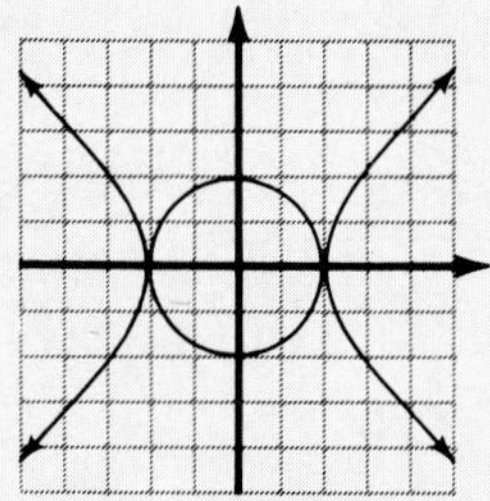

k.

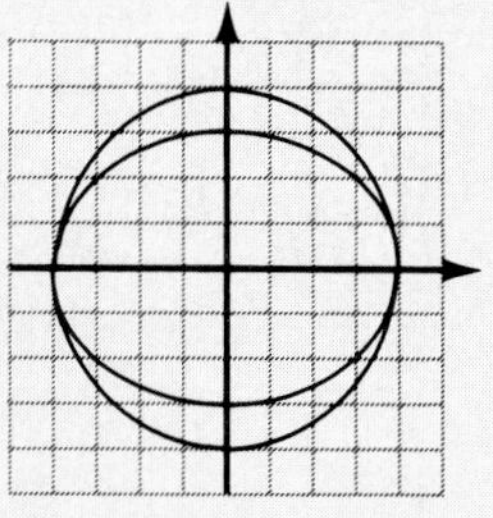

10-6 EXERCISES

A

Tell which conic is defined by each equation.

1. $3x^2 - 2y^2 + 3y - 9 = 0$ Hyperbola

2. $4x^2 + 4y^2 - 9y + 1 = 0$ Circle

3. $7x^2 + 8x - 3y + 7 = 0$ Parabola

4. $-3x^2 - 4y^2 + 8y = 0$ Ellipse

5. $-4x^2 + 4y^2 + 6x - 2y + 3 = 0$ Hyperbola

6. $-x^2 - y^2 - 3x + 2y + 4 = 0$ Circle

7. $\frac{x^2}{16} - \frac{y^2}{4} = 1$ Hyperbola

8. $\frac{y^2}{25} + \frac{x^2}{16} = 1$ Ellipse

9. $20x^2 + y^2 + 10 = 0$ Does not exist

10. $\frac{x^2}{5} + \frac{y^2}{5} = 1$ Circle

Determine the equation represented by the graph.

11.

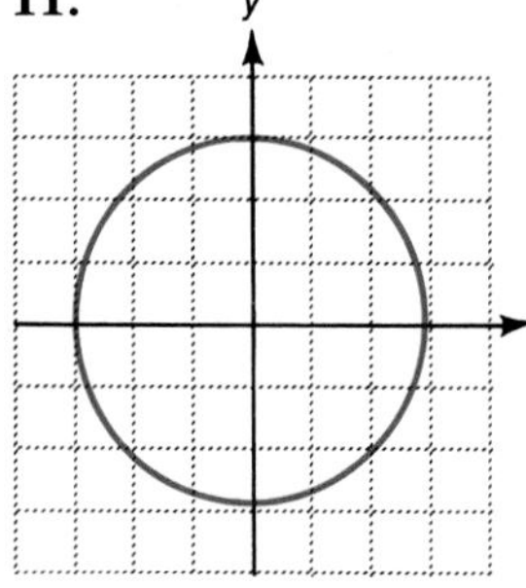

12.

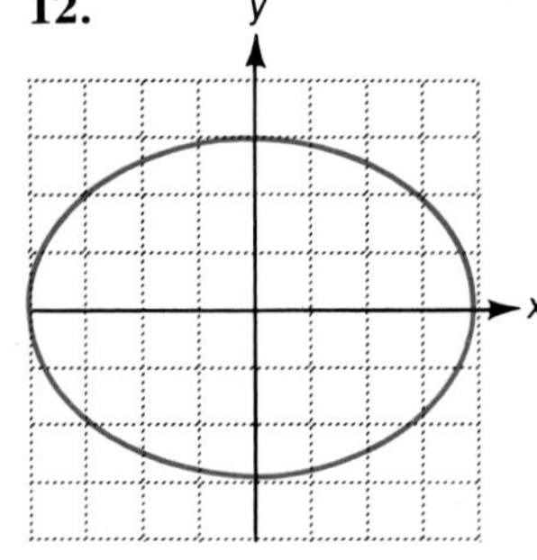

13.

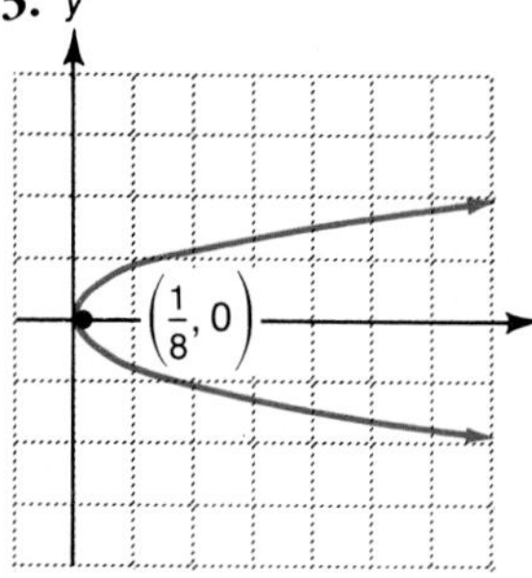

14.

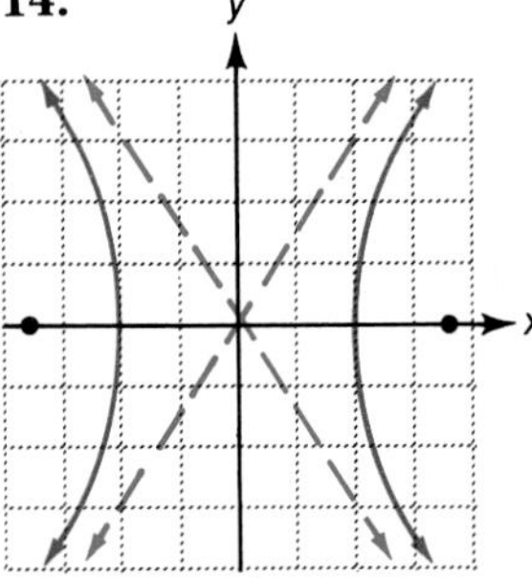

15.

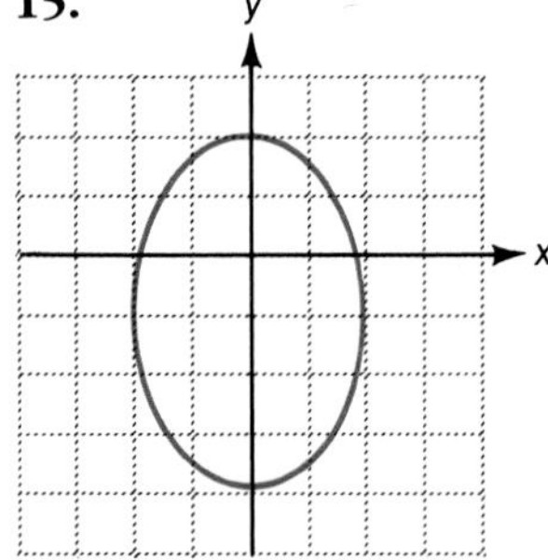

16.

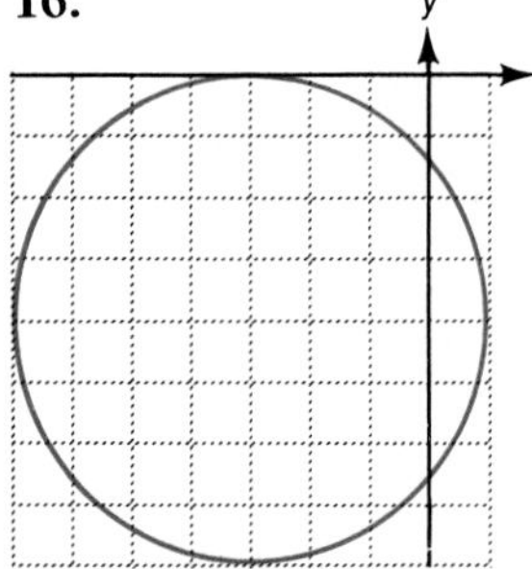

17.

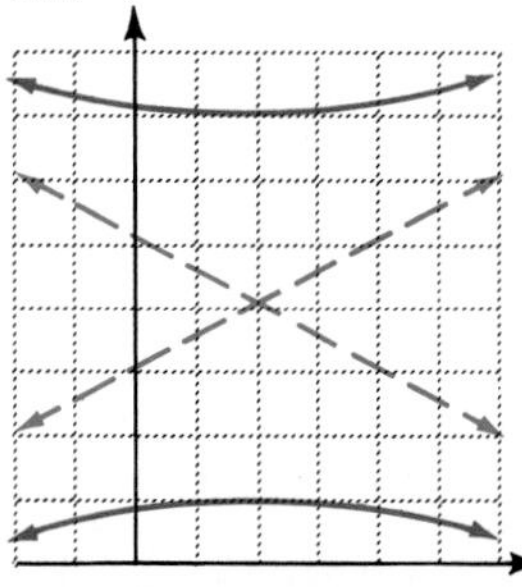

18.

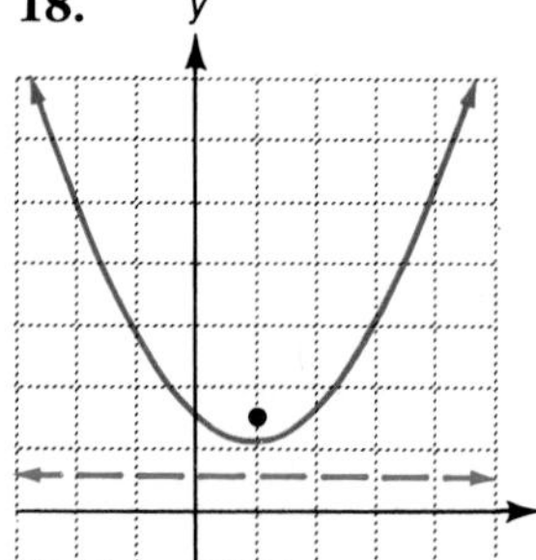

19.

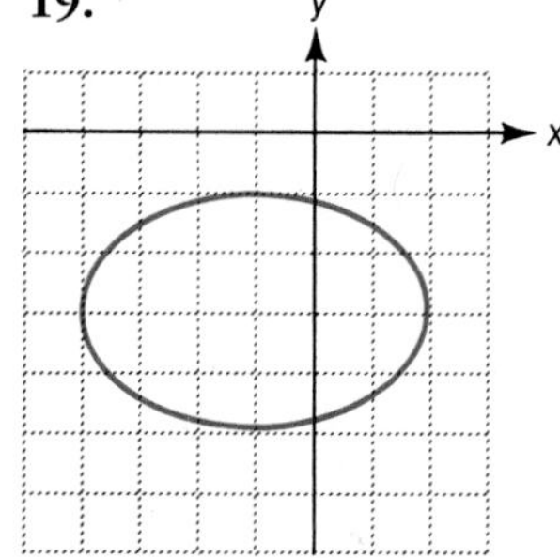

Solve each system graphically.

20. $x^2 + y^2 = 25$
$y - x = 1$ (−4, −3), (3, 4)

21. $x^2 + y^2 = 100$
$y - x = 2$ (−8, −6), (6, 8)

22. $y^2 - x^2 = 9$
$2x - 3 = y$ (4, 5), (0, −3)

23. $x + y = -6$
$xy = -7$ (−7, 1), (1, −7)

24. $4x^2 + 9y^2 = 36$
$3y + 2x = 6$ (0, 2), (3, 0)

25. $9x^2 + 4y^2 = 36$
$3x + 2y = 6$ (0, 3), (2, 0)

26. $y^2 = x + 3$
$2y = x + 4$ (−2, 1)

27. $y = x^2$
$3x = y + 2$ (1, 1), (2, 4)

28. $x^2 + y^2 = 25$
$y^2 = x + 5$ (4, −3), (4, 3), (−5, 0)

29. $y = x^2$
$x = y^2$ (1, 1), (0, 0)

30. $x^2 + y^2 = 9$
$x^2 - y^2 = 9$ (−3, 0), (3, 0)

31. $y^2 - 4x^2 = 4$
$4x^2 + y^2 = 4$ (0, −2), (0, 2)

32. $x^2 + y^2 = 25$
$xy = 12$ (−4, −3), (−3, −4), (3, 4), (4, 3)

33. $x^2 - y^2 = 16$
$x + y^2 = 4$ (−5, −3), (−5, 3), (4, 0)

34. $x^2 + y^2 = 4$
$16x^2 + 9y^2 = 144$ No solution

35. $x^2 + y^2 = 25$
$25x^2 + 16y^2 = 400$ (0, −5), (0, 5)

B

Graph these systems of inequalities.

36. $x^2 + y^2 < 4$
$y < x + 2$

37. $x + 2 > y$
$y > x^2$

38. $x^2 + y^2 \leq 16$
$xy < 10$

39. $y \geq x^2 + 2$
$2x^2 + y^2 \leq 16$

40. $x^2 - y^2 \geq 10$
$x^2 + 4y^2 \geq 8$

41. ***Critical Thinking*** Begin with an equation of the form $Ax^2 + By^2 + Cx + Dy + E = 0$. Determine the conic section it defines. Then change *one* coefficient to obtain a different conic section. Do this two more times, obtaining all four conic sections.

Challenge

42. Graph $\frac{x^2}{4} + \frac{y^2}{12} = 1$. Then graph $x^2 + xy + y^2 = 6$ on a different set of axes. How do the graphs compare?

43. Consider the equation $x^2 + y^2 + 4x + 6y + 13 = 0$.
a. What figure is represented by the equation?
b. What, if any, ordered pairs are solutions of the equation?
c. Determine each coefficient for $Ax^2 + By^2 + Cx + Dy + E = 0$. Then find $C^2 + D^2 - 4AE$ for this equation. What can you generalize from these results?

Mixed Review

Solve. **44.** $x^2 - 7x + 10 = 0$ **45.** $x^4 - 16x^2 = 0$ **46.** $x^4 - 16x^2 + 63 = 0$

Test for symmetry with respect to the origin. **47.** $|y| = 2x + 6$

Find the distance between the points. **48.** $(-4, -6)$ and $(1, 7)$

49. $(-1, 6)$ and $(-1, 3)$ **50.** $(2, -4)$ and $(-4, 4)$ **51.** $(0, 0)$ and $(\sqrt{m}, \sqrt{n})$

Find the coordinates of the midpoint of the segment having the following endpoints.

52. $(-2, 3)$ and $(-7, -1)$ **53.** $(3, 11)$ and $(2, 14)$ **54.** $(6, 0)$ and $(-11, 4)$

Exercises

11. $x^2 + y^2 = 9$
12. $\frac{x^2}{16} + \frac{y^2}{9} = 1$
13. $x = 2y^2$
14. $\frac{x^2}{4} - \frac{y^2}{9} = 1$
15. $\frac{x^2}{9} + \frac{(y-1)^2}{4} = 1$
16. $(x + 3)^2 + (y + 4)^2 = 16$
17. $\frac{(y-4)^2}{9} - \frac{(x-2)^2}{36} = 1$
18. $(x - 1)^2 = 2(y - 1)$
19. $\frac{(x+1)^2}{4} + \frac{(y+3)^2}{9} = 1$

For graphs of Exercises 20–35, see Teacher's Answer Section.
For Exercises 36–40, see Teacher's Answer Section.

41. Answers may vary. Example:
Circle: $x^2 + y^2 + 2x + 2y - 9 = 0$
Ellipse:
$x^2 + 2y^2 + 2x + 2y - 9 = 0$
Hyperbola:
$x^2 - 2y^2 + 2x + 2y - 9 = 0$
Parabola:
$x^2 + 0y^2 + 2x + 2y - 9 = 0$

For Exercise 42, see Teacher's Answer Section.

43. a. A circle
b. The point $(-2, -3)$
c. $A = 1, B = 1, C = 4, D = 6, E = 13$
$C^2 + D^2 - 4AE = 0$
If $C^2 + D^2 - 4AE = 0$, the equation represents a single point.

Mixed Review

44. 2, 5
45. 4, 0, −4
46. 3, −3, $\sqrt{7}$, $-\sqrt{7}$
47. No
48. $13.928 \approx 14$
49. 3
50. 10
51. $\sqrt{m + n}$
52. $\left(-\frac{9}{2}, 1\right)$
53. $\left(\frac{5}{2}, \frac{25}{2}\right)$
54. $\left(-\frac{5}{2}, 2\right)$

10-7

FIRST FIVE MINUTES

1. How many possible solutions are there for the following system?
   $x^2 + y^2 = 100$
   $3x + 2y = 6$
   A line intersects a circle in at most two points.
2. Solve the system graphically.
   $y = 2x - 4$ (1)
   $x^2 + x + y^2 = 6$ (2)
   (1, −2) and (2, 0)

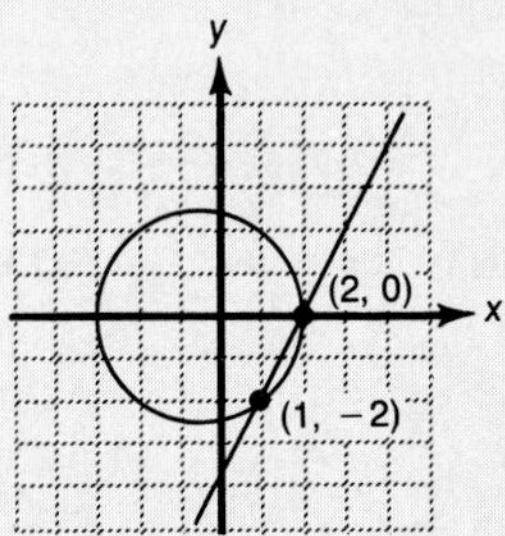

Solving Quadratic Systems Algebraically

Emphasize that recognizing which conics are represented can be very helpful.

Point out that the substitution method is most useful when one of the equations is linear and can be solved for one of the variables without using square roots. In this case the substitution method is used exactly as it is for two linear equations. However, the result will be a second-degree equation that may have one, two, or no solutions.

Key Questions

- Use the substitution method to write an equation that can be used to solve the system
  $9x - y + 28 = 0$
  $4x^2 - 3y^2 + 2x = 60$
  $4x^2 - 3(9x + 28)^2 + 2x = 60$
- How would you find a linear combination that can be used to solve the system
  $2x^2 - 4y^2 + 5y = 13$
  $6x^2 + 20y = 8$
  Multiply the first equation by −3 and add the two equations.

10-7 Solving Quadratic Systems Algebraically

Master Grapher Worksheet 21, *Quadratic-Quadratic Systems*, can be used as a lesson opener.

Remember that we used linear combinations and the substitution method to solve systems of linear equations. In solving systems where one equation is of first degree and one is of second degree, it is preferable to use the substitution method.

EXAMPLE 1 Solve this system algebraically.

$$x^2 + y^2 = 25 \quad ①$$
$$3x - 4y = 0 \quad ②$$

We first solve the linear equation ② for x, finding $x = \frac{4}{3}y$. We then substitute $\frac{4}{3}y$ for x in the first equation and solve for y.

$$\left(\frac{4}{3}y\right)^2 + y^2 = 25$$
$$\frac{16}{9}y^2 + y^2 = 25$$
$$\frac{25}{9}y^2 = 25 \quad \text{Combining like terms}$$
$$\frac{9}{25}\cdot\frac{25}{9}y^2 = \frac{9}{25}\cdot 25 \quad \text{Multiplying both sides by } \frac{9}{25}$$
$$y^2 = 9$$
$$y = \pm 3$$

Now we substitute these numbers into the linear equation and solve for x.

$$3x - 4(3) = 0 \qquad 3x - 4(-3) = 0$$
$$3x = 12 \qquad 3x = -12$$
$$x = 4 \qquad x = -4$$

The pairs (4, 3) and (−4, −3) check and thus are the solutions.

Try This Solve these systems algebraically.

a. $x^2 + y^2 = 25$
$y - x = -1$
(−3, −4), (4, 3)

b. $y = x^2 - 2x - 1$
$y = x + 3$
(4, 7), (−1, 2)

c. $y = \frac{x^2}{4}$
$x + 2y = 4$
(2, 1), (−4, 4)

Sometimes an equation may not take on a familiar form like those studied previously in this chapter. We can still rely on the substitution method for the solution.

EXAMPLE 2 Solve this system.

$$y + 3 = 2x \quad ①$$
$$x^2 + 2xy = -1 \quad ②$$

We first solve the linear equation ① for y.

$$y = 2x - 3$$

We then substitute $2x - 3$ for y in equation ② and solve for x.

$$x^2 + 2x(2x - 3) = -1$$
$$x^2 + 4x^2 - 6x = -1$$
$$5x^2 - 6x + 1 = 0 \quad \text{Combining like terms}$$
$$(5x - 1)(x - 1) = 0 \quad \text{Factoring}$$
$$5x - 1 = 0 \text{ or } x - 1 = 0$$
$$x = \frac{1}{5} \text{ or } x = 1$$

Now we substitute these numbers into the linear equation and solve for y.

$$y + 3 = 2\left(\frac{1}{5}\right) \qquad y + 3 = 2(1)$$
$$y = \frac{2}{5} - 3 \qquad y = 2 - 3$$
$$y = -\frac{13}{5} \qquad y = -1$$

The pairs $\left(\frac{1}{5}, -\frac{13}{5}\right)$ and $(1, -1)$ check and thus are the solutions.

EXAMPLE 3 Solve this system of equations.

$$2x^2 + 5y^2 = 22 \quad ①$$
$$3x^2 - y^2 = -1 \quad ②$$

We recognize these as equations of an ellipse and a hyperbola. Here we use linear combinations.

$$2x^2 + 5y^2 = 22$$
$$15x^2 - 5y^2 = -5 \quad \text{Multiplying ② by 5}$$
$$17x^2 = 17 \quad \text{Adding}$$
$$x^2 = 1$$
$$x = \pm 1$$

If $x = 1, x^2 = 1$, and if $x = -1, x^2 = 1$, so we substitute 1 or -1 for x in equation ②.

$$3 \cdot 1^2 - y^2 = -1$$
$$y^2 = 4$$
$$y = \pm 2$$

Chalkboard Examples

1. Solve.
   $2x^2 - 3y^2 = 5$ (1)
   $2x - y = 5$ (2)
   Solve (2) for y.
   $y = 2x - 5$
   Substitute for y in (1).
   $2x^2 - 3(2x - 5)^2 = 5$
   Expand and simplify.
   $2x^2 - 3(4x^2 - 20x + 25) = 5$
   $10x^2 - 60x + 80 = 0$
   $x^2 - 6x + 8 = 0$
   $(x - 2)(x - 4) = 0$
   $x = 2$ or $x = 4$, and $y = -1$ or $y = 3$.
   The solutions are $(2, -1)$ and $(4, 3)$.
2. Solve.
   $x^2 + y^2 = 13$ (1)
   $x^2 - y = 1$ (2)
   Subtract (2) from (1).
   $y^2 + y - 12 = 0$
   The quadratic equation yields
   $y = \frac{-1 \pm \sqrt{1 + 48}}{2}$
   $y = 3$, or $y = -4$
   Solve equation (2) for x in terms of y.
   $x = \pm\sqrt{y + 1}$
   If $y = 3$, then $x = \pm 2$.
   If $y = -4$, the solution is a complex number.
   Hence the solutions are $(-2, 3)$ and $(2, 3)$.
   Note that this problem was solved in the Chalkboard Example for Solving Systems Graphically.

3. Solve.
$x^2 + y^2 = 5$ (1)
$4x^2 + 9y^2 = 40$ (2)
Add -4 times (1) to (2).
$5y^2 = 20$
$y^2 = 4$
$y = \pm 2$
Substitute for y^2 in (1).
$x^2 + 4 = 5$
$x^2 = 1$
$x = \pm 1$
The four solutions are $(-1, -2)$, $(-1, 2)$, $(1, -2)$, $(1, 2)$.

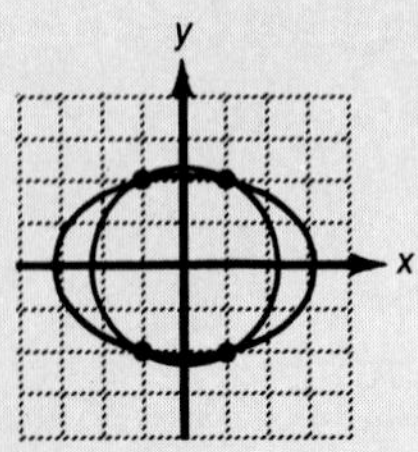

LESSON QUIZ

1. Solve.
$-2(y - 4) = x^2$
$x^2 + y^2 = 16$
$(0, 4)$
2. Solve.
$x^2 + y^2 = 5$
$x^2 - y^2 = 3$
$(-2, -1), (-2, 1), (2, -1), (2, 1)$
3. Solve.
$x + y = 5$
$x^2 + 3y = 13$
$(1, 4), (2, 3)$

Thus if $x = 1$, $y = 2$ or $y = -2$. If $x = -1$, $y = 2$ or $y = -2$. The possible solutions are $(1, 2)$, $(1, -2)$, $(-1, 2)$, and $(-1, -2)$.

Each of these ordered pairs check in the system, so the solutions are $(1, 2)$, $(1, -2)$, $(-1, 2)$, and $(-1, -2)$.

Try This Solve these systems. See additional answers.

d. $x^2 + y^2 = 4$
$\frac{x^2}{25} + \frac{y^2}{4} = 1$

e. $2y^2 - 3x^2 = 6$
$5y^2 + 2x^2 = 53$

f. $y^2 + 2xy + 5 = 2$
$2y + x = -4$

EXAMPLE 4 Solve this system of equations.

$$x^2 + 4y^2 = 20 \quad ①$$
$$xy = 4 \quad ②$$

Here we use the substitution method. First we solve equation ② for y.

$$y = \frac{4}{x}$$

Then we substitute $\frac{4}{x}$ for y in equation ① and solve for x.

$$x^2 + 4\left(\frac{4}{x}\right)^2 = 20$$
$$x^2 + \frac{64}{x^2} = 20$$
$$x^4 + 64 = 20x^2$$
$$x^4 - 20x^2 + 64 = 0$$
$$u^2 - 20u + 64 = 0 \quad \text{Letting } u = x^2$$
$$(u - 16)(u - 4) = 0$$
$$(x^2 - 16)(x^2 - 4) = 0 \quad \text{Substituting } x^2 \text{ for } u$$

Then $x = 4$ or $x = -4$ or $x = 2$ or $x = -2$. Since $y = \frac{4}{x}$, if $x = 4$, $y = 1$; if $x = -4$, $y = -1$; if $x = 2$, $y = 2$; if $x = -2$, $y = -2$. The solutions are $(4, 1)$, $(-4, -1)$, $(2, 2)$, and $(-2, -2)$.

Try This Solve these systems.

g. $x^2 + xy + y^2 = 19$
$xy = 6$ $(-3, -2), (-2, -3), (3, 2), (2, 3)$

h. $xy = 8$
$8x^2 - y^2 = 16$ $(2, 4), (-2, -4)$

10-7 EXERCISES

Solve.

1. $x^2 + 4y^2 = 25$
$x + 2y = 7$

2. $y^2 - x^2 = 16$
$2x - y = 1$

3. $x^2 - xy + 3y^2 = 5$
$x - y = 2$

4. $2y^2 + xy + x^2 = 7$
$x - 2y = 5$

5. $3x + y = 7$
$4x^2 + 5y = 24$

6. $2y^2 + xy = 5$
$4y + x = 7$

7. $x^2 + 3y^2 = 12$
$x + 3y = 6$

8. $2x + 3y = 2$
$2x^2 - 6xy + 3y^2 = -\frac{1}{6}$

9. $xy = -16$
$3x - 46 = 5y$

Solve.

10. $x^2 + y^2 = 16$
$y^2 - 2x^2 = 10$

11. $x^2 + y^2 = 14$
$x^2 - y^2 = 4$

12. $x^2 + y^2 = 5$
$xy = 2$

13. $x^2 + y^2 = 20$
$xy = 8$

14. $x^2 + y^2 = 13$
$xy = 6$

15. $x^2 + 4y^2 = 20$
$xy = 4$

16. $x^2 + y^2 = 7$
$xy = -12$

17. $2xy + 3y^2 = 7$
$3xy - 2y^2 = 4$

18. $y - x^2 = 0$
$x^2 = 20 - y^2$

19. $2x^2 + y^2 = 6$
$3x^2 - y^2 = 11$

B

Solve.

20. $x + y = 4$
$xy = 1$
$(2 + \sqrt{3}, 2 - \sqrt{3}), (2 - \sqrt{3}, 2 + \sqrt{3})$

21. $y = 3x^2$
$y = |x|$
$\left(\frac{1}{3}, \frac{1}{3}\right), \left(-\frac{1}{3}, \frac{1}{3}\right), (0, 0)$

22. $x^2 + y^2 + 6y + 5 = 0$
$x^2 + y^2 - 2x - 8 = 0$
$\left(\frac{5 - 9\sqrt{15}}{20}, \frac{-45 + 3\sqrt{15}}{20}\right), \left(\frac{5 + 9\sqrt{15}}{20}, \frac{-45 - 3\sqrt{15}}{20}\right)$

23. ***Critical Thinking*** Write a system of equations whose graphs are **a)** a line and a circle, **b)** a hyperbola and an ellipse, **c)** a circle and a hyperbola, **d)** a parabola and an ellipse.

Challenge

24. Given the area (A) and the perimeter (P) of a rectangle, show that the length (L) and the width (W) are given by these formulas.

$$L = \frac{1}{4}(P + \sqrt{P^2 - 16A})$$

$$W = \frac{1}{4}(P - \sqrt{P^2 - 16A})$$

25. Show that a hyperbola does not intersect its asymptotes by solving the following system.

$$\frac{x^2}{a^2} - \frac{y^2}{b^2} = 1$$

$$y = \frac{b}{a}x \text{ or } y = -\frac{b}{a}x$$

Assignment Guide
Algebra: Day 1: 1–9, MR
Day 2: 10–19, assign w. Application

Alg w/Finite or Trig: 1–22 e/o, 23, MR

Comprehensive: 1–19 m3, 20–23, 24–28 e/o, MR assign w. Application

ADDITIONAL ANSWERS

Try This

d. $(0, -2), (0, 2)$
e. $(-2, -3), (-2, 3), (2, -3), (2, 3)$
f. $(2, -3), \left(-\frac{14}{3}, \frac{1}{3}\right)$

Exercises

1. $(3, 2), \left(4, \frac{3}{2}\right)$
2. $(3, 5), \left(-\frac{5}{3}, -\frac{13}{3}\right)$
3. $\left(\frac{7}{3}, \frac{1}{3}\right) (1, -1)$
4. $(1, -2), \left(\frac{11}{4}, -\frac{9}{8}\right)$
5. $(1, 4), \left(\frac{11}{4}, -\frac{5}{4}\right)$
6. $\left(-3, \frac{5}{2}\right) (3, 1)$
7. $(0, 2), (3, 1)$
8. $\left(\frac{9}{22}, \frac{13}{33}\right), \left(\frac{1}{2}, \frac{1}{3}\right)$
9. $(2, -8), \left(-\frac{40}{3}, -\frac{6}{5}\right)$
10. $(-\sqrt{2}, -\sqrt{14}), (-\sqrt{2}, \sqrt{14}), (\sqrt{2}, -\sqrt{14}), (\sqrt{2}, \sqrt{14})$
11. $(-3, -\sqrt{5}), (-3, \sqrt{5}), (3, -\sqrt{5}), (3, \sqrt{5})$
12. $(-2, -1), (-1, -2), (1, 2), (2, 1)$
13. $(-4, -2), (-2, -4), (2, 4), (4, 2)$
14. $(-3, -2), (-2, -3), (2, 3), (3, 2)$
15. $(-2, -2), (2, 2), (4, 1), (-4, -1)$
16. No solution
17. $(-2, -1), (2, 1)$
18. $(2, 4), (-2, 4)$
19. No solution

23. Answers may vary. Examples:
a. $y = x$; $x^2 + y^2 = 4$
b. $x^2 - 2y^2 = 4$; $x^2 + 2y^2 = 9$
c. $x^2 + y^2 = 9$; $x^2 - y^2 = 9$
d. $y = x^2 + 2x + 3$; $3x^2 + y^2 = 16$

24. $WL = A$; $2(L + W) = P$;
$L + W = \frac{P}{2}$;
$L = \frac{P}{2} - W$; $W\left(\frac{P}{2} - W\right) = A$;
$W^2 - \frac{WP}{2} + A = 0$;
$W = \frac{\frac{P}{2} \pm \sqrt{\left(\frac{P}{2}\right)^2 - 4A}}{2}$
$= \frac{P}{4} \pm \frac{\sqrt{P^2 - 16A}}{4}$
$= \frac{1}{4}(P \pm \sqrt{P^2 - 16A})$
Since $W < L$, $W = \frac{1}{4}(P - \sqrt{P^2 - 16A})$ and $L = \frac{1}{4}(P + \sqrt{P^2 - 16A})$.

25. There is no number x such that $\frac{x^2}{a^2} - \frac{\left(\frac{b}{a}x\right)^2}{b^2} = 1$, because the left side simplifies to $\frac{x^2}{a^2} - \frac{x^2}{a^2}$, which is 0.

Mixed Review

29. 2
30. $5\sqrt{2}$
31. (0, 0); 7

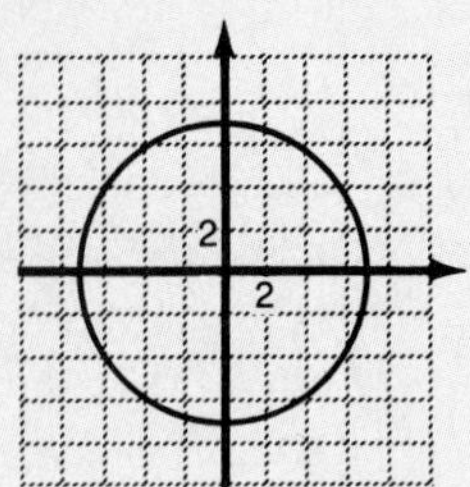

32. a. $f(d) = 0.125d + 273$
b. 1816 feet from the bottom
33. 2 km
34. Yes
35. No
36. Yes
37. No
38. No
39 Yes

26. Find an equation of a circle containing the points (2, 4) and (3, 3), and whose center is on the line $3x - y = 3$. $(x - 2)^2 + (y - 3)^2 = 1$

27. Find an equation of a circle containing the points (7, 3) and (5, 5), and whose center is on the line $y - 4x = 1$. $(x + 1)^2 + (y + 3)^2 = 100$

28. The area of a rectangle inscribed in a unit circle is 1. Find its length and width.
length: $\sqrt{2 + \sqrt{3}} \approx 1.93$
width: $\sqrt{2 - \sqrt{3}} \approx 0.52$

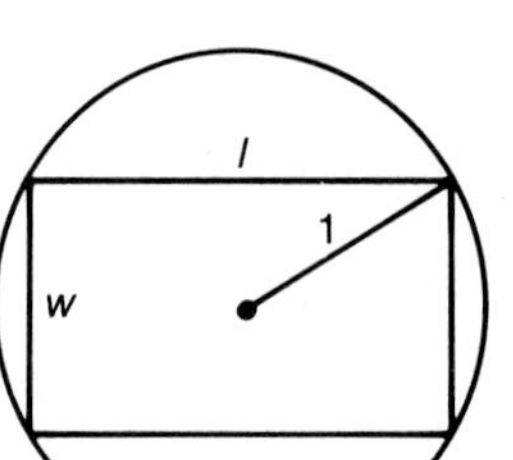

Mixed Review

Find the distance between the points. **29.** (2, 5) and (2, 7)

30. (1, −3) and (6, −8)

31. Consider the circle $x^2 + y^2 = 49$. Find the center and radius. Then draw a graph.

32. The bottom of a hill is at an altitude of 273 feet above sea level. The top of the hill, which is 2640 feet horizontally from the bottom, is 603 feet above sea level.
a. Fit a linear function to the data, relating altitude to horizontal distance.
b. How far along the hill is a spot that is 500 feet above sea level?

33. Calvin used to bicycle to school by travelling east for 3 km, then north for 4 km. A new road was constructed that allowed him to bicycle to school along a straight route. How much distance did the new route save him compared with the old route?

Determine whether the graphs of each pair of equations are perpendicular.

34. $y = 3x - 6$ and $6y = 4 - 2x$
35. $y = 5x + 9$ and $2y = 11 - 10x$
36. $2x + 2y = 4$ and $y - x = 9$
37. $x - 5y = 4$ and $x + 5y = 9$
38. $y = 2$ and $y = -\frac{1}{2}$
39. $y = 2$ and $x = 2$

Problem for Programmers

Write a program that will determine the shape of a conic, given the equation in the form $Ax^2 + By^2 + Cx + Dy + E = 0$, where all coefficients are integers. The program should first complete each square to determine whether real solutions exist. Test your program using Exercises 1 – 10 in Lesson 10-6.

Challenge: Modify the program to display the conic in standard form and list as much information as possible about the conic (vertex/vertices, focus/foci, line of symmetry, radius/constant distance, etc.).

10-8 Problem Solving: Using Systems of Second-Degree Equations

Objective: Solve problems that translate to a system of second-degree equations.

PROBLEM-SOLVING GUIDELINES
■ UNDERSTAND the problem
■ Develop and carry out a PLAN
■ Find the ANSWER and CHECK

Sometimes problem situations translate into a system of equations where one equation is linear and the other is of second degree.

EXAMPLE 1 The perimeter of a rectangular field is 204 m and the area is 2565 m^2. Find the dimensions of the field.

■ UNDERSTAND the problem

Question: What are the dimensions of the field?
Data: The perimeter is 204 m. The area is 2565 m^2.

■ Develop and carry out a PLAN

We first translate the conditions of the problem to equations, using w for width and l for length. We also draw a diagram.

Perimeter: $2w + 2l = 204$ Linear equation

Area: $lw = 2565$ Equation of second degree

We next solve the system.

$$2w + 2l = 204$$
$$lw = 2565$$

The solution of the system is (45, 57).

■ Find the ANSWER and CHECK

The perimeter is $2 \cdot 45 + 2 \cdot 57$, or 204. Thus the perimeter checks. The area is $45 \cdot 57$ or 2565. The area checks.

The dimensions of the field are 45 m by 57 m.

Try This

a. Find the length of the side of each square. 14 m, 9 m

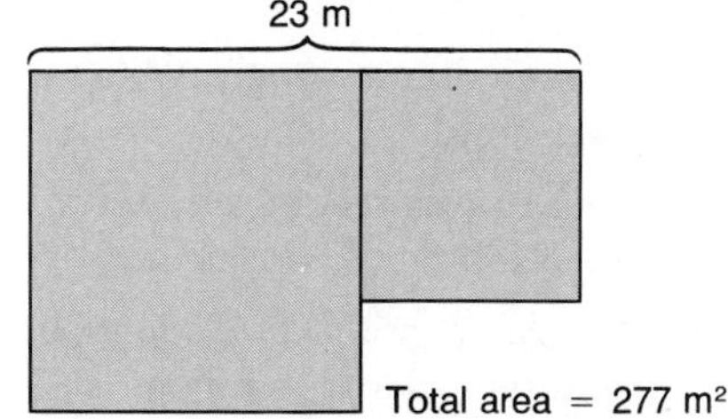

b. The perimeter of a rectangular field is 34 ft and the length of a diagonal is 13 ft. Find the dimensions of the field. $l = 12, w = 5$

10-8

FIRST FIVE MINUTES

1. Solve.
   $y + 1 = x^2$
   $y - 1 = -x^2$
   The solutions are $(-1, 0), (1, 0)$.
2. Solve.
   $3x^2 + 5y^2 = 4$
   $x^2 + y^2 = 2$
   Add -3 times (2) to (1).
   $y^2 = -1$
   There are no real solutions.

Emphasize that solutions that satisfy the equations may not satisfy the word problem; students should check to make sure their answers make sense.

Key Question

- If you had a certain length of fence, would a rectangular or square enclosure give you more area? Square enclosure

Chalkboard Examples

1. Two square pieces of plastic together have an area of 100 square inches. When a square the size of the smaller piece is cut from the larger piece, the remaining area is 28 square inches. What are the lengths of the sides of the two squares?
   Let x be the length of the side of the larger square.
   Let y be the length of the side of the smaller square.
   $x^2 + y^2 = 100$ (1)
   $x^2 - y^2 = 28$ (2)
   Adding (1) and (2) yields
   $2x^2 = 128$
   $x = \pm 8$
   We seek the positive length.
   $x = 8$
   Substitute into (1).
   $64 + y^2 = 100$
   $y = \pm 6$
   The positive length $y = 6$ is the required solution. The larger square has side of length 8. The smaller square has side of length 6.

2. A rectangular beam with cross-sectional area 48 square inches is cut from a circular log with diameter 10 inches. Find the dimensions of the beam.
Let x and y denote the lengths of the sides of the beam in inches. The cross-sectional area of the beam is
$xy = 48$ (1)
The diameter of the log is the hypotenuse of a right triangle with sides x and y.
$x^2 + y^2 = 100$ (2)
Solve (1) for y in terms of x.
$y = \frac{48}{x}$
Substitute into (2).
$$x^2 + \left(\frac{48}{x}\right)^2 = 100$$
$$x^4 + 2304 = 100x^2$$
$$x^4 - 100x^2 + 2304 = 0$$
The quadratic formula yields
$$x^2 = \frac{100 \pm \sqrt{784}}{2} = \frac{100 \pm 28}{2}$$
$x^2 = 36$ or $x^2 = 64$
$x = 6$ or $x = 8$
$y = 8$ or $y = 6$
The lengths of the sides of the beam are 6 and 8 inches.

LESSON QUIZ

1. Find two positive numbers, the sum of whose squares is 74 and the difference of whose squares is 24.
The numbers are 7 and 5.

Assignment Guide
Algebra: 1–12 e/o, MR

Alg w/Finite or Trig: 1–14 e/o, 15, MR

Comprehensive: 1–14 e/o, 15–18, MR, assign w. 10-9

ADDITIONAL ANSWERS

Exercises

1. 6 cm, 8 cm
2. 1 m, 2 m
3. 4 in., 5 in.
4. 1 yd, 2 yd
5. 12, 13 and −12, −13
6. 6, 10 and −6, −10
7. $l = \sqrt{3}$ m, $w = 1$ m
8. $l = \sqrt{2}$ m, $w = 1$ m
9. 16 ft, 24 ft

Some problem situations translate to a system of two second-degree equations.

EXAMPLE 2 The area of a rectangle is 300 yd^2 and the length of a diagonal is 25 yd. Find the dimensions.

First make a *drawing*.

We use l for the length and w for the width and translate to equations.

$$l^2 + w^2 = 25^2 \quad \text{From the Pythagorean theorem}$$
$$lw = 300 \quad \text{Area}$$

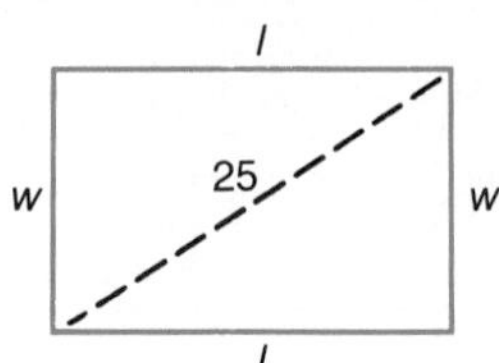

Now we solve the system

$$l^2 + w^2 = 625$$
$$lw = 300$$

and get the solutions (15, 20) and (−15, −20). Now we check in the original problem, $20^2 + 15^2 = 25^2$ and $20 \cdot 15 = 300$, so (15, 20) is a solution of the problem. Lengths of sides cannot be negative, so (−15, −20) is not a solution. The answer is $l = 20$ yd and $w = 15$ yd.

Try This

c. The area of a rectangle is 2 ft^2 and the length of a diagonal is $\sqrt{5}$ ft. Find the dimensions of the rectangle. $w = 1$ ft, $l = 2$ ft

10-8 EXERCISES

A

Solve.

1. A rectangle has perimeter 28 cm and the length of a diagonal is 10 cm. What are its dimensions?
2. A rectangle has perimeter 6 m and the length of a diagonal is $\sqrt{5}$ m. What are its dimensions?
3. A rectangle has area 20 $in.^2$ and perimeter 18 in. Find its dimensions.
4. A rectangle has area 2 yd^2 and perimeter 6 yd. Find its dimensions.
5. Find two numbers whose product is 156 if the sum of their squares is 313.
6. Find two numbers whose product is 60 if the sum of their squares is 136.
7. The area of a rectangle is $\sqrt{3}$ m^2 and the length of a diagonal is 2 m. Find its dimensions.
8. The area of a rectangle is $\sqrt{2}$ m^2 and the length of a diagonal is $\sqrt{3}$ m. Find its dimensions.
9. A garden contains two square beds of peanuts. The sum of their areas is 832 ft^2, and the difference of their areas is 320 ft^2. Find the length of each bed.

10. A certain amount of money saved for 1 yr at a certain interest rate yielded \$7.50. If the principal had been \$25 more and the interest rate 1% less, the interest would have been the same. Find the principal and the rate. \$125, 6%

Find the length of the side of each square.

11. 9.7

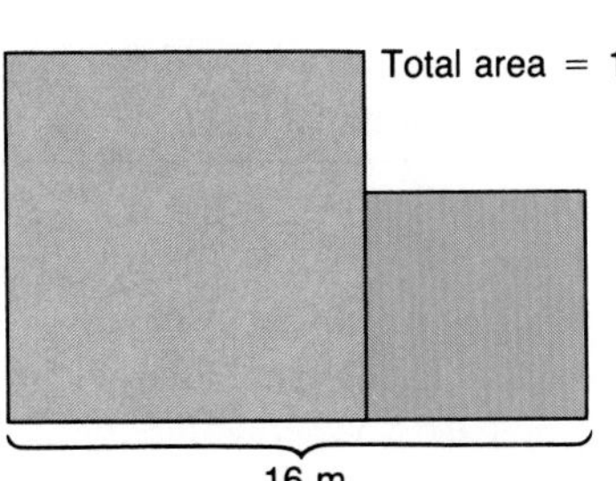

12. 8, 7

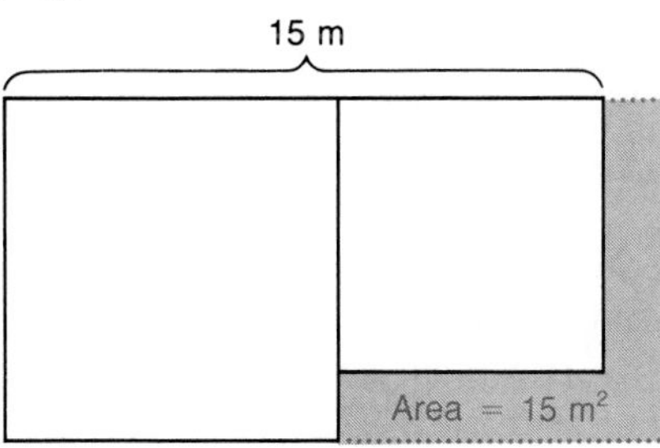

B

13. A right triangle has a hypotenuse of 50 cm and an area of 600 cm^2. Find the lengths of the legs of the triangle. 30 cm, 40 cm

14. A rectangular lot has an area of 60 m^2. The length of a diagonal of the lot is 13 m. What are the length and the width of the lot? 5 m, 12 m

15. ***Critical Thinking*** Suppose the green square in Exercise 11 is actually a rectangle that is half as high as the pink square. What are the new dimensions of each figure? 10 by 10 and 5 by 6

Challenge

16. Starting from some point, Mark walks east and Erin walks north. After three hours, Erin has walked three miles farther than Mark and they are 15 miles apart. Find the rate of speed of each. Erin 4 mi/h, Mark 3 mi/h

17. A carpenter worked alone on a job for two days and then hired a helper. The entire job was completed in $5\frac{5}{7}$ days. Working alone, the carpenter could have completed the job in four days less than the helper could have done the entire job alone. Find the time each would have needed to complete the job alone. Carpenter: 8.3 days, helper: 12.3 days

18. Two identical ellipses with foci on the x-axis are joined such that each ellipse passes through the center of the other. The equation of the first ellipse is $4x^2 + 9y^2 = 36$. The second ellipse is directly to the right of the first.
    a. Find the equation of the second ellipse in standard form. $\frac{(x-3)^2}{9} + \frac{y^2}{4} = 1$
    b. Find their points of intersection. $\left(\frac{3}{2}, \sqrt{3}\right), \left(\frac{3}{2}, -\sqrt{3}\right)$

Mixed Review

Find the coordinates of the midpoint of the segment having the following endpoints.

19. (3, 11) and (3, 9) **20.** (6, −7) and (11, 4)

Find the quadratic function that fits the set of data points.

21. (1, 5), (−1, −7), (−2, −7) **22.** (1, 3), (2, 11), (−1, 5)

Mixed Review

19. (3, 10)

20. $\left(\frac{17}{2}, -\frac{3}{2}\right)$

21. $f(x) = 2x^2 + 6x - 3$

22. $f(x) = 3x^2 - x + 1$

10-9

FIRST FIVE MINUTES

1. Find the GCD (Greatest Common Divisor) of 483 and 1610.
   $483 = 3 \cdot 7 \cdot 23$, $1610 = 2 \cdot 5 \cdot 7 \cdot 23$; so the GCD of 483 and 1610 is $7 \cdot 23 = 161$
2. Your meter stick is broken off at the 24 cm mark. What marks would you cut the stick at to divide the larger part into 4 pieces?
   Make cuts at the 43, 62 and 81 cm marks. (Draw a diagram)

Simplify the Problem

Emphasize that complicated problems are very often solved by looking at simpler problems first. Engineers and mathematicians solve very complex problems by this procedure. Devising a simple problem that relates directly to the complex problem is crucial, and so is the organization of steps going from the simple problem to the complex problem.

Key Questions

- How many squares are in a 7-by-7 square?
  $91 + 49 = 140$ squares
- If you know how many squares are in an n-by-n square, how do you find how many are in an $(n + 1)$-by-$(n + 1)$ square?
  Add $(n + 1)^2$.

Chalkboard Example

1. Suppose you make a pyramid of pennies. The base of the pyramid has 55 pennies arranged in a triangle. How many pennies are in the whole pyramid?
   Simplify the problem.

Base	1	3	6	10	15
Total	1	4	10	20	35

The total number of pennies is the number in the base plus the total number in a pyramid with the next smaller base. Continuing the pattern

Base	21	28	36	45	55
Total	56	84	120	165	220

There are 220 pennies in the pyramid.

10-9 Problem Solving: Strategies

Simplify the Problem

Objective: Solve problems using the strategy *Simplify the Problem*, and other strategies.

Sometimes the numbers in a problem are so large that a direct solution is difficult. The problem-solving strategy called Simplify the Problem can often help. One way to simplify a problem is to find a solution using a small number. Then, using a larger number, find another solution. This process can then be repeated. When you have solutions to simpler problems, organizing the information in a *table* often helps you find a *pattern* and the solution to the original problem.

EXAMPLE

How many squares are in the figure at the right?

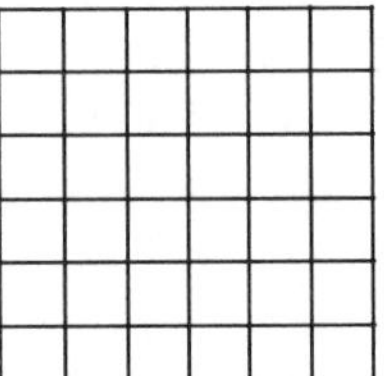

We can simplify the problem by asking how many squares are in a 1-by-1 square, then in a 2-by-2 square, a 3-by-3, and so on. *Drawing a diagram, making a table,* and *looking for a pattern* are other strategies used to help find the solution.

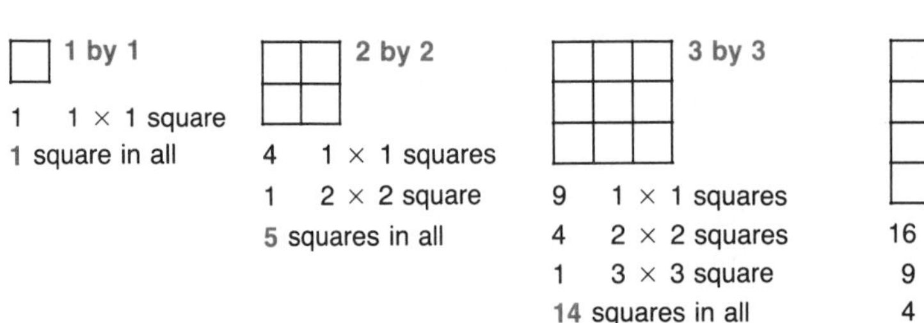

1 by 1: 1 1×1 square; 1 square in all

2 by 2: 4 1×1 squares; 1 2×2 square; 5 squares in all

3 by 3: 9 1×1 squares; 4 2×2 squares; 1 3×3 square; 14 squares in all

4 by 4: 16 1×1 squares; 9 2×2 squares; 4 3×3 squares; 1 4×4 square; 30 squares in all

Size of original square	Number of squares
1 by 1	1
2 by 2	$5 = 1 + 4$
3 by 3	$14 = 1 + 4 + 9$
4 by 4	$30 = 1 + 4 + 9 + 16$
5 by 5	$55 = 1 + 4 + 9 + 16 + 25$

Organizing the data in the *table* helps show the pattern in the number of squares. For an original square with n individual squares on a side, there are $1^2 + 2^2 + 3^2 + \cdots + n^2$ squares in the figure.

For the figure given in the Example, there are 6 individual squares on a side. So there are $1^2 + 2^2 + 3^2 + 4^2 + 5^2 + 6^2$ squares contained within the figure, or 91 squares.

Problem-Solving Strategies		
Write an Equation	Draw a Diagram	Guess, Check, Revise
Make an Organized List	Make a Table	Look for a Pattern
Use Logical Reasoning	Simplify the Problem	Work Backward

10-9 PROBLEMS

Solve using one or more of the strategies.

1. A large circular park is to have six straight walking paths cut through it. The architect has been told to design the park so there will be a maximum number of flower and garden areas inside the park and around the paths. What is the greatest number of flower and garden areas possible with the six straight paths?
2. A tractor-trailer is to carry cartons and boxes. The cartons and boxes are different sizes, but all the cartons are the same size and all the boxes are the same size. When full, the trailer can carry 24 cartons and 20 boxes. When half full, the trailer can carry 6 cartons and 13 boxes. If the trailer is to carry only cartons or only boxes, how many of each can it carry?
3. In a holiday basketball tournament, there were a total of 64 teams. When a team lost, it was eliminated from the tournament and played no more games. To win the tournament, a team could not lose any games. How many games were needed to determine a champion?
4. What should be the dimensions of the bottom row of a pyramid that continues to build like the one at the right, if there are 100 blocks to work with and as many blocks as possible are to be used?

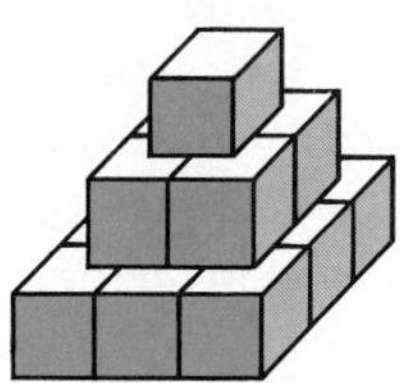

5. Some students were comparing the sizes of the bands in different schools. Roosevelt and Central High's bands have a combined total of 385 students. Roosevelt and Riverside High's bands have a combined total of 320 students. Central's band has 65 more members than Riverside's. Roosevelt's band has 70 more members than Riverside's. How many members are in each school's band?

Hints for Problems

1. Find how many sections there would be with 1 path, then 2 paths, 3 paths, and so on.
2. Draw a diagram showing the two given situations.
3. Simplify the problem. Suppose there were only 2 teams. Then try 3 teams, and so on.
4. Try making a table and looking for the pattern.
5. Draw a diagram to show the given data. Try guessing and checking.

ANSWERS

1. There would be 22 sections with 6 paths.
2. The tractor could carry either 64 cartons or 32 boxes.
3. A total of 63 games (1 less game than the number of teams) were needed to determine the championship.
4. The bottom row should be 6 by 6 to use the most blocks (91).
5. Roosevelt 195, Riverside 125, Central 190

Problem Solving: Application

Students should use calculators for the problems which follow this application.

ANSWERS

1. **a.** 1.8×10^9 mi
   b. 19 AU
   c. $\approx 3 \times 10^{-4}$ light years
2. **a.** 3063 days
   b. 73,512 hours
3. approximately 24,000 miles per hour
4. 6.7×10^8 mi/h
5. $\approx$ 30,400:1
6. approximately 1.26 s
7. 1.62×10^9 miles

Problem Solving: Application

Inferring Data

Often information is presented in journals, articles, papers, and other forms of communication. Problems then can be solved by gathering data and using them to make calculations. Read the following article and answer the questions below.

On January 24, 1986, the Voyager II spacecraft transmitted signals toward Earth. These transmissions were the first to contain explicit data about the planet Uranus. As these transmissions traveled at 186,000 miles per second (the speed of light), scientists on Earth waited for two hours and twenty-five minutes to receive them.

While this was certainly a long wait, scientists had waited much longer for Voyager to reach Uranus. Its trek began September 5, 1977, and its journey utilized the gravitational pull of Jupiter and Saturn to "fling" the spacecraft across the solar system.

Imagine swinging a piece of string with a weight attached, then letting go. This was the effect of the planet's gravitational pull on Voyager. In the same way, the gravitational pull of Uranus sent Voyager to Neptune for an August 24, 1989 rendezvous.

The planets must be in a specific position before this "gravity-powered" trip is possible. In fact, this configuration occurs only once every 177 years.

Because Voyager approached Uranus in a spiral path, its 1.8 billion mile trip was considerably farther than the distance between Earth and Uranus. When describing distances of this magnitude, scientists often use more convenient units such as the astronomical unit (93,000,000 miles, the average distance between the Earth and the Sun), or the lightyear, the distance that light travels in one year.

Voyager II's journey has been a remarkable one. Consider that its scaled equivalent is tossing an atom several hundred yards in order to hit another atom. As Voyager passes the orbit of Neptune and sends information from the edge of the Solar System, the men and women who planned and guided the space mission have succeeded once again.

Problems

1. **a.** How many miles did Voyager travel from Earth to Uranus?
   b. How long was its journey in astronomical units (AU's)?
   c. How far was its trip in lightyears?
2. **a.** How many days did it take Voyager to travel from Earth to Uranus?
   b. How many hours did the trip take?
3. Calculate Voyager's speed, in miles per hour, for the trip from Earth to Uranus.
4. What is the speed of light in miles per hour?
5. Express the ratio of the speed of light to the speed of Voyager.
6. The Earth and the Moon are 234,000 miles apart. How long did it take the words, ". . . one small step for man, . . .", to reach Earth?
7. How many miles apart were Earth and Uranus on January 24, 1986?

Chapter 10 Summary and Review

10-1

The **distance** between any two points (x_1, y_1) and (x_2, y_2) is given by $d = \sqrt{(x_1 - x_2)^2 + (y_1 - y_2)^2}$.

Find the distance between the points.

1. $(-3, 4)$ and $(7, 0)$ $2\sqrt{29}$
2. $(0, 3)$ and $(4, 0)$ 5
3. $(2, -4)$ and $(-9, 6)$ $\sqrt{221}$

If the coordinates of the endpoints of a segment are (x_1, y_1) and (x_2, y_2), then the coordinates of the **midpoint** are $\left(\frac{x_1 + x_2}{2}, \frac{y_1 + y_2}{2}\right)$.

Find the midpoint of the segments having the following endpoints.

4. $(-3, 4)$ and $(7, 0)$ (2, 2)
5. $(-2, 4)$ and $(6, 8)$ (2, 6)
6. $(-8, -1)$ and $(4, 5)$ (−2, 2)
7. $(0, 3)$ and $(10, 7)$ (5, 5)

10-2

The equation (in standard form) of a **circle** with center (h, k) and radius r is $(x - h)^2 + (y - k)^2 = r^2$.

Find an equation of the circle with center and radius as given.

8. $(-2, 6)$; $\sqrt{13}$ $(x + 2)^2 + (y - 6)^2 = 13$
9. $(3, -1)$; 2 $(x - 3)^2 + (y + 1)^2 = 4$

Completing the square can be used to produce the standard form of the equation of a circle.

Find the center and radius of the circle.

10. $(x - 4)^2 + (y + 3)^2 = 12$
11. $x^2 + y^2 = 36$
12. $x^2 + y^2 - 6x + 10y + 24 = 0$
13. $2x^2 + 2y^2 - 3x - 5y + 3 = 0$

10-3

The equation, in standard form, of an **ellipse** centered at (h, k) with foci c units from (h, k), and major axis of length $2a$, is $\frac{(x-h)^2}{a^2} + \frac{(y-k)^2}{b^2} = 1$, for a horizontal major axis, or $\frac{(x-h)^2}{b^2} + \frac{(y-k)^2}{a^2} = 1$, for a vertical major axis, where $c^2 = a^2 - b^2$.
Remember that completing the square can be used to produce the standard form of the equation of an ellipse.

For each ellipse find the center, vertices, and foci. Then draw a graph.

14. $16x^2 + 25y^2 - 64x + 50y - 311 = 0$
15. $9x^2 + 16y^2 + 36x - 32y - 92 = 0$

10-4

The equation, in standard form, of a **hyperbola** centered at (h, k) with foci c units from (h, k) is $\frac{(x-h)^2}{a^2} - \frac{(y-k)^2}{b^2} = 1$, for horizontal foci, or $\frac{(y-k)^2}{a^2} - \frac{(x-h)^2}{b^2} = 1$, for vertical foci, where $c^2 = a^2 + b^2$.

ADDITIONAL ANSWERS

10. Center $(4, -3)$; radius $2\sqrt{3}$
11. Center $(0, 0)$; radius 6
12. Center $(3, -5)$; radius $\sqrt{10}$
13. Center $\left(\frac{3}{4}, \frac{5}{4}\right)$; radius $\frac{\sqrt{10}}{4}$
14. Center: $(2, -1)$; vertices: $(7, -1)$, $(-3, -1)$, $(2, 3)$, $(2, -5)$; foci: $(5, -1)$, $(-1, -1)$

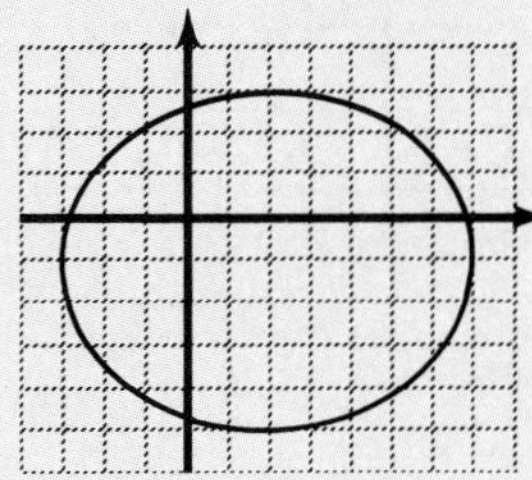

15. Center: $(-2, 1)$; vertices: $(-6, 1)$, $(2, 1)$, $(-2, 4)$, $(-2, -2)$; foci: $(-2 + \sqrt{7}, 1)$, $(-2 - \sqrt{7}, 1)$

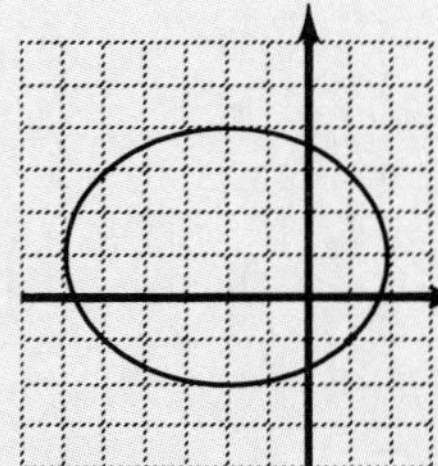

16. Center: $\left(-2, \frac{1}{4}\right)$; vertices: $\left(0, \frac{1}{4}\right)$, $\left(-4, \frac{1}{4}\right)$; foci: $\left(-2 + \sqrt{6}, \frac{1}{4}\right)$, $\left(-2 - \sqrt{6}, \frac{1}{4}\right)$; asymptotes: $y - \frac{1}{4} = \pm \frac{\sqrt{2}}{2}(x + 2)$

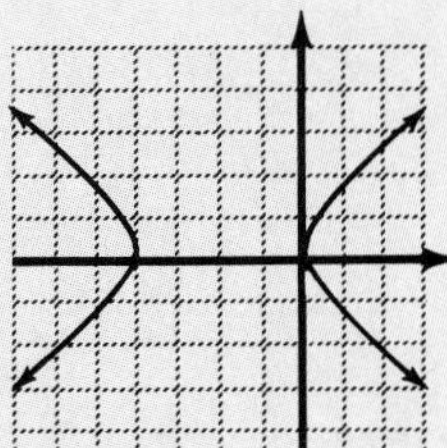

17. Center: (0, 0); vertices: $(\sqrt{6}, 0), (-\sqrt{6}, 0)$; foci: $(\sqrt{22}, 0), (-\sqrt{22}, 0)$; asymptotes: $y = \pm\frac{2\sqrt{6}}{3}x$

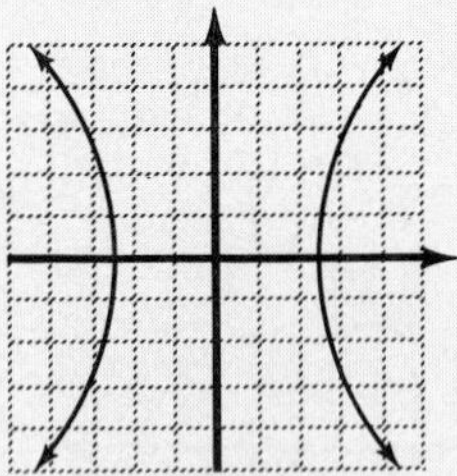

18. Vertex: (0, 0); focus: (−3, 0); directrix: $x = 3$

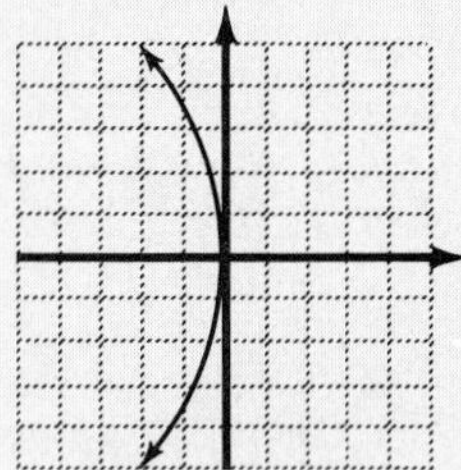

19. Vertex: (1, −1); focus: $\left(1, -\frac{1}{2}\right)$; directrix: $y = -\frac{3}{2}$

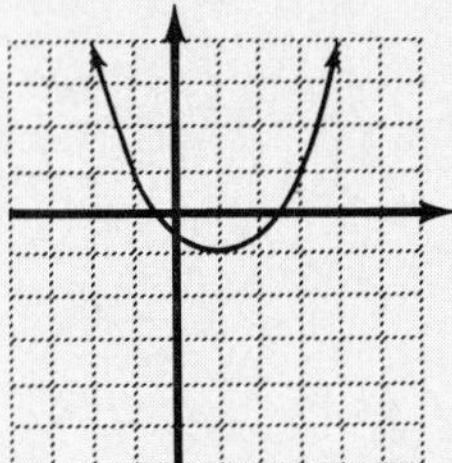

20. Vertex: $\left(\frac{9}{4}, -1\right)$; focus: $\left(\frac{5}{4}, -1\right)$; directrix: $x = \frac{13}{4}$

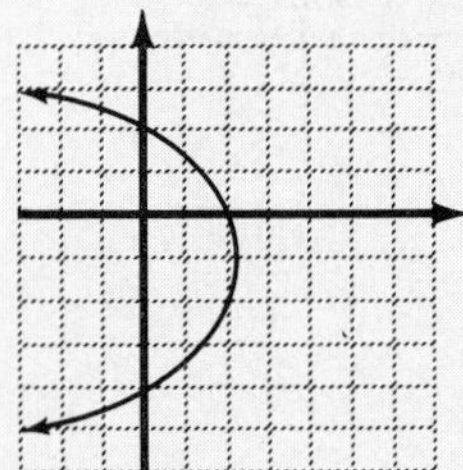

For each hyperbola, find the center, vertices, foci, and asymptotes. Then draw a graph.

16. $x^2 - 2y^2 + 4x + y - \frac{1}{8} = 0$ **17.** $8x^2 - 3y^2 = 48$

10-5

A parabola with vertex (h, k) and axis of symmetry parallel to the y-axis has an equation $(x - h)^2 = 4p(y - k)$ with focus $(h, k + p)$ and directrix $y = k - p$. A parabola with vertex (h, k) and axis of symmetry parallel to the x-axis has an equation $(y - k)^2 = 4p(x - h)$ with focus $(h + p, k)$ and directrix $x = h - p$.

For each parabola find the vertex, focus, and directrix. Then draw a graph.

18. $y^2 = -12x$ **19.** $(x - 1)^2 - 2(y + 1) = 0$ **20.** $y^2 + 2y + 4x - 8 = 0$

10-6

Consider the second-degree equation $Ax^2 + By^2 + Cx + Dy + E = 0$.

1. If $A = B$, the equation may define a circle.
2. If A and B have the same sign and $A \neq B$, the equation may define an ellipse.
3. If A and B have different signs, the equation defines a hyperbola.
4. If either A or B is 0, the equation defines a parabola.

Tell which conic section is defined by the following equations.

21. $2x^2 - 2y^2 + 3x - 2 = 0$ Hyperbola **22.** $5y^2 + 10y + 2x + 2 = 0$ Parabola

23. $2x - 2y^2 - 2x^2 - 3y + 16 = 0$ Circle

24. $\frac{x^2}{5^2} + \frac{y^2}{1} = 1$ Ellipse **25.** $\frac{x^2}{3} + \frac{y^2}{3} + 2 = 1$ No conic

To solve a system of equations graphically, it is helpful to be able to recognize equations of the different conic sections.

Solve graphically.

26. $y^2 = 100 - x^2$
$y = x + 2$ (6, 8), (−8, −6)

27. $y = x^2 + 1$
$x + 2y = 5$ (1, 2), $\left(-\frac{3}{2}, \frac{13}{4}\right)$

Solve graphically.

28. $x^2 + y^2 = 16$
$\frac{x^2}{16} + \frac{y^2}{9} = 1$ (4, 0), (−4, 0)

10-7

When one equation of a system is quadratic, the substitution method is preferable.

Solve.

29. $\frac{x^2}{16} + \frac{y^2}{9} = 1$
$3x + 4y = 12$ (4, 0), (0, 3)

To solve systems of two second-degree equations algebraically, use either the substitution or linear combinations.

Solve.

30. $x^2 + y^2 = 29$
$y^2 - 3x^2 = 13$ (2, 5), (2, −5), (−2, 5), (−2, −5)

31. $4x^2 - 9y^2 = 108$
$xy = -12$ (6, −2), (−6, 2)

10-8

Some problems can be solved after translating to a system of second-degree equations.

32. The area of a rectangle is 240 cm^2 and the length of a diagonal is 26 cm. Find the dimensions of the rectangle. 10 cm by 24 cm

33. Find two numbers whose product is −48 if the sum of their squares is 265. 3, −16 or −3, 16

See also Problem 10, Computer-Assisted Problem Solving, page 845.

Chapter 10 Test

Find the distance between the points.

1. (−3, 4) and (7, 6) $2\sqrt{26}$

2. (4, −1) and (−2, 0) $\sqrt{37}$

Find the midpoint of the segment having the following endpoints.

3. (−3, 4) and (7, 6) (2, 5)

4. (−2, −3) and (0, 1) (−1, −1)

5. Find an equation of the circle with center (4, −1) and radius 5. $(x - 4)^2 + (y + 1)^2 = 25$

6. Find the center and radius of the circle $x^2 + y^2 - 8x + 12y + 49 = 0$.

7. Find the center, vertices, and foci of the ellipse $x^2 + 4y^2 - 6x + 24y + 41 = 0$. Then graph the ellipse.

8. Find the center, vertices, foci, and asymptotes of the hyperbola $25x^2 - 9y^2 = 225$.

9. Find the vertex, focus, and directrix of the parabola $x^2 + 2x + 6y - 11 = 0$. Then graph the parabola.

10. Which conic section is defined by $2x^2 - 5y^2 + 2x - 3y - 6 = 0$?

11. Solve graphically.
$y = x^2 - 2$
$3x - 2y = 2$

12. Solve.
$x^2 + y^2 = 74$
$x - y = 2$

13. Solve graphically.
$x^2 + y^2 = 25$
$x + y = 5$

14. Solve.
$3x^2 - 8y^2 = 3$
$y^2 = x + 4$

15. Two squares whose sides differ in length by 9 m have areas that differ by 153 m^2. Find the length of a side of each. 13 m, 4 m

Challenge

16. Find the equation of a circle containing the points (0, −2) and (6, 6) and whose center is on the line $x - y = 1$. $(x - 3)^2 + (y - 2)^2 = 25$

ADDITIONAL ANSWERS

6. Center (4, −6); radius $\sqrt{3}$

7. Center: (3, −3)
Vertices: (1, −3), (3, −2), (5, −3), (3, −4)
Foci: $(3 + \sqrt{3}, -3)$, $(3 - \sqrt{3}, -3)$

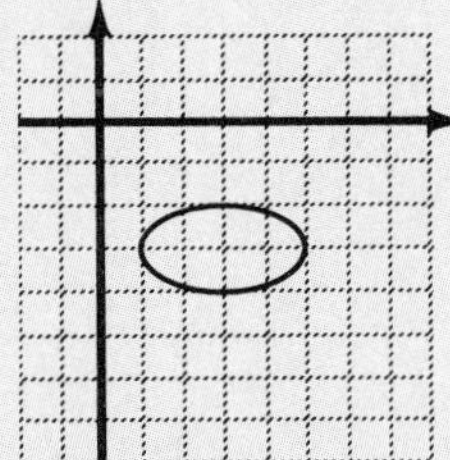

8. Center: (0, 0)
Vertices: (3, 0), (−3, 0)
Foci: $(\sqrt{34}, 0)$, $(-\sqrt{34}, 0)$
Asymptotes: $y = \frac{5}{3}x$, $y = -\frac{5}{3}x$

9. Vertex: (−1, 2); Focus: $\left(-1, \frac{1}{2}\right)$;
Directrix: $y = \frac{7}{2}$

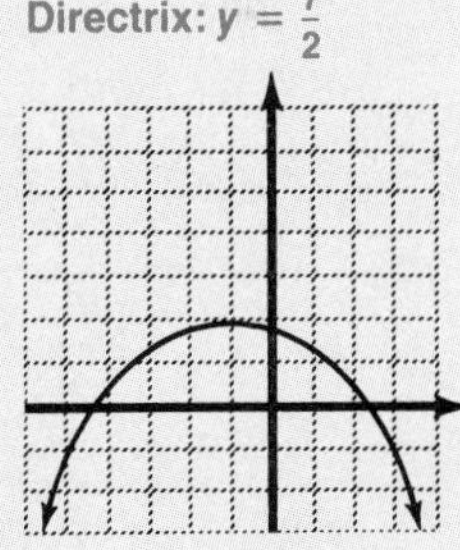

10. Hyperbola

11. (2, 2), $\left(-\frac{1}{2}, -\frac{7}{4}\right)$

12. (7, 5), (−5, −7)

13. (5, 0), (0, 5)

14. (5, 3), (5, −3), $\left(-\frac{7}{3}, \sqrt{\frac{5}{3}}\right)$, $\left(-\frac{7}{3}, -\sqrt{\frac{5}{3}}\right)$

Test Item Analysis

Item	Lesson
1–4	10-1
5, 6	10-2
7	10-3
8	10-4
9	10-5
10	10-7
11–14	10-6
15	10-8
16	10-7

CHAPTER 11

Polynomial Functions

Chapter Overview

Chapter 11 normally concludes the discussion of polynomials, examining the nature of roots, and giving both algorithmic and theoretical methods for considering or solving polynomial equations. The fundamental theorem of algebra, the remainder theorem, factor theorem, rational roots theorem, and Descartes' rule of signs are presented. Higher-degree functions are graphed. The problem-solving strategy *Work Backward* is used.

Objectives

11-1
- Determine whether a number is a root or zero of a polynomial equation or function.
- Determine whether one polynomial is a factor of another by division.

11-2
- Use synthetic division and the remainder theorem to find $P(r)$.
- Determine whether a given number is a root of a polynomial $P(x)$.
- Determine whether $x - r$ is a factor of $P(x)$, and then solve the polynomial equation $P(x) = 0$.

11-3
- Find the roots of a polynomial and determine the multiplicity of each root.
- Find all the roots of a polynomial given its degree and several roots.
- Find polynomials with specific roots.

11-4
- Find rational and other roots of a polynomial with integer coefficients.

11-5
- Use Descartes' rule of signs to find the number of positive roots of a polynomial.
- Use Descartes' rule of signs to find the number of negative roots of a polynomial.

11-6
- Graph polynomial functions.
- Use a graph to aid in approximating solutions to polynomial equations.

11-7
- Solve problems using the strategy *Work Backward,* and other strategies.

TEACHING CHAPTER 11

Cooperative Learning Opportunities

The procedures for finding the roots of a polynomial include some elusive theory and algorithms—synthetic division, attention to complex conjugates, and the rule of signs. These are covered in Lessons 11-2 through 11-5. Quizzes given to pairs of students can help students take the new methods seriously without becoming discouraged. Try this approach, using the same pairs of students, for each of the four lessons. This might lead to the formation of out-of-class study groups.

Assign the **Try This** Exercises to some groups that are spatially separated and assign similar A Exercises to other groups. Students are to work together, without roles, and submit one paper, which you grade for the pair.

There should be no reason for students not agreeing on the answers because factors and roots of polynomials can be checked. You might permit students to check roots through the use of a calculator.

Multicultural Note: *Celestino Beltran*

Graphing calculators and graphing programs for the computer have facilitated the teaching and learning of algebra and trigonometry. As you use these technologies, you might take a moment to remind students that computers and calculators cannot do any more or less than they are programmed to do. Mentioning this will remind students that the computer is neither a god nor is it magic. It might also stimulate interest in computer-related careers.

Celestino Beltran is a Mexican-American engineer and president of Comprehensive Technologies, a software company that is producing products for science and technology. Until the age of 14, Beltran was illiterate, viewed by his teachers as unable to learn. But a remedial summer course changed him. He finished high school, studied engineering in college, and moved to the top of his profession.

For more information, see page 31 of **Multiculturalism in Mathematics, Science, and Technology**.

Alternative Assessment and Communication Ideas

Students can learn to do the mathematics in Chapter 11 and still miss the theoretical subtleties. The **Writing to Learn** activity on page 484 and the **Critical Thinking** Exercise on page 489 taken together can form the nucleus of written alternative assessment.

Ask students to write about polynomials and to include clear explanations of function, equation, zero, solution, root, factor, remainder, coefficient, graph, table of values. Ask students to try to use their own words but to be accurate in their descriptions, to use examples of their own making, and to include the use of the graphing calculator or computer if they wish.

As they take a more careful look at the definitions and theorems, students may notice the differences regarding the coefficients named in the conditions for different theorems: complex, real, rational, integer. Although integer coefficients are used throughout the chapter, the theorems are stated in their most general form.

Investigations and Projects

The graphing calculator can be used to advantage in a number of lessons in Chapter 11. If you have a projector that attaches to the calculator, you might ask students to prepare and do class presentations for some of the lessons. The following are possibilities.

Lesson 11-1: The investigation on page 858 is structured so that a student could easily take the class through the procedures and demonstrate the use of the different functions.

Lesson 11-4: Application of the Rational Roots Theorem through synthetic substitution is the traditional method for checking possible roots. But the graphing calculator can also be used in conjunction with the Rational Roots Theorem in order to identify roots. When the graph shows a decimal approximation, a possible rational root close to the approximation can be tested.

Lesson 11-6: The graphing calculator can be used to show a variety of functions and their graphs.

MANAGING CHAPTER 11

Lesson	PACING CHART (DAYS) Algebra	Algebra w/Finite	Algebra w/Trig	Compre-hensive	Opening Activity	Cooperative Activity	Seat or Group Work
11-1	1.5	1	1	1	First Five Minutes 11-1: **TE** p.480 or ***FFM Transparency Masters*** p.32	Critical Thinking: **SE** p.484 ✂ Manipulative Activity 11: ***Enrichment*** p.52	Try This a–e
11-2	1.5	1	1	1	First Five Minutes 11-2: **TE** p.485 or ***FFM Transparency Masters*** p.33	Explore: **SE** p.485 Critical Thinking: **SE** p.489	Try This a–g
11-3	2	1	1	1	First Five Minutes 11-3: **TE** p.490 or ***FFM Transparency Masters*** p.33	Critical Thinking: **SE** p.495	Try This a–i
11-4	2	1	1	1	First Five Minutes 11-4: **TE** p.496 or ***FFM Transparency Masters*** p.33	Critical Thinking: **SE** p.500	Try This a–d
11-5	1	1	1	1	First Five Minutes 11-5: **TE** p.501 or ***FFM Transparency Masters*** p.33	Critical Thinking: **SE** p.503	Try This a–f
11-6	1	1	1	1	First Five Minutes 11-6: **TE** p.504 or ***FFM Transparency Masters*** p.34	Critical Thinking: **SE** p.508 Looking for Errors 11: ***Enrichment*** p.72	Try This a–e
11-7	1	0.5	0.5	0.5	First Five Minutes 11-7: **TE** p.509 or ***FFM Transparency Masters*** p.34	Strategy Problem Bank 11: ***Problem Bank*** p.12	Problem 1: **SE** p.510
Review	1	0.5	0.5	0.5			
Test	1	1	1	1			

FFM: First Five Minutes   SPMR: Skills Practice Mixed Review

MANAGING CHAPTER 11

Enrichment	Review/Assess	Reteach	Technology	Lesson
Writing to Learn: **SE** p.484 TI-81 Investigation 2: **SE** pp.858–859 ✂ Manipulative Activity 11: ***Enrichment*** p.52 Teacher Demo 2: ***Master Grapher*** pp.7–8(Apple II), pp.141–142(IBM), or pp.277–278(Mac)	Lesson Quiz: **TE** p.482	Skills Practice 30, #1–8: ***SPMR*** p.42	Worksheet 16: ***TI-81 Activities*** pp.67–70 Worksheet 22: ***Master Grapher*** pp.90–93, pp.224–227, or pp.360–363 Calculator Worksheet 17: ***Technology*** p.19 TI-81 Investigation 2: **SE** pp.858–859	**11-1**
Critical Thinking 11: ***Enrichment*** p.32	Lesson Quiz: **TE** p.488 Quiz 21: ***Assessment*** p.29	Skills Practice 30, #9–17: ***SPMR*** p.42	Calculator Worksheet 18: ***Technology*** p.20	**11-2**
Math Point: **TE** p.490 Lesson Enrichment **TE** p.493	Lesson Quiz: **TE** p.493	Skills Practice 31, #1–15: ***SPMR*** p.43	BASIC Computer Project 11: ***Technology*** p.91	**11-3**
Math Point: **TE** p.496	Lesson Quiz: **TE** p.499 Mixed Review 21: ***SPMR*** p.85	Skills Practice 31, #16–21: ***SPMR*** p.43	Calculator Worksheet 19: ***Technology*** p.21	**11-4**
Math Point: **TE** p.502	Lesson Quiz: **TE** p.502 Quiz 22: ***Assessment*** p.30	Skills Practice 32, #1–16: ***SPMR*** p.44	Problem for Programmers: **SE** p.503	**11-5**
Looking for Errors 11: ***Enrichment*** p.72	Lesson Quiz: **TE** p.506	Skills Practice 32, #17–33: ***SPMR*** p.44	Worksheet 17: ***TI-81 Activities*** pp.71–72 Worksheet 23: ***Master Grapher*** pp.94–95, pp.228–229, or pp.364–365 Calculator Worksheet 20: ***Technology*** p.22 Spreadsheet Activity 6: ***Technology*** pp.59–61	**11-6**
Problem 11: Computer Assisted Problem Solving, **SE** pp.846–847	Mixed Review 22: ***SPMR*** p.86	Strategy Problem Bank 11: ***Problem Bank*** p.12	Problem 11: Computer Assisted Problem Solving, **SE** pp.846–847	**11-7**
	Summary and Review: **SE** pp.511–512; Test: **SE** p.513			**Review**
	Chapter 11 Test: ***Assessment*** pp.107–112(reg.), pp.177–178 (adv.); Assessing Strategies 7: ***Assessment*** pp.207–208			**Test**

The solution to the problem posed on the facing page can be found on page 500.

Ready for Polynomial Functions?

5-4, 5-6 Factor.

1. $x^2 + x - 6$ $(x + 3)(x - 2)$ **2.** $x^2 - 5x + 4$ $(x - 4)(x - 1)$ **3.** $3x^2 + 2x - 1$ $(3x - 1)(x + 1$

4. $2x^2 + 7x + 6$ $(x + 2)(2x + 3)$ **5.** $4x^2 + x - 5$ $(x - 1)(4x + 5)$ **6.** $x^2 - 11x + 24$ $(x - 3)(x - 8)$

7-9 Find the conjugate of each.

7. $-3 + 8i$ $-3 - 8i$ **8.** $2 - 4i$ $2 + 4i$

7-9 Multiply.

9. $(1 - 5i)(1 + 5i)$ 26 **10.** $(3 - 2i)(3 + 2i)$ 13

11. $(-6 - i)(-6 + i)$ 37

7-10 Determine whether each of the following is a solution of $x^2 - 2x + 1 = 0$.

12. 1 Yes **13.** $1 + i$ No **14.** $1 - i$ No

15. Find an equation having -2, i, and $3i$ as solutions. $x^3 - 4ix^2 + 2x^2 - 8ix - 3x - 6 = 0$

16. Show that $-1 - i$ is a square root of $2i$. Then find the other square root. $(-1 - i)^2 = 1 + 2i + i^2 = 1 + 2i - 1 = 2i$, $1 + i$

8-4 Find a quadratic equation having the given solutions.

17. $-5, \frac{2}{3}$ $3x^2 + 13x - 10 = 0$ **18.** $\frac{1}{2}, -\frac{3}{2}$ $4x^2 + 4x - 3 = 0$ **19.** $\sqrt{2}, -\sqrt{2}$ $x^2 - 2 = 0$

CHAPTER 11

Polynomial Functions

A box manufacturer makes boxes of volume 48 ft³ from pieces of cardboard 10 ft on a side by cutting squares from each corner and folding up the edges. What is the length of each side of a square?

11-1

FIRST FIVE MINUTES

1. Evaluate $x^2 + 1$ for $x = 3$.
   $(3)^2 + 1 = 10$
2. Solve for x where $x^2 + 6x + 9 = 0$.
   $(x + 3)^2 = 0$
   $x = -3$
3. Solve for x where $(x - 1)(x - 2)(x - 3) = 0$.
   $x = 1$ or $x = 2$ or $x = 3$

Roots and Zeros

Remind students that polynomials have the properties of numbers and can be added, subtracted, multiplied, and divided.

Point out the relationship between roots and zeros. The roots of the equation $x^3 - 5x^2 + x - 5 = 0$ are the same as the zeros of the function $P(x) = x^3 - 5x^2 + x - 5$. Zeros are appropriately named as they are the values for x that make the function zero.

Key Questions

- What are the leading coefficient and the degree of the polynomial $5x^3 + 8x^4 + 9$?
  8, 4
- If 5 is a root of the polynomial equation $x^2 - 10x + 25 = 0$, what is the zero of the function $P(x) = x^2 - 10x + 25$?
  5

Chalkboard Example

Determine whether the given numbers are roots of the polynomial equation $x^3 - 2x^2 - x + 2 = 0$.

1. a. 2
   $P(2) = (2)^3 - 2(2)^2 - (2) + 2 = 0$
   2 is a root of the equation.

   $P(3) = (3)^3 - 2(3)^2 - (3) + 2 = 8$
   3 is not a root of the equation.

11-1 Polynomials and Polynomial Functions

 *Master Grapher* Worksheet 22, *Finding Roots of Polynomial Equations*, can be used as a lesson opener.

TI-81 Investigation 2 (page 858) can be used with this lesson.

Recall that a polynomial in x is any expression of the form

$$a_nx^n + a_{n-1}x^{n-1} + a_{n-2}x^{n-2} + \cdots + a_1x + a_0$$

We will usually assume that the coefficients are complex numbers, but in some cases will restrict them to be real numbers, rational numbers, or integers. Also recall that the coefficient of the term of highest degree, a_n, is the leading coefficient.

Roots and Zeros

Objective: Determine whether a number is a root or zero of a given equation or function.

When a number is substituted for the variable in a polynomial, the result is some unique number. Thus every polynomial defines a function. We often refer to polynomials, therefore, using function notation $P(x)$.

When we set a polynomial equal to 0, we obtain a polynomial equation $P(x) = 0$.

Definition

If a number n is a solution of a polynomial equation $P(x) = 0$, then n is called a **root** of the equation.

If a number n, when substituted for x, makes a polynomial function $P(x)$ zero, then n is called a **zero** of the function.

EXAMPLE 1 Determine whether the given numbers are roots of the polynomial equation $P(x) = 0$, where $P(x) = x^3 - 5x^2 + x - 5$.

$$x^3 - 5x^2 + x - 5 = 0$$

(a) -5;

$$(-5)^3 - 5(-5)^2 + (-5) - 5 = 0 \quad \text{Substituting } -5 \text{ for } x$$
$$-125 - 125 - 5 - 5 = 0$$
$$-260 = 0$$

Substituting -5 for x yields a false equation, so -5 is not a root.

(b) $-i$;

$$(-i)^3 - 5(-i)^2 + (-i) - 5 = 0$$
$$i + 5 - i - 5 = 0 \quad (-i)^3 = -i(-i)^2 = -i(-1) = i$$
$$0 = 0$$

Substituting $-i$ for x yields a true equation, thus $-i$ is a root of the equation $P(x) = 0$.

EXAMPLE 2 Determine whether the given numbers are zeros of the polynomial function $P(x)$, where $P(x)$ is given by $x^3 - 3x^2 + x - 3$.

$$P(x) = x^3 - 3x^2 + x - 3$$

(a) 3; $P(3) = 3^3 - 3(3)^2 + 3 - 3$ Evaluating the function $P(x)$ for $x = 3$

$$= 27 - 27 + 3 - 3$$
$$= 0$$

$P(3) = 0$, so 3 is a zero of the function.

(b) $2i$; $P(2i) = (2i)^3 - 3(2i)^2 + 2i - 3$

$$= -8i + 12 + 2i - 3$$
$$= -6i + 9$$

$P(2i) \neq 0$, so $2i$ is not a zero of the function.

Try This

a. Determine whether the given numbers are roots of the polynomial equation $P(x) = 0$, where $P(x) = x^3 + x^2 - 2x$.

(1) 0 Yes **(2)** i No

b. Determine whether the given numbers are zeros of the polynomial function $P(x)$, where $P(x)$ is given by $x^4 - 2x^3 + 4x^2 - 8x$.

(1) $2i$ Yes **(2)** -2 No

Factors and Division

Objective: Determine whether one polynomial is a factor of another by division.

When we divide one polynomial by another we obtain a quotient and a remainder. If the remainder is 0, then the divisor is a factor of the dividend.

EXAMPLE 3 Divide to determine whether $x^2 + 3$ is a factor of the polynomial $x^3 - x^2 + 5x - 4$.

We use polynomial long division here.

$$\begin{array}{r|l} & x - 1 \\ x^2 + 3 & x^3 - x^2 + 5x - 4 \\ & \underline{x^3 \quad\quad + 3x} \\ & -x^2 + 2x - 4 \\ & \underline{-x^2 \quad\quad - 3} \\ & 2x - 1 \end{array}$$

Since the remainder is not 0, we know that $x^2 + 3$ is not a factor of the polynomial $x^3 - x^2 + 5x - 4$.

Factors and Division

You may want to review synthetic division. Emphasize that it is only used when the divisor is a linear factor.

Chalkboard Examples

1. Divide to find whether $x^2 + 4$ is a factor of $x^4 - 16$.

$$\begin{array}{r|l} & x^2 - 4 \\ x^2 + 4 & x^4 + 0 + 0 - 16 \\ & \underline{x^4 \quad + 4x^2} \\ & -4x^2 - 16 \\ & \underline{-4x^2 - 16} \\ & 0 \end{array}$$

Since the remainder is 0, we know that $x^2 + 4$ is a factor of $x^4 - 16$.

2. Divide to find whether $x^2 + 1$ is a factor of $x^4 + 3x^3 + 2x^2 + 3x + 1$.

$$\begin{array}{r|l} & x^2 + 3x + 1 \\ x^2 + 1 & x^4 + 3x^3 + 2x^2 + 3x + 1 \\ & \underline{x^4 \quad\quad + x^2} \\ & 3x^3 + x^2 + 3x + 1 \\ & \underline{3x^3 + \quad + 3x} \\ & x^2 \quad + 1 \\ & \underline{x^2 \quad + 1} \\ & 0 \end{array}$$

Since the remainder is 0, $x^2 + 1$ is a factor of $x^4 + 3x^3 + 2x^2 + 3x + 1$.

3. If $P(x) = x^3 + 2$ and $D(x) = x + 1$, find $Q(x)$ and $R(x)$.

Divide $P(x)$ by $D(x)$. The quotient is $x^2 - x + 1$ with a remainder of 1. Hence

$x^3 + 2 = (x + 1)(x^2 - x + 1) + 1$

$Q(x) = x^2 - x + 1$

$R(x) = 1$

LESSON QUIZ

1. Determine whether 1 is a root of $P(x) = x^3 + 4x^2 + x - 6$.
   Yes
2. Use division to determine whether $x + 2$ is a factor of $P(x) = x^3 + 4x^2 + x - 6$.
   Yes

EXAMPLE 4 Divide to determine whether $x - 3$ is a factor of the polynomial $x^4 - 3x^3 - x + 3$.

We can use synthetic division here.

$$\begin{array}{r|rrrrr} 3 & 1 & -3 & 0 & -1 & 3 \\ & & 3 & 0 & 0 & -3 \\ \hline & 1 & 0 & 0 & -1 & 0 \end{array}$$

Since the remainder is 0, we know that $x - 3$ is a factor of the polynomial $x^4 - 3x^3 - x + 3$. That is, $x^4 - 3x^3 - x + 3 = (x - 3)(x^3 - 1)$.

Try This

c. Divide to determine whether the following polynomials are factors of the polynomial $x^3 + 2x^2 - 5x - 6$.

(1) $x - 3$ No **(2)** $x + 1$ Yes

d. Divide to determine whether the following polynomials are factors of the polynomial $x^4 + 3x^3 - 3x - 1$.

(1) $x^2 + 3x + 1$ Yes **(2)** $x^3 + 2x^2 - 2x + 1$ No

When we divide a polynomial $P(x)$ by a divisor $D(x)$ we obtain a polynomial $Q(x)$ for a quotient and a polynomial $R(x)$ for a remainder. The remainder must either be 0 or have degree less than that of $D(x)$.

Thus we can express every polynomial division as

$$\underbrace{P(x)}_{\text{dividend}} = \underbrace{D(x)}_{\text{divisor}} \cdot \underbrace{Q(x)}_{\text{quotient}} + \underbrace{R(x)}_{\text{remainder}}$$

EXAMPLE 5

Let $P(x) = 5x^3 - 6x^2 + 18x - 4$ and $D(x) = x^2 - x + 3$. Find $P(x) \div D(x)$, then express the dividend as $P(x) = D(x) \cdot Q(x) + R(x)$.

We divide.

$$\begin{array}{r} 5x \quad - 1 \qquad\qquad\quad \\ x^2 - x + 3\overline{)5x^3 - 6x^2 + 18x - 4} \\ 5x^3 - 5x^2 + 15x \qquad \\ \hline -x^2 + 3x - 4 \\ -x^2 + x - 3 \\ \hline 2x - 1 \end{array}$$

The quotient is $5x - 1$ with a remainder of $2x - 1$. Now we express $P(x)$ as the product of a divisor and a quotient, plus a remainder.

$$\begin{array}{ccccc} P(x) & = & D(x) & \cdot\ Q(x) & +\ R(x) \\ 5x^3 - 6x^2 + 18x - 4 & = & (x^2 - x + 3) & \cdot\ (5x - 1) & +\ 2x - 1 \end{array}$$

Try This

e. Let $P(x) = x^3 + 2x^2 - 5x - 6$ and $D(x) = x - 3$. Find $P(x) \div D(x)$, then express the dividend as $P(x) = D(x) \cdot Q(x) + R(x)$. $x^3 + 2x^2 - 5x - 6 = (x - 3)(x^2 + 5x + 10) + 24$

11-1 EXERCISES

A

Determine whether the following numbers are roots of the polynomial equation $P(x) = 0$.

1. $P(x) = x^3 + 6x^2 - x - 30$; $2, 3, -1$ Yes, no, no

2. $P(x) = 2x^3 - 3x^2 + x - 1$; $2, 3, -1$ No, no, no

Determine whether the given numbers are zeros of the polynomial functions.

3. $P(x) = x^3 - 2x^2 + 8x$; $0, -1, 1 + i\sqrt{7}, 1 - i\sqrt{7}$ Yes, no, yes, yes

4. $P(x) = x^3 - 2x^2 + 2x$; $0, -2, 1 + i, 1 - i$ Yes, no, yes, yes

Divide to determine whether the following polynomials are factors of the polynomial $P(x)$.

5. $P(x) = x^3 + 6x^2 - x - 30$
a. $x - 2$ Yes **b.** $x - 3$ No **c.** $x + 1$ No

6. $P(x) = 2x^3 - 3x^2 + x - 1$
a. $x - 2$ No **b.** $x - 3$ No **c.** $x + 1$ No

7. $P(x) = x^4 - 81$
a. $x - 3$ Yes **b.** $x + 3$ Yes **c.** $x + 9$ No

8. $P(x) = x^5 + 32$
a. $x - 2$ No **b.** $x + 2$ Yes **c.** $x - 4$ No

9. $P(x) = x^6 - 1$
a. $x - 1$ Yes **b.** $x^2 + x + 1$ Yes **c.** $x^2 - x + 1$ Yes

10. $P(x) = 2x^4 + 10x^3 - 3x^2 - 5x + 1$
a. $2x^2 + 1$ No **b.** $2x^2 - 1$ Yes **c.** $x^2 + 5$ No

Divide each $P(x)$ by $D(x)$. Then express the dividend as $P(x) = D(x) \cdot Q(x) + R(x)$.

11. $P(x) = x^3 + 6x^2 - x - 30$
a. $D(x) = x - 2$ **b.** $D(x) = x - 3$

12. $P(x) = 2x^3 - 3x^2 + x - 1$
a. $D(x) = x - 2$ **b.** $D(x) = x - 3$

13. $P(x) = x^3 - 8$
$D(x) = x + 2$

14. $P(x) = x^3 + 27$
$D(x) = x + 1$

15. $P(x) = x^4 + 9x^2 + 20$
$D(x) = x^2 + 4$

16. $P(x) = x^4 + x^2 + 2$
$D(x) = x^2 + x + 1$

17. $P(x) = 5x^5 - 3x^4 + 2x^2 - 3$
$D(x) = 2x^2 - x + 1$

18. $P(x) = 6x^5 + 4x^4 - 3x^2 + x - 2$
$D(x) = 3x^2 + 2x - 1$

Assignment Guide

Algebra: Day 1: 1 – 10, MR
Day 2: 11 – 18 e/o, assign w. 11-2

Alg w/Finite or Trig: 1–21 e/o, 22, MR

Comprehensive: 1–21 m3, 22, 23–26 e/o, MR

ADDITIONAL ANSWERS

Exercises

11. a. $x^3 + 6x^2 - x - 30 = (x - 2)(x^2 + 8x + 15) + 0$
b. $x^3 + 6x^2 - x - 30 = (x - 3)(x^2 + 9x + 26) + 48$

12. a. $2x^3 - 3x^2 + x - 1 = (x - 2)(2x^2 + x + 3) + 5$
b. $2x^3 - 3x^2 + x - 1 = (x - 3)(2x^2 + 3x + 10) + 29$

13. $x^3 - 8 = (x + 2)(x^2 - 2x + 4) + (-16)$

14. $x^3 + 27 = (x + 1)(x^2 - x + 1) + 26$

15. $x^4 + 9x^2 + 20 = (x^2 + 4)(x^2 + 5) + 0$

16. $x^4 + x^2 + 2 = (x^2 + x + 1)(x^2 - x + 1) + 1$

17. $5x^5 - 3x^4 + 2x^2 - 3 = (2x^2 - x + 1) \cdot \left(\frac{5}{2}x^3 - \frac{1}{4}x^2 - \frac{11}{8}x + \frac{7}{16}\right) + \frac{29x - 55}{16}$

18. $6x^5 + 4x^4 - 3x^2 + x - 2 = (3x^2 + 2x - 1) \cdot \left(2x^3 + \frac{2}{3}x - \frac{13}{9}\right) + \frac{41x - 31}{9}$

Mixed Review

27. Even
28. Odd
29. Neither
30. Odd
31.

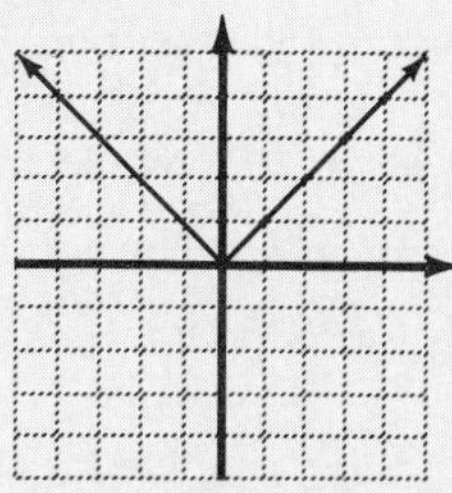

32.

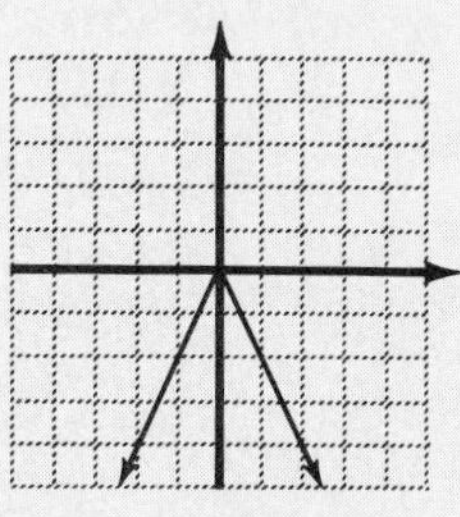

33.

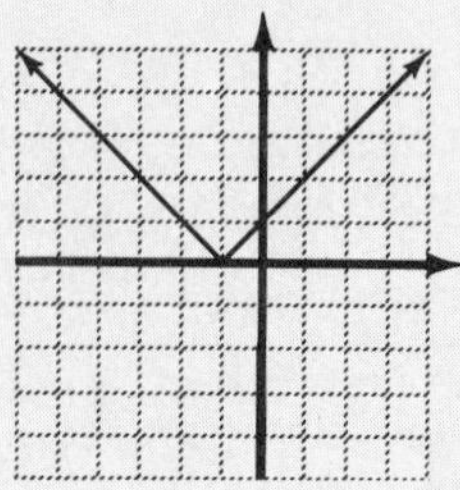

34. 0 or $-\frac{1}{2}$
35. $\frac{1 \pm \sqrt{10}}{3}$
36. 0 or $\frac{m}{n}$
37. a. 7 math, 10 chemistry
b. 88 points

Writing to Learn

Answers may vary.
The equation $P(x) = 0$ is true when the function $P(x)$ crosses the x-axis. The solution of an equation makes the equation true; a zero of a function is the value that makes the function zero.

B

Given $P(x) = D(x) \cdot Q(x) + R(x)$, find $P(x)$ if

19. $D(x) = x + 3$; $Q(x) = 2x^2 + x - 3$; and $R(x) = 4$ $2x^3 + 7x^2 - 5$

20. $D(x) = 4x - 3$; $Q(x) = x^2 + x + 2$; and $R(x) = 2x + 1$ $4x^3 + x^2 + 7x - 5$

21. $D(x) = x^2 - x + 3$; $Q(x) = 6x - 2$; and $R(x) = 3x + 2$ $6x^3 - 8x^2 + 23x - 4$

22. ***Critical Thinking*** Suppose 2 is a zero of a polynomial function. After translating the graph left 3 units, 2 is a zero of the new function. What do you know about the original function? 2 and 5 are zeros

Challenge

23. $P(x) = 2x^2 - ix + 1$
a. Find $P(-i)$. -2
b. Find the remainder when $P(x)$ is divided by $x + i$. -2

24. $P(x) = 2x^2 + ix - 1$
a. Find $P(i)$. -4
b. Find the remainder when $P(x)$ is divided by $x - i$. -4

25. Under what conditions is a polynomial function of real variables an even function, that is, $P(x) = P(-x)$ for all x? Does your answer hold for complex variables? All exponents even; yes

26. Under what conditions is a polynomial function of real variables an odd function, that is, $-P(x) = P(-x)$ for all x? Does your answer hold for complex variables? All exponents odd; yes

Mixed Review

Determine whether each function is odd, even, or neither. **27.** $f(x) = |5x|$

28. $f(x) = \frac{2}{3}x$ **29.** $f(x) = |x| + x$ **30.** $f(x) = x^3 + x$

Graph each equation. **31.** $y = |x|$ **32.** $y = -2|x|$ **33.** $y = |x + 1|$

Solve by completing the square. **34.** $x^2 + \frac{1}{2}x = 0$ **35.** $y^2 - \frac{2}{3}y = 1$

36. $a^2 - \frac{m}{n}a = 0$ (Solve for a.)

37. A contestant in a competition scores 4 points for working a math problem and 6 points for a chemistry problem. There are 12 of each type of problem. The contestant must work 7 math problems and 3 chemistry problems. A timer prevents the person from working more than 17 total problems.
a. How many of each type should the contestant work?
b. What is the maximum score?

WRITING TO LEARN

Write a short paragraph in which you contrast a zero of a polynomial $P(x)$ and the solution of an equation $P(x) = 0$.

11-2 The Remainder and Factor Theorems

Explore

Let $P(x) = x^5 - 64$.

Find $P(2)$. -32
Then find the remainder when $P(x)$ is divided by $x - 2$. -32
Compare your answers.

Find $P(-2)$. Then find the remainder when $P(x)$ is divided by $x + 2$. $-96, -96$

Make a generalization about the results. See Theorem 11-1.

Function Values of Polynomials

Objective: Use synthetic division and the remainder theorem to find $P(r)$.

The exploratory activity suggests the following important theorem about function values.

Theorem 11-1

The Remainder Theorem

For a polynomial $P(x)$, the function value $P(r)$ is the remainder when $P(x)$ is divided by $x - r$.

We can now use synthetic division to find function values for polynomials.

EXAMPLE 1 Let $P(x) = 2x^5 - 3x^4 + x^3 - 2x^2 + x - 8$. Find $P(10)$.

By Theorem 11-1, $P(10)$ is the remainder when $P(x)$ is divided by $x - 10$. We use synthetic division to find that remainder.

10	2	−3	1	−2	1	−8
		20	170	1710	17,080	170,810
	2	17	171	1708	17,081	170,802

Thus $P(10) = 170,802$.

Try This Let $P(x) = x^5 - 2x^4 - 7x^3 + x^2 + 20$.

a. Use synthetic division to find $P(10)$ and $P(-8)$. 73,120; −37,292

11-2

FIRST FIVE MINUTES

1. Is -2 a root of $x^3 + 5x^2 + 6x = 0$?
   Yes
2. Let $P(x) = x^3 + 5$ and $D(x) = x + 1$. Use division to write $P(x)$ in the form $P(x) = D(x) \cdot Q(x) + R(x)$.
   $P(x) = (x + 1)(x^2 - x + 1) + 4$

Explore

Students should note that $P(2)$ is equal to the remainder of $P(x)$ divided by $x - 2$. You may wish to demonstrate the remainder theorem using several different examples.

Function Values of Polynomials

You may want to verify that $P(10) = 170,802$ after working Example 1.

Key Questions

- If $\frac{P(x)}{x - 5} = 6x^7 - 7x^8$, what is $P(5)$?
  0
- If $x - 4$ is a factor of $P(x)$, what is the remainder if $P(x)$ is divided by $x - 4$?
  0

Chalkboard Example

1. $P(x) = 5x^4 + 4x^3 + 3x^2 + 2x + 1$
   Use synthetic division to find $P(3)$.
   $P(3)$ is the remainder when dividing $P(x)$ by $x - 3$.

3	5	4	3	2	1
		15	57	180	546
	5	19	60	182	547

$P(3) = 547$

Roots

Point out that the remainder theorem tells us that if $P(r) = 0$, then $P(x)$ has remainder 0 when divided by $x - r$. And if the remainder is 0, then $x - r$ is a factor of $P(x)$. If $x - r$ is a factor of $P(x)$, then r is a root of $P(x)$.

Explain that this method can be used to find zeros of functions as well as roots of polynomials.

Chalkboard Example

1. Determine whether 3 is a root of $P(x) = x^3 - 7x^2 + 7x + 15$.

3	1	−7	7	15
		3	−12	−15
	1	−4	−5	0

Since $P(3) = 0$, 3 is a root.

The following is a proof of the remainder theorem.

Proof of Theorem 11-1

The equation $P(x) = D(x) \cdot Q(x) + R(x)$ is the basis of this proof. If we divide $P(x)$ by $x - r$, we obtain a quotient $Q(x)$ and a remainder $R(x)$ related as follows.

$$P(x) = (x - r) \cdot Q(x) + R(x)$$

The remainder $R(x)$ must either be 0 or have degree less than the degree of $x - r$. Thus $R(x)$ must have a degree of 0, and thus must be a constant. Let us call this constant R. In the above expression we get a true sentence whenever we replace x by any number.

Let us replace x by r.

$$P(r) = (r - r) \cdot Q(r) + R$$
$$P(r) = 0 \cdot Q(r) + R$$
$$P(r) = R$$

This tells us that the function value $P(r)$ is the remainder obtained when we divide $P(x)$ by $x - r$.

Roots

Objective: Determine whether a given number is a root of a polynomial $P(x)$.

Since the zeros of a polynomial function are the roots of the corresponding equation, we often refer to them as the roots of a polynomial.

Using the remainder theorem and synthetic division we can find $P(r)$. If $P(r) = 0$, then r is a root of $P(x)$.

EXAMPLE 2 Determine whether -4 is a root of $P(x)$, where $P(x) = x^3 + 8x^2 + 8x - 32$.

We use synthetic division and Theorem 11-1 to find $P(-4)$.

−4	1	8	8	−32	
		−4	−16	32	
	1	4	−8	0	The remainder is zero.

Since $P(-4) = 0$, the number -4 is a root of $P(x)$.

Try This Let $P(x) = x^3 + 6x^2 - x - 30$. Using synthetic division, determine whether the given numbers are roots of $P(x)$.

b. 2 Yes **c.** 5 No **d.** -3 Yes

Finding Factors of Polynomials

Objective: Determine whether $x - r$ is a factor of $P(x)$, and solve the equation $P(x) = 0$.

The next theorem follows from the remainder theorem.

Theorem 11-2

The Factor Theorem

For a polynomial $P(x)$, if $P(r) = 0$, then the polynomial $x - r$ is a factor of $P(x)$.

This theorem is very useful in factoring polynomials, and hence, in solving equations.

EXAMPLE 3 Determine whether $x + 6$ is a factor of $P(x)$, where $P(x) = x^4 + 2x^3 - 63x^2 - 288x - 324$.

We apply the factor theorem using synthetic division to divide $P(x)$ by $x + 6$.

$$\begin{array}{r|rrrrr} -6 & 1 & 2 & -63 & -288 & -324 \\ & & -6 & 24 & 234 & 324 \\ \hline & 1 & -4 & -39 & -54 & 0 \end{array}$$

The remainder is 0.

Since $P(-6) = 0$, by Theorem 11-2, $x + 6$ is a factor of $x^4 + 2x^3 - 63x^2 - 288x - 324$.

Try This

e. Determine whether $x - \frac{1}{2}$ is a factor of $4x^4 + 2x^3 + 8x - 1$. No

f. Determine whether $x + 5$ is a factor of $x^4 - 625$. Yes

EXAMPLE 4 Let $P(x) = x^3 + 2x^2 - 5x - 6$. Factor the polynomial $P(x)$. Then solve the equation $P(x) = 0$.

We look for linear factors of the form $x - r$. Let us try $x - 1$. We use synthetic division to see whether $P(1) = 0$.

$$\begin{array}{r|rrrr} 1 & 1 & 2 & -5 & -6 \\ & & 1 & 3 & -2 \\ \hline & 1 & 3 & -2 & -8 \end{array}$$

We know that $x - 1$ is not a factor of $P(x)$. We try $x + 1$.

$$\begin{array}{r|rrrr} -1 & 1 & 2 & -5 & -6 \\ & & -1 & -1 & 6 \\ \hline & 1 & 1 & -6 & 0 \end{array}$$

Finding Factors of Polynomials

Remind students that a function like $P(x) = (x - 1)(x - 3)(x - 5)$ is a polynomial function, and that there is correspondence between linear factors and roots.

Point out that two different polynomial functions can have the same roots. For example, $P(x) = 3(x - 1)(x - 3)$ and $P(x) = 5(x - 1)(x - 3)$ both have roots 1 and 3.

You may wish to review different methods of finding roots. Students can factor $P(x)$, they can find values of r such that $P(r) = 0$, or they can use synthetic division to find values of r such that $\frac{P(x)}{(x - r)}$ has no remainder. Note that Example 4 uses a combination of these techniques; synthetic division is used, and then the quotient is factored.

Key Questions

- What are the roots of $P(x) = 8(x - 2)(x - 4)(x - 6)$? 2, 4, 6
- If the polynomial $P(x)$ has roots 5, 7, and 9, what are some factors of $P(x)$? $x - 5, x - 7, x - 9$

Chalkboard Examples

1. Determine whether $x - 2$ is a factor of $x^3 + x - 10$.

$$\begin{array}{r|rrrr} 2 & 1 & 0 & 1 & -10 \\ & & 2 & 4 & 10 \\ \hline & 1 & 2 & 5 & 0 \end{array}$$

The remainder is 0; $x - 2$ is a factor.

2. Let $P(x) = x^3 - 6x^2 - x + 30$. Factor. Then solve the equation $P(x) = 0$.

If the three roots are integers, then they are factors of 30. By substitution (or inspection) you can see that neither 1 nor -1 are roots. Try -2 using synthetic division.

$$\begin{array}{r|rrrr} -2 & 1 & -6 & -1 & 30 \\ & & -2 & 16 & -30 \\ \hline & 1 & -8 & 15 & 0 \end{array}$$

This shows that -2 is a root and $x + 2$ is a factor.

$P(x) = (x + 2)(x^2 - 8x + 15)$
$= (x + 2)(x - 5)(x - 3)$

The solutions are -2, 5, and 3.

LESSON QUIZ

1. $P(x) = x^3 + 7x^2 + 3x + 1$. Find $P(-2)$.
   15
2. Determine whether 5 is a root of $P(x) = x^3 - 10x - 75$.
   Yes
3. Determine whether $x - 2$ is a factor of the polynomial $P(x) = x^3 - 4x^2 + 8x + 4$.
   No
4. Factor $P(x) = x^3 + 3x^2 - 9x + 5$.
   $P(x) = (x - 1)(x - 1)(x + 5)$

Assignment Guide

Algebra: Day 1: 1 – 8, assign w. 11-1
Day 2: 9 – 24, MR

Alg w/Finite or Trig: 1–24 m3, 25–30 e/o, 31, MR

Comprehensive: 1–30 m3, 31–33, MR

ADDITIONAL ANSWERS

Exercises

1. $P(1) = 0$; $P(-2) = -60$; $P(3) = 0$
2. $P(-3) = 69$; $P(-2) = 41$; $P(1) = -7$
3. $P(20) = 5{,}935{,}988$; $P(-3) = -772$
4. $P(-10) = -220{,}050$; $P(5) = -750$

We know that $x + 1$ is one factor and the quotient, $x^2 + x - 6$, is another.

$$P(x) = (x + 1)(x^2 + x - 6)$$

The trinomial is easily factored.

$$P(x) = (x + 1)(x + 3)(x - 2)$$

To solve the equation $P(x) = 0$, we use the principle of zero products.

$$x + 1 = 0 \quad \text{or} \quad x + 3 = 0 \quad \text{or} \quad x - 2 = 0$$
$$x = -1 \quad \text{or} \quad x = -3 \quad \text{or} \quad x = 2$$

The solutions are -1, -3, and 2.

Try This

g. Let $P(x) = x^3 + 6x^2 - x - 30$. Factor the polynomial $P(x)$. Then solve the equation $P(x) = 0$. $P(x) = (x - 2)(x + 3)(x + 5)$; 2, -3, -5

11-2 EXERCISES

A

Find the function values.

1. $P(x) = x^3 - 6x^2 + 11x - 6$. Find $P(1)$, $P(-2)$, $P(3)$.

2. $P(x) = x^3 + 7x^2 - 12x - 3$. Find $P(-3)$, $P(-2)$, $P(1)$.

3. $P(x) = 2x^5 - 3x^4 + 2x^3 - x + 8$. Find $P(20)$ and $P(-3)$.

4. $P(x) = x^5 - 10x^4 + 20x^3 - 5x - 100$. Find $P(-10)$ and $P(5)$.

Determine whether the numbers are roots of the polynomials.

5. $-3, 2$; $P(x) = 3x^3 + 5x^2 - 6x + 18$ Yes, no

6. $-4, 2$; $P(x) = 3x^3 + 11x^2 - 2x + 8$ Yes, no

7. $-3, \frac{1}{2}$; $P(x) = x^3 - \frac{7}{2}x^2 + x - \frac{3}{2}$ No, no

8. $i, -i, -2$; $P(x) = x^3 + 2x^2 + x + 2$ Yes, yes, yes

Determine whether the expressions of the type $x - r$ are factors of the polynomial $P(x)$.

9. $P(x) = x^3 - 3x^2 - 4x - 12$; $x + 2$ No

10. $P(x) = x^3 - 4x^2 + 3x + 8$; $x + 1$ Yes

11. $P(x) = x^5 - 1$; $x - 1$ Yes

12. $P(x) = x^5 + 1$; $x + 1$ Yes

13. $P(x) = 2x^2 + 2x + 1$; $x - \left(-\frac{1}{2} - \frac{1}{2}i\right)$ Yes

14. $P(x) = 9x^2 + 6x + 2$; $x - \left(\frac{1}{3} - \frac{1}{3}i\right)$ No

15. Let $P(x) = x^3 + 2x^2 - x - 2$.
   a. Determine whether $x - 1$ is a factor of $P(x)$. Yes
   b. Find another factor of $P(x)$. $x^2 + 3x + 2$
   c. Find a complete factorization of $P(x)$. $(x - 1)(x + 2)(x + 1)$
   d. Solve the equation $P(x) = 0$. $1, -2, -1$

16. Let $P(x) = x^3 + 4x^2 - x - 4$.
   a. Determine whether $x + 1$ is a factor of $P(x)$. Yes
   b. Find another factor of $P(x)$. $x^2 + 3x - 4$
   c. Find a complete factorization of $P(x)$. $(x + 1)(x + 4)(x - 1)$
   d. Solve the equation $P(x) = 0$. $-1, -4, 1$

Factor the polynomial $P(x)$. Then solve the equation $P(x) = 0$.

17. $P(x) = x^3 + 4x^2 + x - 6$
18. $P(x) = x^3 + 5x^2 - 2x - 24$
19. $P(x) = x^3 - 6x^2 + 3x + 10$
20. $P(x) = x^3 + 2x^2 - 13x + 10$
21. $P(x) = x^3 - x^2 - 14x + 24$
22. $P(x) = x^3 - 3x^2 - 10x + 24$
23. $P(x) = x^4 - x^3 - 19x^2 + 49x - 30$
24. $P(x) = x^4 + 11x^3 + 41x^2 + 61x + 30$

B

Solve.

25. $x^3 + 2x^2 - 13x + 10 > 0$
26. $x^4 - x^3 - 19x^2 + 49x - 30 < 0$
27. Find k so that $x + 2$ is a factor of $x^3 - kx^2 + 2x + 7k$. 4
28. Find k so that $x - 1$ is a factor of $x^3 - 3x^2 + kx - 1$. 3
29. For what values of k will the remainder be the same when $x^2 + kx + 4$ is divided by $x - 1$ or $x + 1$? 0
30. When $x^2 - 3x + 2k$ is divided by $x + 2$ the remainder is 7. Find the value of k. $-\frac{3}{2}$
31. ***Critical Thinking*** Write a convincing argument that if $A(x)$ is a factor of $B(x)$ and $B(x)$ is a factor of $C(x)$, then $A(x)$ is a factor of $C(x)$.

Challenge

32. Use the factor theorem to prove that $x - a$ is a factor of $x^n - a^n$ for any natural number n.
33. Prove Theorem 11-2.

Mixed Review

For each function find standard form. Then find the vertex, line of symmetry, and the maximum or minimum value for each parabola. **34.** $f(x) = x^2 - 4x$
35. $f(x) = 2x^2 - 10x - 8$ **36.** $f(x) = x^2 + c$

Find the center and radius of each circle. **37.** $(x + 1)^2 + y^2 = 64$
38. $x^2 + y^2 - 6x - 2y - 15 = 0$ **39.** $(x + 1)^2 + (y - 1)^2 = 45$

17. $P(x) = (x - 1)(x + 2)(x + 3)$; $1, -2, -3$
18. $P(x) = (x - 2)(x + 3)(x + 4)$; $2, -3, -4$
19. $P(x) = (x - 2)(x - 5)(x + 1)$; $2, 5, -1$
20. $P(x) = (x - 1)(x - 2)(x + 5)$; $1, 2, -5$
21. $P(x) = (x - 2)(x - 3)(x + 4)$; $2, 3, -4$
22. $P(x) = (x - 2)(x - 4)(x + 3)$; $2, 4, -3$
23. $P(x) = (x - 1)(x - 2)(x - 3)(x + 5)$; $1, 2, 3, -5$
24. $P(x) = (x + 1)(x + 2)(x + 3)(x + 5)$; $-1, -2, -3, -5$
25. $-5 < x < 1$ or $x > 2$
26. $-5 < x < 1$ or $2 < x < 3$

31. Answers may vary. If $A(x)$ is a factor of $B(x)$, then $A(x) \cdot P(x) = B(x)$ for some $P(x)$. Since $P(x)$ is a factor of $C(x)$, $B(x) \cdot Q(x) = C(x)$ for some $Q(x)$. Thus, $A(x) \cdot P(x) \cdot Q(x) = C(x)$, so $A(x)$ is a factor of $C(x)$.
32. $P(a) = a^n - a^n = 0$; since $P(a) = 0$, $x - a$ is a factor of $x^n - a^n$.
33. $P(r)$ is the remainder of $P(x) \div (x - r)$ by the remainder theorem. If $P(r) = 0$, then $P(x) \div (x - r)$ has a remainder of 0. Thus $(x - r)$ must be a factor of $P(x)$.

Mixed Review

34. $f(x - 2)^2 - 4$
Vertex: $(2, -4)$
Line of symmetry: $x = 2$
Minimum: -4
35. $f(x) = 2\left(x - \frac{5}{2}\right)^2 - \frac{41}{2}$
Vertex: $\left(\frac{5}{2}, -\frac{41}{2}\right)$
Line of symmetry: $x = \frac{5}{2}$
Minimum: $-\frac{41}{2}$
36. $f(x) = (x - 0)^2 + c$
Vertex: $(0, c)$
Line of symmetry: $x = 0$
Minimum: c
37. Center $(-1, 0)$; radius 8
38. Center $(3, 1)$; radius 5
39. Center $(-1, 1)$; radius $3\sqrt{5}$

11-3

FIRST FIVE MINUTES

1. $P(x) = 3x^3 + 4x + 1$
   Find $P(-1)$.
   $P(-1) = -6$
2. Determine whether -3 is a root of $P(x) = x^3 + 5x^2 + 15x + 27$.
   $P(-3) = 0$; -3 is a root.
3. Determine whether $x - 1$ is a factor of $x^3 + x^2 + x + 1$.
   Since 1 is not a root, $x - 1$ is not a factor.

Finding Roots by Factoring

Theorem 11-4 is an important consequence of Theorem 11-3 and could be considered to be part of the fundamental theorem of algebra. It follows that if there is at least one linear factor of a polynomial with complex coefficients and degree $n > 1$, there must be another factor of degree $n - 1$. We can continue this reasoning until we have n factors.

Point out that the factor $(x - 0)$ is the same as x.

Math Point
Many brilliant mathematicians of the 18th century attempted to prove the fundamental theorem of algebra. Carl Friedrich Gauss published the first rigorous proof in 1799 and found three other proofs over the next 50 years.

Key Questions

- How many linear factors can the polynomial $x^{17} + 1$ have?
  17
- Which of the following could be linear factors?
  a. 3, b. $x + 7$, c. $x + 3 + 2i$
  b, c

Chalkboard Example

1. Find the roots of the polynomial $P(x) = x^4 - 2x^2 + 1$, and state the multiplicity of each.
   $P(x) = (x^2 - 1)^2$
   $= ((x - 1)(x + 1))^2$
   $= (x - 1)^2(x + 1)^2$
   The root 1 occurs with multiplicity 2. The root -1 occurs with multiplicity 2.

11-3 Theorems About Roots

Carl Friedrich Gauss was one of the great mathematicians of all time. He contributed to many branches of mathematics and science, including non-Euclidean geometry and curvature of surfaces (later used in Einstein's theory of relativity). In 1798, at the age of 20, Gauss proved the fundamental theorem of algebra.

Finding Roots by Factoring

Objective: Find the roots of a polynomial and determine the multiplicity of each root.

Theorem 11-3

The Fundamental Theorem of Algebra

Every polynomial of degree $n > 1$, with complex coefficients, has at least one linear factor.

Using this theorem, Gauss was able to prove another theorem.

Theorem 11-4

Every polynomial of degree $n > 1$, with complex coefficients, can be factored into exactly n linear factors.

Once a polynomial in a polynomial equation is factored into linear factors, its roots can be found using the principle of zero products.

EXAMPLE 1 Find the roots of the polynomial equation.

$$P(x) = x^3 + x^2 - 25x - 25$$
$$= x^2(x + 1) - 25(x + 1) \quad \text{Factoring by grouping}$$
$$= (x^2 - 25)(x + 1)$$
$$= (x + 5)(x - 5)(x + 1) \quad \text{Factoring as a difference of two squares}$$

Setting $P(x) = 0$ to find the roots,

$$0 = (x + 5)(x - 5)(x + 1)$$
$$x + 5 = 0 \text{ or } x - 5 = 0 \text{ or } x + 1 = 0 \quad \text{Using the principle of zero products}$$
$$x = -5 \text{ or } x = 5 \text{ or } x = -1$$

There are 3 linear factors. The roots are -5, 5, and -1.

In Example 1, there are 3 linear factors and 3 roots. A factor may occur more than once. If a factor $(x - r)$ occurs k times, we say that r is a root of multiplicity k.

EXAMPLE 2 Find the roots of the polynomial equation and the multiplicity of each.

$$\begin{aligned} P(x) &= 3x^5 - 15x^4 + 18x^3 + 12x^2 - 24x \\ &= (3x)(x - 2)(x - 2)(x - 2)(x + 1) \quad \text{There are 5 linear factors.} \\ &= 3x(x - 2)^3(x + 1) \end{aligned}$$

Root	Multiplicity	
0	1	The monomial factor x occurs one time.
2	3	$x - 2$ occurs three times.
−1	1	$x + 1$ occurs one time.

The polynomial has 5 linear factors and 5 roots. The root 2 occurs 3 times, however, so we say that the root 2 has a multiplicity of 3.

Try This Find the roots of each polynomial equation and the multiplicity of each.

a. $P(x) = 4(x + 7)^2(x - 3)$ −7(multiplicity 2), 3(multiplicity 1)
b. $P(x) = (x^2 - 7x + 12)^2$ 4(multiplicity 2), 3(multiplicity 2)
c. $P(x) = 5x^2 - 5$ 1(multiplicity 1), −1(multiplicity 1)

Real and Rational Coefficients

Objective: Find all the roots of a polynomial given its degree and several roots.

Consider the quadratic equation $x^2 - 2x + 2 = 0$, with real coefficients. Its roots are $1 + i$ and $1 - i$. Note that they are complex conjugates.

Theorem 11-5

If a polynomial $P(x)$ of degree greater than or equal to 1 with real coefficients has a complex number $a + bi$ as a root, then its conjugate $a - bi$ is also a root. (Complex roots occur in conjugate pairs.)

When a polynomial has rational numbers for coefficients, certain irrational roots also occur in pairs, as described in the following theorem.

Theorem 11-6

Suppose $P(x)$ is a polynomial with rational coefficients and of degree greater than or equal to 1. Then if either of the following is a root, so is the other: $a + c\sqrt{b}$, $a - c\sqrt{b}$, where a, b, and c are rational numbers and $\sqrt{b}$ is irrational.

Real and Rational Coefficients

Point out that to apply Theorem 11-5, it is essential that the coefficients be real numbers. If one of the coefficients is complex, then there may be a complex root without its conjugate.

Key Questions

- What is the conjugate of $5 + 7i$? $5 - 7i$
- What are the roots of $P(x) = (x - i)^2$? i is the single root.
- If one root of the polynomial $x^2 - 6x + 13$ is $3 + 2i$, what is the other root? Since the coefficients are real, complex roots must exist in conjugate pairs. The other root is $3 - 2i$.

Chalkboard Examples

1. Suppose a polynomial of degree 5 with rational coefficients has roots 7, $3 + 2i$, and $2 + \sqrt{5}$. What are the other roots?
   $3 - 2i$, $2 - \sqrt{5}$
2. Let $P(x) = x^4 - 3x^3 - 2x^2 + 2x + 12$. Find all the roots, given that one root is $-1 - i$.
   The conjugate root is $-1 + i$. $x - (-1 - i)$ and $x - (-1 + i)$ are factors, and their product $D(x) = x^2 + 2x + 2$ is a factor of $P(x)$. Divide $P(x)$ by $D(x)$ to get $x^2 - 5x + 6$. This factors into $(x - 2)(x - 3)$. The last two roots are 2 and 3.

Finding Polynomials with Specific Roots

Chalkboard Examples

1. Find a polynomial of degree 3 having roots 3, 5, and $-2i$.
   $P(x) = (x - 3)(x - 5)(x + 2i)$
   $= x^3 + (-8 + 2i)x^2 + (15 - 16i)x + 30i$
2. Find a polynomial of degree 4 having 2 as a root of multiplicity 3 and -5 as a root of multiplicity 1.
   $P(x) = (x - 2)^3(x + 5)$
   $= x^4 - x^3 - 18x^2 + 52x - 40$
3. Find a polynomial of lowest degree with rational coefficients and having roots $3 + i$ and $2 + \sqrt{2}$.
   By Theorems 11-5 and 11-6, the other roots are $3 - i$ and $2 - \sqrt{2}$.
   $P(x) = (x - (3 + i)) \cdot (x - (3 - i)) \cdot (x - (2 + \sqrt{2})) \cdot (x - (2 - \sqrt{2}))$
   $= (x^2 - 6x + 10) \cdot (x^2 - 4x + 2)$
   $= x^4 - 10x^3 + 36x^2 - 52x + 20$

EXAMPLE 3 Suppose a polynomial of degree 3 with real coefficients has $3 - 4i$ and 9 as roots. Find all of the roots.

By Theorem 11-5, since $3 - 4i$ is a root, then $3 + 4i$ is also a root. Since the polynomial is of degree 3, by Theorem 11-4 there can be no more than 3 roots.

The roots are $3 - 4i$, $3 + 4i$, and 9.

EXAMPLE 4 Suppose a polynomial of degree 6 with rational coefficients has $-2 + 5i$, $-i$, and $1 - \sqrt{3}$ as roots. Find all of the roots.

By Theorem 11-5, the conjugates of $-2 + 5i$ and $-i$ are roots. They are $-2 - 5i$ and i. By Theorem 11-6, since $1 - \sqrt{3}$ is a root, $1 + \sqrt{3}$ is also a root. There are no other roots since the degree is 6.

Thus the six roots are $-2 + 5i$, $-2 - 5i$, i, $-i$, $1 + \sqrt{3}$, and $1 - \sqrt{3}$.

Try This

d. Suppose a polynomial of degree 5 with rational coefficients has -4, $7 - 2i$, and $3 + 7\sqrt{5}$ as roots. Find all roots of the polynomial. $7 + 2i$ and $3 - 7\sqrt{5}$ are the other roots.

EXAMPLE 5 Let $P(x) = x^4 - 5x^3 + 10x^2 - 20x + 24$. Find all roots of $P(x)$, given that $2i$ is a root.

Since $2i$ is a root, we know that $-2i$ is also a root.

$$P(x) = (x - 2i)(x + 2i) \cdot Q(x), \text{ for some } Q(x)$$

Since $(x - 2i)(x + 2i) = x^2 + 4$, we write $P(x)$ as follows.

$$P(x) = (x^2 + 4) \cdot Q(x)$$

We find, using division, that $Q(x) = x^2 - 5x + 6$. We factor $x^2 - 5x + 6$.

$$P(x) = (x^2 + 4)(x - 2)(x - 3)$$

Thus the roots are $2i$, $-2i$, 2, and 3.

Try This

e. Find all roots of $x^4 + x^3 - x^2 + x - 2$, given that i is a root. $i, -i, -2, 1$

Finding Polynomials with Specific Roots

Objective: Find polynomials with specific roots.

Given several numbers, we can find a polynomial having them as its roots.

EXAMPLE 6 Find a polynomial of degree three, having the roots -2, 1, and $3i$.

By Theorem 11-2, such a polynomial has factors $x + 2$, $x - 1$, and $x - 3i$, so we have the polynomial $P(x) = a_n(x + 2)(x - 1)(x - 3i)$

The number a_n can be any nonzero number. The simplest polynomial will be obtained if we let $a_n = 1$. If we then multiply the factors we obtain the following.

$$P(x) = x^3 + (1 - 3i)x^2 + (-2 - 3i)x + 6i$$

EXAMPLE 7 Find a polynomial of degree 5 with 0 as a root of multiplicity 1, -1 as a root of multiplicity 3, and 4 as a root of multiplicity 1.

We proceed as in Example 3, letting $a_n = 1$.

$$P(x) = x(x + 1)^3(x - 4)$$
$$P(x) = x^5 - x^4 - 9x^3 - 11x^2 - 4x \quad \text{Multiplying}$$

Try This

f. Find a polynomial of degree 3 that has -1, 2, and 5 as roots. $P(x) = x^3 - 6x^2 + 3x + 10$

g. Find a polynomial of degree 5 with -2 as a root of multiplicity 3 and 0 as a root of multiplicity 2. $P(x) = x^5 + 6x^4 + 12x^3 + 8x^2$

By Theorems 11-5 and 11-6, we know that complex roots occur in conjugate pairs, and certain irrational roots also occur in pairs. We can use these facts to find the polynomial of lowest degree with rational coefficients that has specific roots.

EXAMPLE 8 Find a polynomial of lowest degree with rational coefficients that has $1 - \sqrt{2}$ and $1 + 3i$ as roots.

By Theorem 11-5, $1 - 3i$ is a root. By Theorem 11-6, $1 + \sqrt{2}$ is a root. Thus the polynomial is as follows.

$$P(x) = [x - (1 - \sqrt{2})][x - (1 + \sqrt{2})][x - (1 + 3i)][x - (1 - 3i)] \quad \text{Using the principle of zero products}$$
$$= [(x - 1) + \sqrt{2}][(x - 1) - \sqrt{2}][(x - 1) - 3i][(x - 1) + 3i] \quad \text{Using the associative property}$$
$$= [(x - 1)^2 - (\sqrt{2})^2][(x - 1)^2 - (3i)^2] \quad \text{Multiplying the sum and difference of two expressions}$$
$$= [x^2 - 2x + 1 - 2][x^2 - 2x + 1 + 9] \quad \text{Simplifying}$$
$$= [x^2 - 2x - 1][x^2 - 2x + 10]$$
$$= x^4 - 4x^3 + 13x^2 - 18x - 10$$

The polynomial is of degree 4.

Try This

h. Find a polynomial of lowest degree with rational coefficients that has $2 + \sqrt{3}$ and $1 - i$ as roots. $x^4 - 6x^3 + 11x^2 - 10x + 2$

i. Find a polynomial of lowest degree with real coefficients that has $2i$ and 2 as roots. $x^3 - 2x^2 + 4x - 8$

LESSON ENRICHMENT

Find the cube roots of 1.
The roots are the solution of the equation $x^3 = 1$, or $x^3 - 1 = 0$. By the fundamental theorem of algebra, there are three roots. Factoring as a difference of cubes,
$(x - 1)(x^2 + x + 1) = 0$
$x - 1 = 0$ or $x^2 + x + 1 = 0$
$x = 1$ or $x = -\frac{1}{2} \pm i\frac{\sqrt{3}}{2}$
The cube roots of 1 are
$1, -\frac{1}{2} + i\frac{\sqrt{3}}{2}, -\frac{1}{2} - i\frac{\sqrt{3}}{2}$.

LESSON QUIZ

1. Find the roots and state the multiplicity of each.
$P(x) = (x - 5)^3(x + 2)$
5 is a root with multiplicity 3.
-2 is a root with multiplicity 1.
2. Find a polynomial of degree 3 with roots 5, -6, and 7.
$P(x) = (x - 5)(x + 6)(x - 7)$
3. Find a polynomial of degree 3 with real coefficients having roots i and 3.
$P(x) = x^3 - 3x^2 + x - 3$
4. Find a polynomial of degree 2 with rational coefficients having $\sqrt{5}$ as a root.
$P(x) = x^2 - 5$

Assignment Guide
Algebra: Day 1: 1–18 e/o, MR
Day 2: 19–44 e/o

Alg w/Finite or Trig: 1–34 m4, 35–44 m3, 45–48 e/o, 49, MR

Comprehensive: 1–44 m4, 45–52, MR

ADDITIONAL ANSWERS

Exercises

1. −3(multiplicity 2), 1(multiplicity 1)
2. −2(multiplicity 1), π(multiplicity 5)
3. 3(multiplicity 2), −4(multiplicity 3), 0(multiplicity 4)
4. 0(multiplicity 3), 1(multiplicity 2), −4(multiplicity 1)
5. 2(multiplicity 2), 3(multiplicity 2)
6. 2(multiplicity 2), −1(multiplicity 2)

39. $P(x) = x^4 - 6x^3 + 11x^2 - 10x + 2$
40. $P(x) = x^4 - 10x^3 + 36x^2 - 58x + 35$
41. $P(x) = x^4 + 4x^2 - 45$
42. $P(x) = x^4 + 14x^2 - 32$
43. $P(x) = x^4 - 4x^3 + 9x^2 + 8x - 22$
44. $P(x) = x^4 + 6x^3 + 23x^2 + 54x + 126$

50. For $P(x) = a_nx^n + a_{n-1}x^{n-1} + \cdots + a_0$ with a_i positive, consider any positive x. Every term will be positive, hence $P(x) > 0$.
51. By Theorem 11-3, $P(x)$ can be factored into n linear factors, where n is the degree of $P(x)$. Since by Theorem 11-5 the nonreal roots occur in conjugate pairs, there is at least one factor $(x - a)$ with a real.

For Exercises 52 and 53, see Teacher's Answer Section.

11-3 EXERCISES

A

Find the roots of each polynomial equation, and state the multiplicity of each root.

1. $P(x) = (x + 3)^2(x - 1)$
2. $P(x) = -4(x + 2)(x - \pi)^5$
3. $P(x) = -8(x - 3)^2(x + 4)^3x^4$
4. $P(x) = x^3(x - 1)^2(x + 4)$
5. $P(x) = (x^2 - 5x + 6)^2$
6. $P(x) = (x^2 - x - 2)^2$

Suppose a polynomial of degree 6 with real coefficients has the given roots. Find all roots of the polynomial.

7. $-5, 6, 5 + i, -2i$
$5 - i, 2i$ are the other roots.
8. $8, 6, -3 - 2i, 4i$
$-3 + 2i, -4i$ are the other roots.

Suppose a polynomial of degree 5 with rational coefficients has the given roots. Find all roots of the polynomial.

9. $6, -3 + 4i, 4 - \sqrt{5}$ $\quad -3 - 4i, 4 + \sqrt{5}$
10. $8, 6 - 7i, \frac{1}{2} + \sqrt{11}$ $\quad 6 + 7i, \frac{1}{2} - \sqrt{11}$
11. $-2, 3, 4, 1 - i$ $\quad 1 + i$
12. $3, 4, -5, 7 + i$ $\quad 7 - i$

Given that the polynomial has the given root, find all roots of the polynomial.

13. $P(x) = x^4 - 5x^3 + 7x^2 - 5x + 6; -i$ $\quad i, 3, 2$
14. $P(x) = x^3 - 4x^2 + x - 4; -i$ $\quad i, 4$
15. $P(x) = x^4 - 16; 2i$ $\quad -2i, 2, -2$
16. $P(x) = x^4 - 1; i$ $\quad -i, 1, -1$
17. $P(x) = x^3 - x^2 - 7x + 15; -3$ $\quad 2 + i, 2 - i$
18. $P(x) = x^3 - 6x^2 + 13x - 20; 4$ $\quad 1 + 2i, 1 - 2i$
19. $P(x) = x^3 - 8; 2$ $\quad -1 + i\sqrt{3}, -1 - i\sqrt{3}$
20. $P(x) = x^3 + 8; -2$ $\quad 1 + i\sqrt{3}, 1 - i\sqrt{3}$
21. $P(x) = x^4 - 2x^3 + 7x^2 + 6x - 30; -\sqrt{3}$ $\quad \sqrt{3}, 1 + 3i, 1 - 3i$
22. $P(x) = x^4 + 4x^3 + 2x^2 - 28x - 63; \sqrt{7}$ $\quad -\sqrt{7}, -2 + i\sqrt{5}, -2 - i\sqrt{5}$

Find a polynomial of degree 3 with the given numbers as roots.

23. $-2, 3, 5$ $\quad P(x) = x^3 - 6x^2 - x + 30$
24. $3, 2, -1$ $\quad P(x) = x^3 - 4x^2 + x + 6$
25. $2, i, -i$ $\quad P(x) = x^3 - 2x^2 + x - 2$
26. $-3, 2i, -2i$ $\quad P(x) = x^3 + 3x^2 + 4x + 12$
27. $2 + i, 2 - i, 3$ $\quad P(x) = x^3 - 7x^2 + 17x - 15$
28. $1 + 4i, 1 - 4i, -1$ $\quad P(x) = x^3 - x^2 + 15x + 17$
29. $\sqrt{2}, -\sqrt{2}, \sqrt{3}$ $\quad P(x) = x^3 - \sqrt{3}x^2 - 2x + 2\sqrt{3}$
Are the coefficients rational? No
30. $\sqrt{3}, -\sqrt{3}, \sqrt{2}$ $\quad P(x) = x^3 - \sqrt{2}x^2 - 3x + 3\sqrt{2}$
Are the coefficients rational? No
31. Find a polynomial of degree 4 with 0 as a root of multiplicity 2 and 5 as a root of multiplicity 2. $P(x) = x^4 - 10x^3 + 25x^2$
32. Find a polynomial of degree 4 with 0 as a root of multiplicity 4. $P(x) = x^4$
33. Find a polynomial of degree 4 with −2 as a root of multiplicity 1, 3 as a root of multiplicity 2, and −1 as a root of multiplicity 1. $P(x) = x^4 - 3x^3 - 7x^2 + 15x + 18$
34. Find a polynomial of degree 5 with 4 as a root of multiplicity 3 and −2 as a root of multiplicity 2. $P(x) = x^5 - 8x^4 + 4x^3 + 80x^2 - 64x - 256$

Find a polynomial of lowest degree with rational coefficients that has the given numbers as some of its roots.

35. $1 + i, 2$ $P(x) = x^3 - 4x^2 + 6x - 4$
36. $2 - i, -1$ $P(x) = x^3 - 3x^2 + x + 5$
37. $3i, -2$ $P(x) = x^3 + 2x^2 + 9x + 18$
38. $-4i, 5$ $P(x) = x^3 - 5x^2 + 16x - 80$
39. $2 - \sqrt{3}, 1 + i$
40. $3 + \sqrt{2}, 2 - i$
41. $\sqrt{5}, -3i$
42. $-\sqrt{2}, 4i$
43. $-\sqrt{2}, 2 + i\sqrt{7}$
44. $3i, -3 - i\sqrt{5}$

B

Solve.

45. $ax^3 + bx^2 + ax + b = 0$ $i, -i, -\frac{b}{a}$
46. $ax^3 + ax^2 + bx + b = 0$ $\pm\sqrt{-\frac{b}{a}}, -1$
47. $x^4 - 2x^3 - 2x - 1 = 0$ $i, -i, 1 + \sqrt{2}, 1 - \sqrt{2}$
48. The equation $x^2 + 2ax + b = 0$ has a root of multiplicity 2. Find it. $-a$
49. ***Critical Thinking*** Write a polynomial that has at least one, but no more than three positive real roots. Answers may vary. Ex: $P(x) = x - 2$

Challenge

50. Prove that a polynomial with positive coefficients cannot have a positive root.
51. Prove that every polynomial of odd degree with real coefficients has at least one real root.
52. Prove Theorem 11-5.
53. Prove Theorem 11-6.

Mixed Review

For each of the following graph the function, find the vertex, line of symmetry, and the maximum or minimum value. **54.** $f(x) = (x - 2)^2 + 3$

55. $f(x) = -2(x + 1)^2 - 1$

For each parabola, find the vertex, the focus, and the directrix. **56.** $x^2 = 2y$

57. $x^2 - 8y + 8 = 0$ **58.** $y^2 - 4y - 12x + 28 = 0$

59. The Cup-a-Day coffeehouse has several blends of coffee. Its Mocha-Java blend contains 36% mocha beans. Its Manager's Blend contains 68% mocha beans. How many pounds of each blend should be mixed to make a 20 lb blend that contains 50% mocha beans?
60. What is the minimum product of two numbers whose difference is 27? What are the numbers?
61. The formula $p = \frac{h}{\sqrt[3]{w}}$, where h is a person's height in inches and w is weight in pounds, gives a value called the *ponderal index*.
    a. Find the ponderal index for a 70 in. tall person weighing 165 lb.
    b. Solve the formula for w.
    c. Find the weight of a person with height 62 in. and ponderal index of 12.5.

Mixed Review

54. Vertex: (2, 3)
Line of symmetry: $x = 2$
Minimum: 3

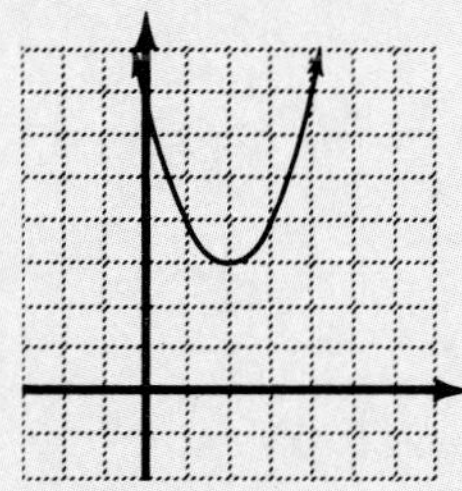

55. Vertex: $(-1, -1)$
Line of symmetry: $x = -1$
Maximum: -1

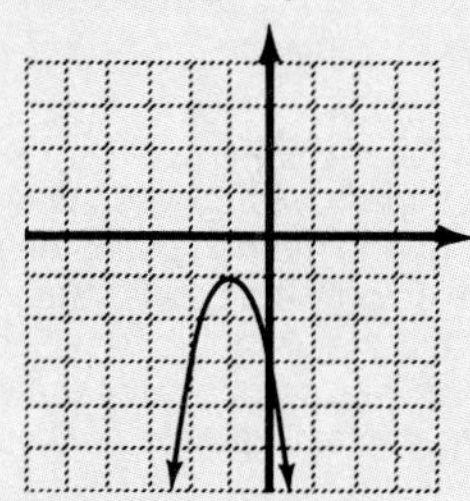

56. Vertex: (0, 0)
Focus: $\left(0, \frac{1}{2}\right)$
Directrix: $y = -\frac{1}{2}$

57. Vertex: (0, 1)
Focus: (0, 3)
Directrix: $y = -1$

58. Vertex: (2, 2)
Focus: (5, 2)
Directrix: $x = -1$

59. $11\frac{1}{4}$ lb of Mocha-Java, $8\frac{3}{4}$ lb of Manager's Blend

60. $-182.25, -13.5, 13.5$

61. a. 12.76
b. $w = \left(\frac{h}{p}\right)^3$
c. 122 lb

11-4

FIRST FIVE MINUTES

1. Find a polynomial having 1, 2, and 3 as roots.
   $P(x) = (x - 1)(x - 2)(x - 3)$
   $= x^3 - 6x^2 + 11x - 6$
2. Find the remaining roots of a polynomial of degree 4 with rational coefficients and having roots $2 + 3i$ and $5 - \sqrt{2}$.
   $2 - 3i$ and $5 + \sqrt{2}$
3. Find the roots of $P(x) = 3x^2 + 4x + 1$.
   $x = \frac{-4 \pm \sqrt{16 - 4 \cdot 3 \cdot 1}}{6}$
   $x = -\frac{1}{3}$ or $x = -1$

You may want to show students the following shorthand method of synthetic division in which only the coefficients of the quotient and the dividend are written down. For example, compare the three synthetic divisions of Example 1 with the following.

	3	−11	0	10	−4
1	3	−8	−8	2	−2
−1	3	−14	14	−4	0
$\frac{2}{3}$	3	−12	6	0	

Students may choose to substitute values of x into $P(x)$ to determine whether they are roots. They may do this either instead of synthetic division or in conjunction with it.

Math Point
Finding the roots of a second-degree polynomial is easy because of the quadratic equation. Third- and fourth-degree polynomials have a similar but much more difficult equation for finding roots. In 1824 Niels Henrik Abel proved that there can be no common formula for finding the roots of polynomials of degree 5 or greater. Abel was 19 when he discovered this extraordinary fact.

11-4 Rational Roots

Objective: Find rational and other roots of a polynomial with integer coefficients.

If a polynomial has integer coefficients, there is a procedure for finding all of the rational roots.

Theorem 11-7

Rational Roots Theorem

Let $P(x) = a_nx^n + a_{n-1}x^{n-1} + \cdots + a_1x + a_0$ where all the coefficients are integers. Consider a rational number denoted by $\frac{c}{d}$, where c and d are relatively prime. For $\frac{c}{d}$ to be a root of $P(x)$, c must be a factor of a_0 (the constant) and d must be a factor of a_n (the leading coefficient).

EXAMPLE 1 Let $P(x) = 3x^4 - 11x^3 + 10x - 4$. Find the rational roots of $P(x)$, if they exist. Find the other roots, if possible.

By the rational roots theorem, if $\frac{c}{d}$ is a root of $P(x)$, then c must be a factor of -4, and d must be a factor of 3. Thus the possibilities for c and d are as follows.

c: 1, −1, 4, −4, 2, −2 Listing all possible values for c and d

d: 1, −1, 3, −3

Then the resulting possibilities for $\frac{c}{d}$ are

$1, -1, 4, -4, 2, -2, \frac{1}{3}, -\frac{1}{3}, \frac{4}{3}, -\frac{4}{3},$ and $\frac{2}{3}, -\frac{2}{3}$ Listing all possible rational roots

Of these 12 possibilities, we know that at most 4 of them could be roots because $P(x)$ is of degree four. To find which are roots, we can use synthetic division.

We try 1.

1	3	−11	0	10	−4
		3	−8	−8	2
	3	−8	−8	2	−2

Testing possible roots

$P(1) = -2$, so 1 is not a root.

We try −1.

−1	3	−11	0	10	−4
		−3	14	−14	4
	3	−14	14	−4	0

$P(-1) = 0$, so -1 is a root. Thus

$$P(x) = (x + 1)(3x^3 - 14x^2 + 14x - 4)$$

We now use $3x^3 - 14x^2 + 14x - 4$ and check the other possible roots.

We try $\frac{2}{3}$.

$\frac{2}{3}$	3	−14	14	−4
		2	−8	4
	3	−12	6	0

$P\left(\frac{2}{3}\right) = 0$, so $\frac{2}{3}$ is a root. We now know that

$$P(x) = (x + 1)\left(x - \frac{2}{3}\right)(3x^2 - 12x + 6)$$

Since the factor $3x^2 - 12x + 6$ is quadratic, we can use the quadratic formula to find the other roots. They are $2 + \sqrt{2}$ and $2 - \sqrt{2}$.

The rational roots of $P(x)$ are -1 and $\frac{2}{3}$. The irrational roots are $2 + \sqrt{2}$ and $2 - \sqrt{2}$.

Try This

a. Let $P(x) = 2x^4 + 3x^3 - 8x^2 - 9x + 6$. Find the rational roots of $P(x)$, if they exist. Find the other roots, if possible. $\frac{1}{2}, -2, \sqrt{3}, -\sqrt{3}$

EXAMPLE 2 Let $P(x) = x^3 + 6x^2 + x + 6$. Find the rational roots of $P(x)$. Find the other roots, if possible.

By the rational roots theorem, if $\frac{c}{d}$ is a root of $P(x)$, then c must be a factor of 6 and d must be a factor of 1. Thus the possibilities for c and d are as follows.

c: 1, −1, 2, −2, 3, −3, 6, −6
d: 1, −1

Then the resulting possibilities for $\frac{c}{d}$ are

1, −1, 2, −2, 3, −3, 6, and −6

These are the same as the possibilities for c alone. Since the leading coefficient is 1, we need only check the factors of the constant term c.

There is another aid in eliminating possibilities for rational roots. Note that all coefficients of $P(x)$ are positive. Thus when any positive number is substituted in $P(x)$, we get a positive value (never 0). No positive number can be a root.

Thus we can eliminate 1, 2, 3, and 6 as possible roots. The only possibilities for roots are −1, −2, −3, and −6.

Key Questions

- What kind of coefficients must a polynomial have for the rational roots theorem to apply?
  The coefficients must be integers.
- What kind of roots does the theorem help us find?
  Rational roots
- If the leading coefficient is 1 on a polynomial with integer coefficients, what can you say about any rational roots?
  They must be integers.

Chalkboard Examples

1. Let $P(x) = 3x^3 + 2x^2 + 3x + 2$. Use the rational roots theorem to find the rational roots. Find all the roots.
   Let $\frac{c}{d}$ be the root.
   c is a factor of 2. Hence $c = \pm1$ or ±2. d is a factor of 3. Hence $d = \pm1$ or ±3.
   The possible rational roots are $-1, 1, -\frac{1}{3}, \frac{1}{3}, -2, 2, -\frac{2}{3}$, or $\frac{2}{3}$.
   The positive numbers cannot be roots since the polynomial will have a positive value. Substitution shows that −1 and −2 are not roots. Try $-\frac{2}{3}$.

$-\frac{2}{3}$	3	2	3	2
		−2	0	−2
	3	0	3	0

   $P\left(-\frac{2}{3}\right) = 0$, so $-\frac{2}{3}$ is a root.
   $P(x) = \left(x + \frac{2}{3}\right)(3x^2 + 3)$
   $= 3\left(x + \frac{2}{3}\right)(x + i)(x - i)$
   The roots are $-\frac{2}{3}$, i, and $-i$.

2. Find the roots of $P(x) = x^3 - 3x^2 - 8x - 10$.
   Let $\frac{c}{d}$ be the rational root. c is a factor of 10. $c = \pm1, \pm2, \pm5$, or ±10. d is a factor of 1, $d = \pm1$. The possible rational roots are ±1, ±2, ±5, or ±10. Substitution shows that 5 is the only rational root. Divide by $x - 5$ to get $P(x) = (x - 5)(x^2 + 2x + 2)$. The quadratic equation yields the roots of the quadratic factor, $-1 + i$ and $-1 - i$.

3. Find the rational roots of $P(x) = x^4 - x^2 - 2$.
Let $\frac{c}{d}$ be the rational root. c is a factor of -2, hence $c = \pm 1$ or ± 2. d is a factor of 1, hence $d = \pm 1$. The possible roots are ± 1 and ± 2. Substitution shows that none of these is a solution. The function $P(x)$ has no rational roots.

We try -6.

$$\begin{array}{r|rrrr} -6 & 1 & 6 & 1 & 6 \\ & & -6 & 0 & -6 \\ \hline & 1 & 0 & 1 & 0 \end{array}$$

$P(-6) = 0$, so -6 is a root. We now know that

$$P(x) = (x + 6)(x^2 + 1)$$

Since $x^2 + 1$ has no real roots, the only rational root of $P(x)$ is -6. The other roots are i and $-i$.

Try This

b. Let $P(x) = x^3 + 7x^2 + 4x + 28$, and let $\frac{c}{d}$ be a rational root of $P(x)$. Find the rational roots, if they exist, of $P(x)$. If possible, find the other roots. $-7, 2i, -2i$

EXAMPLE 3 Find only the rational roots of $x^4 + 2x^3 + 2x^2 - 4x - 8$.

Since the leading coefficient is 1, the only possibilities for rational roots are the factors of the last coefficient, -8.

$$1, -1, 2, -2, 4, -4, 8, -8$$

Using substitution or synthetic division, we find that none of the possibilities is a root. Thus there are no rational roots.

Try This

c. Find only the rational roots of $x^4 + x^2 + 2x + 6$. None

d. Find only the rational roots of $x^5 - 2x^4 + 4x - 8$. 2

Here are some guidelines for finding rational roots.

Finding rational roots

To find possible rational roots of $P(x) = a_nx^n + a_{n-1}x^{n-1} + \cdots + a_0$,
1. find all factors of a_n and a_0.
2. find each rational number $\frac{c}{d}$ such that d is a factor of a_n and c is a factor of a_0.
3. if a_n is 1, test only the factors of a_0.
4. test each $\frac{c}{d}$ using synthetic division.

Once all of the rational roots are found, the polynomial can be simplified by factoring. It is then often possible to find the other roots.

Proof of Theorem 11-7

Since $\frac{c}{d}$ is a root of $P(x)$, we know that

$$a_n\left(\frac{c}{d}\right)^n + a_{n-1}\left(\frac{c}{d}\right)^{n-1} + \cdots + a_1\left(\frac{c}{d}\right) + a_0 = 0 \quad ①$$

We multiply by d^n and get the equation

$$a_nc^n + a_{n-1}c^{n-1}d + \cdots + a_1cd^{n-1} + a_0d^n = 0 \quad ②$$

Then we have

$$a_nc^n = (-a_{n-1}c^{n-1} - \cdots - a_1cd^{n-2} - a_0d^{n-1})\,d$$

Note that d is a factor of a_nc^n. Now d is not a factor of c because c and d are relatively prime. Thus d is not a factor of c^n. So d is a factor of a_n.

In a similar way we can show from equation ② that

$$a_0d^n = (-a_nc^{n-1} - a_{n-1}c^{n-2}d - \cdots - a_1d^{n-1})\,c$$

Thus c is a factor of a_0d^n. Again, c is not a factor of d^n, so it must be a factor of a_0.

11-4 EXERCISES

A

Find the rational roots, if they exist, of each polynomial. Find the other roots, if possible.

1. $P(x) = x^3 + 3x^2 - 2x - 6$
2. $P(x) = x^3 - x^2 - 3x + 3$
3. $P(x) = 5x^4 - 4x^3 + 19x^2 - 16x - 4$
4. $P(x) = 3x^4 - 4x^3 + x^2 + 6x - 2$
5. $P(x) = x^4 - 3x^3 - 20x^2 - 24x - 8$
6. $P(x) = x^3 + 3x^2 - x - 3$
7. $P(x) = x^4 + 5x^3 - 27x^2 + 31x - 10$
8. $P(x) = x^3 + 5x^2 - x - 5$
9. $P(x) = x^3 + 8$
10. $P(x) = x^3 - 8$
11. $P(x) = 4x^3 - 3x^2 + 4x - 3$
12. $P(x) = 2x^3 - 3x^2 - x + 1$

Find only the rational roots.

13. $P(x) = x^5 - 5x^4 + 5x^3 + 15x^2 - 36x + 20$ 1, 2, −2
14. $P(x) = x^5 - 3x^4 - 3x^3 + 9x^2 - 4x + 12$ 2, −2, 3
15. $P(x) = x^4 + 32$ No rational
16. $P(x) = x^6 + 8$ No rational
17. $P(x) = x^3 - x^2 - 4x + 3$ No rational
18. $P(x) = 2x^3 + 3x^2 + 2x + 3$ $-\frac{3}{2}$
19. $P(x) = x^4 + 2x^3 + 2x^2 - 4x - 8$ No rational
20. $P(x) = x^4 + 6x^3 + 17x^2 + 36x + 66$ No rational

LESSON QUIZ

1. Find the rational roots of $P(x) = x^3 - 2x^2 + x - 2$.
   2 is the only rational root.
2. Find the rational roots of $P(x) = x^5 + 3x^3 + 1$.
   There are none.

Assignment Guide

Algebra: Day 1: 1–12
Day 2: 13–20, MR

Alg w/Finite or Trig: 1–12 m3, 13–23 e/o, 24, MR

Comprehensive: 1–23 m3, 24–27, MR

ADDITIONAL ANSWERS

Exercises

1. $-3; \sqrt{2}, -\sqrt{2}$
2. $1; \sqrt{3}, -\sqrt{3}$
3. $1, -\frac{1}{5}; 2i, -2i$
4. $-1, \frac{1}{3}; 1 + i, 1 - i$
5. $-1, -2; 3 + \sqrt{13}, 3 - \sqrt{13}$
6. $1, -1, -3$
7. $1, 2; -4 + \sqrt{21}, -4 - \sqrt{21}$
8. $1, -1, -5$
9. $-2; 1 + i\sqrt{3}, 1 - i\sqrt{3}$
10. $2; -1 + i\sqrt{3}, -1 - i\sqrt{3}$
11. $\frac{3}{4}; i, -i$
12. $\frac{1}{2}; \frac{1+\sqrt{5}}{2}, \frac{1-\sqrt{5}}{2}$

25. The possible rational roots of $x^2 - 5 = 0$ are ± 1, ± 5. None of these are roots.
26. The only possible rational roots of $x^3 - 3 = 0$ are ± 1, ± 3. None of these are roots.

Mixed Review

28. 5
29. $4\sqrt{2}$
30. 10
31. 12
32. Center: $(-7, -1)$, radius: 7
33. $(0, -4)$, $(1, -3)$

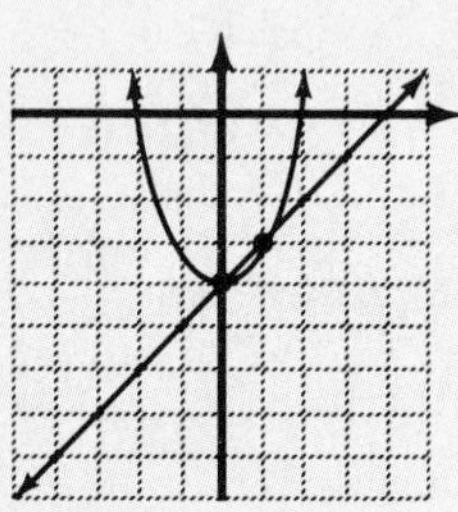

34. $(2, 2)$

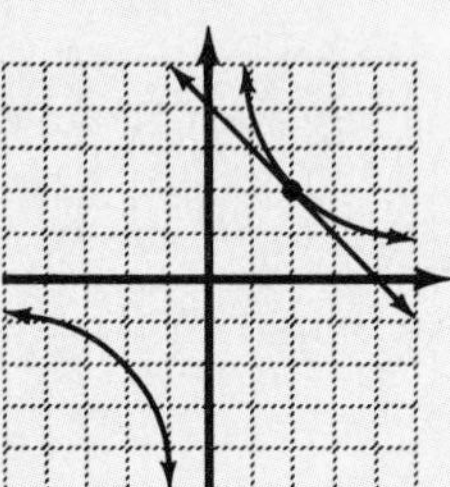

35. Yes, no, yes
36. 63 km

B

21. Find the rational roots of each polynomial. (Hint: Use LCD's.)
 a. $\frac{1}{12}x^3 - \frac{1}{12}x^2 - \frac{2}{3}x + 1$ 2(multiplicity 2), -3(multiplicity 1)
 b. $x^4 - \frac{1}{6}x^3 - \frac{4}{3}x^2 + \frac{1}{6}x + \frac{1}{3}$ $1, -1, \frac{2}{3}, -\frac{1}{2}$
 c. $\frac{1}{3}x^3 - \frac{1}{2}x^2 - \frac{1}{6}x + \frac{1}{6}$ $\frac{1}{2}$
 d. $\frac{2}{3}x^3 - \frac{1}{2}x^2 + \frac{2}{3}x - \frac{1}{2}$ $\frac{3}{4}$

22. A box manufacturer makes boxes of volume 48 ft³ from pieces of cardboard 10 ft on a side by cutting squares from each corner and folding up the edges. Find the length of each side of a square. 3 ft, $\frac{7 - \sqrt{33}}{2}$ ft ($\approx$ 0.6277 ft)

23. A box manufacturer makes boxes of volume 500 cm³ from pieces of tin 20 cm on a side by cutting squares from each corner and folding up the edges. Find the length of each side of a square. 5 cm, $\frac{15 - 5\sqrt{5}}{2}$ cm ($\approx$ 1.9098 cm)

24. ***Critical Thinking*** A polynomial $P(x)$ with all integral coefficients has $\frac{3}{5}$ as one root. The leading coefficient a_n of $P(x)$ is prime and the constant term a_0 is a multiple of 4 that is less than 20. What are a_n and a_0? $a_n = 5$ and $a_0 = 12$

Challenge

25. Show that $\sqrt{5}$ is irrational by considering the equation $x^2 - 5 = 0$.
26. Show that $\sqrt[3]{3}$ is irrational by considering the equation $x^3 - 3 = 0$.
27. A box manufacturer makes boxes of volume 2160 in.² from pieces of tin 38 in. by 32 in. by cutting squares from each corner and folding up the edges. Find the length of each side of a square. 10 in., $\frac{25 - \sqrt{409}}{2}$ in. ($\approx$2.3881 in.)

Mixed Review

Find the distance between each pair of points. **28.** $(3, -2)$, $(6, -6)$
29. $(4, 0)$, $(0, 4)$ **30.** $(9, 1)$, $(15, -7)$ **31.** $(5, 3)$, $(5, -9)$
32. Find the center and radius of the circle $x^2 + y^2 + 14x + 2y + 1 = 0$.

Solve each system graphically. **33.** $y = x^2 - 4$, $y = x - 4$ **34.** $xy = 4$, $x + y = 4$

Determine whether the numbers are roots of the polynomial.

35. $P(x) = x^3 - 6x^2 + 3x + 10$; $5, -2, 2$

36. Callie bicycled in a bike-a-thon for charity. Twenty people pledged $0.25 per kilometer toward her ride. She also had a separate pledge of $35. The total amount pledged was $350. How far did Callie ride?

11-5 Descartes' Rule of Signs

René Descartes (1596–1650) was a French mathematician and philosopher whose work with algebra and geometry led to coordinate geometry. The Cartesian coordinate system is named for him. Descartes lived during the time popularized by the Three Musketeers, and was reputed to be an excellent swordsman.

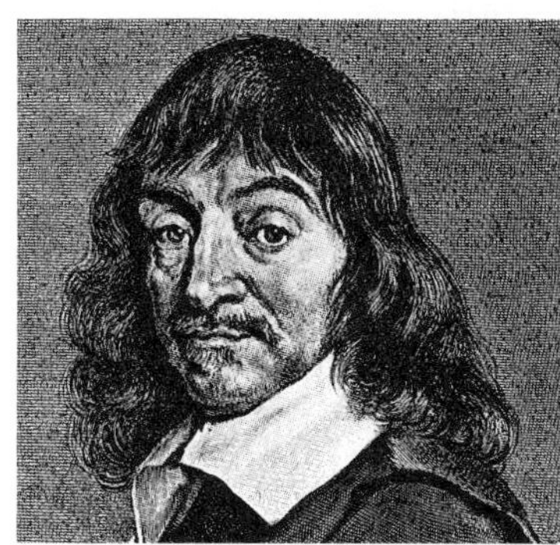

Positive Roots

Objective: Use Descartes' rule of signs to find the number of positive roots of a polynomial.

The number of positive real roots of a polynomial that is arranged in descending order can be found using Descartes' rule of signs. The rule uses the number of variations of sign, that is, the number of times successive coefficients have different signs. For $P(x) = 2x^6 - 3x^2 + x + 4$, the number of variations is 2. For $P(x) = 3x^5 - 2x^3 + x^2 - x + 2$, there are 4 variations.

Theorem 11-8

Descartes' Rule of Signs

The number of positive real roots of a polynomial $P(x)$ with real coefficients is

a. the same as the number of variations of sign of $P(x)$, or
b. less than the number of variations of sign of $P(x)$ by a positive even integer.

Note that a root of multiplicity m is counted m times.

EXAMPLES Determine the number of positive real roots.

1. $P(x) = 2x^5 - 5x^2 + 3x + 6$

The number of variations of sign is two. Therefore, the number of positive real roots is 2 or is less than 2 by 2, 4, 6, etc. Thus the number of positive roots must either be 2 or 0 since a negative number of roots has no meaning. (If one positive root is known, you can be sure there is a second positive real root.)

11-5

FIRST FIVE MINUTES

1. Find the rational roots of $P(x) = x^3 - 3x^2 - 8x - 10$.
   5 is the only rational root.
2. Find the rational roots of $P(x) = x^3 + 7x^2 + 9x + 1$.
   The only possible solutions are 1 and -1. Neither checks. There are no rational roots.

Positive Roots

Point out that a polynomial such as $3x^2 - 2x + 1$ has two variations of sign. Students may forget to count the first variation.

Key Questions

- What kind of coefficients must a polynomial have for the rule of signs to apply?
  The polynomial must have real coefficients.
  How many times does the sign vary for each polynomial?
- $2x^6 - 3x^2 + x + 4$
  2
- $3x^5 + 2x^4 - 5x^3 - 2x^2 + x - 4$
  3
- If a polynomial with real coefficients has seven variations of sign, what are the possible numbers of positive real roots?
  The number of positive real roots is either 7, 5, 3, or 1.

Chalkboard Examples

Use Descartes' rule of signs to find the number of positive real roots.

1. $P(x) = 5x^4 - 3x^3 + 2x^2 - 7x + 1$
   There are four variations of sign. Hence the number of positive real roots is either 4, 2, or 0. There may be no positive real roots, but if there is one, there must be another. If there are three, there must be a fourth.
2. $P(x) = x^7 - x^6 + x^5 - x^4 + x^3 - x^2 + x - 1$
   There are seven variations of sign. Hence the number of positive real roots is either 7, 5, 3, or 1. There must be at least one positive real root.
3. $P(x) = x^2 + x + 1$
   There are no variations of sign. There are no positive real roots.

Negative Roots

Math Point
René Descartes published his revolutionary discoveries about coordinate geometry and equations as an appendix to his book *Discourse on the Method of Reasoning Well and Seeking Truth in the Sciences* in 1637.

Chalkboard Examples

Find the number of negative real roots of the following polynomials.

1. $P(x) = x^4 + x^3 + x^2 + x + 1$
   $P(-x) = x^4 - x^3 + x^2 - x + 1$
   There are four variations of sign. The number of negative real roots of $P(x)$ is 4, 2, or 0.
2. $P(x) = 7x^3 - 3x^2 + 2x - 1$
   $P(-x) = -7x^3 - 3x^2 - 2x - 1$
   There are no variations of sign. Hence $P(x)$ has no negative real roots.

LESSON QUIZ

1. Find the possible number of positive real roots for $P(x) = 3x^5 - 6x^3 + 9x - 1$.
   3 or 1
2. Find the number of negative real roots for $P(x) = 3x^5 - 6x^3 + 9x - 1$.
   $P(-x) = -3x^5 + 6x^3 - 9x - 1$
   $P(x)$ has 2 or 0 negative real roots.

2. $P(x) = 5x^4 - 3x^3 + 7x^2 - 12x + 4$

There are four variations of sign. Thus the number of positive real roots is 4, $4 - 2$, or $4 - 4$; there are 4, 2, or 0 roots.

3. $P(x) = 6x^5 - 2x - 5$

The number of variations of sign is one. Therefore, there is exactly one positive real root.

Try This Determine the number of positive real roots.

a. $P(x) = 5x^3 - 4x - 5$ 1 **b.** $P(x) = 6p^6 - 5p^4 + 3p^3 - 7p^2 + p - 2$ 5, 3, or 1
c. $P(x) = 3x^2 - 2x + 4$ 2 or 0

Negative Roots

Objective: Use Descartes' rule of signs to find the number of negative roots of a polynomial.

Descartes' rule can also be used to help determine the number of negative roots of a polynomial. Recall that the graph of $P(-x)$ is the reflection of the graph of $P(x)$ across the y-axis. The points at which the graph crosses the x-axis are the roots of the polynomial. Thus the positive roots of $P(-x)$ are the negative roots of $P(x)$.

Theorem 11-9

Corollary to Descartes' Rule of Signs

The number of negative real roots of a polynomial $P(x)$ with real coefficients is

a. the number of variations of sign of $P(-x)$, or
b. less than the number of variations of sign $P(-x)$ by a positive even integer.

EXAMPLE Determine the number of negative real roots.

4. $P(x) = 5x^4 + 3x^3 + 7x^2 + 12x + 4$

$$P(-x) = 5(-x)^4 + 3(-x)^3 + 7(-x)^2 + 12(-x) + 4 \quad \text{Substituting } -x \text{ for } x$$
$$= 5x^4 - 3x^3 + 7x^2 - 12x + 4 \quad \text{Simplifying}$$

There are four variations of sign, so the number of negative roots is 4, 2, or 0.

Try This Determine the number of negative real roots.

d. $P(x) = 5x^3 - 4x - 5$ 2 or 0 **e.** $P(x) = 6p^6 - 5p^4 + 3p^3 - 7p^2 + p - 2$ 1
f. $P(x) = 3x^2 - 2x + 4$ 0

11-5 EXERCISES

A

Determine the number of positive real roots.

1. $P(x) = 3x^5 - 2x^2 + x - 1$ 3 or 1
2. $P(x) = 5x^6 - 3x^3 + x^2 - x$ 3 or 1
3. $P(x) = 6x^7 + 2x^2 + 5x + 4$ 0
4. $P(x) = -3x^5 - 7x^3 - 4x - 5$ 0
5. $P(x) = 3x^{18} + 2x^4 - 5x^2 + x + 3$ 2 or 0
6. $P(x) = 5x^{12} - 7x^4 + 3x^2 + x + 1$ 2 or 0
7. $P(x) = 5x^9 - 3x^4 + 7x^3 + x - 2$ 3 or 1
8. $P(x) = -9x^{20} + 5x^{14} - 6x + 2$ 3 or 1
9. $P(x) = 4x^{13} + 4x^{12} - x^3 - 2x + 7$
10. $P(x) = -9x^{13} + x^5 - x^3 + 12x$

B

11.–20. Determine the number of negative real roots for Exercises 1–10.

Without solving, determine the number of positive, negative, and complex roots of the following equations. Assume that n is a natural number.

21. $P(x) = x^4 - 2x^2 - 8$
22. $P(x) = x^3 - 7x^2 + 12$
23. $P(x) = x^4 + 5x^2 + 6$
24. $P(x) = 2x^3 - 2x^2 + 6x - 1$
25. $P(x) = x^{2n} - 1$
26. $P(x) = x^{2n+1} + 1$
27. ***Critical Thinking*** What can you determine about the real roots of $x^3 + bx + c = 0$, given $b > 0$ and $c \neq 0$?

Challenge

28. Prove that for a positive even integer n, $P(x) = x^n - 1$ has only two real roots.
29. Prove that any polynomial equation $P(x) = 0$ that contains only odd powers of x and positive coefficients has no real roots except 0.

Mixed Review

Solve each system of equations. **30.** $y = x^2 - 4$, $y = -2x - 1$ $(-3, 5), (1, -3)$ **31.** $x^2 + y^2 = 25$, $y = x^2 - 13$ $(3, -4), (-3, -4), (4, 3), (-4, 3)$

32. For $x^2 - 9y^2 = 9$, find the center, vertices, foci, asymptotes, and graph.

Problem for Programmers

Write a program to use Descartes' rule of signs to determine the possible number of positive real roots of a polynomial of degree n. Test your program using Exercises 1–10 in Lesson 11-5.

Challenge: Modify the program to also determine the number of negative real roots of a polynomial. Test your program using Exercises 11–20 in Lesson 11-5.

Assignment Guide
Algebra: 1–20 e/o, MR

Alg w/Finite or Trig: 1–26 e/o, 27, MR

Comprehensive: 1–26 e/o, 27–29, MR

ADDITIONAL ANSWERS

Exercises

9. 2 or 0 **10.** 3 or 1 **11.** 0
12. 0 **13.** 3 or 1 **14.** 1
15. 2 or 0 **16.** 4, 2, or 0 **17.** 0
18. 1 **19.** 1 **20.** 3 or 1
21. 1 positive, 1 negative, 2 complex
22. 0 or 2 positive, 1 negative, 0 or 2 complex
23. 0 positive, 0 negative, 4 complex
24. 1 or 3 positive, 0 negative, 0 or 2 complex
25. 1 positive, 1 negative, $2n - 2$ complex
26. 0 positive, 1 negative, $2n$ complex
27. The only real root is negative.
28. Let $P(x) = x^n - 1$. There is one variation of sign, so there is just one positive root. Since n is even, $P(-x) = P(x)$. Hence $P(-x)$ has just one variation of sign, and there is just one negative root. Zero is not a root, so the total number of real roots is two.
29. Let $P(x) = a_n x^n + a_{n-2}x^{n-2} + a_{n-4}x^{n-4} + \cdots + a_3x^3 + a_1x^1$ where n is odd. By Theorem 11-7 there are no positive roots. If we replace x with $(-x)$, every term changes sign. Therefore, by Theorem 11-8, there are no negative roots. We can, however, factor an x from every term; thus $x = 0$ is a root.

Mixed Review

32. Center: (0, 0)
Vertices: (3, 0), (−3, 0)
Foci: $(\sqrt{10}, 0), (-\sqrt{10}, 0)$
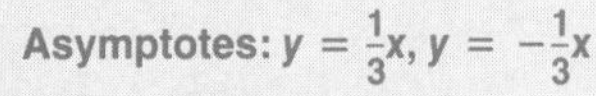
Asymptotes: $y = \frac{1}{3}x$, $y = -\frac{1}{3}x$

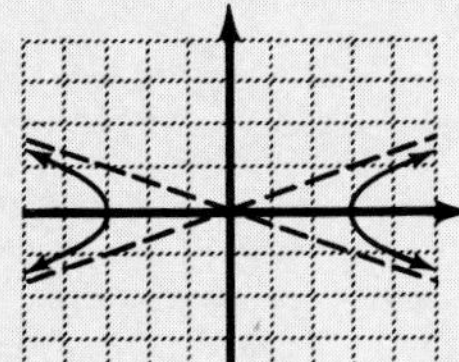

11-6

FIRST FIVE MINUTES

1. Find the number of positive real roots of $P(x) = 9x^5 - 3x^2 - 1$.
   1
2. Find the number of positive real roots of $P(x) = x^7 + x^4 + x + 1$.
   0
3. Find the number of negative real roots of $P(x) = 5x^3 + 4x^2 + 3x + 2$.
   $P(-x) = -5x^3 + 4x^2 - 3x + 2$
   There are 3 or 1 negative real roots of $P(x)$.

11-6 Graphs of Polynomial Functions

Master Grapher Worksheet 23, *Possible Shapes of Polynomial Graphs*, can be used as a lesson opener.

Graphs of first-degree polynomial functions are lines; graphs of second-degree, or quadratic, polynomial functions are parabolas. We now consider polynomials of higher degree with real coefficients.

Graphs of Higher-Degree Polynomial Functions

1. Every polynomial function has as its domain the set of real numbers.
2. The graph of any function is a continuous unbroken curve that must pass the vertical line test.
3. Unless a polynomial function is linear, no part of its graph is straight.
4. A polynomial of degree n cannot have more than n real roots. This means that the graph cannot cross the x-axis more than n times.

Third-degree, or cubic, polynomial functions have graphs like the following.

a.
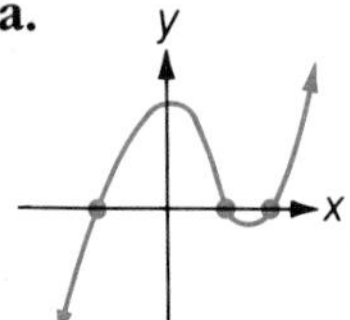

b.
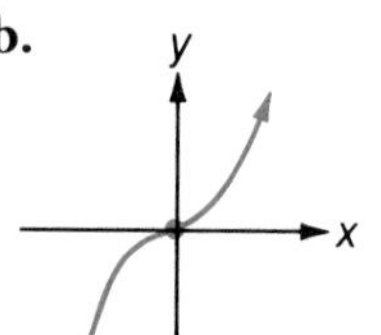

c.
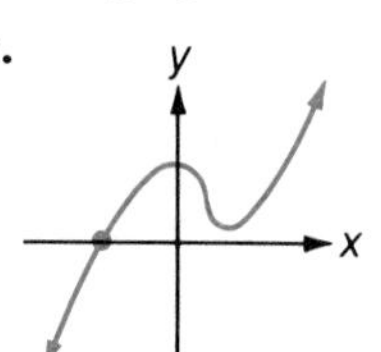

d.
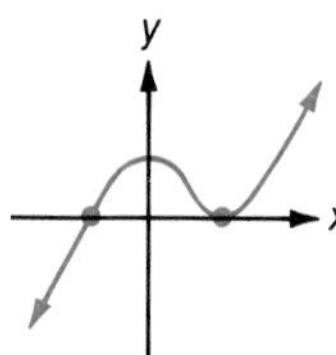

In a the graph crosses the x-axis three times, so there are three real roots. In b and c there is only one x-intercept, so there is only one real root in each case. In d the graph crosses the x-axis once and touches it once, so there are two real roots.

The left and right ends of a graph of an odd-degree function go in opposite directions. In graph c, the left arrow points downward, the right arrow points upward.

Graphs of fourth-degree, or quartic, polynomial functions look like these.

e.
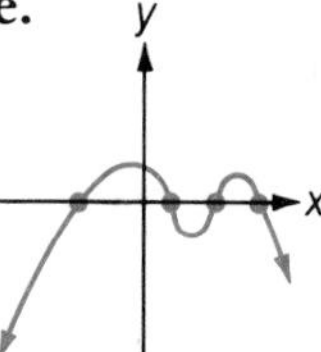

f.
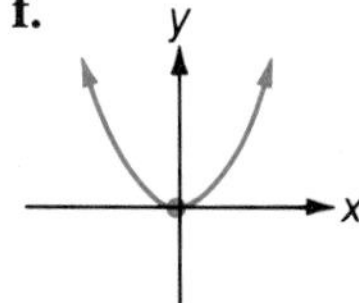

g.
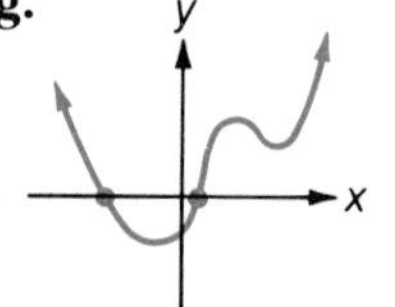

h.
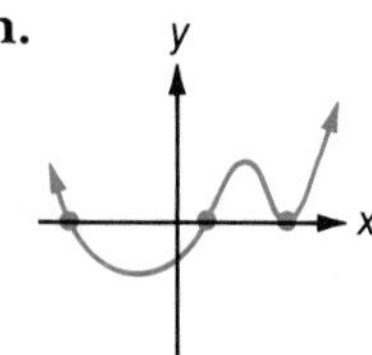

In e there are four real roots, in f there is one, in g there are two, and in h there are three.

The left and right ends of an even-degree function go in the same direction. In graph e, both the left and right arrows point downward.

When multiple real roots occur, they occur at points like the following.

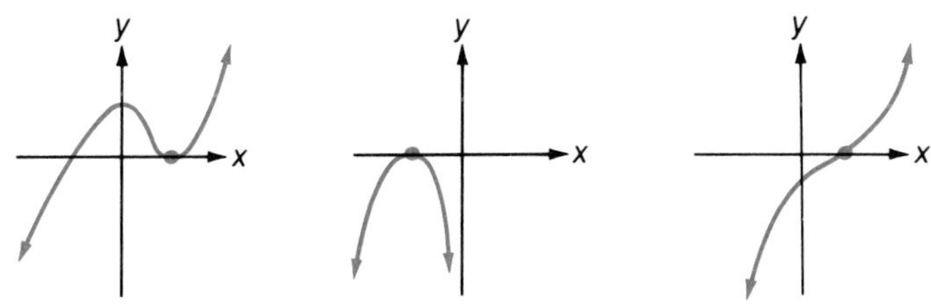

Graphing Polynomials

Objective: Graph polynomial functions.

To graph polynomials, keep in mind previously established results and proceed as follows.

Graphing Polynomials

1. Look at the degree of the polynomial and its leading coefficient. This gives a lot of information about the general shape of the graph.
2. Look for symmetries, as covered in Chapter 9. When symmetrical points occur, the rest of the graph can be plotted quickly.
3. Make a table of values using synthetic division.
4. Find the y-intercept and as many x-intercepts as possible (the latter are roots of the polynomial). In doing this, recall the theorems about roots, including Descartes' rule of signs.
5. Plot the points and connect them appropriately.

EXAMPLE 1 Graph $P(x) = 2x^3 - x + 2$.

1. This polynomial is of degree 3 with leading coefficient positive. The curve will have the general shape of the graph of a cubic function.
2. The function is not odd or even. However, $2x^3 - x$ is an odd function with the origin as a point of symmetry. $P(x)$ is a translation of this, upward 2 units. Hence the point $(0, 2)$ is a point of symmetry.
3. We make a table of values.

x	$f(x)$
0	2
1	3
2	16
−1	1
−2	−12

The points $(1, 3)$, $(2, 16)$, $(-1, 1)$, and $(-2, -12)$ are on the graph.

Graphing Polynomials

Point out that while a polynomial of degree n has n roots, it may have only one distinct root. For example, the polynomial x^n has only one root for any $n \geq 1$.
Have students graph $P(x) = x^3$ as an illustration.

Key Questions

- How many times can a third-degree polynomial cross the x-axis?
  3, 2, or 1
- Can the graph of a polynomial of degree 3 be a straight line along part of its graph?
  No

Chalkboard Example (*T23*)

1. Graph $P(x) = x^3 - 3x^2 + 3x - 1$.

The curve acts like x^3 when x is large positive or large negative. The curve has no obvious symmetry.
There are 3 or 1 positive real roots. There are no negative real roots. The only possible rational roots are ± 1. In fact, 1 is a root.
The polynomial factors as
$$P(x) = (x - 1)(x^2 - 2x + 1) = (x - 1)(x - 1)(x - 1) = (x - 1)^3$$
The curve has the same form as $y = x^3$, but shifted right by 1 unit.
Some values are $(-1, -8)$, $(0, -1)$, $(1, 0)$, $(2, 1)$, $(3, 8)$, $\left(\frac{1}{2}, -\frac{1}{8}\right)$, $\left(\frac{3}{2}, \frac{1}{8}\right)$.

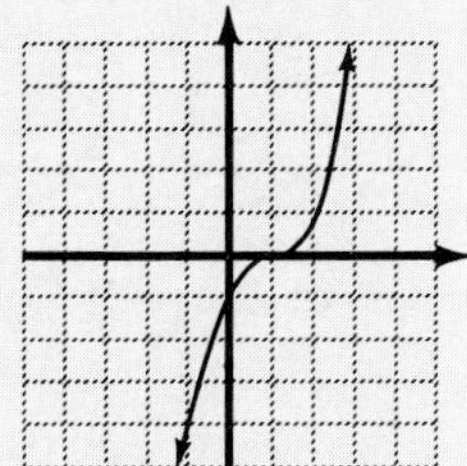

Students may notice that the function in Try This **a** is factorable by grouping.
$$P(x) = x^2(x - 4) - 3(x - 4) = (x^2 - 3)(x - 4)$$
Thus, the roots are $\pm\sqrt{3}, 4$.

Solving Equations

Point out to students that the search technique for finding the roots of a polynomial allows us to find the roots of any polynomial of any degree.

Chalkboard Example (*T24*)

1. Use a calculator to find the positive real root of $P(x) = 2x^3 - 2x - 1$.
   $P(1) = -1$ and $P(2) = 11$, hence the root must be between 1 and 2. Test the midpoint between 1 and 2.
   $P(1.5) = 2.75$, hence the root must be between 1 and 1.5. Test the midpoint between 1 and 1.5.
   $P(1.25) = 0.40625$, hence the root must be between 1 and 1.25.
   $P(1.12) = -0.430144$, hence the root must be between 1.12 and 1.25.
   $P(1.18) = -0.073936$, hence the root must be between 1.18 and 1.25.
   $P(1.21) = 0.12312$, hence the root is between 1.18 and 1.21.

LESSON QUIZ

1. Graph $P(x) = x^3 - x$.
   $P(x) = x(x - 1)(x + 1)$
   The x-intercepts are -1, 0, and 1. The y-intercept is 0.

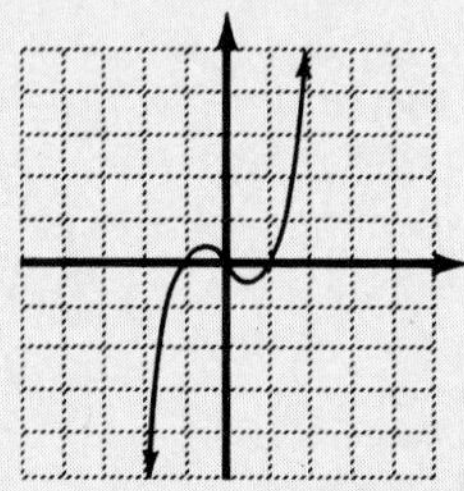

2. Use a calculator to find an approximation, to the nearest tenth, for the positive real root of $P(x) = x^3 - x - 1 = 0$.
   1.3

Assignment Guide

Algebra: 1–16 e/o, MR

Alg w/Finite or Trig: 1–6 m3, 7–20 e/o, 21, MR

Comprehensive: 1–16 m3, 17–20 e/o, 21–23, MR

4. Descartes' rule tells us that there are 2 or 0 positive roots and that there is just one negative root.
5. We plot this information and consider the three possibilities.

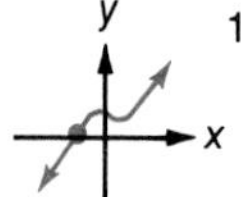

1 negative root

1 negative and 2 positive roots

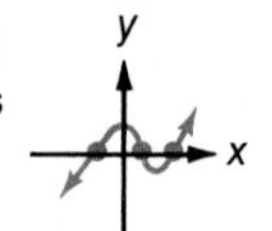

1 negative root and 1 positive root of multiplicity 2

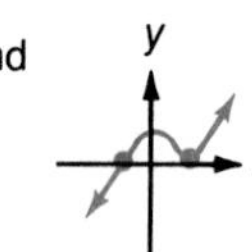

We do not know the shape of the curve between $(-1, 1)$ and $(0, 2)$ and between $(0, 2)$ and $(1, 3)$. We therefore need to plot some more points between -1 and 1. After we determine the points using a calculator, we sketch the complete graph. Computer graphing techniques may also be used to graph the function.

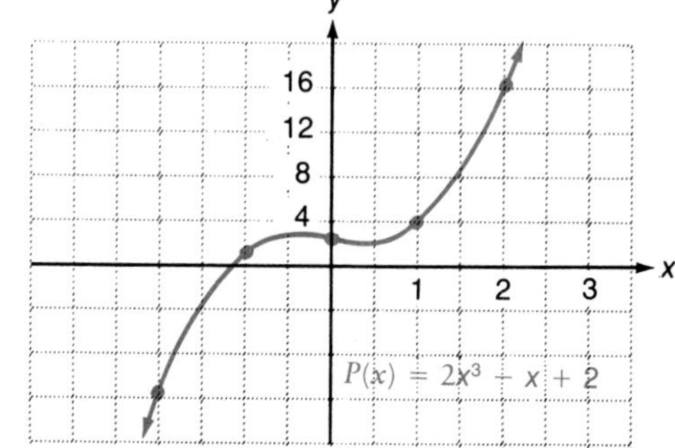

Try This Graph.

a. $P(x) = x^3 - 4x^2 - 3x + 12$ See Additional Answers.

Solving Equations

Objective: Use a graph to aid in approximating solutions to polynomial equations.

Whenever we find the roots, or zeros, of a function $P(x)$, we have solved the equation $P(x) = 0$. One method of finding approximate solutions of polynomial equations is by graphing. We graph the function $y = P(x)$ and note where the graph crosses the x-axis. In Example 1, there is a real solution of the equation $2x^3 - x + 2 = 0$ at about -1.1.

We can approximate roots more precisely by further calculation or by graphing with a computer.

EXAMPLE 2 Use a calculator to find a closer approximation of the root of $P(x) = 2x^3 - x + 2$, which is near -1.1.

We know that $P(-1) = 1$ and $P(-2) = -12$, so there must be a root between -1 and -2. To find a better approximation we use synthetic division.

$P(-1.1) = 0.44$ and $P(-1.2) = -0.26$. Therefore, the graph crosses the x-axis between -1.1 and -1.2. Further calculation shows that $P(-1.16) = 0.04$ and $P(-1.17) = -0.03$, so we have a root between -1.16 and -1.17.

We now have an approximation to hundredths, -1.17.

Try This Graph each polynomial. Find approximate roots to the nearest tenth. See Additional Answers.

b. $P(x) = x^3 - 3x^2 + 1$ 0.7, -0.5, 2.9

c. $P(x) = x^4 + 3x^2 + 2$ No real solution

Computer graphing programs, such as Master Grapher™, can be used to find approximations for both irrational and rational roots of higher-degree polynomial functions.

These programs allow you to change the viewing window so that the graph is enlarged. You can get increasingly better approximations of where a graph crosses the x-axis by "zooming" in.

EXAMPLE 3

Approximate the real roots of $P(x) = 2x^5 - 4x^4 + x^2 - 10$.

Descartes' rule of signs shows that there are 3 or 1 positive real roots, and 2 or 0 negative real roots.

Graphing using the computer shows that there are no negative roots, and there is one positive real root. The positive real root is approximately 2. Using the "zoom" function or changing the limits of x and y allows you to magnify the part of the graph around the intercept of the function.

We can zoom in on the root by changing the borders of the screen. First, we set the limits of x to show from 1.5 to 2.5. Then we set the limits of y to show from -0.5 to 0.5. We can see on the magnified screen that the graph crosses the x-axis at about 2.13.

Continuing to narrow down the x- and y-scales, we can find the root to seven or eight decimal places.

We find x is approximately 2.13200186.

Try This

Approximate the real roots.

d. $2x^4 - 5x - 16 = 0$ $-1.44689491, 1.88857409$ **e.** $x^6 - 6 = 0$ 1.3480062

A graphing calculator may also be used to approximate roots in this manner.

11-6 EXERCISES

A

Graph. A graphing calculator or graphing software may be used.

1. $P(x) = x^3 - 3x^2 - 2x - 6$
2. $P(x) = x^3 + 4x^2 - 3x - 12$
3. $P(x) = 2x^4 + x^3 - 7x^2 - x + 6$
4. $P(x) = 3x^4 + 5x^3 + 5x^2 - 5x - 6$
5. $P(x) = x^5 - 2x^4 - x^3 + 2x^2$
6. $P(x) = x^5 - 2x^4 + x^3 - 2x^2$

Graph each polynomial. Find approximate roots to the nearest tenth.

7. $P(x) = x^3 - 3x - 2$ $-1, 2$
8. $P(x) = x^3 - 3x^2 + 3$ $-0.9, 1.3, 2.6$
9. $P(x) = x^3 - 3x - 4$ 2.2
10. $P(x) = x^3 - 3x^2 + 5$ -1.1

ADDITIONAL ANSWERS

Try This

a.

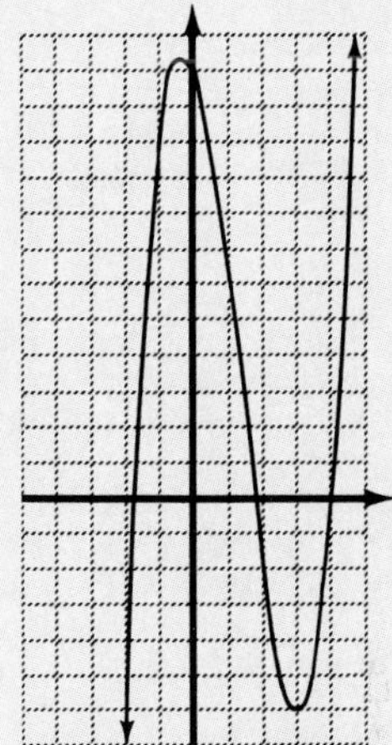

b.

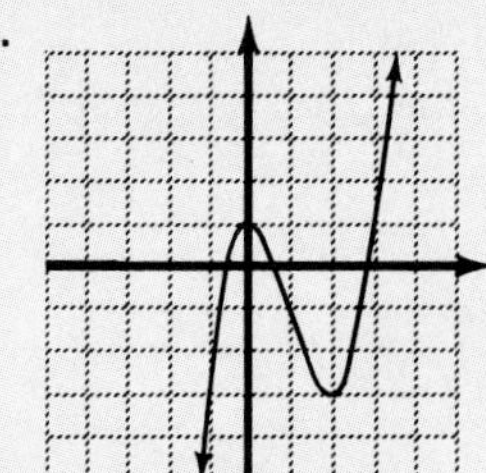

c.

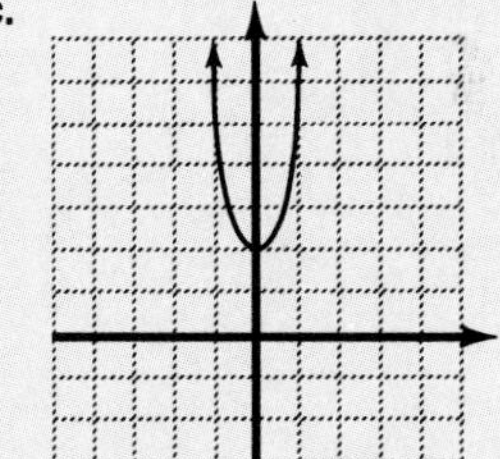

Exercises

For graphs of Exercises 1–16 and 19–20, see Teacher's Answer Section.

21. Answers may vary. Refer students to page 504 for possible answers.

22.

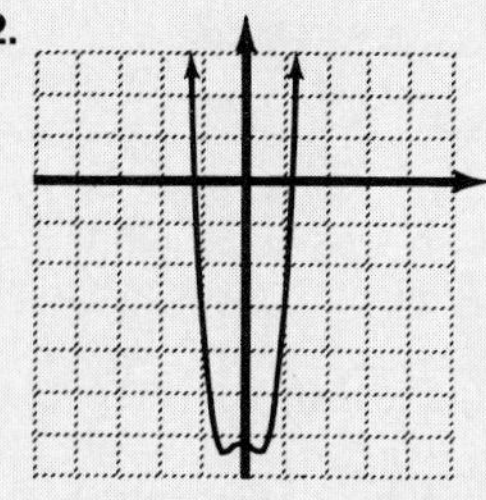

23. $P(x) = 3x^4 - 5x^3 + 4x^2 - 5$
Perform synthetic division using a as the divisor and 3, −5, 4, 0, and −5 as the coefficients to find $P(a) = a[a(a(3a - 5) + 4)] - 5$. This expression is the same expression obtained by factoring to find nested form.

Mixed Review

24. $y = -\frac{2}{3}x + 8$

25. $y = -\frac{1}{2}x + 3$

26. $-\frac{1}{2} \leq x$ and $x \leq \frac{7}{2}$

27. $x \leq -\frac{7}{3}$ or $x \geq 1$

28. $y = 9$
29. No solution
30. $P(2) = -14$; $P(4) = -32$; $P(-1) = -17$; $P(-2) = -50$
31. 6, 2, −1
32. 2, −3, −1
33. (3, 6)
34. (0, 0), (6, 12)

11. $P(x) = x^4 - 6x^2 + 8$ ±1.4, ±2　　**12.** $P(x) = x^4 - 4x^2 + 2$ ±0.8, ±1.8

13. $P(x) = x^5 + x^4 - x^3 - x^2 - 2x - 2$ −1, ±1.4

14. $P(x) = x^5 - 2x^4 - 2x^3 + 4x^2 - 3x + 6$ ±1.7, 2

15. $P(x) = x^4 + x^2 + 1$ No real solution　　**16.** $P(x) = x^4 + 2x^2 + 2$ No real solution

B

17. The equation $2x^5 + 2x^3 - x^2 - 1 = 0$ has a solution between 0 and 1. Use a calculator to approximate it to the nearest hundredth. 0.79

18. The equation $x^4 - 2x^3 - 3x^2 + 4x + 2 = 0$ has a solution between 1 and 2. Use a calculator to approximate it to the nearest hundredth. 1.41

Graph each polynomial. Find the irrational roots. (Use a calculator to approximate to the nearest hundredth.)

19. $P(x) = x^3 - 2x^2 - x + 4$ −1.27

20. $P(x) = x^3 - 4x^2 + x + 3$ −0.7, 1.24, 3.46

21. ***Critical Thinking*** Sketch the graph of a quartic polynomial that has two negative real roots and one nonnegative real root.

Challenge

22. Use a calculator to graph $P(x) = 5.8x^4 - 2.3x^2 - 6.1$.

23. A procedure for evaluating a polynomial, known as nested evaluation, is as follows. Given a polynomial, such as $3x - 5x^3 + 4x^2 - 5$, successively factor out x.

$$x(x(x(3x - 5) + 4)) - 5$$

Given a value of x, substitute it in the innermost parentheses and work your way out, at each step multiplying, then adding or subtracting. Show that this process is identical to synthetic division.

Mixed Review

Write an equation for the line containing the given point and perpendicular to the given line. **24.** $(6, 4)$; $-3x + 2y = 4$　　**25.** $(4, 1)$; $2x - y = 7$

Solve. **26.** $|2x - 3| \leq 4$　　**27.** $|3x + 2| \geq 5$

Solve. **28.** $\sqrt{y - 5} + \sqrt{y} = 5$　　**29.** $\sqrt{x + 3} + \sqrt{x} = -3$

30. $P(x) = x^3 - 7x^2 + 5x - 4$; find $P(2)$, $P(4)$, $P(-1)$, $P(-2)$.

Factor the polynomial $P(x)$, then solve the equation $P(x) = 0$.

31. $P(x) = x^3 - 7x^2 + 4x + 12$　　**32.** $P(x) = x^3 + 2x^2 - 5x - 6$

Solve each system of equations. **33.** $2x^2 - 3y = 0$, $4x - y - 6 = 0$　　**34.** $y = 8x - x^2$, $y = 2x$

11-7 Problem Solving: Strategies

Work Backward

Objective: Solve problems using the strategy *Work Backward* and other strategies.

Sometimes a problem describes a sequence of actions involving numbers, gives the result, and asks for the number with which it started. A problem of this type can be solved by using a strategy called Work Backward.

EXAMPLE

A moving company put $\frac{1}{2}$ of the boxes from a house into a large truck and $\frac{1}{3}$ of the boxes into a smaller truck. Eight boxes were still in the garage of this house, and 6 were in the attic. These were to be moved the next day. How many boxes were in each truck?

To solve this problem, you can start with the number of boxes that were still in the garage and the attic, and then work backward.

DATA IN THE PROBLEM	WORK BACKWARD
↓	$\frac{1}{2}$ of the 84 boxes were on the large truck, or 42 boxes: $\frac{1}{3}$ of the 84 boxes were on the small truck, or 28 boxes
	↑
$\frac{1}{2}$ of the boxes in one truck and $\frac{1}{3}$ of the boxes in another truck	The total number of boxes was $6 \cdot 14$, or 84.
	↑
↓	$\frac{1}{2} + \frac{1}{3} = \frac{5}{6}$, so 14 boxes were $\frac{1}{6}$ of the total boxes.
	↑
8 in the garage and 6 in the attic →	8 + 6, or 14 boxes had yet to be loaded

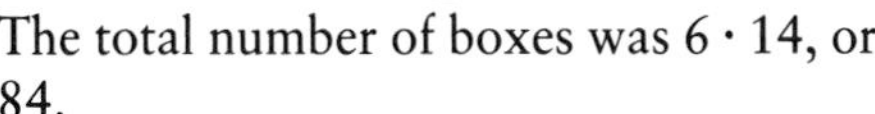

There were 42 boxes on the large truck and 28 on the small truck.

Problem-Solving Strategies

Write an Equation	Draw a Diagram	Guess, Check, Revise
Make an Organized List	Make a Table	Look for a Pattern
Use Logical Reasoning	Simplify the Problem	Work Backward

11-7

FIRST FIVE MINUTES

1. Shelly bicycles around a park at 3 times the rate that Mark jogs. It takes Shelly about 12 minutes to go around the park once. Shelly and Mark start out at 2 pm, but in opposite directions. Assuming they each keep up their pace, how many times will they pass each other before 3 pm? Not including the start, they will pass each other 6 times. (Draw a picture. Think about how long it takes before they meet once.)

Work Backward

Explain that many problems give the result of a sequence of events and ask where the sequence started. The Work Backward strategy is ideal for solving this kind of problem. Note that listing the steps carefully is an important part of the strategy. In the example, the arrows indicate the procedure; write the steps sequentially on the board.

Key Question

- What other strategy could you use to solve the Example? Guess, check, and revise or write an equation

Chalkboard Example

1. On Tuesday, Ms. Revada assigned twice as many math problems as she had assigned on Monday. The next day she assigned $\frac{2}{3}$ as many as the day before. On Thursday, she assigned 8 more than on Wednesday. On Friday, she assigned $\frac{3}{4}$ as many as she assigned on Thursday. If she assigned 21 problems on Friday, how many did she assign on Monday? Work backward. On Thursday, there were $\frac{4}{3}$ as many as on Friday. $\frac{4}{3} \cdot 21 = 28$. On Wednesday, there were 8 fewer, or 20 problems. On Thursday, there were $\frac{3}{2} \cdot 20$, or 30 problems. On Monday, there were half as many, or 15 problems.

Hints for Problems

1. Start with the 40 points they each had and work backward.
2. Simplify the problem. Start with a 3-sided figure, then a 4-sided figure, and so on.
3. Make a table showing the number of generations and the total number of people.
4. Make a table and look for a pattern.
5. Make an organized list of all possible pairings of boxes. Match some of the pairings with the given weights.
6. Draw a diagram, starting with the window.
7. Find how many ways this can be done if there were only 3 filing cabinets. Then try 4 filing cabinets, 5 filing cabinets, and so on.
8. Make a table of possible scores. Look for the first 3 consecutive scores.

ANSWERS

1. They started with 65, 35 and 20 points.
2. The sum of the interior angles of an octagon is 1080.
3. There would be a total of 4094 people in the 11 generations.
4. 41 toothpicks are needed for 10 regular hexagons.
5. The boxes weigh 24, 28, 32, 36, and 41 pounds.
6. A strip 12″ by 48″ would be cut from the side, and a strip 3″ by 96″ would be cut from the top or bottom. 12″ × 48″ + 3″ × 96″ − 3″ × 12″ would be wasted: 828 in² or 5.75 ft².
7. There are 105 ways to divide the 16 filing cabinets among the three stores.
8. The impossible numbers are 1, 2, 4, 5, 7, 10, and 13, so there are seven impossible scores.

11-7 PROBLEMS

Solve using one or more of the strategies.

1. Three friends were playing a game. At one point they decided that they would play three more rounds. The loser of each round had to give each of the other two players as many points as each player had at the start of that round. Each player lost one of the last three rounds. They all ended with 40 points. How many points did each player have before starting the last three rounds?
2. A quadrilateral can be divided into 2 triangles as shown below. This shows that the sum of the interior angles of the quadrilateral is $2 \cdot 180 = 360°$. Use this idea to find the sum of the interior angles of an octagon (8 sides). ◇◇

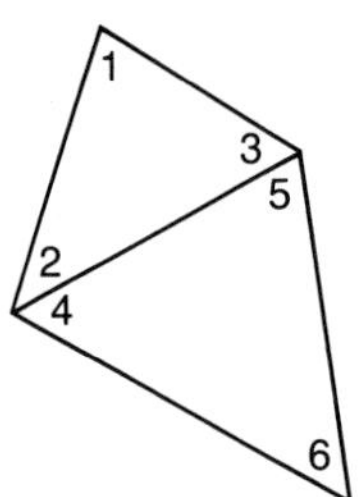

$1 + 2 + 3 = 180$
$4 + 5 + 6 = 180$
so $1 + 2 + 3 + 4 + 5 + 6 = 360$

3. There have been about 11 generations since the American Revolution. Suppose a man and woman were married in 1776 and subsequently had 2 children. Suppose both of these children married and had 2 children, and so on, for the succeeding generations. About how many people would there be in the 11 generations of this family born between 1776 and 1988?
4. What is the least number of toothpicks needed to build a regular hexagonal pattern with 10 hexagons? ◇◇

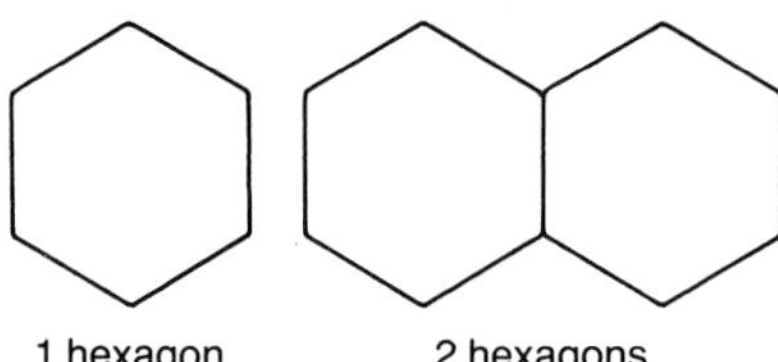

5. A shipping clerk has 5 boxes. The weights of all possible pairs of boxes, in pounds, are 60, 73, 68, 77, 56, 65, 69, 60, 52, and 64. Assume each box weighs a whole number of pounds. How much does each box weigh?
6. You have to cut a piece of wallboard out of a 4 ft by 8 ft sheet. The piece must fit around a window located on part of a wall that is 3 ft by 5 ft. The window must be located 14 in. from the right end, 10 in. from the left end, 6 in. from the bottom, and 3 in. from the top. What are the dimensions of the window? How much material would remain? ◇◇
7. A company has 16 identical filing cabinets to be distributed to its 3 branches. Each branch must receive at least 1 cabinet. In how many ways can the cabinets be distributed?
8. A certain game had 2 possible scoring plays, a 3-point play and an 8-point play. How many different total scores for one player are impossible for this game?

Chapter 11 Summary and Review

11-1

A root is a solution to the polynomial equation $P(x) = 0$. A zero is a value of x that makes the function $P(x)$ equal 0.

Determine whether the given numbers are roots of the polynomial equation $P(x) = 0$.

1. $P(x) = x^3 - x^2 + 25x - 25;\ -1, 5i$

2. $P(x) = x^4 + x^3 - x^2 - 2x - 2;\ \sqrt{2}, i$

Determine whether the given numbers are zeros of the polynomial function.

3. $P(x) = x^3 + 4x^2 - 4x - 16;\ -4, 4i$

4. $P(x) = x^4 - 2x^2 - 3;\ \sqrt{3}, i$

When one polynomial is divided by another, there will be a quotient and a remainder. When the remainder is zero, then the divisor and the quotient are factors of the dividend.

By division, determine whether the following polynomials are factors of the polynomial $P(x) = x^4 - 16$.

5. $x - 2$

6. $x^2 + 3x - 1$

Every polynomial division can be expressed as $P(x) = D(x) \cdot Q(x) + R(x)$, where $P(x)$ is the dividend, $D(x)$ is the divisor, $Q(x)$ is the quotient, and $R(x)$ is the remainder.

7. Let $P(x) = x^3 - 2x^2 + 4$ and $D(x) = x - 1$. Find $P(x) \div D(x)$, then express the dividend as $P(x) = D(x) \cdot Q(x) + R(x)$.

8. Let $P(x) = x^5 + 2x^4 + 2x^3 + 3x^2 + 3x + 3$ and $D(x) = x^2 + 2x + 1$. Find $P(x) \div D(x)$, then express the dividend as $P(x) = D(x) \cdot Q(x) + R(x)$.

11-2

The Remainder Theorem states that for a polynomial $P(x)$, the function value $P(r)$ is the remainder when $P(x)$ is divided by $x - r$.

Find the function values.

9. Let $P(x) = -2x^4 - 8x^3 + 4x^2 - 2x + 1$. Find $P(0)$, $P(1)$, $P(-2)$, and $P(-4)$.

The Factor Theorem states that if $P(r) = 0$, then the polynomial $x - r$ is a factor of $P(x)$. Thus we can use synthetic division to find function values and to check factors.

Factor the polynomial $P(x)$, then solve the equation $P(x) = 0$.

10. $P(x) = x^3 - x^2 - 14x + 24$

11. $P(x) = x^3 - 18x^2 - x + 18$

If a polynomial is of degree n, then it can be factored into exactly n linear factors. A factor may occur more than once. If a factor $x - r$ occurs k times, r is a root of multiplicity k.

Find the roots of the polynomial and the multiplicity of each root.

12. $P(x) = x^2(x - 2)^3(x + 1)$

13. $P(x) = (x^2 - 12x + 11)^2$

ANSWERS

1. No, yes
2. Yes, no
3. Yes, no
4. Yes, yes
5. Yes
6. No
7. $x^3 - 2x^2 + 4 = (x - 1)(x^2 - x - 1) + 3$
8. $x^3 + x + 1$, R2; $(x^2 + 2x + 1) \cdot (x^3 + x + 1) + 2$
9. 1, −7, 53, 73
10. 2, 3, −4
11. −1, 1, 18
12. 0 (multiplicity 2), 2 (multiplicity 3), −1 (multiplicity 1)
13. 1(multiplicity 2), 11(multiplicity 2)

14. $P(x) = x^3 - 13x - 12$
15. $P(x) = x^4 - 6x^3 + 11x^2 - 10x + 2$
16. $P(x) = x^4 - 4x^3 + 11x^2 + 8x - 26$
17. $\frac{1}{2}, \frac{5 + \sqrt{15}}{10}, \frac{5 - \sqrt{15}}{10}$
18. $2, -\frac{3}{2}, i\sqrt{3}, -i\sqrt{3}$
19. Positive 3 or 1, negative 0
20. Positive 3 or 1, negative 2 or 0
21. $-3, 1.4, -1.4$

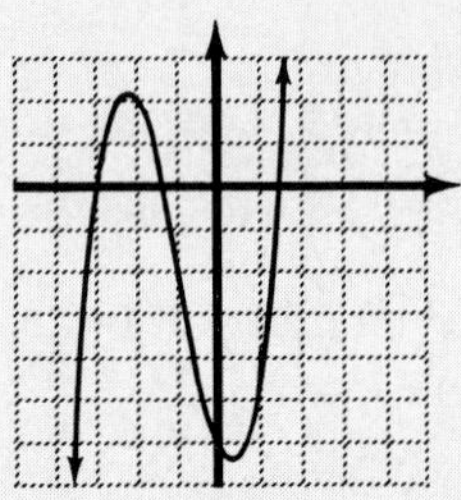

22. $-0.4, 0, 2.4$

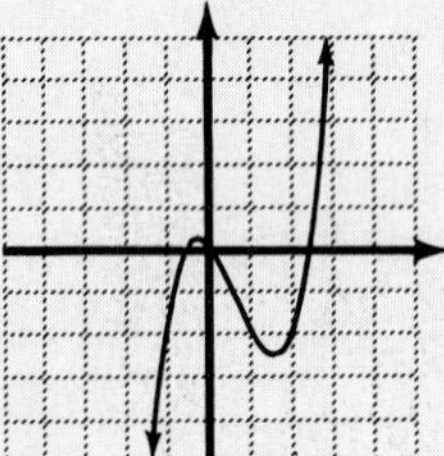

11-3

If r is a root of polynomial $P(x)$, then $x - r$ is a linear factor of $P(x)$.

Find a polynomial of degree 3 with the given numbers as roots.

14. $-1, -3, 4$

Complex roots occur in conjugate pairs in polynomials with real coefficients. Irrational roots occur in pairs in polynomials with rational coefficients.

Find a polynomial of lowest degree with rational coefficients that has the given numbers as some of its roots.

15. $1 - i, 2 + \sqrt{3}$

16. $2 + 3i, -\sqrt{2}$

11-4

To find possible rational roots of $a_nx^n + a_{n-1}x^{n-1} + \cdots + a_0$, find each rational number $\frac{c}{d}$ such that d is a factor of a_n and c is a factor of a_0, then test each $\frac{c}{d}$ using synthetic division.

Find the rational roots, if they exist, of each polynomial. If possible, find the other roots.

17. $P(x) = 20x^3 - 30x^2 + 12x - 1$

18. $P(x) = 2x^4 - x^3 - 3x - 18$

11-5

The number of positive real roots of a polynomial $P(x)$ with real coefficients is either the same as the number of the variations of sign of $P(x)$ or less than the number of variations by a positive even integer.

The number of negative real roots of a polynomial $P(x)$ with real coefficients is either the number of variations of sign of $P(-x)$ or less than the number of variations of sign by a positive even integer.

For each polynomial, determine the number of positive and the number of negative real roots.

19. $P(x) = 4x^5 - 3x^2 + x - 3$

20. $P(x) = 3x^7 - 2x^5 + 3x^2 + x - 1$

11-6

To graph polynomials:
1. look at the degree of the polynomial and its leading coefficient.
2. look for symmetries.
3. use synthetic division to make a table of values.
4. find the y-intercept and as many x-intercepts as possible.
5. plot the points and connect them appropriately.

After graphing, you can use the x-intercepts to aid in approximating roots.

Graph the following polynomial functions and approximate solutions to the nearest tenth.

21. $P(x) = x^3 + 3x^2 - 2x - 6$

22. $P(x) = x^3 - 2x^2 - x$

See also Problem 11, Computer-Assisted Problem Solving, page 846.

Chapter 11 Test

1. Is $x + 1$ a factor of $P(x) = x^3 + 6x^2 + x + 30$?
2. Is $x - 4$ a factor of $x^3 + 64$?
3. Let $P(x) = 4x^3 - 10x + 9$ and $D(x) = x + 2$. Find $P(x) \div D(x)$, then express the dividend as $P(x) = D(x) \cdot Q(x) + R(x)$.
4. If $P(x) = 2x^4 - 3x^3 + x^2 - 3x + 7$, find $P(-2)$, $P(3)$ and $P(-4)$.
5. Factor the polynomial $P(x)$, then solve the equation $P(x) = 0$ for $P(x) = x^4 - x^3 - 6x^2 + 4x + 8$.
6. Find a fourth degree polynomial with rational coefficients that has roots $3 - 2i, 1 + \sqrt{5}$.
7. Suppose a polynomial of degree 5 with rational coefficients has $3 + \sqrt{3}, 1 + 2i, -1$ as roots. Find all the roots of the polynomial.
8. Given that the polynomial $x^4 - 2x^3 + 3x^2 - 2x + 2$ has the root i, find all the roots of the polynomial.
9. Find a polynomial of degree 5 with real coefficients and i as a root of multiplicity 2 and $\sqrt{5}$ as a root of multiplicity 1.
10. Find the rational roots, if they exist, of $x^3 - 7x^2 + 16x - 12$. If possible, find the other roots.
11. Find only the rational roots of $4x^5 + 16x^4 + 15x^3 + 8x^2 - 4x - 3$.
12. For $3x^9 + 2x^6 + 3x^3 + 2x^2 + x - 1$
    a. find the possible number of positive real roots.
    b. find the possible number of negative real roots.
13. For $3x^5 - x^4 + 2x^3 - 5x^2 - 3x - 1$,
    a. find the possible number of positive real roots.
    b. find the possible number of negative real roots.
14. Graph $P(x) = x^3 - 2x^2 + x + 1$.
15. Find zeros of $P(x) = x^3 - 2x^2 + x + 1$. Approximate the zeros to the nearest tenth.

Challenge

16. Factor $x^6 + x^4 - 4x^2 - 4$. (Hint: Substitute z for x^2.)

ANSWERS

1. No
2. No
3. $4x^3 - 10x + 9 = (x + 2)(4x^2 - 8x + 6) - 3$
4. 73, 88, 739
5. $P(x) = (x - 2)^2(x + 2)(x + 1)$, 2 (multiplicity 2), -2, -1
6. $x^4 - 8x^3 + 21x^2 - 2x - 52$
7. $3 + \sqrt{3}, 3 - \sqrt{3}, 1 + 2i, 1 - 2i, -1$
8. $i, -i, 1 + i, 1 - i$
9. $x^5 - \sqrt{5}x^4 + 2x^3 - 2\sqrt{5}x^2 + x - \sqrt{5}$
10. 2, 2, 3
11. $\frac{1}{2}, -\frac{1}{2}, -3$
12. **a.** 1 positive real root
    b. 4, 2, or 0 negative real roots
13. **a.** 3 or 1
    b. 2 or 0
14. 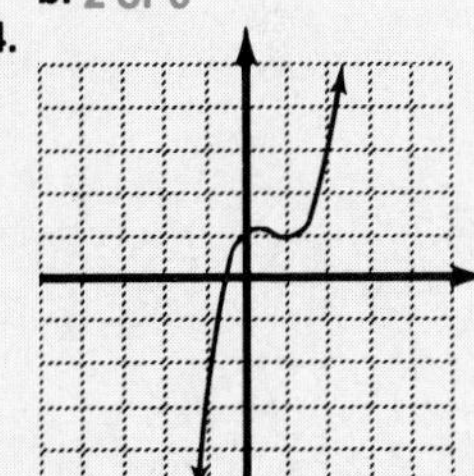
15. -0.5
16. $(x + \sqrt{2})(x - \sqrt{2})(x + i)(x - i)(x + i\sqrt{2})(x - i\sqrt{2})$

Test Item Analysis

Item	Lesson
1-3	11-1
4, 5	11-2
6-9, 16	11-3
10-12	11-4
13	11-5
14, 15	11-6

CHAPTER **12**

Exponential and Logarithmic Functions

Chapter Overview

Chapter 12 presents exponential functions $f(x) = a^x$ and their inverse functions, $f(x) = \log_a x$. Tables and calculators are each emphasized. All necessary properties to find both common and natural logarithms without a calculator, including an optional section on linear interpolation, are taught. Problem-solving applications are emphasized, involving such topics as growth, sound intensity, earthquakes, and radioactive decay. A strategy for solving angle problems on college entrance exams is also taught.

Objectives

12-1
- Write the equation of the inverse of a relation, given the equation of the relation.
- Determine whether the graph of a relation is symmetric with respect to the line $y = x$.
- Find an equation for the inverse function of a given function.

12-2
- Graph exponential functions.
- Graph logarithmic functions.

12-3
- Convert exponential equations to logarithmic equations and vice versa.
- Solve logarithmic equations.
- Simplify expressions of the form $a^{\log_a x}$ and $\log_a a^x$.

12-4
- Apply the basic properties of logarithms.

12-5
- Find common logarithms using a calculator.
- Find common logarithms using a table.
- Find antilogarithms using a calculator or a table.

12-6
- Use a table and linear interpolation to find logarithms.
- Find antilogarithms using a table and linear interpolation.

12-7
- Solve exponential equations.
- Solve logarithmic equations.
- Solve problems involving exponential and logarithmic equations.

12-8
- Graph functions related to the function $y = e^x$.
- Use a calculator or table to find natural logarithms.
- Solve problems involving natural logarithms.
- Change bases to find logarithms of any base in terms of common or natural logarithms.

TEACHING CHAPTER 12

Cooperative Learning Opportunities

Although cooperative learning should generally not be tutoring, on occasion it can be used for that purpose. Sometimes a student can explain a concept or procedure to another student in way that supplements the teacher's approach. If you find students having trouble with inverse, you might suggest a tutoring arrangement.

This approach should be considered especially for the first two lessons of Chapter 12. Ask for a show of hands of students who would like extra help and those who would like to spend a few sessions tutoring. These students might come from different classes or sections.

Ask the tutors to go over the theorems, examples, and several exercises from each set. In particular ask them to review the composition of functions, an important concept that students have not seen for some time. A similar approach can be used for Lesson 12-2.

Multicultural Note: *Hideyo Naguchi*

Hideyo Naguchi was born in Inawashiro, Japan in 1876. He demonstrated academic talents in his early schooling. After working as an apprentice to a pharmacist and as a paramedic, he went through medical school and began to do research on diseases. Naguchi's most important work was in identifying and isolating the organism that causes syphilis. His work contributed to the early detection and treatment of this disease.

Bacterial "growth" or increase in numbers follows an exponential pattern. In such a pattern time relates to numbers of divisions and also to the number of bacteria. Ask students to complete a table like the one below for up to 8 or 10 divisions and then draw a graph for the data.

Time in Minutes	Number of Divisions	Number of Bacteria
0	0	1
20	1	2

For more information, see page 135 of **Multiculturalism in Mathematics, Science, and Technology**.

Alternative Assessment and Communication Ideas

A firm grasp of the workings of exponential and logarithmic functions is most important. This understanding can be achieved, in part, through careful class presentations, home assignments, and review. Sometimes, encouraging speed will help fix fundamental relationships in the minds of students. Even older high school students can enjoy a team contest conducted in a serious but relaxed way. You may recall the mathematics bee shown in the film *Stand and Deliver*.

After covering the first four lessons of Chapter 12, divide the class into two groups. Have a team line up on each side of the classroom. Either orally or with flash cards, ask for the solution to exercises and other the basic relationships.

The following are a few examples.

Find the inverse of $y = 3x - 2$
A logarithm is __________
Convert to a logarithmic equation: $3^x = 10$
Convert to an exponential equation: $y = \log_{10}325$
Express as a sum: $\log_2 xy$.

Investigations and Projects

The origins of logarithms are described briefly on page 549. You might ask students to extend this and do a report on how Napier and Briggs did their calculations and how logarithms were first used. They might also cover the use of the slide rule and how the importance of logarithms has shifted from computation to functions.

The base e is introduced in Lesson 12-8. Although there are many advanced applications, the basic meaning is not too difficult for your more able students. $\left(1 + \frac{1}{n}\right)^n$ can be introduced as an example of compound interest and computed for different values of n. The limit of this expression as n becomes increasingly large can be seen using a scientific calculator. It is a good pre-calculus concept. You might ask if any students wish to study and report on the derivation of the number e.

MANAGING CHAPTER 12

Lesson	PACING CHART (DAYS) Algebra	Algebra w/Finite	Algebra w/Trig	Compre-hensive	Opening Activity	Cooperative Activity	Seat or Group Work
12-1	2	1	1	1	First Five Minutes 12-1: **TE** p.516 or ***FFM Transparency Masters*** p.34	Critical Thinking: **SE** p.520 ✂ Manipulative Activity 12: ***Enrichment*** p.53	Try This a–g
12-2	1	1	1	0.5	First Five Minutes 12-2: **TE** p.521 or ***FFM Transparency Masters*** p.35	Critical Thinking: **SE** p.525	Try This a–f
12-3	1	1	1	0.5	First Five Minutes 12-3: **TE** p.526 or ***FFM Transparency Masters*** p.35	Critical Thinking: **SE** p.528	Try This a–p
12-4	2	1	1	1	First Five Minutes 12-4: **TE** p.529 or ***FFM Transparency Masters*** p.35	Critical Thinking: **SE** p.533	Try This a–i
12-5	1	1	1	1	First Five Minutes 12-5: **TE** p.534 or ***FFM Transparency Masters*** p.35	Critical Thinking: **SE** p.538	Try This a–s
12-6	0	0	0	1	First Five Minutes 12-6: **TE** p.539 or ***FFM Transparency Masters*** p.36	Critical Thinking: **SE** p.542	Try This a–d
12-7	2	1	1	1	First Five Minutes 12-7: **TE** p.543 or ***FFM Transparency Masters*** p.36	Critical Thinking: **SE** p.548	Try This a–j
12-8	4	1	1	1	First Five Minutes 12-8: **TE** p.550 or ***FFM Transparency Masters*** p.36	Critical Thinking: **SE** p.556 Problem Solving: **SE** pp.557–559	Try This a–n
Review	1	1	1	1			
Test	1	1	1	1			
Cum. Review	1	1	1	0			
End-of-year Test	1	0	0	0			

FFM: First Five Minutes SPMR: Skills Practice Mixed Review

MANAGING CHAPTER 12

Enrichment	Review/Assess	Reteach	Technology	Lesson
✂ Manipulative Activity 12: ***Enrichment*** p.53 Teacher Demo 3: ***Master Grapher*** pp.9–10(Apple II), pp.143–144 (IBM), or pp.279–280(Mac)	Lesson Quiz: **TE** p.519	Skills Practice 33, #1–16: ***SPMR*** p.45	Worksheet 18: ***TI-81 Activities*** pp.73–76; Worksheet 24 ***Master Grapher*** pp.96–99, pp.230–233, or pp.366–369	**12-1**
Lesson Enrichment: **TE** p.523 College Entrance Exam 4: ***Problem Bank*** pp.75–78	Lesson Quiz: **TE** p.524	Skills Practice 33, #17–20: ***SPMR*** p.45	Worksheet 19: ***TI-81 Activities*** pp.77–80; Worksheet 20: ***TI-81 Activities*** pp.81–85; Worksheet 25: ***Master Grapher*** pp.100–103, pp.234–237, or pp.370–373; Worksheet 26: ***Master Grapher*** pp.104–108, pp.238–242, or pp.374–378	**12-2**
Critical Thinking 12: ***Enrichment*** p.33	Lesson Quiz: **TE** p.527 Quiz 23: ***Assessment*** p.31	Skills Practice 33, #21–39: ***SPMR*** p.45	Calculator Worksheet 21: ***Technology*** p.23	**12-3**
Bonus Topic 11: ***Enrichment*** p.12	Lesson Quiz: **TE** p.531	Skills Practice 34, #1–23: ***SPMR*** p.46	BASIC Computer Project 12: ***Technology*** p.92	**12-4**
Calculator Worksheet 22: ***Technology*** p.24	Lesson Quiz: **TE** p.537 Mixed Review 23: ***SPMR*** p.87	Skills Practice 34, #24–40: ***SPMR*** p.46	Calculator Worksheet 22: ***Technology*** p.24	**12-5**
Lesson Enrichment: **TE** p.540 Calculator Investigation: **SE** p.542	Lesson Quiz: **TE** p.541		Calculator Investigation: **SE** p.542	**12-6**
Historical Note: **SE** p.549 Worksheet 21: ***TI-81 Activities*** pp.87–89	Lesson Quiz: **TE** p.546 Quiz 24: ***Assessment*** p.32	Skills Practice 35, #1–17: ***SPMR*** p.47 Problem Bank 18: ***Problem Bank*** p.39	Worksheet 21: ***TI-81 Activities*** pp.87–89; Worksheet 27: ***Master Grapher*** pp.109–111, pp.243–245, or pp.379–381	**12-7**
Finding e^x: **SE** p.550 Problem Solving: **SE** pp.557–559 Problem 12: Computer Assisted Problem Solving, **SE** pp.847–848	Lesson Quiz: **TE** p.554 Mixed Review 24: ***SPMR*** p.88	Skills Practice 35, #18–33: ***SPMR*** p.47 Problem Bank 19: ***Problem Bank*** p.40	Calculator Worksheet 23: ***Technology*** p.25; Spreadsheet Activity 7: ***Technology*** pp.61–63; Problem for Programmers: **SE** p.556; Problem 12: Computer Assisted Problem Solving, **SE** pp.847–848	**12-8**
	Summary and Review: **SE** pp.560–561; Test: **SE** p.562			**Review**
	Chapter 12 Test: ***Assessment*** pp.113–118 or pp.179–180			**Test**
	Cumulative Review: **SE** pp.563–565			**Cum. Review**
	End-of-year Test: ***Assessment*** pp.231–234 or pp.237–244			**End-of-year Test**

The solution to the problem posed on the facing page can be found on page 555.

Ready for Exponential and Logarithmic Functions?

1-7 Simplify.

1. 5^1 5 **2.** 8^0 1 **3.** 2^{-3} $\frac{1}{8}$

1-8 Simplify.

4. $x^{-5} \cdot x^3$ x^{-2} or $\frac{1}{x^2}$ **5.** $\frac{x^{-3}}{x^4}$ x^{-7} or $\frac{1}{x^7}$ **6.** $(x^{-3})^4$ x^{-12} or $\frac{1}{x^{12}}$

7. $\frac{24x^2y^2}{-16x^2y}$ $-\frac{3y}{2}$ **8.** $\frac{(2x^3y^{-2})^3}{3y^{-3}}$ $\frac{8x^9}{3y^3}$

1-9

9. Convert 0.0845 to scientific notation. 8.45×10^{-2}

10. Convert 4.335×10^5 to decimal notation. 433,500

9-1 Test for symmetry with respect to the origin.

11. $4x + 4y = 6$ no **12.** $y = 2x^2$ no

CHAPTER

12 Exponential and Logarithmic Functions

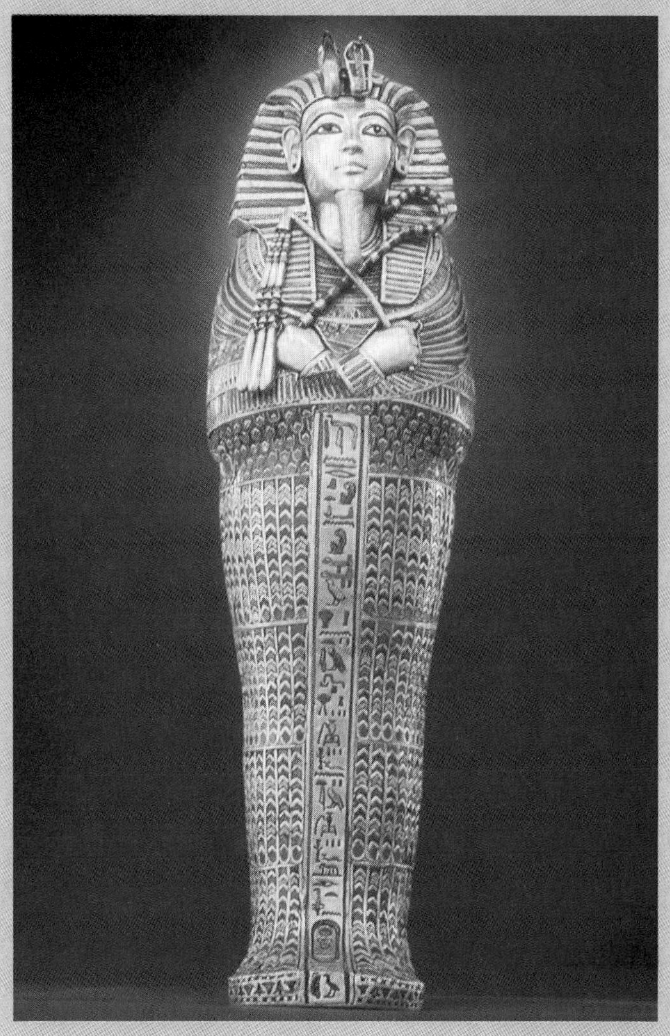

A mummy discovered in a pyramid in the Valley of the Tombs of the Kings had lost 46% of its carbon-14. What is its age?

12-1

FIRST FIVE MINUTES

Let $A = \{1, 2, 3\}$, $B = \{5, 7\}$.

1. List the set of elements of the Cartesian product $A \times B$.
   $\{(1, 5), (1, 7), (2, 5), (2, 7), (3, 5), (3, 7)\}$
2. Using the above relation as the domain, find $\{(x, y) \mid x + y > 9\}$.
   $\{(3, 7)\}$
3. Is the relation $\{(1, 2), (1, 3), (2, 3)\}$ a function?
   No, the first coordinate 1 corresponds to two different second coordinates 2 and 3.

Inverses of Relations

Remind students that a relation is a set of ordered pairs. Any set of ordered pairs is a relation. A function is a special kind of relation for which each first coordinate corresponds to only one second coordinate.

Key Questions

- Is $\{(3, 5), (4, 1)\}$ a relation?
  Yes
- Is $\{(1, 3), (2, 4), (3, 4)\}$ a function?
  Yes
- What is the inverse of the relation $\{(1, 2), (3, 4), (5, 6)\}$?
  $\{(2, 1), (4, 3), (6, 5)\}$

Chalkboard Example

1. Write an equation of the inverse of $y = 3x + 2$.
   $x = 3y + 2$

Inverses and Symmetry

Emphasize that a simple transformation of the equation corresponds to a simple transformation of the graph.

If interchanging x and y leaves the equation unchanged, then the graph will also remain unchanged. We say that the graph is symmetric with respect to the line $x = y$.

12-1 Inverse Relations and Functions

Master Grapher Worksheet 24, *Inverse Relations and Functions*, can be used for lesson closure.

Inverses of Relations

Objective: Write the equation of the inverse of a relation, given the equation of the relation.

If in a relation we interchange the first and second coordinates of each ordered pair, we obtain a relation that is the inverse of the original relation. Thus the inverse of the relation $\{(2, 1), (3, 1), (4, 2)\}$ is $\{(1, 2), (1, 3), (2, 4)\}$.

Theorem 12-1

Interchanging x and y in the equation of a relation produces an equation of the inverse relation.

EXAMPLE 1 Write an equation of the inverse of $y = x^2 - 5$.

We interchange x and y, and obtain $x = y^2 - 5$. This is an equation of the inverse relation.

Try This

a. Write an equation of the inverse of $y = x^2 + 4$. $x = y^2 + 4$

Inverses and Symmetry

Objective: Determine whether the graph of a relation is symmetric with respect to the line $y = x$.

Interchanging first and second coordinates in each ordered pair of a relation has the effect of interchanging the x-axis and the y-axis.

Interchanging the x-axis and the y-axis has the effect of reflecting the graph of those points across the diagonal line whose equation is $y = x$, as shown. Thus the graphs of a relation and its inverse are always reflections of each other across the line $y = x$.

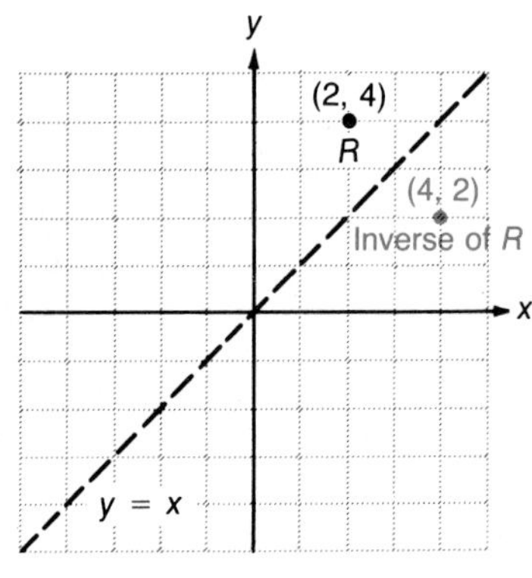

Here are some other graphs of relations and their inverses.

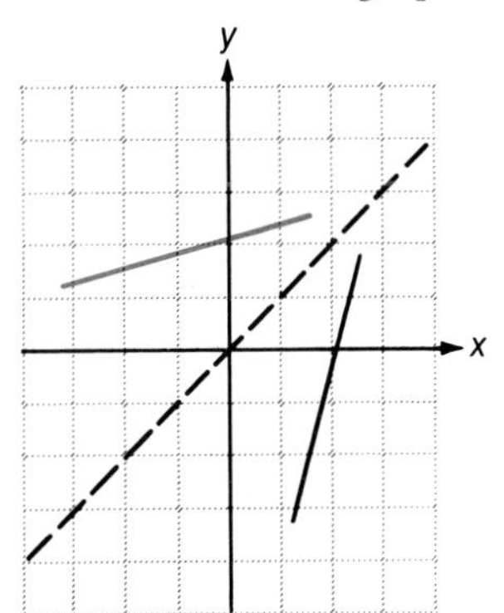

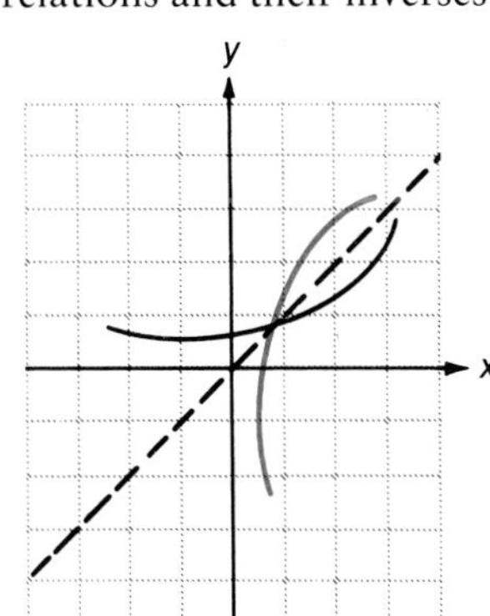

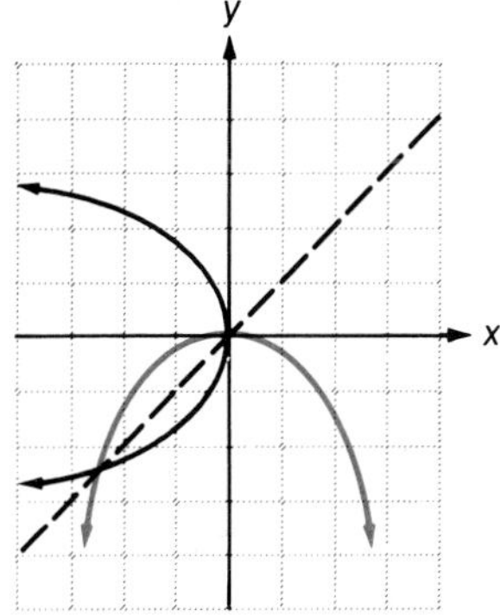

A relation may be its own inverse if, when the relation is reflected across the line $y = x$, the image is unchanged. Such a relation is symmetric with respect to the line $y = x$.

We can test the relation $3x + 3y = 5$ for symmetry with respect to the line $y = x$ by interchanging x and y in the equation. We obtain $3y + 3x = 5$.

This is equivalent to the original equation, so the graph is symmetric with respect to the line $y = x$.

EXAMPLE 2 Test the relation $4x - 4y = 8$ for symmetry with respect to the line $y = x$.

We interchange x and y in the equation, obtaining $4y - 4x = 8$. This is not equivalent to the original equation, so the graph is not symmetric to the line $y = x$.

Try This Test for symmetry with respect to the line $y = x$.

b. $4x + 4y = 6$ Yes

c. $y = 2x^2$ No

Inverses of Functions

Objective: Find an equation for the inverse function of a given function.

All functions have inverses, but the inverse is not necessarily a function. For instance, consider the function

$$G = \{(1, 3), (2, 4), (6, 3), (7, 7)\}$$

The inverse of G, $\{(3, 1), (4, 2), (3, 6), (7, 7)\}$, is not a function because the ordered pairs (3, 1) and (3, 6) have the same first coordinates but different second coordinates.

If the inverse of a function f is also a function, we denote it by f^{-1} (read "f inverse"). Recall that we obtain the inverse of a relation by interchanging the coordinates of each ordered pair. Thus the domain of a function f is the range of f^{-1} and the range of f is the domain of f^{-1}.

Key Questions

- Is the following relation left unchanged when x and y are interchanged? $x^3 + 2xy + y^3 = 1$
  Yes
- Is the following graph left unchanged when it is reflected across the line $x = y$?

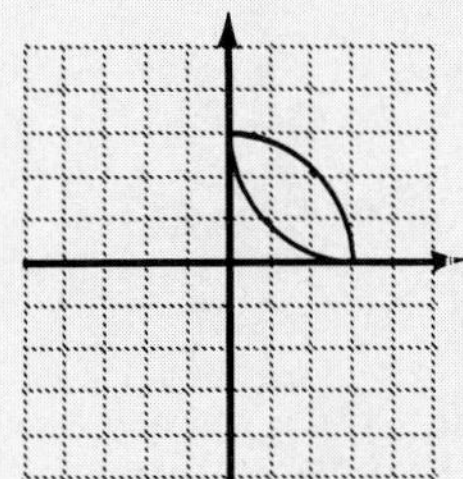

Yes

Chalkboard Example

1. Test whether the relation $x^2 + 3x^2y^2 + y^2 = 1$ is symmetric with respect to the line $x = y$.
   Interchanging x and y yields $y^2 + 3y^2x^2 + x^2 = 1$. This is equivalent to the original equation. The original equation is symmetric with respect to the line $x = y$.

Inverses of Functions

Emphasize that the notation f^{-1} does not mean $\frac{1}{f}$. The exponent notation f^{-1} always means the inverse function.

Point out that a relation that is not a function may have an inverse that is a function. Likewise, a relation that is a function may have an inverse that is not a function.

Note that the domain of the inverse function is the range of the original function. Thus, in Try This **f**, the domain of $f(x)$ is $x \geq -1$, while the domain of $f^{-1}(x)$ is $x \geq 0$.

Explain how inverse function keys work on a calculator. For example, the square and square root functions are inverses. If we enter a number, press the square key, then press the square root key, we obtain the original number.

Key Questions

- Let $A = \{(1, 2), (2, 2), (3, 2)\}$. Is the inverse of this function a function? No, 2 would be assigned to 1, 2, and 3.
- Can a function be its own inverse? Yes, these functions are each their own inverse.
  $f(x) = x$
  $f(x) = -x$
  $f(x) = \frac{1}{x}$

Chalkboard Examples

1. Given $f(x) = 2x + 5$, find an equation for $f^{-1}(x)$.
   $y = 2x + 5$
   Interchange x and y and solve for y.
   $x = 2y + 5$
   $y = \frac{x - 5}{2}$
   $f^{-1}(x) = \frac{x - 5}{2}$
2. Let $T(x) = \sqrt{1 - x}$. Find an equation for $T^{-1}(x)$.
   $y = \sqrt{1 - x}$
   Interchange x and y and solve for y.
   $x = \sqrt{1 - y}$ Note that $x \geq 0$.
   $x^2 = 1 - y$
   $y = 1 - x^2$
   $T^{-1}(x) = 1 - x^2, x \geq 0$
3. For the function $f(x) = 5x - 3$, find $f^{-1}(f(54.32))$ and $f(f^{-1}(87.65))$.
   54.32 and 87.65

When a function is defined by an equation, we can sometimes find an equation for its inverse by interchanging x and y.

EXAMPLE 3 Given $f(x) = 3x + 1$, find an equation for $f^{-1}(x)$.

(a) Let us think of this as $y = 3x + 1$.

(b) To find the inverse we interchange x and y: $x = 3y + 1$.

(c) Now we solve for y: $y = \frac{x - 1}{3}$.

(d) Thus $f^{-1}(x) = \frac{x - 1}{3}$.

In Example 3, f assigns $3x + 1$ to any number x. (This function multiplies each number of the domain by 3 and adds 1.) Its inverse, f^{-1}, assigns the number $\frac{x-1}{3}$ to any number x. (This inverse function subtracts 1 from each member of its domain and divides by 3.) Thus the function and its inverse are inverse operations.

Try This

d. Given $g(x) = x + 2$, find an equation for $g^{-1}(x)$. $g^{-1}(x) = x - 2$

e. Given $g(x) = 5x + 2$, find an equation for $g^{-1}(x)$. $g^{-1}(x) = \frac{1}{5}(x - 2)$

EXAMPLE 4 Let $S(x) = \sqrt{x}$. Find an equation for $S^{-1}(x)$.

(a) Let us think of this as $y = \sqrt{x}$. Note that the domain and range both consist of nonnegative real numbers only.

(b) To find the inverse we interchange x and y: $x = \sqrt{y}$.

(c) Now we solve for y, squaring both sides: $y = x^2$.

(d) Thus $S^{-1}(x) = x^2$, with the understanding that x cannot be negative.

In Example 4, the function S assigns $\sqrt{x}$ to any nonnegative number x. (This function takes the square root of any input.) Its inverse, S^{-1}, assigns x^2 to any nonnegative number x. (This function squares each input.) Thus the function and its inverse use inverse operations.

Try This

f. Let $f(x) = \sqrt{x + 1}$. Find an equation for $f^{-1}(x)$. $f^{-1}(x) = x^2 - 1, x \geq 0$

Suppose $f(x) = 2x + 3$. Then $f^{-1}(x) = \frac{x - 3}{2}$. Note that $f(5) = 13$, and $f^{-1}(13) = \frac{13 - 3}{2} = 5$. Also, $f(8) = 19$ and $f^{-1}(19) = 8$.

It appears that if we find $f(x)$ for some x and then find f^{-1} for this number, we will be back at x. In function notation the statement looks like the following equation.

$$f^{-1}(f(x)) = x$$

The notation $f^{-1}(f(x)) = x$ is read "f inverse of f of x equals x." It means, work from the inside out to take x, then find $f(x)$, and then find f^{-1} for that number. When we do, we will be back where we started, at x. For similar reasons, the following is true.

$$f(f^{-1}(x)) = x$$

For the statements above to be true, x must be in the domain of the function being considered. We summarize these ideas by stating the following theorem.

Theorem 12-2

For any function f whose inverse is a function, $f^{-1}(f(a)) = a$ for any a in the domain of f. Also $f(f^{-1}(a)) = a$ for any a in the domain of f^{-1}.

EXAMPLE 5 For the function $f(x) = 4x + 9$, find $f^{-1}(f(283))$ and $f(f^{-1}(-12{,}045))$.

We note that every real number is in the domain of both f and f^{-1}. Thus using Theorem 12-2, we may immediately write the answers, without calculating.

$$f^{-1}(f(283)) = 283$$
$$f(f^{-1}(-12{,}045)) = -12{,}045$$

Try This

g. For the function $f(x) = \frac{3x - 5}{4}$, find $f^{-1}(f(579))$ and $f(f^{-1}(-83{,}479))$.

$f^{-1}(f(579)) = 579$, $f(f^{-1}(-83{,}479)) = -83{,}479$

12-1 EXERCISES

A

Write an equation of the inverse relation of the following.

1. $y = 4x - 5$ **2.** $y = 3x + 5$ **3.** $y = 3x^2 + 2$
4. $y = 5x^2 - 4$ **5.** $x^2 - 3y^2 = 3$ **6.** $2x^2 + 5y^2 = 4$
7. $xy = 7$ **8.** $xy = -5$ **9.** $xy^2 = 1$
10. $\frac{x^2}{4} + \frac{y^2}{9} = 1$ **11.** $y = \frac{5}{x}$ **12.** $y = \sqrt{x + 1}$

Test for symmetry with respect to the line $y = x$.

13. $3x + 2y = 4$ **14.** $5x - 2y = 7$ **15.** $xy = 10$
16. $xy = 12$ **17.** $4x + 4y = 3$ **18.** $5x + 5y = -1$
19. $3x = \frac{4}{y}$ **20.** $4y = \frac{5}{x}$ **21.** $4x^2 + 4y^2 = 3$
22. $3x^2 + 3y^2 = 5$ **23.** $y = |2x|$ **24.** $3x = |2y|$

LESSON QUIZ

1. Find the inverse of the relation $\{(2, 3), (5, 7), (9, 0)\}$.
   $\{(3, 2), (7, 5), (0, 9)\}$
2. Write an equation for the inverse relation of $x^2 + 2x + xy = 1$.
   $y^2 + 2y + yx = 1$
3. Test $y = \frac{1}{x}$ for symmetry with respect to the diagonal line $y = x$.
   $x = \frac{1}{y}$ is the inverse.
   $y = \frac{1}{x}$ is symmetric to the line $y = x$.
4. Find an equation for $f^{-1}(x)$ where $f(x) = 5x - 7$.
   $f^{-1}(x) = \frac{x + 7}{5}$

Assignment Guide
Algebra: Day 1: 1–24
Day 2: 25–43, MR

Alg w/Finite or Trig: 1–43 m3, 44–55 e/o, 56, MR

Comprehensive: 1–55 m3, 55–60, MR

ADDITIONAL ANSWERS

Exercises

1. $x = 4y - 5$
2. $x = 3y + 5$
3. $x = 3y^2 + 2$
4. $x = 5y^2 - 4$
5. $y^2 - 3x^2 = 3$
6. $2y^2 + 5x^2 = 4$
7. $y \cdot x = 7$
8. $y \cdot x = -5$
9. $yx^2 = 1$
10. $\frac{y^2}{4} + \frac{x^2}{9} = 1$
11. $x = \frac{5}{y}$
12. $x = \sqrt{y + 1}$
13. No
14. No
15. Yes
16. Yes
17. Yes
18. Yes
19. Yes
20. Yes
21. Yes
22. Yes
23. No
24. No

25. $f^{-1}(x) = x + 1$
26. $f^{-1}(x) = x + 2$
27. $f^{-1}(x) = x - 4$
28. $f^{-1}(x) = x - 3$
29. $f^{-1}(x) = x - 8$
30. $f^{-1}(x) = x - 7$
31. $f^{-1}(x) = \frac{x - 5}{2}$
32. $f^{-1}(x) = \frac{x - 2}{3}$
33. $f^{-1}(x) = \frac{x + 1}{3}$
34. $f^{-1}(x) = \frac{x + 3}{4}$
35. $f^{-1}(x) = 2(x - 2)$
36. $f^{-1}(x) = \frac{10(x - 4)}{7}$
37. $f^{-1}(x) = x^2 + 1; x \geq 0$
38. $f^{-1}(x) = x^2 + 2; x \geq 0$
39. $f^{-1}(x) = x^2 - 2; x \geq 0$

For Exercises 44–47, see Teacher's Answer Section.

48. x, x
49. x, x
50. $2x^2 + 2; 4x^2 + 1$
51. $x^2 + 6x + 9; x^2 + 3$
52. $2x - 5; 2x - 1$
53. $12x^2 - 12x + 5; 6x^2 + 3$
54. $\frac{16}{x^2} - 1; \frac{2}{4x^2 - 1}$
55. $x^4 - 2x^2; x^4 - 2x^2$

For graphs of Exercises 57–60, see Teacher's Answer Section.

57. x-axis: no; y-axis: yes; origin: no; $y = x$: no
58. x-axis: yes; y-axis: yes; origin: yes: $y = x$: no
59. x-axis: no; y-axis: no; origin: yes; $y = x$: no
60. x-axis: no; y-axis: no; origin: yes; $y = x$: no

Mixed Review

61. 3^8
62. $64a^6$
63. 9
64. $21x^5y^8$
65. m^{15}
66. $32x^{15}y^{10}$
67. $\frac{m^6}{16n^{14}}$
68. Center: (−7, −1); radius: 7

Find equations for $f^{-1}(x)$ for the following.

25. $f(x) = x - 1$ **26.** $f(x) = x - 2$ **27.** $f(x) = x + 4$

28. $f(x) = x + 3$ **29.** $f(x) = x + 8$ **30.** $f(x) = x + 7$

31. $f(x) = 2x + 5$ **32.** $f(x) = 3x + 2$ **33.** $f(x) = 3x - 1$

34. $f(x) = 4x - 3$ **35.** $f(x) = 0.5x + 2$ **36.** $f(x) = 0.7x + 4$

37. $f(x) = \sqrt{x - 1}$ **38.** $f(x) = \sqrt{x - 2}$ **39.** $f(x) = \sqrt{x + 2}$

40. $f(x) = 35x - 173$. Find $f^{-1}(f(3))$ and $f(f^{-1}(-125))$. 3, −125

41. $g(x) = \frac{-173x + 15}{3}$. Find $g^{-1}(g(5))$ and $g(g^{-1}(-12))$. 5, −12

42. $f(x) = x^3 + 2$. Find $f^{-1}(f(12{,}053))$ and $f(f^{-1}(-17{,}243))$. 12,053, −17,243

43. $g(x) = x^3 - 486$. Find $g^{-1}(g(489))$ and $g(g^{-1}(-17{,}422))$. 489, −17,422

B

44. Graph $y = x^2 + 1$. Then, by reflection across the line $y = x$, graph its inverse.

45. Graph $y = x^2 - 3$. Then, by reflection across the line $y = x$, graph its inverse.

46. Graph $y = |x|$. Then, by reflection across the line $y = x$, graph its inverse.

47. Graph $x = |y|$. Then, by reflection across the line $y = x$, graph its inverse.

Find the composition functions $f(g(x))$ and $g(f(x))$.

48. $f(x) = 3x + 1, g(x) = \frac{x - 1}{3}$ **49.** $f(x) = x^3 - 5, g(x) = \sqrt[3]{x + 5}$

50. $f(x) = 2x, g(x) = x^2 + 1$ **51.** $f(x) = x^2, g(x) = x + 3$

52. $f(x) = 2x + 3, g(x) = x - 4$ **53.** $f(x) = 3x^2 + 2, g(x) = 2x - 1$

54. $f(x) = 4x^2 - 1, g(x) = \frac{2}{x}$ **55.** $f(x) = x^2 - 1, g(x) = x^2 - 1$

56. ***Critical Thinking*** Suppose $f(x) = \frac{1}{x + 1} + 4$.

a. What is the domain of $f(x)$? $\{x|x \neq -1\}$

b. Find $f^{-1}(x)$. What is the domain of $f^{-1}(x)$? $f^{-1}(x) = \frac{5 - x}{x - 4}$; $\{x|x \neq 4\}$

c. For what values of x does $f^{-1}(f(x)) = x$? $\{x|x \neq -1, x \neq 4\}$

Challenge

Graph each equation and its inverse. Then test for symmetry with respect to the x-axis, the y-axis, the origin, and the line $y = x$.

57. $y = \frac{1}{x^2}$ **58.** $|x| - |y| = 1$ **59.** $y = x^3$ **60.** $y = \frac{|x|}{x}$

Mixed Review

Multiply and simplify. **61.** $3^5 3^3$ **62.** $(2a)^2(2a)^4$ **63.** $(-3)^{-5}(-3)^7$

64. $(3x^4y^3)(7xy^5)$ **65.** $(m^5)^3$ **66.** $(2x^3y^2)^5$ **67.** $(4m^{-3}n^7)^{-2}$

68. Find the center and radius of the circle $x^2 + y^2 + 14x + 2y + 1 = 0$.

12-2 Exponential and Logarithmic Functions

Master Grapher Worksheet 25, *Exponential Functions*, can be used as a lesson opener. Worksheet 26, *Logarithmic Functions*, can be used for lesson closure.

We have defined exponential notation for rational exponents. We now consider irrational exponents. Let us consider 2^{π}. The number π has an unending decimal representation.

$$3.1415926535\ldots$$

Now consider this sequence of numbers.

$$3,\quad 3.1,\quad 3.14,\quad 3.141,\quad 3.1415,\quad 3.14159,\ldots$$

Each of these numbers is an approximation to π. The more decimal places, the better the approximation. Let us use these rational numbers to form a sequence as follows.

$$2^{3},\quad 2^{3.1},\quad 2^{3.14},\quad 2^{3.141},\quad 2^{3.1415},\quad 2^{3.14159},\ldots$$

Each of the numbers in this sequence is already defined, the exponent being rational. The numbers in this sequence get closer and closer to some real number. We define that number to be 2^{π}.

We can define exponential notation for any irrational exponent in a similar way. Thus any exponential expression a^x, $a > 0$, now has meaning, whether the exponent is rational or irrational.

Exponential Functions

Objective: Graph exponential functions.

Exponential functions are defined using exponential notation.

Definition

The function $f(x) = a^x$, where a is some positive real-number constant different from 1, is called the **exponential function, base a.**

Here are some exponential functions.

$$f(x) = 2^x \qquad g(x) = \left(\frac{1}{2}\right)^x \qquad h(x) = (0.178)^x$$

Note that the variable is the exponent. The following are *not* exponential functions.

$$f(x) = x^2 \qquad g(x) = x^{\frac{1}{3}} \qquad h(x) = x^{0.178}$$

Note that the variable is not the exponent.

12-2

FIRST FIVE MINUTES

1. Find the equation of the inverse relation for $xy - y^3 = 2$.
   $xy - x^3 = 2$
2. Find $f^{-1}(x)$ for $f(x) = 8x - 1$.
   Switch x and y in $y = 8x - 1$.
   $x = 8y - 1$
   $x - 1 = 8y$
   $\frac{(x-1)}{8} = y$
   So $f^{-1}(x) = \frac{(x-1)}{8}$.

Exponential Functions

Point out that in the definition of an exponential function, we exclude the case where $a = 1$. When $a = 1$, $f(x) = a^x = 1^x = 1$ for all x, which is simply a horizontal line.

Point out that the most commonly used exponential functions are $f(x) = 2^x$, $f(x) = 10^x$, and $f(x) = e^x$ (e^x will be discussed in Lesson 12-8). These functions are often found on scientific calculators.

Avoiding Common Errors

Students will sometimes refer to a function with a variable base and a constant exponent as an exponential function. Point out that an exponential function has the variable in the exponent.

Chalkboard Examples

1. Graph $y = 10^x$. Use the graph to approximate $10^{0.5}$.
   Some pairs of the function are $(-2, 0.01)$, $(-1, 0.1)$, $(0, 1)$, $(1, 10)$, $(2, 100)$.

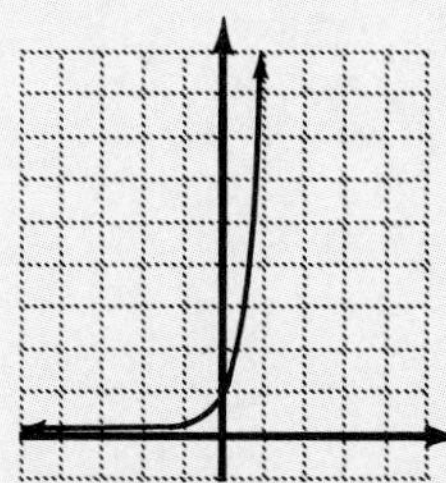

The value of $10^{0.5} \approx 3.2$. We can verify the graphical result since $10^{0.5} = \sqrt{10} \approx 3.1623$.

2. Graph $y = 7^x$.
Some pairs of the function are $(-2, 0.02)$, $(-1, 0.14)$, $(0, 1)$, $(1, 7)$, $(2, 49)$.

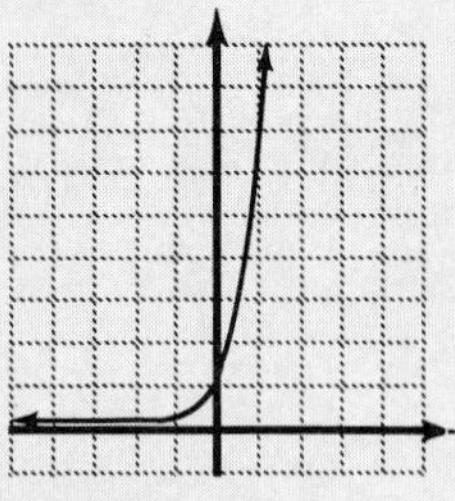

3. Graph $y = \left(\frac{1}{10}\right)^x$.
Some pairs of the function are $(-2, 100)$, $(-1, 10)$, $(0, 1)$, $(1, 0.1)$, $(2, 0.01)$.

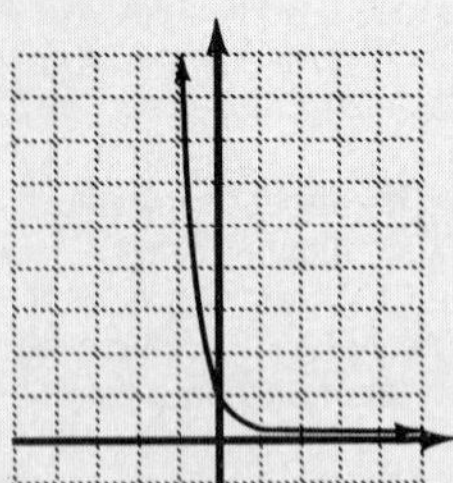

EXAMPLE 1 Graph $y = 2^x$. Use the graph to approximate $2^{\sqrt{2}}$.

We find some solutions, plot them, and then draw the graph.

x	y
0	1
1	2
2	4
3	8
-1	$\frac{1}{2}$
-2	$\frac{1}{4}$
-3	$\frac{1}{8}$

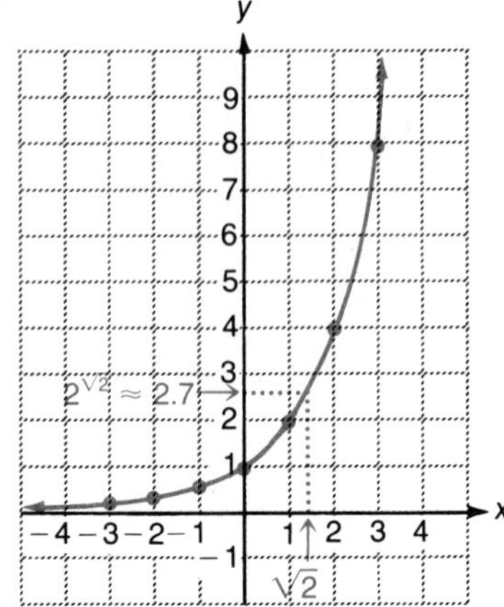

Note that as x increases, the function values increase. Check this on a calculator. As x decreases, the function values decrease toward 0.

To approximate $2^{\sqrt{2}}$ we locate $\sqrt{2}$ on the x-axis, at about 1.4. Then we find the corresponding function value. It is about 2.7. Approximations may be checked using computer graphing techniques.

Try This See Additional Answers.

a. Graph $y = 3^x$. Use the graph to approximate $3^{\frac{1}{2}}$. $3^{\frac{1}{2}} \approx 1.7$

We can make comparisons between functions using transformations.

EXAMPLE 2 Graph $y = 4^x$.

We could plot some points and connect them.

We note that $4^x = (2^2)^x = 2^{2x}$. Compare this with $y = 2^x$, graphed in Example 1. Notice that the graph of $y = 2^{2x}$ approaches the y-axis more rapidly than the graph of $y = 2^x$. The graph of $y = 2^{2x}$ is a shrinking of the graph of $y = 2^x$.

Knowing this allows us to graph $y = 2^{2x}$ at once. Each point on the graph of 2^x is moved half the distance to the y-axis.

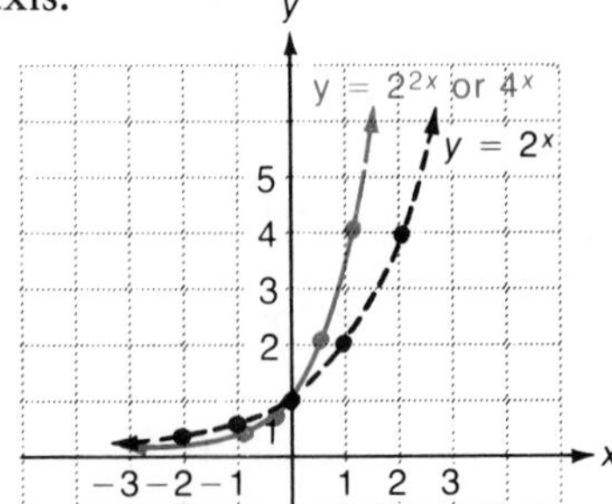

Try This See Additional Answers.

b. Graph $y = 8^x$. **c.** Graph $y = 9^x$.

EXAMPLE 3 Graph $y = \left(\frac{1}{2}\right)^x$.

We could plot some points and connect them, but again let us note that $\left(\frac{1}{2}\right)^x = \frac{1}{2^x} = 2^{-x}$. Compare this with the graph of $y = 2^x$ in Example 1. The graph of $y = 2^{-x}$ is a reflection, across the y-axis, of the graph of $y = 2^x$.

Knowing this allows us to graph $y = 2^{-x}$ at once.

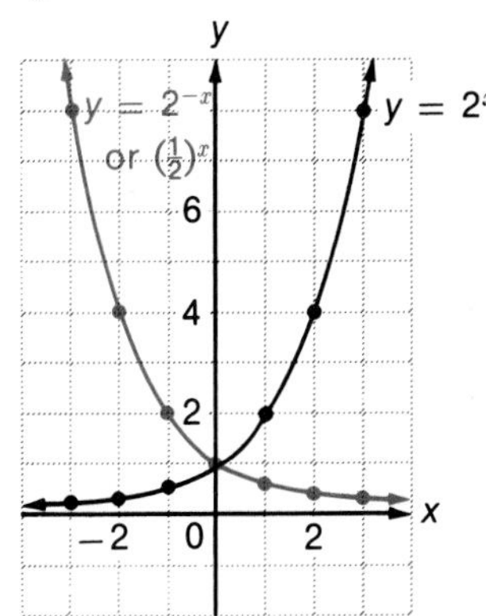

Try This See Selected Answers.

d. Graph $y = \left(\frac{1}{3}\right)^x$.

Logarithmic Functions

Objective: Graph logarithmic functions.

Definition

A **logarithmic function** is the inverse of an exponential function.

One way to describe a logarithmic function is to interchange variables in the equation $y = a^x$. Thus the following equation is logarithmic.

$$x = a^y$$

For logarithmic functions we use the notation $\log_a(x)$ or $\log_a x$, which is read "log, base a, of x."

$$y = \log_a x \text{ means } x = a^y$$

Thus a logarithm is an exponent. That is, we use the symbol $\log_a x$ to denote the second coordinates of a function $x = a^y$.

Logarithmic Functions

Point out that each logarithm is the inverse of the corresponding exponential function, base a. The inverse of a known function is easy to graph since it is the reflection across the diagonal of the original function.

Key Questions

- What is $\log_{10}(10^2)$?
  2
- What is $\log_{10}(1000)$?
  3
- What is $\log_{10}(1)$?
  0
- What is $\log_{10}(0.1)$?
  −1
- What is $\log_2(8)$?
  3
- What is $\log_2(2)$?
  1
- What is $\log_a(a)$?
  1
- What is $\log_a(1)$?
  0

Chalkboard Example (*T25*)

1. Graph $y = \log_6(x)$.
   Some pairs of $y = 6^x$ are (−2, 0.03), (−1, 0.17), (0, 1), (1, 6), (2, 36). The corresponding pairs of the inverse $y = \log_6(x)$ are (0.03, −2), (0.17, −1), (1, 0), (6, 1), (36, 2).

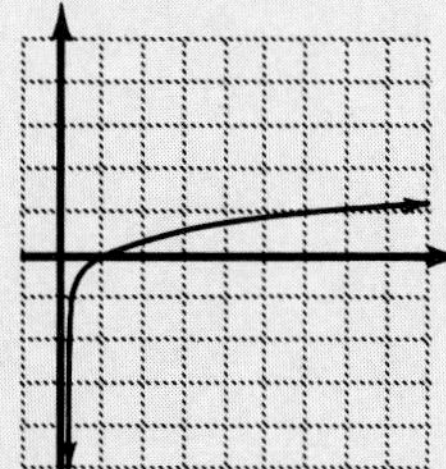

LESSON ENRICHMENT

Have students use logarithmic paper to graph logarithmic and exponential functions. They will discover that these functions graph as straight lines.

LESSON QUIZ

1. Graph $y = 2^x$ for $-3 \le x \le 3$.

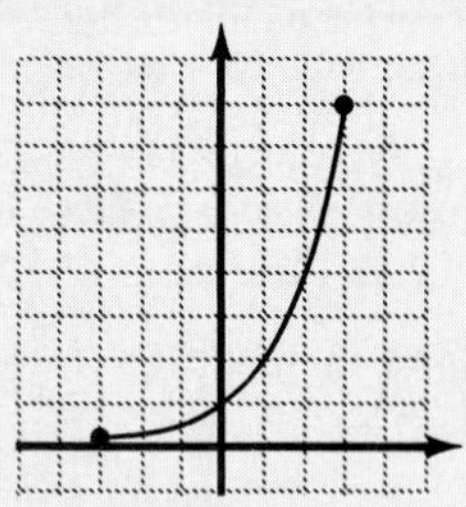

2. Graph $y = \log_2(x)$ for $0 < x \le 8$.

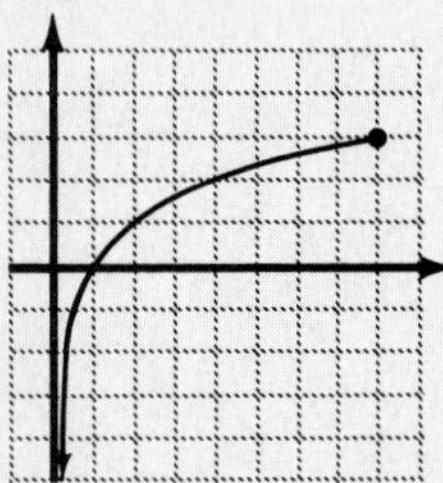

The most useful and interesting logarithmic functions are those for which $a > 1$. The graph of such a function is a reflection of $y = a^x$ across the line $y = x$. The domain of a logarithmic function is the set of all positive real numbers.

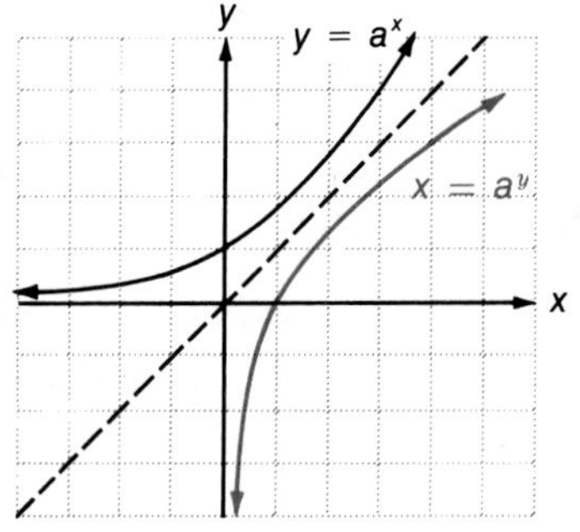

EXAMPLE 4 Graph $y = \log_3 x$.

The equation $y = \log_3 x$ is equivalent to $x = 3^y$. The graph of $x = 3^y$ is a reflection of $y = 3^x$ across the line $y = x$. We make a table of values for $y = 3^x$ and then interchange x and y.

For $y = 3^x$:

x	y
0	1
1	3
2	9
-1	$\frac{1}{3}$
-2	$\frac{1}{9}$

For $y = \log_3 x$ (or $x = 3^y$):

x	y
1	0
3	1
9	2
$\frac{1}{3}$	-1
$\frac{1}{9}$	-2

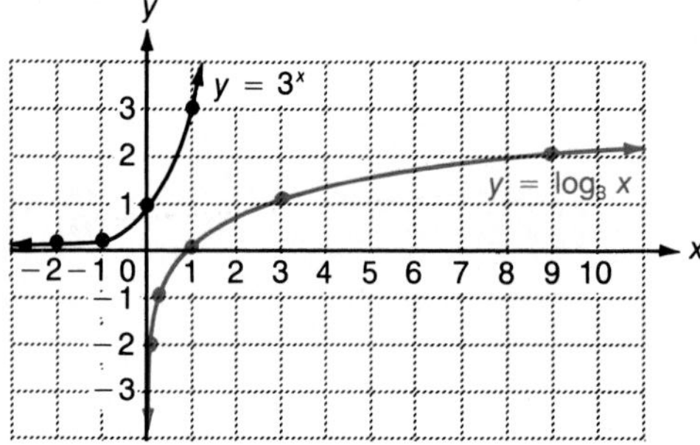

Since $a^0 = 1$ for any $a \neq 0$, the graph of $y = \log_a x$, for any a, has the x-intercept $(1, 0)$.

Try This For graphs, see Selected Answers.

e. Graph $y = \log_2 x$.
What is the domain of this function? What is the range? Domain: positive real numbers; range: all real numbers

f. Graph $y = \log_4 x$.
What is the domain of this function? What is the range? Domain: positive real numbers; range: all real numbers

12-2 EXERCISES

A

Graph. Where possible, use transformations.

1. $y = 2^x$ **2.** $y = 3^x$ **3.** $y = 5^x$ **4.** $y = 6^x$

5. $y = \left(\frac{1}{2}\right)^x$ **6.** $y = \left(\frac{1}{6}\right)^x$ **7.** $y = \left(\frac{1}{4}\right)^x$ **8.** $y = \left(\frac{1}{5}\right)^x$

9. $y = (0.4)^x$ **10.** $y = (0.3)^x$ **11.** $y = (1.5)^x$ **12.** $y = (2.5)^x$

Graph. Where possible, use transformations.

13. $y = \log_2 x$ **14.** $y = \log_5 x$ **15.** $y = \log_3 x$ **16.** $y = \log_4 x$

17. $y = \log_7 x$ **18.** $y = \log_{10} x$ **19.** $y = \log_{1.5} x$ **20.** $y = \log_{3.5} x$

B

Consider the graph of $y = 4^x$ in Example 2.

21. What is the domain of $y = 4^x$? Set of all real numbers

22. What is the range? Set of all positive numbers

23. What is the y-intercept? 1

24. Use the graph to approximate $4^{0.7}$. 2.6

Graph.

25. $y = 2^{x-1}$ **26.** $y = 2^{x+1}$ **27.** $y = 3^{x+1}$

28. $y = \log_2 (x + 1)$ **29.** $y = \log_3 (x - 2)$ **30.** $f(x) = 3^{|x|}$

31. $f(x) = 2^{|x-1|}$ **32.** $y = 2^x + 2^{-x}$ **33.** $y = \log_2 |x|$

What is the domain of each function?

34. $f(x) = 3^x$ **35.** $f(x) = \log_{10} x$ **36.** $f(x) = \log_a x^2$

37. $f(x) = \log_4 x^3$ **38.** $f(x) = \log_{10} (3x - 4)$ **39.** $f(x) = \log_5 |x|$

40. Use a calculator to estimate each of the following to six decimal places.

a. 2^3 **b.** $2^{3.1}$ **c.** $2^{3.14}$ **d.** $2^{3.141}$ **e.** $2^{3.1415}$ **f.** $2^{3.14159}$

Use a calculator to determine which of the two numbers is larger.

41. 5^π or π^5 π^5

42. $\sqrt{8^3}$ or $8^{\sqrt{3}}$ $8^{\sqrt{3}}$

43. ***Critical Thinking*** Solve $3^{2x^2+5x-3} = 1$. $\frac{1}{2}, -3$

Challenge

Graph.

44. $y = 2^{-x^2}$ **45.** $y = 3^{-(x+1)^2}$ **46.** $y = |2^{x^2} - 8|$

Mixed Review

Convert to scientific notation. **47.** 3,007,114 **48.** 0.002385

Convert to decimal notation. **49.** 5.709×10^{-5} **50.** 6.03791×10^8

51. Find an equation of a parabola with focus (6, 0) and vertex at the origin.

52. Find a polynomial of degree 3 with 6, 2, and -1 as roots.

Assignment Guide

Algebra: 1–20 e/o, MR

Alg w/Finite or Trig: 1–20 m3, 21–42 e/o, 43, MR

Comprehensive: 1–42 m3, 43–46, MR, assign w. 12-3

ADDITIONAL ANSWERS

Try This

a.

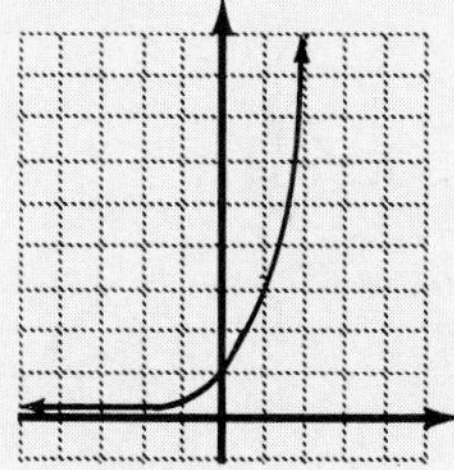

b.

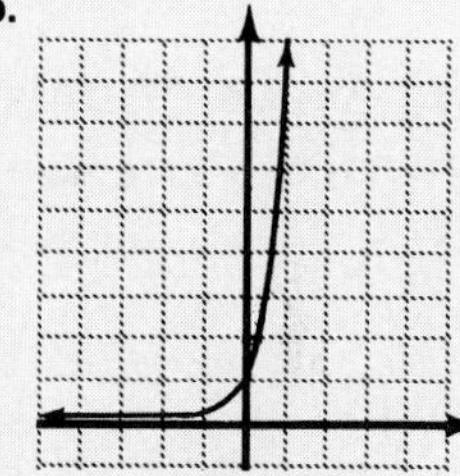

c.

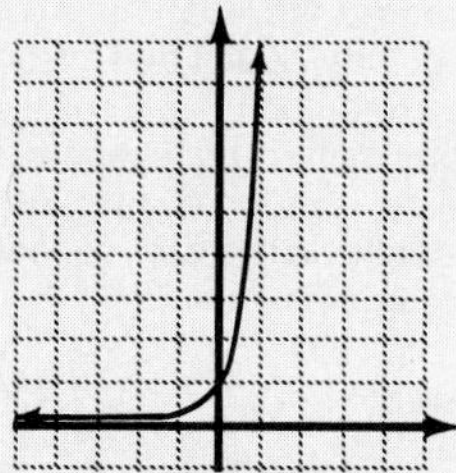

For Exercises 1–20, 25–40, and 44–46, see Teacher's Answer Section.

Mixed Review

47. 3.007114×10^6
48. 2.385×10^{-3}
49. 0.00005709
50. 603,791,000
51. $y^2 = 24x$
52. $x^3 - 7x^2 + 4x + 12$

12-3

FIRST FIVE MINUTES

1. Graph $y = 2^x$ for $-3 \le x \le 3$.

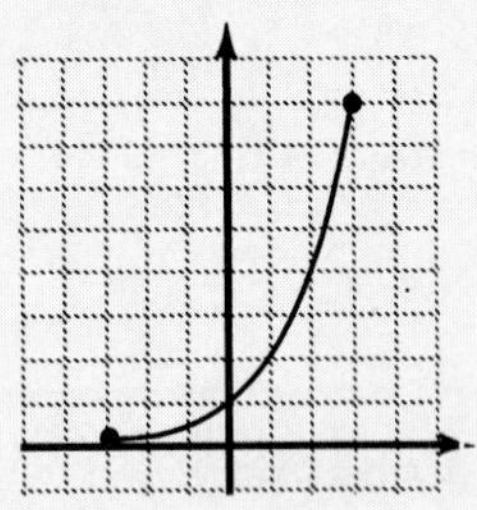

2. Graph $y = \log_2(x)$ for $0 < x < 4$.

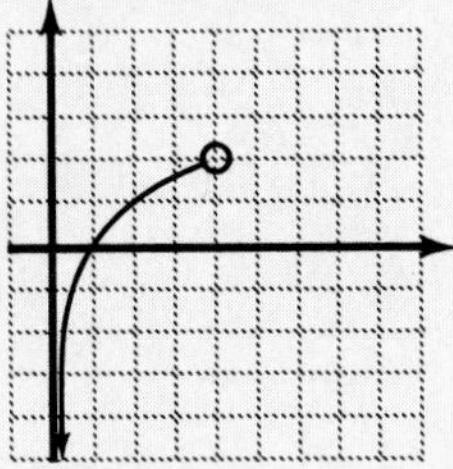

Converting Exponential and Logarithmic Equations

Remind students that the exponential function and the logarithmic function are inverses of one another. The ordered pairs of the exponential function are the same as the pairs of the logarithmic function, except that the first and second coordinates are interchanged. Similarly, the equation that defines the exponential function is the same as the equation that defines the logarithmic function, except that x and y are interchanged.

Key Questions

- If $y = 3^x$ defines an exponential function, what equation defines the corresponding inverse function? $x = 3^y$
- How do we write the equation $x = 3^y$ in logarithmic notation? $y = \log_3(x)$ or $y = \log_3 x$

12-3 Exponential and Logarithmic Relationships

Converting Exponential and Logarithmic Equations

Objective: Convert exponential equations to logarithmic equations and vice versa.

It is often helpful to be able to convert from an exponential equation to a logarithmic equation.

Recall that the following are equivalent.

$$x = a^y \text{ and } y = \log_a x$$

EXAMPLES Convert to logarithmic equations.

1. $2^x = 8 \rightarrow x = \log_2 8$ The logarithm is the exponent.
2. $y^{-1} = 4 \rightarrow -1 = \log_y 4$
3. $10^3 = 1000 \rightarrow 3 = \log_{10} 1000$

In general, for an equation $a^b = c$ where $a > 0$, $b = \log_a c$.

Try This Convert to logarithmic equations.

a. $6^0 = 1$ $\log_6 1 = 0$

b. $10^{-3} = 0.001$ $\log_{10} 0.001 = -3$

c. $16^{\frac{1}{4}} = 2$ $\log_{16} 2 = \frac{1}{4}$

d. $\left(\frac{6}{5}\right)^{-2} = \frac{25}{36}$ $\log_{\frac{6}{5}} \frac{25}{36} = -2$

It is also useful to be able to convert from a logarithmic equation to an exponential equation.

EXAMPLES Convert to exponential equations.

4. $y = \log_3 5 \rightarrow 3^y = 5$
5. $-2 = \log_a 7 \rightarrow a^{-2} = 7$
6. $a = \log_b d \rightarrow b^a = d$

Try This Convert to exponential equations.

e. $\log_2 32 = 5$ $2^5 = 32$

f. $\log_{10} 1000 = 3$ $10^3 = 1000$

g. $\log_{10} 0.01 = -2$ $10^{-2} = 0.01$

h. $\log_{\sqrt{5}} 5 = 2$ $(\sqrt{5})^2 = 5$

Note that the domain of logarithmic functions is restricted to values greater than 0. Therefore, exponential equations with a negative base, such as $(-2)^y = 16$, cannot be converted to a logarithmic equation. This allows exponential functions and logarithmic functions to be inverses of each other. For this reason, many calculators will not calculate exponents with negative bases.

Solving Logarithmic Equations

Objective: Solve logarithmic equations.

Certain equations containing logarithmic notation can be solved by first converting to exponential notation.

EXAMPLES

7. Solve $\log_2 x = -3$.
$\log_2 x = -3$ is equivalent to $2^{-3} = x$. So $x = \frac{1}{8}$.

8. Solve $\log_{27} 3 = x$.
$\log_{27} 3 = x$ is equivalent to $27^x = 3$. Since $27^{\frac{1}{3}} = 3$, we have $x = \frac{1}{3}$.

9. Solve $\log_x 4 = \frac{1}{2}$.
$\log_x 4 = \frac{1}{2}$ is equivalent to $x^{\frac{1}{2}} = 4$. Since $(x^{\frac{1}{2}})^2 = 4^2$, we have $x = 16$.

Try This Solve.

i. $\log_{10} x = 4$ 10,000 **j.** $\log_x 81 = 4$ 3 **k.** $\log_2 16 = x$ 4 **l.** $\log_5 \frac{1}{25} = x$ −2

Simplifying the Expressions $a^{\log_a x}$ and $\log_a a^x$

Objective: Simplify expressions of the form $a^{\log_a x}$ and $\log_a a^x$.

From Theorem 12-2 we know that $f^{-1}(f(x)) = x$ and $f(f^{-1}(x)) = x$ with appropriate restrictions on the domains of the functions. Since exponential and logarithmic functions are inverses of each other, Theorem 12-2 applies to them. Thus if $f(x) = a^x$, then $f^{-1}(x) = \log_a x$.

Therefore, $f(f^{-1}(x)) = f(\log_a x) = a^{\log_a x} = x$.
Likewise, $f^{-1}(f(x)) = f^{-1}(a^x) = \log_a a^x = x$

Theorem 12-3

For any positive number a, where $a \neq 1$,

$a^{\log_a x} = x$, for any positive number x and
$\log_a a^x = x$, for any number x.

EXAMPLES Simplify.

10. $2^{\log_2 5} = 5$ **11.** $10^{\log_{10} t} = t$ **12.** $\log_{10} 10^{5.6} = 5.6$

Try This Simplify.

m. $4^{\log_4 3}$ 3 **n.** $b^{\log_b 42}$ 42 **o.** $\log_5 5^{37}$ 37 **p.** $\log_{10} 10^{3.2}$ 3.2

Chalkboard Examples

Convert to logarithmic equations.
1. $3 = 2^x$ $\log_2 3 = x$
2. $a^2 = 5$ $\log_a 5 = 2$
3. $x^y = z$ $\log_x z = y$

Convert to exponential equations.
4. $y = \log_5 3$ $5^y = 3$
5. $-5 = \log_x 8$ $x^{-5} = 8$
6. $x = \log_y z$ $y^x = z$

Solving Logarithmic Equations

Chalkboard Examples

1. Solve $\log_2 x = -4$.
$2^{-4} = x$
$\frac{1}{16} = x$
2. Solve $\log_4 16 = x$.
$4^x = 16$
$x = 2$
3. Solve $\log_x 64 = 3$.
$x^3 = 64$
$x = 4$

Simplifying the Expressions $a^{\log_a x}$ and $\log_a a^x$

Chalkboard Examples

Simplify.
1. $3^{\log_3 8}$
8
2. $5^{\log_5 x}$
x
3. $\log_2 2^{3.7}$
3.7

LESSON QUIZ

Convert to logarithmic equations.
1. $2^{0.2} = 1.1487$
$\log_2 1.1487 = 0.2$
2. $32^{1/5} = 2$
$\log_{32} 2 = \frac{1}{5}$

Convert to exponential equations.
3. $x = \log_t y$
$t^x = y$
4. $\log_{10} 0.1 = -1$
$10^{-1} = 0.1$
5. Solve $\log_2 x = 4$.
$x = 16$
6. Simplify $9^{\log_9 0.5}$. 0.5

Assignment Guide
Algebra: 1–30 e/o, MR

Alg w/Finite or Trig: 1–30 m3, 31–42 e/o, 43, MR

Comprehensive: 1–42 m3, 43–46, MR, assign w. 12-2

ADDITIONAL ANSWERS

Exercises

1. $5 = \log_{10} 100{,}000$
2. $2 = \log_{10} 100$
3. $\frac{1}{3} = \log_8 2$
4. $\frac{1}{4} = \log_{16} 2$
5. $-3 = \log_5 \frac{1}{125}$
6. $-5 = \log_4 \frac{1}{1024}$
7. $0.3010 = \log_{10} 2$
8. $-b = \log_a c$
9. $3^t = 8$
10. $7^h = 10$
11. $5^2 = 25$
12. $6^1 = 6$
13. $10^{-1} = 0.1$
14. $10^{-2} = 0.01$
15. $10^{0.845} = 7$
16. $10^{0.4771} = 3$
17. $k^c = A$

Mixed Review

47. $x^5 - x^4 - 2x^3 + 2x^2 + x - 1$
48. $x^5 - 2x^4 + 22x^3 - 44x^2 - 75x + 150$
49. $f(x) = 3x^2 - 6x - 5$
50. $f(x) = x^2 - 5x + 2$

12-3 EXERCISES

A

Convert to logarithmic equations.

1. $10^5 = 100{,}000$ **2.** $10^2 = 100$ **3.** $8^{\frac{1}{3}} = 2$ **4.** $16^{\frac{1}{4}} = 2$

5. $5^{-3} = \frac{1}{125}$ **6.** $4^{-5} = \frac{1}{1024}$ **7.** $10^{0.3010} = 2$ **8.** $a^{-b} = c$

Convert to exponential equations.

9. $t = \log_3 8$ **10.** $h = \log_7 10$ **11.** $\log_5 25 = 2$

12. $\log_6 6 = 1$ **13.** $\log_{10} 0.1 = -1$ **14.** $\log_{10} 0.01 = -2$

15. $\log_{10} 7 = 0.845$ **16.** $\log_{10} 3 = 0.4771$ **17.** $\log_k A = c$

Solve.

18. $\log_3 x = 2$ 9 **19.** $\log_4 x = 3$ 64 **20.** $\log_x 16 = 2$ 4

21. $\log_x 64 = 3$ 4 **22.** $\log_2 x = -1$ $\frac{1}{2}$ **23.** $\log_3 x = -2$ $\frac{1}{9}$

24. $\log_8 x = \frac{1}{3}$ 2 **25.** $\log_{32} x = \frac{1}{5}$ 2 **26.** $\log_9 x = \frac{1}{2}$ 3

Simplify.

27. $3^{\log_3 4}$ 4 **28.** $7^{\log_7 10}$ 10 **29.** $\log_t t^9$ 9 **30.** $\log_p p^a$ a

B

Simplify.

31. $\log_2 64$ 6 **32.** $\log_4 64$ 3 **33.** $\log_{10} 10^2$ 2 **34.** $\log_3 3^4$ 4

35. $\log_{10} 0.1$ −1 **36.** $\log_{10} 10{,}000$ 4 **37.** $\log_{10} 1$ 0 **38.** $\log_{10} 10$ 1

Solve, using graphing.

39. $2^x > 1$ $\{x \mid x > 0\}$ **40.** $3^x \le 1$ $\{x \mid x \le 0\}$ **41.** $\log_2 x < 0$ $\{x \mid 0 < x < 1\}$ **42.** $\log_2 x \ge 4$ $\{x \mid x \ge 16\}$

43. ***Critical Thinking*** Find $\log_{\sqrt{2}} 16$. 8

Challenge

Solve.

44. $3^{(2^x)} = 6561$ 3 **45.** $81^{(4^x)} = 9$ $-\frac{1}{2}$ **46.** $3^{(3^x)} = 1$ No solution

Mixed Review

47. Find a polynomial of degree 5 with 1 as a root of multiplicity 3 and −1 as a root of multiplicity 2.

48. Find a polynomial of lowest degree with rational coefficients that has $\sqrt{3}$, 2, and $-5i$ as some of its roots.

Find the quadratic function that fits the data points.

49. (1, −8), (2, −5), (−1, 4) **50.** (2, −4), (−3, 26), (5, 2)

12-4 Properties of Logarithmic Functions

Objective: Apply the basic properties of logarithms.

Let us now establish some basic properties of logarithmic functions.

Theorem 12-4

For any positive numbers x and y,

$$\log_a (x \cdot y) = \log_a x + \log_a y$$

where a is any positive number different from 1.

Theorem 12-4 says that the logarithm of a product is the sum of the logarithms of the factors. Note that the base a must remain constant. The logarithm of a sum is *not* the sum of the logarithms of the addends.

Proof of Theorem 12-4

Since a is positive and different from 1, it can serve as a logarithm base. Since x and y are assumed positive, they are in the domain of $f(x) = \log_a x$. Now let $b = \log_a x$ and $c = \log_a y$. We write equivalent exponential equations.

$$x = a^b \text{ and } y = a^c$$

Next we multiply.

$$\begin{aligned} xy &= a^b a^c \\ &= a^{b+c} \end{aligned}$$

Now writing an equivalent logarithmic equation, we obtain

$$\log_a (xy) = b + c$$

Substituting for b and c, we obtain

$$\log_a (xy) = \log_a x + \log_a y$$

EXAMPLE 1 Express as a sum of logarithms. Simplify, if possible.

$$\begin{aligned} \log_2 (4 \cdot 16) &= \log_2 4 + \log_2 16 \\ &= 2 + 4 = 6 \end{aligned}$$

EXAMPLE 2 Express as a single logarithm.

$$\begin{aligned} \log_5 19 + \log_5 3 &= \log_5 (19 \cdot 3) \\ &= \log_5 57 \end{aligned}$$

12-4

FIRST FIVE MINUTES

1. Convert to logarithmic notation.
   $3^5 = 243$
   $\log_3 243 = 5$
2. Convert to exponential notation.
   $\log_3 a = b$
   $3^b = a$
3. Solve for x where
   $\log_2 x = 3.$
   $2^3 = x$
   $x = 8$
4. Solve for x where
   $\log_x 2 = 1.$
   $x^1 = 2$
   $x = 2$

Emphasize the parallel between the properties of logarithmic functions and exponential functions. For example, Theorem 12-4, $\log_a xy = \log_a x + \log_a y$, is equivalent to $a^x a^y = a^{x+y}$. Likewise, Theorem 12-6, $\log_a \frac{x}{y} = \log_a x - \log_a y$, is equivalent to $\frac{a^x}{a^y} = a^{x-y}$.

This analogy can also be seen in Example 1.
$\log_2 64 = \log_2 4 + \log_2 16$
$= \log_2 2^6 = \log_2 2^2 + \log_2 2^4$, which is equivalent to $2^6 = 2^2 \cdot 2^4$

Avoiding Common Errors

Students may try to "extend" the properties of logarithmic functions
$\log (x + y) \neq \log x + \log y$
$\log (x - y) \neq \frac{\log x}{\log y}$
$\log (x + y) \neq \log x \cdot \log y$
Point out the correct form of the properties and compare them to the above. They could also try substituting numbers for the variables and checking the results.
$\log (1 + 10) \neq \log 1 + \log 10 \neq \log 1 \cdot \log 10$
$\log 11 \neq 0 + 1 \neq 0 \cdot 1$

Key Questions

- If $\log_{10} 100 = 2$ and $\log_{10} 1000 = 3$, what is $\log_{10}(100 \cdot 1000)$?
  $2 + 3 = 5$
- If $\log_2 a = 5$ and $\log_2 b = 7$, what is $\log_2 \frac{a}{b}$?
  $5 - 7 = -2$
- If $\log_2 a = 5$, what is $\log_2 a^3$?
  $3 \cdot 5 = 15$

Chalkboard Examples

1. Express as a sum of logarithms.
$\log_{10}(3 \cdot 7)$
$\log_{10} 3 + \log_{10} 7$
2. Express as a single logarithm.
$\log_2 5 + \log_2 9$
$\log_2 45$

Express as a product.

3. $\log_a 3^{10}$
$10 \log_a 3$
4. $\log_{10} 2^{20}$
$20 \log_{10} 2$
5. Express in terms of $\log_2 a$ and $\log_2 b$.
$\log_2 \sqrt[3]{\frac{5a^2}{b^4}}$
$\log_2 \left(\frac{5a^2}{b^4}\right)^{1/3}$
$= \frac{1}{3}\left(\log_2 \frac{5a^2}{b^4}\right)$
$= \frac{1}{3}(\log_2 5 + \log_2 a^2 - \log_2 b^4)$
$= \frac{1}{3}(\log_2 5 + 2\log_2 a - 4\log_2 b)$
6. Express as a single logarithm.
$\frac{1}{2}\log_a 9 + 2\log_a 5 - \frac{1}{3}\log_a 125$
$= \log_a 9^{1/2} + \log_a 25 - \log_a 125^{1/3}$
$= \log_a \frac{3 \cdot 25}{5}$
$= \log_a 15$
7. Given that $\log_{10} 5 \approx 0.699$ and $\log_{10} 8 \approx 0.903$, find the following.
   a. $\log_{10} 40 = \log_{10}(5 \cdot 8)$
   $= \log_{10} 5 + \log_{10} 8 \approx 0.699 + 0.903 \approx 1.602$
   b. $\log_{10} 5^6$
   $6 \log_{10} 5 \approx 6 \cdot 0.699 \approx 4.194$
   c. $\log_{10} \sqrt{8}$
   $\log_{10} 8^{1/2}$
   $= \frac{1}{2}\log_{10} 8$
   $\approx \frac{1}{2} \cdot 0.903 \approx 0.451$
   d. $\log_{10} \frac{8}{5}$
   $\log_{10} 8 - \log_{10} 5$
   $\approx 0.903 - 0.699 \approx 0.204$
   e. $\log_{10} 11$
   There is no way to get the result using the given information.
   f. $\frac{\log_{10} 5}{\log_{10} 8}$
   $\approx \frac{0.699}{0.903} \approx 0.774$

Try This

a. Express as a sum of logarithms. Simplify, if possible.
(1) $\log_a MN$ $\log_a M + \log_a N$ **(2)** $\log_5 (25 \cdot 5)$ $\log_5 25 + \log_5 5 = 3$

b. Express as a single logarithm.
(1) $\log_3 7 + \log_3 5$ $\log_3 35$ **(2)** $\log_a C + \log_a A + \log_a B + \log_a I + \log_a N$ $\log_a CABIN$

Theorem 12-5

For any positive number x, any number p, and any logarithm base a,

$$\log_a x^p = p \cdot \log_a x$$

Theorem 12-5 says that the logarithm of a power of a number is the exponent times the logarithm of the number.

Proof of Theorem 12-5

Let $b = \log_a x$. Then, writing an equivalent exponential equation, we have $x = a^b$. Next we raise both sides of the latter equation to the pth power.

$$x^p = (a^b)^p = a^{bp}, \text{ or } a^{pb}$$

Now we can write an equivalent logarithmic equation.

$$\log_a x^p = \log_a a^{pb}$$
$$= pb \quad \text{Using Theorem 12-3}$$

But $b = \log_a x$, so we have $\log_a x^p = p \cdot \log_a x$.

EXAMPLES Express as a product.

3. $\log_b 9^{-5} = -5 \cdot \log_b 9$

4. $\log_a \sqrt[4]{5} = \log_a 5^{\frac{1}{4}} = \frac{1}{4} \log_a 5$

Try This Express as a product.

c. $\log_7 4^5$ $5\log_7 4$ **d.** $\log_a \sqrt{5}$ $\frac{1}{2}\log_a 5$

Theorem 12-6

For any positive numbers x, y, and any logarithm base a,

$$\log_a \frac{x}{y} = \log_a x - \log_a y$$

Theorem 12-6 says that the logarithm of a quotient is the logarithm of the dividend minus the logarithm of the divisor.

Proof of Theorem 12-6

Since a is positive and different from 1, it can serve as a logarithm base. Since x and y are assumed positive, they are in the domain of $f(x) = \log_a x$. Now let $b = \log_a x$ and $c = \log_a y$. We write equivalent exponential equations.

$$x = a^b \text{ and } y = a^c$$

Next we divide.

$$\frac{x}{y} = \frac{a^b}{a^c}$$
$$= a^{b-c}$$

Now writing an equivalent logarithmic equation, we obtain

$$\log_a\left(\frac{x}{y}\right) = b - c, \text{ or}$$

Substituting for b and c, we obtain

$$\log_a \frac{x}{y} = \log_a x - \log_a y$$

EXAMPLE 5 Express in terms of logarithms of x, y, and z.

$$\log_a \sqrt[4]{\frac{xy}{z^3}} = \log_a\left(\frac{xy}{z^3}\right)^{\frac{1}{4}}$$

$$= \frac{1}{4}\cdot \log_a \frac{xy}{z^3}$$ Using Theorem 12-5

$$= \frac{1}{4}[\log_a xy - \log_a z^3]$$ Using Theorem 12-6

$$= \frac{1}{4}[\log_a x + \log_a y - 3\log_a z]$$ Using Theorems 12-4 and 12-6

$$= \frac{1}{4}\log_a x + \frac{1}{4}\log_a y - \frac{3}{4}\log_a z$$ Using the distributive property

Try This

e. Express as a difference.

(1) $\log_a \frac{M}{N}$ $\log_a M - \log_a N$

(2) $\log_c \frac{1}{4}$ $\log_c 1 - \log_c 4$

f. Express as sums and differences of logarithms and without exponential notation or radicals.

$\log_{10} \frac{4\pi}{\sqrt{23}}$ $\log_{10} 4 + \log_{10} \pi - \frac{1}{2}\log_{10} 23$

g. Express in terms of logarithms of x, y, and z.

$\log_a \sqrt{\frac{z^3}{xy}}$ $\frac{3}{2}\log_a z - \frac{1}{2}\log_a x - \frac{1}{2}\log_a y$

LESSON QUIZ

1. Express as a sum of logarithms.
   $\log_{10}(11 \cdot 13)$
   $\log_{10} 11 + \log_{10} 13$
2. Express as a single logarithm.
   $\log_a 7 + \log_a 11$
   $\log_a(7 \cdot 11)$
3. Express as a product.
   $\log_a(5^7)$
   $7\log_a(5)$
4. Express as a difference of logarithms.
   $\log_a \frac{13}{17}$
   $\log_a 13 - \log_a 17$
5. Express as a single logarithm and simplify.
   $\frac{2}{3}\log_{10}(8) + 2\log_{10}(5)$
   $\log_{10} 100 = 2$

Assignment Guide
Algebra: Day 1: 1–18, MR
Day 2: 19–36

Alg w/Finite or Trig: 1–48 m3, 49, MR

Comprehensive: 1–48 m3, 49, 50–54 e/o, MR

ADDITIONAL ANSWERS

Exercises

1. $\log_2 32 + \log_2 8 = 5 + 3 = 8$
2. $\log_3 27 + \log_3 81 = 3 + 4 = 7$
3. $\log_4 64 + \log_4 16 = 3 + 2 = 5$
4. $\log_5 25 + \log_5 125 = 2 + 3 = 5$
5. $\log_c B + \log_c x$
6. $\log_t 5 + \log_t Y$
7. $\log_a (6 \cdot 70)$
8. $\log_b (65 \cdot 2)$
9. $\log_c (K \cdot y)$
10. $3 \log_a x$
11. $5 \log_b t$
12. $6 \log_c y$
13. $\log_a 67 - \log_a 5$
14. $\log_t T - \log_t 7$
15. $\log_b 3 - \log_b 4$

EXAMPLE 6 Express as a single logarithm.

$$\frac{1}{2}\log_a x - 7\log_a y + \log_a z = \log_a \sqrt{x} - \log_a y^7 + \log_a z$$
$$= \log_a \frac{\sqrt{x}}{y^7} + \log_a z = \log_a \frac{z\sqrt{x}}{y^7}$$

Try This

h. Express $5\log_a x - \log_a y + \frac{1}{4}\log_a z$ as a single logarithm. $\log_a \frac{x^5\sqrt[4]{z}}{y}$

EXAMPLE 7 Given that $\log_a 2 \approx 0.301$ and $\log_a 3 \approx 0.477$, find the following.

(a) $\log_a 6 = \log_a 2 \cdot 3 = \log_a 2 + \log_a 3 \approx 0.301 + 0.477 \approx 0.778$

(b) $\log_a \sqrt{3} = \log_a 3^{\frac{1}{2}} = \frac{1}{2} \cdot \log_a 3 \approx \frac{1}{2} \cdot 0.477 \approx 0.2385$

(c) $\log_a \frac{2}{3} = \log_a 2 - \log_a 3 \approx 0.301 - 0.477 \approx -0.176$

(d) $\log_a 5$ Using Theorems 12-4, 12-5 and 12-6, there is no way to find $\log_a 5$: $\log_a 5 \neq \log_a 2 + \log_a 3$.

(e) $\frac{\log_a 2}{\log_a 3} \approx \frac{0.301}{0.477} \approx 0.63$ Note that we could not use Theorems 12-4, 12-5, 12-6; we simply divided.

Try This

i. Given that $\log_a 2 \approx 0.301$ and $\log_a 3 \approx 0.477$, find the following.

(1) $\log_a 9$ 0.954 **(2)** $\log_a \sqrt{2}$ 0.1505 **(3)** $\log_a \sqrt[3]{2}$ 0.1003 **(4)** $\log_a \frac{3}{2}$ 0.176 **(5)** $\frac{\log_a 3}{\log_a 2}$ 1.585

12-4 EXERCISES

A

Express as a sum of logarithms. Simplify, if possible.

1. $\log_2 (32 \cdot 8)$ **2.** $\log_3 (27 \cdot 81)$ **3.** $\log_4 (64 \cdot 16)$

4. $\log_5 (25 \cdot 125)$ **5.** $\log_c Bx$ **6.** $\log_t 5Y$

Express as a single logarithm.

7. $\log_a 6 + \log_a 70$ **8.** $\log_b 65 + \log_b 2$ **9.** $\log_c K + \log_c y$

Express as a product.

10. $\log_a x^3$ **11.** $\log_b t^5$ **12.** $\log_c y^6$

Express as a difference of logarithms.

13. $\log_a \frac{67}{5}$ **14.** $\log_t \frac{T}{7}$ **15.** $\log_b \frac{3}{4}$

Express in terms of logarithms of x, y, and z.

16. $\log_a x^2y^3z$ 17. $\log_a 5xy^4z^3$ 18. $\log_b \frac{xy^2}{z^3}$

Express as a single logarithm. Simplify, if possible.

19. $\frac{2}{3}\log_a x - \frac{1}{2}\log_a y$ 20. $\frac{1}{2}\log_a x + 3\log_a y - 2\log_a x$

21. $\log_a 2x + 3(\log_a x - \log_a y)$ 22. $\log_a x^2 - 2\log_a \sqrt{x}$

23. $\log_a \frac{a}{\sqrt{x}} - \log_a \sqrt{ax}$ 24. $\log_a (x^2 - 4) - \log_a (x - 2)$

Given $\log_{10} 2 \approx 0.301$, $\log_{10} 3 \approx 0.477$, and $\log_{10} 10 = 1$, find the following.

25. $\log_{10} 4$ 26. $\log_{10} 5$ 27. $\log_{10} 50$ 28. $\log_{10} 12$

29. $\log_{10} 60$ 30. $\log_{10} \frac{1}{3}$ 31. $\log_{10} \sqrt{\frac{2}{3}}$ 32. $\log_{10} \sqrt[5]{12}$

33. $\log_{10} 90$ 34. $\log_{10} \frac{9}{8}$ 35. $\log_{10} \frac{1}{4}$ 36. $\log_{10} \frac{9}{10}$

B

Which of the following are false?

37. $\frac{\log_a M}{\log_a N} = \log_a M - \log_a N$ False 38. $\frac{\log_a M}{\log_a N} = \log_a \frac{M}{N}$ False

39. $\log_a 2x = 2\log_a x$ False 40. $\log_a 2x = \log_a 2 + \log_a x$ True

41. $\log_a (M + N) = \log_a M + \log_a N$ False 42. $\log_a x^3 = 3\log_a x$ True

Solve.

43. $\log_\pi \pi^{2x+3} = 4$ $\frac{1}{2}$ 44. $3^{\log_3 (8x-4)} = 5$ $\frac{9}{8}$ 45. $4^{2\log_4 x} = 7$ $\sqrt{7}$

46. $8^{2\log_8 x + \log_8 x} = 27$ 3 47. $(x + 3)\cdot\log_a a^x = x$ $-2, 0$ 48. $\log_a 5x = \log_a 5 + \log_a x$ $\{x \mid x > 0\}$

49. ***Critical Thinking*** If $\log x^2y^3 = a$ and $\log\left(\frac{x}{y}\right) = b$, what are the values of $\log x$ and $\log y$?

Challenge

50. If $\log_a x = 2$, what is $\log_a \left(\frac{1}{x}\right)$? -2 51. If $\log_a x = 2$, what is $\log_{\frac{1}{a}} x$? -2

Prove the following for any base a and any positive number x.

52. $\log_a \left(\frac{1}{x}\right) = -\log_a x$ 53. $\log_a \left(\frac{1}{x}\right) = \log_{\frac{1}{a}} x$

54. Show that $\log_a \left(\frac{x + \sqrt{x^2 - 5}}{5}\right) = -\log_a (x - \sqrt{x^2 - 5})$.

Mixed Review

Given that the polynomial has the given root, find all the roots of the polynomial.

55. $x^3 - 2x^2 + x - 2;\ i$ 56. $x^4 - 3x^2 - 28;\ -2i$

Find the rational roots, if they exist, of each polynomial. Then find the other roots.

57. $x^4 - 6x^3 + 30x - 25$ 58. $x^3 - 6x^2 + 3x + 10$

16. $2\log_a x + 3\log_a y + \log_a z$
17. $\log_a 5 + \log_a x + 4\log_a y + 3\log_a z$
18. $\log_b x + 2\log_b y - 3\log_b z$
19. $\log_a \frac{\sqrt[3]{x^2}\sqrt{y}}{y}$
20. $\log_a \frac{\sqrt{x}y^3}{x^2}$
21. $\log_a \frac{2x^4}{y^3}$
22. $\log_a x$
23. $\log_a \frac{\sqrt{a}}{x}$
24. $\log_a (x + 2)$
25. 0.602
26. 0.699
27. 1.699
28. 1.079
29. 1.778
30. −0.477
31. −0.088
32. 0.2158
33. 1.954
34. 0.051
35. −0.602
36. −0.046

49. $\log x = \frac{a + 3b}{5}$, $\log y = \frac{a - 2b}{5}$

52. $\log_a\left(\frac{1}{x}\right) = \log_a 1 - \log_a x = 0 - \log_a x = -\log_a x$

53. Let $\log_a\left(\frac{1}{x}\right) = M$. Then $a^M = \frac{1}{x}$, so $a^{-M} = x$ or $\left(\frac{1}{a}\right)^M = x$. Thus $\log_{1/a} x = \log_a\left(\frac{1}{x}\right)$.

54. $\log_a\left(\frac{x + \sqrt{x^2 - 5}}{5} \cdot \frac{x - \sqrt{x^2 - 5}}{x - \sqrt{x^2 - 5}}\right)$
$= \log_a\left(\frac{x^2 - (x^2 - 5)}{5(x - \sqrt{x^2 - 5})}\right)$
$= \log_a\left(\frac{1}{x - \sqrt{x^2 - 5}}\right)$
$= -\log_a (x - \sqrt{x^2 - 5})$

Mixed Review

55. $i, -i, 2$
56. $\sqrt{7}, -\sqrt{7}, 2i, -2i$
57. $5, 1; \sqrt{5}, -\sqrt{5}$
58. $5, 2, -1$

12-5

FIRST FIVE MINUTES

1. Simplify $\frac{1}{4}\log_{10}16$.

   $\log_{10} 16^{1/4} = \log_{10} 2$

2. Simplify $3\log_2 2 - \frac{1}{2}\log_2 64$.

   $\log_2 2^3 - \log_2 64^{1/2}$
   $= \log_2 8 - \log_2 8 = 0$

Finding Common Logarithms: Calculators

If you want students using calculators to show the mantissa and characteristic when finding logarithms of decimals, show them how to convert negative answers by adding 10 and subtracting 10.

$\log 0.003 = (-2.5228787 + 10) - 10$
$= 7.4771213 - 10$
or $7.4771 - 10$ rounded to 4 decimal places

Key Questions

- What is log(10)? 1
- What is log(0.1)? −1
- What is log(10,000)? 4

Chalkboard Examples

1. Find log 13. ≈1.11394335
2. Find log 0.01234. ≈ −1.9086848

Finding Common Logarithms: Tables

The computation method used in Examples 4, 5, 6, and 7 is useful only when the base is 10.

When working with tables, and without a calculator, it is most efficient to keep the characteristic and mantissa separate.

You may want to review scientific notation.

Note that most logarithms are irrational numbers. Tables and calculators only give approximations of these.

12-5 Logarithmic Function Values

Base 10 logarithms are called common logarithms. They are useful because they are of the same base as the decimal numeration system. Before calculators became so widely available, common logarithms were used extensively for calculations.

The abbreviation log is used for the logarithmic function base 10. Thus a symbol log 23 means $\log_{10} 23$.

Finding Common Logarithms: Calculators

Objective: Find common logarithms using a calculator.

On scientific calculators the key for the common logarithm is marked [log]. To find the common logarithm of a number, we enter that number and then press the [log] key.

EXAMPLE 1 Find log 475,000.

We enter 475,000 and press [log]. We find $\log 475{,}000 \approx 5.67669361$.

EXAMPLE 2 Find log 0.00372.

We enter 0.00372 and press [log]. We find that $\log 0.00372 \approx -2.42945706$.

Try This Use a calculator to find these logarithms.

a. log 210.78 2.3238 **b.** log 658,629 5.8186 **c.** log 2.90043 0.4625 **d.** log 0.000043 −4.3665

Finding Common Logarithms: Tables

Objective: Find common logarithms using a table.

If a scientific calculator is not available, logarithms can be found using a table. Table 2, in the appendix p. 872, is a table of common logarithms for numbers from 1 to 10. The values in the table are the same as those stored in the calculator except that the values in the table have been rounded to four decimal places. Part of that table is shown below.

x	0	1	2	3	4	5	6	7	8	9
5.0	0.6990	0.6998	0.7007	0.7016	0.7024	0.7033	0.7042	0.7050	0.7059	0.7067
5.1	0.7076	0.7084	0.7093	0.7101	0.7110	0.7118	0.7126	0.7135	0.7143	0.7152
5.2	0.7160	0.7168	0.7177	0.7185	0.7193	0.7202	0.7210	0.7218	0.7226	0.7235
5.3	0.7243	0.7251	0.7259	0.7267	0.7275	0.7284	0.7292	0.7300	0.7308	0.7316
5.4	0.7324	0.7332	0.7340	0.7348	0.7356	0.7364	0.7372	0.7380	0.7388	0.7396

EXAMPLE 3 Find log 5.24.

At the left of the table we find the row headed 5.2. Then we move across the table to the column headed 4. At the intersection of this row and column we find log 5.24.

$$\log 5.24 \approx 0.7193$$

Try This Use Table 2 to find these logarithms.

e. log 7.09 0.8506 **f.** log 4.00 0.6021 **g.** log 9.99 0.9996

Using Table 2 and scientific notation we can approximate logarithms of numbers that are not between 1 and 10. First recall the following.

$$\log_a a^k = k \text{ for any number } k \quad \text{Theorem 12-3}$$

Thus $\log_{10} 10^k = k$ for any number k.

EXAMPLES Use scientific notation and Table 2 to find each logarithm.

4. $\log 52.4 = \log (5.24 \times 10^1)$ Converting to scientific notation
$= \log 5.24 + \log 10^1$ Using Theorem 12-4
$\approx 0.7193 + 1$

5. $\log 0.524 = \log (5.24 \times 10^{-1})$
$= \log 5.24 + \log 10^{-1}$
$\approx 0.7193 + (-1)$

6. $\log 52{,}400 = \log (5.24 \times 10^4)$
$= \log 5.24 + \log 10^4$
$\approx 0.7193 + 4$

7. $\log 0.00524 = \log (5.24 \times 10^{-3})$
$= \log 5.24 + \log 10^{-3}$
$\approx 0.7193 + (-3)$

Try This Use scientific notation and Table 2 to find each logarithm.

h log 289 0.4609 + 2 **i.** log 0.000289 0.4609 + (−4)

In Examples 4 – 7, the integer part of the logarithm is the exponent in the scientific notation. This integer is called the **characteristic** of the logarithm. The other part of the logarithm, a number between 0 and 1, is called the **mantissa** of the logarithm. Table 2 contains only mantissas.

EXAMPLE 8 Find log 0.0538, indicating the characteristic and mantissa.

We first write scientific notation for the number.

$$5.38 \times 10^{-2}$$

Then we find log 5.38. This is the mantissa.

$$\log 5.38 \approx 0.7308$$

Key Questions

- What is 54,321 in scientific notation? $5.4321 \cdot 10^4$
- What is 0.0054321 in scientific notation? $5.4321 \cdot 10^{-3}$

Chalkboard Examples

Use Table 2 to find these logarithms.

1. log 5.01
   ≈ 0.6998
2. log 564
   $\log(5.64 \cdot 10^2)$
   $\approx 0.7513 + 2$
3. log 0.0599
   $\log(5.99 \cdot 10^{-2})$
   $\approx 0.7774 + (-2)$
4. log 50,000
   $\log(5.00 \cdot 10^4)$
   $\approx 0.6990 + 4$
5. log 0.000500
   $\log(5.00 \cdot 10^{-4})$
   $\approx 0.6990 + (-4)$
6. log 0.523
   $\log(5.23 \cdot 10^{-1})$
   $\approx 0.7185 + (-1)$
   $\approx 0.7185 + (9 - 10)$
   $\approx 9.7185 + (-10)$
7. log 0.000987
   $\log(9.87 \cdot 10^{-4})$
   $\approx 0.9943 + (-4)$
   $\approx 0.9943 + (6 - 10)$
   $\approx 6.9943 + (-10)$

Finding Antilogarithms

Chalkboard Examples

Use a calculator to find these antilogs.

1. antilog 0.8451
   ≈ 7.00003159
2. antilog 3.321
   ≈ 2094.11245

Use Table 2 to find these antilogs.

3. antilog 3.7505
   antilog $3.7505 = 10^{3.7505}$
   $= 10^3 \cdot 10^{0.7505}$
   $\approx 10^3 \cdot 5.630$
   ≈ 5630
4. antilog$(5.1431 - 10)$
   antilog$(0.1431 - 5)$
   $= 10^{0.1431} \cdot 10^{-5}$
   $\approx 1.39 \cdot 10^{-5}$
   ≈ 0.0000139
5. antilog -3.2104
   antilog$(-3.2104 + 10 - 10)$
   $=$ antilog$(6.7896 - 10)$
   $=$ antilog$(0.7896 - 4)$
   $= 10^{0.7896} \cdot 10^{-4}$
   $\approx 6.16 \cdot 10^{-4}$
   ≈ 0.000616

The characteristic of the logarithm is the exponent -2. Now log 0.0538 $\approx 0.7308 + (-2)$, or -1.2692. When negative characteristics occur, it is often best to name the logarithm so that the characteristic and mantissa are preserved.

$$\log 0.0538 \approx 0.7308 + (-2) = -1.2692$$

The latter notation displays neither the characteristic nor the mantissa. We can rename the characteristic, -2, as $8 - 10$, and then add the mantissa to preserve both the mantissa and characteristic.

$$8.7308 - 10$$

The characteristic and mantissa are useful when working with logarithm tables, but are not needed on a calculator. For example, on a calculator with a ten-digit readout, we find the following.

$$\log 0.0538 = -1.269217724$$

This shows neither the characteristic nor the mantissa. Check this on your calculator. How can you find the characteristic and mantissa?

EXAMPLE 9 Find log 0.00687.

We write scientific notation.

$$0.00687 = 6.87 \times 10^{-3}$$

The characteristic is

$$-3, \text{ or } 7 - 10$$

The mantissa, from the table, is

$$0.8370$$

Thus log $0.00687 = 7.8370 - 10$.

Try This Use Table 2 to find these logarithms.

j. 0.0462 8.6646 − 10 **k.** 0.607 9.7832 − 10 **l.** 0.000639 6.8055 − 10

Finding Antilogarithms

Objective: Find antilogarithms using a calculator or a table.

When we find the common logarithm of a number M, we find an exponent x such that $10^x = M$. When we find the antilogarithm, we reverse this process. We start with the exponent x (logarithm) and find the number M such that $M = 10^x$.

On a calculator, there is generally no key marked "antilog." Many scientific calculators have an "inverse" key [inv], and pressing [inv] followed by [log] will give the antilog. Or, a key marked [10^x] will find the antilog. If these keys are not on your calculator, use the [y^x] key to raise 10 to a power.

EXAMPLES Use a calculator to find these antilogarithms.

10. Find antilog 3.2546.
We enter 3.2546, then press [inv] and [log],
or we enter 10, press [y^x], and enter 3.2546.
We find antilog 3.2546 ≈ 1797.2149.

11. Find antilog −2.36589.
We enter −2.36589, then press [inv] and [log],
or we enter 10, press [y^x], and enter −2.36589.
We find antilog −2.36589 ≈ 0.0043064.

Try This Use a calculator to find these antilogarithms.

m. antilog 4.3425 22,003.92
n. antilog 3.0098 1022.8219
o. antilog −3.0067 0.00098469
p. antilog −6.7628 0.00000017

To find antilogs using Table 2, we reverse the process for finding logarithms.

EXAMPLE 12 Find antilog 2.7251.

$$\text{antilog } 2.7251 = 10^{2.7251} = 10^{2+0.7251} = 10^2 \cdot 10^{0.7251}$$

From the table we find $10^{0.7251}$. We find 0.7251 inside the table and see that the antilog is approximately 5.31. Thus, antilog 2.7251 ≈ $10^2 \times 5.31$ or 531.

Note that in this example, we separated 2.7251 into an integer (2) and a number between 0 and 1.0 (0.7251). We use the latter number with Table 2, after which we have scientific notation for our answer.

EXAMPLE 13 Find antilog (7.7143 − 10).

The characteristic is −3 and the mantissa is 0.7143.
From the table we find that antilog 0.7143 ≈ 5.18.

$$\begin{aligned}\text{antilog } (7.7143 - 10) &\approx 5.18 \times 10^{-3}\\ &\approx 0.00518\end{aligned}$$

EXAMPLE 14 Find antilog −2.2857.

We are to find the antilog of a number, but the number is given so that the mantissa is not apparent. To find the mantissa we add 10 − 10.

$$\begin{aligned}-2.2857 &= -2.2857 + (10 - 10)\\ &= (-2.2857 + 10) - 10 = 7.7143 - 10\end{aligned}$$

Then we proceed as in Example 13. The answer is approximately 0.00518.

Try This Use Table 2 to find these antilogs.

q. antilog 4.8069 64106.2
r. antilog (6.6284 − 10) 4.25×10^{-4}
s. antilog −1.9788 0.0105

LESSON QUIZ

Use a calculator or Table 2 to find the following.

1. log 3.67
≈ 0.5647
2. log 588,000
≈ 5.7694
3. antilog 0.9754
≈ 9.45
4. antilog 3.6321
≈ 4286.47

Assignment Guide
Algebra: 1–39 e/o, MR

Alg w/Finite or Trig: 1–39 m3, 40–45 e/o, 46, MR

Comprehensive: 1–45 m3, 46–50, MR

ADDITIONAL ANSWERS

Exercises

17. 5.7952
18. 7.1271 − 10, or −2.8729
19. 8.8463 − 10, or −1.1537
20. 9.8062 − 10, or −0.1938
21. 6.3345 − 10, or −3.6655
22. 9.2380 − 10, or −0.7620
23. 7.5403 − 10, or −2.4597
24. 5.6064 − 10, or −4.3936

40. 6.34
41. 15,500
42. 0.613
43. 0.0951
44. 2.5378
45. 3.7536

47. $10^{1/3 \log 8} = 2$
48. $10^{3 \log 2} = 8$
49. $10^{\log 14 - \log 2} = 7$
50. $10^{\log 4 + \log 2} = 8$

Mixed Review

51. Parabola
52. $P(x) = (x^2 + 5x + 6)(x - 1) + 0$

12-5 EXERCISES

A

Use a calculator or Table 2 to find these logarithms.

1. log 2.46 0.3909 **2.** log 7.65 0.8837 **3.** log 5.31 0.7251 **4.** log 8.57 0.9330
5. log 3.72 0.5705 **6.** log 9.04 0.9562 **7.** log 1.07 0.0294 **8.** log 4.60 0.6628
9. log 6.32 0.8007 **10.** log 347 2.5403 **11.** log 8720 3.9405 **12.** log 52.5 1.7202
13. log 20.6 1.3139 **14.** log 834 2.9212 **15.** log 92.4 1.9657 **16.** log 3870 3.5877
17. log 624,000 **18.** log 0.00134 **19.** log 0.0702 **20.** log 0.64
21. log 0.000216 **22.** log 0.173 **23.** log 0.00347 **24.** log 0.0000404

Use a calculator or Table 2 to find these antilogarithms.

25. antilog 0.8657 7.34 **26.** antilog 0.3502 2.24 **27.** antilog 0.6803 4.79
28. antilog 0.1399 1.38 **29.** antilog 0.7574 5.72 **30.** antilog 0.9191 8.30
31. antilog 3.3674 2330 **32.** antilog 4.9222 83,600 **33.** antilog 1.2553 18
34. antilog (9.7875 − 10) 0.613 **35.** antilog (8.9881 − 10) 0.0973
36. antilog (7.9881 − 10) 0.00973 **37.** antilog (8.5391 − 10) 0.0346
38. antilog (6.7875 − 10) 0.000613 **39.** antilog (4.6294 − 10) 0.00000426

B

Find x.

40. $\log x = 0.8021$ **41.** $\log x = 4.1903$ **42.** $\log x = 9.7875 - 10$
43. $\log x = -1.0218$ **44.** $10^x = 345$ **45.** $10^x = 5670$

46. ***Critical Thinking***
   a. How many digits are there in 8^{1000}? 904
   b. What power of 8 has 1000 digits? 8^{1107}
   c. What number to the 1000th power has 500 digits? ±3.1622777 ($\pm\sqrt{10}$)

Challenge

Use the properties of logarithms to do these calculations.

Example: Find $\sqrt[4]{16}$ using common logarithms.

$$\log_{10} \sqrt[4]{16} = \log_{10} 16^{\frac{1}{4}} = \frac{1}{4} \cdot \log_{10} 16 \approx \frac{1}{4} \cdot 1.2041 \approx 0.3010$$
$$\sqrt[4]{16} \approx \text{antilog}_{10}\, 0.3010 \approx 2$$

47. $\sqrt[3]{8}$ **48.** 2^3 **49.** $\frac{14}{2}$ **50.** 4×2

Mixed Review

Tell which conic is defined by the equation. **51.** $y^2 + 3x - 5y + 8 = 0$

Divide $P(x)$ by $D(x)$. Then express the dividend as $P(x) = D(x) \cdot Q(x) + R(x)$.

52. $P(x) = x^3 + 4x^2 + x - 6;\ D(x) = (x^2 + 5x + 6)$

12-6 Interpolation

(Optional)

Tables are often prepared giving function values for a continuous function. Suppose the table gives four-digit precision. By using a procedure called interpolation, we can estimate values between those listed in the table.

Interpolation can be done in various ways, the simplest and most common being linear interpolation. We describe it now in relation to Table 2 for common logarithms. Remember that this method applies to a table for *any* continuous function.

Linear Interpolation

Objective: Use a table and linear interpolation to find logarithms.

Consider how a table of values for any function is made. We select members of the domain x_1, x_2, x_3, and so on. Then we compute or somehow determine the corresponding function values $f(x_1)$, $f(x_2)$, $f(x_3)$, and so on. Then we tabulate the results. We might also graph the results.

x	x_1	x_2	x_3	x_4	...
$f(x)$	$f(x_1)$	$f(x_2)$	$f(x_3)$	$f(x_4)$	...

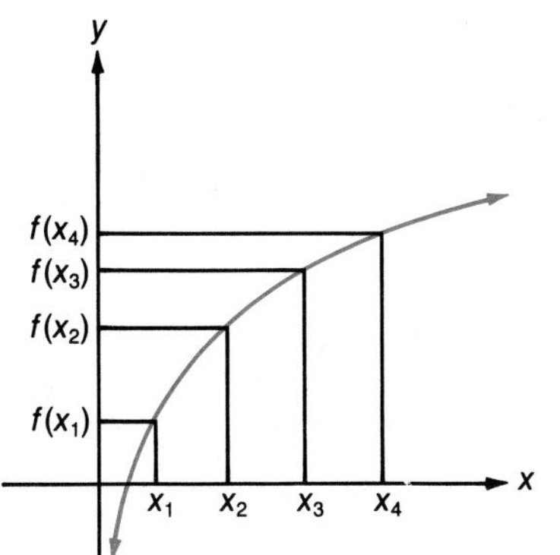

Suppose we want to find the function value $f(x)$ for an x not in the table. If x is halfway between x_1 and x_2, then we can take the number halfway between $f(x_1)$ and $f(x_2)$ as an approximation to $f(x)$. If x is one fifth of the way between x_1 and x_2, we take the number that is one fifth of the way between $f(x_1)$ and $f(x_2)$ as an approximation to $f(x)$. We divide the length from x_1 to x_2 in a certain ratio, and then divide the length from $f(x_1)$ to $f(x_2)$ in the same ratio. This is linear interpolation.

To interpolate, we fit a linear function to the two closest known data points. In the figure at the right, the approximation for $f(x)$ is obtained from the linear function, and not from the function itself. Let us apply linear interpolation to the common logarithms given in Table 2. (Note that if you use a calculator to find logarithms, interpolation is not necessary.)

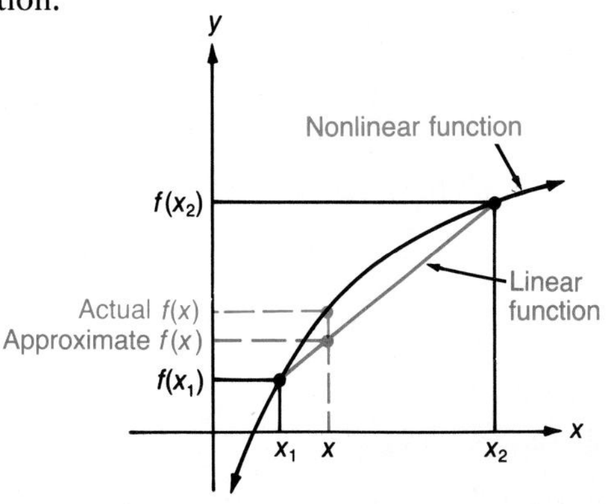

12-6

FIRST FIVE MINUTES

Find the missing number in each sequence.

1. 5.3, 5.5, ?, 5.9
   5.7
2. 0.125, 0.129, ?, 0.137
   0.133
3. Find the number halfway between 2.1 and 2.5.
   2.3
4. Find the number $\frac{1}{3}$ of the way from 3 to 36.
   14
5. Solve $\frac{5}{7} = \frac{x}{3}$ for x.
   $\frac{15}{7}$

Linear Interpolation

Emphasize that linear interpolation gives an exact value if the function is linear but only an approximate value if the function is quadratic, exponential, logarithmic, etc.

Encourage students to check answers to see if they are reasonable. For example, if x is about halfway between x_1 and x_2, then $f(x)$ should be about halfway between $f(x_1)$ and $f(x_2)$.

Key Question

- Look at the graph at the bottom of page 539. Where is interpolation most accurate?
  Interpolation is most accurate close to x_1 or x_2 because the linear function is closest to the nonlinear function near these points.

Chalkboard Examples

1. Find log 4591.
   a. **Since $4591 = 4.591 \cdot 10^3$, the characteristic is 3.**
   b. **Find the mantissa. From Table 2, log 4.59 = 0.6618 and log 4.60 = 0.6628. Since 4.591 is $\frac{1}{10}$ of the distance from 4.59 to 4.60, the mantissa is $0.6618 + 0.1(0.6628 - 0.6618) = 0.6619$.**
   c. **Add the characteristic and mantissa. log 4591 = 3 + 0.6619 = 3.6619.**

2. Find log 0.01359.
   a. Since $0.01359 = 1.359 \cdot 10^{-2}$, the characteristic is -2.
   b. Find the mantissa. From Table 2, log 1.35 = 0.1303 and log 1.36 = 0.1335. Since 1.359 is $\frac{9}{10}$ of the distance from 1.35 to 1.36, the mantissa is $0.1303 + 0.9(0.1335 - 0.1303) = 0.1332$.
   c. Add the characteristic and mantissa. $\log 0.01359 = -2 + 0.1332$ or $8.1332 - 10$ or -1.8668

LESSON ENRICHMENT

Use interpolation to estimate the following.

1. $\sqrt{19}$ $\sqrt{16} = 4, \sqrt{25} = 5,$ $\sqrt{19} \approx 4\frac{3}{9} \approx 4\frac{1}{3}$
2. $\sqrt[3]{50}$ $\sqrt[3]{27} = 3, \sqrt{64} = 4,$ $\sqrt[3]{50} \approx 3\frac{23}{37}$
3. $5^{2.6}$ $5^2 = 25, 5^3 = 125,$ $5^{2.6} \approx 25 + 0.6 \cdot 100 \approx 85$

EXAMPLE 1 Find log 34,870.

(a) Since $34{,}870 = 3.487 \times 10^4$, the characteristic is 4.

(b) Find the mantissa. From Table 2 we have log 3.48 = 0.5416 and log 3.49 = 0.5428. We know that 3.487 is $\frac{7}{10}$ of the distance between 3.48 and 3.49. Thus to estimate log 3.487, we find the number $\frac{7}{10}$ of the way from 0.5416 to 0.5428.

0.5416	?	0.5428
(log 3.48)	(log 3.487)	(log 3.49)

The difference between log 3.48 and log 3.49 is 0.0012. Thus we take $\frac{7}{10}$ of 0.0012 and add it to 0.5416.

$$\begin{aligned} &0.5416 + 0.7(0.0012) \\ &= 0.5416 + 0.00084 \\ &= 0.54244 \end{aligned}$$

We round the result to 0.5424.

(c) Add the characteristic and mantissa.

$$\log 34{,}870 \approx 4.5424$$

EXAMPLE 2 Find log 0.01413.

(a) Since $0.01413 = 1.413 \times 10^{-2}$, the characteristic is -2, or $8 - 10$.

(b) Find the mantissa. From Table 2, we have

0.1492	?	0.1523
(log 1.41)	(log 1.413)	(log 1.42)

The difference between log 1.41 and log 1.42 is 0.0031. We know 1.413 is $\frac{3}{10}$ of the distance between 1.41 and 1.42, so we take $\frac{3}{10}$ of 0.0031 and add it to 0.1492.

$$\begin{aligned} &0.1492 + 0.3(0.0031) \\ &= 0.1492 + 0.00093 \\ &= 0.15013 \end{aligned}$$

We round the result to 0.1501.

(c) Add the characteristic and mantissa.

$$\log 0.01413 \approx 8.1501 - 10, \text{ or } -1.8499$$

Try This

a. Find log 4562. 3.6592

b. Find log 0.02387. $8.3779 - 10$ or -1.6221

Finding Antilogarithms

Objective: Find antilogarithms using a table and linear interpolation.

EXAMPLE 3 Find antilog (7.4122 − 10).

(a) The characteristic is −3. The mantissa is 0.4122. From Table 2 we have

0.4116	0.4122	0.4133
(log 2.58)	(log ?)	(log 2.59)

The difference between 0.4116 and 0.4133 is 0.0017. We know that 0.4122 is $\frac{6}{17}$ of the distance between 0.4116 and 0.4133. So the antilog of 0.4122 is $\frac{6}{17}$ of the way from 2.58 to 2.59. We take $\frac{6}{17}$ of 0.01 and add it to 2.58.

$$2.58 + \frac{6}{17}(0.01)$$
$$\approx 2.58 + 0.0035$$
$$\approx 2.5835$$

We round the result to 2.584. Thus antilog (7.4122 − 10) ≈ 2.584×10^{-3}, or 0.002584.

Try This

c. Find antilog 3.4557. 2856 **d.** Find antilog (6.7749 − 10). 0.0005956

12-6 EXERCISES

A

Find the following logarithms using interpolation and Table 2.

1. log 41.63 1.6194 **2.** log 472.1 2.6740 **3.** log 2.944 0.4689
4. log 21.76 1.3377 **5.** log 650.2 2.8130 **6.** log 37.37 1.5725
7. log 0.1425 9.1538 − 10 **8.** log 0.09045 8.9564 − 10 **9.** log 0.004257 7.6291 − 10
10. log 4518 3.6549 **11.** log 0.1776 9.2494 − 10 **12.** log 0.08356 8.9220 − 10
13. log 600.6 2.7786 **14.** log 500.2 2.6991 **15.** log 800.1 2.9031

Find the following antilogarithms using interpolation and Table 2.

16. antilog 1.6350 43.15 **17.** antilog 2.3512 224.5 **18.** antilog 0.6478 4.444
19. antilog 1.1624 14.53 **20.** antilog 0.0342 1.082 **21.** antilog 4.8453 70,030
22. antilog (9.8564 − 10) **23.** antilog (8.9659 − 10)

Finding Antilogarithms

Chalkboard Examples

1. Find the antilog of 2.7158.
antilog 2.7158
= antilog(0.7158) · 10^2
antilog 0.7158 = ?
antilog 0.7152 = 5.19
antilog 0.7160 = 5.20
$\frac{0.7158 - 0.7152}{0.7160 - 0.7152} = \frac{6}{8} = 0.75$
0.75 · (5.20 − 5.19) = 0.0075
antilog 0.7158
≈ antilog 0.7152 + 0.0075
≈ 5.198
antilog 2.7158 ≈ 5.198 · 10^2
= 519.8
2. Find antilog(8.2145 − 10).
antilog(8.2145 − 10)
= antilog(0.2145 − 2)
= antilog(0.2145) · 10^{-2}
antilog 0.2145 = ?
antilog 0.2122 = 1.63
antilog 0.2148 = 1.64
$\frac{0.2145 - 0.2122}{0.2148 - 0.2122} = \frac{0.0023}{0.0026} = 0.88$
0.88 · (1.64 − 1.63) = 0.0088
antilog 0.2145 = 1.63 + 0.0088
≈ 1.639
antilog (8.2145 − 10)
≈ 1.639 · 10^{-2} = 0.01639

LESSON QUIZ

1. Find log 4.761 using interpolation and Table 2.
0.6777
2. Find antilog 1.3142 using interpolation and Table 2.
20.61

Assignment Guide
Algebra: omit

Alg w/Finite or Trig: omit

Comprehensive: 1–27 m3, 28–33, MR

ADDITIONAL ANSWERS

Exercises

22. 0.7185
23. 0.09245

24. 0.002587
25. 0.5343
26. 0.01589
27. 0.007295

32. 773.4
33. 0.8268

Mixed Review

34. 2 or 0
35. 3 or 1
36. 2 or 0
37. 0
38. No
39. Yes
40. No
41. Yes
42. $f^{-1}(x) = x - 2$
43. $f^{-1}(x) = x^2 - 3$
44. $113\frac{1}{3}$ yards

24. antilog (7.4128 − 10) **25.** antilog (9.7278 − 10)

26. antilog (8.2010 − 10) **27.** antilog (7.8630 − 10)

B

Find.

28. log (log 3) 9.6786 − 10 **29.** log (log 5) 9.8445 − 10 **30.** log (log 7) 9.9269 − 10

31. ***Critical Thinking*** Compare estimates of logarithms as found by linear interpolation with those found using a table or calculator. Values found by interpolation are slightly less.

Challenge

Use logarithms and interpolation to do the following calculations. Use four-digit precision. Answers may be checked using a calculator.

32. $\dfrac{35.24 \times (16.77)^3}{12.93 \times \sqrt{276.2}}$ **33.** $\sqrt[5]{\dfrac{16.79 \times (4.234)^3}{18.81 \times 175.3}}$

Mixed Review

Use Descartes' rule of signs to determine the number of positive real roots.

34. $5x^4 + 2x^3 - 6x^2 + 11x + 6$ **35.** $-4x^3 + 5x^2 - 8x + 10$

Use Descartes' rule of signs to determine the number of negative real roots.

36. $5x^4 + 2x^3 - 6x^2 + 11x + 6$ **37.** $-4x^3 + 5x^2 - 8x + 10$

Test for symmetry with respect to the line $x = y$.

38. $2x + 3y = 5$ **39.** $xy = 2$ **40.** $7x - 7y = 1$ **41.** $3x^2 + 3y^2 = 7$

For each $f(x)$, find $f^{-1}(x)$. **42.** $f(x) = x + 2$ **43.** $f(x) = \sqrt{x + 3}$

44. A rectangular field is $53\frac{1}{3}$ yards wide and 100 yards long. How long is a diagonal of the rectangle?

Calculator Investigation

1. Enter the largest number you can on your calculator. Most calculators allow you to enter 9.9999×10^{99} (9.9999 EXP 99. Press LOG four times. What is the result? −0.5213902 or -5.2139×10^{-1}

   What happens if you press LOG again? Why? An error occurs. Negative numbers do not have logarithms.

2. Enter the smallest number you can on your calculator. Most calculators allow you to enter 1×10^{-99} (1 EXP −99). Press 2nd LOG three times. What is the result? 10^{10}

   What happens if you press 2nd LOG again? Why? An error occurs. The result, 10^{100}, is too large for the calculator.

3. Use function notation to explain these procedures $f(f(f(f(x))))$, where $f(x) = \log(x)$, $f(f(f(f(x))))$, where $f(x) = 10^x$

4. Compare the results of taking successive logs of logs with taking successive powers of powers. Logs of logs decrease rapidly while powers of powers increase rapidly.

12-7 Exponential and Logarithmic Equations

Master Grapher Worksheet 27, *Solving Exponential and Logarithmic Equations*, can be used as a lesson opener.

Earthquake intensity, loudness of sound, and compound interest are all applications of exponential and logarithmic equations.

Exponential Equations

Objective: Solve exponential equations.

An equation with variables in exponents, such as $3^{2x-1} = 4$, is called an **exponential equation.** We can solve such equations by taking logarithms of both sides and then using Theorem 12-5.

EXAMPLE 1 Solve $3^x = 8$.

$$\log 3^x = \log 8 \quad \text{Taking the log of both sides (Remember } \log m = \log_{10} m.)$$
$$x \log 3 = \log 8 \quad \text{Using Theorem 12-5}$$
$$x = \frac{\log 8}{\log 3} \quad \text{Solving for } x$$
$$x \approx \frac{0.9031}{0.4771} \approx 1.8929 \quad \text{We look up the logs, or find them on a calculator, and divide.}$$

EXAMPLE 2 Solve $2^{3x-5} = 16$.

$$\log 2^{3x-5} = \log 16 \quad \text{Taking the log of both sides}$$
$$(3x - 5) \log 2 = \log 16 \quad \text{Using Theorem 12-5}$$
$$3x - 5 = \frac{\log 16}{\log 2}$$
$$3x = \frac{\log 16}{\log 2} + 5$$
$$x = \frac{\frac{\log 16}{\log 2} + 5}{3}$$
$$x \approx \frac{\frac{1.2041}{0.3010} + 5}{3} \quad \text{Solving for } x \text{ and evaluating logarithms}$$
$$x \approx 3.0001 \quad \text{Calculating}$$

The answer is approximate because the logarithms are approximate. We can see that 3 is the solution since $2^{3(3)-5} = 2^4 = 16$.

12-7

FIRST FIVE MINUTES

Use a calculator or Table 2.

1. Find log 2.13.
   0.3284
2. Find log 432.
   2.6355
3. Find antilog 0.3263.
   2.12
4. Find antilog −0.4413.
   0.362

Exponential Equations

Calculators should be used for this section, if available.

Note that Example 3 could also be solved by taking the logarithm of both sides.

Key Questions

- What is the value of 2^{5x+1} when $x = 0$?
  2
- What is the value of 10^{2x+1} when $x = -1$?
  0.1
- What is a simpler expression for $\log(10^{2x+3})$?
  $2x + 3$

Chalkboard Examples

1. Solve $5^x = 7$.
   $\log(5^x) = \log 7$
   $x\log 5 = \log 7$
   $x = \frac{\log 7}{\log 5}$
   $\approx \frac{0.8451}{0.6990} \approx 1.2091$
2. Solve $3^{5x-2} = 8$.
   $\log(3^{5x-2}) = \log 8$
   $(5x - 2)\log 3 = \log 8$
   $5x - 2 = \frac{\log 8}{\log 3}$
   $x = \frac{1}{5}\left(\frac{\log 8}{\log 3} + 2\right)$
   ≈ 0.7786
3. Solve $3^{5x-2} = 27$.
   $3^{5x-2} = 3^3$
   $5x - 2 = 3$
   $x = 1$

Logarithmic Equations

Remind students that logarithmic functions and exponential functions are inverses of each other.

Key Questions

- What is the result of taking the antilog on both sides of the equation $\log x = 3$?
  $x = 10^3$
- What is the result of taking the antilog on both sides of the equation $\log(3x + 1) = 5$?
  $3x + 1 = 10^5$

Chalkboard Examples

1. Solve $\log(2x - 1) = 4$.
   $2x - 1 = 10^4$
   $x = \frac{10^4 + 1}{2}$
2. Solve $\log(x - 1) + \log(x + 1) = 1$.
   $\log((x - 1)(x + 1)) = 1$
   $(x - 1)(x + 1) = 10^1$
   $x^2 - 1 = 10$
   $x^2 = 11$
   $x = \pm\sqrt{11}$
   The solution is $\sqrt{11}$, since negative numbers do not have logarithms.

The following is another method of solving exponential equations.

EXAMPLE 3 Solve $2^{3x-5} = 16$.

Note that $16 = 2^4$. Then we have $2^{3x-5} = 2^4$.

Since the base, 2, is the same on both sides, the exponents must be the same. Thus we can solve for x as follows.

$$3x - 5 = 4$$
$$x = 3$$

Try This

a. Solve $2^x = 7$. 2.8074 **b.** Solve $4^x = 6$. 1.2925

c. Solve $4^{2x-3} = 64$. Use the method in Example 3. 3

Logarithmic Equations

Objective: Solve logarithmic equations.

Equations that contain logarithmic expressions are logarithmic equations. We solve them by converting to an equivalent exponential equation. For example, to solve $\log_2 x = -3$, we convert to $x = 2^{-3}$ and find that $x = \frac{1}{8}$.

To solve logarithmic equations we first try to obtain a single logarithmic expression on one side of the equation and then write an equivalent exponential equation.

EXAMPLE 4 Solve $\log_3(5x + 7) = 2$.

We already have a single logarithmic expression, so we write an equivalent exponential equation.

$$5x + 7 = 3^2$$
$$5x + 7 = 9$$
$$x = \frac{2}{5}$$

Check:

$\log_3(5x + 7)$	$= 2$
$\log_3\left(5 \cdot \frac{2}{5} + 7\right)$	2
$\log_3(2 + 7)$	2
$\log_3 9$	2
2	2 ✓

EXAMPLE 5 Solve $\log x + \log(x - 3) = 1$.

Here we must first obtain a single logarithmic equation.

$$\log x + \log(x - 3) = 1$$
$$\log x(x - 3) = 1 \quad \text{Using Theorem 12-4 to obtain a single logarithm}$$
$$x(x - 3) = 10^1 \quad \text{Converting to an equivalent exponential equation}$$
$$x^2 - 3x = 10$$
$$x^2 - 3x - 10 = 0$$
$$(x + 2)(x - 5) = 0 \quad \text{Factoring and using the principle of zero products}$$
$$x = -2 \text{ or } x = 5$$

Possible solutions to logarithmic equations must be checked because domains of logarithmic functions consist only of positive numbers.

Check:

$\log x + \log(x-3) = 1$	
$\log(-2) + \log(-2-3)$	1
$\log(-2) + \log(-5)$	1

$\log x + \log(x-3) = 1$	
$\log 5 + \log(5-3)$	1
$\log 5 + \log 2$	1
$\log 10$	1
1	1 ✓

The number -2 is not a solution because negative numbers do not have logarithms. The solution is 5.

Try This Solve.

d. $\log_5 x = 3$ 125 **e.** $\log_4(8x - 6) = 3$ 8.75 **f.** $\log x + \log(x + 3) = 1$ 2

Problem Solving: Logarithms

Objective: Solve problems involving exponential and logarithmic equations.

The amount A that principal P will be worth after t years at interest rate r, compounded annually, is given by the formula $A = P(1 + r)^t$.

EXAMPLE 6

Suppose $4000 principal is invested at 6% interest and yields $5353. For how many years was it invested?

We use the formula $A = P(1 + r)^t$.

$$5353 = 4000(1 + 0.06)^t, \text{ or } 5353 = 4000(1.06)^t$$

Then we solve for t.

$$\log 5353 = \log(4000(1.06)^t) \quad \text{Taking the log of both sides}$$

$$\log 5353 = \log 4000 + t \log 1.06 \quad \text{Using Theorems 12-4 and 12-5}$$

$$\frac{\log 5353 - \log 4000}{\log 1.06} = t \quad \text{Solving for } t$$

$$\frac{3.7286 - 3.6021}{0.0253} \approx t \quad \text{Evaluating logarithms}$$

$$5 \approx t$$

The money was invested for approximately 5 years. We can use a calculator to check.

$4000(1.06)^5 \approx 5352.9023$ The solution checks.

Try This

g. Suppose $5000 was invested at 14%, compounded annually, and it yielded $18,540. For how long was it invested? Approximately 10 years

Problem Solving: Logarithms

Chalkboard Examples

1. Suppose $1000 is invested at 8% interest, compounded yearly. How long will it take for the investment to grow to $2000?
$2000 = 1000(1 + 0.08)^t$
$2 = (1.08)^t$
$\log 2 = \log(1.08)^t$
$\log 2 = t \log 1.08$
$t = \frac{\log 2}{\log 1.08}$
≈ 9.0 years
2. Find the loudness in decibels of a sound whose intensity I is 1000 times I_0.
$L = 10 \log \frac{1000 \cdot I_0}{I_0}$
$= 10 \log 1000 = 30$ decibels
3. Find the Richter scale magnitude of an earthquake whose intensity I is 10,000 times I_0.
$R = \log \frac{10000 \cdot I_0}{I_0}$
$= \log 10000 = 4$

LESSON QUIZ

1. Solve $2^x = 12$.
   $x \approx 3.5850$
2. Solve $5^{7x-2} = 3$.
   ≈ 0.3832
3. Solve $\log(x + 2) + \log(x - 2) = 1$.
   $x = \sqrt{14} \approx 3.7417$
4. How many years will it take an investment of one dollar to double if it is invested at 7% interest, compounded yearly?
   ≈ 10.24 years

The sensation of loudness of sound is not proportional to the energy intensity, but rather is a logarithmic function.

Loudness is measured in bels (after Alexander Graham Bell) or in smaller units, *decibels*. Loudness in decibels of a sound of intensity (I) is defined to be

$$L = 10 \log \frac{I}{I_0}$$

where I_0 is the minimum intensity detectable by the human ear (such as the tick of a watch at 6 meters under quiet conditions). When a sound is 10 times as intense as another, its loudness is 10 decibels greater. If a sound is 100 times as intense as another, it is louder by 20 decibels, and so on.

EXAMPLE 7

(a) Find the loudness in decibels of the background noise in a radio studio, for which the intensity (I) is 199 times I_0.

We substitute into the formula and calculate, using a calculator.

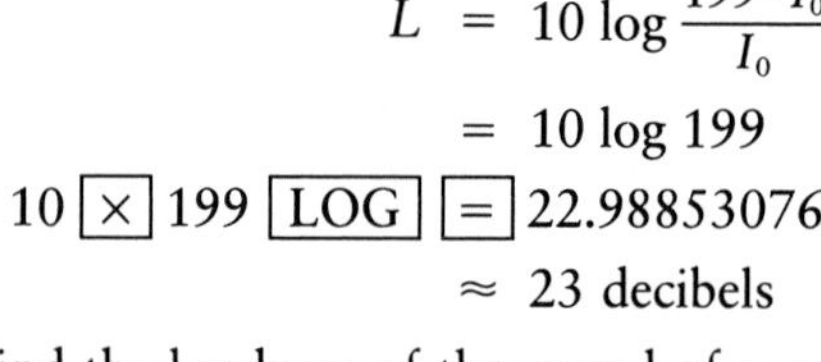

$$L = 10 \log \frac{199 \cdot I_0}{I_0}$$

$$= 10 \log 199$$

10 [×] 199 [LOG] [=] 22.98853076

$$\approx 23 \text{ decibels}$$

(b) Find the loudness of the sound of a rock concert, for which the intensity is $10^{11}\ I_0$.

$$L = 10 \log \frac{10^{11} \cdot I_0}{I_0}$$

$$= 10 \log 10^{11}$$

$$= 10 \cdot 11$$

$$= 110 \text{ decibels}$$

Try This

h. Find the loudness in decibels of the sound in a library, for which the intensity is 2510 times I_0. 34 decibels

i. Find the loudness in decibels of conversational speech, for which the intensity is 10^6 times I_0. 60 decibels

---

The magnitude R (on the Richter scale) of an earthquake of intensity I is defined as

$$R = \log \frac{I}{I_0}$$

where I_0 is a minimum intensity used for comparison.

EXAMPLE 8

An earthquake has an intensity 4×10^8 times I_0. What is its magnitude on the Richter scale?

We substitute into the formula.

$$R = \log \frac{4 \times 10^8 \cdot I_0}{I_0}$$
$$= \log \frac{4 \cdot I_0}{I_0} + \log \frac{10^8 I_0}{I_0}$$
$$= \log 4 + \log 10^8$$

4 [LOG] [+] 8 [=] 8.602059991 ≈ 8.6

The magnitude on the Richter scale is about 8.6.

Try This

j. The earthquake in Anchorage, Alaska, on March 27, 1964, had an intensity 2.5×10^8 times I_0. What was its magnitude on the Richter scale? ≈ 8.4

12-7 EXERCISES

A

Solve.

1. $2^x = 8$ **2.** $2^x = 32$ **3.** $2^x = 10$

4. $2^x = 33$ **5.** $5^{4x-7} = 125$ **6.** $4^{3x+5} = 16$

7. $3^{x^2+4x} = \frac{1}{27}$ **8.** $3^{5x} \cdot 9^{x^2} = 27$ **9.** $4^x = 7$

10. $8^x = 10$ **11.** $2^x = 3^{x-1}$ **12.** $3^{x+2} = 5^{x-1}$

13. $(2.8)^x = 41$ **14.** $(3.4)^x = 80$ **15.** $(1.7)^x = 20$

Solve.

16. $\log x + \log (x - 9) = 1$ 10

17. $\log x + \log (x + 9) = 1$ 1

18. $\log x - \log (x + 3) = -1$ $\frac{1}{3}$

19. $\log (x + 9) - \log x = 1$ 1

20. $\log_4 (x + 3) + \log_4 (x - 3) = 2$ 5

21. $\log_5 (x + 4) + \log_5 (x - 4) = 2$ $\sqrt{41}$

22. $\log \sqrt[3]{x} = \sqrt{\log x}$ 1, 10^9

23. $\log \sqrt[4]{x} = \sqrt{\log x}$ 1, 10^{16}

24. $\log_5 \sqrt{x^2 + 1} = 1$ $\pm 2\sqrt{6}$

25. $\log \sqrt[3]{x^2} + \log \sqrt[3]{x^4} = \log 2^{-3}$ $\pm\frac{\sqrt{2}}{4}$

Solve.

26. How many years will it take an investment of \$1000 to double itself when interest is compounded annually at 6%? 11.9

27. How many years will it take an investment of \$1000 to triple itself when interest is compounded annually at 5%? 22.5

28. Find the loudness in decibels of the sound of an automobile having an intensity 3,100,000 times I_0. 65 decibels

29. Find the loudness in decibels of the sound of a dishwasher having an intensity 2,500,000 times I_0. 64 decibels

Assignment Guide

Algebra: Day 1: 1–15, MR
Day 2: 16–25, 26–37 e/o

Alg w/Finite or Trig: 1–51 m3, 52, MR

Comprehensive: 1–51 m3, 52, 53–62 e/o, MR

ADDITIONAL ANSWERS

Exercises

1. 3
2. 5
3. 3.3219
4. 5.0444
5. $\frac{5}{2}$
6. −1
7. −3, −1
8. −3, $\frac{1}{2}$
9. 1.4036
10. 1.1073
11. 2.7093
12. 7.4520
13. 3.6064
14. 3.5806
15. 5.6467

38. 1; 10,000
39. $\pm 4\sqrt{39}$
40. No solution
41. $25, \frac{1}{25}$
42. $-9; 9$
43. $100, \frac{1}{100}$
44. $\frac{7}{4}$
45. $-\frac{1}{2}$
46. $\log_x y - \log_x a$
47. $t = \frac{\log_b y - \log_b k}{a}$
48. $t = -\frac{1}{k}\log\left[\frac{T - T_0}{T_1 - T_0}\right]$
49. $n = \log_v c - \log_v P$, or $\log_v \frac{c}{P}$
50. $Q = a^b \cdot \sqrt[3]{y}$
51. $y = xa^{2x}$
52. a. $\log_2 8 = 3, \log_8 2 = \frac{1}{3}$

b. $\log_3 9 = 2, \log_9 3 = \frac{1}{2}$

c. $\log_4 16 = 2, \log_{16} 4 = \frac{1}{2}$

In general, $\log_a b = \frac{1}{\log_b a}$.

53. 10, 100
54. $100, \frac{1}{10}$
55. 5
56. $\{x|x \geq 1\}$ for bases a such that $a > 1$

30. Find the loudness in decibels of the threshold of sound pain, for which the intensity is 10^{14} times I_0. 140 decibels
31. Find the loudness in decibels of a jet aircraft having an intensity 10^{12} times I_0. 120 decibels
32. The Los Angeles earthquake of 1971 had an intensity 5×10^6 times I_0. What was its magnitude on the Richter scale? ≈ 6.7
33. The San Francisco earthquake of 1906 had an intensity 1.8×10^8 times I_0. What was its magnitude on the Richter scale? ≈ 8.25
34. An earthquake has a magnitude of 5 on the Richter scale. What is its intensity? 10^5 times I_0
35. An earthquake has a magnitude of 7.8 on the Richter scale. What is its intensity? $\approx 6.3 \times 10^7 I_0$

In chemistry, pH is defined as

$$\text{pH} = -\log\,[\text{H}^+]$$

where $[\text{H}^+]$ is the hydrogen ion concentration in moles per liter. For example, the hydrogen ion concentration in milk is 4×10^{-7} moles per liter, so

$$\text{pH} = -\log\,(4 \times 10^{-7}) = -[\log 4 + (-7)] \approx 6.4$$

36. For tomatoes, $[\text{H}^+]$ is about 6.3×10^{-5}. Find the pH. 4.2
37. For eggs, $[\text{H}^+]$ is about 1.6×10^{-8}. Find the pH. 7.8

B

Solve.

38. $\log \sqrt{x} = \sqrt{\log x}$
39. $\log_5 \sqrt{x^2 + 1} = 2$
40. $(\log_a x)^{-1} = \log_a x^{-1}$
41. $|\log_5 x| = 2$
42. $\log_3 |x| = 2$
43. $\log x^{\log x} = 4$
44. $\frac{\sqrt{(a^{2x} \cdot a^{-5x})^{-4}}}{a^x \div a^{-x}} = a^7$
45. $\frac{(a^{3x + 1})^2}{a^4} = a^{10x}$
46. Solve $y = ax^n$, for n. Use $\log_x$.
47. Solve $y = kb^{at}$, for t. Use $\log_b$.
48. Solve $T = T_0 + (T_1 - T_0)\,10^{-kt}$, for t.
49. Solve $PV^n = c$, for n. Use $\log_V$.
50. Solve $\log_a Q = \frac{1}{3}\log_a y + b$, for Q.
51. Solve $\log_a y = 2x + \log_a x$, for y.
52. ***Critical Thinking*** Determine the relationship between (**a**), $\log_2 8$ and $\log_8 2$, (**b**) $\log_3 9$ and $\log_9 3$, and (**c**) $\log_4 16$ and $\log_{16} 4$. In general, how do $\log_a b$ and $\log_b a$ compare?

Challenge

Solve for x.

53. $x^{\log x} = \frac{x^3}{100}$
54. $x^{\log x} = 100x$
55. $|\log_5 x| + 3\log_5 |x| = 4$
56. $|\log_a x| = \log_a |x|$

57. $(0.5)^x < \frac{4}{5}$

58. $8x^{0.3} - 8x^{-0.3} = 63$

59. Solve the system of equations.

$$5^{x+y} = 100$$
$$3^{2x-y} = 1000$$

60. Find $x + y + z$, given that

$$\log_2 [\log_3 (\log_4 x)] = 0,$$
$$\log_3 [\log_2 (\log_4 y)] = 0,$$
$$\log_4 [\log_3 (\log_2 z)] = 0$$

61. If $2 \log_3 (x - 2y) = \log_3 x + \log_3 y$, find $\frac{x}{y}$.

62. Find the rational ordered pair (x, y) for which $4^{\log_{16} 27} = 2^x 3^y$.

Mixed Review

Given $f(x) = 2x + 5$, find the following. **63.** $f^{-1}(f(4))$ **64.** $f(f^{-1}(-7))$

Find an equation for $f^{-1}(x)$. **65.** $f(x) = 0.2x - 1$ **66.** $f(x) = \sqrt{x - 5}$

Convert to logarithmic equations. **67.** $10^3 = 1{,}000$ **68.** $2^{-4} = \frac{1}{16}$

69. $81^{\frac{1}{2}} = 9$ **70.** $r^s = t$

Convert to exponential equations. **71.** $\log_8 8 = 1$ **72.** $\log_3 9 = 2$

73. $\log_2 64 = 6$ **74.** $\log_5 625 = 4$

Find only the rational roots. **75.** $x^4 - 12x^2 + 35$ **76.** $x^4 - 28x^2 + 75$

77. $x^3 - x^2 - 4x + 4$

HISTORICAL NOTE: LOGARITHMS

John Napier, although not a mathematician, was responsible for the development of logarithms. In the late 1500s, he developed a method of making powers of numbers nearly continuous—that is, finding powers over small increments. By finding successive powers of numbers very close to 1, he was able to create tables of exponents using repeated multiplications. It was a tedious process, but with it he created a system that was, although inaccurate, the basis for logarithms as we know them today.

A geometry professor, Henry Briggs, was fascinated by Napier's work. Briggs and Napier began working together and decided to extend logarithms to base 10, beginning with log 1 = 0 and log 10 = 1. Napier, however, died within 3 years, and Briggs was left to develop a table of common logarithms on his own.

Briggs used successive roots to find accurate common logarithms of numbers from 1 to 20,000 and from 90,000 to 100,000. Many mathematicians of the time immediately began extending the use of logarithms to such topics as trigonometry and astronomy.

57. $\{x \mid x < \frac{\log 0.8}{\log 0.5} \approx 0.3219\}$
58. 2^{10}
59. $\left(\frac{\log 1125}{(\log 125)(\log 3)}, \frac{\log \frac{81}{125}}{(\log 125)(\log 3)}\right) \approx (3.05, -0.19)$
60. 88
61. 4
62. $\left(0, \frac{3}{2}\right)$

Mixed Review

63. 4
64. −7
65. $f^{-1}(x) = 5x + 5$
66. $f^{-1}(x) = x^2 + 5, x \geq 0$
67. $3 = \log_{10} 1000$
68. $-4 = \log_2 \frac{1}{16}$
69. $\frac{1}{2} = \log_{81} 9$
70. $s = \log_r t$
71. $8^1 = 8$
72. $3^2 = 9$
73. $2^6 = 64$
74. $5^4 = 625$
75. None
76. 5, −5
77. 1, 2, −2

12-8

FIRST FIVE MINUTES

1. Solve $4^x = 9$.
   $x\log(4) = \log 9$
   $x = \frac{\log 9}{\log 4} \approx 1.5850$
2. Solve $\log(x - 3) + \log(x + 3) = 2$.
   $\log(x^2 - 9) = 2$
   $x^2 - 9 = 10^2$
   $x = \sqrt{109} \approx 10.4403$

Exponential Functions, Base *e*

Point out that *e* is used in such applications as continuously compounded interest, radioactive decay, population growth, statistics, and many other topics in math, science, and social science.

Key Questions

- What is the value of *e*?
  $e \approx 2.7$
- What is the value of e^0?
  1
- What is the value of e^1?
  $e \approx 2.7$

Chalkboard Example

1. Use Table 4 or a calculator to graph $y = e^{2x}$.

x	−2	−1	0	1	2
y	0.02	0.14	1	7.4	54.6

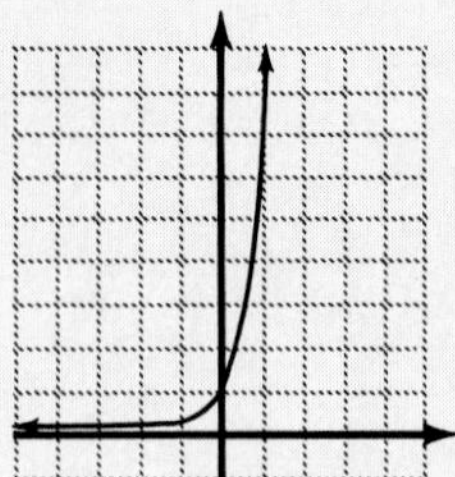

12-8 Natural Logarithms and the Number *e*

Exponential Functions, Base *e*

Objective: Graph functions related to the function $y = e^x$.

One of the most important numbers, an irrational number called *e*, occurs in advanced mathematics, economics, statistics, probability, and in many situations involving growth.

$$e \approx 2.718281828459\ldots$$

The exponential function, base *e*, and its inverse, the logarithm function base *e*, are important in mathematical theory and in applications as well. Logarithms to the base *e* are called **natural logarithms.** Table 4 on page 876 gives function values for e^x and e^{-x}. Using a calculator or these tables we can construct graphs of $y = e^x$ and $y = \log_e x$.

EXAMPLE 1 Use Table 4 or a calculator to graph $y = e^x$.

x	y
0	1
1	2.7
1.5	4.5
2	7.4
−1	0.37
−2	0.13

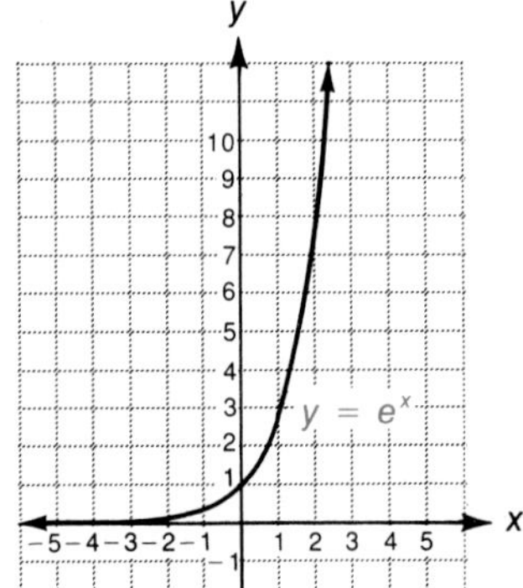

Finding e^x

You can use a scientific calculator to find base *e* exponential functions using the e^x key or the keys 2nd ln .

Find e^2.

2 e^x → 7.389056099

For additional calculator practice, see Calculator Worksheet 23.

Try This Use Table 4 or a calculator to graph. See Additional Answers.

a. $y = e^{-x}$ **b.** $y = e^{\frac{1}{2}x}$

Natural Logarithms

Objective: Use a calculator or table to find natural logarithms.

The number $\log_e x$ is abbreviated $\ln x$; that is, $\ln x = \log_e x$. If you have an [ln] key on your calculator, you can find such logarithms directly. You can also use Table 3 on page 858.

EXAMPLES Use a calculator or Table 3 to find each logarithm.

2. $\ln 5.24 \approx 1.6563$ Using Table 3

3. $$\begin{aligned} \ln 52.4 &= \ln (5.24 \times 5 \times 2) \\ &= \ln 5.24 + \ln 5 + \ln 2 \\ &\approx 1.6563 + 1.6094 + 0.6931 \quad \text{Using Table 3} \\ &\approx 3.9588 \end{aligned}$$

4. $\ln 0.001277 \approx -6.663242$ Using a calculator

From ln 5.24 and ln 52.4 we note that natural logarithms do not have characteristics and mantissas. Common logarithms have characteristics and mantissas because our numeration system is based on 10. For any base other than 10, logarithms have neither characteristics nor mantissas.

Try This Use a calculator or Table 3 to find each logarithm.

c. ln 2 0.693147 **d.** ln 100 4.605170 **e.** ln 0.07432 −2.599375 **f.** ln 0.9999 −0.000100

Problem Solving: Natural Logarithms

Objective: Solve problems involving natural logarithms.

There are many applications of exponential functions, base *e*. We consider a few.

EXAMPLE 5

One mathematical model for describing population growth is the formula

$$P = P_0 e^{kt}$$

where P_0 is the number of people at time 0, P is the number of people at time t, and k is a positive constant depending on the situation. The population of the United States in 1970 was about 203 million. In 1989 it was about 247 million. Use these data to find the value of k and then use the model to predict the population in 2000.

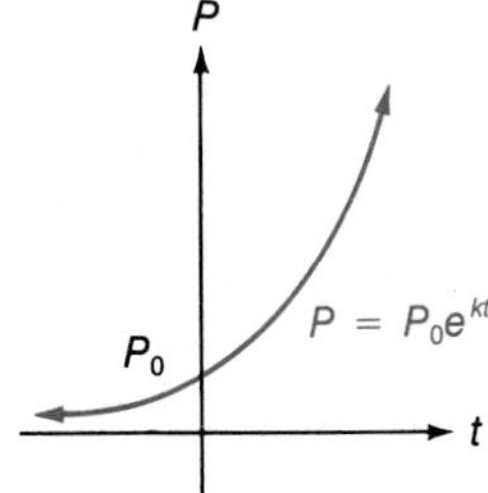

Time t begins with 1970. That is, $t = 0$ in 1970, $t = 19$ in 1989, and so on. Substituting the data into the formula, we get the equation $247 = 203e^{k \cdot 19}$.

Natural Logarithms

Note that Table 3 uses values from 0 to 9.99. To use Table 3 with smaller or larger values, students must first convert to scientific notation, and then use the fact that $10 = 2 \cdot 5$. For example, $\ln 750 = \ln (7.5 \times 10^2) = \ln (7.5 \times 2^2 \times 5^2) = \ln 7.5 + 2 \cdot \ln 2 + 2 \cdot \ln 5$.

Chalkboard Examples

Use a calculator or Table 3 to find the following.

1. ln 2
   ≈ 0.69314718
2. ln 2.718281828
   $\approx 0.99999999 \approx 1$
   Point out that $\ln(e^1) = 1$.
3. ln 1
   0
   Point out that $\ln(e^0) = 0$.

Problem Solving: Natural Logarithms

Explain that values of k can be checked by substitution into the previous equation. For instance, in Example 6, we can check the value for k, 0.0277.

$$\ln \frac{1}{2} = \ln e^{-25k}$$

$$\ln \frac{1}{2} \approx \ln e^{-0.6925}$$

$$\ln \frac{1}{2} \approx \ln \frac{1}{2}$$

Chalkboard Examples

1. The U.S. population grows according to the population growth formula with $k = 0.008$. If there are currently 240 million people in the U.S., how many years will it take for the population to double to 480 million?

$$480 = 240e^{0.008t}$$
$$2 = e^{0.008t}$$
$$\ln 2 = 0.008t$$
$$t = \frac{\ln 2}{0.008} \approx \frac{0.693}{0.008} \approx 86.6 \text{ years}$$

2. Radioactive plutonium decays according to the radioactive decay law. The half-life of plutonium is 24,000 years. Find the decay constant k and then use the formula to find how much of a 2-gram sample will remain in 1000 years.

$\frac{1}{2}N_0 = N_0e^{-k \cdot 24000}$

$\frac{1}{2} = e^{-k \cdot 24000}$

$\ln\frac{1}{2} = -k \cdot 24000$

$k = \frac{-\ln\frac{1}{2}}{24000}$

≈ 0.000028881

The amount after 1000 years is

$N = 2e^{-k \cdot 1000}$

$\approx 2e^{-0.028881}$

≈ 1.943 grams

We solve for k.

$$\ln 247 = \ln 203e^{19k} \quad \text{Taking the natural logarithm on both sides}$$

$$\ln 247 = \ln 203 + \ln e^{19k} \quad \text{Theorem 12-4}$$

$$\ln 247 = \ln 203 + 19k \quad \text{Theorem 12-3}$$

$$k = \frac{\ln 247 - \ln 203}{19} \quad \text{Solving for } k$$

$$k \approx \frac{5.5094 - 5.3132}{19} \quad \text{Using a calculator}$$

$$k \approx 0.0103 \quad \text{Calculating}$$

To find the population in 2000, we will use $P_0 = 203$ (population in millions in 1970).

$$P \approx 203e^{0.0103t}$$

In 2000, t will be 30.

$$P \approx 203e^{(0.0103)(30)} \approx 203e^{0.31}$$

Using a calculator or Table 4, we find that $e^{0.31} \approx 1.3634$. Multiplying by 203 gives us about 277 million. This is our prediction for the population of the United States in the year 2000.

Try This

g. The population of Tempe, Arizona, was 64,000 in 1970. In 1980 it was 107,000.
  (1) Use these data to determine k in the growth model. 0.0514
  (2) Use these data to predict the population of Tempe in 1995. 231,000

EXAMPLE 6

In a radioactive element some of the atoms are always transforming themselves into other elements. Thus the amount of a radioactive substance decreases. This is called *radioactive decay*. A model for radioactive decay is

$$N = N_0e^{-kt}$$

where N_0 is the amount of a radioactive substance at time 0, N is the amount at time t, and k is a positive constant depending on the rate at which a particular element decays. Strontium-90, a radioactive substance, has a half-life of 25 years. This means that half of a sample of the substance will remain as the original element in 25 years. Find k in the formula and then use the formula to find how much of a 36-gram sample will remain after 100 years.

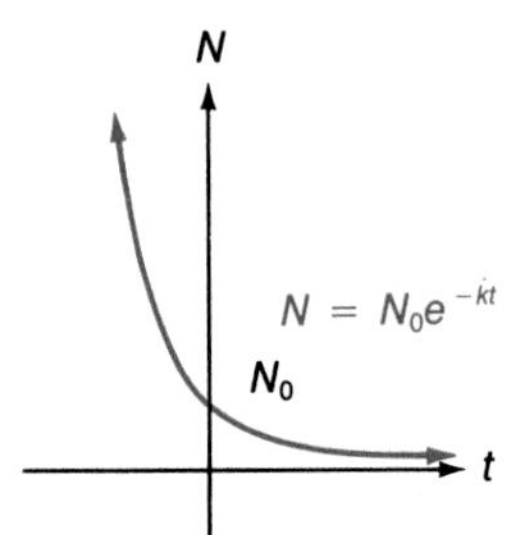

When $t = 25$ (half-life), N will be half of N_0.

$$\frac{1}{2}N_0 = N_0e^{-25k} \text{ or } \frac{1}{2} = e^{-25k}$$

We take the natural log on both sides.

$$\ln \frac{1}{2} = \ln e^{-25k}$$

$$\ln \frac{1}{2} = -25k$$

Thus $k = -\frac{\ln 0.5}{25} \approx 0.0277$ 0.5 [LN] [÷] 25 [=] [+/−] → 0.027725887

Now to find the amount remaining after 100 years, we use the following formula.

$$N \approx 36e^{-0.0277 \cdot 100}$$

$$\approx 36e^{-2.77}$$ 2.77 [+/−] [2nd] [LN] [×] 36 [=] 2.255832171

Using a calculator, we find that $N \approx 2.26$ grams.

Try This

h. Radioactive bismuth has a half-life of 5 days. A scientist buys 224 grams of it. How much of it will remain as the original bismuth in 30 days? 3.5 grams

Logarithm Tables and Change of Base

Objective: Change bases to find logarithms of any base in terms of common or natural logarithms.

The following theorem shows how we can change logarithm bases. The theorem can be applied to find the logarithm of a number to any base, using a table of common or natural logarithms.

Theorem 12-7

For any bases a and b, and any positive number M,

$$\log_b M = \frac{\log_a M}{\log_a b}$$

Proof of Theorem 12-7

Let $x = \log_b M$.

$b^x = M$ Converting to exponential form

$\log_a b^x = \log_a M$ Taking the log of both sides

$x \log_a b = \log_a M$ Using Theorem 12-5

$x = \frac{\log_a M}{\log_a b}$ Solving for x

$\log_b M = \frac{\log_a M}{\log_a b}$ Substituting $\log_b M$ for x

Logarithm Tables and Change of Base

You may want to encourage students to rederive these formulas when needed rather than memorize them.

You may want to point out that a logarithm to any base can be found on a scientific calculator with the common or natural log key using Theorem 12-7. For example, $\log_2 8 = \frac{\log 8}{\log 2}$ or $\frac{\ln 8}{\ln 2}$.

Chalkboard Examples

1. Find $\log_2 7$.

$$\log_2 7 = \frac{\log_{10} 7}{\log_{10} 2} \approx \frac{0.8451}{0.3010} \approx 2.8074$$

2. Find $\log_e 7$.

$$\log_e 7 = \frac{\log_{10} 7}{\log_{10} e} \approx \frac{0.8451}{0.4343} \approx 1.9459$$

3. Solve $5^x = 3$.

$$\log_{10}(5^x) = \log_{10} 3$$
$$x \log_{10} 5 = \log_{10} 3$$
$$x = \frac{\log_{10} 3}{\log_{10} 5} \approx 0.6826$$

LESSON QUIZ

1. Graph $y = e^{0.2x}$.

x	−2	−1	0	1	2
y	0.67	0.82	1	1.22	1.49

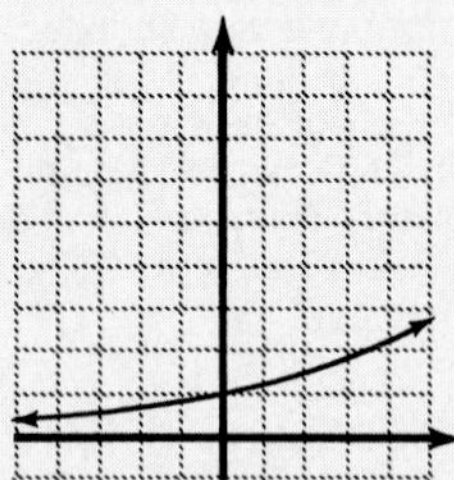

2. Use a calculator or Table 3 to find ln 1.59 to four decimal places. ≈ 0.4637
3. If a population doubles in 10 years, what is the growth rate k? ≈ 0.0693
4. Find $\log_6 9$. 1.2226

EXAMPLE 7 Find $\log_5 346$.

$$\log_5 346 = \frac{\log_{10} 346}{\log_{10} 5}$$

$$\approx \frac{2.5391}{0.6990} \approx 3.6325$$

Try This

i. Find $\log_5 125$. 3

j. Find $\log_6 4870$. 4.7385

k. Find $\log_{10} e$. Use 2.718 for e. 0.4342

We can use Theorem 12-7 to convert between common logarithms and natural logarithms.

$$\log_e M = \frac{\log_{10} M}{\log_{10} e} \text{ and } \log_{10} M = \frac{\log_e M}{\log_e 10}$$

Abbreviating the notation, we can state these in a theorem.

Theorem 12-8

$$\ln M = \frac{\log M}{\log e} \text{ and } \log M = \frac{\ln M}{\ln 10}$$

Using approximations, $\log e \approx 0.4343$ and $\ln 10 \approx 2.3026$, so we have

$$\ln M \approx \frac{\log M}{0.4343} \text{ and } \log M \approx \frac{\ln M}{2.3026}$$

EXAMPLE 8 Use common (base 10) logarithms to find ln 257.

$$\ln 257 \approx \frac{\log 257}{\log e} \approx \frac{2.4099}{0.4343} \approx 5.5489$$

We can make use of this change-of-base procedure to solve certain exponential equations.

EXAMPLE 9 Solve $3^x = 8$.

$\log_3 3^x = \log_3 8$ Taking logarithms, base 3, on both sides

$x = \log_3 8$ Theorem 12-3

$$= \frac{\log 8}{\log 3} \approx \frac{0.9031}{0.4771} \approx 1.8929$$

Compare this with Example 1 in Section 12-7.

Try This Use common (base 10) logarithms.

l. Find ln 1030. 6.937

m. Find ln 0.457. −0.783

n. Solve $2^x = 7$. 2.8076

12-8 EXERCISES

A For Exercises 1–6, See Teacher's Answer Section.

Graph. A graphing calculator or software may be used.

1. $y = e^{2x}$ **2.** $y = e^{0.5x}$ **3.** $y = e^{-2x}$ **4.** $y = e^{-0.5x}$

5. $y = 1 - e^{-x}$, for $x \geq 0$ **6.** $y = 2(1 - e^{-x})$, for $x \geq 0$

Find each natural logarithm. Use a calculator or Table 3.

7. ln 1.88 **8.** ln 18.8 **9.** ln 0.0188 **10.** ln 0.188

11. ln 2.13 **12.** ln 213 **13.** ln 0.213 **14.** ln 0.00213

15. ln 4500 **16.** ln 81,000 **17.** ln 0.00056 **18.** ln 0.999

19. ln 0.08 **20.** ln 0.0471 **21.** ln 980,000

22. The approximate population of Dallas was 680,000 in 1960. In 1980 it was 905,000. Find k in the growth formula and estimate the population in 2000.

23. The approximate population of San Jose was 460,000 in 1970. In 1980 it was 630,000. Find k in the growth formula and estimate the population in 2000.

24. The half-life of polonium-218 is 3 minutes. After 30 minutes, how much of a 410-gram sample will remain as the original polonium? 0.4 gram

25. The half-life of a lead isotope is 22 years. After 66 years, how much of a 1000-gram sample will remain as the original isotope? 125 grams

26. A certain radioactive substance decays from 66,560 grams to 6.5 grams in 16 days. What is its half-life? 1.2 days

27. Ten grams of uranium will decay to 2.5 grams in 496,000 years. What is its half-life? 248,000 years

28. When an organism dies, it takes in no more carbon. By determining the amount of carbon-14, it is possible to determine how long an organism has been dead, hence its age. Carbon-14 has a half-life of 5730 years.

a. How old is an animal bone that has lost 30% of its carbon-14? 2948 years

b. A mummy discovered in a pyramid in the Valley of the Tombs of the Kings had lost 46% of its carbon-14. What is its age? 5093 years

29. The Mesopotamian civilization was dated by using carbon-14 dating. A piece of wood discovered in an archaeological dig was found to have lost 62% of its carbon-14. Determine its age. (See Exercise 28.) 7997 years

Assignment Guide

Algebra: Day 1: 1–21
Day 2: 22–29 e/o, 30–36, MR

Alg w/Finite or Trig: 1–38 e/o, 39, 40, MR

Comprehensive: 1–38 m3, 39, 40, 41–45 e/o, MR

ADDITIONAL ANSWERS

Try This

a.

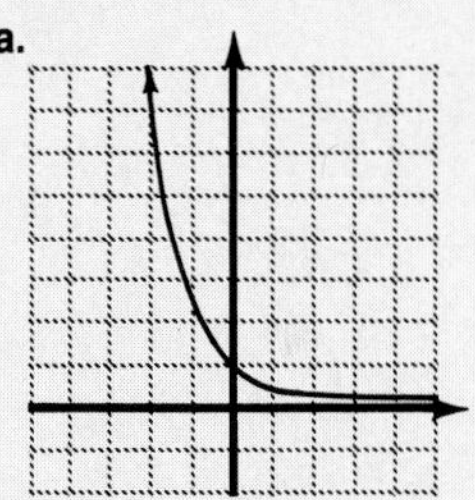

b.

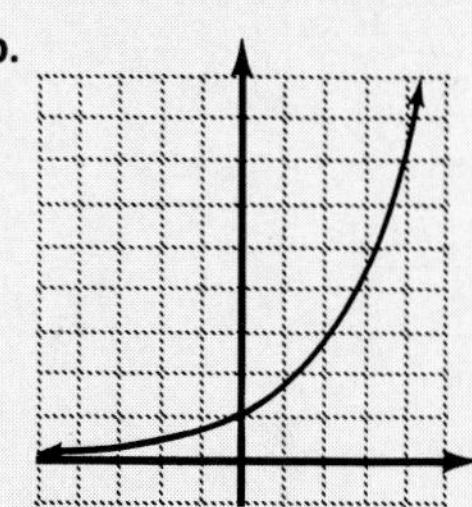

Exercises

These answers have been found using Table 3. If students use a calculator, there may be some variance in the last decimal place.

7. 0.6313
8. 2.9339
9. −3.9739
10. −1.6713
11. 0.7561
12. 5.3613
13. −1.5465
14. −6.1517
15. 8.4119
16. 11.3022
17. −7.4872
18. −0.001
19. −2.5256
20. −3.0555
21. 13.7953
22. $k \approx 0.01426$; $P \approx 1,204,000$
23. $k \approx 0.03148$; $P \approx 1,182,000$

40.

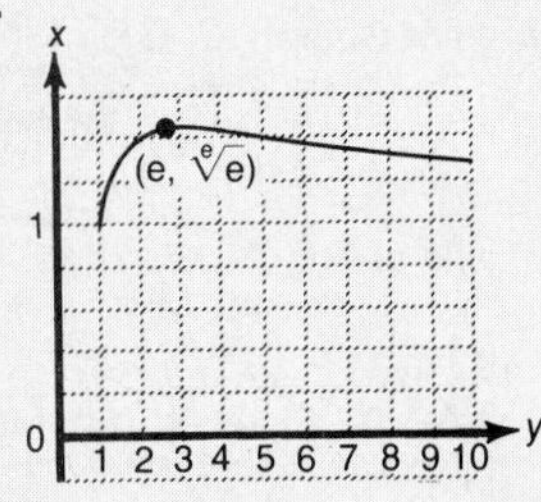

41. $N = N_0 2^{-t/H}$

42. By Theorem 12-7, $\log_a b = \frac{\log_b b}{\log_b a} = \frac{1}{\log_b a}$

43. By Theorem 12-7, $a^{(\log_b M) \div (\log_b a)} = a^{\log_a M} = M$, by Theorem 12-4.

44. By Theorem 12-7, $\log_M a = \frac{\log_b a}{\log_b M}$, so $(\log_b M)(\log_M a) = \log_b a$. Then, by Theorem 12-5, $\log_M a^{\log_b M} = \log_b a$. Then, by definition of logarithms, $a^{\log_b M} = M^{\log_b a}$. Now raise both sides to the power, $\log_b a$, and the result follows.

45. $\log_a(\log_a x) = \log_a\left(\frac{\log_b x}{\log_b a}\right)$, by Theorem 12-7, $\log_a(\log_a x) = \log_a(\log_b x - \log_b a)$, by Theorem 12-6.

Mixed Review

46. Yes, no, no
47. No, yes, no
48. 26
49. −9

30. The *consumer price index* compares the costs of goods and services over various years. The base year is 1967. The same goods and services that cost \$100 in 1967 cost \$325 in 1986. Assuming the exponential model,

a. find the value k and write the equation. $k \approx 0.062$; $P \approx \$100e^{0.062t}$

b. estimate what the same goods and services would cost in 2000. \$774.65

c. find when the same goods and services cost five times that of 1967. 1993

Use common (base 10) logarithms to find the following.

31. $\log_4 20$ 2.1610 **32.** $\log_8 0.99$ −0.0048 **33.** $\log_5 0.78$ −0.1544

34. $\log_{12} 15{,}000$ 3.8697 **35.** $\ln 12$ 2.4849 **36.** $\ln 0.77$ −0.2614

B

Solve for t.

37. $P = P_0 e^{kt}$ $t = \frac{\ln P - \ln P_0}{k}$ **38.** $P = P_0 e^{-kt}$ $t = \frac{\ln P_0 - \ln P}{k}$

39. Banks use **compound interest.** The amount received after one year at an interest rate of 12% for each dollar deposited is given by $\left(1 + \frac{0.12}{n}\right)^n$, where n is the number of times interest is compounded. How much is received per dollar deposited for each?

a. $n = 4$ (quarterly compounding) \$1.1255 **b.** $n = 12$ (monthly compounding) \$1.126825

c. $n = 365$ (daily compounding) \$1.1274746

d. Evaluate $e^{0.12}$. What can you conclude from this result? 1.1274969 is the maximum

40. ***Critical Thinking*** Graph $\sqrt[x]{x}$ from 1 to 10. For what value of x is $\sqrt[x]{x}$ a maximum? e

Use a calculator to find the maximum value for the function ≈ 1.444667861

Challenge

41. Find a general formula for radioactive decay involving H, the half-life.

Prove the following for any logarithm bases a and b.

42. $\log_a b = \frac{1}{\log_b a}$ **43.** $a^{(\log_b M) \div (\log_b a)} = M$

44. $a^{(\log_b M)(\log_b a)} = M^{(\log_b a)^2}$ **45.** $\log_a(\log_a x) = \log_a(\log_b x) - \log_a(\log_b a)$

Mixed Review

Determine whether the polynomials are factors of the polynomial $P(x)$.

46. $P(x) = x^3 - 3x^2 - 6x + 8$ **a.** $x - 1$ **b.** $x + 4$ **c.** $x - 3$

47. $P(x) = x^3 - 10x^2 + 11x + 70$ **a.** $x - 1$ **b.** $x + 2$ **c.** $x + 5$

Given $f(x) = x^2 + 7$ **48.** find $f^{-1}(f(26))$. **49.** find $f(f^{-1}(-9))$.

Problem for Programmers

Write a program to find an exponential function containing two ordered pairs. Use the program to predict other function values. Test your program using Exercises 22 and 23 in Lesson 12-8.

Problem Solving: College Entrance Exams

Angle Problems

Many problems on college entrance exams involve work with angles and angle measures. The following facts are helpful in solving angle problems on college entrance exams.

Fact 1 The sum of the measures of the three angles of a triangle equals 180°.

$m\angle 1 + m\angle 2 + m\angle 3 = 180°$

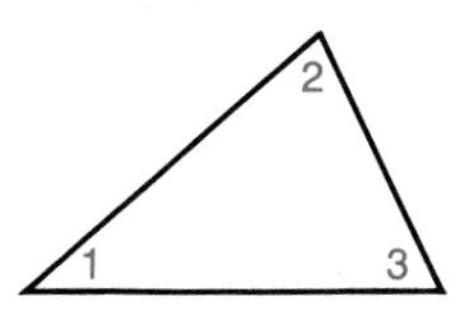

Fact 2 Vertical angles are congruent.

$m\angle 4 = m\angle 5$

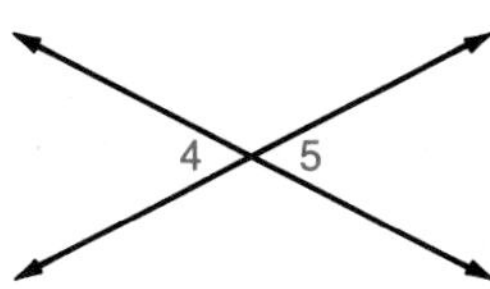

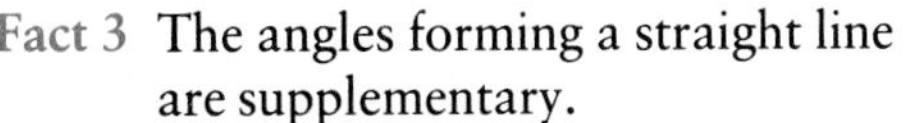

Fact 3 The angles forming a straight line are supplementary.

$m\angle 6 + m\angle 7 = 180°$

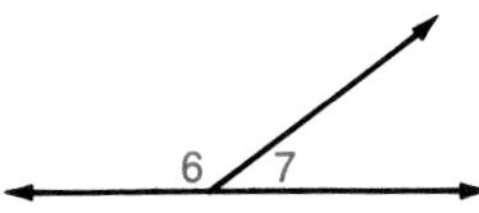

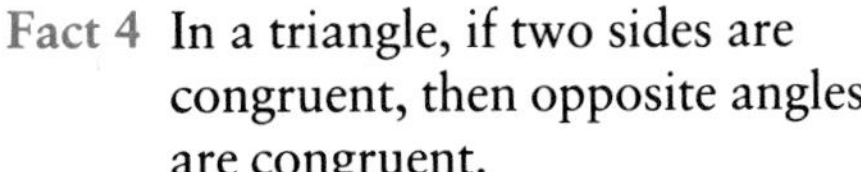

Fact 4 In a triangle, if two sides are congruent, then opposite angles are congruent.

$\overline{AC} = \overline{BC} \rightarrow m\angle 3 = m\angle 4$

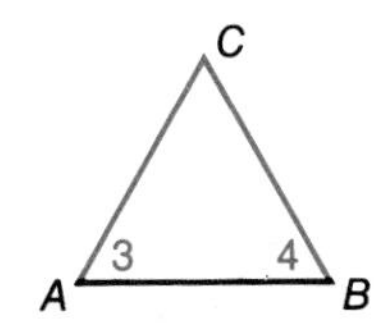

Fact 5 The sum of the measures of the four angles of a quadrilateral is 360°.

$m\angle 1 + m\angle 2 + m\angle 3 + m\angle 4 = 360°$

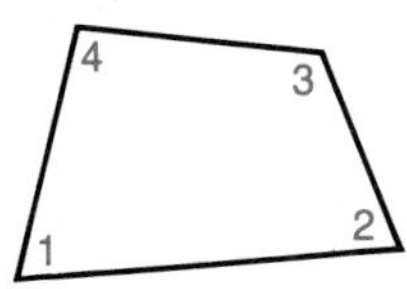

Fact 6 If a series of angles forms a complete "circle," then the sum of their measures is 360°.

$m\angle 1 + m\angle 2 + m\angle 3 + m\angle 4 + m\angle 5 = 360°$

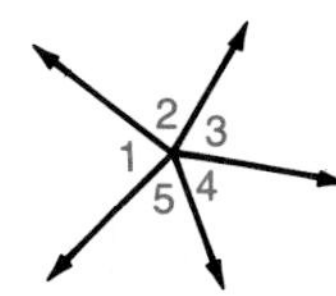

Fact 7 In a triangle, the largest angle is opposite the largest side.

$\overline{AB} > \overline{AC} \rightarrow m\angle 1 > m\angle 2$

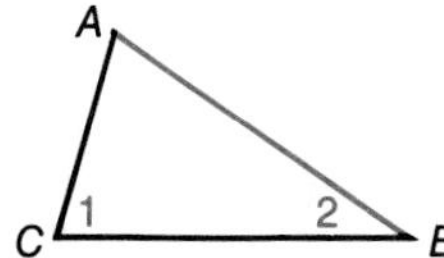

Problem Solving: College Entrance Exams

Start by reintroducing students to the eight fundamental theorems about angles that are given in the text. Work through the examples in the book. Be sure to point out that sketches of problems are usually not drawn to scale. You may want to ask students to design their own problems.

Fact 8 In a triangle, the measure of an exterior angle is the sum of the measures of the two remote interior angles.

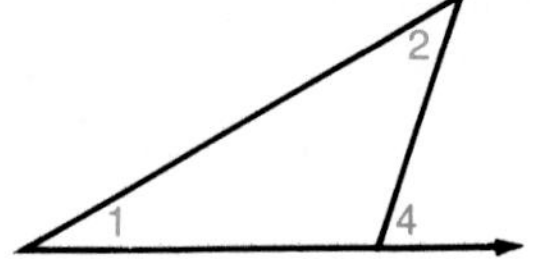

$m\angle 4 = m\angle 1 + m\angle 2$

Most items on college entrance exams involving angles require that several of the facts given above be applied to arrive at a solution.

EXAMPLE 1

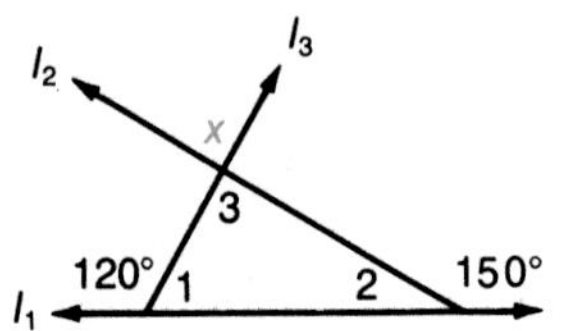

If l_1, l_2, and l_3 intersect as shown, then $x =$

(A) 60° **(B)** 70° **(C)** 80° **(D)** 90° **(E)** 100°

Solving this problem is a 3-step process.

First, we would use Fact 3 to conclude

$$m\angle 1 + 120° = 180° \rightarrow m\angle 1 = 60°$$
$$m\angle 2 + 150° = 180° \rightarrow m\angle 2 = 30°$$

Second, we would use Fact 1 to conclude

$$m\angle 1 + m\angle 2 + m\angle 3 = 180° \rightarrow m\angle 3 = 90°$$
$$60° + 30° + m\angle 3 = 180°$$

Finally, we would use Fact 2 to conclude

$$x = m\angle 3 \rightarrow x = 90°$$

So the correct answer is choice D.

EXAMPLE 2

Find the sum of the marked angles.

(A) 180° **(B)** 270° **(C)** 360° **(D)** 540° **(E)** 720°

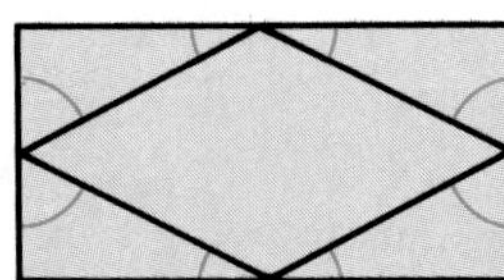

We can first find the sum of all blue and all red angles shown.

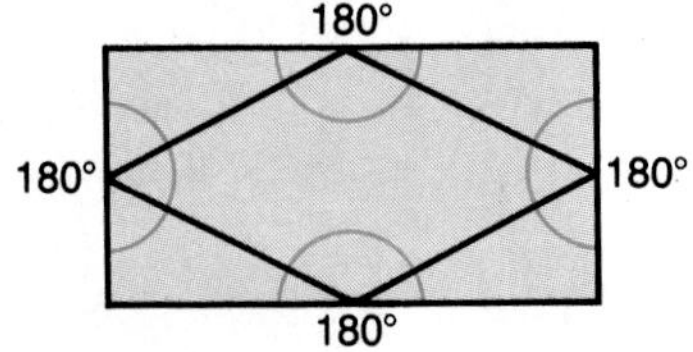

Next, we can find the sum of the red angles. Fact 5 tells us that the sum of the red angles will be 360°.

Finally, we can find the sum of the blue angles by subtracting the sum of the red angles from the sum of the blue and red angles.

$$\begin{aligned}\text{sum of blue angles} &= \text{sum (red and blue angles)} - \text{sum of red angles}\\ &= 720^\circ - 360^\circ\\ &= 360^\circ\end{aligned}$$

So the correct answer is choice C.

Problems

1.

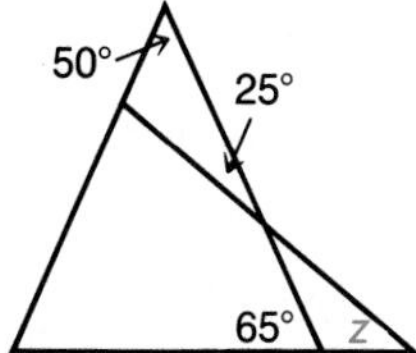

In the figure above, $z =$

(A) 55° **(B)** 50° **(C)** 45°
(D) 40° **(E)** 35°

2.

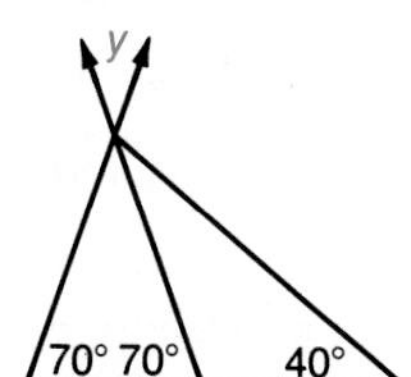

In the figure above, $y =$

(A) 70° **(B)** 65° **(C)** 60°
(D) 50° **(E)** 40°

3.

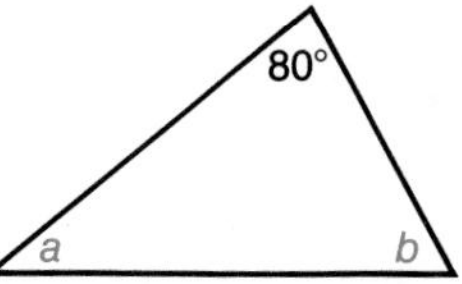

In the figure above,

$\frac{1}{2}(a + b) =$

(A) 40° **(B)** 50° **(C)** 60°
(D) 70° **(E)** 80°

4.

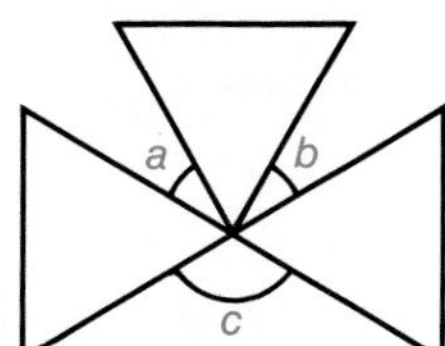

In the figure above, if the three equilateral triangles have a common vertex, then $a + b + c =$

(A) 120° **(B)** 150° **(C)** 180°
(D) 210° **(E)** 240°

5.

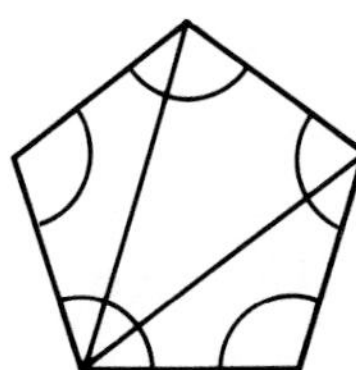

In the figure above, what is the average degree measure of the 5 marked angles?

(A) 75° **(B)** 108° **(C)** 90°
(D) 120° **(E)** 135°

6.

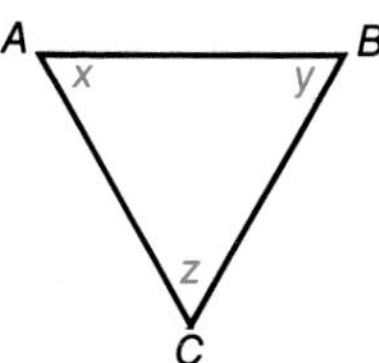

In ABC above, if $AB < BC < AC$, then which of the following is false?

(A) $x > z$ **(B)** $y > x$ **(C)** $y > z$
(D) $z > 60°$ **(E)** $y > 60°$

ANSWERS

1. (D)
2. (E)
3. (B)
4. (C)
5. (B)
6. (D)

ANSWERS

1. $y = \frac{1}{3}x + \frac{1}{3}$
2. $x = 3y^2 + 2y - 1$
3. (1, 4), (8, −3), (−5, −1)
4. (3, 2), (7, 5), (−4, 6)
5. Yes
6. No
7. $g^{-1}(x) = x^2 - 4x + 4, x \geq 2$
8. $h^{-1}(x) = 2x + 2$
9. Set of all real numbers, set of all positive numbers; (0, 1)

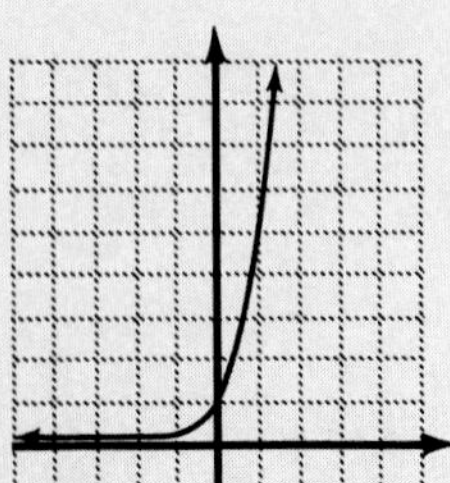

10.

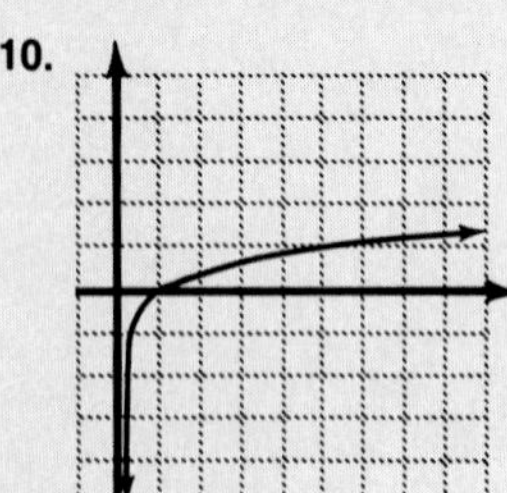

11. $2.3 = \log_7 x$
12. $\frac{1}{3} = \log_8 2$
13. $3^4 = 81$
14. $8^t = M$
15. 4
16. $\frac{1}{2}$
17. 3
18. t

Chapter 12 Summary and Review

12-1

Interchanging x and y in the equation of a relation produces an equation of inverse relation.

Write an equation of inverse relation.

1. $y = 3x - 1$

2. $y = 3x^2 + 2x - 1$

Find the inverse of the relation.

3. (4, 1), (−3, 8), (−1, −5)

4. (2, 3), (5, 7), (6, −4)

The graphs of a relation and its inverse are always reflections of each other across the line $y = x$.

Test each of the following for symmetry with respect to the line $y = x$.

5. $6x + 6y = 7$

6. $2x - y = 1$

Remember that $f^{-1}(x)$ is the inverse of $f(x)$.

Write an equation of the inverse relation.

7. Given $g(x) = \sqrt{x} + 2$, find an equation for $g^{-1}(x)$.

8. Given $h(x) = 0.5x - 1$, find an equation for $h^{-1}(x)$.

12-2

To graph exponential or logarithmic functions, find some solutions, then graph.

9. Graph $y = 5^x$. Give the domain, range, and y-intercept.

10. Graph $y = \log_5 x$.

The statements $x = a^y$ and $y = \log_a x$ are equivalent.

Write equivalent logarithmic equations.

11. $7^{2.3} = x$

12. $8^{\frac{1}{3}} = 2$

Write equivalent exponential equations.

13. $\log_3 81 = 4$

14. $\log_8 M = t$

12-3

Certain equations containing logarithmic notation can be solved by first converting to exponential notation.

15. Solve $\log_x 64 = 3$.

16. Solve $\log_{16} 4 = x$.

For any number a suitable as a logarithm base, $a^{\log_a x} = x$ for $x > 0$ and $\log_a a^x = x$ for any x.

17. Simplify $\log_b b^3$.

18. Simplify $3^{\log_3 t}$.

12-4

For any positive number x and y, where a is any positive number different from 1, $\log_a (x \cdot y) = \log_a x + \log_a y$, $\log_a x^p = p \cdot \log_a x$, and $\log_a \frac{x}{y} = \log_a x - \log_a y$.

19. Express $\frac{1}{2}\log_b a + \frac{3}{2}\log_b c - 4\log_b d$ as a single logarithm.

20. Express $\log \sqrt[3]{\frac{M^2}{N}}$ in terms of logarithms of M and N.

Given that $\log_a 2 \approx 0.301$, $\log_a 3 \approx 0.477$, and $\log_a 7 \approx 0.845$, find the following.

21. $\log_a 18$ **22.** $\log_a \frac{7}{2}$ **23.** $\log_a \frac{1}{4}$ **24.** $\log_a \sqrt{3}$

12-5

Finding $\log_{10} 1.23$, or finding x such that $10^x = 1.23$, are different ways of stating the same problem. Table 2 or a calculator will be helpful.

Use Table 2 or a calculator to find the following.

25. $\log 26.2$ **26.** $\log_{10} 0.00806$ **27.** $10^x = 5.82$

28. antilog 0.7686 **29.** antilog (7.3617 − 10) **30.** antilog 2.3304

12-6 (Optional)

Interpolation can be used to estimate values between those listed in a table.

31. Find log 18.75 using interpolation and Table 2. Check using a calculator.

32. Find antilog 1.1629 using interpolation and Table 2. Check using a calculator.

12-7

Taking logarithms of both sides can be useful in solving exponential equations.

33. $3^{-1-x} = 9^{2x}$ **34.** $4^{2x} = 8^{x-1}$

Logarithmic equations can be solved by converting to exponential equations.

Solve.

35. $\log(x^2 - 1) - \log(x - 1) = 1$ **36.** $\log_4 \sqrt{x - 2} = 2$

Exponential and logarithmic functions and equations have many applications.

37. How many years will it take an investment of \$1000 to double itself if interest is compounded annually at 5%?

12-8

Logarithms to the base e are called natural logarithms.

Find each natural logarithm to four decimal places.

38. ln 1.6 **39.** ln 1600

For any bases a and b, and any positive number M, $\log_b M = \frac{\log_a M}{\log_a b}$.

40. Find $\log_4 80$.

See also Problem 12, Computer-Assisted Problem Solving, page 847.

19. $\log_b \left[\frac{(ac^3)^{1/2}}{d^4}\right]$
20. $\frac{1}{3}(2 \log M - \log N)$
21. 1.255
22. 0.544
23. −0.602
24. 0.2385
25. 1.4183
26. 7.9063 − 10
27. 0.7649
28. 5.87
29. 0.00230
30. 214
31. 1.2730
32. 14.55
33. $-\frac{1}{5}$
34. −3
35. 9
36. 258
37. 14.2 years
38. 0.4700
39. 7.3778
40. 3.1610

ANSWERS

1. $x = 2y^2 - 3y + 1$
2. Yes
3. $f^{-1}(x) = 9x^2 - 18x + 9$
4. 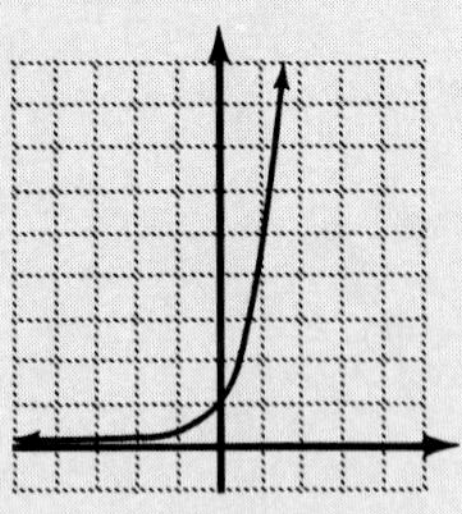
5. 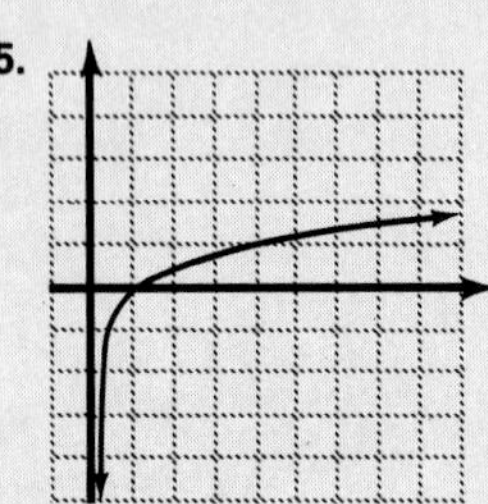
6. $x = \log_3 25$
7. $\frac{1}{2} = \log_{25} 5$
8. $3^2 = 9$
9. $6^y = x$
10. 5
11. $\frac{1}{2}$
12. $7t$
13. $\log_2\left(\frac{3^{1/3}}{4}\right)$
14. 0.902
15. 0.118
16. 1.155
17. 0.00342
18. 6
19. 5
20. 7 years
21. 0.5306
22. $k \approx 0.5135$; 3,099,000 cells
23. 2.096
24. 2.25
25. -1

Test Item Analysis

Item	Lesson
1–3	12-1
4–9	12-2
10–12	12-3
13–15, 25	12-4
16, 17	12-5
18–20	12-7
21–24	12-8

Chapter 12 Test

1. Write an equation of the inverse relation of $y = 2x^2 - 3x + 1$.
2. Test $x + y = 7$ for symmetry with respect to the line $y = x$.
3. Given $f(x) = \frac{\sqrt{x}}{3} + 1$, find an equation for $f^{-1}(x)$.

Graph.

4. $y = 4^x$
5. $y = \log_4 x$

Write the equivalent logarithmic expressions.

6. $3^x = 25$
7. $25^{\frac{1}{2}} = 5$

Write equivalent exponential equations.

8. $\log_3 9 = 2$
9. $\log_6 x = y$

Solve.

10. $\log_x 125 = 3$
11. $\log_{25} 5 = x$

Simplify.

12. $14^{\log_{14} 7t}$

Express as a single logarithm.

13. $\frac{2}{3}\log_2 8 + \frac{1}{3}\log_2 3 - 2\log_2 4$

Given that $\log_a 3 = 0.451$ and $\log_a 4 = 0.569$, find the following.

14. $\log_a 9$
15. $\log_a \frac{4}{3}$

Use Table 2 to find the following.

16. $\log 14.3$
17. antilog $(7.5340 - 10)$

Solve.

18. $2^{x-1} = 32$
19. $\log 4x + \log x = 2$
20. Suppose $10,000 is invested at 10% interest compounded annually. The investment yields $19,487. For how many years was it invested?
21. Find ln 1.7 to four decimal places.

Solve.

22. The population of a colony of cells growing exponentially in a culture is 300 after 2 minutes and 1400 after 5 minutes. Find k in the growth formula and estimate the population of the colony after 20 minutes.

Use common logarithms to find the following.

23. $\log_9 100$
24. $\log_{16} 512$

Challenge

25. If $\log_a x = 1$, what is $\log_a\left(\frac{1}{x}\right)$?

Chapters 1-12 Cumulative Review

1-3 Evaluate each expression for $a = 5$ and $c = -2$.

1. $-|a + c| + (3a + c)$ 10
2. $ac + c^2 + |6c|$ 6
3. $|a + c| - |a| - |c|$ −4
4. $|a - c| + |c - a|$ 14

2-4 Solve.

5. $4x - 3 \leq 5x + 2$
6. $-2x \leq 2(x + 3) - 1$
7. $-\frac{2}{5}x < -24$

3-6 Find an equation in standard form for the line containing

8. $(-1, 1)$ and $(-2, 1)$. $y - 1 = 0$
9. $(6, 3)$ and $(6, -3)$. $x - 6 = 0$

4-2 Solve.

10. $4x - 2y = 10$
    $-x + 2y = -7$ $(1, -3)$
11. $16x + 6y = -11$
    $-7x + 9y = -1$
    $\left(-\frac{1}{2}, -\frac{1}{2}\right)$
12. $19x + 18y = -12$
    $14x + 9y = -6$
    $\left(0, -\frac{2}{3}\right)$

4-3

13. Solution *A* is 12% acid and Solution *B* is 60% acid. How many liters of each should be mixed together to get 24 liters of a solution that is 50% acid?
5 liters of *A* and 19 liters of *B*

4-7 Graph.

14. $x < y$
15. $x - y > 0$
16. $y + x < 1$

5-3 Multiply.

17. $(2z + 4y)^2$
18. $(x - 5)^3$
19. $(a^2 + 2b)^3$

5-4 – 5-6 Factor.

20. $400x^2 - 441y^2$
21. $a^{16} - 1$
22. $x^4y^2 - x^2$
23. $y^3 + 125$
24. $y^3 + 2y^2 - 4y - 8$
25. $4x^3 - 16x^2 - 9x + 36$

5-7 Solve.

26. $2x^2 = 15 + x$
27. $3x^2 + 6 = 19x$
28. $20x^2 - 3 = -28x$

6-3 Simplify.

29. $\left(\frac{3x}{y} - x\right) \div \left(\frac{y}{x} - y\right)$
30. $\left(\frac{x - 1}{x} + \frac{x}{1 + x}\right) \div \left(\frac{x}{1 - x} + \frac{1 + x}{x}\right)$

ADDITIONAL ANSWERS

5. $-5 \leq x$
6. $x \geq -\frac{5}{4}$
7. $x > 60$
14.

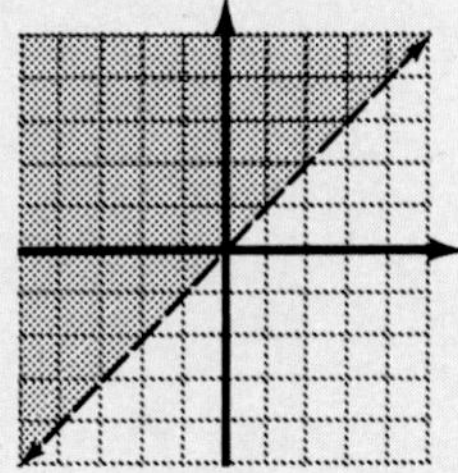

15.

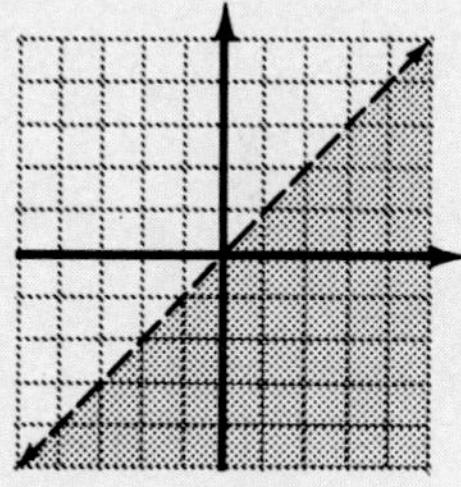

16.

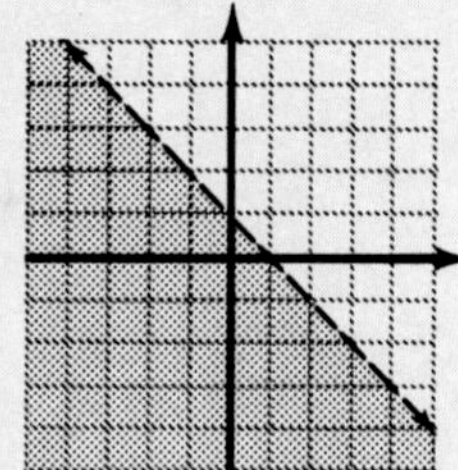

17. $4z^2 + 16yz + 16y^2$
18. $x^3 - 15x^2 + 75x - 125$
19. $a^6 + 6a^4b + 12a^2b^2 + 8b^3$
20. $(20x + 21y)(20x - 21y)$
21. $(a^8 + 1)(a^4 + 1)(a^2 + 1)(a + 1)(a - 1)$
22. $x^2(xy + 1)(xy - 1)$
23. $(y + 5)(y^2 - 5y + 25)$
24. $(y + 2)^2(y - 2)$
25. $(x - 4)(2x + 3)(2x - 3)$
26. $3, -\frac{5}{2}$
27. $\frac{1}{3}, 6$
28. $-\frac{3}{2}, \frac{1}{10}$
29. $\frac{x^2(y - 3)}{y^2(x - 1)}$
30. $\frac{(2x^2 - 1)(1 - x)}{1 + x}$

31. $x^3 + 3x^2 + x - 9$
32. $x = -\frac{10}{3}$
33. $x = \frac{1}{2}, x = -\frac{2}{7}$
34. $6|x|$
35. -5
36. $2|x|y^2$
37. 3
38. $3\sqrt{5x}$
39. $4y\sqrt{3y}$
40. $4\sqrt{2}$
41. $6 + \sqrt{35}$
42. $\frac{\sqrt{6}}{3}$
43. $\frac{2}{3}a\sqrt{3}$
44. $x\frac{\sqrt{2}(\sqrt[3]{12})}{6}$
45. $x = 21$
46. $x = 5$
47. $21 + 20i$
48. $\frac{-1 + 5i}{13}$
49. i
50. $-\frac{3}{4}, 2$
51. $0, \frac{4}{5}$
52. $\frac{-1 \pm i\sqrt{5}}{2}$
53. $12x^2 + 11x - 15 = 0$
54. $x^2 - 2x - 2 = 0$

6-4 Divide.

31. $(2x^4 + 7x^3 + 5x^2 - 17x - 9)$ by $(2x + 1)$

6-6 Solve.

32. $\frac{7}{5x - 2} = \frac{5}{4x}$ **33.** $\frac{1}{x} + \frac{2x + 3}{2} = 8x$

7-1 – 7-4 Simplify.

34. $\sqrt{36x^2}$ **35.** $\sqrt[3]{-125}$ **36.** $\sqrt[4]{16x^4y^8}$ **37.** $\sqrt{(-3)^2}$

38. $\sqrt{45x}$ **39.** $\sqrt{48y^3}$ **40.** $\sqrt{18} - \sqrt{50} + 2\sqrt{8} + \sqrt{8}$

41. $\frac{\sqrt{7} + \sqrt{5}}{\sqrt{7} - \sqrt{5}}$ **42.** $\frac{\sqrt{10}}{\sqrt{15}}$ **43.** $\frac{\sqrt{48a^5}}{\sqrt{36a^3}}$ **44.** $\frac{\sqrt[3]{96x^6}}{\sqrt{72x^2}}$

7-6 Solve.

45. $\sqrt{5x + 39} = x - 9$ **46.** $\sqrt[3]{4x + 7} + 2 = 5$

7-9 Simplify.

47. $(5 + 2i)^2$ **48.** $(1 + i) \div (2 - 3i)$ **49.** $-(-i^9)(i^4)$

8-1 – 8-3 Solve.

50. $4x^2 - 5x - 6 = 0$ **51.** $5x^2 - 4x = 0$ **52.** $2x^2 + 2x + 3 = 0$

8-4 Find a quadratic equation whose solutions are the following.

53. $\frac{3}{4}, -\frac{5}{3}$ **54.** $1 + \sqrt{3}, 1 - \sqrt{3}$

9-1 Test the following equations for symmetry with respect to the x-axis and the y-axis.

55. $4y = 3x^2 - 1$ y-axis **56.** $2x^2 - 3y^2 = 5$ Both axes **57.** $x^3 + 3y^3 = 10$ Neither axis

Determine whether each function is even, odd, or neither.

58. $f(x) = 5$ Even **59.** $f(x) = x^{23}$ Odd **60.** $f(x) = \sqrt{x} + 1$ Neither

9-6

61. For $f(x) = -3x^2 + 12x - 5$,
   a. find standard form for the quadratic function. $f(x) = -3(x - 2)^2 + 7$
   b. find the vertex, the line of symmetry, and the maximum or minimum value. $(2, 7)$, $x = 2$, max 7

9-7

62. Find the x-intercepts, if they exist.
   a. $f(x) = 4x^2 + 12x + 9$ $-\frac{3}{2}$ **b.** $f(x) = 9x^2 - 12x - 1$ $\frac{2 \pm \sqrt{5}}{3}$

10-1

63. Find the distance between the points $(-2, 5)$ and $(3, -4)$. $\sqrt{106}$

10-4, 10-5

64. Find the vertices, foci, and asymptotes of the hyperbola $8x^2 - 3y^2 = 48$. Then graph the hyperbola.

65. Find the vertex, focus, and directrix of the parabola $x^2 + 2x + 6y - 11 = 0$. Then graph the parabola.

10-7 Solve the system.

66. $y^2 + x^2 = 13$
$x - 2y = 1$ $(-3, -2), \left(\frac{17}{5}, \frac{6}{5}\right)$

67. $x^2 + y^2 = 20$
$xy = 8$ $(2, 4), (-2, -4), (4, 2), (-4, -2)$

11-2–11-5 Solve.

68. Use synthetic division to find $P(-3)$ if $P(x) = -2x^3 + x^2 - 1$. 62

69. Find a polynomial of degree 3 with roots $3, i, -i$. $x^3 - 3x^2 + x - 3 = 0$

70. Find all roots of $2x^4 - 7x^3 + 5x^2 + 9x - 5$. $\frac{1}{2}, -1, 2 + i, 2 - i$

71. What does Descartes' rule of signs tell you about the number of positive real roots and negative real roots of $4x^5 + 3x^4 - 2x^3 + 2x^2 + 3x - 1$?
3 or 1 positive roots, 2 or 0 negative roots

12-1

72. Find $f^{-1}(x)$ if $f(x) = 2x - 3$. $f^{-1}(x) = \frac{x + 3}{2}$

12-3

73. Solve $x = \log_4 16$. 2

74. Solve $\log_4 x = 3$. 64

12-4 Express as a single logarithm. Simplify if possible.

75. $\frac{1}{2}\log_5 x - 3 \log_5 y$ $\log_5\left(\frac{\sqrt{x}}{y^3}\right)$

76. $\log_a 3x + 2(\log_a 2x - \log_a x)$ $\log_a 12x$

12-5 Use Table 2 or a calculator to find the following.

77. $\log 0.00332$ $7.5211 - 10$

78. antilog $(8.3215 - 10)$ .021

12-7 Solve.

79. $3^{3x-2} = 27$ $\frac{5}{3}$

80. $\log(x + 19) - \log 2x = 1$ 1

12-8

81. Find ln 73.2. 4.2932

82. Find $\log_3 45$. 3.465

64. Center: $(0, 0)$;
vertices: $(\sqrt{6}, 0), (-\sqrt{6}, 0)$;
foci: $(\sqrt{22}, 0), (-\sqrt{22}, 0)$;
asymptotes $y = \frac{2\sqrt{6}}{3}x$,
$y = \frac{-2\sqrt{6}}{3}x$

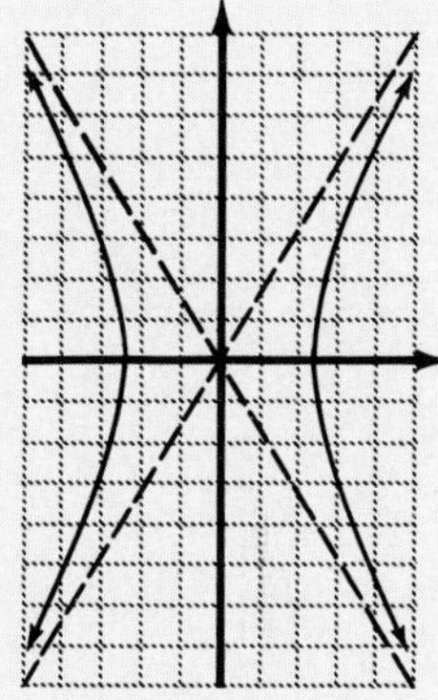

65. Vertex: $(-1, 2)$;
focus: $\left(-1, \frac{1}{2}\right)$;
directrix: $y = \frac{7}{2}$

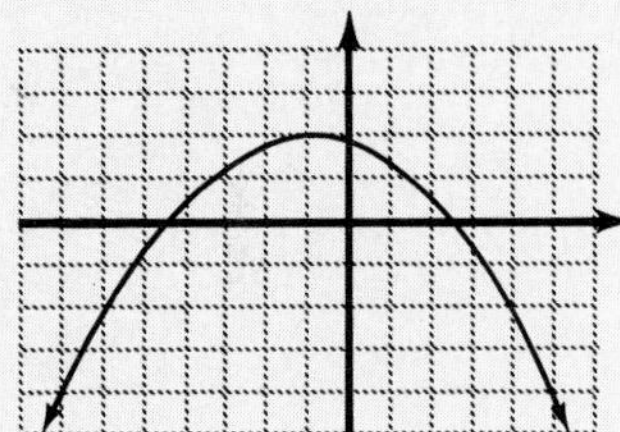

CHAPTER 13

Matrices and Determinants

Chapter Overview

Chapter 13 begins the study of finite math. Properties of matrices and determinants and their use in solving systems of equations are highlighted. Row-equivalent operations are used to find the inverse of a matrix. Problem-solving lessons involve translation to matrices, an application of matrices to cryptography, and a college entrance exam strategy for solving quantitative comparisons.

Objectives

13-1
- State the dimensions of a matrix.
- Solve systems of equations using matrices.

13-2
- Add matrices.
- Subtract matrices and find the additive inverse of a matrix.

13-3
- Evaluate a 2×2 determinant.
- Solve a system of two equations in two variables using Cramer's rule.
- Evaluate a 3×3 determinant.
- Solve a system of three equations in three variables using Cramer's rule.

13-4
- Find the product of a scalar and a matrix, and the product of two matrices.
- Write a matrix equation equivalent to a system of equations.

13-5
- Determine whether two matrices are inverses.
- Find the inverse of a 2×2 matrix.

13-6
- Calculate the inverse of a square matrix.
- Solve systems of equations using the inverse of a matrix.

13-7
- Solve problems by translating to matrices.

TEACHING CHAPTER 13

Cooperative Learning Opportunities

The topics in Chapter 13 will be new to most students. Operations with matrices and determinants are not difficult but they demand close attention. The concepts and skills build systematically on one another and a student who becomes lost early will have difficulty regaining understanding. All of these factors make the chapter a good candidate for study groups. You might assign these groups, have them meet several times a week in class, and encourage them to meet out of class. Each group should contain three to five students. The following are suggestions to help the study groups get started.

Lesson 13-1: Assign Exercise 9, 10, or 11.

Lesson 13-3: Assign one of the **Try This** Exercises for example 4.
Lesson 13-5: Have groups meet in or out of class to review operations on matrices and inverses.
Lesson 13-6: Finding the inverse of a 3×3 matrix is best done individually. But the work is tedious. Assign the same exercises to a group. Have one student explain to the others the steps he or she used to obtain the inverse.

Multicultural Note: *Two Friends—Cayley and Sylvester*

Arthur Cayley (1821–1895) studied at Cambridge, earning degrees in law as well as mathematics. While he practiced law for 14 years he also wrote hundreds of mathematical papers. His contributions were primarily in abstract algebra but he also worked in geometry.

James Joseph Sylvester (1814–1897) also studied at Cambridge and was a lawyer with an active practice for about 10 years. Sylvester worked on the theory of determinants for 50 years. He taught at several universities including Johns Hopkins and Oxford.

Starting in about 1850, Cayley and Sylvester became good friends encouraging each other's work through the following years. Cayley was mild mannered and methodical while Sylvester was impatient and intuitive. Sylvester frequently published brilliant guesses rather than mathematical proofs. Both men helped establish the role of algebra in contemporary mathematics.

Alternative Assessment and Communication Ideas

Lesson 13-7 covers applications of matrices. But the procedures can be introduced earlier to assess whether students' difficulties are with the abstract nature of matrices or with the specific manipulations. This concrete reference will also aid students' understanding.

For Lesson 13-2 on the addition and subtraction of matrices, you can suggest a 2×4 matrix in which the rows stand for methods of recording music: tapes and compact discs; and the columns stand for different kinds of music: country, folk, rock, and jazz. A store's inventory will be represented by a matrix and adding would result in a matrix showing the total for two stores.

Relating to Lesson 13-4, you could use a 1×2 matrix for prices of tapes and discs and multiply it by a 2×4 matrix for quantity of sales by category (folk, etc.). The resulting 1×4 matrix contains total dollar sales for each category.

Investigations and Projects

Transformations of different kinds were covered in connection with conic sections and other curves. Some students will be interested to find that matrices can effect transformations. As a start on a project, you might show students a triangle with vertices $A(3, -1)$ and $B(-2, 5)$ and $C(4, 6)$. These coordinates can be put into matrix form.

$$\begin{array}{c} \\ x \\ y \end{array} \begin{array}{c} \begin{array}{ccc} A & B & C \end{array} \\ \begin{bmatrix} 3 & -2 & 4 \\ -1 & 5 & 6 \end{bmatrix} \end{array}$$

A transformation can be effected by the product:

$$\begin{bmatrix} -1 & 0 \\ 0 & 1 \end{bmatrix} \quad \begin{bmatrix} 3 & -2 & 4 \\ -1 & 5 & 6 \end{bmatrix}$$

Have students graph the original and resulting triangle and describe the transformation. Based on the results ask what matrix would effect a reflection over the x-axis. Have students try other transformations using matrices composed of 1's and -1's. Ask them to write a paper or develop a display for the bulletin board.

MANAGING CHAPTER 13

Lesson	PACING CHART (DAYS) Algebra	Algebra w/Finite	Algebra w/Trig	Compre-hensive	Opening Activity	Cooperative Activity	Seat or Group Work
13-1	0	0.5	0	0.5	First Five Minutes 13-1: **TE** p.568 or ***FFM Transparency Masters*** p.37	Critical Thinking: **SE** p.572 Strategy Problem Bank 12: ***Problem Bank*** p.13 Critical Thinking 13: ***Enrichment*** p.34	Try This a–h
13-2	0	0.5	0	0.5	First Five Minutes 13-2: **TE** p.573 or ***FFM Transparency Masters*** p.37	Critical Thinking: **SE** p.575 Looking for Errors 12: ***Enrichment*** p.73	Try This a–g
13-3	0	1	0	1	First Five Minutes 13-3: **TE** p.576 or ***FFM Transparency Masters*** p.37	Critical Thinking: **SE** p.581	Try This a–j
13-4	0	1	0	1	First Five Minutes 13-4: **TE** p.582 or ***FFM Transparency Masters*** p.38	Critical Thinking: **SE** p.588 Looking for Errors 13: ***Enrichment*** p.74	Try This a–l
13-5	0	1	0	1	First Five Minutes 13-5: **TE** p.589 or ***FFM Transparency Masters*** p.38	Explore: **SE** p.589 Critical Thinking: **SE** p.592 ✂ Manipulative Activity 13: ***Enrichment*** p.54	Try This a–e
13-6	0	1	0	1	First Five Minutes 13-6: **TE** p.593 or ***FFM Transparency Masters*** p.38	Critical Thinking: **SE** p.597	Try This a–d
13-7	0	2	0	1	First Five Minutes 13-7: **TE** p.598 or ***FFM Transparency Masters*** p.39	Critical Thinking: **SE** p.601 Problem Solving: **SE** pp.602–603 Problem Solving: **SE** pp.604–605	Try This a
Review	0	1	0	1			
Test	0	1	0	1			

FFM: First Five Minutes SPMR: Skills Practice Mixed Review

Enrichment	Review/Assess	Reteach	Technology	Lesson
Critical Thinking 13: ***Enrichment*** p.34 Bonus Topic 12: ***Enrichment*** p.13	Lesson Quiz: **TE** p.571	Skills Practice 36, #1–15: ***SPMR*** p.48	BASIC Computer Project 13: ***Technology*** p.93	**13-1**
Looking for Errors 12: ***Enrichment*** p.73	Lesson Quiz: **TE** p.574	Skills Practice 36, #16–25: ***SPMR*** p.48		**13-2**
TI-81 Investigation 3: **SE** pp.860–862	Lesson Quiz: **TE** p.580 Quiz 25: ***Assessment*** p.33	Skills Practice 37, #1–15: ***SPMR*** p.49	Calculator Worksheet 24: ***Technology*** p.26 TI-81 Investigation 3: **SE** pp.860–862	**13-3**
Looking for Errors 13: ***Enrichment*** p.74	Lesson Quiz: **TE** p.586	Skills Practice 37, #16–23: ***SPMR*** p.49		**13-4**
✂ Manipulative Activity 13: ***Enrichment*** p.54 Bonus Topic 13: ***Enrichment*** p.14	Lesson Quiz: **TE** p.591 Mixed Review 25: ***SPMR*** p.89	Skills Practice 38, #1–8: ***SPMR*** p.50	Calculator Worksheet 25: ***Technology*** p.27	**13-5**
Lesson Enrichment: **TE** p.595 TI-81 Investigation 4: **SE** pp.863–865	Lesson Quiz: **TE** p.596 Quiz 26: ***Assessment*** p.34	Skills Practice 38, #9–20: ***SPMR*** p.50	Spreadsheet Activity 8: ***Technology*** pp.64–66 Problem for Programmers: **SE** p.592 TI-81 Investigation 4: **SE** pp.863–865	**13-6**
Problem Solving: **SE** pp.602–603 Problem Solving: **SE** pp.604–605 Problem 13: Computer Assisted Problem Solving, **SE** pp.848–849	Lesson Quiz: **TE** p.599 Mixed Review 26: ***SPMR*** p.90	Skills Practice 38, #21–22: ***SPMR*** p.50 Problem Bank 20: ***Problem Bank*** p.41	Problem 13: Computer Assisted Problem Solving, **SE** pp.848–849 BASIC Computer Project 14: ***Technology*** p.94	**13-7**
	Summary and Review: **SE** pp.606–608; Test: **SE** p.609			**Review**
	Chapter 13 Test: ***Assessment*** pp.119–124(reg.), pp.181–182 (adv.)			**Test**

The solution to the problem posed on the facing page can be found on page 598.

Ready for Matrices and Determinants?

1-3 Evaluate for $x = -2$, $y = -3$, and $z = 8$.

1. $x(y + z)$ −10

2. $xy(yz - xz)$ −48

4-2, 4-4 Solve.

3. $5x + 3y = 7$
$3x - 5y = -23$ −1, 4

4. $2x - y + 4z = -3$
$x - 4z = 5$
$6x - y + 2z = 10$ 3, 7, $-\frac{1}{2}$

5. $x + y - 2z = 9$
$2x + y - z = 4$
$x + 2y + z = 5$ −2, 5, −3

C H A P T E R

13 Matrices and Determinants

The table shows the number of boxes of apples sold to each market.

Apples	***Markets***	
	Al's	***Bell***
McIntosh	*200*	*180*
Gravenstein	*150*	*250*
Jonathan	*300*	*200*

The profit is \$5.75 on a box of McIntosh apples, \$3.25 on Gravensteins, and \$2.00 on Jonathans. How much profit is generated by sales to each market?

13-1

FIRST FIVE MINUTES

1. Solve the system.
   $3x + 2y = 13$
   $y = x - 6$
   $x = 5, y = -1$
2. Solve the system.
   $2x - 3y = 1$
   $5x + 3y = 55$
   $x = 8, y = 5$

Dimensions of a Matrix

Emphasize that the solution of a system of equations is completely determined by the coefficients of the equations. The variables serve essentially as place holders. An array containing the coefficients captures the important information about the system of equations.

If the desks in your classroom are in rows and columns, you may want to use them as elements of a matrix. Designate the front left desk as element a_{11}, the desk behind it as a_{21}, and so on. Ask students where they and other students are sitting.

You may wish to point out the different ways of representing matrix elements. A 2 × 2 matrix may be represented as

$$\begin{bmatrix} a_{11} & a_{12} \\ a_{21} & a_{22} \end{bmatrix}, \begin{bmatrix} a_1 & b_1 \\ a_2 & b_2 \end{bmatrix}, \text{ or } \begin{bmatrix} a & b \\ c & d \end{bmatrix}.$$

Using the notation a_{ij}, i represents the row and j represents the column.

You may also point out that matrices, like synthetic division, represent equations using only their coefficients, making it an efficient method of representation.

Key Questions

Put the following matrix on the board.

$$\begin{bmatrix} 9 & 7 & 2 \\ 0 & 3 & 1 \\ 5 & 4 & 6 \end{bmatrix}$$

- What are the elements of row 1? 9, 7, 2
- What are the elements of column 3? 2 1 6
- What is the element at row 3, column 1? 5
- What is the element a_{21}? 0
- What is the array element where the number 1 occurs? a_{23}

13-1 Matrices and Systems of Equations

To solve systems of equations, we perform computations with the coefficients and constants. After the equations are in the form $Ax + By = C$, the variables play no important role in the process until we state the solution. We can simplify the process by omitting the variables. For example, the system

$$\begin{aligned} 3x + 4y &= 5 \\ x - 2y &= 1 \end{aligned} \quad \text{simplifies to} \quad \begin{matrix} 3 & 4 & 5 \\ 1 & -2 & 1 \end{matrix}$$

In the above example we have written a rectangular array of numbers. Such an array is called a **matrix** (plural: **matrices**). We ordinarily write brackets around matrices.

$$\begin{bmatrix} 3 & 4 & 5 \\ 1 & -2 & 1 \end{bmatrix}$$

Definition

An $m \times n$ **matrix,** where m and n are positive integers, is an array of the form

$$\begin{bmatrix} a_{11} & a_{12} & a_{13} & \cdots & a_{1n} \\ a_{21} & a_{22} & a_{23} & \cdots & a_{2n} \\ a_{31} & a_{32} & a_{33} & \cdots & a_{3n} \\ \vdots & \vdots & \vdots & & \vdots \\ a_{m1} & a_{m2} & a_{m3} & \cdots & a_{mn} \end{bmatrix}$$

Each **element** a_{ij} of the matrix is a real number.

Dimensions of a Matrix

Objective: State the dimensions of a matrix.

An $m \times n$ matrix (read "m by n") has m horizontal **rows** and n vertical **columns.** In the following 4 × 3 matrix, a_{12} (read "a sub one two") is the element in row 1, column 2, so a_{12} is -2. The element a_{21} is 9, the element a_{33} is -7, and so on.

	column 1 ↘	column 2 ↓	column 3 ↙
row 1	5	−2	2
row 2	9	0	4
row 3	0	1	−7
row 4	−3	6	8

Definition

A matrix of m rows and n columns is called a matrix with **dimensions** $m \times n$.

EXAMPLES Find the dimensions of each matrix.

1. $\begin{bmatrix} 2 & -3 & 4 \\ -1 & \frac{1}{2} & \pi \end{bmatrix}$

2×3 matrix

2. $\begin{bmatrix} -3 & 8 & 9 \\ \pi & -2 & 5 \\ -6 & 7 & 8 \end{bmatrix}$

3×3 matrix

3. $\begin{bmatrix} 10 \\ -7 \end{bmatrix}$

2×1 matrix

4. $[-3 \quad 4]$

1×2 matrix

Note that the row dimension is always listed first. A row matrix is any matrix with dimensions $1 \times n$. A column matrix is any matrix with dimensions $m \times 1$.

Try This Find the dimensions of each matrix.

a. $\begin{bmatrix} -3 & 5 \\ 4 & \frac{1}{4} \\ -\pi & 0 \end{bmatrix}$ 3×2

b. $\begin{bmatrix} -3 & 0 \\ 0 & 3 \end{bmatrix}$ 2×2

c. $\begin{bmatrix} 1 & 2 & 3 \\ 0 & 1 & 8 \\ 0 & 0 & 1 \end{bmatrix}$ 3×3

d. $[\pi \quad \sqrt{2}]$ 1×2

e. $\begin{bmatrix} -5 \\ \pi \end{bmatrix}$ 2×1

f. $[-3]$ 1×1

Systems of Linear Equations

Objective: Solve systems of equations using matrices.

We can use matrices to solve systems of linear equations. All the operations used on the matrices correspond to operations with the equations. Since the operations produce equivalent matrices, we call them row equivalent operations. The matrices are said to be **row equivalent.**

Theorem 13-1

Each of the following row-equivalent operations produces equivalent matrices.

A. interchanging any two rows of a matrix
B. multiplying each element of a row by the same nonzero constant
C. multiplying each element of a row by a nonzero number and adding the result to another row

Chalkboard Examples

Find the dimensions of each matrix.

1. $\begin{bmatrix} 2 & 5 & 8 & 9 \\ 4 & 1 & 3 & 7 \end{bmatrix}$
   2 by 4
2. $[9 \quad 8 \quad 7 \quad 6 \quad 5 \quad 4]$
   1 by 6
3. $[0]$
   1 by 1
4. $\begin{bmatrix} 3 \\ 5 \\ 7 \end{bmatrix}$
   3 by 1

Systems of Linear Equations

Emphasize that at each stage of the solution of a system of equations, we have a new matrix and thus a simpler system of equations. The new system and the corresponding new matrix are obtained by three elementary row operations: exchanging rows, multiplying a row by a constant, or adding a multiple of one row to a multiple of another.

As an illustration of the parallel between solving by matrices and solving by the addition method, solve

$$3x + 4y = 25$$
$$4x + 3y = 24$$

using both methods simultaneously.

Chalkboard Examples

1. Solve using matrices.
$x + 2y = 3$
$3x + 8y = 1$
The matrix is
$\begin{bmatrix} 1 & 2 & 3 \\ 3 & 8 & 1 \end{bmatrix}$ ① ②
Multiply ① by −3.
$\begin{bmatrix} -3 & -6 & -9 \\ 3 & 8 & 1 \end{bmatrix}$ −3 · ① ②
Add ① and ②.
$\begin{bmatrix} 0 & 2 & -8 \\ 3 & 8 & 1 \end{bmatrix}$ ① + ② ②
Returning the variables, we have
$2y = -8$
$y = -4$
Substituting,
$3x + 8(-4) = 1$
$3x = 33$
$x = 11$

When solving a system of equations with matrices, our goal will be to get the matrix in the form where there are just 0's below the main diagonal formed by a, e, and h. Such a matrix is said to be in triangular form. Then we put the variables back and complete the solution.

$$\begin{bmatrix} a & b & c & d \\ 0 & e & f & g \\ 0 & 0 & h & k \end{bmatrix}$$ The dashed line indicates the main diagonal.

EXAMPLE 5 Solve using matrices.

$$2x - y = -1$$
$$3x + 2y = 16$$

We write the matrix using only the coefficients and constants.

$$\begin{bmatrix} 2 & -1 & -1 \\ 3 & 2 & 16 \end{bmatrix}$$

We do the same calculations using the matrix that we would do with the system of equations. Our goal is to put the matrix in triangular form.

The first step is to multiply the first row by 3 and the second row by −2.

$$\begin{bmatrix} 6 & -3 & -3 \\ -6 & -4 & -32 \end{bmatrix}$$ This corresponds to multiplying equation ① by 3 and equation ② by −2.

Now we add the first row to the second row to make $a_{21} = 0$.

$$\begin{bmatrix} 6 & -3 & -3 \\ 0 & -7 & -35 \end{bmatrix}$$ This corresponds to adding equation ① to equation ②, thus eliminating the x-term of equation ②.

We now have the matrix in triangular form. If we put the variables back, we have the following.

$$6x - 3y = -3$$
$$-7y = -35$$

We solve ② for y and get $y = 5$. Substituting 5 for y in ① and solving for x, we get $x = 2$. The solution is (2, 5).

EXAMPLE 6 Solve using matrices.

$$2x - y + 4z = -3$$
$$x - 4z = 5$$
$$6x - y + 2z = 10$$

We first write a matrix, using only the coefficients and constants. Note that where there are missing terms we must write 0's.

$$\begin{bmatrix} 2 & -1 & 4 & -3 \\ 1 & 0 & -4 & 5 \\ 6 & -1 & 2 & 10 \end{bmatrix}$$

We do exactly the same calculations using the matrix that we would do if we used the equations. The first step, if possible, is to interchange the rows so that each number in the first column is a multiple of a_{11}. We do this by interchanging rows 1 and 2.

$$\begin{bmatrix} 1 & 0 & -4 & 5 \\ 2 & -1 & 4 & -3 \\ 6 & -1 & 2 & 10 \end{bmatrix}$$ This corresponds to interchanging equation ① and equation ②.

Next we multiply the first row by -2 and add it to the second row to make $a_{21} = 0$.

$$\begin{bmatrix} 1 & 0 & -4 & 5 \\ 0 & -1 & 12 & -13 \\ 6 & -1 & 2 & 10 \end{bmatrix}$$ This corresponds to multiplying equation ① by -2 and adding it to equation ②, thus eliminating the x-term in equation ②.

Now we multiply the first row by -6 and add it to the third row to make $a_{31} = 0$.

$$\begin{bmatrix} 1 & 0 & -4 & 5 \\ 0 & -1 & 12 & -13 \\ 0 & -1 & 26 & -20 \end{bmatrix}$$ This corresponds to multiplying equation ① by -6 and adding it to equation ③, thus eliminating the x-term in equation ③.

Next we multiply row 2 by -1 and add it to the third row to make $a_{32} = 0$.

$$\begin{bmatrix} 1 & 0 & -4 & 5 \\ 0 & -1 & 12 & -13 \\ 0 & 0 & 14 & -7 \end{bmatrix}$$ This corresponds to multiplying equation ② by -1 and adding it to equation ③, thus eliminating the y-term in equation ③.

We now have the matrix in triangular form.

If we put the variables back, we have the following.

$$x - 4z = 5$$
$$-y + 12z = -13$$
$$14z = -7$$

We solve ③ for z and get $z = -\frac{1}{2}$.

Next we substitute $-\frac{1}{2}$ for z in ② and solve for y.

$$-y + 12\left(-\frac{1}{2}\right) = -13, \text{ so } y = 7$$

Since there is no y-term in ①, we need only substitute $-\frac{1}{2}$ for z in ① and solve for x: $x - 4(-\frac{1}{2}) = 5$, so $x = 3$.

The solution is $(3, 7, -\frac{1}{2})$.

Try This Solve using matrices.

g. $5x - 2y = -44$
$x + 5y = 2$ $(-8, 2)$

h. $x - 2y + 3z = 4$
$2x - y + z = -1$
$4x + y + z = 1$ $(-1, 2, 3)$

2. Solve using matrices.
$2x + 4y + 8z = 6$
$x + 3y + 5z = 4$
$3x + 8y + 6z = 19$

$$\begin{bmatrix} 2 & 4 & 8 & 6 \\ 1 & 3 & 5 & 4 \\ 3 & 8 & 6 & 19 \end{bmatrix}$$

Interchange ① and ②.

$$\begin{bmatrix} 1 & 3 & 5 & 4 \\ 2 & 4 & 8 & 6 \\ 3 & 8 & 6 & 19 \end{bmatrix} \begin{matrix} ② \\ ① \\ \\ \end{matrix}$$

Multiply ① by -2 and add it to ②.
Multiply ① by -3 and add it to ③.

$$\begin{bmatrix} 1 & 3 & 5 & 4 \\ 0 & -2 & -2 & -2 \\ 0 & -1 & -9 & 7 \end{bmatrix} \begin{matrix} \\ -2① + ② \\ -3① + ③ \end{matrix}$$

Interchange ② and ③.

$$\begin{bmatrix} 1 & 3 & 5 & 4 \\ 0 & -1 & -9 & 7 \\ 0 & -2 & -2 & -2 \end{bmatrix} \begin{matrix} \\ ③ \\ ② \end{matrix}$$

Multiply ② by -2 and add it to ③.

$$\begin{bmatrix} 1 & 3 & 5 & 4 \\ 0 & -1 & -9 & 7 \\ 0 & 0 & 16 & -16 \end{bmatrix}$$

We now have the system
$x + 3y + 5z = 4$
$-y - 9z = 7$
$16z = -16$
Solving, $z = -1$
$-y - 9(-1) = 7$, so $y = 2$
$x + 3(2) + 5(-1) = 4$, so $x = 3$

LESSON QUIZ

1. Find the dimensions of the matrix.
$$\begin{bmatrix} 5 & 8 & 3 \\ 2 & 1 & 0 \end{bmatrix}$$
2 by 3
2. Solve using matrices.
$3x + 6y = 12$
$2x + 5y = 11$
$x = -2$
$y = 3$

Assignment Guide
Algebra: omit

Alg w/Finite Math: 1–13 e/o, 14, MR, assign w. 13-2.

Comprehensive: 1–13 e/o, 14–16, MR, assign w. 13-2.

ADDITIONAL ANSWERS

Exercises

9. $(-1, 2, -2)$
10. $\left(\frac{1}{2}, 2, 1\right)$
11. $\left(2, \frac{1}{2}, -2\right)$

14. Answers may vary. Since both multiplication and subtraction (addition with inverses) are row equivalent operations, the result is a row equivalent matrix.
15. $(2, -1, 3, 4, 1)$
16. $(2, -2, 3, -29, 9)$

Mixed Review

17. $\frac{x(x-21)}{(x+3)(x-3)}$
18. $\frac{a+b}{a^2+ab+b^2}$
19. -0.3036
20. 3.141
21. 0.9562
22. 5.9562
23. 12, -12

13-1 EXERCISES

A

Find the dimensions of each matrix.

1. $\begin{bmatrix} 2 & -5 & 3 \\ 1 & 4 & -6 \end{bmatrix}$ 2×3

2. $\begin{bmatrix} \pi & -8 & 3 & 5 \\ \frac{1}{2} & 0 & 0 & 7 \\ -8 & 0 & 0 & 0 \end{bmatrix}$ 3×4

3. $\begin{bmatrix} 0 & 3 \\ 1 & -1 \\ 5 & -5 \\ 2 & 7 \\ 8 & 1.9 \end{bmatrix}$ 5×2

4. $\begin{bmatrix} -3 \\ 4 \\ 12 \end{bmatrix}$ 3×1

Solve using matrices.

5. $4x + 2y = 11$
   $3x - y = 2$ $\left(\frac{3}{2}, \frac{5}{2}\right)$

6. $3x - 3y = -6$
   $9x - 2y = 3$ $(1, 3)$

7. $5x + 2 = 3y$
   $4x + 2y - 5 = 0$ $\left(\frac{1}{2}, \frac{3}{2}\right)$

8. $3x + 3y - 2 = 0$
   $2y = -1 + 5x$ $\left(\frac{1}{3}, \frac{1}{3}\right)$

9. $x + 2y - 3z = 9$
   $2x - y + 2z = -8$
   $3x - y - 4z = 3$

10. $4x + y - 3z = 1$
    $8x + y - z = 5$
    $2x + y + 2z = 5$

11. $3x + 2y + 2z = 3$
    $x + 2y - z = 5$
    $2x - 4y + z = 0$

B

Solve using matrices.

12. $2w - 2x - 2y + 2z = 10$
    $w + x + y + z = -5$
    $3w + x - y + 4z = -2$
    $w + 3x - 2y + 2z = -6$ $(1, -3, -2, -1)$

13. $w - 2x + 3y - z = 8$
    $w - x - y + z = 4$
    $w + 2x + y + z = 26$
    $w - x + y + z = 14$ $(7, 4, 5, 6)$

14. ***Critical Thinking*** Show that subtracting a multiple of one row of a matrix from another row results in a row-equivalent matrix.

Challenge

Solve using matrices.

15. $x + y - 2z + 3w + 2n = 9$
    $8x + 5y - 2z - w + 2n = 3$
    $2x + 2y - z + w - 2n = 1$
    $3x + 3y - z + w + n = 5$
    $4x + 4y + z - 3n = 4$

16. $2x + 2y + 4z + 4w + 13n = 13$
    $x - y + 2z + 2w + 6n = 6$
    $y - z - w - 3n = -3$
    $3x - 2y + 4z + 4w + 12n = 14$
    $2x - 2y + 4z + 5w + 15n = 10$

Mixed Review

Subtract. **17.** $\frac{4x}{x+3} - \frac{3x}{x-3}$ **18.** $\frac{5a^2 + 4ab + 3b^2}{a^3 - b^3} - \frac{4}{a-b}$

Evaluate. **19.** log 0.497 **20.** antilog 0.497 **21.** log 9.04

22. log (9.04×10^5)

23. Four more than the square of a number is 148. Find the number.

13-2 Addition and Subtraction of Matrices

In 1857, Arthur Cayley, an English mathematician, developed the idea of matrix algebra. In this section we begin the study of operations with matrices.

Matrix Addition

Objective: Add matrices.

To *add* matrices, we add the corresponding elements. The matrices must have the same dimensions. Capital letters are used to denote matrices. Addition of matrices is both commutative and associative.

EXAMPLES Add.

1. $A = \begin{bmatrix} -5 & 0 \\ 4 & 1 \end{bmatrix}$ $B = \begin{bmatrix} 6 & -3 \\ 2 & 3 \end{bmatrix}$ $A + B = \begin{bmatrix} -5+6 & 0-3 \\ 4+2 & 1+3 \end{bmatrix} = \begin{bmatrix} 1 & -3 \\ 6 & 4 \end{bmatrix}$

A matrix having zeros for all of its members is called a zero matrix and is often denoted by O. When a zero matrix is added to another matrix of the same dimensions, that same matrix is obtained. Thus a zero matrix is an additive identity.

2. $\begin{bmatrix} 2 & -1 & 3 \\ 1 & 0 & -1 \end{bmatrix} + \begin{bmatrix} 0 & 0 & 0 \\ 0 & 0 & 0 \end{bmatrix} = \begin{bmatrix} 2 & -1 & 3 \\ 1 & 0 & -1 \end{bmatrix}$

Try This Add.

a. Let $A = \begin{bmatrix} 4 & -1 \\ 6 & -3 \end{bmatrix}$, $B = \begin{bmatrix} -6 & -5 \\ 7 & 3 \end{bmatrix}$, $O = \begin{bmatrix} 0 & 0 \\ 0 & 0 \end{bmatrix}$

(1) $A + B$ $\begin{bmatrix} -2 & -6 \\ 13 & 0 \end{bmatrix}$ **(2)** $B + A$ $\begin{bmatrix} -2 & -6 \\ 13 & 0 \end{bmatrix}$ **(3)** $O + A$ $\begin{bmatrix} 4 & -1 \\ 6 & -3 \end{bmatrix}$

Additive Inverses and Subtraction

Objective: Subtract matrices and find the additive inverse of a matrix.

To subtract matrices, we subtract the corresponding elements. The matrices must have the same dimensions.

EXAMPLE 3 Subtract.

$$\begin{bmatrix} 1 & 2 \\ -2 & 0 \\ -3 & -1 \end{bmatrix} - \begin{bmatrix} 1 & -1 \\ 1 & 3 \\ 2 & 3 \end{bmatrix} = \begin{bmatrix} 0 & 3 \\ -3 & -3 \\ -5 & -4 \end{bmatrix}$$

13-2

FIRST FIVE MINUTES

1. Solve using matrix methods.
$2x + 6y = 2$
$5x + 16y = 4$

$\begin{bmatrix} 2 & 6 & 2 \\ 5 & 16 & 4 \end{bmatrix}$ ① ②

Multiply ① by $\frac{1}{2}$.

$\begin{bmatrix} 1 & 3 & 1 \\ 5 & 16 & 4 \end{bmatrix}$ $\frac{1}{2}$①

Multiply ① by -5 and add it to ②.

$\begin{bmatrix} 1 & 3 & 1 \\ 0 & 1 & -1 \end{bmatrix}$ $-5$① + 2

Solve.
$x + 3y = 1$
$y = -1$
The solution is
$x = 4$
$y = -1$

Matrix Addition

Remind students of the properties of real numbers. The real numbers under addition and multiplication are closed, associative, commutative, and distributive, and have identity elements and inverses. While a matrix is made up of real numbers, it is not a real number. Therefore, we cannot assume that all of these properties are true for matrices and, in fact, they are not.

Chalkboard Examples

Add.

1. $\begin{bmatrix} 1 & 2 \\ 3 & 4 \end{bmatrix} + \begin{bmatrix} 4 & 3 \\ 2 & 1 \end{bmatrix}$ $\begin{bmatrix} 5 & 5 \\ 5 & 5 \end{bmatrix}$
2. $\begin{bmatrix} 1 & 2 & 3 \\ 4 & 5 & 6 \\ 7 & 8 & 9 \end{bmatrix} + \begin{bmatrix} -1 & -2 & -3 \\ -4 & -5 & -6 \\ -7 & -8 & -9 \end{bmatrix}$ $\begin{bmatrix} 0 & 0 & 0 \\ 0 & 0 & 0 \\ 0 & 0 & 0 \end{bmatrix}$
3. $\begin{bmatrix} 9 & 8 \end{bmatrix} + \begin{bmatrix} 0 & 0 \end{bmatrix}$ $\begin{bmatrix} 9 & 8 \end{bmatrix}$

Additive Inverses and Subtraction

Chalkboard Examples

1. Subtract.
$\begin{bmatrix} 5 & 4 \\ 3 & 2 \end{bmatrix} - \begin{bmatrix} 1 & 2 \\ 3 & 4 \end{bmatrix}$ $\begin{bmatrix} 4 & 2 \\ 0 & -2 \end{bmatrix}$

2. Find the additive inverse of

$$\begin{bmatrix} 2 & 3 & -4 \\ 5 & -6 & 7 \\ 8 & 9 & 0 \end{bmatrix}$$

$$\begin{bmatrix} -2 & -3 & +4 \\ -5 & +6 & -7 \\ -8 & -9 & 0 \end{bmatrix}$$

3. Subtract by adding an inverse.

$$\begin{bmatrix} 1 & 3 & 5 \\ 7 & 9 & 1 \end{bmatrix} - \begin{bmatrix} 0 & 2 & 4 \\ 6 & 8 & 0 \end{bmatrix}$$

$$\begin{bmatrix} 1 & 3 & 5 \\ 7 & 9 & 1 \end{bmatrix} + \begin{bmatrix} 0 & -2 & -4 \\ -6 & -8 & 0 \end{bmatrix}$$

$$= \begin{bmatrix} 1 & 1 & 1 \\ 1 & 1 & 1 \end{bmatrix}$$

LESSON QUIZ

1. Add.

$$\begin{bmatrix} 1 & 4 & 7 \\ 0 & 3 & 6 \\ 9 & 2 & 5 \end{bmatrix} + \begin{bmatrix} 5 & 9 & 3 \\ 7 & 1 & 5 \\ 9 & 3 & 7 \end{bmatrix}$$

$$\begin{bmatrix} 6 & 13 & 10 \\ 7 & 4 & 11 \\ 18 & 5 & 12 \end{bmatrix}$$

2. Subtract.

$$\begin{bmatrix} 3 & 6 & 1 \\ 0 & 2 & 9 \\ 4 & 5 & 7 \end{bmatrix} - \begin{bmatrix} 7 & 5 & 8 \\ 4 & 3 & 2 \\ 1 & 2 & 6 \end{bmatrix}$$

$$\begin{bmatrix} -4 & 1 & -7 \\ -4 & -1 & 7 \\ 3 & 3 & 1 \end{bmatrix}$$

3. Find the additive inverse of

$$\begin{bmatrix} 7 & 2 & 0 \\ 4 & 1 & 5 \\ 6 & 8 & 9 \end{bmatrix}$$

$$\begin{bmatrix} -7 & -2 & 0 \\ -4 & -1 & -5 \\ -6 & -8 & -9 \end{bmatrix}$$

Try This Subtract.

b. $\begin{bmatrix} 1 & 3 & -2 \\ 4 & 0 & 5 \end{bmatrix} - \begin{bmatrix} 2 & -1 & 5 \\ 6 & 4 & -3 \end{bmatrix}$ $\begin{bmatrix} -1 & 4 & -7 \\ -2 & -4 & 8 \end{bmatrix}$

c. $\begin{bmatrix} 1 & 2 \\ 4 & 1 \\ -5 & 4 \end{bmatrix} - \begin{bmatrix} 7 & -4 \\ 3 & 5 \\ 2 & -1 \end{bmatrix}$ $\begin{bmatrix} -6 & 6 \\ 1 & -4 \\ -7 & 5 \end{bmatrix}$

The additive inverse of a matrix can be obtained by replacing each element by its additive inverse. For a matrix A, the additive inverse is $-A$. When two matrices that are additive inverses of each other are added, a zero matrix is obtained.

EXAMPLE 4 Find the additive inverse.

$$A = \begin{bmatrix} 1 & 0 & 2 \\ 3 & -1 & 5 \end{bmatrix} \quad -A = \begin{bmatrix} -1 & 0 & -2 \\ -3 & 1 & -5 \end{bmatrix}$$

Try This Find the additive inverse.

d. $\begin{bmatrix} 2 & -1 & 5 \\ 6 & 4 & -3 \end{bmatrix}$ $\begin{bmatrix} -2 & 1 & -5 \\ -6 & -4 & 3 \end{bmatrix}$

e. $\begin{bmatrix} 1 & 3 & -5 \\ -2 & 0 & 0 \\ 6 & -10 & 7 \end{bmatrix}$ $\begin{bmatrix} -1 & -3 & 5 \\ 2 & 0 & 0 \\ -6 & 10 & -7 \end{bmatrix}$

If we denote matrices by A and B and an additive inverse by $-B$, we can subtract by adding an inverse as we do with numbers.

Theorem 13-2

For any matrices A and B, $A - B = A + (-B)$.

EXAMPLE 5 Subtract by adding an additive inverse.

$$\begin{matrix} A & - & B \end{matrix}$$

$$\begin{bmatrix} 3 & -1 \\ -2 & 4 \end{bmatrix} - \begin{bmatrix} 2 & 1 \\ 3 & -2 \end{bmatrix} = \begin{bmatrix} 1 & -2 \\ -5 & 6 \end{bmatrix}$$

$$= \quad A \quad + \quad (-B)$$

$$\begin{bmatrix} 3 & -1 \\ -2 & 4 \end{bmatrix} + \begin{bmatrix} -2 & -1 \\ -3 & 2 \end{bmatrix} = \begin{bmatrix} 1 & -2 \\ -5 & 6 \end{bmatrix}$$

Try This Subtract by adding an additive inverse.

f. $\begin{bmatrix} 1 & 3 & -2 \\ 4 & 0 & 5 \end{bmatrix} - \begin{bmatrix} -2 & 1 & -5 \\ -6 & -4 & 3 \end{bmatrix}$ $\begin{bmatrix} 3 & 2 & 3 \\ 10 & 4 & 2 \end{bmatrix}$

g. $\begin{bmatrix} 9 & 3 & 7 \\ -1 & 5 & -3 \\ 0 & -4 & -6 \end{bmatrix} - \begin{bmatrix} -2 & 5 & 14 \\ 2 & -8 & 2 \\ -7 & -6 & 0 \end{bmatrix}$ $\begin{bmatrix} 11 & -2 & -7 \\ -3 & 13 & -5 \\ 7 & 2 & -6 \end{bmatrix}$

13-2 EXERCISES

A

For Exercises 1 – 34, let

$A = \begin{bmatrix}1 & 2\\4 & -3\end{bmatrix}$ $B = \begin{bmatrix}-3 & -5\\2 & -1\end{bmatrix}$ $C = \begin{bmatrix}1 & -1\\-1 & 1\end{bmatrix}$ $D = \begin{bmatrix}1 & 1\\1 & 1\end{bmatrix}$ $E = \begin{bmatrix}1 & 3\\2 & 6\end{bmatrix}$

$F = \begin{bmatrix}3 & 3\\-1 & -1\\0 & 0\end{bmatrix}$ $G = \begin{bmatrix}1 & 0 & -2\\0 & -1 & 3\\3 & -2 & 4\end{bmatrix}$ $H = \begin{bmatrix}-1 & -2 & 5\\1 & 0 & -1\\-2 & -3 & 1\end{bmatrix}$ $J = \begin{bmatrix}-2 & 3 & 4\\8 & 0 & -1\end{bmatrix}$

$M = \begin{bmatrix}-4 & 5 & -2\\1 & 0 & -4\\-2 & -3 & -5\end{bmatrix}$ $O = \begin{bmatrix}0 & 0\\0 & 0\end{bmatrix}$ $Q = \begin{bmatrix}-3 & -3 & 7\\-5 & 2 & 1\end{bmatrix}$ $R = \begin{bmatrix}-1 & 0 & 0\\0 & 2 & 0\end{bmatrix}$

Find the dimensions of each matrix.

1. A 2×2 **2.** G 3×3 **3.** Q 2×3 **4.** O 2×2

Add or subtract.

5. $A + B$ **6.** $B + C$ **7.** $J + Q$ **8.** $R + J$ **9.** $H + G$
10. $M + H$ **11.** $G + J$ **12.** $R + F$ **13.** $A - B$ **14.** $C - B$
15. $F - D$ **16.** $H - M$ **17.** $G - H$ **18.** $Q - J$ **19.** $M - R$

Find the additive inverse of each matrix.

20. D **21.** Q **22.** E **23.** M

Subtract by adding an additive inverse.

24. $D - C$ **25.** $M - H$ **26.** $J - Q$ **27.** $O - F$

B

Find the value of each sum.

28. $(A + B) + C$ and $A + (B + C)$ **29.** $(G + H) + M$ and $(M + H) + G$

30. ***Critical Thinking*** The transpose of A, A^t, is formed by exchanging the rows and columns of A. (For $A = \begin{bmatrix}a & b\\c & d\end{bmatrix}$, $A^t = \begin{bmatrix}a & c\\b & d\end{bmatrix}$.) Show that $A^t + B^t = (A + B)^t$.

$\begin{bmatrix}a & b\\c & d\end{bmatrix}^t + \begin{bmatrix}e & f\\g & h\end{bmatrix}^t = \begin{bmatrix}a & c\\b & d\end{bmatrix} + \begin{bmatrix}e & g\\f & h\end{bmatrix} = \begin{bmatrix}a+e & c+g\\b+f & d+h\end{bmatrix}$

$\begin{bmatrix}a & b\\c & d\end{bmatrix} + \begin{bmatrix}e & f\\g & h\end{bmatrix} = \begin{bmatrix}a+e & b+f\\c+g & d+h\end{bmatrix}, \begin{bmatrix}a+e & b+f\\c+g & d+h\end{bmatrix}^t = \begin{bmatrix}a+e & c+g\\b+f & d+h\end{bmatrix}$

Challenge

31. Prove Theorem 13-2.

32. Prove that for any $m \times n$ matrices A and B, $A + B = B + A$.

Mixed Review

Solve. **33.** $7^x = 10$ **34.** $\log x + \log (x + 8) = 1$ **35.** $2x^2 = 5$
36. $2x^2 - 9x = 5$ **37.** $x^2 + 2x = 15$

38. Twenty-four less than the square of n is five times n. Find n.

Assignment Guide
Algebra: omit

Alg w/Finite or Trig: 1–29 e/o, 30, MR, assign w. 13-1.

Comprehensive: 1–27 m3, 28–32, MR, assign w. 13-1.

ADDITIONAL ANSWERS

Exercises

5. $\begin{bmatrix}-2 & -3\\6 & -4\end{bmatrix}$

6. $\begin{bmatrix}-2 & -6\\1 & 0\end{bmatrix}$

7. $\begin{bmatrix}-5 & 0 & 11\\3 & 2 & 0\end{bmatrix}$

8. $\begin{bmatrix}-3 & 3 & 4\\8 & 2 & -1\end{bmatrix}$

9. $\begin{bmatrix}0 & -2 & 3\\1 & -1 & 2\\1 & -5 & 5\end{bmatrix}$

10. $\begin{bmatrix}-5 & 3 & 3\\2 & 0 & -5\\-4 & -6 & -4\end{bmatrix}$

11. Cannot be added

12. Cannot be added

13. $\begin{bmatrix}4 & 7\\2 & -2\end{bmatrix}$

14. $\begin{bmatrix}4 & 4\\-3 & 2\end{bmatrix}$

15. Cannot be subtracted

16. $\begin{bmatrix}3 & -7 & 7\\0 & 0 & 3\\0 & 0 & 6\end{bmatrix}$

17. $\begin{bmatrix}2 & 2 & -7\\-1 & -1 & 4\\5 & 1 & 3\end{bmatrix}$

18. $\begin{bmatrix}-1 & -6 & 3\\-13 & 2 & 2\end{bmatrix}$

19. Cannot be subtracted

For Exercises 20–32, see Teacher's Answer Section.

Mixed Review

33. 1.183 **34.** $-4 + \sqrt{26}$

35. $\pm\frac{\sqrt{10}}{2}$ **36.** $5, -\frac{1}{2}$

37. $-5, 3$ **38.** $8, -3$

13-3

FIRST FIVE MINUTES

1. Subtract.

$$\begin{bmatrix} 9 & 7 & 8 \\ 5 & 6 & 4 \\ 8 & 7 & 3 \end{bmatrix} - \begin{bmatrix} 7 & 5 & 4 \\ 2 & 4 & 1 \\ 3 & 5 & 7 \end{bmatrix}$$

$$\begin{bmatrix} 2 & 2 & 4 \\ 3 & 2 & 3 \\ 5 & 2 & -4 \end{bmatrix}$$

Determinants of 2 × 2 Matrices

Avoiding Common Errors

The vertical bars enclosing a determinant *do not* signify absolute value. Determinants may be negative; absolute value is always nonnegative.

Key Question

- What kind of matrices have determinants?
  Square matrices

Chalkboard Example

1. Evaluate.

$$\begin{vmatrix} 5 & -2 \\ 1 & -3 \end{vmatrix}$$

$5 \cdot (-3) - 1 \cdot (-2) = -13$

Cramer's Rule for Two Equations

Remind students that a system of two linear equations in two unknowns corresponds to a pair of lines. If the lines are parallel and distinct, then there are no solutions to the system. In this case the system is *inconsistent*. If the lines are identical, then there are many solutions. In this case the system is said to be *dependent*. If the two lines meet in a single point, then there is a single solution to the system. In this case the system is *consistent* and *independent*. The determinant of coefficients is nonzero if and only if the system is consistent and independent.

13-3 Determinants and Cramer's Rule

TI-81 Investigation 3 (page 860) can be used with this lesson.

Determinants of 2 × 2 Matrices

Objective: Evaluate a 2 × 2 determinant.

A matrix with the same number of rows and columns is called a square matrix. With every square matrix is associated a number called its determinant. The determinant of a matrix A is denoted $|A|$. The determinant of a 2 × 2 matrix is defined as follows.

Definition

The **determinant** of the matrix $\begin{bmatrix} a_1 & b_1 \\ a_2 & b_2 \end{bmatrix}$ is denoted $\begin{vmatrix} a_1 & b_1 \\ a_2 & b_2 \end{vmatrix}$ and is defined as

$$\begin{vmatrix} a_1 & b_1 \\ a_2 & b_2 \end{vmatrix} = a_1b_2 - a_2b_1$$

EXAMPLE 1 Evaluate $\begin{vmatrix} 7 & -3 \\ -4 & -8 \end{vmatrix}$.

$$\begin{vmatrix} 7 & -3 \\ -4 & -8 \end{vmatrix} = 7(-8) - (-4)(-3) = -68$$

The arrows indicate the products involved.

Try This Evaluate.

a. $\begin{vmatrix} -4 & -5 \\ -2 & -6 \end{vmatrix}$ 14

b. $\begin{vmatrix} 1 & 2 \\ 3 & 4 \end{vmatrix}$ −2

c. $\begin{vmatrix} -2 & -3 \\ 4 & x \end{vmatrix}$ $-2x + 12$

Cramer's Rule for Two Equations

Objective: Solve a system of two equations in two variables using Cramer's rule.

Determinants have many uses. One of these is in solving systems of linear equations in which the number of variables is the same as the number of equations. Let us consider a system of two equations, each in the form $ax + by = c$.

$$a_1x + b_1y = c_1$$
$$a_2x + b_2y = c_2$$

If we solve this system by elimination of variables, we obtain the following solution.

$$x = \frac{c_1b_2 - c_2b_1}{a_1b_2 - a_2b_1} \text{ and } y = \frac{a_1c_2 - a_2c_1}{a_1b_2 - a_2b_1}$$

We note that the numerators and denominators of the expressions for x and y are determinants. Thus we have the following theorem.

Theorem 13-3

Cramer's Rule (2 Equations)

The system of two equations in two variables

$$\begin{aligned} a_1x + b_1y &= c_1 \\ a_2x + b_2y &= c_2 \end{aligned}$$ has a solution given by

$$x = \frac{\begin{vmatrix} c_1 & b_1 \\ c_2 & b_2 \end{vmatrix}}{\begin{vmatrix} a_1 & b_1 \\ a_2 & b_2 \end{vmatrix}} \text{ and } y = \frac{\begin{vmatrix} a_1 & c_1 \\ a_2 & c_2 \end{vmatrix}}{\begin{vmatrix} a_1 & b_1 \\ a_2 & b_2 \end{vmatrix}}, \text{ where } \begin{vmatrix} a_1 & b_1 \\ a_2 & b_2 \end{vmatrix} \neq 0$$

Note that the denominator is the same for both variables, and it contains the coefficients of x and y in the same position as in the original equations. We refer to this determinant as D.

For x, the numerator is obtained by replacing the x-coefficients (the a's) in D by the constants (the c's). For y, the numerator is obtained by replacing the y-coefficients (the b's) in D by the c's.

If $D = 0$, then one of these situations occurs:

1. If $D = 0$ and the determinants of the numerators are also 0, then the system of equations is dependent.
2. If $D = 0$ and at least one of the other determinants is nonzero, then the system is inconsistent.

EXAMPLE 2 Solve using Cramer's rule.

$$\begin{aligned} 2x + 5y &= 7 \\ 4x - 2y &= -3 \end{aligned}$$

$$D = \begin{vmatrix} 2 & 5 \\ 4 & -2 \end{vmatrix} = 2(-2) - 4(5) = -24.$$

$$x = \frac{\begin{vmatrix} 7 & 5 \\ -3 & -2 \end{vmatrix}}{-24} \qquad y = \frac{\begin{vmatrix} 2 & 7 \\ 4 & -3 \end{vmatrix}}{-24}$$

$$x = \frac{7(-2) - (-3)(5)}{-24} \qquad y = \frac{2(-3) - 4(7)}{-24}$$

$$x = \frac{-1}{24} \qquad y = \frac{17}{12}$$

The solution is $\left(-\frac{1}{24}, \frac{17}{12}\right)$.

Key Questions

- Is the system
  $3x + 2y = 1$
  $4x + 6y = 3$
  consistent and independent?
  Yes
- Is the system
  $2x + 3y = 1$
  $4x + 6y = 3$
  consistent and independent?
  No

Chalkboard Example

1. Solve using Cramer's rule.
   $4x + 3y = 1$
   $2x + \ \ y = 5$
   $\begin{vmatrix} 4 & 3 \\ 2 & 1 \end{vmatrix} = 4 \cdot 1 - 2 \cdot 3 = -2$
   $x = \frac{\begin{vmatrix} 1 & 3 \\ 5 & 1 \end{vmatrix}}{-2} = \frac{1 \cdot 1 - 5 \cdot 3}{-2} = 7$
   $y = \frac{\begin{vmatrix} 4 & 1 \\ 2 & 5 \end{vmatrix}}{-2} = \frac{4 \cdot 5 - 2 \cdot 1}{-2} = -9$

Determinants of 3 × 3 Matrices

Chalkboard Example

1. Evaluate.

$$\begin{vmatrix} 2 & 4 & 8 \\ 1 & 3 & 5 \\ 3 & 8 & 6 \end{vmatrix}$$

$$2 \cdot \begin{vmatrix} 3 & 5 \\ 8 & 6 \end{vmatrix} - 1 \cdot \begin{vmatrix} 4 & 8 \\ 8 & 6 \end{vmatrix} + 3 \cdot \begin{vmatrix} 4 & 8 \\ 3 & 5 \end{vmatrix}$$
$= 2(-22) - 1(-40) + 3(-4)$
$= -16$

Try This Solve using Cramer's rule.

d. $2x - y = 5$
$x - 2y = 1$ (3, 1)

e. $3x + 4y = -2$
$5x - 7y = 1$ $\left(-\frac{10}{41}, -\frac{13}{41}\right)$

Determinants of 3 × 3 Matrices

Objective: Evaluate a 3 × 3 determinant.

Definition

The **determinant** of a 3 × 3 matrix is defined as follows.

$$\begin{vmatrix} a_1 & b_1 & c_1 \\ a_2 & b_2 & c_2 \\ a_3 & b_3 & c_3 \end{vmatrix} = a_1 \cdot \begin{vmatrix} b_2 & c_2 \\ b_3 & c_3 \end{vmatrix} - a_2 \cdot \begin{vmatrix} b_1 & c_1 \\ b_3 & c_3 \end{vmatrix} + a_3 \cdot \begin{vmatrix} b_1 & c_1 \\ b_2 & c_2 \end{vmatrix}$$
$$= a_1b_2c_3 - a_1b_3c_2 - a_2b_1c_3 + a_2b_3c_1 + a_3b_1c_2 - a_3b_2c_1$$

Each 2 × 2 determinant may be obtained by crossing out the row and column in which the a-coefficient occurs.

$$a_1 \begin{vmatrix} a_1 & b_1 & c_1 \\ a_2 & b_2 & c_2 \\ a_3 & b_3 & c_3 \end{vmatrix} - a_2 \begin{vmatrix} a_1 & b_1 & c_1 \\ a_2 & b_2 & c_2 \\ a_3 & b_3 & c_3 \end{vmatrix} + a_3 \begin{vmatrix} a_1 & b_1 & c_1 \\ a_2 & b_2 & c_2 \\ a_3 & b_3 & c_3 \end{vmatrix}$$

EXAMPLE 3 Evaluate.

$$\begin{vmatrix} -1 & 0 & 1 \\ -5 & 1 & -1 \\ 4 & 8 & 1 \end{vmatrix} = -1 \cdot \begin{vmatrix} 1 & -1 \\ 8 & 1 \end{vmatrix} - (-5) \cdot \begin{vmatrix} 0 & 1 \\ 8 & 1 \end{vmatrix} + 4 \cdot \begin{vmatrix} 0 & 1 \\ 1 & -1 \end{vmatrix}$$
$$= -1(1 + 8) + 5(0 - 8) + 4(0 - 1) = -53$$

EXAMPLE 4 Evaluate.

$$\begin{vmatrix} -3 & 3 & 0 \\ 1 & -6 & 1 \\ -1 & 0 & -3 \end{vmatrix} = -3 \begin{vmatrix} -6 & 1 \\ 0 & -3 \end{vmatrix} - 1 \begin{vmatrix} 3 & 0 \\ 0 & -3 \end{vmatrix} + (-1) \begin{vmatrix} 3 & 0 \\ -6 & 1 \end{vmatrix}$$

$$a_1b_2c_3 - a_1b_3c_2 - a_2b_1c_3 + a_2b_3c_1 + a_3b_1c_2 - a_3b_2c_1$$
$$= -54 - 0 - (-9) + 0 + (-3) - 0 = -48$$

Try This Evaluate.

f. $\begin{vmatrix} 3 & 2 & 2 \\ -2 & 1 & 4 \\ 4 & -3 & 3 \end{vmatrix}$ 93 **g.** $\begin{vmatrix} -5 & 0 & 0 \\ 4 & 2 & 0 \\ -3 & 5 & -6 \end{vmatrix}$ 60 **h.** $\begin{vmatrix} 5 & 0 & 5 \\ 0 & 5 & 0 \\ 1 & 0 & 5 \end{vmatrix}$ 100

Cramer's Rule for Three Equations

Objective: Solve a system of three equations in three variables using Cramer's rule.

Cramer's rule uses determinants to solve systems of three equations the same way we solved systems of two equations.

Theorem 13-4

Cramer's Rule (3 Equations)

The system of three equations in three variables

$$\begin{aligned} a_1x + b_1y + c_1z &= d_1 \\ a_2x + b_2y + c_2z &= d_2 \\ a_3x + b_3y + c_3z &= d_3 \end{aligned} \quad \text{has a solution given by}$$

$$x = \frac{D_x}{D}, y = \frac{D_y}{D}, z = \frac{D_z}{D}, \text{ where } D = \begin{vmatrix} a_1 & b_1 & c_1 \\ a_2 & b_2 & c_2 \\ a_3 & b_3 & c_3 \end{vmatrix}, D \neq 0,$$

$$D_x = \begin{vmatrix} d_1 & b_1 & c_1 \\ d_2 & b_2 & c_2 \\ d_3 & b_3 & c_3 \end{vmatrix}, D_y = \begin{vmatrix} a_1 & d_1 & c_1 \\ a_2 & d_2 & c_2 \\ a_3 & d_3 & c_3 \end{vmatrix}, \text{ and } D_z = \begin{vmatrix} a_1 & b_1 & d_1 \\ a_2 & b_2 & d_2 \\ a_3 & b_3 & d_3 \end{vmatrix}$$

Note that we obtain the determinant D_x, the numerator of x, by substituting the constants d_1, d_2, and d_3 for the x-coefficients. We obtain D_y and D_z similarly. We have thus extended Cramer's rule to solve systems of three equations in three variables.

EXAMPLE 5 Solve using Cramer's rule.

$$\begin{aligned} x - 3y + 7z &= 13 \\ x + y + z &= 1 \\ x - 2y + 3z &= 4 \end{aligned}$$

$$D = \begin{vmatrix} 1 & -3 & 7 \\ 1 & 1 & 1 \\ 1 & -2 & 3 \end{vmatrix} = -10 \qquad D_x = \begin{vmatrix} 13 & -3 & 7 \\ 1 & 1 & 1 \\ 4 & -2 & 3 \end{vmatrix} = 20$$

$$D_y = \begin{vmatrix} 1 & 13 & 7 \\ 1 & 1 & 1 \\ 1 & 4 & 3 \end{vmatrix} = -6 \qquad D_z = \begin{vmatrix} 1 & -3 & 13 \\ 1 & 1 & 1 \\ 1 & -2 & 4 \end{vmatrix} = -24$$

$$x = \frac{D_x}{D} = \frac{20}{-10} = -2, \; y = \frac{D_y}{D} = \frac{-6}{-10} = \frac{3}{5}, \; z = \frac{D_z}{D} = \frac{-24}{-10} = \frac{12}{5}$$

The solution is $\left(-2, \frac{3}{5}, \frac{12}{5}\right)$. In practice, it is not necessary to evaluate D_z. When we find values for x and y we can substitute them into an equation to find z.

Cramer's Rule for Three Equations

Point out that the determinant of a three by three matrix of coefficients can be used to determine whether a system of three equations in three unknowns is consistent and independent. If the determinant is nonzero, then the system has a unique solution.

Math Point
Given any two points and the origin, a parallelogram is uniquely determined, as in the figure below.

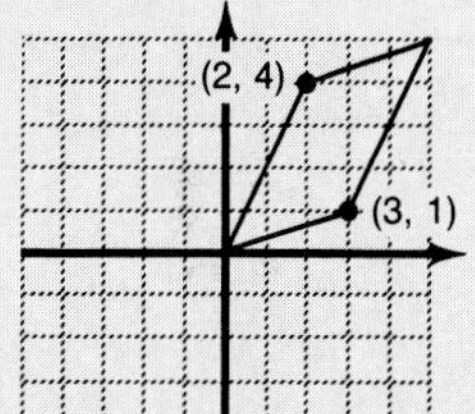

If the two points are used as the rows of a matrix, then we get the following:

$$\begin{bmatrix} 3 & 1 \\ 2 & 4 \end{bmatrix}$$

The area of the parallelogram equals the absolute value of the determinant. In this example, the area of the parallelogram is 10.

Chalkboard Example

1. Solve using Cramer's rule.

$$\begin{aligned} 2x + 4y + 8z &= 6 \\ x + 3y + 5z &= 4 \\ 3x + 8y + 6z &= 19 \end{aligned}$$

$$D = \begin{vmatrix} 2 & 4 & 8 \\ 1 & 3 & 5 \\ 3 & 8 & 6 \end{vmatrix} = -16$$

$$D_x = \begin{vmatrix} 6 & 4 & 8 \\ 4 & 3 & 5 \\ 19 & 8 & 6 \end{vmatrix} = -48$$

$$D_y = \begin{vmatrix} 2 & 6 & 8 \\ 1 & 4 & 5 \\ 3 & 19 & 6 \end{vmatrix} = -32$$

$$D_z = \begin{vmatrix} 2 & 4 & 6 \\ 1 & 3 & 4 \\ 3 & 8 & 19 \end{vmatrix} = 16$$

$$x = \frac{D_x}{D} = \frac{-48}{-16} = 3$$

$$y = \frac{D_y}{D} = \frac{-32}{-16} = 2$$

$$z = \frac{D_z}{D} = \frac{16}{-16} = -1$$

LESSON QUIZ

1. Solve using Cramer's rule.
   $4x + 2y = 2$
   $3x + 5y = -9$
   $(2, -3)$

Assignment Guide
Algebra: omit

Alg w/Finite or Trig: 1–20 m3, 21–33 e/o, 34, MR

Comprehensive: 1–33 m3, 34 35–39 e/o, MR

Try This Solve using Cramer's rule.

i. $x - 3y - 7z = 6$
$2x + 3y + z = 9$
$4x + y = 7$ $(1, 3, -2)$

j. $x + 2y - z = 2$
$2x - 2y + z = -1$
$6x + 4y + 3z = 5$ $\left(\frac{1}{3}, \frac{4}{5}, -\frac{1}{15}\right)$

13-3 EXERCISES

A

Evaluate.

1. $\begin{vmatrix} 2 & 7 \\ 1 & 5 \end{vmatrix}$ 3

2. $\begin{vmatrix} 3 & 2 \\ 2 & -3 \end{vmatrix}$ -13

3. $\begin{vmatrix} 6 & -9 \\ 2 & 3 \end{vmatrix}$ 36

4. $\begin{vmatrix} 3 & 2 \\ -7 & 5 \end{vmatrix}$ 29

5. $\begin{vmatrix} 1.3 & 2.7 \\ 4.2 & 0.8 \end{vmatrix}$ -10.3

6. $\begin{vmatrix} 2.4 & 1.6 \\ 0.9 & 1.8 \end{vmatrix}$ 2.88

7. $\begin{vmatrix} -7 & -7 \\ 3 & 3 \end{vmatrix}$ 0

8. $\begin{vmatrix} 8 & -1 \\ 8 & -1 \end{vmatrix}$ 0

Solve using Cramer's rule.

9. $3x - 4y = 6$
$5x + 9y = 10$ $(2, 0)$

10. $5x + 8y = 1$
$3x + 7y = 5$ $(-3, 2)$

11. $2x - 2y = 2$
$6x - 5y = 1$ $(-4, -5)$

12. $5x - 6y = 8$
$2x - 5y = -2$ $(4, 2)$

13. $4x - 4y = 4$
$7x + 2y = 1$ $\left(\frac{1}{3}, -\frac{2}{3}\right)$

14. $-2x + 4y = 3$
$3x - 7y = 1$ $\left(-\frac{25}{2}, -\frac{11}{2}\right)$

Evaluate.

15. $\begin{vmatrix} 0 & 2 & 0 \\ 3 & -1 & 1 \\ 1 & -2 & 2 \end{vmatrix}$ -10

16. $\begin{vmatrix} 3 & 0 & -2 \\ 5 & 1 & 2 \\ 2 & 0 & -1 \end{vmatrix}$ 1

17. $\begin{vmatrix} -1 & -2 & -3 \\ 3 & 4 & 2 \\ 0 & 1 & 2 \end{vmatrix}$ -3

18. $\begin{vmatrix} 1 & 2 & 2 \\ 2 & 1 & 0 \\ 3 & 3 & 1 \end{vmatrix}$ 3

19. $\begin{vmatrix} 3 & -2 & -2 \\ -2 & 1 & -4 \\ 4 & -3 & 3 \end{vmatrix}$ -11

20. $\begin{vmatrix} 2 & -1 & 1 \\ 1 & 2 & -1 \\ 3 & 4 & -3 \end{vmatrix}$ -6

Solve using Cramer's rule.

21. $2x - 3y + 5z = 27$
$x + 2y - z = -4$
$5x - y + 4z = 27$ $(2, -1, 4)$

22. $x - y + 2z = -3$
$x + 2y + 3z = 4$
$2x + y + z = -3$ $(-3, 2, 1)$

23. $r - 2s + 3t = 6$
$2r - s - t = -3$
$r + s + t = 6$ $(1, 2, 3)$

24. $a - 3c = 6$
$b + 2c = 2$
$7a - 3b - 5c = 14$ $(3, 4, -1)$

25. $3x + 2y - z = 4$
$3x - 2y + z = 5$
$4x - 5y - z = -1$ $\left(\frac{3}{2}, \frac{13}{14}, \frac{33}{14}\right)$

26. $3x - y + 2z = 1$
$x - y + 2z = 3$
$-2x + 3y + z = 1$ $\left(-1, -\frac{6}{7}, \frac{11}{7}\right)$

B

Evaluate.

27. $\begin{vmatrix} x & 4 \\ x & x^2 \end{vmatrix}$ $x^3 - 4x$

28. $\begin{vmatrix} y^2 & -2 \\ y & 3 \end{vmatrix}$ $3y^2 + 2y$

29. $\begin{vmatrix} z & -3 \\ z^2 & 1 \end{vmatrix}$ $z + 3z^2$

Solve for x.

30. $\begin{vmatrix} 4 & 2 \\ 3 & x \end{vmatrix} = x$ 2

31. $\begin{vmatrix} x & 5 \\ -4 & x \end{vmatrix} = 24$ 2 or −2

32. $\begin{vmatrix} x+3 & 4 \\ x-3 & 5 \end{vmatrix} = -7$ −34

33. Solve using Cramer's rule.
$\sqrt{3}x + \pi y = -5$
$\left(\frac{15 - 4\pi}{-3\sqrt{3} - \pi^2}, \frac{4\sqrt{3} + 5\pi}{-3\sqrt{3} - \pi^2}\right)$

34. ***Critical Thinking*** Is a determinant a *function* of an $n \times n$ matrix? Explain.

Challenge

35. Evaluate. $\begin{vmatrix} 1 & x & y \\ 1 & x & y \\ 1 & 1 & 1 \end{vmatrix}$ 0

36. Verify. $\begin{vmatrix} 1 & x & x^2 \\ 1 & y & y^2 \\ 1 & z & z^2 \end{vmatrix} = (x - y)(y - z)(z - x)$

37. Use linear combinations to prove Cramer's rule for a system of two equations. That is, verify that the solution of the system

$$\begin{aligned} a_1x + b_1y &= c_1 \\ a_2x + b_2y &= c_2 \end{aligned} \text{ is given by } x = \frac{c_1b_2 - c_2b_1}{a_1b_2 - a_2b_1} \text{ and } y = \frac{a_1c_2 - a_2c_1}{a_1b_2 - a_2b_1}$$

when $a_1b_2 - a_2b_1 \neq 0$.

38. Rewrite each expression as a determinant two different ways.
a. $2l + w$ **b.** $a^2 + b^2$

39. Find the determinant of A^t for $A = \begin{bmatrix} a_1 & b_1 & c_1 \\ a_2 & b_2 & c_2 \\ a_3 & b_3 & c_3 \end{bmatrix}$. What is true of the determinant of a transposed matrix? (See Lesson 13-2, Exercise 30.) It is the same as the determinant of the original matrix.

Mixed Review

Solve. 40. $x + 2 = 3x^2$ 41. $v^{\frac{4}{3}} = 16$ 42. $\frac{6}{y} + \frac{2y}{3} = 5$

43. $z^{\frac{2}{3}} - 2z^{\frac{1}{3}} - 48 = 0$

44. $3(x^2 - 2x + 5) - 2(3x - 5) = 4(x^2 - x - 5) - (x^2 + 3)$

Divide. 45. $y^5 - 2y^4 - 2y^3 + 9y^2 - 10 \div y^2 - 2$

46. Beth can wash and wax a car in 90 minutes. Toni can wash and wax a car in 75 minutes. How long will it take them to wash and wax a car if they work together?

ADDITIONAL ANSWERS

Exercises

34. Since a given $n \times n$ matrix can only have one value for its determinant, the determinant is a function. Its domain is the set of $n \times n$ matrices and its range is the set of real numbers.

36. $\begin{vmatrix} 1 & x & x^2 \\ 1 & y & y^2 \\ 1 & z & z^2 \end{vmatrix}$
$= \begin{vmatrix} y & y^2 \\ z & z^2 \end{vmatrix} - \begin{vmatrix} x & x^2 \\ z & z^2 \end{vmatrix} + \begin{vmatrix} x & x^2 \\ y & y^2 \end{vmatrix}$
$= yz^2 - zy^2 - (xz^2 - zx^2) + (xy^2 - yx^2)$
$= yz^2 - zy^2 - xz^2 + zx^2 + xy^2 - yx^2$
$= (x - y)(y - z)(z - x)$

37. Multiplying ① by $-a_2$ and ② by a_1,
$$\begin{aligned} -a_1a_2x - a_2b_1y &= -a_2c_1 \\ + \quad a_1a_2x + a_1b_2y &= a_1c_2 \\ \hline a_1b_2y - a_2b_1y &= a_1c_2 - a_2c_1 \\ y(a_1b_2 - a_2b_1) &= a_1c_2 - a_2c_1 \end{aligned}$$
$$y = \frac{a_1c_2 - a_2c_1}{a_1b_2 - a_2b_1}$$
Similarly, multiplying ① by b_2 and ② by $-b_1$
$$\begin{aligned} a_1b_2x + b_1b_2y &= c_1b_2 \\ + \; -a_2b_1x - b_1b_2y &= -c_2b_1 \\ \hline a_1b_2x - a_2b_1x &= c_1b_2 - c_2b_1 \\ x(a_1b_2 - a_2b_1) &= c_1b_2 - c_2b_1 \end{aligned}$$
$$x = \frac{c_1b_2 - c_2b_1}{a_1b_2 - a_2b_1}$$

38. Answers may vary.
a. $\begin{vmatrix} 2 & w \\ -1 & l \end{vmatrix}$ or $\begin{vmatrix} 2l & -w \\ 1 & 1 \end{vmatrix}$
b. $\begin{vmatrix} a^2 & b \\ -b & 1 \end{vmatrix}$ or $\begin{vmatrix} a & -1 \\ b^2 & a \end{vmatrix}$

Mixed Review

40. $1, -\frac{2}{3}$
41. $8, -8$
42. $6, \frac{3}{2}$
43. $512, -216$
44. 6
45. $y^3 - 2y^2 + 5$
46. 40.9 min

13-4

FIRST FIVE MINUTES

1. Solve using Cramer's rule.
   $4x + 3y = 2$
   $2x + 5y = 8$
   $D = \begin{vmatrix} 4 & 3 \\ 2 & 5 \end{vmatrix} = 14$
   $D_x = \begin{vmatrix} 2 & 3 \\ 8 & 5 \end{vmatrix} = -14$
   $D_y = \begin{vmatrix} 4 & 2 \\ 2 & 8 \end{vmatrix} = 28$
   $x = \frac{-14}{14} = -1$
   $y = \frac{28}{14} = 2$

Multiplying Matrices

Remind students that matrices can be added and subtracted, but point out that addition or subtraction of a matrix and a real number is not defined. However, the multiplication of a matrix and a real number, or scalar, is defined, as is the multiplication of two matrices.

Emphasize that not every pair of matrices can be multiplied. Furthermore, AB and BA are not necessarily equal; that is, matrix multiplication is not commutative.

Key Questions

$M = \begin{bmatrix} 0 & 1 \\ 2 & 3 \end{bmatrix}$

- What is $M + M + M$?
  $\begin{bmatrix} 0 & 3 \\ 6 & 9 \end{bmatrix}$
- What is $10M$?
  $\begin{bmatrix} 0 & 10 \\ 20 & 30 \end{bmatrix}$

What is the dimension of the matrix product of the following matrices?

- $[2 \quad 5 \quad 3] \begin{bmatrix} 9 \\ 8 \\ 7 \end{bmatrix}$
  1 by 1
- $\begin{bmatrix} 1 \\ 2 \\ 3 \end{bmatrix} [9 \quad 8 \quad 7]$
  3 by 3
- $\begin{bmatrix} 1 & 5 \\ 2 & 6 \\ 3 & 7 \\ 4 & 8 \end{bmatrix} \begin{bmatrix} 6 & 7 & 8 & 9 & 0 \\ 1 & 2 & 3 & 4 & 5 \end{bmatrix}$
  4 by 5

13-4 Multiplying Matrices

Multiplying Matrices

Objective: Find the product of a scalar and a matrix, and the product of two matrices.

There are two kinds of products involving matrices. First we define a product of a matrix and a number.

Definition

The **product** of a number k, called a scalar, and a **matrix** A is the matrix, denoted kA, obtained by multiplying each number in A by the number k.

EXAMPLES Multiply.

1. $3\begin{bmatrix} -3 & 0 \\ 4 & 5 \end{bmatrix} = \begin{bmatrix} -9 & 0 \\ 12 & 15 \end{bmatrix}$

2. $-\frac{1}{2}\begin{bmatrix} -3 & 0 \\ 4 & 5 \end{bmatrix} = \begin{bmatrix} \frac{3}{2} & 0 \\ -2 & -\frac{5}{2} \end{bmatrix}$

Try This Multiply.

a. $5\begin{bmatrix} 1 & -2 & x \\ 4 & y & 1 \\ 0 & -5 & x^2 \end{bmatrix}$ $\begin{bmatrix} 5 & -10 & 5x \\ 20 & 5y & 5 \\ 0 & -25 & 5x^2 \end{bmatrix}$

b. $-3t\begin{bmatrix} 1 & -1 & 4 & x \\ y & 3 & -2 & y \\ 1 & 4 & -5 & y \end{bmatrix}$ $\begin{bmatrix} -3t & 3t & -12t & -3xt \\ -3yt & -9t & 6t & -3yt \\ -3t & -12t & 15t & -3yt \end{bmatrix}$

Now we consider the product of two matrices. We do not multiply two matrices by multiplying their corresponding members. The motivation for defining matrix products comes from systems of equations.

Let us begin by considering a system of equations.

$$3x + 2y - 2z = 4$$
$$2x - y + 5z = 3$$
$$-x + y + 4z = 7$$

Consider the following matrices.

$$\underset{A}{\begin{bmatrix} 3 & 2 & -2 \\ 2 & -1 & 5 \\ -1 & 1 & 4 \end{bmatrix}} \underset{X}{\begin{bmatrix} x \\ y \\ z \end{bmatrix}} = \underset{B}{\begin{bmatrix} 4 \\ 3 \\ 7 \end{bmatrix}}$$

If we multiply the first row of A by X, we get $3x + 2y - 2z$. If we multiply the second row of A by X, we get $2x - y + 5z$. If we then multiply the third row of A by X, we get $-x + y + 4z$.

Note that the first members are multiplied, the second members are multiplied, the third members are multiplied, and the results are added to get a single number with three terms.

We define the product AX to be the following 3×1 column matrix.

$$\begin{bmatrix} 3x + 2y - 2z \\ 2x - y + 5z \\ -x + y + 4z \end{bmatrix}$$

Now consider this matrix equation.

$$\begin{bmatrix} 3x + 2y - 2z \\ 2x - y + 5z \\ -x + y + 4z \end{bmatrix} = \begin{bmatrix} 4 \\ 3 \\ 7 \end{bmatrix}$$

Two matrices are equal if their corresponding elements are equal. In the above equation, the "two" matrices are really the same matrix. This means that $3x + 2y - 2z$ is 4, $2x - y + 5z$ is 3, and $-x + y + 4z$ is 7.

$$3x + 2y - 2z = 4$$
$$2x - y + 5z = 3$$
$$-x + y + 4z = 7$$

Thus the matrix equation $AX = B$ is equivalent to the original system of equations.

EXAMPLE 3 Multiply.

$$\begin{bmatrix} 3 & 1 & -1 \\ 1 & 2 & 2 \\ -1 & 0 & 5 \\ 4 & 1 & 2 \end{bmatrix} \begin{bmatrix} 1 \\ 2 \\ 1 \end{bmatrix}$$

$$= \begin{bmatrix} 3 \cdot 1 + 1 \cdot 2 - 1 \cdot 1 \\ 1 \cdot 1 + 2 \cdot 2 + 2 \cdot 1 \\ -1 \cdot 1 + 0 \cdot 2 + 5 \cdot 1 \\ 4 \cdot 1 + 1 \cdot 2 + 2 \cdot 1 \end{bmatrix} = \begin{bmatrix} 4 \\ 7 \\ 4 \\ 8 \end{bmatrix}$$

Try This Multiply.

c. $\begin{bmatrix} 1 & 4 & 2 \\ -1 & 6 & 3 \\ 3 & 2 & -1 \\ 5 & 0 & 2 \end{bmatrix} \begin{bmatrix} 2 \\ 1 \\ 3 \end{bmatrix}$ $\begin{bmatrix} 12 \\ 13 \\ 5 \\ 16 \end{bmatrix}$

In the examples discussed so far, the second matrix had only one column. If it has more than one column, we multiply each row of the first matrix by each column of the second matrix separately. The product matrix will have as many columns as the second matrix.

Chalkboard Examples

Multiply.

1. $5\begin{bmatrix} 3 & 2 \\ 1 & 4 \end{bmatrix}$ $\begin{bmatrix} 15 & 10 \\ 5 & 20 \end{bmatrix}$

2. $3\begin{bmatrix} 7 & -1 \\ 4 & 8 \end{bmatrix}$ $\begin{bmatrix} 21 & -3 \\ 12 & 24 \end{bmatrix}$

3. $\begin{bmatrix} 1 & 2 \\ 3 & 4 \end{bmatrix}\begin{bmatrix} 5 \\ 6 \end{bmatrix}$ $\begin{bmatrix} 1 \cdot 5 + 2 \cdot 6 \\ 3 \cdot 5 + 4 \cdot 6 \end{bmatrix} = \begin{bmatrix} 17 \\ 39 \end{bmatrix}$

4. $\begin{bmatrix} 1 & 0 & 2 \\ 4 & 1 & 5 \\ 7 & 2 & 3 \end{bmatrix}\begin{bmatrix} 3 \\ 0 \\ 8 \end{bmatrix}$ $\begin{bmatrix} 1 \cdot 3 + 0 \cdot 0 + 2 \cdot 8 \\ 4 \cdot 3 + 1 \cdot 0 + 5 \cdot 8 \\ 7 \cdot 3 + 2 \cdot 0 + 3 \cdot 8 \end{bmatrix} = \begin{bmatrix} 19 \\ 52 \\ 45 \end{bmatrix}$

5. $\begin{bmatrix} 5 & 1 & 2 \\ 2 & 0 & 3 \end{bmatrix}\begin{bmatrix} 3 & 1 & 2 \\ 1 & 7 & 4 \\ 8 & 0 & 5 \end{bmatrix}$ $\begin{bmatrix} 32 & 12 & 24 \\ 30 & 2 & 19 \end{bmatrix}$

$A = \begin{bmatrix} 0 & 2 & 4 \\ 6 & 8 & 0 \\ 2 & 4 & 6 \end{bmatrix}$

$B = \begin{bmatrix} 1 & 3 & 5 \\ 7 & 9 & 1 \\ 3 & 5 & 7 \end{bmatrix}$

6. Find AB.

$AB = \begin{bmatrix} 26 & 38 & 30 \\ 62 & 90 & 38 \\ 48 & 72 & 56 \end{bmatrix}$

7. Find BA.

$BA = \begin{bmatrix} 28 & 46 & 34 \\ 56 & 90 & 34 \\ 44 & 74 & 54 \end{bmatrix}$

EXAMPLE 4 Multiply. (Compare with Example 3.)

$$\underset{A}{\begin{bmatrix} 3 & 1 & -1 \\ 1 & 2 & 2 \\ -1 & 0 & 5 \\ 4 & 1 & 2 \end{bmatrix}} \underset{B}{\begin{bmatrix} 1 & 0 \\ 2 & 1 \\ 1 & 3 \end{bmatrix}} = \begin{bmatrix} 4 & 3\cdot 0 + 1\cdot 1 + (-1)\cdot 3 \\ 7 & 1\cdot 0 + 2\cdot 1 + 2\cdot 3 \\ 4 & -1\cdot 0 + 0\cdot 1 + 5\cdot 3 \\ 8 & 4\cdot 0 + 1\cdot 1 + 2\cdot 3 \end{bmatrix} = \begin{bmatrix} 4 & -2 \\ 7 & 8 \\ 4 & 15 \\ 8 & 7 \end{bmatrix}$$

Same as in Example 3 (first column)

The rows of A multiplied by the second column of B

EXAMPLE 5 Multiply.

$$\begin{bmatrix} 3 & 1 & -1 \\ 2 & 0 & 3 \end{bmatrix} \begin{bmatrix} 1 & 4 & 6 \\ 3 & -1 & 9 \\ 2 & 5 & 1 \end{bmatrix}$$

$$= \begin{bmatrix} 3\cdot 1 + 1\cdot 3 - 1\cdot 2 & 3\cdot 4 + 1(-1) - 1\cdot 5 & 3\cdot 6 + 1\cdot 9 - 1\cdot 1 \\ 2\cdot 1 + 0\cdot 3 + 3\cdot 2 & 2\cdot 4 + 0\cdot(-1) + 3\cdot 5 & 2\cdot 6 + 0\cdot 9 + 3\cdot 1 \end{bmatrix}$$

$$= \begin{bmatrix} 4 & 6 & 26 \\ 8 & 23 & 15 \end{bmatrix}$$

Try This Multiply.

d. $\begin{bmatrix} 4 & 1 & 2 \\ -3 & 2 & 3 \\ 2 & 0 & 5 \\ 3 & 1 & 4 \end{bmatrix} \begin{bmatrix} 1 & 4 \\ 2 & 0 \\ -3 & 5 \end{bmatrix}$ $\begin{bmatrix} 0 & 26 \\ -8 & 3 \\ -13 & 33 \\ -7 & 32 \end{bmatrix}$

e. $\begin{bmatrix} 4 & 1 & 0 & 2 \end{bmatrix} \begin{bmatrix} 1 & 0 & 1 \\ 2 & -1 & 0 \\ 3 & 5 & 1 \\ 1 & 3 & 0 \end{bmatrix}$ $\begin{bmatrix} 8 & 5 & 4 \end{bmatrix}$

If matrix A has n columns and matrix B has n rows, then we can compute the product AB, regardless of the other dimensions. The product will have as many rows as A and as many columns as B. The element in row i, column j, of the product AB is found by multiplying the elements in row i of A by the elements in column j of B, and adding.

Theorem 13-5

The product of an $m \times n$ matrix and an $n \times p$ matrix is an $m \times p$ matrix.

$$\begin{array}{ccccc} A & \times & B & = & AB \\ \textcircled{m} \times n & & n \times \textcircled{p} & & \textcircled{m} \times \textcircled{p} \end{array}$$

$$A = \begin{bmatrix} 3 & 1 & -1 \\ 2 & 0 & 3 \end{bmatrix} \text{ and } B = \begin{bmatrix} 1 & 4 & 6 \\ 3 & -1 & 9 \\ 2 & 5 & 1 \end{bmatrix}$$

$A + B$ and $A - B$ do not exist because the dimensions of A and B are not the same. AB does exist because the number of columns in A, 3, is the same as the number of rows in B, 3. But BA does not exist because the number of columns in B, 3, is not the same as the number of rows in A, 2. Since AB exists, and BA does not, matrix multiplication is not commutative.

EXAMPLES Find the product, if possible.

$$A = \begin{bmatrix} -2 & 3 & 1 \\ 1 & 0 & 4 \end{bmatrix} \quad B = \begin{bmatrix} -2 & 0 & -1 \\ 1 & 5 & 6 \\ 0 & 2 & 3 \end{bmatrix}$$

6. $AB = \begin{bmatrix} -2 & 3 & 1 \\ 1 & 0 & 4 \end{bmatrix} \begin{bmatrix} -2 & 0 & -1 \\ 1 & 5 & 6 \\ 0 & 2 & 3 \end{bmatrix}$

$$= \begin{bmatrix} 7 & 17 & 23 \\ -2 & 8 & 11 \end{bmatrix}$$

7. BA We cannot find BA since B has 3 columns and A has only 2 rows.

Try This Find each product, if possible.

$$A = \begin{bmatrix} -2 & 4 & 0 \\ -3 & 0 & -8 \end{bmatrix} \quad B = \begin{bmatrix} -1 & -2 & -3 \\ 0 & 1 & 0 \\ 4 & 5 & 2 \end{bmatrix} \quad C = \begin{bmatrix} 1 & -1 \\ 2 & -1 \end{bmatrix}$$

f. AB $\begin{bmatrix} 2 & 8 & 6 \\ -29 & -34 & -7 \end{bmatrix}$ **g.** AC Undefined **h.** CA $\begin{bmatrix} 1 & 4 & 8 \\ -1 & 8 & 8 \end{bmatrix}$

Equivalent Matrix Equations

Objective: Write a matrix equation equivalent to a system of equations.

For later purposes it is important to be able to write a matrix equation equivalent to a system of equations.

EXAMPLE 8 Write a matrix equation equivalent to this system of equations.

$$\begin{aligned} 4x + 2y - z &= 3 \\ 9x + z &= 5 \\ 4x + 5y - 2z &= 1 \\ x + y + z &= 0 \end{aligned}$$

We write the coefficients on the left in a matrix. We write the product of that matrix by the column matrix containing the variables, and set the result equal to the column matrix containing the constants on the right.

$$\begin{bmatrix} 4 & 2 & -1 \\ 9 & 0 & 1 \\ 4 & 5 & -2 \\ 1 & 1 & 1 \end{bmatrix} \begin{bmatrix} x \\ y \\ z \end{bmatrix} = \begin{bmatrix} 3 \\ 5 \\ 1 \\ 0 \end{bmatrix}$$

Equivalent Matrix Equations

Chalkboard Example

1. Write a matrix equation equivalent to the following system.
$5x + 3y + 2z = 7$
$4x + 8y + 9z = 1$
$2x + 1y + 7z = 3$
$\begin{bmatrix} 5 & 3 & 2 \\ 4 & 8 & 9 \\ 2 & 1 & 7 \end{bmatrix} \begin{bmatrix} x \\ y \\ z \end{bmatrix} = \begin{bmatrix} 7 \\ 1 \\ 3 \end{bmatrix}$

LESSON QUIZ

1. Multiply.

$$\begin{bmatrix} 0 & 1 & 2 \\ 3 & 0 & 1 \\ 1 & 4 & 2 \end{bmatrix}\begin{bmatrix} 3 & 2 & 1 \\ 4 & 0 & 2 \\ 1 & 2 & 0 \end{bmatrix}$$

$$\begin{bmatrix} 6 & 4 & 2 \\ 10 & 8 & 3 \\ 21 & 6 & 9 \end{bmatrix}$$

2. Write a matrix equation equivalent to the following system.

$7x + 3y + 2z = 9$
$8x + 2y + 4z = 7$
$x + 5y + 6z = 8$

$$\begin{bmatrix} 7 & 3 & 2 \\ 8 & 2 & 4 \\ 1 & 5 & 6 \end{bmatrix}\begin{bmatrix} x \\ y \\ z \end{bmatrix} = \begin{bmatrix} 9 \\ 7 \\ 8 \end{bmatrix}$$

Try This Write a matrix equation equivalent to each system of equations.
See Additional Answers.

i. $3x + 4y - 2z = 5$
$2x - 2y + 5z = 3$
$6x + 7y - z = 0$

j. $5x + 7y = 19$
$3x - 2y + z = 1$
$-2x + 3y - z = -12$

k. $3v + 2x - 7y = 13$
$w - 2x = 0$
$5v + 5w - 3y = -5$
$10x - 3y = 15$
$v - x - y = 2$

l. $4w + 1 = 0$
$4w + x + 3 = 0$
$4w + 2x + y + 6 = 0$
$4w + 3x + 2y + z + 10 = 0$

The following theorem summarizes some of the properties of square matrices of the same dimensions whose elements are real numbers. We restrict the theorem to square matrices so that all additions and multiplications are possible. Some of the proofs will be considered in the Challenge Exercises. Note that not all field properties hold.

Theorem 13-6

For any square matrices A, B, and C of the same dimensions, the following properties hold.

Commutative Property

$A + B = B + A$

Associative Property

$A + (B + C) = (A + B) + C,\ A(BC) = (AB)C$

Identity

There exists a unique matrix O, such that

$A + O = O + A = A.$

Inverses

There exists a unique matrix $-A$, such that

$A + (-A) = -A + A = O.$

Distributive Property

$A(B + C) = AB + AC$

For any square matrices A and B of the same dimensions, and any real numbers k and m,

$k(A + B) = kA + kB$

$(k + m)A = kA + mA$

$(km)A = k(mA).$

13-4 EXERCISES

A

For Exercises 1 – 28, let

$A = \begin{bmatrix} 1 & 2 \\ 4 & 3 \end{bmatrix}$ $B = \begin{bmatrix} -3 & 5 \\ 2 & -1 \end{bmatrix}$ $C = \begin{bmatrix} 1 & -1 \\ -1 & 1 \end{bmatrix}$ $D = \begin{bmatrix} 1 & 1 \\ 1 & 1 \end{bmatrix}$

$E = \begin{bmatrix} 1 & 3 \\ 2 & 6 \end{bmatrix}$ $F = \begin{bmatrix} 3 & 3 \\ -1 & -1 \end{bmatrix}$ $I = \begin{bmatrix} 1 & 0 \\ 0 & 1 \end{bmatrix}$ $G = \begin{bmatrix} 1 & 0 & -2 \\ 0 & -1 & 3 \\ 3 & 2 & 4 \end{bmatrix}$

$H = \begin{bmatrix} -1 & -2 & 5 \\ 1 & 0 & -1 \\ 2 & -3 & 1 \end{bmatrix}$ $J = [-2 \quad 3 \quad -4]$ $K = [8 \quad -1]$

$L = [-1 \quad -2 \quad -3 \quad 4]$ $M = \begin{bmatrix} -2 \\ -4 \\ 7 \end{bmatrix}$ $N = \begin{bmatrix} 8 \\ -6 \\ \frac{1}{2} \end{bmatrix}$ $P = \begin{bmatrix} -3 \\ -2 \end{bmatrix}$

$Q = \begin{bmatrix} 10 \\ -4 \\ 5 \\ 2 \end{bmatrix}$ $Z = \begin{bmatrix} -2 & 9 & 6 \\ -3 & 3 & 4 \\ 2 & -2 & 1 \end{bmatrix}$

Multiply.

1. $(-2)A$ **2.** $(-5)B$ **3.** $14C$ **4.** $12D$
5. tE **6.** pF **7.** $(-1)Z$ **8.** $(-1)H$

Find each product, if possible.

9. KP **10.** JM **11.** JN **12.** LQ **13.** AB
14. BC **15.** CD **16.** EF **17.** JG **18.** KF
19. JZ **20.** FP **21.** FI **22.** IB **23.** GH
24. HG **25.** AP **26.** KC **27.** HA **28.** CG

Write a matrix equation equivalent to each of the following systems of equations.

29. $3x - 2y + 4z = 17$
$2x + y - 5z = 13$

30. $3x + 2y + 5z = 9$
$4x - 3y + 2z = 10$

31. $x - y + 2z - 4w = 12$
$2x - y - z + w = 0$
$x + 4y - 3z - w = 1$
$3x + 5y - 7z + 2w = 9$

32. $2x + 4y - 5z + 12w = 2$
$4x - y + 12z - w = 5$
$-x + 4y + 2w = 13$
$2x + 10y + z = 5$

B

33. For $A = \begin{bmatrix} 3 & 1 & 0 \\ 6 & 4 & 0 \\ 2 & 3 & 1 \end{bmatrix}$ and $B = \begin{bmatrix} 2 & 1 & 0 \\ 3 & 3 & 9 \\ 6 & 4 & 6 \end{bmatrix}$, find $3A + 2B$ and $B - 2A$. $\begin{bmatrix} 13 & 5 & 0 \\ 24 & 18 & 18 \\ 18 & 17 & 15 \end{bmatrix}$; $\begin{bmatrix} -4 & -1 & 0 \\ -9 & -5 & 9 \\ 2 & -2 & 4 \end{bmatrix}$

Assignment Guide
Algebra: omit

Alg w/Finite or Trig: 1–28 m3, 29–38 e/o, 39, MR

Comprehensive: 1–28 m4, 29–38 m3, 39, 40–46 e/o, MR

ADDITIONAL ANSWERS

Try This

i. $\begin{bmatrix} 3 & 4 & -2 \\ 2 & -2 & 5 \\ 6 & 7 & -1 \end{bmatrix} \begin{bmatrix} x \\ y \\ z \end{bmatrix} = \begin{bmatrix} 5 \\ 3 \\ 0 \end{bmatrix}$

j. $\begin{bmatrix} 5 & 7 & 0 \\ 3 & -2 & 1 \\ -2 & 3 & -1 \end{bmatrix} \begin{bmatrix} x \\ y \\ z \end{bmatrix} = \begin{bmatrix} 19 \\ 1 \\ -12 \end{bmatrix}$

k. $\begin{bmatrix} 3 & 0 & 2 & -7 \\ 0 & 1 & -2 & 0 \\ 5 & 5 & 0 & -3 \\ 0 & 0 & 10 & -3 \\ 1 & 0 & -1 & -1 \end{bmatrix} \begin{bmatrix} v \\ w \\ x \\ y \end{bmatrix} = \begin{bmatrix} 13 \\ 0 \\ -5 \\ 15 \\ 2 \end{bmatrix}$

l. $\begin{bmatrix} 4 & 0 & 0 & 0 \\ 4 & 1 & 0 & 0 \\ 4 & 2 & 1 & 0 \\ 4 & 3 & 2 & 1 \end{bmatrix} \begin{bmatrix} w \\ x \\ y \\ z \end{bmatrix} + \begin{bmatrix} 1 \\ 3 \\ 6 \\ 10 \end{bmatrix} = \begin{bmatrix} 0 \\ 0 \\ 0 \\ 0 \end{bmatrix}$

Exercises

1. $\begin{bmatrix} -2 & -4 \\ -8 & -6 \end{bmatrix}$

2. $\begin{bmatrix} 15 & -25 \\ -10 & 5 \end{bmatrix}$

3. $\begin{bmatrix} 14 & -14 \\ -14 & 14 \end{bmatrix}$

4. $\begin{bmatrix} 12 & 12 \\ 12 & 12 \end{bmatrix}$

5. $\begin{bmatrix} t & 3t \\ 2t & 6t \end{bmatrix}$

6. $\begin{bmatrix} 3p & 3p \\ -p & -p \end{bmatrix}$

7. $\begin{bmatrix} 2 & -9 & -6 \\ 3 & -3 & -4 \\ -2 & 2 & -1 \end{bmatrix}$

8. $\begin{bmatrix} 1 & 2 & -5 \\ -1 & 0 & 1 \\ -2 & 3 & -1 \end{bmatrix}$

9. $[-22]$ **10.** $[-36]$
11. $[-36]$ **12.** $[-9]$

13. $\begin{bmatrix} 1 & 3 \\ -6 & 17 \end{bmatrix}$ **14.** $\begin{bmatrix} -8 & 8 \\ 3 & -3 \end{bmatrix}$

15. $\begin{bmatrix} 0 & 0 \\ 0 & 0 \end{bmatrix}$ **16.** $\begin{bmatrix} 0 & 0 \\ 0 & 0 \end{bmatrix}$

17. $[-14 \quad -11 \quad -3]$
18. $[25 \quad 25]$

19. $\begin{bmatrix} -13 & -1 & -4 \end{bmatrix}$

20. $\begin{bmatrix} -15 \\ 5 \end{bmatrix}$

21. $\begin{bmatrix} 3 & 3 \\ -1 & -1 \end{bmatrix}$

22. $\begin{bmatrix} -3 & 5 \\ 2 & -1 \end{bmatrix}$

23. $\begin{bmatrix} -5 & 4 & 3 \\ 5 & -9 & 4 \\ 7 & -18 & 17 \end{bmatrix}$

24. $\begin{bmatrix} 14 & 12 & 16 \\ -2 & -2 & -6 \\ 5 & 5 & -9 \end{bmatrix}$

25. $\begin{bmatrix} -7 \\ -18 \end{bmatrix}$

26. $\begin{bmatrix} 9 & -9 \end{bmatrix}$

27. Not possible

28. Not possible

29. $\begin{bmatrix} 3 & -2 & 4 \\ 2 & 1 & -5 \end{bmatrix}\begin{bmatrix} x \\ y \\ z \end{bmatrix} = \begin{bmatrix} 17 \\ 13 \end{bmatrix}$

30. $\begin{bmatrix} 3 & 2 & 5 \\ 4 & -3 & 2 \end{bmatrix}\begin{bmatrix} x \\ y \\ z \end{bmatrix} = \begin{bmatrix} 9 \\ 10 \end{bmatrix}$

31. $\begin{bmatrix} 1 & -1 & 2 & -4 \\ 2 & -1 & -1 & 1 \\ 1 & 4 & -3 & -1 \\ 3 & 5 & -7 & 2 \end{bmatrix}\begin{bmatrix} x \\ y \\ z \\ w \end{bmatrix} = \begin{bmatrix} 12 \\ 0 \\ 1 \\ 9 \end{bmatrix}$

32. $\begin{bmatrix} 2 & 4 & -5 & 12 \\ 4 & -1 & 12 & -1 \\ -1 & 4 & 0 & 2 \\ 2 & 10 & 1 & 0 \end{bmatrix}\begin{bmatrix} x \\ y \\ z \\ w \end{bmatrix} = \begin{bmatrix} 2 \\ 5 \\ 13 \\ 5 \end{bmatrix}$

For Exercises 40–46, see Teacher's Answer Section.

Mixed Review

47. $x^4 - 6x^2y + 9y^2$

48. $\frac{9}{x}$

49. $\frac{4m^2\sqrt[3]{z}}{9n^4z^5}$

50. $\pm 8, \pm 4, \pm 2, \pm 1, \pm\frac{1}{2}$

51. 1 positive, 1 or 3 negative

52. $\frac{1}{2}, -2, 2i, -2i$

53. $P(3) = 325; P(-1) = -15;$ $P(0) = -8; P\left(\frac{1}{2}\right) = 0$

54. 25 m, 13 m

34. For $A = \begin{bmatrix} 3 & 2 \\ -1 & 5 \end{bmatrix}$ and $I = \begin{bmatrix} 1 & 0 \\ 0 & 1 \end{bmatrix}$, find AI and IA. $AI = \begin{bmatrix} 3 & 2 \\ -1 & 5 \end{bmatrix} = IA = A$

35. What can you conclude about matrix I in Exercise 34? I is a multiplicative identity.

36. Factor so that all matrix elements are integers.

$$\begin{bmatrix} \frac{1}{24} & -\frac{1}{6} & \frac{3}{8} \\ \frac{5}{12} & -\frac{1}{2} & \frac{7}{36} \end{bmatrix}$$

$\frac{1}{72}\begin{bmatrix} 3 & -12 & 27 \\ 30 & -36 & 14 \end{bmatrix}$

Do the following products exist? If they do, determine how many rows and columns are in the product matrix. Do not carry out the multiplication.

37. $\begin{bmatrix} 3 & 6 & 1 \\ 4 & 9 & 0 \\ 2 & 8 & 3 \end{bmatrix}\begin{bmatrix} 2 & 3 & 6 \\ 4 & 9 & 1 \end{bmatrix}$ No

38. $\begin{bmatrix} 4 & 3 & 2 & 1 & 5 \\ 6 & 9 & 3 & 25 & 6 \\ 4 & 18 & 2 & 18 & 2 \\ 3 & 6 & 1 & 1 & 2 \\ 2 & 4 & 8 & 25 & 23 \end{bmatrix}\begin{bmatrix} 6 & 3 & 7 & 9 & 11 & 24 \\ 4 & 7 & 59 & 8 & 2 & 12 \\ 3 & 2 & 6 & 0 & 1 & 7 \\ 2 & 19 & 4 & 2 & 4 & 1 \\ 1 & 23 & 3 & 9 & 0 & 1 \end{bmatrix}$ Yes; 5 rows and 6 columns

39. ***Critical Thinking*** If for two matrices A and B, both AB and BA exist, what can you determine about A, B, and their products? If A is $m \times n$, B is $n \times m$; AB is $m \times m$ and BA is $n \times n$.

Challenge

40. Let $A = \begin{bmatrix} -1 & 0 \\ 2 & 1 \end{bmatrix}$ and $B = \begin{bmatrix} 1 & -1 \\ 0 & 2 \end{bmatrix}$.

a. Show that $(A + B)(A - B) \neq A^2 - B^2$, where $A^2 = AA$ and $B^2 = BB$.
b. Show that $(A + B)(A + B) \neq A^2 + 2AB + B^2$.

For Exercises 41–46, let $A = \begin{bmatrix} a & c \\ b & d \end{bmatrix}$, $B = \begin{bmatrix} e & g \\ f & h \end{bmatrix}$, and $C = \begin{bmatrix} p & r \\ q & s \end{bmatrix}$.

Prove.

41. $A + B = B + A$

42. $(A + B) + C = A + (B + C)$

43. $A - B = A + (-B)$

44. $(-1)A = -A$

45. $k(A + B) = kA + kB$

46. $(k + m)A = kA + mA$

Mixed Review

Simplify. **47.** $(x^2 - 3y)^2$ **48.** $x^2(-3y)^2x^{-3}(-y)^{-2}$ **49.** $\left(\frac{8m^3n^{-2}}{27n^4z^7}\right)^{\frac{2}{3}}$

Let $P(x) = 2x^4 + 3x^3 + 6x^2 + 12x - 8$.

50. List the possible rational roots of $P(x)$.

51. Determine the number of positive and negative real roots.

52. Solve $P(x) = 0$. **53.** Find $P(3)$, $P(-1)$, $P(0)$, $P\left(\frac{1}{2}\right)$.

54. The length of a rectangular swimming pool is 12 m longer than the width. The area is 325 m^2. Find the length and width.

13-5 Inverses of Matrices

Explore

Let $A = \begin{bmatrix} 2 & 7 \\ 1 & 4 \end{bmatrix}$, $B = \begin{bmatrix} 1 & 0 \\ 0 & 1 \end{bmatrix}$, and $C = \begin{bmatrix} 4 & -7 \\ -1 & 2 \end{bmatrix}$.

Find AB, BA, AC, and CA. What relationships do you see?

Inverses

Objective: Determine whether two matrices are inverses.

Square matrices with 1's from the upper left to the lower right along the main diagonal are represented by the symbol I. The matrix I is the **identity matrix.**

Theorem 13-7

For any $n \times n$ matrices A and I, $AI = IA = A$ (I is a multiplicative identity).

Suppose a matrix A has a **multiplicative inverse** or simply an **inverse,** A^{-1}. Then A^{-1} is a matrix for which $A \cdot A^{-1} = A^{-1} \cdot A = I$.

EXAMPLE 1 Determine whether A and B are inverses.

$$A = \begin{bmatrix} 4 & 6 \\ 3 & 1 \end{bmatrix} \quad B = \begin{bmatrix} -\frac{1}{14} & \frac{3}{7} \\ \frac{3}{14} & -\frac{2}{7} \end{bmatrix}$$

We can test whether $AB = BA = I$ by multiplying.

$$AB = \begin{bmatrix} 4 & 6 \\ 3 & 1 \end{bmatrix} \begin{bmatrix} -\frac{1}{14} & \frac{3}{7} \\ \frac{3}{14} & -\frac{2}{7} \end{bmatrix} = \begin{bmatrix} -\frac{1}{14} & \frac{3}{7} \\ \frac{3}{14} & -\frac{2}{7} \end{bmatrix} \begin{bmatrix} 4 & 6 \\ 3 & 1 \end{bmatrix} = \begin{bmatrix} 1 & 0 \\ 0 & 1 \end{bmatrix}$$

A and B are inverses. Thus $B = A^{-1}$, and $A = B^{-1}$.

Try This Determine whether A and B are inverses.

a. $A = \begin{bmatrix} 5 & -3 \\ -7 & 4 \end{bmatrix}$ $\quad B = \begin{bmatrix} -4 & 3 \\ -7 & 5 \end{bmatrix}$ No, $AB = \begin{bmatrix} 1 & 0 \\ 0 & -1 \end{bmatrix}$

b. $A = \begin{bmatrix} 3 & 1 & 0 \\ 1 & -1 & 2 \\ 1 & 1 & 1 \end{bmatrix}$ $\quad B = \begin{bmatrix} \frac{3}{8} & \frac{1}{8} & -\frac{2}{8} \\ -\frac{1}{8} & -\frac{3}{8} & \frac{6}{8} \\ -\frac{2}{8} & \frac{2}{8} & \frac{4}{8} \end{bmatrix}$ Yes, $AB = BA = I$

13-5

FIRST FIVE MINUTES

1. Multiply.

$$\begin{bmatrix} 2 & 3 & 0 \\ 1 & 0 & 2 \\ 0 & 4 & 1 \end{bmatrix} \begin{bmatrix} 4 & 0 & 1 \\ 3 & 1 & 2 \\ 0 & 2 & 3 \end{bmatrix}$$

$$\begin{bmatrix} 17 & 3 & 8 \\ 4 & 4 & 7 \\ 12 & 6 & 11 \end{bmatrix}$$

EXPLORE

$AB = BA = \begin{bmatrix} 2 & 7 \\ 1 & 4 \end{bmatrix}$

$AC = CA = \begin{bmatrix} 1 & 0 \\ 0 & 1 \end{bmatrix}$

AC is the identity matrix.

Inverses

Point out the parallel between the real numbers and matrices. Compare $A \cdot A^{-1} = I$ with $x \cdot x^{-1} = 1$.

Emphasize that only a square matrix may have an inverse. However, there are square matrices that do not have inverses, just as there is a real number, 0, that does not have a multiplicative inverse.

Key Questions

- What is the product?

$$\begin{bmatrix} 1 & 2 & 3 \\ 4 & 5 & 6 \\ 7 & 8 & 9 \end{bmatrix} \begin{bmatrix} 1 & 0 & 0 \\ 0 & 1 & 0 \\ 0 & 0 & 1 \end{bmatrix}$$

$$\begin{bmatrix} 1 & 2 & 3 \\ 4 & 5 & 6 \\ 7 & 8 & 9 \end{bmatrix}$$

- What is the product?

$$\begin{bmatrix} 1 & 0 & 0 \\ 0 & 1 & 0 \\ 0 & 0 & 1 \end{bmatrix} \begin{bmatrix} 1 & 2 & 3 \\ 4 & 5 & 6 \\ 7 & 8 & 9 \end{bmatrix}$$

$$\begin{bmatrix} 1 & 2 & 3 \\ 4 & 5 & 6 \\ 7 & 8 & 9 \end{bmatrix}$$

Chalkboard Example

1. Determine whether A and B are inverses.

$A = \begin{bmatrix} 4 & 3 \\ 1 & 1 \end{bmatrix}$ and $B = \begin{bmatrix} 1 & -3 \\ -1 & 4 \end{bmatrix}$

$AB = \begin{bmatrix} 4 & 3 \\ 1 & 1 \end{bmatrix} \begin{bmatrix} 1 & -3 \\ -1 & 4 \end{bmatrix} = \begin{bmatrix} 1 & 0 \\ 0 & 1 \end{bmatrix}$

A and B are inverses.

Inverses of 2 × 2 Matrices

Chalkboard Example

1. Find A^{-1} where
$A = \begin{bmatrix} 3 & 1 \\ 4 & 2 \end{bmatrix}$.
$|A| = 2$
$A^{-1} = \frac{1}{2}\begin{bmatrix} 2 & -1 \\ -4 & 3 \end{bmatrix} = \begin{bmatrix} 1 & -\frac{1}{2} \\ -2 & \frac{3}{2} \end{bmatrix}$

Inverses of 2 × 2 Matrices

Objective: Find the inverse of a 2 × 2 matrix.

We can find the inverse of any 2 × 2 matrix, if it exists, using the following theorem.

Theorem 13-8

If $A = \begin{bmatrix} a & b \\ c & d \end{bmatrix}$ and $|A| \neq 0$, then

$$A^{-1} = \frac{1}{|A|}\begin{bmatrix} d & -b \\ -c & a \end{bmatrix}$$

If the determinant of A is nonzero, then A^{-1} exists.

EXAMPLES Find A^{-1}, if it exists.

2. $A = \begin{bmatrix} 2 & 1 \\ 4 & 0 \end{bmatrix}$ $a = 2$ $b = 1$ $c = 4$ $d = 0$

First find $|A|$.

$$|A| = 2 \cdot 0 - 4 \cdot 1 = -4$$

Since $|A| \neq 0$, we know A^{-1} exists.

Next, we interchange a and d and find the additive inverses of b and c.

$$\begin{bmatrix} 0 & -1 \\ -4 & 2 \end{bmatrix}$$ $d = 0$ $-b = -1$ $-c = -4$ $a = 2$

We multiply by $\frac{1}{|A|}$ or $-\frac{1}{4}$.

Thus $A^{-1} = -\frac{1}{4}\begin{bmatrix} 0 & -1 \\ -4 & 2 \end{bmatrix} = \begin{bmatrix} 0 & \frac{1}{4} \\ 1 & -\frac{1}{2} \end{bmatrix}$

We can verify this by finding $A \cdot A^{-1}$.

3. $A = \begin{bmatrix} 3 & 6 \\ -1 & -2 \end{bmatrix}$

We find $|A| = 0$. Thus A^{-1} does not exist.

Try This Find A^{-1}, if it exists.

c. $A = \begin{bmatrix} 5 & 10 \\ 2 & 4 \end{bmatrix}$ Does not exist **d.** $A = \begin{bmatrix} 1 & 3 \\ -1 & 2 \end{bmatrix}$ $\begin{bmatrix} \frac{2}{5} & -\frac{3}{5} \\ \frac{1}{5} & \frac{1}{5} \end{bmatrix}$ **e.** $A = \begin{bmatrix} 3 & 5 \\ -3 & 5 \end{bmatrix}$ $\begin{bmatrix} \frac{1}{6} & -\frac{1}{6} \\ \frac{1}{10} & \frac{1}{10} \end{bmatrix}$

Proof of Theorem 13-8

Consider the 2×2 matrix $A = \begin{bmatrix} a & b \\ c & d \end{bmatrix}$. If A^{-1} exists, it is a matrix $\begin{bmatrix} x & y \\ w & z \end{bmatrix}$ such that $A \cdot A^{-1} = I$.

Thus $\begin{bmatrix} a & b \\ c & d \end{bmatrix}\begin{bmatrix} x & y \\ w & z \end{bmatrix} = \begin{bmatrix} ax + bw & ay + bz \\ cx + dw & cy + dz \end{bmatrix} = \begin{bmatrix} 1 & 0 \\ 0 & 1 \end{bmatrix}$

Since we are interested in the values of x, y, z, and w, we consider these as two systems of equations.

$$\begin{aligned} ax + bw &= 1 \\ cx + dw &= 0 \end{aligned} \quad \text{and} \quad \begin{aligned} ay + bz &= 0 \\ cy + dz &= 1 \end{aligned}$$

We solve these systems and find the following:

$$x = \frac{d}{ad - bc} \qquad y = \frac{-b}{ad - bc}$$

$$w = \frac{-c}{ad - bc} \qquad z = \frac{a}{ad - bc}$$

Thus $\begin{bmatrix} x & y \\ w & z \end{bmatrix} = \dfrac{1}{ad - bc}\begin{bmatrix} d & -b \\ -c & a \end{bmatrix} = \dfrac{1}{|A|}\begin{bmatrix} d & -b \\ -c & a \end{bmatrix}$

LESSON QUIZ

1. Determine whether A and B are inverses.
   $A = \begin{bmatrix} 1 & 3 \\ 2 & 7 \end{bmatrix}$ $B = \begin{bmatrix} 7 & 3 \\ -2 & -1 \end{bmatrix}$
   No, $AB = \begin{bmatrix} 1 & 0 \\ 0 & -1 \end{bmatrix}$
2. Find A^{-1} where
   $A = \begin{bmatrix} 3 & 5 \\ 2 & 4 \end{bmatrix}$
   $A^{-1} = \frac{1}{2}\begin{bmatrix} 4 & -5 \\ -2 & 3 \end{bmatrix}$

Assignment Guide
Algebra: omit

Alg w/Finite or Trig: 1–18 e/o, 19, MR

Comprehensive: 1–18 m3, 19–21, MR

13-5 EXERCISES

A

Determine whether A and B are inverses.

1. $A = \begin{bmatrix} 1 & 2 \\ 3 & 4 \end{bmatrix}$

$B = \begin{bmatrix} -2 & 1 \\ \frac{3}{2} & -\frac{1}{2} \end{bmatrix}$ Yes

2. $A = \begin{bmatrix} 3 & 4 \\ 2 & 6 \end{bmatrix}$

$B = \begin{bmatrix} \frac{3}{5} & -\frac{2}{5} \\ -\frac{1}{5} & -\frac{3}{10} \end{bmatrix}$ No

3. $A = \begin{bmatrix} 7 & 4 \\ 3 & 2 \end{bmatrix}$

$B = \begin{bmatrix} 1 & -2 \\ -\frac{3}{2} & \frac{11}{2} \end{bmatrix}$ No

4. $A = \begin{bmatrix} 2 & 3 \\ 3 & 6 \end{bmatrix}$

$B = \begin{bmatrix} 2 & -1 \\ -1 & \frac{2}{3} \end{bmatrix}$ Yes

Find A^{-1}, if it exists. Check your answers by calculating AA^{-1} and $A^{-1}A$.

5. $A = \begin{bmatrix} 3 & 2 \\ 5 & 3 \end{bmatrix}$ $\begin{bmatrix} -3 & 2 \\ 5 & -3 \end{bmatrix}$

6. $A = \begin{bmatrix} 3 & 5 \\ 1 & 2 \end{bmatrix}$ $\begin{bmatrix} 2 & -5 \\ -1 & 3 \end{bmatrix}$

7. $A = \begin{bmatrix} 11 & 3 \\ 7 & 2 \end{bmatrix}$ $\begin{bmatrix} 2 & -3 \\ -7 & 11 \end{bmatrix}$

ADDITIONAL ANSWERS

Exercises

14. $8\begin{bmatrix} \frac{1}{4} & 0 \\ -1 & \frac{1}{2} \end{bmatrix}$ or $\begin{bmatrix} 2 & 0 \\ -8 & 4 \end{bmatrix}$

15. $-\frac{1}{0.05}\begin{bmatrix} 0.2 & -0.1 \\ -1.5 & 0.5 \end{bmatrix}$ or $\begin{bmatrix} -4 & 2 \\ 30 & -10 \end{bmatrix}$

16. $\frac{1}{xy}\begin{bmatrix} y & 0 \\ 0 & x \end{bmatrix}$ or $\begin{bmatrix} \frac{1}{x} & 0 \\ 0 & \frac{1}{y} \end{bmatrix}$, $xy \neq 0$

17. $-\frac{1}{xy}\begin{bmatrix} 0 & -x \\ -y & 0 \end{bmatrix}$ or $\begin{bmatrix} 0 & \frac{1}{y} \\ \frac{1}{x} & 0 \end{bmatrix}$, $xy \neq 0$

18. $\begin{bmatrix} \frac{1}{x} \end{bmatrix}$, $x \neq 0$

20. Let $A = \begin{bmatrix} 0 & 0 \\ a & b \end{bmatrix}$. Then $|A| = 0$ and A^{-1} does not exist.
Let $A = \begin{bmatrix} 0 & a \\ 0 & b \end{bmatrix}$. Then $|A| = 0$ and A^{-1} does not exist.

21. Let $A = \begin{bmatrix} a & a \\ b & b \end{bmatrix}$. Then $|A| = ab - ba = 0$ and A^{-1} does not exist.
Let $A = \begin{bmatrix} a & b \\ a & b \end{bmatrix}$. Then $|A| = ab - ab = 0$ and A^{-1} does not exist.

22. Let $A = \begin{bmatrix} a & b \\ ka & kb \end{bmatrix}$. Then $|A| = akb - kab = 0$ and A^{-1} does not exist.
Let $A = \begin{bmatrix} a & ka \\ b & kb \end{bmatrix}$. Then $|A| = akb - bka = 0$ and A^{-1} does not exist.

Mixed Review

23. $(x^2 + 9y^4)(x + 3y^2)(x - 3y^2)$
24. $(a + 5b + c)(a + 5b - c)$
25. $(2m - 3n)(3m - 2n)$
26. $\frac{b^4}{a^8}$
27. $3yz^3\sqrt[3]{2y}$
28. $\frac{8x^3z^3}{y^6}$
29. $-\frac{8n^{12}}{m^{12}}$
30. $\frac{3}{5}$
31. 30 m × 30 m; 900 m²

8. $A = \begin{bmatrix} 8 & 5 \\ 5 & 3 \end{bmatrix}$ $\begin{bmatrix} -3 & 5 \\ 5 & -8 \end{bmatrix}$
9. $A = \begin{bmatrix} 4 & -3 \\ 1 & 2 \end{bmatrix}$ $\begin{bmatrix} \frac{2}{11} & \frac{3}{11} \\ -\frac{1}{11} & \frac{4}{11} \end{bmatrix}$
10. $A = \begin{bmatrix} 0 & -1 \\ 1 & 0 \end{bmatrix}$ $\begin{bmatrix} 0 & 1 \\ -1 & 0 \end{bmatrix}$

11. $A = \begin{bmatrix} 6 & 3 \\ 4 & 2 \end{bmatrix}$ Does not exist
12. $A = \begin{bmatrix} 4 & 0 \\ 0 & 1 \end{bmatrix}$ $\begin{bmatrix} \frac{1}{4} & 0 \\ 0 & 1 \end{bmatrix}$
13. $A = \begin{bmatrix} 1 & 1 \\ -1 & -1 \end{bmatrix}$ Does not exist

B

Find A^{-1}, if it exists.

14. $A = \begin{bmatrix} \frac{1}{2} & 0 \\ 1 & \frac{1}{4} \end{bmatrix}$
15. $A = \begin{bmatrix} 0.5 & 0.1 \\ 1.5 & 0.2 \end{bmatrix}$

Find A^{-1}.

16. $A = \begin{bmatrix} x & 0 \\ 0 & y \end{bmatrix}$
17. $A = \begin{bmatrix} 0 & x \\ y & 0 \end{bmatrix}$
18. $A = [x]$

19. ***Critical Thinking*** The inverse of a matrix A is $\begin{bmatrix} \frac{1}{11} & -\frac{2}{11} \\ \frac{3}{11} & \frac{5}{11} \end{bmatrix}$. Find A $\begin{bmatrix} 5 & 2 \\ -3 & 1 \end{bmatrix}$

Challenge

Prove that for any 2 × 2 matrix A, A^{-1} does not exist if

20. an entire row or column has elements which are 0.
21. either both rows or both columns have the same elements.
22. one row or column is a multiple of the other row or column.

Mixed Review

Factor. **23.** $x^4 - 81y^8$ **24.** $a^2 + 10ab + 25b^2 - c^2$
25. $6m^2 - 13mn + 6n^2$

Simplify. **26.** $((((a^{-2}b)^{-1})^4)^{-\frac{1}{2}})^2$ **27.** $\sqrt[3]{54y^4z^9}$ **28.** $\left(\frac{16x^4y^{-3}}{y^5z^{-4}}\right)^{\frac{3}{4}}$

29. $\left(\frac{-4^{-2}m^3n^{-2}}{2^{-3}m^{-1}n^2}\right)^{-3}$ **30.** $\frac{3r^{-1} + 3s^{-1} - 6r^{-1}s^{-1}}{5r^{-1} + 5s^{-1} - 10r^{-1}s^{-1}}$

Solve.

31. A farmer is fencing off a rectangular area with a fixed perimeter of 120 m. What dimensions would yield the maximum area? What is the maximum area?

Problem for Programmers

Write a program to find the inverse A^{-1} for any 2 × 2 matrix. The program should determine whether the inverse exists and verify that A^{-1} is the inverse by multiplying. Test your program using Exercises 5 – 15 in Lesson 13-5.

13-6 Inverses and Systems

TI-81 Investigation 4 (page 863) can be used with this lesson.

Calculating Matrix Inverses

Objective: Calculate the inverse of a square matrix.

In this lesson we consider a way of calculating the inverse of any square matrix, which, as with 2×2 matrices, exists only when the determinant of the matrix is nonzero.

Suppose we want to find the inverse of the following matrix.

$$A = \begin{bmatrix} 2 & -1 & 1 \\ 1 & -2 & 3 \\ 4 & 1 & 2 \end{bmatrix}$$

First we form a new **augmented matrix** consisting, on the left, of the matrix A and, on the right, of the corresponding identity matrix I.

$$\left[\begin{array}{ccc|ccc} 2 & -1 & 1 & 1 & 0 & 0 \\ 1 & -2 & 3 & 0 & 1 & 0 \\ 4 & 1 & 2 & 0 & 0 & 1 \end{array}\right]$$

The matrix A The identity matrix I

We now proceed by applying Theorem 13-1. Using row-equivalent operations we attempt to transform A into the identity matrix. Whatever operations we perform, we do on the entire augmented matrix. We will get a matrix like the following.

$$\left[\begin{array}{ccc|ccc} 1 & 0 & 0 & a & b & c \\ 0 & 1 & 0 & d & e & f \\ 0 & 0 & 1 & g & h & i \end{array}\right]$$

Elements of the identity matrix I Elements of the matrix A^{-1}

EXAMPLE 1 Find A^{-1}.

$$A = \begin{bmatrix} 2 & -1 & 1 \\ 1 & -2 & 3 \\ 4 & 1 & 2 \end{bmatrix}$$

(a) We begin with the augmented matrix consisting of A and I.

$$\left[\begin{array}{ccc|ccc} 2 & -1 & 1 & 1 & 0 & 0 \\ 1 & -2 & 3 & 0 & 1 & 0 \\ 4 & 1 & 2 & 0 & 0 & 1 \end{array}\right]$$

13-6

FIRST FIVE MINUTES

1. Write the 3×3 identity matrix.

$$\begin{bmatrix} 1 & 0 & 0 \\ 0 & 1 & 0 \\ 0 & 0 & 1 \end{bmatrix}$$

2. Find the inverse of the matrix.

$$A = \begin{bmatrix} 2 & 6 \\ 1 & 4 \end{bmatrix}$$

$$A^{-1} = \frac{1}{2}\begin{bmatrix} 4 & -6 \\ -1 & 2 \end{bmatrix} = \begin{bmatrix} 2 & -3 \\ -\frac{1}{2} & 1 \end{bmatrix}$$

Calculating Matrix Inverses

Remind students of the 3 row-equivalent operations: multiplying a row by a constant, exchanging two rows, and adding a multiple of one row to another.

Point out that this lesson uses row-equivalent operations just as Lesson 13-1 does.

Note that there is no one right sequence of steps when calculating an inverse; students may find the inverse using a different number of steps. However, there is only one right answer.

Key Questions

- What row-equivalent operation changes the matrix

$$\begin{bmatrix} 2 & 4 & 1 & 0 \\ 3 & 7 & 0 & 1 \end{bmatrix} \begin{matrix} (1) \\ (2) \end{matrix}$$

to the matrix

$$\begin{bmatrix} 1 & 2 & \frac{1}{2} & 0 \\ 3 & 7 & 0 & 1 \end{bmatrix}? \begin{matrix} (1) \\ (2) \end{matrix}$$

Row (1) was multiplied by $\frac{1}{2}$.

- What row-equivalent operation changes the matrix

$$\begin{bmatrix} 1 & 2 & \frac{1}{2} & 0 \\ 3 & 7 & 0 & 1 \end{bmatrix} \begin{matrix} (1) \\ (2) \end{matrix}$$

to the matrix

$$\begin{bmatrix} 1 & 2 & \frac{1}{2} & 0 \\ 0 & 1 & -\frac{3}{2} & 1 \end{bmatrix}? \begin{matrix} (1) \\ (2) \end{matrix}$$

Subtract $3 \cdot$ (1) from (2).

Chalkboard Example

1. Find A^{-1} where

$$A = \begin{bmatrix} 2 & 4 & 0 \\ 1 & 4 & 2 \\ 3 & 7 & 2 \end{bmatrix}$$

The augmented matrix is

$$\left[\begin{array}{ccc|ccc} 2 & 4 & 0 & 1 & 0 & 0 \\ 1 & 4 & 2 & 0 & 1 & 0 \\ 3 & 7 & 2 & 0 & 0 & 1 \end{array}\right]$$

Exchange ① and ②.

$$\left[\begin{array}{ccc|ccc} 1 & 4 & 2 & 0 & 1 & 0 \\ 2 & 4 & 0 & 1 & 0 & 0 \\ 3 & 7 & 2 & 0 & 0 & 1 \end{array}\right]$$

Multiply ① by −2 and add ②.
Multiply ① by −3 and add ③.

$$\left[\begin{array}{ccc|ccc} 1 & 4 & 2 & 0 & 1 & 0 \\ 0 & -4 & -4 & 1 & -2 & 0 \\ 0 & -5 & -4 & 0 & -3 & 1 \end{array}\right]$$

Multiply ③ by 4.

$$\left[\begin{array}{ccc|ccc} 1 & 4 & 2 & 0 & 1 & 0 \\ 0 & -4 & -4 & 1 & -2 & 0 \\ 0 & -20 & -16 & 0 & -12 & 4 \end{array}\right]$$

Add ② and ①.
Multiply ② by −5 and add ③.

$$\left[\begin{array}{ccc|ccc} 1 & 0 & -2 & 1 & -1 & 0 \\ 0 & -4 & -4 & 1 & -2 & 0 \\ 0 & 0 & 4 & -5 & -2 & 4 \end{array}\right]$$

Multiply ① by 2.

$$\left[\begin{array}{ccc|ccc} 2 & 0 & -4 & 2 & -2 & 0 \\ 0 & -4 & -4 & 1 & -2 & 0 \\ 0 & 0 & 4 & -5 & -2 & 4 \end{array}\right]$$

Add ③ and ①.
Add ③ and ②.

$$\left[\begin{array}{ccc|ccc} 2 & 0 & 0 & -3 & -4 & 4 \\ 0 & -4 & 0 & -4 & -4 & 4 \\ 0 & 0 & 4 & -5 & -2 & 4 \end{array}\right]$$

Multiply ① by $\frac{1}{2}$, ② by $-\frac{1}{4}$, and ③ by $\frac{1}{4}$.

$$\left[\begin{array}{ccc|ccc} 1 & 0 & 0 & -\frac{3}{2} & -2 & 2 \\ 0 & 1 & 0 & 1 & 1 & -1 \\ 0 & 0 & 1 & -\frac{5}{4} & -\frac{1}{2} & 1 \end{array}\right]$$

$$A^{-1} = \begin{bmatrix} -\frac{3}{2} & -2 & 2 \\ 1 & 1 & -1 \\ -\frac{5}{4} & -\frac{1}{2} & 1 \end{bmatrix}$$

(b) We interchange the first and second rows so that the elements of the first column are multiples of the top number on the main diagonal.

$$\left[\begin{array}{ccc|ccc} 1 & -2 & 3 & 0 & 1 & 0 \\ 2 & -1 & 1 & 1 & 0 & 0 \\ 4 & 1 & 2 & 0 & 0 & 1 \end{array}\right]$$

(c) Next we obtain 0's in the rest of the first column. We multiply the first row by −2 and add it to the second row. Then we multiply the first row by −4 and add it to the third row.

$$\left[\begin{array}{ccc|ccc} 1 & -2 & 3 & 0 & 1 & 0 \\ 0 & 3 & -5 & 1 & -2 & 0 \\ 0 & 9 & -10 & 0 & -4 & 1 \end{array}\right] \quad \begin{array}{l} \\ -2① + ② \\ -4① + ③ \end{array}$$

(d) Now we multiply row ② by 2 and add it to 3 times row ①. We also multiply row ② by −3 and add it to row ③.

$$\left[\begin{array}{ccc|ccc} 3 & 0 & -1 & 2 & -1 & 0 \\ 0 & 3 & -5 & 1 & -2 & 0 \\ 0 & 0 & 5 & -3 & 2 & 1 \end{array}\right] \quad \begin{array}{l} 2② + 3① \\ \\ -3② + ③ \end{array}$$

(e) We can now use the 5 in column 3 to get zeros above it in that column.

$$\left[\begin{array}{ccc|ccc} 15 & 0 & 0 & 7 & -3 & 1 \\ 0 & 3 & 0 & -2 & 0 & 1 \\ 0 & 0 & 5 & -3 & 2 & 1 \end{array}\right] \quad \begin{array}{l} ③ + 5① \\ ③ + ② \\ \end{array}$$

(f) Finally, we get all 1's on the main diagonal. We multiply the first row by $\frac{1}{15}$, the second by $\frac{1}{3}$, and the third by $\frac{1}{5}$.

$$\left[\begin{array}{ccc|ccc} 1 & 0 & 0 & \frac{7}{15} & -\frac{1}{5} & \frac{1}{15} \\ 0 & 1 & 0 & -\frac{2}{3} & 0 & \frac{1}{3} \\ 0 & 0 & 1 & -\frac{3}{5} & \frac{2}{5} & \frac{1}{5} \end{array}\right] \quad \begin{array}{l} \frac{1}{15}① \\ \frac{1}{3}② \\ \frac{1}{5}③ \end{array}$$

We now have the matrix I on the left and A^{-1} on the right.

$$A^{-1} = \begin{bmatrix} \frac{7}{15} & -\frac{1}{5} & \frac{1}{15} \\ -\frac{2}{3} & 0 & \frac{1}{3} \\ -\frac{3}{5} & \frac{2}{5} & \frac{1}{5} \end{bmatrix}$$

You can check by doing the multiplication $A^{-1}A$ or AA^{-1}. If we cannot obtain the identity matrix on the left, as would be the case when a system has no solution or infinitely many solutions, then A^{-1} does not exist.

Try This Find A^{-1}.

a. $A = \begin{bmatrix} 1 & 0 & 1 \\ 2 & 1 & 0 \\ 1 & -1 & 1 \end{bmatrix}$ $A^{-1} = \begin{bmatrix} -\frac{1}{2} & \frac{1}{2} & \frac{1}{2} \\ 1 & 0 & -1 \\ \frac{3}{2} & -\frac{1}{2} & -\frac{1}{2} \end{bmatrix}$

b. $A = \begin{bmatrix} 1 & 2 & 3 \\ 4 & 5 & 6 \\ 7 & 8 & 9 \end{bmatrix}$ A^{-1} does not exist.

Solving Systems Using Inverses

Objective: Solve systems of equations using the inverse of a matrix.

One application of inverses of square matrices is to solve certain kinds of systems of equations.

When we solve a system using matrices, we solve $AX = B$, where A is the coefficient matrix, X is the variable matrix, and B is the constant matrix. Solving,

$$AX = B$$

$$A^{-1}AX = A^{-1}B \quad \text{Multiplying both sides by } A^{-1}$$

$$IX = A^{-1}B \quad A^{-1} \cdot A = I$$

$$X = A^{-1}B \quad \text{Since } I \text{ is an identity, } IX = X.$$

The solution of the matrix equation $AX = B$ can thus be found by multiplying the inverse matrix A^{-1} by the constant matrix B.

EXAMPLE 2 Solve this system using matrices.

$$3x + 5y = -1$$
$$x - 2y = 4$$

We write a matrix equation equivalent to this system.

$$\underset{A}{\begin{bmatrix} 3 & 5 \\ 1 & -2 \end{bmatrix}} \cdot \underset{X}{\begin{bmatrix} x \\ y \end{bmatrix}} = \underset{B}{\begin{bmatrix} -1 \\ 4 \end{bmatrix}}$$

Then we solve the following equation.

$$AX = B$$

To solve this equation, we first find A^{-1}.

$$A^{-1} = \frac{1}{11}\begin{bmatrix} 2 & 5 \\ 1 & -3 \end{bmatrix}$$

Now we substitute.

$$X = A^{-1}B$$

$$\begin{bmatrix} x \\ y \end{bmatrix} = \frac{1}{11}\begin{bmatrix} 2 & 5 \\ 1 & -3 \end{bmatrix} \cdot \begin{bmatrix} -1 \\ 4 \end{bmatrix}$$

$$= \frac{1}{11}\begin{bmatrix} 18 \\ -13 \end{bmatrix}$$

$$= \begin{bmatrix} \frac{18}{11} \\ -\frac{13}{11} \end{bmatrix}$$

The solution of the system of equations is $x = \frac{18}{11}$ and $y = -\frac{13}{11}$.

Solving Systems Using Inverses

Chalkboard Example

1. Solve using matrices.
   $4x + 3y = 2$
   $2x + 4y = 6$
   The system is equivalent to
   $$\begin{bmatrix} 4 & 3 \\ 2 & 4 \end{bmatrix}\begin{bmatrix} x \\ y \end{bmatrix} = \begin{bmatrix} 2 \\ 6 \end{bmatrix}$$
   We find the inverse of the matrix
   $$A = \begin{bmatrix} 4 & 3 \\ 2 & 4 \end{bmatrix}$$
   $$A^{-1} = \frac{1}{10}\begin{bmatrix} 4 & -3 \\ -2 & 4 \end{bmatrix}$$
   Substituting,
   $$X = A^{-1}B$$
   $$\begin{bmatrix} x \\ y \end{bmatrix} = \frac{1}{10}\begin{bmatrix} 4 & -3 \\ -2 & 4 \end{bmatrix}\begin{bmatrix} 2 \\ 6 \end{bmatrix}$$
   $$= \frac{1}{10}\begin{bmatrix} -10 \\ 20 \end{bmatrix} = \begin{bmatrix} -1 \\ 2 \end{bmatrix}$$
   Hence
   $x = -1$
   $y = 2$

LESSON ENRICHMENT

Which step is incorrect?

1. $AX = B$
2. $AA^{-1}X = BA^{-1}$
3. $IX = BA^{-1}$
4. $X = BA^{-1}$
5. $XA = BA^{-1}A$
6. $XA = B$, which is false.

Step 2; AX can be multiplied on the left or right, but not "within."

LESSON QUIZ

1. Find A^{-1} where

$$A = \begin{bmatrix} 1 & 2 & 3 \\ 2 & 5 & 7 \\ 3 & 7 & 11 \end{bmatrix}.$$

$$A^{-1} = \begin{bmatrix} 6 & -1 & -1 \\ -1 & 2 & -1 \\ -1 & -1 & 1 \end{bmatrix}$$

2. Solve using matrices.

$2x + 3y = 1$
$5x + 7y = 2$

$$\begin{bmatrix} x \\ y \end{bmatrix} = \frac{1}{-1}\begin{bmatrix} 7 & -3 \\ -5 & 2 \end{bmatrix}\begin{bmatrix} 1 \\ 2 \end{bmatrix}$$

$x = -1$
$y = 1$

Assignment Guide
Algebra: omit

Alg w/Finite or Trig: 1–15 e/o, 16, MR

Comprehensive: 1–15 m3, 16–18, MR

ADDITIONAL ANSWERS

Exercises

1. $A^{-1} = \begin{bmatrix} -1 & 1 & 0 \\ -1 & 0 & 1 \\ 6 & -2 & -3 \end{bmatrix}$

2. $A^{-1} = \begin{bmatrix} -\frac{2}{5} & \frac{3}{5} & \frac{1}{5} \\ \frac{3}{5} & \frac{3}{5} & \frac{1}{5} \\ -\frac{2}{5} & \frac{8}{5} & \frac{1}{5} \end{bmatrix}$

3. $A^{-1} = \begin{bmatrix} -\frac{4}{3} & -\frac{5}{3} & 1 \\ -\frac{4}{3} & -\frac{8}{3} & 1 \\ \frac{1}{3} & \frac{2}{3} & 0 \end{bmatrix}$

4. $A^{-1} = \begin{bmatrix} \frac{3}{8} & -\frac{1}{4} & \frac{1}{8} \\ -\frac{1}{8} & \frac{3}{4} & -\frac{3}{8} \\ -\frac{1}{4} & \frac{1}{2} & \frac{1}{4} \end{bmatrix}$

5. $A^{-1} = \begin{bmatrix} -\frac{1}{2} & \frac{1}{2} & \frac{1}{2} \\ 1 & 0 & -1 \\ \frac{3}{2} & -\frac{1}{2} & -\frac{1}{2} \end{bmatrix}$

6. Does not exist

EXAMPLE 3 Solve this system using matrices.

$$\begin{aligned} -x + 3y + 5z &= -15 \\ 2x + y \quad\quad &= 1 \\ -9x - 8y - 4z &= 12 \end{aligned}$$

The matrix equation equivalent to the system is

$$\underset{A}{\begin{bmatrix} -1 & 3 & 5 \\ 2 & 1 & 0 \\ -9 & -8 & -4 \end{bmatrix}} \underset{X}{\begin{bmatrix} x \\ y \\ z \end{bmatrix}} = \underset{B}{\begin{bmatrix} -15 \\ 1 \\ 12 \end{bmatrix}}$$

We know $X = A^{-1}B$. We find the inverse of A.

$$A^{-1} = \begin{bmatrix} \frac{4}{7} & 4 & \frac{5}{7} \\ -\frac{8}{7} & -7 & -\frac{10}{7} \\ 1 & 5 & 1 \end{bmatrix}$$

$$A^{-1}B = \begin{bmatrix} \frac{4}{7} & 4 & \frac{5}{7} \\ -\frac{8}{7} & -7 & -\frac{10}{7} \\ 1 & 5 & 1 \end{bmatrix}\begin{bmatrix} -15 \\ 1 \\ 12 \end{bmatrix} = \begin{bmatrix} 4 \\ -7 \\ 2 \end{bmatrix}$$

The solution of the system of equations is $(4, -7, 2)$.

Try This Solve using matrices.

c. $4x - 2y = -1$
$x + 5y = 1$ $\left(-\frac{3}{22}, \frac{5}{22}\right)$

d. $x + 3y - 4z = -14$
$-2x + 2y - 5z = 0$
$y - 6z = 0$ $\left(-\frac{14}{5}, -\frac{24}{5}, -\frac{4}{5}\right)$

13-6 EXERCISES

A

Find A^{-1}, if it exists.

1. $A = \begin{bmatrix} 2 & 3 & 1 \\ 3 & 3 & 1 \\ 2 & 4 & 1 \end{bmatrix}$

2. $A = \begin{bmatrix} -1 & 1 & 0 \\ -1 & 0 & 1 \\ 6 & 2 & -3 \end{bmatrix}$

3. $A = \begin{bmatrix} -2 & 2 & 3 \\ 1 & -1 & 0 \\ 0 & 1 & 4 \end{bmatrix}$

4. $A = \begin{bmatrix} 3 & 1 & 0 \\ 1 & 1 & 1 \\ 1 & -1 & 2 \end{bmatrix}$

5. $A = \begin{bmatrix} 1 & 0 & 1 \\ 2 & 1 & 0 \\ 1 & -1 & 1 \end{bmatrix}$

6. $A = \begin{bmatrix} 1 & -1 & 2 \\ 0 & 0 & 0 \\ 2 & 1 & 2 \end{bmatrix}$

Solve using matrices.

7. $7x - 2y = 10$
   $9x + 3y = 24$ (2, 2)

8. $5x + 3y = 29$
   $4x - y = 13$ (4, 3)

9. $2x + 3y = 5$
   $x + 4y = 10$ (−2, 3)

10. $2x + 4y = 2$
    $x + 2y = 1$ Dependent system

11. $x + z = 1$
    $2x + y = 3$
    $x - y + z = 4$ (3, −3, −2)

12. $x + 2y + 3z = -1$
    $2x - 3y + 4z = 2$
    $-3x + 5y - 6z = 4$ (124, 14, −51)

B

Find A^{-1}, if it exists.

13. $A = \begin{bmatrix} x & 0 & 0 \\ 0 & y & 0 \\ 0 & 0 & z \end{bmatrix}$

14. $A = \begin{bmatrix} 1 & 2 & 3 & 4 \\ 2 & 3 & 4 & 1 \\ 3 & 4 & 1 & 2 \\ 4 & 1 & 2 & 3 \end{bmatrix}$

15. Find X such that $AX = B$.

$$A = \begin{bmatrix} 3 & 2 \\ 7 & 5 \end{bmatrix} \quad B = \begin{bmatrix} 3 & 2 \\ 11 & 8 \end{bmatrix}$$

16. ***Critical Thinking*** Write a 2×2 matrix. Apply the augmented matrix technique for finding the inverse. Does this technique work for 2×2 matrices?

Challenge

17. Prove that $(A^{-1})^{-1} = A$.

18. Find A^{-1}.

$$A = \begin{bmatrix} 0 & t & t \\ t & 0 & t \\ t & t & 0 \end{bmatrix}$$

19. Find X such that $AX = B$.

$$A = \begin{bmatrix} 2 & -2 & 4 \\ -3 & 1 & -4 \\ 1 & 0 & 3 \end{bmatrix} \quad B = \begin{bmatrix} 8 & 4 & 2 \\ -3 & 0 & 3 \\ 2 & -1 & -5 \end{bmatrix}$$

Mixed Review

Solve. 20. $2y + 3x = 18$
$3y + x = 13$

21. $4y + 3x = 24$
$5y - x = 49$

Simplify. 22. $\dfrac{\sqrt{u^3 + v^3}}{\sqrt{u + v}}$ 23. $\dfrac{5}{8 - \sqrt{6}}$ 24. $\dfrac{3}{4 - 3i}$ 25. $\dfrac{\sqrt[3]{2u^4}}{\sqrt[3]{6v^4}}$

26. $\sqrt[3]{108} - 2\sqrt{75} + \sqrt{98}$

Solve. 27. $2x - 6 < 5x - 9$ 28. $-1 < x + 2 \leq 6$

29. Tao scored a total of 244 points on three tests. His first score exceeded his second score by 2 points; his third score exceeded his first by 6 points. Find the three scores.

30. The cost of renting a car and driving it 250 miles is \$150. The cost of renting a car and driving it 380 miles is \$202.
    a. Fit a linear function to the data points.
    b. Use the function to find the cost of renting a car and driving it 300 miles.

---

13. $A^{-1} = \begin{bmatrix} \frac{1}{x} & 0 & 0 \\ 0 & \frac{1}{y} & 0 \\ 0 & 0 & \frac{1}{z} \end{bmatrix}$, $x, y, z \neq 0$

14. $A^{-1} = \frac{1}{40}\begin{bmatrix} -9 & 1 & 1 & 11 \\ 1 & 1 & 11 & -9 \\ 1 & 11 & -9 & 1 \\ 11 & -9 & 1 & 1 \end{bmatrix}$

15. $X = \begin{bmatrix} -7 & -6 \\ 12 & 10 \end{bmatrix}$

16. Yes.

17. By definition of the inverse of a matrix,
$A^{-1}A = I$ and $(A^{-1})(A^{-1})^{-1} = I$
$A^{-1}A = A^{-1}(A^{-1})^{-1}$
$A(A^{-1}A) = A[A^{-1}(A^{-1})^{-1}]$
Apply associative property of multiplication of matrices.
$(AA^{-1})A = (AA^{-1})(A^{-1})^{-1}$
$IA = I(A^{-1})^{-1}$
$A = (A^{-1})^{-1}$

18. $\frac{1}{2t}\begin{bmatrix} -1 & 1 & 1 \\ 1 & -1 & 1 \\ 1 & 1 & -1 \end{bmatrix}$, $t \neq 0$

19. $\begin{bmatrix} -\frac{7}{4} & -1 & -\frac{1}{2} \\ -\frac{13}{4} & -3 & -\frac{9}{2} \\ \frac{5}{4} & 0 & -\frac{3}{2} \end{bmatrix}$

Mixed Review

20. (4, 3)
21. (−4, 9)
22. $\sqrt{u^2 - uv + v^2}$
23. $\dfrac{40 + 5\sqrt{6}}{58}$
24. $\frac{12}{25} + \frac{9}{25}i$
25. $\dfrac{u\sqrt[3]{9uv^2}}{3v^2}$
26. $3\sqrt[3]{4} - 10\sqrt{3} + 7\sqrt{2}$
27. $1 < x$
28. $-3 < x \leq 4$
29. 80, 78, 86
30. a. $y = 0.4x + 50$
    b. \$170

13-7

FIRST FIVE MINUTES

1. Find A^{-1} where
$$A = \begin{bmatrix} 6 & 5 \\ 4 & 4 \end{bmatrix}.$$
$$A^{-1} = \frac{1}{4}\begin{bmatrix} 4 & -5 \\ -4 & 6 \end{bmatrix}$$

2. Find A^{-1} where
$$A = \begin{bmatrix} 2 & 1 & 3 \\ 2 & 2 & 4 \\ 4 & 4 & 9 \end{bmatrix}.$$
$$A^{-1} = \begin{bmatrix} 1 & \frac{3}{2} & -1 \\ -1 & 3 & -1 \\ 0 & -2 & 1 \end{bmatrix}$$

Point out that matrix notation gives us a quick and efficient way to store large amounts of data. Furthermore, large repetitive tasks can be specified easily. For example, if M is a large matrix of numbers, each of which must be multiplied by 3, we can describe the operation by the simple expression $3M$. Every computer language has matrix operations built in, or can easily be extended to do so.

Key Questions

A and B are large arrays of numbers.

- How do you express the operation of adding the corresponding elements of each matrix together?
  $A + B$
- How would you express the operation of taking 10% of each of the numbers in array A?
  $(0.10)A$
- How would you express the operation of adding twice each number in A to the corresponding number in B?
  $2A + B$

13-7 Problem Solving: Using Matrices

Objective: Solve problems by translating to matrices.

PROBLEM-SOLVING GUIDELINES
■ UNDERSTAND the problem
■ Develop and carry out a PLAN
■ Find the ANSWER and CHECK

We know that some problems can be solved by translating to a system of equations. We can then use matrices to solve the system of equations. Other problems can be solved by translating directly to a matrix and then performing matrix operations.

EXAMPLE 1

An orchard grows McIntosh, Gravenstein, and Jonathan apples. The apples are sold in boxes to two different markets. The profit is \$5.75 on a box of McIntosh apples, \$3.25 on Gravensteins, and \$2.00 on Jonathans. The table shows the number of boxes sold.

Apples	Markets	
	Al's	Bell
McIntosh	200	180
Gravenstein	150	250
Jonathan	300	200

Find the amount of profit generated by sales to each market.

■ **UNDERSTAND the problem**

Question: What is the orchard's profit from each market? — Clarifying the question

Data: The quantities are given in the table. The profits on each box of the three types are \$5.75, \$3.25, and \$2.00. — Identifying the given data

■ **Develop and carry out a PLAN**

We can represent the market data in a 3×2 matrix as shown below.

$$M = \begin{bmatrix} 200 & 180 \\ 150 & 250 \\ 300 & 200 \end{bmatrix}$$

Likewise, we can write a 1×3 matrix to represent the respective profits $P = [5.75 \quad 3.25 \quad 2.00]$.

The product PM will then be a 1×2 matrix which will determine the profit from each market.

$$PM = [5.75 \quad 3.25 \quad 2.00] \begin{bmatrix} 200 & 180 \\ 150 & 250 \\ 300 & 200 \end{bmatrix}$$

$$= [2237.50 \quad 2247.50]$$

Find the ANSWER and CHECK

The profit from Al's is $2237.50, while the profit from Bell is $2247.50. This is reasonable because 650 boxes were sent to Al's and 630 to Bell, and the average profit from each was between $2.00 and $5.75.

EXAMPLE 2

Five students had the following currency. How much money did each student have?

	$10 bills	$5 bills	$1 bills	Quarters	Dimes	Nickels	Cents
Teresa	2		3	5	1		3
Rick		1	8	2	3	1	1
Leah	1				2	2	
Chan	1	1	2	9		4	4
Sandi			2	3	3	3	16

We represent the data in matrices and multiply.

$$\begin{bmatrix} 2 & 0 & 3 & 5 & 1 & 0 & 3 \\ 0 & 1 & 8 & 2 & 3 & 1 & 1 \\ 1 & 0 & 0 & 0 & 2 & 2 & 0 \\ 1 & 1 & 2 & 9 & 0 & 4 & 4 \\ 0 & 0 & 2 & 3 & 3 & 3 & 16 \end{bmatrix} \begin{bmatrix} 10 \\ 5 \\ 1 \\ 0.25 \\ 0.10 \\ 0.05 \\ 0.01 \end{bmatrix} = \begin{bmatrix} 24.38 \\ 13.86 \\ 10.30 \\ 19.49 \\ 3.36 \end{bmatrix}$$

Teresa had $24.38, Reggie had $13.86, Leah had $10.30, Chan had $19,49, and Aretha had $3.36.

Try This

a. A farm raises two crops, which are shipped to three distributors. The table below shows the number of crates shipped to each distributor.

	Distributor A	B	C
Crop 1	400	250	600
Crop 2	180	300	250

Profit
A: $1467
B: $1507.50
C: $2137.50

The profit on crop 1 is $2.25 per crate and the profit on crop 2 is $3.15 per crate. Find the amount of profit from each distributor.

Chalkboard Example

1. A delivery company with offices in three cities distributes four types of equipment to its clients: typewriters, computers, copy machines, and printers. The number of units shipped from each office during the month of October is shown in the table below.

	Office A	B	C
Typewriters	73	69	100
Computers	80	41	82
Copy machines	30	13	41
Printers	150	120	90

Profit on a single unit is: typewriter $30, computer $42, copy machine $65, printer $27. Find the amount of profit made by each office for the month of October.

$$[30 \quad 42 \quad 65 \quad 27] \begin{bmatrix} 73 & 69 & 100 \\ 80 & 41 & 82 \\ 30 & 13 & 41 \\ 150 & 120 & 90 \end{bmatrix}$$

$$= [11{,}550 \quad 7{,}877 \quad 11{,}539]$$

Office A made $11,550.
Office B made $ 7,877.
Office C made $11,539.

LESSON QUIZ

1. A bakery sells three types of bread: white, whole wheat, and rye. Each week four schools in a district order the amounts shown in the table below.

	School A	B	C	D
White	10	8	7	13
Whole wheat	8	5	9	10
Rye	4	2	1	5

The cost per loaf for each type of bread is: white $1.10, whole wheat $1.40, rye $1.25. Find the cost to each school for bread per week.
A $27.20
B $18.30
C $21.55
D $34.55

Assignment Guide
Algebra: omit

Alg w/Finite Math: 1–4 e/o, 5, MR, assign w. Application

Comprehensive: 1–4 e/o, 5–7, MR, assign w. Application

13-7 EXERCISES

A

1. A bread company has four different bakeries, each of which produces three types of bread: white, rye, and whole wheat. The number of loaves of bread produced daily at each bakery is shown in the table below.

	Bakery			
	A	B	C	D
White	180	200	250	100
Rye	50	75	100	50
Whole wheat	200	250	300	175
	$248.50	$298.75	$370	$180

Profit on each loaf of bread is 70¢ for white, 45¢ for rye, and 50¢ for whole wheat. Find the amount of profit the company receives from each bakery.

2. A nursery raises five kinds of trees: spruce, dogwood, pine, yew, and hemlock. The trees are shipped to three retail outlets. The number of trees shipped to each outlet is shown in the table below.

	Outlet		
	A	B	C
Spruce	25	50	100
Dogwood	15	75	25
Pine	50	25	50
Yew	25	100	75
Hemlock	50	50	125
	$428.75	$818.75	$968.75

Profit on each tree is as follows: spruce $3.50, dogwood $4.00, pine $2.75, yew $1.75, and hemlock $2.00. Find the amount of profit from each outlet.

3. A tournament is to be organized with eight winning teams from different leagues. To determine pairings, points are awarded as follows: three points for a win, one point for a tie, and no points for a loss. The records of the eight teams are shown below. How many points did each team earn?

Team	Wins	Ties	Losses	
Hawks	9	2	4	29
Eagles	10	2	3	32
Angels	9	4	2	31
Tornadoes	11	3	1	36
Cyclones	14	1	0	43
Zephyrs	12	2	1	38
Jays	13	1	1	40
Dynamos	12	1	2	37

B

4. Seventy high-school football coaches ranked county teams for a newspaper poll. The first matrix shows the number of first-place votes, second-place votes, and so on received by each school. The second matrix shows the value, in points, for each first-place vote, second-place vote, and so on. Determine the number of points received by each school and the ranking of the schools in the poll.

	1	2	3	4	5	6	7
Third Avenue	13	4	12	21	9	0	0
Northpoint	3	12	25	19	0	0	1
Don Ramos	10	10	8	4	9	11	0
St. Cecilia	0	0	5	15	21	11	2
Kennedy	26	17	7	2	3	1	1
Washington	0	0	0	0	1	19	33
Riverside	18	27	11	0	1	0	0

First	10
Second	8
Third	6
Fourth	4
Fifth	3
Sixth	2
Seventh	1

5. ***Critical Thinking*** Find the cost of each item, given the number purchased by each customer. Then find the total spent for each item by all the customers.

	Item 1	Item 2	Item 3	Total Paid
Customer A	2	3	5	\$82.50
Customer B	1	3	4	\$69.00
Customer C	4	2	1	\$48.50

Challenge

6. A store sold the following amounts of three products over a three-week period. Find the wholesale and retail costs per item for each product.

	Silky Shampoo	Face It Scrub	Incandessence	Total Wholesale	Total Retail
Week 1	36	25	11	\$140.50	\$206.25
Week 2	29	16	27	\$157.25	\$228.75
Week 3	25	18	51	\$229.25	\$329.75

7. The number of direct flights between cities is shown in the matrix. Show that squaring the matrix gives the number of two-flight routes between cities.

	Peoria	Detroit	St. Louis	Denver
Peoria	0	1	3	2
Detroit	1	0	2	1
St. Louis	3	2	0	2
Denver	2	1	2	0

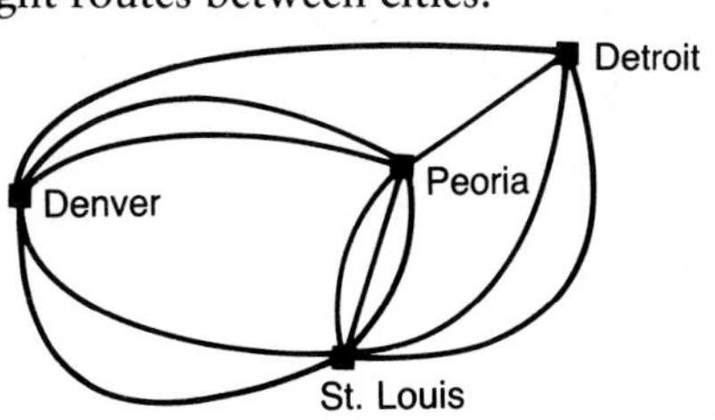

Mixed Review

Solve. **8.** $-10 \le 3x - 5 \le -1$ **9.** $|x| \le 5$ **10.** $|3y - 4| > 8$

11. Ricardo scores 82, 77, and 91 on three biology quizzes. He must have a total of 340 to get a B in the course. What score on the last test will give him a B?

ADDITIONAL ANSWERS

Exercises

4. Riverside 465
Kennedy 458
Northpoint 353
Third Avenue 345
Don Ramos 293
St. Cecilia 177
Washington 74

5. Item 1: cost \$5.00; total \$35.00
Item 2: cost \$10.00; total \$80.00
Item 3: cost \$8.50; total \$85.00

6.

	Wholesale	Retail
Silky	\$1.25	\$2.00
Face It	2.50	3.50
Incan.	3.00	4.25

7. The square of the matrix is

$$\begin{bmatrix} 14 & 8 & 6 & 7 \\ 8 & 6 & 5 & 6 \\ 6 & 5 & 17 & 8 \\ 7 & 6 & 8 & 9 \end{bmatrix}.$$

The element a_{12} represents the two-flight routes between Peoria and Detroit. $a_{12} = 0 \cdot 1 + 1 \cdot 0 + 3 \cdot 2 + 2 \cdot 1$. $0 \cdot 1$ indicates that there is no two-flight route with Peoria as the intermediate stop. $1 \cdot 0$ indicates that there is no route with Detroit as the intermediate stop. $3 \cdot 2$ indicates that there are 6 routes with St. Louis as the intermediate stop, and $2 \cdot 1$ indicates that there are two routes with Denver as the intermediate stop.

8. $-\frac{5}{3} \le x \le \frac{4}{3}$

9. $-5 \le x \le 5$

10. $y > 4$ or $y < -\frac{4}{3}$

11. $s \ge 90$

Problem Solving: College Entrance Exams

Solving qualitative comparison problems involves the use of concepts developed during the study of inequalities. Be sure to point out that when multiplying or dividing by a negative number, the inequality reverses.

The most general and immediate strategy is to simplify expressions. Other strategies include breaking problems down into cases, quickly sketching graphs, or analyzing the signs of expressions.

Problem Solving: College Entrance Exams

Quantitative Comparisons

One type of problem encountered on college entrance exams requires you to compare two expressions, one in column A and one in column B. The choices are often:

(A) if the quantity in column A is greater;
(B) if the quantity in column B is greater;
(C) if the two quantities are equal;
(D) if the relationship cannot be determined

A strategy that is often helpful for solving this type of problem is to simplify the expressions using the addition and multiplication principles. In the examples below, decide which of the choices above is correct.

EXAMPLE 1

	Column A	Column B
	$-x^2 + 1$	$-x^2 + 2$
We can subtract $-x^2$.		
	1	2

Since $1 < 2$, $-x^2 + 1 < -x^2 + 2$, the correct answer is B.

EXAMPLE 2

	Column A	Column B
Often, additional information is presented between the columns. →	$x > -2$	
	$(x + 2)(x + 3)$	$(x + 2)^2$
We first divide by $x + 2$ in each column.		
	$x + 3$	$x + 2$
Then we subtract x from each column.		
	3	2

Since $3 > 2$, the answer is A.

In the second example, dividing by $x + 2$ was an effective strategy, since $x + 2$ could not be negative. In inequality problems, when you multiply or divide by a negative number, you change the direction of the inequality symbol. In quantitative comparison problems, there is no inequality symbol, so we must be sure not to divide by numbers that could be negative.

EXAMPLE 3

Column A		Column B
	$x < y < 0$	
xy		x

We cannot divide by x, a negative number. Since xy is a product of negative numbers, xy is positive. We know x is negative, so the correct answer is A.

Problems

(A) if the quantity in column A is greater;
(B) if the quantity in column B is greater;
(C) if the two quantities are equal;
(D) if the relationship cannot be determined

Decide which of the above choices is correct.

	Column A		Column B
		$a > b > c$	
1.	ab		bc
		$n < m$	
2.	$m \times 8{,}765$		$n \times 8{,}765$
		$e > 1$ $f < 0$	
3.	$\frac{f}{e}$		ef
		$a > 0$	
4.	$(a - 3)(a + 6)$		$(a - 3)$
		$w > 1$	
5.	$w(x + y)$		$x + y$
6.	0.4×10^x		$40 \times 10^{x-2}$
		$m, n > 0$	
7.	$0.6m + 0.7n$		$0.6(m + n)$
		a and b are positive integers	
8.	$\frac{a}{b}$		$\frac{a + 1}{b + 1}$
9.	$6ab$		$(2a)(3b)$
		$mn > 0$	
10.	$m + n$		$m - n$

ANSWERS

1. (D)
2. (A)
3. (A)
4. (D)
5. (D)
6. (C)
7. (A)
8. (D)
9. (C)
10. (D)

Problem Solving: Application

There are other mathematical methods to encode and decode messages.

We could encode by multiplying the "value" of each letter by some whole number from 1 to 26 and using the modulus or mod function. If 3 is the multiplier, we would encode V, the 22nd letter, as follows: $3 \times 22 = 66$, $66 = 14$ MOD 26 (66 has a remainder 14 when divided by 26). Since N is the 14th letter, V is encoded as N.

The following is an encoding table for the multiplier 3:

Letter	A B C D E F G H I
Encoded as	C F I L O R U X A
	J K L M N O P Q R
	D G J M P S V Y B
	S T U V W X Y Z
	E H K N Q T W Z

To decode N, $\frac{14}{3} = 4\frac{2}{3}$, so we can multiply 26 by 2 (the numerator of the fractional part), add 14 to get 66, divide by 3 to get 22, and convert to V.

Discuss which multipliers are not possible (all multiples of 2 and 13, since they are factors of 26. The multiplier and 26 must be relatively prime). See the following encoding table for the multiplier 2:

Letter	A B C D E F G H I
Encoded as	B D F H J L N O R
	J K L M N O P Q R
	T V X Z B D F H J
	S T U V W X Y Z
	L N O R T V X Z

The letter B in a coded message could represent an A or an N. Thus the message could not be decoded.

Problem Solving: Application

Cryptography

Cryptography is the science of creating and deciphering codes. For centuries, codes have been used in diplomatic, intelligence, and military communications. Today, with so much secret data stored in computers, concealing computerized information with codes has become important to industry.

Matrices are often used to develop systems for creating codes. A first step in creating a code is to assign numbers to the letters of the alphabet.

A	01	G	07	L	12	Q	17	V	22
B	02	H	08	M	13	R	18	W	23
C	03	I	09	N	14	S	19	X	24
D	04	J	10	O	15	T	20	Y	25
E	05	K	11	P	16	U	21	Z	26
F	06								

Then, write any 2×2 matrix that has an inverse. For example, consider the matrix

$$E = \begin{bmatrix} 1 & 2 \\ 3 & 4 \end{bmatrix}$$

It will be used as an *encoding matrix*.

Encode the message:

STUDY MATH IT COUNTS

First, break it into pairs of letters.

ST UD YM AT HI TC OU NT SQ

The Q at the end is a "dummy" to complete the pairing. Using the numerical assignment of the alphabet shown above, these pairs can be written as the 2×1 matrices

$$\begin{bmatrix} 19 \\ 20 \end{bmatrix} \begin{bmatrix} 21 \\ 04 \end{bmatrix} \begin{bmatrix} 25 \\ 13 \end{bmatrix} \begin{bmatrix} 01 \\ 20 \end{bmatrix} \begin{bmatrix} 08 \\ 09 \end{bmatrix} \begin{bmatrix} 20 \\ 03 \end{bmatrix} \begin{bmatrix} 15 \\ 21 \end{bmatrix} \begin{bmatrix} 14 \\ 20 \end{bmatrix} \begin{bmatrix} 19 \\ 17 \end{bmatrix}$$

Multiply each of these these 2×1 matrices by the 2×2 encoding matrix $E = \begin{bmatrix} 1 & 2 \\ 3 & 4 \end{bmatrix}$.

This gives the following matrices.

$$\begin{bmatrix} 59 \\ 137 \end{bmatrix} \begin{bmatrix} 29 \\ 79 \end{bmatrix} \begin{bmatrix} 51 \\ 127 \end{bmatrix} \begin{bmatrix} 41 \\ 83 \end{bmatrix} \begin{bmatrix} 26 \\ 60 \end{bmatrix} \begin{bmatrix} 26 \\ 72 \end{bmatrix} \begin{bmatrix} 57 \\ 129 \end{bmatrix} \begin{bmatrix} 54 \\ 122 \end{bmatrix} \begin{bmatrix} 53 \\ 125 \end{bmatrix}$$

The encoded message could then be sent as

59 137 29 79 51 127 41 83 26 60 26 72 57 129 54 122 53 125

Having encoded a message, you should be able to decode it. To decode a message you need a *decoding matrix, D,* which is simply the inverse of the encoding matrix. That is, $D = E^{-1}$, where E is the encoding matrix. Therefore, if

$$E = \begin{bmatrix} 1 & 2 \\ 3 & 4 \end{bmatrix} \text{ then } D = \begin{bmatrix} -2 & 1 \\ \frac{3}{2} & -\frac{1}{2} \end{bmatrix}$$

Multiplying the coded matrices by D yields the original (uncoded) 2×1 matrices. For example,

$$D\begin{bmatrix} 59 \\ 137 \end{bmatrix} = \begin{bmatrix} -2 & 1 \\ \frac{3}{2} & -\frac{1}{2} \end{bmatrix}\begin{bmatrix} 59 \\ 137 \end{bmatrix} = \begin{bmatrix} 19 \\ 20 \end{bmatrix}$$

The matrix $\begin{bmatrix} 19 \\ 20 \end{bmatrix}$ corresponds to the 19th and 20th letters of the alphabet, ST.

A message can be coded by breaking it into groups of three letters or more. In general, the greater the length of the units into which the message is broken, the more difficult it is for an unauthorized party to *break* the code. To encode a message broken into units of three letters, use a 3×3 encoding matrix that has an inverse and proceed as in the example above. For units of four letters use a 4×4 matrix, and so forth.

Problems

1. Decode the following messages based on the same coding used for STUDY MATH IT COUNTS.

a. 40 96 51 103 4 10 36 84

b. 29 77 22 58 43 99 24 62 73 171

2. Select a new 2×2 encoding matrix. Write a message and encode it. Find the decoding matrix.

3. Encode the message PEACE ASSURED, using the 3×3 encoding matrix below. Remember to group the letters into units of three letters.

$$\begin{bmatrix} 1 & -2 & 3 \\ -3 & 2 & 4 \\ 5 & -1 & -2 \end{bmatrix}$$

4. Decode the following message, which was encoded using $\begin{bmatrix} 4 & 3 \\ -1 & 12 \end{bmatrix}$.

51 0 126 147 36 93 31 56 51 0 115 35 55 152

5. Decode the following message, which was encoded using $\begin{bmatrix} 1 & -2 & 3 \\ -3 & 2 & 4 \\ 5 & -1 & -2 \end{bmatrix}$.

25 48 32 8 21 0 1 −2 15 26 −20 73 33 9 69 57 47 64

ANSWERS

1. a. PLAY BALL
   b. SEND MONEY
3. 9 −34 73 −4 5 8 44 65 34 20 −28 77
4. LAUNCH DELAYED
5. PROCEED CAREFULLY

ANSWERS

1. 2×3
2. 3×1
3. $(1, -2)$
4. $\left(\frac{41}{22}, -\frac{16}{11}, -\frac{45}{22}\right)$
5. $\begin{bmatrix} -2 & 0 \\ 1 & -4 \end{bmatrix}$
6. $\begin{bmatrix} -4 & 10 \\ 7 & 0 \end{bmatrix}$
7. 14
8. 6
9. $(2, -1)$
10. $\left(\frac{46}{17}, \frac{14}{17}\right)$

Chapter 13 Summary and Review

13-1

A matrix of m rows and n columns has **dimensions** $m \times n$.

Find the dimensions of each matrix.

1. $\begin{bmatrix} 3 & -1 & 4 \\ 2 & -3 & -1 \end{bmatrix}$

2. $\begin{bmatrix} 1 \\ 0 \\ -2 \end{bmatrix}$

To solve a system of equations using matrices, use **row-equivalent operations** to transform the matrix into a matrix that has only 0's below the main diagonal.

Solve using matrices.

3. $3x - 2y = 7$
$5x + 3y = -1$

4. $3x - y + z = 5$
$2x - y + 4z = -3$
$x + 2y - z = 1$

13-2

To add matrices, add the corresponding elements. To subtract matrices, subtract the corresponding elements. In either case, the matrices must have the same dimensions.

5. Find $\begin{bmatrix} -3 & 5 \\ 4 & -2 \end{bmatrix} + \begin{bmatrix} 1 & -5 \\ -3 & -2 \end{bmatrix}$

6. Find $\begin{bmatrix} -3 & 5 \\ 4 & -2 \end{bmatrix} - \begin{bmatrix} 1 & -5 \\ -3 & -2 \end{bmatrix}$

13-3

The **determinant** of $\begin{bmatrix} a_1 & a_2 \\ b_1 & b_2 \end{bmatrix}$ is written as $\begin{vmatrix} a_1 & a_2 \\ b_1 & b_2 \end{vmatrix}$ and is evaluated as $a_1b_2 - b_1a_2$.

Evaluate.

7. $\begin{vmatrix} 3 & -2 \\ 1 & 4 \end{vmatrix}$

8. $\begin{vmatrix} -2 & 3 \\ 0 & -3 \end{vmatrix}$

Cramer's rule for 2 equations in the form

$$\begin{aligned} a_1x + b_1y &= c_1 \\ a_2x + b_2y &= c_2 \end{aligned} \quad \text{has a solution } x = \frac{\begin{vmatrix} c_1 & b_1 \\ c_2 & b_2 \end{vmatrix}}{\begin{vmatrix} a_1 & b_1 \\ a_2 & b_2 \end{vmatrix}} \text{ and } y = \frac{\begin{vmatrix} a_1 & c_1 \\ a_2 & c_2 \end{vmatrix}}{\begin{vmatrix} a_1 & b_1 \\ a_2 & b_2 \end{vmatrix}}.$$

Solve using Cramer's rule.

9. $2x - 5y = 9$
$-3x + y = -7$

10. $4x - y = 10$
$-3x + 5y = -4$

The determinant of a 3×3 matrix can be evaluated as follows.

$$\begin{vmatrix} a_1 & b_1 & c_1 \\ a_2 & b_2 & c_2 \\ a_3 & b_3 & c_3 \end{vmatrix} = a_1\begin{vmatrix} b_2 & c_2 \\ b_3 & c_3 \end{vmatrix} - a_2\begin{vmatrix} b_1 & c_1 \\ b_3 & c_3 \end{vmatrix} + a_3\begin{vmatrix} b_1 & c_1 \\ b_2 & c_2 \end{vmatrix}$$

Evaluate.

11. $\begin{vmatrix} 3 & 2 & -3 \\ 1 & -1 & 1 \\ 0 & 1 & -1 \end{vmatrix}$

12. $\begin{vmatrix} -2 & 2 & -4 \\ -1 & 0 & 0 \\ 3 & -1 & 1 \end{vmatrix}$

Cramer's rule for 3 equations in the form

$$\begin{aligned} a_1x + b_1y + c_1z &= d_1 \\ a_2x + b_2y + c_2z &= d_2 \\ a_3x + b_3y + c_3z &= d_3 \end{aligned}$$ has a solution given by

$x = \frac{D_x}{D}$, $y = \frac{D_y}{D}$, $z = \frac{D_z}{D}$, where $D \neq 0$,

$$D = \begin{vmatrix} a_1 & b_1 & c_1 \\ a_2 & b_2 & c_2 \\ a_3 & b_3 & c_3 \end{vmatrix}, \; D_x = \begin{vmatrix} d_1 & b_1 & c_1 \\ d_2 & b_2 & c_2 \\ d_3 & b_3 & c_3 \end{vmatrix}, \; D_y = \begin{vmatrix} a_1 & d_1 & c_1 \\ a_2 & d_2 & c_2 \\ a_3 & d_3 & c_3 \end{vmatrix}, \text{ and } D_z = \begin{vmatrix} a_1 & b_1 & d_1 \\ a_2 & b_2 & d_2 \\ a_3 & b_3 & d_3 \end{vmatrix}.$$

Solve using Cramer's rule.

13. $\begin{aligned} 3x - 2y - z &= -1 \\ 2x + y + z &= 8 \\ -x + 3y - 2z &= 5 \end{aligned}$

14. $\begin{aligned} 2x - 2y + z &= 3 \\ -4x + y - 3z &= 1 \\ -2x - 3y + z &= 0 \end{aligned}$

13-4

The **product** of a number k, called a scalar, and a matrix A is the matrix, denoted kA, obtained by multiplying each number in A by the number k.

If $A = \begin{bmatrix} -3 & 0 \\ 2 & -1 \end{bmatrix}$,

15. find $-3A$.

16. find $4A$.

If matrix A has n columns and matrix B has n rows, then we can compute the product AB, which will have as many rows as A and as many columns as B. The element in row i, column j, of the product AB is found by multiplying the elements in row i of A by the elements in column j of B, and adding.

If $A = \begin{bmatrix} -3 & 0 \\ 2 & -1 \end{bmatrix}$ $B = \begin{bmatrix} 2 & 1 & -1 \\ -1 & 0 & 2 \end{bmatrix}$ $C = \begin{bmatrix} -2 & 0 & 3 \\ -1 & 1 & 1 \\ 0 & 2 & 0 \end{bmatrix}$

Find each product, if it exists.

17. AB

18. BC

19. AC

The system of equations $\begin{aligned} a_1x + b_1y + c_1z &= d_1 \\ a_2x + b_2y + c_2z &= d_2 \\ a_3x + b_3y + c_3z &= d_3 \end{aligned}$ has an equivalent matrix equation

$$\begin{bmatrix} a_1 & b_1 & c_1 \\ a_2 & b_2 & c_2 \\ a_3 & b_3 & c_3 \end{bmatrix} \begin{bmatrix} x \\ y \\ z \end{bmatrix} = \begin{bmatrix} d_1 \\ d_2 \\ d_3 \end{bmatrix}$$

11. -1
12. -2
13. $(2, 3, 1)$
14. $\left(\frac{25}{22}, -\frac{17}{11}, -\frac{26}{11}\right)$
15. $\begin{bmatrix} 9 & 0 \\ -6 & 3 \end{bmatrix}$
16. $\begin{bmatrix} -12 & 0 \\ 8 & -4 \end{bmatrix}$
17. $\begin{bmatrix} -6 & -3 & 3 \\ 5 & 2 & -4 \end{bmatrix}$
18. $\begin{bmatrix} -5 & -1 & 7 \\ 2 & 4 & -3 \end{bmatrix}$
19. Does not exist

20. $\begin{bmatrix} 5 & 2 & -4 \\ -3 & -4 & -2 \\ 6 & 7 & 5 \end{bmatrix}\begin{bmatrix} x \\ y \\ z \end{bmatrix} = \begin{bmatrix} 0 \\ 6 \\ 15 \end{bmatrix}$

21. $\begin{bmatrix} 2 & -3 \\ -1 & 2 \end{bmatrix}$

22. Does not exist

23. $\begin{bmatrix} \frac{2}{3} & -\frac{1}{6} & -\frac{1}{6} \\ 0 & -\frac{1}{2} & \frac{1}{2} \\ -\frac{1}{3} & \frac{1}{3} & \frac{1}{3} \end{bmatrix}$

24. $\begin{bmatrix} -\frac{1}{2} & \frac{3}{2} & -\frac{1}{2} \\ \frac{3}{2} & -\frac{7}{2} & \frac{1}{2} \\ \frac{1}{2} & -\frac{1}{2} & \frac{1}{2} \end{bmatrix}$

25. (1, −2)

26. (6, −2)

27. Pens $7.20, pencils $7.00, erasers $28.00

20. Write a matrix equation equivalent to the system of equations.

$$\begin{aligned} 5x + 2y - 4z &= 0 \\ -3x - 4y - 2z &= 6 \\ 6x + 7y + 5z &= 15 \end{aligned}$$

13-5

If $A = \begin{bmatrix} a & b \\ c & d \end{bmatrix}$, then to find the inverse of A, denoted A^{-1}, $A^{-1} = \frac{1}{|A|}\begin{bmatrix} d & -b \\ -c & a \end{bmatrix}$

Find A^{-1}, if it exists. Check by calculating AA^{-1}.

21. $A = \begin{bmatrix} 2 & 3 \\ 1 & 2 \end{bmatrix}$

22. $A = \begin{bmatrix} -3 & -1 \\ 6 & 2 \end{bmatrix}$

13-6

The inverse of any square matrix A exists only when the determinant of the matrix is nonzero. To find this inverse, form a new augmented matrix consisting of matrix A on the left and the corresponding identity matrix I on the right. Use row-equivalent operations to transform the left half of the augmented matrix into the identity matrix. Once this is done, the inverse, A^{-1}, will appear as the right half of the augmented matrix.

Find A^{-1} if it exists.

23. $\begin{bmatrix} 2 & 0 & 1 \\ 1 & -1 & 2 \\ 1 & 1 & 2 \end{bmatrix}$

24. $\begin{bmatrix} 3 & 1 & 2 \\ 1 & 0 & 1 \\ -2 & -1 & 1 \end{bmatrix}$

To solve $\begin{aligned} a_1x + b_1y &= c_1 \\ a_2x + b_2y &= c_2 \end{aligned}$, the variable matrix $\begin{bmatrix} x \\ y \end{bmatrix}$ equals the product of the inverse of the coefficient matrix $\begin{bmatrix} a_1 & b_1 \\ a_2 & b_2 \end{bmatrix}$ and the constant matrix $\begin{bmatrix} c_1 \\ c_2 \end{bmatrix}$.

Solve using matrices.

25. $\begin{aligned} 3x - 2y &= 7 \\ 5x + 3y &= -1 \end{aligned}$

26. $\begin{aligned} 2x + 3y &= 6 \\ x + 2y &= 2 \end{aligned}$

13-7

Some problems can be translated into a system of equations that can be solved by using matrices.

27. The Ticon Co. produces pens, pencils, and erasers. The items are sold by stores A, B, and C as indicated in this table.

	Stores		
	A	B	C
Pens	40	30	20
Pencils	50	30	60
Erasers	40	40	60

The profit on pencils is 5¢, on pens 8¢, and on erasers 20¢. Find the amount of profit from each item sold.

See also Problem 13, Computer-Assisted Problem Solving, page 848.

Chapter 13 Test

1. Find the dimensions of $\begin{bmatrix} -2 & 3 \\ 1 & 2 \\ 0 & 5 \end{bmatrix}$.

2. Solve using matrices. $\begin{aligned} 2x - 5y &= 1 \\ 3x + 2y &= -2 \end{aligned}$

3. Add $\begin{bmatrix} 3 & -4 \\ 2 & 0 \\ 1 & -1 \end{bmatrix} + \begin{bmatrix} -2 & 4 \\ 3 & -3 \\ 1 & 1 \end{bmatrix}$.

4. Evaluate $\begin{vmatrix} 1 & -4 \\ -2 & 3 \end{vmatrix}$.

5. Solve $\begin{aligned} -4x - 2y &= 3 \\ 3x - 5y &= -4 \end{aligned}$ using Cramer's rule.

6. Evaluate $\begin{vmatrix} 3 & 0 & -2 \\ -2 & 1 & 0 \\ 1 & -1 & -3 \end{vmatrix}$.

7. Solve $\begin{aligned} 2x - 3y + z &= 2 \\ x - 2y + 3z &= 0 \\ 3x + y - z &= -1 \end{aligned}$ using Cramer's rule.

8. If $A = \begin{bmatrix} 2 & -1 & 0 \\ 0 & 1 & -4 \end{bmatrix}$, find $-2A$.

If $A = \begin{bmatrix} -3 & 2 & 0 \\ 1 & 1 & 1 \\ 0 & -1 & 0 \end{bmatrix}$ and $B = \begin{bmatrix} 2 & 3 & -1 \\ -1 & 0 & 1 \\ 1 & 1 & -2 \end{bmatrix}$

9. find $A \cdot B$.

10. find $B \cdot A$.

11. Write a matrix equation equivalent to this system of equations.

$$\begin{aligned} 2x - y + 3z &= 5 \\ 3x + 2y - z &= 1 \\ x - 3y + 4z &= 0 \end{aligned}$$

12. If $A = \begin{bmatrix} 3 & 1 \\ -5 & 0 \end{bmatrix}$, find A^{-1}, if it exists.

13. If $B = \begin{bmatrix} 1 & 2 & 0 \\ 0 & -2 & 1 \\ -1 & 1 & -1 \end{bmatrix}$, find B^{-1}, if it exists.

14. This chart represents the standings at the end of a soccer season. If 2 points are awarded for a win, 1 point for a tie, and 0 points for a loss, how many points did each team earn?

Team	Wins	Losses	Ties
Fireballs	8	8	0
Blue Angels	5	8	3
Tigers	7	6	3
Dynamite	9	5	2
Rangers	4	6	6

ANSWERS

1. 3×2
2. $\left(-\frac{8}{19}, -\frac{7}{19}\right)$
3. $\begin{bmatrix} 1 & 0 \\ 5 & -3 \\ 2 & 0 \end{bmatrix}$
4. -5
5. $\left(-\frac{23}{26}, \frac{7}{26}\right)$
6. -11
7. $\left(-\frac{1}{5}, -1, -\frac{3}{5}\right)$
8. $\begin{bmatrix} -4 & 2 & 0 \\ 0 & -2 & 8 \end{bmatrix}$
9. $\begin{bmatrix} -8 & -9 & 5 \\ 2 & 4 & -2 \\ 1 & 0 & -1 \end{bmatrix}$
10. $\begin{bmatrix} -3 & 8 & 3 \\ 3 & -3 & 0 \\ -2 & 5 & 1 \end{bmatrix}$
11. $\begin{bmatrix} 2 & -1 & 3 \\ 3 & 2 & -1 \\ 1 & -3 & 4 \end{bmatrix} \begin{bmatrix} x \\ y \\ z \end{bmatrix} = \begin{bmatrix} 5 \\ 1 \\ 0 \end{bmatrix}$
12. $\begin{bmatrix} 0 & -\frac{1}{5} \\ 1 & \frac{3}{5} \end{bmatrix}$
13. $\begin{bmatrix} -1 & -2 & -2 \\ 1 & 1 & 1 \\ 2 & 3 & 2 \end{bmatrix}$
14. Fireballs 16 points; Blue Angels 13 points; Tigers 17 points; Dynamite 20 points; Rangers 14 points

Test Item Analysis

Item	Lesson
1	13-1
2	13-6
3	13-2
4–7	13-3
8	13-6
9, 10	13-4
11	13-6
12	13-5
13	13-6
14	13-7

CHAPTER 14

Sequences, Series, and Mathematical Induction

Chapter Overview

Chapter 14 introduces sequences, partial sums, series, sigma notation, and mathematical induction. Advanced concepts are considered, such as limits of infinite series and inductive proofs, to prepare students for ideas studied in detail in higher mathematics courses such as calculus. A problem-solving lesson emphasizes the need to systematically *combine strategies* to solve problems.

Objectives

14-1
- Find specific terms of a sequence, given the n-th term of the sequence.
- Find a general term for a sequence.
- Find partial sums for a sequence.
- Use sigma notation.

14-2
- Find the first term and common difference of an arithmetic sequence.
- Solve problems involving the n-th term of an arithmetic sequence.
- Construct an arithmetic sequence, given specific terms of the sequence.
- Find partial sums of arithmetic series.

14-3
- Find the common ratio of a given geometric sequence.
- Solve problems involving the n-th term of a geometric sequence.
- Find partial sums of a geometric series.

14-4
- Determine whether a given geometric series has a sum.
- Find the sum of an infinite geometric series.

14-5
- Prove statements about positive integers using the principle of mathematical induction.

14-6
- Solve nonroutine problems using a combination of strategies.

TEACHING CHAPTER 14

Cooperative Learning Opportunities

Chapter 14 lends itself to paired checking. There are many concepts and procedures that can be learned in isolation but that fit together like stones forming a great building. Also, with the exception of some earlier work on patterns, students will not have had much experience with sequences and series. Therefore, it will be helpful to check understanding at each step.

Each of the example sets in Lesson 14-1 covers a new idea or kind of notation. Consequently, you should assign each of the **Try This** Exercises in class. After they are done by individuals, assign pairs to review each other's work. For about five minutes, let them discuss the exercises, the meaning of the words, and their answers. Take questions to settle any remaining confusion and then proceed to the next example.

If time permits, the method described above would also be helpful for Lessons 14-2 through 14-4. The follow-up on examples explained will help students retain the ideas and methods.

Multicultural Note: *Kovalevsky and Cauchy*

Sonya Kovalevsky (1850–1891) taught herself trigonometry and calculus. At 18, she left Russia and went to Germany, where she worked extensively on the theory of infinite series. A French contemporary of Kovalevsky, Augustin-Louis Cauchy (1789–1867) also worked with series and developed a test for convergence.

Kovalevsky and Cauchy independently developed an important theorem on the existence of solutions to certain kinds of partial differential equations. This theorem belongs to advanced mathematics, but you might wish to broaden students' thinking by discussing existence ideas.

Mathematicians work not only to solve problems and create comprehensive structures but also to determine the conditions for which certain classes of equations have solutions. **Theorem 14-6** with its innocent looking test for convergence was only obtained after a great deal of trial and error by the best mathematicians.

For more information, see page 99 of **Multiculturalism in Mathematics, Science, and Technology**.

Alternative Assessment and Communication Ideas

There are a number of possible sources of confusion in the vocabulary and concepts associated with sequences and series. While it is necessary that students be able to use the formulas in Chapter 14, it is also important that they intuitively grasp the basic concepts. You can assess this understanding through quizzes or test items in which you ask for written responses in complete sentences (not symbols). The following are sample items.

(1) What is a sequence?
(2) What is a series?
(3) Write a sequence and the series associated with it.
(4) What is the difference between a sequence and a series?
(5) What is the difference between an arithmetic and a geometric series?
(6) What does converge mean?
(7) Explain how the sum of an endless set of numbers can be a small whole number.

Investigations and Projects

In Lesson 14-3, Example 6 discusses a geometric sequence for the payment of interest. You might have students do a project on the interest for an investment and how this is related to geometric series. You could suggest the following guidelines as a start.

The amount of principal and interest for an investment can be calculated for $1. Then whatever amount is invested is multiplied by the amount for $1. For example $1 invested at 7% will grow as follows after 4 years: $(1.07)^4 = 1.3108$

Ask students to write the sum of accumulated principles and interest for $1 invested at the beginning of each of n years. If we write the last dollar invested first, then the sum will be:

$$1 + (1.07) + (1.07)^2 + \quad + (1.07)^{n-1}$$

Students can see that this is a geometric series and after identifying the terms and common ratio they can devise and use the formula to calculate the investments **Ans:** $\left(\frac{(1.07)^n - 1}{.07}\right)$ **Use (1 + 0.07) as the common ratio.**

MANAGING CHAPTER 14

Lesson	PACING CHART (DAYS) Algebra	Algebra w/Finite	Algebra w/Trig	Comprehensive	Opening Activity	Cooperative Activity	Seat or Group Work
14-1	0	1	0	1	First Five Minutes 14-1: **TE** p.612 or ***FFM Transparency Masters*** p.39	Critical Thinking: **SE** p.616 Strategy Problem Bank 13: ***Problem Bank*** p.14	Try This a–m
14-2	0	1	0	1	First Five Minutes 14-2: **TE** p.617 or ***FFM Transparency Masters*** p.40	Critical Thinking: **SE** p.623	Try This a–l
14-3	0	1	0	1	First Five Minutes 14-3: **TE** p.624 or ***FFM Transparency Masters*** p.40	Critical Thinking: **SE** p.629	Try This a–k
14-4	0	1	0	1	First Five Minutes 14-4: **TE** p.630 or ***FFM Transparency Masters*** p.40	Critical Thinking: **SE** p.632 ✂ Manipulative Activity 14: ***Enrichment*** p.55	Try This a–e
14-5	0	0.5	0	0.5	First Five Minutes 14-5: **TE** p.634 or ***FFM Transparency Masters*** p.41	Critical Thinking: **SE** p.636 Looking for Errors 14: ***Enrichment*** p.75	Try This a–b
14-6	0	0.5	0	0.5	First Five Minutes 14-6: **TE** p.637 or ***FFM Transparency Masters*** p.41	Strategy Problem Bank 14: ***Problem Bank*** p.15	Problem 4: **SE** p.638
Review	0	1	0	1			
Test	0	1	0	1			

FFM: First Five Minutes SPMR: Skills Practice Mixed Review

MANAGING CHAPTER 14

Enrichment	Review/Assess	Reteach	Technology	Lesson
Critical Thinking 14: ***Enrichment*** p.35	Lesson Quiz: **TE** p.615	Skills Practice 39, #1–13: ***SPMR*** p.51	BASIC Computer Project 15: ***Technology*** p.95	**14-1**
Math Point: **TE** p.620 Lesson Enrichment **TE** p.621	Lesson Quiz: **TE** p.621 Quiz 27: ***Assessment*** p.35	Skills Practice 39, #14–25: ***SPMR*** p.51	Worksheet 22: ***TI-81 Activities*** pp.91–93 Worksheet 28: ***Master Grapher*** pp.112–114, pp.246–248, or pp.382–384 Calculator Worksheet 26: ***Technology*** p.28	**14-2**
Writing to Learn: **SE** p.629	Lesson Quiz: **TE** p.627 Mixed Review 27: ***SPMR*** p.91	Skills Practice 40, #1–25: ***SPMR*** p.52	Worksheet 29: ***Master Grapher*** pp.115–118, pp.249–252, or pp.385–388 Calculator Worksheet 27: ***Technology*** p.29 Spreadsheet Activity 9: ***Technology*** pp.67–69	**14-3**
✂ Manipulative Activity 14: ***Enrichment*** p.55	Lesson Quiz: **TE** p.631 Quiz 28: ***Assessment*** p.36	Skills Practice 41, #1–20: ***SPMR*** p.53	Worksheet 23: ***TI-81 Activities*** pp.95–98 Calculator Worksheet 28: ***Technology*** p.30 Problem for Programmers: **SE** p.633	**14-4**
Looking for Errors 14: ***Enrichment*** p.75	Lesson Quiz: **TE** p.636	Skills Practice 41, #21–26: ***SPMR*** p.53	BASIC Computer Project 16: ***Technology*** p.96	**14-5**
Problem 14: Computer Assisted Problem Solving, **SE** pp.849–850	Mixed Review 28: ***SPMR*** p.92	Strategy Problem Bank 14: ***Problem Bank*** p.15	Problem 14: Computer Assisted Problem Solving, **SE** pp.849–850	**14-6**
	Summary and Review: **SE** pp.639–640; Test: **SE** p.641			**Review**
	Chapter 14 Test: ***Assessment*** pp.125–130(reg.), pp.183–184 (adv.) Assessing Strategies 8, 9: ***Assessment*** pp.209–212			**Test**

The solution to the problem posed on the facing page can be found on page 616.

Ready for Sequences, Series, and Mathematical Induction?

1-3 Evaluate each expression for $n = 5$.

1. $n(n - 1)$ 20

2. $n(n - 1)(n - 2)$ 60

3. $\dfrac{2n^2 - 3n - 5}{n - 3}$ 15

1-7 Evaluate each expression for $n = 5$ and $r = 3$.

4. n^r 125

5. $(r - 1)^n$ 32

6. $\dfrac{(3r - 2n)^r}{2nr}$ $-\frac{1}{30}$

3-3, 12-2 Given each function f, find $f(1)$, $f(2)$, $f(3)$.

7. $f(x) = 3x + 2$ 5, 8, 11

8. $f(x) = 3x^2 - 1$ 2, 11, 26

9. $f(x) = (-1)^x 3^x$ $-3, 9, -27$

10. $f(x) = \left(\frac{1}{2}\right)^x$ $\frac{1}{2}, \frac{1}{4}, \frac{1}{8}$

CHAPTER 14

Sequences, Series, and Mathematical Induction

How many pairs of rabbits will there be in a year if every month each pair gives birth to a new pair which, from the second month on, also gives birth each month?

14-1

FIRST FIVE MINUTES

1. What is the missing number?
   1, 3, 5, ___ , 9
   7
2. What is the missing number?
   1, 2, 4, ___ , 16
   8
3. What is the missing number?
   0, 3, 6, ___ , 12
   9

Sequences and General Terms

Point out that a sequence may or may not have a rule.

Three-period notation is called an "ellipsis," and means "and so on."

Key Questions

$a_n = 3n + 2$

- What is the value of a_1?
  $a_1 = 3(1) + 2 = 5$
- What is the value of a_2?
  $a_2 = 3(2) + 2 = 8$
- In the sequence 7, 4, 8, 3, 9, . . . , what is a_4?
  $a_4 = 3$

Chalkboard Examples

1. Given that $a_n = 2n - 3$, find the first three terms of the sequence.
   $a_1 = 2(1) - 3 = -1$
   $a_2 = 2(2) - 3 = 1$
   $a_3 = 2(3) - 3 = 3$
2. Given that $a_1 = 0$ and $a_{n+1} = (-1)^{a_n} + a_n$, find the first five terms of the sequence.
   0, 1, 0, 1, 0

14-1 Sequences and Series

Leonardo Fibonacci, perhaps the best mathematician of the Middle Ages, included the following problem in his famous work *Liber abaci.*

How many pairs of rabbits can be produced from a single pair in a year if every month each pair begets a new pair which, from the second month on, become productive?

This problem gave rise to the famous Fibonacci sequence.

Sequences and General Terms

Objective: Find specific terms of a sequence, given the n-th term of the sequence.

Definition

A **sequence** is an ordered set of numbers.

Here is an example of a sequence: 3, 5, 7, 9, . . .

The dots mean that there are more numbers in the sequence. A sequence that does not end is called an infinite sequence.

Each number is called a term of the sequence. The first term, a_1, is 3; the second term, a_2, is 5; the third term, a_3, is 7; and so on.

Some sequences have a rule which describes the n-th term or general term. The above sequence could be described as 3, 5, 7, 9, . . . , $2n + 1$, . . . , where the n-th term, a_n, is $2n + 1$. We also say

$$a_n = 2n + 1$$

We can find the terms of the sequence by consecutively substituting the natural numbers, 1, 2, 3, . . . , for n in the general term.

EXAMPLE 1 The general term of a sequence is given by $a_n = \frac{(-1)^n}{n+1}$. Find the first three terms, the 10th term, and the 15th term.

$$a_1 = \frac{(-1)^1}{1+1} = -\frac{1}{2} \qquad a_2 = \frac{(-1)^2}{2+1} = \frac{1}{3} \qquad a_3 = \frac{(-1)^3}{3+1} = -\frac{1}{4}$$

$$a_{10} = \frac{(-1)^{10}}{10+1} = \frac{1}{11} \qquad a_{15} = \frac{(-1)^{15}}{15+1} = -\frac{1}{16}$$

Try This

For each of the following, the general term of a sequence is given. Find the first three terms, the 10th term, and the 15th term.

a. $a_n = 2^n - 1$
$a_1 = 1, a_2 = 3, a_3 = 7, a_{10} = 1023, a_{15} = 32,767$

b. $a_n = (-1)^n n^2$
$a_1 = -1, a_2 = 4, a_3 = -9, a_{10} = 100, a_{15} = -225$

Some sequences can be defined by **recursion.** We give a value of a_1 and then tell how each subsequent term is related to the term before it in the sequence.

EXAMPLE 2 Find the first five terms of this recursively defined sequence: $a_1 = 1$ and $a_{n+1} = 3a_n - 1$.

$$a_1 = 1, \quad a_2 = 3a_1 - 1 = 3 \cdot 1 - 1 = 2, \quad a_3 = 3a_2 - 1 = 3 \cdot 2 - 1 = 5, \quad a_4 = 3a_3 - 1 = 3 \cdot 5 - 1 = 14, \quad a_5 = 3a_4 - 1 = 3 \cdot 14 - 1 = 41$$

Try This Find the first five terms of these recursively defined sequences.

c. $a_1 = 0, \quad a_{n+1} = a_n + 4$
0, 4, 8, 12, 16

d. $a_1 = 4, \quad a_{n+1} = a_n - 2$
4, 2, 0, −2, −4

Finding General Terms

Objective: Find a general term for a sequence.

We may know the first few terms of a sequence, but not the general term. In such a case we cannot know for sure what the general term is, but we can look for a pattern.

EXAMPLES For each sequence, find a general term.

3. 1, 4, 9, 16, 25, . . .

These are squares of numbers, so a rule for the n-th term would be $a_n = n^2$.

4. −1, 2, −4, 8, −16, . . .

If we ignore the negative signs we have the powers of 2, which have a general term of $a_n = 2^{n-1}$. We can multiply each term by $(-1)^n$. This will multiply each odd term by −1 and each even term by 1. Thus, a general term would be $a_n = (-1)^n 2^{n-1}$.

Try This For each sequence, find a general term. Answers may vary.

e. 2, 4, 6, 8, 10, . . . $a_n = 2n$

f. −1, 2, −3, 4, −5, 6, . . . $a_n = (-1)^n(n)$

g. 1, 8, 27, 64, 125, . . . $a_n = n^3$

h. 1, 2, 4, 8, 16, 32, . . . $a_n = 2^{n-1}$

Series

Objective: Find partial sums for a sequence.

If we add the terms of a sequence we have a series. Given the sequence 1, 3, 5, 7, 9, . . . , $2n - 1$, . . . , we have the series $1 + 3 + 5 + 7 + 9 + \cdots + (2n - 1) + \cdots$.

Finding General Terms

Illustrate that a sequence is never completely determined by its first few terms. For example, 1, 2, 4, 8, and 16 are the first five terms of the sequence $a_n = 2^{n-1}$. However, they are also the first five terms of the different sequence $a_n = \frac{n^4}{24} - \frac{n^3}{4} + \frac{23n^2}{24} - \frac{3n}{4} + 1$.

You may want to have students write out the terms of $(-1)^n$ and $(-1)^{n+1}$ as an illustration of the difference.

Chalkboard Examples

Find the rule for the general term of each sequence.

1. 4, 8, 12, 16, 20, 24, . . .
   $a_n = 4n$
2. 1, −1, 1, −1, 1, . . .
   $a_n = (-1)^{n-1}$ or $a_n = (-1)^{n+1}$

Series

Chalkboard Example

1. Find the partial sum S_5 for the sequence 1, 3, 5, 7, 9, 11, 13, . . .
   $1 + 3 + 5 + 7 + 9 = 25$

Sigma Notation

Explain that

$\sum_{n=1}^{3} 2n - 3 = \left(\sum_{n=1}^{3} 2n\right) - 3$
$= 2 + 4 + 6 - 3 = 9$

While

$\sum_{n=1}^{3} (2n - 3) = -1 + 1 + 3 = 3$

Chalkboard Examples

Express the following without sigma notation and evaluate.

1. $\sum_{n=1}^{4} 3n$
   $3(1) + 3(2) + 3(3) + 3(4) = 30$
2. $\sum_{n=1}^{3} 2^n$
   $2^1 + 2^2 + 2^3 = 2 + 4 + 8 = 14$

Write sigma notation for each sum.

3. $5 + 10 + 15 + 20 + 25$
   $\sum_{n=1}^{5} 5n$
4. $1 - 2 + 4 - 8 + 16$
   $\sum_{n=1}^{5} (-1)^{n-1} 2^{n-1}$ or $\sum_{n=1}^{5} (-2)^{n-1}$
5. $1 + 8 + 27 + 64 + 125$
   $\sum_{n=1}^{5} n^3$

Definition

An indicated sum of the terms of a sequence

$$S_n = a_1 + a_2 + a_3 + \cdots + a_n$$

is called a **series**.

Since many sequences are infinite, it is often convenient to consider the sum of only a finite number of terms of a sequence. We call this a **partial sum**. For the sequence $1, 3, 5, 7, 9, \ldots, 2n - 1, \ldots$, we construct some partial sums.

$S_1 = a_1 = 1$ — Finding the first term of the given sequence

$S_2 = a_1 + a_2 = 1 + 3 = 4$ — Finding the sum of the first two terms

$S_3 = a_1 + a_2 + a_3 = 1 + 3 + 5 = 9$ — Finding the sum of the first three terms

EXAMPLE 5 Find S_5 for the sequence $-2, 4, -6, 8, -10, 12, -14, \ldots$.

$S_5 = -2 + 4 + (-6) + 8 + (-10) = -6$ — Finding the sum of the first five terms

Try This

i. Find S_1, S_2, S_3, and S_4 for the sequence $\frac{1}{2}, \frac{1}{4}, \frac{1}{8}, \frac{1}{16}, \frac{1}{32}, \ldots$. $S_1 = \frac{1}{2}, S_2 = \frac{3}{4}, S_3 = \frac{7}{8}, S_4 = \frac{15}{16}$

Sigma Notation

Objective: Use sigma notation.

The Greek letter Σ (sigma) can be used to simplify notation when a series has a formula for the general term.

The sum of the first four terms of the sequence $3, 5, 7, 9, \ldots, 2n + 1$, can be denoted

$\sum_{n=1}^{4} (2n + 1)$ Read "the sum as n goes from 1 to 4 of $(2n + 1)$"

EXAMPLES Rename and evaluate the following sums.

6. $\sum_{n=1}^{5} n^2 = 1^2 + 2^2 + 3^2 + 4^2 + 5^2 = 1 + 4 + 9 + 16 + 25 = 55$

7. $\sum_{n=1}^{4} (-1)^n(2n) = (-1)^1(2 \cdot 1) + (-1)^2(2 \cdot 2) + (-1)^3(2 \cdot 3) + (-1)^4(2 \cdot 4) = -2 + 4 - 6 + 8 = 4$

Try This Rename and evaluate the following sums.

j. $\sum_{n=1}^{3}\left(2 + \frac{1}{n}\right)$ $7\frac{5}{6}$ **k.** $\sum_{n=1}^{4}(5^n - 1)$ 776

EXAMPLES Write sigma notation for each sum.

8. $1 + 3 + 5 + 7$

This is the sum of the first four odd numbers. A general term for an odd number is $2n - 1$. So, sigma notation is

$$\sum_{n=1}^{4}(2n - 1)$$

9. $1 - 3 + 5 - 7$

This is the sum of the first four odd numbers, but with alternating signs. The first is positive, the second negative, and so on. To cause this pattern we can multiply each term by $(-1)^{n+1}$. So sigma notation is

$$\sum_{n=1}^{4}(-1)^{n+1}(2n - 1)$$

10. $3 + 9 + 27 + 81 + \cdots$

This is a sum of powers of 3, and it is also an unending or infinite series. We use the symbol ∞ to represent infinity.

$$\sum_{n=1}^{\infty} 3^n$$

Try This Write sigma notation for each sum.

l. $2 + 4 + 6 + 8 + 10$ $\sum_{n=1}^{5} 2n$ **m.** $2 - 3 + 4 - 5 + \cdots$ $\sum_{n=1}^{\infty}(-1)^{n+1}(n + 1)$

14-1 EXERCISES

A

The general term of a sequence is given. In each case find the first four terms, the 10th term, and the 15th term.

1. $a_n = 3n + 1$ **2.** $a_n = 3n - 1$ **3.** $a_n = \frac{n}{n + 1}$ **4.** $a_n = n^2 + 1$

5. $a_n = n^2 - 2n$ **6.** $a_n = \frac{n^2 - 1}{n^2 + 1}$ **7.** $a_n = n + \frac{1}{n}$ **8.** $a_n = \left(-\frac{1}{2}\right)^{n-1}$

Find the first five terms of these recursively defined sequences.

9. $a_1 = 2, a_{n+1} = 4a_n - 3$ **10.** $a_1 = -3, a_{n+1} = 2a_n - 5$

11. $a_1 = 8, a_{n+1} = \frac{1}{2}a_n + 2$ **12.** $a_1 = 3, a_2 = 3, a_{n+1} = a_n - a_{n-1}$

LESSON QUIZ

1. Find a_5, given that $a_n = 3n - 5$. $a_5 = 10$
2. Find the general term a_n of the sequence 5, 7, 9, 11, 13, . . . $a_n = 3 + 2n$
3. Write without sigma notation and evaluate. $\sum_{n=1}^{4} 6n$ $6 + 12 + 18 + 24 = 60$
4. Write using sigma notation. $7^1 + 7^2 + 7^3 + 7^4 + 7^5 + 7^6$ $\sum_{n=1}^{6} 7^n$

Assignment Guide

Algebra: Omit

Alg w/Finite Math: 1–41 m3, 42, MR

Comprehensive: 1–36 m4, 37–41 e/o, 42–44, MR

ADDITIONAL ANSWERS

Exercises

1. 4, 7, 10, 13; 31; 46
2. 2, 5, 8, 11; 29; 44
3. $\frac{1}{2}, \frac{2}{3}, \frac{3}{4}, \frac{4}{5}; \frac{10}{11}; \frac{15}{16}$
4. 2, 5, 10, 17; 101; 226
5. −1, 0, 3, 8; 80; 195
6. $0, \frac{3}{5}, \frac{4}{5}, \frac{15}{17}; \frac{99}{101}; \frac{112}{113}$
7. $2, 2\frac{1}{2}, 3\frac{1}{3}, 4\frac{1}{4}; 10\frac{1}{10}; 15\frac{1}{15}$
8. $1, -\frac{1}{2}, \frac{1}{4}, -\frac{1}{8}; -\frac{1}{512}; \frac{1}{16{,}384}$
9. 2, 5, 17, 65, 257
10. −3, −11, −27, −59, −123
11. $8, 6, 5, 4\frac{1}{2}, 4\frac{1}{4}$
12. 3, 3, 0, −3, −3

21. $S_1 = \frac{1}{3}, S_2 = \frac{1}{2}, S_3 = \frac{7}{12}, S_4 = \frac{5}{8}$

22. $S_1 = -1, S_2 = 2, S_3 = -3, S_4 = 4$

23. $S_1 = 4, S_2 = 11, S_3 = 21, S_4 = 34$

24. $S_1 = -3, S_2 = 6, S_3 = -21, S_4 = 60$

25. $\frac{1}{2} + \frac{1}{4} + \frac{1}{6} + \frac{1}{8} + \frac{1}{10} = \frac{137}{120}$

26. $\frac{1}{3} + \frac{1}{5} + \frac{1}{7} + \frac{1}{9} + \frac{1}{11} + \frac{1}{13} = \frac{43024}{45045}$

27. $2^1 + 2^2 + 2^3 + 2^4 + 2^5 = 62$

28. $\sqrt{7} + \sqrt{9} + \sqrt{11} + \sqrt{13} = \sqrt{7} + 3 + \sqrt{11} + \sqrt{13}$

29. $\log 7 + \log 8 + \log 9 + \log 10 = \log (7 \cdot 8 \cdot 9 \cdot 10) = \log 5040$

30. $0 + \pi + 2\pi + 3\pi + 4\pi = 10\pi$

31. $\sum_{n=1}^{6} \frac{n}{n+1}$

32. $\sum_{n=1}^{5} 3n$

33. $\sum_{n=1}^{6} (-1)^n 2^n$

34. $\sum_{n=1}^{5} \frac{1}{n^2}$

35. $\sum_{n=2}^{\infty} (-1)^n n^2$

36. $\sum_{n=3}^{\infty} (-1)^{n+1} n^2$

37. $\frac{3}{2}, \frac{3}{2}, \frac{3}{2}, \frac{3}{2}, \frac{3}{2}$

38. $i, -1, -i, 1, i$

39. 0, 0.693, 1.792, 3.178, 4.787

42. 1, 1, 2, 3, 5, 8, 13, 21, 34, 55, 89, 144, 233; 233

Mixed Review

45. $\begin{bmatrix} 15 & 14 & 20 \\ 8 & 2 & 22 \\ 9 & 32 & 26 \end{bmatrix}$

46. $\begin{bmatrix} 4t+3 & 5t-1 & 6t+2 \\ 3t-1 & 2 & 7t+1 \\ 2t+3 & 9t+5 & 8t+2 \end{bmatrix}$

47. $\begin{bmatrix} 13 & 33 & 27 \\ 4 & 4 & 16 \\ 31 & 33 & 69 \end{bmatrix}$

48. $\begin{bmatrix} 21 \\ 8 \\ 51 \end{bmatrix}$

49. Not possible

50. $\begin{bmatrix} 73 \\ 46 \\ 89 \end{bmatrix}$

For each sequence, find a general term. Answers may vary.

13. 1, 3, 5, 7, 9, . . . $a_n = 2n - 1$

14. 3, 9, 27, 81, 243, . . . $a_n = 3^n$

15. $\frac{2}{3}, \frac{3}{4}, \frac{4}{5}, \frac{5}{6}, \frac{6}{7}, \ldots$ $a_n = \frac{n+1}{n+2}$

16. $\sqrt{2}, \sqrt{4}, \sqrt{6}, \sqrt{8}, \sqrt{10}, \ldots$ $a_n = \sqrt{2n}$

17. $\sqrt{3}, 3, 3\sqrt{3}, 9, 9\sqrt{3}, \ldots$ $a_n = 3^{n/2}$

18. 1·2, 2·3, 3·4, 4·5, . . . $a_n = n(n + 1)$

19. $-1, -4, -7, -10, -13, \ldots$ $a_n = -3n + 2$

20. log 1, log 10, log 100, log 1000, . . . $a_n = n - 1$

Find S_1, S_2, S_3, and S_4 for each sequence.

21. $\frac{1}{3}, \frac{1}{6}, \frac{1}{12}, \frac{1}{24}, \frac{1}{48}, \ldots$

22. $-1, 3, -5, 7, -9, \ldots$

23. 4, 7, 10, 13, 16, . . .

24. $-3, 9, -27, 81, -243, \ldots$

Rename and evaluate each sum.

25. $\sum_{n=1}^{5} \frac{1}{2n}$

26. $\sum_{n=1}^{6} \frac{1}{2n+1}$

27. $\sum_{n=1}^{5} 2^n$

28. $\sum_{n=4}^{7} \sqrt{2n-1}$

29. $\sum_{n=7}^{10} \log n$

30. $\sum_{n=0}^{4} \pi n$

Write sigma notation for each sum.

31. $\frac{1}{2} + \frac{2}{3} + \frac{3}{4} + \frac{4}{5} + \frac{5}{6} + \frac{6}{7}$

32. $3 + 6 + 9 + 12 + 15$

33. $-2 + 4 - 8 + 16 - 32 + 64$

34. $\frac{1}{1^2} + \frac{1}{2^2} + \frac{1}{3^2} + \frac{1}{4^2} + \frac{1}{5^2}$

35. $4 - 9 + 16 - 25 + \cdots$

36. $9 - 16 + 25 - 36 + 49 - 64 + \cdots$

B

Find the first five terms of each sequence.

37. $a_n = \frac{1}{2n} \log 1000^n$

38. $a_n = i^n, i = \sqrt{-1}$

39. $a_n = \ln (1 \cdot 2 \cdot 3 \ldots n)$

Use a calculator to find S_6 rounded to six decimal places.

40. $a_n = \left(1 + \frac{1}{n}\right)^n$ 14.071723

41. $a_n = \sqrt{n+1} - \sqrt{n}$ 1.645751

42. ***Critical Thinking*** Determine the first twelve terms of the Fibonacci sequence and then give the answer to Fibonacci's problem. (Hint: In the first and second months there is only one pair of rabbits.)

Challenge

43. Find a formula for S_n, given that $a_n = \frac{1}{n} \cdot \frac{1}{n+1}$. $1 - \frac{1}{n+1}$

44. Write a recursive definition of the Fibonacci sequence. $a_n = a_{n-1} + a_{n-2}$

Mixed Review

Let $A = \begin{bmatrix} 3 & -1 & 2 \\ -1 & 2 & 1 \\ 3 & 5 & 2 \end{bmatrix}$ $B = \begin{bmatrix} 6 \\ 5 \\ 4 \end{bmatrix}$ $C = \begin{bmatrix} 4 & 5 & 6 \\ 3 & 0 & 7 \\ 2 & 9 & 8 \end{bmatrix}$ Evaluate, if possible.

45. $A + 3C$ **46.** $tC + A$ **47.** AC **48.** AB **49.** BC **50.** CB

14-2 Arithmetic Sequences and Series

Master Grapher Worksheet 28, *Infinite Arithmetic Sequences and Series*, can be used for lesson closure.

At a temperature of 1°C, the speed of sound in air is about 332.1 meters per second. The speed increases about 0.6 m/s for each increase of 1°C. This gives the sequence

332.1   332.7   333.3   333.9   334.5

0.6   0.6   0.6   0.6

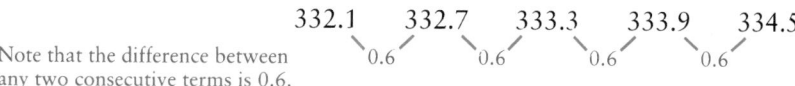

Note that the difference between any two consecutive terms is 0.6.

Arithmetic Sequences

Objective: Find the first term and common difference of an arithmetic sequence.

Definition

A sequence in which a constant d can be added to each term to get the next term is called an **arithmetic sequence**. The constant d is called the **common difference**.

In an arithmetic sequence with n terms, the terms are denoted $a_1, a_2, \ldots, a_n$.

To find the common difference, subtract any term from the one that follows it.

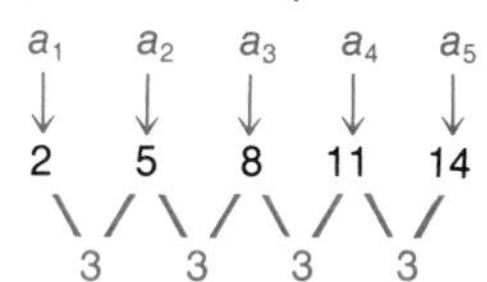

EXAMPLES Find the first term and the common difference of each arithmetic sequence.

	Sequence	First term	Common difference
1.	4, 9, 14, 19, 24, ...	4	5
2.	34, 27, 20, 13, 6, −1, −8, ...	34	−7
3.	$2, 2\frac{1}{2}, 3, 3\frac{1}{2}, 4, 4\frac{1}{2}, \ldots$	2	$\frac{1}{2}$

Try This Find the first term and the common difference of each arithmetic sequence.

a. 2, 3, 4, 5, 6, . . . $a_1 = 2, d = 1$

b. 1, 4, 7, 10, 13, . . . $a_1 = 1, d = 3$

c. 19, 14, 9, 4, −1, −6, . . . $a_1 = 19, d = -5$

d. $10, 9\frac{1}{2}, 9, 8\frac{1}{2}, 8, 7\frac{1}{2}, \ldots$ $a_1 = 10, d = -\frac{1}{2}$

14-2

FIRST FIVE MINUTES

1. Find the general term a_n of the sequence 4, 16, 64, 256, ...
   $a_n = 4^n$
2. Evaluate.
   $\sum_{n=1}^{3} n^3$
   1 + 8 + 27 = 36
3. Write in sigma notation.
   1 + 3 + 5 + 7 + 9
   $\sum_{n=1}^{5} (2n - 1)$

Arithmetic Sequences

Point out that when "arithmetic" is used as an adjective, as in the phrase "arithmetic sequences," it is pronounced "ar′ith met′ik."

Key Questions

What is the next term in each of the following arithmetic sequences?

- 0, 5, 10, 15, . . .
  20
- 1, 3, 5, 7, . . .
  9
- 2, 7, 12, . . .
  17

Chalkboard Examples

Find the first term and the common difference for each of the following arithmetic sequences.

1. 6, 9, 12, 15, . . .
   First term 6, difference 3
2. 42, 39, 36, 33, . . .
   First term 42, difference −3
3. $1, 1\frac{1}{3}, 1\frac{2}{3}, 2, 2\frac{1}{3}, 2\frac{2}{3}, 3, \ldots$
   First term 1, difference $\frac{1}{3}$

The n-th Term

Mention some common situations where arithmetic sequences occur. For example, a taxi ride may cost \$2 plus \$1 per mile, or a telephone company may charge 50 cents for the first minute and 30 cents for each additional minute.

Chalkboard Examples

1. Find the 21st term of the arithmetic sequence 4, 9, 14, 19, ...
   The general term is
   $a_n = 4 + (n - 1)5$.
   The 21st term is
   $a_{21} = 4 + (20)5 = 104$.
2. In the arithmetic sequence 2, 9, 16, 23, . . . which term has a value of 702?

$$a_n = 2 + (n - 1)7$$
$$2 + (n - 1)7 = 702$$
$$(n - 1)7 = 700$$
$$n - 1 = 100$$
$$n = 101$$

The n-th Term

Objective: Solve problems involving the n-th term of an arithmetic sequence.

The first term of an arithmetic sequence is a_1. We add d to get the next term, $a_1 + d$. We add d again to get the next term, $(a_1 + d) + d$, and so on. There is a pattern.

$$a_1 = a_1$$
$$a_2 = a_1 + d$$
$$a_3 = (a_1 + d) + d = a_1 + 2d$$
$$a_4 = (a_1 + 2d) + d = a_1 + 3d$$
$$\vdots$$
$$a_n = a_1 + (n - 1)d$$

Theorem 14-1

The **n-th term** of an arithmetic sequence is given by

$$a_n = a_1 + (n - 1)d$$

EXAMPLE 4 Find the 14th term of the arithmetic sequence 4, 7, 10, 13, ...

First note that $a_1 = 4$, $d = 3$, and $n = 14$. Then, using the formula of Theorem 14-1, we have the following.

$$a_{14} = 4 + (14 - 1)3 = 4 + 39 = 43$$

Thus the 14th term, a_{14}, is 43.

EXAMPLE 5 In the arithmetic sequence 4, 7, 10, 13, . . . , which term has a value of 301?

$$a_n = a_1 + (n - 1)d \quad \text{Theorem 14-1}$$
$$301 = 4 + (n - 1)3 \quad \text{Substituting}$$
$$300 = 3n$$
$$100 = n$$

Thus the 100th term, a_{100}, is 301.

In a similar manner we can find a_1 if we know n, a_n, and d. Also, we can find d if we know a_1, n, and a_n.

Try This

e. Find the 13th term of the sequence 2, 6, 10, 14, ... 50

f. In the sequence 2, 6, 10, 14, . . . , which term has a value of 286? a_{72}

Constructing Sequences

Objective: Construct an arithmetic sequence, given specific terms of the sequence.

Given two terms in a sequence, we can find a_1 and d, and construct the sequence.

EXAMPLE 6 The 3rd term of an arithmetic sequence is 8 and the 16th term is 47. Find a_1 and d. Construct the sequence.

We use the formula $a_n = a_1 + (n - 1)d$, where $a_3 = 8$.

$$8 = a_1 + (3 - 1)d \text{ or } 8 = a_1 + 2d$$

We use the same formula, where $a_{16} = 47$.

$$47 = a_1 + (16 - 1)d \text{ or } 47 = a_1 + 15d$$

Now we solve the system of equations.

$$a_1 + 15d = 47 \rightarrow \quad a_1 + 15d = 47$$

$$a_1 + 2d = 8 \rightarrow \quad -a_1 - 2d = -8 \qquad \text{Multiplying by } -1$$

$$13d = 39 \qquad \text{Adding}$$

$$d = 3 \qquad \text{Solving for } d$$

$$a_1 + 2 \cdot 3 = 8 \qquad \text{Substituting}$$

$$a_1 = 2 \qquad \text{Solving for } a_1$$

Thus a_1 is 2, d is 3, and the sequence is 2, 5, 8, 11, 14, ... The sequence may be graphed by hand or computer (see p. 633).

Try This

g. The 7th term of an arithmetic sequence is 79 and the 13th term is 151. Find a_1 and d. Construct the sequence. $a_1 = 7, d = 12$; 7, 19, 31, 43, . . .

An arithmetic mean of two numbers, a and b, is simply their average, $\frac{a + b}{2}$. Notice that the numbers $a, \frac{a + b}{2}, b$ form an arithmetic sequence. Numbers $m_1, m_2, m_3, \ldots, m_n$ are called arithmetic means between a and b if $a, m_1, m_2, m_3, \ldots, m_n, b$ form an arithmetic sequence.

EXAMPLE 7 Insert three arithmetic means between 8 and 16.

Let 8 be the 1st term. Then 16 will be the 5th term. We use $a_n = a_1 + (n - 1)d$.

$$16 = 8 + (5 - 1)d \text{ or } d = 2$$

So we have 8, 10, 12, 14, 16.

Try This

h. Insert two arithmetic means between 3 and 24. 3, 10, 17, 24

Constructing Sequences

After solving Example 6, students should check that $a_{16} = 47$.

Chalkboard Examples

1. The second term of an arithmetic sequence is 11 and the tenth term is 35. Construct the sequence.
   $a_n = a_1 + (n - 1)d$
   $a_2 = a_1 + (2 - 1)d = 11$ (1)
   $a_{10} = a_1 + (10 - 1)d = 35$ (2)
   Hence,
   $a_1 + d = 11$ (1)
   $a_1 + 9d = 35$ (2)
   Subtract (1) from (2).
   $8d = 24$
   $d = 3$
   Substitute into (1).
   $a_1 = 8$
   The general term is
   $a_n = 8 + (n - 1)3$.
   The sequence is
   8, 11, 14, 17, 20, ...
2. Insert three arithmetic means between 10 and 34.
   The first term is 10. The fifth term is 34.
   $a_n = a_1 + (n - 1)d$
   $a_1 = 10$
   $a_5 = 10 + (5 - 1)d = 34$
   $4d = 24$
   $d = 6$
   The general term is
   $a_n = 10 + (n - 1)6$.
   The series is
   10, 16, 22, 28, 34.

Arithmetic Series

Math Point
When the great mathematician Carl Friedrich Gauss was a schoolboy, his teacher gave the class the problem of finding the sum of all the whole numbers from 1 to 100. Young Gauss had the answer almost immediately. He reasoned that there were 50 pairs of numbers and the sum of each pair was 101.

$1 + 2 + 3 + \cdots + 98 + 99 + 100$

The answer is $50 \cdot 101 = 5050$.

Chalkboard Examples

1. Find the sum of the first 50 natural numbers.

$S_n = \frac{n}{2}(a_1 + a_n)$

$= \frac{50}{2}(1 + 50)$

$= 25 \cdot 51 = 1275$

2. Find the sum of the first 20 odd numbers.

The general term is $a_n = 1 + (n - 1)2$.
Hence $a_1 = 1$ and $d = 2$.

$S_n = \frac{n}{2}(2a_1 + (n - 1)d)$

$= 10(2 + 19 \cdot 2)$
$= 400$

3. Find the sum of the series.

$\sum_{n=1}^{20} (3n + 1)$

In this case we have the sum of an arithmetic series with $a_1 = 4$, $d = 3$, and $n = 20$.

$S_n = \frac{n}{2}(2a_1 + (n - 1)d)$

$S_{20} = \frac{20}{2}(2(4) + (19)3)$

$= 650$

Arithmetic Series

Objective: Find partial sums of arithmetic series.

An arithmetic series is a series associated with an arithmetic sequence. Two theorems give useful formulas for finding the sum of the first n terms.

Theorem 14-2

The sum of the first n terms of an arithmetic series is given by

$$S_n = \frac{n}{2}(a_1 + a_n)$$

This formula is useful when we know the first and last terms, a_1 and a_n. If we do not know the last term of the series, we can substitute $a_1 + (n - 1)d$ for a_n in the above formula. This gives us our next theorem.

Theorem 14-3

The sum of the first n terms of an arithmetic series is given by

$$S_n = \frac{n}{2}[2a_1 + (n - 1)d]$$

EXAMPLE 8 Find the sum of the first 100 natural numbers.

The sum of the first 100 natural numbers is $1 + 2 + 3 + \cdots + 100$.

This is an arithmetic series.

$a = 1$, $a_n = 100$, and $n = 100$. We use Theorem 14-2.

$$S_n = \frac{n}{2}(a_1 + a_n)$$

Substituting, we get the following.

$$S_{100} = \frac{100}{2}(1 + 100)$$

$$= 50(101) = 5050$$

The sum of the first 100 natural numbers is 5050.

Try This

i. Find the sum of the first 200 natural numbers. 20,100

j. Find the sum of the first 473 natural numbers. 112,101

EXAMPLE 9 Find the sum of the first 14 terms of the arithmetic series $2 + 5 + 8 + 11 + 14 + 17 + \cdots$.

Note that $a_1 = 2$, $d = 3$, and $n = 14$. We use Theorem 14-3.

$$S_n = \frac{n}{2}[2a_1 + (n - 1)d]$$

$$S_{14} = \frac{14}{2}\cdot[2\cdot 2 + (14 - 1)3]$$

$$= 7\cdot[4 + 13\cdot 3]$$

$$= 7\cdot 43$$

$$S_{14} = 301$$

The sum of the first 14 terms of the series is 301.

Try This

k. Find the sum of the first 15 terms of the arithmetic series $1 + 3 + 5 + 7 + 9 + \cdots$. 225

EXAMPLE 10 Find the sum of the series $\sum_{n=1}^{13} (4n + 5)$.

First find a few terms.

$$9 + 13 + 17 + \cdots$$

We see that this is an arithmetic series with $a_1 = 9$, $d = 4$, and $n = 13$. We use Theorem 14-3.

$$S_n = \frac{n}{2}[2a_1 + (n - 1)d]$$

$$S_{13} = \frac{13}{2}[2\cdot 9 + (13 - 1)4]$$

$$= \frac{13}{2}[18 + 12\cdot 4] = \frac{13}{2}\cdot 66 = 429$$

The sum of the series is 429.

EXAMPLE 11 Find the sum of the series $\sum_{n=1}^{20} (-2n + 21)$.

The first 3 terms are 19, 17, 15, $a_1 = 19$, $d = -2$, and $n = 20$.

$$S_{20} = \frac{20}{2}[2\cdot 19 + (20 - 1)(-2)]$$

$$= 10[38 + 19(-2)] = 10(0) = 0$$

The sum of the series is zero.

Try This

l. Find the sum of the series $\sum_{n=1}^{10} (9n - 4)$. 455

LESSON ENRICHMENT

Show that the sum of the first n odd numbers equals n^2.

$$S_n = \frac{n}{2}(2a_1 + (n - 1)d)$$

$$= \frac{n}{2}(2(1) + (n - 1)2)$$

$$= n^2$$

LESSON QUIZ

1. Find the first term and the common difference for the arithmetic sequence 10, 16, 22, 28, 34, ...
   The first term is 10.
   The common difference is 6.
2. Find the general term a_n for the arithmetic sequence 5, 8, 11, 14, 17, ...
   $a_n = 5 + (n - 1)3$
3. Find the 100th term of the arithmetic sequence 3, 5, 7, 9, 11, ...
   201
4. Find the sum of the first 30 natural numbers.
   465

Assignment Guide
Algebra: omit

Alg w/Finite Math: 1–35 e/o, 36, MR

Comprehensive: 1–35 m3, 36, 37–42 e/o, MR

14-2 EXERCISES

A

For the arithmetic sequences in Exercises 1 – 6, find the first term and the common difference.

1. 2, 7, 12, 17, . . . $a_1 = 2, d = 5$

2. 1.06, 1.12, 1.18, 1.24, . . . $a_1 = 1.06, d = 0.06$

3. 7, 3, −1, −5, . . . $a_1 = 7, d = -4$

4. −9, −6, −3, 0, . . . $a_1 = -9, d = 3$

5. $\frac{3}{2}, \frac{9}{4}, 3, \frac{15}{4}, \ldots$ $a_1 = \frac{3}{2}, d = \frac{3}{4}$

6. $\frac{3}{5}, \frac{1}{10}, -\frac{2}{5}, \ldots$ $a_1 = \frac{3}{5}, d = -\frac{1}{2}$

7. Find the 12th term of the arithmetic sequence 2, 6, 10, ... $a_{12} = 46$

8. Find the 11th term of the arithmetic sequence 0.07, 0.12, 0.17, ... $a_{11} = 0.57$

9. Find the 17th term of the arithmetic sequence 7, 4, 1, ... $a_{17} = -41$

10. Find the 14th term of the arithmetic sequence $3, \frac{7}{3}, \frac{5}{3}, \ldots$. $a_{14} = -\frac{17}{3}$

11. In the sequence 2, 6, 10, . . . , what term has a value of 106? a_{27}

12. In the sequence 0.07, 0.12, 0.17, . . . , what term has a value of 1.67? a_{33}

13. In the sequence 7, 4, 1, . . . , what term has a value of −296? a_{102}

14. In the sequence $3, \frac{7}{3}, \frac{5}{3}, \ldots$, what term has a value of −27? a_{46}

15. The 17th term of an arithmetic sequence is −40 and the 28th term is −73. Find a_1 and d. Construct the sequence. $a_1 = 8, d = -3$; 8, 5, 2, −1, . . .

16. The 17th term of an arithmetic sequence is $\frac{25}{3}$, and the 32nd term is $\frac{95}{6}$. Find a_1 and d. Construct the sequence. $a_1 = \frac{1}{3}, d = \frac{1}{2}; \frac{1}{3}, \frac{5}{6}, \frac{4}{3}, \frac{11}{6}, \ldots$

17. Insert three arithmetic means between 2 and 22. 2, 7, 12, 17, 22

18. Insert four arithmetic means between 8 and 23. 8, 11, 14, 17, 20, 23

19. Find the sum of the even numbers from 2 to 100, inclusive. 2550

20. Find the sum of the odd numbers from 1 to 99, inclusive. 2500

21. Find the sum of the first 20 terms of the series 5 + 8 + 11 + 14 + · · · . 670

22. Find the sum of the first 14 terms of the series 11 + 7 + 3 + · · · . −210

Find the sum of each series.

23. $\sum_{n=1}^{12} (6n - 3)$ 432

24. $\sum_{n=1}^{16} (7n - 76)$ −264

25. $\sum_{n=1}^{18} 5n$ 855

26. $\sum_{n=1}^{20} 3n$ 630

B

27. How many poles will be in a pile of telephone poles if there are 30 in the bottom layer, 29 in the second, and so on, until there is one in the top layer? 465

28. If 10¢ is saved on October 1, 20¢ on October 2, 30¢ on October 3, and so on, how much is saved during October? (October has 31 days.) $49.60

29. Find a formula for the sum of the first n odd natural numbers. $S_n = n^2$

30. Find three numbers in an arithmetic sequence such that the sum of the first and third is 10 and the product of the first and second is 15. 3, 5, 7

31. Insert enough arithmetic means between 1 and 50 so that the sum of the resulting arithmetic series will be 459. 16 means, $d = \frac{49}{17}$

32. Find the first term and the common difference for the arithmetic sequence $3x + 2y, 4x + y, 5x, 6x - y, \ldots$. $a_1 = 3x + 2y, d = x - y$

33. Find the first term and the common difference for the arithmetic sequence where $a_2 = 4p - 3q$ and $a_4 = 10p + q$. $a_1 = p - 5q, d = 3p + 2q$

34. Use a calculator to find the first 10 terms of the arithmetic sequence for which $a_1 = \$8760$ and $d = -\$798.23$.

35. Use a calculator to find the sum of the first ten terms of the sequence given in Exercise 34.

36. ***Critical Thinking*** A **harmonic sequence** is a sequence whose reciprocals form an arithmetic sequence. Make up a harmonic sequence.

Challenge

37. Inserting a **harmonic mean** creates a sequence whose reciprocals form an arithmetic sequence. Insert four harmonic means between $\frac{1}{5}$ and $\frac{1}{20}$.

38. Prove that if p, m, and q form an arithmetic sequence, then $m = \dfrac{p + q}{2}$.

39. Prove Theorem 14-2.

40. Prove Theorem 14-3.

41. Prove that if x, y, and z are three consecutive terms of an arithmetic sequence, then $x + y + z = 3y$.

42. Let S be the sum of terms in a finite arithmetic sequence. Prove that if there are an odd number of terms in a finite arithmetic sequence, then the middle term is $\dfrac{S}{n}$, and if there are an even number of terms, the sum of the middle terms is $\dfrac{2S}{n}$.

Mixed Review

Solve. **43.** $|x| \geq 5$ **44.** $|3y - 4| < 8$

Let $A = \begin{bmatrix} -2 & 1 \\ 5 & 3 \end{bmatrix}$ $B = \begin{bmatrix} 3 & -1 & 2 \\ -1 & 2 & 1 \\ 3 & 5 & 2 \end{bmatrix}$

Find. **45.** $|A|$ **46.** $|B|$ **47.** A^{-1} **48.** B^{-1}

Find $f^{-1}(x)$ for the given function. **49.** $f(x) = x^3 + 8$ **50.** $f(x) = \sqrt[3]{x + 1}$
51. $f(x) = x^3$ **52.** $f(x) = 3^x$ **53.** $f(x) = \log_3 x$

Convert to logarithmic equations. **54.** $7^x = 5$ **55.** $x^5 = 7$ **56.** $5^7 = x$

57. In triangle ABC, the measure of angle A is 10° more than the measure of angle B, and the measure of angle B is 10° more than the measure of angle C. Find the angle measures.

ADDITIONAL ANSWERS

Exercises

34. 8760, 7961.77, 7163.54, 6365.31, 5567.08, 4768.85, 3970.62, 3172.39, 2374.16, 1575.93
35. 51,679.65
36. Answers may vary. $1, \frac{1}{2}, \frac{1}{3}, \frac{1}{4}, \ldots$
37. $\frac{1}{8}, \frac{1}{11}, \frac{1}{14}, \frac{1}{17}$
38. p, m, q are an arithmetic sequence, so $m = p + d$, $q = p + 2d$. Now $\frac{p+q}{2} = \frac{p + (p + 2d)}{2} = p + d = m$.

For Exercises 39-42, see Teacher's Answer Section.

Mixed Review

43. $x \leq -5$ or $x \geq 5$
44. $y > -\frac{4}{3}$ and $y < 4$
45. -11
46. -30
47. $-\frac{1}{11}\begin{bmatrix} 3 & -1 \\ -5 & -2 \end{bmatrix}$
48. $\begin{bmatrix} \frac{1}{30} & -\frac{2}{5} & \frac{1}{6} \\ -\frac{1}{6} & 0 & \frac{1}{6} \\ \frac{11}{30} & \frac{3}{5} & -\frac{1}{6} \end{bmatrix}$
49. $f^{-1}(x) = \sqrt[3]{x - 8}$
50. $f^{-1}(x) = x^3 - 1$
51. $f^{-1}(x) = x^{1/3}$
52. $f^{-1}(x) = \log_3 x$
53. $f^{-1}(x) = 3^x$
54. $\log_7 5 = x$
55. $\log_x 7 = 5$
56. $\log_5 x = 7$
57. $m\angle A = 70°$, $m\angle B = 60°$, $m\angle C = 50°$

14-3

FIRST FIVE MINUTES

1. Find the general term a_n for the arithmetic sequence 7, 10, 13, 16, 19, ...
   $a_n = 7 + (n - 1)3$
2. Find the sum.
   $1 + 2 + 3 + \cdots + 80$
   $S_n = \frac{n}{2}(a_1 + a_n)$
   $= \frac{80}{2}(1 + 80)$
   $= 3240$

Geometric Sequences

Point out some common situations where geometric sequences occur. For example, a population may grow 2% per year, a radioactive substance may decay 2% per year, or a savings account may increase 5% per year.

Key Question

- Is the following a geometric sequence?
  $7 \times 10^{-4}, 7 \times 10^{-3}, 7 \times 10^{-2}, \ldots$
  Yes, the common ratio is 10.

Chalkboard Examples

Find the common ratio of each of the following geometric sequences.

1. 1, 2, 4, 8, . . .
   2
2. 1, −1, 1, −1, . . .
   −1
3. $\frac{1}{10}, \frac{1}{100}, \frac{1}{1000}, \frac{1}{10{,}000}, \ldots$
   $\frac{1}{10}$

14-3 Geometric Sequences and Series

Master Grapher Worksheet 29, *Infinite Geometric Sequences and Series*, can be used for lesson closure.

The value of a car is reduced, or *depreciates*, a certain amount each year. Here is the value of a \$20,000 car year by year.

\$18,000   \$16,200   \$14,580   \$13,122

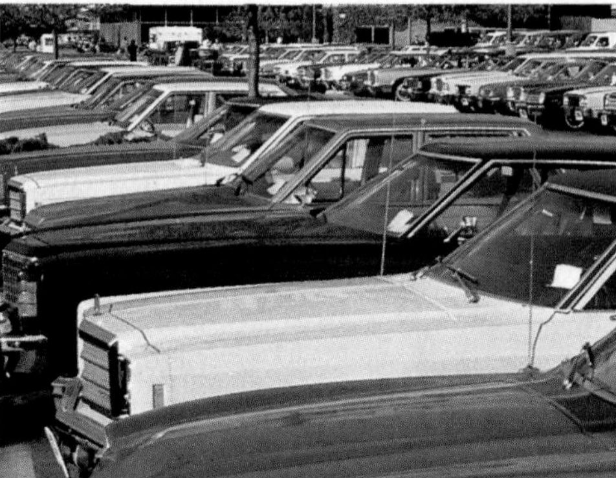

This is not an *arithmetic* sequence because there is no common difference. However, multiplying any term by 0.9 gives us the next term. So the *ratio* of each term to the preceding one is 0.9 to 1.

Geometric Sequences

Objective: Find the common ratio of a given geometric sequence.

Definition

A sequence in which a constant r can be multiplied by each term to get the next is called a **geometric sequence.**

The constant r is called the **common ratio.**

The notation for geometric sequences is the same as the notation for arithmetic sequences: a_1 is the first term, a_2 is the second term, a_3 is the third term, and so on.

To find the common ratio, divide any term by the one before it.

EXAMPLES Find the common ratio of each geometric sequence.

1. $3, 6, 12, 24, \ldots$ $\quad 6 \div 3 = 2, 12 \div 6 = 2, \ldots$ $\quad$ The common ratio is 2
2. $3, -6, 12, -24, \ldots$ $\quad -6 \div 3 = -2, 12 \div -6 = -2, \ldots$ $\quad$ The common ratio is -2
3. $1, \frac{1}{2}, \frac{1}{4}, \frac{1}{8}, \ldots$ $\quad \frac{1}{2} \div 1 = \frac{1}{2}, \frac{1}{4} \div \frac{1}{2} = \frac{1}{2}, \ldots$ $\quad$ The common ratio is $\frac{1}{2}$

Try This Find the common ratio of each geometric sequence.

a. 1, 5, 25, 125, . . . 5

b. 3, −9, 27, −81, . . . −3

c. 48, −12, 3, . . . $-\frac{1}{4}$

d. 54, 18, 6, . . . $\frac{1}{3}$

The n-th Term

Objective: Solve problems involving the n-th term of a geometric sequence.

We can think of the sequence 3, 6, 12, 24, . . . as

$$3 \cdot 2^0, \quad 3 \cdot 2^1, \quad 3 \cdot 2^2, \quad 3 \cdot 2^3, \quad \ldots$$

The pattern suggests that the n-th term is $3 \cdot 2^{n-1}$. Likewise, in any geometric sequence, if we let a_1 be the first term and r be the common ratio, then $a_1 r$ is the second term, $a_1 r^2$ is the third term, and so on. Generalizing, we have the following.

Theorem 14-4

In a geometric sequence, the n-th term is given by $a_n = a_1 r^{n-1}$.

Note that the exponent is one less than the number of the term.

EXAMPLE 4 Find the 11th term of the geometric sequence 64, −32, 16, −8, ...

Note that $a_1 = 64$, $n = 11$, and $r = \frac{-32}{64}$, or $-\frac{1}{2}$.

$$a_n = a_1 r^{n-1}$$

$$a_{11} = 64 \cdot \left(-\frac{1}{2}\right)^{11-1}$$

$$= 64 \cdot \left(-\frac{1}{2}\right)^{10} = 2^6 \cdot \frac{1}{2^{10}} = 2^{-4}, \text{ or } \frac{1}{16}$$

This result can be verified by graphing the sequence (see p. 633).

Try This

e. Find the 6th term of the geometric sequence 3, −15, 75, ... −9375

Numbers $m_1, m_2, m_3, \ldots m_n$, are called geometric means of the numbers a and b if a, $m_1, m_2, m_3, \ldots, m_n$, b form a geometric sequence. We can use Theorem 14-4 to insert geometric means between two numbers.

EXAMPLE 5 Insert two geometric means between 3 and 24.

3 is the 1st term and 24 is the 4th term.

$$24 = 3(r)^{4-1} \quad \text{Using Theorem 14-4; } a_n = a_1 r^{n-1}$$

$$8 = r^3$$

$$2 = r$$

So we have 3, 6, 12, 24.

The n-th Term

In Example 6, $n = 37$ because the end of the 36th month is the beginning of the 37th month.

Note that for Try This f, 5, −10, 20 forms a geometric sequence, but −10 is *not* between 5 and 20.

Students should use calculators for Try This g.

Chalkboard Examples

1. Find the 10th term of the geometric sequence 2, 6, 18, 54, ...
   The general term is
   $a_n = 2 \cdot 3^{n-1}$
   $a_{10} = 2 \cdot 3^9 = 39{,}366$
2. Insert two geometric means between 4 and 108.
   $a_n = a_1 r^{n-1}$
   The first term is 4. The 4th term is 108.
   $a_1 = 4$
   $a_4 = 4r^3$
   $a_4 = 108$
   $r^3 = 27$
   $r = 3$
   The general term is $a_n = 4 \cdot 3^{n-1}$.
   The sequence is 4, 12, 36, 108.
3. Two hundred dollars is invested in a savings account that pays 6% annual interest compounded monthly. How much money is in the account at the end of three years?
   Each month the amount grows by $\frac{6\%}{12}$ or $\frac{1}{2}\%$. We have a geometric sequence with $a_1 = 200$, $r = 1.005$, $n = 37$.
   $a_n = a_1 r^{n-1}$
   $a_n = 200 \cdot 1.005^{37-1} \approx 239.34$
   There will be $239.34 in the bank at the end of three years.

Geometric Series

Illustrate the principle with a particular case. For example, find the sum of

$$S = \frac{1}{2} + \frac{1}{4} + \frac{1}{8} + \cdots \frac{1}{2^9} + \frac{1}{2^{10}}$$

We find $2S$.

$$2S = 1 + \frac{1}{2} + \frac{1}{4} + \frac{1}{8} + \cdots + \frac{1}{2^9}$$

When we subtract S from $2S$, all but two terms "cancel."

$$2S - S = 1 - \frac{1}{2^{10}}$$

$$S = 1 - \frac{1}{2^{10}}$$

Students may find the following form of the formula easier to memorize.

$$S_n = a_1\left(\frac{r^n - 1}{r - 1}\right)$$

Key Question

- What happens if $r = 1$?
  The sequence is *arithmetic*, not geometric. The formula would have a zero denominator.

Chalkboard Examples

1. Find the sum of the first 8 terms of the geometric series
   $1 + 3 + 3^2 + 3^3 + 3^4 + \cdots$.
   $a_1 = 1, r = 3, n = 8$
   $$S_n = \frac{a_1 - a_1r^n}{1 - r} = \frac{1 - 1 \cdot 3^8}{1 - 3} = \frac{1 - 3^8}{-2} = 3280$$
2. Find the sum of the geometric series.
   $$\sum_{n=1}^{5}\left(\frac{1}{10}\right)^n$$
   $a_1 = \frac{1}{10}, r = \frac{1}{10}, n = 5$
   $$S_5 = \frac{\frac{1}{10} - \frac{1}{10}\cdot\left(\frac{1}{10}\right)^5}{1 - \frac{1}{10}} = \frac{1 - \left(\frac{1}{10}\right)^5}{9} = \frac{1 - 0.00001}{9} = \frac{0.99999}{9} = 0.11111$$

Try This

f. Insert one geometric mean between 5 and 20. 10

EXAMPLE 6

A student borrows \$600 at 12% interest compounded monthly. The student pays the loan in one payment at the end of 36 months. How much does the student pay?

For any principal (P), at 12% annual or 1% monthly interest, the student will owe $P + 0.01P$ at the end of 1 month, or $1.01P$. Then $1.01P$ is the principal for the second month. Thus at the end of the second month the student owes $1.01(1.01P)$. Then the principal at the beginning of the third month is $1.01(1.01P)$. It appears that the following sequence is being formed.

$$P, 1.01P, 1.01(1.01P), \ldots$$

This is a geometric sequence with $a_1 = 600$, $n = 37$, and $r = 1.01$.

$a_n = a_1r^{n-1}$ Using Theorem 14-4

$a_{37} = 600 \cdot (1.01)^{37-1}$ Finding the 37th term (the principal at the *beginning* of the 37th month or *end* of the 36th month)

$= 600 \cdot 1.01^{36}$

$= 600 \cdot 1.430769 \approx 858.46$

Thus the student pays \$858.46 (rounded to the nearest cent).

Try This

g. A college student borrows \$400 at 12% interest compounded monthly. The loan is repaid in one lump-sum payment at the end of 24 months. How much does the student pay? \$507.89

Geometric Series

Objective: Find partial sums of a geometric series.

A geometric series is a series associated with a geometric sequence. Suppose that we want to find the sum S_n of the first n terms of a geometric sequence.

$$S_n = a_1 + a_1r + a_1r^2 + \cdots + a_1r^{n-1}$$

If we multiply both sides by r, we have

$$rS_n = a_1r + a_1r^2 + a_1r^3 + \cdots + a_1r^{n-1} + a_1r^n$$

Subtracting the second equation from the first, we have

$S_n - rS_n = a_1 - a_1r^n$

$S_n(1 - r) = a_1(1 - r^n)$ Factoring

$S_n = \dfrac{a_1(1 - r^n)}{1 - r}$ Dividing both sides by $1 - r$

This gives us a formula for the sum of the first n terms of a geometric series.

Theorem 14-5

The sum of the first n terms of a geometric series is given by

$$S_n = \frac{a_1(1 - r^n)}{1 - r}$$

EXAMPLE 7 Find the sum of the first 6 terms of the geometric series $3 + 6 + 12 + 24 + \cdots$.

$a_1 = 3, n = 6$, and $r = \frac{6}{3}$, or 2

$$S_n = \frac{a_1(1 - r^n)}{1 - r} \quad \text{Using Theorem 14-5}$$

$$S_6 = \frac{3(1 - 2^6)}{1 - 2} \quad \text{Substituting}$$

$$= \frac{3(-63)}{-1} = 189$$

Try This

h. Find the sum of the first 6 terms of the geometric series $3 + 15 + 75 + 375 + \cdots$. 11,718

i. Find the sum of the first 10 terms of the geometric series $2 - 1 + \frac{1}{2} - \frac{1}{4} + \cdots$. $\frac{341}{256}$

EXAMPLE 8 Find the sum of the geometric series $\sum_{n=1}^{5} \left(\frac{1}{2}\right)^{n+1}$.

First find a few terms.

$$\left(\frac{1}{2}\right)^2 + \left(\frac{1}{2}\right)^3 + \left(\frac{1}{2}\right)^4 + \cdots$$

In this geometric series we have $a_1 = \frac{1}{4}, n = 5$, and $r = \frac{1}{2}$.

$$S_n = \frac{a_1(1 - r^n)}{1 - r} \quad \text{Using Theorem 14-5}$$

$$S_5 = \frac{\frac{1}{4}\left(1 - \left(\frac{1}{2}\right)^5\right)}{1 - \frac{1}{2}} = \frac{\frac{1}{4}\left(\frac{31}{32}\right)}{\frac{1}{2}}$$

$$= \frac{31}{64}$$

Try This Find the sum of each geometric series.

j. $\sum_{n=1}^{5} 3^n$ 363 **k.** $\sum_{n=1}^{4} \left(\frac{2}{3}\right)^{n-1}$ $\frac{65}{27}$

LESSON QUIZ

1. Find the common ratio for the geometric series $\frac{3}{2}, 3, 6, 12, \ldots$.
   2
2. Find the general term a_n for the geometric sequence 3, 12, 48, ...
   $a_n = 3 \cdot 4^{n-1}$
3. Write an expression for the sum of the first 100 terms of the geometric sequence 1, 2, 4, 8, 16, ...
   $2^{100} - 1$

Assignment Guide
Algebra: Omit

Alg w/Finite Math: 1–31 e/o, 32, MR

Comprehensive: 1–26 m3, 27–31 e/o, 32, 33–40 e/o, MR

14-3 EXERCISES

A

Find the common ratio for each geometric sequence.

1. 4, 8, 16, 32, . . . 2

2. $12, -4, \frac{4}{3}, -\frac{4}{9}, \ldots$ $-\frac{1}{3}$

3. $1, -1, 1, -1, 1, \ldots$ -1

4. $-5, -0.5, -0.05, -0.005, \ldots$ 0.1

5. $\frac{1}{x}, \frac{1}{x^2}, \frac{1}{x^3}, \ldots$ $\frac{1}{x}$

6. $5, \frac{5m}{2}, \frac{5m^2}{4}, \frac{5m^3}{8}, \ldots$ $\frac{m}{2}$

7. Find the 6th term of the geometric sequence 1, 3, 9, ... 243

8. Find the 10th term of the geometric sequence $\frac{8}{243}, \frac{4}{81}, \frac{2}{27}, \ldots$. $\frac{81}{64}$

9. Find the 5th term of the geometric sequence $2, -10, 50, \ldots$. 1250

10. Find the 9th term of the geometric sequence $2, 2\sqrt{3}, 6, \ldots$. 162

11. Insert one geometric mean between 3 and 48. 3, 12, 48

12. Insert two geometric means between 4 and 32. 4, 8, 16, 32

13. Insert three geometric means between $\frac{1}{4}$ and $\frac{1}{64}$. $\frac{1}{4}, \frac{1}{8}, \frac{1}{16}, \frac{1}{32}, \frac{1}{64}$

14. Insert four geometric means between $\frac{1}{9}$ and 27. $\frac{1}{9}, \frac{1}{3}$, 1, 3, 9, 27

15. A college student borrowed \$800 at 12% interest compounded monthly. The loan is paid in one lump sum at the end of 2 years. How much did the student pay? \$1015.79

16. A college student borrowed \$1000 at 10% interest compounded monthly. The loan is paid in one lump sum at the end of 4 years. How much did the student pay? \$1489.35

17. Find the sum of the first 7 terms of the geometric series $6 + 12 + 24 + \cdots$. 762

18. Find the sum of the first 6 terms of the geometric series $16 - 8 + 4 - \cdots$. $10\frac{1}{2}$

19. Find the sum of the first 7 terms of the geometric series $\frac{1}{18} - \frac{1}{6} + \frac{1}{2} - \cdots$. $\frac{547}{18}$

20. Find the sum of the first 5 terms of the geometric series $6 + 0.6 + 0.06 + \cdots$. $\frac{33{,}333}{5000}$

21. Find the sum of the first 8 terms of the series $1 + x + x^2 + x^3 + \cdots$. $\frac{1 - x^8}{1 - x}$

22. Find the sum of the first 10 terms of the series $1 + x^2 + x^4 + x^6 + \cdots$. $\frac{1 - x^{20}}{1 - x^2}$

Find the sum of each geometric series.

23. $\sum_{n=1}^{6} \left(\frac{1}{2}\right)^{n-1}$ $\frac{63}{32}$

24. $\sum_{n=1}^{8} 2^n$ 510

25. $\sum_{n=1}^{7} 4^n$ 21,844

26. $\sum_{n=1}^{5} \left(\frac{1}{3}\right)^{n-1}$ $\frac{121}{81}$

B

27. A Ping-Pong ball is dropped from a height of 16 ft and always rebounds $\frac{1}{4}$ of the distance of the previous fall.

a. What distance does it rebound the 6th time? $\frac{1}{256}$ ft

b. What is the total distance the ball has travelled after this time? $26\frac{169}{256}$ ft

28. A town has a population of 100,000 now and the population is increasing 10% every year. What will be the population in 5 years? 161,051

29. Use a calculator to find the sum of the first 5 terms of each geometric sequence. Round to the nearest cent.
   a. \$1000, \$1000(1.08), \$1000(1.08)^2, . . . \$5866.60
   b. \$200, \$200(1.13), \$200(1.13)^2, . . . \$1296.05

30. Find the sum of the first n terms of $1 + x + x^2 + x^3 + \cdots$. $\frac{1-x^n}{1-x}$

31. Find the geometric mean between each pair of numbers.
   a. 4 and 9 6
   b. 2 and 6 $2\sqrt{3}$
   c. $\frac{1}{2}$ and $\frac{1}{3}$ $\frac{\sqrt{6}}{6}$
   d. $\sqrt{5} + \sqrt{2}$ and $\sqrt{5} - \sqrt{2}$ $\sqrt{3}$

32. ***Critical Thinking*** The third term of a geometric sequence is 4. What is the product of the first five terms? 1024

Challenge

33. If each term of a geometric sequence is multiplied by some number c, is the resulting sequence necessarily geometric? Yes

34. If some number c is added to each term of a geometric sequence, is the resulting sequence necessarily geometric? No

35. Show that each sequence is always a geometric sequence, given that $a_1, a_2, a_3, \ldots$ is a geometric sequence.
   a. $a_1^2, a_2^2, a_3^2, \ldots$
   b. $a_1^{-3}, a_2^{-3}, a_3^{-3}, \ldots$

36. A piece of paper is 0.01 in. thick. It is folded 20 times in such a way that its thickness is doubled each time. How thick is the result? (Use a calculator.) 10,485.76 in.

37. A person decides to save money in a savings account for retirement. At the beginning of each year \$1000 is invested at 14% compounded annually. How much is in the retirement fund at the end of 40 years? (Hint: Remember that the end of year 40 is the beginning of year 41.) \$1,529,908.60

38. Prove that if the corresponding terms of two geometric sequences are multiplied, then the products form a geometric sequence.

39. Suppose x, y, and z are three consecutive terms in a geometric sequence. Prove that $\frac{1}{y-x}$, $\frac{1}{2y}$, and $\frac{1}{y-z}$ are terms in an arithmetic sequence.

40. Explain why the number zero cannot be a term of a geometric sequence.

Mixed Review

Solve. 41. $x^2 + y^2 - 25 = 0$, $y^2 + 8x - 40 = 0$ 42. $xy - 25 = 0$, $y - x = 0$

43. The area of a triangle is 27 cm². The base is 3 cm shorter than the height. Find the height.

WRITING TO LEARN

Suppose you are an investigative reporter assigned to interview a sequence. Make a list of at least four questions that you would ask.

ADDITIONAL ANSWERS

Exercises

35. a. $\frac{a_n}{a_{n-1}} = r$, so $\frac{a_n^2}{a_{n-1}^2} = r^2$; hence $a_1^2, a_2^2, \ldots$, is geometric, with ratio r^2.

b. $\frac{a_n}{a_{n-1}} = r$, so $\frac{a_n^{-3}}{a_{n-1}^{-3}} = r^{-3}$; thus $a_1^{-3}, a_2^{-3}, \ldots$ is geometric, with ratio r^{-3}.

38. Let one geometric series be $a_1, a_1r, a_1r^2, \ldots, a_1r^n \ldots$, the other $a_2, a_2R, a_2R^2, \ldots, a_2R^n \ldots$ The new series is $a_1a_2, a_1a_2rR, a_1a_2r^2R^2, \ldots, a_1a_2r^nR^n \ldots$ Let $a_1a_2 = b$ and $rR = q$. The new series is $b, bq, bq^2, \ldots, bq^n \ldots$, which is a geometric series.

39. Let $y = xr$ and $z = xr^2$.

Then $\frac{1}{2y} - \frac{1}{y-x} = \frac{1}{2xr} - \frac{1}{x(r-1)} = \frac{1+r}{2xr(1-r)}$

$\frac{1}{y-x} - \frac{1}{2y} = \frac{1}{xr - xr^2} - \frac{1}{2xr} = \frac{1+r}{2xr(1-r)}$

Since the differences are the same, the terms make up an arithmetic sequence with $d = \frac{1+r}{2xr(1-r)}$.

40. If 0 is a term of a geometric sequence, the next term must be $r \cdot 0 = 0$, the next after that $r \cdot 0 = 0$, etc. Previous terms cannot be nonzero for the common ratio to be the same. Thus every term must be 0. But the common ratio of this sequence is $\frac{0}{0}$, which is undefined, so this sequence is not geometric.

Mixed Review

41. (5, 0), (3, 4), (3, −4)
42. (5, 5), (−5, −5)
43. 9 cm

Writing to Learn

You may wish to divide the class into pairs for this exercise.
Answers may vary. Examples:
Are you geometric or arithmetic?
Are you finite or infinite?
What is your first term?
What is your common ratio (or common difference)?

14-4

FIRST FIVE MINUTES

1. Find the general term a_n of the geometric sequence 256, 128, 64, 32, ...

   $a_n = 256 \cdot \left(\frac{1}{2}\right)^{n-1}$

2. Find the sum.
   $1 + 3 + 3^2 + 3^3 + 3^4$

   $\frac{a_1 - a_1 r^5}{1 - r} = \frac{1 - 3^5}{1 - 3} = \frac{1 - 243}{-2} = 121$

Convergent Geometric Series

Emphasize that a series can be increasing and still be bounded; for example,

$\frac{1}{2} + \frac{1}{4} + \frac{1}{8} + \frac{1}{16} + \cdots$

is less than one.

Students may think that the series in Example 3 must have a sum of zero since

$(1 + -1) + (1 + -1) + \cdots$
$= \quad 0 \quad + \quad 0 \quad + \cdots$

But grouped differently, it appears to have a sum of 1.

$1 + (-1 + 1) + (-1 + 1) + \cdots$
$= 1 + \quad 0 \quad + \quad 0 \quad + \cdots$

Key Question

- A snail travels halfway across a sidewalk in one day. Each following day it travels one-half of the remaining distance. Will the snail ever reach the other side? No

Chalkboard Examples

Determine which geometric series have sums.

1. $1 - \frac{1}{3} + \frac{1}{9} - \frac{1}{27} + \frac{1}{81} \cdots$

   $r = -\frac{1}{3}, |r| < 1$

   The series has a sum.

2. $3 + \frac{3}{5} + \frac{3}{25} + \frac{3}{125} + \frac{3}{625} + \ldots$

   $r = \frac{1}{5}, |r| < 1$

   The series has a sum.

14-4 Infinite Geometric Series

Convergent Geometric Series

Objective: Determine whether a given geometric series has a sum.

Let us consider an infinite geometric series.

$$2 + 4 + 8 + 16 + 32 + 64 + \cdots + 2^n + \cdots$$

As n becomes larger and larger, the sum of the first n terms gets larger without bound. The next example, however, is different.

$$\frac{1}{2} + \frac{1}{4} + \frac{1}{8} + \frac{1}{16} + \cdots + \frac{1}{2^n} + \cdots$$

Let us look at the sum of the first n terms for some values of n.

$$S_1 = \frac{1}{2}$$
$$S_2 = \frac{1}{2} + \frac{1}{4} = \frac{3}{4}$$
$$S_3 = \frac{1}{2} + \frac{1}{4} + \frac{1}{8} = \frac{7}{8}$$
$$S_4 = \frac{1}{2} + \frac{1}{4} + \frac{1}{8} + \frac{1}{16} = \frac{15}{16}$$

Each denominator is in the form 2^n. Each numerator appears to be one less than the denominator. There is a pattern, which can be described as $S_n = \frac{2^n - 1}{2^n}$. As n gets very large, S_n gets very close to 1. We say S_n approaches a limit of 1. We define the sum of this infinite series to be 1.

Definition

If, in an infinite series, S_n approaches some limit as n becomes very large, that limit is defined to be the sum of the series. If an infinite series has a sum, it is said to **converge** or to be **convergent.**

Some infinite series have sums (converge) and some do not.

Theorem 14-6

An infinite geometric series is convergent and thus has a sum if and only if $|r| < 1$ (the absolute value of the common ratio is less than 1).

EXAMPLES Determine which geometric series have sums.

1. $1 - \frac{1}{2} + \frac{1}{4} - \frac{1}{8} + \frac{1}{16} + \cdots \quad r = -\frac{1}{2}, |r| < 1$

   The series has a sum, by Theorem 14-6.

2. $1 + 5 + 25 + 125 + \cdots \quad r = 5, |r| > 1$

   The series does not have a sum.

3. $1 + (-1) + 1 + (-1) + \cdots \quad r = -1, |r| = 1$

   The series does not have a sum.

Try This Determine which geometric series have sums.

a. $4 + 16 + 64 + \cdots$ No **b.** $5 - 30 + 180 - \cdots$ No **c.** $1 + \frac{1}{3} + \frac{1}{9} + \frac{1}{27} + \cdots$ Yes

Finding Sums

Objective: Find the sum of an infinite geometric series.

Theorem 14-7

The sum of an infinite geometric series, with $|r| < 1$, is given by $S = \frac{a_1}{1 - r}$.

EXAMPLE 4 Find the sum of the infinite geometric series $5 + \frac{5}{2} + \frac{5}{4} + \frac{5}{8} + \cdots$.

Note that $a_1 = 5$ and $r = \frac{1}{2}$. We use Theorem 14-7.

$$S = \frac{5}{1 - \frac{1}{2}} = 10$$

Try This Find the sum of each infinite geometric series.

d. $1 + \frac{1}{3} + \frac{1}{9} + \frac{1}{27} + \cdots$ $\frac{3}{2}$ **e.** $4 - 1 + \frac{1}{4} - \frac{1}{16} + \cdots$ $\frac{16}{5}$

Proof of Theorem 14-7

The sum of the first n terms of an infinite geometric series is $S_n = \frac{a_1(1 - r^n)}{1 - r}$.

As n gets very large, we look at r^n and see that, since $|r| < 1$, r^n gets very small, approaching 0. Thus the numerator approaches a_1. The limit of S_n as n gets very large is, therefore, $\frac{a_1}{1 - r}$, and we have $S = \frac{a_1}{1 - r}$.

Finding Sums

Chalkboard Example

1. Find the sum of the infinite geometric series.

   $2 + \frac{1}{2} + \frac{1}{8} + \frac{1}{16} + \cdots$

   $a_1 = 2, r = \frac{1}{4}$

   $S = \frac{2}{1 - \frac{1}{4}}$

   $S = \frac{8}{3}$

LESSON QUIZ

1. Determine whether the geometric series has a sum.

   $1 - 1 + 1 - 1 + \cdots$

   No

2. Find the sum of the infinite series.

   $1 - \frac{1}{4} + \frac{1}{16} - \frac{1}{64} + \frac{1}{128} - \cdots$

   $\frac{4}{5}$

Assignment Guide
Algebra: Omit

Alg w/Finite Math: 1–21 e/o, 22, MR

Comprehensive: 1–21 e/o, 22–26, MR

ADDITIONAL ANSWERS

Exercises

26. The sum of each group is greater than $\frac{1}{2}$. Thus, the series is greater than $1 + \frac{1}{2} + \frac{1}{2} + \frac{1}{2} + \cdots$, which does not converge.

Mixed Review

27. $\pm 80, \pm 40, \pm 20, \pm 16, \pm 10, \pm 8, \pm 5, \pm 4, \pm 2, \pm 1$
28. 1 positive, 0, 2, or 4 negative
29. $P(2) = -336$; $P(5) = 1740$; $P(0) = -80$; $P(-5) = 0$
30. $-1, -5, 4, 2i, -2i$
31. $-1, -5, 4; -1, -5, 4, 2i, -2i$
32.

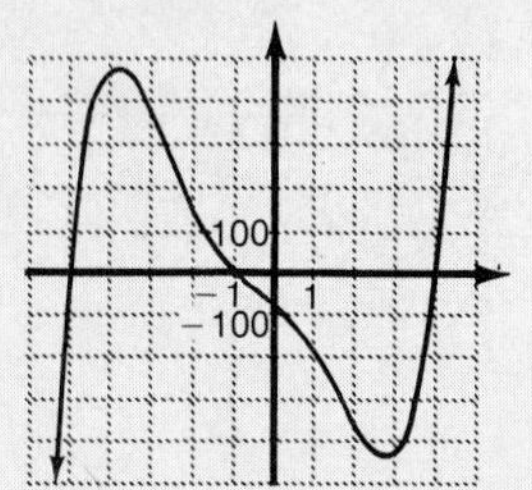

33. $-6, -3, 2, 137$
34. 27, 37, 47, 137

14-4 EXERCISES

A

Determine which geometric series have sums.

1. $5 + 10 + 20 + 40 + \cdots$ No

2. $16 + 8 + 4 + 2 + \cdots$ Yes

3. $6 + 2 + \frac{2}{3} + \frac{2}{9} + \cdots$ Yes

4. $2 - 4 + 8 - 16 + 32 - \cdots$ No

5. $1 + 0.1 + 0.01 + 0.001 + \cdots$ Yes

6. $-\frac{5}{3} - \frac{10}{9} - \frac{20}{27} - \frac{40}{81} - \cdots$ Yes

7. $1 - \frac{1}{5} + \frac{1}{25} - \frac{1}{125} + \cdots$ Yes

8. $6 + \frac{42}{5} + \frac{294}{25} + \cdots$ No

Find the sum of each infinite geometric series.

9. $4 + 2 + 1 + \cdots$ 8

10. $7 + 3 + \frac{9}{7} + \cdots$ $\frac{49}{4}$

11. $1 + \frac{1}{2} + \frac{1}{4} + \cdots$ 2

12. $\frac{8}{3} + \frac{4}{3} + \frac{2}{3} + \cdots$ $\frac{16}{3}$

13. $16 + 1.6 + 0.16 + \cdots$ $\frac{160}{9}$

14. $4 + 2.4 + 1.44 + \cdots$ 10

B

Repeating decimals represent infinite geometric series. For example, $0.\overline{6}$ represents $0.6 + 0.06 + 0.006 + 0.0006 + \cdots$.

We can use Theorem 14-7 to find rational notation, using 0.6 for a_1 and 0.1 for r. Find rational notation for each number.

15. $0.\overline{7}$ $\frac{7}{9}$

16. $0.\overline{3}$ $\frac{1}{3}$

17. $0.\overline{21}$ $\frac{7}{33}$

18. $0.\overline{63}$ $\frac{7}{11}$

19. $5.\overline{15}$ $\frac{170}{33}$

20. $4.\overline{125}$ $\frac{4121}{999}$

21. How far up and down will a ball travel before stopping if it is dropped from a height of 12 m, and each rebound is $\frac{1}{3}$ of the previous distance? (Hint: Use an infinite geometric series.) 24 m

22. ***Critical Thinking*** The number 2 is the first term of an infinite geometric series with a sum of 3. List the first 5 terms of the series. $2, \frac{2}{3}, \frac{2}{9}, \frac{2}{27}, \frac{2}{81}$

Challenge

23. The sides of a square are each 16 cm long. A second square is inscribed by joining the midpoints of the sides, successively. In the second square we repeat the process, inscribing a third square. If this process is continued indefinitely, what is the sum of the areas of all the squares? (Hint: Use an infinite geometric series.) 512 cm^2

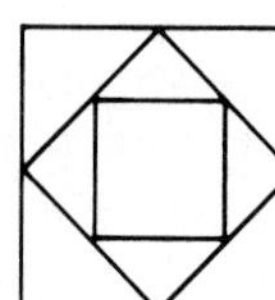

24. The infinite series

$$2 + \frac{1}{2} + \frac{1}{2 \cdot 3} + \frac{1}{2 \cdot 3 \cdot 4} + \frac{1}{2 \cdot 3 \cdot 4 \cdot 5} + \frac{1}{2 \cdot 3 \cdot 4 \cdot 5 \cdot 6} + \cdots$$

is not geometric, but does have a sum. Find values of S_1, S_2, S_3, S_4, S_5, and S_6. Make a conjecture about the value of S. $2, 2.5, 2.\overline{6}, 2.708\overline{3}, 2.71\overline{6}, 2.7180\overline{5}; S = e$

25. Find rational notation for 0.010101 . . . , which is in binary notation. $\frac{1}{3}$ decimal, or $\frac{1}{11}$ binary

26. Consider the **harmonic series** $1 + \frac{1}{2} + \frac{1}{3} + \frac{1}{4} + \frac{1}{5} + \cdots$. Drop the first term and consider the remaining terms in the following way: put $\frac{1}{2}$ in the first group, the next two terms in the second group, the next four terms in the third group, the next eight terms in the fourth group. Compare the sum of each group with $\frac{1}{2}$ and use the result to argue whether the series converges.

Mixed Review

Let $P(x) = x^5 + 2x^4 - 15x^3 - 12x^2 - 76x - 80$.

27. List the possible rational roots of $P(x)$.

28. Determine the number of possible positive and negative roots.

29. Find $P(2)$, $P(5)$, $P(0)$, $P(-5)$. 30. Solve $P(x) = 0$.

31. List the x-intercepts and roots of $P(x)$. 32. Graph $P(x)$.

Find the first three terms and the 12th term for each sequence.

33. $a_n = n^2 - 7$ 34. $a_n = 10n + 17$

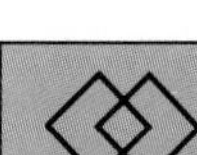

GRAPHING SEQUENCES

Suppose we think of a sequence as a function. That is, to the number 1 is assigned the first term, to the number 2 is assigned the second term, and so on. We can graph a sequence by plotting a point for each term, or by using computer graphing techniques.

Graph.

a. $4, 2, 1, \frac{1}{2}, \ldots$ b. $a_n = 2n - 3$ c. $a_n = 10(0.8)^n$

Problem for Programmers

Write a program to find the sum of an infinite geometric series, if it exists, given the first three terms. Test your program using Exercises 9 – 14 in Lesson 14-4.

Graphing Sequences

Note that arithmetic sequences are points on a line with slope d, geometric sequences are points on exponential or logarithmic curves.

a.

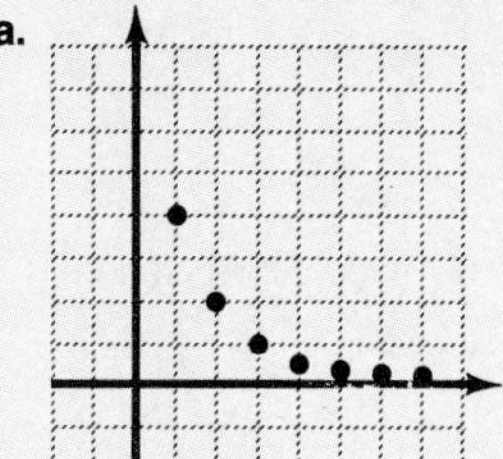

b.

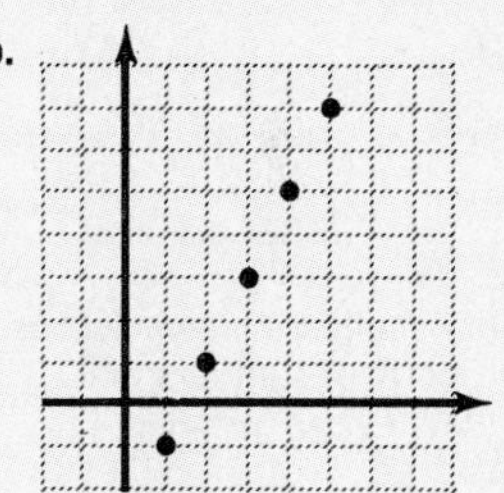

c.

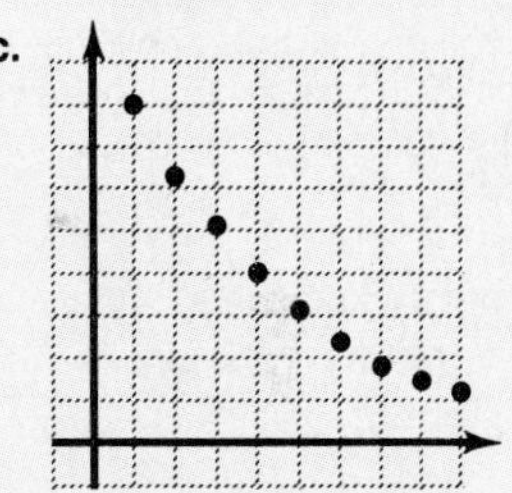

14-5

FIRST FIVE MINUTES

1. Determine whether the following series has a sum.

   $1 + \frac{1}{2} + \frac{1}{4} + \frac{1}{8} + \frac{1}{16} + \cdots$

   $r = \frac{1}{2}, |r| < 1$

   The series has a sum.

2. Find the sum of the infinite series.

   $1 + \frac{1}{6} + \frac{1}{36} + \frac{1}{216} + \cdots$

   $S = \frac{a_1}{1 - r}$

   $= \frac{1}{1 - \frac{1}{6}} = \frac{6}{5}$

The principle of mathematical induction is the only property of numbers that guarantees that there is an infinite number of numbers.

When showing a statement is true for $n = k + 1$, you may wish to show the result of substituting n's for all $k + 1$'s in the final step.

Key Question

- What are some statements P_n that are true for any positive integer n?
  $0 < n$
  $n < n + 1$
  $(n + 1)^2 = n^2 + 2n + 1$
  etc.

14-5 Mathematical Induction

Objective: Prove statements about positive integers using mathematical induction.

Earlier we observed the sequence of odd numbers 1, 3, 5, 7, 9 . . . , $(2n - 1)$. The sequence of partial sums 1, 4, 9, 16, 25, . . . suggests that the sum of the first n odd integers is n^2. It is impossible to prove this by considering all possible cases. In order to deal with such problems we use the **principle of mathematical induction.**

The Principle of Mathematical Induction

If P_n is a statement concerning the positive integers n and

A. P_1 is true,
B. assuming P_k is true implies that P_{k+1} is true

then P_n must be true for all positive integers n.

The logic of the principle of mathematical induction is very reasonable. Suppose parts A and B hold for some statement. Then, part A tells us that the statement P_1 is true. Part B tells us that since P_1 is true, then P_2 must be true. Since P_2 is true, P_3 must be true, and so on. To justify a statement using the principle of mathematical induction, both parts must be shown to be true.

EXAMPLE 1 Use the principle of mathematical induction to prove that the sum of n consecutive positive odd integers is n^2.

We are trying to prove that $1 + 3 + 5 + \cdots + (2n - 1) = n^2$.

A. First we must show that the statement is true for $n = 1$.

$$1 = n^2$$
$$1 = 1 \checkmark$$

B. Now suppose that the statement is true when n is some integer k.

That is, $1 + 3 + 5 + \cdots + (2k - 1) = k^2$.

We must show that the statement is true when n is $k + 1$. That is, we must show that if the sum of the first k odd positive integers is k^2, then the sum of the first $k + 1$ odd positive integers is $(k + 1)^2$.

$$1 + 3 + 5 + \cdots + (2k - 1) = k^2 \quad \text{Assumed true for } k$$

$$\begin{aligned} 1 + 3 + 5 + \cdots + (2k - 1) + [2(k + 1) - 1] &= k^2 + [2(k + 1) - 1] \quad \text{Adding } 2(k+1) - 1 \text{ to both sides} \\ &= k^2 + 2k + 2 - 1 \\ &= k^2 + 2k + 1 \\ &= (k + 1)^2 \checkmark \end{aligned}$$

We first showed that the statement is true for $n = 1$. Then we showed that if the statement is true when n is some integer k, it must be true when n is the next integer $k + 1$. This means that if it is true for $n = 1$, it is true for $n = 2$. If it is true for $n = 2$, then it must be true for $n = 3$, and so on. The principle of mathematical induction tells us that the statement is true for *all* odd positive integers n.

Now consider the sequence $1, 2, 4, 8, \ldots, 2^{n-1}$. Forming a series, we have $S_n = 1 + 2 + 4 + 8 + \cdots + 2^{n-1}$.

$$S_1 = 1$$
$$S_2 = 1 + 2 = 3$$
$$S_3 = 1 + 2 + 4 = 7$$
$$S_4 = 1 + 2 + 4 + 8 = 15$$

If we examine each partial sum, we see that in each case we have 1 less than a power of 2. This suggests that $S_n = 2^n - 1$.

EXAMPLE 2 Use the principle of mathematical induction to prove that $1 + 2 + 4 + 8 + \cdots + 2^{n-1} = 2^n - 1$.

A. First we must show that this is true for $n = 1$.

$$2^{1-1} = 2^1 - 1$$
$$2^0 = 2 - 1$$
$$1 = 1 \checkmark$$

B. Now suppose that the statement is true when n is some integer k. That is, $1 + 2 + 4 + 8 + \cdots + 2^{k-1} = 2^k - 1$.

We must show that the statement is true when $n = k + 1$. That is, adding the $k + 1$st term should give us $2^{k+1} - 1$.

$$1 + 2 + 4 + 8 + \cdots + 2^{k-1} = 2^k - 1 \quad \text{Assumed true for } k$$
$$1 + 2 + 4 + 8 + \cdots + 2^{k-1} + [2^{(k+1)-1}] = 2^k - 1 + [2^{(k+1)-1}] \quad \text{Adding } 2^{(k+1)-1} \text{ to both sides}$$
$$= 2^k - 1 + 2^k$$
$$= 2(2^k) - 1$$
$$= 2^{k+1} - 1 \checkmark$$

We have shown that if the statement $1 + 2 + 4 + 8 + \cdots + 2^{n-1} = 2^n - 1$ is true when n is some integer k, then it is true when n is $k + 1$. The principle of mathematical induction tells us that the statement is true for all positive integers.

Try This See Selected Answers.

a. Use the principle of mathematical induction to prove that $1 + 2 + 3 + 4 + \cdots + n = \frac{n(n + 1)}{2}$.

b. Use the principle of mathematical induction to prove that $1 + 3 + 7 + 15 + \cdots + (2^n - 1) = 2^{n+1} - n - 2$.

Chalkboard Examples

1. Use the principle of mathematical induction to prove that $1 \cdot 2 + 2 \cdot 3 + 3 \cdot 4 + \cdots + n(n + 1) = \frac{n(n + 1)(n + 2)}{3}$.

First we check that the statement is true for $n = 1$; that is,

$1 \cdot (1 + 1) = \frac{1(1 + 1)(1 + 2)}{3}$.

Next, suppose that the statement is true for some integer k.

$1 \cdot 2 + 2 \cdot 3 + 3 \cdot 4 + \cdots + k(k + 1) = \frac{k(k + 1)(k + 2)}{3}$

We must show that the statement is true for $k + 1$. Add $(k + 1)(k + 2)$ to both sides to get

$1 \cdot 2 + 2 \cdot 3 + \cdots + (k + 1)(k + 2)$

$= \frac{k(k + 1)(k + 2)}{3} + (k + 1)(k + 2)$

$= \frac{k(k + 1)(k + 2)}{3} + \frac{3(k + 1)(k + 2)}{3}$

$= \frac{k(k + 1)(k + 2) + 3(k + 1)(k + 2)}{3}$

$= \frac{(k + 1)(k + 2)(k + 3)}{3}$

But this is just the statement for $n = k + 1$

$= \frac{(k + 1)[(k + 1) + 1][(k + 1) + 2]}{3}$.

Therefore, the statement is proved.

2. Use the principle of mathematical induction to prove that

$1 + 3 + 9 + \cdots + 3^{n-1} = \frac{3^n - 1}{2}$.

First note that the statement is true for $n = 1$; that is,

$3^{1-1} = \frac{3^1 - 1}{2}$.

The theorem is true for $n = 1$. Next suppose the statement is true for some number k; that is,

$1 + 3 + 9 + \cdots + 3^{k-1} = \frac{3^k - 1}{2}$.

Add 3^k to both sides of the equation to get

$1 + 3 + 9 + \cdots + 3^{k-1} + 3^k$

$= \frac{3^k - 1}{2} + 3^k = \frac{3^k - 1 + 2 \cdot 3^k}{2}$

$= \frac{3^k(1 + 2) - 1}{2} = \frac{3^{k+1} - 1}{2}$

But this is just the statement for $n = k + 1$. Therefore the statement is true for all positive integers.

LESSON QUIZ

1. What are the two steps necessary to prove that a statement P_n is true for all positive integers n?
   First show that the statement is true for $n = 1$.
   Next show that for any positive integer k if the statement P_k is true, then the statement P_{k+1} must be true.
2. Use the principle of mathematical induction to prove that $2 + 2 \cdot 3 + 2 \cdot 3^2 + \cdots + 2 \cdot 3^{n-1} = 3^n - 1$.
   The statement is true for $n = 1$, since $2 \cdot 3^{1-1} = 3^1 - 1$.
   Suppose the theorem is true for some positive integer k; that is, $2 + 2 \cdot 3 + 2 \cdot 3^2 + \cdots + 2 \cdot 3^{k-1} = 3^k - 1$.
   Add $2 \cdot 3^k$ to both sides. Hence
   $2 + 2 \cdot 3 + 2 \cdot 3^2 + \cdots + 2 \cdot 3^k$
   $= 3^k - 1 + 2 \cdot 3^k$
   $= 3^k(1 + 2) - 1$
   $= 3^{k+1} - 1$
   The statement is true for $k + 1$. By mathematical induction the statement is true for all positive integers.

Assignment Guide:

Algebra: omit

Alg w/Finite Math: 1–12 e/o, 13, MR, assign w. 14-6

Comprehensive: 1–12 e/o, 13–16, MR, assign w. 14-6

ADDITIONAL ANSWERS

Exercises

For Exercises 1–16, see Teacher's Answer Section.

Mixed Review

17. 2, −2, $2i$, $-2i$, −1
18. $P(x) = (x^4 + 4x^3 + 12x + 36x + 92) \cdot (x - 3) + 260$
19. $10\sqrt{2}$
20. 5
21. 5, −5
22. 3
23. 3, −3, $3i$, $-3i$

14-5 EXERCISES

A

Use the principle of mathematical induction to prove each of the following.

1. $3 + 4 + 5 + \cdots + (n + 2) = \frac{1}{2}n(n + 5)$

2. $3 + 5 + 7 + \cdots + (2n + 1) = n(n + 2)$

3. $-2 - 3 - 4 - 5 - \cdots - (n + 1) = -\frac{1}{2}n(n + 3)$

4. $4 + 4^2 + 4^3 + \cdots + 4^n = \frac{4}{3}(4^n - 1)$

5. $1^2 + 2^2 + 3^2 + 4^2 + \cdots + n^2 = \frac{n(n + 1)(2n + 1)}{6}$

6. $1^3 + 2^3 + 3^3 + 4^3 + \cdots + n^3 = \frac{n^2(n + 1)^2}{4}$

7. $\frac{1}{1 \cdot 2} + \frac{1}{2 \cdot 3} + \frac{1}{3 \cdot 4} + \frac{1}{4 \cdot 5} + \cdots + \frac{1}{n(n + 1)} = \frac{n}{n + 1}$

8. $2 + 5 + 8 + \cdots + (3n - 1) = \frac{n}{2}(3n + 1)$

9. $4 + 3 + 2 + \cdots + (5 - n) = \frac{1}{2}n(9 - n)$

10. $1 + \frac{1}{3} + \frac{1}{9} + \cdots + 3^{1-n} = \frac{3}{2}\left(1 - \left(\frac{1}{3}\right)^n\right)$

B

11. Prove that $\sum_{k=1}^{n} (2k + 3) = n(n + 4)$.

12. Prove that $\sum_{k=1}^{n} 2^k = 2(2^n - 1)$.

13. ***Critical Thinking*** Explain how using the principle of mathematical induction is like knocking over an infinite arrangement of dominoes.

Challenge

14. Prove that $\left(1 + \frac{1}{1}\right)\left(1 + \frac{1}{2}\right)\left(1 + \frac{1}{3}\right)\cdots\left(1 + \frac{1}{n}\right) = n + 1$.

15. Prove that $\sum_{k=1}^{n} k^5 = \frac{n^2(n + 1)^2(2n^2 + 2n - 1)}{12}$.

16. Use Exercises 5 and 6 to find and prove a formula for $\sum_{k=1}^{n} (k^3 - k^2)$.

Mixed Review

Let $P(x) = x^5 + x^4 - 16x - 16$. **17.** Solve $P(x) = 0$.

18. For $D(x) = x - 3$, write $P(x) = Q(x) \cdot D(x) + R(x)$.

Find the distance between **19.** $(5, -5)$ and $(-5, 5)$. **20.** $(\log 10, 3)$ and $(4, 7)$.

Solve. **21.** $x^2 - 25 = 0$ **22.** $x^3 = 27$ **23.** $x^4 - 81 = 0$

14-6 Problem Solving: Strategies

Combine Strategies

Objective: Solve nonroutine problems using a combination of strategies.

The chart below shows the strategies that you have been introduced to in this book. We have seen that most problems are solved using a combination of strategies and that many problems can be solved in more than one way, that is, by using different strategies.

Problem-Solving Strategies		
Write an Equation	Draw a Diagram	Guess, Check, Revise
Make an Organized List	Make a Table	Look for a Pattern
Use Logical Reasoning	Simplify the Problem	Work Backward

EXAMPLE How many rectangular arrays can be built using 36 blocks if all the blocks must be used?

■ UNDERSTAND the problem

The statement of the problem is simple. Understanding what the problem is asking us to find, however, may not be immediately clear. The strategies *Simplify the Problem* and *Draw a Diagram* can help us understand this problem. Suppose we had 6 blocks. What is a rectangular array? By drawing diagrams we can find that there are 4 rectangular arrays that can be made using 6 blocks. This helps us understand what we must do, but we must use 36 blocks, not just 6.

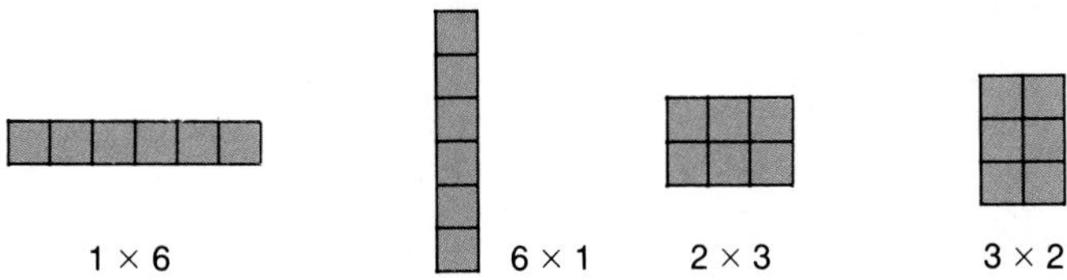

■ Develop and carry out a PLAN

We are asked to solve this problem for a large number of blocks, we might try to *Simplify the Problem* using arrays with 1 block, 2 blocks, 3 blocks, and so on. We will still *Draw a Diagram*.

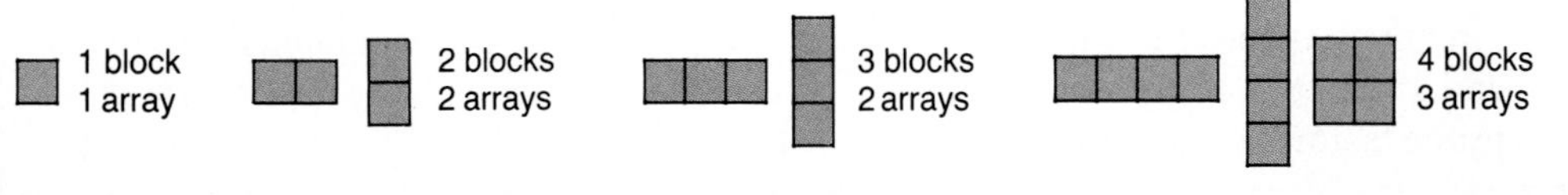

14-6

FIRST FIVE MINUTES

1. What is the greatest number contained in each set?
   a. $A = \{x \mid x = -|x|, x \text{ is an integer} \neq 0\}$
   A is the set of negative integers. Therefore, -1 is the greatest.
   b. $B = \{x \mid x^2 - 2 \leq 0, x \text{ is a real number}\}$ **$\sqrt{2}$ is largest.**

Combine Strategies

Past problem-solving lessons have focused on a few of the many different problem-solving strategies. These strategies provide students with a starting point from which they can develop and carry out problem-solving plans of their own.

You may wish to review the strategies studied so far. Ask students to give an example of a problem which could be solved using each strategy.

Key Question

- What other strategy might you use to solve the Example?
  Make an Organized List

Chalkboard Example

1. Three aliens, Ao, Beex, and Qdi each made several trips to Earth. One took 3 trips during the Dark Ages, 2 during the Renaissance, and 5 in the 1980s. The trips took 21 total days. Another took 6 trips during the Renaissance and 2 in the 1980s over a 14-day period. The third took 3 trips in the Dark Ages and 8 in the 1980s over a 20-day period. Qdi took the most 2-day trips, Ao didn't take any. How many days did each alien travel?
   Solving the system
   $3D + 2R + 5N = 21$
   $6R + 2N = 14$
   $3D + 8N = 20$
   we get $D = 4$, $R = 2$, and $N = 1$. Thus a Renaissance trip takes 2 days. Using Logical Reasoning, the alien who took 6 Renaissance trips was Qdi, thus Qdi traveled 14 days. The alien who took 0 Renaissance trips was Ao, so Ao traveled 20 days. The only one left is Beex, who thus traveled 21 days.

Hints for Problems

1. Write an expression for the salary after the 20% cut.
2. Make an organized list of the possible ways to distribute the doggy treats.
3. Simplify the equations until you have the values for ac, ab, and bc.
4. Make an organized list of all pairs of cubes.
5. Try writing an equation for the number of points earned and the number lost.
6. If you add 1 to each exponent of the factors in the prime factorization and take their product, you get the number of factors of the number. For example, $300 = 2^2 \cdot 3^1 \cdot 5^2$, $(2 + 1)(1 + 1)(2 + 1) = 18$ different factors.

ANSWERS

1. They needed a 25% raise the following year.
2. She could distribute them 66 ways.
3. The values are $a = 4, b = 5$, and $c = 6$ or $a = -4, b = -5, c = -6$.
4. The code number is 1729, which is $9^3 + 10^3$ and $1^3 + 12^3$
5. This person had 12 items correct on the test.
6. The smallest positive integer with 8 different positive factors is 24.

To organize our findings, we could *Make a Table* and *Look for a Pattern*. The table below has been completed through 10 blocks.

Number of blocks	1	2	3	4	5	6	7	8	9	10
Number of arrays	1	2	2	3	2	4	2	4	3	4

The pattern here is not like others you have seen before. The diagrams shown above, together with the table, help show the pattern. In the diagrams above for 6 blocks, we see arrays with these dimensions: $1 \times 6, 2 \times 3, 3 \times 2$, and 6×1. There are 4 arrays. Notice the first number in each array. They are 1, 2, 3, and 6. Notice that these are the factors of the number 6. There are 4 factors and 4 arrays. If we test this pattern with other numbers in the table, we find this always holds true. Thus if we find the factors of 36, we will know how many rectangular arrays can be made.

Find the ANSWER and CHECK

The factors of 36 are 1, 2, 3, 4, 6, 9, 12, 18, and 36. Thus there are 9 rectangular arrays possible using 36 blocks. The best way to check our work in this problem is to retrace our steps through the solution. Doing this shows that we have not made any errors, so the solution checks.

14-6 PROBLEMS

Solve using one or more strategies.

1. All employees in a certain company agreed to take a 20% cut in wages for one year. What percent raise did they receive the following year in order to return to their original salaries?
2. Nancy has 16 identical doggy treats to be distributed among her 3 dogs. Each dog must receive at least 2 doggy treats. In how many ways can she distribute the doggy treats?
3. Find a, b, and c given the following conditions: $a(b + c) = 44$, $b(a + c) = 50$, and $c(a + b) = 54$.
4. A computer access-code number was designated in a special way. It was a 4-digit number. The number is the smallest integer that can be written as the sum of two positive cubes in two different ways, and the number is between 1000 and 2000. What is the code number?
5. A math test had 20 items. Students received 2 points for each correct answer and lost 1 point for each incorrect or missing answer. A student had a score of 16. How many items were answered correctly on the test?
6. Find the least positive integer with 8 different positive factors, including the number and 1. (Hint: Compare the number of factors of a number with the exponents in the prime factorization of the number.)

Chapter 14 Summary and Review

14-1

You can find the terms of a sequence by substituting values for n.

The n-th term of a sequence is given. Find the first four terms, the 10th term, and the 15th term.

1. $a_n = \frac{n-1}{n+1}$

2. $a_n = n - \frac{1}{n}$

Some sequences can be defined by recursion.

3. Find the first five terms of the sequence, when $a_1 = 2$ and $a_{n+1} = \frac{a_n}{1 - a_n}$.

Looking for a pattern in a sequence will help you find a general term. For each sequence, find a rule for the general term.

4. 0, 3, 8, 15, 24, . . .

5. $2, \frac{3}{2}, \frac{4}{3}, \frac{5}{4}, \frac{6}{5}, \ldots$

The Greek letter Σ (sigma) can be used to simplify notation when a series has a formula for the general term.

6. Rename $\sum_{n=1}^{3} 3^n$ without using sigma notation.

Write sigma notation for this sum.

7. $4 - 8 + 12 - 16 + 20 - 24$

14-2

a_n, the n-th term of an arithmetic sequence, is found by using the formula $a_n = a_1 + (n - 1)d$, where a_1 is the first term and d is the common difference.

For the arithmetic sequence $3, 4\frac{1}{2}, 6, 7\frac{1}{2}, \ldots,$

8. Find a_1, d and find the 10th term.

9. what term has a value of 24?

Numbers $m_1, m_2, m_3, \ldots, m_n$ are called arithmetic means between a and b if $a, m_1, m_2, m_3, \ldots, m_n, b$ form an arithmetic sequence.

10. Insert three arithmetic means between 2 and 22.

There are two formulas for finding the sum of an arithmetic series.

$$S_n = \frac{n}{2}(a_1 + a_n) \qquad S_n = \frac{n}{2}(2a_1 + (n - 1)d)$$

11. Find the sum of the first thirty positive integers.

12. Find the sum of this series.

$$\sum_{k=1}^{20} (3k - 15)$$

ANSWERS

1. $0, \frac{1}{3}, \frac{2}{4}, \frac{3}{5}; \frac{9}{11}; \frac{14}{16}$
2. $0, 1\frac{1}{2}, 2\frac{2}{3}, 3\frac{3}{4}; 9\frac{9}{10}; 14\frac{14}{15}$
3. $2, -2, -\frac{2}{3}, -\frac{2}{5}, -\frac{2}{7}$
4. $n^2 - 1$
5. $\frac{n+1}{n}$
6. $3 + 9 + 27$
7. $\sum_{n=1}^{6} (4n)(-1)^{n+1}$
8. $a_1 = 3, d = 1\frac{1}{2}$ and $16\frac{1}{2}$
9. 15th term
10. 7, 12, 17
11. 465
12. 330

13. -2
14. 256
15. 8th term
16. 36, 18
17. $3\frac{15}{16}$
18. -1641
19. No
20. Yes
21. 40
22. $8\frac{1}{3}$
23. A. True for $n = 1$
B. Assume true for $n = k$. Show that statement is true for $n = k + 1$.
$1 + 4 + 7 + \cdots + (3k - 2) + [3(k + 1) - 2]$
$= \frac{k(3k - 1)}{2} + [3(k + 1) - 2]$
$= \frac{3k^2 - k + 6k + 2}{2}$
$= \frac{3k^2 + 5k + 2}{2}$
$= \frac{(k + 1)(3k + 2)}{2}$
$= \frac{(k + 1)[3(k + 1) - 1]}{2}$

14-3

a_n, the n-th term of a geometric sequence, is found by using the formula $a_n = a_1r^{n-1}$ where a_1 is the first term and r is the common ratio.

For the geometric sequence $4, -8, 16, -32, \ldots,$

13. find the common ratio.

14. find the seventh term.

15. what term has a value of -512?

Numbers $m_1, m_2, \ldots, m_n$ are geometric means of a and b if $a, m_1, m_2, \ldots m_n, b$ form a geometric sequence.

16. Insert two geometric means between 72 and 9.

The sum of the first n terms of a geometric series is given by

$$S_n = \frac{a_1(1 - r^n)}{1 - r}$$

17. Find the sum of the first six terms of the geometric series $2, 1, \frac{1}{2}, \frac{1}{4}, \ldots.$

18. Evaluate.

$$\sum_{n=1}^{7} (-3)^n$$

14-4

An infinite geometric series is convergent and has a sum if and only if $|r| < 1$.

Determine which series have sums.

19. $1 - 2 + 4 - 8 + \cdots$

20. $3.2 + 1.6 + 0.8 + \cdots$

The sum, S, of an infinite geometric series with $|r| < 1$ is given by

$$S = \frac{a_1}{1 - r}$$

21. Find the sum of the geometric series $20, 10, 5, \ldots.$

22. Find the sum of the geometric series $10, -2, 0.4, -0.08, \ldots.$

14-5

We can use mathematical induction to prove statements.
If P_n is a statement concerning the positive integers n and

A. P_1 is true,
B. assuming P_k is true implies that P_{k+1} is true

then P_n must be true for all positive integers.

Use mathematical induction to prove the following.

23. $1 + 4 + 7 + \cdots + (3n - 2) = \frac{n(3n - 1)}{2}$

See also Problem 14, Computer-Assisted Problem Solving, page 849.

Chapter 14 Test

1. If $a_n = \frac{1}{2n + 1}$, find the first four terms, the tenth term, and the fifteenth term.
2. Find the first five terms of the sequence, where $a_1 = -3$ and $a_{n+1} = \frac{a_n}{1 + a_n}$.
3. Find a rule for a general term for the sequence.

   $-1, \frac{1}{2}, -\frac{1}{3}, \frac{1}{4}, -\frac{1}{5}, \ldots$

4. Rename without using sigma notation.

   $\sum_{n=1}^{4} 2^{n-1}$

5. Write using sigma notation.

   $-6 - 3 + 0 + 3 + 6 + 9 + 12$

For the arithmetic sequence $-4, -1\frac{1}{2}, 1, 3\frac{1}{2}, 6, \ldots,$

6. find a_1, d, and find the 20th term.
7. what term has a value of 41?
8. Insert 4 arithmetic means between 2 and 8.
9. Find the sum of the first 84 positive integers.
10. Find the sum of this series.

    $\sum_{n=1}^{30} (7 - 2n)$

For the geometric sequence $24, 16, \frac{32}{3}, \ldots,$

11. find the common ratio.
12. find the sixth term.
13. find the sum of the first six terms.
14. What term is $\frac{1024}{729}$?
15. Insert 5 geometric means between $\frac{1}{16}$ and 4.
16. Find the sum of the first six terms of the geometric series.

    $\frac{2}{3} + \frac{1}{3} + \frac{1}{6} + \frac{1}{12} + \cdots$

17. Evaluate $\sum_{n=1}^{5} 4\left(-\frac{1}{2}\right)^n$.
18. Does this series have a sum?

    $\frac{1}{128} + \frac{1}{64} + \frac{1}{32} + \cdots$

19. Find the sum of the geometric series $81 - 27 + 9 - 3 + \cdots$.
20. Use mathematical induction to prove $2 + 6 + 10 + 14 + \cdots + (4n - 2) = 2n^2$

ANSWERS

1. $\frac{1}{3}, \frac{1}{5}, \frac{1}{7}, \frac{1}{9}; \frac{1}{21}; \frac{1}{31}$
2. $-3, \frac{3}{2}, \frac{3}{5}, \frac{3}{8}, \frac{3}{11}$
3. $a_n = \frac{(-1)^n}{n}$
4. $1 + 2 + 4 + 8 = 15$
5. $\sum_{n=1}^{7} (3n - 9)$
6. $a_1 = -4, d = 2\frac{1}{2}$ and $43\frac{1}{2}$
7. 19th term
8. $3\frac{1}{5}, 4\frac{2}{5}, 5\frac{3}{5}, 6\frac{4}{5}$
9. 3570
10. -720
11. $\frac{2}{3}$
12. $\frac{256}{81}$
13. $65\frac{55}{81}$
14. 8th term
15. $\frac{1}{8}, \frac{1}{4}, \frac{1}{2}, 1, 2$
16. $\frac{21}{16}$
17. $-\frac{11}{8}$
18. No
19. $60\frac{3}{4}$
20. a. $2 = 2(1)^2; 2 = 2$

    b. Assume true for $n = k$, show true for $n = k + 1$

    $2 + 6 + 10 + 14 + \cdots + (4k - 2) + (4(k + 1) - 2)$
    $= 2k^2 + (4(k + 1) - 2)$
    $= 2k^2 + 4k + 2$
    $= 2(k^2 + 2k + 1)$
    $= 2(k + 1)^2$

Test Item Analysis

Item	Lesson
1–5	14-1
6–10	14-2
11–17	14-3
18, 19	14-4
20	14-5

CHAPTER **15**

Counting and Probability

Chapter Overview

Chapter 15 presents the fundamental counting principle and uses this concept to introduce permutations. Permutations of objects are calculated with and without replacement as well as permutations with repeated objects and circular permutations. Combinations are developed as unordered permutations. The binomial theorem is presented along with formulas to find the r-th term of a binomial expansion. Probabilities of a simple event are explained and expanded to include probabilities of the union or intersection in compound events.

The last two lessons employ simulations using random devices, such as spinners, random number tables, and computer programs to determine experimental probability. An application applies probability to check digits in an array of numbers.

Objectives

15-1
- Determine the number of ways a compound event may occur.
- Find the total number of permutations of a set of n objects.
- Evaluate factorial notation.
- Find the number of permutations of n objects taken r at a time without replacement.

15-2
- Find the number of permutations of n objects taken r at a time with replacements.
- Find permutations of a set of objects that are not all different.
- Find circular permutations.

15-3
- Find the number of combinations of a set of n objects taken r at a time.

15-4
- Find the r-th term of the binomial expansion of $(a + b)^n$.
- Use the binomial theorem to expand powers of binomials.
- Determine the number of subsets of a finite set.

15-5
- Compute the probability of a simple event.

15-6
- Find the probability that one event or another will occur.
- Find the probability that one event and another event will occur.

15-7
- Design and use simulations to determine experimental probability.
- Use a random number table to simulate an event and determine experimental probability.

15-8
- Use computer software to simulate events and determine experimental probability.

TEACHING CHAPTER 15

Cooperative Learning Opportunities

Chapter 15 is a good candidate for a four-step method that stresses group process rather than roles. Assign students in groups of three or four, then explain and monitor the process. Try this with Lesson 15-2, Exercises 1, 5, 10, and 20.

(1) **Read Silently:** Each group member reads the problem slowly, thinks about what is to be found and how to go about it.

(2) **Read Aloud:** An assigned member of each group reads the problem out loud.

(3) **Discussion:** The group members talk about what is asked for and how to do the problem. They look back at examples and formulas as needed and try to agree on the method.

(4) **Working:** The group does the work needed. One student may emerge as a leader and another as the one who writes things down. They should check and agree on the solution.

Multicultural Note: *Chu Shih-Chieh*

Pascal's triangle, simple in itself yet rich in applications, has been independently discovered several times in the history of mathematics. In 1303, the Chinese mathematician Chu Shih-Chieh displayed the triangle in his book, *Precious Mirror of the Four Elements*, and called it an old method for finding binomial coefficients.

An interesting application of the triangle relates to a process for selecting foods. Consider wheat, rice, corn, and beans. Each supplies certain necessary proteins but they are most nutritious when eaten in combination.

If we list all the combinations of wheat and rice, we find that we could have neither, one or the other, or both.

There is only one way to have 0 items; two ways to have 1 item; and one way to have 2 items. Explain this and have students figure the numbers for combinations of 3, 4, and 5 items. Chu Shih-Chieh's triangle emerges.

For more information, see page 45 of **Multiculturalism in Mathematics, Science, and Technology**.

Alternative Assessment and Communication Ideas

The phrase "write a convincing argument" is used throughout the text for exercises and activities intended to get students to do some reasoning about math and how it works. This phrase could be used with each of the first eight theorems of Chapter 15 to provide the basis for a test item or homework assignment.

The theorems of probability need to be understood rather than proved. If students can write an example to demonstrate the reasons for a formula, they will be less dependent on memory. For example, Theorem 15-6 is about permutations of *n* objects with a certain number alike. Give students the formula and ask them to explain what it means and why it works.

A summary assessment of understanding would be to provide all of the first eight formulas and have students write a situation or problem for each one.

Investigations and Projects

The **Bonus Topic** on binomial probabilities (page 677) could provide the basis for a project that would demonstrate to students how an abstract method can have very important concrete results. Have students study and work through the bonus topic and when you have checked their work propose the problem described below.

A medical screening test is intended to identify the presence of a particular disease in an individual. A positive result will send the person for further tests and diagnosis. But on occasion a test gives a false positive. That is, the test indicates the disease where it is not present.

Suppose that a medical screening test has a false positive rate of 0.05. About how many people out of 1,000 will test false positive? **(Ans: 50)** Of 10 people tested for the disease, find the probability that exactly one will test false positive. **(Ans: ~0.315)** What is the probability that at least one will test false positive? **(Ans: ~0.34)**

MANAGING CHAPTER 15

Lesson	PACING CHART (DAYS) Algebra	Algebra w/Finite	Algebra w/Trig	Comprehensive	Opening Activity	Cooperative Activity	Seat or Group Work
15-1	0	0.5	0	0.5	First Five Minutes 15-1: **TE** p.644 or ***FFM Transparency Masters*** p.41	Critical Thinking: **SE** p.650	Try This a–p
15-2	0	0.5	0	0.5	First Five Minutes 15-2: **TE** p.651 or ***FFM Transparency Masters*** p.41	Critical Thinking: **SE** p.655 Critical Thinking 15: ***Enrichment*** p.36	Try This a–e
15-3	0	1	0	1	First Five Minutes 15-3: **TE** p.656 or ***FFM Transparency Masters*** p.42	Critical Thinking: **SE** p.659	Try This a–f
15-4	0	1	0	1	First Five Minutes 15-4: **TE** p.660 or ***FFM Transparency Masters*** p.42	Critical Thinking: **SE** p.663 Probability/Statistics 1: ***Enrichment*** p.82	Try This a–f
15-5	0	0.5	0	0.5	First Five Minutes 15-5: **TE** p.664 or ***FFM Transparency Masters*** p.42	Critical Thinking: **SE** p.666 Looking for Errors 15: ***Enrichment*** p.76	Try This a–c
15-6	0	0.5	0	0.5	First Five Minutes 15-6: **TE** p.667 or ***FFM Transparency Masters*** p.43	Critical Thinking: **SE** p.671 Probability/Statistics 2: ***Enrichment*** p.83	Try This a–d
15-7	0	0.5	0	0.5	First Five Minutes 15-7: **TE** p.672 or ***FFM Transparency Masters*** p.43	Critical Thinking: **SE** p.677 Probability/Statistics 3: ***Enrichment*** p.84 Bonus Topic: **SE** p.677	Try This a–d
15-8	0	0.5	0	0.5	First Five Minutes 15-8: **TE** p.678 or ***FFM Transparency Masters*** p.43	Critical Thinking: **SE** p.682 Problem Solving: **SE** pp.683–684	Try This a–d
Review	0	1	0	1			
Test	0	1	0	1			

FFM: First Five Minutes   SPMR: Skills Practice Mixed Review

MANAGING CHAPTER 15

Enrichment	Review/Assess	Reteach	Technology	Lesson
✂ Manipulative Activity 15: ***Enrichment*** p.56	Lesson Quiz: **TE** p.648	Skills Practice 42, #1–14: ***SPMR*** p.54	Calculator Worksheet 29: ***Technology*** p.31	**15-1**
Critical Thinking 15: ***Enrichment*** p.36	Lesson Quiz: **TE** p.653 Quiz 29: ***Assessment*** p.37	Skills Practice 42, #15–22: ***SPMR*** p.54	Calculator Worksheet 30: ***Technology*** p.32	**15-2**
Bonus Topic 14: ***Enrichment*** p.15	Lesson Quiz: **TE** p.658	Skills Practice 42, #23–28: ***SPMR*** p.54	Calculator Worksheet 31: ***Technology*** p.33	**15-3**
Math Point: **TE** p.661 Probability/Statistics 1: ***Enrichment*** p.82	Lesson Quiz: **TE** p.662	Skills Practice 43, #1–12: ***SPMR*** p.55	Problem for Programmers: **SE** p.663	**15-4**
Looking for Errors 15: ***Enrichment*** p.76	Lesson Quiz: **TE** p.665 Mixed Review 29: ***SPMR*** p.93	Skills Practice 43, #13–18: ***SPMR*** p.55	BASIC Computer Project 17: ***Technology*** p.97	**15-5**
Probability/Statistics 2: ***Enrichment*** p.83	Lesson Quiz: **TE** p.670 Quiz 30: ***Assessment*** p.38	Skills Practice 43, #19–22: ***SPMR*** p.55 Problem Bank 21: ***Problem Bank*** p.42	BASIC Computer Project 18: ***Technology*** p.98	**15-6**
Probability/Statistics 3: ***Enrichment*** p.84 Bonus Topic 15: ***Enrichment*** p.16	Lesson Quiz: **TE** p.675	Spreadsheet Activity 10: ***Technology*** pp.71–73	Spreadsheet Activity 10: ***Technology*** pp.70–72	**15-7**
Math Point: **TE** p.679 Lesson Enrichment: **TE** p.680 Problem Solving: **SE** pp.683–684 Problem 15: Computer Assisted Problem Solving, **SE** pp.850–851	Lesson Quiz: **TE** p.681 Mixed Review 30: ***SPMR*** p.94	Problem 15: Computer Assisted Problem Solving, **SE** pp.850–851	Lesson Enrichment: **TE** p.680 Problem 15: Computer Assisted Problem Solving, **SE** pp.850–851	**15-8**
	Summary and Review: **SE** pp.685–687; Test: **SE** p.687			**Review**
	Chapter 15 Test: ***Assessment*** pp.131–136(reg.), pp.185–186 (adv.)			**Test**

The solution to the problem posed on the facing page can be found on page 657.

Ready for Counting and Probability?

1-2 Simplify.

1. $\frac{3}{8} \cdot \frac{4}{9} \cdot \frac{5}{10}$ $\frac{1}{12}$

2. $\frac{1}{9} \cdot \frac{2}{10} \cdot \frac{3}{11} \cdot \frac{4}{12}$ $\frac{1}{495}$

3. $\frac{13}{52} \cdot \frac{12}{51} \cdot \frac{11}{50}$ $\frac{11}{850}$

5-3 Multiply.

4. $(3x + 1)(3x + 1)$ $9x^2 + 6x + 1$

5. $(2 - 3x)^2$ $4 - 12x + 9x^2$

6. $(x - 1)^3$ $x^3 - 3x^2 + 3x - 1$

7. $(x + 2)^4$ $x^4 + 8x^3 + 24x^2 + 32x + 16$

CHAPTER 15

Counting and Probability

How many ways can a congressional committee be formed from a set of 5 senators and 7 representatives if a committee contains 3 senators and 4 representatives?

15-1

FIRST FIVE MINUTES

1. Write down all possible pairs with a 0 or 1 in the first position and an A, B, or C in the second position.
   0A, 0B, 0C, 1A, 1B, 1C
2. Write down all possible outcomes of two coin flips.
   HH, HT, TH, TT

The Fundamental Counting Principle

Before using the fundamental counting principle to solve an example, have students work a simple example by listing all possibilities. For example, two models of cars, the X19 and the Comanche, each have three possible colors: black, red, and silver. Ask students to list the six possibilities.

Key Questions

- In listing the dinner salads, does it matter in what order you list the items? No
- If you list possible combinations of digits for area codes, does it matter in what order you list the digits? Yes

Chalkboard Examples

1. Margaret has three pairs of shoes, four skirts, and five blouses. How many different outfits can she assemble?
   There are three ways to choose the shoes, four ways to choose a skirt, and five ways to choose a blouse. There are $3 \cdot 4 \cdot 5 = 60$ ways to choose an outfit.
2. A license plate for a particular state has three letters followed by three numbers. How many different license plates are possible?
   For each of the three letters, there are 26 possible outcomes. For each of the three numbers, there are 10 possible outcomes. Using the fundamental counting principle, the number of possible outcomes is $26 \cdot 26 \cdot 26 \cdot 10 \cdot 10 \cdot 10 = 17{,}576{,}000$.

15-1 Counting Problems and Permutations

The Fundamental Counting Principle

Objective: Determine the number of ways a compound event may occur.

Many problems are concerned with the number of ways a set of objects can be arranged, combined, or chosen, or the number of ways a succession of events can occur. The study of such problems is called combinatorics.

EXAMPLE 1

A restaurant offers a dinner salad for $3.75. There is a choice of a lettuce salad or a spinach salad. Then there is a choice of one topping from mushrooms, beans, or cheese. Finally, there is a choice of dressing from ranchstyle or oil and vinegar. How many different salad combinations are possible?

The possibilities are illustrated by this tree diagram.

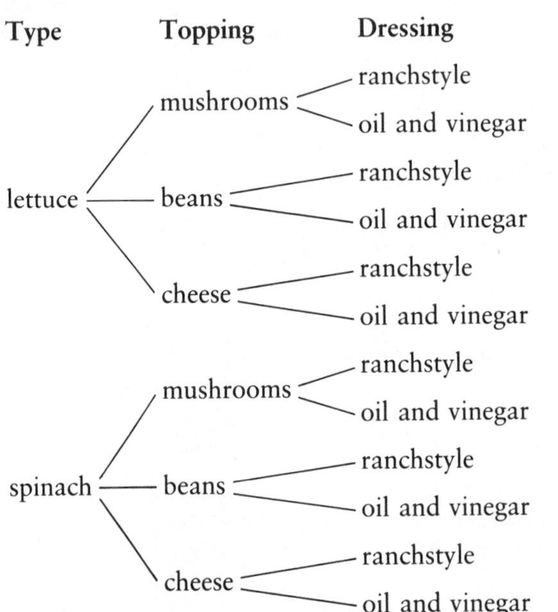

Combination

1 lettuce, mushrooms, ranchstyle
2 lettuce, mushrooms, oil and vinegar
3 lettuce, beans, ranchstyle
4 lettuce, beans, oil and vinegar
5 lettuce, cheese, ranchstyle
6 lettuce, cheese, oil and vinegar
7 spinach, mushrooms, ranchstyle
8 spinach, mushrooms, oil and vinegar
9 spinach, beans, ranchstyle
10 spinach, beans, oil and vinegar
11 spinach, cheese, ranchstyle
12 spinach, cheese, oil and vinegar

There are 12 possible salad combinations.

In situations where we consider combinations of items, or a succession of events such as flips of a coin or the drawing of cards, each result is called an outcome. An event is a subset of outcomes. When several events occur together, such as choosing a card followed by choosing another card, we have a compound event.

Theorem 15-1

The Fundamental Counting Principle

In a compound event in which the first event may occur in n_1 different ways, the second event may occur in n_2 different ways and so on, and the k-th event may occur in n_k different ways, the total number of ways the compound event may occur is

$$n_1 \cdot n_2 \cdot n_3 \cdot \ldots \cdot n_k$$

For Example 1, there were $2 \cdot 3 \cdot 2 = 12$ salad combinations.

Try This

a. Jani can choose from gray or blue jeans, a navy, white, green, or striped shirt, and running shoes, boots, or penny loafers. How many outfits can she form? 24

b. A restaurant offers four sizes of pizza, two types of crust, and eight toppings. How many possible combinations of pizza with one topping are there? 64

Permutations

Objective: Find the total number of permutations of a set of n objects.

Consider a set of 3 objects, $\{A, B, C\}$. How many ways are there to arrange these objects? We can select any of the objects to be first, so there are 3 choices for the first object. Once the first object has been selected, there are 2 choices for the second object. The third object is then already determined, since it is the only one remaining. Thus there is 1 choice for the third object. By the fundamental counting principle, there are $3 \cdot 2 \cdot 1$ possible arrangements. The set of all of the arrangements is $\{ABC, ACB, BAC, BCA, CAB, CBA\}$.

We can generalize this to a set of n objects. We have n choices for the first selection, $n - 1$ for the second, $n - 2$ for the third, and so on. For the n-th selection, there is only one choice.

Definition

A **permutation** of a set of n objects is an ordered arrangement of the objects.

The number of permutations of a set of n objects taken n at a time is denoted ${}_nP_n$.

Theorem 15-2

The total number of permutations of a set of n objects is given by ${}_nP_n = n(n - 1) \cdot (n - 2) \cdot \ldots \cdot 3 \cdot 2 \cdot 1$.

Permutations

Emphasize that a permutation applies when order is important.

Chalkboard Examples

1. In how many different ways can Anne, Bob, Carmine, and Della be arranged in a line?
   There are four choices for the first position. There are three remaining choices for the second position. There are two remaining choices for the third position. There is one remaining choice for the last position. By the fundamental counting principle, there are $4 \cdot 3 \cdot 2 \cdot 1 = 24$ possible choices.

Find the following.

2. ${}_1P_1$
   1
3. ${}_8P_8$
   $8 \cdot 7 \cdot 6 \cdot 5 \cdot 4 \cdot 3 \cdot 2 \cdot 1 = 40{,}320$
4. In how many different ways can six circus elephants be arranged in a line?
   ${}_6P_6 = 6 \cdot 5 \cdot 4 \cdot 3 \cdot 2 \cdot 1 = 720$

Factorial Notation

Point out that factorials are defined only for the nonnegative integers.

Key Question

- How many ways are there to order no things? 1
  This is a basis for defining 0! as 1.

Chalkboard Examples

1. Find 5!.
   5! = 120
2. Rewrite 12! with a factor of 10!.
   $12! = 12 \cdot 11 \cdot 10!$

EXAMPLES Find the following.

2. ${}_4P_4 = 4 \cdot 3 \cdot 2 \cdot 1 = 24$

3. ${}_7P_7 = 7 \cdot 6 \cdot 5 \cdot 4 \cdot 3 \cdot 2 \cdot 1 = 5040$

Try This Evaluate.

c. ${}_3P_3$ 6

d. ${}_5P_5$ 120

e. ${}_6P_6$ 720

EXAMPLE 4 How many ways can 5 paintings be lined up on a wall?

Since this is an arrangement of objects, we use Theorem 15-2. There are ${}_5P_5$ ways.

$${}_5P_5 = 5 \cdot 4 \cdot 3 \cdot 2 \cdot 1 = 120$$

Try This

f. In how many ways can 6 people line up at a ticket window? 720

Factorial Notation

Objective: Evaluate factorial notation.

For the product $5 \cdot 4 \cdot 3 \cdot 2 \cdot 1$, we write 5!, read "5 factorial."

Definition

***n* factorial** or ***n*!** $= n(n - 1)(n - 2) \cdot \ldots \cdot 3 \cdot 2 \cdot 1$

EXAMPLES

5. $7! = 7 \cdot 6 \cdot 5 \cdot 4 \cdot 3 \cdot 2 \cdot 1 = 5040$

6. $3! = 3 \cdot 2 \cdot 1 = 6$

7. $1! = 1$

By Theorem 15-2 and the definition of $n!$, the total number of permutations of a set of n objects, ${}_nP_n$, is given by $n!$. We also define 0! to be 1 so that certain formulas and theorems can be stated concisely.

Try This

g. Evaluate 9!. 362,880

h. Using factorial notation only, represent the number of permutations of 18 objects. 18!

Note the following.

$$\begin{aligned} 8! &= 8 \cdot 7 \cdot 6 \cdot 5 \cdot 4 \cdot 3 \cdot 2 \cdot 1 \\ &= 8 \cdot (7 \cdot 6 \cdot 5 \cdot 4 \cdot 3 \cdot 2 \cdot 1) \\ &= 8 \cdot 7! \end{aligned}$$

Theorem 15-3

For any natural number n,

$$n! = n(n - 1)!$$

By using Theorem 15-3 repeatedly, we can further manipulate factorial notation.

EXAMPLE 8 Rewrite 7! with a factor of 5!.

$$7! = 7 \cdot 6 \cdot 5!$$

Try This

i. Represent 10! in the form $n(n - 1)!$. $10 \cdot 9!$

j. Rewrite 11! with a factor of 8!. $11 \cdot 10 \cdot 9 \cdot 8!$

Permutations of *n* Objects Taken *r* at a Time

Objective: Find the number of permutations of n objects taken r at a time without replacement.

Consider a set of 7 objects. In how many ways can we construct an ordered subset having three members? We can select the first object in 7 ways. There are then 6 choices for the second and 5 choices for the third. By the fundamental counting principle, there are then $7 \cdot 6 \cdot 5$ ways to construct the subset. In other words, there are $7 \cdot 6 \cdot 5$ permutations of a set of 7 objects taken 3 at a time. Note that $7 \cdot 6 \cdot 5$ is equal to $\frac{7 \cdot 6 \cdot 5 \cdot 4!}{4!}$, or $\frac{7!}{4!}$. Generalizing gives us a theorem.

Theorem 15-4

The number of permutations of a set of n objects taken r at a time, denoted ${}_nP_r$, is given by

$${}_nP_r = \frac{n!}{(n - r)!}$$

Each permutation is an ordered arrangement of r objects taken from the set of n objects.

EXAMPLES Compute.

9. ${}_6P_4 = \frac{6!}{(6 - 4)!}$ By Theorem 15-4

$= \frac{6!}{2!}$

$= \frac{6 \cdot 5 \cdot 4 \cdot 3 \cdot 2!}{2!}$ By Theorem 15-3

$= 6 \cdot 5 \cdot 4 \cdot 3 = 360$

Permutations of *n* Objects Taken *r* at a Time

Emphasize that Theorem 15-4 is a direct result of the fundamental counting theorem.

Key Questions

- In how many ways can one choose a card from a deck of 52 cards?
  52
- In how many ways can one choose a sequence of two cards from a full deck?
  $52 \cdot 51 = 2652$

Chalkboard Examples

Compute.

1. ${}_4P_2$
   $\frac{4!}{2!} = \frac{4 \cdot 3 \cdot 2!}{2!} = 4 \cdot 3 = 12$
2. ${}_7P_3$
   $\frac{7!}{4!} = 7 \cdot 6 \cdot 5 = 210$
3. In an Olympic event with five competitors, how many different orderings are there for the gold medal, silver medal, and bronze medal winners?
   ${}_5P_3 = 5 \cdot 4 \cdot 3 = 60$

LESSON QUIZ

1. In how many different ways can the four symbols *!@# be arranged? 24
2. Find $_4P_4$. 24
3. Compute $_5P_2$. 20
4. In how many ways can one write three letters on a tag, using each of the letters A, B, C, D, and E at most once? 60

Assignment Guide
Algebra: Omit

Alg w/Finite Math: 1–47 m3, 48, MR assign w. 15-2

Comprehensive: 1–47 m3, 48–51, MR assign w. 15-2

10. $_5P_2 = \frac{5!}{(5-2)!}$ By Theorem 15-4

$= \frac{5!}{3!}$

$= \frac{5 \cdot 4 \cdot 3!}{3!}$ By Theorem 15-3

$= 5 \cdot 4 = 20$

Try This Compute.

k. $_7P_3$ 210 **l.** $_{10}P_4$ 5040 **m.** $_8P_2$ 56 **n.** $_{11}P_5$ 55,440

EXAMPLE 11 In how many ways can letters of the set $\{R, S, T, U\}$ be arranged to form ordered codes of 2 letters? (No letters are repeated.)

$$_4P_2 = \frac{4!}{(4-2)!} = \frac{4 \cdot 3 \cdot 2!}{2!} = 12 \text{ ways}$$

The 12 arrangements are *RS, RT, RU, ST, SU, TU, SR, TR, UR, TS, US, UT*.

EXAMPLE 12 In how many ways can letters of the set $\{A, B, C, D, E, F, G\}$ be arranged to form ordered codes of **(a)** 7 letters? **(b)** 5 letters? **(c)** 2 letters?

(a) $_7P_7 = 7 \cdot 6 \cdot 5 \cdot 4 \cdot 3 \cdot 2 \cdot 1 = 5040$ ways

(b) $_7P_5 = 7 \cdot 6 \cdot 5 \cdot 4 \cdot 3 = 2520$ ways

(c) $_7P_2 = 7 \cdot 6 = 42$ ways

Try This

o. A teacher wants to write an ordered 6-question test from a pool of 10 questions. How many different forms of the test can the teacher write? 151,200

p. How many 7-digit numbers can be named, without repetition, using the digits 2, 3, 4, 5, 6, 7, and 8 if an even digit must come first? 2880

15-1 EXERCISES

A

Solve.

1. How many 4-letter code symbols can be formed with the letters *P, D, Q, X* without repetition? 24
2. How many 5-digit numbers can be formed using all the digits 0, 1, 2, 3, 4 without repetition? 120
3. In how many ways can 6 bicycles be parked in a row? 720
4. In how many ways can 7 different cards be laid out on a table in a row? 5040

5. A woman is going out for the evening. She will put on one of 6 dresses, one pair out of 8 pairs of shoes, and go to one of 7 restaurants. In how many ways can this be done? 336

6. A man is going out for the evening. He will put on one of 7 suits, one pair out of 4 pairs of shoes, and go to one of 10 restaurants. In how many ways can this be done? 280

Evaluate.

7. ${}_6P_6$ 720 8. ${}_5P_5$ 120 9. ${}_4P_4$ 24 10. ${}_2P_2$ 2

11. In how many ways can 7 people line up in a row? 5040

12. In how many ways can 8 motorcycles be parked in a row? 40,320

13. How many permutations are there of the letters in the set $\{R, S, T, U, V, W\}$? 720

14. How many permutations are there of the letters in the set $\{M, N, O, P, Q, R, S\}$? 5040

15. The owner of a business hires 8 secretaries, one for each of 8 department managers. How many different assignments of the secretaries are possible? 40,320

16. A fruit stand sells 9 different varieties of apples. How many different ways can the names of the apples be arranged on a sign? 362,880

Evaluate.

17. $5!$ 120 18. $6!$ 720 19. $1!$ 1 20. $0!$ 1

Represent each in the form $n(n - 1)!$.

21. $9!$ $9 \cdot 8!$ 22. $13!$ $13 \cdot 12!$ 23. $a!$ $a \cdot (a - 1)!$ 24. $m!$ $m \cdot (m - 1)!$

25. Rewrite $27!$ with a factor of $22!$. $27 \cdot 26 \cdot 25 \cdot 24 \cdot 23 \cdot 22!$

26. Rewrite $13!$ with a factor of $5!$. $13 \cdot 12 \cdot 11 \cdot 10 \cdot 9 \cdot 8 \cdot 7 \cdot 6 \cdot 5!$

Compute.

27. ${}_4P_3$ 28. ${}_7P_5$ 29. ${}_{10}P_7$ 30. ${}_{10}P_3$ 31. ${}_{20}P_2$ 32. ${}_{30}P_2$ 33. ${}_8P_3$ 34. ${}_7P_4$

35. In how many ways can the letters of the set $\{M, N, O, P, Q\}$ be arranged to form ordered codes of 4 letters? 3 letters? 120, 60

36. In how many ways can the letters of the set $\{P, D, Q, W, T, Z\}$ be arranged to form ordered codes of 3 letters? 5 letters? 120, 720

37. In how many ways can 4 people be assigned to 6 one-person offices? ${}_6P_4 = 360$

38. In how many ways can 3 people be assigned to 5 one-person offices? ${}_5P_3 = 60$

39. A special classroom has 8 sets of headphones for students who have difficulty hearing. How many possible combinations of students and headphones are there if 6 students in a class need to use headphones? 20,160

40. A special classroom has 10 sets of headphones for students who have difficulty hearing. How many possible combinations of students and headphones are there if 7 students in a class need to use headphones? 604,800

ADDITIONAL ANSWERS

Exercises

27. 24
28. 2520
29. 604,800
30. 720
31. 380
32. 870
33. 336
34. 840

48. When $n = 3$ we have $3! = 6 < 8 = 2^3$. For 4, we have $4! = 24 > 16 = 2^4$. From this point on, each additional factor on the left is larger than 2, while the new factors on the right are always two; hence the left side grows faster.
49. We can factor a 2 from each factor. There are n factors, thus $2^n[1 \cdot 2 \cdot 3 \cdot \cdots \cdot (n)] = 2^n n!$.
50. For $n > 1$, $n!$ will always contain a factor of 2, therefore it must be even.
51. For $n > 4$, $n!$ always contains a factor of 5 and 2, therefore $n!$ is divisible by 10, so it must end in a zero.

Mixed Review

52. $-6, -7$
53. $\pm 3, \pm 6i$
54. $\frac{5}{6}, \frac{6}{5}$
55. 100
56. 3.3
57. -98
58. 5.55
59. 1581
60. 42
61. 2132
62. ≈ 0.5
63. $\approx 8.34 \times 10^{15}$
64. $\approx \frac{4}{3}$
65. A: 31, B: 28; C: 27
66. a. $E = 1000 + 0.06g$
b. $1510

B

41. How many 7-digit telephone numbers can be formed, assuming that no digit is used more than once and the first digit is not 0? $9 \cdot 9 \cdot 8 \cdot 7 \cdot 6 \cdot 5 \cdot 4$, or 544,320

42. **a.** In how many ways can a penny, nickel, dime, quarter, and half dollar be arranged in a straight line? 120

b. Considering the coins and heads and tails, in how many ways can they be lined up? $2^5 \cdot 5! = 3840$

43. Use a calculator. Answers may vary.

a. What is the largest value of n for which the calculator will display $n!$ in standard notation? 11!

b. What is the largest value of n for which the calculator will find $n!$? $69! \approx 1.7 \times 10^{98}$

Solve for n.

44. ${}_nP_5 = 7 \cdot {}_nP_4$ 11

45. ${}_nP_4 = 8 \cdot {}_{n-1}P_3$ 8

46. ${}_nP_5 = 9 \cdot {}_{n-1}P_4$ 9

47. ${}_nP_4 = 8 \cdot {}_nP_3$ 11

48. ***Critical Thinking*** Give a convincing argument that $n! > 2^n$ for $n > 3$.

Challenge

49. Show that $2 \cdot 4 \cdot 6 \cdot \ldots \cdot (2n) = 2^n n!$.

50. Show that $n!$ is even for any $n > 1$.

51. Show that $n!$ ends in a zero for any $n > 4$.

Mixed Review

Solve. **52.** $x^3 + 20x^2 + 133x + 294 = 0$ **53.** $x^4 + 27x^2 = 324$

54. $30x^2 - 61x + 30 = 0$

For an arithmetic sequence find **55.** a_{50} when $a_{17} = 1$ and $d = 3$.

56. d when $a_3 = 0$ and $a_{13} = 33$. **57.** a_{17} when $a_{50} = 1$ and $d = 3$.

58. d when $a_{515} = 222$ and $a_{555} = 444$.

Find the sum. **59.** $\sum_{n=3}^{33} (3n - 3)$ **60.** $\sum_{n=2}^{22} (2n - 22)$ **61.** $\sum_{n=4}^{44} (4n - 44)$

62. $\sum_{n=2}^{22} \left(\frac{1}{2}\right)^n$ **63.** $\sum_{n=3}^{33} 3^n$ **64.** $\sum_{n=4}^{44} \left(\frac{1}{4}\right)^{n-4}$

65. Three assemblers, A, B, and C, can produce 86 circuit boards per hour. A and B together can produce 59 circuit boards per hour, while A and C together can produce 58 circuit boards per hour. How many circuit boards can each assembler produce in an hour?

66. Thanh Nguyen is a salesman who earns a salary plus commission. In a week when his gross sales are $5000, he earns $1300. In a week when his gross sales are $7500, he earns $1450.

a. Fit a linear function to the data points.

b. Use the function to find his earnings on gross sales of $8500.

15-2 Permutations for Special Counts

Repeated Use of the Same Object

Objective: Find the number of permutations of n objects taken r at a time with replacement.

For an arrangement of objects to be a permutation, we cannot repeat any of the objects. In some situations, it is possible to use an object more than once.

Theorem 15-5

The number of orderings of n objects taken r at a time, with repetition, is n^r.

EXAMPLE 1 How many 5-letter ordered codes can be formed with the letters A, B, C, and D if we allow repeated use of the same letter?

We can select the first letter in 4 ways, the second in 4 ways, and so on. Thus there are 4^5, or 1024 orderings.

Try This

a. How many 5-letter ordered codes can be formed by repeated use of the letters of the alphabet? Find an expression. Do not evaluate. 26^5

EXAMPLE 2 A standard deck of cards has 52 different cards. How many 3-card ordered arrangements can be made by selecting the 3 cards **(a)** without replacement? **(b)** with replacement?

(a) The case 'without replacement' is the number of permutations of 52 objects taken 3 at a time.

$${}_{52}P_3 = 52 \cdot 51 \cdot 50 = 132{,}600 \quad \text{By Theorem 15-4}$$

(b) The case 'with replacement' is the number of arrangements of 52 objects taken 3 at a time, with repetition.

$$52 \cdot 52 \cdot 52 = 52^3 = 140{,}608 \quad \text{By Theorem 15-5}$$

Thus there are 132,600 possible ordered arrangements without replacement, and 140,608 with replacement.

15-2

FIRST FIVE MINUTES

1. Find the number of ways that five people can finish a 500-meter run in first through fifth place, with no ties.
   $5 \cdot 4 \cdot 3 \cdot 2 \cdot 1 = 120$
2. Find 6!.
   $6 \cdot 5 \cdot 4 \cdot 3 \cdot 2 \cdot 1 = 720$

Repeated Use of the Same Object

Key Questions

- If you select 52 cards from a deck of 52, replacing the card after each selection, how many possibilities are there for the 52nd card?
  52
- If you select 52 cards without replacement, how many possibilities are there for the 52nd card?
  1

Chalkboard Examples

1. Glenda has forgotten Kelly's phone number, but she remembers that each of the seven digits is either a 7 or an 8. How many phone numbers are possibilities?
   $2^7 = 128$
   There are 128 possible numbers. (126 if we eliminate all 7's and all 8's)
2. In how many different ways can a sequence of 4 cards be dealt from a full deck of 52 cards, without replacement?
   $52 \cdot 51 \cdot 50 \cdot 49 = 6{,}497{,}400$
3. In how many different ways can a sequence of 4 cards be dealt from a full deck of 52 cards, with replacement after each card is drawn?
   $52 \cdot 52 \cdot 52 \cdot 52 = 7{,}311{,}616$

Permutations with Identical Objects

Point out that Theorem 15-6 can be used regardless of whether any of the objects are identical. For example, the number of permutations, P, of the letters ABCD is $\frac{4!}{1!\,1!\,1!\,1!} = 4!$.

Key Questions

- How many permutations of letters of the word DAD are there?
  $\frac{3!}{2!} = 3$
- How many permutations of letters of the word Dad are there?
  $3! = 6$
- Which word has more permutations of its letters, HAWAII or OREGON?
  OREGON

Chalkboard Examples

1. Find the number of permutations of the word ENTREPRENEUR.
   There are 12 letters involved with 4 E's, 3 R's, 2 N's. By Theorem 15-6, $\frac{12!}{4!\,3!\,2!} = 1{,}663{,}200$.
2. Find the number of permutations of the word ASSESSES.
   There are 8 letters involved with 1 A, 5 S's, and 2 E's. By Theorem 15-6, $\frac{8!}{1!5!2!} = 168$.

Try This

b. How many 2-card ordered arrangements can be made by selecting 2 cards from a deck of 52
 (1) without replacement? 2652
 (2) with replacement? 2704

Permutations with Identical Objects

Objective: Find permutations of a set of objects that are not all different.

Consider the letters of the word HOOT. If the two O's were somehow different from each other, then the number of permutations of the four letters would be ${}_4P_4 = 4! = 24$. However, we cannot distinguish between the two O's.

There are only 12 permutations.
HOOT, HOTO, HTOO, TOOH, TOHO, THOO,
OTOH, OHOT, OHTO, OTHO, OOTH, OOHT

If the O's had been different, say Oo, there would have been 2! permutations of Oo (Oo and oO). If P is the number of permutations of the letters in HOOT, $P \cdot 2! = 4!$.

Hence, we have $P = \frac{4!}{2!} = 12$.

This method generalizes to the following theorem.

Theorem 15-6

The number of permutations, P, of n objects taken n at a time, with r objects alike, s of another kind alike, t of another kind alike, is

$$P = \frac{n!}{r!\,s!\,t!}$$

EXAMPLE 3 Find the number of permutations of the letters in DADDA.

There are five letters, including two A's and three D's. Thus, by Theorem 15-6 we have

$$\begin{aligned} P &= \frac{5!}{3!\,2!} \\ &= \frac{5\cdot4\cdot3\cdot2\cdot1}{3\cdot2\cdot1\cdot2\cdot1} \\ &= 10 \end{aligned}$$

There are 10 permutations.

Try This

c. Find the number of permutations of the letters of the word BANANAS. 420

d. In how many ways can the product $a^2b^3c^2$ be written without using exponents? 210

Circular Permutations

Objective: Find circular permutations.

Consider the problem of seating four diplomats, X, Y, Z, and W, around a circular table. We cannot distinguish among these four arrangements.

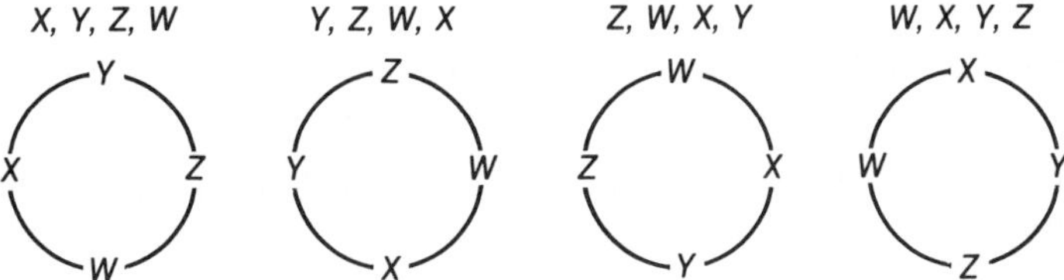

One way to think about the problem of circular permutations is to "fix" one of the objects and then consider how the other objects are arranged with respect to the "fixed" object. In the case of the four diplomats, suppose we fix diplomat X as shown. Then we arrange the three other diplomats.

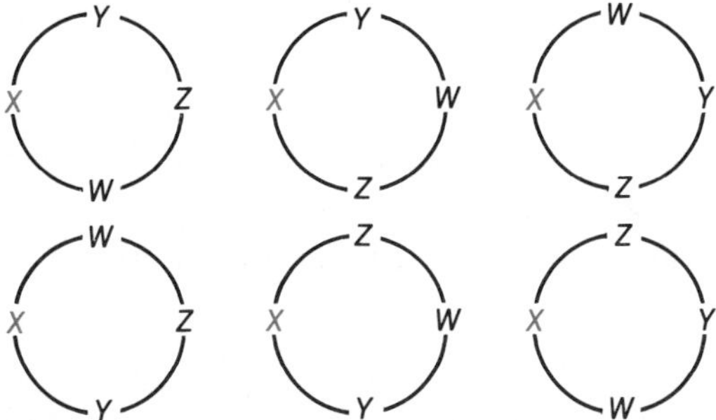

There are 6 circular permutations for the diplomats. Note that there were 4 permutations for the 4 diplomats that were indistinguishable (n permutations). This suggests the following theorem.

Theorem 15-7

The number of circular permutations of n objects is $\frac{n!}{n}$, or $(n - 1)!$.

EXAMPLE 4 Find the number of circular permutations of six people.

$$(n - 1)! = (6 - 1)! = 5! = 120$$

There are 120 circular permutations.

Try This

e. In how many ways can King Arthur arrange 8 knights around the Round Table? 5040

Circular Permutations

Chalkboard Example

1. Find the number of permutations of five people around a table.
$(5 - 1)! = 4! = 24$

LESSON QUIZ

1. In how many ways can one write three letters on a tag, using each of the letters A, B, C, D, and E zero or more times?
125
2. Find the number of permutations of the letters of the word MAMMAL.
$\frac{6!}{3!\,2!} = 60$
3. Find the number of circular permutations of seven persons around a table.
$(7 - 1)! = 720$

Assignment Guide
Algebra: Omit

Alg w/Finite Math: 1–28 m3, 29, MR assign w. 15-1

Comprehensive: 1–28 m3, 29, 30–35 e/o, MR assign w. 15-1

15-2 EXERCISES

A

1. How many 4-number license plates can be made using the digits 0, 1, 2, 3, 4, 5 if repetitions are allowed? not allowed? 1296; 360
2. How many 5-number license plates can be made using the digits 1, 2, 3, 4, 5, 6, 7 if repetitions are allowed? not allowed? 16,807; 2520
3. A teacher wants to write an ordered 4-question test from a pool of 12 questions. How many different forms of the test can the teacher write? 11,880
4. A teacher wants to write an ordered 5-question test from a pool of 8 questions. How many different forms of the test can the teacher write? 6720
5. How many 4-number license plates can be made using the digits 0, 1, 2, 3, 4, 5 if an even digit must come first and repetitions are allowed? not allowed? 648; 180
6. How many 5-number license plates can be made using the digits 1, 2, 3, 4, 5, 6, 7 if an odd digit must come first and repetitions are allowed? not allowed? 9604; 1440
7. Suppose in Exercise 1 the license number must be even. Solve. 648; 180
8. Suppose in Exercise 2 the license number must be odd. Solve. 9604; 1440
9. A state forms its license plates by first listing a two-digit number that corresponds to the county in which the owner lives, then listing a letter of the alphabet, and finally a number from 1 to 9999. How many such plates are possible if there are 80 counties? $80 \cdot 26 \cdot 9999 = 20{,}797{,}920$

Find the number of permutations of the letters of these words.

10. DEED 6
11. ABBA 6
12. COMMITTEE 45,360
13. MISSISSIPPI 34,650
14. CINCINNATI 50,400
15. SUBSTITUTE 151,200
16. SATELLITE 45,360
17. ICICLE 180
18. MASSACHUSETTS 64,864,800
19. In how many ways can four blue flags, three red flags, and two green flags be arranged on a staff? 1260
20. A player in a word game has the letters E, E, B, D, G, G, G. In how many ways can these letters be arranged? 420
21. Find the number of permutations of five people around a circular table. 24
22. Find the number of permutations of six numbers on a spinner. 120
23. Find the number of circular permutations of eight cheerleaders. 5040
24. In how many ways can the 10 swimmers on an aquatic ballet team be arranged in a circular pattern? 362,880

B

25. How many ordered codes can be formed using 4 of the letters of A, B, C, D, E if the letters
    a. are not repeated? 120
    b. can be repeated? 625
    c. are not repeated but must begin with D? 24
    d. are not repeated but must end with DE? 6

26. How many different numbers can be represented using the digits 1, 0, 0, 1, 5, 5, 6, 6, 6? 7560

27. How many five-digit integers can be represented when 2, 6, and 7 may be used once and 0 may be used twice? 36

28. How many even five-digit integers can be represented when 1, 3, and 5 may be used once and 6 may be used twice? 24

29. ***Critical Thinking*** Provide an argument that the two following forms for the number of permutations for n objects taken r at a time are equivalent.

$$n \cdot (n-1) \cdot (n-2) \cdot \ldots \cdot (n-r+1) \text{ and } \frac{n!}{(n-r)!}$$

Challenge

30. Find the number of permutations of five keys on a ring if two keys are identical. 12

31. In how many ways can King Arthur seat himself and eight knights, including Sir Lancelot, around the Round Table when Lancelot sits directly to the left of King Arthur? 5040

For each problem, express your answer in terms of n.

32. In a sports tournament consisting of n teams, a team is eliminated when it loses one game. How many games are required to complete the tournament? $n - 1$

33. In a softball tournament consisting of n teams, a team is eliminated when it loses two games. At most, how many games are required to complete the tournament? $2n - 1$

34. In how many ways can a 9-player baseball lineup be made if the pitcher always bats last, the shortstop always bats 6th or 7th, and the left fielder always bats 1st, 2nd, or 8th? $1 \cdot 2 \cdot 3 \cdot 6! = 4320$

35. Show that ${}_nP_r = n(n-1)(n-2)\cdots(n-r+1)$.

$${}_nP_r = \frac{n!}{(n-r)!} = \frac{n(n-1)(n-2)\ldots(n-r+1)(n-r)!}{(n-r)!} = n(n-1)(n-2)\ldots(n-r+1)$$

Mixed Review

Let $P(x) = x^4 + 2x^3 - 13x^2 - 14x + 24$.

36. Determine whether $-1, -2, -3$, and i are roots of $P(x)$.

37. Determine whether $(x+1)$, $(x+2)$, and $(x+4)$ are factors of $P(x)$.

38. Find $P(5)$, $P(0)$, $P(-4)$, $P(-5)$.

39. Factor $P(x)$, solve $P(x) = 0$, and graph $P(x)$.

Find the sum of the following series. **40.** $8 + 4 + 2 + \cdots$ **41.** $\frac{1}{2} + \frac{1}{4} + \frac{1}{8} + \cdots$

Insert three geometric means between **42.** 3 and 243. **43.** x^2 and x^4.

44. Find the dimensions of a rectangle with area 192 cm^2 and perimeter 56 cm.

ADDITIONAL ANSWERS

Exercises

29. Multiply the left side of the equation by $(n - r)!$: $n \cdot (n-1) \cdot \ldots \cdot (n-r+1) \cdot (n-r)! = n!$
Multiply the right side of the equation by $(n-r)!$: $\frac{n!}{(n-r)!} \cdot (n-r)! = n!$
If $ac = bc$ and $a, b, c \neq 0$, then $a = b$, so the two forms are equivalent.

Mixed Review

36. No, yes, no, no
37. No, yes, yes
38. $P(5) = 504$; $P(0) = 24$; $P(-4) = 0$; $P(-5) = 144$
39. $P(x) = (x-1)(x+2)(x-3)(x+4)$
1, −2, 3, −4

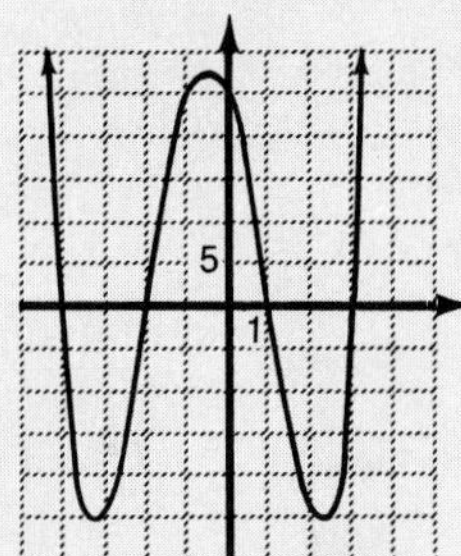

40. 16
41. 1
42. 9, 27, 81
43. $x^{5/2}$, x^3, $x^{7/2}$
44. 16 cm, 12 cm

15-3

FIRST FIVE MINUTES

1. Compute.
$\frac{5!}{3!2!}$
10
2. Find the number of permutations of the letters in the word TENNESSEE.
$\frac{9!}{4!\,2!\,2!} = 3780$
3. Find the number of ways to seat five people around a circular table.
$(5 - 1)! = 24$

Emphasize that permutations are concerned with order, whereas combinations are concerned with selection.

You should point out that the symbol $\binom{n}{r}$ is sometimes written ${}_nC_r$ and is read "combination n r."

You may wish to illustrate the following.

$\binom{n}{n} = \binom{n}{0} = 1$ and $\frac{n!}{n!0!} = \frac{n!}{n!} = 1$

$\binom{n}{1} = \binom{n}{n-1} = n$ and

$\frac{n!}{(n-1)!\,1!} = \frac{n!}{(n-1)!} = \frac{n(n-1)!}{(n-1)!} = n$

Key Questions

- Does the set $\{a, b, c\}$ have more combinations of three elements or more permutations of three elements?
More permutations
- How many combinations are there of the set $\{a, b, c, d, e, f\}$ taken six at a time?
One

Chalkboard Examples

1. How many combinations are there of the set $\{A, B, C, D\}$ taken two at a time?
The combinations are six subsets.
$\{A, B\}, \{A, C\}, \{A, D\}, \{B, C\}, \{B, D\}, \{C, D\}$

Simplify.

2. $\binom{4}{0}$ $\frac{4!}{0!4!} = \frac{4!}{1 \cdot 4!} = 1$
3. $\binom{6}{2}$ $\frac{6!}{2!4!} = 15$

15-3 Combinations

Objective: Find the number of combinations of a set of n objects taken r at a time.

Permutations of a set are arrangements of the elements of the set. Often we are concerned only with the number of ways we can select elements from a set. These are combinations.

EXAMPLE 1 How many combinations are there of the set $\{A, B, C, D\}$ taken 3 at a time?

The combinations are the following subsets.

$$\{A, B, C\} \quad \{B, C, D\} \quad \{A, C, D\} \quad \{A, B, D\}$$

Note that the set $\{A, B, C\}$ is the same as the set $\{B, A, C\}$, since they contain the same objects.

Try This

a. Consider the set $\{A, B, C, D\}$. How many combinations are there taken

(1) 4 at a time? 1 **(2)** 3 at a time? 4 **(3)** 2 at a time? 6
(4) 1 at a time? 4 **(5)** 0 at a time? 1

Let us use the symbol $\binom{n}{r}$ to denote the number of ways we can select r elements from a set containing n elements. We read the symbol $\binom{n}{r}$ as "n choose r."

Consider the problem of finding the number of permutations of n objects taken r at a time, ${}_nP_r$. We can think of this process in two steps.

1. We *select* the r objects. 2. We *arrange* the r objects.

We can select the r objects from the n objects in $\binom{n}{r}$ ways. Then we can arrange the r objects in $r!$ ways. Thus by the fundamental counting principle we can select and then arrange in $\binom{n}{r} \cdot r!$ ways.

This means $\binom{n}{r} \cdot r! = {}_nP_r$. But we know ${}_nP_r = \frac{n!}{(n-r)!}$. Thus we now have

$\binom{n}{r} \cdot r! = \frac{n!}{(n-r)!}$, which implies $\binom{n}{r} = \frac{n!}{r!\,(n-r)!}$.

Theorem 15-8

The number of combinations of a set of n objects taken r at a time is

$$\binom{n}{r} = \frac{n!}{r!(n-r)!}$$

EXAMPLES Simplify.

2. $\binom{5}{2} = \frac{5!}{2!(5-2)!}$ By definition of $\binom{5}{2}$

$= \frac{5!}{2!3!}$

$= \frac{5 \cdot 4 \cdot 3!}{2!3!}$ By Theorem 15-3

$= 10$

3. $\binom{7}{4} = \frac{7!}{4!(7-4)!} = \frac{7!}{4!3!} = \frac{7 \cdot 6 \cdot 5 \cdot 4!}{3!4!} = \frac{7 \cdot 6 \cdot 5}{3 \cdot 2 \cdot 1} = 35$

4. $\binom{n}{3} = \frac{n!}{3!(n-3)!} = \frac{n(n-1)(n-2)(n-3)!}{3!(n-3)!} = \frac{n(n-1)(n-2)}{3!}$

Try This Simplify.

b. $\binom{10}{8}$ 45 **c.** $\binom{10}{2}$ 45 **d.** $\binom{n}{1}$ n

---

EXAMPLE 5 For a sociological study 4 people are chosen at random from a group of 10 people. In how many ways can this be done?

No order is implied here, so the number of ways 4 people can be selected is $\binom{10}{4}$, by Theorem 15-8.

$$\binom{10}{4} = \frac{10!}{4!\,6!} = \frac{10 \cdot 9 \cdot 8 \cdot 7 \cdot 6!}{4!\,6!} = \frac{10 \cdot 9 \cdot 8 \cdot 7}{4 \cdot 3 \cdot 2 \cdot 1} = 210$$

EXAMPLE 6

How many ways can a congressional committee be formed from a set of 5 senators and 7 representatives if a committee contains 3 senators and 4 representatives?

The 3 senators can be selected in $\binom{5}{3}$ ways, the 4 senators in $\binom{7}{4}$ ways. Using the fundamental counting principle, $\binom{5}{3}\binom{7}{4} = 10 \cdot 35 = 350$.

Try This

e. In how many ways can a 5-player starting unit be selected from a 12-member basketball squad? 792

---

4. A class of 20 persons selects a different committee of three each week to take notes and distribute them to the rest of the class. In how many ways can a committee of three be chosen from 20 people?

$\binom{20}{3} = \frac{20!}{3!17!} = 1140$

5. How many committees can be formed from a class having 12 women and 8 men, if the committee must have 3 women and 2 men?

The 3 women can be chosen from 12 in $\binom{12}{3} = 220$ ways.

The 2 men can be chosen from the 8 in $\binom{8}{2} = 28$ ways. By the fundamental counting principle, there are $220 \cdot 28 = 6160$ ways to create the committee.

6. How many subsets, of all sizes, can be chosen from a set of size 5?

$\binom{5}{0} = 1$ subset of size 0

$\binom{5}{1} = 5$ subsets of size 1

$\binom{5}{2} = 10$ subsets of size 2

$\binom{5}{3} = 10$ subsets of size 3

$\binom{5}{4} = 5$ subsets of size 4

$\binom{5}{5} = 1$ subset of size 5

$1 + 5 + 10 + 10 + 5 + 1$
$= 32$ possible subsets

LESSON QUIZ

1. Evaluate $\binom{5}{3}$.
   10
2. Find the number of subsets of 5 elements in a set of 7 elements.
   $\binom{7}{5} = 21$
3. In how many ways can a committee of 3 be chosen from a group of 7 people?
   $\binom{7}{3} = 35$

Assignment Guide
Algebra: Omit

Alg w/Finite Math: 1–27 e/o, 28, MR

Comprehensive: 1–27 e/o, 28–30, MR

ADDITIONAL ANSWERS

Exercises

1. 126
2. 91
3. 1225
4. 9880
5. 495
6. 2002
7. $\frac{n(n-1)(n-2)}{6}$
8. $\frac{n(n-1)}{2}$

EXAMPLE 7

A hamburger restaurant advertises "We Fix Hamburgers 256 Ways!". This is accomplished using various combinations of catsup, onion, mustard, pickle, mayonnaise, relish, tomato, and lettuce. Of course, one can also have a plain hamburger. Use combination notation to show the number of possible hamburgers. Do not evaluate.

There are 8 basic seasonings. Each way of fixing a hamburger is a combination, or subset, of these toppings. There are $\binom{8}{0}$ subsets with 0 toppings, $\binom{8}{1}$ subsets with 1 topping, $\binom{8}{2}$ subsets with 2 toppings, and so on, up to $\binom{8}{8}$ subsets with 8 toppings. Thus the total number of combinations, or subsets, is given by the following expression.

$$\sum_{r=0}^{8} \binom{8}{r} = \binom{8}{0} + \binom{8}{1} + \binom{8}{2} + \cdots + \binom{8}{8}$$

Try This

f. Including cheese as a possibility, use combination notation to show the number of ways the restaurant could fix hamburgers. You do not need to evaluate your expression. $\binom{9}{0} + \binom{9}{1} + \binom{9}{2} + \cdots + \binom{9}{9}$ or 512

15-3 EXERCISES

A

Simplify.

1. $\binom{9}{5}$ **2.** $\binom{14}{2}$ **3.** $\binom{50}{2}$ **4.** $\binom{40}{3}$

5. $\binom{12}{8}$ **6.** $\binom{14}{9}$ **7.** $\binom{n}{3}$ **8.** $\binom{n}{2}$

9. There are 23 students in a club. How many ways can 4 officers be selected? 8855

10. On a test a student is to select 6 out of 10 questions, without regard to order. How many ways can this be done? 210

11. How many basketball games are played in a 9-team league if each team plays all other teams twice? 72

12. How many basketball games are played in a 10-team league if each team plays all other teams twice? 90

13. How many lines are determined by 8 points, no 3 of which are collinear? How many triangles are determined by the same points if no 4 are coplanar? 28, 56

14. How many lines are determined by 7 points, no 3 of which are collinear? How many triangles are determined by the same points if no 4 are coplanar? 21, 35

15. Of the first 10 questions on a test, a student must answer 7. Of the next 5 questions, 3 must be answered. In how many ways can this be done? 1200

16. Of the first 8 questions on a test, a student must answer 6. Of the next 4 questions, 3 must be answered. In how many ways can this be done? 112

17. Suppose the Senate of the United States consisted of 58 Democrats and 42 Republicans. How many committees consisting of 6 Democrats and 4 Republicans could be formed? You do not need to simplify the expression. $\binom{58}{6}\cdot\binom{42}{4}$

18. Suppose the Senate of the United States consisted of 63 Republicans and 37 Democrats. How many committees consisting of 12 Republicans and 8 Democrats could be formed? You need not simplify the expression. $\binom{63}{12}\cdot\binom{37}{8}$

B

19. There are 8 points on a circle. How many triangles can be inscribed with these points as vertices?

Simplify.

20. $\binom{n}{n-1}$ 21. $\binom{n}{n}$ 22. $\binom{n+1}{n}$ 23. $\binom{n+1}{n-1}$

Solve for n.

24. $\binom{n+1}{3} = 2\cdot\binom{n}{2}$ 25. $\binom{n}{n-2} = 6$

26. $\binom{n+2}{4} = 6\cdot\binom{n}{2}$ 27. $\binom{n}{3} = \binom{n-1}{1}\cdot\binom{n}{1}$

28. ***Critical Thinking*** Prove that for any natural numbers n and $r \leq n$,

$$\binom{n}{r} = \binom{n}{n-r}$$

Explain what this means in terms of combinations.

Challenge

29. How many line segments are determined by the n vertices of an n-gon? Of these, how many are diagonals?

30. For a wrestling exhibition, 2 wrestlers per weight class were chosen from each of the following: 5 wrestlers at 106 lb, 3 at 115 lb, 2 at 126, 6 at 137, 5 at 150, 8 at 163, 7 at 181, 3 at 198, 2 at 220, and 4 over 220 lb. In how many ways could the wrestlers be chosen?

Mixed Review

Let $A = \begin{bmatrix} 2 & 1 & 4 \\ 3 & 0 & 7 \\ 4 & 5 & 6 \end{bmatrix}$ $B = \begin{bmatrix} 1 & 1 & 1 \\ 1 & 2 & 2 \\ 2 & 1 & 0 \end{bmatrix}$

Find. 31. $3A + B$ 32. $|A|$ 33. $|B|$ 34. B^{-1} 35. BA 36. AB^{-1}

Find an equation for $f^{-1}(x)$. 37. $f(x) = x^{\frac{2}{3}}$ 38. $f(x) = 3^x$ 39. $f(x) = 3x + \frac{3}{2}$

Evaluate. 40. $|5 + 12i|$ 41. $|6 + 8i|$ 42. $|15 - 8i|$

Solve. 43. $|3x + 4| \leq 10$ 44. $|-8x + 9| < 1$

45. Find the dimensions of a rectangle with area 120 m² and perimeter 44 m.

19. 56
20. n
21. 1
22. $n + 1$
23. $\frac{(n+1)n}{2}$
24. 5
25. 4
26. 7
27. 8
28. $\binom{n}{r} = \frac{n!}{r!\,(n-r)!} = \frac{n!}{(n-r)!\,r!}$
$= \frac{n!}{(n-r)!\,[n-(n-r)]!} = \binom{n}{n-r}$
The number of combinations of a set of n objects taken r at a time is equal to the number of combinations of a set of n objects taken $n - r$ at a time.
29. $\frac{n(n-1)}{2}$; $\frac{n(n-3)}{2}$
30. 47,628,000 ways

Mixed Review

31. $\begin{bmatrix} 7 & 4 & 13 \\ 10 & 2 & 23 \\ 14 & 16 & 18 \end{bmatrix}$
32. 0
33. −1
34. $\begin{bmatrix} 2 & -1 & 0 \\ -4 & 2 & 1 \\ 3 & -1 & -1 \end{bmatrix}$
35. $\begin{bmatrix} 9 & 6 & 17 \\ 16 & 11 & 30 \\ 7 & 2 & 15 \end{bmatrix}$
36. $\begin{bmatrix} 12 & -4 & -3 \\ 27 & -10 & -7 \\ 6 & 0 & -1 \end{bmatrix}$
37. $f^{-1}(x) = x^{3/2}, x \geq 0$
38. $f^{-1}(x) = \log_3 x, x \geq 0$
39. $f^{-1}(x) = \frac{1}{3}x - \frac{1}{2}$
40. 13
41. 10
42. 17
43. $-\frac{14}{3} \leq x \leq 2$
44. $1 < x < \frac{5}{4}$
45. 12 m, 10 m

15-4

FIRST FIVE MINUTES

1. Compute $\binom{6}{2}$.
   15
2. In how many ways can a committee of 5 be chosen from 7 persons?
   $\binom{7}{5} = 21$

15-4 The Binomial Theorem

Consider the following expanded powers of $(a + b)^n$ where $a + b$ is any binomial. Look for patterns.

$$(a + b)^0 = 1$$
$$(a + b)^1 = a + b$$
$$(a + b)^2 = a^2 + 2ab + b^2$$
$$(a + b)^3 = a^3 + 3a^2b + 3ab^2 + b^3$$
$$(a + b)^4 = a^4 + 4a^3b + 6a^2b^2 + 4ab^3 + b^4$$
$$(a + b)^5 = a^5 + 5a^4b + 10a^3b^2 + 10a^2b^3 + 5ab^4 + b^5$$
$$\uparrow \quad \uparrow \quad \uparrow \quad \uparrow \quad \uparrow \quad \uparrow$$
$$\binom{5}{0}a^5b^0 + \binom{5}{1}a^4b^1 + \binom{5}{2}a^3b^2 + \binom{5}{3}a^2b^3 + \binom{5}{4}a^1b^4 + \binom{5}{5}a^0b^5$$

Note that each expansion is a polynomial. It is also a series, though not arithmetic or geometric. Notice these patterns.

1. In each term, the sum of the exponents is n.
2. The exponents of a start with n and decrease to 0. The exponents of b start with 0 and increase to n.
3. There is one more term than the degree of the polynomial. The expansion of $(a + b)^n$ has $n + 1$ terms.
4. The coefficients start with $\binom{n}{0}$ and go to $\binom{n}{n}$.

We generalize the expansion of a binomial raised to a whole number exponent as follows.

Theorem 15-9

The Binomial Theorem

For any binomial $(a + b)$ and any whole number n, $(a + b)^n =$

$$\binom{n}{0}a^n + \binom{n}{1}a^{n-1}b + \binom{n}{2}a^{n-2}b^2 + \cdots + \binom{n}{n-2}a^2b^{n-2} + \binom{n}{n-1}ab^{n-1} + \binom{n}{n}b^n.$$

The statement of Theorem 15-9 in sigma notation is as follows.

$$(a + b)^n = \sum_{r=0}^{n} \binom{n}{r}a^{n-r}b^r$$

Because of this theorem $\binom{n}{r}$ is called a binomial coefficient.

Finding the r-th Term

Objective: Find the r-th term of the binomial expansion of $(a + b)^n$.

Looking at the statement of the theorem we see that the $(r + 1)$-th term is $\binom{n}{r}a^{n-r}b^r$. That is, the 1st term is $\binom{n}{0}a^{n-0}b^0$, the 2nd term is $\binom{n}{1}a^{n-1}b^1$, the 3rd term is $\binom{n}{2}a^{n-2}b^2$, the 8th term is $\binom{n}{7}a^{n-7}b^7$, and so on.

EXAMPLE 1 Find the 7th term of $(4x - y^2)^9$.

We let $r = 6, n = 9, a = 4x$, and $b = -y^2$ in the formula $\binom{n}{r}a^{n-r}b^r$.

$$\binom{9}{6}(4x)^3(-y^2)^6 = \frac{9!}{6!3!}(4x)^3(-y^2)^6$$
$$= \frac{9 \cdot 8 \cdot 7}{3!}(64x^3y^{12})$$
$$= 5376x^3y^{12}$$

Try This

a. Find the 4th term of $(x - 3)^8$. $-1512x^5$

b. Find the 6th term of $(y^2 + 2)^{10}$. $8064y^{10}$

Binomial Expansion

Objective: Use the binomial theorem to expand powers of binomials.

EXAMPLE 2 Expand $(x^2 - 2y)^5$.

Note that $a = x^2, b = -2y$, and $n = 5$.

$$(x^2 - 2y)^5 = \binom{5}{0}(x^2)^5 + \binom{5}{1}(x^2)^4(-2y) + \binom{5}{2}(x^2)^3(-2y)^2 + \binom{5}{3}(x^2)^2(-2y)^3 +$$
$$\binom{5}{4}x^2(-2y)^4 + \binom{5}{5}(-2y)^5 \quad \text{Using Theorem 15-9}$$
$$= \frac{5!}{0!5!}x^{10} + \frac{5!}{1!4!}x^8(-2y) + \frac{5!}{2!3!}x^6(-2y)^2 +$$
$$\frac{5!}{3!2!}x^4(-2y)^3 + \frac{5!}{4!1!}x^2(-2y)^4 + \frac{5!}{5!0!}(-2y)^5$$
$$= x^{10} - 10x^8y + 40x^6y^2 - 80x^4y^3 + 80x^2y^4 - 32y^5$$

Try This Expand.

c. $(x^2 - 1)^5$ $x^{10} - 5x^8 + 10x^6 - 10x^4 + 5x^2 - 1$

d. $\left(2x + \frac{1}{y}\right)^4$ $16x^4 + 32\frac{x^3}{y} + 24\frac{x^2}{y^2} + 8\frac{x}{y^3} + \frac{1}{y^4}$

Finding the r-th Term

Ask students to find a formula for the r-th term rather than the $(r + 1)$-th term. By substituting $r - 1$ for r, they should obtain $\binom{n}{r-1}a^{n-(r-1)}b^{r-1}$.

Chalkboard Example

1. Find the fourth term of $(x + y)^5$.
   $\binom{5}{3}x^2y^3 = 10x^2y^3$

Binomial Expansion

Math Point

The binomial coefficients can be arranged in a triangular form.

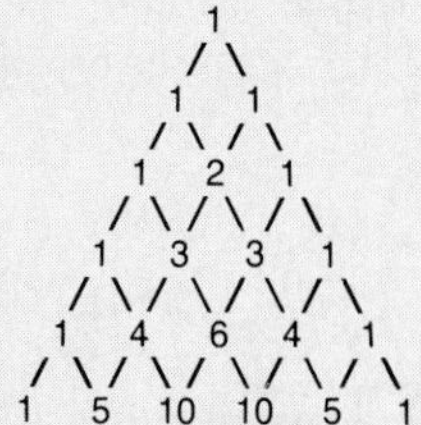

Each number is the sum of the one or two numbers above it in the triangle. This triangle is known as Pascal's Triangle, named after Blaise Pascal who investigated the properties of the triangle around 1650.

However, Chu Shih-Chieh, a Chinese mathematician, published extensive results on the triangle in 1303. It is believed that Omar Khayyam, a Persian mathematician and poet, also worked with the triangle around 1100.

Chalkboard Example

1. Expand $(x + y)^4$.
   $(x + y)^4$
   $= \binom{4}{0}x^4y^0 + \binom{4}{1}x^3y^1 + \binom{4}{2}x^2y^2$
   $+ \binom{4}{3}x^1y^3 + \binom{4}{4}x^0y^4$
   $= x^4 + 4x^3y + 6x^2y^2 + 4xy^3 + y^4$

Subsets

Some students might enjoy the following indirect proof of Theorem 15-10 using the fundamental counting principle.

Consider a subset of a set of n elements. Each element in the set is either in the subset or not in the subset. That is, for each of the n elements there are two possibilities. By the fundamental counting principle, there are 2^n possible choices.

Chalkboard Examples

1. How many subsets can be made from a set of 8 elements?
   $2^8 = 256$
2. If there are 10 different toppings for a pizza, how many different kinds of pizza can be made?
   $2^{10} = 1024$

LESSON QUIZ

1. Find the fifth term of the expansion of $(x + y)^6$.
   $\binom{6}{4}x^2y^4$
2. Expand $(a + b)^5$.
   $a^5 + 5a^4b + 10a^3b^2 + 10a^2b^3 + 5ab^4 + b^5$
3. Determine the number of subsets of a set of 6 objects.
   $2^6 = 64$

Assignment Guide
Algebra: Omit

Alg w/Finite Math: 1–22 e/o, 23, MR

Comprehensive: 1–22 e/o, 23, 24–28 e/o, MR

ADDITIONAL ANSWERS

Exercises

1. $15a^4b^2$
2. $21x^2y^5$
3. $-745{,}472a^3$
4. $3{,}897{,}234x^2$
5. $-1{,}959{,}552u^5v^{10}$
6. $30x\sqrt{x}, 30x\sqrt{3}$
7. $m^5 + 5m^4n + 10m^3n^2 + 10m^2n^3 + 5mn^4 + n^5$
8. $a^4 - 4a^3b + 6a^2b^2 - 4ab^3 + b^4$
9. $x^{10} - 15x^8y + 90x^6y^2 - 270x^4y^3 + 405x^2y^4 - 243y^5$

Subsets

Objective: Determine the number of subsets of a finite set.

Suppose a set has n objects. The number of subsets containing r members is $\binom{n}{r}$, by Theorem 15-8. The total number of subsets of a set is the number with 0 elements, plus the number with 1 element, plus the number with two elements, and so on. The total number of subsets of a set with n members is $\binom{n}{0} + \binom{n}{1} + \binom{n}{2} + \cdots + \binom{n}{n}$. Now let us expand $(1 + 1)^n$, $(1 + 1)^n = \binom{n}{0} + \binom{n}{1} + \binom{n}{2} + \cdots + \binom{n}{n}$. Thus the total number of subsets is $(1 + 1)^n$ or 2^n.

Theorem 15-10

The total number of subsets of a set with n members is 2^n.

EXAMPLES

3. How many subsets are in the set $\{A, B, C, D, E\}$?

   The set has 5 members, so the number of subsets is 2^5, or 32.

4. Show how a restaurant makes hamburgers 256 ways using 8 seasonings.

$$\binom{8}{0} + \binom{8}{1} + \cdots + \binom{8}{8} = 2^8 = 256$$

Try This

e. How many subsets are in the set of states of the United States? 2^{50}

f. In 10-pin bowling, how many possible pin combinations can remain after the first ball of a frame is thrown? 2^{10}

15-4 EXERCISES

A

Find the indicated term of the binomial expression.

1. 3rd, $(a + b)^6$ **2.** 6th, $(x + y)^7$

3. 12th, $(a - 2)^{14}$ **4.** 11th, $(x - 3)^{12}$

5. Middle, $(2u - 3v^2)^{10}$ **6.** Middle two, $(\sqrt{x} + \sqrt{3})^5$

Expand.

7. $(m + n)^5$ **8.** $(a - b)^4$ **9.** $(x^2 - 3y)^5$ **10.** $(3c - d)^6$

11. $(1 - 1)^n$ **12.** $(1 + 3)^n$ **13.** $(\sqrt{2} + 1)^6$ **14.** $(1 - \sqrt{2})^4$

Determine the number of subsets of each of the following sets.

15. A set of 7 members 128

16. A set of 6 members 64

17. A set of 26 letters 2^{26}

18. A set of 24 letters 2^{24}

B

19. Expand and simplify $(\sqrt{2} - i)^4$. $-7 - 4i\sqrt{2}$

20. Expand and simplify $(1 + i)^6$. $-8i$

21. Find a formula for $(a - b)^n$. Use sigma notation.

22. Expand and simplify $\frac{(x + h)^n - x^n}{h}$. Use sigma notation.

23. *Critical Thinking* In the expansion of $(x + y)^3$, explain in terms of combinatorics, why the coefficient for x^2y is the number of combinations of 3 things taken 1 at a time.

Challenge

Solve for x.

24. $\sum_{r=0}^{8} \binom{8}{r} x^{8-r} 3^r = 0$ -3

25. $\sum_{r=0}^{4} \binom{4}{r} 5^{4-r} x^r = 64$ $-5 \pm \sqrt{8}$

26. $\sum_{r=0}^{5} \binom{5}{r} (-1)^r x^{5-r} 3^r = 32$ 5

27. Show that $\binom{n}{r} = \binom{n-1}{r-1} + \binom{n-1}{r}$.

28. Use Exercise 27 and the principle of mathematical induction to prove Theorem 15-9. See Teacher's Answer Section.

Mixed Review

Let $P(x) = x^4 - 8x^3 + 24x^2 - 32x + 16$.

29. List all the possible rational roots of $P(x)$.

30. Solve $P(x) = 0$.

31. Find $P(-3)$, $P(-1)$, $P(0)$, $P(2)$, $P(30)$.

32. Graph $P(x)$.

Simplify. **33.** $\frac{1}{2 + 2i}$ **34.** $(x - 2i)^{-1} - \frac{2i}{x^2 + 4}$

Evaluate. **35.** ${}_{10}P_{10}$ **36.** ${}_{69}P_{69}$

37. Atiba is planning to invest \$12,000, part at 15% and part at 9%. What is the most that he can invest at 9% in order to make at least \$1200 interest per year?

Problem for Programmers

Write a program to expand $(ax + by)^n$ for any integers a and b, and any positive integer n. Test your program using Exercises 7–14 in Lesson 15-4.

10. $729c^6 - 1458c^5d + 1215c^4d^2 - 540c^3d^3 + 135c^2d^4 - 18cd^5 + d^6$

11. $\binom{n}{0} - \binom{n}{1} + \binom{n}{2} - \binom{n}{3} + \cdots + \binom{n}{n}(-1)^n$

12. $\binom{n}{0} + \binom{n}{1}3 + \binom{n}{2}9 + \binom{n}{3}27 + \cdots + \binom{n}{n}3^n$

13. $99 + 70\sqrt{2}$

14. $17 - 12\sqrt{2}$

21. $\sum_{r=0}^{n} \binom{n}{r}(-1)^r a^{n-r}b^r$

22. $\sum_{r=1}^{n} \binom{n}{r} x^{n-r}h^{r-1}$

23. The product $(x + y)(x + y)(x + y)$ is $x^3 + x^2y + x^2y + x^2y + xy^2 + xy^2 + xy^2 + y^3$. There are 3 ways to select 1 term of the form x^2y.

27. $\binom{n-1}{r-1} + \binom{n-1}{r}$

$= \frac{(n-1)!}{(r-1)!(n-1-r+1)!} + \frac{(n-1)!}{r!(n-1-r)!}$

$= \frac{(n-1)!}{(r-1)!(n-r)!} + \frac{(n-1)!}{r!(n-r-1)!}$

$= \frac{(n-1)!(r) + (n-1)!(n-r)}{(r)!(n-r)!}$

$= \frac{(n-1)!(r+n-r)}{(r)!(n-r)!} = \frac{(n-1)!(n)}{r!(n-r)!}$

$= \frac{(n)!}{r!(n-r)!} = \binom{n}{r}$

Mixed Review

29. $\pm 16, \pm 8, \pm 4, \pm 2, \pm 1$

30. 2

31. $P(-3) = 625$; $P(-1) = 81$; $P(0) = 16$; $P(2) = 0$; $P(30) = 614{,}656$

32.

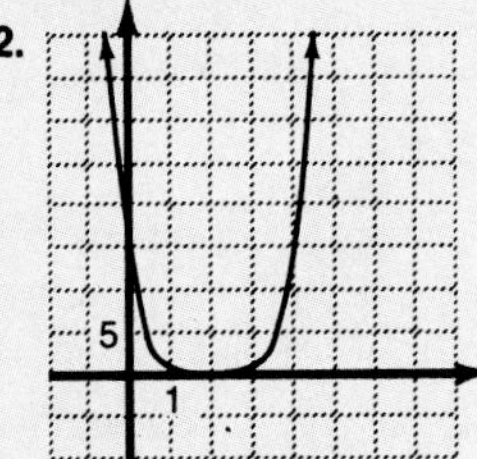

33. $\frac{1}{4} - \frac{i}{4}$

34. $\frac{x}{x^2 + 4}$

35. 3,628,800

36. 1.71×10^{98}

37. \$10,000

15-5

FIRST FIVE MINUTES

1. Find the fourth term of $(x + 2)^4$.
   $32x$
2. In how many different ways can a subset be chosen from a set of 7 people?
   $2^7 = 128$

A probability is a fraction. The numerator is the number of outcomes that lead to a particular event. The denominator is the total number of possible outcomes.

Explain that a fair die simply means that all of the six outcomes are equally likely.

For Try This (a), remind students that 1 is not prime.

Key Questions

- What is the probability of getting a 7 on the roll of a die?
  0
- What is the probability of getting a head or a tail in a coin flip?
  1
- If a pair of dice is rolled, is a 7 or a 12 more likely?
  7

Chalkboard Examples

1. What is the probability of rolling a 2 on a fair die?
   $P(2) = \frac{1}{6}$
2. What is the probability of rolling a 2 or higher?
   The event is the set of outcomes $E = \{2, 3, 4, 5, 6\}$.
   $P(E) = \frac{5}{6}$
3. What is the probability of drawing a red card from a deck of 52 cards?
   26 of the 52 cards are red.
   $P(\text{red}) = \frac{26}{52} = \frac{1}{2}$

15-5 Probability

Objective: Compute the probability of a simple event.

Suppose we perform an experiment such as flipping a coin, throwing a dart, drawing a card from a deck, or checking an item from an assembly line for quality. The result of an experiment is called an outcome. The set of all possible outcomes is called a sample space. An event is a set of outcomes, that is, a subset of the sample space. For example, for the experiment "throwing a dart" at a 3-colored dart board, the sample space is made up of the three outcomes, {red, yellow, blue}. When we throw a dart, an event may be to hit the yellow.

Definition

If an event E can occur m ways out of n possible equally likely outcomes of sample space S, the **probability** of that event is given by $P(E)$, where

$$P(E) = \frac{m}{n}$$

When the outcomes of an experiment all have the same probability of occurring, we say that they are *equally likely*.

A die is a cube with six faces, each containing a number of dots from 1 to 6.

EXAMPLES

1. What is the probability of rolling a 3 on a die?

On a fair die there are 6 equally likely outcomes and there is 1 way to get a 3. By the definition of probability, $P(3) = \frac{1}{6}$.

2. What is the probability of rolling an even number on a die?

The event $P(\text{even})$ can occur in 3 ways (getting a 2, 4, or 6). The number of possible outcomes is 6, so $P(\text{even}) = \frac{3}{6} = \frac{1}{2}$.

Try This

a. What is the probability of rolling a prime number on a die? $\frac{1}{2}$

EXAMPLE 3 What is the probability of drawing an ace from a deck of 52 cards?

An ace can be drawn in 4 ways. There are 52 equally likely outcomes (cards in the deck).

$$P\text{ (drawing an ace)} = \frac{4}{52}, \text{ or } \frac{1}{13}$$

Theorem 15-11

The probability of any event is a number from 0 to 1. If an event cannot occur its probability is 0. If an event is certain to occur its probability is 1.

EXAMPLE 4 Suppose 2 cards are drawn from a deck of 52 cards. What is the probability that both of them are spades?

13 of the 52 cards are spades, so the number m of ways of drawing 2 spades is $\binom{13}{2}$. The number of ways of drawing any two cards is $\binom{52}{2}$.

$$P(\text{getting 2 spades}) = \frac{m}{n} = \frac{\binom{13}{2}}{\binom{52}{2}} = \frac{78}{1326} = \frac{1}{17}$$

EXAMPLE 5 What is the probability of getting 8 on a roll of a pair of dice?

On each die there are 6 possible outcomes. There are $6 \cdot 6$, or 36, possible outcomes for the pair. There are 5 ways of getting a total of 8, (2, 6), (3, 5), (4, 4), (5, 3), and (6, 2). Thus the probability of getting an 8 is $\frac{5}{36}$.

Try This

b. Suppose 3 cards are drawn from a deck of 52 cards. What is the probability that all three of them are diamonds? $\frac{11}{850}$

c. What is the probability of getting a total of 7 on a roll of a pair of dice? $\frac{1}{6}$

15-5 EXERCISES

A

Suppose we draw a card from a deck of 52 cards. What is the probability of drawing

1. a heart? $\frac{1}{4}$ **2.** a queen? $\frac{1}{13}$ **3.** a 4? $\frac{1}{13}$ **4.** a club? $\frac{1}{4}$

5. a black card? $\frac{1}{2}$ **6.** a red card? $\frac{1}{2}$ **7.** a 9 or a king? $\frac{2}{13}$ **8.** an ace or a two? $\frac{2}{13}$

Suppose we select, without looking, one marble from a bag containing 4 red marbles and 10 green marbles. What is the probability of selecting

9. a red marble? $\frac{2}{7}$ **10.** a green marble? $\frac{5}{7}$ **11.** a purple marble? 0

Suppose 4 cards are drawn from a deck of 52 cards. What is the probability that

12. all 4 are spades? $\frac{11}{4165}$ **13.** all 4 are hearts? $\frac{11}{4165}$

14. What is the probability of getting a total of 6 on a roll of a pair of dice? $\frac{5}{36}$

15. What is the probability of getting a total of 3 on a roll of a pair of dice? $\frac{1}{18}$

4. Three cards are drawn from a deck of 52 cards. What is the probability that all three are red?
The outcomes are subsets of size 3. There are $\binom{52}{3} = 22100$ subsets of size 3. There are $\binom{26}{3} = 2600$ ways to choose 3 red cards from the 26 available red cards. The probability that all three cards are red is $\left(\frac{2600}{22100}\right) \approx 0.1176$.

5. What is the probability of getting a total of 3 when rolling two dice?
The outcomes in this situation are pairs of numbers. There are $6 \cdot 6 = 36$ possible outcomes. The pairs that sum to 3 are (1, 2) and (2, 1). $P(3) = \frac{2}{36} = \frac{1}{18}$.

LESSON QUIZ

1. What is the probability of drawing a red king from a deck of 52 cards?
$\frac{2}{52} = \frac{1}{26}$

2. What is the probability of rolling 4 or more on a fair die?
$\frac{3}{6} = \frac{1}{2}$

3. What is the probability of rolling a sum of exactly 11 with two dice?
$\frac{1}{18}$

Assignment Guide

Algebra: Omit

Alg w/Finite Math: 1–21 m3, 22, MR assign w. 15-6

Comprehensive: 1–21 m3, 22–24, MR assign w. 15-6

ADDITIONAL ANSWERS

Exercises

20. 2,598,960
21. a. $13 \cdot 48 = 624$
    b. $\frac{624}{2,598,960} = \frac{1}{4165}$
22. For any event, the event must either occur or not occur. Thus, $P(A) + P(\text{not } A) = 1$, so $P(A) = 1 - P(\text{not } A)$.

Mixed Review

25. Vertex: $(4, -3)$
    Line of symmetry: $x = 4$
    Focus: $(4, -2)$
    Directrix: $y = -4$
26. Vertex: $(4, -2)$
    Line of symmetry: $y = -2$
    Focus: $(8, -2)$
    Directrix: $x = 0$
27. 360360
28. 1680
29. 504
30. 462
31. \$2500

16. If 4 marbles are drawn at random all at once from a bag containing 8 white marbles and 6 black marbles, what is the probability that 2 will be white and 2 will be black? $\frac{60}{143}$
17. From a group of 8 men and 7 women, a committee of 4 is chosen. What is the probability that 2 men and 2 women will be chosen? $\frac{28}{65}$
18. From a bag containing 5 nickels, 8 dimes, and 7 quarters, 5 coins are drawn at random all at once. What is the probability of getting 2 nickels, 2 dimes, and 1 quarter? $\frac{245}{1938}$
19. From a bag containing 6 nickels, 10 dimes, and 4 quarters, 6 coins are drawn at random all at once. What is the probability of getting 3 nickels, 2 dimes, and 1 quarter? $\frac{30}{323}$

B

There are 52 colored balls in a large tumbler, 13 red, 13 blue, 13 yellow, and 13 green. The balls of each color are lettered A through M. Five balls are chosen at random.

20. How many 5-ball choices are there?
21. **a.** How many 5-ball choices consist of exactly four balls with the same letter?
    b. What is the probability of choosing exactly four balls with the same letter?
22. ***Critical Thinking*** Given that an event A either occurs (A) or does not occur (not A), give a convincing argument that $P(A) = 1 - P(\text{not } A)$.

Challenge

There are 52 colored balls in a large tumbler, 13 red, 13 blue, 13 yellow, and 13 green. The balls of each color are lettered A through M. Five balls are chosen at random.

23. **a.** How many 5-ball choices have two of the same letter and three other, different letters? $\binom{13}{1}\binom{4}{2}\binom{12}{3}\binom{4}{1}\binom{4}{1}\binom{4}{1} = 1,098,240$
    b. What is the probability of choosing two of the same letter and three other, different letters? 0.423
24. **a.** How many 5-ball choices have two of the same letter, two of a second letter and the fifth a different letter? $\binom{13}{2}\binom{4}{2}\binom{4}{2}\binom{11}{1}\binom{4}{1} = 123,552$
    b. What is the probability of choosing two of the same letter, two of a second letter, and the fifth a different letter? 0.048

Mixed Review

Find the vertex, line of symmetry, focus, and directrix. **25.** $4y = x^2 - 8x + 4$

26. $y^2 + 4y + 68 = 16x$

Compute. **27.** ${}_{15}P_5$ **28.** ${}_{8}P_4$ **29.** ${}_{9}P_3$ **30.** ${}_{22}P_2$

31. Mara has \$5000 to invest in two plans. Plan A earns 10%, and plan B earns 8%. What is the most she can invest at 8% in order to make at least \$450 per year?

15-6 Compound Probability

Since the sample space of an experiment is the set of all possible outcomes, it will be helpful to consider some basic ideas about sets. Suppose $A = \{a, b, c, d\}$ and $B = \{b, c, e, f, g\}$. One important set of elements is the set containing those elements common to both A and B. This set is called the intersection of A and B, is symbolized by $A \cap B$, and is read "A intersect B."

Thus for sets A and B, we have $A \cap B = \{b, c\}$.

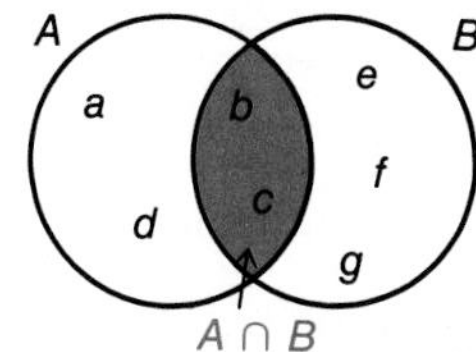

Another set that we can consider is the set of elements which belong to either A or B. This set is called the union of A and B and is symbolized by $A \cup B$, read "A union B."

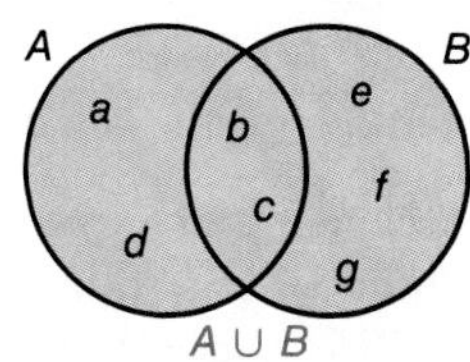

Adding Probabilities

Objective: Find the probability that one event or another will occur.

Consider again the experiment of rolling a die. The sample space for this experiment is $S = \{1, 2, 3, 4, 5, 6\}$. What is the probability of rolling a prime number **or** an odd number? These two events can be represented by the sets $A = \{2, 3, 5\}$ and $B = \{1, 3, 5\}$. The diagram below shows the relationship between these two sets.

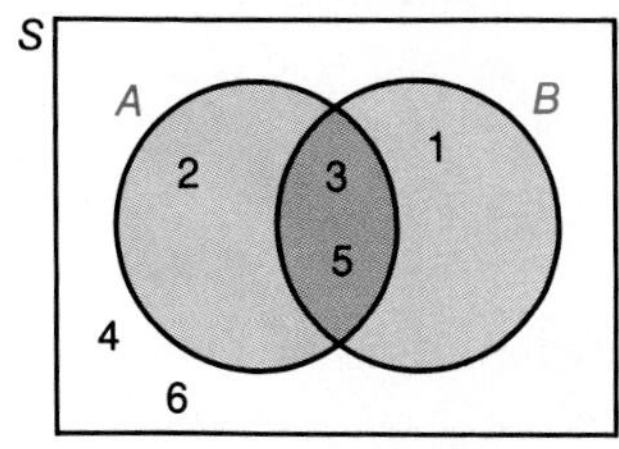

15-6

FIRST FIVE MINUTES

1. What is the probability of rolling 5 or less on a fair die?
   $\frac{5}{6}$
2. What is the probability of rolling a sum of 10 with two fair dice?
   The pairs that sum to 10 are (4, 6), (5, 5), (6, 4).
   $P(10) = \frac{3}{36} = \frac{1}{12}$

Adding Probabilities

In the discussion of Theorem 15-12, emphasize that simply adding the probabilities counts the intersection elements twice. One copy of the intersection must be subtracted to adjust for the double counting.

Key Questions

- What is the union of the sets {2, 0} and {2}?
  {2, 0}
- What is the intersection of the sets {2, 0} and {2}?
  {2}

Chalkboard Example

1. When rolling a die, what is the probability of rolling a number from 2 to 5, or rolling a number 4 or greater?
   Let A be the probability of rolling a 2, 3, 4, or 5.
   $P(A) = \frac{4}{6}$
   Let B be the probability of rolling a 4, 5, or 6.
   $P(B) = \frac{3}{6}$
   $P(A \cap B) = P(\{4, 5\}) = \frac{2}{6}$
   $P(A \cup B)$
   $= P(A) + P(B) - P(A \cap B)$
   $= \frac{4}{6} + \frac{3}{6} - \frac{2}{6} = \frac{5}{6}$

We know that $P(A) = \frac{3}{6}$ and $P(B) = \frac{3}{6}$. Thus it would seem reasonable to add the probabilities to find $P(A \cup B)$. However, the diagram shows that events A and B have something in common, namely, the outcomes 3 and 5. If we add the probabilities we would count the probabilities of these outcomes twice. To avoid this problem we can subtract $P(A \cap B)$. Thus $P(A \cup B) = P(A) + P(B) - P(A \cap B) = \frac{3}{6} + \frac{3}{6} - \frac{2}{6} = \frac{4}{6} = \frac{2}{3}$. Therefore, the probability of rolling a prime number **or** an odd number is $\frac{2}{3}$.

Theorem 15-12

If A and B are events from a sample space S, then

$$P(A \cup B) = P(A) + P(B) - P(A \cap B)$$

EXAMPLE 1 When rolling a die, what is the probability of rolling a prime number or an even number?

Let $A = \{2, 3, 5\}$ represent the event of rolling a prime number. Then $P(A) = \frac{3}{6}$.

Let $B = \{2, 4, 6\}$ represent the event of rolling an even number. Then $P(B) = \frac{3}{6}$.

$$A \cap B = \{2\}, \text{so } P(A \cap B) = \frac{1}{6}$$

$$P(A \cup B) = P(A) + P(B) - P(A \cap B) = \frac{3}{6} + \frac{3}{6} - \frac{1}{6} = \frac{5}{6}$$

The probability of rolling a prime number or an even number is $\frac{5}{6}$.

Two events which have no common elements are said to be mutually exclusive. In the one die experiment, rolling an even number and rolling an odd number are mutually exclusive events. If A and B are mutually exclusive then $P(A \cup B) = P(A) + P(B)$.

EXAMPLE 2 When rolling a die, what is the probability of rolling a number less than 3 or a number greater than 3?

Let $A = \{1, 2\}$ represent the event of rolling a number less than 3. Then $P(A) = \frac{2}{6}$.

Let $B = \{4, 5, 6\}$ represent the event of rolling a number greater than 3. Then $P(B) = \frac{3}{6}$.

$$A \cap B = \emptyset, \text{so } P(A \cap B) = 0$$

$$P(A \cup B) = P(A) + P(B) = \frac{2}{6} + \frac{3}{6} = \frac{5}{6}$$

The probability of rolling a number less than 3 or a number greater than 3 is $\frac{5}{6}$.

Try This

a. When rolling a die, what is the probability of rolling an even number or a divisor of 10? $\frac{5}{6}$

b. What is the probability of drawing an ace or a red card from a deck of cards? $\frac{7}{13}$

Multiplying Probabilities

Objective: Find the probability that one event and another event will occur.

Suppose a die and a coin are tossed. The sample space for this experiment is {(1, *H*), (1, *T*), (2, *H*), (2, *T*), (3, *H*), (3, *T*), (4, *H*), (4, *T*), (5, *H*), (5, *T*), (6, *H*), (6, *T*)}. The probability of any of these compound events occurring is the **compound probability.**

If A is the event that the die comes up 3, then $A = \{(3, H), (3, T)\}$. If B is the event that the coin lands heads, then $B = \{(1, H), (2, H)\ (3, H), (4, H), (5, H), (6, H)\}$. Notice that the events are not mutually exclusive, since $A \cap B = \{(3, H)\}$. We also note that event A occurring has no effect on event B occurring and vice versa. Such events are said to be **independent.**

What is $P(A \cap B)$? This is the same as asking what the probability is of tossing a 3 **and** a head. This corresponds to outcome (3, *H*). Since there are 12 possible outcomes we have $P(3, H) = \frac{1}{12}$. We can see that $P(A) = \frac{1}{2}$ and that $P(B) = \frac{1}{6}$. Notice also that $\left(\frac{1}{2}\right)\left(\frac{1}{6}\right) = \frac{1}{12}$. This suggests the following theorem.

Theorem 15-13

Two events A and B are independent if and only if
$$P(A \cap B) = P(A) \cdot P(B)$$

EXAMPLE 3

A bag contains three red marbles and five blue marbles. A marble is drawn and then replaced. A second marble is drawn. What is the probability that a blue marble will be drawn both times?

Let event A be that the first marble is blue and event B that the second marble is blue. Then we have $P(A) = \frac{5}{8}$ and $P(B) = \frac{5}{8}$. The events are independent, since replacing the marble means there is no effect on the second draw.

Thus we can apply Theorem 15-13.

$$P(A \cap B) = P(A) \cdot P(B) = \frac{5}{8} \cdot \frac{5}{8} = \frac{25}{64}$$

The probability of a blue marble being drawn both times is $\frac{25}{64}$.

Try This

c. A nickel and dime are tossed. What is the probability they both come up heads? $\frac{1}{4}$

d. One die has A, B, C, D, E, and F on its faces. Another die has 1, 2, 3, 4, 5, and 6 on its faces. What is the probability that when both dice are rolled a D and an odd number will come up? What is the probability that a vowel and a 6 will come up? $\frac{1}{12}, \frac{1}{18}$

Multiplying Probabilities

Point out that from our experience and from experiments, we know that some events are independent. For example, the outcome of a coin toss does *not* influence the outcome of the next toss. If, however, a card is pulled from a deck and *not* replaced, the outcome of the second card that is pulled *depends* on the outcome of the first card. (If, for example, the first card was the king of hearts, the second card cannot be the king of hearts.)

Key Questions

- If a card is drawn from a deck of cards and then replaced, and a second card is drawn, are these independent events?
  Yes
- If a fair coin is tossed ten times, all ten landing heads, is the next toss an independent event?
  Yes, although the probability that a coin will land heads eleven times in a row is $\left(\frac{1}{2}\right)^{11}$. Each individual toss is an independent event and has a probability of $\frac{1}{2}$ of landing heads.

Chalkboard Example

1. A die is rolled and a coin is tossed. What is the probability that a 4 is rolled and a head is tossed?
   Let *A* be the event that a 4 occurs on the die and any outcome occurs on the coin. Let *B* be the event that any outcome occurs on the die and a head is tossed on the coin. *A* and *B* are independent. $A \cap B$ is the event that a 4 occurs on the die and a head occurs on the coin.
   $$P(A \cap B) = P(A) \cdot P(B) = \frac{1}{6} \cdot \frac{1}{2} = \frac{1}{12}$$

LESSON QUIZ

A bag contains many marbles, colored red, black, and white. The probability of drawing a red marble is 0.5, the probability of drawing a black marble is 0.3, and the probability of drawing a white marble is 0.2.

1. If one marble is drawn at random, what is the probability that the marble will be either black or white?
   The events are mutually exclusive, hence $0.3 + 0.2 = 0.5$.
2. If two marbles are drawn, with replacement after the first draw, what is the probability that the marbles are both red?
   The events are independent.
   $P = 0.5 \cdot 0.5 = 0.25$
3. A die is rolled three times. What is the probability of rolling 1, 2, and 3 in that order?
   The events are independent.
   $P = \frac{1}{6} \cdot \frac{1}{6} \cdot \frac{1}{6} = \frac{1}{216}$

Assignment Guide
Algebra: Omit

Alg w/Finite Math: 1–25 m3, 26, MR assign w. 15-5

Comprehensive: 1–25 m3, 26, 27–30 e/o, MR assign w. 15-5

15-6 EXERCISES

A

A bag contains five red marbles, seven blue marbles, and ten green marbles. One marble is drawn at random.

1. What is the probability that it will be either red or green? $\frac{15}{22}$
2. What is the probability that it will be either blue or green? $\frac{17}{22}$
3. What is the probability that it will be either red or blue? $\frac{6}{11}$

A die is rolled.

4. What is the probability of rolling an odd number or a power of two? $\frac{5}{6}$
5. What is the probability of rolling an even number or a multiple of 6? $\frac{1}{2}$
6. What is the probability of rolling a number less than 5 or a divisor of 12? $\frac{5}{6}$
7. What is the probability of rolling a multiple of three or a prime number? $\frac{2}{3}$

A die with A, B, C, D, E, and F on its faces is rolled.

8. What is the probability of rolling a consonant or a letter in the word ALGEBRA? 1
9. What is the probability of rolling a vowel or a letter made with only straight lines? $\frac{1}{2}$
10. What is the probability of rolling a letter in the word PROBABILITY or a letter in your name? Answers may vary.

A card is drawn from an ordinary deck of 52 cards.

11. What is the probability that the card will be a spade or an ace? $\frac{4}{13}$
12. What is the probability that the card will be a heart or a face card? $\frac{11}{26}$
13. What is the probability that the card will be a red card or a card with a value less than six? $\frac{9}{13}$

A die is rolled twice.

14. What is the probability of rolling a 6 on the first roll and a 2 on the second roll? $\frac{1}{36}$
15. What is the probability of rolling a 3 on the first roll and a prime number on the second roll? $\frac{1}{12}$
16. What is the probability of rolling an odd number on the first roll and a power of 5 on the second roll? $\frac{1}{12}$

A die is rolled three times.

17. What is the probability of rolling an even number on all three rolls? $\frac{1}{8}$
18. What is the probability of rolling an odd number on the first roll, an even number on the second roll, and a prime number on the third roll? $\frac{1}{8}$
19. What is the probability of rolling a multiple of two on the first roll, an odd number on the second roll, and a divisor of 12 on the third roll? $\frac{5}{24}$
20. One die has A, B, C, D, E, and F on its faces. Another die has 1, 2, 3, 4, 5, and 6 on its faces. When the pair of dice is rolled, what is the probability that a consonant and a prime number come up? $\frac{1}{3}$

B

21. A bag contains three red marbles and four green marbles. A marble is drawn from the bag and *not* put back before a second marble is drawn. What is the probability that the second marble is red? $\frac{3}{7}$

22. Suppose S is a sample space and A is an event in S. The complement of A, which is symbolized $\overline{A}$, is the set of elements in S, which are not in A. What is $P(A \cup \overline{A})$? What is $P(A \cap \overline{A})$? 1; 0

23. Dave, Tom, Bob, Roger, and Sergio left their hats at the hat-check room in a restaurant. When they asked for their hats they found that their hats had not been marked. Their hats were returned to them at random. What is the probability that they all received the correct hats? $\frac{1}{120}$

24. Multicolored balloons come in a package of 1000. There are 150 red and yellow balloons, 250 blue and red, 100 white and red, 300 yellow and white, and 200 yellow and blue.
 a. What is the probability of picking a balloon with yellow or white on it? 0.75
 b. What is the probability of picking a balloon without blue or red on it? 0.30

25. The kennel club has 400 dogs, of which 150 are poodles and 150 have shaggy hair. Fifty of the poodles have shaggy hair. What is the probability of picking a poodle or shaggy-haired dog from the kennel? $\frac{5}{8}$

26. ***Critical Thinking*** Suppose S is a sample space with A and B events in S. Show that $\overline{A \cap B} = \overline{A} \cup \overline{B}$. (Hint: Draw a diagram. Also see Exercise 22.)

Challenge

27. Suppose two cards are drawn from an ordinary deck of 52 cards. What is the probability that at least one will not be a king or at least one will be red? $\frac{1325}{1326}$

28. The letters of the word PROBABILITY are printed on file cards and the cards are shuffled. What is the probability that when the cards are dealt out, face up from left to right, they will spell PROBABILITY? $\frac{1}{9{,}979{,}200}$

29. In Dave's drawer there are 4 pairs of different-colored socks, but they are all mixed up. Dave reaches into the drawer and pulls out 3 socks without looking. What is the probability that 2 of them match? $\frac{3}{7}$

30. Sandra is one of 20 people entered in a drawing for a prize. Each person is given a sealed envelope which, when opened, will reveal whether or not they are winners. What is the probability that Sandra is a winner after 5 other people open their envelopes and are not winners? $\frac{1}{15}$

Mixed Review

Find a parabola with **31.** focus $(-8, -2)$, vertex $(-4, -2)$.

32. focus $(-4, -2)$, vertex $(-4, -3)$. **33.** vertex $(4, -2)$, containing the point $(5, 2)$.

34. vertex $(4, -3)$, containing the point $(2, -2)$.

35. Find the variation constant and an equation of variation where y varies directly as x, and the following are true.
 a. $y = 3$ when $x = 6$ **b.** $y = -4$ when $x = -2$ **c.** $y = 4$ when $x = 7$

ADDITIONAL ANSWERS

Exercises

26.

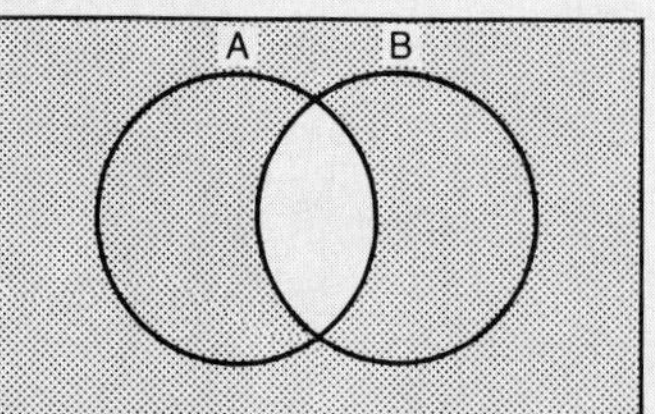

Mixed Review

31. $(y + 2)^2 = -16(x + 4)$
32. $(x + 4)^2 = 4(y + 3)$
33. $(y + 2)^2 = 16(x - 4)$
 or $(x - 4)^2 = \frac{1}{4}(y + 2)$
34. $(x - 4)^2 = 4(y + 3)$
 or $(y + 3)^2 = -\frac{1}{2}(x - 4)$
35. a. $y = \frac{1}{2}x$
 b. $y = 2x$
 c. $y = \frac{4}{7}x$

15-7

FIRST FIVE MINUTES

1. What is the probability of drawing either a heart or a king from a deck of 52 cards?
   $P(H \cup K)$
   $= P(H) + P(K) - P(H \cap K)$
   $= \frac{13}{52} + \frac{4}{52} - \frac{1}{52}$
   $= \frac{16}{52} = \frac{4}{13}$
2. A coin is tossed three times. What is the probability of three heads occurring?
   $\frac{1}{2} \cdot \frac{1}{2} \cdot \frac{1}{2} = \frac{1}{8}$

Simulations and Probability

Emphasize the importance of selecting an appropriate model. Point out that flipping a coin is an appropriate model if the probability of an event is 0.5 but not if it is 0.6.

Point out that if you repeat a simulation, you are likely to get a different answer, and that the more trials you do, the closer you are likely to be to the theoretical probability of an event.

In Example 1, a trial could also consist of spinning one spinner twice. In Example 2, a trial could also consist of flipping one coin 4 times.

Key Questions

- What is the probability that the player in Example 1 will make the first free-throw? 0.60
- What is the probability that she will make the second free-throw? 0.60
- What would be an appropriate model if the player had a 0.67 average from the free-throw line?
  Answers may vary. The spinners could be marked with $\frac{2}{3}$ marked "made" and $\frac{1}{3}$ marked "missed," or two dice could be thrown, with 1 and 2 indicating "missed" and 3, 4, 5, and 6 representing "made."

15-7 Simulating Events

Simulations and Probability

Objective: Design and use simulations to determine experimental probability.

It is not always possible to list the elements of the sample space for an event or calculate the actual or theoretical probability. In this case, we can design an experiment to determine the experimental probability.

For example, if we flip a coin 1000 times and heads comes up 489 times, we would have an experimental probability of $\frac{489}{1000}$, or 0.489.

Often it is either impractical or impossible to perform an experiment directly. For example, suppose the probability that a computer chip is defective is 0.02. What is the probability that there are no more than 10 defective chips in a shipment of 1000? Testing every chip could take hundreds of hours and tie up all of a company's resources. We could simulate the situation quickly and easily, however, with a model.

To use a simulation to approximate the probability of an event, we first *define the problem,* then *select a model* and *define a trial.* Finally, we *collect data* by *running trials.* These steps are illustrated in the following example.

EXAMPLE 1

In a college playoff game, a player was fouled at the final buzzer with her team down by one point. The player has a 0.60 average from the free-throw line. What is the probability that she will make both shots to win the game?

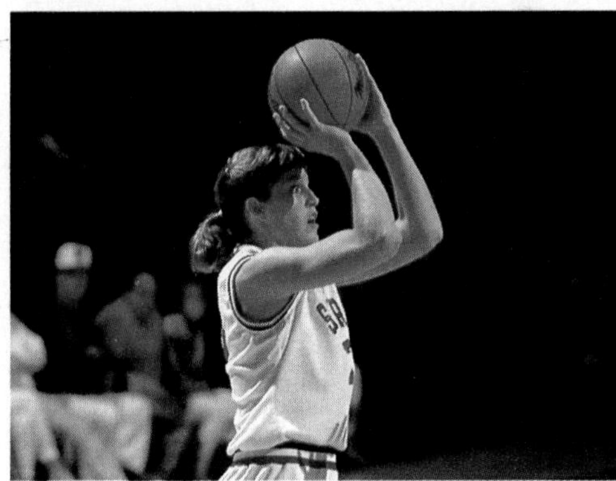

UNDERSTAND the problem

Question: Find the probability that a player, who averages 0.60 from the free-throw line, will make two consecutive free-throws.

Develop and carry out a PLAN

This can be modeled with two spinners that have $\frac{3}{5}$ of their areas labeled "made" and $\frac{2}{5}$ labeled "missed." One spinner can be marked "first shot" and the other second shot." A *trial* would then consist of spinning each of the spinners once.

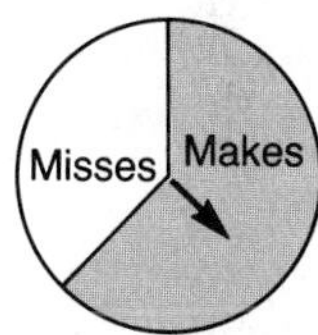

First Shot

Misses Makes

Second Shot

Using a chart to *record* the *data collected,* the results of 50 *trials* were as follows:

Makes both shots	𝍸 𝍸 𝍸 ||||
Does not make both shots	𝍸 𝍸 𝍸 𝍸 𝍸 𝍸 |

■ **Find the ANSWER and CHECK**

There were 19 successes in 50 trials. This suggests that about 38% of the time, we would expect the player to make both shots and win the game.

In this case the theoretical probability is $0.6(0.6) = 0.36$. The difference between the theoretical probability of 0.36 and 0.38 from the simulation is that a simulation results in an approximation. The more trials that are run, the better the approximation.

Try This

a. Use a simulation to find the probability of making exactly one of two shots if the player averages 0.75 from the free-throw line? Theoretical probability is 0.375.

EXAMPLE 2 What is the probability that a family with four children has three girls and one boy?

The problem can be modeled by flipping four coins, letting a head represent a girl and a tail represent a boy. Thus, a trial is represented by flipping the four coins, and a success is represented by 3 heads and 1 tail. We carry out 50 trials. Our results look like this:

HHTH	THTH	HHTH	HTTT	TTHH	HTHT	HHHT	HTHH	THTT	HHHH
HHHT	TTHT	HHTT	THHT	THHT	HHHT	HTHH	TTTT	TTTH	THTH
HTTT	HTHT	THTT	TTHT	THTH	THTH	TTHT	TTTT	TTTT	THTT
HHHT	HTHT	TTHH	TTTT	HTHT	THHT	TTHH	HHHT	HTHH	THHT
TTTT	HTHH	HHTT	THTH	TTTT	HTTH	HTHH	HHHH	HTHH	HHTT

After 50 trials, we had 13 successes. Thus, we conclude that the probability is about $\frac{13}{50} = 0.26$.

Try This

b. What is the probability that a four-child family has two boys and two girls?
Theoretical probability is 0.375.

Other problems require even more ingenuity in setting up the models. Sometimes they require the use of dice or other random devices.

Chalkboard Example

1. The probability that it will rain on each of the next 5 days is 50%. What is the probability that it will rain for 3 of the next 5 days?
   Toss a coin 5 times to simulate the event, letting heads represent rain and tails represent no rain. You may wish to have each student in your class toss a coin 5 times. The number of trials will be the same as the number of students. Ask students who tossed 3 tails to raise their hands. The experimental probability that it will rain for 3 of the next 5 days is the number of students with raised hands divided by the total number of students. (The theoretical probability is 0.31.)

Using a Random Number Table

Point out that a random number table can be used to simulate many probabilities other than 0.1.

Key Questions

- How would you use a random number table to simulate a probability of 0.2 for an event?
  Let 0 and 1 represent the event occurring and the other digits represent it not occurring.
- How would you simulate a probability of $\frac{2}{9}$?
  Ignore the digit 0 and let 1 and 2 represent the event occurring.

Chalkboard Example

1. A gas station is giving away free glasses with 5 different designs. What is the probability of collecting all 5 in 15 visits to the gas station?
   Divide the digits into 5 pairs, 0 and 1, 2 and 3, 4 and 5, 6 and 7, and 8 and 9. Using the random number table, look through groups of 15 digits. If at least one digit of each pair appears, the trial is a success. Beginning with row 1 and using 50 trials, there are 42 successes. The simulated probability of collecting all 5 glasses is 0.84.

EXAMPLE 3 A restaurant is giving away six different toy figures with children's meals. What is the probability of getting all six figures when purchasing ten meals?

The probability of getting any one figure is $\frac{1}{6}$. This can easily be modeled by the roll of a die. A trial for the problem could consist of rolling a die ten times and determining whether all six numbers turn up in the ten rolls. If they do, the trial is a success.

We carry out 25 trials and find that there are 7 successes. The experimental probability of getting all six of the figures in ten meals is $\frac{7}{25}$, or 0.28.

Try This

c. Suppose that a restaurant gives away one of three different figures with each child's meal. What is the probability you will get all three figures when purchasing five meals? [Hint: Use groups of digits from the die.] Theoretical probability is 0.625.

Using a Random Number Table

Objective: Use a random number table to simulate an event and determine experimental probability.

A table of random digits may also be used to simulate an event. Such a table contains the digits 0 through 9, generated so that each digit has the same probability of occurring. In the sample shown below, we see 4 rows of 50 digits, blocked in groups of five. The entire table is shown in the Appendix.

Row										
1	82350	90391	34806	35773	37006	34566	12787	35876	01956	45032
2	88640	70497	48430	23118	28843	63970	27630	48165	75403	56046
3	88866	78271	21214	37408	13072	74208	46567	72124	21437	58899
4	22024	15249	05312	06293	89938	86283	37555	47539	45303	79801

Of the 200 digits, there are approximately the same number of each of the digits 0 to 9.

Digit	0	1	2	3	4	5	6	7	8	9
Count	22	15	21	26	21	18	18	22	24	13

For a large number of rows, each count would approximate $\frac{1}{10}$ of the total number of digits.

EXAMPLE 4

The manager of a river canoeing company estimates that one tenth of the individuals who purchase tickets for a 9-person trip will not show up. Therefore, 10 tickets are sold for each trip. What is the probability that more than 9 people will show up for a trip?

We model the situation using the random number table, letting the digit 0 represent an individual who does not show up for a given trip. Because 10 tickets are sold for each trip, a trial will consist of examining 10 random numbers drawn from the table. If one or more zeros appear in a list of 10 digits, the manager's policy works. If not, the trip is overbooked.

We can start with row 1 of the table, which is given on page 866. We run 50 trials.

82350 90391
34806 35773
37006 34566 and so on.

We find that in 18 of the 50 trials, all 10 ticketholders show up. Thus, the probability that more than 9 people show up is $\frac{18}{50}$, or 0.36.

Try This

d. What is the probability that more than 8 individuals holding tickets show up, if 10 tickets are sold for each trip? (Begin with row 12 of the random number table.) 0.80

15-7 EXERCISES

A

Answers may vary.

Use simulations to answer the following questions. Theoretical probabilities are given.

1. If a basketball player has a free-throw average of 0.80, what is the probability that the player will make two free-throws in a row? ≈0.64
2. If a basketball player has a free-throw average of 0.50, what is the probability that the player will make two free-throws in a row? ≈0.25
3. If a basketball player has a free-throw average of 0.25, what is the probability that the player will miss two free-throws in a row? ≈0.563
4. If a basketball player has a free-throw average of 0.75, what is the probability that the player will miss two free-throws in a row? ≈0.0625
5. What is the probability that a family with 5 children has 3 boys and 2 girls? ≈0.313
6. What is the probability that a family with 5 children has 1 boy and 4 girls? ≈0.156
7. What is the probability that a family with 5 children has either all boys or all girls? ≈0.06
8. If a baseball club is giving out 5 different baseball posters to people attending games, what is the probability that a fan will get all 5 posters in 10 trips to the park? ≈0.52
9. If a baseball club is giving out 10 different team pictures, what is the probability that a fan will get one of each in 20 trips to the park? ≈0.22

To use the table with Example 3, we can use only the digits 0 through 5 to represent the six figures, ignoring digits greater than 5. When 10 of these are found, we check whether each of the digits was represented. Using the first row of the table, the first trial would have consisted of the digits below.

82350 90391 3480

We would skip the digits 6, 7, 8, and 9 when they occur.

We can see that each of the digits 0 through 5 is represented. Hence, this trial would have been considered a success in getting all six of the figures.

Lesson Quiz

1. A bicycle manufacturer makes an equal number of red, black, and yellow bikes. If he ships 3 at random to a store, what is the probability that the store will receive 1 of each color?
   Theoretical probability is 0.22.
2. Frank is practicing free-throws. He has a 0.60 average. Use the random number table to find the probability that he will make 3 out of 5 shots.
   Theoretical probability is 0.3456.

Assignment Guide
Algebra: Omit

Alg w/Finite Math: 1–25 m3, 26, MR assign w. 15-8

Comprehensive: 1–25 m3, 26–28, MR assign w. 15-8

10. Suppose the junior class made a mistake in ordering and selling tickets for its play. The class accidentally sold 25 tickets for each row of 24 seats. If there is a 10% chance that a ticketholder will not show up, at what proportion of the showings will there be enough seats in a given row? ≈0.92

11. A commuter airline normally books seats on its flights by selling 15 tickets for each flight capable of carrying 13 passengers. What proportion of the flights have more ticketholders present than seats for passengers if, on average, 10% of the ticketholders do not show up? ≈0.55

Driving from home to school, a mathematics teacher passes through 4 traffic signals, A, B, C, and D. The probability that any one light is green is 0.4 and the probability that it is not green is 0.6. Use this information and a simulation to answer the following.

12. What is the probability that the teacher will hit each light on green? ≈0.03

13. What is the probability that the teacher will hit each light on red? ≈0.13

14. What is the probability that the teacher will find at least one light red? ≈0.97

15. What is the probability that the teacher will find the first light green and the last two lights red? ≈0.14

16. What is the probability that the teacher will find the last light green? ≈0.40

17. Suppose that a racing car tire manufacturer claims that only one tire in twenty is defective (will not run 100 miles). Find the probability that in a set of 10 tires, exactly 2 tires are defective. ≈0.075

18. A doctor knows that, on average, a given medicine is effective in $\frac{4}{5}$ of the cases for which it is prescribed. What is the probability that it is effective in five straight cases? ≈0.328

19. There was a major defect in 10% of the cars produced by Lemon Motors. What is the probability of a business getting two or more such cars if it buys five company cars from Lemon? ≈0.08

20. Police estimate that the probability of a driver not wearing a seatbelt is about 30 percent. If they stop 20 cars, what is the probability that they will find at least 10 such drivers? ≈0.048

B

21. Make your own table of 100 random digits. Count the frequency of each of the digits. Compare your frequencies with the results of a table made from the first 100 digits in the random number table on page 865. Answers may vary.

22. A student takes a ten-question, multiple-choice test with four choices per item. If the student guesses, what is the expected score for the examination? ≈2.5

23. What is the probability that in a group of four people, at least two were born in the same month? 0.42

24. What is the probability that any two people were born in the same month? ≈0.08

25. The probability that an event does not happen is known as the **complement** of the event. Using the fact that the probability of an event plus the probability of the complement of the event is 1, find the solution to Exercise 24 using theoretical probability. 0.083

26. ***Critical Thinking*** Explain why the following digits probably are not random. (Hint: make a table of digits and study row 3 of table 6.)

27439 16058 35641 79082 03864 57219 38502 71694 60591 82437

Challenge

27. If a car attendant at a theater gets the keys to six cars mixed up, what is the probability that randomly putting the keys back on the six pegs will result in at least one of the keys being correctly assigned to the car to which it belongs?
28. What is the probability that exactly 5 keys in Exercise 27 are placed on the correct pegs?

Mixed Review

29. Divide $\frac{x^2 - 9}{x^2 + 6x + 9}$ by $\frac{x^2 + 4x - 21}{x^2 - 4x - 21}$.

Convert to exponential notation. **30.** $\log_a 7 = 4$ **31.** $\ln u = 8$

Convert to logarithmic notation. **32.** $14^2 = 196$ **33.** $e^{t+1} = t$

Bonus Topic: Binomial Probabilities

Given that an event can either occur or not occur, the probability of r successes in a sample of size n is given by $\binom{n}{r} p^r(1 - p)^{n-r}$.

EXAMPLE 1 What is the probability that a family with 9 children has 7 girls?

This is the binominal probability of 7 successes in a sample of size 9, where $p = 0.5$. The probability is $\binom{9}{7}(0.5)^7(0.5)^{9-7} = 36(0.5)^9 \approx 0.07$.

EXAMPLE 2 A baseball player is a .300 hitter (hits safely 30% of the time). What is the probability that the player will get at least 4 hits in 5 times at bat?

This is the probability of 4 hits + the probability of 5 hits.

$$\binom{5}{4}(0.3)^4(0.7)^1 + \binom{5}{5}(0.3)^5(0.7)^0 = 5(0.0081)(0.7) + 0.00243 = 0.03078$$

Find the following using binomial probabilities.

1. What is the probability that a family with 7 children has at least 5 boys?
2. The probability that a medicine is effective is 0.9. What is the probability that it will be effective in at least 9 of 10 cases?
3. Use the binomial theorem to expand $(p + (1 - p))^n$. What is the sum of the terms? (Hint: Simplify $(p + (1 - p)^n)$. How can you relate this to what you know about probability?

ADDITIONAL ANSWERS

26. Each set of 10 digits includes all 10 digits. It is unlikely that 5 sets of 10 digits would be randomly generated with no repetitions.
27. ≈ 0.34
28. 0. If 5 keys are successfully placed, the 6th must be also.

Mixed Review

29. $\frac{x - 7}{x + 7}$
30. $a^4 = 7$
31. $e^8 = u$
32. $\log_{14} 196 = 2$
33. $\ln t = t + 1$

Bonus Topic

1. ≈ 0.23
2. ≈ 0.74
3. $(p + (1 - p))^n = \binom{n}{0}p^n(1 - p)^0 + \binom{n}{1}p^{n-1}(1 - p)^1 + \ldots \binom{n}{n}p^0(1 - p)^n$ but $p + (1 - p) = 1$, so $(p + (1 - p))^n = 1^n = 1$ Thus the sum of the terms of the binomial expansion is 1. The probability of r successes in a sample of size n, for $r = 0$ to $r = n$, is thus 1.

15-8

FIRST FIVE MINUTES

1. A pen manufacturer makes red, blue, and black pens, and randomly packages them in sets of 4. What is the probability that a set will have at least one of each color?
   ≈0.44

RND(1) generates a number from 0 to 0.999999999. Multiplying it by 4 gives a number from 0 to 3.999999996. Taking the integer part of this number gives 0, 1, 2, or 3, with approximately equal probability.

The following lines should be added to the program for the computer to calculate the probability of 4 or more PhD's on a staff of 12:

```
55 IF X = 0 THEN PHD = PHD + 1
70 IF PHD > 3 THEN SUCCESS =
   SUCCESS + 1
75 PHD = 0
90 PRINT : PRINT
   SUCCESS,SUCCESS/T
```

This will print the successes and the probability as:

```
   78          .39
```

The method in Example 1 could be used to determine whether a company discriminates. We could, for example, find the probability that a company hired a certain percentage of women for a particular job. If the probability is very low, we might conclude that a company with a smaller percentage of women in that job is discriminatory.

Key Questions

- If 25% of the qualified workers are PhD's, about how many PhD's would you expect to find on a 12-person staff? 3
- If 50% of the qualified workers are PhD's, would you need to change the program? No
- How would you interpret the output? Let 0 and 1 represent PhD's.

15-8 Advanced Simulations

Objective: Use a computer to simulate events and find experimental probability.

Lesson 15-8 is recommended only for classes with access to a computer.

Simulating events by hand or using a random number table can also be quite time-consuming. Using computer software makes the process much easier. In this lesson we use a computer to list the trials. Then we can check the output to find the successful trials. In some cases, the computer can even do the checking for us.

A second advantage in using a computer to run trials is that many more trials can be conducted in the time available. This allows for better approximations, since the difference between an approximation and the true answer narrows as the number of trials increases.

Methods that use simulations to determine the probability of a certain event occurring are known as **Monte Carlo** methods.

EXAMPLE 1 If 25% of the qualified workers for a certain job in a geographical area have PhD's, what is the probability that there would be more than 3 PhD's on a 12-person staff?

We need to find the probability that a 12-person staff would contain 4 or more PhD's.

The BASIC program below randomly makes lists of 12 numbers, each representing a staff member. The numbers range from 0 to 3. We let one of the four numbers (25%) represent PhD's.

PhD's: 0 Not PhD's: 1, 2, 3

```
10 INPUT "TRIALS?";T
20 FOR N = 1 TO T
30 FOR I = 1 TO 12
40 LET X = INT(4*RND(1))      Generates an integer from 0 to 3
50 PRINT X;" ";
60 NEXT I
70 PRINT
80 NEXT N
```

When we run the program by typing

RUN <Return>

TRIALS? 200

we get output such as the following. Each line represents one trial.

```
2 2 2 0 0 2 3 3 1 3 2 2      Each number represents a worker. The number
                             0 represents a PhD.
1 0 3 1 0 2 0 0 1 1 3 0
```

The first trial corresponds to two PhD's on the staff, the second trial has five.

After 200 trials, 78 of the trials have 4 or more PhD's, so the experimental probability of 4 or more PhD's on a staff of 12 workers is 0.39.

Try This

a. If fifty percent of the qualified workers for a certain job in a geographical area are male, what is the probability that a company would have 3 or fewer males on a staff of 10? (Hint: Adapt the program from Example 1.) ≈0.29

EXAMPLE 2 Suppose a quarterback on a football team throws a pass on first down 60% of the time. Suppose that his receivers catch his passes 40% of the time. What is the probability that the team will successfully complete a pass on a first-down play?

We can use a similar program to run 200 trials consisting of two-digit pairs. Each digit is a number from 0 to 9. The first digit indicates whether the team passes or not. Because there was a 60% chance of a pass, the digits 0–5 represent a pass. The second digit represents whether the pass was caught. The digits 0–3 represent a successful catch.

```
10 INPUT "TRIALS?";T
20 FOR N = 1 TO T
30 LET X = INT(10*RND(1))
40 LET Y = INT(10*RND(1))
50 PRINT X;Y
60 NEXT N
```

The output for the first three trials is shown below.

27	2 is a pass, 7 means it is not caught
64	6 is not a pass (we can ignore the 4)
31	3 is a pass, 1 means it is caught

After 200 trials, 44 show a pass that is caught. The experimental probability of a successful pass on first down is 0.22.

Try This

b. Suppose a quarterback on a football team throws a pass 70% of the time on the third down, and the receivers catch her passes 60% of the time. What is the probability that the team will complete a third-down pass? ≈0.42

EXAMPLE 3 For every 1000 balloons manufactured by PoP! Corporation, there are 200 red, 200 white, 100 yellow, 100 green, and 400 blue. A machine packs 4 balloons randomly in a package. What is the probability that a package contains balloons that are all different colors?

In this case, the computer is asked to generate 200 lists of four digits selected from the digits 0 through 9. The digits 0 and 1 represent a red balloon, 2 and 3 represent white, 4 yellow, 5 green, and 6, 7, 8, and 9 represent a blue balloon.

Math Point
Monte Carlo methods were developed to estimate risks in the nuclear industry, where using experimental methods to estimate probabilities would be dangerous to humans and destructive to the atmosphere.

Chalkboard Example

1. On an engine assembly line, there is a 20% chance that an engine will be defective the first time it passes through quality control. Of the defective engines, 80% can be repaired, and the rest must be discarded. What is the probability that out of 20 engines, more than 1 will be discarded?
   Using the program from Example 2, the computer will be asked to print out 200 trials of 20 pairs of digits selected from 0 through 9. The first digit indicates whether the engine is defective, with 0 and 1 being defective. The second digit indicates whether a defective engine can be repaired, with 0 and 1 indicating that the engine must be discarded. Scan for pairs in the form 00, 01, 10, and 11. Two or more such pairs in a set of 20 represents that more than 1 engine must be discarded. The probability is approximately 0.19.

LESSON ENRICHMENT

Rewrite the program given in Example 2 so that it will automatically calculate the experimental probability of completing a pass. You need not print the list of trials.

```
10 INPUT "TRIALS?";T
20 SUCCESS = 0
30 FOR N = 1 TO T
40 LET X = INT(10*RND(1))
50 LET Y = INT(10*RND(1))
60 IF X < 5 and Y <= 3 THEN
   SUCCESS = SUCCESS + 1
70 NEXT N
80 PRINT : PRINT
   SUCCESS,SUCCESS/T
```

```
10 INPUT "TRIALS?";T
20 FOR N = 1 TO T
30 FOR I = 1 TO 4
40 LET X = INT(10*RND(1))
50 PRINT X;
60 NEXT I
70 PRINT
80 NEXT N
```

A trial output of 8 3 5 2 might represent a selection consisting of a blue balloon, a white balloon, a green balloon, and a white balloon.

It would be tedious to translate each line of numerical output. We can program the computer to translate from numbers to the colors they represent.

```
10 INPUT "TRIALS?";T
20 FOR N = 1 TO T
30 FOR I = 1 TO 4
40 LET X = INT(10*RND(1))
50 If X < 2 THEN PRINT "R";
52 IF X = 2 OR X = 3 THEN PRINT "W";
54 IF X = 4 THEN PRINT "Y";
56 IF X = 5 THEN PRINT "G";
58 IF X > 5 THEN PRINT "B";
60 NEXT I
70 NEXT N
```

Our output would look like

BWGW   for blue, white, green, white

After 200 trials, 24 show four different colored balloons. The experimental probability is 0.12.

Try This

c. What is the probability that a three-balloon package contains balloons that are all the same color? ≈ 0.08

EXAMPLE 4 Any of four different safety systems can shut down a machine in case of a problem. Any one of the systems can shut the machine off. Each has a 0.5 probability of shutting down the machine. What is the probability that the machine will be shut down if a problem occurs?

In this case, each trial consists of a list of 4 digits. Because the probability of a machine shutdown for each system is 0.5, we let the digits from 0 to 4 stand for the system being shut down and 5 to 9 stand for no intervention by the safety system. Hence, any trial with a digit less than 5 in it will indicate that the machine was shut down.

We can use the first program from Example 3. The output would look like

2 7 4 3
0 6 3 9
8 8 4 7 and so on

After 200 trials, there were 186 trials where at least one of the digits was less than 5. The experimental probability is $\frac{186}{200}$, or 0.93, that the machine will be shut down by a safety system if a problem occurs.

Try This

d. The systems are improved so that the probability that a particular system will shut down the machine if there is a problem is 0.60. System 4 is then removed. What is the probability that at least one safety system will shut down the machine if there is a problem? ≈0.94

15-8 EXERCISES

A

Use a simulation to solve each problem.

1. A basketball player has a free-throw average of 0.80. What is the probability that the player will make two free-throws in a row? ≈0.64
2. A basketball player has a free-throw average of 0.60. What is the probability that the player will make four free-throws in a row? ≈0.13
3. Assume that 30% of the qualified individuals for a certain job are male. What is the probability that a company would have at most 2 males out of the 10 individuals assigned to that job? ≈0.38
4. Assume that 60% of the qualified individuals for a certain job are male. What is the probability that a company would have at most 3 males out of the 11 individuals assigned to that job? ≈0.05
5. If a local movie theater is giving away posters of 5 movie stars, what is the probability that you will get one of each of the posters in 10 trips to the theater? ≈0.52
6. If a cereal box contains one of 4 different Loco Men, what is the probability that you will get one of each after buying 10 boxes of cereal? ≈0.80
7. If 10 people are in a room, what is the probability that at least 3 were born in the same month? (Assume an equal probability for each month.) ≈0.47
8. If 8 people are in a room, what is the probability that each was born in a different month? (Assume an equal probability for each month.) ≈0.05
9. A baseball player is known to bunt about 30% of the time on the first pitch. Further, he bunts successfully about 60% of the time that he bunts. What is the probability that he will bunt successfully on the first pitch on a given trip to the plate? ≈0.18

LESSON QUIZ

1. 60% of the qualified workers for a certain job in Arkenville are women. What is the probability that a staff of 15 will have 5 or fewer women? ≈0.034

Assignment Guide

Algebra: Omit

Alg w/Finite Math: 1–19 m3, 20, MR assign w. 15-7

Comprehensive: 1–16 m4, 17–19 e/o, 20–23, MR assign w. 15-7

ADDITIONAL ANSWERS

Mixed Review

25. $\frac{3 - a}{a(a + 3)}$
26. x
27. 36

10. A hockey player shoots about 20% of the time she has the puck in the offensive zone. Further, she scores a goal on about 30% of her shots. What is the probability that she will score a goal when she has the puck in the offensive zone? ≈ 0.06

11. A successful launch of a three-stage rocket requires that all three motors fire on time. The probability that the first engine will ignite properly is 0.9. The probability that the second and third engines will fire properly is 0.8 and 0.7, respectively. What is the probability that on a given launch all three engines will fire correctly? ≈ 0.504

12–16. Reconsider problems 12–16 from Exercise Set 15.7, this time using a greater number of trials. Compare your results with the answers you found in your previous work. Answers may vary.

B

A mixture of a large number of balloons in a sack consists of about $\frac{1}{3}$ red balloons, $\frac{1}{2}$ blue balloons, and $\frac{1}{6}$ yellow balloons. Assuming that picking a balloon has no effect on these probabilities, answer the following questions.

17. What is the probability that the first five balloons drawn at random from the sack will be only red or blue? ≈ 0.4

18. What is the probability that 4 out of the first 5 balloons drawn from the sack will be only blue or yellow? ≈ 0.33

19. Find the probability that in a World Series between two equally matched teams that one team will win the first 3 games but lose the 7-game series. ≈ 0.016

20. ***Critical Thinking*** Find the exact probability, using theoretical methods, for the problem in Exercise 19 and compare your answers. ≈ 0.016

Challenge

21. A deck of cards is composed of 10 red cards and 20 blue cards. We pick 5 cards. What is the probability that there are more red cards than blue cards chosen? ≈ 0.19

22. On average, how many people would you need to ask before you found someone who has the same birthday as you do? (If you were born February 29, consider that your birthday occurs every 1461 days.) about 253, or about 1012 for Feb. 29

23. A football team plays a 16-game season. If the team has a 0.5 probability of winning each game, what is the probability that the team will have no winning or losing streaks of 4 or more games? ≈ 0.33

24. Suppose the home team has a 70% chance of winning a basketball game. In a 7-game playoff, where the series ends when one team wins 4 games, team A plays at home for games 1, 2, 6, and 7. If the teams are evenly matched, what is the probability that team A wins the series? ≈ 0.58

Mixed Review

Simplify. **25.** $\frac{a + 2}{a^2 + 3a} \cdot \frac{a^2 - 5a + 6}{4 - a^2}$ **26.** $\frac{8x^3 + 19x^2 - 15x}{x^2 + 7x + 12} \div \frac{8x^2 + 35x - 25}{x^2 + 9x + 20}$

27. Simplify $\sqrt[6]{6^{12}}$

Problem Solving: Application

Space Message Error Codes

Satellites and space probes send messages to earth in the form of electromagnetic impulses that are read as either 0 or 1. A 12-digit message might be read 001001101010. Sometimes radiation, lightning, heat, or other factors interfere with a message and cause an error. To determine whether a single error exists in a message, the following procedure is used.

The message is grouped into three rows with four columns each. The message above would be grouped like this:

0010
0110
1010

If a row or column has an even number of 1's, a 0 is added to the row or column as a **check digit.** If a row or a column has an odd number of 1's, a 1 is added to the row or column as a check digit. So after the 0's and 1's have been added, every row or column will have an even number of 1's. The message to be sent would now look like this:

00101
01100
10100
11101

Now, suppose that radiation caused a single error in the message, and when it was received it looked like this:

00111
01100
10100
11101

By examining the rows and columns you can see an odd number of 1's in the first row and in the fourth column. This means that the digit at the intersection of this row and column must be incorrect.

The "error correcting code" described above is called a **rectangular code** because the information is arranged in a row-column format. The check digit added to each row and column can be used to detect and correct a *single* error. However, an even number of errors could remain undetected. Also, an odd number of errors greater than or equal to 3 could give the appearance of a single error. Although the rectangular code has these limitations, it can be used in applications for which the probability of more than one error in 20 digits (4 rows, 5 columns) is extremely low.

Problem Solving: Application

Check digits are used extensively in many areas. Scanners reading bar codes on supermarket items read the widths of the black and white lines and assign numbers to them. If the check digit doesn't match the number the scanner generates, the item will not register.

Here is a more detailed explanation of the check digit procedure shown:
The original message was

0010
0110
1010

Each *row* is *augmented* by a check digit.

0010**1**
0110**0**
1010**0**

Each *column* is augmented by a check digit.

00101
01100
10100
11101

Note that the bottom right 1 could have been generated either from the bottom row data or from the right-hand column data.

ANSWERS

1. 00011
   10010
   11101
   01100
2. 11000
   00011
   01001
   10010
3. 01100
   11011
   11011
   01100
4. 00000
   11000
   00011
   11011
5. no error
6. 0.608
7. 0.017
8. 0.00019
9. 0.0000019
10. 0.5
11. ≈ 0.3012
12. 0.976

Suppose that transmission errors are random and occur with probability p for each digit. The probability that more than one error occurs among the 20 digits is

$$1 - (\text{probability of no error } \textbf{or} \text{ one error})$$

Finding the probability of no errors:

The probability of no errors for a single digit is $1 - p$. So, using the fundamental counting principle, the probability of no errors among the 20 digits is

$$(1 - p)(1 - p)(1 - p) \ldots (1 - p) \text{ or } (1 - p)^{20}$$

Finding the probability of one error:

If exactly one error is to occur, it could occur on the first digit *or* the second digit *or* the third digit, and so on. If a given digit is to be the single error, then all the other 19 digits cannot be the error. So the probability that a given digit is the only error is $p(1 - p)^{19}$. Since there are 20 such cases we have the probability of one error as $20p(1 - p)^{19}$.

Finding the probability of no errors or *one error:*

The probability of no errors or one error is the sum of their probabilities.

$$(1 - p)^{20} + 20p(1 - p)^{19}$$

Thus, the probability T of two or more errors among the 20 digits is

$$T = 1 - [P(\text{no errors}) + P(\text{one error})]$$
$$T = 1 - [(1 - p)^{20} + 20p(1 - p)^{19}]$$

For $p = 0.05$, for example,

$$T = 1 - [(0.95)^{20} + 20(0.05)(0.95)^{19}]$$
$$\approx 1 - [0.358 + 0.377]$$
$$\approx 1 - 0.735$$
$$\approx 0.265$$

Problems

Examine each message. Determine whether a single error exists in each message, and correct the errors.

1.	**2.**	**3.**	**4.**	**5.**
00011	11000	00100	00000	10001
10010	00011	11011	11000	01001
11001	01101	11011	00011	10100
01100	10010	01100	11010	01100

Find the probability of two or more errors, T, for the following values of p.

6. $p = 0.1$ **7.** $p = 0.01$ **8.** $p = 0.001$ **9.** $p = 0.0001$ **10.** $p = 0.0825$

11. Suppose a 90-digit message is sent in a 10×11 matrix (a 9×10 matrix with a row and column of check digits added.)

Find T for $p = 0.01$.

12. Find the probability of two or more errors for $p = 0.05$.

Chapter 15 Summary and Review

ANSWERS
1. 24
2. 24
3. 720
4. 40,320
5. 1
6. 1
7. $14 \cdot 13!$
8. 210
9. 1,814,400
10. 1296
11. 3360
12. 5040

15-1

In a compound event in which the first event may occur in n_1 different ways, the second event in n_2 different ways, and so on, and the k-th event may occur in n_k ways, the total number of ways the compound event may occur is $n_1 \cdot n_2 \cdot n_3 \cdot \cdots \cdot n_k$.

1. When Carla made her yogurt sundae, she had a choice of vanilla, strawberry, or chocolate yogurt. On top of her yogurt, she had a choice of granola, fruit, carob bits, or no topping. She also had a choice of a large or a small sundae. From how many different combinations did Carla have to choose?

A permutation of a set of n objects is an ordered arrangement of the objects, and the total number of these permutations is given by
${}_nP_n = n \cdot (n - 1) \cdot (n - 2) \cdot \cdots \cdot 3 \cdot 2 \cdot 1.$

Find the following.

2. ${}_4P_4$
3. ${}_6P_6$

n factorial or $n! = n \cdot (n - 1) \cdot (n - 2) \cdot \cdots \cdot 3 \cdot 2 \cdot 1$

Find the following.

4. $8!$
5. $1!$
6. $0!$

For any natural number n, $n! = n(n - 1)!$.

7. Represent $14!$ in the form $n(n - 1)!$.

The number of permutations of a set of n objects taken r at a time is given by
${}_nP_r = \frac{n!}{(n - r)!}$ where each permutation is an ordered arrangement.

Compute.

8. ${}_7P_3$
9. ${}_{10}P_8$

15-2

The number of orderings of n objects taken r at a time, with repetition, is n^r.

10. How many different 4-digit numbers can be formed using the digits 3, 4, 5, 6, 7, and 8 if you are allowed to repeat digits?

If P represents the number of permutations of n things taken n at a time, and if there are r things all alike, s other things all alike, t things all alike, then $P = \frac{n!}{r!s!t!}$.

11. Find the number of permutations of the letters of the word TOMORROW.

The number of circular permutations of n objects is $(n - 1)!$.

12. Find the number of permutations of 8 numbers on a spinner.

13. 3003
14. 10
15. 120
16. $-48{,}384x^5$
17. $32x^5 - 320x^4 + 1280x^3 - 2560x^2 + 2560x - 1024$
18. 256
19. $\frac{25}{102}$
20. $\frac{1}{9}$
21. $\frac{4}{13}$
22. $\frac{9}{25}$
23. ≈ 0.65

15-3

Combinations concern the number of ways we can select r elements from n elements and are symbolized by $\binom{n}{r} = \frac{n!}{r!(n-r)!}$.

13. From a class of 15 students, 5 are chosen to represent the class in a contest. In how many ways could the five students be chosen?

Evaluate.

14. $\binom{5}{2}$

15. $\binom{10}{7}$

15-4

For any binomial $(a + b)$ and any natural number n,

$$(a + b)^n = \binom{n}{0}a^n + \binom{n}{1}a^{n-1}b + \binom{n}{2}a^{n-2}b^2 + \cdots + \binom{n}{n}b^n.$$

16. Find the 4th term of $(2x - 3)^8$.

17. Expand $(2x - 4)^5$.

The total number of subsets of a set with n members is 2^n.

18. How many subsets does a set with 8 members have?

15-5

If an event E can occur m ways out of n possible equally likely outcomes of sample space S, the probability of that event is given by $P(E) = \frac{m}{n}$.

19. Suppose 2 cards are drawn from a deck of 52 cards. What is the probability that both cards are black?

20. What is the probability of getting 5 on a roll of a pair of dice?

15-6

If A and B are events from a sample space S then
$P(A \text{ or } B) = P(A \cup B) = P(A) + P(B) - P(A \cap B)$.

21. What is the probability of drawing a king or a heart from a well-shuffled deck of cards in one draw?

Two events, A and B, are independent if and only if $P(A \cap B) = P(A) \cdot P(B)$.

22. A bag contains 4 red marbles and 6 green marbles. A marble is drawn and then replaced. A second drawing is made. What is the probability that a green marble is drawn both times?

15-7

A simulation requires that one define a problem, select a model, define a trial, and collect data through running a large number of trials.

23. A grocer gives out game cards with each purchase. Fifty percent have a W, 40% have an N, and 10% have an I. What is the probability of getting at least one of each with 10 purchases?

15-8

Accurate approximations of events are found through Monte Carlo methods where the simulation's trials are run by a computer, giving a large number of trials.

24. A game consists of one player rolling two dice and the other rolling one. The first player wins if the higher of the numbers showing is greater than the other player's die. What is the probability that the first player wins? ≈0.58

See also Problem 15, Computer-Assisted Problem Solving, page 850.

Test Item Analysis

Item	Lesson
1–6	15-1
7–9	15-2
10, 11	15-3
12–14	15-4
15, 16	15-5
17, 18	15-6
19	15-7

Chapter 15 Test

1. Joe has 4 different colored pairs of jeans, 4 different colored shirts, and 2 belts. How many different outfits can he make? 32

2. Find ${}_5P_5$. 120 **3.** Find 7!. 5040 **4.** Find 0!. 1

5. Represent 11! in the form $n(n - 1)!$. $11 \cdot 10!$

6. Compute ${}_9P_4$. 3024

7. In how many ways can a sedan, a coupe, a sports car, a station wagon, and a van be parked in a row? 120

8. Find the number of permutations of the letters of the word MEMENTO. 1260

9. Find the number of permutations of five people sitting at a round table. 24

10. In how many ways can 9 players be chosen from a team with 14 players? 2002

11. Evaluate $\binom{8}{3}$. 56

12. Find the 5th term of $(x^2 - 2)^6$. $240x^4$

13. Expand $(3x - 2)^4$. $81x^4 - 216x^3 + 216x^2 - 96x + 16$

14. How many subsets does a set with 6 members have? 64

15. Suppose 3 cards are drawn from a well-shuffled deck of 52 cards. What is the probability that all three cards are clubs? $\frac{11}{850}$

16. What is the probability of getting 7 on a roll of a pair of dice? $\frac{1}{6}$

17. What is the probability of drawing a queen or a diamond from a well-shuffled deck of 52 cards in one draw? $\frac{4}{13}$

18. A bag contains 3 red marbles and 6 green marbles. A marble is drawn and then replaced. A second marble is drawn and replaced, and then a third marble is drawn. What is the probability that a red marble is drawn all 3 times? $\frac{1}{27}$

19. The probability of a defect in a manufacturing process is 0.2. Use the random numbers below to find the probability of 2 or more defects in 5 randomly sampled items. 0.25, using 0 and 1

38321	22226	40307	74347	79972	67851	32300	76354	87500	49716
87073	68858	90416	01915	36139	26589	35492	19669	36504	28157
95751	41919	30546	03902	40274	26484	03784	02472	08932	52209
22716	42951	14478	28692	58257	82510	69084	68465	09410	73160

CHAPTER 16 Statistics and Data Analysis

Chapter Overview

Chapter 16 begins with the organization of data, covering stem-and-leaf diagrams, frequency distributions, and box and whisker plots. The chapter moves on to attributes of data, measures of central tendency, and measures of dispersion. The last three lessons teach the normal distribution, effective sampling methods and bias, and statistical experiments and hypothesis testing using chi-square.

Objectives

16-1
- Construct a stem-and-leaf diagram for a set of data.
- Construct a frequency distribution for a set of data.

16-2
- Find the mean, median, and mode of a set of data.
- Construct a box and whisker plot of a set of data.

16-3
- Find the range and mean deviation of a set of data.
- Find the variance of a set of data.
- Find the standard deviation of a set of data.

16-4
- Determine the proportion of data falling within a range of standard deviations.
- Find and use z-scores to determine probability.
- Solve problems involving normal distributions.

16-5
- Evaluate and select sampling methods.
- Describe how to take a stratified random sample.

16-6
- Calculate chi-square values.
- Test a hypothesis by using chi-square.

TEACHING CHAPTER 16

Cooperative Learning Opportunities

As a change of pace you might want to check homework Lessons 16-1 through 16-4 in cooperative groups of four. Most students will not have much difficulty but since the material is new you can assign the following roles and then follow up with a brief class discussion.

(1) **Discussion moderator:** This student calls on one of the others to explain each exercise, is responsible to be sure that the groups remain on task, that everyone contributes, and that the discussion moves along.

(2) **Checker:** Looks at each of the papers and notes any places where answers or graphs differ.

(3) **Note taker:** Writes down any uncertainties and later brings them up in class discussion.

(4) **Questioner:** Looks back at the examples and instructional material to see how concepts are reviewed and verified, raises questions about the homework's relationship to previous learning.

Multicultural Note: *Granville T. Woods*

Granville T. Woods (1856–1910) was an African-American inventor whose primary interest was in the field of electricity. His most important achievement was the development of equipment that permitted messages to be transmitted from moving trains to stations. Woods registered over 60 patents. They included inventions or improvements for an incubator that could hatch 50,000 chicken eggs, an amusement park railway, a phonograph, and an automatic circuit breaker.

The physical sciences sometimes use statistical methods. To study static electricity, have students inflate balloons and then "charge" them by rubbing them against wool fabric. The balloon will stick to a wall. Have students repeat this experiment a number of times, measuring the number of seconds of sticking time for each trial. Have them list and then order the data and ask what conclusions can be drawn.

For more information, see page 155 of **Multiculturalism in Mathematics, Science, and Technology**.

Alternative Assessment and Communication Ideas

The activity suggested on page 714 can easily be expanded into an alternative assessment. Have a small group of interested students develop a questionnaire on several topics of interest. Suggest that they think ahead about what they would like to find out, how they will try to obtain a representative sample, and how they will analyze and display their data.

A possibility would be a "student profile." In this area they might ask for age, major interests, hours spent doing homework, hours spent watching TV, subjects studied. Responses to items in these areas could lead to various interpretations and presentations.

As a follow up you might explain that statisticians often do studies that are related to or overlap with previous studies. You might suggest that they look for statistical profiles of high school students and compare them with the results of their survey.

Investigations and Projects

Statistics are used very extensively to examine and report on practically every area of life. Have students select a particular area of interest and then collect statistical information as presented in newspapers, magazines, on television, and on radio. They should explain what exactly is being said, what the evidence is, and how the different claims or presentations are related. Students should then do a general evaluation based on the statistics presented and on common sense. The following are possible areas to investigate.

Advertising. What are the claims? On what are they based? What are the underlying assumptions? What actions should one take?

Politics. What do particular polls say about people's concerns? How should they be used by public office holders?

Health. What is the statistical evidence about particular health hazards? How was it obtained? Based on the evidence, what decision can be made?

MANAGING CHAPTER 16

Lesson	PACING CHART (DAYS) Algebra	Algebra w/Finite	Algebra w/Trig	Comprehensive	Opening Activity	Cooperative Activity	Seat or Group Work
16-1	0	1	0	1	First Five Minutes 16-1: **TE** p.690 or ***FFM Transparency Masters*** p.43	Critical Thinking: **SE** p.693 Strategy Problem Bank 15: ***Problem Bank*** p.16	Try This a–c
16-2	0	1	0	1	First Five Minutes 16-2: **TE** p.694 or ***FFM Transparency Masters*** p.44	Critical Thinking: **SE** p.699 Probability/Statistics 4: ***Enrichment*** p.85	Try This a–d
16-3	0	1	0	1	First Five Minutes 16-3: **TE** p.700 or ***FFM Transparency Masters*** p.44	Critical Thinking: **SE** p.703	Try This a–c
16-4	0	1	0	1	First Five Minutes 16-4: **TE** p.704 or ***FFM Transparency Masters*** p.44	Critical Thinking: **SE** p.709 ✂ Manipulative Activity 16: ***Enrichment*** p.57	Try This a–j
16-5	0	1	0	1	First Five Minutes 16-5: **TE** p.710 or ***FFM Transparency Masters*** p.45	Critical Thinking: **SE** p.714 Activity: **SE** p.714	Try This a–e
16-6	0	2	0	1	First Five Minutes 16-6: **TE** p.715 or ***FFM Transparency Masters*** p.45	Explore: **SE** p.715 Critical Thinking: **SE** p.720 Problem Solving: **SE** p.721	Try This a–c
Review	0	1	0	1			
Test	0	1	0	1			
Cum. Review	0	1	0	0			
End-of-year Test	0	1	0	0			

FFM: First Five Minutes SPMR: Skills Practice Mixed Review

MANAGING CHAPTER 16

Enrichment	Review/Assess	Reteach	Technology	Lesson
Critical Thinking 16: ***Enrichment*** p.37	Lesson Quiz: **TE** p. 692	Skills Practice 44, #1–4: ***SPMR*** p.56	Problem for Programmers: **SE** p.693	**16-1**
Probability/Statistics 4: ***Enrichment*** p.85	Lesson Quiz: **TE** p.697	Skills Practice 44, #5–7: ***SPMR*** p.56	Calculator Worksheet 32: ***Technology*** p.34	**16-2**
Statistics Keys: **SE** p.703 TI-81 Investigation 5: **SE** pp.866–868	Lesson Quiz: **TE** p.702 Quiz 31: ***Assessment*** p.39	Spreadsheet Activity 11: ***Technology*** pp.74–76	Calculator Worksheet 33: ***Technology*** p.35 Spreadsheet Activity 11: ***Technology*** pp.73–75 Statistics Keys: **SE** p.703 TI-81 Investigation 5: **SE** pp.866–868	**16-3**
Writing to Learn: **SE** p.709 ✂ Manipulative Activity 16: ***Enrichment*** p.57	Lesson Quiz: **TE** p.707 Mixed Review 31: ***SPMR*** p.95	Skills Practice 45, #1–4: ***SPMR*** p.57		**16-4**
Math Point: **TE** p.712 Activity: **SE** p.714	Lesson Quiz: **TE** p.712	Skills Practice 45, #5: ***SPMR*** p.57	BASIC Computer Project 19: ***Technology*** p.99	**16-5**
Writing to Learn: **SE** p.720 Problem Solving: **SE** p.721 Problem 16: Computer Assisted Problem Solving, **SE** pp.851–852	Lesson Quiz: **TE** p.718 Quiz 32: ***Assessment*** p.40	Skills Practice 45, #6–7: ***SPMR*** p.57	Calculator Worksheet 34: ***Technology*** p.36 Problem 16: Computer Assisted Problem Solving, **SE** pp.851–852	**16-6**
	Summary and Review: **SE** pp.722–724 Test: **SE** p.725			**Review**
	Chapter 16 Test: ***Assessment*** pp.137–142(reg.), pp.187–188 (adv.)			**Test**
	Cumulative Review: **SE** pp.834–837			**Cum Review**
	End-of-year Test: ***Assessment*** pp.231–234(reg.), pp.237–244(reg.), p.235(finite), or pp.245–246(finite)			**End-of-year Test**

The solution to the problem posed on the facing page can be found on page 697.

Ready for Statistics and Data Analysis?

12-5 Use Table 2 to find these logarithms.

1. log 9.14 0.9609
2. log 5.27 0.7218
3. log 0.000124 6.0934 − 10 or −3.9066
4. log 67100 5.1733 − 10 or 4.8267

12-8 Use Table 3 to find these natural logarithms.

5. ln 1.85 0.6152
6. ln 0.0376 −3.2806
7. ln 12.9 2.4131

14-1 Rename and evaluate each sum.

8. $\sum_{n=1}^{8} \frac{n}{2}$ $\frac{1}{2} + \frac{2}{2} + \frac{3}{2} + \frac{4}{2} + \frac{5}{2} + \frac{6}{2} + \frac{7}{2} + \frac{8}{2} = 18$

9. $\sum_{n=1}^{5} 3^n$ $3 + 9 + 27 + 81 + 243 = 363$

10. $\sum_{n=1}^{4} \left(\frac{2^n - 5}{4}\right)$ $-\frac{3}{4} + -\frac{1}{4} + \frac{3}{4} + \frac{11}{4} = \frac{10}{4} = 2.5$

CHAPTER 16

Statistics and Data Analysis

The Dow Jones Industrial Average is a measure of stock market performance using the performance of 30 well-known stocks. Construct a box and whisker plot of the gains and losses of the 30 stocks.

Stock	Change	Stock	Change
Allied-sig	−3/8	IntPaper	−3/8
Alcoa	−1/2	McDonalds	−1 1/4
AmerExp	−5/8	Merck	−5/8
AmerT&T	−1/4	MinnM&M	−1 3/8
BethSteel	−1/4	Navistar	+1/8
Boeing	−1 3/8	PhilMorr	−3/4
Chevron	−1/8	Primerica	−3/4
CocaCola	−3/8	Proct&Gm	−7/8
DuPont	−1 3/4	SearsRoe	−1/8
EastKod	−5/8	Texaco	+1/8
Exxon	−	USX	+3/8
GenElec	−1/8	UnionCarb	−3/8
GenMotors	−1 1/2	UnitedTch	+1/2
Goodyear	−3/4	Westnghs	−1
IBM	−3/8	Woolworth	+1 1/4

16-1

FIRST FIVE MINUTES

1. The organizers of a race are giving away t-shirts with 5 different logos. Use a simulation to find the probability that in a group of 4 people, at least 2 receive the same shirt.
   Answers will vary. The probability is about 0.65.

Stem-and-Leaf Diagrams

Point out that a stem-and-leaf diagram that is rotated one-quarter turn counterclockwise resembles a histogram.

Point out that the stem-and-leaf diagram is a quick and easy way to organize a set of numeric data. There is a choice for the stem. For example, if the data consist of numbers like 15, 23, 52, then single-digit stems are appropriate. On the other hand, if the data consist of numbers like 54,222, 54,541, 54,833, then stems like 542, 543, 545, . . . are more appropriate.

Key Questions

What stems would you use for each of the following data sets?

- 76, 54, 63, 14, 87, 59, 64, 26, 91
  1, 2, . . . , 9
- 123, 134, 146, 132, 144
  12, 13, 14
- 2345, 2130, 2556, 2483, 2200, 2312
  21, 22, 23, 24, 25

16-1 Statistics: Organizing Data

Statistics is the branch of mathematics that is concerned with the collection, organization, display, and interpretation of data. Many problems are solved and important decisions made using statistical methods.

Stem-and-Leaf Diagrams

Objective: Construct a stem-and-leaf diagram for a set of data.

We can organize data by placing them in charts and tables or ordering them in some way. Another useful way to organize data is to construct a **stem-and-leaf diagram.**

EXAMPLE 1 Here is a set of systolic blood pressures of 40 patients.

Construct a stem-and-leaf diagram.

122, 143, 156, 162, 134, 122, 119, 136, 148, 160, 146, 154, 132, 116, 153, 143, 129, 121, 143, 154, 127, 118, 128, 120, 163, 156, 117, 128, 149, 135, 143, 167, 139, 121, 115, 163, 157, 138, 129, 143

As we look at this set of data we see that there are some numbers in the 110s, some in the 120s, some in the 130s and so on. We use this idea to construct a stem-and-leaf diagram. We split each numeral into two parts: a stem, such as 11 or 15, and a leaf, such as 2 or 5. The first value, 122, is split into 12 and 2. We write the leaf, 2, in the row opposite the stem, 12.

Stem	Leaf
11	9, 6, 8, 7, 5
12	2, 2, 9, 1, 7, 8, 0, 8, 1, 9
13	4, 6, 2, 5, 9, 8
14	3, 8, 6, 3, 3, 9, 3, 3
15	6, 4, 3, 4, 6, 7
16	2, 0, 3, 7, 3

We can see that the stem-and-leaf diagram has organized the data for us. It is easy to find the lowest blood pressure, 115, and the highest, 167. Also, it is obvious that in this set of patients, most had a systolic blood pressure in the 120s.

Try This See Selected Answers.

a. Here is a set of cholesterol readings for 35 male patients in the 40-year age bracket. Construct a stem-and-leaf diagram.
132, 122, 143, 126, 154, 164, 126, 121, 148, 132, 135, 125, 137, 120, 129, 127, 132, 145, 164, 154, 143, 153, 123, 128, 132, 148, 144, 153, 132, 126, 143, 125, 131, 173, 123

EXAMPLE 2 Here is the set of gasoline octane ratings of a sample of 21 producers. Construct a stem-and-leaf diagram.

87.6, 84.8, 84.9, 86.2, 88.6, 89.5, 84.6, 85.4, 84.8, 86.3, 87.6, 86.7, 85.2, 86.5, 87.3, 88.8, 85.3, 86.2, 85.3, 87.3, 91.2

To eliminate the decimal point we multiply each value by 10. When reading from the diagram we must remember to reverse the process.

Stem	Leaf
84	8, 9, 6, 8
85	4, 2, 3, 3
86	2, 3, 7, 5, 2
87	6, 6, 3, 3
88	6, 8
89	5
90	
91	2

Sometimes the leaves in a stem-and-leaf diagram are arranged in order from least to greatest. This is called a **ranked stem-and-leaf diagram.**

Try This See Selected Answers.

b. Here is a set of earned-run averages for former big-league pitcher Red Ruffing. Construct a stem-and-leaf diagram.
6.65, 5.01, 4.39, 4.66, 3.89, 4.86, 4.38, 4.41, 3.09, 3.91, 3.93, 3.12, 3.85, 2.98, 3.31, 2.93, 3.38, 3.54, 3.21, 2.89, 1.77, 6.11

Frequency Distributions

Objective: Construct a frequency distribution for a set of data.

A stem-and-leaf diagram records every value. We can also organize data by constructing a **frequency distribution.** In a frequency distribution we may group data into intervals. Then we indicate how frequently values fall within that interval. A general rule is to form 10 to 15 intervals. We can also show the **relative frequency** by dividing the frequency by the total number of values.

EXAMPLE 3 Here is the height, in feet, of 20 of the world's waterfalls. Construct a frequency distribution. Show the relative frequency.

2415, 2154, 3212, 1304, 1500, 1612, 1841, 1259, 2625, 1904, 2000, 1325, 3110, 1650, 2120, 1280, 1600, 1476, 1400, 2540

We see that the highest waterfall is 3212 ft and the lowest is 1259 ft. The difference between 3212 and 1259 is 1953. Suppose we decide to have about ten intervals. We divide 1953 by 10. This gives us 195.3, which suggests that the interval be 200. Thus the intervals can be 1201–1400, 1401–1600, and so on.

Chalkboard Examples

1. Construct a stem-and-leaf diagram for the following set of weights.
110, 132, 174, 102, 176, 157, 193, 135, 128, 153, 173, 147, 183, 175

Stem	Leaf
10	2
11	0
12	8
13	2, 5
14	7
15	7, 3
16	
17	4, 6, 3, 5
18	3
19	3

2. Construct a stem-and-leaf diagram for the temperature readings below.
98.2, 97.7, 99.7, 93.3, 95.6, 96.0, 97.3, 95.2, 96.2, 97.8, 94.6, 98.5, 96.9, 97.6, 93.8, 95.4, 96.1, 97.0, 95.2, 98.7

Stem	Leaf
93	3, 8
94	6
95	6, 2, 4, 2
96	0, 2, 9, 1
97	7, 3, 8, 6, 0
98	2, 5, 7
99	7

Frequency Distributions

Chalkboard Example

1. Here are the weights, in pounds, of twenty elk that were tagged and weighed for scientific study. Construct a frequency distribution and show the relative frequency.
243, 642, 823, 561, 784, 357, 685, 946, 802, 380, 582, 190, 476, 387, 631, 578, 694, 574, 604, 485

Interval	Tally	Freq	Rel f
100–199	I	1	0.05
200–299	I	1	0.05
300–399	III	3	0.15
400–499	II	2	0.10
500–599	IIII	4	0.20
600–699	~~IIII~~	5	0.25
700–799	I	1	0.05
800–899	II	2	0.10
900–999	I	1	0.05

LESSON QUIZ

1. Construct a stem-and-leaf diagram for the following data.
24, 54, 65, 87, 59, 31, 76, 92, 67, 83

Stem	Leaf
1	
2	4
3	1
4	
5	4, 9
6	5, 7
7	6
8	7, 3
9	2

2. Construct a frequency distribution for the following data.
641, 755, 356, 912, 239, 416, 588, 383, 527, 748, 673, 589, 436, 540

Interval	Tally	Frequency
200 – 299	I	1
300 – 399	II	2
400 – 499	II	2
500 – 599	IIII	4
600 – 699	II	2
700 – 799	II	2
800 – 899		0
900 – 999	I	1

Assignment Guide
Algebra: Omit

Alg w/Finite Math: 1–10 e/o, 11, MR

Comprehensive: 1–10 e/o, 11, 12, MR

ADDITIONAL ANSWERS

Exercises

1.

Stem	Leaf
0	0, 4, 3, 2, 6
1	1
2	9, 5, 2
3	5, 4
4	1, 6, 7, 6, 9, 6, 1
5	4, 9, 4
6	0

For Exercises 2 and 3, see Teacher's Answer Section.

Interval	Tally	f Frequency	f/n Relative Frequency
1201 – 1400	IIII̸	5	0.25
1401 – 1600	III	3	0.15
1601 – 1800	II	2	0.10
1801 – 2000	III	3	0.15
2001 – 2200	II	2	0.10
2201 – 2400		0	0.00
2401 – 2600	II	2	0.10
2601 – 2800	I	1	0.05
2801 – 3000		0	0.00
3001 – 3200	I	1	0.05
3201 – 3400	I	1	0.05

Try This See Selected Answers.

c. Here is a set of raw scores on a standardized algebra test. Construct a frequency distribution. Show the relative frequency.

32, 21, 40, 22, 15, 14, 23, 34, 19, 22, 26, 34, 36, 21, 29, 23, 38, 15, 27, 26, 38, 31, 20, 25, 33, 24, 21, 17, 16, 25, 35, 37, 23, 32, 19, 27, 28, 32

16-1 EXERCISES

A

Here are four sets of data. Construct a stem-and-leaf diagram for

1. the numbers of home runs hit by Babe Ruth each year of his career.

0, 4, 3, 2, 11, 29, 54, 59, 35, 41, 46, 25, 47, 60, 54, 46, 49, 46, 41, 34, 22, 6

2. the radar-recorded speeds, in miles per hour, of cars traveling on an interstate highway.

56, 63, 49, 56, 55, 49, 61, 60, 63, 58, 59, 60, 49, 57, 68, 56, 55, 46, 65, 67, 54, 53, 58, 63, 61, 64, 56, 64, 48

3. the number of ounces dispensed per drink from a sample of vending machines that are supposed to serve seven ounces.

5.5, 6.5, 7.0, 6.7, 3.9, 5.6, 6.7, 7.1, 4.5, 6.7, 6.8, 6.9, 7.0, 5.9, 6.8, 4.6, 3.8, 4.8, 6.5, 4.9, 4.0, 6.8, 7.2, 5.6, 7.0, 6.9, 6.5, 6.7, 4.8, 4.9, 4.9, 5.9

4. the height, in inches, of a sample of a variety of wheat.

13.6, 16.4, 14.8, 16.9, 17.2, 13.6, 17.4, 18.3, 16.4, 15.8, 13.9, 21.5, 16.5, 14.7, 23.9, 15.2, 13.8, 20.6, 12.5, 16.8, 15.4, 18.9, 25.4, 23.8, 17.9, 13.6, 22.4, 18.5, 17.4, 19.0, 20.7, 22.5, 21.2, 14.6, 18.9, 17.6, 14.2, 21.3, 15.6, 17.4, 12.5, 21.5, 19.6, 14.8, 19.2

Construct a frequency distribution showing the relative frequency for

5. the numbers of hours it took for a sample of 40 light bulbs to burn out.

990, 987, 1065, 1203, 996, 1206, 1332, 1502, 1563, 1290, 1339, 1432, 898, 1356, 1465, 1604, 1365, 989, 1546, 1453, 1676, 1221, 1546, 1453, 987, 1205, 1546, 1332, 1435, 1543, 1632, 1365, 1229, 1548, 1453, 1332, 1602, 1544, 1475, 1322

6. the time, in seconds, of 28 runners to run the 200-yard dash.

25.4, 27.6, 24.9, 25.7, 25.6, 24.8, 27.8, 25.6, 26.7, 27.8, 26.9, 25.8, 28.8, 26.8, 25.7, 26.9, 27.2, 26.5, 25.9, 26.6, 27.8, 25.9, 25.2, 27.4, 27.4, 28.1, 27.3, 26.4

7. the height, in feet, of some of the principal active volcanoes of the world.

19,882, 19,652, 19,347, 19,167, 18,504, 17,887, 17,159, 16,197, 15,913, 15,604, 13,812, 13,680, 13,350, 13,333, 12,582, 12,450, 12,224, 12,198, 12,080, 12,060, 11,385, 11,339, 11,268, 11,253, 11,247, 11,070, 10,705, 10,453, 9,351

8. the diastolic blood pressure of 42 patients.

89, 99, 72, 87, 69, 78, 74, 69, 90, 88, 76, 65, 99, 78, 89, 87, 69, 90, 102, 86, 76, 84, 100, 89, 73, 78, 89, 76, 70, 64, 87, 79, 97, 90, 76, 69, 78, 89, 69, 70, 74, 73

B

9. Study the stem-and-leaf diagrams made in Exercises 1-4. How can you draw a simple bar graph of the data?

10. List some advantages and disadvantages of using a stem-and-leaf diagram for a set of data. Do the same for a frequency distribution.

11. ***Critical Thinking*** Given only the frequency distribution from Example 3, devise a method of estimating the average height of the 20 waterfalls.

Challenge

12. Use your frequency distribution from Exercise 5. What is the probability that a light bulb will burn at least 1500 hours?

Mixed Review

For each hyperbola find the center, vertices, foci, and asymptotes, and then graph the hyperbola. **13.** $x^2 - 4x - y^2 - 10y = 30$ **14.** $16y^2 + 96y - 25x^2 - 50x = 281$

Find the number of permutations of the letters of these words.

15. MULTIDIMENSIONAL **16.** NANOSECOND **17.** TERRITORIALISM

18. Find the variation constant and an equation of variation where y varies inversely as x and the following are true.
a. $y = 3$ when $x = 6$ **b.** $y = -4$ when $x = -2$ **c.** $y = 4$ when $x = 7$

Problem for Programmers

Write a program to construct a frequency distribution for a set of data. Test your program using Example 3 and Try This c.

4.

Stem	Leaf
12	5, 5
13	6, 6, 9, 8, 6
14	8, 7, 6, 2, 8
15	8, 2, 4, 6
16	4, 9, 4, 5, 8
17	2, 4, 9, 4, 6, 4
18	3, 9, 5, 9
19	0, 6, 2
20	6, 7
21	5, 2, 3, 5
22	4, 5
23	9, 8
24	
25	4

5.

Interval	Frequency	Rel f
801 – 900	1	0.025
901 – 1000	5	0.125
1001 – 1100	1	0.025
1101 – 1200	0	0
1201 – 1300	6	0.15
1301 – 1400	8	0.2
1401 – 1500	7	0.175
1501 – 1600	8	0.2
1601 – 1700	4	0.1

For Exercises 6–12, see Teacher's Answer Section.

Mixed Review

For graphs of Exercises 13 and 14, see Teacher's Answer Section.

13. Center: (2, −5)
Vertices: (−1, −5), (5, −5)
Foci: $(2 - 3\sqrt{2}, -5)$, $(2 + 3\sqrt{2}, -5)$
Asymptotes: $y + 5 = \pm(x - 2)$

14. Center: (−1, −3)
Vertices: (−1, −8), (−1, 2)
Foci: $(-1, -3 - \sqrt{41})$, $(-1, -3 + \sqrt{41})$
Asymptotes: $y + 3 = \pm\frac{5}{4}(x + 1)$

15. 4.35891×10^{11}
16. 302,400
17. 1.2108×10^9
18. a. $y = \frac{18}{x}$
b. $y = \frac{8}{x}$
c. $y = \frac{28}{x}$

16-2

FIRST FIVE MINUTES

1. Construct a frequency distribution for the following set of data.
935, 654, 123, 453, 765, 846, 246, 943, 567, 456, 764, 568, 432, 569

Interval	Tally	Frequency
100–199	I	1
200–299	I	1
300–399		0
400–499	III	3
500–599	III	3
600–699	I	1
700–799	II	2
800–899	I	1
900–999	II	2

Central Tendency

Note that a measure of central tendency may be misleading for some sets of data. Give the following three examples as an illustration.

For 1, 2, 3, 5, 89, the mean is 20, yet 20 does not seem to be representative of the data. The median may be a better measure here.

For 1, 2, 4, 3, 5, 56, 56, the mode is 56; however, 56 does not seem to be very representative of the data. The mean or median may be a better measure.

For 1, 2, 3, 99, 100, the median is 3; this is also not very representative. The mean may be a better measure.

Also note that any set of data has only one mean and one median, but may have more than one mode. A set of data with two modes, such as 1, 2, 5, 8, 5, 6, 2, is said to be **bimodal.** A set of data with more than one mode is **multimodal.**

Key Questions

- Must the mean appear in a set of data?
No
- Does every set of data have a mode?
No
- If a set of data has a mode, must it appear in the data?
Yes
- If there are 5 values in a data set that are less than the median, how many values are higher than the median?
5

16-2 Using Measures of Central Tendency

Central Tendency

Objective: Find the mean, median, and mode of a set of data.

When considering a set of data, it is reasonable to look for a single number that is representative of the entire set. Numbers at the middle or center of the set of data serve this purpose well. There are a variety of ways of thinking of the center of a set of data. One way that is often used is the **mean** or **average.** To find the mean of a set of data, we add all the values and divide by the number of values. The mean is usually denoted by $\bar{x}$ and the formula for finding the mean is

$$\bar{x} = \frac{\sum_{i=1}^{n} x_i}{n}$$

EXAMPLE 1 Here is a set of golf scores for a club tournament. Find the mean score.

81, 78, 79, 80, 76, 88, 83, 90, 87, 76, 79, 83, 74, 82, 76

There are 15 scores, so $n = 15$.

First we find the sum, then we divide by 15.

$$\bar{x} = \frac{\sum_{i=1}^{15} x_i}{15} = \frac{1212}{15} = 80.8$$

The mean score is 80.8.

When we look at the scores in Example 1 we can see that they tend to fall around 80. Thus the mean 80.8 is a representative score.

Try This

a. Here is a set of weights, in pounds, of players on a high school football team. Find the mean weight. 189.4 pounds

178, 192, 201, 217, 195, 176, 202, 183, 179, 221, 203, 188, 192, 178, 187, 203, 221, 234, 196, 184, 173, 183, 180, 191, 179, 173, 182, 187, 191, 178, 172, 184, 179, 177, 185, 183, 179

Another value which can be used to represent a set of data is the **mode.** The mode is the value that occurs most often.

EXAMPLE 2 Here is a stem-and-leaf diagram of a set of pulse rates. Find the mode.

Stem	Leaf
6	8, 8, 3, 7, 9
7	1, 2, 3, 2, 1, 0, 0, 5, 2, 3, 1, 1, 4, 8, 1, 1
8	0, 1, 1, 0, 3, 2, 2, 0

By inspecting the stem-and-leaf diagram, we see that the mode is 71.

Try This

b. Here is a set of diastolic blood pressures. Find the mode. 78

Stem	Leaf
6	7, 9, 4, 7, 9
7	8, 8, 9, 0, 3, 2, 5, 8, 6, 8, 0, 2, 2, 6, 8, 4, 8, 4
8	2, 6, 4, 7, 9, 0, 0, 3, 1
9	1, 8, 7, 2, 0, 4
10	0, 9, 7, 4, 0, 2, 3, 7

A third central value which can be used to represent a set of data is the median. The median is the middle value when all the values are arranged in order. For instance, the median of the five numbers 11, 16, 27, 34 and 51 is the third number, 27.

EXAMPLE 3 Here is a stem-and-leaf diagram showing the number of home runs hit each year from 1954 to 1976 by Hank Aaron. Find the median number of home runs.

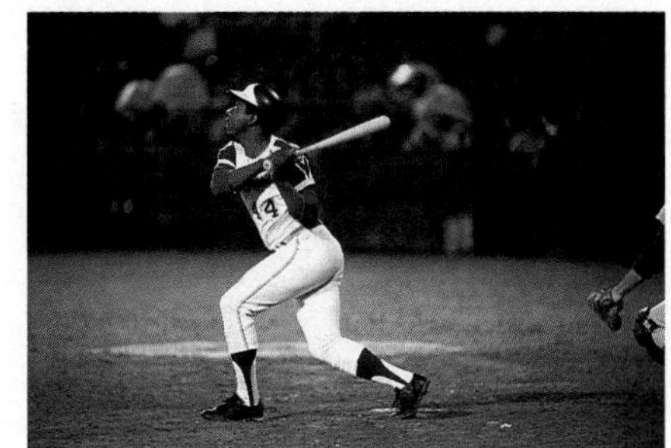

Stem	Leaf
1	3, 2, 0
2	7, 6, 4, 9, 0
3	0, 9, 4, 2, 9, 8, 4
4	4, 0, 5, 4, 4, 4, 7, 0

The stem-and-leaf diagram makes it easy to arrange the numbers from least to greatest.

10, 12, 13, 20, 24, 26, 27, 29, 30, 32, 34, 34, 38, 39, 39, 40, 40, 44, 44, 44, 44, 45, 47

There are 23 numbers. Thus the median is the 12th number, 34. The median number of home runs hit by Hank Aaron is 34.

There will always be exactly one middle value if there is an odd number of values. If the number of values is even, then we use the average of the two middle values as the median. For instance, the median of 17, 20, 24, 33, 41, and 52 is $\frac{24 + 33}{2}$ or 28.5.

Chalkboard Examples

1. Find the mean for the following set of numbers.

   3, 2, 3, 4, 6, 6, 4, 3, 2, 7 $\frac{40}{10} = 4$

2. Find the mode of the data presented in the following stem-and-leaf diagram.

Stem	Leaf
5	1, 5, 2, 1, 1, 3
6	4, 0, 1
7	6, 2, 3, 5

   The mode is 51.

3. Find the median for the data in the following stem-and-leaf diagram.

Stem	Leaf
12	1, 5, 7
13	6, 2, 3, 5, 0
14	8, 1, 0
15	5, 2

   The median is 135.

Box and Whisker Plots

You may want to point out that the lower whisker, lower hinge, upper hinge, and upper whisker are also known as the first, second, third, and fourth quartiles, respectively.

Chalkboard Example (*T26*)

1. Here is a stem-and-leaf diagram of a data set. Construct a box and whisker plot.

Stem	Leaf
5	2
6	5, 2
7	4, 9, 2, 3
8	1, 0, 8, 3
9	6, 9, 2, 5, 1
10	0, 3, 1
11	4, 6, 2
12	2, 5
13	4

The median is 92. There are 12 values above and 12 values below the median. The lower hinge is at 76.5. The upper hinge is at 107.5. We use these values to construct a box and whisker plot.

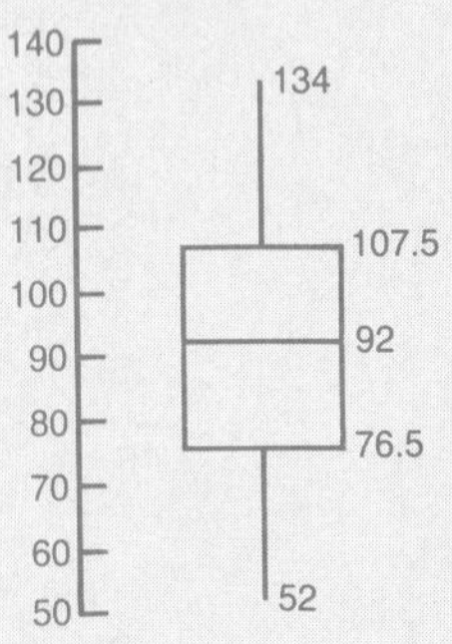

Try This

c. Here is a stem-and-leaf diagram of the number of home run hits by Willie Mays from 1951 to 1973. Find the median. 31.5

Stem	Leaf
0	4, 8, 6
1	3, 8
2	0, 9, 9, 2, 3, 8
3	6, 5, 4, 8, 7
4	1, 0, 9, 7
5	1, 2

Box and Whisker Plots

Objective: Construct a box and whisker plot of a set of data.

Data can be displayed in charts, graphs, and tables. Another method of displaying a set of data is a box and whisker plot. To make a box and whisker plot we first find the median. This divides the set of data in half. We then find the upper hinge, or the median of the upper half of the data. Next we find the lower hinge, or the median of the lower half of the data. A box is then drawn that encloses the middle half of the data. A thin whisker is drawn from the box to the highest value and lowest value. Here is a box and whisker plot of the number of home runs hit by Hank Aaron.

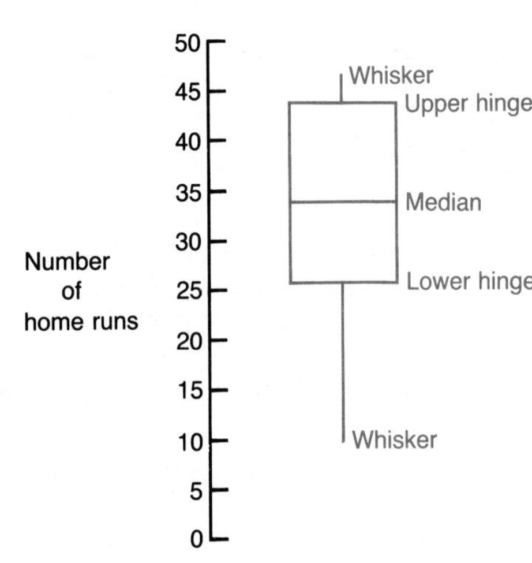

The box and whisker plot gives us a picture of the set of data. We can easily see that in most years Hank Aaron hit over 25 home runs.

EXAMPLE 4

Here is a stem-and-leaf diagram of the number of stories in 29 buildings.
Construct a box and whisker plot of the data.

Stem	Leaf
2	8
3	3
4	8, 6
5	4, 2, 7, 2, 7, 9
6	0, 0, 4, 0, 4, 0, 2, 7
7	0, 4, 1, 1, 2, 7
8	0
10	0, 2
11	0, 0

We find that the median is the 15th value or 62. There are 14 values above and below the median. The lower hinge is the median of the 14 lower values. Thus the lower hinge is midway between the seventh and eighth values of 54 and 57. It is 55.5. The upper hinge is the median of the 14 upper values. Thus it is between the seventh and eighth values above the median, or between the 22nd and 23rd values of 72 and 74. It is 73. We use these numbers to construct the box and whisker plot.

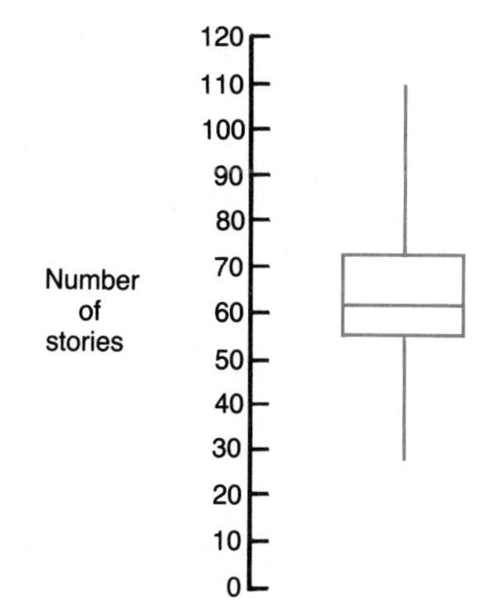

EXAMPLE 5 The Dow Jones Industrial Average is a measure of stock market performance using the performance of 30 well-known stocks. Construct a box and whisker plot of the gains and losses of the 30 stocks.

The range is from $-1\frac{3}{4}$ to $1\frac{1}{4}$. Writing the values in order,

$-1\frac{3}{4}, -1\frac{1}{2}, -1\frac{3}{8}, -1\frac{3}{8}, -1\frac{1}{4}, -1,$

$-\frac{7}{8}, -\frac{3}{4}, -\frac{3}{4}, -\frac{3}{4}, -\frac{5}{8}, -\frac{5}{8}, -\frac{5}{8}, -\frac{1}{2},$

$-\frac{3}{8}, -\frac{3}{8}, -\frac{3}{8}, -\frac{3}{8}, -\frac{3}{8}, -\frac{1}{4}, -\frac{1}{4},$

$-\frac{1}{8}, -\frac{1}{8}, -\frac{1}{8}, 0, \frac{1}{8}, \frac{1}{8}, \frac{3}{8}, \frac{1}{2}, 1\frac{1}{4}$

Allied-sig	−3/8	IntPaper	−3/8
Alcoa	−1/2	McDonalds	−1 1/4
AmerExp	−5/8	Merck	−5/8
AmerT&T	−1/4	MinnM&M	−1 3/8
BethSteel	−1/4	Navistar	+1/8
Boeing	−1 3/8	PhilMorr	−3/4
Chevron	−1/8	Primerica	−3/4
CocaCola	−3/8	Proct&Gm	−7/8
DuPont	−1 3/4	SearsRoe	−1/8
EastKod	−5/8	Texaco	+1/8
Exxon	−	USX	+3/8
GenElec	−1/8	UnionCarb	−3/8
GenMotors	−1 1/2	UnitedTch	+1/2
Goodyear	−3/4	Westnghs	−1
IBM	−3/8	Woolworth	+1 1/4

LESSON QUIZ

1. Find the mean of the following data set.
   4, 7, 3, 5, 7, 2, 3, 6, 7, 6
   $\frac{50}{10} = 5$
2. Find the median of the following data set.
   7, 3, 5, 6, 8, 2, 1, 1, 9
   5
3. Find the mode of the following data set
   1, 4, 5, 1, 2, 6, 4, 1, 4, 1, 5, 4, 4, 3, 5
   4

Assignment Guide
Algebra: Omit

Alg w/Finite Math: 1–15 m3, 16, MR

Comprehensive: 1–15 m3, 16–18, MR

ADDITIONAL ANSWERS

Try This

d.

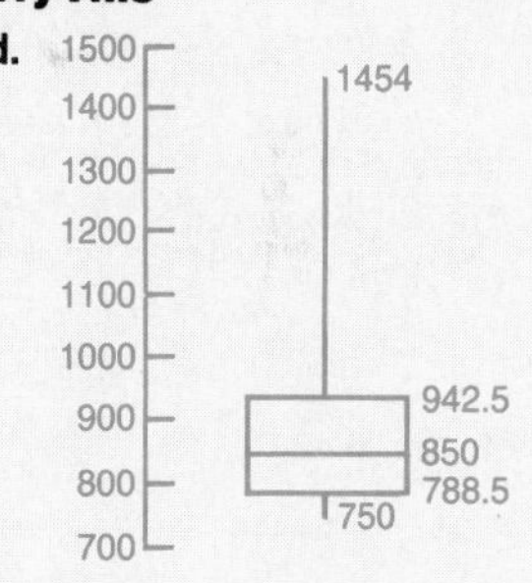

Exercises

1. Mean 831, median 794, mode 794
2. Mean 73.6, median 74, mode 74
3. Mean 99.97, median 98.7, mode 98.6
4. Mean 61.3, median 54.9, mode none
5. Mean 273.6, median 106, mode none
6. Mean 14.1, median 16, mode 20

7.
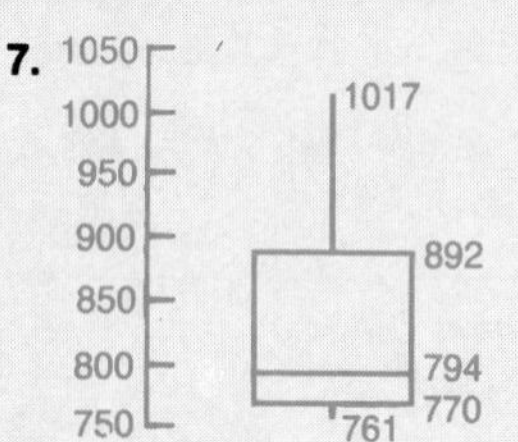

8.
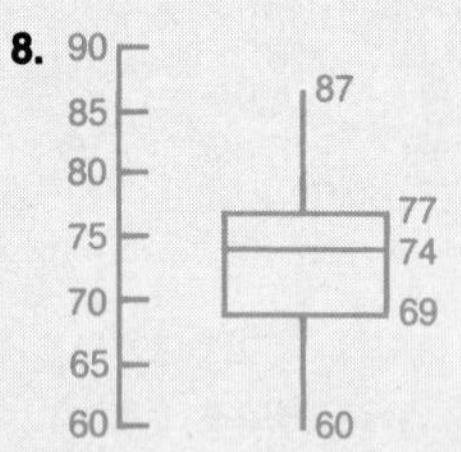

9.
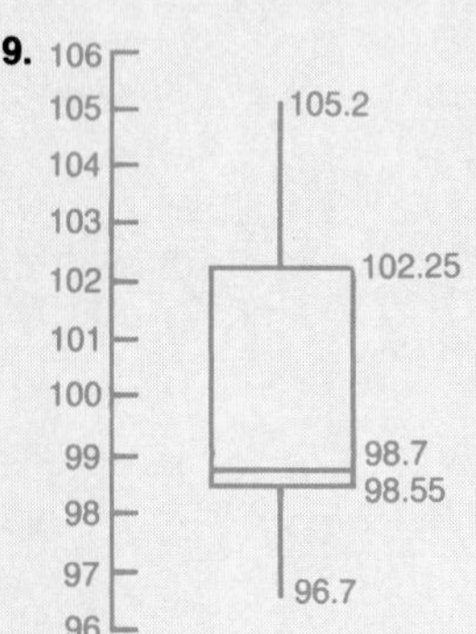

10.
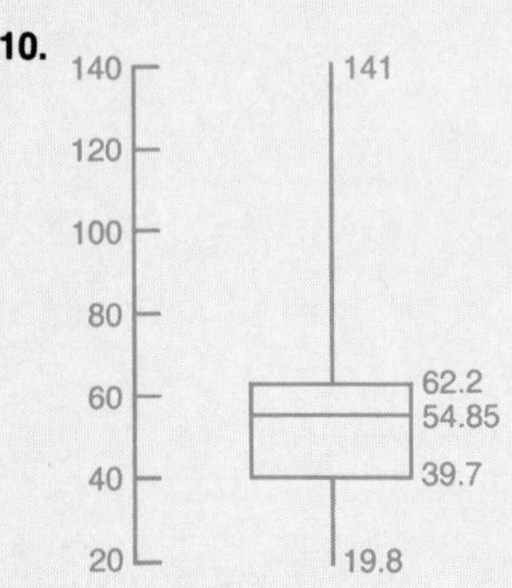

The median change is the average of the 15th and 16th values. These are both $-\frac{3}{8}$, so the median is $-\frac{3}{8}$.

There are 15 values below the median, so the lower hinge is the 8th value, $-\frac{3}{4}$. There are 15 values above the median, so the upper hinge is the 8th value from the end, $-\frac{1}{8}$.

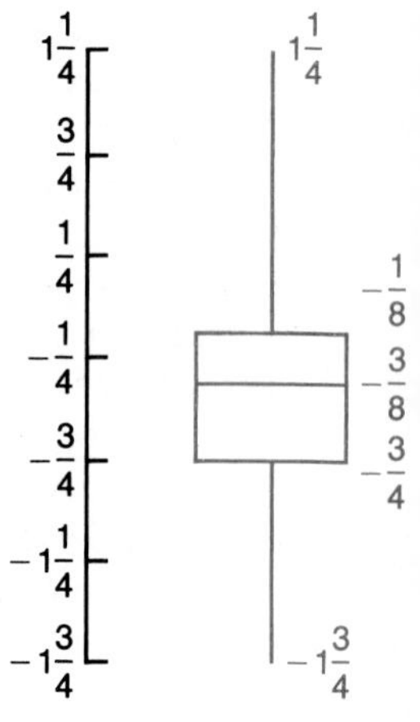

Try This See Additional Answers.

d. Here is a stem-and-leaf diagram of the heights, in feet, of 29 of the world's tallest buildings. Construct a box and whisker plot.

Stem	Leaf
7	50, 50, 56, 64, 78, 84, 87, 90, 92
8	00, 08, 13, 41, 50, 50, 53, 58, 59
9	00, 14, 27, 35, 50
10	46
11	27, 36
12	50
13	50
14	54

16-2 EXERCISES

A

Here are six sets of data. For each set of data find the mean, median, and mode of

1. the heights, in feet, of some of the world's highest dams.

Stem	Leaf
7	64, 77, 61, 70, 94, 78, 94
8	92, 58
9	32
10	17

2. the pulse rate for a set of 30 patients.

Stem	Leaf
6	8, 6, 7, 5, 3, 9, 0, 6
7	3, 7, 4, 8, 2, 1, 2, 7, 4, 4, 6, 4, 5, 4, 3, 4
8	0, 5, 2, 2, 7, 1

3. the temperatures, in degrees Fahrenheit, for a set of 40 patients.

97.8, 96.7, 98.6, 100.3, 102.1, 97.8, 98.8, 98.6, 98.5, 102.4, 103.2, 104.1, 98.6, 98.5, 97.3, 98.7, 103.6, 102.4, 98.6, 98.6, 97.9, 99.9, 97.4, 98.6, 98.6, 99.7, 101.7, 104.8, 103.6, 98.7, 99.0, 98.6, 105.2, 98.6, 99.3, 97.9, 98.5, 102.7, 103.8, 98.9

4. the lengths, in miles, of ten of the world's longest canals.

53, 62.2, 28, 39.7, 141, 60.9, 50.7, 19.8, 100.6, 56.7

5. the distances, in light years from earth, of 22 of the brightest stars.

8.7, 200, 4.4, 36, 26, 42, 850, 11, 127, 360, 16, 650, 65, 270, 260, 430, 35, 23, 1500, 530, 85, 490

6. the number of games won per year by former Orioles pitcher Jim Palmer.

5, 15, 3, 16, 20, 20, 21, 22, 7, 21, 10, 16, 23, 22, 20, 7, 15, 5, 0

7–12. Construct a box and whisker plot for each set of data in Exercises 1 – 6.

B

13. The mean of a set of data can be affected by any extreme value. Recalculate the mean of the distances in Exercise 5, but omit the distance to Deneb of 1500 light years. How are the mean and median affected? The median decreases to 85; the mean decreases to 215.2.

14. Collect a set of data on some topic that is of interest to you. Find the mean, median, and mode for the set of data, and construct a box and whisker plot. Answers may vary.

15. If a set of data has two modes it is said to be **bimodal**. Are any of the six sets of data in Exercises 1 – 6 bimodal? No

16. ***Critical Thinking*** Make up small sets of data with the following conditions.

a. mean < median < mode Ex. 1, 5, 6,6, mean = 4.5, median = 5.5, mode = 6

b. mode < mean < median Ex. 1, 1, 7, 8, 9, mode = 1, mean = 5.2, median = 7

c. median < mean < mode Ex. 1, 2, 3, 9, 9, median = 3, mean = 4.8, mode = 9

Challenge

17. The mean is sensitive to extremely high or low values. A **trimmed** mean is found by ordering the values from least to greatest, deleting an equal number from each end, and finding the mean of the remaining values. The **trimming percentage** is the percentage of values that were deleted. Find a trimmed mean for the distances to the brightest stars in Exercise 5 by deleting two values from each end, and find the trimming percentage. 203.1; 18.2%

18. Suppose an element is added to a set of data that has a greater value than any element already present in the set. Of the mean, median, and mode, which will be affected the least by the new element? Why?

Mixed Review

Find the center, vertices, and foci of each ellipse.

19. $x^2 - 2x + 4y^2 - 16y = -13$ 20. $16x^2 - 64x + 25y^2 + 150y = 111$

Find a polynomial of lowest degree with

21. rational coefficients and $(3 - 2i)$, $\sqrt{6}$ as some of its roots.

11.

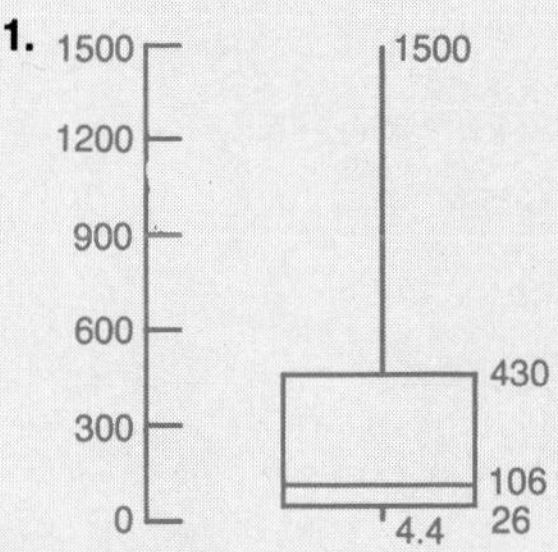

12.

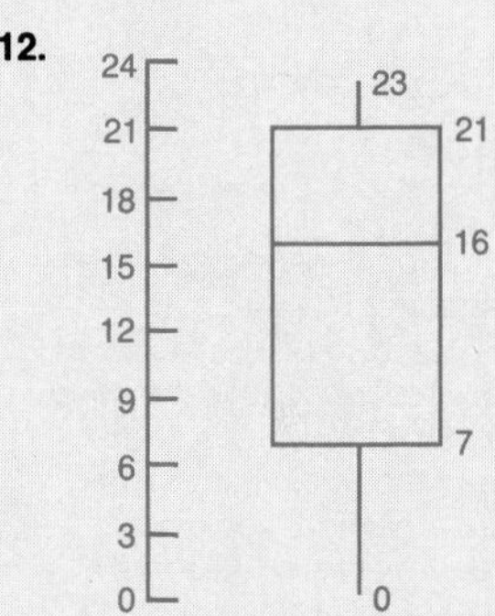

18. **Since it is the only element with this value, it will not effect the mode.**

Mixed Review

19. **Center: (1, 2)**
Vertices: (−1, 2), (3, 2), (1, 1), (1, 3)
Foci: $(1 - \sqrt{3}, 2), (1 + \sqrt{3}, 2)$

20. **Center: (2, −3)**
Vertices: (−3, −3), (7, −3), (2, −7), (2, 1)
Foci: (−1, −3), (5, −3)

21. $f(x) = x^4 - 6x^3 + 7x^2 + 36x - 78$

16-3

FIRST FIVE MINUTES

Here is a set of data.
6, 7, 4, 3, 1, 7, 7

1. Find the mean.
   5
2. Find the median.
   6
3. Find the mode.
   7

Range and Mean Deviation

Point out that while the range is the easiest measure of variation to calculate, it can also be the most misleading. This is because the range depends on only two entries, the minimum and the maximum.

The mean deviation, however, considers every entry of data and is a better measure of variance.

Key Questions

- Can a set have a range of 0? If so, give an example.
  Yes, any set of data that is made up of the same entry
- Can the mean be negative?
  Yes
- Can the mean deviation be negative?
  No

Chalkboard Example

1. Find the mean deviation for the following data set.
   5, 7, 3, 2, 1, 8, 3, 6, 9, 6
   The mean is $\frac{50}{10} = 5$. The absolute deviations from 5 are 0, 2, 2, 3, 4, 3, 2, 1, 4, 1. The average of the absolute deviations is $\frac{22}{10} = 2.2$.

16-3 Measures of Variation

 TI-81 Investigation 5 (page 866) can be used with this lesson.

We have seen that the various measures of central tendency give us a representative value for a set of data. Two other important questions concerning a set of data have to do with how spread out the data are, and how much the data vary. In this lesson we shall consider several measures of variation or dispersion.

Range and Mean Deviation

Objective: Find the range and mean deviation of a set of data.

One way to get a feeling for the variation, or spread, of a set of data is to find the difference between the greatest value and the least value. This difference is called the **range**.

For instance, here is a set of scores on a chemistry test.

98, 78, 60, 87, 83, 56, 99, 76, 73, 81, 75, 89, 71, 70, 68, 93, 67, 85

The highest score is 99 and the lowest score is 56.

$$99 - 56 = 43$$

Thus the range of the set of scores is 43.

Another possibility for measuring the variability of a set of data is to find the difference between each value x_i and the mean $\overline{x}$, and then find the sum of these differences. It turns out, however, that this sum is always 0, since the positive and negative differences offset each other. To avoid the problem of positive and negative differences we can find the absolute value of each difference.

This measure of spread, or variation, is called the **mean deviation**, or the average amount that a set of data deviates from the mean. To find the mean deviation we first find the deviation of each value from the mean. We do this by finding the absolute value of the difference between each value and the mean. Then we find the mean of these deviations.

EXAMPLE 1

Consider this set of high-school basketball scores.

59, 73, 68, 81, 65, 78, 88, 72, 69, 59, 76, 81

Find the range and the mean deviation.

The highest score is 88, the lowest is 59, so the range is 29.

The sum of the scores is 869.

$$869 \div 12 \approx 72.4$$

The mean of the set of data is 72.4.

We now find the absolute value of the difference between each value and the mean.

The mean deviation is $\frac{\sum_{i=1}^{n} |\bar{x} - x_i|}{n}$.

$|72.4 - 59| = 13.4, |72.4 - 73| = 0.6, |72.4 - 68| = 4.4 \ldots, |72.4 - 81| = 8.6$

Next we find the mean of these deviations. The sum of the deviations is 85.

$85 \div 12 \approx 7.08$

The mean deviation is 7.08. This tells us that, typically, each score was about 7 greater or less than the mean of 72.4.

Try This

a. Here is a set of temperatures, in degrees Celsius, for a winter week in Richmond, Virginia. Find the range and the mean deviation. 5, 1.3

10, 12, 9, 10, 8, 9, 13

Variance

Objective: Find the variance of a set of data.

The spread of a set of data can be measured using a statistic called the variance. To find the variance we square the deviation of each value from the mean and then find the mean of these squares. Note that since we square each deviation, avoiding the problem of positive and negative differences, it is not necessary to find absolute values. We denote the variance by σ^2.

$$\sigma^2 = \frac{\sum_{i=1}^{n} (\bar{x} - x_i)^2}{n}$$

EXAMPLE 2 Find the variance for this set of temperatures.

10, 12, 9, 10, 8, 9, 13

The mean is 10.1. The deviations from the mean are 0.1, −1.9, 1.1, 0.1, 2.1, 1.1, and −2.9. Squaring each of these values we have 0.01, 3.61, 1.21, 0.01, 4.41, 1.21 and 8.41. We next find the mean of these squares.

The sum of the squares is 18.87. Dividing by n, $\frac{18.87}{7} \approx 2.7$

The variance of the set of temperatures is 2.7.

When using measures of spread such as the range, the mean deviation, and the variance, we note that the larger the number found, the greater the spread of the set of data.

Try This

b. Find the variance of the set of scores in Example 1. 73.4

Variance

Point out that σ is the lowercase of the Greek letter, sigma. Remind students that Σ, used for series, is an uppercase sigma.

Chalkboard Example

1. Find the variance for the following data set.
   5, 7, 3, 2, 1, 8, 3, 6, 9, 6

   The mean is $\frac{50}{10} = 5$.

   The deviations from the mean are 0, 2, −2, −3, −4, 3, −2, 1, 4, 1.
   The squares of the deviations are 0, 4, 4, 9, 16, 9, 4, 1, 16, 1.
   The average of the squared deviations is $\frac{64}{10} = 6.4$.

Standard Deviation

Chalkboard Example

1. Find the standard deviation for the data set.
   5, 7, 3, 2, 1, 8, 3, 6, 9, 6
   We found that the variance was 6.4. The standard deviation is $\sqrt{6.4} \approx 2.53$.

LESSON QUIZ

Given the following data set,
4, 3, 5, 7, 2, 1, 8, 2

1. find the range.
   $8 - 1 = 7$
2. find the mean deviation.
   2
3. find the variance.
   5.5
4. find the standard deviation.
   $\sqrt{5.5} \approx 2.35$

Assignment Guide
Algebra: Omit

Alg w/Finite Math: 1–7 e/o, 8, MR, assign w. Application

Comprehensive: 1–7 e/o, 8–10, MR, assign w. Application

ADDITIONAL ANSWERS

Exercises

1. Range = 1642, mean deviation = 537.7, variance = 366337.49, standard deviation = 605.3
2. Range = 8.41, mean deviation = 2.39, variance = 8.27, standard deviation = 2.88
3. Range = 5.9, mean deviation = 1.68, variance = 4.01, standard deviation = 2.00
4. Range = 9.1, mean deviation = 2.03, variance = 6.81, standard deviation = 2.61

Standard Deviation

Objective: Find the standard deviation of a set of data.

When we find the variance, we square the deviations. This tends to magnify the measure of variation. Thus we can use another measure of the variation called the standard deviation. To find the standard deviation of a set of data we find the square root of the variance. The standard deviation is denoted by σ.

$$\sigma = \sqrt{\frac{\sum_{i=1}^{n} (\overline{x} - x_i)^2}{n}}$$

The standard deviation is the most frequently used measure of the spread of a set of data.

EXAMPLE 3 Find the standard deviation of the set of temperatures in Example 2.

In Example 2 we found that the variance was 2.7. We find $\sqrt{2.7} \approx 1.64$. The standard deviation of the set of temperatures is 1.64.

Try This

c. Find the standard deviation of the set of scores in Example 1. 8.57

16-3 EXERCISES

A

Find the range, mean deviation, variance, and standard deviation for

1. passenger capacities of the ten largest cruise ships.
   1499, 1022, 2400, 1970, 821, 2400, 2217, 1146, 758, 1636
2. the lengths, in miles, of the 12 longest highway tunnels.
   2.0, 2.1, 1.8, 2.8, 1.73, 1.7, 7.2, 8.7, 10.01, 3.6, 1.6, 3.1
3. the percentages of fat found in ten samples of ground beef at a grocery store.
   23.5, 22.4, 25.6, 26.8, 28.1, 22.3, 25.6, 24.5, 25.7, 28.2
4. the production costs, in millions of dollars, of 12 recent movies.
   1.4, 4.5, 2.0, 7.0, 4.8, 7.0, 5.0, 7.0, 2.9, 10.5, 1.4, 4.8
5. the distances, in feet, of the left-field foul line in American League baseball parks.
   309, 315, 333, 341, 320, 340, 330, 315, 343, 312, 330, 316, 330, 330
6. the scores of ten girls on the balance beam in a girls' gymnastics meet.
   8.5, 7.9, 8.2, 9.0, 8.3, 7.8, 9.1, 9.2, 8.4, 9.2

B

7. Consider these two sets of data: {20, 22, 30, 36} and {20, 22, 30, 1000}. Find the mean deviation and the standard deviation for each set of data. Which measure of variation is less affected by an extreme value? Mean deviation

8. ***Critical Thinking*** Set A has a mean of 42 and a standard deviation of 2.5. Set B has a mean of 50 and a standard deviation of 27.
   a. Which set is more likely to contain a value of 34? B
   b. Which set is more likely to have a range of 11? A
   c. Which set is likely to have more elements? Cannot be determined
   d. For which set would the standard deviation decrease if a value of 46 were added to the set? B

Challenge

9. Here is a formula for the variance, which can be used with a large set of data to simplify calculations. The calculations are equal.

$$\sigma^2 = \frac{\sum_{i=1}^{n} x_i^2 - \frac{\left(\sum_{i=1}^{n} x_i\right)^2}{n}}{n}$$

Use this formula to calculate the variance of any of the sets of data in Exercises 1 – 6. Compare this to the variance already calculated.

10. For technical reasons beyond the scope of our discussion, statisticians sometimes use the following formula to compute the standard deviation.

$$s = \sqrt{\frac{\sum_{i=1}^{n} (\bar{x} - x_i)^2}{n-1}}$$ where $\bar{x}$ is the mean of the set of data

Use this formula to calculate the standard deviation of any of the sets of data in Exercises 1 – 6. Compare this to the standard deviation already calculated. The new calculation is larger.

Mixed Review

Given two points $A(-2, -6)$ and $B(4, 2)$ find **11.** the slope of $\overline{AB}$.

12. the distance between A and B. **13.** the midpoint of $\overline{AB}$.

Statistics Keys

The $\Sigma+$ key can be used to collect data so that the mean and standard deviation of the data can be found. MODE STAT may not be required.

Find the mean and standard deviation of 7, 13, 25, and 4.

										mean		standard deviation
MODE	STAT	7	$\Sigma+$	13	$\Sigma+$	25	$\Sigma+$	4	$\Sigma+$	$\bar{x}$ 12.25	σ_n	8.0428540

See Calculator Worksheets 32 and 33.

5. Range = 34, mean deviation = 9.9, variance = 120.4, standard deviation = 10.97
6. Range = 1.4, mean deviation = 0.45, variance = 0.25, standard deviation = 0.50
7. Set A, mean deviation = 6, standard deviation = 6.4. Set B, mean deviation = 366, standard deviation = 423.

Mixed Review

11. $\frac{4}{3}$
12. 10
13. (1, −2)

16-4

FIRST FIVE MINUTES

1. Find the standard deviation for the following set of data:
   12, 14, 10, 18, 18, 15
   2.93

Proportion

You may wish to review histograms with your students and point out that the normal curve can be thought of as an "ideal" histogram.

Note that the normal curve gives a method for approximating proportions of data falling within a range of the mean. Few sets of data have a perfect normal distribution, but many are very close.

Key Questions

- What percent of the data is represented by the normal curve? 100%
- What percent of values is greater than the mean in a normal distribution? 50%

Chalkboard Examples

1. A list of the heights of girls in the sophomore class has a normal distribution. The mean is 63 inches and the standard deviation is 2.5 inches. What percent of girls in the class is more than 65.5 inches tall?
   65.5 is 1 standard deviation above the mean. We expect 50% of the girls to be less than 63 in. tall, and 34% to be between 63 in. and 65.5 in. tall.
   100% − 50% − 34% = 16%, so we expect 16% of the girls in the sophomore class to be taller than 65.5 in.

16-4 The Normal Distribution

The heights of 16-year-old girls are not distributed uniformly, or evenly. Many more girls are average height than are very short or very tall. The values are distributed so that they are frequent near the mean, and become more rare and infrequent the farther they are from the mean. The most common distribution with this characteristic is a **normal distribution.**

When data are distributed in a bell-shaped, or **normal curve,** about 68% of the data lie within one standard deviation on either side of the mean, and about 95% lie within two standard deviations of the mean.

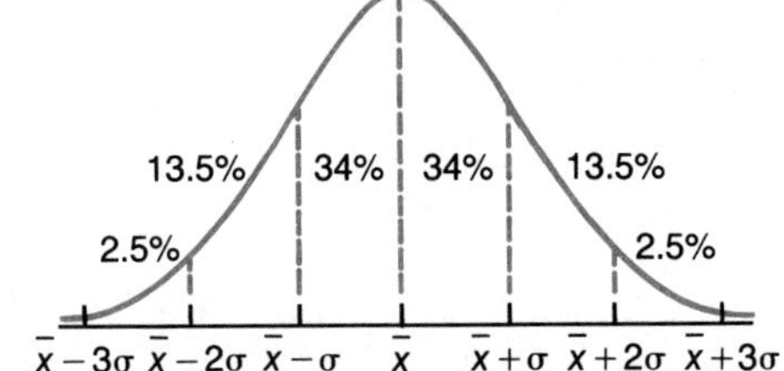

Normal curves are symmetric with respect to the vertical line at the mean. The spread of each curve is defined by its standard deviation. For a large standard deviation, the height of the curve at the mean decreases, and the range increases.

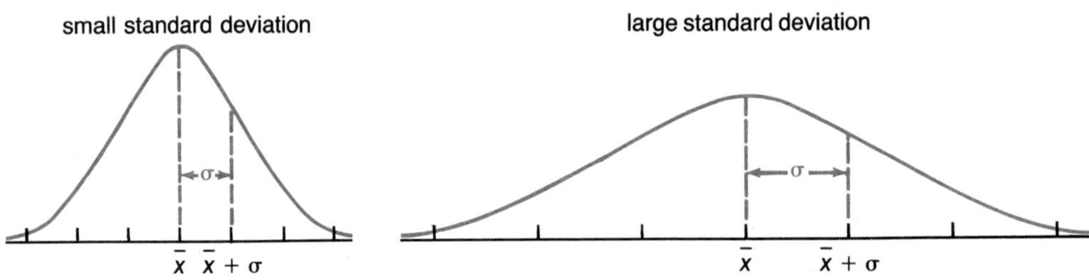

Proportion

Objective: Determine the proportion of data falling within a range of standard deviations.

EXAMPLE 1

Consider the bell-shaped distribution of IQ scores for students in a school. The mean is 100 and the standard deviation is 15. What percent of students in the school would we expect to have IQs between 85 and 115?

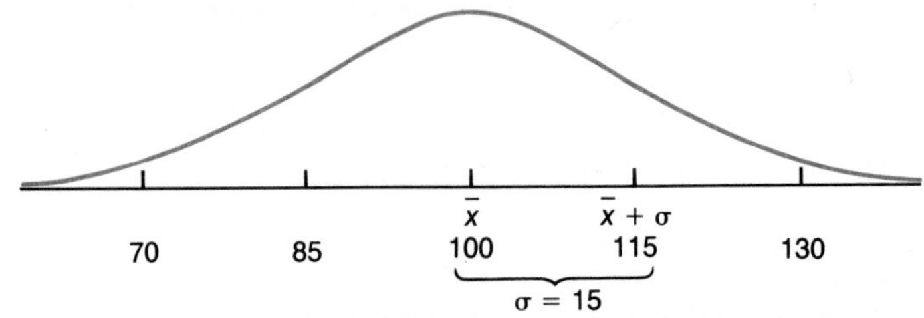

Since 115 and 85 mark positions in the distribution one standard deviation above and below the mean, we would expect 34% of the scores to fall between 85 and 100, and another 34% to fall between 100 and 115.

We can expect 68% of the students' scores to fall between 85 and 115.

EXAMPLE 2

What percent of the students can we expect to have IQs between 70 and 115?

Since 70 is two standard deviations below the mean of 100, $13.5 + 34 = 47.5\%$ of the distribution lies between the 70 and 100. Also, 115 is one standard deviation above the mean and 34% of the distribution is between the mean and this point.

Thus, we can expect $47.5 + 34 = 81.5\%$ of the students' IQs to fall in the range from 70 to 115.

Try This

a. What percent of students in the school can we expect to have IQs above 115? 16%
b. What percent of the students in the school can we expect to have IQs in the range from 85 to 145? 84%

z-scores and Probability

Objective: Find and use *z*-scores to determine probability.

A *z*-score for a value is the number of standard deviations the value is from the mean. The sign of the *z*-score is its direction from the mean. For example, if a value has a *z*-score of -2, it is two standard deviations below the mean.

The *z*-score for x is found by dividing the difference between x and the mean by the standard deviation.

$$z = \frac{x - \bar{x}}{\sigma}$$

z-scores translate any normal distribution to a standard normal distribution with a mean of 0 and a standard deviation of 1.

EXAMPLE 3

What is the *z*-score for 46 in a normal distribution whose mean is 44 and whose standard deviation is 2?

For this distribution, $\bar{x} = 44$ and $\sigma = 2$.

Using the formula, we have $z = \frac{46 - 44}{2} = 1$.

The *z*-score for 46 is 1. Thus, 46 is one standard deviation above the mean.

2. The freshman class at one college has an average score on the math SAT of about 500 with a standard deviation of about 60 points. What percent of the class scored between 560 and 620? What percent scored less than 380?
560 is 1 standard deviation above the mean and 620 is 2 standard deviations above the mean, so 13.5% of the class scored between 560 and 620.
380 is 2 standard deviations below the mean, so 2.5% of the class scored below 380.

z-Scores and Probability

Note that to simplify the discussion, we let the probability that a value has a *z*-score of less than x equal the probability that the *z*-score is less than or equal to x.

Key Questions

- A normal distribution has a mean of 20. The value 26 has a *z*-score of 2. What is the standard deviation?
3
- A normal distribution has a standard deviation of 30. The value 100 has a *z*-score of -2. What is the mean?
160
- Distributions A and B have the same mean. The standard deviation of A is twice that of B. How would their *z*-scores compare for any data point?
the *z*-score for B would be half of the *z*-score for A.

Chalkboard Examples

1. A set of data has a mean of 95 and a standard deviation of 8. What is the *z*-score for 88?
$z = \frac{88 - 95}{8}$
$= -0.875$
2. A set of data has a mean of 15 and a standard deviation of 1.5. What is the *z*-score for 19?
$z = \frac{19 - 15}{1.5}$
$= 2.67$

3. Find the probability that a z-score of greater than 1.7 will be selected from a normal distribution.
The probability that a z-score of greater than 1.7 will be selected is equivalent to the area to the right of the point associated with z = 1.7. Using the table, we find that the probability of selecting a point to the left of the point is 0.9554. Thus, the probability of selecting a point to the right of the point is 0.0446, so the probability of selecting a point with a z-score greater than 1.7 is 0.0446, or about 4.5%.

Try This

What are the z-scores for the following?

c. 45, where $\overline{x} = 50$ and $\sigma = 4$ −1.25
d. 90, where $\overline{x} = 70$ and $\sigma = 8$ 2.5
e. 56, where $\overline{x} = 60$ and $\sigma = 10$ −0.4
f. 120, where $\overline{x} = 120$ and $\sigma = 17$ 0

Normal curves are useful for probability. The area under the curve represents the entire distribution. The area under any section of the curve describes the probability that a value falls within a given range.

Table 7 on page 883 gives the probability that a value in the distribution has a z-score that is less than a given value.

EXAMPLE 4 A value is selected randomly from a normal distribution. What is the probability that its z-score is less than -1.46?

The probability that a value has a z-score less than -1.46 is equivalent to the ratio of the shaded area to the entire area under the curve. Proportion of the area below that is shaded. This value is given in Table 7, a portion of which is shown below.

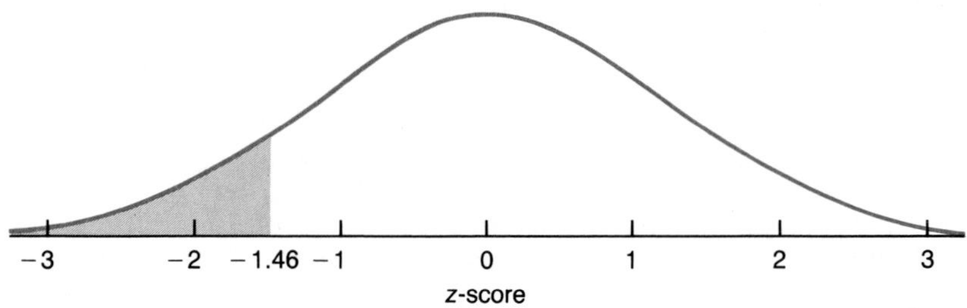

We find -1.4 in the column headed z on the left side of the table and go across the row to the column headed 6.

z	0	1	2	3	4	5	6	7	8	9
−1.5	.0668	.0655	.0643	.0630	.0618	.0606	.0594	.0582	.0571	.0559
−1.4	.0808	.0793	.0778	.0764	.0749	.0735	**.0721**	.0708	.0694	.0681
−1.3	.0968	.0951	.0934	.0918	.0901	.0885	.0869	.0853	.0838	.0823

The probability that a z-score is less than -1.46 is 0.0721 (7.21% of the area under the curve is shaded). We write $P(z < -1.46) = 0.0721$.

EXAMPLE 5 A value is selected randomly from a normal distribution. Find $P(z > -1.46)$.

In Example 4 we found the probability of a z-score *less* than -1.46 is 0.0721. Since the area under the entire curve is 1, the probability of a greater z-score is $1 - 0.0721$, or 0.9279.

Thus $P(z > -1.46) = 0.9279$.

Try This

g. A value is selected randomly from a normal distribution. What is the probability that its z-score is less than 1.65? 0.9505

h. A value is selected randomly from a normal distribution. Find $P(z > -0.7)$. 0.7580

Problem Solving

Objective: Solve problems involving normal distributions.

EXAMPLE 6

A student received a score of 56 on a normally distributed standardized test. The test had a mean of 50 and a standard deviation of 5. What is the probability that a randomly selected student achieved a higher score?

We need to find the probability that a value greater than 56 is selected from a normal distribution with a mean of 50 and standard deviation of 5.

$$z = \frac{x - \bar{x}}{\sigma} = \frac{56 - 50}{5} = 1.2$$

The value 56 has a z-score of 1.2 (56 is 1.2 standard deviations above the mean), so we look up 1.2 in Table 7. The probability that a value is less than 56 is 0.8849. Thus, the probability of a greater value is $1 - 0.8849 = 0.1151$.

The probability that a randomly selected student has a higher score is about 0.12.

EXAMPLE 7

How often would we expect to find an IQ greater than 142 in a sample of students whose mean IQ was 110 where the standard deviation was 16?

A value of 142 would have a z-score of $\frac{142 - 110}{16}$, or 2.0 in this distribution. Thus, we want to find $P(z > 2.0)$.

Using the table, we find $P(z < 2.0) = 0.9772$. Thus, the probability of a greater value is $1 - 0.9772$, or 0.0228.

We can expect to find such a score in a similar distribution about 2 times out of 100.

Try This

Mountain Mineral Water bottles have a mean volume of 12 oz with a standard deviation of 0.4 oz.

i. What is the probability that a bottle contains less than 11 oz of water? 0.0062

j. How often can we expect to find a bottle containing more than 12.5 oz of water? ≈11 times in 100

Problem Solving

Chalkboard Example

1. The number of cars that pass a certain stop sign on an average day is 215 with a standard deviation of 42. What is the probability that fewer than 150 cars will pass the stop sign on a given day?
   First we need to find the z-score of 150.
   $$z = \frac{150 - 215}{42} = -1.55$$
   Looking up −1.55 in the table, we find that the probability that a value is less than 150 is 0.0606. Thus, the probability that fewer than 150 cars will pass the stop sign is 0.0606.

LESSON QUIZ

1. What is the z-score of 220 if the mean is 230 and the standard deviation is 19?
   0.526
2. The mean height of a group of men is 69 inches with a standard deviation of 2.5 inches. What is the probability that the first man to be measured is shorter than 67 inches?
   0.2119

Assignment Guide
Algebra: Omit

Alg w/Finite Math: 1–40 e/o, 41, MR

Comprehensive: 1–40 e/o, 41, 42–44 e/o, MR

ADDITIONAL ANSWERS

Exercises

27. 0.2258
28. 0.0793
29. 0.2511
30. 0.3086
31. 0.9817
32. 0.3067
33. 0.0990
34. 0.5992
35. 0.7745
36. 0.6687
37. 0.6915
38. 0.1151
39. 0.0062
40. 0.6171
41. Yes; 4, 5, and 6 are within 1 standard deviation of the mean and account for 66% of the data; 2, 3, 4, 5, 6, 7, and 8 are within 2 standard deviations of the mean and account for 98% of the data. This is close to a normal distribution.

16-4 EXERCISES

A

A set of test scores is normally distributed with mean 50 and standard deviation 10. Use the figure at the top of page 704.

1. What percent of the scores can you expect to fall between 40 and 50? ≈34%
2. What percent of the scores can you expect to be less than 30? ≈2.5%
3. What percent of the scores can you expect to find between 40 and 70? ≈81.5%
4. What percent of the scores can you expect to find above 70? ≈2.5%
5. What percent of the scores can you expect to find between 30 and 70? ≈95%
6. What percent of the scores can you expect to find between 0 and 40? ≈16%

Find the z-score associated with each of the following test scores.

7. 67, where $\overline{x} = 50$ and $\sigma = 10$ 1.7
8. 74, where $\overline{x} = 40$ and $\sigma = 17$ 2
9. 137, where $\overline{x} = 170$ and $\sigma = 44$ −0.75
10. 108, where $\overline{x} = 112$ and $\sigma = 40$ −0.1

Use Table 7 to determine the probability of observing z-scores in each range.

11. $P(z < -1.79)$ 0.0367
12. $P(z > 2.4)$ 0.0082
13. $P(z > 1.92)$ 0.0274
14. $P(z < -2.43)$ 0.0075
15. $P(z > -2.88)$ 0.9980
16. $P(z < 0.43)$ 0.6664

For Exercises 17–20, assume a normal distribution.

17. A battery is found to have a mean life of 219 hours and a standard deviation of 70 hours. What is the probability that a battery will not last 100 hours? 0.0446
18. Students in one grade have an average height of 66 in. and a standard deviation of 3 in. What is the probability that a student is less than 68 inches tall? 0.7486
19. A bolt manufacturer makes bolts that have a mean diameter of 1 cm and a standard deviation of 0.05 cm. What is the probability that the diameter of a bolt will exceed 1.03 cm? 0.2742
20. Of popcorn kernels that pop successfully, the mean popping time for one batch is 4 minutes with a standard deviation of 1 minute. What is the probability that a specific kernel will pop after $5\frac{1}{2}$ minutes? 0.0668

B

Use Table 7 to find x.

21. $P(z < x) = 0.9066$ 1.32
22. $P(z > x) = 0.9783$ −2.02
23. $P(z < x) = 0.1056$ −1.25
24. $P(z < x) = 0.0244$ −1.97
25. $P(z > x) = 0.3622$ 0.35
26. $P(z > x) = 0.4404$ 0.15

Use Table 7 to find the probability of observing z-scores in the following ranges.

27. $P(0 < z < 0.6)$
28. $P(-0.2 < z < 0)$
29. $P(-0.5 < z < 0.15)$
30. $P(0.43 < z < 1.96)$
31. $P(-2.12 < z < 3.0)$
32. $P(0.48 < z < 2.37)$
33. $P(|z| > 1.65)$
34. $P(|z| < 0.84)$

The College Entrance Examination Board scores are developed to approximate a normal distribution with mean 500 and standard deviation 100. What proportion of test takers can we expect to score in the following ranges?

35. Between 350 and 600 **36.** Between 450 and 700 **37.** Below 550

38. Above 620 **39.** Above 750 **40.** Below 450 or above 550

41. ***Critical Thinking*** Suppose ten coins were flipped and the number of heads was recorded. This was done 1000 times and the following data were recorded.

Number of heads	0	1	2	3	4	5	6	7	8	9	10
Frequency	1	10	44	117	205	246	205	117	44	10	1

If the mean of the data is 5 and the standard deviation is 1.58, does the proportion of the scores between the mean and the standard z-scores suggest that the sums observed are normally distributed?

Challenge

42. Half of normal data lie within x standard deviations of the mean. Find x. ≈ 0.675

43. A company manufactures cover plates for boxes with lengths of 4 inches. Due to variation in the process, the lengths of the plates are normally distributed about a mean of 4 inches with a standard deviation of 0.01 inch. A plate is considered a "reject" if its length is less than 3.98 inches or greater than 4.02 inches. What percent of the production are considered "rejects"? 4.56%

44. Suppose a coin is flipped n times. If n is a large number, and p is the probability of a head on any given toss, the mean number of heads is given by np, and the standard deviation by $\sqrt{np(1-p)}$. A coin is tossed 10,000 times.

a. Find $\overline{x}$ and σ. 5000, 50

b. What is the probability of throwing between 4900 and 5100 heads? ≈ 0.955

Mixed Review

Expand. **45.** $(x + 2y)^5$ **46.** $\left(y - \frac{1}{2}x\right)^4$ **47.** $(x - 1)^3$

Find the 3rd and 7th term of the expression. **48.** $(p + q)^6$ **49.** $(x - 3)^7$

50. The stopping distance (d) of a car after brakes are applied varies directly as the square of the speed (r). A car traveling 60 km/h can stop in 80 m. How many meters will it take the same car to stop when it is traveling 75 km/h?

Find a polynomial of lowest degree with

51. roots 3, 4, and with root -3 having multiplicity 2.

52. root -2 of multiplicity 4.

WRITING TO LEARN

Is a normal distribution an accurate model for predicting the probability that a person will live to a certain age? Write a convincing argument why or why not.

Mixed Review

45. $x^5 + 10x^4y + 40x^3y^2 + 80x^2y^3 + 80xy^4 + 32y^5$

46. $y^4 - 2y^3x + \frac{3}{2}y^2x^2 - \frac{1}{2}yx^3 + \frac{1}{16}x^4$

47. $x^3 - 3x^2 + 3x - 1$

48. $15p^4q^2$, q^6

49. $189x^5$, $5103x$

50. 125 m

51. $f(x) = x^4 - x^3 - 21x^2 + 9x + 108$

52. $f(x) = x^4 + 8x^3 + 24x^2 + 32x + 16$

Writing to Learn

No. Reasons may vary.

16-5

FIRST FIVE MINUTES

1. What is the z-score of 68 if the mean is 74 and the standard deviation is 12?
   -0.5
2. Two hundred students take a test on which a passing grade is 60. The scores are normally distributed, the mean is 76, and the standard deviation is 16. How many students passed?
   168

Random Sampling

Note that the method with which the data are collected and the care with which they are recorded are equally important.

Key Questions

- Name some types of information that are obtained through random sampling.
  Television ratings, market surveys, etc.
- How can random numbers from 1–400 be generated using a random number table?
  Scan the table until you find a 0, 1, 2, 3, or 4. Look at the three-digit number beginning there. If it is between 001 and 400, add the number to your list. If not, keep going. For example, using
  52118 67017 94236
  the first number is 211
  the second is 017
  423 is too high
  the third number is 236

Chalkboard Examples

1. How would you select a random sample of books in your school's library?
   You could generate a list of random numbers between 1 and the number of books in the library. Then use these numbers to select cards from the card catalog or entries from the microfiche catalog.

16-5 Collecting Data: Randomness and Bias

To prevent over- or underrepresentation of some population group that the data are to represent, statisticians use methods of sampling, or effectively drawing and examining samples from a population to make accurate statements about the population's characteristics. Samples are used because obtaining information about each member of a population may be expensive, difficult, time-consuming, or even impossible.

Random Sampling

Objective: Evaluate and select sampling methods.

Definition

A **random sample** is a sample selected such that

1. each object (person) in the population has an equal chance of being selected for the sample.
2. each object (person) in the sample is chosen independently of any other objects in the sample.

EXAMPLE 1

A scientist is studying the weight gain or loss of mice that are given a certain treatment. When choosing mice for the experiment, the scientist reaches into a cage with 30 mice and selects the 5 heaviest mice in the cage. Is the sample random?

No. The scientist did not choose randomly. Each mouse did not have an equal chance of being chosen.

EXAMPLE 2

Describe how a random sample of 10 individuals might be chosen from a high school graduating class of 202 to receive a gift certificate.

A random sample of 10 individuals from the graduating class might be selected by placing each class member's name on a slip of paper, placing the slips in a large bowl, and mixing them thoroughly. Ten names could then be drawn from the bowl to determine the winners.

This process has allowed each class member an equal chance to be selected when each name is drawn. In addition, there were no connections between the names drawn, that is, a name being drawn or not drawn did not affect the probability of another name being drawn or not drawn.

Try This For Answer to Try This b, see Selected Answers.

a. Is a survey of students in this algebra class a random sample of the students in your grade? No

b. Describe how to select a random sample of 10 individuals attending a movie.

A table of random numbers or a random number generator on a computer is a helpful tool to select objects for a random sample. In Example 1, each class member could have been assigned a number from 1 to 202. Then, the table or computer program could have selected 10 random numbers from 1 to 202.

EXAMPLE 3

Describe how to use a random number table or generator to select a random sample of 15 watchbands for a quality control inspection from a line of 400 watchbands.

This process might be handled by developing a list of 15 random numbers between 1 and 400, ordering the list from smallest to largest, such as 10, 32, 55, and so on, then selecting the tenth band, the thirty-second band, the fifty-fifth band, and so on.

Try This

c. A news magazine has asked for a random sampling of community members to be interviewed. Describe how you might use a table of random numbers to select 20 people from your community for this purpose. See Selected Answers.

Although the processes involved in the development of a random sample guarantee that requirements of equal probability and independence are satisfied, they do not guarantee that the sample drawn will be **representative.**

EXAMPLE 4

A town newsletter is doing an article on the interests of high school students. A questionnaire is sent to a random sample of school-aged students. Are the data representative?

No. A sample of students from kindergarten through grade 12 would not give results representative of high school students.

Even when the sample is restricted to high school students, the data may not be representative. Data might have been collected largely from members of the high school chorus. In this case, the data would most likely be **biased.** That is, it is likely that the data would be overly influenced by factors that are related to musical interests.

2. A magazine prints a reader's poll and asks readers to mail in their responses. Is this a representative sample of the magazine's readers? **No; readers who respond by mailing in the poll are likely to be ones who feel strongly about the issue. This sample is likely to be biased.**

Stratified Random Sampling

Survey statisticians attempt to develop sampling plans that will be both random and representative. Point out that when students read the results of a survey or hear someone quoting statistics, they should carefully consider whether the data could be biased.

Math Point
Other ways to control bias include cluster sampling, in which data are collected in a number of clusters of interests throughout the population. The responses to questions are averaged within each cluster to give one data point for each cluster. Another method is systematic sampling, in which every 10th, or 15th, person to pass a point is polled. Cluster and systematic sampling are appropriate in many cases, but neither satisfies the requirements for random sampling.

Chalkboard Example

1. At Tyler Senior High School, 38% of the students are in the 12th grade, 28% in the 11th, and 34% in the 10th. In each class, 53% are female and 47% are male. There are 2000 students. Describe a stratified random sample of 100 students.
   Since we want 100 students, we must find the percent of males and females in each class. 53% of 38%, or 20%, of the students are 12th grade girls. So out of 100 students, we want 20 to be 12th grade girls. Likewise, the sample should include 18 12th grade boys, 15 11th grade girls, 13 11th grade boys, 18 10th grade girls, and 16 10th grade boys.

LESSON QUIZ

1. Does picking names out of a phone book give you a random sample of a population of the city?
   No; some people are unlisted, and not everybody in a household will be listed, particularly children.

Try This See Selected Answers.

d. A polling organization would like to know how a community feels about irradiation of produce. Discuss the representatives of each sampling method.
   1. Taking a random sample of customers outside a health food store.
   2. Calling random numbers from a telephone book.
   3. Questioning owners of large farms.

Stratified Random Sampling

Objective: Describe how to take a stratified random sample.

To draw a representative sample, we may need to divide the population into distinct subgroups, called **strata.** Then we can use **stratified random sampling** to assure that the sample has the same characteristics as the population.

Each member of the population must be placed in one and only one stratum. A random sample is drawn so that the sample has the same distribution among the strata as the population. For example, if $\frac{2}{3}$ of the voting population in an area are Democrats, we would want a sample of voters to contain $\frac{2}{3}$ Democrats.

EXAMPLE 5 A college has 1260 freshmen, 1176 sophomores, 840 juniors, and 924 seniors. Describe how to take a stratified random sample of 200 students.

These are a total of 4200 students. 30% are freshmen, 28% are sophomores, 20% are juniors, and 22% are seniors. We want 30% of the sample of 200 to be freshmen, so we sample 60 freshmen, and so on for sophomores, juniors, and seniors.

	Freshmen	Sophomores	Juniors	Seniors	Total
Population	1260	1176	840	924	4200
	30%	28%	20%	22%	
Sample	60	56	40	44	200
	30%	28%	20%	22%	

We would randomly sample 60 freshmen, 56 sophomores, 40 juniors, and 44 seniors.

Try This

e. In a given community, 40% of the voters are under 35 years old, 20% are 35–44 years old, 20% are age 45–54, 15% are age 55–64, and the remaining 5% are age 65 or older. If there are 10,000 registered voters, describe how to take a stratified random sample to predict the election outcome. See Selected Answers.

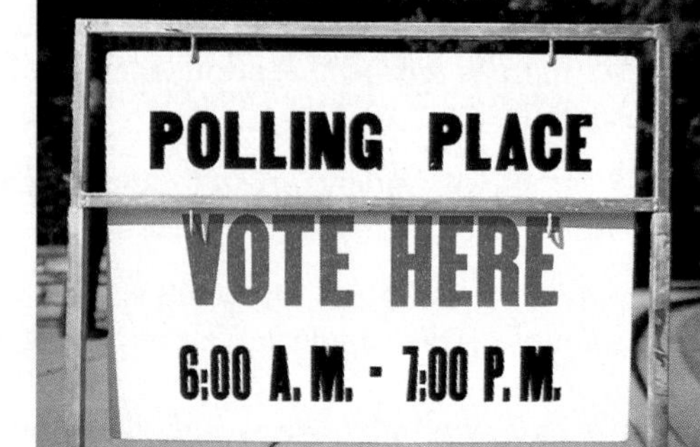

16-5 EXERCISES

Which of the following methods of drawing a sample will result in random samples? Explain why or why not.

1. Selecting six friends you meet at a basketball game to participate in a survey about clothing styles at your high school.
2. Surveying five people leaving a hardware store on their views about new construction in the community.
3. Forty students are assigned random numbers from 1 to 40. Two ten-sided dice are rolled and the first ten two-digit numbers selected are used to determine the sample members.
4. A survey is conducted to get a sample of 5000 individuals from a state by selecting 50 cities in the state and interviewing 100 individuals in each city.
5. Each individual in a population of 300 is assigned a random number from 1 to 300. First a number less than 100 is selected, then a number from 100 to 199, and finally a number from 200 to 300.
6. Describe how a random sample of 15 sophomores might be chosen from a class of 431.
7. Describe how the 5 mice in Example 1 could have been chosen randomly.

Discuss the representativeness of the samples. Mention possible sources of bias.

8. The results of a reader response survey to an advice columnist's poll in the newspaper
9. The results of a poll taken on a street corner outside the county court building
10. The results of a sample survey conducted via a computer telecommunications network for personal computer users
11. The results of a survey about the use of preferred brands of hair curling irons at a wrestling meet
12. The results of a survey about knowledge of the warning signs of heart problems at a hospital cardiac care ward
13. The results of a poll about a state governor's election race taken outside of the largest polling place in each county
14. Describe how you might select a random sample of 20% of the students from your school to collect data to determine students' wishes concerning the school lunch program.
15. Delaware has a population of about 595,000; 98,000 people live in Kent County, 399,000 live in New Castle County, and 98,000 live in Sussex County. Describe how you might take a random sample of 200 Delaware residents.

2. Describe a stratified sample of 200 in a population of 47% Democrats, 42% Republicans, and 11% Independents.
Select randomly 94 Democrats, 84 Republicans, and 22 Independents.

Assignment Guide
Algebra: Omit

Alg w/Finite Math: 1–17 e/o, 18, MR

Comprehensive: 1–17 e/o, 18, 19, MR

ADDITIONAL ANSWERS

Exercises

1. Not a random sample because each student at the high school did not have an equal chance of participating.
2. Not a random sample because each person in the community did not have an equal chance to participate.
3. Not a random sample because each student did not have a chance to be selected.
4. Not a random sample because individuals not living in cities did not have an opportunity to participate.
5. Not a random sample because there are 99 possible selections for the first number, 100 for the second, and 101 for the third.
6. Each student could be assigned a number from 1 to 431, then 15 numbers between 1 and 431 could be selected using a random number table or random number generator.
7. The scientist could have given each mouse a number between 1 and 30, then used a random number table to select 5 numbers between 1 and 30.
8. This is only representative of people who read the advice column. It may be biased because not everyone reads the advice column.
9. This is only representative of people who walk past the county court building. This may be biased because not everyone will walk past the building.

10. This could be a representative sample if the survey only concerned owners of personal computers that participated in this network. It could be biased because individuals who spend a lot of time on their computers have a better chance of being selected.
11. This is only representative of individuals who attend wrestling meets.
12. This is only representative of individuals who are involved with cardiac problems. This survey would be biased because people who are in such close contact with cardiac problems will know more about them.
13. This is representative of people who live in densely populated areas. It would be biased because it does not include voters living in rural areas.
14. By giving each student in the school a number, then using either a random number table or a random number generator to choose 20% of the population from each grade.
15. By randomly selecting 33 people from Kent County, 134 people from New Castle County, and 33 from Sussex County.
16. By first dividing the lists of names into lists by political wards, and randomly selecting 24% of the names from the first ward, 33% from the second, 23% from the third, and 20% from the fourth.
17. Assign each of the 20,000 people a number, then use a random number generator to select 12 people.
18. The selection process was representative, random, and unbiased.
19. Roosevelt won by a landslide. Poorer people could not afford the luxuries of telephones, clubs, or mail, and many were illiterate. They favored Roosevelt but were not represented in the poll.

Mixed Review

20. $(x + 6)(x^2 - 6x + 36)$
21. $(y + 1)^3$
22. $(x + 2)(x^3 + 3x^2 + x - 9)$
23. 4 oz of Happy Trail Mix and 8 oz of Mountain Top Trail Mix
24. $y = 4x^2$

B

16. Describe how to set up stratified sampling design for a situation having four strata representing 24, 33, 23, and 20 percent of the population respectively. Suppose that the population is the citizens of a town and the four strata represent political wards in the town. The only information you have are the individual's names, the locations of their homes, and their ages.

17. Describe how 12 people might be randomly selected from 20,000 names in a 480-page telephone book.

18. ***Critical Thinking*** In 1969, the Selective Service System began a draft lottery. Each 19-year-old male was eligible to be drafted. Capsules containing slips of paper with each of the 366 days of the year were mixed, drawn randomly, and the order of selection was determined by the order of the draw. September 14 was chosen first, and so on. Was the selection process representative, random, biased? Discuss.

Challenge

19. In 1936, near the end of the Great Depression, the *Literary Digest* took a poll of 10 million people regarding the upcoming presidential election. Names were chosen from telephone books and club membership lists. Almost 2.5 million people responded to the poll by mail. The magazine used the results to predict that Alf Landon would defeat Franklin D. Roosevelt by a landslide. What was the actual result? Interpret the relationship between the poll and the actual result.

Mixed Review

Factor **20.** $x^3 + 216$ **21.** $y^3 + 3y^2 + 3y + 1$

22. Divide $x^4 + 5x^3 + 7x^2 - 7x - 18$ by $x + 2$.

23. Happy Trail Mix is 70% peanuts; Mountain Top Trail Mix is 55% peanuts. How many ounces of each should be mixed together to get 12 ounces of trail mix that is 60% peanuts?

24. Find the equation of variation where y varies inversely as the square of x, and $y = 12$ when $x = 3$.

ACTIVITY

Design a sample survey questionnaire with your classmates. Decide on a topic of current interest to members of your school. Then have each member of the class collect data from 20 randomly chosen students. Compare the results from the individual surveys; then pool all of the data and consider the overall picture. To what extent do the individual results mirror the overall class results?

16-6 Testing Hypotheses

Explore

A coin is tossed 30 times and lands tails 23 times. Did this result occur by chance or was it due to some other circumstances? Can you repeat this experiment and get 23 tails in 30 tosses?

Calculating Chi-Square

Objective: Calculate chi-square values.

Statisticians are often asked to test whether a given set of observational data represents what one would expect to observe by chance or whether it differs greatly from what one might expect.

To determine what constitutes a significant difference, statisticians establish a level of error they are willing to tolerate. For example, if we throw a coin 30 times and the coin shows tails 23 times, we may decide either that

1. The results occurred by chance.
   The coin is fair and randomly showed 23 tails, although the likelihood that a coin lands tails 23 times is remote.
2. The results did *not* occur by chance.
   The coin is unevenly weighted or was tossed so that tails had a higher probability of being thrown.

Usually, we want to be sure the probability that the results occurred by chance is 5% or less before we state that the results were biased or were due to other circumstances. Then we can state that the coin is fair at the 5% level of significance.

In fact, the probability of throwing tails 23 times in 30 throws is 0.0026, or less than 0.1%. Since the probability is less than 5%, we may state that at the 5% level of significance, the results did *not* occur by chance.

One of the most common ways to test whether a given set of data differs from what one would expect by chance is to use the chi-square (χ^2) test. This test is used to compare observed data with expected data, using the following formula.

$$\chi^2 = \sum \frac{(\text{observed} - \text{expected})^2}{\text{expected}}$$

If there is a large difference between observed and expected data, we get a large value for χ^2. If there is no difference, $\chi^2 = 0$.

16-6

FIRST FIVE MINUTES

1. Describe a stratified random sample of 50 children from a group of day care centers where 48 are 2 years old, 72 are 3 years old, and 80 are 4 years old.
   The sample should include 20 4-year-olds, 18 3-year-olds, and 12 2-year-olds.

Calculating Chi-Square

A 5% level of significance means that the probability of concluding that something did not occur randomly when it in fact did is 5%. In other words, we will be wrong about 1 time in 20.

Key Questions

- How many tails would you expect if you tossed a coin 30 times?
  About 15
- If you asked 50 people to name a number from 1 to 5, would you expect each number to be chosen about the same number of times?
  Probably
- If this did not occur, what would you conclude?
  That people were biased toward or against a particular number.

Chalkboard Examples

1. 400 people were asked to select a number from 1 to 5. 200 people selected either 3 or 4. Calculate chi-square for this result.
   We expect each number to have an equal chance of being selected, so 3 and 4 should each be selected about $\frac{1}{5}$ of the time.
   $\frac{1}{5} \cdot 400 = 80$, so we expect 80 3's and 80 4's, or 160 altogether.
   We expect 240 1's, 2's, and 5's, and we received 200.
   $\frac{(200 - 160)^2}{160} + \frac{(200 - 240)^2}{240}$
   $= \frac{1600}{160} + \frac{1600}{240} = 10 + 6\frac{2}{3} = 16\frac{2}{3}$
   Chi-square is approximately 16.67.

2. A spinner with 10 equal spaces is spun 150 times. Numbers less than 5 turn up 68 times. Calculate chi-square for this result.
We expect the numbers 1–4 to turn up $\frac{4}{10}$ of the time, or 60 times, and the numbers 5–10 to turn up 90 times.
$\frac{(68-60)^2}{60} + \frac{(82-90)^2}{90}$
$= \frac{64}{60} + \frac{64}{90} = 1\frac{7}{9}$
$\chi^2 \approx 1.78$

Testing Hypotheses Using Chi-Square

Emphasize that, in general, large values of chi-square mean that the observed frequencies are far from the expected ones.

The values in the table are computed using advanced statistical methods and the theoretical chi-square distribution.

The choice of significance level should be based upon the risks involved in being wrong.

Key Questions

What does it mean to *reject* the null hypothesis at the 10% significance level?

That we are willing to state that a nonrandom element caused the results to be different from expected, even though we have a 1 in 10 chance of being wrong.

What does it mean to *accept* the null hypothesis at the 0.1% significance level?

That we are *not* willing to state that a nonrandom element caused the results to be different from expected, since we want no more than a 1 in 1000 chance of being wrong.

EXAMPLE 1

Calculate chi-square for the coin experiment given in the Explore.

Since the coin was tossed 30 times, we must account for all 30 events when computing chi-square. There are 2 possible outcomes—heads and tails. Each contributes one term to the value of χ^2.

	Heads	Tails	
We observe	23	7	There are 30 events observed
We expect	15	15	There are also 30 events expected
$\frac{(\text{observed} - \text{expected})^2}{\text{expected}}$	$\frac{(23-15)^2}{15}$	$\frac{(7-15)^2}{15}$	

$$\chi^2 = \frac{(23-15)^2}{15} + \frac{(7-15)^2}{15} = \frac{128}{15} = 8.5\overline{3}$$

Thus, the value of chi-square associated with the coin toss is $8.5\overline{3}$.

Try This

a. A die was rolled 90 times. It showed a six 19 times. Calculate chi-square.
We expect 15 sixes and 75 other numbers. $\chi^2 = \frac{16}{15} + \frac{16}{75} + \frac{96}{75} \approx 1.28$

Testing Hypotheses Using Chi-Square

Objective: Test a hypothesis by using chi-square.

The chi-square test is typically used to *accept* or *reject* a hypothesis about a set of data and to generalize about a population. The hypothesis usually tested is the **null hypothesis.** The null hypothesis most often tested is: *There is no statistical difference between the expected and the observed data. Thus, the observed results occurred by chance.* The larger the value of χ^2, the higher the probability the null hypothesis is false.

How large must χ^2 be for us to *reject* the above hypothesis? For a specific level of significance, we reject the hypothesis if the calculated value of chi-square exceeds the table value for the number of possible outcomes.

Possible Outcomes	Level of significance 10%	5%	2.5%	1%	0.1%
2	2.71	3.84	5.02	6.63	7.88
3	4.61	5.99	7.38	9.21	10.6
4	6.25	7.81	9.35	11.3	12.8
5	7.78	9.59	11.1	13.3	14.9
6	9.24	11.1	12.8	15.1	16.7
7	10.6	12.6	14.4	16.8	18.5
8	12.0	14.1	16.0	18.5	20.3
9	13.4	15.5	17.5	20.1	22.0
10	14.7	16.9	19.0	21.7	23.6

We can see for Example 1, the χ^2 value of $8.5\overline{3}$ was greater than the 7.88 table value for a 0.1% level of significance. We can *reject* the null hypothesis that the results occurred by chance.

EXAMPLE 2

Suppose we rolled a die 72 times and found that we had 13 ones, 18 threes, and 12 sixes. Determine whether these results occurred by chance. Use a 5% level of significance. The null hypothesis is that the results occurred by chance.

The expected outcome for each of the three possible outcomes is $\frac{1}{6}$ of the total number of rolls, so we expected one, three, and six to have occurred 12 times each. We also expected the other three numbers to have occurred 12 times each, or a total of 36 times. To compute the value of chi-square we make the following table.

Outcome	Observed	Expected	Difference	(Difference)^2	$\frac{(\text{Difference})^2}{\text{Expected}}$
One	13	12	1	1	$\frac{1}{12}$
Three	18	12	6	36	$\frac{36}{12}$
Six	12	12	0	0	$\frac{0}{12}$
Other	29	36	−7	49	$\frac{49}{36}$
	72	72			Total $\frac{160}{36}$

Thus, $\chi^2 = \frac{160}{36} \approx 4.44.$

There are 4 possible outcomes. The chi-square value for a 5% significance level for 4 possible outcomes is 7.81. Since 4.44 does not exceed this value, we can state that our results occurred by chance. Thus, we can *accept* the null hypothesis.

Try This

b. One hundred students are asked, "On a multiple-choice question, if you were to guess, would you choose a, b, c, or d?" Thirty-nine students chose c, 16 chose a. Determine whether this result occurred by chance. Use a 1% level of significance.
No. $\chi^2 = 11.58$, which is greater than 9.21, the table value for 3 possible outcomes at the 1% level.

EXAMPLE 3

For two years, the winners in eighty-eight 100-meter dashes held at Central High School's new track were distributed as follows:

Lane of track	1	2	3	4	5	6	7	8
Number of winners	15	12	19	13	11	6	7	5

Chalkboard Examples

1. 300 students were asked to choose their favorite color from the following list: blue, green, red, orange, yellow, and purple. 63 chose red, 38 chose orange, 45 chose yellow, 59 chose blue, 55 chose purple, and 40 chose green. Determine whether these results were due to chance. Use a 5% level of significance.
   The expected outcome if the results were due to chance is $\frac{1}{6}$ of the total number, or 50 responses for each color.

Color	Difference	$\frac{\text{Difference}^2}{\text{Expected}}$
red	13	3.38
orange	−12	2.88
yellow	−5	0.50
blue	9	1.62
purple	5	0.50
green	−10	2.00

   Chi-square = 10.88

   The table value for 6 possible outcomes at a 5% level is 11.1. Since 10.88 is less than this value, we can conclude the results occurred by chance.
2. A record company is including with an album posters—posters in three different designs with an album. One poster is of the entire band, one is of the lead singer, and one is of the drummer. A record store ordered 120 copies of the album, and received 27 posters of the lead singer, 54 of the entire band, and 39 of the drummer. Test the null hypothesis that these numbers resulted by chance. Use a 2.5% level of significance.
   We would expect the store to receive $\frac{1}{3} \cdot 120$, or 40, of each poster.

Outcome	Difference	$\frac{\text{Difference}^2}{\text{Expected}}$
band	14	4.9
lead	−13	4.225
drummer	−1	0.025

   Chi-square = 9.15

   The table value for 3 possible outcomes at a 2.5% level is 7.38. We would reject the null hypothesis that the numbers occurred by chance.

LESSON QUIZ

1. A die is thrown 60 times and 14 fours are thrown. Calculate chi-square.
   1.92
2. A coin is tossed 100 times and 62 heads come up. Determine whether this result is due to chance at a 5% level of significance.
   The results were not due to chance (chi-square = 5.76 > 3.84).

Test the hypothesis that there is no difference between the respective lanes in terms of the number of race winners associated with each lane

a. at the 5% level of significance.

b. at the 2.5% level of significance.

There were a total of 88 races, so we would expect 11 winners from each lane if runners were assigned randomly to lanes.

Using the formula for chi-square we calculate the value associated with the data.

$$\chi^2 = \frac{(15-11)^2}{11} + \frac{(12-11)^2}{11} + \frac{(19-11)^2}{11} + \frac{(13-11)^2}{11} + \frac{(11-11)^2}{11} + \frac{(6-11)^2}{11} + \frac{(7-11)^2}{11} + \frac{(5-11)^2}{11}$$

$$= \frac{16}{11} + \frac{1}{11} + \frac{64}{11} + \frac{4}{11} + 0 + \frac{25}{11} + \frac{16}{11} + \frac{36}{11} + \frac{162}{11} \approx 14.73$$

There are 8 possible outcomes. The chi-square value 14.73 exceeds the table value of 14.1 for a 5% level of significance. We would *reject* the null hypothesis that there is no difference between the lanes at the 5% level of significance.

A chi-square of 14.73 does *not* exceed the table value of 16.0 for a 2.5% level of significance. We would *accept* the null hypothesis that there is no difference between the lanes at the 2.5% level of significance.

Try This

c. Group the data in Example 3 so that there are 4 possible outcomes—lanes 1 and 2, lanes 3 and 4, lanes 5 and 6, lanes 7 and 8. Test the hypothesis that there is no difference between each pair of lanes in terms of the number of race winners
1. at the 5% level of significance. **2.** at the 1% level of significance.
$\chi^2 = 11.36$; it is significant at both the 5% and 1% levels. We would conclude that there is a difference between the pairs of lanes at three levels, and reject the null hypothesis.

16-6 EXERCISES

Calculate the value of chi-square.

1. A coin is tossed 55 times and lands heads 24 times.

2. A die is tossed 30 times and shows a one 7 times.

3. One hundred students are asked to pick a number from 1 to 10; 35 pick 7, 28 pick 3, and the rest pick another number.

4. In a class of 260, 65 have last names beginning with J, 56 have last names beginning with T, and the others have last names beginning with a different letter.

Complete the table and determine chi-square.

5.

Outcome	Observed	Expected	Difference	(Difference)^2	$\frac{(\text{Difference})^2}{\text{Expected}}$
1	14	12	2	4	4/12
2	14	12	2	4	4/12
3	8	12	−4	16	16/12
4	6	12	−6	36	36/12
5	9	12	−3	9	9/12
6	21	12	9	81	81/12 $\chi^2 = 12.5$

6.

Outcome	Observed	Expected	Difference	(Difference)^2	$\frac{(\text{Difference})^2}{\text{Expected}}$
1	13	12	1	1	1/12
2	11	12	−1	1	1/12
3	14	12	2	4	4/12
4	16	12	4	16	16/12
5	8	12	−4	16	16/12
6	10	12	−2	4	4/12 $\chi^2 = 3.5$

7.

Outcome	Observed	Expected	Difference	(Difference)^2	$\frac{(\text{Difference})^2}{\text{Expected}}$
1	20	12	8	64	64/12
2	19	15	4	16	16/15
3	18	18	0	0	0/18
4	24	21	3	9	9/21
5	17	21	−4	16	16/21
6	10	18	−8	64	64/18
7	14	15	−1	1	1/15
8	10	12	−2	4	4/12 $\chi^2 \approx 11.546$

8.

Outcome	Observed	Expected	Difference	(Difference)^2	$\frac{(\text{Difference})^2}{\text{Expected}}$
1	2	5	−3	9	9/5
2	12	8	4	16	16/8
3	23	11	12	144	144/11
4	16	14	2	4	4/14
5	14	17	−3	9	9/17
6	8	20	−12	144	144/20 $\chi^2 \approx 24.906$

9. In testing metal bars for breaks under a series of laboratory tests, technicians obtained the following data relating the distributions of theoretical and observed breaks. Test the null hypothesis at the 1% level.
$\chi^2 \approx 31.83$; we reject the null hypothesis at the 1% level of significance.

Number of Breaks	0	1	2	3	4	5 or more
Observed breaks	157	125	35	17	1	1
Expected breaks	131	107	54	27	11	6

Assignment Guide
Algebra: Omit

Alg w/Finite Math: 1–11 e/o, 12, MR

Comprehensive: 1–11 e/o, 12, 13, MR

Additional Answers

Exercises

1. $\frac{2}{25} = 0.08$
2. $\frac{24}{25} = 0.96$
3. $\frac{9441}{80} = 118.0125$
4. $\frac{133585}{240} = 556.6$

Mixed Review

14. $\frac{27}{8}$
15. $\frac{9}{4}$
16. $\frac{3}{2}$

Writing to Learn

Most people don't get enough same digits and consecutive digits because they don't feel they are random.

10. The expected frequency of students passing through the school computer center was calculated and a survey taken to see how closely the predictions matched the theoretical solution. Test the null hypothesis at the 0.1% level of significance.

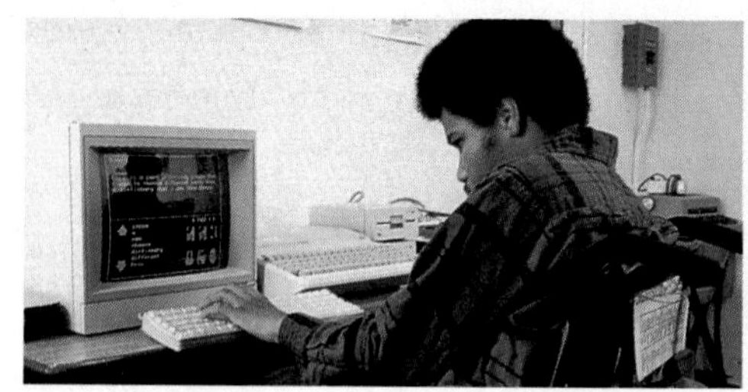

Period of Observation	1	2	3	4	5	6	7	8
Observed number	43	27	28	67	43	31	25	46
Expected number	30	40	40	60	50	30	30	30

$\chi^2 = 24.655$; we reject the null hypothesis.

B

11. Are chi-square values for the *proportion* of observed values equal to the chi-square values for the data? Give an example. No. For Example 1, $\chi^2 \approx 0.28$ using proportions.

12. ***Critical Thinking***
 a. Write a 51-digit string of "random" digits.
 b. Count the number of times you have the same digit following itself. Count the number of times a number one less or one greater follows a digit (± 1 number).
 c. Fill in the table and test the data at a 5% level of significance.
 Answers may vary.

	Number observed	Number expected
Same follower		0.1(50) = 5
±1 number		0.2(50) = 10
Other		35

Challenge

13. Chi-square tests are not recommended when expected values are 5 or less. Why? Can you think of a way to test the following data for significance at the 5% level? Small expected values have too much effect on the value of χ^2. We can group the data so that expected values are greater than 5.

Observed	0	3	7	15	18	11	10
Expected	1	6	15	20	15	6	1

Mixed Review

Simplify. **14.** $\frac{\sqrt{729}}{\sqrt{64}}$ **15.** $\frac{\sqrt[3]{729}}{\sqrt[3]{64}}$ **16.** $\frac{\sqrt[6]{729}}{\sqrt[6]{64}}$

WRITING TO LEARN

Write an explanation why most people do not get enough of the same followers and ± 1 numbers in their strings of "random" numbers in the experiment described in Exercise 12.

Problem Solving: Application

Statistical Studies

You have been asked by the principal of a school to do a statistical study of the previous year's grades. She needs to know the following:

a. The grade point average, or mean grade, for each subject and for the total of all subjects.

b. The distribution of grades for different subjects and for the total.

c. How the distribution of grades for a subject and for the total compares with the expected distribution of grades—20%A's, 25% B's, 30% C's, 20% D's, and 5% F's.

After asking the appropriate teachers and school records office for the number of A's, B's, C's, D's, and F's for each class, you find the following grade distributions.

	A	B	C	D	F	
Mathematics	67	112	84	43	32	338
Science	51	70	86	53	21	281
History	111	103	75	40	11	340
English	101	110	73	46	29	359
Social Studies	49	84	89	37	19	278
Languages	38	57	41	22	6	164
Total	417	536	448	241	118	1760

The grades are assigned the numerical values 4 for A, 3 for B, 2 for C, 1 for D, and 0 for F. To find the grade point average, or mean grade, for English, $\bar{x} = \frac{\sum_{i=1}^{5} f_i w_i}{n}$, where w_i is the value of each grade and f_i is the frequency of grade i.

$$\bar{x} = \frac{101(4) + 110(3) + 73(2) + 46(1) + 29(0)}{359} = \frac{926}{359} \approx 2.58,$$ which is just over halfway from C to B.

Problems

1. What is the grade point average for each subject? for the total?
2. Choose an appropriate level of significance. Use chi-square to test whether the grades were as expected for each subject; for the total.
3. Are the grades normally distributed for each subject? for the total?
4. What is the expected grade point average for any or all subjects?
5. What other statistical information could you present?
6. To find the variance, $\sigma^2 = \frac{\sum_{i=1}^{5} f_i(w_i - \bar{x})^2}{n}$. Find the standard deviation of grades for the total.

Problem Solving: Application

The method of finding the mean here is essentially the same as the method shown on page 334 Example 2 of finding a weighted average:

To use that method,

The average of 101 numbers is 4, the average of 110 numbers is 3, and so on.

$4 = \frac{\text{the first sum}}{101}$, so

the first sum $= 4(101) = 404$ and so on.
total sum $= 404 + 330 + 146 + 46 + 0 = 926$.

Average $= \frac{926}{359} \approx 2.58$

ANSWERS

1. Math 2.41, Science 2.27, History 2.77, English 2.58, Social Studies 2.38, Languages 2.60, total 2.51
2. Chi-square scores are: Math 34.4, Science 4.1, History 51.8, English 43.7, Social Studies 12.3, Languages 12.6, total 90.3. Grades for Math, History, English, and the total are significantly different from expected values for any level of significance. Grades for Social Studies and Languages are significant at 2.5% or more. Science grades do not differ from expected values at 10% or more.
3. No, they are not symmetric about the mean.
4. 2.35
5. You could show histograms, give median and mode grades, and break down the data further to see why the grades deviated from expected grades.
6. $\sigma \approx 1.16$

Chapter 16 Summary and Review

16-1

Stem-and-leaf diagrams and frequency distributions are helpful in organizing data.

1. Construct a stem-and-leaf diagram for these math test scores.

   92, 73, 82, 53, 67, 77, 78, 63, 93, 96, 80, 71, 63, 90, 81, 74, 76, 72, 73, 80, 91, 65, 49, 50, 74, 80, 77, 80, 83, 70, 72

2. Construct a frequency distribution showing the relative frequency for the following latitudes, in degrees, of some North American cities.

   32, 41, 42, 35, 40, 82, 40, 35, 38, 62, 33, 39, 33, 44, 30, 64, 35, 39, 44, 30, 32, 42, 51, 43, 30, 44, 64, 48, 37, 40, 45, 40

16-2

The following are three important measures of central tendency.

The mean or average is $\bar{x} = \dfrac{\sum_{i=1}^{n} x_i}{n}$.

The mode is the value that occurs most often.

The median is the middle value when all the values are arranged in order. If there is no middle value, then the median is the average of the two middle values.

3. Find the mean, mode, and median for the length, in miles, of some major United States rivers.

   3710, 1243, 1306, 1900, 135, 2533, 900, 1270, 680, 780, 1038, 1459, 280, 620, 300, 444, 270, 735, 720, 530, 490, 525, 720, 310, 470

A box and whisker plot is a valuable method of displaying data.

4. Construct a box and whisker plot of the average speed of winds, in mi/h, in some North American cities.

   9.1, 6.8, 9.1, 10.3, 12.4, 12.1, 11.4, 6.2, 10.3, 10.7, 8.9, 10.2

16-3

The range is the difference between the greatest and least values.

5. The Rams scored 14, 15, 22, 20, 27, 24, and 18 points in 7 games. What is the range?

The mean deviation is the average amount that a set of data differs from the mean. To find the mean deviation, first we find the deviation of each value from the mean. We do this by finding the absolute value of the difference between each value and the mean. Then we find the mean of these deviations.

6. Find the mean deviation for these basketball scores.

   80, 99, 89, 125, 113, 117, 142, 131, 103, 111, 123, 135, 97, 109, 86, 117, 107, 125, 94, 121

ANSWERS

1.

Stem	Leaf
4	9
5	3, 0
6	7, 3, 3, 5
7	3, 7, 8, 1, 4, 6, 2, 3, 4, 7, 0, 2
8	2, 0, 1, 0, 0, 0, 3
9	2, 3, 6, 0, 1

2.

Interval	Frequency	Rel f
30–39	14	0.4375
40–49	13	0.40625
50–59	1	0.03125
60–69	3	0.09375
70–79	0	0
80–89	1	0.03125

3. Mean 935, mode 720, median 720

4.

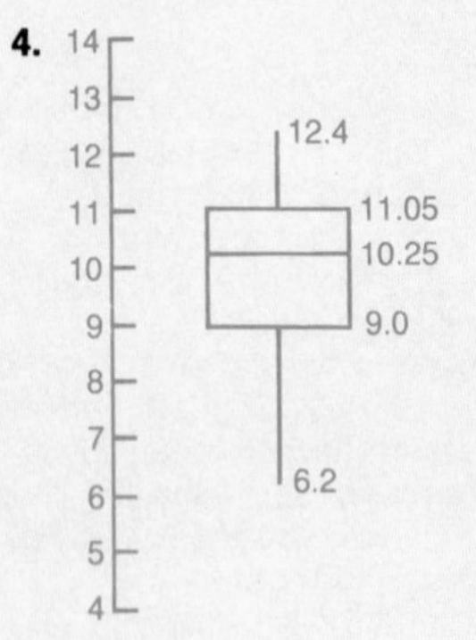

5. 13
6. 13.7

To find the variance, square the deviation of each value from the mean and then find the mean of these squares.

7. Find the variance for the following running speeds, in mi/h, of various animals.

   50, 40, 45, 35, 30, 70, 25, 30, 39, 47, 61, 11, 28, 35, 45, 50, 32, 20

To find the standard deviation, σ, take the square root of the variance.

8. Find the standard deviation for the height, in meters, of the world's highest dams.

   243, 237, 261, 272, 237, 226, 300, 285, 267, 233, 335, 262, 253, 230, 237, 242, 245

16-4

When data are distributed in a bell-shaped, or normal curve, about 68% of the data lie within one standard deviation on either side of the mean, and about 95% lie within two standard deviations of the mean.

9. A test has a mean score of 23 with a standard deviation of 4. What percent of the students would we expect to have a score below 19?

The z-score for x is found by dividing the difference between x and the mean by the standard deviation. The probability of a lower z-score is given in Table 7.

10. Find the z-score for 90, where $\bar{x} = 120$ and $\sigma = 37.5$.

11. Rolling Wheels tires have a mean lifetime of 40,000 miles with a standard deviation of 8000 miles. What is the probability that a specific tire will go more than 50,000 miles? Assume a normal distribution.

16-5

A random sample is a sample selected such that each object (person) in the population has an equal chance of being selected for the sample, and each object (person) in the sample is chosen independently of any other objects in the sample.

12. If we are surveying students' ice cream flavor preferences and the first student picks chocolate, are we taking a random sample if we make sure the second student picks a flavor other than chocolate?

13. Describe how to select a random sample of 5 physicians from a telephone listing of 200 for a health survey.

To draw a representative sample, we may need to divide the population into distinct subgroups, called strata. Then we can use stratified random sampling to assure that the sample has the same characteristics as the population.

14. A college has 1400 freshmen, 1800 sophomores, 1200 juniors, and 600 seniors. Describe how to take a stratified random sample of 200 students.

7. 195.8
8. 27.8
9. 16%
10. −0.8
11. 0.1056
12. No. This is not random because students are not chosen independently.
13. Assign each of the 200 doctors a number between 1 and 200, then randomly select five numbers between 1 and 200.
14. To select a stratified random sample of 200 students, you would randomly choose 56 freshmen, 72 sophomores, 48 juniors, and 24 seniors.

15. $\chi^2 = 3.30625$
16. $3.30625 < 3.84$, accept the null hypothesis
17. $\chi^2 = 31.63$, so we reject the null hypothesis.

16-6

The chi-square (χ^2) test is used to compare observed data with expected data, using the formula

$$\chi^2 = \sum \frac{(\text{observed} - \text{expected})^2}{\text{expected}}$$

15. A rub-off game card has 5 scratch-off spots. There is one winning spot and 4 losing spots. The player scratches off exactly one spot. Out of 1000 game cards, there were 223 winners. Calculate chi-square.

The hypothesis usually tested is the null hypothesis, which states

> There is no statistical difference between the expected and the observed data. Thus, the observed results occurred by chance.

To reject the null hypothesis at a specific level of significance, the calculated value of chi-square must exceed the value given for the number of possible outcomes reported.

Possible Outcomes	Level of significance 10%	5%	2.5%	1%	0.1%
2	2.71	3.84	5.02	6.63	7.88
3	4.61	5.99	7.38	9.21	10.6
4	6.25	7.81	9.35	11.3	12.8
5	7.78	9.59	11.1	13.3	14.9
6	9.24	11.1	12.8	15.1	16.7
7	10.6	12.6	14.4	16.8	18.5
8	12.0	14.1	16.0	18.5	20.3
9	13.4	15.5	17.5	20.1	22.0
10	14.7	16.9	19.0	21.7	23.6

16. Test the null hypothesis for Exercise 15 at the 5% level of significance.

17. The manager of a fast-food restaurant noticed the following numbers of customers served by the different cashiers during one day.

Cashier	Customers
1	85
2	68
3	41
4	78
5	96
6	72
7	50

Test the null hypothesis at the 5% level of significance.

See also Problem 16, Computer-Assisted Problem Solving, page 851.

Chapter 16 Test

Use the data for Problems 1–8.

The temperatures in several western cities on a certain date were as follows.

40	43	44	44	47
51	70	68	56	56
52	67	53	63	56

1. Construct a stem-and-leaf diagram for this data.

2. Construct a frequency distribution showing the relative frequency for this data.

3. Find the mean, mode, and median for this data.

4. Construct a box and whisker plot for this data.

5. What is the range for this data?

6. Find the mean deviation for this data.

7. Find the variance for this data.

8. Find the standard deviation for this data.

9. A test has a mean score of 73 with a standard deviation of 12. Students with scores of 85 and up receive an A. What percent of the students would we expect to get an A? Assume a normal distribution. 16

10. Find the z-score for 29, where $\overline{x} = 31$ and $\sigma = 1.25$. −1.6

11. A tool withstands an average pressure of 38 lb, with a standard deviation of 1.6 lb. The manufacturer must throw out tools that cannot withstand pressures of 40 lb or more. What is the probability that a certain tool must be thrown out? Assume a normal distribution. 0.1056

12. If we are studying customer satisfaction for Leopard XX cars, are we taking a random sample if we select every third customer from a list of customers who have purchased two Leopard XX cars?

13. Describe how to select a random sample of 25 athletes for a sports trivia contest.

14. There are three high schools in a town. There are 1350 students at Martin Luther King High, 925 at Wayne High, and 1475 at Jordan School. Describe how to take a stratified random sample of 150 students.

15. A game show asks the contestants to choose door 1, 2, or 3. The big prize is behind one of the doors. Of 60 contestants, 29 chose the door with the big prize. Calculate chi-square. $\chi^2 = 6.075$

16. Test the null hypothesis for Problem 15 at the 5% level of significance.
$\chi^2 > 5.99$, so we reject the null hyposthesis.

17. A toll collector noticed that the following numbers of cars came through the different toll booths during one day.

Toll booth	1	2	3	4
Customers	131	185	172	112

$\chi^2 = 23.4$, so we reject the null hypothesis.

Test the null hypothesis at the 1% level of significance.

ADDITIONAL ANSWERS

1.

Stem	Leaf
4	0, 3, 4, 4, 7
5	1, 6, 6, 2, 3, 6
6	8, 7, 3
7	0

2.

Interval	Frequency	Rel f
39–41	1	0.07
42–44	3	0.2
45–47	1	0.07
48–50	0	0.0
51–53	3	0.2
54–56	3	0.2
57–59	0	0.0
60–62	0	0.0
63–65	1	0.07
66–68	2	0.13
69–71	1	0.07

3. Mean 54, mode 56, median 53

4.

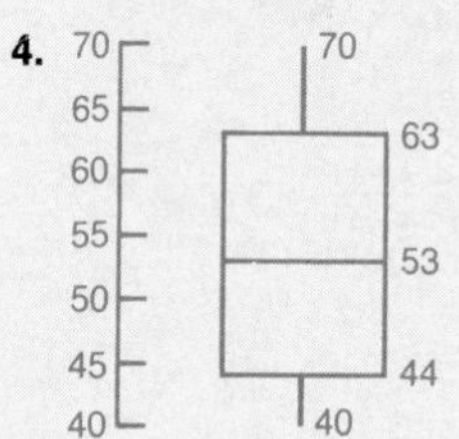

5. 30

6. 7.73

7. 86.27

8. 9.29

12. This is not a random sample because each person in the population (individuals who own Leopard XX cars) does not have an equal chance of being selected.

13. Assign all the athletes a number, then use a random number generator or a random number table to select 25 numbers.

14. To select a stratified random sample, select 54 students from Martin Luther King High, 37 from Wayne High, and 59 from Jordan High.

Test Item Analysis

Item	Lesson
1, 2	16-1
3, 4	16-2
5–8	16-3
9, 10	16-4
11–14	16-5
15–17	16-6

CHAPTER **17**

Trigonometric Functions

Chapter Overview

Chapter 17 examines the basic functions and graphs of trigonometry. The six trigonometric functions are defined as ratios of sides in a right triangle. The measure of angles are explained and used to define reference angles. The relationship between radian and degree measure is considered. The concepts of arc length and angular speed are used for problem-solving applications. Conversion between decimal degree and degree and minute notation is presented in order to use tables in finding the values of trigonometric functions. Periodicity and amplitude of a function are defined to aid in the graphing of periodic functions. The quotient, Pythagorean, and cofunction identities are used to find related identities. More complex graphs are presented with changes in amplitude and/or period. Algebraic manipulation is used in simplifying trigonometric expressions or equations. A situational problem-solving lesson concludes the chapter material.

Objectives

17-1
- Find the sine, cosine, and tangent for an angle of a right triangle.
- Find the lengths of sides in special triangles.
- Find the six trigonometric function values for an angle given one of the function values.

17-2
- Find the quadrant in which the terminal side of an angle lies.
- Find the trigonometric function values of an angle, or of a rotation.
- Find trigonometric function values for angles whose terminal side lies on an axis.
- Find the reference angle of a rotation and use it to find trigonometric function values.

17-3
- Convert from degree to radian measure and vice versa.
- Find arc length given the radian measure of an angle and vice versa.
- Use cofunction identities to find trigonometric function values.
- Solve problems concerning angular speed.

17-4
- Find trigonometric function values using a table.
- Convert between degree and minute notation and decimal degree notation.
- Use a table and linear interpolation to find trigonometric function values.

17-5
- Identify periodic functions from their graphs.
- Graph the sine and cosine functions and interpret their graphs.
- Graph the other trigonometric functions and interpret their graphs.

17-6
- Derive identities from the quotient and Pythagorean identities.
- Derive identities from the cofunction identities.

17-7
- Sketch graphs in which the amplitude or period is changed.
- Sketch graphs in which the amplitude and period are changed.

17-8
- Compute and simplify trigonometric expressions.
- Solve equations involving trigonometric expressions.

TEACHING CHAPTER 17

Cooperative Learning Opportunities

The A exercises in Lessons 17-1 through 17-3 can serve as class exercises for cooperative learning groups. After explaining the introductory material, assign groups of five and have them go around the group answering one exercise after another. All students should be attentive to each response. An individual should raise his or her hand when wishing to correct a mistake. The student doing that exercise will call on the one with the raised hand. When two different answers are proposed, the group will discuss them to decide which is correct.

In Lessons 17-4 and 17-5, have individuals do five of the A Exercises before the groups form. Then have them compare their results and correct any mistakes.

Identities are quickly grasped by some students but are quite difficult for others. For this reason you may want to assign study partners to first review the examples and later check homework for Lesson 17-7.

Multicultural Note: *Surveying and Astronomy in Early America*

In both surveying and astronomy, calculations are made based on trigonometric relationships. Surveying was a highly respected profession in colonial times. Both George Washington and Thomas Jefferson worked for a time as surveyors.

Although astronomy seems at first to be quite distinct from surveying, the two were often used together in determining boundaries between territories. Andrew Ellicott, the son of a Pennsylvania clock maker, exhibited a rare combination of mechanical and mathematical skills. He was active in the early years of the United States as a surveyor, astronomer, and instrument maker.

Ellicott worked on surveys for the northern boundary of Pennsylvania, the boundary between Virginia and Pennsylvania, and the boundaries of Washington, D.C. He reported on the methods he used to calculate the eccentricity of the planetary orbits. In general, Ellicott was a practical scientist using what he knew to serve the needs of early America.

Alternative Assessment and Communication Ideas

There are several reasons for using alternative assessment. You can give students a different way of answering questions or expressing themselves. At the same time you will learn more about students' learning styles. Some forms of alternative assessment allow you to see whether students are making connections.

The relationships existing among trigonometric functions are literally endless. In Chapter 17, the **Critical Thinking** exercises are well suited to help you find out not only whether students have learned the basic relationships but whether they can use this learning to think in a larger context. These **Critical Thinking** questions can be used as part of a quiz or as test items.

The **Writing to Learn** activity on page 762 provides an excellent opportunity to think through and express all of the essential elements of a trig function. Ask the class to think about the descriptions offered and comment on whether anything has been left out.

Investigations and Projects

Although a great deal of time and energy are spent on trigonometric graphs, some students seem never to get beyond the idea that trigonometry means triangles. Use this project to introduce interested students to further applications and graphs of periodic functions. Have students start by looking up and writing about the meaning of "sinusoidal."

After they have looked through reference books and other texts, suggest that individuals or small groups work on short reports that include a clear definition or description of the necessary vocabulary, a description of topics or subject areas that use sinusoidal functions, and a specific example, clearly explained, of a sinusoidal function and its graph. Even if these examples are taken directly from reference materials, the research and effort to explain them will be most beneficial. Topics might include the length of days as a function of time, the phases of the moon, sound waves, or height of a point on a rotating wheel.

MANAGING CHAPTER 17

Lesson	PACING CHART (DAYS) Algebra	Algebra w/Finite	Algebra w/Trig	Compre-hensive	Opening Activity	Cooperative Activity	Seat or Group Work
17-1	0	0	1	1	First Five Minutes 17-1: **TE** p.728 or ***FFM Transparency Masters*** p.45	Critical Thinking: **SE** p.733 Strategy Problem Bank 16: ***Problem Bank*** p.17 ✂ Manipulative Activity 17: ***Enrichment*** p.58	Try This a–d
17-2	0	0	2	1	First Five Minutes 17-2: **TE** p.734 or ***FFM Transparency Masters*** p.46	Critical Thinking: **SE** p.740 Critical Thinking 17: ***Enrichment*** p.38	Try This a–n
17-3	0	0	2	1	First Five Minutes 17-3: **TE** p.741 or ***FFM Transparency Masters*** p.46	Critical Thinking: **SE** p.748	Try This a–m
17-4	0	0	2	1	First Five Minutes 17-4: **TE** p.749 or ***FFM Transparency Masters*** p.46	Critical Thinking: **SE** p.754 Looking for Errors 16: ***Enrichment*** p.77	Try This a–k
17-5	0	0	2	2	First Five Minutes 17-5: **TE** p.755 or ***FFM Transparency Masters*** p.47	Critical Thinking: **SE** p.762	Try This a–j
17-6	0	0	2	1	First Five Minutes 17-6: **TE** p.763 or ***FFM Transparency Masters*** p.47	Critical Thinking: **SE** p.768 Probability/Statistics 5: ***Enrichment*** p.86	Try This a–g
17-7	0	0	1	1	First Five Minutes 17-7: **TE** p.769 or ***FFM Transparency Masters*** p.47	Critical Thinking: **SE** p.771 Probability/Statistics 6: ***Enrichment*** p.87	Try This a–c
17-8	0	0	3	3	First Five Minutes 17-8: **TE** p.772 or ***FFM Transparency Masters*** p.47	Critical Thinking: **SE** p.774 Problem Solving: **SE** p.775	Try This a–d
Review	0	0	1	1			
Test	0	0	1	1			

FFM: First Five Minutes   SPMR: Skills Practice Mixed Review

Enrichment	Review/Assess	Reteach	Technology	Lesson
✂ Manipulative Activity 17: ***Enrichment*** p.58 Bonus Topic 16: ***Enrichment*** p.17	Lesson Quiz: **TE** p.731	Skills Practice 46, #1–7: ***SPMR*** p.58	Calculator Worksheet 35: ***Technology*** p.37	**17-1**
Critical Thinking 17: ***Enrichment*** p.38	Lesson Quiz: **TE** p.738 Mixed Review 32: ***SPMR*** p.96	Skills Practice 46, #8–25: ***SPMR*** p.58		**17-2**
Calculator Investigation: **SE** p.748	Lesson Quiz: **TE** p.745 Quiz 33: ***Assessment*** p.41	Skills Practice 47, #1–16: ***SPMR*** p.59 Problem Bank 22: ***Problem Bank*** p.43	Calculator Worksheet 36: ***Technology*** p.38 Calculator Investigation: **SE** p.748	**17-3**
Looking for Errors 16: ***Enrichment*** p.77	Lesson Quiz: **TE** p.752	Skills Practice 47, #17–31: ***SPMR*** p.59	Calculator Worksheet 37: ***Technology*** p.39 Problem for Programmers: **SE** p.754	**17-4**
Writing to Learn: **SE** p.762 Teacher Demo 4: ***Master Grapher*** pp.11–12(Apple II), pp.145–146(IBM), or pp.281–282(Mac)	Lesson Quiz: **TE** p.759 Mixed Review 33: ***SPMR*** p.97	Skills Practice 47, #32–35: ***SPMR*** p.59	Worksheet 24: ***TI-81 Activities*** pp.99–102 Worksheet 30: ***Master Grapher*** pp.119–122, pp.253–256, or pp.389–392	**17-5**
Probability/Statistics 5: ***Enrichment*** p.86	Lesson Quiz: **TE** p.766	Skills Practice 48, #1–6: ***SPMR*** p.60	Spreadsheet Activity 12: ***Technology*** pp.76–78	**17-6**
Probability/Statistics 6: ***Enrichment*** p.87 Bonus Topic 17: ***Enrichment*** p.18	Lesson Quiz: **TE** p.770 Quiz 34: ***Assessment*** p.42	Skills Practice 48, #7–12: ***SPMR*** p.60	Worksheet 25: ***TI-81 Activities*** pp.103–106 Worksheet 31: ***Master Grapher*** pp.123–126, pp.257–260, or pp.393–396	**17-7**
Problem Solving: **SE** p.775 Problem 17: Computer Assisted Problem Solving, **SE** pp.852–853	Lesson Quiz: **TE** p.773 Mixed Review 34: ***SPMR*** p.98	Skills Practice 48, #13–24: ***SPMR*** p.60	Problem 17: Computer Assisted Problem Solving, **SE** pp.852–853	**17-8**
	Summary and Review: **SE** pp.776–778; Test: **SE** p.779			**Review**
	Chapter 17 Test: ***Assessment*** pp.143–148(reg.), pp.189–190 (adv.)			**Test**

The solution to the problem posed on the facing page can be found on page 747.

Ready for Trigonometric Functions?

3-3

1. Given $f(x) = 2x^2 + 1$, find $f(3)$ and $f(-2)$. 19, 9

5-3 Simplify.

2. $(3t + 2)(t - 4)$ $3t^2 - 10t - 8$

5-4, 5-5, 5-6 Factor completely.

3. $24a^2 - 96b^2$ $24(a - 2b)(a + 2b)$

4. $3x^3y - 15x^2y^2 + 18xy^3$ $3xy(x - 3y)(x - 2y)$

6-1 Simplify.

5. $\dfrac{(a^2 - 4)}{-2a - 6} \cdot \dfrac{a + 3}{a - 2}$ $\dfrac{a + 2}{-2}$

6-2 Simplify.

6. $\dfrac{4}{-x} + \dfrac{6}{x}$ $\dfrac{2}{x}$

7. $\dfrac{5cd}{4c^2 - 1} - \dfrac{c - d}{2c + 1}$ $\dfrac{-2c^2 + 7dc + c - d}{(2c - 1)(2c + 1)}$

8-1, 8-3, 8-5 Solve.

8. $a^2 + a - 12 = 0$ $3, -4$

9. $6y^2 + 20y = 16$ $\frac{2}{3}, -4$

10. $1 + \dfrac{3}{x^2} = \dfrac{1}{x}$ $\dfrac{1 \pm i\sqrt{11}}{2}$

11. $2x + x(x - 1) = 1$ $\dfrac{-1 \pm \sqrt{5}}{2}$

9-1

12. Show that $f(x) = x^3 - x$ is odd. $f(-x) = (-x)^3 - (-x) = -x^3 + x = -(x^3 - x) = -f(x)$

13. Show that $g(x) = 2x^2 - x^4$ is even. $g(-x) = 2(-x)^2 - (-x)^4 = 2x^2 - x^4 = g(x)$

CHAPTER

Trigonometric Functions 17

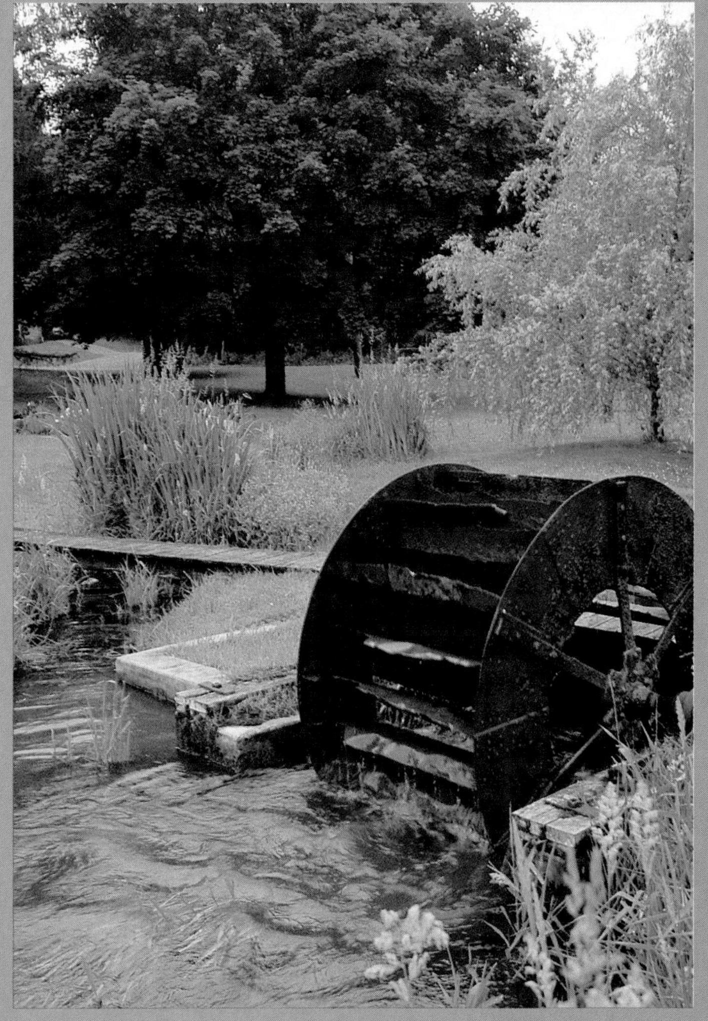

A water wheel has a 10-ft radius. The wheel revolves 16 times per minute. What is the speed of the river, in mi/h?

17-1

FIRST FIVE MINUTES

1. How many degrees are in a right angle?
   90°
2. Use the Pythagorean theorem to find the length of side c.
   10

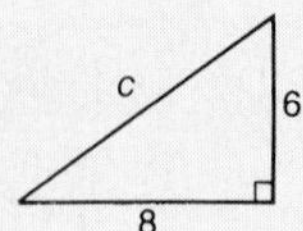

Trigonometric Ratios

Point out that the angles of a right triangle can be found given the ratio of any two sides of the triangle. For example, given the ratio of the length of side a to side b, one could construct a triangle similar to the original.

Emphasize that every right triangle has two sine ratios, two cosine ratios, and two tangent ratios.

Key Question

- What are the six possible ratios of sides for the following right triangle?

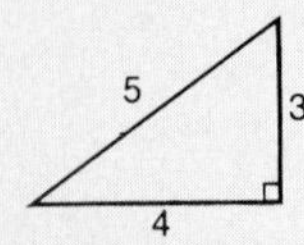

$\frac{3}{5}, \frac{4}{5}, \frac{3}{4}, \frac{5}{3}, \frac{5}{4}, \frac{4}{3}$

Chalkboard Example

1. Find $\sin \theta$, $\cos \theta$, and $\tan \theta$ for the following right triangle.

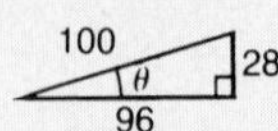

$\sin \theta = \frac{28}{100} = \frac{7}{25}$

$\cos \theta = \frac{96}{100} = \frac{24}{25}$

$\tan \theta = \frac{28}{96} = \frac{7}{24}$

17-1 Trigonometric Functions in Triangles

We now consider an important class of functions, known as **trigonometric functions.** The word **trigonometry** means "triangle measurement." The Greeks and Hindus saw trigonometry mainly as a tool for use in astronomy. The early Arabian mathematicians are credited with using all six trigonometric functions.

Trigonometric Ratios

Objective: Find the sine, cosine, and tangent for an angle of a right triangle.

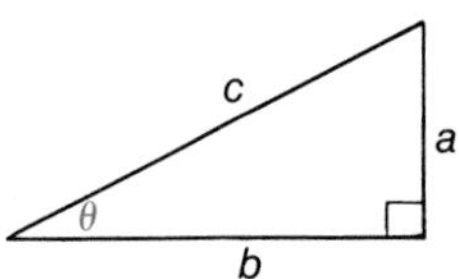

In a right triangle, the side opposite the right angle is the **hypotenuse.** In the triangle shown, the hypotenuse has length c, the side **opposite** the angle θ (**theta**) has length a, and the side **adjacent** to θ has length b.

The ratio $\frac{a}{b}$ depends on θ, and thus is a function of θ. This function is the **sine** function. There are six such functions, three of which are defined as follows.

Definition

sine function: $\sin \theta = \frac{\text{length of the side opposite } \theta}{\text{length of the hypotenuse}}$

cosine function: $\cos \theta = \frac{\text{length of the side adjacent to } \theta}{\text{length of the hypotenuse}}$

tangent function: $\tan \theta = \frac{\text{length of the side opposite } \theta}{\text{length of the side adjacent to } \theta}$

Because all right triangles with an angle of measure θ are similar, function values depend only on the size of the angle, not the size of the triangle.

EXAMPLE 1 In this triangle find $\sin \theta$, $\cos \theta$, and $\tan \theta$.

$$\sin \theta = \frac{\text{side opposite } \theta}{\text{hypotenuse}} = \frac{3}{5}$$

$$\cos \theta = \frac{\text{side adjacent to } \theta}{\text{hypotenuse}} = \frac{4}{5}$$

$$\tan \theta = \frac{\text{side opposite } \theta}{\text{side adjacent to } \theta} = \frac{3}{4}$$

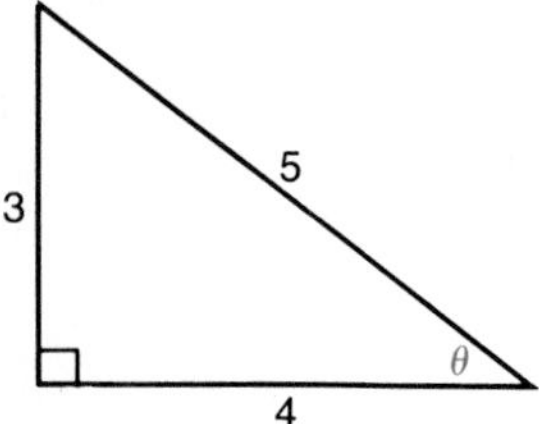

Try This

a. In this triangle find $\sin \theta$, $\cos \theta$, and $\tan \theta$.
$\sin \theta = \frac{4}{5}$, $\cos \theta = \frac{3}{5}$, $\tan \theta = \frac{4}{3}$

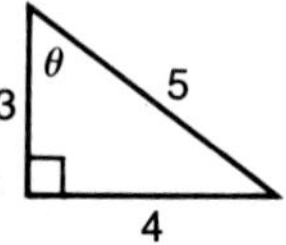

Special Angles

Objective: Find the lengths of sides in special triangles.

Our knowledge of triangles enables us to determine trigonometric function values for certain angles. First recall the Pythagorean theorem. It says that in any right triangle $a^2 + b^2 = c^2$, where c is the length of the hypotenuse.

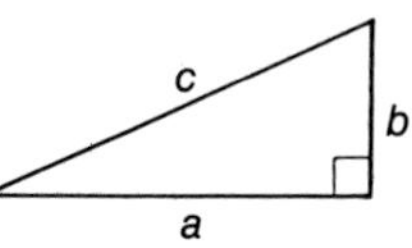

In a 45° right triangle the legs are the same length. Let us consider such a triangle whose legs have length 1. Then its hypotenuse has length c.

$$1^2 + 1^2 = c^2, \text{ or } c^2 = 2, \text{ or } c = \sqrt{2}$$

Such a triangle is shown below. From this diagram we can easily determine the trigonometric function values for 45°.

$$\sin 45° = \frac{1}{\sqrt{2}} = \frac{\sqrt{2}}{2}$$

$$\cos 45° = \frac{1}{\sqrt{2}} = \frac{\sqrt{2}}{2}$$

$$\tan 45° = \frac{1}{1} = 1$$

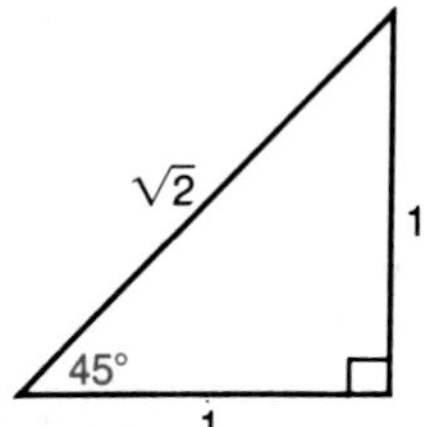

Next we consider an equilateral triangle with sides of length 2. If we bisect one angle, we obtain a right triangle that has a hypotenuse of length 2 and a leg of length 1. The other leg has length a, given by the Pythagorean theorem as follows.

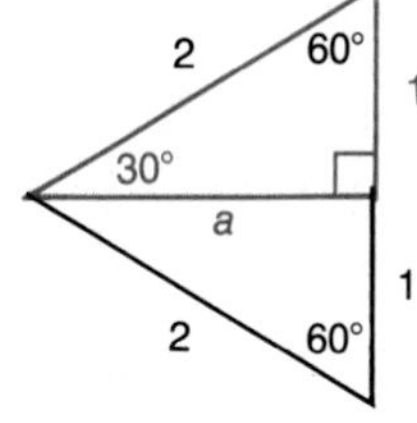

$$a^2 + 1^2 = 2^2, \text{ or } a^2 = 3, \text{ or } a = \sqrt{3}$$

The acute angles of this triangle have measures of 30° and 60°. We can now determine function values for 30° and 60°.

$$\sin 30° = \frac{1}{2} \qquad \sin 60° = \frac{\sqrt{3}}{2}$$

$$\cos 30° = \frac{\sqrt{3}}{2} \qquad \cos 60° = \frac{1}{2}$$

$$\tan 30° = \frac{1}{\sqrt{3}} = \frac{\sqrt{3}}{3} \qquad \tan 60° = \sqrt{3}$$

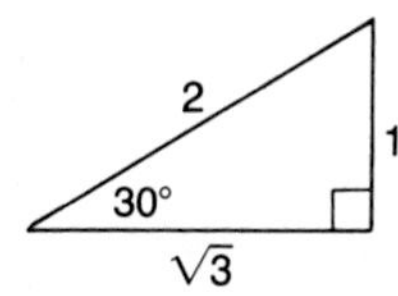

We can use what we have learned about trigonometry to solve problems.

Special Angles

Stress the importance of memorizing or quickly deriving the sin, cos, and tan of the special angles 0°, 30°, 45°, 60°, and 90°.

You may want to show students the following pattern.

$\sin 0° = \frac{\sqrt{0}}{2}$	$\cos 0° = \frac{\sqrt{4}}{2}$
$\sin 30° = \frac{\sqrt{1}}{2}$	$\cos 30° = \frac{\sqrt{3}}{2}$
$\sin 45° = \frac{\sqrt{2}}{2}$	$\cos 45° = \frac{\sqrt{2}}{2}$
$\sin 60° = \frac{\sqrt{3}}{2}$	$\cos 60° = \frac{\sqrt{1}}{2}$
$\sin 90° = \frac{\sqrt{4}}{2}$	$\cos 90° = \frac{\sqrt{0}}{2}$

Key Questions

- What is sin 45°?
  $\frac{\sqrt{2}}{2}$
- What is sin 30°?
  $\frac{1}{2}$
- What is cos 60°?
  $\frac{1}{2}$
- What is cos 90°?
  0

Chalkboard Example

1. In ABC, $a = 20$ and $m\angle A = 30°$. Find the length of side c.

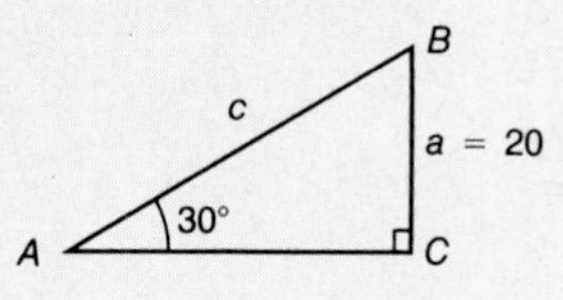

$\sin 30° = \frac{a}{c}$

$\frac{1}{2} = \frac{20}{c}$

$c = 2 \cdot 20$

$c = 40$

Reciprocal Functions

Emphasize that the cosecant is the reciprocal of the sine and that the secant is the reciprocal of the cosine.

Chalkboard Examples

1. Find csc θ, sec θ, and cot θ.

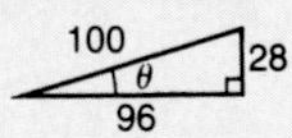

$\csc\theta = \frac{100}{28}$

$\sec\theta = \frac{100}{96}$

$\cot\theta = \frac{96}{28}$

2. If $\cos\theta = \frac{21}{29}$, find the values of the other five trigonometric functions of θ.
Consider a right triangle with side adjacent to θ of length 21 and hypotenuse 29.

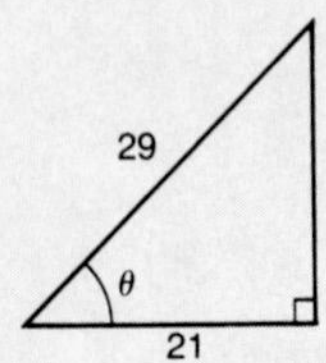

By the Pythagorean theorem the remaining side is $\sqrt{29^2 - 21^2} = 20$, hence,

$\sin\theta = \frac{20}{29}$

$\tan\theta = \frac{20}{21}$

$\csc\theta = \frac{29}{20}$

$\sec\theta = \frac{29}{21}$

$\cot\theta = \frac{21}{20}$

EXAMPLE 2 In $\triangle ABC$, $b = 40$ cm and $m\angle A = 60°$. What is the length of side c?

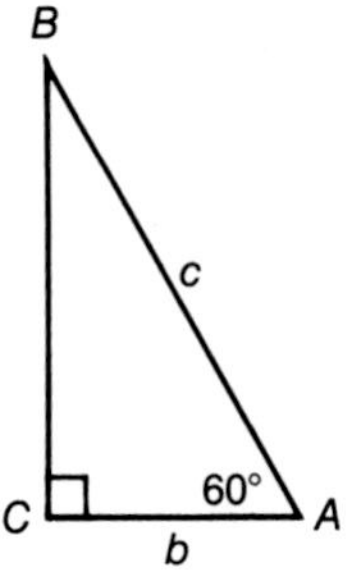

$\cos A = \frac{b}{c}$

$\cos 60° = \frac{40}{c}$ Substituting

$\frac{1}{2} = \frac{40}{c}$ Using $\cos 60° = \frac{1}{2}$

$c = 80$ cm

Try This

b. In $\triangle PQR$, $q = 12$ ft. Use the cosine function to find the length of side r. $r = 12\sqrt{2}$ ft

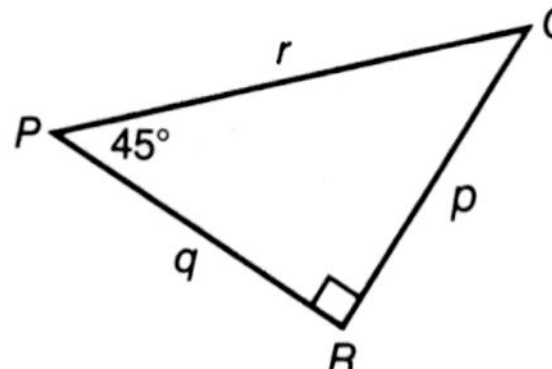

Reciprocal Functions

Objective: Find the six trigonometric function values for an angle given one of the function values.

We define the three other trigonometric functions by finding the reciprocals of the sine, cosine, and tangent functions.

Definition

The **cotangent, secant,** and **cosecant** functions are the respective reciprocals of the tangent, cosine, and sine functions.

$$\cot\theta = \frac{1}{\tan\theta} = \frac{\text{length of the side adjacent to }\theta}{\text{length of the side opposite }\theta}$$

$$\sec\theta = \frac{1}{\cos\theta} = \frac{\text{length of the hypotenuse}}{\text{length of the side adjacent to }\theta}$$

$$\csc\theta = \frac{1}{\sin\theta} = \frac{\text{length of the hypotenuse}}{\text{length of the side opposite }\theta}$$

EXAMPLE 3 Find the cotangent, secant, and cosecant of the angle shown. Approximate to two decimal places.

$$\cot\theta = \frac{\text{side adjacent to }\theta}{\text{side opposite }\theta} = \frac{3}{4} = 0.75$$

$$\sec\theta = \frac{\text{hypotenuse}}{\text{side adjacent to }\theta} = \frac{5}{3} \approx 1.67$$

$$\csc\theta = \frac{\text{hypotenuse}}{\text{side opposite }\theta} = \frac{5}{4} = 1.25$$

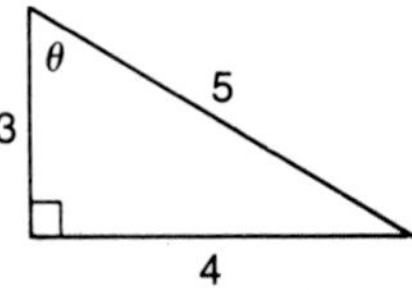

Try This

c. Approximate cot θ, sec θ, and csc θ to two decimal places.
cot $\theta \approx 1.33$, sec $\theta = 1.25$, csc $\theta \approx 1.67$

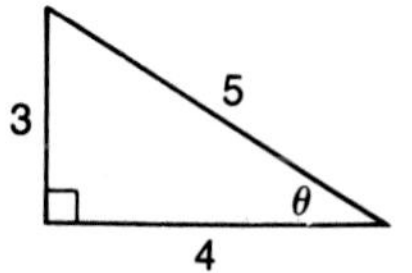

By using the Pythagorean theorem we can find all six trigonometric function values of θ when one of the ratios is known.

EXAMPLE 4 If $\sin\theta = \frac{12}{13}$, find the other five trigonometric function values for θ.

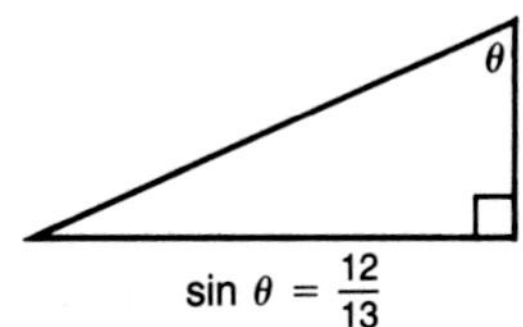

$\sin\theta = \frac{12}{13}$

We know from the definition of the sine function that the ratio

$$\frac{\text{side opposite } \theta}{\text{hypotenuse}} \text{ is } \frac{12}{13}$$

Let us consider a similar right triangle in which the hypotenuse has length 13 and the side opposite θ has length 12.

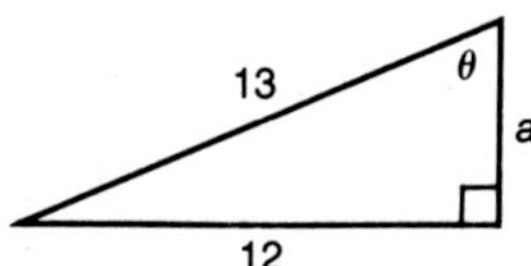

To find the length of the side adjacent to θ, we use the Pythagorean theorem.

$$a^2 + 12^2 = 13^2$$
$$a^2 = 169 - 144 = 25$$
$$a = 5$$ Choosing the positive square root, since we are finding length

We can use $a = 5$, $b = 12$, and $c = 13$ to find all of the ratios in our original triangle.

$$\sin\theta = \frac{12}{13} \qquad \csc\theta = \frac{13}{12}$$

$$\cos\theta = \frac{5}{13} \qquad \sec\theta = \frac{13}{5}$$

$$\tan\theta = \frac{12}{5} \qquad \cot\theta = \frac{5}{12}$$

Try This See Additional Answers.

d. If $\cos\theta = \frac{8}{17}$, find the other five trigonometric function values for θ.

LESSON QUIZ

1.

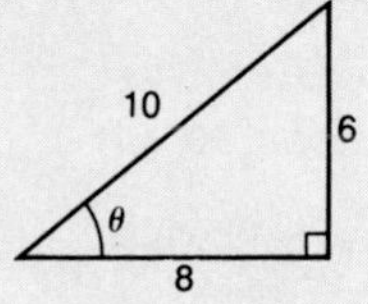

Find sin θ, cos θ, and tan θ.

$\sin\theta = \frac{6}{10} = \frac{3}{5}$

$\cos\theta = \frac{8}{10} = \frac{4}{5}$

$\tan\theta = \frac{6}{8} = \frac{3}{4}$

2.

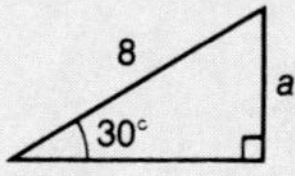

Find the length of side a.

$\sin 30° = \frac{a}{8}$

$\frac{1}{2} = \frac{a}{8}$

$a = 4$

3.

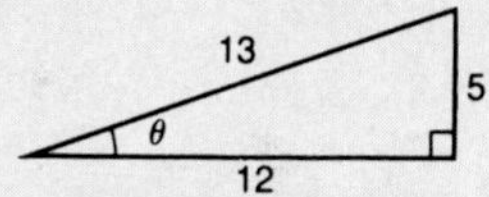

Find csc θ, sec θ, and cot θ.

$\csc\theta = \frac{13}{5}$

$\sec\theta = \frac{13}{12}$

$\cot\theta = \frac{12}{5}$

Assignment Guide
Algebra: Omit

Alg w/Trig: 1–19 e/o, 20, MR

Comprehensive: 1–19 e/o, 20, 21–23 e/o, MR

ADDITIONAL ANSWERS

Try This

d. $\sin\theta = \frac{15}{17}$

$\tan\theta = \frac{15}{8}$

$\csc\theta = \frac{17}{15}$

$\sec\theta = \frac{17}{8}$

$\cot\theta = \frac{8}{15}$

Exercises

9. $\cot\theta = 3.43$, $\sec\theta = 1.04$, $\csc\theta = 3.57$
10. $\cot\theta = 0.29$, $\sec\theta = 3.57$, $\csc\theta = 1.04$
11. $\cot\theta = 1.88$, $\sec\theta = 1.13$, $\csc\theta = 2.13$
12. $\cot\theta = 2.4$, $\sec\theta = 1.08$, $\csc\theta = 2.6$

17-1 EXERCISES

A

Find the indicated trigonometric function values for θ in each of the following triangles. Use rational notation.

1. Find $\sin\theta$, $\cos\theta$, and $\tan\theta$.

$\sin\theta = \frac{7}{25}$
$\cos\theta = \frac{24}{25}$
$\tan\theta = \frac{7}{24}$

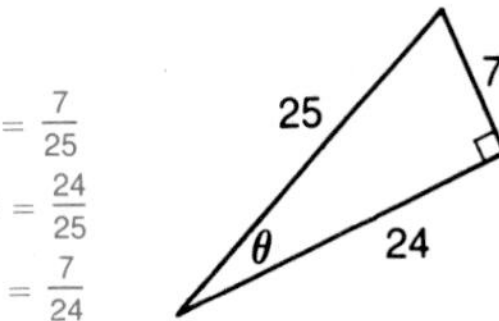

2. Find $\sin\theta$, $\cos\theta$, and $\tan\theta$.

$\sin\theta = \frac{24}{25}$
$\cos\theta = \frac{7}{25}$
$\tan\theta = \frac{24}{7}$

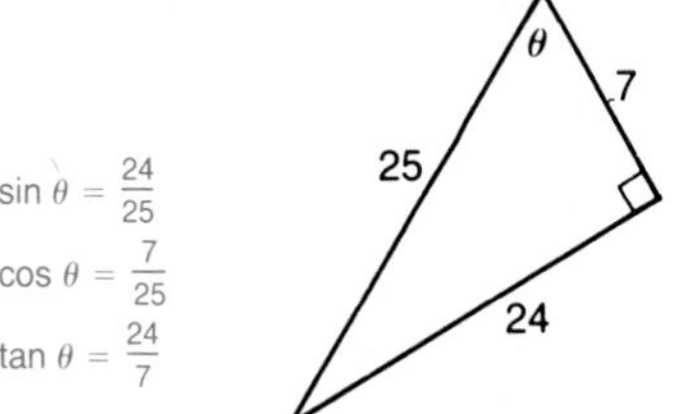

3. Find $\sin\theta$, $\cos\theta$, and $\tan\theta$.

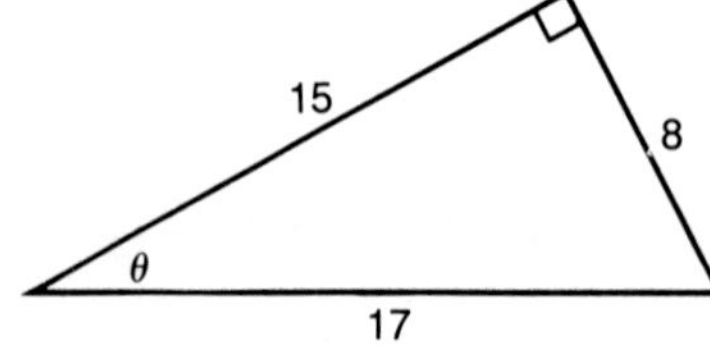

$\sin\theta = \frac{8}{17}$
$\cos\theta = \frac{15}{17}$
$\tan\theta = \frac{8}{15}$

4. Find $\sin\theta$, $\cos\theta$, and $\tan\theta$.

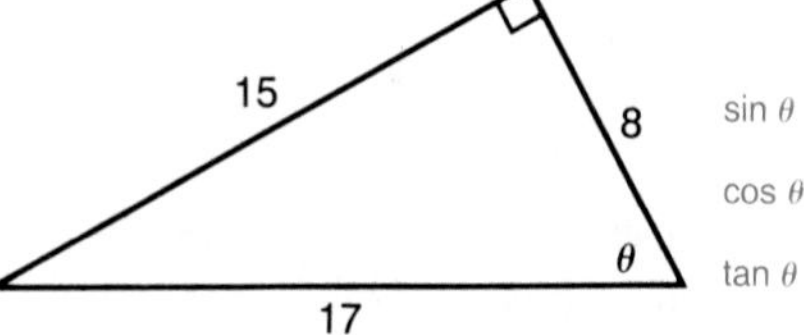

$\sin\theta = \frac{15}{17}$
$\cos\theta = \frac{8}{17}$
$\tan\theta = \frac{15}{8}$

Find the length of each labeled side.

5.

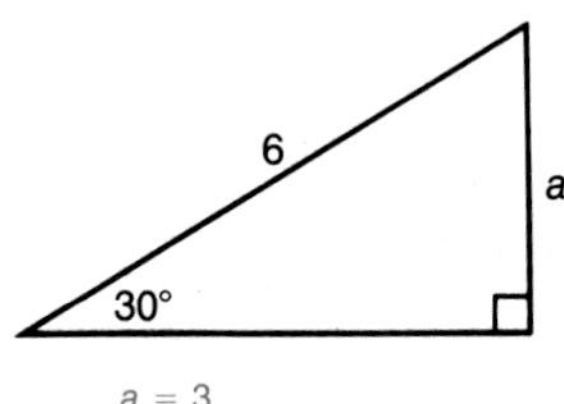

$a = 3$

6.

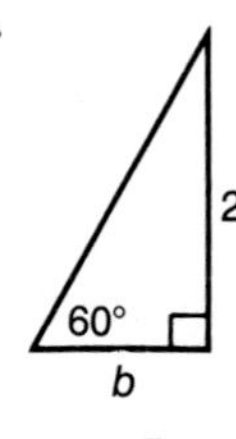

$b = 9\sqrt{3}$

7.

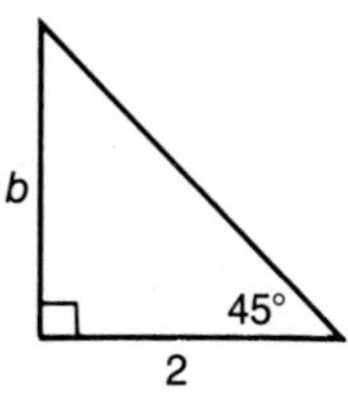

$b = 2$

8.

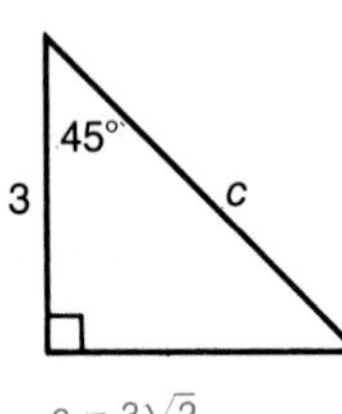

$c = 3\sqrt{2}$

Find the cotangent, secant, and cosecant of the angles shown. Approximate to two decimal places.

9.

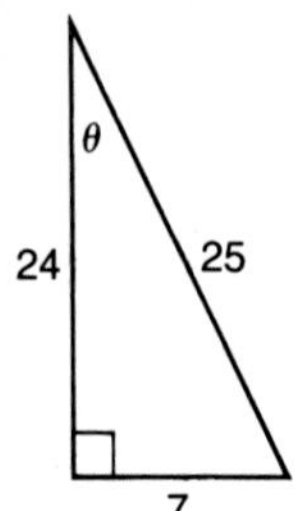

10.

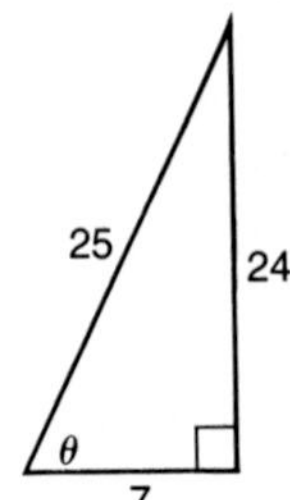

11.

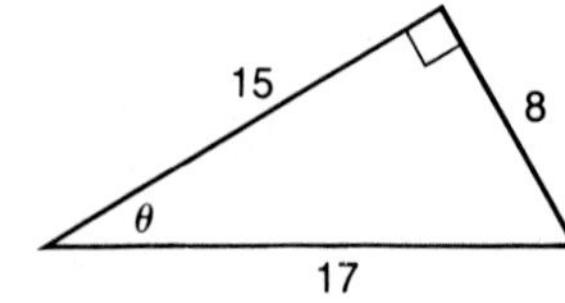

12.

5
12
θ
13

For Exercises 13 – 16, assume all angles are in the first quadrant.

13. If $\tan\theta = \frac{\sqrt{3}}{1}$, find the other five trigonometric function values for θ.

14. If $\cos\theta = \frac{\sqrt{2}}{2}$, find the other five trigonometric function values for θ.

15. If $\sin\theta = \frac{1}{2}$, find the other five trigonometric function values for θ.

16. If $\sec\theta = 2$, find the other five trigonometric function values for θ.

B

Find the six trigonometric function values for each of the following angles. Do not convert the values to decimal notation.

17. 30° **18.** 60° **19.** 45°

20. ***Critical Thinking*** Write a convincing argument that $\tan\theta = \frac{\sin\theta}{\cos\theta}$.

Challenge

21. A guy wire is attached to a 28-ft pole and makes an angle of 60° with the ground. Find

a. the distance b from A to the pole. $\frac{28\sqrt{3}}{3}$ ft

b. the length of the wire. $\frac{56\sqrt{3}}{3}$ ft

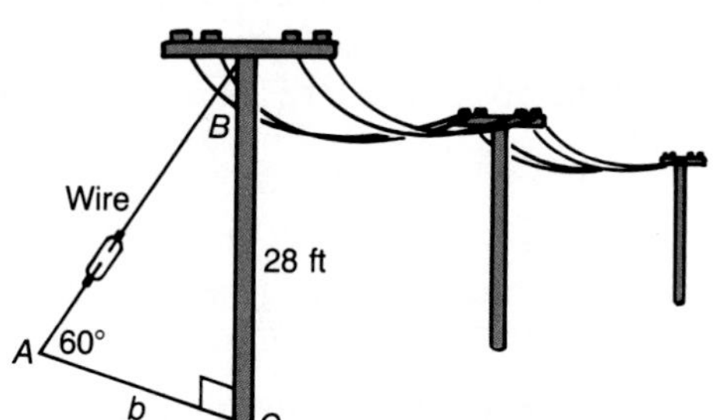

22. An observer stands 120 m from a tree and finds that the line of sight to the top of the tree is 30° above the horizontal. Find the height of the tree above eye level. $40\sqrt{3}$ m

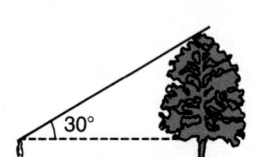

23. Find a. (Hint: Recall from geometry that the altitude of an isosceles triangle from the vertex angle bisects the base and the vertex angle.) $5\sqrt{3}$

Mixed Review

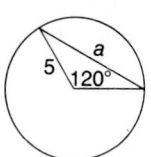

Simplify. **24.** $\sqrt[3]{16x^4}\sqrt[3]{256x^6y^6}$ **25.** $5\sqrt{13} - 18\sqrt[4]{7} + 8\sqrt{13} + 11\sqrt[4]{7}$

26. $\frac{\sqrt{b}}{\sqrt{b} + \sqrt{a}}\left(\frac{1}{b + \sqrt{ab}}\right)^{-1}$

Write without rational exponents. **27.** $a^{\frac{2}{5}}b^{\frac{3}{4}}$ **28.** $b^{-\frac{3}{4}}c$ **29.** $(4096)^{\frac{1}{3}}(4096)^{\frac{1}{4}}$

Evaluate. **30.** $\log_{10} 10^4$ **31.** $3^{\log_3 \pi}$

32. Two pipes carry water to the same tank. Pipe A can fill the tank in 6 hours. Pipe B can fill the tank in 4 hours. If both pipes are used simultaneously, how long will it take to fill the tank?

13. $\sin\theta = \frac{\sqrt{3}}{2}$, $\sec\theta = 2$, $\cos\theta = \frac{1}{2}$, $\csc\theta = \frac{2\sqrt{3}}{3}$, $\cot\theta = \frac{\sqrt{3}}{3}$

14. $\sin\theta = \frac{\sqrt{2}}{2}$, $\tan\theta = 1$, $\cot\theta = 1$, $\sec\theta = \sqrt{2}$, $\csc\theta = \sqrt{2}$

15. $\cos\theta = \frac{\sqrt{3}}{2}$, $\tan\theta = \frac{\sqrt{3}}{3}$, $\cot\theta = \sqrt{3}$, $\sec\theta = \frac{2\sqrt{3}}{3}$, $\csc\theta = 2$

16. $\sin\theta = \frac{\sqrt{3}}{2}$, $\cos\theta = \frac{1}{2}$, $\tan\theta = \sqrt{3}$, $\cot\theta = \frac{\sqrt{3}}{3}$, $\csc\theta = \frac{2\sqrt{3}}{3}$

17. $\sin\theta = \frac{1}{2}$, $\cos\theta = \frac{\sqrt{3}}{2}$, $\tan\theta = \frac{\sqrt{3}}{3}$, $\cot\theta = \sqrt{3}$, $\sec\theta = \frac{2\sqrt{3}}{3}$, $\csc\theta = 2$

18. $\sin\theta = \frac{\sqrt{3}}{2}$, $\cos\theta = \frac{1}{2}$, $\tan\theta = \sqrt{3}$, $\cot\theta = \frac{\sqrt{3}}{3}$, $\sec\theta = 2$, $\csc\theta = \frac{2\sqrt{3}}{3}$

19. $\sin\theta = \frac{\sqrt{2}}{2}$, $\cos\theta = \frac{\sqrt{2}}{2}$, $\tan\theta = 1$, $\cot\theta = 1$, $\sec\theta = \sqrt{2}$, $\csc\theta = \sqrt{2}$

20. $\frac{\sin\theta}{\cos\theta} = \frac{\text{opposite}}{\text{hypotenuse}} \div \frac{\text{adjacent}}{\text{hypotenuse}} = \frac{\text{opposite}}{\text{hypotenuse}} \cdot \frac{\text{hypotenuse}}{\text{adjacent}} = \frac{\text{opposite}}{\text{adjacent}} = \tan\theta$

Mixed Review

24. $16x^3y^2\sqrt[3]{x}$

25. $13\sqrt{13} - 7\sqrt[4]{7}$

26. b

27. $\sqrt[20]{a^8b^{15}}$

28. $\sqrt[4]{\frac{c^4}{b^3}}$

29. 128

30. 4

31. π

32. $2\frac{2}{5}$ h

17-2

FIRST FIVE MINUTES

1.

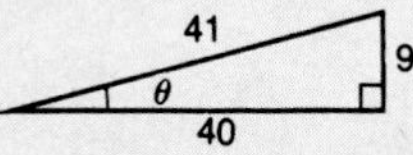

Find sin θ, cos θ, and tan θ.
Then find csc θ, sec θ, and cot θ.

$\sin\theta = \frac{9}{41}$, $\cos\theta = \frac{40}{41}$,

$\tan\theta = \frac{9}{40}$, $\csc\theta = \frac{41}{9}$,

$\sec\theta = \frac{41}{40}$, $\cot\theta = \frac{40}{9}$

2.

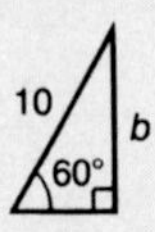

Find b.

$\frac{b}{10} = \sin 60°$

$\frac{b}{10} = \frac{\sqrt{3}}{2}$

$b = 5\sqrt{3}$

Measures of Rotations of Angles

Emphasize that angle measure is based on the arbitrary decision to divide a circle into 360 congruent arcs.

Note that 360 is divisible by 1, 2, 3, 4, 5, 6, 8, 9, 10, 12, 15, and 18.

Chalkboard Examples

In which quadrant does the terminal side of each angle lie?

1. 75°
   First quadrant
2. 275°
   Fourth quadrant
3. −30°
   Fourth quadrant
4. −190°
   Second quadrant
5. 730°
   First quadrant

17-2 More on Trigonometric Functions

Consider a rotating ray with its endpoint at the origin. The ray starts in position along the positive half of the x-axis. Counterclockwise rotations will be called positive. Clockwise rotations will be called negative.

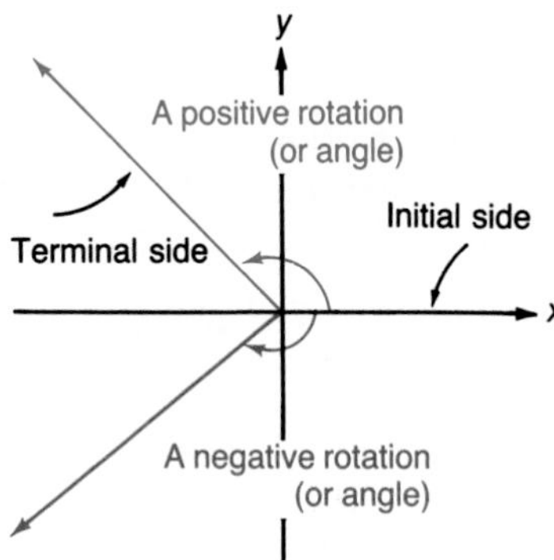

Note that the rotating ray and the positive half of the x-axis form an angle. Thus we often speak of "rotations" and "angles" interchangeably. The rotating ray is often called the **terminal side** of the angle, and the positive half of the x-axis is called the **initial side**.

Measures of Rotations of Angles

Objective: Find the quadrant in which the terminal side of an angle lies.

The measure of an angle, or rotation, may be given in degrees. For example, a complete revolution has a measure of 360°, half a revolution has a measure of 180°, a triple revolution has a measure of $360° \cdot 3$ or 1080°, and so on. We also speak of angles of 90° or 720° or −240°.

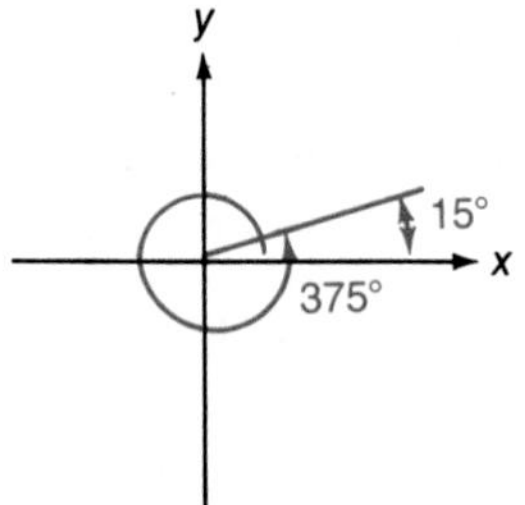

An angle between 0° and 90° has its terminal side in the first quadrant. An angle between 90° and 180° has its terminal side in the second quadrant. An angle between 0° and −90° has its terminal side in the fourth quadrant, and so on.

When the measure of an angle is greater than 360°, the rotating ray has gone through at least one complete revolution. For example, an angle of 375° will have the same terminal side as an angle of 15°. Thus the terminal side will be in the first quadrant.

EXAMPLES In which quadrant does the terminal side of each angle lie?

1. 53° First quadrant
2. 253° Third quadrant
3. −126° Third quadrant
4. −373° Fourth quadrant
5. 460° Second quadrant

Try This In which quadrant does the terminal side of each angle lie?

a. 47° First
b. 212° Third
c. −43° Fourth
d. −135° Third
e. 365° First
f. 740° First

Trigonometric Functions of Rotations

Objective: Find the trigonometric function values of an angle, or rotation.

In the preceding discussion of trigonometric functions we worked with right triangles, so the angle θ was always less than 90°. We can use rotations to apply trigonometric functions to angles of any measure.

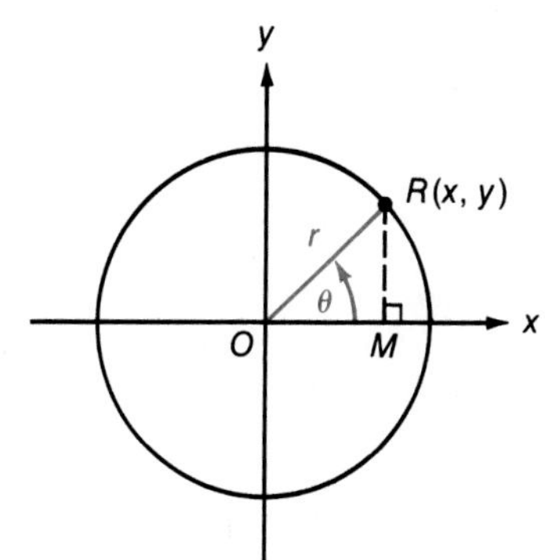

Consider a right triangle with one vertex at the origin of a coordinate system and one vertex on the positive x-axis. The other vertex is at R, a point of the circle whose center is at the origin and whose radius (r) is the length of the hypotenuse of the triangle.

Note that three of the trigonometric functions of θ are defined as follows.

$$\sin\theta = \frac{\text{side opposite } \theta}{\text{hypotenuse}} = \frac{y}{r} \qquad \cos\theta = \frac{\text{side adjacent to } \theta}{\text{hypotenuse}} = \frac{x}{r}$$

$$\tan\theta = \frac{\text{side opposite } \theta}{\text{side adjacent to } \theta} = \frac{y}{x}$$

Since x and y are coordinates of the point R, we could also define these functions as follows.

$$\sin\theta = \frac{y\text{-coordinate}}{\text{radius}} \qquad \cos\theta = \frac{x\text{-coordinate}}{\text{radius}} \qquad \tan\theta = \frac{y\text{-coordinate}}{x\text{-coordinate}}$$

We will use these definitions for functions of angles of any measure. Note that while x and y may be either positive, negative, or 0, r is always positive.

EXAMPLES Find $\sin\theta$, $\cos\theta$, and $\tan\theta$ for the angle θ.

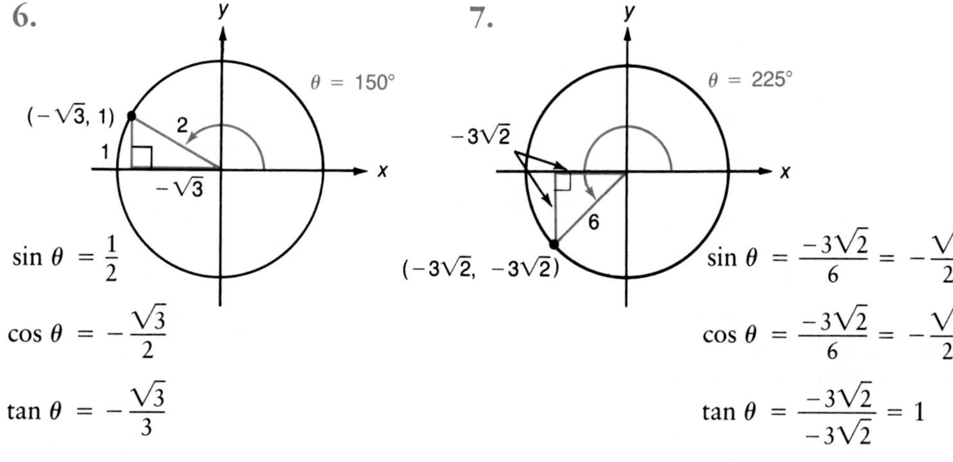

6.

$$\sin\theta = \frac{1}{2}$$

$$\cos\theta = -\frac{\sqrt{3}}{2}$$

$$\tan\theta = -\frac{\sqrt{3}}{3}$$

7.

$$\sin\theta = \frac{-3\sqrt{2}}{6} = -\frac{\sqrt{2}}{2}$$

$$\cos\theta = \frac{-3\sqrt{2}}{6} = -\frac{\sqrt{2}}{2}$$

$$\tan\theta = \frac{-3\sqrt{2}}{-3\sqrt{2}} = 1$$

Trigonometric Functions of Rotations

Note that $r > 0$ because r is the length of the radius.

You might want to have your class construct the following chart on the blackboard.

	Quadrant I	II	III	IV	
x	+	−	−	+	
cos	+	−	−	+	cos is $\frac{x}{r}$, $r > 0$
sec	+	−	−	+	sec is $\frac{1}{\cos}$
y	+	+	−	−	
sin	+	+	−	−	sin is $\frac{y}{r}$, $r > 0$
csc	+	+	−	−	csc is $\frac{1}{\sin}$
tan	+	−	+	−	tan is $\frac{\sin}{\cos}$
cot	+	−	+	−	cot is $\frac{1}{\tan}$

Chalkboard Examples

1. Find $\sin\theta$, $\cos\theta$, and $\tan\theta$.

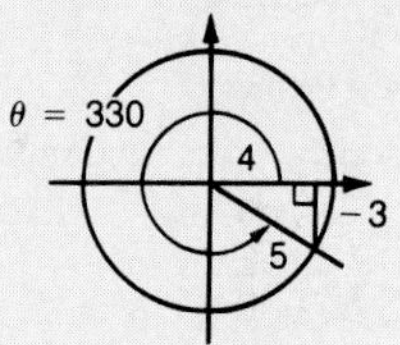

$\sin\theta = -\frac{3}{5}$

$\cos\theta = \frac{4}{5}$

$\tan\theta = -\frac{3}{4}$

2. Find sin θ, cos θ, and tan θ.

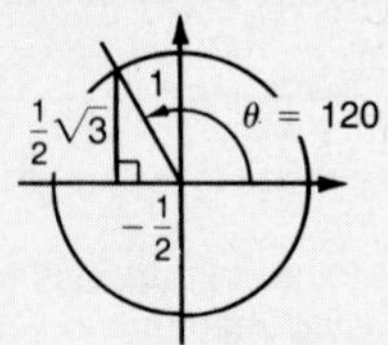

$$\sin\theta = \frac{\frac{\sqrt{3}}{2}}{1} = \frac{\sqrt{3}}{2}$$

$$\cos\theta = \frac{-\frac{1}{2}}{1} = -\frac{1}{2}$$

$$\tan\theta = \frac{\frac{\sqrt{3}}{2}}{-\frac{1}{2}} = -\sqrt{3}$$

3. Find the sign of each of the six trigonometric functions for a rotation of 290°.

$270 < 290 < 360$ $R(x, y)$ is in the fourth quadrant. The cosine and secant are positive and the other four functions are negative.

Terminal Side on an Axis

Chalkboard Example

1. Find the sine, cosine, and tangent for −90°.

$\sin -90° = \frac{-r}{r} = -1$

$\cos -90° = \frac{0}{r} = 0$

$\tan -90° = -\frac{r}{0}$, undefined

Try This

g. Find sin θ, cos θ, and tan θ for the angle θ shown. $\sin\theta = -\frac{1}{2}$ $\cos\theta = \frac{\sqrt{3}}{2}$ $\tan\theta = -\frac{\sqrt{3}}{3}$

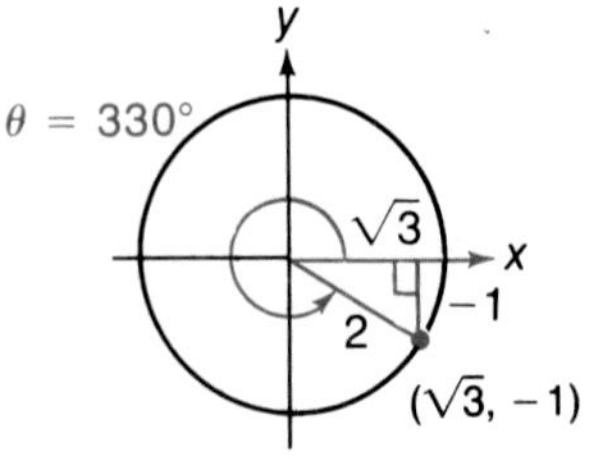

The cosecant, secant, and cotangent functions can also be defined in terms of x, y, and r. We find the reciprocals of the sine, cosine, and tangent, respectively.

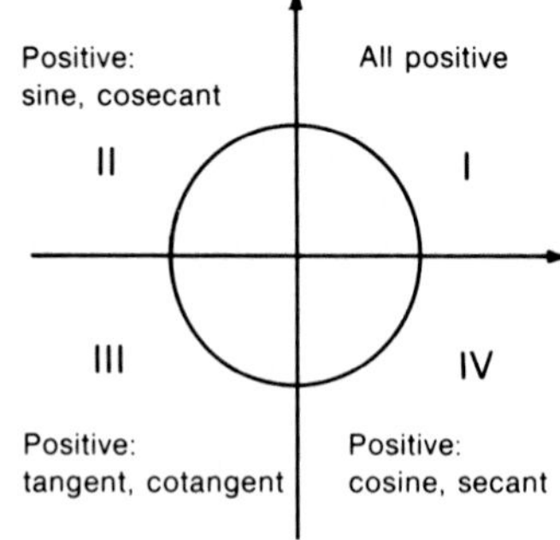

$$\csc\theta = \frac{r}{y} \qquad \sec\theta = \frac{r}{x} \qquad \cot\theta = \frac{x}{y}$$

The values of the trigonometric functions can be positive, negative, or zero, depending on where the terminal side of the angle lies. The figure at the right shows which of the trigonometric function values are positive in each of the quadrants.

EXAMPLE 8 Give the sign of the six trigonometric function values for a rotation of 225°.

$180 < 225 < 270$, so R(x, y) is in the third quadrant.

The tangent and cotangent are positive, and the other four function values are negative.

Try This

h. Give the signs of the six trigonometric function values for a rotation of −30°. Cosine and secant values are positive; the other four function values are negative.

Terminal Side on an Axis

Objective: Find trigonometric function values for angles whose terminal side lies on an axis.

If the terminal side of an angle falls on one of the axes, the definitions of the functions still apply, but in some cases functions will not be defined because a denominator will be 0. Notice the coordinates of the points for angles of 0°, 90°, 180°, and 270°. For example, the coordinates for an angle of 90° are $x = 0$ and $y = r$.

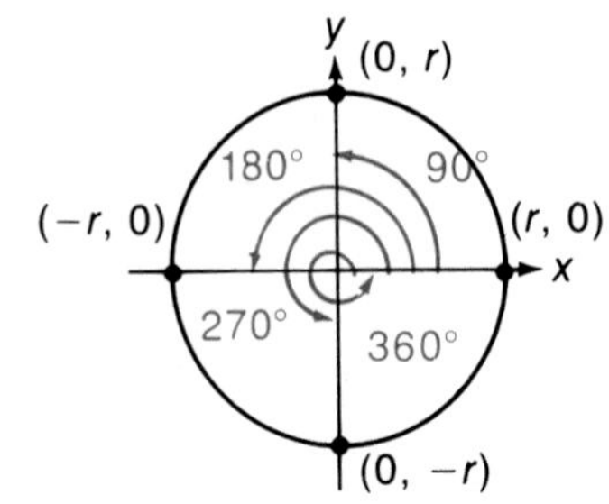

EXAMPLE 9 Find the sine, cosine, and tangent function values for 0° and 90°.

$$\sin 0° = \frac{y}{r} = \frac{0}{r} = 0 \qquad \sin 90° = \frac{y}{r} = \frac{r}{r} = 1$$

$$\cos 0° = \frac{x}{r} = \frac{r}{r} = 1 \qquad \cos 90° = \frac{x}{r} = \frac{0}{r} = 0$$

$$\tan 0° = \frac{y}{x} = \frac{0}{r} = 0 \qquad \tan 90° = \frac{y}{x} = \frac{r}{0} \quad \text{Undefined}$$

Try This

i. Find the sine, cosine, and tangent function values for 180° and 270°.
sin 180° = 0, cos 180° = −1, tan 180° = 0, sin 270° = −1, cos 270° = 0, tan 270° is undefined.

Reference Angles

Objective: Find the reference angle of a rotation and use it to find trigonometric function values.

We can now determine the trigonometric function values for angles in other quadrants by using the values of the functions for angles between 0° and 90°. We do so by using a reference angle.

Definition

The **reference angle** for a rotation is the acute angle formed by the terminal side and the x-axis.

EXAMPLES Find the reference angle for θ.

10.

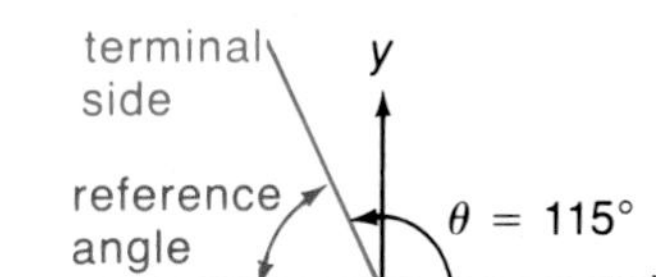

To find the measure of the acute angle formed by the terminal side and the x-axis, we subtract the measure of θ from 180°.

$$180 - 115 = 65$$

The reference angle is 65°.

11.

y
θ = 225°
x
reference
angle

We are looking for the acute angle formed by the terminal side and the x-axis. We subtract 180° from 225° to get the reference angle.

$$225 - 180 = 45$$

The reference angle is 45°.

Reference Angles

Chalkboard Examples

1. Find the reference angle for θ.

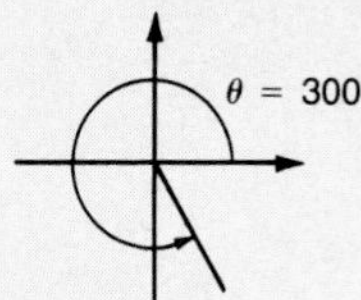

$360° - 300° = 60°$

2. Find the reference angle for θ.

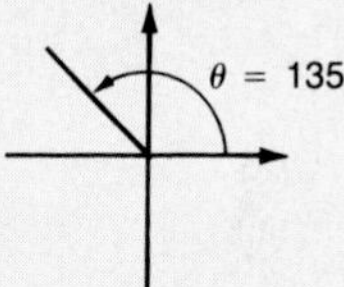

$180° - 135° = 45°$

3. Find the sine, cosine and tangent of 930°.
$930° = 5 \cdot 180° + 30°$
The terminal position is in the third quadrant.
The reference angle is 30°.
$\sin 930° = -\sin 30° = -\frac{1}{2}$
$\cos 930° = -\cos 30° = -\frac{\sqrt{3}}{2}$
$\tan 930° = \tan 30° = \frac{\sqrt{3}}{3}$

LESSON QUIZ

1. In which quadrant does the terminal side of 420° lie?
   First quadrant
2. Find sin 210°.
   $-\frac{1}{2}$
3. Find cos 330°.
   $\frac{\sqrt{3}}{2}$
4. Find tan 765°.
   1

Try This Find the reference angle for θ.

j. 30°

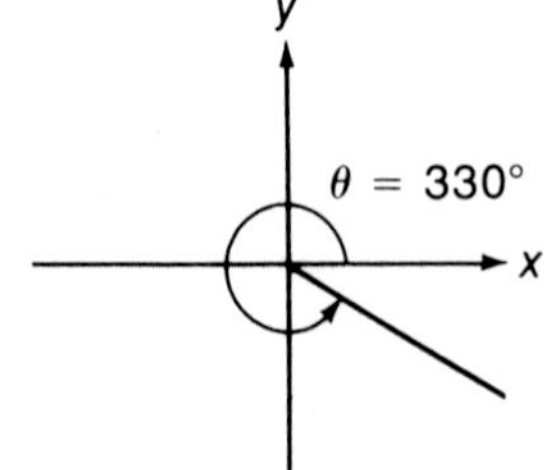

k. 30°

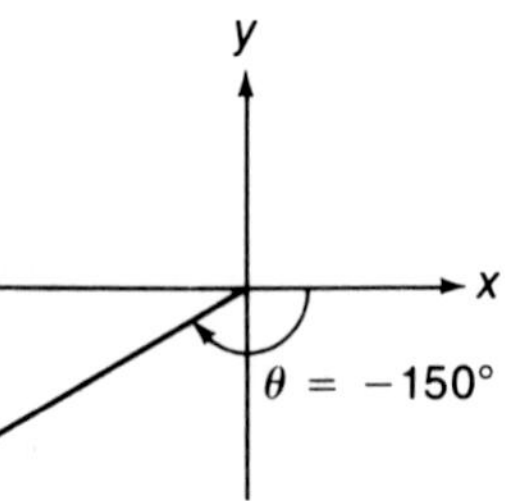

We now use the reference angle to determine trigonometric function values. Consider, for example, an angle of 150°. The terminal side makes a 30° angle with the x-axis, since $180 - 150 = 30$. As the diagram shows, triangle ONR is congruent to triangle $ON'R'$. Hence the ratios of the lengths of the sides of the two triangles are the same.

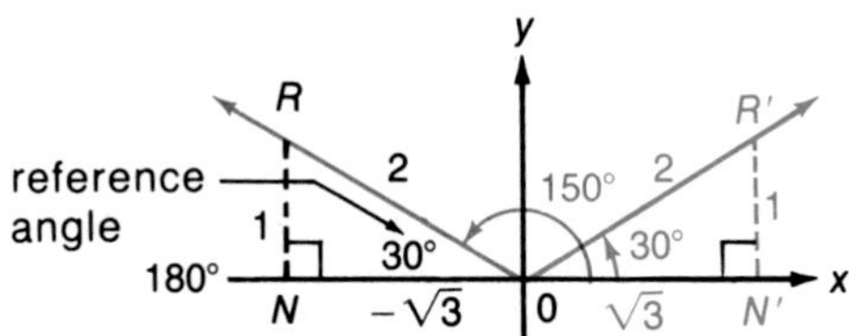

We could determine the function values directly from triangle ONR, but this is not necessary. If we remember that the sine is positive in quadrant II and that the cosine and tangent are negative, we can simply use the values for 30°, prefixing the appropriate sign.

EXAMPLE 12 Find the sine, cosine, and tangent of 1320°.

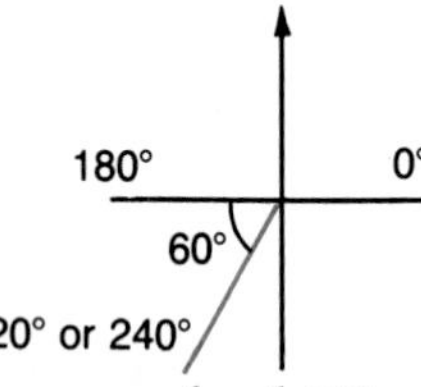

We can subtract multiples of 360°. We do this by dividing 1320 by 360 and taking the integer part. Thus we subtract three multiples of 360.

$$1320 - 3(360) = 240$$

The angle with the same terminal side is 240°. This gives us a reference angle of 60°. Since 1320° is in the third quadrant, $\sin 1320° = -\frac{\sqrt{3}}{2}$, $\cos 1320° = -\frac{1}{2}$, and $\tan 1320° = \sqrt{3}$.

EXAMPLE 13 Find the sine, cosine, and tangent of $-1665°$.

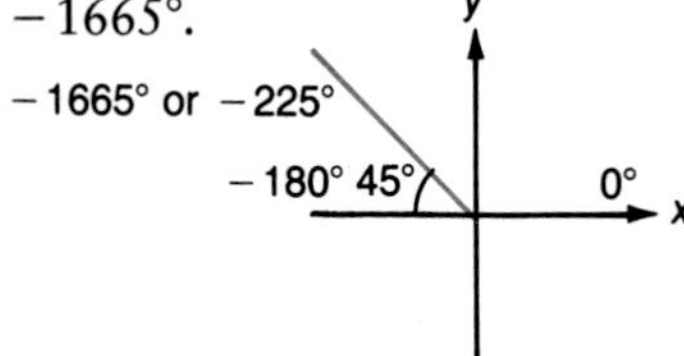

We can add multiples of 360°. We divide 1665 by 360 and take the integer part. Thus we add four multiples of 360.

$$-1665 + 4(360) = -225$$

The angle with the same terminal side is $-225°$. This gives us a reference angle of 45°. Since $-1665°$ is in the second quadrant, $\sin -1665° = \frac{\sqrt{2}}{2}$, $\cos -1665° = -\frac{\sqrt{2}}{2}$, and $\tan -1665° = -1$.

In general, to find the function values of an angle, we find them for the reference angle and then prefix the appropriate sign.

Try This Find the sine, cosine, and tangent of each angle.

l. 2370° $-\frac{1}{2}, -\frac{\sqrt{3}}{2}, \frac{\sqrt{3}}{3}$ **m.** −765° $-\frac{\sqrt{2}}{2}, \frac{\sqrt{2}}{2}, -1$ **n.** −2340° 0, −1, 0

17-2 EXERCISES

A

In which quadrant does the terminal side of each angle lie?

1. 34° First **2.** 320° Fourth **3.** −120° Third **4.** −175° Third
5. 60° First **6.** −135° Third **7.** 495° Second **8.** 855° Second
9. 160° Second **10.** 230° Third **11.** −400° Fourth **12.** −555° Second

Find sin θ, cos θ, and tan θ for the angle θ shown.

13.

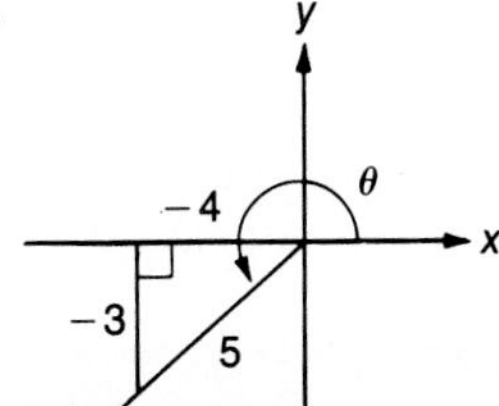

14.

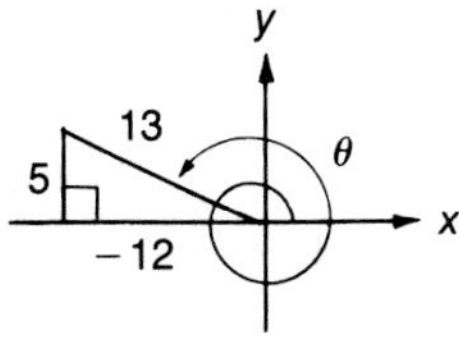

15.

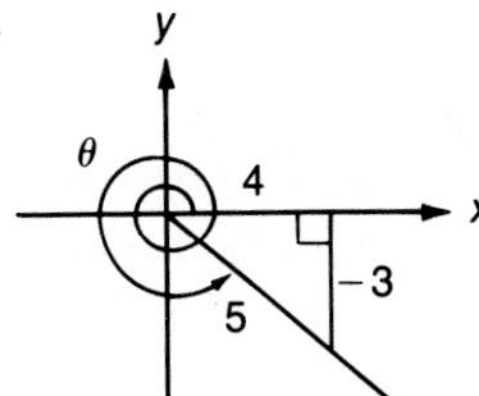

16.

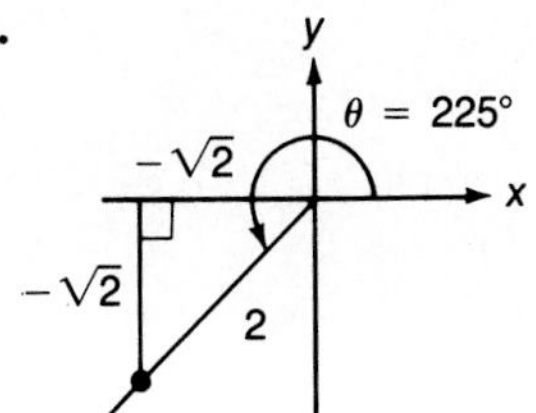

17.

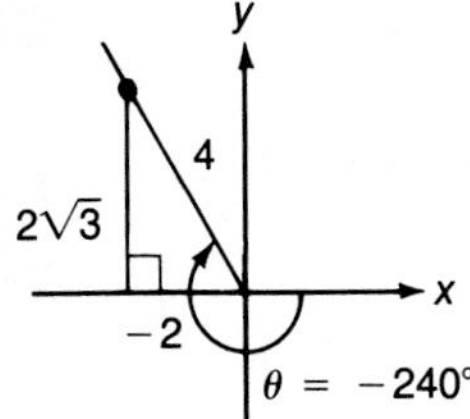

18.

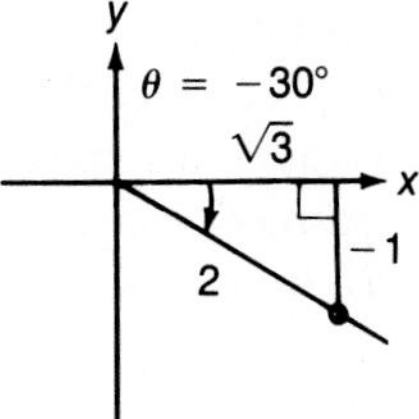

Give the sign of the six trigonometric function values for the following angles of rotation.

19. 57° **20.** −57° **21.** 315° **22.** −100° **23.** 760° **24.** 460°

25. Find the cotangent, secant, and cosecant function values for 0°, 90°, 180°, and 270°.

Find the reference angle for the following angles of rotation.

26. 405° 45° **27.** 210° 30° **28.** −300° 60° **29.** 315° 45° **30.** 240° 60° **31.** −225° 45°

Assignment Guide
Algebra: Omit

Alg w/Trig: Day 1: 1–31 e/o, MR
Day 2: 32–61 e/o, 62

Comprehensive: 1–61 m3, 62, 63, MR

ADDITIONAL ANSWERS
Exercises

13. $\sin\theta = -\frac{3}{5}$; $\cos\theta = -\frac{4}{5}$, $\tan\theta = \frac{3}{4}$

14. $\sin\theta = \frac{5}{13}$; $\cos\theta = -\frac{12}{13}$, $\tan\theta = -\frac{5}{12}$

15. $\sin\theta = -\frac{3}{5}$; $\cos\theta = \frac{4}{5}$, $\tan\theta = -\frac{3}{4}$

16. $\sin\theta = -\frac{\sqrt{2}}{2}$; $\cos\theta = -\frac{\sqrt{2}}{2}$; $\tan\theta = 1$

17. $\sin\theta = \frac{\sqrt{3}}{2}$; $\cos\theta = -\frac{1}{2}$, $\tan\theta = -\sqrt{3}$

18. $\sin\theta = -\frac{1}{2}$; $\cos\theta = \frac{\sqrt{3}}{2}$; $\tan\theta = -\frac{\sqrt{3}}{3}$

19. All function values are positive.
20. The cosine and secant function values are positive; the other four are negative.
21. Same as 20
22. The tangent and cotangent function values are positive; the other four are negative.
23. All function values are positive.
24. The sine and cosecant function values are positive; the other four are negative.
25.

θ	cot θ	sec θ	csc θ
0°	—	1	—
90°	0	—	1
180°	—	−1	—
270°	0	—	−1

48. $\frac{1}{2}, -\frac{\sqrt{3}}{2}, -\frac{\sqrt{3}}{3}$

49. $-\frac{\sqrt{3}}{2}, -\frac{1}{2}, \sqrt{3}$

50. $-\frac{\sqrt{2}}{2}, -\frac{\sqrt{2}}{2}, 1$

51. 0, −1, 0
52. 0, 1, 0

53. sin 30° = 0.500, cos 30° = 0.866, tan 30° = 0.577, csc 30° = 2.000, sec 30° = 1.155, cot 30° = 1.732
54. sin 60° = 0.866, cos 60° = 0.500, tan 60° = 1.732, csc 60° = 1.155, sec 60° = 2.000, cot 60° = 0.577
55. sin 120° = 0.866, cos 120° = −0.500, tan 120° = −1.732, csc 120° = 1.155, sec 120° = −2.000, cot 120° = −0.577
56. sin 225° = −0.707, cos 225° = −0.707, tan 225° = 1.000, csc 225° = −1.414, sec 225° = −1.414, cot 225° = 1.000
57. sin θ = 0.866, cos θ = 0.5, tan θ = 1.732, sec θ = 2, csc θ = 1.155, cot θ = 0.577
58. sin θ = 0.707, cos θ = −0.707, tan θ = −1, sec θ = −1.414, csc θ = 1.414, cot θ = −1

59. $\sin\theta = -\frac{8}{17}$, $\cos\theta = -\frac{15}{17}$, $\tan\theta = \frac{8}{15}$, $\csc\theta = -\frac{17}{8}$, $\sec\theta = -\frac{17}{15}$, $\cot\theta = \frac{15}{8}$

60. $\sin\theta = \frac{4}{7}$, $\cos\theta = -\frac{\sqrt{33}}{7}$, $\tan\theta = -\frac{4\sqrt{33}}{33}$, $\csc\theta = \frac{7}{4}$, $\sec\theta = -\frac{7\sqrt{33}}{33}$, $\cot\theta = -\frac{\sqrt{33}}{4}$

61. $\sin\theta = -\frac{5}{13}$, $\cos\theta = \frac{12}{13}$, $\tan\theta = -\frac{5}{12}$, $\csc\theta = -\frac{13}{5}$, $\sec\theta = \frac{13}{12}$, $\cot\theta = -\frac{12}{5}$

62. $\sin\theta = -\frac{2}{3}$, $\cos\theta = -\frac{\sqrt{5}}{3}$, $\sec\theta = -\frac{3\sqrt{5}}{5}$, $\csc\theta = -\frac{3}{2}$, $\cot\theta = \frac{\sqrt{5}}{2}$

Mixed Review

64. Yes 65. No
66. 27 67. $\pm\frac{1}{5}$
68. $\pm 5, \pm 5i$ 69. $\frac{7}{13}$
70. $\frac{4}{13}$ 71. $\frac{11}{26}$
72. 15 mi/h

Find each of the following, or indicate those that are undefined.

32. cos 180° −1 **33.** sin 360° 0 **34.** tan 90° Undefined **35.** cot 180° Undefined
36. sec 720° 1 **37.** csc 720° Undefined **38.** sin (−135°) $-\frac{\sqrt{2}}{2}$ **39.** cos 135° $-\frac{\sqrt{2}}{2}$
40. sin 150° $\frac{1}{2}$ **41.** cos 150° $-\frac{\sqrt{3}}{2}$ **42.** tan 240° $\sqrt{3}$ **43.** cot 240° $\frac{\sqrt{3}}{3}$
44. sec 315° $\sqrt{2}$ **45.** csc 315° $-\sqrt{2}$ **46.** tan (−315°) 1 **47.** cot (−315°) 1

Find the sine, cosine, and tangent of each angle.

48. 1590° **49.** −3000° **50.** −4095° **51.** 2700° **52.** −4680°

B

Find decimal notation to three places for the six trigonometric functions of each of the following angles. Use the fact that $\sqrt{2} \approx 1.414$ and $\sqrt{3} \approx 1.732$.

53. 30° **54.** 60° **55.** 120° **56.** 225° **57.** −1020° **58.** 2295°

Find the six trigonometric function values for the angle θ shown.

59.

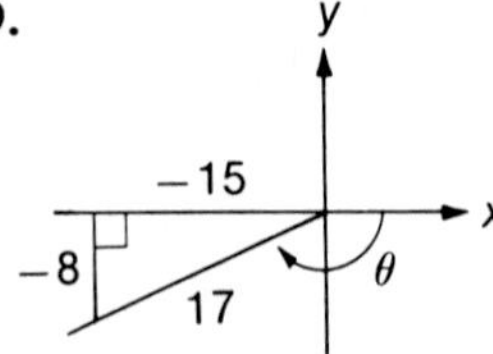

60.

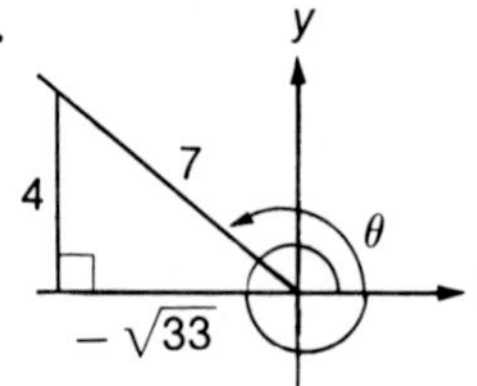

61.

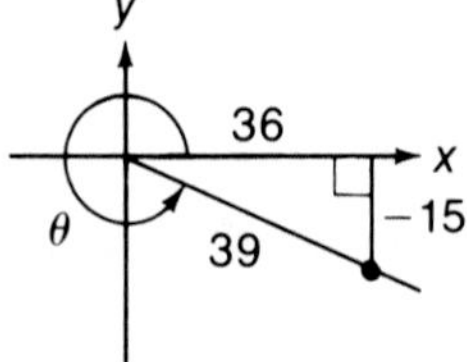

62. ***Critical Thinking*** Given that $\tan\theta = \frac{2\sqrt{5}}{5}$ and the terminal side is in quadrant III, what are the values of the other five trigonometric functions?

Challenge

63. The valve cap on a bicycle wheel is 24.5 in. from the center of the wheel. From the position shown, the wheel starts rolling. After the wheel has turned 390°, how far above the ground is the valve cap? Assume that the outer radius of the tire is 26 in. 38.25 in.

Mixed Review

Test for symmetry about the x-axis. **64.** $x^2 + y^2 = 36$ **65.** $xy = 25$

Solve. **66.** $\log_9 x = \frac{3}{2}$ **67.** $x^2 = \frac{1}{25}$ **68.** $x^4 = 625$

Suppose a card is drawn from an ordinary deck. Find the probability of drawing a

69. red card or king. **70.** spade or ace. **71.** club or face card.

72. A barge travels 90 mi downstream in the same time that it travels 60 mi upstream. The speed of the current is 3 mi/h. Find the speed of the barge in still water.

17-3 Radians, Cofunctions, and Problem Solving

Radian Measure

Objective: Convert from degree to radian measure and vice versa.

So far we have measured angles using degrees. Another useful angle measure is a radian. Consider a circle of radius 1, a unit circle. Since the circumference of a circle is $2\pi r$, the unit circle has a circumference of 2π. A rotation of 360° (1 revolution) has a measure of 2π radians. Half of a revolution is a rotation of 180°, or π radians. A quarter of a revolution is a rotation of 90°, or $\frac{\pi}{2}$ radians, and so on.

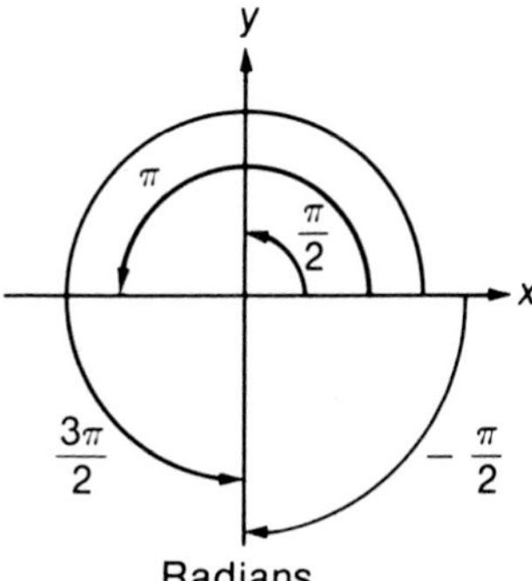

Radians

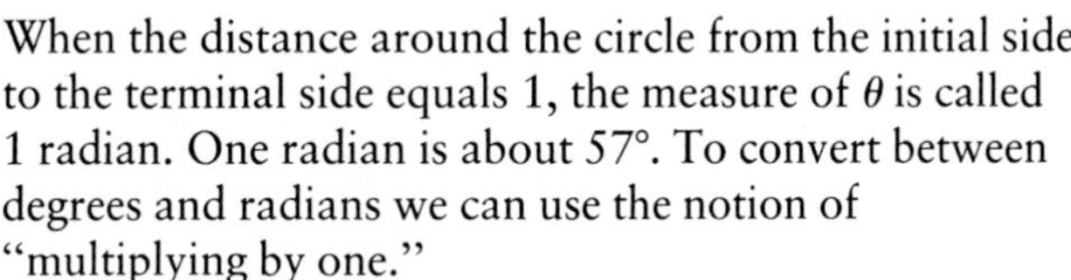

When the distance around the circle from the initial side to the terminal side equals 1, the measure of θ is called 1 radian. One radian is about 57°. To convert between degrees and radians we can use the notion of "multiplying by one."

$$\frac{1 \text{ revolution}}{1 \text{ revolution}} = 1 = \frac{2\pi \text{ radians}}{360 \text{ degrees}} = \frac{\pi \text{ radians}}{180 \text{ degrees}}$$

The following equation is also true.

$$\frac{180 \text{ degrees}}{\pi \text{ radians}} = 1$$

When a rotation is given in radians, the word "radians" is optional and often omitted. Thus if no unit is given for a rotation, it is understood to be in radians.

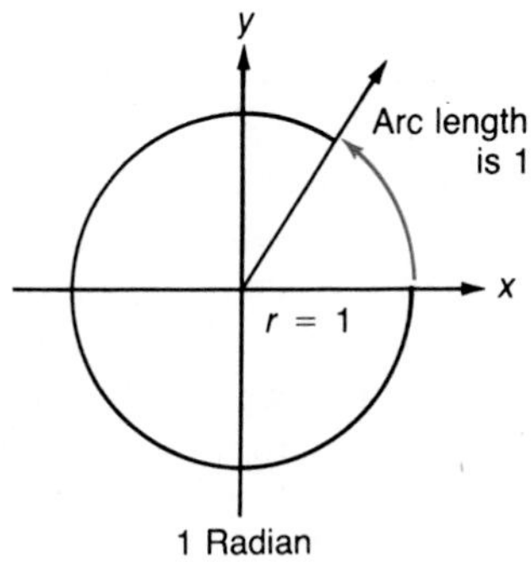

1 Radian

EXAMPLE 1 Convert 60° to radians.

$$60° = 60° \cdot \frac{\pi \text{ radians}}{180°} \quad \text{Multiplying by 1}$$

$$= \frac{60°}{180°} \pi \text{ radians}$$

$$= \frac{\pi}{3} \text{ radians, or } \frac{\pi}{3}$$

Try This Convert to radian measure. Give answers in terms of π.

a. 225° $\frac{5}{4}\pi$ **b.** 300° $\frac{5}{3}\pi$ **c.** −315° $-\frac{7}{4}\pi$

17-3

FIRST FIVE MINUTES

1. Find sin 135°.
   $\sin 135° = \sin 45° = \frac{\sqrt{2}}{2}$
2. Find cos 225°.
   $\cos 225° = -\cos 45° = -\frac{\sqrt{2}}{2}$
3. Find tan 300°.
   $\tan 300° = -\tan 60° = -\sqrt{3}$

Radian Measure

Note that the radian measures of 30°, 45°, 60°, and 90° are easy to find because these numbers are factors of 180.
For example, $\frac{30}{180}$ is $\frac{1}{6}$,
therefore 30° is $\frac{\pi}{6}$ radians.

Key Questions

- What is the radian measure of a 0° angle?
  0
- What is the radian measure of a 360° angle?
  2π

Chalkboard Examples (*T27*)

1. Convert 30° to radians.
   $$30° = 30° \cdot \frac{\pi \text{ radians}}{180°}$$
   $$= \frac{30°}{180°} \cdot \pi \text{ radians}$$
   $$= \frac{\pi}{6} \text{ radians, or } \frac{\pi}{6}$$
2. Convert $\frac{\pi}{3}$ radians to degrees.
   $$\frac{\pi}{3} \text{ radians} = \frac{\pi}{3} \cdot \frac{180°}{\pi \text{ radians}}$$
   $$= \frac{\pi}{3\pi} \cdot 180°$$
   $$= 60°$$

Arc Length and Central Angles

The word radian is often omitted when it is implied through context. When angle measures are given in degrees, the word degrees (or the degree mark °) should never be omitted.

Chalkboard Examples

1. Find the length of an arc associated with an angle of π radians in a circle of radius 10.
   $s = r\theta = 10\pi$
2. Find the radian measure of the angle of rotation when a point moves 5 inches along the circumference of a circle of radius 15 inches.
   The radian measure is the ratio of the arc length divided by the radius. The radian measure is $\frac{5 \text{ inches}}{15 \text{ inches}} = \frac{1}{3}$.

EXAMPLE 2 Convert $\frac{3\pi}{4}$ to degrees.

$$\frac{3\pi}{4} \text{ radians} = \frac{3\pi}{4} \text{ radians} \cdot \frac{180°}{\pi \text{ radians}} \quad \text{Multiplying by 1}$$
$$= \frac{3\pi}{4\pi} \cdot 180°$$
$$= 135°$$

The diagram below shows a unit circle marked in both radians and degrees.

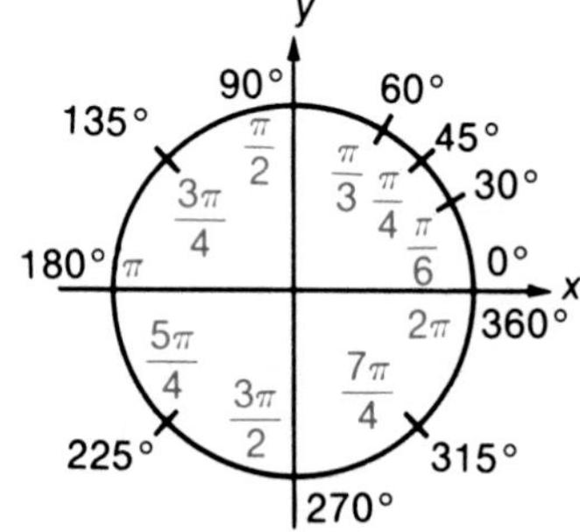

Try This Convert to degree measure.

d. $\frac{4\pi}{3}$ radians 240° **e.** $\frac{5\pi}{2}$ radians 450° **f.** $-\frac{4\pi}{5}$ radians −144°

Arc Length and Central Angles

Objective: Find arc length given the radian measure of an angle and vice versa.

Radian measure can be determined using a circle other than a unit circle. In the following drawing a unit circle is shown along with another circle. The angle shown is a central angle of both circles. Hence the lengths of the intercepted arcs are proportional to the radii of the circles. The radii of the circles are r and 1.

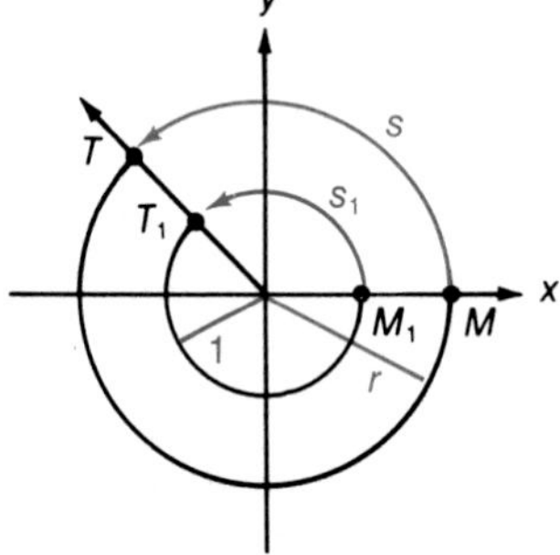

The corresponding arc lengths are MT and M_1T_1, or more simply, s and s_1. We therefore have the proportion

$$\frac{s}{r} = \frac{s_1}{1}$$

Now s_1 is the radian measure of the rotation in question. It is more common to use a Greek letter, such as θ, for the measure of an angle or rotation. We commonly use the letter s for arc length. Adopting this convention, the above proportion becomes $\theta = \frac{s}{r}$. In any circle, arc length, central angle, and length of the radius are related in this fashion. Or, in general, the following is true.

Theorem 17-1

The **radian measure** θ of a rotation is the ratio of the distance s traveled by a point at a radius r from the center of rotation to the length of the radius.

$$\theta = \frac{s}{r}$$

EXAMPLE 3 Find the length of an arc of a circle of 5 cm radius associated with a central angle of $\frac{\pi}{3}$ radians.

$$\theta = \frac{s}{r}, \text{ or } s = r\theta$$

Therefore, $s = 5 \cdot \frac{\pi}{3}$ cm, or using 3.14 for π, about 5.23 cm.

EXAMPLE 4 Find the measure of a rotation in radians where a point 2 m from the center of rotation travels 4 m.

$$\theta = \frac{s}{r} = \frac{4\text{ m}}{2\text{ m}} = 2$$ The unit is understood to be radians.

In using the formula $\theta = \frac{s}{r}$, we must be sure that θ is in radians and that s and r are expressed in the same unit.

Try This

g. Find the length of an arc of a circle with 10-cm radius, associated with a central angle of measure $\frac{11\pi}{6}$. (Use 3.14 for π.) 57.6 cm

h. Find the radian measure of a rotation where a point 2.5 cm from the center of rotation travels 15 cm. 6 radians

Cofunctions and Complements

Objective: Use cofunction identities to find trigonometric function values.

Since the sum of all three angle measures of a triangle is 180°, and the right angle accounts for 90° of this total, the acute angles are complementary. Thus if one acute angle of a right triangle is θ, the other is $90° - \theta$, $\left(\text{or } \frac{\pi}{2} - \theta\right)$. Note that the sine of $\angle A$ is also the cosine of $\angle B$, its complement.

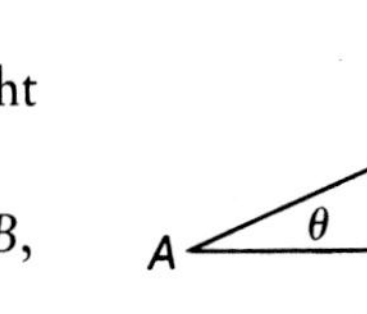

$$\sin \theta = \frac{a}{c} \qquad \cos(90° - \theta) = \frac{a}{c}$$

Similarly, the tangent of $\angle A$ is the cotangent of its complement and the secant of $\angle A$ is the cosecant of its complement.

Cofunctions and Complements

You may wish to have students complete a table for all special angles from 0° to 360°, converting each angle to radians and finding each trigonometric function. For example,

Deg	Rad	sin	cos	tan	csc	sec	cot
0°	0	0	1	0	–	0	–
30°	$\frac{\pi}{6}$	$\frac{1}{2}$	$\frac{\sqrt{3}}{2}$	$\frac{\sqrt{3}}{3}$	2	$\frac{2\sqrt{3}}{3}$	$\sqrt{3}$

and so on.

Chalkboard Examples

Find the function values.

1. cot 45°

$\cot 45° = \tan(90° - 45°)$
$= \tan 45°$
$= 1$

2. csc 60°

$\csc 60° = \sec(90° - 60°)$
$= \sec 30°$
$= \frac{1}{\cos 30°}$
$= \frac{1}{\frac{\sqrt{3}}{2}}$
$= \frac{2\sqrt{3}}{3}$

Problem Solving: Angular Speed

Chalkboard Example

1. While riding your bike, a piece of gum becomes stuck to your front tire, which is 25 inches in diameter. What is the linear speed of the piece of gum, if your tires are making four revolutions per second?
   $d = 25$ inches
   $r = 12.5$ inches
   $w = \frac{2\pi \text{ radians}}{0.25 \text{ sec}}$
   $w = 8\pi$ radians/sec
   $v = rw$
   $v = 12.5$ inches $\cdot\, 8\pi$/sec
   $v = 100\pi$ inches/sec
   $v = 314$ inches/sec

These pairs of functions are called **cofunctions.** The name *cosine* originally meant the sine of the complement. The name *cotangent* meant the tangent of the complement, and *cosecant* meant the secant of the complement. A complete list of the cofunction relations follows. Equations that hold for all acceptable replacements for the variables are known as **identities.** We use the identity symbol $\equiv$ when stating identities.

Cofunction Identities

$\sin\theta \equiv \cos(90° - \theta)$	$\cos\theta \equiv \sin(90° - \theta)$	$\tan\theta \equiv \cot(90° - \theta)$
$\cot\theta \equiv \tan(90° - \theta)$	$\sec\theta \equiv \csc(90° - \theta)$	$\csc\theta \equiv \sec(90° - \theta)$

EXAMPLES Find the function values.

5. $\cot 60° = \tan(90° - 60°) = \tan 30° = \frac{\sqrt{3}}{3}$

6. $\csc 30° = \sec(90° - 30°) = \sec 60° = \frac{1}{\cos 60°} = \frac{1}{\frac{1}{2}} = 2$

Try This Find the function values.

i. $\sec 60°$ 2 **j.** $\cot 30°$ $\sqrt{3}$ **k.** $\csc 45°$ $\sqrt{2}$

Problem Solving: Angular Speed

Objective: Solve problems concerning angular speed.

Speed is defined as the distance traveled per unit of time. Similarly, **angular speed** is defined as the amount of rotation per unit of time. For example, we might speak of the angular speed of a wheel as 150 revolutions per minute or the angular speed of the earth as 2π radians per day. The Greek letter ω (omega) is usually used for angular speed. Thus angular speed is defined as

$$\omega = \frac{\theta}{t} \quad \theta \text{ is the angle of rotation.}$$

For many applications it is important to know a relationship between angular speed and linear speed. For example, we might wish to find the linear speed of a point on the earth, knowing its angular speed. Or, we might wish to know the linear speed of an earth satellite, knowing its angular speed. To develop the relationship we seek, we recall the relation between angle and distance from the preceding section, $\theta = \frac{s}{r}$. This is equivalent to $s = r\theta$.

We divide by the time (t) to obtain $\frac{s}{t} = r\frac{\theta}{t}$.

Now $\frac{s}{t}$ is linear speed v, and $\frac{\theta}{t}$ is angular speed ω. We thus have the relation we seek.

Definition

The **linear speed** v of a point a distance of r from the center of rotation is given by

$$v = r\omega$$

where ω is the angular speed in radians per unit of time.

In deriving this formula we used the equations $s = r\theta$, in which the units for s and r must be the same and θ must be in radians. Thus for our new formula $v = r\omega$, the units of distance for v and r must be the same, ω must be in radians per unit of time, and the units of time must be the same for v and ω.

EXAMPLE 7

An earth satellite in a circular orbit 1200 km high makes one complete revolution every 90 min. What is its linear speed? Use 6400 km for the length of a radius of the earth.

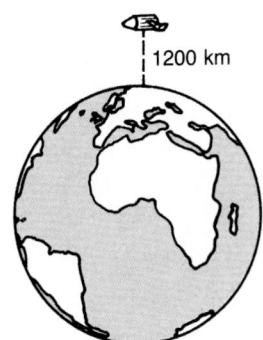

Use the formula $v = r\omega$.

$$\begin{aligned} r &= \text{radius of the earth} + \text{height of satellite} \\ &= 6400 \text{ km} + 1200 \text{ km} \\ &= 7600 \text{ km} \end{aligned}$$

$$\omega = \frac{2\pi \text{ radians}}{90 \text{ min}} = \frac{\pi}{45 \text{ min}} \quad \text{Finding the angular speed}$$

$$v = r\omega$$

$$\begin{aligned} v &= 7600 \text{ km} \cdot \frac{\pi}{45 \text{ min}} \quad \text{Substituting} \\ &= 7600 \cdot \frac{\pi}{45} \cdot \frac{\text{km}}{\text{min}} \\ &\approx 7600 \cdot \frac{3.14}{45} \cdot \frac{\text{km}}{\text{min}} \\ &\approx 530 \frac{\text{km}}{\text{min}} \end{aligned}$$

The linear speed of the satellite is about 530 km/min.

Try This

1. A wheel with 12-cm diameter is rotating at 10 revolutions per second. What is the velocity of a point on the rim? 377 cm/sec

LESSON QUIZ

1. Convert 120° to radian measure.
   $\frac{2\pi}{3}$ radians
2. Convert $\frac{\pi}{12}$ radians to degrees.
   15 degrees
3. Find the length of the arc associated with a central angle of $\frac{\pi}{3}$ radians on a circle of radius 30.
   $s = 30 \cdot \frac{\pi}{3} = 10\pi$

Assignment Guide
Algebra: Omit

Alg w/Trig: Day 1: 1–31 e/o, MR
Day 2: 32–46 e/o, 47

Comprehensive: 1–46 m3, 47–49, MR

ADDITIONAL ANSWERS

Exercises

1. $\frac{\pi}{6} \approx 0.52$
2. $\frac{\pi}{12} \approx 0.26$
3. $\frac{5\pi}{9} \approx 1.74$
4. $\frac{10\pi}{9} \approx 3.49$
5. $\frac{5\pi}{12} \approx 1.31$
6. $\frac{7\pi}{12} \approx 1.83$
7. $\frac{2\pi}{3} \approx 2.09$
8. $\frac{4\pi}{3} \approx 4.19$
9. $-\frac{16\pi}{9} \approx -5.58$
10. $-\frac{25\pi}{18} \approx -4.36$
11. $-\frac{17\pi}{36} \approx -1.48$
12. $-\frac{35\pi}{36} \approx -3.05$
13. 57.3°
14. 114.6°
15. 1440°
16. −2160°
17. 135°
18. 225°
19. 20.9 cm
20. 10.5 m

EXAMPLE 8

An anchor is being hoisted at 2 ft/sec, winding the chain around a capstan with a 1.8-yd diameter. What is the angular speed of the capstan?

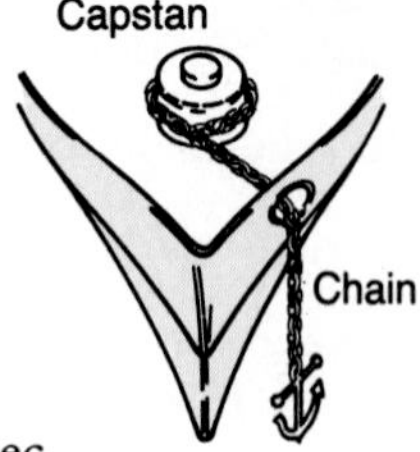

We will use the formula $\omega = \frac{v}{r}$, taking care to use the proper units. Since v is in ft/sec, we need r in ft. Then ω will be in radians/sec.

$$r = \frac{1.8}{2}\,\text{yd} \cdot \frac{3\text{ ft}}{\text{yd}} = 2.7\text{ ft}$$

$$\omega = \frac{v}{r} = \frac{2}{2.7} \approx 0.741 \text{ radian/sec}$$

In applying the formula $v = r\omega$, we must be sure that the units for v and r are the same and that ω is in radians per unit of time. The units of time must be the same for v and ω.

Try This

m. A bucket is being raised at 3 ft/sec. The radius of the drum is 10 in. What is the angular speed of the handle? 3.6 radians/sec

17-3 EXERCISES

A

Convert to radian measure. Give answers in terms of π.

1. 30° **2.** 15° **3.** 100° **4.** 200°
5. 75° **6.** 105° **7.** 120° **8.** 240°
9. −320° **10.** −250° **11.** −85° **12.** −175°

Convert to degree measure.

13. 1 radian **14.** 2 radians **15.** 8π
16. -12π **17.** $\frac{3\pi}{4}$ **18.** $\frac{5\pi}{4}$

19. Find the length of an arc of a circle with a 10-cm radius associated with a central angle of $\frac{2\pi}{3}$ radians.

20. Find the length of an arc of a circle with a 5 m radius associated with a central angle of 2.1 radians.

21. Find the radian measure of rotation where a point 3.5 cm from the center of rotation travels 20 cm.

22. Find the radian measure of rotation where a point 5 m from the center of rotation travels 30 m.

For each of the following, find the function value using cofunctions.

23. tan 60° 24. csc 60° 25. sec 30°

26. csc 30° 27. cot 45° 28. sec 45°

29. cot 60° 30. sec 60° 31. cos 90°

32. A flywheel is rotating at 7 radians/sec. It has a 15-cm diameter. What is the speed of a point on its rim, in cm/min?

33. A wheel is rotating at 3 radians/sec. The wheel has a 30-cm radius. What is the speed of a point on its rim, in m/min?

34. A $33\frac{1}{3}$-rpm record has a radius of 15 cm. What is the linear velocity of a point on the rim, in cm/sec?

35. A 45-rpm record has a radius of 8.7 cm. What is the linear velocity of a point on the rim, in cm/sec?

36. The earth has a 4000-mile radius and rotates one revolution every 24 hours. What is the linear speed of a point on the equator, in mi/h?

37. The earth is 93,000,000 miles from the sun and traverses its orbit, which is nearly circular, every 365.25 days. What is the linear velocity of the earth in its orbit, in mi/h?

38. A wheel has a 32-cm diameter. The speed of a point on its rim is 11 m/s. What is its angular speed?

39. A horse on a merry-go-round is 7 m from the center and travels at 10 km/h. What is its angular speed?

40. A water wheel has a 20-ft radius. The wheel revolves 7 times per minute. What is the speed of the river, in mi/h?

41. A water wheel has a 10-ft radius. The wheel revolves 16 times per minute. What is the speed of the river, in mi/h?

B

42. Through how many radians does the minute hand of a clock rotate in 50 min?

43. The *grad* is a unit of angle measure similar to a degree. A right angle has a measure of 100 grads. Convert the following to grads.

a. 48° **b.** 153° **c.** $\frac{\pi}{8}$ radians **d.** $\frac{5\pi}{7}$ radians

21. 5.7
22. 6
23. $\sqrt{3}$
24. $\frac{2\sqrt{3}}{3}$
25. $\frac{2\sqrt{3}}{3}$
26. 2
27. 1
28. $\sqrt{2}$
29. $\frac{\sqrt{3}}{3}$
30. 2
31. 0
32. 3150 cm/min
33. 54 m/min
34. 52.3 cm/sec
35. 41.0 cm/sec
36. 1047 mi/h
37. 66,626 mi/h
38. 68.8 radians/sec
39. 1429 radians/hr
40. 10 mi/h
41. 11.4 mi/h
42. $\frac{5\pi}{3} \approx 5.233$
43. a. 53.33
b. 170
c. 25
d. 142.86
44. a. 5.6°
b. 19.7°
45. 111.6 km; 69.8 mi

46. Circumference: 21,600 nautical mi; radius: 3439 nautical mi
47. Yes, for all angles
48. $\frac{1}{30}$ radian
49. 25,000 mi

Mixed Review

50. Yes
51. No
52. Yes
53. $f^{-1}(x) = x^{1/3}$
54. $f^{-1}(x) = \log_3 x, x \geq 0$
55. $f^{-1}(x) = \sqrt[4]{x^2 + 1}$
56. 3
57. e
58. $\frac{5}{6}$
59. $\frac{10}{9}$
60. mean = 3.25, median = 3.5, mode = 4

44. The *mil* is a unit of angle measure. A right angle has a measure of 1600 mils. Convert the following to degrees. Use 3.14 for π.

a. 100 mils **b.** 350 mils

45. On the earth, one degree of latitude is how many kilometers? how many miles? Use 3.14 for π. (Assume that the radius of the earth is $\approx$ 6400 km, or 4000 mi).

46. One degree of latitude on the earth is equivalent to sixty *nautical miles*. Find the circumference and radius of the earth in nautical miles. Use 3.14 for π.

47. ***Critical Thinking*** For any acute angle θ, $\cos(90 - \theta) = \sin \theta$. Consider angles other than acute angles. Does this relation still hold, and if so, to what extent?

Challenge

48. An astronaut on the moon observes the earth, about 240,000 miles away. The diameter of the earth is about 8000 miles. Find the angle α.

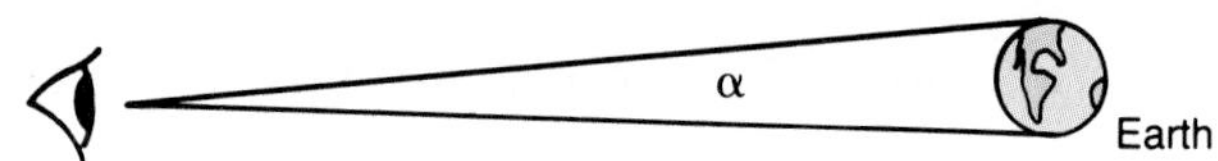

49. The circumference of the earth was computed by Eratosthenes (276-195 B.C.). He knew the distance from Aswan to Alexandria to be about 500 miles. From each town he observed the sun at noon, finding the angular difference to be 7.2°. Do Eratosthenes' calculation.

Mixed Review

Test for symmetry with respect to the y-axis. **50.** $x^2 + y^2 = 36$ **51.** $xy = 25$
52. $y = x^4 + 3x^2 - 2$

In each of the following, find equations for $f^{-1}(x)$. **53.** $f(x) = x^3$
54. $f(x) = 3^x$ **55.** $f(x) = \sqrt{x^4 - 1}$

Evaluate. **56.** $\log_7 343$ **57.** $7^{\log_7 e}$

Find the sum. **58.** $1 - \frac{1}{5} + \frac{1}{25} + \cdots$ **59.** $1 + 0.1 + 0.01 + \cdots$

60. Find the mean, median and mode for {5, 4, 0, 1, 3, 0, 4, 7, 3, 4, 1, 7}

Calculator Investigation

The formula $\sin x = x - \frac{x^3}{3!} + \frac{x^5}{5!} - \frac{x^7}{7!} + \cdots$
gives sine values when x is in radians. Use the formula to approximate sin 0.5 using the first 3 terms of the series. Compare your answer with the value in Table 5. 0.4794

17-4 Finding Function Values: Tables and Calculators

The early Greeks, Hindus, and Arabians created tables of various trigonometric function values. George Rheticus, an associate of Copernicus, spent 12 years developing two tables of values that are still useful.

Scientific calculators give approximations of the sine, cosine, and tangent. The cosecant, secant, and cotangent can be found by taking reciprocals. Some calculators require angles to be entered in degrees. For most, degrees or radians may be used. To find sin 28°, enter 28 and press [SIN]. We find sin 28° ≈ 0.4694716. To find the cosine of π radians, press [π], press [DRG] to use radians, then press [COS]. We find $\cos \pi = -1$.

Finding Function Values

Objective: Find trigonometric function values using a table.

Table 5, in the back of the book, is a table of trigonometric functions with four-digit accuracy. A portion of Table 5 is shown below.

Degrees	Radians	Sin	Cos	Tan	Cot	Sec	Csc		
43° 00′	0.7505	0.6820	0.7314	0.9325	1.072	1.367	1.466	0.8203	47° 00′
10	534	841	294	380	066	371	462	174	50
20	563	862	274	435	060	375	457	145	40
30	0.7592	0.6884	0.7254	0.9490	1.054	1.379	1.453	0.8116	30
40	621	905	234	545	048	382	448	087	20
50	650	926	214	601	042	386	444	058	10
44° 00′	0.7679	0.6947	0.7193	0.9657	1.036	1.390	1.440	0.8029	46° 00′
10	709	967	173	713	030	394	435	999	50
20	738	988	153	770	024	398	431	970	40
30	0.7767	0.7009	0.7133	0.9827	1.018	1.402	1.427	0.7941	30
40	796	030	112	884	012	406	423	912	20
50	825	050	092	942	006	410	418	883	10
45° 00′	0.7854	0.7071	0.7071	1.0000	1.000	1.414	1.414	0.7854	45° 00′
		Cos	Sin	Cot	Tan	Csc	Sec	Radians	Degrees

The headings on the left of Table 5 range only from 0° to 45°. For angles from 45° to 90° the headings on the right are used, together with the headings at the bottom, because these values are the same as the cofunction values of their complements. For example, sin 43° is found to be 0.6820 using the top and left headings. The cosine of 47° (the complement of 43°) is found also to be 0.6820 using the bottom and right headings.

A subunit of a degree is a minute, which is designated by an apostrophe. There are 60 minutes in a degree. The table gives trigonometric function values for intervals of 10′.

17-4

FIRST FIVE MINUTES

1. Convert 15° to radians.

$$15° = 15° \cdot \frac{\pi \text{ radians}}{180°}$$
$$= \frac{15°}{180°} \cdot \pi \text{ radians}$$
$$= \frac{\pi}{12} \text{ radians or } \frac{\pi}{12}$$

2. Convert 3π radians to degrees.

$$3\pi \text{ radians} = 3\pi \text{ radians} \cdot \frac{180°}{\pi \text{ radians}}$$
$$= \frac{3\pi}{\pi} \cdot 180°$$
$$= 540°$$

3. If a wheel with radius 12 turns through an angle of $\frac{\pi}{3}$ radians, how far does a point on the circumference of the wheel move?

$$s = 12 \cdot \frac{\pi}{3} = 4\pi$$

Finding Function Values

Some students may notice that their calculators have a third mode of angle measurement called a *grad*. You may want to point out that there are 100 grads in a right angle and that this unit of measure is often used in the measure of slopes.

[DRG] switches between degrees, radians, and grads. The display should indicate which unit is in use. Pressing [AC/ON] to clear the display will also reset the calculator to degrees.

Avoiding Common Errors

Students will often enter a radian measure with their calculators set in degree mode, or vice versa. Students should check that their calculators are in the correct mode.

EXAMPLE 1 Find cos 37°20′.

We find 37°20′ in the left column of Table 5 and then Cos at the top. At the intersection of this row and column we find the entry we seek.

$$\cos 37°20' = 0.7951$$

Try This Use Table 5 to find the following.

a. sin 15°20′ 0.2644 **b.** cot 64°50′ 0.4699

Table 5 gives function values for angles from 0° to 90°. To find the function value for any other angle, we first find the reference angle, which is the angle the terminal side makes with the x-axis. We then look up the function values for the reference angle in the table and use the appropriate sign, depending on the quadrant in which the terminal side lies.

EXAMPLE 2 Find sin 285°40′.

To find sin 285°40′, we determine that the terminal side of the angle is in the fourth quadrant.

$$\begin{aligned} 360° &= 359°60' \\ &- \underline{285°40'} \\ &\quad 74°20' \end{aligned}$$

The reference angle is 74°20′.

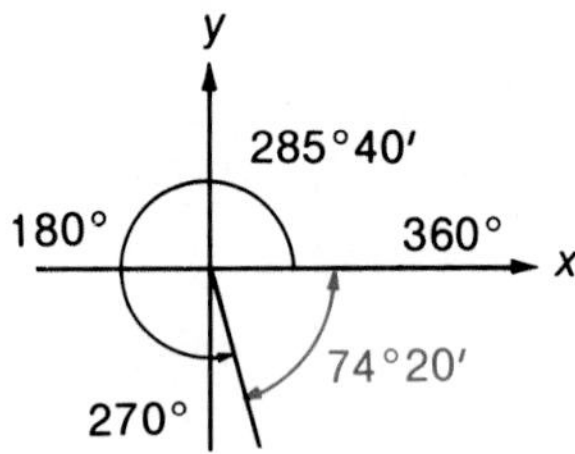

We find sin 74°20′ = 0.9628. In quadrant IV the sine is negative, so sin 285°40′ = −0.9628.

Try This

c. Find cos 410°20′. 0.6383 **d.** Find sin 260°40′. −0.9868

There are many occasions when we will have to use the table in reverse. That is, we will have a trigonometric function value and will want to find the measure of the angle.

EXAMPLE 3 Given tan B = 0.9545, find B (between 0° and 90°).

In the column headed Tan, we find 0.9545. That value is in the row headed 43°40′. Thus B = 43°40′.

Try This

e. Given sec B = 1.655, find B (between 0° and 90°). 52°50′

Decimal Notation for Degrees and Minutes

Objective: Convert between degree and minute notation and decimal degree notation.

If we use a scientific calculator to find an angle when given a trigonometric function value, we find the angle expressed in tenths and hundredths of a degree. For instance, suppose that we know that $\cos B = 0.7030$ and we use a calculator to find B. We enter 0.7030 and press [INV] [COS], or [COS^{-1}]. The display shows 45.33180728. Thus $B \approx 45.33°$.

EXAMPLE 4 Convert 16.35° to degrees and minutes.

$$\begin{aligned} 16.35° &= 16° + (0.35 \times 1°) && 1° = 60' \\ &= 16° + (0.35 \times 60') && \text{Substituting } 60' \text{ for } 1° \\ &= 16° + 21' && \text{Multiplying} \\ 16.35° &= 16°21' \end{aligned}$$

EXAMPLE 5 Convert 34°39′ to degrees and decimal parts of degrees.

$$\begin{aligned} 34°39' &= 34° + 39' \\ &= 34° + \left(\frac{39}{60}\right)° && 1' = \left(\frac{1}{60}\right)° \\ &= 34° + 0.65° && \text{Dividing} \\ 34°39' &= 34.65° \end{aligned}$$

Try This

f. Convert 37.45° to degrees and minutes. 37°27′

g. Convert 43°55′ to degrees and decimal parts of degrees. 43.917°

Interpolation (Optional)

Objective: Use a table and linear interpolation to find trigonometric function values.

The process of linear interpolation used with logarithmic functions can be applied to tables of any function. We can use it with tables of the trigonometric functions.

EXAMPLE 6 Find tan 27°43′.

0.5243	?	0.5280
(tan 27°40′)	(tan 27°43′)	(tan 27°50′)

The difference between tan 27°40′ and tan 27°50′ is 0.0037. Because 43′ is $\frac{3}{10}$ of the distance from 40′ to 50′, we take $\frac{3}{10}$ of 0.0037 and add it to 0.5243.

$$0.5243 + 0.3\,(0.0037) = 0.5243 + 0.00111 = 0.52541$$

$\tan 27°43' \approx 0.5254$

Decimal Notation for Degrees and Minutes

Point out that degrees of longitude and latitude are also divided into minutes and seconds.

Many calculators will convert between decimal degrees (DD) and degrees, minutes, and seconds (DMS). The function may be indicated by DMS > DD and DD > DMS, or simply >DD and >DMS. Using a calculator for Example 5:
34.39 [>DD] 34.65

Chalkboard Examples

1. Convert 24.25° to degrees and minutes.
   $24.25° = 24° + 0.25 \cdot 1°$
   $= 24° + 0.25 \cdot 60'$
   $= 24° + 15' = 24°15'$
2. Convert 57°15′ to degrees and decimal parts of degrees.
   $57°15' = 57° + \frac{15°}{60}$
   $= 57° + 0.25° = 57.25°$
3. Convert 6°12′18″ to degrees and decimal parts of degrees.
   $5°12'18'' = 6° + \frac{12°}{60} + \frac{18°}{3600}$
   $= 6° + 0.2° + 0.005°$
   $= 6.205°$

Interpolation

Chalkboard Examples

1. Find cos 44°15′.
   cos 44°15′ is approximately $\frac{5}{10}$ of the way between cos 44°10′, 0.7173, and cos 44°20′, 0.7153.
   $\frac{5}{10} \cdot (0.7173 - 0.7153) = 0.0010$
   $\cos 44°15' \approx 0.7153 + 0.0010$
   $\cos 44°15' \approx 0.7163$
2. Find A (between 0° and 90°), given that $\tan A = 0.9501$.
   From Table 5, tan 43°30′ = 0.9490 and tan 43°40′ = 0.9545.
   $0.9501 - 0.9490 = 0.0011$
   $0.9545 - 0.9490 = 0.0055$
   $\frac{0.0011}{0.0055} = \frac{1}{5}$
   $A = 43°30' + \frac{1}{5} \cdot 10' = 43°32'$

LESSON QUIZ

Use Table 5 to find each of the following.

1. sin 25°50′
   ≈ 0.4358
2. cos 72°10′
   0.3062
3. $m\angle B$(between 0° and 90°) given that tan B = 0.5243
   ≈ 27°40′
4. Convert 37.05° to degrees and minutes.
   37°3′
5. Convert 56°12′ to degrees and decimal parts of degrees.
   56.2°
6. Use Table 5 and interpolation to find cot 29°44′.
   ≈ 1.751

EXAMPLE 7 Find cot 6°18′.

9.255	?	9.010
(cot 6°10′)	(cot 6°18′)	(cot 6°20′)

The difference between cot 6°10′ and cot 6°20′ is 0.245. We know 18′ is $\frac{8}{10}$ of the distance from 10′ to 20′. We take $\frac{8}{10}$ of 0.245 and subtract it from 9.255, since the cotangent function decreases over this interval.

$$\begin{aligned} &9.255 - 0.8\,(0.245) \\ &= 9.255 - 0.196 \\ &= 9.059 \end{aligned}$$

cot 6°18′ ≈ 9.059

Try This Use Table 5 and interpolation to find the following.

h. sin 38°47′ 0.6264 **i.** cot 27°45′ 1.900

Once the process of interpolation is understood, it will not be necessary to write as much as we did in the examples above. After a bit of practice you will find that interpolation is rather easy, and you can accomplish some of the steps without writing them.

Let us look at an example of using the tables in reverse, that is, given a function value to find the measure of an angle.

EXAMPLE 8 Given tan B = 0.6193, find $m\angle B$ (between 0° and 90°).

0.6168	0.6193	0.6208
(tan 31°40′)	(tan ?)	(tan 31°50′)

The difference between 0.6168 and 0.6208 is 0.0040. We know that 0.6193 is $\frac{25}{40}$ of the distance between 0.6168 and 0.6208. The tabular difference is 10′. We take $\frac{25}{40}$ of 10′ and add it to 31°40′.

$$\begin{aligned} &31°40' + \frac{25}{40}(10') \\ &= 31°40' + 6.25' \\ &= 31°46.25' \end{aligned}$$

Thus $m\angle B \approx 31°46'$.

Try This

j. Given sin θ = 0.3624, find θ. ≈ 21°15′

k. Given cot θ = 1.614, find θ. ≈ 31°47′

17-4 EXERCISES

A

Use Table 5 to find the following.

1. sin 13°20′ **2.** sin 41°40′ **3.** cos 56°30′ **4.** cos 71°50′
5. tan 28°40′ **6.** tan 57°10′ **7.** csc 62°30′ **8.** csc 70°10′

Use Table 5 to find the following.

9. sin 307°10′ **10.** sin 336°30′ **11.** cos 410°20′ **12.** cos 456°40′
13. tan 208°20′ **14.** csc 324°40′ **15.** cot 375°10′ **16.** sec 520°10′

Given the following function values, find B (between 0° and 90°).

17. $\sin B = 0.9881$ **18.** $\cos B = 0.9983$ **19.** $\sec B = 1.435$
20. $\csc B = 1.111$ **21.** $\tan B = 0.2432$ **22.** $\cot B = 1.199$

Convert to degrees and minutes.

23. 46.65° **24.** 85.2° **25.** 67.05° **26.** 38.45°
27. −48.95° **28.** −94.8° **29.** 412.55° **30.** 714.1°

Convert to degrees and decimal parts of degrees.

31. 45°25′ **32.** 36°17′ **33.** 76°53′ **34.** 12°23′
35. −68°47′ **36.** −113°22′ **37.** 225°33′ **38.** 414°07′

Use Table 5 and interpolation to find the following.

39. sin 28°31′ **40.** sin 36°42′ **41.** cos 53°55′
42. cos 80°33′ **43.** tan 24°12′ **44.** cot 54°18′

Given the following function values, use interpolation to find θ (between 0° and 90°).

45. $\sin\theta = 0.6391$ **46.** $\cot\theta = 1.655$ **47.** $\tan\theta = 1.026$
48. $\cos\theta = 0.5771$ **49.** $\sec\theta = 3.835$ **50.** $\csc\theta = 2.916$

B

Use a calculator to convert to radian measure. Leave answers in terms of π.

51. 37.71° **52.** 12.73° **53.** 214.6° **54.** 73.87°

Use a calculator to convert these radian measures to degree measure.

55. 1.303 **56.** 2.347 **57.** 37.89 **58.** 7.005
59. 8.206π **60.** -14.13π **61.** 0.7532π **62.** -1.205π

Use a calculator to find the following function values.

63. tan 29°43′ **64.** cot 73°21′ **65.** sin 213.56°
66. tan −545°29′ **67.** cot −2.556° **68.** cos 4.223°

For each function value, use a calculator to find the angle in radians.

69. $\cot A = 11.546$ **70.** $\tan A = 15.234$
71. $\sin A = -0.0089$ **72.** $\tan A = -43.467$

Assignment Guide
Algebra: Omit

Alg w/Trig: Day 1: 1–35 e/o, MR
Day 2: 36–72 m4, 73

Comprehensive: 1–72 m4, 73, 74–79 e/o, MR

ADDITIONAL ANSWERS

Exercises

1. 0.2306 **2.** 0.6648
3. 0.5519 **4.** 0.3118
5. 0.5467 **6.** 1.550
7. 1.127 **8.** 1.063
9. −0.7969 **10.** −0.3987
11. 0.6383 **12.** −0.1161
13. 0.5392 **14.** −1.729
15. 3.689 **16.** −1.063
17. 81°10′ **18.** 3°20′
19. 45°50′ **20.** 64°10′
21. 13°40′ **22.** 39°50′
23. 46°39′ **24.** 85°12′
25. 67°3′ **26.** 38°27′
27. −48°57′ **28.** −94°48′
29. 412°33′ **30.** 714°6′
31. 45.42° **32.** 36.28°
33. 76.88° **34.** 12.38°
35. −68.78° **36.** −113.37°
37. 225.55° **38.** 414.12°
39. 0.4775 **40.** 0.5977
41. 0.5889 **42.** 0.1642
43. 0.4494 **44.** 0.7186
45. 39°43′ **46.** 31°8′
47. 45°44′ **48.** 54°45′
49. 74°53′ **50.** 20°3′

51. 0.2095π
52. 0.0707222π
53. 1.1922222π
54. 0.4103889π
55. 74.694267°
56. 134.54140°
57. 2172.0382°
58. 401.56051°
59. 1477.08°
60. −2543.4°
61. 135.576°
62. −216.9°
63. 0.5708
64. 0.2991
65. −0.5582
66. −0.0960
67. −22.4013
68. 0.9973
69. 0.0864
70. 1.5052
71. −0.0089
72. −1.5478

73. Find the reciprocal of 1.706 using the $\frac{1}{x}$ key, then press the inv and cos, or $\cos^{-1}$ keys.
74. Convert to decimal degrees, press the sin key, then press the $\frac{1}{x}$ key.
75. $\sin\theta \approx \theta$ for small angles
76. $\tan\theta \approx \theta$ for small angles
77. 61.63944°
78. -0.0764; $0 + 360k < \theta < 180 + 360k$, k an integer ($\sin\theta$ must be positive)
79. 8.65689×10^5 mi is the diameter

Mixed Review

80. Yes, yes
81. Yes, yes
82. No, no
83. Yes, no
84. $\left(2, \frac{1}{2}\right)$
85. $(-1, -2, 3)$
86. $x < -1$ or $x > 6$
87. All real numbers
88. 370
89. 242
90. 2,391,483
91. 0.05556, or $\frac{1}{18}$
92. $p < 125$

73. ***Critical Thinking*** How would you use a calculator to find θ given $\sec\theta = 1.706$?

Challenge

74. How would you use a calculator to find csc 27°32′?
75. Use a calculator. Find $\sin\theta$ for some very small values of θ in radians. What can you conclude?
76. Use a calculator. Find $\tan\theta$ for some very small values of θ in radians. What can you conclude?
77. Use a calculator. Convert 61°38′22″ to degrees and decimal parts of degrees. (Hint: 22″ means 22 seconds. 60″ = 1′)
78. Find log sin 57° (the logarithm of the sine of 57°). What is the domain of the log sin function?
79. Calculate the diameter of the sun. The sun is 93 million miles away from the earth, and the angle it forms at the earth's surface is about 0°32′.

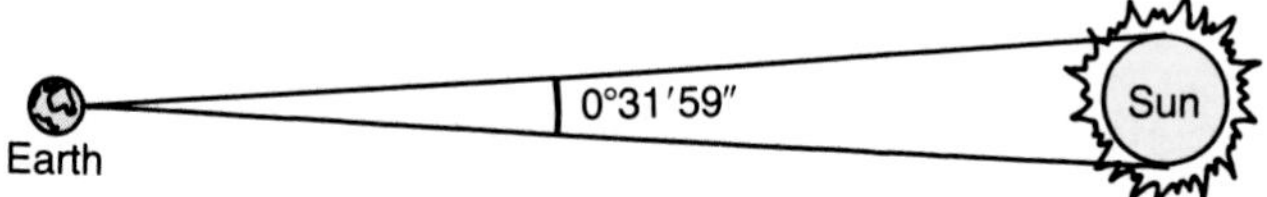

Mixed Review

Test for symmetry about the origin and the line $x = y$. **80.** $x^2 + y^2 = 36$
81. $xy = 25$ **82.** $4(x-3)^2 + (y-3)^2 = 25$ **83.** $f(x) = x^3 - x$

Solve each system using Cramer's rule. **84.** $4x + 2y = 9$
$7x + 4y = 16$

85. $x + y + z = 0$
$2x + y + 2z = 2$
$x + 2y = -5$

Solve. **86.** $|5 - 2x| > 7$ **87.** $|3 + 7x| \geq -11$

Find the sum. **88.** $\sum_{n=1}^{10} 6n + 4$ **89.** $\sum_{n=5}^{15} 2n + 2$ **90.** $\sum_{n=1}^{13} 3^n$
91. $\sum_{n=3}^{13} \left(\frac{1}{3}\right)^n$

92. A typist can be paid in two ways.
Plan *A*: \$50 plus \$0.15 per page
Plan *B*: straight \$0.55 per page
For what number of pages is plan *A* better than plan *B*?

Problem for Programmers

Write a program to find the six trigonometric ratios for an angle given in degrees and minutes. Test your program using Exercises 1–16 and 39–44 in Lesson 17-4.

17-5 Graphs of Trigonometric Functions

Master Grapher Worksheet 30, *Trigonometric Functions*, can be used for lesson closure.

Periodic Functions

Objective: Identify periodic functions from their graphs.

Certain functions with a repeating pattern are called periodic. The function whose graph is shown is periodic. The function values repeat every two units as we move from left to right. In other words, for any x, we have $f(x) = f(x + 2)$. To see this another way, think of the part of the graph between 0 and 2 on the x-axis, and note that the rest of the graph consists of copies of it. If we translate the graph two units to the left or right, the original graph will be obtained. We say f has a period of 2.

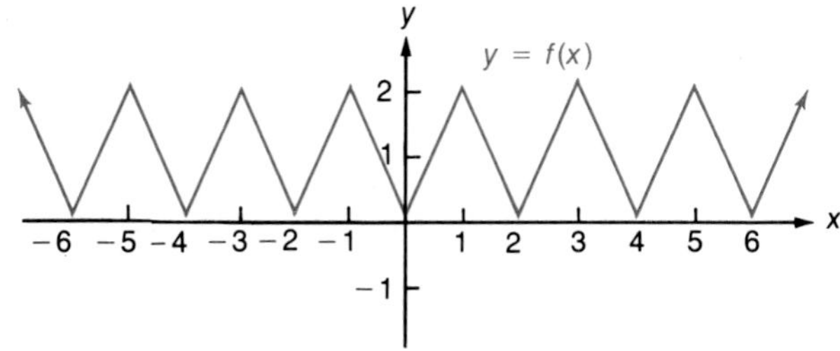

EXAMPLE 1 What is the period of this function?

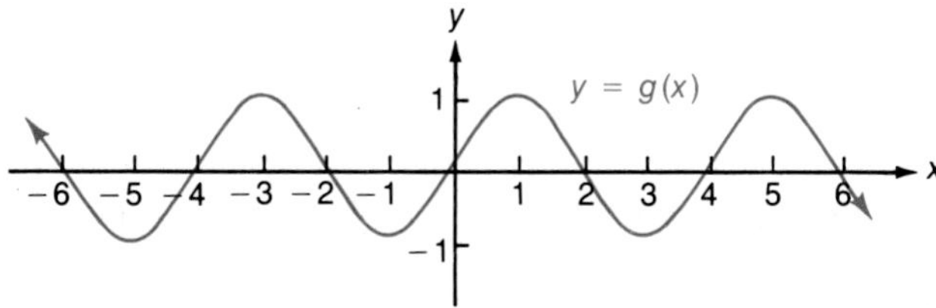

In the function g, the function values repeat every four units. Hence $g(x) = g(x + 4)$ for any x, and if the graph is translated four units to the left or right, it will coincide with itself. The period of g is 4.

Definition

If a function f has the property that $f(x + p) = f(x)$ for all x in the domain where p is a constant, then f is said to be **periodic**. The smallest positive number p, (if there is one) for which $f(x + p) = f(x)$ for all x, is the **period** of the function.

17-5

FIRST FIVE MINUTES

1. Convert 37.2° to degrees and minutes.
   $37° + 0.2° = 37° + 0.2 \cdot 60' = 37°12'$
2. Convert 48°15′ to degrees and decimal parts of degrees.
   $48° + 15' = 48° + \left(\frac{15}{60}\right)^{\circ} = 48.25°$

Periodic Functions

Discuss situations which are periodic. The cycle of days and nights, the repetition of Sundays, the 28-day cycle of the moon, and the ticking of a clock are all periodic.

Key Questions

- If $f(x) = f(x - p)$, is f a periodic function?
  Yes
- If $f(x)$ equals $f(x + 2p)$ but does not equal $f(x + p)$, is f a periodic function?
  Yes

Chalkboard Example

1. What is the period of the function graphed below?

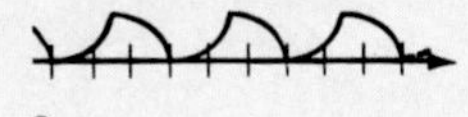

3

The Sine and Cosine Functions (*T28*)

Observe that the values chosen for the arguments of the sine function are the angles whose values we know, 0°, 30°, 45°, 60°, 90°, etc.

Chalkboard Examples

1. Is the function $f(\theta) = -\sin\theta$ periodic? If so, what is its period? Is the function even? Is it odd?

   The graph of the function $f(\theta) = -\sin\theta$ is the graph of $\sin\theta$, reflected across the x-axis. It is periodic, with the same period as $\sin\theta$, namely 2π. The function is odd, since
   $$f(-\theta) = -\sin(-\theta) = -(-\sin\theta) = -f(\theta)$$
   The function is not even since $f(-\theta)$ is not equal to $f(\theta)$.

2. What is the amplitude of the function $f(\theta) = 3\cos\theta$? Is the function odd or even? What is its domain and range?
   The maximum value is 3. The minimum value is -3. Thus the amplitude is 3. The function is even since
   $$f(-\theta) = 3\cos(-\theta) = 3\cos\theta = f(\theta)$$
   The function is not odd. The domain is all real numbers. The range is the set of real numbers from -3 to 3.

Try This

a. What is the period of this function? 3

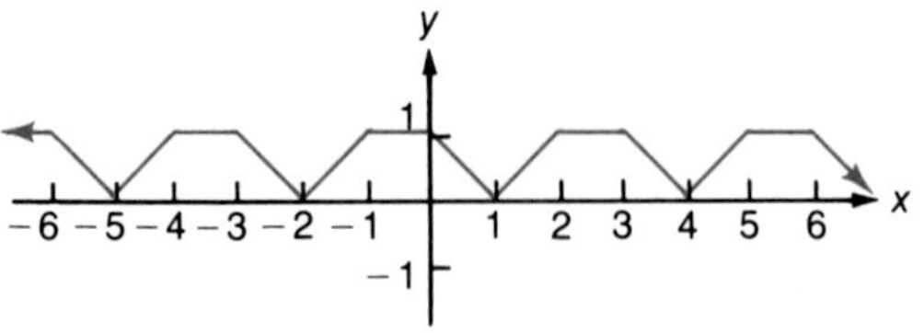

The Sine and Cosine Functions

Objective: Graph the sine and cosine functions and interpret their graphs.

To graph the sine function we look at special angles in the first two quadrants. We will use radian measure for the angles.

θ	0	$\frac{\pi}{6}$	$\frac{\pi}{4}$	$\frac{\pi}{3}$	$\frac{\pi}{2}$	$\frac{2\pi}{3}$	$\frac{3\pi}{4}$	$\frac{5\pi}{6}$	π
$\sin\theta$ (exact)	0	$\frac{1}{2}$	$\frac{\sqrt{2}}{2}$	$\frac{\sqrt{3}}{2}$	1	$\frac{\sqrt{3}}{2}$	$\frac{\sqrt{2}}{2}$	$\frac{1}{2}$	0
$\sin\theta$ (approximate)	0	0.5	0.7	0.9	1	0.9	0.7	0.5	0

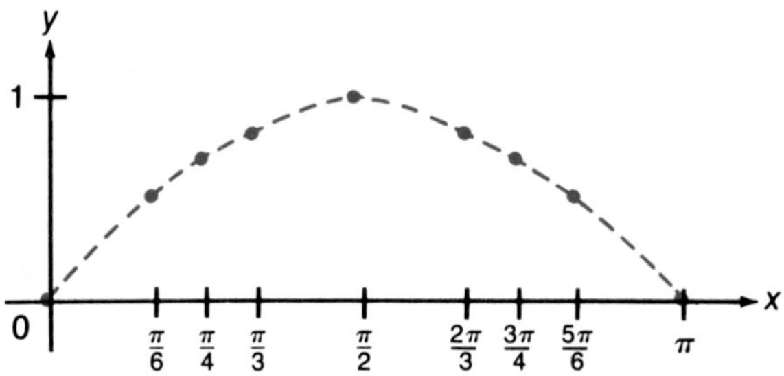

In Section 17-4 we used tables that gave us the values for angles between 0 and $\frac{\pi}{2}$. Thus it seems reasonable that we join the above points with a smooth curve. If we choose negative values for θ, we will be choosing rotations from the third and fourth quadrants.

θ	$-\pi$	$-\frac{5\pi}{6}$	$-\frac{3\pi}{4}$	$-\frac{2\pi}{3}$	$-\frac{\pi}{2}$	$-\frac{\pi}{3}$	$-\frac{\pi}{4}$	$-\frac{\pi}{6}$	0
$\sin\theta$ (exact)	0	$-\frac{1}{2}$	$-\frac{\sqrt{2}}{2}$	$-\frac{\sqrt{3}}{2}$	-1	$-\frac{\sqrt{3}}{2}$	$-\frac{\sqrt{2}}{2}$	$-\frac{1}{2}$	0
$\sin\theta$ (approximate)	0	-0.5	-0.7	-0.9	-1	-0.9	-0.7	-0.5	0

Here is a graph of the sine function. Function values increase to a maximum of 1 at $\frac{\pi}{2}$, then decrease to 0 at π, decrease further to -1 at $\frac{3}{2}\pi$, then increase to 0 at 2π, and so on.

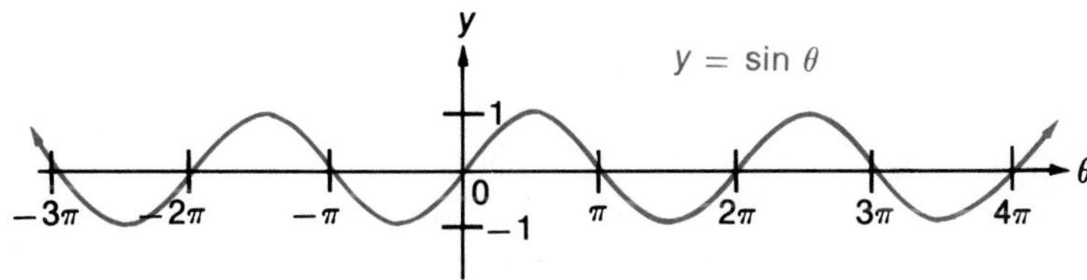

EXAMPLE 2

(a) Is the sine function periodic? If so, what is its period?
(b) Is the sine function even? odd?

From the graph of the sine function, certain properties are apparent.

(a) The sine function is periodic, with period 2π.
(b) The sine function is an odd function because it is symmetric with respect to the origin. Thus we know that $\sin(-\theta) = -\sin\theta$ for all real numbers θ.

Try This

b. What are the domain and range of the sine function? D: The set of all real numbers; R: $-1 \leq \sin x \leq 1$

The amplitude of a periodic function is half the difference between its maximum and minimum function values. It is always positive. The maximum value of the sine function can be seen to be 1, either from the graph or the unit circle, while the minimum value is -1. Thus the amplitude of the sine function is 1.

Here is the graph of the cosine function.

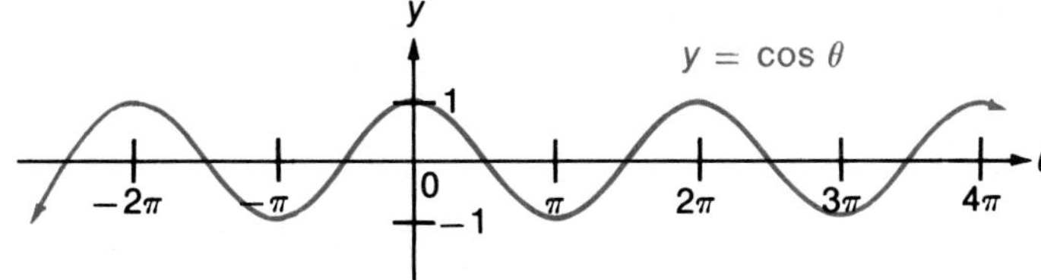

EXAMPLE 3

(a) What is the amplitude of the cosine function?
(b) Is the cosine function even? odd?
(c) What is the domain? What is the range?

From the graph of the cosine function, we notice certain properties.

(a) The range is the set of all real numbers from -1 to 1 inclusive. Thus the amplitude is 1.
(b) The cosine function is an even function, by symmetry with respect to the y-axis. Thus we know that $\cos(-\theta) = \cos\theta$ for all real numbers θ.
(c) The domain is the set of all real numbers. The range is -1 to 1 inclusive.

Graphs of Other Trigonometric Functions

Chalkboard Examples

1. Is the function $f(\theta) = 3\tan\theta$ periodic? If so, what is its period? Is it even or odd? What is its domain and range?
   The graph of the function is the graph of $\tan\theta$ stretched by a factor of 3 in the y direction. The function is periodic, with the same period as $\tan\theta$, namely π. The function is odd since
   $f(-\theta) = 3\tan(-\theta)$
   $= 3(-\tan\theta)$
   $= -f(\theta)$
   The domain of the function is the set of all real numbers, except for $\frac{(2k+1)\pi}{2}$, where k is an integer.
   The range is all real numbers.
2. Is the function $f(\theta) = 3\sec\theta$ periodic? If so, what is its period? Is the function even or odd? What is the domain and range of the function?
   The graph of the function $f(\theta)$ is the graph of $\sec\theta$ stretched by a multiple of 3 in the y direction. The function is periodic with the same period, 2π, as $\sec\theta$.
   The function is even since
   $f(-\theta) = 3\sec(-\theta)$
   $= 3\sec\theta$
   $= f(\theta)$
   The domain of f is the set of all real numbers, except for $\frac{(2k+1)\pi}{2}$ where k is an integer. The range is all real numbers ≥ 1 or ≤ -1.

Try This

c. Is the cosine function periodic? If so, what is its period? Yes; 2π

The following theorem summarizes some properties of the sine and cosine functions.

Theorem 17-2

The sine function is periodic, with period 2π.
$\sin\theta = \sin(\theta + 2\pi) = \sin(\theta - 2\pi) = \sin(\theta + 4\pi)$, and so on,
or $\sin\theta = \sin(\theta \pm 2\pi k)$ where k is an integer
The cosine function is periodic, with period 2π.
$\cos\theta = \cos(\theta + 2\pi) = \cos(\theta - 2\pi) = \cos(\theta + 4\pi)$, and so on,
or $\cos\theta = \cos(\theta \pm 2\pi k)$ where k is an integer

Graphs of Other Trigonometric Functions

Objective: Graph the other trigonometric functions and interpret their graphs.

Not every angle has a tangent. For example, using the relationship $\tan\theta = \frac{\sin\theta}{\cos\theta}$, the tangent ratio for $\frac{\pi}{2}$ would be $\frac{1}{0}$, since $\cos\frac{\pi}{2} = 0$.

Since division by 0 is undefined, $\tan\frac{\pi}{2}$ is meaningless. In this graph of the tangent function we use x instead of θ. The variable x represents any real number. Note that the function value is 0 when $x = 0$, and the values increase as x increases toward $\frac{\pi}{2}$. As we approach $\frac{\pi}{2}$ the tangent values become very large. In fact, they increase without bound. The dashed vertical lines are not part of the graph. They are asymptotes. The graph approaches each asymptote, but never reaches it because there are no values of the function for $\frac{\pi}{2}$, $\frac{3\pi}{2}$, etc.

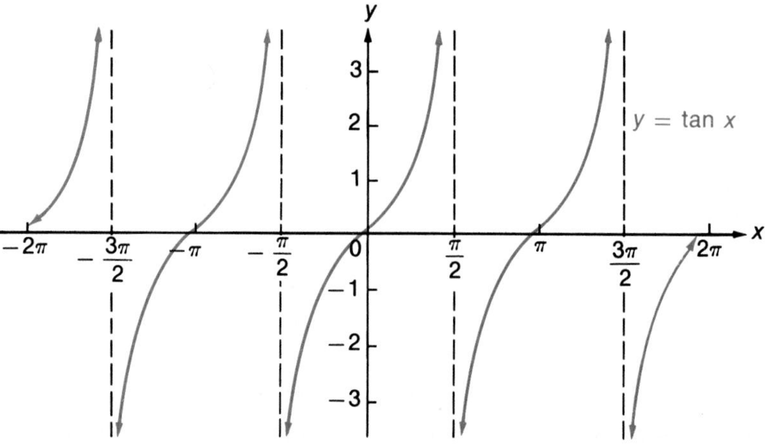

EXAMPLE 4 Is the tangent function periodic? If so, what is its period? What is its domain? What is its range?

We see that the graph from $-\frac{\pi}{2}$ to $\frac{\pi}{2}$ repeats in the interval from $\frac{\pi}{2}$ to $\frac{3\pi}{2}$. Consequently, the tangent function is periodic, with a period of π.

Its domain is $\{x \mid x \neq \frac{\pi}{2} + k\pi, k \text{ an integer}\}$.

Its range is the set of all real numbers.

Try This

d. Is the tangent function even or odd? Odd

The secant and cosine functions are reciprocals. The secant function is undefined for those numbers for which $\cos x = 0$.

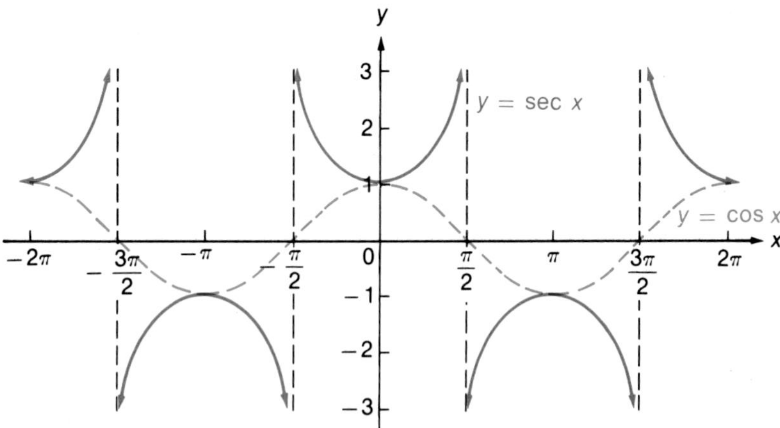

EXAMPLE 5 What is the domain of the secant function?

The domain of the secant function is the set of all real numbers except $\frac{\pi}{2} + k\pi$, k an integer; that is

$$\{x \mid x \neq \frac{\pi}{2} + k\pi, k \text{ an integer}\}$$

Try This

e. What is the period of the secant function? 2π

f. What is the range of the secant function? $\{y \mid y \geq 1 \text{ or } y \leq -1\}$

g. Graph the cotangent function. See Selected Answer Section

h. What is the period of the cotangent function? π

i. What is the domain of the cotangent function? What is the range?
Domain: $\{x \mid x \neq k\pi, k \text{ an integer}\}$; Range: All reals

j. Is the cotangent function even or odd? Odd

LESSON QUIZ

Consider the function shown below.

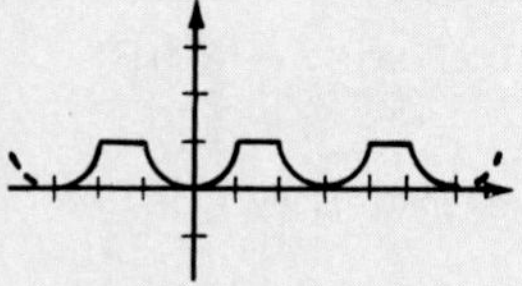

1. Is the function periodic? If so, what is its period?
   Yes, 3
2. Is the function even or odd?
   Even
3. What is the domain of the function?
   All real numbers
4. What is the amplitude of the function?
   $\frac{1}{2}$
5. What is the range of the function?
   All real numbers from 0 to 1

Assignment Guide
Algebra: Omit

Alg w/Trig: Day 1: 1–12, MR,
Day 2: 13–24

Comprehensive: Day 1: 1–15, MR
Day 2: 16–28

ADDITIONAL ANSWERS

Exercises

9.

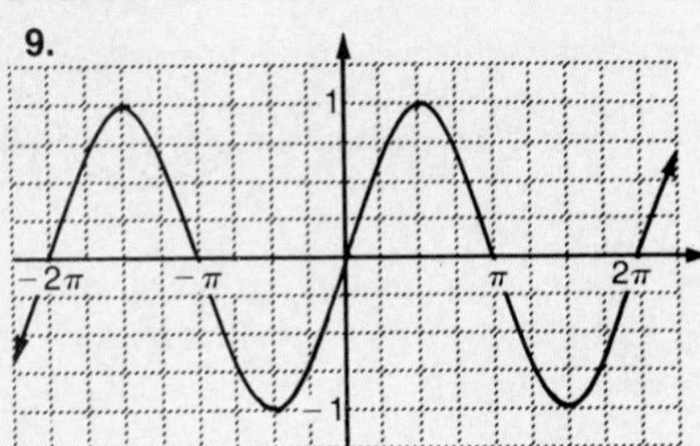

12.

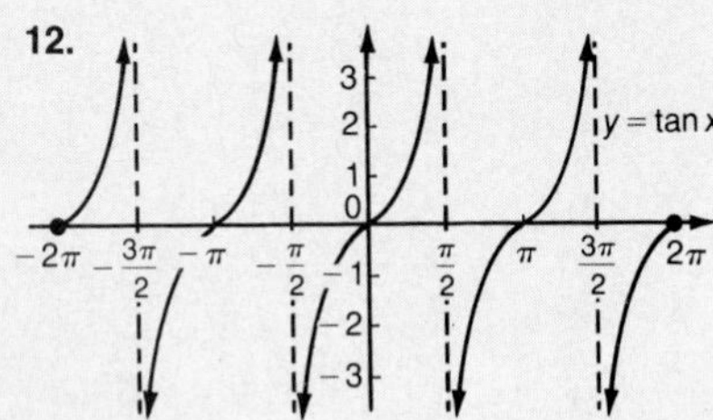

13.

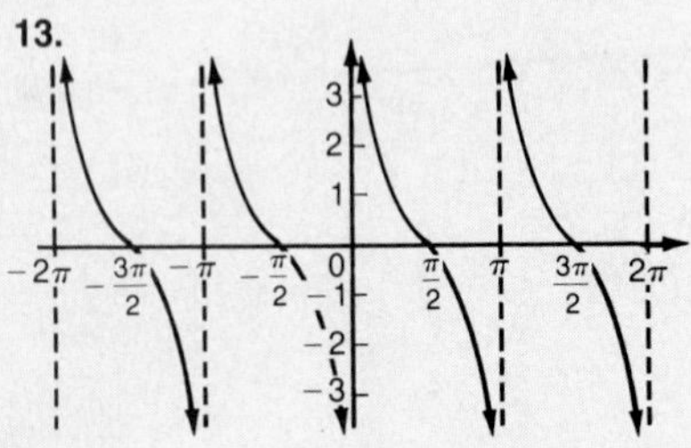

14.

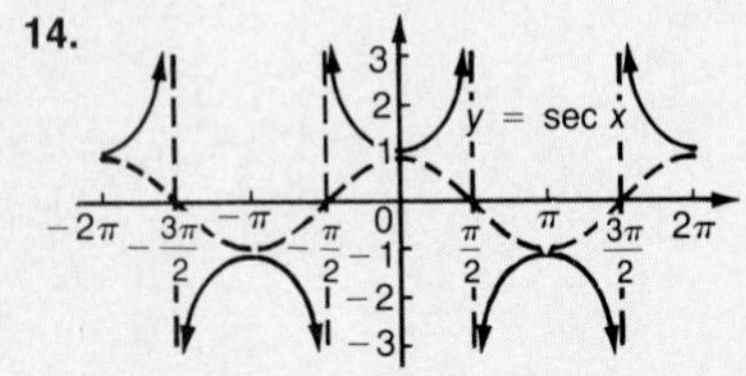

15.

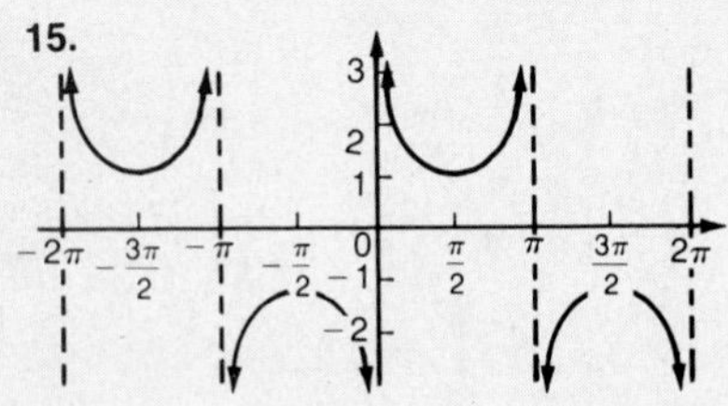

17-5 EXERCISES

A

Which of the following functions are periodic?

1. No

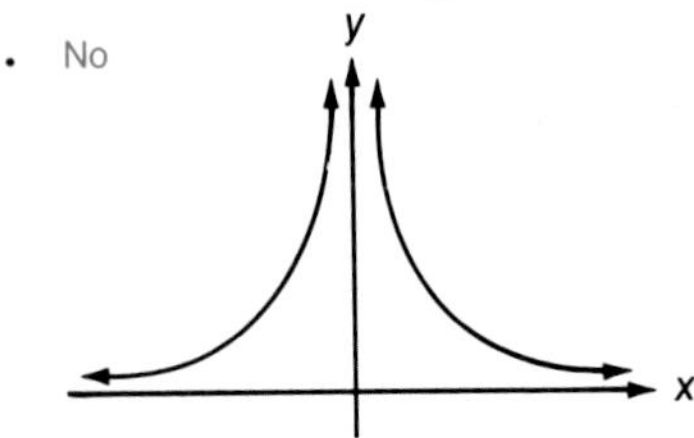

2. Yes

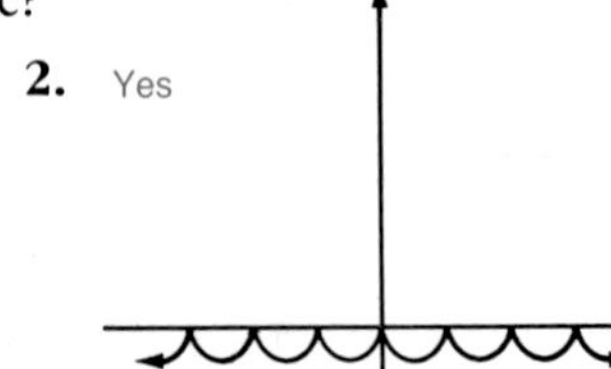

3. Yes

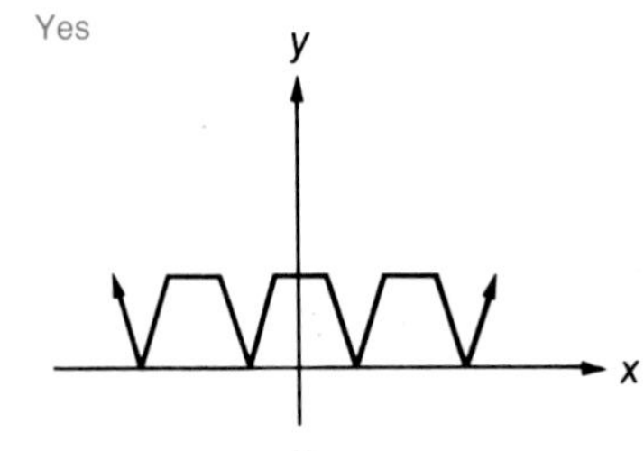

4. No

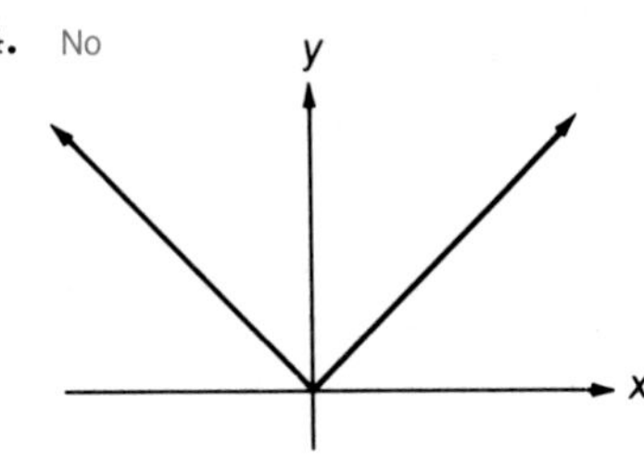

5. Yes

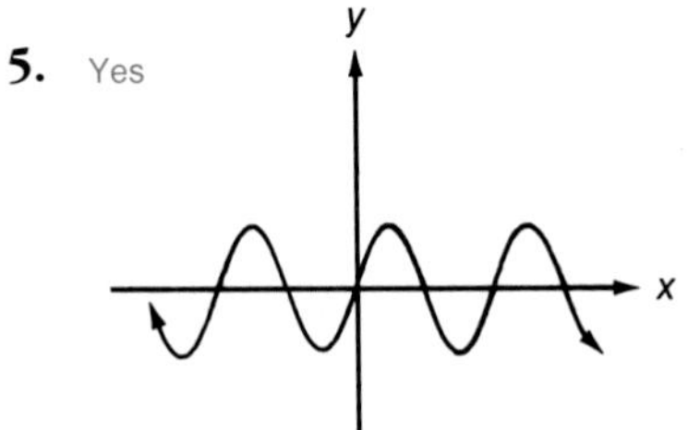

6. Yes

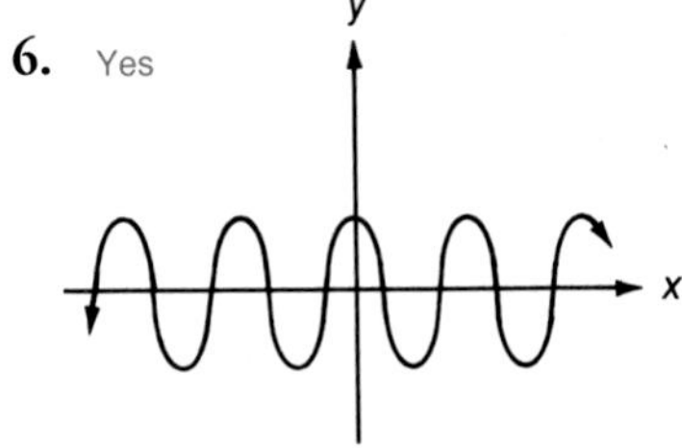

7. What is the period of this function? 4

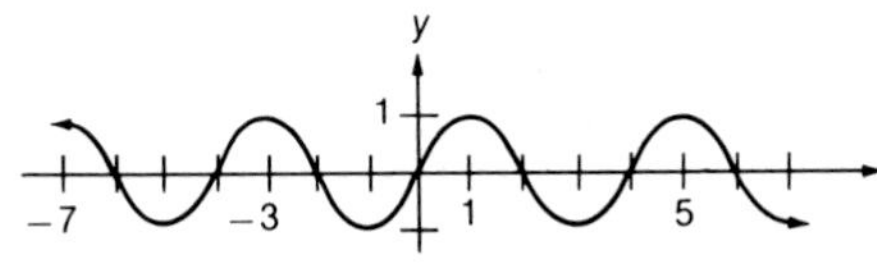

8. What is the period of this function? 2

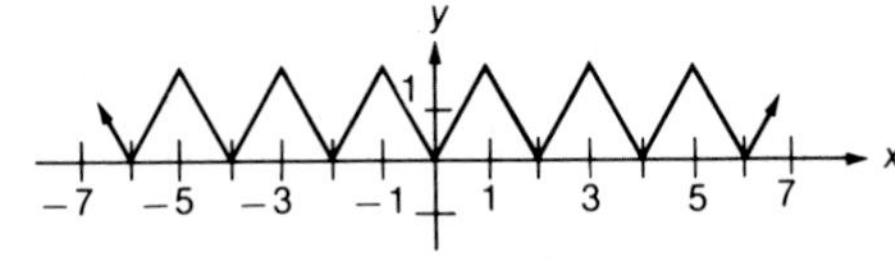

9. Use Table 5 in the back of the book to plot the points and sketch the sine curve.

10. Copy and complete this table of values for the cosine function in the first and second quadrants.

θ	0	$\frac{\pi}{6}$	$\frac{\pi}{4}$	$\frac{\pi}{3}$	$\frac{\pi}{2}$	$\frac{2\pi}{3}$	$\frac{3\pi}{4}$	$\frac{5\pi}{6}$	π
cos θ (exact)	1	$\frac{\sqrt{3}}{2}$	$\frac{\sqrt{2}}{2}$	$\frac{1}{2}$	0	$-\frac{1}{2}$	$-\frac{\sqrt{2}}{2}$	$-\frac{\sqrt{3}}{2}$	−1
cos θ (approximate)	1	0.866	0.707	0.5	0	−0.5	−0.707	−0.866	−1

11. Copy and complete this table of values for the cosine function in the third and fourth quadrants.

θ	$-\pi$	$-\frac{5\pi}{6}$	$-\frac{3\pi}{4}$	$-\frac{2\pi}{3}$	$-\frac{\pi}{2}$	$-\frac{\pi}{3}$	$-\frac{\pi}{4}$	$-\frac{\pi}{6}$	0
$\cos\theta$ (exact)	-1	$-\frac{\sqrt{3}}{2}$	$-\frac{\sqrt{2}}{2}$	$-\frac{1}{2}$	0	$\frac{1}{2}$	$\frac{\sqrt{2}}{2}$	$\frac{\sqrt{3}}{2}$	1
$\cos\theta$ (approximate)	-1	-0.866	-0.707	-0.5	0	0.5	0.707	0.866	1

Here is a table of approximate values of functions. Use this table, plus your knowledge of the properties of the functions, to make graphs.

	$\frac{\pi}{16}$	$\frac{\pi}{8}$	$\frac{\pi}{6}$	$\frac{\pi}{4}$	$\frac{\pi}{3}$	$\frac{3\pi}{8}$	$\frac{7\pi}{16}$	$-\frac{\pi}{16}$	$-\frac{\pi}{8}$	$-\frac{\pi}{6}$	$-\frac{\pi}{4}$
tan	0.2	0.4	0.6	1	1.7	2.4	4.9	-0.2	-0.4	-0.6	-1
cot	4.9	2.4	1.7	1	0.6	0.4	0.2	-4.9	-2.4	-1.7	-1
sec	1.02	1.1	1.2	1.4	2	2.6	5.0	1.02	1.1	1.2	1.4
csc	5.0	2.6	2	1.4	1.2	1.08	1.02	-5.0	-2.6	-2	-1.4

12. Graph the tangent function between -2π and 2π.

13. Graph the cotangent function between -2π and 2π.

14. Graph the secant function between -2π and 2π.

15. Graph the cosecant function between -2π and 2π.

B

16. **a.** Sketch a graph of $y = \sin x$.
    b. By reflecting the graph in **a.**, sketch a graph of $y = \sin(-x)$.
    c. By reflecting the graph in **a.**, sketch a graph of $y = -\sin x$.
    d. How do the graphs in **b.** and **c.** compare?

17. **a.** Sketch a graph of $y = \cos x$.
    b. By reflecting the graph in **a.**, sketch a graph of $y = \cos(-x)$.
    c. By reflecting the graph in **a.**, sketch a graph of $y = -\cos x$.
    d. How do the graphs in **a.** and **b.** compare?

18. **a.** Sketch a graph of $y = \sin x$.
    b. By translating, sketch a graph of $y = \sin(x + \pi)$.
    c. By reflecting the graph of **a.**, sketch a graph of $y = -\sin x$.
    d. How do the graphs in **b.** and **c.** compare?

19. **a.** Sketch a graph of $y = \sin x$.
    b. By translating, sketch a graph of $y = \sin(x - \pi)$.
    c. By reflecting the graph of **a.**, sketch a graph of $y = -\sin x$.
    d. How do the graphs in **b.** and **c.** compare?

16. a. Sine curve
b. Curve through $(-\pi, 0)$, $\left(-\frac{\pi}{2}, 1\right)$, $(0, 0)$, $\left(\frac{\pi}{2}, -1\right)$, $(\pi, 0)$
c. Curve through points listed in 16b
d. They are the same.

17. a. Cosine curve
b. Cosine curve
c. Curve through $(-\pi, 1)$, $\left(-\frac{\pi}{2}, 0\right)$, $(0, -1)$, $\left(\frac{\pi}{2}, 0\right)$, $(\pi, 1)$
d. They are the same.

18. a. Sine curve
b. Curve through points listed in 16b, above
c. Curve through points listed in 16b, above
d. They are the same.

19. a. Sine curve
b. Curve through points listed in 16b, above
c. Curve through points listed in 16b, above
d. They are the same.

20. a. Cosine curve
b. Curve through points listed in 17c, above
c. Curve through points listed in 17c, above
d. They are the same.

21. a. Cosine curve
b. Curve through points listed in 17c, above
c. Curve through points listed in 17c, above
d. They are the same.

22. The sin and tan functions; the cos and cot functions

23.

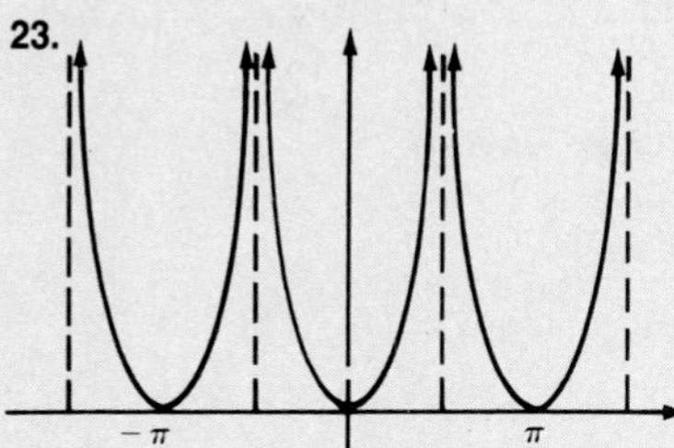

24. a. If the graph of tan x were reflected across the y-axis and then translated to the right a distance of $\frac{\pi}{2}$, the graph of cot x could be obtained. There are other ways to describe the relation.
b. If the graph of sec x were translated to the right $\frac{\pi}{2}$ units, the graph of csc x would be obtained. There are other descriptions.

25. $\left\{x \mid -\frac{\pi}{2} + 2k\pi < x < \frac{\pi}{2} + 2k\pi,\ k \text{ an integer}\right\}$

26. $\left\{x \mid (2k + 1)\pi < x < (2k + 2)\pi,\ x \neq \frac{3\pi}{2} + 2\pi k,\ k \text{ an integer}\right\}$

27.

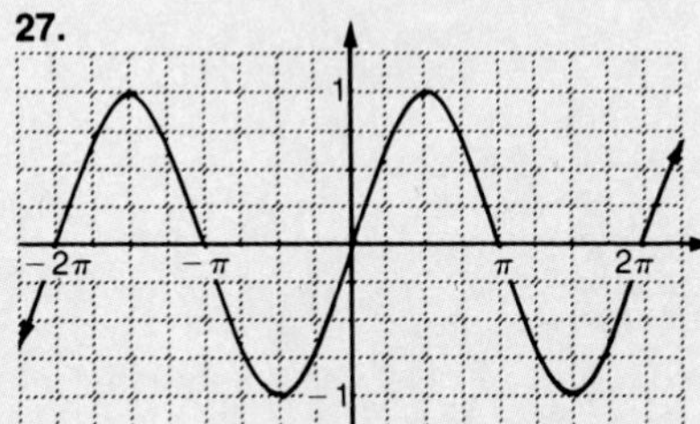

28.

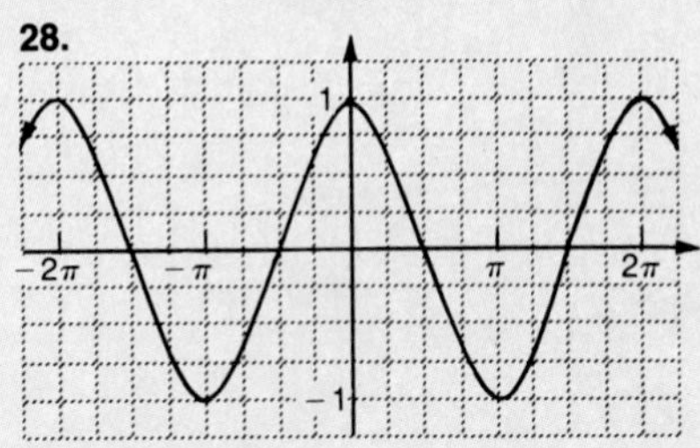

Mixed Review

29. Odd
30. Odd
31. Even
32. Neither
33. 10

20. **a.** Sketch a graph of $y = \cos x$.
b. By translating, sketch a graph of $y = \cos(x + \pi)$.
c. By reflecting the graph of **a.**, sketch a graph of $y = -\cos x$.
d. How do the graphs in **b.** and **c.** compare?

21. **a.** Sketch a graph of $y = \cos x$.
b. By translating, sketch a graph of $y = \cos(x - \pi)$.
c. By reflecting the graph of **a.**, sketch a graph of $y = -\cos x$.
d. How do the graphs in **b.** and **c.** compare?

22. Which pairs of circular functions have the same zeros?

23. Graph $f(x) = |\tan x|$.

24. ***Critical Thinking***
a. Describe how the graphs of the tangent and cotangent functions are related.
b. Describe how the graphs of the secant and cosecant functions are related.

Challenge

25. Solve $\cos x \leq \sec x$.

26. Solve $\sin x > \csc x$.

27. Construct a graph of the sine function by copying the coordinate axes on other paper. Then, from the unit circle shown here, transfer vertical distances with a compass.

28. Construct a graph of the cosine function. Follow the instructions for Exercise 31, but transfer *horizontal* distances from the unit circle with a compass.

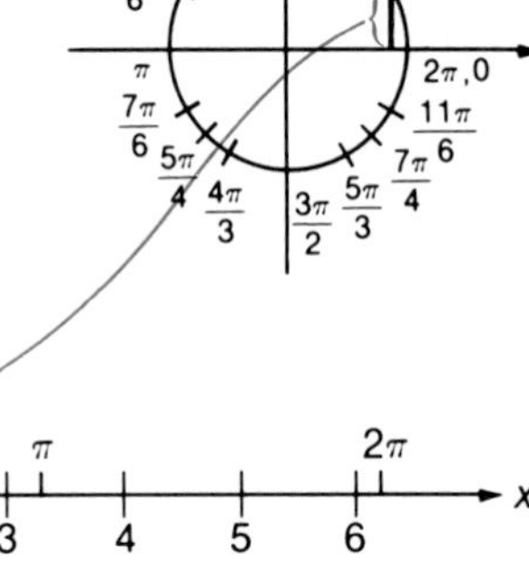

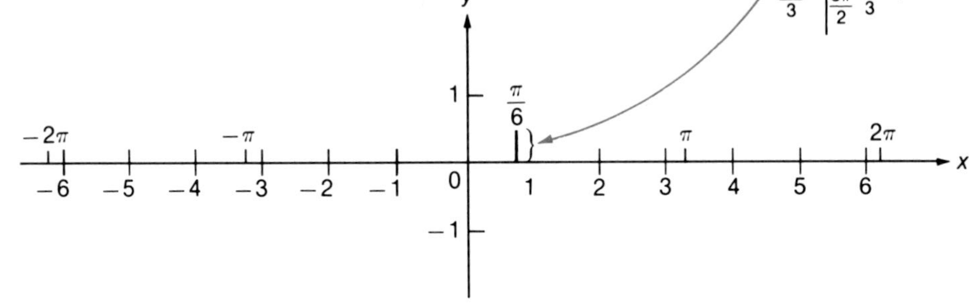

Mixed Review

Tell whether the function is odd, even, or neither. **29.** $f(x) = \sin x$

30. $f(x) = x^3 - x$ **31.** $f(x) = \cos x$ **32.** $f(x) = x^4 - x^2 + x$

For an arithmetic sequence **33.** find d when $a_{25} = 10$ and $a_{50} = 260$.

WRITING TO LEARN

Write a description of the graph of any trigonometric function. Read your description to the class. See if anyone can identify the function from your description. Answers may vary.

17-6 Trigonometric Function Relationships

We have already seen some of the important relationships that exist among the six trigonometric functions. There are certain other relationships called identities. Recall that an identity is an equation that is true for all acceptable replacements for the variables.

Quotient and Pythagorean Identities

Objective: Derive identities from the quotient and Pythagorean identities.

The tangent and cotangent functions can be expressed in terms of the sine and cosine functions.

Theorem 17-3

The Quotient Identities

$$\tan \theta \equiv \frac{\sin \theta}{\cos \theta}, \cos \theta \neq 0 \qquad \cot \theta \equiv \frac{\cos \theta}{\sin \theta}, \sin \theta \neq 0$$

EXAMPLE 1 Derive an identity that gives $\sin \theta$ in terms of $\tan \theta$ and $\cos \theta$.

By Theorem 17-3 we have $\tan \theta \equiv \frac{\sin \theta}{\cos \theta}$. Solving for $\sin \theta$ we have

$$\sin \theta \equiv \tan \theta \cdot \cos \theta$$

Try This

a. Derive an identity that gives $\cos \theta$ in terms of $\sin \theta$ and $\cot \theta$. $\cos \theta \equiv \cot \theta \cdot \sin \theta$

Suppose θ determines a point T on the unit circle, with coordinates (x, y). By the Pythagorean theorem, $x^2 + y^2 = 1$. Since $x = \cos \theta$ and $y = \sin \theta$, we obtain the following identity.

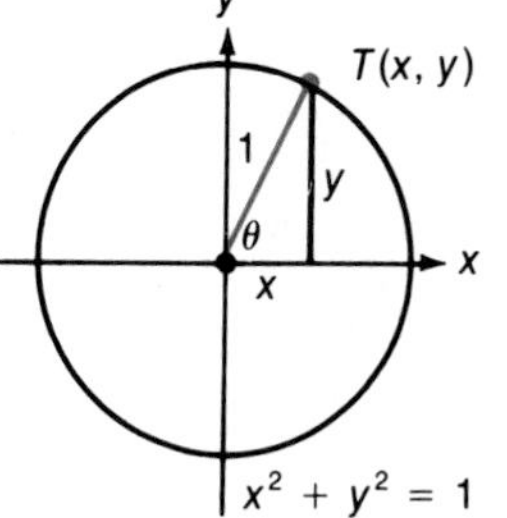

$$\sin^2 \theta + \cos^2 \theta \equiv 1$$ When exponents are used with the trigonometric functions, we write $\sin^2 \theta$ instead of $(\sin \theta)^2$.

This identity relates the sine and cosine of any angle. It is known as one of the Pythagorean identities. Now we will divide the above identity by $\sin^2 \theta$.

$$\frac{\sin^2 \theta}{\sin^2 \theta} + \frac{\cos^2 \theta}{\sin^2 \theta} \equiv \frac{1}{\sin^2 \theta}$$

17-6

FIRST FIVE MINUTES

1. What is the period of $\cos \theta$?
   2π
2. What is the domain of $\sin \theta$?
   All real numbers
3. What is the range of $\csc \theta$?
   All real numbers ≥ 1 or ≤ -1.
4. For the functions cosine, sine, tangent, and secant, which are odd and which are even?
   Cosine and secant are even.
   Sine and tangent are odd.

Quotient and Pythagorean Identities

Point out to students that the angles of a right triangle are completely determined if any one of the six trigonometric ratios is known. Hence, knowing any one of the six trigonometric functions determines the others. In this section we investigate the algebraic relations between the trigonometric functions.

Key Questions

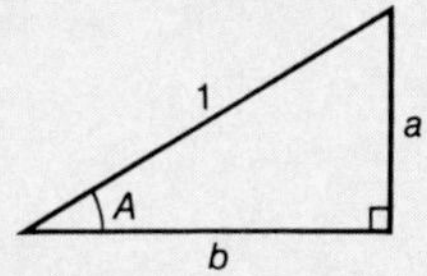

- What is the algebraic relationship between a and b?
  $a^2 + b^2 = 1$
- What is $\sin A$?
  a
- What is $\cos A$?
  b
- What is $\tan A$?
  $\frac{a}{b}$
- What is $\sec A$?
  $\frac{1}{b}$

Chalkboard Examples

1. Simplify the expression $\tan\theta \cdot \csc\theta$.

   $\frac{\sin\theta}{\cos\theta}\cdot\frac{1}{\sin\theta} = \sec\theta$

2. Simplify the expression $\sin^2\theta + \frac{1}{\sec^2\theta}$.

   $\sin^2\theta + \cos^2\theta = 1$

3. Use the identity $1 + \tan^2\theta \equiv \sec^2\theta$ to derive an equation for the cosine in terms of the tangent, for θ between $-\frac{\pi}{2}$ and $\frac{\pi}{2}$.

   $1 + \tan^2\theta = \frac{1}{\cos^2\theta}$

   $\frac{1}{1+\tan^2\theta} = \cos^2\theta$

   $\frac{1}{\sqrt{1+\tan^2\theta}} = \cos\theta$

Since the cosecant is the reciprocal of the sine, this can be further simplified.

$$1 + \cot^2\theta \equiv \csc^2\theta$$

This identity is valid for any rotation θ for which $\sin^2\theta \neq 0$, since we divided by $\sin^2\theta$.

The third Pythagorean identity is obtained by dividing the first by $\cos^2\theta$.

$$1 + \tan^2\theta \equiv \sec^2\theta$$

Theorem 17-4

The Pythagorean Identities

$$\sin^2\theta + \cos^2\theta \equiv 1 \qquad 1 + \cot^2\theta \equiv \csc^2\theta \qquad 1 + \tan^2\theta \equiv \sec^2\theta$$

EXAMPLE 2 Derive identities that give $\cos^2\theta$ and $\cos\theta$ in terms of $\sin\theta$.

$\sin^2\theta + \cos^2\theta \equiv 1$ — Pythagorean identity

$\cos^2\theta \equiv 1 - \sin^2\theta$ — Solving for $\cos^2\theta$

$|\cos\theta| \equiv \sqrt{1 - \sin^2\theta}$ — Finding the principal square root

$\cos\theta \equiv \pm\sqrt{1 - \sin^2\theta}$

The sign of $\cos\theta$ is positive if the terminal side of θ is in the first or fourth quadrant. Otherwise, it is negative.

Try This

b. Derive an identity for $\sin^2\theta$ in terms of $\cos\theta$. $\sin^2\theta \equiv 1 - \cos^2\theta$

c. Derive an identity for $\sin\theta$ in terms of $\cos\theta$. $\sin\theta \equiv \pm\sqrt{1 - \cos^2\theta}$

EXAMPLE 3 Derive two other identities from $1 + \cot^2\theta \equiv \csc^2\theta$.

We obtain

$$\csc^2\theta - \cot^2\theta \equiv 1 \text{ and } \cot^2\theta \equiv \csc^2\theta - 1$$

EXAMPLE 4 Derive an identity for $\cot\theta$ in terms of $\sin\theta$.

$\cot^2\theta \equiv \csc^2\theta - 1$ — From the identity derived in Example 3

$\cot^2\theta \equiv \frac{1}{\sin^2\theta} - 1$

$\cot\theta \equiv \pm\sqrt{\frac{1}{\sin^2\theta} - 1}$

Try This

d. From the identity $1 + \tan^2\theta \equiv \sec^2\theta$, derive two other identities.
$\sec^2\theta - \tan^2\theta \equiv 1$ $\tan^2\theta \equiv \sec^2\theta - 1$

e. Derive an identity for $\sec\theta$ in terms of $\sin\theta$ and $\cos\theta$. $\sec\theta \equiv \pm\sqrt{1 + \frac{\sin^2\theta}{\cos^2\theta}}$

The Cofunction Identities

Objective: Derive identities from the cofunction identities.

We know that the sine and cosine are called cofunctions of each other. Another class of identities gives functions in terms of their cofunctions.

Consider this graph. The graph of $y = \sin\theta$ has been translated to the left a distance of $\frac{\pi}{2}$. Thus we obtain the graph of $y = \sin\left(\theta + \frac{\pi}{2}\right)$. The latter is also a graph of the cosine function. Thus we obtain the identity $\sin\left(\theta + \frac{\pi}{2}\right) \equiv \cos\theta$.

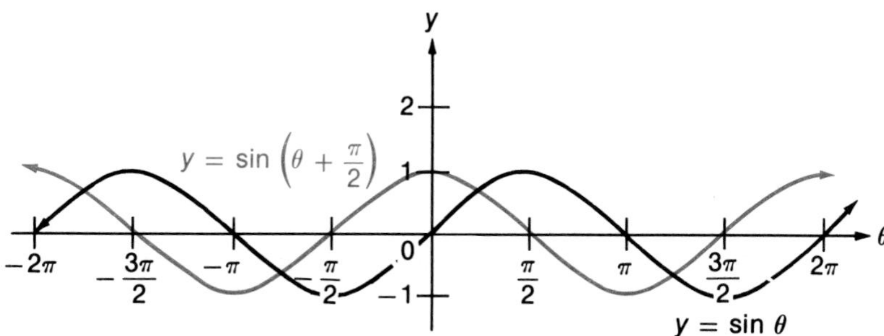

EXAMPLE 5 Check the identity $\sin\left(\theta + \frac{\pi}{2}\right) \equiv \cos\theta$ by using $\theta = \frac{\pi}{6}$.

$$\sin\left(\theta + \frac{\pi}{2}\right) = \sin\left(\frac{\pi}{6} + \frac{\pi}{2}\right) = \sin\left(\frac{2\pi}{3}\right) = \frac{\sqrt{3}}{2} = \cos\frac{\pi}{6}$$

By translating the graph of $y = \cos\theta$ to the right a distance of $\frac{\pi}{2}$, we obtain the following identity.

$$\cos\left(\theta - \frac{\pi}{2}\right) \equiv \sin\theta$$

Try This

f. Check the identity $\cos\left(\theta - \frac{\pi}{2}\right) \equiv \sin\theta$ by using $\theta = 0$ radians. $\cos\left(0 - \frac{\pi}{2}\right) = \cos\left(-\frac{\pi}{2}\right) = 0 = \sin 0$

If the graph of $y = \sin\theta$ is translated to the right a distance of $\frac{\pi}{2}$, we obtain the graph of $y = \sin\left(\theta - \frac{\pi}{2}\right)$. The latter is a reflection of the cosine function across the x-axis. In other words, it is a graph of $y = -\cos\theta$. We thus obtain the following identity.

$$\sin\left(\theta - \frac{\pi}{2}\right) \equiv -\cos\theta$$

By means similar to those above, we obtain this identity.

$$\cos\left(\theta + \frac{\pi}{2}\right) \equiv -\sin\theta$$

The Cofunction Identities

Remind students that the sine function is an odd function and the cosine function is an even function.

Chalkboard Examples

1. Check the identity $\cos\left(\theta + \frac{\pi}{2}\right) \equiv -\sin\theta$ using the value $\theta = \frac{\pi}{2}$.

$\cos\left(\frac{\pi}{2} + \frac{\pi}{2}\right)$
$= \cos(\pi)$
$= -1$
$= -\sin\frac{\pi}{2}$

2. Find an identity for $\tan\left(\theta - \frac{\pi}{2}\right)$.

$\tan\left(\theta - \frac{\pi}{2}\right)$
$= \dfrac{\sin\left(\theta - \frac{\pi}{2}\right)}{\cos\left(\theta - \frac{\pi}{2}\right)}$
$= \dfrac{-\cos\theta}{\sin\theta}$
$= -\cot\theta$

LESSON QUIZ

1. Write an identity for $\sin\theta$ in terms of $\cos\theta$.
   $\sin\theta \equiv \pm\sqrt{1-\cos^2\theta}$
2. Write an identity for $\sin\theta$ in terms of $\cos\theta$ and $\tan\theta$.
   $\sin\theta \equiv \cos\theta \cdot \tan\theta$
3. Write an identity relating $\tan\theta$ and $\sec\theta$.
   $1+\tan^2\theta \equiv \sec^2\theta$

We now consider function values at $\frac{\pi}{2} - \theta$. Since the sine function is odd, we know the following.

$$\sin\left(\frac{\pi}{2} - \theta\right) \equiv \sin\left[-\left(\theta - \frac{\pi}{2}\right)\right] \equiv -\sin\left(\theta - \frac{\pi}{2}\right)$$

Now consider the identity already established.

$$\sin\left(\theta - \frac{\pi}{2}\right) \equiv -\cos\theta$$

This is equivalent to the following.

$$-\sin\left(\theta - \frac{\pi}{2}\right) \equiv \cos\theta \quad \text{Multiplying by } -1$$

Since the sine function is odd, we now have the following identity.

$$\sin\left(\frac{\pi}{2} - \theta\right) \equiv \cos\theta$$

Similarly, we can establish the identity $\cos\left(\frac{\pi}{2} - \theta\right) \equiv \sin\theta$.

The following theorem summarizes the cofunction identities. These identities should be memorized.

Theorem 17-5

The Cofunction Identities

$$\sin\left(\theta + \frac{\pi}{2}\right) \equiv \cos\theta \qquad \cos\left(\theta + \frac{\pi}{2}\right) \equiv -\sin\theta$$

$$\sin\left(\theta - \frac{\pi}{2}\right) \equiv -\cos\theta \qquad \cos\left(\theta - \frac{\pi}{2}\right) \equiv \sin\theta$$

$$\sin\left(\frac{\pi}{2} - \theta\right) \equiv \cos\theta \qquad \cos\left(\frac{\pi}{2} - \theta\right) \equiv \sin\theta$$

EXAMPLE 6 Find an identity for $\tan\left(\theta + \frac{\pi}{2}\right)$.

$$\tan\left(\theta + \frac{\pi}{2}\right) \equiv \frac{\sin\left(\theta + \frac{\pi}{2}\right)}{\cos\left(\theta + \frac{\pi}{2}\right)} \quad \text{Theorem 16-3 (quotient identity)}$$

$$\equiv \frac{\cos\theta}{-\sin\theta} \quad \text{Theorem 16-5 (cofunction identity)}$$

$$\equiv -\cot\theta \quad \text{Theorem 16-3 (quotient identity)}$$

Try This

g. Find an identity for $\cot\left(\theta + \frac{\pi}{2}\right)$. $\cot\left(\theta + \frac{\pi}{2}\right) \equiv -\tan\theta$

17-6 EXERCISES

A

1. Derive an identity for $\cos\theta$ in terms of $\sin\theta$ and $\tan\theta$. $\cos\theta \equiv \frac{\sin\theta}{\tan\theta}$
2. Derive an identity for $\sin\theta$ in terms of $\cot\theta$ and $\cos\theta$. $\sin\theta \equiv \frac{\cos\theta}{\cot\theta}$

Use the Pythagorean identities to derive an identity for

3. $\csc\theta$ in terms of $\cot\theta$. $\csc\theta \equiv \pm\sqrt{1+\cot^2\theta}$
4. $\tan\theta$ in terms of $\sec\theta$. $\tan\theta \equiv \pm\sqrt{\sec^2\theta - 1}$
5. $\cot\theta$ in terms of $\csc\theta$. $\cot\theta \equiv \pm\sqrt{\csc^2\theta - 1}$
6. $\sec\theta$ in terms of $\tan\theta$. $\sec\theta \equiv \pm\sqrt{1+\tan^2\theta}$
7. $\tan\theta$ in terms of $\cos\theta$. $\tan\theta \equiv \pm\sqrt{\frac{1}{\cos^2\theta} - 1}$
8. $\csc\theta$ in terms of $\cos\theta$. $\csc\theta \equiv \pm\sqrt{\frac{1}{1-\cos^2\theta}}$
9. Check the identity $\sin\left(\theta - \frac{\pi}{2}\right) \equiv -\cos\theta$ by using $\theta = \frac{\pi}{4}$.
10. Check the identity $\cos\left(\theta - \frac{\pi}{2}\right) \equiv \sin\theta$ by using $\theta = 0$.
11. Check the identity $\sin\left(\frac{\pi}{2} - \theta\right) \equiv \cos\theta$ by using $\theta = \frac{5\pi}{4}$.
12. Check the identity $\cos\left(\frac{\pi}{2} - \theta\right) \equiv \sin\theta$ by using $\theta = \frac{\pi}{3}$.

Use the cofunction identities to derive an identity for the following.

13. $\tan\left(\theta - \frac{\pi}{2}\right)$ $\tan\left(\theta - \frac{\pi}{2}\right) \equiv -\cot\theta$
14. $\cot\left(\theta - \frac{\pi}{2}\right)$ $\cot\left(\theta - \frac{\pi}{2}\right) \equiv -\tan\theta$
15. $\sec\left(\frac{\pi}{2} - \theta\right)$ $\sec\left(\frac{\pi}{2} - \theta\right) \equiv \csc\theta$
16. $\csc\left(\frac{\pi}{2} - \theta\right)$ $\csc\left(\frac{\pi}{2} - \theta\right) \equiv \sec\theta$

B

Use the given function values to find the six function values of the complement angle.

17. $\sin 65° = 0.9063$ $\cos 65° = 0.4226$
    $\tan 65° = 2.145$ $\cot 65° = 0.4663$
    $\sec 65° = 2.366$ $\csc 65° = 1.103$
18. $\sin 32° = 0.5299$ $\cos 32° = 0.8480$
    $\tan 32° = 0.6249$ $\cot 32° = 1.600$
    $\sec 32° = 1.179$ $\csc 32° = 1.887$

Write an equivalent expression for each of the following.

19. $\sin(\theta + \pi)$ $-\sin\theta$
20. $\sin(\theta - \pi)$ $-\sin\theta$
21. $\cos(\pi - \theta)$ $-\cos\theta$
22. $\sin(\pi - \theta)$ $\sin\theta$
23. $\cos(\theta + 2k\pi)$ $\cos\theta$
24. $\sin(\theta + 2k\pi)$ $\sin\theta$
25. $\cos(\theta - \pi)$ $-\cos\theta$
26. $\cos(\theta + \pi)$ $-\cos\theta$

Assignment Guide
Algebra: Omit

Alg w/Trig: Day 1: 1–16, MR
Day 2: 17–33

Comprehensive: 1–32 e/o, 33–37, MR

ADDITIONAL ANSWERS

Exercises

9. $\sin\left(\frac{\pi}{4} - \frac{\pi}{2}\right) = \sin\left(-\frac{\pi}{4}\right) = -\frac{\sqrt{2}}{2} = -\cos\frac{\pi}{4}$

10. $\cos\left(0 - \frac{\pi}{2}\right) = \cos\left(-\frac{\pi}{2}\right) = 0 = \sin 0$

11. $\sin\left(\frac{\pi}{2} - \frac{5\pi}{4}\right) = \sin\left(-\frac{3\pi}{4}\right) = -\frac{\sqrt{2}}{2} = \cos\frac{5\pi}{4}$

12. $\cos\left(\frac{\pi}{2} - \frac{\pi}{3}\right) = \cos\frac{\pi}{6} = \frac{\sqrt{3}}{2} = \sin\frac{\pi}{3}$

17. $\sin 25° = 0.4226$, $\cos 25° = 0.9063$, $\tan 25° = 0.4663$, $\cot 25° = 2.145$, $\sec 25° = 1.103$, $\csc 25° = 2.366$

18. $\sin 58° = 0.8480$, $\cos 58° = 0.5299$, $\tan 58° = 1.600$, $\cot 58° = 0.6249$, $\sec 58° = 1.887$, $\csc 58° = 1.179$

33. $\sin\theta \equiv \cos\left(\frac{\pi}{2} - \theta\right)$, $\cos\theta \equiv \sin\left(\frac{\pi}{2} - \theta\right)$, $\tan\theta \equiv \cot\left(\frac{\pi}{2} - \theta\right)$, $\cot\theta \equiv \tan\left(\frac{\pi}{2} - \theta\right)$, $\sec\theta \equiv \csc\left(\frac{\pi}{2} - \theta\right)$, $\csc\theta \equiv \sec\left(\frac{\pi}{2} - \theta\right)$
The function of an angle is equal to the cofunction of its complement.

34. $\theta = 30°; \frac{1 - \sin 30°}{\cos 30°} = \frac{\cos 30°}{1 + \sin 30°};$

$\frac{\frac{1}{2}}{\frac{\sqrt{3}}{2}} = \frac{\frac{\sqrt{3}}{2}}{\frac{3}{2}}; \frac{\sqrt{3}}{3} = \frac{\sqrt{3}}{3}$

35. $\theta = 60°; \frac{1 - \cos 60°}{\sin 60°} = \frac{\sin 60°}{1 + \cos 60°};$

$\frac{\frac{1}{2}}{\frac{\sqrt{3}}{2}} = \frac{\frac{\sqrt{3}}{2}}{\frac{3}{2}}; \frac{\sqrt{3}}{3} = \frac{\sqrt{3}}{3}$

36. $x = \frac{\pi}{2}; \csc\frac{\pi}{2} - \cos\frac{\pi}{2}\cot\frac{\pi}{2}$

$= \sin\frac{\pi}{2}; 1 - 0 \cdot 0 = 1; 1 = 1$

37. $x = \frac{\pi}{4}; \sec\frac{\pi}{4} - \sin\frac{\pi}{4}\tan\frac{\pi}{4}$

$= \cos\frac{\pi}{4}; \sqrt{2} - \frac{\sqrt{2}}{2} \cdot 1 = \frac{\sqrt{2}}{2};$

$\frac{\sqrt{2}}{2} = \frac{\sqrt{2}}{2}$

Mixed Review

38. $(2x - 3)(3x - 2)$
39. $(x^2 + 25)(x + 5)(x - 5)$
40. $6xy^2(2x - 3y)(2x + 3y)$
41. $(x + 4)(x + 5)(x + 6)$
42. $x^2 - 3x + 2$
43. $x^3 - x^2 + x - 1$
44. $\frac{-8a^6c^3d\sqrt[5]{d}}{b^3}$
45. $\frac{-3125l^{10}n^6\sqrt[3]{n^2}}{16807m^{15}}$
46. $\frac{\sqrt[4]{8}}{2}$, or $\frac{1}{2}8^{1/4}$
47. $\sin\alpha = \frac{12}{13}$ $\sin\theta = \frac{5}{13}$

$\cos\alpha = \frac{5}{13}$ $\cos\theta = \frac{12}{13}$

$\tan\alpha = \frac{12}{5}$ $\tan\theta = \frac{5}{12}$

$\cot\alpha = \frac{5}{12}$ $\cot\theta = \frac{12}{5}$

$\csc\alpha = \frac{13}{12}$ $\csc\theta = \frac{13}{5}$

$\sec\alpha = \frac{13}{5}$ $\sec\theta = \frac{13}{12}$

48. $a = 1, b = 2$
49. $a = \sqrt{2}, b = 2$

Given that $\sin\frac{\pi}{8} = 0.38268$, use identities to find the following.

27. $\cos\frac{\pi}{8}$ 0.92388

28. $\cos\frac{5\pi}{8}$ −0.38268

29. $\sin\frac{5\pi}{8}$ 0.92388

30. $\sin -\frac{3\pi}{8}$ −0.92388

31. $\cos -\frac{3\pi}{8}$ 0.38268

32. $\cos -\frac{\pi}{8}$ 0.92388

33. ***Critical Thinking***

a. For the six trigonometric functions, find the cofunction identities for $\frac{\pi}{2} - \theta$.

b. Describe the pattern you see in part a.

Challenge

Choose values for θ or x. Then check these identities. Answers may vary.

34. $\frac{1 - \sin\theta}{\cos\theta} \equiv \frac{\cos\theta}{1 + \sin\theta}$

35. $\frac{1 - \cos\theta}{\sin\theta} \equiv \frac{\sin\theta}{1 + \cos\theta}$

36. $\csc x - \cos x \cot x \equiv \sin x$

37. $\sec x - \sin x \tan x \equiv \cos x$

Mixed Review

Factor **38.** $6x^2 - 13x + 6$ **39.** $x^4 - 625$ **40.** $24x^3y^2 - 54xy^4$

41. $x^3 + 15x^2 + 74x + 120$

Divide. **42.** $(x^3 - 4x^2 + 5x - 2) \div (x - 1)$

43. $(3x^4 + x^3 - x^2 + x - 4) \div (3x + 4)$

Simplify. **44.** $\left(\frac{-32a^{12}b^{-3}c^7d^4}{a^2b^2c^2d^2}\right)^{\frac{3}{5}}$ **45.** $\left(\frac{-125n^7m^{-7}l^7}{343n^3m^2l}\right)^{\frac{5}{3}}$

46. Use rational exponents to simplify. $\sqrt{\frac{\sqrt{2}}{2}}$

Find the six trigonometric function values for θ and α. Leave answers as fractions.

47.

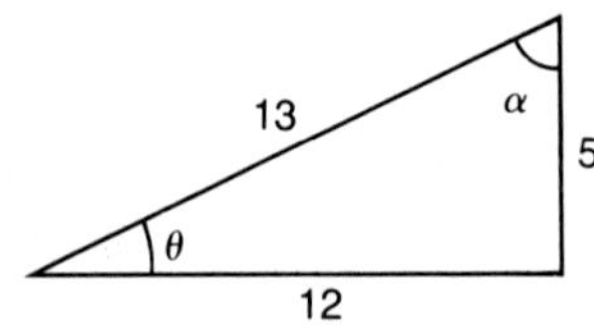

Find the length of a and b.

48.

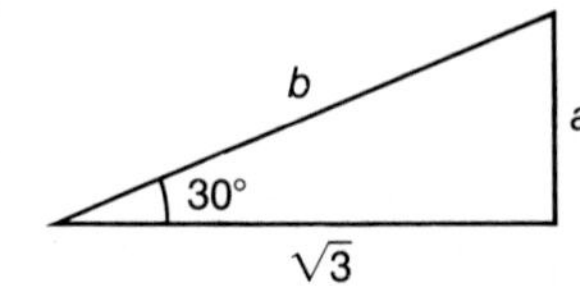

49.

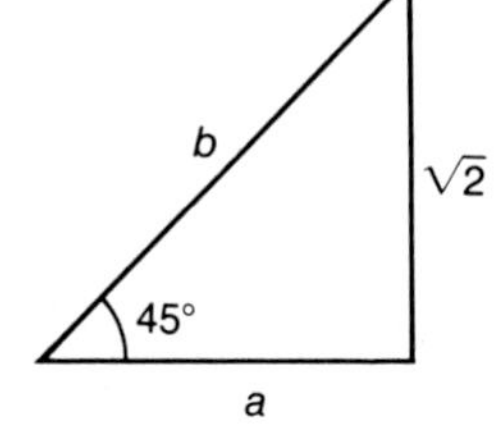

17-7 More Trigonometric Graphs

Master Grapher Worksheet 31, *Transformations of Sine, Cosine, and Tangent Functions*, can be used for lesson closure.

We will consider graphs of some variations of the sine and cosine function. In particular, we are interested in $y = A \sin B\theta$ and $y = A \cos B\theta$ where A and B are constants.

Change of Amplitude or Period

Objective: Sketch graphs in which the amplitude or period is changed.

Changing the constant A in $y = A \sin \theta$ causes a vertical stretching or shrinking of the graph and thus a change in the amplitude.

EXAMPLE 1 Sketch a graph of $y = 2 \sin \theta$. What is the amplitude?

The function $y = 2 \sin \theta$ is equivalent to $\frac{y}{2} = \sin \theta$. Thus the graph is a vertical stretching of the graph of $y = \sin \theta$. The amplitude of this function is 2. That is, $A = 2$.

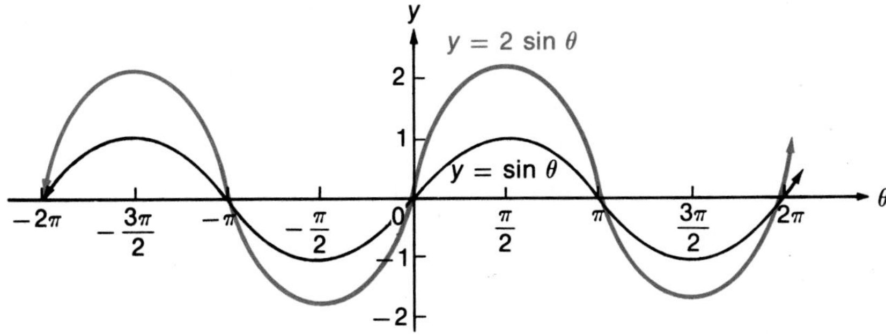

If the constant A in $y = A \sin x$ is negative, there will also be a reflection across the x-axis. If the absolute value of A is less than 1, then there will be a vertical shrinking. The amplitude will be $|A|$. Thus the graph of $y = -\frac{1}{2} \sin \theta$ is a reflection of $y = \sin \theta$ and has an amplitude of $\left|-\frac{1}{2}\right|$ or $\frac{1}{2}$.

Try This See Additional Answers.

a. Sketch a graph of $y = 2 \cos \theta$. What is the amplitude? 2

Changing the constant B in $y = \sin B\theta$ causes a horizontal stretching or shrinking of the graph and thus a change in the period.

17-7

FIRST FIVE MINUTES

1. Write an expression relating $\sin \theta$ and $\cos \theta$.
   $\sin^2 \theta + \cos^2 \theta = 1$
2. Simplify.
   $\cos^2 \theta \cdot (1 + \tan^2 \theta)$
   $\cos^2 \theta + \cos^2 \theta \cdot \tan^2 \theta$
   $= \cos^2 \theta + \sin^2 \theta = 1$

Change of Amplitude or Period (*T28*)

Point out that the sine and cosine functions are used to describe sound waves. The amplitude corresponds to the loudness of the sound and the constant factor corresponds to the frequency, or pitch, of the sound.

Key Questions

- What is the period of the function $y = \pi \cos 2\theta$?
  π
- Which function has the greater amplitude,
  $y = \frac{\pi}{4} \cos \theta$ or
  $y = \cos \theta$?
  $y = \cos \theta$

Chalkboard Examples

1. Sketch the graph of $y = 3\cos \theta$. What is its amplitude?

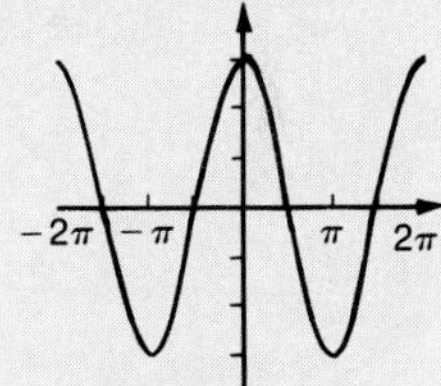

The amplitude is 3.

2. Sketch the graph of $y = \cos 3\theta$. What is the period of the function?

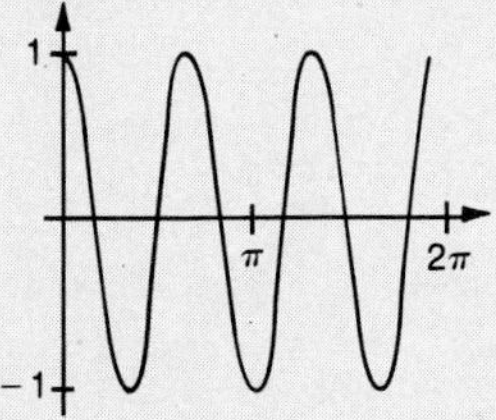

The period is $\frac{2\pi}{3}$.

Change of Amplitude and Period

Chalkboard Example

1. Sketch the graph of $y = 2\cos 2\theta$. What are the amplitude and period?

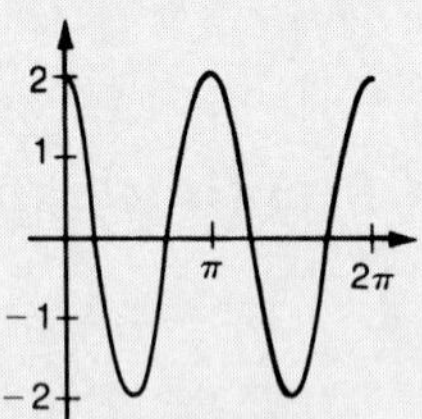

The amplitude is 2.

The period is π.

LESSON QUIZ

1. Sketch the graph of the function $y = \frac{1}{3}\cos\theta$.

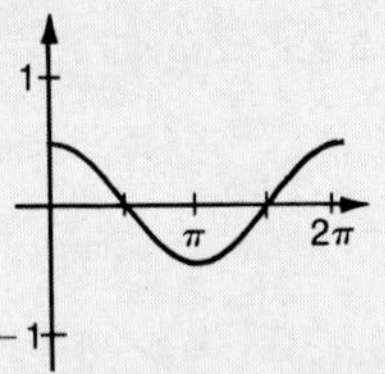

2. Sketch the graph of the function $y = \cos 4\theta$.

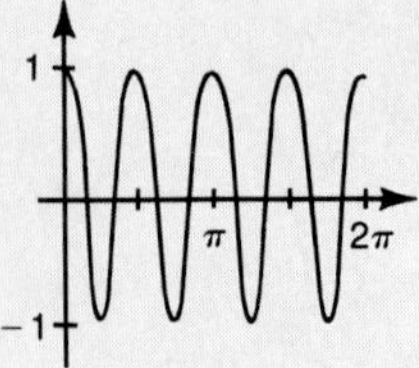

3. Sketch the graph of the function $y = \frac{1}{2}\sin 2\theta$.

EXAMPLE 2 Sketch a graph of $y = \sin 2\theta$. What is the period?

The function $y = \sin 2\theta$ is equivalent to $y = \sin \frac{\theta}{\frac{1}{2}}$. Thus the graph is a horizontal shrinking of the graph of $y = \sin\theta$.
The period of this function is π.

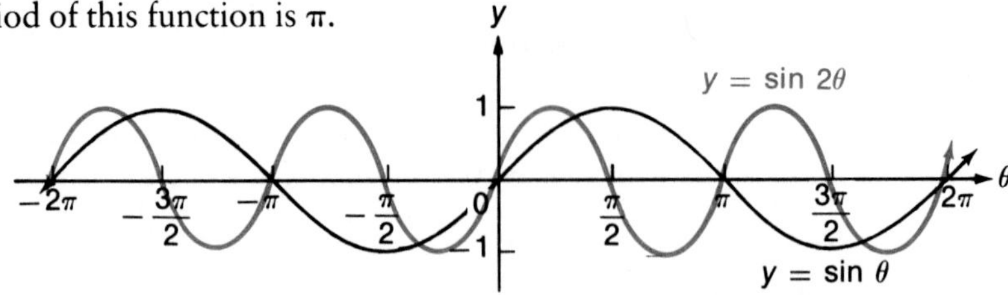

If $|B| > 1$, there will be a horizontal shrink. If $|B| < 1$, there will be a horizontal stretch. If B is negative, there will also be a reflection across the y-axis. The period will be $\frac{2\pi}{|B|}$. Thus the graph of $y = \sin\left(-\frac{1}{2}\theta\right)$ is a reflection of $y = \sin\theta$, and has a period of $\frac{2\pi}{\left|-\frac{1}{2}\right|}$ or 4π.

Try This See Additional Answers.

b. Sketch a graph of $y = \cos 2\theta$. What is the period? π

Change of Amplitude and Period

Objective: Sketch graphs in which the amplitude and period are changed.

Changing the constants A and B in $y = A\sin B\theta$ causes both a vertical and a horizontal stretching or shrinking of the graph.

EXAMPLE 3 Sketch a graph of $y = 3\sin 2\theta$. What is the amplitude and period?

The graph is a vertical stretching and a horizontal shrinking of the graph of $y = \sin\theta$. The function $y = 3\sin 2\theta$ is equivalent to

$$\frac{y}{3} = \sin\frac{\theta}{\frac{1}{2}}$$

The amplitude is 3.
The period is π.

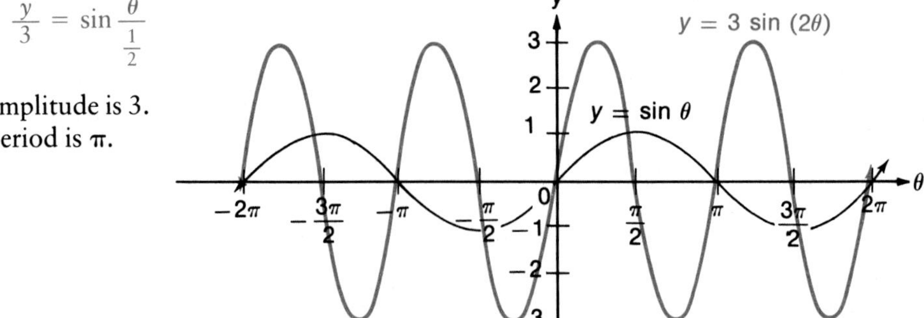

Try This See Additional Answers.

c. Sketch a graph of $y = 3\cos 2\theta$. What is the amplitude and the period? $A = 3$, period $= \pi$

17-7 EXERCISES

A

Sketch graphs of these functions. Determine the amplitude.

1. $y = \frac{1}{2}\sin\theta$ $A = \frac{1}{2}$
2. $y = \frac{1}{2}\cos\theta$ $A = \frac{1}{2}$
3. $y = 3\sin\theta$ $A = 3$
4. $y = 3\cos\theta$ $A = 3$
5. $y = -\frac{1}{3}\sin\theta$ $A = \frac{1}{3}$
6. $y = -\frac{1}{3}\cos\theta$ $A = \frac{1}{3}$
7. $y = 4\sin\theta$ $A = 4$
8. $y = 4\cos\theta$ $A = 4$
9. $y = -2\sin\theta$ $A = 2$

Sketch graphs of these functions. Determine the period.

10. $y = \sin 3\theta$ $\frac{2\pi}{3}$
11. $y = \cos 3\theta$ $\frac{2\pi}{3}$
12. $y = \sin\frac{1}{2}\theta$ 4π
13. $y = \cos\frac{1}{2}\theta$ 4π
14. $y = \sin\left(-\frac{1}{3}\theta\right)$ 6π
15. $y = \cos\left(-\frac{1}{3}\theta\right)$ 6π
16. $y = \sin(-2\theta)$ π
17. $y = \cos(-2\theta)$ π
18. $y = \sin(-3\theta)$ $\frac{2\pi}{3}$

Sketch graphs of these functions. Determine the amplitude and the period.

19. $y = 2\sin 2\theta$
20. $y = 2\cos 2\theta$
21. $y = \frac{1}{2}\sin 2\theta$
22. $y = \frac{1}{2}\cos 2\theta$
23. $y = -2\sin\frac{1}{2}\theta$
24. $y = -2\cos\frac{1}{2}\theta$
25. $y = \frac{1}{2}\sin(-2\theta)$
26. $y = \frac{1}{2}\cos(-2\theta)$
27. $y = -\frac{1}{2}\sin(-2\theta)$

B

Sketch graphs of these functions.

28. $y = \cos(2\theta - \pi)$
29. $y = \sin(2\theta + \pi)$
30. $y = 2 + \sin\theta$
31. ***Critical Thinking*** Write a function to quadruple the amplitude of $\sin\theta$, stretch its graph horizontally by a factor of 3, and reflect the graph across the x-axis.

Challenge

Sketch graphs of these functions. Determine the amplitude and period.

32. $y = 2 + 2\sin(2\theta + \pi)$
    $A = 2$, period $= \pi$
33. $y = -3 + \frac{1}{2}\sin\left(\frac{1}{2}\theta - \pi\right)$
    $A = \frac{1}{2}$, period $= 4\pi$

Mixed Review

Let $P(x) = x^3 + 6x^2 + 11x + 6$.

34. Determine the number of positive and negative real roots of $P(x)$.
35. Determine whether the following are factors of $P(x)$: $(x - 1)$, $(x + 1)$, $(x - 2)$.
36. Determine whether the following are zeros of $P(x)$: $-2, 0, 3$.
37. Find $P(-5)$, $P(-3)$, $P(2)$, $P(4)$.
38. Factor $P(x)$, list the x-intercepts, and then graph $P(x)$.

Assignment Guide
Algebra: Omit

Alg w/Trig: 1–30 e/o, 31, MR

Comprehensive: 1–30 e/o, 31–33, MR

ADDITIONAL ANSWERS

Try This

a.

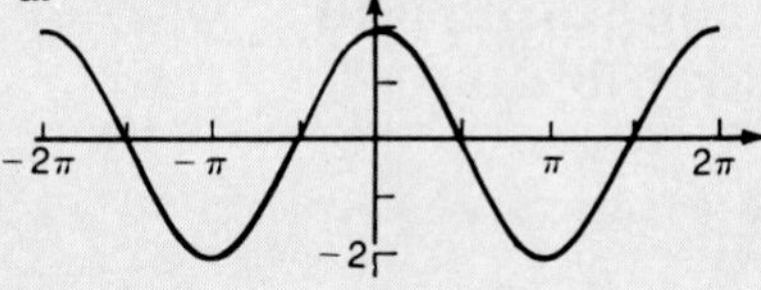

b.

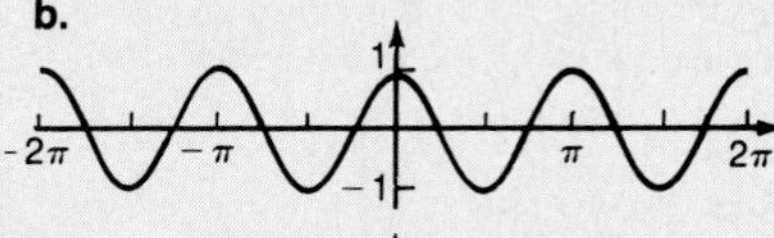

c.

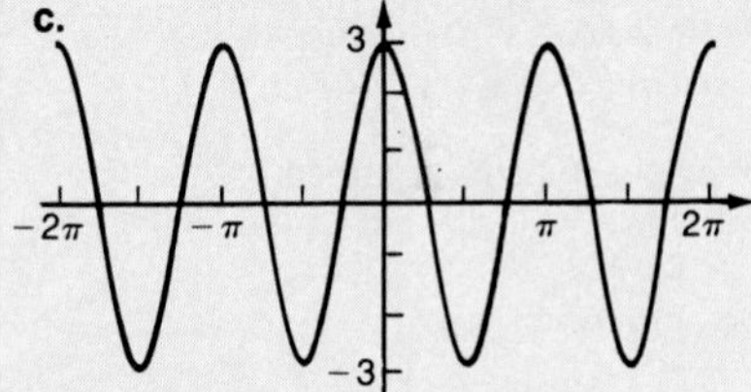

Exercises

For graphs of Exercises 1–18, 32–33, see Teacher's Answer Section.

For Exercises 19–30, see Teacher's Answer Section.

31. $y = -4\sin\left(\frac{1}{3}\theta\right)$

Mixed Review

34. No positive, 1 or 3 negative
35. No, yes, no
36. Yes, no, no
37. $P(-5) = -24$; $P(-3) = 0$; $P(2) = 60$; $P(4) = 210$
38. $P(x) = (x + 1)(x + 2)(x + 3)$ x-intercepts: $(-1, 0)$, $(-2, 0)$, $(-3, 0)$

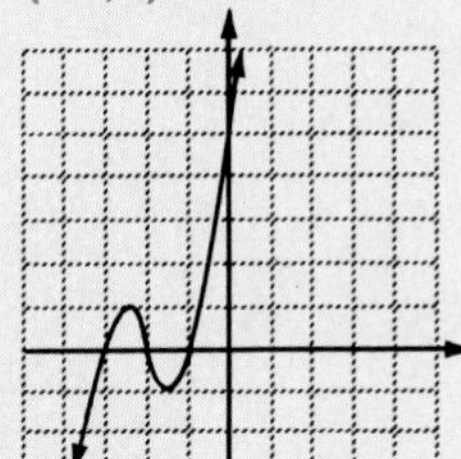

17-8

FIRST FIVE MINUTES

1. Graph $2\sin 3\theta$.

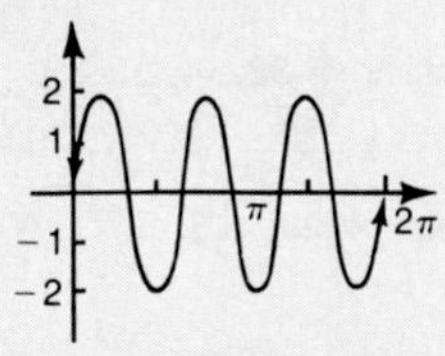

Computing and Simplifying

Emphasize that a trigonometric expression such as $\cos 3\theta$ is not a product of two factors. Many students will try to factor the 3 or the θ from $\cos 3\theta$.

Key Questions

- What expression represents the phrase "twice the sine of θ"? $2\sin\theta$
- What expression represents the phrase "one plus the square of the cosine of θ"? $1 + \cos^2\theta$

Chalkboard Examples

1. Multiply and simplify.

   $\sin x \cot x - \sin^2 x$

   $= \sin x \frac{\cos x}{\sin x} - \sin^2 x$

   $= \cos x - \sin^2 x$
2. Factor and simplify.
   $\tan x \sin^2 x + \tan x \cos^2 x$
   $\tan x(\sin^2 x + \cos^2 x) = \tan x$
3. Simplify.

   $\sin\left(x + \frac{\pi}{2}\right) \cdot \sec x$

   $\cos x \cdot \sec x = 1$

17-8 Algebraic Manipulations

Trigonometric expressions such as $\sin 2\theta$ or $\tan(x - \pi)$ represent numbers, just as algebraic expressions represent numbers. Thus we can work with trigonometric expressions in much the same way as we work with purely algebraic expressions.

Computing and Simplifying

Objective: Compute and simplify trigonometric expressions.

EXAMPLE 1 Multiply and simplify $\cos y(\tan y - \sec y)$.

$$\cos y(\tan y - \sec y) = \cos y \tan y - \cos y \sec y \quad \text{Multiplying}$$
$$= \cos y \frac{\sin y}{\cos y} - \cos y \frac{1}{\cos y} \quad \text{Simplifying}$$
$$= \sin y - 1$$

In Example 1, we used certain identities to accomplish simplification. There is no general rule for doing this, but it is often helpful to put everything in terms of sines and cosines, as we did here.

EXAMPLE 2 Factor and simplify $\sin^2 x \cos^2 x + \cos^4 x$.

$$\sin^2 x \cos^2 x + \cos^4 x = \cos^2 x(\sin^2 x + \cos^2 x) \quad \text{Factoring}$$
$$= \cos^2 x(1) \quad \text{Substituting 1 for } \sin^2 x + \cos^2 x\text{; Pythagorean identity}$$
$$= \cos^2 x$$

EXAMPLE 3 Simplify $\sin\left(\frac{\pi}{2} - x\right)(\sec x - \cos x)$.

$$\sin\left(\frac{\pi}{2} - x\right)(\sec x - \cos x) = \cos x(\sec x - \cos x) \quad \text{Using an identity for } \sin\left(\frac{\pi}{2} - x\right)$$
$$= \cos x\left(\frac{1}{\cos x} - \cos x\right) \quad \sec x \text{ is } \frac{1}{\cos x}$$
$$= \frac{\cos x}{\cos x} - \cos^2 x \quad \text{Multiplying}$$
$$= 1 - \cos^2 x \quad \text{Dividing}$$
$$= \sin^2 x \quad \text{Using an identity for } \cos^2 x$$

Try This

a. Multiply and simplify $\sin x(\cot x + \csc x)$. $\cos x + 1$

b. Factor $\sin^3\theta + \sin\theta\cos^2\theta$. $\sin\theta$

c. Simplify $\dfrac{1 - \cos^2 x}{\cos\left(\frac{\pi}{2} - x\right)}$. $\sin x$

Solving Equations

Objective: Solve equations involving trigonometric expressions.

EXAMPLE 4 Solve for tan x: $\tan^2 x + \tan x = 56$.

$$\tan^2 x + \tan x - 56 = 0 \quad \text{Rewriting as a quadratic equation}$$
$$(\tan x + 8)(\tan x - 7) = 0 \quad \text{Factoring}$$
$$\tan x + 8 = 0 \text{ or } \tan x - 7 = 0$$
$$\tan x = -8 \text{ or } \tan x = 7$$

EXAMPLE 5 Solve for sec x: $\sec^2 x - \frac{3}{4}\sec x = \frac{1}{2}$.

$$\sec^2 x - \frac{3}{4}\sec x - \frac{1}{2} = 0$$

We now use the quadratic formula, and obtain

$$\sec x = \frac{\frac{3}{4} \pm \sqrt{\frac{9}{16} - 4 \cdot 1 \cdot \left(-\frac{1}{2}\right)}}{2} = \frac{\frac{3}{4} \pm \sqrt{\frac{41}{16}}}{2} = \frac{\frac{3}{4} \pm \frac{\sqrt{41}}{4}}{2} = \frac{3 \pm \sqrt{41}}{8}$$

Since $\frac{3 - \sqrt{41}}{8} \approx -0.43$, which is not within the range of the secant function, the solution is $\frac{3 + \sqrt{41}}{8}$.

Try This

d. Solve for cot x in $\cot^2 x + \cot x = 12$. $\cot x = -4$ or $\cot x = 3$

17-8 EXERCISES

A

Multiply and simplify.

1. $(\sin x - \cos x)(\sin x + \cos x)$

2. $(\tan \theta - \cot \theta)(\tan \theta + \cot \theta)$

3. $\tan x (\cos x - \csc x)$

4. $\cot x (\sin x + \sec x)$

5. $\cos \theta \sin \theta (\sec \theta + \csc \theta)$

6. $\tan y \sin y (\cot y - \csc y)$

7. $(\sin x + \cos x)(\csc x - \sec x)$

8. $(\sin x + \cos x)(\sec x + \csc x)$

9. $(\sin y - \cos y)^2$

10. $(\sin \theta + \cos \theta)^2$

11. $(1 + \tan \theta)^2$

12. $(1 + \cot x)^2$

Factor and simplify.

13. $\sin x \cos x + \cos^2 x$ $\cos x (\sin x + \cos x)$

14. $\sec x \csc x - \csc^2 x$ $\csc x (\sec x - \csc x)$

15. $\sin^2 y - \cos^2 y$ $(\sin y - \cos y)(\sin y + \cos y)$

16. $\tan^2 y - \cot^2 y$ $(\tan y - \cot y)(\tan y + \cot y)$

Solving Equations

Remind students that $\tan^2 x = (\tan x)^2$. However, $\tan x^2 \neq (\tan x)^2$.

Chalkboard Examples

1. Solve for $\cos x$ where $\cos^2 x + 3\cos x = -2$.
   $\cos^2 x + 3\cos x + 2 = 0$
   $(\cos x + 1)(\cos x + 2) = 0$
   $\cos x = -1$ or $\cos x = -2$
   There is no x such that $\cos x = -2$, therefore $\cos x = -1$.
2. Solve for $\sin x$ where $\sin x (\sin x - 2) = -1$.
   $\sin^2 x - 2\sin x + 1 = 0$
   $(\sin x - 1)^2 = 0$
   $\sin x = 1$

LESSON QUIZ

1. Multiply and simplify. $(\sin x - \cos x)^2$
   $1 - 2\sin x \cos x$
2. Factor and simplify. $\sin^4 x + \sin^2 x \cos^2 x$
   $\sin^2 x$
3. Solve for $\cos x$ where $2\cos^2 x - 3\cos x = -1$.
   $\cos x = 1$ or $\cos x = \frac{1}{2}$

Assignment Guide

Algebra: Omit

Alg w/Trig: Day 1: 23, MR
Day 2: 24–47

Comprehensive: Day 1: 1–30, MR
Day 2: 31–51

ADDITIONAL ANSWERS

Exercises

1. $\sin^2 x - \cos^2 x$
2. $\tan^2 \theta - \cot^2 \theta$
3. $\sin x - \sec x$
4. $\cos x + \csc x$
5. $\sin \theta + \cos \theta$
6. $\sin y - \tan y$
7. $\cot x - \tan x$
8. $\tan x + \cot x + 2$
9. $1 - 2 \sin y \cos y$
10. $1 + 2 \sin \theta \cos \theta$
11. $\sec^2 \theta + 2 \tan \theta$
12. $\csc^2 x + 2 \cot x$

33. $\tan x = -7$ or $\tan x = 3$
34. $\sec \theta = 5$ or $\sec \theta = 2$
35. $\sin \theta = \frac{3}{4}$ or $\sin \theta = -\frac{1}{2}$
36. $\cos x = -\frac{1}{3}$
37. $\cot x = -10$ or $\cot x = 1$
38. $\csc \theta = -5$ or $\csc \theta = 2$
39. No solution
40. $\tan \theta = 3 \pm \sqrt{13}$
41. $\csc x = \frac{3 + \sqrt{41}}{4}$
42. $\sin x = -\frac{1}{2}$
43. $\frac{1}{\sin \theta} - \cos \theta \frac{\cos \theta}{\sin \theta} = \frac{1 - \cos^2 \theta}{\sin \theta} = \frac{\sin^2 \theta}{\sin \theta} = \sin \theta$
44. $\frac{1}{\cos \theta} - \sin \theta \frac{\sin \theta}{\cos \theta} = \frac{1 - \sin^2 \theta}{\cos \theta} = \frac{\cos^2 \theta}{\cos \theta} = \cos \theta$
45. $\frac{(1 - \sin \theta)}{\cos \theta} = \frac{(1 - \sin \theta)(1 + \sin \theta)}{\cos \theta (1 + \sin \theta)} = \frac{(1 - \sin^2 \theta)}{\cos \theta (1 + \sin \theta)} = \frac{\cos^2 \theta}{\cos \theta (1 + \sin \theta)} = \frac{\cos \theta}{1 + \sin \theta}$
46. $\frac{(1 - \cos \theta)}{\sin \theta} = \frac{(1 - \cos \theta)(1 + \cos \theta)}{\sin \theta (1 + \cos \theta)} = \frac{(1 - \cos^2 \theta)}{\sin \theta (1 + \cos \theta)} = \frac{\sin^2 \theta}{\sin \theta (1 + \cos \theta)} = \frac{\sin \theta}{1 + \cos \theta}$
47. No; $\sin\left(\frac{\pi}{2} + \frac{\pi}{2}\right) = \sin \pi = 1$
$\sin \frac{\pi}{2} + \sin \frac{\pi}{2} = 1 + 1 = 2$
48. $|\sin x \cos x|$
49. $4 - |\tan y|$
50. $\frac{\sqrt{\sin x \cos x}}{|\cos x|}$
51. $\frac{\cos x}{|1 - \sin x|}$

Mixed Review

52. $(x + 3)(x + 4)(x + 5)$
53. $(x + 2)^4$
54. $\frac{\pi}{4}$
55. $\frac{2\pi}{5}$
56. $-\frac{3\pi}{2}$
57. $\frac{7\pi}{6}$
58. $120°$
59. $315°$
60. $-150°$
61. $30°$
62. 265.8 cm^2

17. $\sin^2\left(\frac{\pi}{2} - x\right)(\sec^2 x - \tan^2 x)$ $\cos^2 x$

18. $\cot \theta - \cos(\pi - \theta)$ $\cot \theta + \cos \theta$

19. $\sin^4 \theta - \cos^4 \theta$ $\sin^2 \theta - \cos^2 \theta$

20. $\tan^4 x - \sec^4 x$ $-(\tan^2 x + \sec^2 x)$

21. $3 \cot^2 y + 6 \cot y + 3$ $3(\cot y + 1)^2$

22. $4 \sin^2 y + 8 \sin y + 4$ $4(\sin y + 1)^2$

23. $\csc^4 \theta + 4 \csc^2 \theta - 5$ $(\csc^2 \theta + 5)(\cot^2 \theta)$

24. $\tan^4 x - 2 \tan^2 x - 3$ $(\tan^2 x - 3)(\sec^2 x)$

25. $\frac{\sin^2 x \cos x}{\cos^2 x \sin x}$ $\tan x$

26. $\frac{\cos^2 x \sin x}{\sin^2 x \cos x}$ $\cot x$

27. $\frac{4 \sin \theta \cos^3 \theta}{18 \sin^2 \theta \cos \theta}$ $\frac{2}{9} \cos \theta \cot \theta$

28. $\frac{30 \sin^3 x \cos x}{6 \cos^2 x \sin x}$ $5 \tan x \sin x$

29. $\frac{\cos^2 x - 2 \cos x + 1}{\cos x - 1}$ $\cos x - 1$

30. $\frac{\sin^2 x + 2 \sin x + 1}{\sin x + 1}$ $\sin x + 1$

31. $\frac{\cos^2 x - 1}{\cos x - 1}$ $\cos x + 1$

32. $\frac{\sin^2 \theta - 1}{\sin \theta + 1}$ $\sin \theta - 1$

Solve for the indicated trigonometric expression.

33. $\tan^2 x + 4 \tan x = 21$, for $\tan x$

34. $\sec^2 \theta - 7 \sec \theta = -10$, for $\sec \theta$

35. $8 \sin^2 \theta - 2 \sin \theta = 3$, for $\sin \theta$

36. $6 \cos^2 x + 17 \cos x = -5$, for $\cos x$

37. $\cot^2 x + 9 \cot x - 10 = 0$, for $\cot x$

38. $\csc^2 \theta + 3 \csc \theta - 10 = 0$, for $\csc \theta$

39. $\sin^2 \theta + \cos\left(\theta + \frac{\pi}{2}\right) = 6$, for $\sin \theta$

40. $\tan^2 \theta - 6 \tan \theta = 4$, for $\tan \theta$

41. $2 \csc^2 x - 3 \csc x - 4 = 0$, for $\csc x$

42. $2 \cos^2\left(x - \frac{\pi}{2}\right) - 3 \cos\left(x - \frac{\pi}{2}\right) - 2 = 0$, for $\sin x$

B

Show that the following identities are true.

43. $\csc \theta - \cos \theta \cot \theta \equiv \sin \theta$

44. $\sec \theta - \sin \theta \tan \theta \equiv \cos \theta$

45. $\frac{1 - \sin \theta}{\cos \theta} \equiv \frac{\cos \theta}{1 + \sin \theta}$

46. $\frac{1 - \cos \theta}{\sin \theta} \equiv \frac{\sin \theta}{1 + \cos \theta}$

47. ***Critical Thinking*** Does $\sin(A + B) = \sin A + \sin B$? If not, give a counterexample.

Challenge

Simplify.

48. $\sqrt{\sin^2 x \cos x} \cdot \sqrt{\cos x}$

49. $(2 - \sqrt{\tan y})(\sqrt{\tan y} + 2)$

50. $\sqrt{\frac{\sin x}{\cos x}}$

51. $\sqrt{\frac{1 + \sin x}{1 - \sin x}}$

Mixed Review

Factor. **52.** $x^3 + 12x^2 + 47x + 60$ **53.** $x^4 + 8x^3 + 24x^2 + 32x + 16$

Convert to radian measure. **54.** $45°$ **55.** $72°$ **56.** $-270°$ **57.** $210°$

Convert to degree measure. **58.** $\frac{2\pi}{3}$ **59.** $\frac{7\pi}{4}$ **60.** $-\frac{5\pi}{6}$ **61.** $\frac{\pi}{6}$

62. The area of a circle varies directly as the square of the radius. A circle with radius 6.4 cm has area 128.6 cm^2. What is the area of a circle with radius 9.2 cm?

Problem Solving: Situational Problem Solving

Making a Business Plan

In the problems presented so far, the data have been given and the questions have been easily identified. In real-world situations you need to clarify the assumptions and what you are being asked to do, and collect the data from a variety of sources. You may need to solve many subproblems before arriving at the answer. These are situational problems.

Situational Problem

You have been asked to develop a rental plan for a new video store. The new store owner has invested $90,000 to lease a store and buy videotapes and furniture for the store. The store owner wants to spend an additional $300 per month for new and replacement videotapes and wants $2000 per month for personal expenses. Determine a rental plan that will allow the store owner to meet the necessary costs, be competitive, and have a return on the initial investment in about 2 years.

Possible Assumptions

1. The utilities and miscellaneous expenses for the store will cost about $600 per month after an initial $1000 fee.
2. The store owner can purchase videotapes for $15 each.
3. Additional furniture and equipment can be purchased for $3500.
4. No one else will be hired to work in the store.
5. A nearby video store, which charges $3.50 per day to rent a videotape, rents about 500 videos each weekend and 125 videos each weekday.
6. Another store, with a $40 per year membership club, rents tapes for $2.50 to members and $4.00 to nonmembers. About 40% of their customers join their club. They rent about 525 videos each weekend and 110 videos each weekday.

Possible Subproblems

1. What will the total expenses be for the first year?
2. What will the total expenses be for subsequent years?
3. How many tapes can the store owner expect to rent each month?
4. Would it be advisable to have a special video club with reduced prices for members?

Problem Solving: Situational Problem Solving

Before students begin to work the situational problem, discuss possible modifications of the Problem-Solving Guideline subsections that can apply to situational problem solving.
For example,
Phase 1:
What am I trying to find?
What assumptions need to be made?
What data will I need?
Phase 2:
What subproblems need to be solved?
What strategies will I use to solve these problems?
Phase 3:
What is the answer to the problem?
Does the answer seem reasonable?
Have I stated the answer clearly?

Large, complex problems that cannot be solved directly using mathematics can be considered situational problems. Mathematics may not be the sole basis for making decisions, although it often plays a large role. Models can be created, such as large-scale computer simulations, but mathematical results must often be tempered by intuition and new information. The possible consequences of an incorrect decision must be considered, and quickly changing conditions may render a model obsolete. Predictions for economics, weather forecasting, locating fire stations, and determining staff levels for a company are examples of inexact situational problems that must be solved.

You may want to have students work in groups of four to create a business plan. After each group has completed its plan, have them present the plan to the class, stating their reasons for each decision.

Vary the assumptions with data from local video stores. Have the students compare their rental policies with ones in the community.

ANSWERS

1. 20 cm
2. $\sin\theta = \frac{1}{2}, \cos\theta = \frac{\sqrt{3}}{2},$
   $\cot\theta = \sqrt{3}, \sec\theta = \frac{2\sqrt{3}}{3},$
   $\csc\theta = 2$ or $\sin\theta = -\frac{1}{2},$
   $\cos\theta = -\frac{\sqrt{3}}{2}, \cot\theta = \sqrt{3},$
   $\sec\theta = \frac{-2\sqrt{3}}{3}, \csc\theta = -2$
3. First
4. Third
5. Second
6. Third
7. $\sin\theta = -\frac{4}{7}, \cos\theta = \frac{\sqrt{33}}{7},$
   $\tan\theta = \frac{-4\sqrt{33}}{33}, \cot\theta = -\frac{\sqrt{33}}{4},$
   $\csc\theta = -\frac{7}{4}, \sec\theta = \frac{7\sqrt{33}}{33}$
8. 30°
9. 30°
10. 40°
11. Undefined
12. 1
13. $\frac{\sqrt{2}}{2}$

Chapter 17 Summary and Review

17-1

$$\sin\theta = \frac{\text{length of the side opposite } \theta}{\text{length of the hypotenuse}} = \frac{1}{\csc\theta}$$

$$\cos\theta = \frac{\text{length of the side adjacent } \theta}{\text{length of the hypotenuse}} = \frac{1}{\sec\theta}$$

$$\tan\theta = \frac{\text{length of the side opposite } \theta}{\text{length of the side adjacent } \theta} = \frac{1}{\cot\theta}$$

1. In triangle ABC, $\angle C$ is a right angle, $b = 10$ cm, and $m\angle A = 60°$. If sides a, b, and c are opposite angles A, B, and C respectively, what is the length of side c?
2. If $\tan\theta = \frac{\sqrt{3}}{3}$, find the other five trigonometric function values.

17-2

An angle between 0° and 90° has its **terminal side** in the first quadrant. An angle between 90° and 180° has its terminal side in the second quadrant. An angle between 0° and −90° has its terminal side in the fourth quadrant, and so on.

In which quadrant does the terminal side of each angle lie?

3. 14° **4.** 201° **5.** 116° **6.** −131°

If a right triangle has one vertex at the origin, one vertex on the positive x-axis, and one vertex at R, with coordinates (x, y), a point of the circle whose center is at the origin and whose radius r is the length of the hypotenuse, then we can define these functions.

$$\sin\theta = \frac{y\text{-coordinate}}{\text{radius}}$$

$$\cos\theta = \frac{x\text{-coordinate}}{\text{radius}}$$

$$\tan\theta = \frac{y\text{-coordinate}}{x\text{-coordinate}}$$

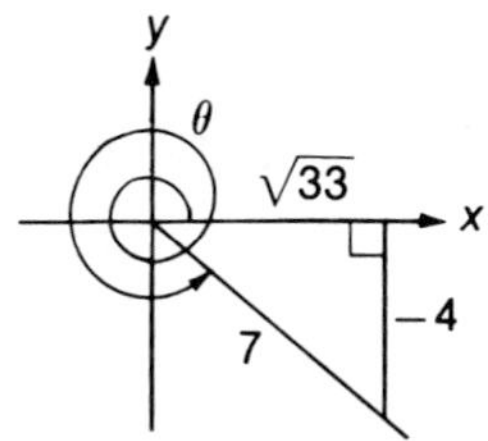

7. Find the six trigonometric function values for the angle θ shown.

The **reference angle** for a rotation is the acute angle formed by the terminal side and the x-axis.

Find the reference angles for the following angles of rotation.

8. 330° **9.** −510° **10.** 220°

If the terminal side of an angle falls on one of the axes, then in some cases trigonometric functions will not be defined because a denominator is 0. Pay special attention to angles that are multiples of 90.

Find each of the following function values, or indicate if it is undefined.

11. tan 270° **12.** tan −315° **13.** sin 495°

17-3

To convert between degrees and radians we can use the notion of multiplying by one and the equation $\frac{180 \text{ degrees}}{\pi \text{ radians}}$ radians $= 1$.

Convert to radian measure. Give answers in terms of π.

14. $45°$ **15.** $150°$ **16.** $270°$ **17.** $-60°$

Convert to degree measure.

18. $\frac{7\pi}{6}$ **19.** $-\frac{\pi}{3}$ **20.** 4π

The cofunction identities are

$$\sin\theta \equiv \cos(90 - \theta) \qquad \cos\theta \equiv \sin(90 - \theta)$$
$$\tan\theta \equiv \cot(90 - \theta) \qquad \cot\theta \equiv \tan(90 - \theta)$$
$$\sec\theta \equiv \csc(90 - \theta) \qquad \csc\theta \equiv \sec(90 - \theta)$$

Find the function value using cofunctions.

21. $\csc 45°$ **22.** $\cot 30°$ **23.** $\sin 90°$

The following equations can be helpful in problem solving.

$\theta = \frac{s}{r}$ where θ is the radian measure of a rotation and s is the distance traveled by a point at a radius r from the center of rotation

$\omega = \frac{\theta}{t}$ where ω is angular speed, θ is radian measure of a rotation, and t is time

$v = r\omega$ where v is linear speed, r is the distance from the center of rotation, and ω is the angular speed in radians per unit of time

24. A wheel has a 60-cm radius. The speed of a point on its rim is 30 cm/s. What is its angular speed?

17-4

Table 5 or a calculator may be used to find trigonometric function values.

Find the following. Interpolate, if necessary.

25. $\sin 8°20'$ **26.** $\cos 391°30'$ **27.** $\tan 27°14'$ **28.** $\sin 42°18'$

Occasionally you will have to use a table or calculator to find the measure of an angle.

Express θ in degrees and minutes, between $0°$ and $90°$.

29. $\cos\theta = 0.9094$ **30.** $\tan\theta = 1.103$

17-5

To sketch a graph of a trigonometric function, look at special angles in the first two quadrants, using radian measure for the angles.

31. Sketch a graph of the secant function.

14. $\frac{\pi}{4}$
15. $\frac{5\pi}{6}$
16. $\frac{3\pi}{2}$
17. $-\frac{\pi}{3}$
18. $210°$
19. $-60°$
20. $720°$
21. $\sqrt{2}$
22. $\sqrt{3}$
23. 1
24. $\frac{1}{2}$ radians/sec
25. 0.1449
26. 0.8526
27. 0.515
28. 0.6730
29. $24°35'$
30. $47°48'$
31.

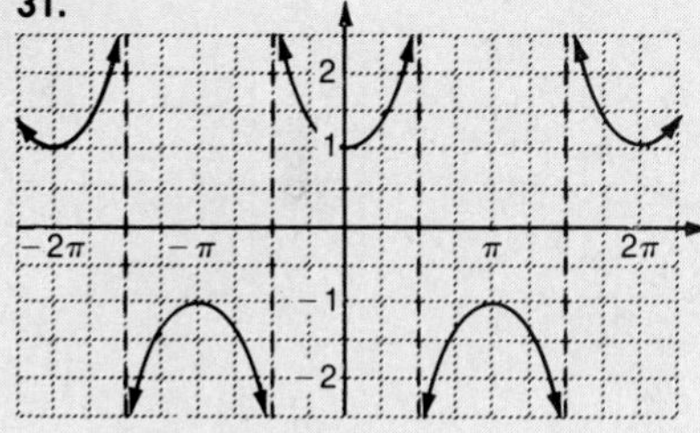

17-6

It is useful to learn certain identities.

The quotient identities

$$\tan\theta \equiv \frac{\sin\theta}{\cos\theta},\ \cos\theta \neq 0$$

$$\cot\theta \equiv \frac{\cos\theta}{\sin\theta},\ \sin\theta \neq 0$$

The Pythagorean identities

$$\sin^2\theta + \cos^2\theta \equiv 1$$
$$1 + \cot^2\theta \equiv \csc^2\theta$$
$$1 + \tan^2\theta \equiv \sec^2\theta$$

The cofunction identities

$$\sin\left(\theta + \frac{\pi}{2}\right) \equiv \cos\theta \qquad \cos\left(\theta + \frac{\pi}{2}\right) \equiv -\sin\theta$$

$$\sin\left(\theta - \frac{\pi}{2}\right) \equiv -\cos\theta \qquad \cos\left(\theta - \frac{\pi}{2}\right) \equiv \sin\theta$$

$$\sin\left(\frac{\pi}{2} - \theta\right) \equiv \cos\theta \qquad \cos\left(\frac{\pi}{2} - \theta\right) \equiv \sin\theta$$

Check each identity by using $\theta = \frac{\pi}{4}$.

32. $\tan\theta \equiv \frac{\sin\theta}{\cos\theta}$

33. $\sin\left(\frac{\pi}{2} - \theta\right) \equiv \cos\theta$

The quotient identities, Pythagorean identities, and cofunction identities given above can be used to derive other identities.

Use the Pythagorean identities to derive an identity for

34. $\cot\theta$ in terms of $\csc\theta$.

35. $\csc\theta$ in terms of $\cos\theta$.

36. Use the cofunction identities to derive an identity for $\cot\left(\theta - \frac{\pi}{2}\right)$.

Use the given function values to find the function value of each complement.

37. $\sin 75° = 0.9659$ **38.** $\cos 75° = 0.2588$ **39.** $\tan 75° = 3.732$

40. $\cot 75° = 0.2679$ **41.** $\sec 75° = 3.864$ **42.** $\csc 75° = 1.035$

17-7

Changing the constant A in $y = A\sin\theta$ causes a vertical stretching or shrinking of the graph and thus a change in the amplitude. Changing the constant B in $y = \sin B\theta$ causes a horizontal stretching or shrinking of the graph and thus a change in the period.

43. Sketch a graph of $y = 3\cos\theta$. What is the amplitude of the function?

44. Sketch a graph of $y = \sin 2\theta$. What is the period of the function?

17-8

Trigonometric expressions can be changed or simplified by using algebraic manipulations and trigonometric identities.

45. Simplify $\cos\theta(\tan\theta + \cot\theta)$.

46. Solve $3\tan^2\theta - 2\tan\theta - 2 = 0$ for $\tan\theta$.

See also Problem 17, Computer-Assisted Problem Solving, page 852.

32. $1 = \frac{\frac{\sqrt{2}}{2}}{\frac{\sqrt{2}}{2}}$

33. $\sin\left(\frac{\pi}{2} - \frac{\pi}{4}\right)$

$\sin\frac{\pi}{4} = \frac{\sqrt{2}}{2} = \cos\frac{\pi}{4}$

34. $\cot\theta \equiv \pm\sqrt{\csc^2\theta - 1}$

35. $\csc\theta \equiv \pm\sqrt{\frac{1}{1 - \cos^2\theta}}$

36. $\cot\left(\theta - \frac{\pi}{2}\right) \equiv -\tan\theta$

37. $\sin 15° = 0.2588$
38. $\cos 15° = 0.9659$
39. $\tan 15° = 0.2679$
40. $\cot 15° = 3.732$
41. $\sec 15° = 1.035$
42. $\csc 15° = 3.864$
43. 3

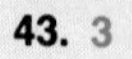

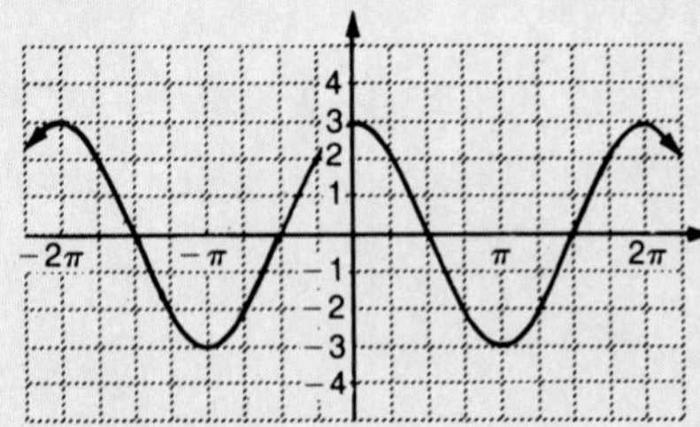

44. π

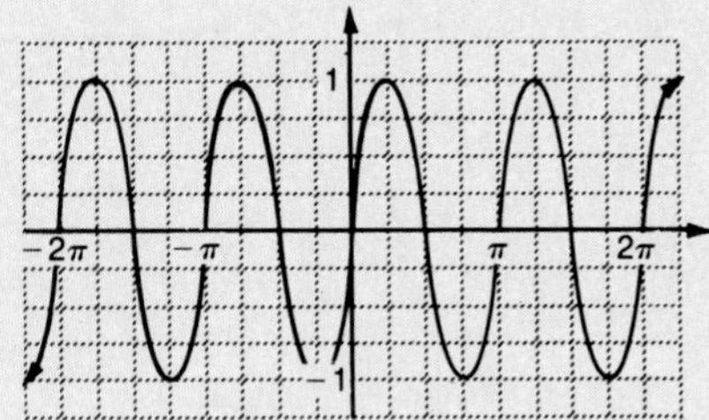

45. $\csc\theta$

46. $\frac{1 \pm \sqrt{7}}{3}$

Chapter 17 Test

1. In triangle ABC, $\angle C$ is a right angle, $b = 10$ cm, and $m\angle A = 45$. What is the length of side c?
2. If $\sin\theta = \frac{\sqrt{5}}{5}$, find the other five trigonometric function values.
3. Find the six trigonometric function values for the angle θ shown.

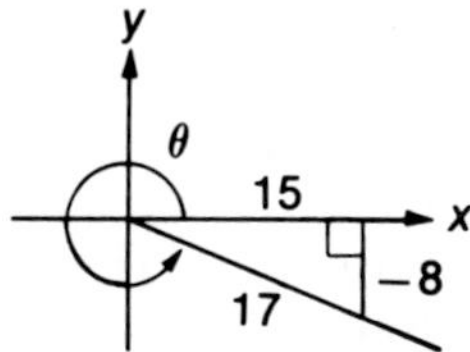

Find each of the following function values or indicate if it is undefined.

4. $\sin(-135°)$
5. $\tan 540°$
6. Convert $-225°$ to radian measure, in terms of π.
7. Convert $-\frac{3\pi}{2}$ to degree measure.
8. A wheel with a 150-cm diameter is rotating at a rate of 15 radians/sec. Find the speed of a point on its rim in cm/sec.

Use Table 5 and interpolation to find the following.

9. $\cos 32°24'$
10. $\tan 54°18'$

Find θ in degrees and minutes between 0° and 90°.

11. $\sin\theta = 0.6259$
12. $\tan\theta = 1.331$
13. Use the given function values to find the six function values of the complement of 54°.

$$\sin 54° = 0.8090, \cos 54° = 0.5878, \tan 54° = 1.376$$

14. Sketch a graph of $y = 4\sin\theta$. What is the amplitude of the function?
15. Sketch a graph of $y = \sin\frac{1}{2}\theta$. What is the period of the function?
16. Simplify $\dfrac{\csc\theta(\sin^2\theta + \cos^2\theta\tan\theta)}{\sin\theta + \cos\theta}$.
17. Solve $6\sec^2\theta - 5\sec\theta - 2 = 0$ for $\sec\theta$.

Use the Pythagorean identities to derive an identity for

18. $\sec\theta$ in terms of $\sin\theta$.

Use the cofunction identities to derive an identity for

19. $\cot\left(\frac{\pi}{2} - \theta\right)$.

Challenge

20. Solve for θ between 0° and 360°.

$$2\sin^2\theta - 3\sin\theta + 1 = 0$$

ANSWERS

1. $10\sqrt{2}$ cm
2. $\cos\theta = \frac{2\sqrt{5}}{5}$, $\tan\theta = \frac{1}{2}$, $\cot\theta = 2$, $\sec\theta = \frac{\sqrt{5}}{2}$, $\csc\theta = \sqrt{5}$
3. $\sin\theta = \frac{-8}{17}$, $\cos\theta = \frac{15}{17}$, $\tan\theta = \frac{-8}{15}$, $\cot\theta = \frac{15}{-8}$, $\sec\theta = \frac{17}{15}$, $\csc\theta = \frac{17}{-8}$
4. $-\frac{\sqrt{2}}{2}$
5. 0
6. $-\frac{5\pi}{4}$
7. $-270°$
8. 1125 cm/sec
9. 0.8444
10. 1.391
11. 38°45′
12. 53°05′
13. $\sin 36° = 0.5878$, $\cos 36° = 0.8090$, $\tan 36° = 0.7265$, $\cot 36° = 1.376$, $\sec 36° = 1.236$, $\csc 36° = 1.701$
14. Sine curve with amplitude 4 through $(-\pi, 0)$, $\left(-\frac{\pi}{2}, -4\right)$, $(0,0)$, $\left(\frac{\pi}{2}, 4\right)$, $(\pi, 0)$
15. Sine curve with period 4π through $(-2\pi, 0)$, $(-\pi, -1)$, $(0,0)$, $(\pi, 1)$, and $(2\pi, 0)$
16. 1
17. $\sec\theta = \frac{5 + \sqrt{73}}{12}$
18. $\sec\theta \equiv \pm\sqrt{\frac{1}{1 - \sin^2\theta}}$
19. $\cot\left(\frac{\pi}{2} - \theta\right) \equiv \tan\theta$
20. $\theta = 30°, 90°$, or $150°$

Test Item Analysis

Item	Lesson
1, 2	17-1
3–5	17-2
6–8	17-3
9–12	17-4
13	17-6
14, 15	17-7
16–20	17-8

CHAPTER 18 Trigonometric Identities and Equations

Chapter Overview

Chapter 18 primarily concerns identities and applications. Students are expected to solve, prove, and derive identities. Special identities covered include the sum and difference identities, double-angle and half-angle identities, and the law of sines and law of cosines. The inverse trigonometric functions are introduced and the principle values of these functions are defined. Trigonometric equations are solved for an unknown angle. Problem solving involves right triangle applications. Complex numbers are shown to be represented by trigonometric expressions. DeMoivre's theorem is presented to find powers and roots of complex numbers. Situational and application problem-solving lessons conclude the chapter material.

Objectives

18-1
- Use the sum and difference identities for cosine to simplify trigonometric expressions.
- Use the sum and difference identities for sine and tangent to simplify trigonometric expressions.

18-2
- Use the double-angle identities to find function values.
- Use the half-angle identities to find function values.

18-3
- Prove trigonometric identities.

18-4
- Find values of arcsin, arccos, and arctan.
- Find principal values of the inverses of the trigonometric functions.

18-5
- Solve simple trigonometric equations.

18-6
- Solve right triangles.
- Solve problems using right triangles.

18-7
- Use the law of sines to solve triangles, given two angles and a side opposite one of them.
- Use the law of sines to solve triangles, given two sides and an angle opposite one of them.
- Use the law of sines to find the area of a triangle.

18-8
- Solve a triangle, given two sides and an included angle.
- Use the law of cosines to solve a triangle given three sides.

18-9
- Change from rectangular notation for a complex number to trigonometric notation and vice versa.
- Use trigonometric notation to multiply and divide complex numbers.
- Use DeMoivre's theorem to find powers and roots of complex numbers.

TEACHING CHAPTER 18

Cooperative Learning Opportunities

Students as individuals must learn and be able to use the trigonometric identities contained in Chapter 18. But some find these difficult to remember and group work can help the learning process.

If you wish to use groups to drill on the identities it will be helpful to have them get together for about five minutes every day for a week or more. As you go through each lesson, have students write out the identities on index cards. They should write the left-hand side of the identity on one side of a card and the right-hand side on the other.

Have students meet in groups of three and use the following roles in rotation. Student A asks the questions by showing the index cards; Student B answers; Student C keeps score writing down the total number of questions asked and total answered correctly. After five questions, rotate roles. These scores should be kept not as grades but as an on-going self-assessment.

Multicultural Note: *Nicholas Copernicus*

Some students may think that learning and working with the details in mathematics and other subjects is not so important. They want to get to the big ideas. If this problem arises, you can take the opportunity to point out that a great new idea about the solar system came about only after years of painstaking work with the details. Such was the case of Copernicus.

Nicholas Copernicus was born in 1473 in Poland. He later studied at the University of Cracow, a renowned center of learning, particularly for mathematics and astronomy.

Copernicus worked extensively in trigonometry, which at that time was used in astronomy. His observations, measurements, and calculations eventually led him to put forward the proposition that the sun and not the earth was at the center of the solar system. Thus, a really big idea that changed everyone's thinking about the universe was supported by trigonometric details.

Alternative Assessment and Communication Ideas

Chapter 18 contains a number of trigonometric concepts that are usually tested through exercises. If a student can work out a problem on inverse functions, for example, you might assume that he or she understands the basic theory of inverses. But this understanding can also be tested in other ways. The following questions seem simple but you may find students complaining that they are difficult to answer. Try them either as test items, for homework, or as the basis of a small portfolio.

(1) What is a trigonometric identity?
(2) Of what use are trigonometric identities?
(3) What is the inverse of a function?
(4) What is the meaning of principal values in the discussion of trigonometric functions?
(5) How are principal values used?
(6) Why does a trigonometric equation have many solutions?
(7) Explain the ambiguous case with respect to the law of sines.

Investigations and Projects

Scientific calculators in general, and graphing calculators in particular, should be helpful to students not only as time savers but also as aids to understanding. Students must understand how each key stroke and each parameter affects the result. Some students catch on to the use of the calculator and computer much more quickly than others. You might ask interested students to take on the project of preparing a class presentation covering the following areas.

Use the calculator to verify identities and check equations. Students can show how identities can be verified by entering values for both sides and seeing that the same result is obtained. Grouping and operating symbols must be use with care.

Explain the parameters and range values used to graph functions and inverse functions.

As an additional project you might ask students to research and report on the law of tangents.

MANAGING CHAPTER 18

Lesson	PACING CHART (DAYS) Algebra	Algebra w/Finite	Algebra w/Trig	Compre-hensive	Opening Activity	Cooperative Activity	Seat or Group Work
18-1	0	0	2	1	First Five Minutes 18-1: **TE** p.782 or ***FFM Transparency Masters*** p.48	Critical Thinking: **SE** p.787 Strategy Problem Bank 17: ***Problem Bank*** p.18 ✂ Manipulative Activity 18: ***Enrichment*** p.59	Try This a–e
18-2	0	0	1	1	First Five Minutes 18-2: **TE** p.788 or ***FFM Transparency Masters*** p.48	Critical Thinking: **SE** p.792 Critical Thinking 18: ***Enrichment*** p.39	Try This a–e
18-3	0	0	1	1	First Five Minutes 18-3: **TE** p.793 or ***FFM Transparency Masters*** p.48	Critical Thinking: **SE** p.795	Try This a–b
18-4	0	0	2	1	First Five Minutes 18-4: **TE** p.796 or ***FFM Transparency Masters*** p.48	Critical Thinking: **SE** p.800 Looking for Errors 17: ***Enrichment*** p.78	Try This a–i
18-5	0	0	2	1	First Five Minutes 18-5: **TE** p.801 or ***FFM Transparency Masters*** p.49	Critical Thinking: **SE** p.803	Try This a–d
18-6	0	0	2	1	First Five Minutes 18-6: **TE** p.804 or ***FFM Transparency Masters*** p.49	Critical Thinking: **SE** p.809 Looking for Errors 18: ***Enrichment*** p.79	Try This a–f
18-7	0	0	1	1	First Five Minutes 18-7: **TE** p.810 or ***FFM Transparency Masters*** p.49	Critical Thinking: **SE** p.816	Try This a–g
18-8	0	0	1	1	First Five Minutes 18-8: **TE** p.817 or ***FFM Transparency Masters*** p.50	Critical Thinking: **SE** p.820	Try This a–b
18-9	0	0	3	2	First Five Minutes 18-9: **TE** p.821 or ***FFM Transparency Masters*** p.50	Problem Solving: **SE** p.827, pp.828–829 Strategy Problem Bank 18: ***Problem Bank*** p.19	Try This a–h
Review	0	0	1	1			
Test	0	0	1	1			
Cum. Review	0	0	1	1			
End-of-year Test	0	0	1	1			

FFM: First Five Minutes SPMR: Skills Practice Mixed Review

MANAGING CHAPTER 18

Enrichment	Review/Assess	Reteach	Technology	Lesson
✂ Manipulative Activity 18: ***Enrichment*** p.59	Lesson Quiz: **TE** p.785	Skills Practice 49, #1–11: ***SPMR*** p.61	Worksheet 26: ***TI-81 Activities*** pp.107–110; Worksheet 32: ***Master Grapher*** pp.127–130, pp.261–264, or pp.397–400	**18-1**
Critical Thinking 18: ***Enrichment*** p.39	Lesson Quiz: **TE** p.791	Skills Practice 49, #12–21: ***SPMR*** p.61	BASIC Computer Project 20: ***Technology*** p.100	**18-2**
TI-81 Investigation 6: **SE** pp.869–870	Lesson Quiz: **TE** p.794 Quiz 35: ***Assessment*** p.43	Skills Practice 49, #22–27: ***SPMR*** p.61	TI-81 Investigation 6: **SE** pp.869–870	**18-3**
Looking for Errors 17: ***Enrichment*** p.78	Lesson Quiz: **TE** p.798	Skills Practice 50, #1–14: ***SPMR*** p.62	Worksheet 27: ***TI-81 Activities*** pp.111–114; Worksheet 33: ***Master Grapher*** pp.131–134, pp.265–268, or pp.401–404	**18-4**
Worksheet 34: ***Master Grapher*** pp.135–137(Apple II), pp.269–271 (IBM), or pp.405–407(Mac)	Lesson Quiz: **TE** p.802	Skills Practice 50, #15–24: ***SPMR*** p.62	Worksheet 28: ***TI-81 Activities*** pp.115–117; Worksheet 34: ***Master Grapher*** pp.135–137, pp.269–271, or pp.405–407 Calculator Worksheet 38: ***Technology*** p.40	**18-5**
Looking for Errors 18: ***Enrichment*** p.79	Lesson Quiz: **TE** p.807 Mixed Review 35: ***SPMR*** p.99	Skills Practice 50, #25–31: ***SPMR*** p.62 Problem Bank 23: ***Problem Bank*** p.44	Calculator Worksheet 39: ***Technology*** p.41; Problem for Programmers: **SE** p.809	**18-6**
Connections: **SE** p.816	Lesson Quiz: **TE** p.814 Quiz 36: ***Assessment*** p.44	Skills Practice 51, #1–10: ***SPMR*** p.63		**18-7**
Writing to Learn: **SE** p.820	Lesson Quiz: **TE** p.818	Skills Practice 51, #11–16: ***SPMR*** p.63		**18-8**
Problem Solving: **SE** p.827, pp.828–829 Bonus Topic 18: ***Enrichment*** p.19	Lesson Quiz: **TE** p.824 Mixed Review 36: ***SPMR*** p.100	Skills Practice 51, #17–28: ***SPMR*** p.63	Problem 18: Computer Assisted Problem Solving, **SE** p.853	**18-9**
	Summary and Review: **SE** pp.830–832; Test: **SE** p.833			**Review**
	Chapter 18 Test: ***Assessment*** pp.149–154(reg.), pp.191–192 (adv.)			**Test**
	Cumulative Review: **SE** pp.834–837			**Cum. Review**
	End-of-year Test: ***Assessment*** pp.231–234(reg.), pp.237–244 (reg.), p.236(trig.), pp.247–248 (trig.), or pp.249–254(adv.)			**End-of-year Test**

The solution to the problem posed on the facing page can be found on page 800.

Ready for Trigonometric Identities and Equations?

7-1 Simplify.

1. $\sqrt{(-81)^2}$ 81

2. $\sqrt{(9c)^2}$ $9|c|$

7-4 Simplify by rationalizing the denominators.

3. $\dfrac{\sqrt[3]{4m}}{\sqrt[3]{5n}}$ $\dfrac{\sqrt[3]{100mn^2}}{5n}$

4. $\dfrac{5\sqrt{5} - 2\sqrt{3}}{2\sqrt{3} - 3\sqrt{5}}$ $-\dfrac{63 + 4\sqrt{15}}{33}$

7-8 Find the absolute value of each complex number.

5. $|-a + bi|$ $\sqrt{a^2 + b^2}$

6. $|5 - 12i|$ 13

12-1 Find $f^{-1}(x)$.

7. $f(x) = 3x - 2$ $f^{-1}(x) = \frac{1}{3}x + \frac{2}{3}$

8. $f(x) = 2 + \sqrt{x + 3}$ $f^{-1}(x) = x^2 - 4x + 1$

17-5 Find an identity for $\tan\theta$ in terms of each function.

9. $\sin\theta$ $\pm\sqrt{\dfrac{\sin^2\theta}{1 - \sin^2\theta}}$

10. $\cos\theta$ $\pm\dfrac{\sqrt{1 - \cos^2\theta}}{\cos\theta}$

11. $\csc\theta$ $\pm\dfrac{\sqrt{\csc^2\theta - 1}}{\csc^2\theta - 1}$

12. $\cot\theta$ $\dfrac{1}{\cot\theta}$

13. $\sec\theta$ $\pm\sqrt{\sec^2\theta - 1}$

CHAPTER 18

Trigonometric Identities and Equations

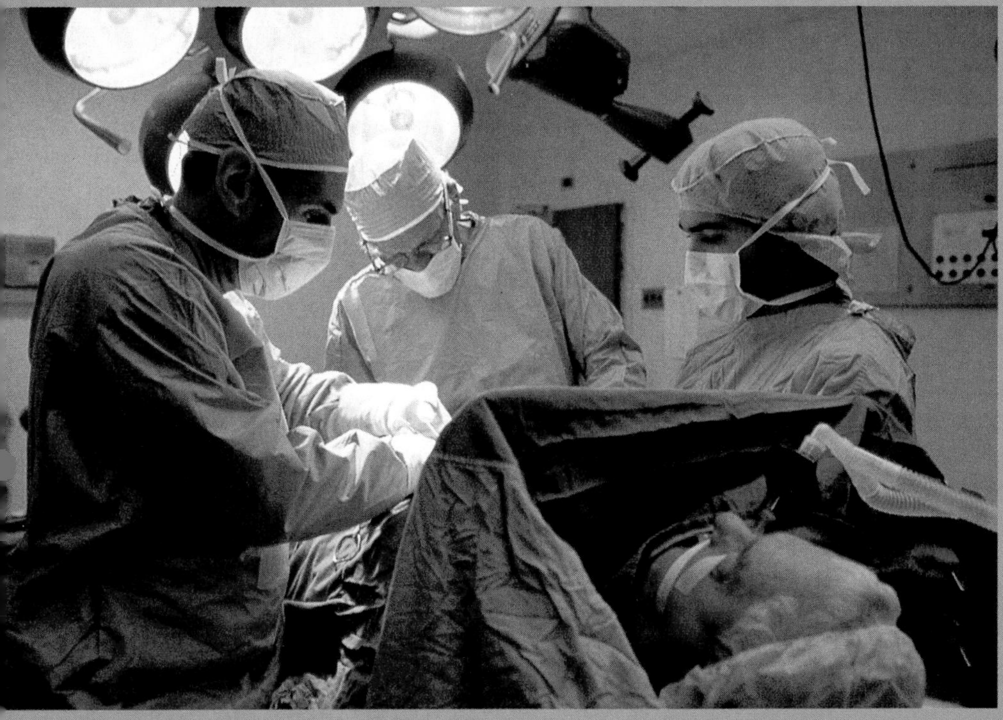

The angle to minimize friction in the flow of blood where two arteries meet is found using $\mathrm{Cos}^{-1}\left(\frac{r^4}{R^4}\right)$, *where* r *is the radius of the smaller artery and* R *is the radius of the larger artery. A heart surgeon must join arteries with radii of 4 mm and 5 mm. What angle should be formed?*

18-1

FIRST FIVE MINUTES

1. Multiply and simplify.
   $(\cos a - \sin a)^2$
   $\cos^2 a - 2\cos a \sin a + \sin^2 a$
   $= 1 - 2\cos a \sin a$
2. Write $\tan(a + b)$ in terms of sine and cosine.
   $\tan(a + b) = \frac{\sin(a + b)}{\cos(a + b)}$

Cosines of Sums or Differences

Key Questions

- What is an equivalent expression for $\cos(x - y)$?
  $\cos x \cos y + \sin x \sin y$
- What is an equivalent expression for $\cos A \cos B + \sin A \sin B$?
  $\cos (A - B)$

Chalkboard Examples

1. Write an equivalent expression and simplify $\cos\left(\frac{\pi}{2} - \frac{\pi}{3}\right)$.
   $\cos\frac{\pi}{2}\cos\frac{\pi}{3} + \sin\frac{\pi}{2}\sin\frac{\pi}{3}$
   $= (0)\left(\frac{1}{2}\right) + (1)\left(\frac{\sqrt{3}}{2}\right)$
   $= \frac{\sqrt{3}}{2}$
2. Find $\cos 75°$.
   $\cos 75° = \cos(30° + 45°)$
   $= \cos 30° \cos 45° - \sin 30° \sin 45°$
   $= \frac{\sqrt{3}}{2}\cdot\frac{\sqrt{2}}{2} - \frac{1}{2}\cdot\frac{\sqrt{2}}{2}$
   $= \frac{1}{4}(\sqrt{6} - \sqrt{2})$ or $= \frac{\sqrt{2}}{4}(\sqrt{3} - 1)$

18-1 Sum and Difference Identities

Master Grapher Worksheet 32, *Trigonometric Identities*, can be used as a lesson opener.

Cosines of Sums or Differences

Objective: Use the sum and difference identities for cosine to simplify trigonometric expressions.

We will now consider identities involving sums or differences of angles or rotations.

A basic identity shows that the cosine of the difference of two angles is related to the cosines and sines of the angles themselves. This identity can be used to simplify expressions.

$$\cos(\alpha - \beta) \equiv \cos\alpha\cos\beta + \sin\alpha\sin\beta$$

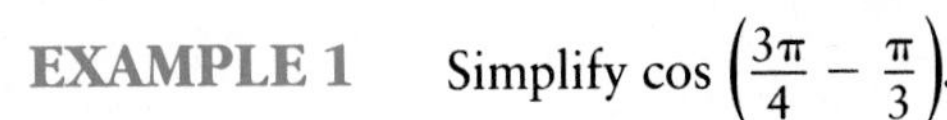

EXAMPLE 1 Simplify $\cos\left(\frac{3\pi}{4} - \frac{\pi}{3}\right)$.

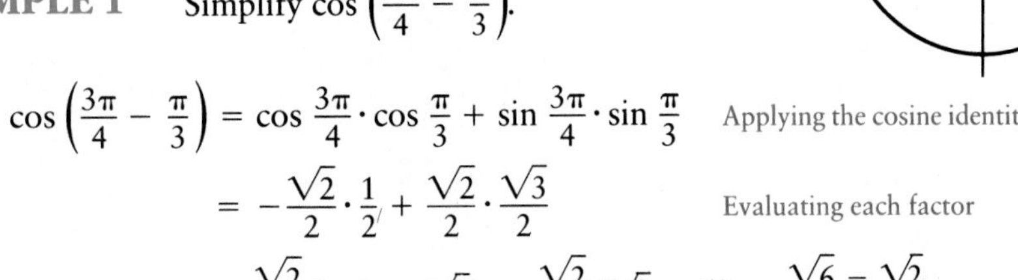

$$\cos\left(\frac{3\pi}{4} - \frac{\pi}{3}\right) = \cos\frac{3\pi}{4}\cdot\cos\frac{\pi}{3} + \sin\frac{3\pi}{4}\cdot\sin\frac{\pi}{3} \quad \text{Applying the cosine identity}$$

$$= -\frac{\sqrt{2}}{2}\cdot\frac{1}{2} + \frac{\sqrt{2}}{2}\cdot\frac{\sqrt{3}}{2} \quad \text{Evaluating each factor}$$

$$= \frac{\sqrt{2}}{4}(-1 + \sqrt{3}), \text{ or } \frac{\sqrt{2}}{4}(\sqrt{3} - 1), \text{ or } \frac{\sqrt{6} - \sqrt{2}}{4}$$

Try This

a. Simplify $\cos\left(\frac{\pi}{2} - \frac{\pi}{6}\right)$. $\frac{1}{2}$

We can use known values of the functions to find other values.

EXAMPLE 2 Find $\cos 15°$.

$$\cos 15° = \cos(45° - 30°) \quad \text{Writing 15° in terms of angles with known function values}$$

$$= \cos 45° \cos 30° + \sin 45° \sin 30°$$

$$= \frac{\sqrt{2}}{2}\cdot\frac{\sqrt{3}}{2} + \frac{\sqrt{2}}{2}\cdot\frac{1}{2}$$

$$= \frac{\sqrt{2}}{4}(\sqrt{3} + 1), \text{ or } \frac{\sqrt{6} + \sqrt{2}}{4}$$

Try This

b. Find $\cos 105°$ by evaluating $\cos(150° - 45°)$. $\frac{\sqrt{2} - \sqrt{6}}{4}$

Proof of the Cosine Identity

We have applied the identity $\cos(\alpha - \beta) \equiv \cos\alpha\cos\beta + \sin\alpha\sin\beta$. Let us see how this identity is developed.

Consider the unit circle where angles α and β have coordinates as shown.

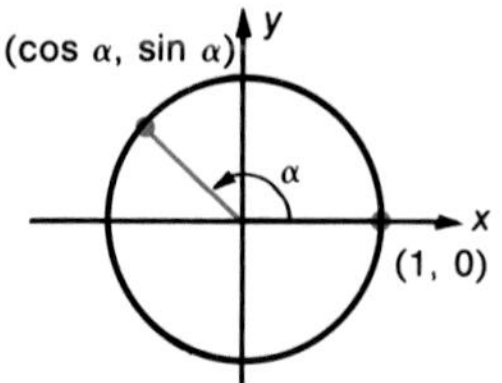

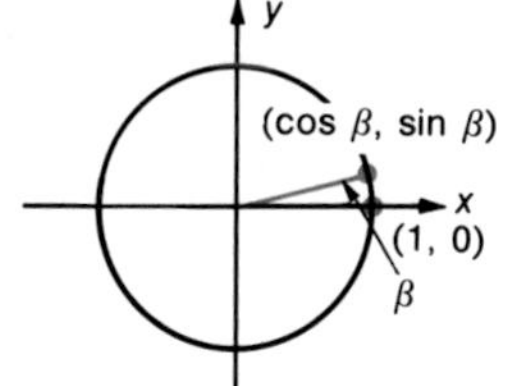

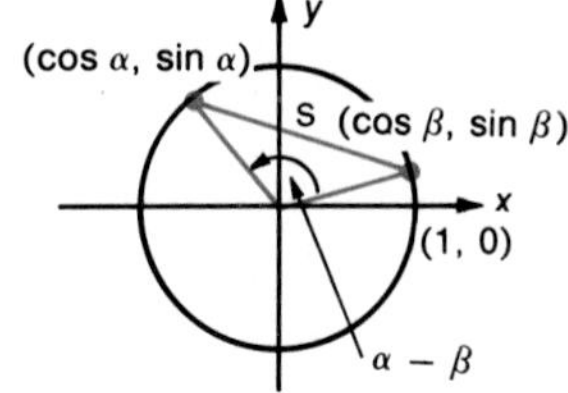

The figure on the right shows these angles on the same coordinate axes. Notice that the size of the angle between them is $\alpha - \beta$. We use the distance formula to write an expression for s, the length of the segment between $(\cos\alpha, \sin\alpha)$ and $(\cos\beta, \sin\beta)$.

$$
\begin{aligned}
s^2 &= (\cos\alpha - \cos\beta)^2 + (\sin\alpha - \sin\beta)^2 \\
&= (\cos^2\alpha - 2\cos\alpha\cos\beta + \cos^2\beta) + (\sin^2\alpha - 2\sin\alpha\sin\beta + \sin^2\beta) \\
&= (\cos^2\alpha + \sin^2\alpha) + (\cos^2\beta + \sin^2\beta) - 2\cos\alpha\cos\beta - 2\sin\alpha\cos\beta \\
&= 1 + 1 - 2\cos\alpha\cos\beta - 2\sin\alpha\sin\beta \\
&= 2 - 2(\cos\alpha\cos\beta + \sin\alpha\sin\beta)
\end{aligned}
$$

Now imagine that the unit circle above is rotated so that $(\cos\beta, \sin\beta)$ is at $(1, 0)$. The length s has not changed.

$$
\begin{aligned}
s^2 &= [\cos(\alpha - \beta) - 1]^2 + [\sin(\alpha - \beta) - 0]^2 \\
&= [\cos^2(\alpha - \beta) - 2\cos(\alpha - \beta) + 1] + \sin^2(\alpha - \beta) \\
&= [\cos^2(\alpha - \beta) + \sin^2(\alpha - \beta)] + 1 - 2\cos(\alpha - \beta) \\
&= 2 - 2\cos(\alpha - \beta)
\end{aligned}
$$

Equating our two expressions for s^2, we obtain

$$2 - 2\cos(\alpha - \beta) = 2 - 2(\cos\alpha\cos\beta + \sin\alpha\sin\beta)$$

This simplifies to the identity

$$\cos(\alpha - \beta) \equiv \cos\alpha\cos\beta + \sin\alpha\sin\beta$$

Next let us consider $\cos(\alpha + \beta)$. This is equal to $\cos[\alpha - (-\beta)]$, and by the cosine of a difference identity, we have the following.

$$\cos(\alpha + \beta) \equiv \cos\alpha\cos(-\beta) + \sin\alpha\sin(-\beta)$$

But $\cos(-\beta) \equiv \cos\beta$ and $\sin(-\beta) \equiv -\sin\beta$, so the identity we seek is the following.

$$\cos(\alpha + \beta) \equiv \cos\alpha\cos\beta - \sin\alpha\sin\beta$$

Other Identities

After deriving the identity for the sine of a sum, have students derive the identity for the sine of a difference. Remind them that $\cos(-x) = \cos x$ and that $\sin(-x) = -\sin x$. Therefore,

$\sin(\alpha + (-\beta))$
$= \sin\alpha\cos(-\beta) + \cos\alpha\sin(-\beta)$
$= \sin\alpha\cos\beta + \cos\alpha(-\sin\beta)$
$= \sin\alpha\cos\beta - \cos\alpha\sin\beta$

Chalkboard Examples

1. Simplify $\sin\left(\frac{\pi}{2} + \frac{\pi}{6}\right)$.

$\sin\frac{\pi}{2}\cos\frac{\pi}{6} + \cos\frac{\pi}{2}\sin\frac{\pi}{6}$
$= 1\cdot\frac{\sqrt{3}}{2} + 0\cdot\frac{1}{2}$
$= \frac{\sqrt{3}}{2}$

2. Find tan 75°.

$\tan(45° + 30°)$
$= \frac{\tan 45° + \tan 30°}{1 - \tan 45° \tan 30°}$
$= \frac{1 + \frac{\sqrt{3}}{3}}{1 - 1\cdot\frac{\sqrt{3}}{3}}$
$= \frac{3 + \sqrt{3}}{3 - \sqrt{3}}$
$= \frac{12 + 6\sqrt{3}}{6}$
$= 2 + \sqrt{3}$

EXAMPLE 3 Find cos 105°.

$$\begin{aligned}\cos 105° &= \cos(60° + 45°)\\ &= \cos 60°\cos 45° - \sin 60°\sin 45°\\ &= \frac{1}{2}\cdot\frac{\sqrt{2}}{2} - \frac{\sqrt{3}}{2}\cdot\frac{\sqrt{2}}{2}\\ &= \frac{\sqrt{2} - \sqrt{6}}{4}\end{aligned}$$

Writing 105° in terms of angles with known function values

Try This

c. Find cos 75° by evaluating cos (30° + 45°). $\frac{\sqrt{6} - \sqrt{2}}{4}$

Other Identities

Objective: Use sum and difference identities for sin and tan to simplify trigonometric expressions.

To develop an identity for the sine of a sum $\alpha + \beta$, we recall the following.

$$\sin\theta \equiv \cos\left(\frac{\pi}{2} - \theta\right)$$

In this identity we shall substitute $\alpha + \beta$ for θ.

$$\sin(\alpha + \beta) \equiv \cos\left[\frac{\pi}{2} - (\alpha + \beta)\right]$$

We can now use the identity for the cosine of a difference.

$$\begin{aligned}\sin(\alpha + \beta) &\equiv \cos\left[\frac{\pi}{2} - (\alpha + \beta)\right]\\ &\equiv \cos\left[\left(\frac{\pi}{2} - \alpha\right) - \beta\right]\\ &\equiv \cos\left(\frac{\pi}{2} - \alpha\right)\cos\beta + \sin\left(\frac{\pi}{2} - \alpha\right)\sin\beta\\ &\equiv \sin\alpha\cos\beta + \cos\alpha\sin\beta\end{aligned}$$

Thus, $\sin(\alpha + \beta) \equiv \sin\alpha\cos\beta + \cos\alpha\sin\beta$.

EXAMPLE 4 Simplify $\sin\left(\frac{5\pi}{4} + \frac{\pi}{3}\right)$.

$$\begin{aligned}\sin\left(\frac{5\pi}{4} + \frac{\pi}{3}\right) &= \sin\frac{5\pi}{4}\cos\frac{\pi}{3} + \cos\frac{5\pi}{4}\sin\frac{\pi}{3}\\ &= -\frac{\sqrt{2}}{2}\cdot\frac{1}{2} + \left(-\frac{\sqrt{2}}{2}\right)\frac{\sqrt{3}}{2}\\ &= \frac{-\sqrt{2}}{4} - \frac{\sqrt{6}}{4}\\ &= \frac{-\sqrt{2} - \sqrt{6}}{4}\end{aligned}$$

Try This

d. Simplify $\sin\left(\frac{\pi}{4} + \frac{\pi}{3}\right)$. $\frac{\sqrt{2} + \sqrt{6}}{4}$

To find an identity for the sine of a difference, we can use the identity just derived, substituting $-\beta$ for β.

$$\sin(\alpha - \beta) \equiv \sin \alpha \cos \beta - \cos \alpha \sin \beta$$

An identity for the tangent of a sum can be derived as follows, using identities already established.

$$\tan(\alpha + \beta) \equiv \frac{\sin(\alpha + \beta)}{\cos(\alpha + \beta)}$$

$$\equiv \frac{\sin \alpha \cos \beta + \cos \alpha \sin \beta}{\cos \alpha \cos \beta - \sin \alpha \sin \beta} \cdot \frac{\frac{1}{\cos \alpha \cos \beta}}{\frac{1}{\cos \alpha \cos \beta}}$$

$$\equiv \frac{\frac{\sin \alpha \cos \beta}{\cos \alpha \cos \beta} + \frac{\cos \alpha \sin \beta}{\cos \alpha \cos \beta}}{\frac{\cos \alpha \cos \beta}{\cos \alpha \cos \beta} - \frac{\sin \alpha \sin \beta}{\cos \alpha \cos \beta}}$$

$$\equiv \frac{\frac{\sin \alpha}{\cos \alpha} + \frac{\sin \beta}{\cos \beta}}{1 - \frac{\sin \alpha \sin \beta}{\cos \alpha \cos \beta}}$$

$$\tan(\alpha + \beta) \equiv \frac{\tan \alpha + \tan \beta}{1 - \tan \alpha \tan \beta}$$

Similarly, an identity for the tangent of a difference can be established. The following theorem summarizes the sum and difference formulas. These should be memorized.

Theorem 18-1

$$\cos(\alpha - \beta) \equiv \cos \alpha \cos \beta + \sin \alpha \sin \beta$$

$$\cos(\alpha + \beta) \equiv \cos \alpha \cos \beta - \sin \alpha \sin \beta$$

$$\sin(\alpha - \beta) \equiv \sin \alpha \cos \beta - \cos \alpha \sin \beta$$

$$\sin(\alpha + \beta) \equiv \sin \alpha \cos \beta + \cos \alpha \sin \beta$$

$$\tan(\alpha - \beta) \equiv \frac{\tan \alpha - \tan \beta}{1 + \tan \alpha \tan \beta}$$

$$\tan(\alpha + \beta) \equiv \frac{\tan \alpha + \tan \beta}{1 - \tan \alpha \tan \beta}$$

The identities involving sines and tangents can be used in the same way as those involving cosines in the earlier examples. Simply write the angle as a sum or difference of angles with known function values.

LESSON QUIZ

1. Write an equivalent expression for $\cos(x - y)$.
   $\cos x \cos y + \sin x \sin y$
2. Simplify $\sin(45° + 30°)$.
   $\frac{1}{4}(\sqrt{6} + \sqrt{2})$, or $\frac{\sqrt{2}}{4}(\sqrt{3} + 1)$

Assignment Guide
Algebra: Omit

Alg w/Trig: Day 1: 1–32 e/o, MR
Day 2: 33–54 e/o, 55

Comprehensive: 1–54 m3, 55, 56–61 e/o, MR

ANSWERS

Exercises

1. $\cos A \cos B + \sin A \sin B$
2. $\cos A \cos B - \sin A \sin B$
3. $\frac{\sqrt{2}+\sqrt{6}}{4}$ 4. $\frac{\sqrt{6}-\sqrt{2}}{4}$
5. $\frac{\sqrt{2}-\sqrt{6}}{4}$ 6. $\frac{\sqrt{2}+\sqrt{6}}{4}$
7. $-\frac{\sqrt{3}}{2}$ 8. $-\frac{\sqrt{3}}{2}$
9. $\frac{-\sqrt{2}-\sqrt{6}}{4}$ 10. $\frac{-\sqrt{2}-\sqrt{6}}{4}$
11. $-\frac{\sqrt{2}}{2}$ 12. $-\frac{\sqrt{2}}{2}$
13. $\sin P \cos Q + \cos P \sin Q$
14. $\sin P \cos Q - \cos P \sin Q$
15. $\frac{\tan P - \tan Q}{1 + \tan P \tan Q}$
16. $\frac{\tan P + \tan Q}{1 - \tan P \tan Q}$
17. $\frac{\sqrt{2}+\sqrt{6}}{4}$ 18. $\frac{\sqrt{6}-\sqrt{2}}{4}$
19. $2-\sqrt{3}$ 20. $-2-\sqrt{3}$
21. $\frac{\sqrt{6}-\sqrt{2}}{4}$ 22. $\frac{\sqrt{2}+\sqrt{6}}{4}$
23. $2+\sqrt{3}$ 24. $2-\sqrt{3}$
25. $\frac{\sqrt{6}-\sqrt{2}}{4}$ 26. $\frac{\sqrt{2}+\sqrt{6}}{4}$
27. $\frac{\sqrt{2}}{2}$ 28. $\frac{1}{2}$
29. $2+\sqrt{3}$ 30. $-2-\sqrt{3}$
31. $2-\sqrt{3}$ 32. -1
33. $\cos 3\pi = -1$
34. $\cos \frac{7\pi}{12} = \frac{-\sqrt{6}+\sqrt{2}}{4}$
35. $\cos (A - B)$
36. $\cos (A + B)$

EXAMPLE 5 Find tan 15°.

$$\tan 15° = \tan (45° - 30°)$$
$$= \frac{\tan 45° - \tan 30°}{1 + \tan 45° \tan 30°}$$
$$= \frac{1 - \frac{\sqrt{3}}{3}}{1 + \frac{\sqrt{3}}{3}} = \frac{3 - \sqrt{3}}{3 + \sqrt{3}} = 2 - \sqrt{3}$$

Try This

e. Find tan 105° by evaluating tan (45° + 60°). $-2-\sqrt{3}$

18-1 EXERCISES

A

Use the cosine sum and difference identities to simplify the following.

1. $\cos (A - B)$ **2.** $\cos (A + B)$ **3.** $\cos (45° - 30°)$
4. $\cos (45° + 30°)$ **5.** $\cos (60° + 45°)$ **6.** $\cos (60° - 45°)$
7. $\cos \left(\frac{\pi}{2} + \frac{\pi}{3}\right)$ **8.** $\cos \left(\frac{3\pi}{2} - \frac{\pi}{3}\right)$

Use the cosine sum and difference identities to find the following.

9. cos 165° **10.** cos 195° **11.** cos 225° **12.** cos 135°

Use sine and tangent sum and difference identities to simplify the following.

13. $\sin (P + Q)$ **14.** $\sin (P - Q)$ **15.** $\tan (P - Q)$ **16.** $\tan (P + Q)$
17. $\sin (60° + 45°)$ **18.** $\sin (60° - 45°)$ **19.** $\tan (60° - 45°)$ **20.** $\tan (60° + 45°)$
21. $\sin \left(\frac{\pi}{4} - \frac{\pi}{6}\right)$ **22.** $\sin \left(\frac{\pi}{4} + \frac{\pi}{6}\right)$ **23.** $\tan \left(\frac{\pi}{4} + \frac{\pi}{6}\right)$ **24.** $\tan \left(\frac{\pi}{4} - \frac{\pi}{6}\right)$

Use sum and difference formulas to find the following.

25. sin 15° **26.** sin 105° **27.** sin 135° **28.** sin 150°
29. tan 75° **30.** tan 105° **31.** tan 15° **32.** tan 135°

B

Use the cosine, sine, and tangent sum and difference identities to simplify each of the following.

33. $\sin \left(-\frac{5\pi}{2}\right) \cdot \sin \frac{\pi}{2} + \cos \frac{\pi}{2} \cdot \cos \left(-\frac{5\pi}{2}\right)$

34. $\sin \frac{\pi}{3} \cdot \sin \left(-\frac{\pi}{4}\right) + \cos \left(-\frac{\pi}{4}\right) \cdot \cos \frac{\pi}{3}$

35. $\cos A \cos B + \sin A \sin B$ **36.** $\cos A \cos B - \sin A \sin B$

37. $\cos(\alpha + \beta) + \cos(\alpha - \beta)$

38. $\cos(\alpha + \beta) - \cos(\alpha - \beta)$

39. $\dfrac{\tan A - \tan B}{1 + \tan A \tan B}$

40. $\dfrac{\tan A + \tan B}{1 - \tan A \tan B}$

41. $\dfrac{\tan 20° + \tan 32°}{1 - \tan 20° \tan 32°}$

42. $\dfrac{\tan 35° - \tan 12°}{1 + \tan 35° \tan 12°}$

43. $\sin(\alpha + \beta) + \sin(\alpha - \beta)$

44. $\sin(\alpha + \beta) - \sin(\alpha - \beta)$

45. $\sin \frac{\pi}{3} \cdot \cos \pi + \sin \pi \cdot \cos \frac{\pi}{3}$

46. $\sin \frac{\pi}{2} \cdot \cos \frac{\pi}{3} - \sin \frac{\pi}{3} \cdot \cos \frac{\pi}{2}$

47. Derive an identity for $\cot(\alpha + \beta)$ in terms of $\cot \alpha$ and $\cot \beta$.

48. Derive an identity for $\cot(\alpha - \beta)$ in terms of $\cot \alpha$ and $\cot \beta$.

The cofunction identities can be derived from the sum and difference formulas. Derive the following cofunction identities.

49. $\sin\left(\frac{\pi}{2} - x\right)$ 50. $\sin\left(x - \frac{\pi}{2}\right)$ 51. $\cos\left(\frac{\pi}{2} - x\right)$ 52. $\cos\left(x + \frac{\pi}{2}\right)$

53. Find $\sin 45° + \sin 30°$ and compare with $\sin 75°$. (Use Table 3.)

54. Find $\cos 45° - \cos 30°$ and compare with $\cos 15°$. (Use Table 3.)

55. ***Critical Thinking*** Find identities for $\sin 2\theta$, $\cos 2\theta$, and $\tan 2\theta$. (Hint: Think of 2θ as a sum.)

Challenge

Given that $\sin \theta = 0.6249$ and $\cos \phi = 0.1102$, and that θ and ϕ are both first-quadrant angles, use a calculator to find the following.

56. $\sin(\theta + \phi)$ 57. $\cos(\theta + \phi)$ 58. $\tan(\theta + \phi)$

Use the idea of *composition of functions* to find a formula for each of the following. You may use the following substitutions.

$u = \sin x$ and $v = \sin y$

59. $\sin(\sin x + \sin y)$ 60. $\cos(\cos x + \cos y)$ 61. $\sin(x + y + z)$

Mixed Review

Simplify. 62. $\dfrac{2}{q^2 - 1} - \dfrac{1}{q^2 - q}$ 63. $\dfrac{1 - m}{1 - m^{-1}}$

64. $\dfrac{\dfrac{4}{x - 5} + \dfrac{2}{x + 2}}{\dfrac{-3x}{x^2 - 3x - 10} + \dfrac{3}{x - 5}}$ 65. $\sqrt{\dfrac{2}{3}} + \sqrt{\dfrac{3}{2}}$ 66. $\sqrt[3]{9}\,\sqrt[6]{9}$

Evaluate. 67. sin 20.4167 68. cos 36.8699 69. log 6.95 70. tan 80.5

Solve. 71. $v^{\frac{2}{5}} = 9$ 72. $x^{\frac{2}{3}} - x^{\frac{1}{3}} - 12 = 0$

73. The distance s that an object falls when dropped from some point above the ground varies directly as the square of the time t it falls. If the object falls 19.6 meters in 2 seconds, how far will the object fall in 15 seconds?

37. $2 \cos \alpha \cos \beta$
38. $-2 \sin \alpha \sin \beta$
39. $\tan(A - B)$
40. $\tan(A + B)$
41. $\tan 52° = 1.280$
42. $\tan 23° = 0.425$
43. $2 \sin \alpha \cos \beta$
44. $2 \sin \beta \cos \alpha$
45. $-\frac{\sqrt{3}}{2}$
46. $\frac{1}{2}$
47. $\dfrac{\cot \alpha \cot \beta - 1}{\cot \beta + \cot \alpha}$
48. $\dfrac{\cot \alpha \cot \beta + 1}{\cot \beta - \cot \alpha}$
49. $\sin \frac{\pi}{2} \cos x - \cos \frac{\pi}{2} \sin x$
$= 1 \cdot \cos x - 0 \cdot \sin x = \cos x$
50. $-\cos x$
51. $\cos \frac{\pi}{2} \cos x + \sin \frac{\pi}{2} \sin x$
$= 0 + \sin x = \sin x$
52. $-\sin x$
53. 1.2071; 0.9659
54. −0.1589; 0.9659
55. $\cos 2\theta = \cos\theta\cos\theta - \sin\theta\sin\theta$
$= \cos^2\theta - \sin^2\theta$
$\sin 2\theta = \sin\theta\cos\theta + \cos\theta\sin\theta$
$= 2\sin\theta\cos\theta$
$\tan 2\theta = \dfrac{\tan\theta + \tan\theta}{1 - \tan\theta\tan\theta} = \dfrac{2\tan\theta}{1 - \tan^2\theta}$
56. 0.8448
57. −0.5351
58. −1.5789
59. sin (sin x) cos (sin y)
+ cos (sin x) sin (sin y)
60. cos (cos x) cos (cos y)
− sin (cos x) sin (cos y)
61. sin x cos y cos z
+ cos x sin y cos z
+ cos x cos y sin z
− sin x sin y sin z

Mixed Review

62. $\dfrac{1}{q(q + 1)}$
63. $-m$
64. $x - \frac{1}{3}$
65. $\frac{5\sqrt{6}}{6}$
66. 3
67. 0.3488
68. 0.8
69. 0.8420
70. 5.9758
71. 243
72. −27, 64
73. 1102.5 m

18-2

FIRST FIVE MINUTES

1. Write an equivalent expression for $\sin(x + x)$ in terms of $\sin x$ and $\cos x$.
   $\sin x \cos x + \cos x \sin x$
   $= 2 \sin x \cos x$
2. Simplify $\cos 135°$.
   $\cos(90° + 45°)$
   $= \cos 90° \cos 45° - \sin 90° \sin 45°$
   $= 0 \cdot \frac{\sqrt{2}}{2} - 1 \cdot \frac{\sqrt{2}}{2}$
   $= -\frac{\sqrt{2}}{2}$

Double-Angle Identities

Point out that the double-angle identities are special cases of the sum identities.

Emphasize that all of the identities in Theorem 18-2 are derived from the sum identities for sine and cosine.

Key Questions

What is an equivalent expression involving both sine and cosine for

- $\sin 4x$?
  $2\sin 2x \cos 2x$
- $\sin A$?
  $2\sin\frac{A}{2}\cos\frac{A}{2}$
- $\cos 6ab$?
  $\cos^2 3ab - \sin^2 3ab$
- $\cos B$?
  $\cos^2\frac{B}{2} - \sin^2\frac{B}{2}$

Chalkboard Examples

1. If $\sin\theta = \frac{8}{10}$ and θ is in the first quadrant, what is $\sin 2\theta$?
   $\sin 2\theta = 2\sin\theta\cos\theta$
   $= 2\sin\theta\sqrt{1 - \sin^2\theta}$
   $= 2 \cdot \frac{8}{10} \cdot \sqrt{1 - \frac{64}{100}}$
   $= 2 \cdot \frac{8}{10} \cdot \frac{6}{10}$
   $= \frac{96}{100} = \frac{24}{25}$

18-2 Double-Angle and Half-Angle Identities

Two important classes of trigonometric identities are known as the double-angle identities and the half-angle identities.

Double-Angle Identities

Objective: Use the double-angle identities to find function values.

Identities involving $\sin 2\theta$ or $\cos 2\theta$ are called double-angle identities. To develop these identities we shall use the sum identities from the preceding lesson.

We first develop an identity for $\sin 2\theta$. We shall consider an angle θ and substitute it for both α and β in the identity for $\sin(\alpha + \beta)$.

$$\begin{aligned} \sin 2\theta &\equiv \sin(\theta + \theta) \\ &\equiv \sin\theta\cos\theta + \cos\theta\sin\theta \\ &\equiv \sin\theta\cos\theta + \sin\theta\cos\theta \quad \text{Using the commutative property} \\ &\equiv 2\sin\theta\cos\theta \end{aligned}$$

Thus we have the following identity.

$$\boldsymbol{\sin 2\theta \equiv 2\sin\theta\cos\theta}$$

EXAMPLE 1 If $\sin\theta = \frac{3}{8}$ and θ is in the first quadrant, what is $\sin 2\theta$?

From the diagram, we see that $\cos\theta = \frac{\sqrt{55}}{8}$.

$$\begin{aligned} \sin 2\theta &\equiv 2\sin\theta\cos\theta \\ &= 2 \cdot \frac{3}{8} \cdot \frac{\sqrt{55}}{8} \\ &= \frac{3\sqrt{55}}{32} \end{aligned}$$

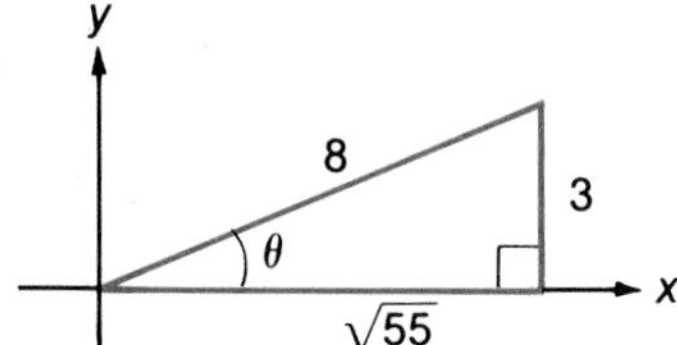

Try This

a. If $\sin\theta = \frac{3}{5}$ and θ is in the first quadrant, what is $\sin 2\theta$? $\frac{24}{25}$

Double-angle identities for the cosine and tangent functions can be derived in much the same way as the identity above.

$$\begin{aligned} \cos 2\theta &\equiv \cos(\theta + \theta) \\ &\equiv \cos\theta\cos\theta - \sin\theta\sin\theta \\ &\equiv \cos^2\theta - \sin^2\theta \end{aligned}$$

Thus we have the following identity.

$$\cos 2\theta \equiv \cos^2 \theta - \sin^2 \theta$$

By using the same kind of substitution, we can derive the double-angle identity for the tangent function.

$$\tan 2\theta \equiv \frac{2 \tan \theta}{1 - \tan^2 \theta}$$

EXAMPLE 2 Given that $\tan \theta = -\frac{3}{4}$ and θ is in the second quadrant, find $\sin 2\theta$, $\cos 2\theta$, $\tan 2\theta$, and the quadrant in which 2θ lies.

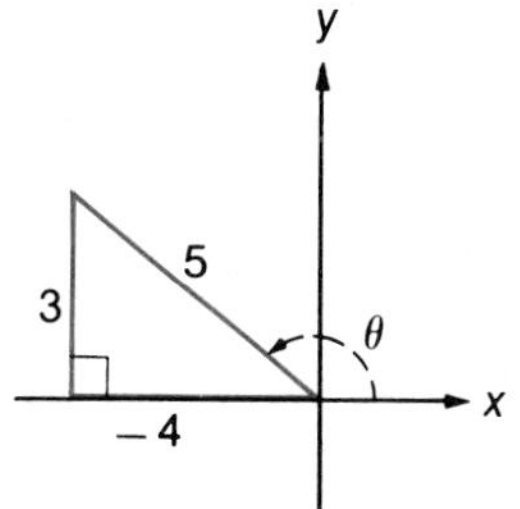

By drawing a diagram as shown, we find that $\sin \theta = \frac{3}{5}$ and $\cos \theta = -\frac{4}{5}$.

$$\sin 2\theta = 2 \sin \theta \cos \theta = 2 \cdot \frac{3}{5} \cdot \left(-\frac{4}{5}\right) = -\frac{24}{25}$$

$$\cos 2\theta = \cos^2 \theta - \sin^2 \theta = \left(-\frac{4}{5}\right)^2 - \left(\frac{3}{5}\right)^2 = \frac{16}{25} - \frac{9}{25} = \frac{7}{25}$$

$$\tan 2\theta = \frac{2 \tan \theta}{1 - \tan^2 \theta} = \frac{2 \cdot \left(-\frac{3}{4}\right)}{1 - \left(-\frac{3}{4}\right)^2} = \frac{-\frac{3}{2}}{1 - \frac{9}{16}} = \frac{-\frac{24}{16}}{\frac{7}{16}} = -\frac{24}{7}$$

Since $\sin 2\theta$ is negative and $\cos 2\theta$ is positive, we know that 2θ is in quadrant IV. Note that $\tan 2\theta$ could have been found more easily in this case by dividing the values of $\sin 2\theta$ and $\cos 2\theta$; that is, $-\frac{24}{25} \div \frac{7}{25} = -\frac{24}{7}$.

Try This

$\sin 2\theta = \frac{120}{169}$, $\cos 2\theta = -\frac{119}{169}$, $\tan 2\theta = -\frac{120}{119}$, second quadrant

b. Given that $\cos \theta = -\frac{5}{13}$ with θ in the third quadrant, find $\sin 2\theta$, $\cos 2\theta$, and $\tan 2\theta$. Also, determine the quadrant in which 2θ lies.

Two other useful identities for $\cos 2\theta$ can easily be derived as follows.

$$\begin{aligned} \cos 2\theta &\equiv \cos^2 \theta - \sin^2 \theta \\ &\equiv (1 - \sin^2 \theta) - \sin^2 \theta && \text{Using } \cos^2 \theta = 1 - \sin^2 \theta \\ &\equiv 1 - 2 \sin^2 \theta \end{aligned}$$

$$\begin{aligned} \cos 2\theta &\equiv \cos^2 \theta - \sin^2 \theta \\ &\equiv \cos^2 \theta - (1 - \cos^2 \theta) && \text{Using } \sin^2 \theta = 1 - \cos^2 \theta \\ &\equiv 2 \cos^2 \theta - 1 \end{aligned}$$

Solving these two identities for $\sin^2 \theta$ and $\cos^2 \theta$, respectively, we obtain two more identities, which are often useful. The following theorem summarizes the double-angle identities and three important derivations. They should be memorized.

2. Given that $\tan \theta = 3$ and θ is in the first quadrant, find $\tan 2\theta$.

$$\tan 2\theta = \frac{2 \tan \theta}{1 - \tan^2 \theta} = \frac{6}{1 - 9} = -\frac{6}{8} = -\frac{3}{4}$$

3. Find a formula for $\sin 4\theta$.

$\sin (2 \cdot 2\theta)$
$= 2\sin 2\theta \cos 2\theta$
$= 2(2\sin \theta \cos \theta)(1 - 2\sin^2 \theta)$
$= 4(\sin \theta \cos \theta)(1 - 2\sin^2 \theta)$
or
$= 4\sin \theta \cos \theta - 8\sin^3 \theta \cos \theta$

Half-Angle Identities

Note the following equivalencies, which you may wish students to verify.

$$\frac{\sqrt{6}+\sqrt{2}}{4}=\frac{\sqrt{2+\sqrt{3}}}{2}$$

$$\frac{\sqrt{6}-\sqrt{2}}{4}=\frac{\sqrt{2-\sqrt{3}}}{2}$$

Answers using different identities may result in either form of an expression. For example, on page 782, we found $\cos 15° = \frac{\sqrt{6}+\sqrt{2}}{4}$. Using the half-angle formula, we obtain the equivalent form in Chalkboard Example 1 below.

Chalkboard Example

1. Find cos 15°.

$$\cos\left(\frac{30}{2}\right)^{\circ} = \pm\sqrt{\frac{1+\cos 30°}{2}}$$

$$= \pm\sqrt{\frac{1+\frac{\sqrt{3}}{2}}{2}}$$

$$= \frac{\sqrt{2+\sqrt{3}}}{2}$$

Theorem 18-2

$$\sin 2\theta \equiv 2\sin\theta\cos\theta \qquad \sin^2\theta \equiv \frac{1-\cos 2\theta}{2}$$

$$\cos 2\theta \equiv \cos^2\theta - \sin^2\theta$$

$$\cos 2\theta \equiv 1 - 2\sin^2\theta \qquad \cos^2\theta \equiv \frac{1+\cos 2\theta}{2}$$

$$\cos 2\theta \equiv 2\cos^2\theta - 1$$

$$\tan 2\theta \equiv \frac{2\tan\theta}{1-\tan^2\theta} \qquad \tan^2\theta \equiv \frac{1-\cos 2\theta}{1+\cos 2\theta}$$

From the basic identities listed in Theorems 18-1 and 18-2, others can be obtained.

EXAMPLE 3 Find a formula for $\sin 3\theta$ in terms of function values of θ.

$$\begin{aligned}\sin 3\theta &\equiv \sin(2\theta+\theta)\\ &\equiv \sin 2\theta\cos\theta + \cos 2\theta\sin\theta\\ &\equiv (2\sin\theta\cos\theta)\cos\theta + (2\cos^2\theta - 1)\sin\theta\\ &\equiv 2\sin\theta\cos^2\theta + 2\sin\theta\cos^2\theta - \sin\theta\\ &\equiv 4\sin\theta\cos^2\theta - \sin\theta\end{aligned}$$

Try This Answers may vary.

c. Find a formula for $\cos 3\theta$ in terms of function values of θ.
$\cos^3\theta - 3\sin^2\theta\cos\theta$ or $\cos\theta - 4\sin^2\theta\cos\theta$ or $2\cos^3\theta - \cos\theta - 2\sin^2\theta\cos\theta$

Half-Angle Identities

Objective: Use the half-angle identities to find function values.

To develop these identities, we use previously developed ones. Consider the following identity.

$$\sin^2\theta \equiv \frac{1-\cos 2\theta}{2}$$

Note that the right side of this identity is in terms of 2θ. Letting $2\theta = \phi$ we have $\theta = \frac{\phi}{2}$. Taking the square roots gives the following.

$$\left|\sin\frac{\phi}{2}\right| \equiv \sqrt{\frac{1-\cos\phi}{2}}$$

Similarly for cosine and tangent, by taking square roots and replacing θ by $\frac{\phi}{2}$ we derive the following.

$$\left|\cos\frac{\phi}{2}\right| \equiv \sqrt{\frac{1+\cos\phi}{2}} \qquad \left|\tan\frac{\phi}{2}\right| \equiv \sqrt{\frac{1-\cos\phi}{1+\cos\phi}}$$

We can eliminate the absolute value signs by introducing ± signs with the understanding that we use + or − depending on the quadrant in which the angle lies. We thus obtain the formulas summarized in the following theorem.

Theorem 18-3

$$\sin \frac{\phi}{2} \equiv \pm \sqrt{\frac{1 - \cos \phi}{2}} \qquad \cos \frac{\phi}{2} \equiv \pm \sqrt{\frac{1 + \cos \phi}{2}} \qquad \tan \frac{\phi}{2} \equiv \pm \sqrt{\frac{1 - \cos \phi}{1 + \cos \phi}}$$

EXAMPLE 4 Use Theorem 18-3 to find sin 15°.

$$\begin{aligned} \sin 15° &= \sin \frac{30°}{2} \\ &= \pm \sqrt{\frac{1 - \cos 30°}{2}} \\ &= \pm \sqrt{\frac{1 - \left(\frac{\sqrt{3}}{2}\right)}{2}} \\ &= \pm \sqrt{\frac{2 - \sqrt{3}}{4}} = \frac{\sqrt{2 - \sqrt{3}}}{2} \end{aligned}$$

The expression is positive, because 15° is in the first quadrant.

Two other formulas for $\tan \frac{\phi}{2}$ can be obtained. These formulas give the correct sign of $\tan \left(\frac{\phi}{2}\right)$ directly.

Theorem 18-4

$$\tan \frac{\phi}{2} \equiv \frac{\sin \phi}{1 + \cos \phi} \qquad \tan \frac{\phi}{2} \equiv \frac{1 - \cos \phi}{\sin \phi}$$

EXAMPLE 5 Use Theorem 18-4 to find tan 15°.

$$\begin{aligned} \tan 15° &= \tan \frac{30°}{2} \\ &= \frac{1 - \cos 30°}{\sin 30°} \\ &= \frac{1 - \left(\frac{\sqrt{3}}{2}\right)}{\frac{1}{2}} \\ &= \frac{\frac{2}{2} - \frac{\sqrt{3}}{2}}{\frac{1}{2}} = 2 - \sqrt{3} \end{aligned}$$

Try This

d. Use Theorem 18-3 to find cos 15°. $\frac{\sqrt{2 + \sqrt{3}}}{2}$ **e.** Use Theorem 18-4 to find tan 45°. 1

LESSON QUIZ

1. Find cos 2θ, given that $\cos \theta = \frac{1}{3}$.

   $\cos 2\theta = -\frac{7}{9}$

2. Find sin 22.5°.

   $\sin 22.5° = \frac{\sqrt{2 - \sqrt{2}}}{2}$

Assignment Guide
Algebra: Omit

Alg w/Trig: 1–26 e/o, 27, MR

Comprehensive: 1–26 e/o, 27, 28–30 e/o, MR

ADDITIONAL ANSWERS

Exercises

1. $\frac{24}{25}, -\frac{7}{25}, -\frac{24}{7}$, II
2. $\frac{120}{169}, \frac{119}{169}, \frac{120}{119}$, I
3. $\frac{24}{25}, \frac{7}{25}, \frac{24}{7}$, I
4. $\frac{24}{25}, -\frac{7}{25}, -\frac{24}{7}$, II
5. $\frac{24}{25}, -\frac{7}{25}, -\frac{24}{7}$, II
6. $\frac{24}{25}, \frac{7}{25}, \frac{24}{7}$, I

27. $8 \sin\theta\cos^3\theta - 4\sin\theta\cos\theta$, or $4\sin\theta\cos^3\theta - 4\sin^3\theta\cos\theta$, or $4\sin\theta\cos\theta - 8\sin^3\theta\cos\theta$; $\cos^4\theta - 6\cos^2\theta\sin^2\theta + \sin^4\theta$, or $8\cos^4\theta - 8\cos^2\theta + 1$, or $1 - 8\sin^2\theta\cos^2\theta$
28. $\frac{1}{8}(3 - 4\cos 2\theta + \cos 4\theta)$
29. $\frac{1}{8}(3 + 4\cos 2\theta + \cos 4\theta)$
30. Using Theorem 18-1

$$\tan(\theta + \theta) = \frac{\tan\theta + \tan\theta}{1 - \tan\theta\tan\theta} = \frac{2\tan\theta}{1 - \tan^2\theta}$$

Mixed Review

31. $f^{-1}(x) = \sqrt{x^3 - 1}$
32. $f^{-1}(x) = 4^x$
33. $f^{-1}(x) = \ln x$
34. $f^{-1}(x) = \frac{1}{2}x + 3$
35.

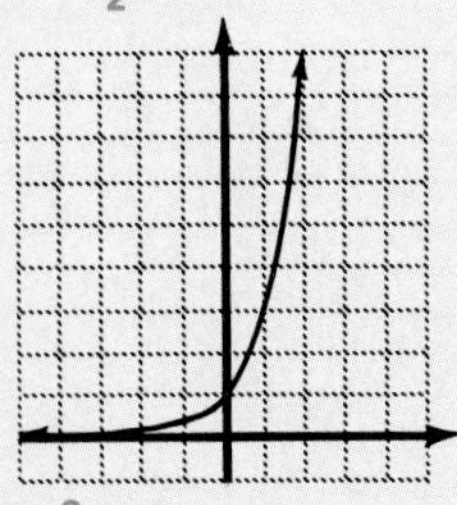

36. 6 cm, 8 cm

18-2 EXERCISES

A

Find $\sin 2\theta$, $\cos 2\theta$, $\tan 2\theta$, and the quadrant in which 2θ lies.

1. $\sin\theta = \frac{4}{5}$ (θ in quadrant I)
2. $\sin\theta = \frac{5}{13}$ (θ in quadrant I)
3. $\cos\theta = -\frac{4}{5}$ (θ in quadrant III)
4. $\cos\theta = -\frac{3}{5}$ (θ in quadrant III)
5. $\tan\theta = \frac{4}{3}$ (θ in quadrant III)
6. $\tan\theta = \frac{3}{4}$ (θ in quadrant III)

Use Theorem 18-3 and Theorem 18-4 to find the following.

7. $\sin 75°$ $\frac{\sqrt{2+\sqrt{3}}}{2}$
8. $\cos 75°$ $\frac{\sqrt{2-\sqrt{3}}}{2}$
9. $\tan 75°$ $2 + \sqrt{3}$
10. $\tan 67.5°$ $\sqrt{2} + 1$
11. $\sin\frac{5\pi}{8}$ $\frac{\sqrt{2+\sqrt{2}}}{2}$
12. $\cos\frac{5\pi}{8}$ $-\frac{\sqrt{2-\sqrt{2}}}{2}$
13. $\sin\frac{3\pi}{8}$ $\frac{\sqrt{2+\sqrt{2}}}{2}$
14. $\cos\frac{3\pi}{8}$ $\frac{\sqrt{2-\sqrt{2}}}{2}$
15. $\tan\frac{\pi}{8}$ $\sqrt{2} - 1$

B

Simplify.

16. $1 - 2\sin^2\frac{x}{2}$ $\cos x$
17. $2\cos^2\frac{x}{2} - 1$ $\cos x$
18. $2\sin\frac{x}{2}\cos\frac{x}{2}$ $\sin x$
19. $2\sin 2x\cos 2x$ $\sin 4x$
20. $\cos^2\frac{x}{2} - \sin^2\frac{x}{2}$ $\cos x$
21. $2\sin^2\frac{x}{2} + \cos x$ 1
22. $\cos^4 x - \sin^4 x$ $\cos 2x$
23. $(\sin x + \cos x)^2 - \sin 2x$ 1
24. $(\sin x - \cos x)^2 + \sin 2x$ 1
25. $2\sin x\cos^3 x + 2\sin^3 x\cos x$ $\sin 2x$
26. $2\sin x\cos^3 x - 2\sin^3 x\cos x$ $\sin 2x\cos 2x$
27. ***Critical Thinking*** Find formulas for $\sin 4\theta$ and $\cos 4\theta$ in terms of function values of θ.

Challenge

Find a formula for

28. $\sin^4\theta$ in terms of function values of θ or 2θ or 4θ, raised only to the first power.
29. $\cos^4\theta$ in terms of function values of θ or 2θ or 4θ, raised only to the first power.
30. Derive the formula for $\tan 2\theta$ given in Theorem 18-2.

Mixed Review

Find an equation for $f^{-1}(x)$. **31.** $f(x) = \sqrt[3]{x^2 + 1}$ **32.** $f(x) = \log_4 x$
33. $f(x) = e^x$ **34.** $f(x) = 2x - 6$
35. Graph the equation $f(x) = 3^x$.
36. The hypotenuse of a right triangle is 10 cm long. One leg is 2 cm less than the other. Find the lengths of the legs.

18-3 Proving Identities

Objective: Prove trigonometric identities.

TI-81 Investigation 6 (page 869) can be used with this lesson.

Following is a minimal list of identities that should be memorized. Most formulas involving secants, cosecants, and cotangents can be easily derived because these functions are reciprocals of the sine, cosine, and tangent.

Basic Identities

$$\sin(-x) \equiv -\sin x$$
$$\cos(-x) \equiv \cos x$$
$$\tan(-x) \equiv -\tan x$$

Pythagorean Identities

$$\sin^2 x + \cos^2 x \equiv 1$$
$$1 + \tan^2 x \equiv \sec^2 x$$
$$1 + \cot^2 x \equiv \csc^2 x$$

Cofunction Identities

$$\sin\left(x \pm \frac{\pi}{2}\right) \equiv \pm \cos x$$
$$\cos\left(x \pm \frac{\pi}{2}\right) \equiv \mp \sin x$$

Sum and Difference Identities

$$\sin(\alpha \pm \beta) \equiv \sin\alpha\cos\beta \pm \cos\alpha\sin\beta$$
$$\cos(\alpha \pm \beta) \equiv \cos\alpha\cos\beta \mp \sin\alpha\sin\beta$$
$$\tan(\alpha \pm \beta) \equiv \frac{\tan\alpha \pm \tan\beta}{1 \mp \tan\alpha\tan\beta}$$

Double-angle Identities

$$\sin 2x \equiv 2\sin x\cos x$$
$$\cos 2x \equiv \cos^2 x - \sin^2 x$$
$$\equiv 1 - 2\sin^2 x \equiv 2\cos^2 x - 1$$
$$\tan 2x \equiv \frac{2\tan x}{1 - \tan^2 x}$$
$$\sin^2 x \equiv \frac{1 - \cos 2x}{2}$$
$$\cos^2 x \equiv \frac{1 + \cos 2x}{2}$$

Half-angle Identities

$$\sin\frac{x}{2} \equiv \pm\sqrt{\frac{1 - \cos x}{2}}$$
$$\cos\frac{x}{2} \equiv \pm\sqrt{\frac{1 + \cos x}{2}}$$
$$\tan\frac{x}{2} \equiv \pm\sqrt{\frac{1 - \cos x}{1 + \cos x}}$$
$$\equiv \frac{\sin x}{1 + \cos x} \equiv \frac{1 - \cos x}{\sin x}$$

EXAMPLE 1 Prove the following identity.

$$\tan^2 x - \sin^2 x \equiv \sin^2 x \tan^2 x$$

$\tan^2 x - \sin^2 x$	$\sin^2 x \tan^2 x$	
$\frac{\sin^2 x}{\cos^2 x} - \sin^2 x$	$\sin^2 x \frac{\sin^2 x}{\cos^2 x}$	Writing each side in terms of sin x and cos x
$\frac{\sin^2 x - \sin^2 x\cos^2 x}{\cos^2 x}$		Finding common denominators and subtracting
$\frac{\sin^2 x(1 - \cos^2 x)}{\cos^2 x}$		
$\frac{\sin^2 x(\sin^2 x)}{\cos^2 x}$		
$\sin^2 x \frac{\sin^2 x}{\cos^2 x}$		

Therefore, $\tan^2 x - \sin^2 x \equiv \sin^2 x \tan^2 x$.

18-3

FIRST FIVE MINUTES

1. Write $\cos(a + b)$ in terms of the sine and cosine of a and b.
   $\cos a \cos b - \sin a \sin b$
2. Write $\cos 2\theta$ in terms of the cosine of θ.
   $\cos 2\theta = 2\cos^2\theta - 1$
3. Write $\cos\frac{\theta}{2}$ in terms of the cosine of θ.
   $\pm\sqrt{\frac{1 + \cos\theta}{2}}$

As a general rule for proving identities, first rewrite both sides in terms of sine and cosine. Then use double-angle and half-angle identities to obtain an expression with single-angle arguments.

Key Questions

The circle below has radius 1. What are the indicated sides for

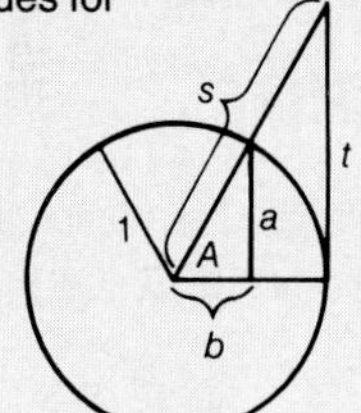

- $a = ?$ $\sin A$
- $b = ?$ $\cos A$
- $t = ?$ $t = \tan A$
- $s = ?$ $s = \sec A$
- $a^2 + b^2 = ?$ 1

Chalkboard Example

1. Prove the identity
   $\sec^2 x - \cos^2 x \equiv \tan^2 x + \sin^2 x$.

$\sec^2 x - \cos^2 x$	$\tan^2 x + \sin^2 x$
$\frac{1}{\cos^2 x} - \cos^2 x\left(\frac{\cos^2 x}{\cos^2 x}\right)$	$\tan^2 x + \sin^2 x$
$\frac{1}{\cos^2 x} - \frac{\cos^4 x}{\cos^2 x}$	
$\frac{1 - \cos^4 x}{\cos^2 x}$	
$\frac{(1 - \cos^2 x)(1 + \cos^2 x)}{\cos^2 x}$	
$\frac{(\sin^2 x)(1 + \cos^2 x)}{\cos^2 x}$	
$\frac{\sin^2 x + \sin^2 x\cos^2 x}{\cos^2 x}$	
$\frac{\sin^2 x}{\cos^2 x} + \frac{\sin^2 x\cos^2 x}{\cos^2 x}$	
$\tan^2 x + \sin^2 x$	

LESSON QUIZ

Prove the identities.

1. $(\cos x - \sin x)^2 \equiv 1 - \sin 2x$

$$\begin{array}{l|l} \multicolumn{2}{c}{(\cos x - \sin x)^2 \equiv 1 - \sin 2x} \\ \hline \cos^2 x - 2\cos x \sin x + \sin^2 x & 1 - \sin 2x \\ (\cos^2 x + \sin^2 x) - 2\sin x \cos x & \\ 1 - \sin 2x & \end{array}$$

2. $\cos^4 x - \sin^4 x \equiv \cos 2x$

$$\begin{array}{l|l} \multicolumn{2}{c}{\cos^4 x - \sin^4 x \equiv \cos 2x} \\ \hline (\cos^2 x - \sin^2 x)(\cos^2 x + \sin^2 x) & \cos 2x \\ (\cos 2x)(1) & \\ \cos 2x & \end{array}$$

Assignment Guide

Algebra: Omit

Alg w/Trig: 1–28 e/o, 29, MR

Comprehensive: 1–28 e/o, 29, 30–33 e/o, MR

ADDITIONAL ANSWERS

Try This

a.

$$\begin{array}{l|l} \multicolumn{2}{c}{\cot^2 x - \cos^2 x \equiv \cos^2 x \cot^2 x} \\ \hline \frac{\cos^2 x}{\sin^2 x} - \cos^2 x & \cos^2 x \frac{\cos^2 x}{\sin^2 x} \\ \frac{\cos^2 x - \cos^2 x \sin^2 x}{\sin^2 x} & \\ \frac{\cos^2 x (1 - \sin^2 x)}{\sin^2 x} & \\ \frac{\cos^2 x \cos^2 x}{\sin^2 x} & \end{array}$$

b.

$$\begin{array}{l|l} \multicolumn{2}{c}{\frac{\sin 2\theta + \sin \theta}{\cos 2\theta + \cos \theta + 1} \equiv \tan \theta} \\ \hline \frac{2 \sin \theta \cos \theta + \sin \theta}{2\cos^2 \theta + \cos \theta} & \frac{\sin \theta}{\cos \theta} \\ \frac{\sin \theta (2 \cos \theta + 1)}{\cos \theta (2 \cos \theta + 1)} & \\ \frac{\sin \theta}{\cos \theta} & \end{array}$$

Exercises

1.

$$\begin{array}{l|l} \multicolumn{2}{c}{\csc x - \cos x \cot x \equiv \sin x} \\ \hline \frac{1}{\sin x} - \cos x \frac{\cos x}{\sin x} & \sin x \\ \frac{1 - \cos^2 x}{\sin x} & \\ \frac{\sin^2 x}{\sin x} & \\ \sin x & \end{array}$$

Try This Prove the following identity. See Additional Answers.

a. $\cot^2 x - \cos^2 x \equiv \cos^2 x \cot^2 x$

The next identity shows the use of double-angle formulas.

EXAMPLE 2 Prove the following identity.

$$\begin{array}{r|l} \multicolumn{2}{c}{\frac{\sin 2\theta}{\sin \theta} - \frac{\cos 2\theta}{\cos \theta} \equiv \sec \theta} \\ \hline \frac{2 \sin \theta \cos \theta}{\sin \theta} - \frac{\cos^2 \theta - \sin^2 \theta}{\cos \theta} & \frac{1}{\cos \theta} \\ \frac{2 \cos^2 \theta - \cos^2 \theta + \sin^2 \theta}{\cos \theta} & \\ \frac{\cos^2 \theta + \sin^2 \theta}{\cos \theta} & \\ \frac{1}{\cos \theta} & \end{array}$$

Therefore, $\frac{\sin 2\theta}{\sin \theta} - \frac{\cos 2\theta}{\cos \theta} \equiv \sec \theta$.

Try This Prove the following identity. See Additional Answers.

b. $\frac{\sin 2\theta + \sin \theta}{\cos 2\theta + \cos \theta + 1} \equiv \tan \theta$

18-3 EXERCISES

A

Prove these identities.

1. $\csc x - \cos x \cot x \equiv \sin x$
2. $\sec x - \sin x \tan x \equiv \cos x$
3. $\frac{1 + \cos \theta}{\sin \theta} + \frac{\sin \theta}{\cos \theta} \equiv \frac{\cos \theta + 1}{\sin \theta \cos \theta}$
4. $\frac{1}{\sin \theta \cos \theta} - \frac{\cos \theta}{\sin \theta} \equiv \frac{\sin \theta \cos \theta}{1 - \sin^2 \theta}$
5. $\frac{1 - \sin x}{\cos x} \equiv \frac{\cos x}{1 + \sin x}$
6. $\frac{1 - \cos x}{\sin x} \equiv \frac{\sin x}{1 + \cos x}$
7. $\frac{1 + \tan \theta}{1 + \cot \theta} \equiv \frac{\sec \theta}{\csc \theta}$
8. $\frac{\cot \theta - 1}{1 - \tan \theta} \equiv \frac{\csc \theta}{\sec \theta}$
9. $\frac{\sin x + \cos x}{\sec x + \csc x} \equiv \frac{\sin x}{\sec x}$
10. $\frac{\sin x - \cos x}{\sec x - \csc x} \equiv \frac{\cos x}{\csc x}$
11. $\frac{1 + \tan \theta}{1 - \tan \theta} + \frac{1 + \cot \theta}{1 - \cot \theta} \equiv 0$
12. $\frac{\cos^2 \theta + \cot \theta}{\cos^2 \theta - \cot \theta} \equiv \frac{\cos^2 \theta \tan \theta + 1}{\cos^2 \theta \tan \theta - 1}$
13. $\frac{1 + \cos 2\theta}{\sin 2\theta} \equiv \cot \theta$
14. $\frac{2 \tan \theta}{1 + \tan^2 \theta} \equiv \sin 2\theta$

15. $\sec 2\theta \equiv \dfrac{\sec^2\theta}{2 - \sec^2\theta}$

16. $\cot 2\theta \equiv \dfrac{\cot^2\theta - 1}{2\cot\theta}$

B

17. $\dfrac{\sin(\alpha+\beta)}{\cos\alpha\cos\beta} \equiv \tan\alpha + \tan\beta$

18. $\dfrac{\cos(\alpha-\beta)}{\cos\alpha\sin\beta} \equiv \tan\alpha + \cot\beta$

19. $\dfrac{\tan\theta + \sin\theta}{2\tan\theta} \equiv \cos^2\dfrac{\theta}{2}$

20. $\dfrac{\tan\theta - \sin\theta}{2\tan\theta} \equiv \sin^2\dfrac{\theta}{2}$

21. $\cos^4 x - \sin^4 x \equiv \cos 2x$

22. $\dfrac{\cos^4 x - \sin^4 x}{1 - \tan^4 x} \equiv \cos^4 x$

23. $\dfrac{\tan 3\theta - \tan\theta}{1 + \tan 3\theta\tan\theta} \equiv \dfrac{2\tan\theta}{1 - \tan^2\theta}$

24. $\left(\dfrac{1+\tan\theta}{1-\tan\theta}\right)^2 \equiv \dfrac{1+\sin 2\theta}{1-\sin 2\theta}$

25. $\sin(\alpha+\beta)\sin(\alpha-\beta) \equiv \sin^2\alpha - \sin^2\beta$

26. $\cos(\alpha+\beta)\cos(\alpha-\beta) \equiv \cos^2\alpha - \sin^2\beta$

27. $\cos(\alpha+\beta) + \cos(\alpha-\beta) \equiv 2\cos\alpha\cos\beta$

28. $\sin(\alpha+\beta) + \sin(\alpha-\beta) \equiv 2\sin\alpha\cos\beta$

29. ***Critical Thinking*** Create a trigonometric identity. (Hint: Start with a simple trigonometric expression and work backward.)

Challenge

30. Show that $\log(\cos x - \sin x) + \log(\cos x + \sin x) \equiv \log(\cos 2x)$.

31. The equation $\sin\theta = \dfrac{I_1\cos\phi}{\sqrt{(I_1\cos\phi)^2 + (I_2\sin\phi)^2}}$ occurs in the study of mechanics.

    It can happen that $I_1 = I_2$. Assuming that this happens, simplify the equation.

32. The equation $R = \dfrac{1}{\omega C(\tan\theta + \tan\phi)}$ occurs in the theory of alternating current.

    Show that this equation is equivalent to $R = \dfrac{\cos\theta\cos\phi}{\omega C\sin(\theta+\phi)}$.

33. In electrical theory the following equations occur.

$$E_1 = \sqrt{2}E_t\cos\left(\theta + \frac{\pi}{P}\right), \qquad E_2 = \sqrt{2}E_t\cos\left(\theta - \frac{\pi}{P}\right)$$

Show that $\dfrac{E_1 + E_2}{2} = \sqrt{2}E_t\cos\theta\cos\dfrac{\pi}{P}$ and $\dfrac{E_1 - E_2}{2} = -\sqrt{2}E_t\sin\theta\sin\dfrac{\pi}{P}$.

Mixed Review

Sketch the graph of each equation. 34. $y = 2\sin(-2x)$

35. $y = -4\cos\left(\frac{1}{2}x\right)$ 36. $y = -6\sin\left(\frac{1}{3}x\right)$

Solve. 37. $\log_8 x = \frac{2}{3}$ 38. $x^4 = 1$

39. A ladder 25 ft long leans against a wall. The bottom of the ladder is 15 ft from the wall. How much would the lower end of the ladder have to be pulled away so that the top of the ladder would be pulled down the same distance?

---

2. $\sec x - \sin x\tan x \equiv \cos x$

$\frac{1}{\cos x} - \sin x\frac{\sin x}{\cos x}$	$\cos x$
$\frac{1-\sin^2 x}{\cos x}$	
$\frac{\cos^2 x}{\cos x}$	
$\cos x$	

3. $\frac{1+\cos\theta}{\sin\theta} + \frac{\sin\theta}{\cos\theta} \equiv \frac{\cos\theta+1}{\sin\theta\cos\theta}$

$\frac{1+\cos\theta}{\sin\theta}\cdot\frac{\cos\theta}{\cos\theta} + \frac{\sin\theta}{\cos\theta}\cdot\frac{\sin\theta}{\sin\theta}$	$\frac{\cos\theta+1}{\sin\theta\cos\theta}$
$\frac{\cos\theta + \cos^2\theta + \sin^2\theta}{\sin\theta\cos\theta}$	
$\frac{\cos\theta+1}{\sin\theta\cos\theta}$	

4. $\frac{1}{\sin\theta\cos\theta} - \frac{\cos\theta}{\sin\theta} \equiv \frac{\sin\theta\cos\theta}{1-\sin^2\theta}$

$\frac{1}{\sin\theta\cos\theta} - \frac{\cos\theta}{\sin\theta}\cdot\frac{\cos\theta}{\cos\theta}$	$\frac{\sin\theta\cos\theta}{\cos^2\theta}$
$\frac{1-\cos^2\theta}{\sin\theta\cos\theta}$	$\frac{\sin\theta}{\cos\theta}$
$\frac{\sin^2\theta}{\sin\theta\cos\theta}$	
$\frac{\sin\theta}{\cos\theta}$	

5. $\frac{1-\sin x}{\cos x} \equiv \frac{\cos x}{1+\sin x}$

$\frac{1-\sin x}{\cos x}\cdot\frac{\cos x}{\cos x}$	$\frac{\cos x}{1+\sin x}\cdot\frac{1-\sin x}{1-\sin x}$
$\frac{\cos x - \sin x\cos x}{\cos^2 x}$	$\frac{\cos x - \cos x\sin x}{1-\sin^2 x}$
	$\frac{\cos x - \sin x\cos x}{\cos^2 x}$

6. $\frac{1-\cos x}{\sin x} \equiv \frac{\sin x}{1+\cos x}$

$\frac{1-\cos x}{\sin x}\cdot\frac{\sin x}{\sin x}$	$\frac{\sin x}{1+\cos x}\cdot\frac{1-\cos x}{1-\cos x}$
$\frac{\sin x - \cos x\sin x}{\sin^2 x}$	$\frac{\sin x - \sin x\cos x}{1-\cos^2 x}$
	$\frac{\sin x - \cos x\sin x}{\sin^2 x}$

For Exercises 7–33, see Teacher's Answer Section.

Mixed Review

For graphs of Exercises 34–36, see Teacher's Answer Section.

37. 4
38. $\pm 1, \pm i$
39. 5 ft

18-4

FIRST FIVE MINUTES

Prove the identity.

1. $\sin(x + y) + \sin(x - y) \equiv 2\sin x \cos y$

$\sin(x + y) + \sin(x - y) \equiv 2\sin x \cos y$	
$\sin x \cos y + \cos x \sin y$	$2\sin x \cos y$
$+ \sin x \cos y - \cos x \sin y$	
$2\sin x \cos y$	

Finding Inverse Values

Point out that the tables for sine, cosine, and tangent are also the tables for inverse functions. The table gives the angle that corresponds to the function value.

The prefix "arc" is used because arcsin x is the length of the arc corresponding to the central angle for which the sine is x.

Point out that the graphs of trigonometric inverses serve as a check.

Key Questions

- If $\sin x = y$, what is arcsin y?
  arcsin $y = x$
- What is $\cos^{-1} 1$?
  0, or any integer multiple of 2π
- What is $\tan^{-1} 0$?
  0, or any integer multiple of π
- What is $\sec^{-1}\left(\frac{1}{2}\right)$?
  Does not exist since $\sec x = \frac{1}{\cos x}$, and $\cos x$ cannot be 2

Chalkboard Examples (*T29*)

1. Sketch the graph of $\sin^{-1} x$. Is the relation a function?
   The relation is not a function.

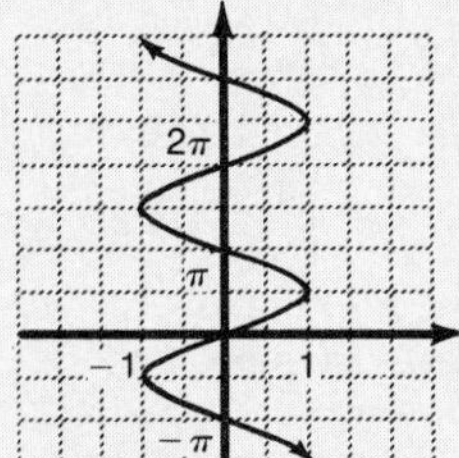

2. Find all the values of arccos 0.
   From the graph of $y = \cos x$, or from the unit circle, we can see that y is 0 when $x = \frac{\pi}{2} + k\pi$.
   Hence, $\arccos 0 = \frac{\pi}{2} + k\pi$.

18-4 Inverses of the Trigonometric Functions

Master Grapher Worksheet 33, *Trigonometric Inverses*, can be used for lesson closure.

Finding Inverse Values

Objective: Find values of arcsin, arccos, and arctan.

To obtain the inverse of any relation, we interchange the first and second members of each ordered pair in the relation. If a relation is defined by an equation, say in x and y, interchanging x and y produces an equation of the inverse relation. The graphs of a relation and its inverse are reflections of each other across the line $y = x$.

Let us consider the inverse of the sine function, $y = \sin x$. The inverse may be denoted several ways as follows.

$$x = \sin y \qquad y = \sin^{-1} x$$
$$y = \arcsin x$$

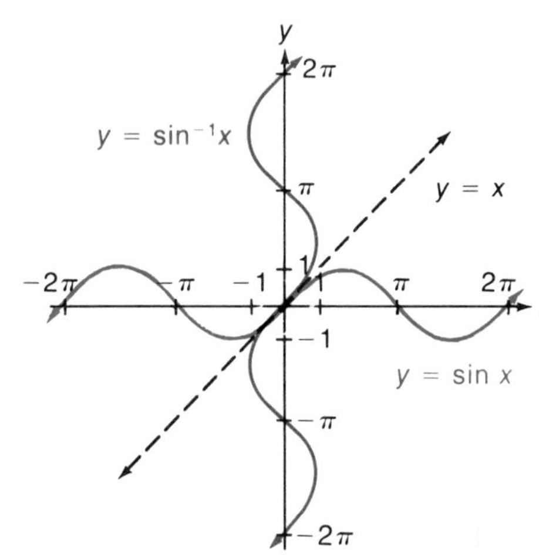

Thus $\sin^{-1} x$ is a number whose sine is x. The notation $\sin^{-1} x$ is not exponential notation. It does *not* mean $\frac{1}{\sin x}$. Either of the latter two kinds of notation above can be read "the inverse sine of x" or "the arc sine of x" or "the number (or angle) whose sine is x." Notation is chosen similarly for the inverses of the other trigonometric functions: $\cos^{-1} x$ or arccos x, $\tan^{-1} x$ or arctan x, and so on.

EXAMPLE 1 Sketch a graph of $y = \cos^{-1} x$. Is this relation a function?

First sketch a graph of $y = \cos x$.

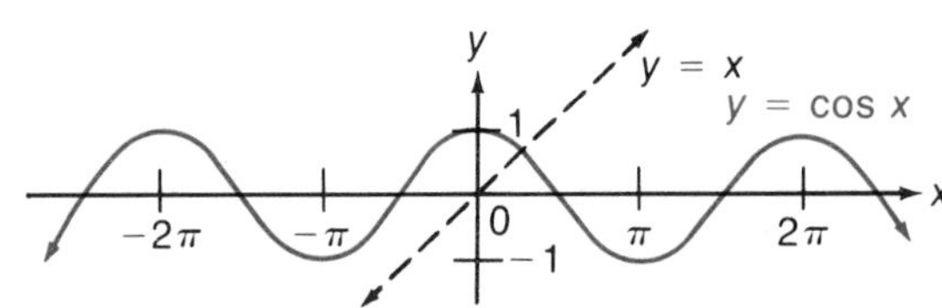

Then reflect this graph over the line $y = x$. The graph is not a function because there is more than one value of y for each x.

Try This See Additional Answers.

a. Sketch a graph of $y = \cot^{-1} x$. Is this relation a function? Not a function

We can find inverse values using either a graph or a unit circle. In practice the unit circle is easier to use.

EXAMPLE 2 Find all values of arcsin $\frac{1}{2}$.

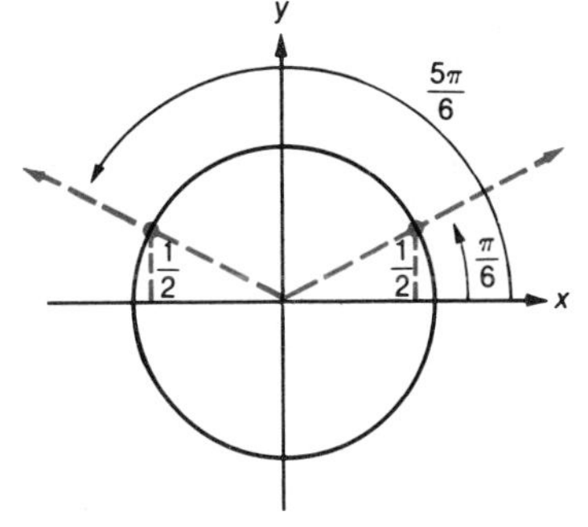

We can use the unit circle to find inverse values. On the unit circle there are two points at which the sine is $\frac{1}{2}$. The rotation for the point in the first quadrant is $\frac{\pi}{6}$ plus any multiple of 2π. The rotation for the point in the second quadrant is $\frac{5\pi}{6}$ plus any multiple of 2π. Hence we obtain all values of arcsin $\frac{1}{2}$ as follows.

$$\frac{\pi}{6} + 2k\pi \text{ and } \frac{5\pi}{6} + 2k\pi, k \text{ an integer}$$

In degree notation, we write $30° + k \cdot 360°$ and $150° + k \cdot 360°$.

Try This Find all values of the following.

b. $\arccos \frac{\sqrt{2}}{2}$ $\frac{\pi}{4} + 2k\pi, \frac{7\pi}{4} + 2k\pi$ **c.** $\sin^{-1} \frac{\sqrt{3}}{2}$ $\frac{\pi}{3} + 2k\pi, \frac{2\pi}{3} + 2k\pi$

We can also use a graph to find inverse values.

On the graph of $y = \arcsin x$, we draw a vertical line at $x = \frac{1}{2}$ as shown. It intersects the graph at points whose y-value is arcsin $\frac{1}{2}$. Some of the numbers whose sine is $\frac{1}{2}$ are seen to be $\frac{\pi}{6}$, $\frac{5\pi}{6}$, $-\frac{7\pi}{6}$, and so on. From the graph we can see that $\frac{\pi}{6}$ plus any multiple of 2π is such a number. Also, $\frac{5\pi}{6}$ plus any multiple of 2π is such a number. The complete set of values is given by $\frac{\pi}{6} + 2k\pi$, and $\frac{5\pi}{6} + 2k\pi$, k an integer.

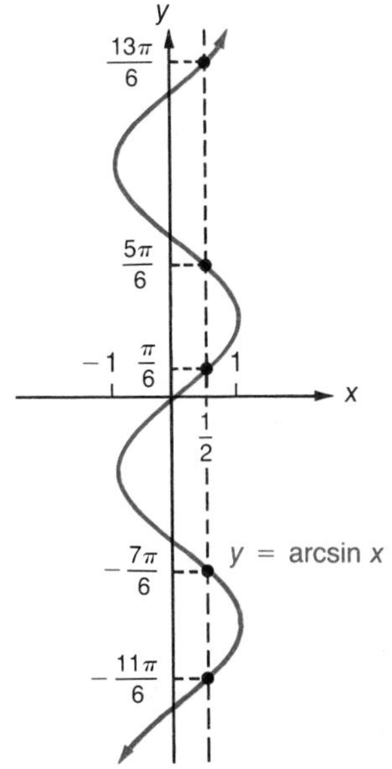

3. Find all the values, in degrees, of $\sin^{-1} 0.7660$.
From Table 5 or a calculator, we find that 50° is an angle whose sine is 0.7660. This is the reference angle.
A second such angle is $180° - 50° = 130°$. These angles plus any multiple of 360° have a sine of 0.7660. Hence $\sin^{-1} 0.7760 = 50° + k \cdot 360°$ or $130° + k \cdot 360°$.

4. Find all the values, in degrees, of $\tan^{-1} 0.1763$.
From Table 5 or a calculator, we find that 10° is an angle whose tangent is 0.1763. From the graph of tan x or from the unit circle, we see that 10° plus any multiple of 180° has a tangent of 0.1763. Hence,
$\tan^{-1} 0.1763 = 10° + k \cdot 180°$

Principal Values

Point out that the principal value is denoted by capitalizing the first letter of an inverse trigonometric function. For example, while Arccos, Sin^{-1}, and Arcsec all denote principal values, arccos, $\sin^{-1}$, and arcsec do not.

Chalkboard Examples

Find the following, in degrees.

1. Arctan 0.3640
   20°
2. $\mathrm{Sin}^{-1}\, 0.7193$
   46°
3. Arccos 0.9877
   9°

LESSON QUIZ

1. Find all the values, in degrees, of arcsin 0.5.
   $30° + k \cdot 360°$ or $150° + k \cdot 360°$
2. Find all the values, in radians, of $\tan^{-1} 1$.
   $\frac{\pi}{4} + k\pi$
3. Find, in degrees, $\mathrm{Cos}^{-1}\, 0.3420$.
   70°

EXAMPLE 3 Find all values of $\cos^{-1}(-0.9397)$ in degrees.

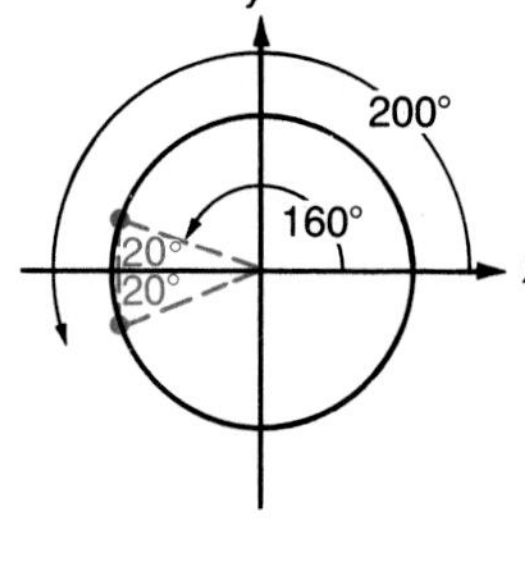

From Table 5 or a calculator, we find that the angle whose cosine is 0.9397 is 20°. This is the reference angle. We sketch this on a unit circle to find the two points where the cosine is -0.9397. The angles are 160° and 200°, plus any multiple of 360°. Thus the values of $\cos^{-1}(-0.9397)$ are

$$160° + k \cdot 360° \quad \text{or} \quad 200° + k \cdot 360°$$

where k is any integer.

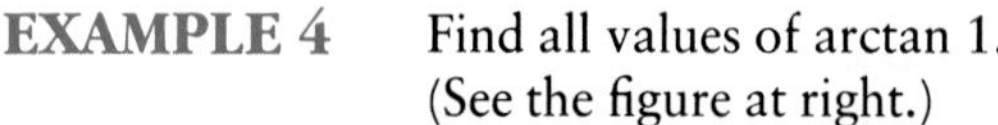

EXAMPLE 4 Find all values of arctan 1. (See the figure at right.)

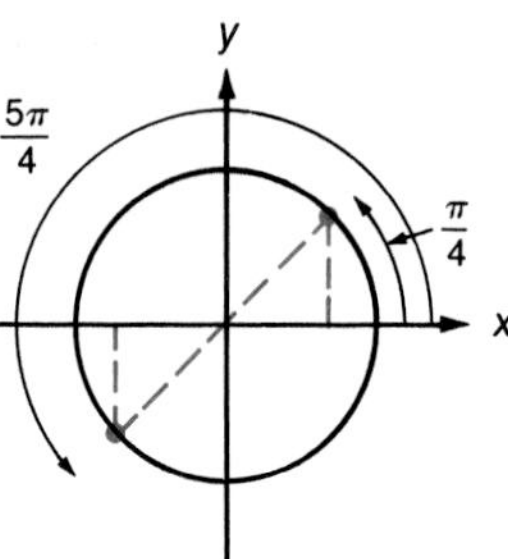

We find the two points on the unit circle at which the tangent is 1. These points are opposite ends of a diameter. Hence the arc lengths differ by π. Thus we have for all values of arctan 1

$$\frac{\pi}{4} + k\pi,\ k \text{ an integer}$$

Try This

d. Find all values of $\sin^{-1} 0.4226$ in degrees. $25° + k \cdot 360°$, $155° + k \cdot 360°$

e. Find all values of arctan -1. $\frac{3\pi}{4} + k\pi$

Principal Values

Objective: Find principal values of the inverses of the trigonometric functions.

The inverses of the trigonometric functions are not themselves functions. However, if we restrict the ranges of these relations, we can obtain functions. The following graphs show how this restriction is made.

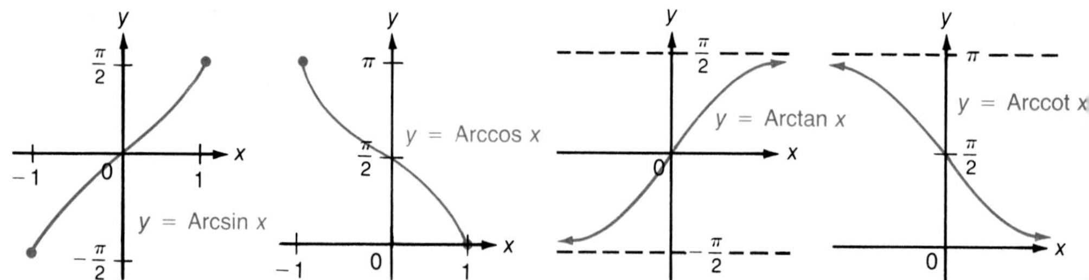

These relations with their ranges so restricted are functions, and the values in these restricted ranges are called principal values. To denote principal values we shall capitalize as follows: Arcsin x, $\mathrm{Sin}^{-1} x$, Arccos x, $\mathrm{Cos}^{-1} x$, and so on. Thus whereas arcsin $\frac{1}{2}$ represents an infinite set of numbers, Arcsin $\frac{1}{2}$ represents the single number $\frac{\pi}{6}$.

Note that for the function $y = \text{Arcsin } x$ the range is $\{y \mid -\frac{\pi}{2} \leq y \leq \frac{\pi}{2}\}$.

For the function $y = \text{Arctan } x$ the range is $\{y \mid -\frac{\pi}{2} < y < \frac{\pi}{2}\}$.

For the function $y = \text{Arccos } x$ the range is $\{y \mid 0 \leq y \leq \pi\}$.

For the function $y = \text{Arccot } x$ the range is $\{y \mid 0 < y < \pi\}$.

EXAMPLE 5 Find Arcsin $\frac{\sqrt{2}}{2}$ and $\text{Cos}^{-1}\left(-\frac{1}{2}\right)$.

In the restricted range as shown in the figure, the only number whose sine is $\frac{\sqrt{2}}{2}$ is $\frac{\pi}{4}$. Hence Arcsin $\frac{\sqrt{2}}{2} = \frac{\pi}{4}$. The only number whose cosine is $-\frac{1}{2}$ in the restricted range is $\frac{2\pi}{3}$. Hence $\text{Cos}^{-1}\left(-\frac{1}{2}\right) = \frac{2\pi}{3}$.

Try This Find each of the following.

f. Arcsin $\frac{\sqrt{3}}{2}$ $\frac{\pi}{3}$ **g.** $\text{Cos}^{-1} -\frac{\sqrt{2}}{2}$ $\frac{3\pi}{4}$ **h.** Arccot (-1) $\frac{3\pi}{4}$ **i.** $\text{Tan}^{-1}(-1)$ $-\frac{\pi}{4}$

18-4 EXERCISES

A

Find all values of the following.

1. arcsin $\frac{\sqrt{2}}{2}$ **2.** arcsin $\frac{\sqrt{3}}{2}$ **3.** $\cos^{-1}\frac{\sqrt{2}}{2}$ **4.** $\cos^{-1}\frac{\sqrt{3}}{2}$

5. $\sin^{-1}\left(-\frac{\sqrt{2}}{2}\right)$ **6.** $\sin^{-1}\left(-\frac{\sqrt{3}}{2}\right)$ **7.** arccos $\left(-\frac{\sqrt{2}}{2}\right)$ **8.** arccos $\left(-\frac{\sqrt{3}}{2}\right)$

9. arctan $\sqrt{3}$ **10.** arctan $\frac{\sqrt{3}}{3}$ **11.** $\cot^{-1} 1$ **12.** $\cot^{-1}\sqrt{3}$

13. arctan $\left(-\frac{\sqrt{3}}{3}\right)$ **14.** arctan $(-\sqrt{3})$ **15.** arccot (-1) **16.** arccot $(-\sqrt{3})$

17. arcsec 1 **18.** arcsec 2 **19.** $\csc^{-1} 1$ **20.** $\csc^{-1} 2$

Use a table or calculator to find, in degrees, all values of the following.

21. arcsin 0.3907 **22.** arcsin 0.9613 **23.** $\sin^{-1} 0.6293$ **24.** $\sin^{-1} 0.8746$

25. arccos 0.7990 **26.** arccos 0.9265 **27.** $\cos^{-1} 0.9310$ **28.** $\cos^{-1} 0.2735$

29. $\tan^{-1} 0.3673$ **30.** $\tan^{-1} 1.091$ **31.** $\cot^{-1} 1.265$ **32.** $\cot^{-1} 0.4770$

33. $\sec^{-1} 1.167$ **34.** $\sec^{-1} 1.440$ **35.** arccsc 6.277 **36.** arccsc 1.111

Find the following without using a table or a calculator.

37. Arcsin $\frac{\sqrt{2}}{2}$ $\frac{\pi}{4}$ **38.** Arcsin $\frac{1}{2}$ $\frac{\pi}{6}$ **39.** $\text{Cos}^{-1}\frac{1}{2}$ $\frac{\pi}{3}$

40. $\text{Cos}^{-1}\frac{\sqrt{2}}{2}$ $\frac{\pi}{4}$ **41.** $\text{Sin}^{-1}\left(-\frac{\sqrt{3}}{2}\right)$ $-\frac{\pi}{3}$ **42.** $\text{Sin}^{-1}\left(-\frac{1}{2}\right)$ $-\frac{\pi}{6}$

Assignment Guide
Algebra: Omit

Alg w/Trig: Day 1: 1–36 e/o, MR
Day 2: 37–67 e/o, 68

Comprehensive: 1–67 m4, 68, 69–74 e/o, MR

ADDITIONAL ANSWERS

Try This

a.

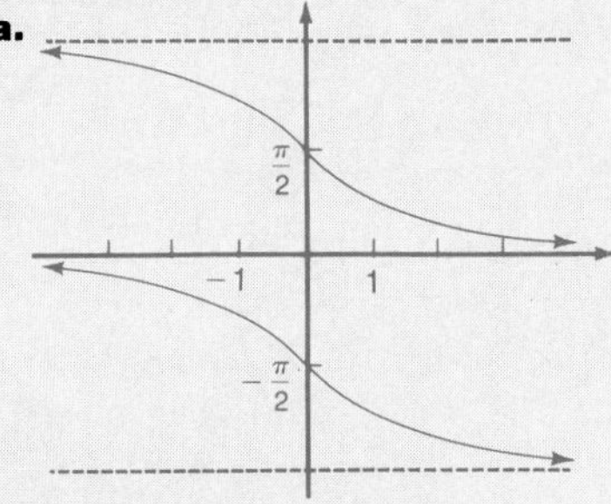

Exercises

1. $\frac{\pi}{4} + 2k\pi, \frac{3\pi}{4} + 2k\pi$
2. $\frac{\pi}{3} + 2k\pi, \frac{2\pi}{3} + 2k\pi$
3. $\frac{\pi}{4} + 2k\pi, -\frac{\pi}{4} + 2k\pi$
4. $\frac{\pi}{6} + 2k\pi, -\frac{\pi}{6} + 2k\pi$
5. $\frac{5\pi}{4} + 2k\pi, -\frac{\pi}{4} + 2k\pi$
6. $\frac{4\pi}{3} + 2k\pi, -\frac{\pi}{3} + 2k\pi$
7. $\frac{3\pi}{4} + 2k\pi, \frac{5\pi}{4} + 2k\pi$
8. $\frac{5\pi}{6} + 2k\pi, \frac{7\pi}{6} + 2k\pi$
9. $\frac{\pi}{3} + k\pi$ **10.** $\frac{\pi}{6} + k\pi$
11. $\frac{\pi}{4} + k\pi$ **12.** $\frac{\pi}{6} + k\pi$
13. $\frac{5\pi}{6} + k\pi$ **14.** $\frac{2\pi}{3} + k\pi$
15. $\frac{3\pi}{4} + k\pi$ **16.** $\frac{5\pi}{6} + k\pi$
17. $0 + 2k\pi$
18. $\frac{\pi}{3} + 2k\pi, -\frac{\pi}{3} + 2k\pi$
19. $\frac{\pi}{2} + 2k\pi$
20. $\frac{\pi}{6} + 2k\pi, \frac{5\pi}{6} + 2k\pi$
21. $23° + k \cdot 360°, 157° + k \cdot 360°$
22. $74° + k \cdot 360°, 106° + k \cdot 360°$
23. $39° + k \cdot 360°, 141° + k \cdot 360°$
24. $61° + k \cdot 360°, 119° + k \cdot 360°$

25. $36°58' + k \cdot 360°$, $323°02' + k \cdot 360°$
26. $22°06' + k \cdot 360°$, $337°54' + k \cdot 360°$
27. $21°25' + k \cdot 360°$, $338°35' + k \cdot 360°$
28. $74°08' + k \cdot 360°$, $285°52' + k \cdot 360°$
29. $20°10' + k \cdot 180°$
30. $47°30' + k \cdot 180°$
31. $38°20' + k \cdot 180°$
32. $64°30' + k \cdot 180°$
33. $31° + k \cdot 360°$, $329° + k \cdot 360°$
34. $46° + k \cdot 360°$, $314° + k \cdot 360°$
35. $9°10' + k \cdot 360°$, $170°50' + k \cdot 360°$
36. $64°10' + k \cdot 360°$, $115°50' + k \cdot 360°$
49. $\frac{3\pi}{4} + k\pi$ (k an integer)
50. $\frac{5\pi}{6} + k\pi$ (k an integer)
51. $2k\pi$ (k an integer)
52. $\frac{\pi}{3} + 2k\pi, \frac{5\pi}{3} + 2k\pi$ (k an integer)
53. $\frac{\pi}{2} + 2k\pi$ (k an integer)
54. $\frac{\pi}{6} + 2k\pi, \frac{5\pi}{6} + 2k\pi$ (k an integer)
55. The semicircle to the right of the y-axis from (and including) $-\frac{\pi}{2}$ to (and including) $\frac{\pi}{2}$
56. The semicircle above the x-axis from (and including) 0 to (and including) π
57. The semicircle to the right of the y-axis from (not including) $-\frac{\pi}{2}$ to (not including) $\frac{\pi}{2}$
58. The semicircle above the x-axis from (not including) 0 to (not including) π
59. 0.2356 radians
60. 0.4683 radians
61. -0.6894 radians
62. -0.96 radians
63. 2.6675 radians
64. 1.8675 radians
65. -0.3869 radians
66. -0.2356 radians
67. 2.9583 radians

Mixed Review

75. $y = -12.5x + 3750$
76. 1.66
77. $1, -1, \frac{-1 + i\sqrt{3}}{2}, \frac{-1 - i\sqrt{3}}{2}$
78. ± 1.468
79. 5 km/h, 12 km/h

43. $\text{Arccos}\left(-\frac{\sqrt{2}}{2}\right)$ $\frac{3\pi}{4}$ **44.** $\text{Arccos}\left(-\frac{\sqrt{3}}{2}\right)$ $\frac{5\pi}{6}$ **45.** $\text{Tan}^{-1}\left(-\frac{\sqrt{3}}{3}\right)$ $-\frac{\pi}{6}$

46. $\text{Tan}^{-1}(-\sqrt{3})$ $-\frac{\pi}{3}$ **47.** $\text{Arccot}\left(-\frac{\sqrt{3}}{3}\right)$ $\frac{2\pi}{3}$ **48.** $\text{Arccot}(-\sqrt{3})$ $\frac{5\pi}{6}$

B

Find all values of the following by sketching the graph.

49. $\text{arccot}(-1)$ **50.** $\text{arccot}(-\sqrt{3})$ **51.** arcsec 1

52. arcsec 2 **53.** $\csc^{-1} 1$ **54.** $\csc^{-1} 2$

For each of the following, indicate on separate graphs of the unit circle where principal values are found.

55. Arcsin **56.** Arccos **57.** Arctan **58.** Arccot

Find the following, in radians, using a calculator.

59. Arcsin 0.2334 **60.** Arcsin 0.4514 **61.** $\text{Sin}^{-1}(-0.6361)$

62. $\text{Sin}^{-1}(-0.8192)$ **63.** $\text{Arccos}(-0.8897)$ **64.** $\text{Arccos}(-0.2924)$

65. $\text{Tan}^{-1}(-0.4074)$ **66.** $\text{Tan}^{-1}(-0.2401)$ **67.** $\text{Cot}^{-1}(-5.396)$

68. ***Critical Thinking*** The angle to minimize friction in the flow of blood where two arteries meet is found using $\text{Cos}^{-1}\left(\frac{r^4}{R^4}\right)$, where r is the radius of the smaller artery and R is the radius of the larger artery.

a. A heart surgeon must join arteries with radii of 4 mm and 5 mm. What angle should be formed? $\approx 66°$

b. Under what condition will the formula not work? Why? If $r = R$, the angle must be 0°.

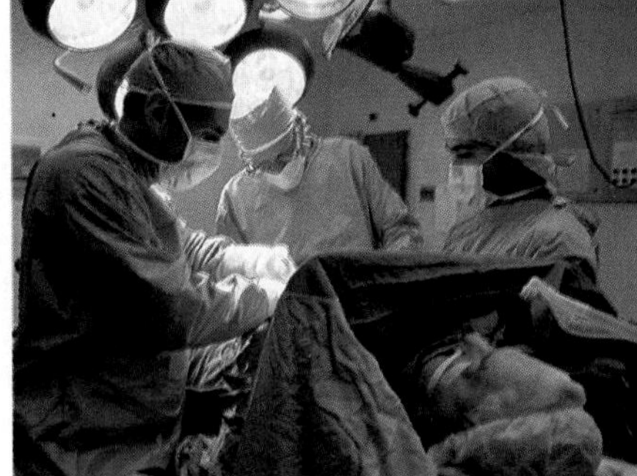

Challenge

Evaluate or simplify.

69. $\text{Cos}^{-1}\left(\cos\frac{\pi}{7}\right)$ $\frac{\pi}{7}$ **70.** $\text{Tan}^{-1}\left(\tan\frac{2\pi}{3}\right)$ $-\frac{\pi}{3}$ **71.** $\tan(\text{Tan}^{-1} -4.2)$ -4.2

72. $\sin(\text{Arctan}\sqrt{3})$ $\frac{\sqrt{3}}{2}$ **73.** $\sin(\text{Arccot}\, x)$ $\frac{\sqrt{1+x^2}}{1+x^2}$ **74.** $\text{Sin}^{-1}\left(\tan -\frac{\pi}{4}\right)$ $-\frac{\pi}{2}$

Mixed Review

75. Find the equation of the line containing (100, 2500) with slope -12.5.

Solve. **76.** $4^x = 10$ **77.** $x^4 + x^3 - x - 1 = 0$ **78.** $x^6 = 10$

79. Bob and Phil ride their bikes, headed west and north respectively, from the same point (P), starting at the same time. Bob rides 7 km/h faster than Phil. After two hours, they are 26 km apart. Find the speed of each.

18-5 Trigonometric Equations

Objective: Solve simple trigonometric equations.

Master Grapher Worksheet 34, *Solving Trigonometric Equations*, can be used for lesson closure.

When an equation contains a trigonometric expression with a variable such as $\sin x$, it is called a trigonometric equation. To solve such an equation, we find all replacements for the variable that make the equation true.

EXAMPLE 1 Solve $2 \sin x = 1$.

We first solve for $\sin x$.

$$\sin x = \frac{1}{2}$$

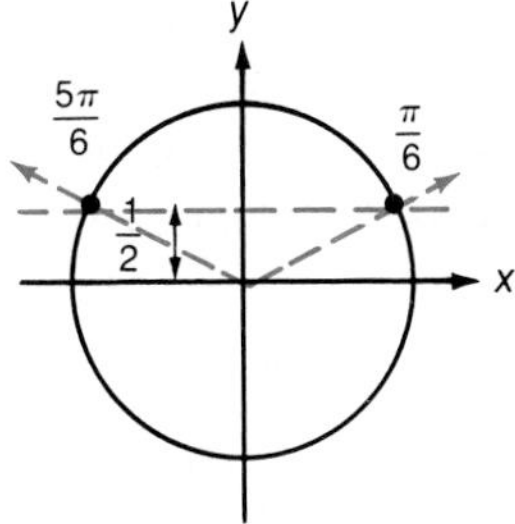

Now we note that the solutions are those angles having a sine of $\frac{1}{2}$. We look for them. The unit circle is helpful. There are just two points on it for which the sine is $\frac{1}{2}$, as shown. They are points for $\frac{\pi}{6}$ and $\frac{5\pi}{6}$. These angles, plus any multiple of 2π, are the solutions.

$$\frac{\pi}{6} + 2k\pi \text{ and } \frac{5\pi}{6} + 2k\pi \text{ where } k \text{ is any integer}$$

In degrees, the solutions are $30° + k \cdot 360°$ and $150° + k \cdot 360°$ where k is any integer.

EXAMPLE 2 Solve $4 \cos^2 x = 1$.

$$\cos^2 x = \frac{1}{4}$$

$$|\cos x| = \frac{1}{2} \quad \text{Taking principal square roots}$$

$$\cos x = \pm\frac{1}{2}$$

Now we use the unit circle to find those numbers having a cosine of $\pm\frac{1}{2}$. The solutions are $\frac{\pi}{3}, \frac{2\pi}{3}, \frac{4\pi}{3}, \frac{5\pi}{3}$, plus any multiple of 2π.

In solving trigonometric equations, it is usually sufficient to find just the solutions from 0 to 2π. Any multiple of 2π may be added to obtain all the solutions.

Try This Solve.

a. $4 \sin^2 x = 1$ $\frac{\pi}{6}, \frac{5\pi}{6}, \frac{7\pi}{6}, \frac{11\pi}{6}$ plus $2k\pi$

The following example illustrates that when we look for solutions to equations involving a double angle, we must be cautious.

18-5

FIRST FIVE MINUTES

1. Find all the values, in degrees, of $\arccos \frac{1}{2}$.
   $60° + k \cdot 360°$ or $-60° + k \cdot 360°$
2. Find all the values, in degrees, of $\tan^{-1} \sqrt{3}$.
   $60° + k \cdot 180°$

Point out that solving for a trigonometric function involves the same steps as solving for a variable. The only difference is that once we have obtained a value for the trigonometric function, we then must find the inverse function value.

Key Questions

- What is $\sin x$, if $(\sin x)^2 = 1$?
  $\sin x = \pm 1$
- What is x, if $\sin x = 1$?
  $x = 90° + k \cdot 360°$
- What is a value for x, if $\sin x = -1$?
  $x = 270°$, or $x = -90°$, for example. $270° + k \cdot 360°$ gives all solutions.

Chalkboard Examples

1. Solve, in radian measure, $(\sin x)^2 = 1$.
   $\sin x = 1$ or $\sin x = -1$
   $x = \frac{\pi}{2} + 2k\pi$ or $x = -\frac{\pi}{2} + 2k\pi$
   $x = \frac{\pi}{2} + k\pi$ gives all solutions.
2. Solve, in radian measure, $\cos^2 \theta = \frac{1}{2}$.
   $\cos \theta = \frac{\sqrt{2}}{2}$ or $\cos \theta = -\frac{\sqrt{2}}{2}$
   $\theta = \frac{\pi}{4} + 2k\pi$ or $\theta = \frac{3\pi}{4} + 2k\pi$ or
   $\theta = -\frac{\pi}{4} + 2k\pi$ or $\theta = -\frac{3\pi}{4} + 2k\pi$
   $\theta = \frac{\pi}{4} + k\pi$ or $\theta = \frac{3\pi}{4} + k\pi$ gives all solutions
3. Find the solutions of $2\sin 3x = 1$.
   $\sin 3x = \frac{1}{2}$
   $3x = \frac{\pi}{6} + 2k\pi$ or
   $3x = \frac{5\pi}{6} + 2k\pi$
   $x = \frac{\pi}{18} + \frac{2k\pi}{3}$ or
   $x = \frac{5\pi}{18} + \frac{2k\pi}{3}$

4. Solve $\sin^2\theta - 6\sin\theta + 5 = 0$.
$(\sin\theta - 1)(\sin\theta - 5) = 0$
$\sin\theta = 1$ or $\sin\theta = 5$
$\sin\theta$ is never equal to 5.
Hence
$\sin\theta = 1$

$\theta = \frac{\pi}{2} + 2k\pi$

LESSON QUIZ

1. Solve, finding all solutions from 0° to 360°.
$\sin 3x - 1 = 0$
30°, 150°, or 270°
2. Solve, finding all solutions from 0 to 2π.
$\cos^2\theta - 4\cos\theta + 3 = 0$
$\theta = 0, 2\pi$

Assignment Guide
Algebra: Omit

Alg w/Trig: Day 1: 1–20 e/o, MR
Day 2: 21–38 e/o, 39

Comprehensive: 1–38 m3, 39, 40–45 e/o, MR

ADDITIONAL ANSWERS

Exercises

1. $\frac{4\pi}{3}, \frac{5\pi}{3}$ or 240°, 300°
2. $\frac{5\pi}{6}, \frac{11\pi}{6}$ or 150°, 330°
3. $\frac{\pi}{6}, \frac{5\pi}{6}, \frac{7\pi}{6}, \frac{11\pi}{6}$ or 30°, 150°, 210°, 330°
4. $\frac{\pi}{4}, \frac{3\pi}{4}, \frac{5\pi}{4}, \frac{7\pi}{4}$ or 45°, 135°, 225°, 315°
5. $\frac{\pi}{6}, \frac{5\pi}{6}, \frac{3\pi}{2}$ or 30°, 150°, 270°
6. $\frac{2\pi}{3}, \pi, \frac{4\pi}{3}$ or 120°, 180°, 240°
7. $0, 2\pi$ or 0°, 360°
8. $\frac{3\pi}{2}$ or 270°
9. $\frac{\pi}{6}, \frac{5\pi}{6}$ or 30°, 150°
10. $\frac{\pi}{6}, \frac{5\pi}{6}$ or 30°, 150°

EXAMPLE 3 Find the solutions of $2\sin 2x = 1$ from 0 to 2π.

We first solve for $\sin 2x$: $\sin 2x = \frac{1}{2}$. Points on the unit circle for which $\sin 2x = \frac{1}{2}$ are points where $2x = \frac{\pi}{6}$ and $2x = \frac{5\pi}{6}$. So $\frac{\pi}{12}$ and $\frac{5\pi}{12}$ are solutions. However, since x values must be in the interval from 0 to 2π, $2x$ must be in the interval from 0 to 4π. Thus other values of $2x$ are $\frac{13\pi}{6}$ and $\frac{17\pi}{6}$. Therefore, $\frac{13\pi}{12}$ and $\frac{17\pi}{12}$ are also solutions.

$$x = \frac{\pi}{12}, \frac{5\pi}{12}, \frac{13\pi}{12}, \frac{17\pi}{12}$$

Try This Find all solutions (in terms of π) from 0 to 2π.

b. $2\cos 2x = 1$ $\frac{\pi}{6}, \frac{5\pi}{6}, \frac{7\pi}{6}, \frac{11\pi}{6}$

In solving trigonometric equations, we often apply algebraic manipulations before working with the trigonometric part. In the next example, we recognize that the equation is reducible to a quadratic, with $\cos\theta$ as the variable. We begin by putting the equation in standard form.

EXAMPLE 4 Solve $8\cos^2\theta - 2\cos\theta = 1$, finding all solutions from 0° to 360°.

$8\cos^2\theta - 2\cos\theta - 1 = 0$ Getting 0 on one side
$(4\cos\theta + 1)(2\cos\theta - 1) = 0$ Factoring
$4\cos\theta + 1 = 0$ or $2\cos\theta - 1 = 0$ Principle of zero products
$\cos\theta = -\frac{1}{4}$ or $\cos\theta = \frac{1}{2}$
$= -0.25$

From Table 5 we find that for $\cos\theta = -0.25$, $\theta = 104°30'$ or $255°30'$. For $\cos\theta = \frac{1}{2}$, $\theta = 60°$ or $300°$. The solutions from 0 to 360° are 104°30′, 255°30′, 60°, and 300°.

Try This Solve. Find all solutions from 0° to 360°.

c. $8\cos^2\theta + 2\cos\theta = 1$ 75°30′, 284°30′, 120°, 240° **d.** $2\cos^2\phi + \cos\phi = 0$ 90°, 120°, 240°, 270°

18-5 EXERCISES

A

Solve. Find all solutions from 0 to 2π or 0° to 360°.

1. $2\sin x + \sqrt{3} = 0$
2. $\sqrt{3}\tan x + 1 = 0$
3. $4\sin^2 x - 1 = 0$
4. $2\cos^2 x = 1$
5. $2\sin^2 x + \sin x = 1$
6. $2\cos^2 x + 3\cos x = -1$
7. $\cos^2 x + 2\cos x = 3$
8. $2\sin^2 x - \sin x = 3$
9. $2\sin^2\theta + 7\sin\theta = 4$
10. $2\sin^2\theta - 5\sin\theta + 2 = 0$

Solve. Find all solutions from 0° to 360°.

11. $2 \tan x + 3 = 0$ **12.** $4 \sin x - 1 = 0$

13. $6 \cos^2 \phi + 5 \cos \phi + 1 = 0$ **14.** $2 \sin^2 \phi + \sin \phi - 1 = 0$

Find all solutions of the following equations from 0 to 2π.

15. $\cos 2x \sin x + \sin x = 0$ **16.** $\sin 2x \cos x - \cos x = 0$

17. $\tan x \sin x - \tan x = 0$ **18.** $2 \sin x \cos x + \sin x = 0$

19. $2 \sec x \tan x + 2 \sec x + \tan x + 1 = 0$

20. $2 \csc x \cos x - 4 \cos x - \csc x + 2 = 0$

21. $\sin 2x \sin x - \cos x = 0$ **22.** $\sin 2x \cos x - \sin x = 0$

23. $\sin 2x + 2 \sin x \cos x = 0$ **24.** $\cos 2x \sin x + \sin x = 0$

25. $\cos 2x \cos x + \sin 2x \sin x = 1$ $0, 2\pi$

26. $\sin 2x \sin x - \cos 2x \cos x = -\cos x$ $0, \frac{\pi}{2}, \pi, \frac{3\pi}{2}, 2\pi$

27. $\sin 2x + 2 \sin x - \cos x - 1 = 0$ $\frac{\pi}{6}, \frac{5\pi}{6}, \pi$

28. $\sin 2x + \sin x + 2 \cos x + 1 = 0$ $\frac{2\pi}{3}, \frac{4\pi}{3}, \frac{3\pi}{2}$

29. $\sec^2 x = 4 \tan^2 x$ $\frac{\pi}{6}, \frac{5\pi}{6}, \frac{7\pi}{6}, \frac{11\pi}{6}$ **30.** $\sec^2 x - 2 \tan^2 x = 0$ $\frac{\pi}{4}, \frac{3\pi}{4}, \frac{5\pi}{4}, \frac{7\pi}{4}$

31. $\sec^2 x + 3 \tan x - 11 = 0$ 1.7682, 4.9098, 1.1071, 4.2487 **32.** $\tan^2 x + 4 = 2 \sec^2 x + \tan x$ $\frac{\pi}{4}, \frac{5\pi}{4}$, 2.0344, 5.176

B

33. $\cos(\pi - x) + \sin\left(x - \frac{\pi}{2}\right) = 1$ $\frac{2\pi}{3}, \frac{4\pi}{3}$ **34.** $\sin(\pi - x) + \cos\left(\frac{\pi}{2} - x\right) = 1$ $\frac{\pi}{6}, \frac{5\pi}{6}$

35. $2 \cos x + 2 \sin x = \sqrt{6}$ $\frac{\pi}{12}, \frac{5\pi}{12}$ **36.** $2 \cos x + 2 \sin x = \sqrt{2}$ $\frac{7\pi}{12}, \frac{23\pi}{12}$

37. $\sqrt{3} \cos x - \sin x = 1$ $\frac{\pi}{6}, \frac{3\pi}{2}$ **38.** $\sqrt{2} \cos x - \sqrt{2} \sin x = 2$ $\frac{7\pi}{4}$

39. ***Critical Thinking*** Make up a trigonometric equation with solutions of $\frac{\pi}{12}, \frac{5\pi}{12}$, and $\frac{3\pi}{4}$ in the domain $\{0, 2\pi\}$.

Challenge

Find solutions to the following equations from 0 to 2π.

40. $|\sin x| = \frac{\sqrt{3}}{2}$ **41.** $|\cos x| = \frac{1}{2}$

42. $\sqrt{\tan x} = \sqrt[4]{3}$ **43.** $12 \sin x - 7\sqrt{\sin x} + 1 = 0$

44. $16 \cos^4 x - 16 \cos^2 x + 3 = 0$

45. Find the solution to $\text{Arccos } x = \text{Arccos } \frac{3}{5} - \text{Arcsin } \frac{4}{5}$ from 0 to 1.

Mixed Review

Let $P(x) = x^4 + x^3 + 7x^2 + 9x - 18$. **46.** Find the zeros and x-intercepts.

47. Find $P(-5)$, $P(-3)$, $P(0)$, $P(2)$, $P(4)$. **48.** Factor $P(x)$, then graph $P(x)$.

Solve. **49.** $\sqrt{x + 2} = x + 2$ **50.** $z^4 + 7z^2 = 144$

Evaluate. **51.** ${}_6P_6$ **52.** ${}_{10}P_5$ **53.** ${}_9P_4$ **54.** $\binom{9}{4}$ **55.** $\binom{10}{5}$

11. 123°41′, 303°41′
12. 14°29′, 165°31′
13. 109°28′, 120°, 240°, 250°32′
14. 30°, 150°, 270°
15. $0, \frac{\pi}{2}, \pi, \frac{3\pi}{2}, 2\pi$
16. $\frac{\pi}{4}, \frac{\pi}{2}, \frac{5\pi}{4}, \frac{3\pi}{2}$
17. $0, \pi, 2\pi$
18. $0, \frac{2\pi}{3}, \pi, \frac{4\pi}{3}, 2\pi$
19. $\frac{3\pi}{4}, \frac{7\pi}{4}$
20. $\frac{\pi}{6}, \frac{\pi}{3}, \frac{5\pi}{6}, \frac{5\pi}{3}$
21. $\frac{\pi}{4}, \frac{\pi}{2}, \frac{3\pi}{4}, \frac{5\pi}{4}, \frac{3\pi}{2}, \frac{7\pi}{4}$
22. $0, \frac{\pi}{4}, \frac{3\pi}{4}, \pi, \frac{5\pi}{4}, \frac{7\pi}{4}, 2\pi$
23. $0, \frac{\pi}{2}, \pi, \frac{3\pi}{2}, 2\pi$
24. $0, \frac{\pi}{2}, \pi, \frac{3\pi}{2}, 2\pi$
39. Answers may vary. Ex: $6 \cos\left(x - \frac{\pi}{3}\right) = 1$
40. 60°, 120°, 240°, 300°
41. 60°, 120°, 240°, 300°
42. 60°, 240°
43. 3°35′, 6°23′, 173°37′, 176°25′
44. 30°, 60°, 120°, 150°, 210°, 240°, 300°, 330°
45. 1

Mixed Review

46. Zeros: $3i, -3i, 1, -2$; x-intercepts: $1, -2$
47. $P(-5) = 612$; $P(-3) = 72$; $P(0) = -18$; $P(2) = 52$; $P(4) = 450$
48. $P(x) = (x^2 + 9)(x + 2)(x - 1)$

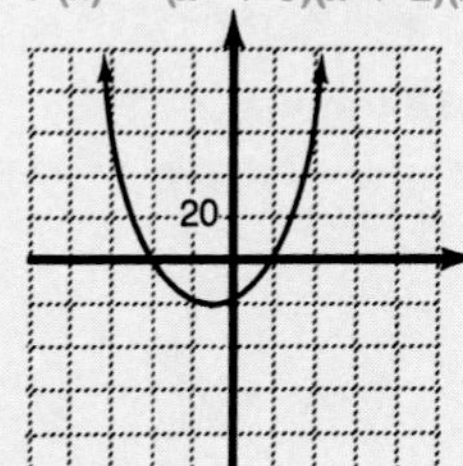

49. $-1, -2$
50. $\pm 3, \pm 4i$
51. 720
52. 30240
53. 3024
54. 126
55. 252

18-6

FIRST FIVE MINUTES

1. Find all solutions from 0° to 90° for $10\sin 4x = 5$.

   $\sin 4x = \frac{1}{2}$

   $4x = 30°$ or $4x = 150°$
   $x = 7.5°$ or $x = 37.5°$

2. Find all solutions from 0° to 360° for $\sin^2 x - 3\sin x + 2 = 0$.
   $(\sin x - 1)(\sin x - 2) = 0$
   $\sin x = 1$ or $\sin x = 2$
   $\sin x$ is never equal to 2.
   Hence
   $\sin x = 1$
   $x = 90°$

Solving Triangles

Point out that the desired accuracy of a measure depends on the situation. For a surveying job, precision to a fraction of a second may be required. The building of a gate, however, may only require accuracy to the nearest degree.

The precision to which we can find an angle, using a trigonometric ratio, depends on how precisely we know the lengths of the sides. The following table shows the relationship.

Number of Digits in Ratio	Precision of Angle Measure
4	To nearest minute
3	To nearest ten minutes
2	To nearest degree

Some of the exercises in this lesson may use unwarranted precision, from the standpoint of reality, in order to provide valid practice in calculating.

Chalkboard Example

1. For the triangle below, find length a to four-digit precision.

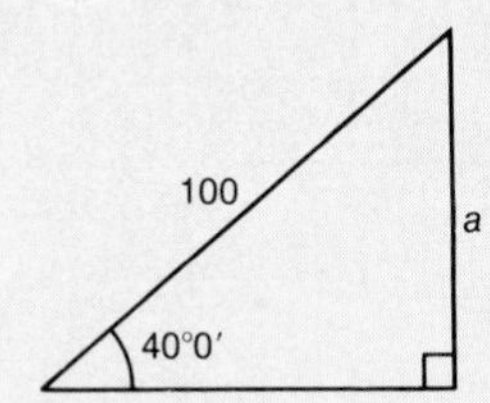

$a = 100\sin 40°0'$
$\approx 100 \cdot 0.6428$
≈ 64.28 to four digits of accuracy

18-6 Right Triangles and Problem Solving

Solving Triangles

Objective: Solve right triangles.

In Chapter 17 the trigonometric functions were defined, solving of right triangles was introduced, and tables were considered. We continue consideration of solving right triangles, a topic important in many applications of trigonometry.

EXAMPLE 1 Find the length b in this triangle. Use four-digit precision.

The known side is the hypotenuse. The side we seek is adjacent to the known angle. Thus we shall use the cosine $\cos A = \frac{b}{70}$. We solve for b.

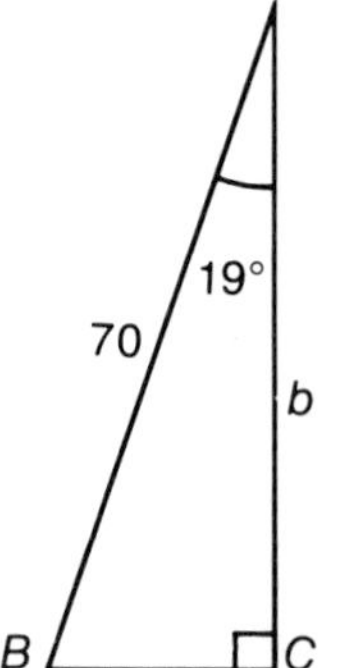

$$\text{cosine} = \frac{\text{adjacent}}{\text{hypotenuse}}$$

$$\cos 19° = \frac{b}{70}$$

$$b = 70 \cdot \cos 19°$$

$$b \approx 70 \cdot 0.9455$$

$$b \approx 66.19$$

When we solve a triangle, we find the *measures* of its sides and angles not already known. We sometimes shorten this by saying that we "find the angles" or "find the sides."

Try This

a. Find the lengths a and b in this triangle. Angle A is given to the nearest minute, and length AB to four-digit precision. $a \approx 38.43$, $b \approx 54.88$

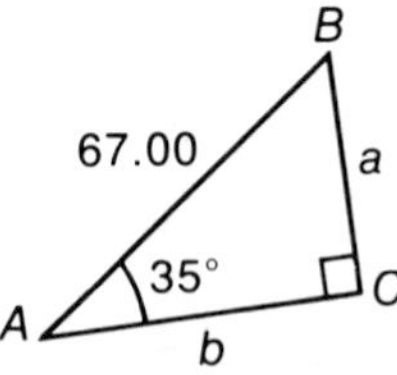

b. Solve this triangle. Use four-digit precision. $m\angle A \approx 56°19'$, $m\angle B \approx 33°41'$, $c \approx 7.211$

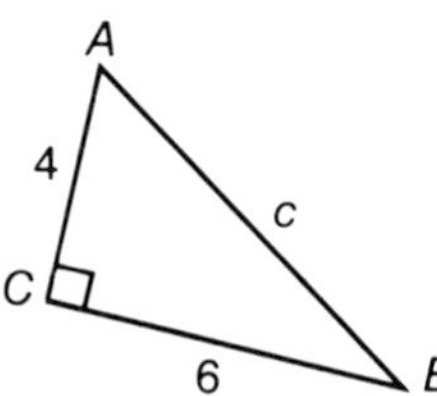

Problem Solving: Using Right Triangles

Objective: Solve problems using right triangles.

Right triangles have many applications. To solve a problem, we locate a right triangle and then solve that triangle to find a solution to the problem. There are many real-world applications or situations that involve right triangles.

EXAMPLE 2

A device for measuring cloud height at night consists of a vertical beam of light that makes a spot on the clouds. The spot is viewed from a point 135 m away. The angle of elevation is 67°40′. (The angle between the horizontal and a line of sight is called an **angle of elevation** or an **angle of depression,** the latter if the line of sight is below the horizontal.) Find the height of the clouds.

h

67°40′

135 m

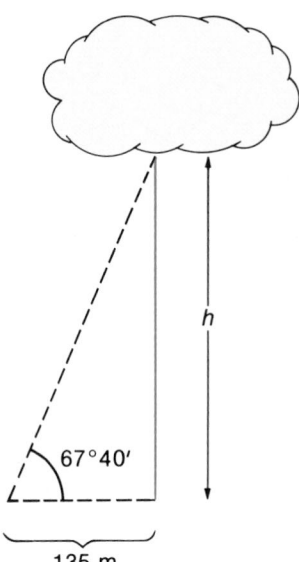

From the drawing we have

$$\text{tangent} = \frac{\text{opposite}}{\text{adjacent}}$$

$$\tan 67°40' = \frac{h}{135}$$

$$135 \cdot \tan 67°40' = h$$

$$135 \cdot 2.434 \approx h$$

$$329 \approx h$$

The cloud is approximately 329 m high.

EXAMPLE 3

An observer stands on level ground, 200 m from the base of a TV tower, and looks up at an angle of 26.5° to see the top of the tower. How high is the tower above the observer's eye level?

We draw a diagram and see that a right triangle is formed. We use one of the trigonometric functions. The tangent function is most convenient. From the definition of the tangent function, we have

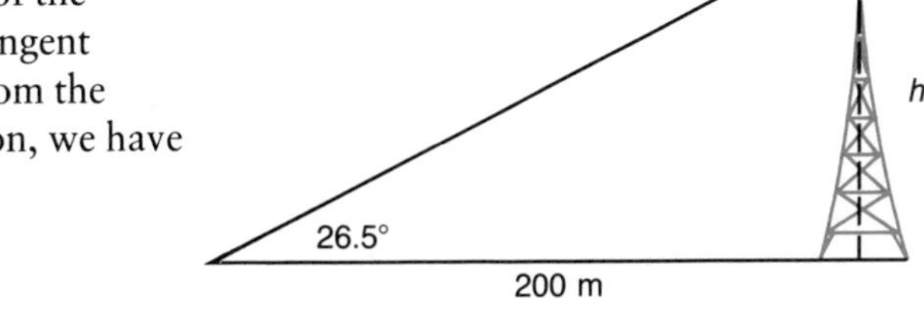

$$\text{tangent} = \frac{\text{opposite}}{\text{adjacent}}$$

$$\tan 26.5° = \frac{h}{200}$$

Then $h = 200 \tan 26.5°$. We find, from a table or calculator, that $\tan 26.5° \approx 0.4986$. Thus $h \approx 200 \cdot 0.4986 \approx 99.7$.

Problem Solving: Using Right Triangles

Chalkboard Examples

1. A balloon pilot notes that she is directly above one of the goal lines of a 100-yard playing field. Using a sextant, she estimates that the angle formed by the first goal line, the second goal line, and herself measures 10°. How high is the balloon?

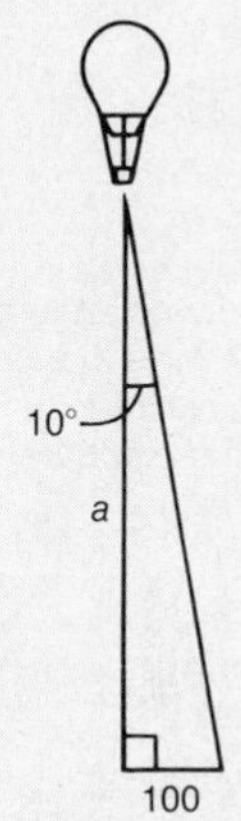

$$\tan 10° = \frac{100}{a}$$

$$a = \frac{100}{\tan 10°}$$

$$\approx \frac{100}{0.1763}$$

$$\approx 567$$

The balloon is approximately 567 yards above the ground.

2. A forester stands 200 feet away from the base of a tree. Viewing the top of the tree, he estimates the angle of elevation to be 20°. How far does the tree rise above eye level?

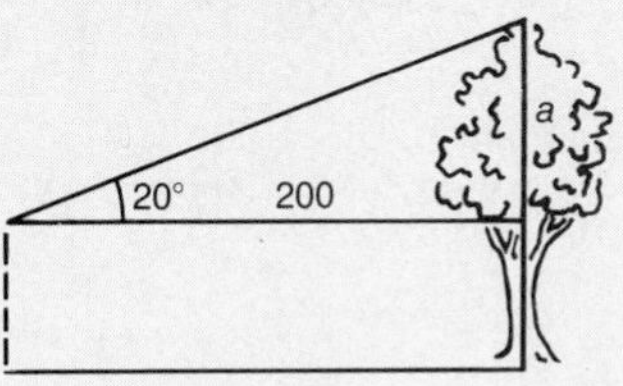

$$\tan 20° = \frac{a}{200}$$

$$a = 200 \tan 20$$

$$\approx 200 \cdot 0.3640$$

$$\approx 73$$

The tree is 73 feet above eye level.

3. A hiker notices a spot at eye level on the trail ahead. The hiker counts her paces and finds that the distance to the spot is 50 feet. The hiker's eyes are five feet above the ground. At what angle does the hill rise, measured with respect to the horizontal?

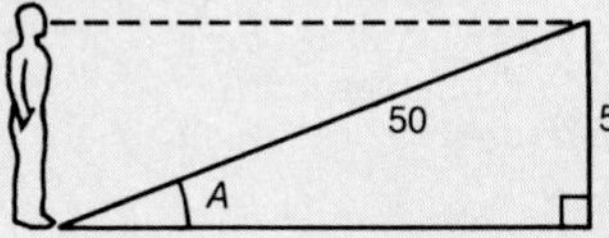

$\sin A = \frac{5}{50}$

$\sin A = 0.1$

$\sin^{-1} 0.1 \approx 5.74°$

The hill rises with a slope of 5.74°.

4. An airplane leaves an airport and travels for 50 miles in a direction 10° east of north. How far north and how far east has the plane travelled?

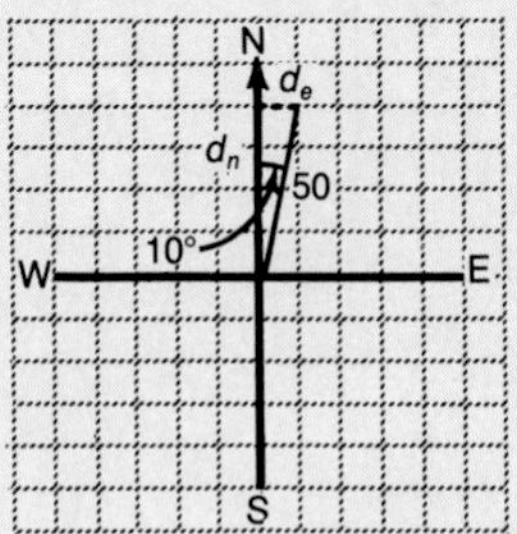

Let d_e denote the distance east.
Let d_n denote the distance north.

$\cos 10° = \frac{d_n}{50}$

$d_n = 50 \cos 10° \approx 50 \cdot 0.9848 = 49.24$

$\sin 10° = \frac{d_e}{50}$

$d_e = 50 \sin 10° \approx 50 \cdot 0.1736 \approx 8.68$

The plane has travelled approximately 49.2 miles north and 8.7 miles east.

Try This

c. An observer stands 120 m from a tree, and finds that the line of sight to the top of the tree is 32.3° above the horizontal. The tangent of 32.3° is 0.632. Find the height of the tree above eye level. ≈75.8 m

d. A guy wire is 13.6 m long, and is fastened from the ground to a pole 6.5 m above the ground. What angle does the wire make with the ground? ≈28°30′

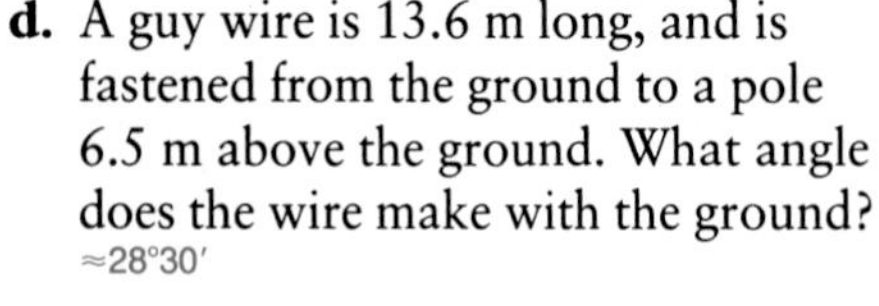

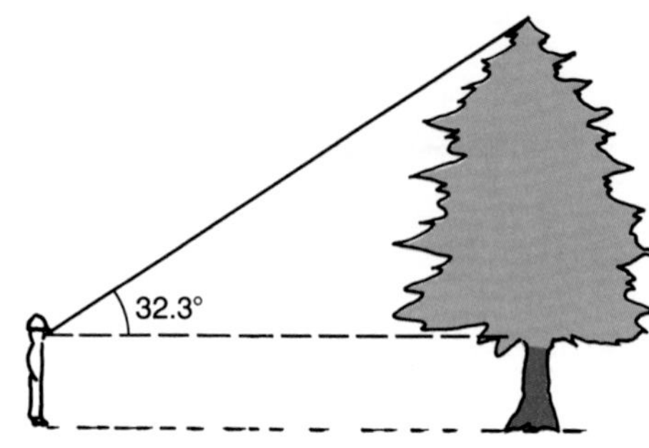

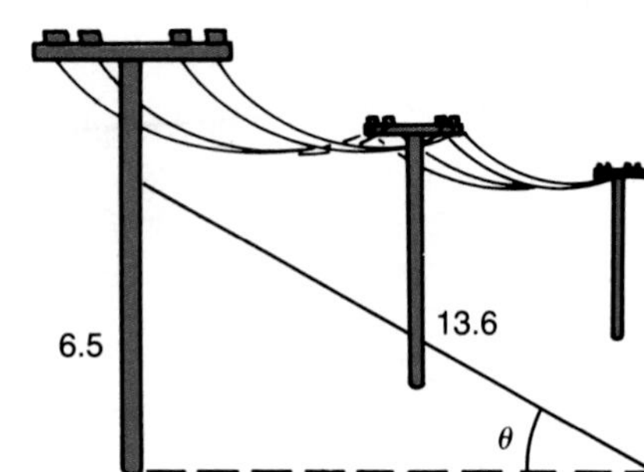

EXAMPLE 4

In surveying, horizontal distances must often be measured, even where terrain is not level. One way of doing it is as follows. Distance down a slope is measured with a surveyor's tape, and the distance d is measured by making a level sighting from A to a pole held vertically at B, or the angle α is measured by an instrument placed at A. Suppose that a slope distance L is measured to be 121.3 ft and the angle α is measured to be 3°25′. Find the horizontal distance H.

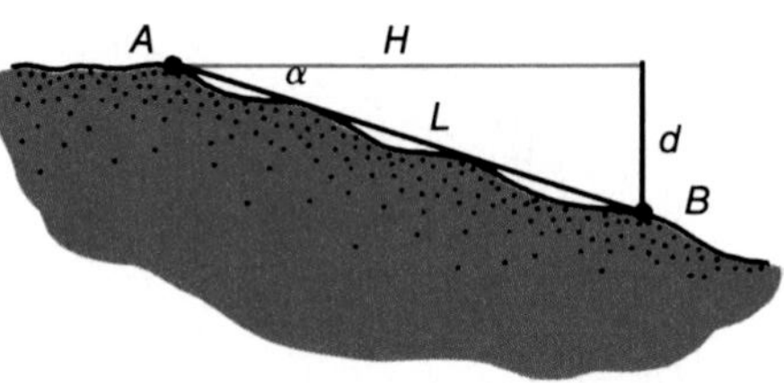

From the drawing we see that $\frac{H}{L} = \cos \alpha$. Thus $H = L \cos \alpha$, and in this case,

$$H = 121.3 \times 0.9982$$
$$= 121.1 \text{ ft}$$

EXAMPLE 5

In aerial navigation, directions are given in degrees, clockwise from north. Thus east is 90°, south is 180°, and so on. An airplane leaves an airport and travels for 100 miles in a direction 300°. How far north and how far west of the airport is the plane?

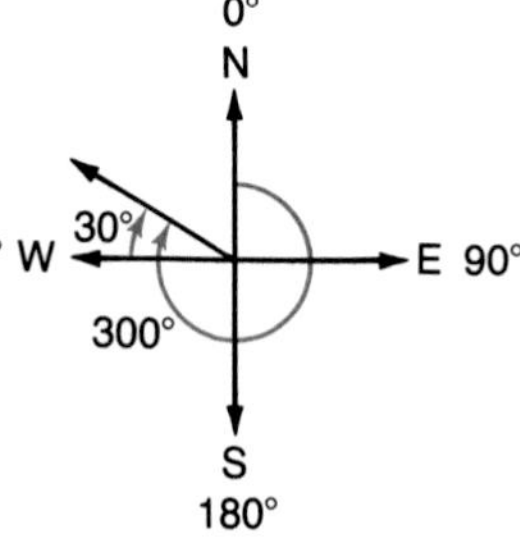

The direction of flight is as shown.

In the triangle, d_1 is the northerly distance and d_2 is the westerly distance. Then

$$\frac{d_1}{100} = \sin 30° \quad \text{and} \quad \frac{d_2}{100} = \cos 30°$$

$$d_1 = 100 \sin 30° = 100 \times 0.5 = 50 \text{ mi}$$

$$d_2 = 100 \cos 30° = 100 \times 0.866 = 87 \text{ mi (to the nearest mile)}$$

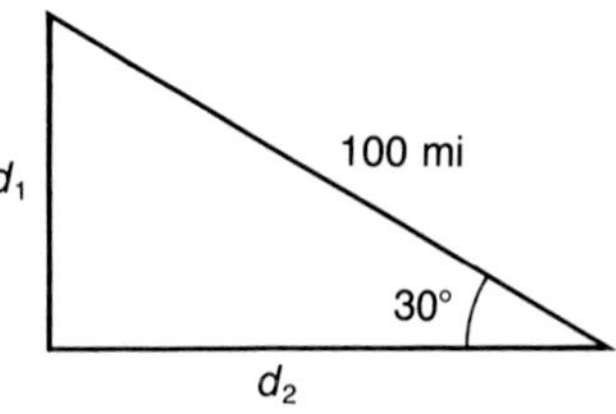

The plane is about 50 miles north and 87 miles west of the airport.

Guidelines for Solving a Triangle Problem

1. Draw a sketch of the problem situation.
2. Look for triangles and sketch them in.
3. Mark the known and unknown sides and angles.
4. Express the desired side or angle in terms of known trigonometric ratios. Then solve.

Try This

e. A downslope distance is measured to be 241.3 ft and the angle of depression α is measured to be 5°15′. Find the horizontal distance. 240.3 ft

f. An airplane flies 150 km from an airport in a direction of 115°. It is then how far east of the airport? how far south? 136 km; 63.4 km

18-6 EXERCISES

A

In Exercises 1 – 18, standard lettering for a right triangle will be used. A, B, and C are the angles, C being the right angle. The sides opposite A, B, and C are a, b, and c, respectively. Solve the triangles using three-digit precision.

1. $\angle A = 36°10', a = 27.2$
2. $\angle A = 87°40', a = 9.73$
3. $\angle B = 12°40', b = 98.1$
4. $\angle B = 69°50', b = 127$
5. $\angle A = 17°20', b = 13.6$
6. $\angle A = 78°40', b = 1340$
7. $\angle B = 23°10', a = 0.0345$
8. $\angle A = 47°30', c = 48.3$
9. $\angle B = 69°20', a = 0.0049$
10. $\angle A = 88°50', c = 3950$
11. $\angle B = 56°30', c = 0.0447$
12. $\angle B = 82°20', c = 0.982$
13. $a = 12.0, b = 18.0$
14. $a = 10.0, b = 20.0$
15. $a = 16.0, c = 20.0$
16. $a = 15.0, c = 45.0$
17. $b = 1.80, c = 4.00$
18. $b = 100, c = 450$

A
b
c
C
a
B

LESSON QUIZ

Given the triangle below, solve these problems.

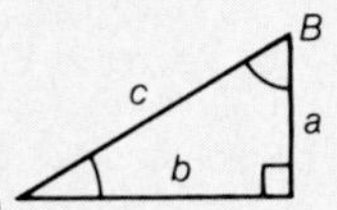

1. If $A = 20°$ and $c = 100$, what is a? 34
2. If $a = 2$ and $b = 5$, what is $m\angle A$? 22°
3. A road rises 50 vertical feet per 200 horizontal feet. What angle does the road make with respect to the horizontal? ≈ 14°

Assignment Guide

Algebra: Omit

Alg w/Trig: Day 1: 1–25 e/o, MR
Day 2: 26–43 e/o, 44

Comprehensive: 1–43 m3, 44, 45, MR

ANSWERS

Exercises

1. $\angle B = 53°50', b = 37.2, c = 46.1$
2. $\angle B = 2°20', b = 0.40, c = 9.74$
3. $\angle A = 77°20', a = 436.5, c = 447.4$
4. $\angle A = 20°10', a = 46.6, c = 135.3$
5. $\angle B = 72°40', a = 4.2, c = 14.2$
6. $\angle B = 11°20', a = 6686, c = 6819$
7. $\angle A = 66°50', b = 0.0148, c = 0.0375$
8. $\angle B = 42°30', a = 35.6, b = 32.6$
9. $\angle A = 20°40', b = 0.0129, c = 0.0138$
10. $\angle B = 1°10', a = 3949, b = 80.4$
11. $\angle A = 33°30', a = 0.0247, b = 0.0373$
12. $\angle A = 7°40', a = 0.131, b = 0.973$
13. $c = 21.6, \angle A = 33°40', \angle B = 56°20'$
14. $c = 22.4, \angle A = 26°30', \angle B = 63°30'$
15. $b = 12.0, \angle A = 53°10', \angle B = 36°50'$
16. $b = 42.4, \angle A = 19°30', \angle B = 70°30'$
17. $a = 3.57, \angle A = 63°20', \angle B = 26°40'$
18. $a = 439, \angle A = 77°10', \angle B = 12°50'$

19. 47.9 ft
20. 9.59 ft
21. 239 ft
22. 171.5 ft
23. 1°40′
24. 10°20′
25. 30°10′
26. 60°20′
27. 18,572 ft
28. 274.4 ft
29. 328 ft
30. 609.9 ft
31. 109 km
32. 201 km
33. 25.9 cm
34. 29.5 cm
35. 8.33 cm
36. 96.7 cm
37. 355 ft
38. 44.9 ft

19. A guy wire attached to a pole makes an angle of 73°10′ with the level ground, and is 14.5 ft from the pole at the ground. How far above the ground is the wire attached to the pole?

20. A guy wire attached to a pole makes an angle of 74°20′ with the level ground and is attached to the pole 34.2 ft above the ground. How far from the base of the pole is the wire attached to the ground?

21. A kite string makes an angle of 31°40′ with the level ground, and 455 ft of string is out. How high is the kite?

22. A kite string makes an angle of 41°40′ with the level ground when the kite is 114 ft high. How long is the string?

23. A road rises 3 m per 100 horizontal m. What angle does it make with the horizontal?

24. A kite is 120 ft high when 670 ft of string is out. What angle does the kite make with the ground?

25. What is the angle of elevation of the sun when a 6-ft man casts a 10.3-ft shadow?

26. What is the angle of elevation of the sun when a 35-ft mast casts a 20-ft shadow?

27. From a balloon 2500 ft high, a command post is seen with an angle of depression of 7°40′. How far is it from a point on the ground below the balloon to the command post?

28. From a lighthouse 55 ft above sea level, the angle of depression to a small boat is 11°20′. How far from the foot of the lighthouse is the boat?

29. An observer sights the top of a building 173 ft higher than the eye at an angle of elevation of 27°50′. How far is it from the observer to the building?

30. An observer sights the top of a building 212 ft higher than the eye at an angle of elevation of 19°10′. How far is it from the observer to the building?

31. An airplane travels at 120 km/h for 2 hr in a direction of 243° from Chicago. At the end of this time, how far south of Chicago is the plane?

32. An airplane travels at 150 km/h for 2 hr in a direction of 138° from Omaha. At the end of this time, how far east of Omaha is the plane?

33. A regular pentagon has sides 30.5 cm long. Find the radius of the circumscribed circle.

34. A regular pentagon has sides 42.8 cm long. Find the radius of the inscribed circle.

35. A hexagon has a perimeter of 50 cm and is inscribed in a circle. Find the radius of the circle.

36. An octagon is inscribed in a circle of radius 15.8 cm. Find the perimeter of the octagon.

37. A vertical antenna is mounted on top of a 50 ft pole. From a point on the level ground 75 ft from the base of the pole, the antenna subtends an angle of 10.5°. Find the length of the antenna.

38. An observer on a ladder looks at a building 100 ft away, noting that the angle of elevation of the top of the building is 18°40′ and the angle of depression of the bottom of the building is 6°20′. How tall is the building?

39. From a balloon 2 km high, the angles of depression to two towns in line with the balloon are 81°20′ and 13°40′. How far apart are the towns?

40. From a balloon 1000 km high, the angles of depression to two artillery posts in line with the balloon are 11°50′ and 84°10′. How far apart are the artillery posts?

41. A weather balloon is directly west of two observing stations 10 km apart. The angles of elevation of the balloon from the two stations are 17°50′ and 78°10′. How high is the balloon?

42. From two points south of a hill on level ground and 1000 ft apart, the angles of elevation of the hill are 12°20′ and 82°40′. How high is the hill?

B

43. Show that the area of a right triangle is $\frac{1}{2}bc\sin A$.

44. ***Critical Thinking*** Use the information given in the diagram to find y without using a table or calculator. (Hint: Use a double-angle identity).

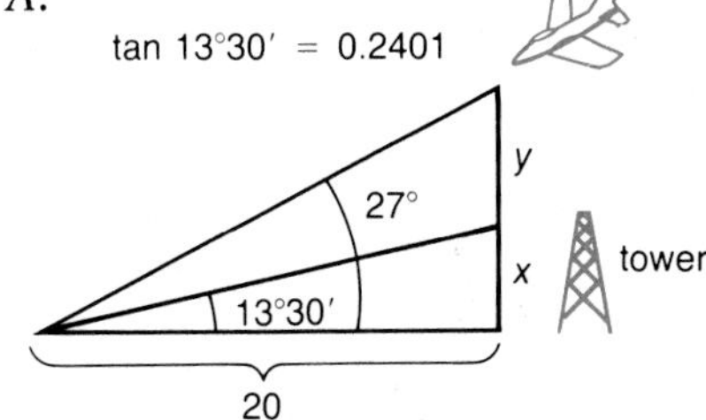

Challenge

45. Find a formula for the distance to the horizon as a function of the height of the observer above the earth. Calculate the distance to the horizon from an airplane at an altitude of 1000 ft. (You will need to look up the radius of the earth.)

Mixed Review

Solve. **46.** $x^3 + 24x^2 + 191x + 504 = 0$ **47.** $25x^2 + 49 = 0$
48. $\sqrt[3]{4y + 7} - 3 = 0$

Problem for Programmers

Write a program to find any of the six inverse trigonometric functions in degrees. Note that many computer languages only have the arctan function (ATN) built in. Use trigonometric identities to relate the tan function to the other functions. Test your program using Exercises 21–36 in Lesson 18-4. See Exercises 9–13, page 726.

39. 7.92 km
40. 4.67 km
41. 3.45 km
42. 225 ft
43. Area = $\frac{ab}{2}$, $\frac{a}{c} = \sin A$, $a = c\sin A$. Substituting, area = $\frac{bc}{2}\sin A$
44. $y = 5.3895$
45. $d \approx \sqrt{h^2 + 2(3963)h}$, where d and h are in miles; 38.7 miles

Mixed Review

46. −7, −8, −9
47. $\pm\frac{7}{5}i$
48. 5

18-7

FIRST FIVE MINUTES

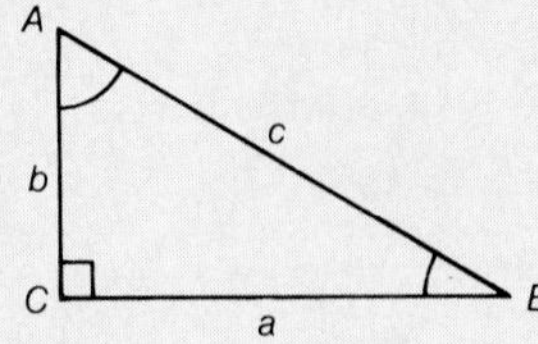

1. If $m\angle A = 20$, what is $m\angle B$?
   70
2. If $c = 2$ and $b = \sqrt{3}$, what is angle B?
   $\sin B = \frac{b}{c} = \frac{\sqrt{3}}{2}$
   $m\angle B = 60$
3. If $c = 13$ and $b = 12$, what is a?
   $a^2 = c^2 - b^2 = 169 - 144 = 25$
   $a = 5$

18-7 The Law of Sines

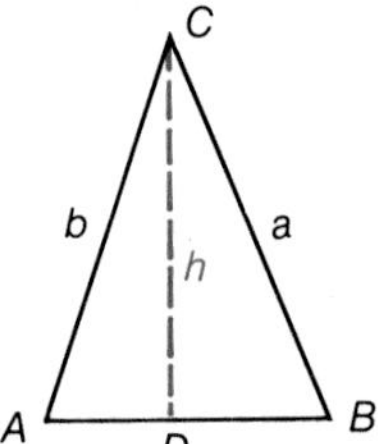

The trigonometric functions can be used to solve triangles that are not right triangles (oblique triangles). In order to solve oblique triangles we need to derive some properties, one of which is called the law of sines. We shall consider any oblique triangle. It may or may not have an obtuse angle. We will consider both cases, but the derivations are essentially the same.

The triangles are lettered in the standard way, with angles A, B, and C, and the sides opposite them a, b, and c, respectively. The altitude from vertex C has length h. In either triangle we now have, from triangle ADC,

$$\frac{h}{b} = \sin A, \text{ or } h = b \sin A$$

From triangle DBC we have $\frac{h}{a} = \sin B$, or $h = a \sin B$.

Thus we have $\frac{h}{a} = \sin \angle CBD = \sin (180° - B) = \sin B$. So in either kind of triangle we now have

$$h = a \sin B \text{ and } h = b \sin A$$

Thus it follows that $a \sin B = b \sin A$.

$$\frac{a}{\sin A} = \frac{b}{\sin B}$$

If we were to consider an altitude from vertex A in the triangles shown, the same argument would give us the following.

$$\frac{b}{\sin B} = \frac{c}{\sin C}$$

We combine these results to obtain the law of sines, which holds for right triangles as well as oblique triangles.

Theorem 18-5

The Law of Sines

In any triangle ABC, $\frac{a}{\sin A} = \frac{b}{\sin B} = \frac{c}{\sin C}$.

(The sides are proportional to the sines of the opposite angles.)

Solving Triangles (AAS)

Objective: Use the law of sines to solve triangles, given two angles and a side opposite one of them.

When two angles and a side of any triangle are known, the law of sines can be used to solve the triangle.

EXAMPLE 1

In triangle ABC, $a = 4.56$, $m\angle A = 43$, and $m\angle C = 57$. Solve the triangle.

We first draw a sketch. We find $m\angle B$, as follows.

$$m\angle B = 180° - (43° + 57°)$$
$$= 80°$$

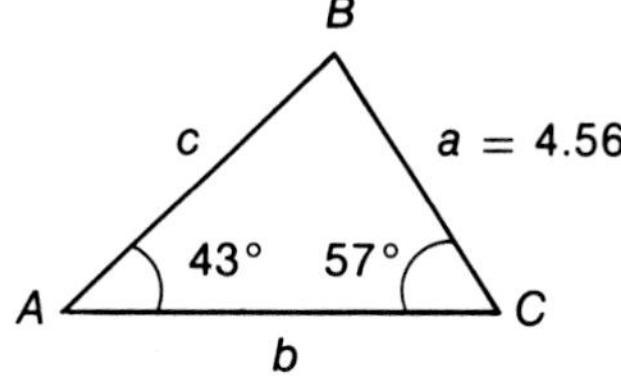

We can now find the other two sides, using the law of sines.

$$\frac{c}{\sin C} = \frac{a}{\sin A}$$
$$c = \frac{a \sin C}{\sin A}$$
$$= \frac{4.56 \sin 57°}{\sin 43°}$$
$$\approx \frac{4.56 \times 0.8387}{0.6820}$$
$$\approx 5.61$$
$$\frac{b}{\sin B} = \frac{a}{\sin A}$$
$$b = \frac{a \sin B}{\sin A}$$
$$= \frac{4.56 \sin 80°}{0.6820}$$
$$\approx \frac{4.56 \times 0.9848}{0.6820}$$
$$\approx 6.58$$

We have now found the unknown parts of the triangle, $B = 80°$, $c \approx 5.61$, and $b \approx 6.58$. A calculator is of great help in doing calculations like these.

Try This

a. In triangle ABC, $m\angle A = 41$, $m\angle C = 52$, and $a = 6.53$. Solve the triangle.
$m\angle B = 87$, $b \approx 9.94$, $c \approx 7.84$

b. In triangle ABC, $m\angle B = 2$, $m\angle C = 119$, and $b = 9$. Solve the triangle.
$m\angle A = 59$, $a \approx 221.05$, $c \approx 225.55$

Solving Triangles (AAS)

Explain that an oblique triangle can also be solved by drawing altitudes and forming right triangles.

An easy method for using the law of sines is given below.

Since the length of a side divided by the sine of its opposite angle is a constant for all angles of a triangle, we can use this triangle quotient, T, to solve the triangle.

In Example 1

$$T = \frac{a}{\sin A} = \frac{4.56}{\sin 43°} \approx 6.686$$

By the law of sines, T is the ratio of any side length to its opposite angle in the triangle. Thus,

$\frac{b}{\sin B} = T$, so $b \approx 6.686 \sin 80 \approx 6.58$

$\frac{c}{\sin C} = T$, so $c \approx 6.686 \sin 57 \approx 5.61$

We now have all three angles and all three side lengths, thus we have solved the triangle.

Once we find T for a triangle, we can find any angle if we know its opposite side length, and we can find any side length if we know its opposite angle.

Chalkboard Example

1. In triangle ABC, $a = 10$, $m\angle A = 40$, and $m\angle C = 60$. Solve for the remaining sides and angle.
The measure of the remaining angle, $m\angle B$, is $180 - (40 + 60) = 80$.
$$\frac{c}{\sin C} = \frac{a}{\sin A}$$
$$c = \frac{a \cdot \sin C}{\sin A}$$
$$= \frac{10 \cdot \sin 60}{\sin 40}$$
$$\approx 13.47$$
$$\frac{b}{\sin B} = \frac{a}{\sin A}$$
$$b = \frac{a \cdot \sin B}{\sin A}$$
$$= \frac{10 \cdot \sin 80}{\sin 40}$$
$$\approx 15.32.$$

The Ambiguous Case (SSA)

Before presenting the four possible cases of triangles when two sides and an angle opposite one of them are known, have students try to draw them. For example, give them two sides and an angle of a triangle that has no solution, as well as one that has two solutions.

Chalkboard Examples

1. In triangle ABC, $m\angle A = 30$, $a = 10$, $b = 100$. Solve the triangle.
   We look first for $m\angle B$.
   $\frac{\sin A}{a} = \frac{\sin B}{b}$
   $\sin B = \frac{b \cdot \sin A}{a}$
   $\sin B = \frac{100 \cdot \sin 30}{10}$
   $\sin B = 5$
   No angle has a sine of 5, thus there is no solution.
2. In triangle ABC, $m\angle A = 35$, $a = 57.36$, $b = 100$. Solve the triangle.
   We look first for $m\angle B$.
   $\frac{\sin A}{a} = \frac{\sin B}{b}$
   $\sin B = \frac{b \cdot \sin A}{a}$
   $= \frac{100 \cdot \sin 35}{57.36}$
   $= 1$
   Hence $m\angle B = 90$.
   $m\angle C = 180 - (90 + 35) = 55$
   $c = 100\cos 35° = 81.92$

The Ambiguous Case (SSA)

Objective: Use the law of sines to solve triangles, given two sides and an angle opposite one of them.

When two sides of a triangle and an angle opposite one of them are known, the law of sines can be used to solve the triangle. However, there may be more than one solution. Thus this is known as the ambiguous case. Suppose a, b, and $m\angle A$ are given. The various possibilities are shown in the four cases below.

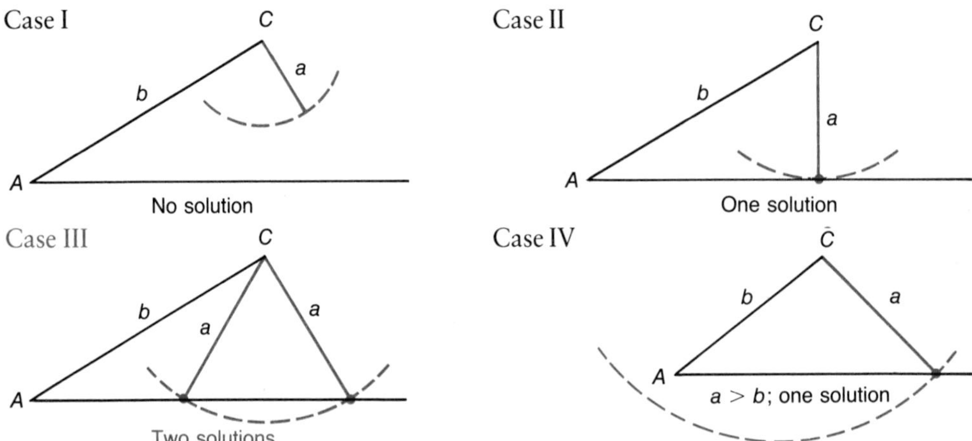

EXAMPLE 2 In triangle ABC, $a = 15$, $b = 25$, and $m\angle A = 47$. Solve the triangle.

This is Case I. We look for $m\angle B$.

$$\frac{a}{\sin A} = \frac{b}{\sin B}$$

Then $\sin B = \frac{b \sin A}{a} = \frac{25 \sin 47°}{15} \approx \frac{25 \times 0.7314}{15} \approx 1.219.$

Since there is no angle having a sine greater than 1, there is no solution.

EXAMPLE 3 In triangle ABC, $a = 12$, $b = 5$, and $\angle B = 24°38'$. Solve the triangle.

This is Case II. We look for $m\angle A$.

$$\frac{a}{\sin A} = \frac{b}{\sin B}$$

Then $\sin A = \frac{a \sin B}{b} = \frac{12 \sin 24°38'}{5} \approx \frac{12 \times 0.4168}{5} \approx 1.000.$

$$m\angle A \approx 90$$

Thus $\angle C \approx 90° - 24°38' \approx 65°22'$.

Since $\frac{c}{a} = \cos B$, $c = a \cos B \approx 12 \times 0.9090 \approx 10.9$.

Try This Solve triangle ABC.

c. $a = 40, b = 12, m\angle B = 57$ No solution

d. $a = 4, b = 3, \angle A = 53°08'$ $\angle B = 36°52', \angle C = 90°, c = 5$

EXAMPLE 4 In triangle ABC, $a = 20$, $b = 15$, and $m\angle B = 30$. Solve the triangle.

This is Case III. We look for $m\angle A$.

$$\frac{a}{\sin A} = \frac{b}{\sin B}$$

$$\sin A = \frac{a \sin B}{b} = \frac{20 \sin 30°}{15} = \frac{20 \times 0.5}{15} \approx 0.667$$

There are two angles less than 180° having a sine of approximately 0.667. They are 42° and 138°. This gives us two possible solutions.

Possible solution 1

C
b = 15
108°
a = 20
42°
30°
A
c = 28.5
B

We know that $m\angle A = 42$.
Then $\angle C = 180° - (30° + 42°) = 108°$.

We now find c.

$$\frac{c}{\sin C} = \frac{b}{\sin B}$$

$$c = \frac{b \sin C}{\sin B} = \frac{15 \sin 108°}{\sin 30°} \approx \frac{15 \times 0.9511}{0.5} \approx 28.5$$

These parts make a triangle, as shown. Hence we have a solution.

Possible solution 2

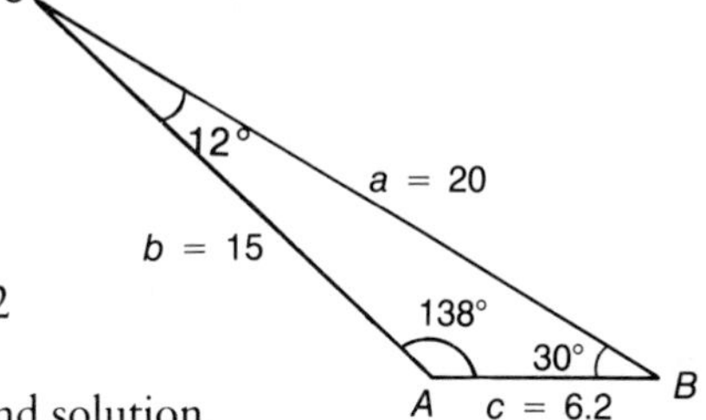

$m\angle A = 138$
$m\angle C = 12$

We now find c.

$$c = \frac{b \sin C}{\sin B} = \frac{15 \sin 12°}{\sin 30°} \approx \frac{15 \times 0.2079}{0.5} \approx 6.2$$

These parts make a triangle. Hence we have a second solution.

EXAMPLE 5 In triangle ABC, $a = 25$, $b = 10$, and $m\angle A = 42$. Solve the triangle.

This is Case IV. We look for $m\angle B$.

$$\frac{b}{\sin B} = \frac{a}{\sin A}$$

$$\sin B = \frac{b \sin A}{a} = \frac{10 \sin 42°}{25}$$

$$\approx \frac{10 \times 0.6691}{25} \approx 0.2676$$

3. In triangle ABC, $a = 171$, $c = 383$, $m\angle A = 20$. Solve the triangle.
We look first for $m\angle C$.
$\frac{\sin A}{a} = \frac{\sin C}{c}$
$\sin C = \frac{c \cdot \sin A}{a}$
$\sin C = \frac{383 \cdot \sin 20}{171}$
$= 0.7660$
$m\angle C = 50$ or 130
If $m\angle C = 50$, then
$m\angle B = 180 - 20 - 50 = 110°$.
$\frac{\sin B}{b} = \frac{\sin A}{a}$
$b = \frac{a \cdot \sin B}{\sin A}$
$= \frac{171 \cdot \sin 110}{\sin 20}$
$= 469.82$
If $m\angle C = 130$,
$m\angle B = 180 - 20 - 130 = 30$.
$b = \frac{171 \cdot \sin 30}{\sin 20}$
≈ 250

4. In triangle ABC, $a = 374$, $b = 199$, $m\angle A = 40$. Solve the triangle.
$\frac{\sin A}{a} = \frac{\sin B}{b}$
$\sin B = \frac{b \cdot \sin A}{a}$
$= \frac{199 \cdot \sin 40}{374}$
$= 0.3420$
$m\angle B = 20$
Hence $m\angle C = 180 - 40 - 20 = 120°$.
$\frac{\sin C}{c} = \frac{\sin A}{a}$
$c = \frac{a \cdot \sin C}{\sin A}$
$= \frac{374 \cdot \sin 120}{\sin 40}$
≈ 504

Area of a Triangle

Chalkboard Examples

Find the area of triangle ABC.

1. $b = 5, c = 8$, and $m\angle A = 30$

$\text{area} = \frac{1}{2}bc \sin A$

$= \frac{1}{2} \cdot 5 \cdot 8 \cdot \sin 30°$

$= 10$

2. $b = 10, c = 9\sqrt{3}$, and $m\angle A = 86$

$\text{area} = \frac{1}{2}bc \sin A$

$= \frac{1}{2} \cdot 10 \cdot 9\sqrt{3} \cdot \sin 86°$

≈ 77.75

LESSON QUIZ

1. In triangle ABC, $m\angle A = 30$, $c = 10$, and $m\angle B = 40$. Solve the triangle.
   $m\angle C = 110°, a \approx 5.32, b \approx 6.84$
2. Find the area of triangle ABC where $b = 7, c = 10$, and $m\angle A = 30$.
   17.5

Then $\angle B = 15°30'$ or $\angle B = 164°30'$. Since $a > b$, we know there is only one solution. An angle of $164°30'$ cannot be an angle of this triangle because it already has an angle of $42°$, and these two would total more than $180°$.

$$\angle C = 180° - (42° + 15°30') = 122°30'$$

$$\frac{c}{\sin C} = \frac{a}{\sin A}$$

$$c = \frac{a \sin C}{\sin A} \approx \frac{25 \sin 122°30'}{\sin 42°} \quad \text{Solving for } c$$

$$c \approx \frac{25 \times 0.8434}{0.6691} \approx 31.5$$

Try This Solve triangle ABC.

e. $a = 25, b = 20, m\angle B = 33$

f. $b = 20, c = 10, m\angle B = 38$

e. $m\angle A \approx 43, m\angle C \approx 104, c \approx 35.6$ or $m\angle A \approx 137, m\angle C \approx 10, c \approx 6.4$
f. $m\angle A \approx 124, m\angle C \approx 18, a \approx 26.9$

Area of a Triangle

Objective: Use the law of sines to find the area of a triangle.

We can use the law of sines in finding areas of triangles. Look again at the triangles at the beginning of this section. Each triangle has area $\frac{1}{2}hc$. Remember that $h = b \sin A$. Thus area $= \frac{1}{2}(b \sin A)c$.

$$\text{area} = \frac{1}{2}bc \sin A$$

EXAMPLE 6 In triangle ABC, $b = 9, c = 12$, and $m\angle A = 40$. Find the area.

Using area $= \frac{1}{2}bc \sin A$, we have the following.

$$\text{area} \approx \frac{1}{2} \times 9 \times 12 \times 0.6428 \approx 34.7 \text{ square units}$$

EXAMPLE 7 Find the area of the triangle.

We assign $\angle A$ to the known angle. The side lengths b and c can be assigned arbitrarily to 7 m and 10 m.

$$m\angle A = 35, \quad b = 7 \text{ m}, \quad c = 10 \text{ m}$$

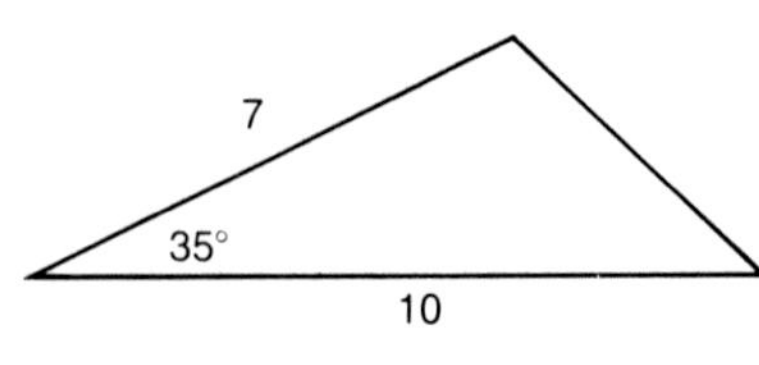

$$\text{area} = \frac{1}{2}bc \sin A$$

$$= \frac{1}{2}(7)(10) \sin 35$$

$$\approx 35 \cdot 0.5736 \approx 20.1 \text{ m}^2$$

Try This

g. In triangle ABC, $b = 5, c = 8$, and $m\angle A = 25$. Find the area. ≈ 8.452

18-7 EXERCISES

A

Solve triangle ABC.

1. $m\angle A = 60, m\angle B = 70, b = 20$
2. $m\angle A = 48, m\angle B = 62, b = 35$
3. $m\angle A = 36, m\angle B = 48, a = 12$
4. $m\angle A = 40, m\angle B = 60, b = 100$
5. $m\angle A = 133, m\angle B = 30, b = 18$
6. $m\angle B = 120, m\angle C = 30, a = 16$
7. $m\angle B = 38, m\angle C = 21, b = 24$
8. $m\angle A = 131, m\angle C = 23, b = 10$
9. $m\angle A = 68°30', m\angle C = 42°40', c = 23.5$
10. $m\angle B = 118°20', m\angle C = 45°40', b = 42.1$
11. $m\angle B = 150, a = 3, b = 7$
12. $m\angle A = 30, a = 6, c = 9$
13. $m\angle C = 60, a = 12, c = 30$
14. $m\angle B = 45, a = 15, b = 17$
15. $m\angle A = 36, a = 24, b = 34$
16. $m\angle C = 43, c = 28, b = 27$
17. $\angle A = 116°20', a = 17.2, c = 13.5$
18. $\angle A = 47°50', a = 28.3, b = 18.2$
19. $\angle C = 61°10', c = 30.3, b = 24.2$
20. $\angle B = 58°40', a = 25.1, b = 32.6$

Find the area of triangle ABC.

21. $b = 8, c = 15, m\angle A = 30$
22. $b = 7, c = 18, m\angle A = 54$
23. $b = 1, c = 1, m\angle A = 10$
24. $b = 100, c = 75, m\angle A = 170$

Find the area of each triangle.

25. $\approx 5.438 \text{ m}^2$

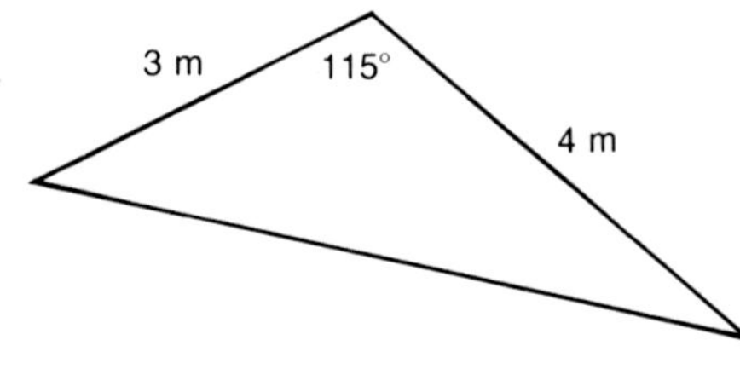

26. $\approx 51.08 \text{ cm}^2$

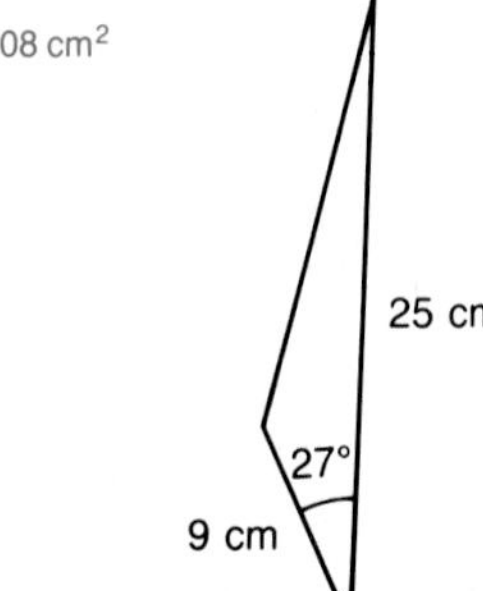

B

Solve.

27. Points A and B are on opposite sides of a lunar crater. Point C is 50 m from A. The measure of $\angle BAC$ is determined to be 112° and the measure of $\angle ACB$ is determined to be 42°. What is the width of the crater? 76.3 m

28. A guy wire to the top of a pole makes a 71° angle with level ground. At a point 25 ft farther from the pole than the guy wire, the angle of elevation of the top of the pole is 37°. How long is the guy wire? 26.9 ft

Assignment Guide

Algebra: Omit

Alg w/Trig: 1–33 m3, 34, MR, assign w. Application

Comprehensive: 1–33 m3, 34–36, MR, assign w. Application

ADDITIONAL ANSWERS

Exercises

1. $m\angle C = 50, a = 18.4, c = 16.3$
2. $m\angle C = 70, a = 29.5, c = 37.3$
3. $m\angle C = 96, b = 15.2, c = 20.3$
4. $m\angle C = 80, a = 74.2, c = 113.7$
5. $m\angle C = 17, a = 26.3, c = 10.5$
6. $m\angle A = 30, b = 27.7, c = 16.0$
7. $m\angle A = 121, a = 33.4, c = 14.0$
8. $m\angle B = 26, a = 17.2, c = 8.9$
9. $\angle B = 68°50', a = 32.3, b = 32.3$
10. $m\angle A = 16, a = 13.2, c = 34.2$
11. $\angle A = 12°20', \angle C = 17°40', c = 4.25$
12. $\angle C = 48°40', \angle B = 101°20', b = 11.8$ or $\angle C = 131°20', \angle B = 18°40', b = 3.84$
13. $\angle A = 20°20', \angle B = 99°40', b = 34.1$
14. $\angle A = 38°40', \angle C = 96°20', c = 23.9$
15. $\angle B = 56°20', \angle C = 87°40', c = 40.8$ or $\angle B = 123°40', \angle C = 20°20', c = 14.2$
16. $\angle B = 41°10', \angle A = 95°50', a = 40.8$
17. $\angle C = 44°40', \angle B = 19, b = 6.25$
18. $\angle B = 28°30', \angle C = 103°40', c = 37.1$
19. $\angle B = 44°20', \angle A = 74°30', a = 33.3$
20. $\angle A = 41°10', \angle C = 80°10', c = 37.6$
21. 30
22. 51
23. ≈ 0.0868
24. ≈ 651

35. Area $= \frac{1}{2}bd \sin \theta + \frac{1}{2}ac \sin \theta + \frac{1}{2}ad \sin (180° - \theta) + \frac{1}{2}bc \sin (180° - \theta) = \frac{1}{2}(bd + ac + ad + bc) \sin \theta = \frac{1}{2}(a + b)(c + d) \sin \theta$

36. The paths of the two objects are straight and the distance between them is decreasing, so their paths cross, forming a vertical angle, $\angle C$. The straight line distance between the objects thus forms side c of a triangle with the two paths as sides a and b. $\angle A$ is then the bearing (the angle formed by sides b and c). Since the bearing is constant and $\angle C$ is constant, $\angle B$ is constant, and as the objects advance, the triangles formed are similar. By the law of sines, $\frac{a}{\sin A} = \frac{b}{\sin B} = \frac{c}{\sin C}$. So when c decreases to 0, $\frac{a}{\sin A} = \frac{b}{\sin B} = \frac{0}{\sin C} = 0$, a and b must be 0, thus the objects collide.

Mixed Review

37. $\frac{36b^2d^2\sqrt[3]{d^2}}{a^4c^4}$
38. $-7 - 24i$
39. 1
40. $\frac{1}{2} + \frac{i}{2}$
41. 54
42. 15.875
43. -209715
44. $\frac{7}{9}$
45. $f(x) = x^4 + 10x^2 - 96$
46. $f(x) = x^4 - 5x^3 + 13x^2 - 19x + 10$

29. A pole leans away from the sun at an angle of 7° to the vertical. When the angle of elevation of the sun is 51°, the pole casts a shadow 47 ft long on level ground. How long is the pole? 50.8 ft

30. A vertical pole stands by a road that is inclined 10° to the horizontal. When the angle of elevation of the sun is 23°, the pole casts a shadow 38 ft long directly downhill along the road. How long is the pole? 9.29 ft

31. A reconnaissance airplane leaves its airport on the east coast of the United States and flies in a direction of 85°. Because of bad weather it returns to another airport 230 km to the north of its home base. For the return it flies in a direction of 283°. What is the total distance flown? 1467 km

32. Station B is 10.2 km east of station A. The bearing of a fire from A is S 10°40′W. The bearing of the fire from B is S 31°20′W. How far is the fire from A? from B? 24.7 km, 28.4 km

33. A boat leaves lighthouse A and sails 5.1 km. At this time it is sighted from lighthouse B, 7.2 km west of A. The bearing of the boat from B is N 65°10′E. How far is the boat from B? 10.6 km or 2.4 km

34. ***Critical Thinking*** Find a formula for the area of a parallelogram in terms of two sides, a and b, and an included angle θ. Area $= ab \sin \theta$.

Challenge

35. Prove that the area of a quadrilateral is half the product of the lengths of its diagonals and the sine of an angle between the diagonals.

36. Consider two objects, such as ships, airplanes, or runners, moving in straight-line paths. If the distance between them is decreasing, and if the bearing from one of them to the other is constant, they will collide. ("Constant bearing means collision," as mariners put it.) Prove that this statement is true.

Mixed Review

Simplify. **37.** $\left(\frac{216a^{-2}b^5c^4d^2}{a^4b^2c^{10}d^{-2}}\right)^{\frac{2}{3}}$ **38.** $(2 - i)^4$ **39.** $\left|\frac{1}{2} - \frac{\sqrt{3}}{2}i\right|$ **40.** $\frac{i}{1 + i}$

Find the sum. **41.** $\sum_{n=-4}^{4} (4n + 6)$ **42.** $\sum_{n=-3}^{3} \left(\frac{1}{2}\right)^n$ **43.** $\sum_{n=1}^{10} (-4)^{n-1}$

44. $0.7 + 0.07 + 0.007 + \cdots$.

Find the function of lowest degree with rational coefficients

45. with roots $4i, -\sqrt{6}$. **46.** with roots $1, 2, 1 + 2i$.

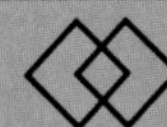

CONNECTIONS: GEOMETRY

Draw a circle with a diameter of 3 in. Mark the center of the circle as point M. Then choose 3 points A, B, and C on the circle so that when you draw a triangle with these points as vertices, M is inside the triangle.

Measure the angles and side lengths. Then find $\frac{a}{\sin A}$, $\frac{b}{\sin B}$, and $\frac{c}{\sin C}$. Compare these ratios to the diameter of the circle. They are approximately equal.

18-8 The Law of Cosines

A second property used for solving oblique triangles is the law of sines. This law can be thought of as a generalization of the Pythagorean theorem. At the end of Book II of Euclid's Elements, there are two propositions that establish this law.

Consider any triangle ABC placed on a coordinate system. We will place the origin at one of the vertices, say C, and the positive half of the x-axis along one of the sides, say CB. Then the coordinates of B are $(a, 0)$, and the coordinates of A are $(b \cos C, b \sin C)$. We use the distance formula to determine c^2.

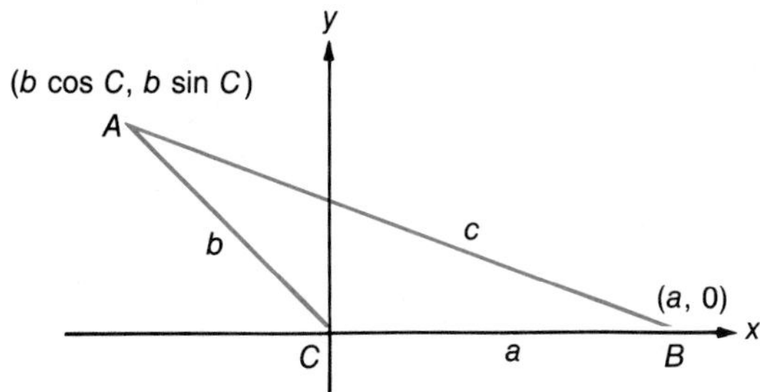

$$c^2 = (b \cos C - a)^2 + (b \sin C - 0)^2$$
$$c^2 = b^2 \cos^2 C - 2ab \cos C + a^2 + b^2 \sin^2 C \quad \text{Multiplying and simplifying}$$
$$c^2 = a^2 + b^2(\sin^2 C + \cos^2 C) - 2ab \cos C$$
$$c^2 = a^2 + b^2 - 2ab \cos C$$

Had we placed the origin at one of the other vertices, we would have obtained $a^2 = b^2 + c^2 - 2bc \cos A$, or $b^2 = a^2 + c^2 - 2ac \cos B$.

This result can be summarized as follows.

Theorem 18-6

The Law of Cosines

In any triangle ABC,

$$a^2 = b^2 + c^2 - 2bc \cos A$$
$$b^2 = a^2 + c^2 - 2ac \cos B$$
$$c^2 = a^2 + b^2 - 2ab \cos C$$

(In any triangle, the square of a side is the sum of the squares of the other two sides, minus twice the product of those sides and the cosine of the included angle.)

Only one of the above formulas needs to be memorized. The other two can be obtained by a change of letters.

18-8

FIRST FIVE MINUTES

1. In triangle ABC, $m\angle A = 10$, $c = 10$, $m\angle B = 150$. Find a.
   $m\angle C = 180 - 10 - 150 = 20$
   $\frac{\sin A}{a} = \frac{\sin C}{c}$
   $a = \frac{c \cdot \sin A}{\sin C} = 5.08$

Solving Triangles (SAS)

Point out that the law of cosines is a generalization of the Pythagorean theorem.

Illustrate this by using the law of cosines to find the hypotenuse of a right triangle. The cosine of the angle opposite the hypotenuse is 0, and the law of cosines will reduce to the Pythagorean theorem.

Chalkboard Example

1. In triangle ABC, $b = 5, c = 3,$ $m\angle A = 60$. Find a.
$a^2 = b^2 + c^2 - 2bc \cos A$
$= 25 + 9 - 2 \cdot 5 \cdot 3 \cdot \cos 60$
$= 19$
$a = \sqrt{19}$

Solving Triangles (SSS)

Chalkboard Example

1. In triangle ABC, $a = 2, b = 4,$ $c = 5$. Find $m\angle A$.
$a^2 = b^2 + c^2 - 2bc \cos A$
$\cos A = \frac{a^2 - b^2 - c^2}{-2bc}$
$= \frac{4 - 16 - 25}{-2 \cdot 4 \cdot 5}$
$= \frac{37}{40} = 0.9250$
$\angle A \approx 22°20'$

LESSON QUIZ

1. In triangle ABC, $b = 6, c = 3,$ $m\angle A = 60$. Find length a.
$a^2 = b^2 + c^2 - 2bc \cos A$
$= 36 + 9 - 2 \cdot 6 \cdot 3 \cdot \frac{1}{2}$
$= 27$
$a = \sqrt{27} = 3\sqrt{3}$
2. In triangle ABC, $a = 2, b = 3,$ $c = 4$. Find $m\angle A$.
$a^2 = b^2 + c^2 - 2bc \cos A$
$\cos A = \frac{a^2 - b^2 - c^2}{-2bc}$
$= \frac{21}{24} = 0.8750$
$\angle A \approx 28.95° \approx 28°57'$

Solving Triangles (SAS)

Objective: Solve a triangle given two sides and an included angle.

When two sides of a triangle and the included angle are known, we can use the law of cosines to find the third side. The law of sines can then be used to solve the triangle.

EXAMPLE 1 In triangle ABC, $a = 24$, $c = 32$, and $m\angle B = 115$. Solve the triangle.

We first find the third side. From the law of cosines

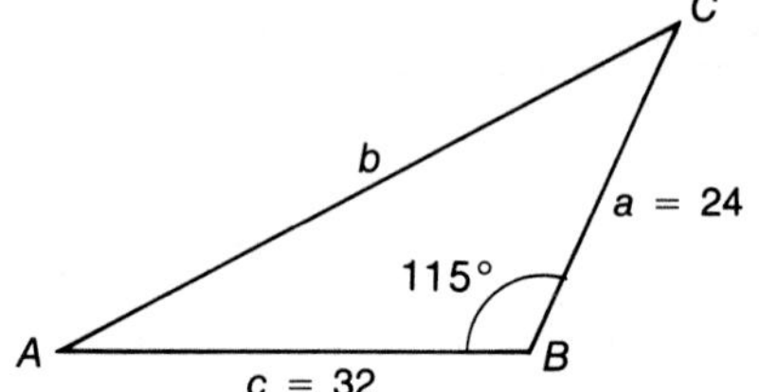

$$b^2 = a^2 + c^2 - 2ac \cos B$$
$$\approx 24^2 + 32^2 - 2 \cdot 24 \cdot 32(-0.4226)$$
$$\approx 2249$$
$$b \approx \sqrt{2249} \approx 47.4$$

Next we use the law of sines to find a second angle.

$$\frac{a}{\sin A} = \frac{b}{\sin B}, \sin A = \frac{a \sin B}{b} = \frac{24 \sin 115°}{47.4} \approx \frac{24 \times 0.9063}{47.4} \approx 0.4589$$
$$\angle A = 27°20'$$
$$\angle C = 180° - (115° + 27°20') = 37°40'$$

Try This Solve the triangle by using the law of cosines.

a. In triangle ABC, $b = 18$, $c = 28$, and $m\angle A = 122$. $a = 40.5$, $\angle B = 22°10'$, $\angle C = 35°50'$

Solving Triangles (SSS)

Objective: Use the law of cosines to solve a triangle given three sides.

When all three sides are known, the law of cosines can be used to solve the triangle.

EXAMPLE 2 In triangle ABC, $a = 18$, $b = 25$, and $c = 12$. Solve the triangle.

Let us first find $m\angle B$. We select the formula from the law of cosines that contains $\cos B$; in other words, $b^2 = a^2 + c^2 - 2ac \cos B$. We solve this for $\cos B$ and substitute.

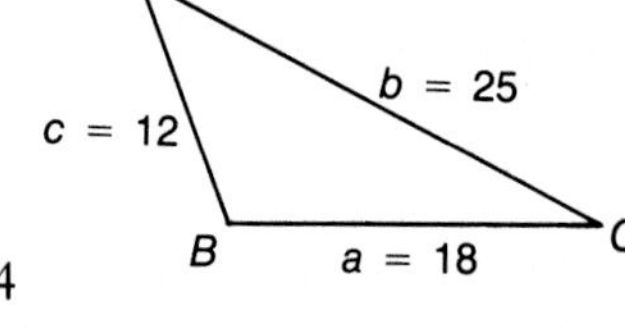

$$\cos B = \frac{a^2 + c^2 - b^2}{2ac} = \frac{18^2 + 12^2 - 25^2}{2 \cdot 18 \cdot 12} = -0.3634$$
$$m\angle B = 111°20'$$

By using the formula that contains $\cos A$ we find that $\cos A = 0.7417$, so $\angle A = 42°10'$. Then $\angle C = 180° - (111°20' + 42°10') = 26°30'$.

Try This Solve the triangle by using the law of cosines.

b. In triangle ABC, $a = 25$, $b = 10$, and $c = 20$. $\angle A = 108°10'$, $\angle B = 22°20'$, $\angle C = 49°30'$

18-8 EXERCISES

A

Solve the triangles.

1. $m\angle C = 135, a = 6, b = 7$

2. $m\angle A = 116, b = 31, c = 25$

3. $m\angle A = 30, b = 12, c = 24$

4. $m\angle C = 120, a = 5, b = 8$

5. $m\angle A = 133, b = 12, c = 15$

6. $m\angle C = 60, a = 15, b = 12$

7. $\angle B = 72°40', c = 16, a = 78$

8. $\angle A = 24°30', b = 68, c = 109.8$

Solve the triangles.

9. $a = 2, b = 3, c = 4$

10. $a = 7, b = 9, c = 10$

11. $a = 4, b = 6, c = 7$

12. $a = 7, b = 8, c = 10$

13. $a = 12, b = 14, c = 20$

14. $a = 22, b = 22, c = 35$

15. $a = 3.3, b = 2.7, c = 2.8$

16. $a = 16, b = 20, c = 32$

17. $a = 2.2, b = 4.1, c = 2.4$

18. $a = 3.6, b = 6.2, c = 4.1$

B

19. Two ships leave harbor at the same time. The first sails N 15°W at 25 knots (a knot is one nautical mile per hour). The second sails N 32°E at 20 knots. After 2 hours, how far apart are the ships? 37 nautical miles

20. Two airplanes leave an airport at the same time. The first flies 150 km/h in a direction of 320°. The second flies 200 km/h in a direction of 200°. After 3 hours, how far apart are the planes? 912 km

21. A hill is inclined 5° to the horizontal. A 45-ft pole stands at the top of the hill. How long a rope will it take to reach from the top of the pole to a point 35 ft downhill from the base of the pole? 59.4 ft

22. A hill is inclined 15° to the horizontal. A 40-ft pole stands at the top of the hill. How long a rope will it take to reach from the top of the pole to a point 68 ft downhill from the base of the pole? 87.4 ft

23. A piece of wire 5.5 m long is bent into a triangular shape. One side is 1.5 m long and another is 2 m long. Find the angles of the triangle. 68°, 68°, 44°

24. A triangular lot has sides 120 ft long, 150 ft long, and 100 ft long. Find the angles of the lot. 52°50′, 85°30′, 41°40′

25. A slow-pitch softball diamond is a square 60 ft on a side. The pitcher's mound is 46 ft from home. How far is it from the pitcher's mound to first base? 42.6 ft

26. A baseball diamond is a square 90 ft on a side. The pitcher's mound is 60.5 ft from home. How far does the pitcher have to run to cover first? 63.7 ft

Assignment Guide
Algebra: Omit

Alg w/Trig: 1–28 e/o, 29, MR

Comprehensive: 1–28 m3, 29, 30–32 e/o, MR

ADDITIONAL ANSWERS

Exercises

1. $c = 12.0$, $\angle A = 20°40'$, $\angle B = 24°20'$
2. $a = 47.6$, $\angle B = 35°50'$, $\angle C = 28°10'$
3. $a = 14.9$, $\angle B = 23°40'$, $\angle C = 126°20'$
4. $c = 11.4$, $\angle A = 22°20'$, $\angle B = 37°40'$
5. $a = 24.8$, $\angle B = 20°40'$, $\angle C = 26°20'$
6. $c = 13.7$, $\angle A = 71°30'$, $\angle C = 48°30'$
7. $b = 74.8$, $\angle A = 95°30'$, $\angle C = 11°50'$
8. $a = 55.6$, $\angle B = 30°30'$, $\angle C = 125°$
9. $\angle A = 29°$, $\angle B = 46°30'$, $\angle C = 104°30'$
10. $\angle A = 42°50'$, $\angle B = 61°$, $\angle C = 76°10'$
11. $\angle A = 34°50'$, $\angle B = 58°50'$, $\angle C = 86°20'$
12. $\angle A = 44°$, $\angle B = 52°40'$, $\angle C = 83°20'$
13. $\angle A = 36°10'$, $\angle B = 43°30'$, $\angle C = 100°20'$
14. $\angle A = 37°20'$, $\angle B = 37°20'$, $\angle C = 105°20'$
15. $\angle A = 73°40'$, $\angle B = 51°50'$, $\angle C = 54°30'$
16. $\angle A = 24°10'$, $\angle B = 30°40'$, $\angle C = 125°10'$
17. $\angle A = 25°40'$, $\angle B = 126°$, $\angle C = 28°20'$
18. $\angle A = 33°40'$, $\angle B = 107°$, $\angle C = 39°20'$

29. $a^2 + b^2 + c^2 = 2abc\left(\frac{\cos A}{a} + \frac{\cos B}{b} + \frac{\cos C}{c}\right)$

30. $\approx$ 9381 ft

31. Area $= \frac{1}{2}a^2 \sin \theta$; $\theta = 90°$

32. $\frac{\cos A}{a} + \frac{\cos B}{b} + \frac{\cos C}{c}$

$= \frac{bc \cos A + ac \cos B + ab \cos C}{abc}$

$= \frac{2(bc \cos A + ac \cos B + ab \cos C)}{2abc}$

$= \frac{a^2 + b^2 + c^2}{2abc}$

Mixed Review

33. 2
34. −4
35. 2
36. 0
37. 10
38. $\frac{1}{2}x^3 - \frac{1}{3}x + 2$
39. $4x^3 + 4x^2 + 2x + 5$, R: 1
40. $x^3 + 5x - 1$, R: $15x - 3$
41. $(x^4 + 4y^2)(x^2 + 2y)(x^2 - 2y)$
42. $(x + 2)(x - 2)(x + 3)(x - 3)$
43. $2(c - 15)(c + 1)$

Writing to Learn

When we know 3 side lengths or 2 side lengths and the angle opposite the unknown side, we can use the law of cosines to solve the triangle. If we know two angles and any side length, or two side lengths and an angle opposite one of them, we can use the law of sines to solve the triangle.

27. The longer base of an isosceles trapezoid measures 14 ft. The nonparallel sides measure 10 ft, and the base angles measure 80°.
a. Find the length of a diagonal. 15.73 ft **b.** Find the area. 120.8 ft^2

28. After flying 75 miles of a 180-mile trip, an aircraft is 10 miles off course. How much should the heading be corrected to then fly straight to the destination, assuming no wind correction? $\approx$ 13°5′

29. ***Critical Thinking*** Find a formula for $a^2 + b^2 + c^2$ in any triangle.

Challenge

30. A bridge is being built across a canyon. The length of the bridge is 5042 ft. From the deepest point in the canyon, the angles of elevation of the ends of the bridge are 78° and 72°. How deep is the canyon?

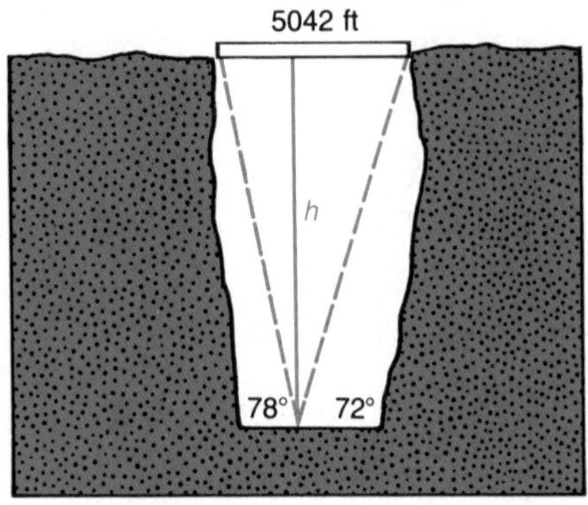

31. Find a formula for the area of an isosceles triangle in terms of the congruent sides and their included angle. Under what conditions will the area of a triangle with fixed congruent sides be a maximum?

Show that in any triangle ABC each of the following is true.

32. $\frac{\cos A}{a} + \frac{\cos B}{b} + \frac{\cos C}{c} = \frac{a^2 + b^2 + c^2}{2abc}$

Mixed Review

Solve. **33.** $\frac{1}{4}x + \frac{1}{6}x + \frac{1}{8}x = \frac{13}{12}$ **34.** $0.3x + 0.02x - 0.004x = -1.264$

35. $2^x \cdot 2^{2x} = 2^6$ **36.** $16^x = 1$ **37.** $x^3 = 1000$

Divide. **38.** $(3x^4 - 2x^2 + 12x) \div 6x$ **39.** $(4x^4 - 2x^2 + 3x - 4) \div (x - 1)$

40. $(x^5 + 2x^3 - x^2) \div (x^2 - 3)$

Factor. **41.** $x^8 - 16y^4$ **42.** $x^4 - 13x^2 + 36$ **43.** $2c^2 - 28c - 30$

WRITING TO LEARN

Write a short paragraph in which you contrast the law of sines and the law of cosines.

18-9 Trigonometric Notation for Complex Numbers

In Chapter 7, we studied complex numbers. We now use our knowledge of trigonometry to develop trigonometric notation for complex numbers.

Consider any complex number $a + bi$. Recall that the length r of the segment from the origin to $a + bi$ is $\sqrt{a^2 + b^2}$. This distance r is called the **absolute value of a complex number** $a + bi$.

Suppose that the segment makes an angle θ with the real axis. As the diagram shows,

$$a = r \cos \theta \text{ and } b = r \sin \theta$$

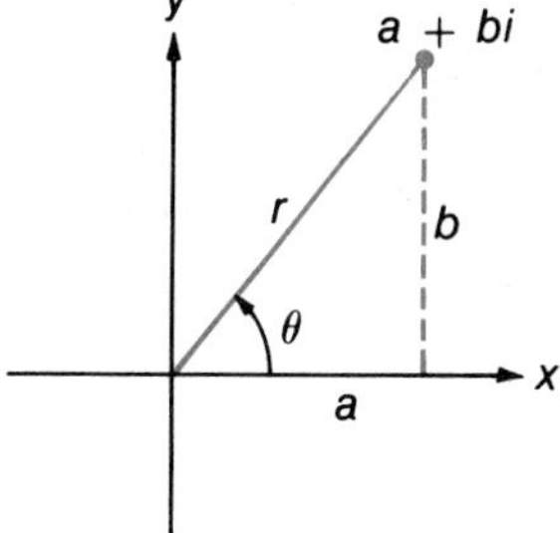

Thus

$$\begin{aligned} a + bi &= r \cos \theta + ir \sin \theta \\ &= r (\cos \theta + i \sin \theta) \end{aligned}$$

This is trigonometric notation for $a + bi$. The angle θ is called the **argument.**

Definition

Trigonometric, or **polar, notation** for the complex number $a + bi$ is

$$r (\cos \theta + i \sin \theta)$$

where $r = |a + bi|$ and θ is the argument. This is often shortened to $\boldsymbol{r \text{ cis } \theta}$.

Change of Notation

Objective: Change from rectangular to trigonometric notation for a complex number and vice versa.

To change from trigonometric notation to **rectangular notation** $a + bi$, we use the formulas $a = r \cos \theta$ and $b = r \sin \theta$.

EXAMPLE 1 Write rectangular notation for $2 (\cos 120° + i \sin 120°)$.

$a = 2 \cos 120° = -1$ Identifying and evaluating a and b
$b = 2 \sin 120° = \sqrt{3}$

Thus $2 (\cos 120° + i \sin 120°) = -1 + i\sqrt{3}$.

To change from rectangular notation to trigonometric notation, we remember that $r = \sqrt{a^2 + b^2}$ and θ is an angle for which $\sin \theta = \frac{b}{r}$ and $\cos \theta = \frac{a}{r}$.

18-9

FIRST FIVE MINUTES

1. In triangle ABC, $m\angle A = 60°$, $b = 2$, $c = 7$. Find the length of side a.
   $a^2 = b^2 + c^2 - 2bc \cos A$
   $= 4 + 49 - 2 \cdot 2 \cdot 7 \cdot \frac{1}{2}$
   $= 39$
   $a = \sqrt{39}$
2. In triangle ABC, $a = 2$, $b = 5$, $c = 6$. Find $m\angle A$.
   $a^2 = b^2 + c^2 - 2bc \cos A$
   $\cos A = \dfrac{a^2 - b^2 - c^2}{-2bc}$
   $m\angle A \approx 18.19° \approx 18°12'$

Change of Notation

Chalkboard Examples

1. Write rectangular notation for $5(\cos 30° + i \sin 30°)$.
   $a = 5\cos 30 = \frac{5\sqrt{3}}{2}$
   $b = 5\sin 30 = \frac{5}{2}$
   Thus,
   $5(\cos 30 + i \sin 30)$
   $= \frac{5\sqrt{3}}{2} + \frac{5i}{2}$
2. Find the trigonometric, or polar, notation for
   $\frac{1}{2} + \frac{i\sqrt{3}}{2}$.
   $r^2 = \frac{1}{4} + \frac{3}{4} = 1$
   $r = 1$
   $\cos \theta = \frac{1}{2}, \sin \theta = \frac{\sqrt{3}}{2}$
   $\theta = 60°$
   Thus,
   $\frac{1}{2} + \frac{i\sqrt{3}}{2}$
   $= \text{cis } 60°$

Multiplication and Trigonometric Notation

Illustrate the geometric significance of Theorem 18-7 by graphing two complex numbers and their product. Explain that the product has an angle measure of $\theta_1 + \theta_2$ and has length r_1r_2.

Chalkboard Examples

1. Find the product of 5 cis 30° and 2 cis 15°.
   $5 \text{ cis } 30° \cdot 2 \text{ cis } 15°$
   $= 5 \cdot 2 \text{ cis } (30° + 15°)$
   $= 10 \text{ cis } 45°$
2. Divide 6 cis 15° by 3 cis 5°.
   $\frac{6 \text{ cis } 15°}{3 \text{ cis } 5°} = \frac{6}{3} \text{ cis } (15° - 5°)$
   $= 2 \text{ cis } 10°$

EXAMPLE 2 Find trigonometric, or polar, notation for $1 + i$.

We note that $a = 1$ and $b = 1$.

$$r = \sqrt{1^2 + 1^2} = \sqrt{2}$$

$$\sin\theta = \frac{1}{\sqrt{2}} \text{ and } \cos\theta = \frac{1}{\sqrt{2}}$$ $\sin\theta = \frac{b}{r}, \cos\theta = \frac{a}{r}$

Thus $\theta = \frac{\pi}{4}$, or 45°, and we have the following.

$$1 + i = \sqrt{2} \text{ cis } \frac{\pi}{4} \text{ or } 1 + i = \sqrt{2} \text{ cis } 45°$$

In changing to trigonometric, or polar, notation, note that there are many angles satisfying the given conditions. We ordinarily choose the smallest positive angle between 0° and 360°.

Try This

a. Write rectangular notation for $\sqrt{2}(\cos 315° + i \sin 315°)$. $1 - i$

b. Write trigonometric, or polar, notation for $1 - i$. $\sqrt{2}(\cos 315° + i \sin 315°)$

Multiplication and Trigonometric Notation

Objective: use trigonometric notation to multiply and divide complex numbers.

Multiplication of complex numbers is somewhat easier to do with trigonometric notation than with rectangular notation. We simply multiply the absolute values and add the arguments. To divide, we divide absolute values and subtract arguments.

Theorem 18-7

For any complex numbers $r_1 \text{ cis } \theta_1$ and $r_2 \text{ cis } \theta_2$,

$$(r_1 \text{ cis } \theta_1)(r_2 \text{ cis } \theta_2) = r_1 \cdot r_2 \text{ cis } (\theta_1 + \theta_2)$$

Theorem 18-8

For any complex numbers $r_1 \text{ cis } \theta_1$ and $r_2 \text{ cis } \theta_2$, $(r_2 \neq 0)$,

$$\frac{r_1 \text{ cis } \theta_1}{r_2 \text{ cis } \theta_2} = \frac{r_1}{r_2} \text{ cis } (\theta_1 - \theta_2)$$

EXAMPLE 3 Find the product of 3 cis 40° and 7 cis 20°.

$$3 \text{ cis } 40° \cdot 7 \text{ cis } 20° = 3 \cdot 7 \text{ cis } (40° + 20°)$$
$$= 21 \text{ cis } 60°$$

EXAMPLE 4 Divide 2 cis π by 4 cis $\frac{\pi}{2}$.

$$\frac{2 \text{ cis } \pi}{4 \text{ cis } \frac{\pi}{2}} = \frac{2}{4} \text{ cis } \left(\pi - \frac{\pi}{2}\right) = \frac{1}{2} \text{ cis } \frac{\pi}{2}$$

Try This

c. Multiply 5 cis 25° by 4 cis 30°. 20 cis 55°

d. Divide 10 cis $\frac{\pi}{2}$ by 5 cis $\frac{\pi}{4}$. 2 cis $\frac{\pi}{4}$

DeMoivre's Theorem

Objective: Use DeMoivre's theorem to find powers and roots of complex numbers.

An important theorem about powers and roots of complex numbers is named for French mathematician DeMoivre (1667 – 1754). Let us consider a number r cis θ and its square.

$$\begin{aligned}(r \text{ cis } \theta)^2 &= (r \text{ cis } \theta)(r \text{ cis } \theta)\\ &= r \cdot r \text{ cis } (\theta + \theta)\\ &= r^2 \text{ cis } 2\theta\end{aligned}$$

Similarly, we see that $(r \text{ cis } \theta)^3 = r \cdot r \cdot r \text{ cis } (\theta + \theta + \theta) = r^3 \text{ cis } 3\theta$. The generalization of this is DeMoivre's theorem.

Theorem 18-9

DeMoivre's Theorem

For any complex number r cis θ and any natural number n, $(r \text{ cis } \theta)^n = r^n \text{ cis } n\theta$.

EXAMPLE 5 Find $(1 + i)^9$.

We first find polar notation.

$$1 + i = \sqrt{2} \text{ cis } 45°$$

Then

$$\begin{aligned}(1 + i)^9 &= (\sqrt{2} \text{ cis } 45°)^9\\ &= (\sqrt{2})^9 \text{ cis } 9 \cdot 45°\\ &= 2^{\frac{9}{2}} \text{ cis } 405°\\ &= 16\sqrt{2} \text{ cis } 45°\end{aligned}$$

405° has the same terminal side as 45°.

Try This

e. Find $(1 - i)^{10}$. 32 cis 270°

f. Find $(\sqrt{3} + i)^4$. 16 cis 120°

DeMoivre's Theorem

Chalkboard Examples

1. Find $(1 + i\sqrt{3})^8$.
   Change $1 + i\sqrt{3}$ to polar notation.
   $r = \sqrt{1 + 3} = 2$
   $\cos \theta = \frac{1}{2}$
   $\theta = 60°$
   $1 + i\sqrt{3} = 2 \text{ cis } 60$
   $(2 \text{ cis } 60°)^8$
   $= 2^8 \text{ cis } 8 \cdot 60$
   $= 256 \text{ cis } 480$
   $= 256 \text{ cis } 120$
   $= 256\cos 120° + i256\sin 120°$
   $= 256\left(-\frac{1}{2}\right) + i\left(256 \cdot \frac{1}{2}\sqrt{3}\right)$
   $= -128 + 128i\sqrt{3}$
2. Find the square roots of $\sqrt{2} + i\sqrt{2}$.
   Change to cis notation.
   $r = \sqrt{2 + 2} = 2$
   $\cos \theta = \frac{\sqrt{2}}{2}$
   $\theta = 45°$
   $\sqrt{2} + i\sqrt{2} = 2 \text{ cis } 45°$
   $(\sqrt{2} + i\sqrt{2})^{1/2}$
   $= \sqrt{2} \text{ cis } \left(\frac{45}{2} + k \cdot \frac{360}{2}\right)$,
   for $k = 0, 1$
   Thus the square roots are
   $\sqrt{2}$cis 22.5 and $\sqrt{2}$cis 202.5, or in rectangular notation
   $1.3066 + 0.5412i$ and
   $-1.3066 - 0.5412i$.

LESSON QUIZ

1. Convert $2(\cos 30° + i \sin 30°)$ to rectangular notation.
   $\sqrt{3} + i$
2. Convert $5\sqrt{3} + 5i$ to polar form.
   10 cis 30°
3. Multiply $(2 + 3i)(1 + 5i)$.
   $-13 + 13i$
4. Find the square root of i.
   $\cos 45° + i \sin 45°$
   $= \frac{\sqrt{2}}{2} + \frac{i\sqrt{2}}{2}$
   or
   $\cos 225° + i \sin 225°$
   $= \frac{-\sqrt{2}}{2} - \frac{i\sqrt{2}}{2}$

As we shall see, every nonzero complex number has two square roots, three cube roots, four fourth roots, and so on. In general, a nonzero complex number has n different n-th roots. These can be found by the formula, which we now state and prove.

Theorem 18-10

The n-th roots of a complex number r cis θ are given by

$$r^{\frac{1}{n}} \text{cis}\left(\frac{\theta}{n} + k \cdot \frac{360°}{n}\right), \text{ where } k = 0, 1, 2, \ldots, n - 1$$

Proof of Theorem 18-10

We show that this formula gives us n different roots by using DeMoivre's theorem. We take the expression for the n-th roots and raise it to the n-th power to show that we get r cis θ.

$$\left[r^{\frac{1}{n}} \text{cis}\left(\frac{\theta}{n} + k \cdot \frac{360°}{n}\right)\right]^n = (r^{\frac{1}{n}})^n \text{cis}\left(\frac{\theta}{n} \cdot n + k \cdot n \cdot \frac{360°}{n}\right)$$

$$= r \text{ cis } (\theta + k \cdot 360°) = r \text{ cis } \theta$$

Thus we know that the formula gives us n-th roots for any natural number k. Next we show that there are at least n different roots. To see this, consider substituting 0, 1, 2, and so on, for k. From 0 to $n - 1$ the angles obtained and their sines and cosines are all different. But when $k = n$ the cycle begins to repeat. There cannot be more than n different n-th roots. This fact follows from the **Fundamental Theorem of Algebra**, considered in Chapter 11.

EXAMPLE 6 Find the square roots of $2 + 2\sqrt{3}i$.

We first find trigonometric notation.

$$2 + 2\sqrt{3}i = 4 \text{ cis } 60°$$

Then

$$(4 \text{ cis } 60°)^{\frac{1}{2}} = 4^{\frac{1}{2}} \text{cis}\left(\frac{60°}{2} + k \cdot \frac{360°}{2}\right), k = 0, 1$$

$$= 2 \text{ cis}\left(30° + k \cdot \frac{360°}{2}\right), k = 0, 1$$

Thus the roots are 2 cis 30° and 2 cis 210°, or $\sqrt{3} + i$ and $-\sqrt{3} - i$.

Try This

g. Find the square roots of $2i$. $1 + i, -1 - i$

h. Find the cube roots of $8i$. $\sqrt{3} + i, -\sqrt{3} + i, -2i$

18-9 EXERCISES

A

Find rectangular notation.

1. $3(\cos 30° + i \sin 30°)$ $\frac{3\sqrt{3}}{2} + \frac{3}{2}i$

2. $5(\cos 60° + i \sin 60°)$ $\frac{5}{2} + \frac{5\sqrt{3}}{2}i$

3. $4(\cos 135° + i \sin 135°)$ $-2\sqrt{2} + 2i\sqrt{2}$

4. $6(\cos 150° + i \sin 150°)$ $-3\sqrt{3} + 3i$

5. $10 \text{ cis } 270°$ $-10i$

6. $12 \text{ cis } 90°$ $12i$

7. $5 \text{ cis } (-45°)$ $\frac{5\sqrt{2}}{2} - \frac{5\sqrt{2}}{2}i$

8. $5 \text{ cis } (-60°)$ $\frac{5}{2} - \frac{5\sqrt{3}}{2}i$

9. $\sqrt{8}\left(\cos \frac{\pi}{4} + i \sin \frac{\pi}{4}\right)$ $2 + 2i$

10. $\sqrt{8}\left(\cos \frac{3\pi}{4} + i \sin \frac{3\pi}{4}\right)$ $-2 + 2i$

11. $4\left(\cos \frac{\pi}{6} + i \sin \frac{\pi}{6}\right)$ $2\sqrt{3} + 2i$

12. $5\left(\cos \frac{\pi}{3} + i \sin \frac{\pi}{3}\right)$ $\frac{5}{2} + \frac{5\sqrt{3}}{2}i$

13. $\sqrt{8} \text{ cis } \frac{5\pi}{4}$ $-2 - 2i$

14. $\sqrt{8} \text{ cis } \left(-\frac{\pi}{4}\right)$ $2 - 2i$

Find trigonometric notation.

15. $-1 + i$ $\sqrt{2} \text{ cis } \frac{3\pi}{4}$ or $\sqrt{2} \text{ cis } 135°$

16. $-1 - i$ $\sqrt{2} \text{ cis } \frac{5\pi}{4}$ or $\sqrt{2} \text{ cis } 225°$

17. $\sqrt{3} + i$ $2 \text{ cis } \frac{\pi}{6}$ or $2 \text{ cis } 30°$

18. $-\sqrt{3} + i$ $2 \text{ cis } \frac{5\pi}{6}$ or $2 \text{ cis } 150°$

19. $10\sqrt{3} - 10i$ $20 \text{ cis } \frac{11\pi}{6}$ or $20 \text{ cis } 330°$

20. $-10\sqrt{3} + 10i$ $20 \text{ cis } \frac{5\pi}{6}$ or $20 \text{ cis } 150°$

21. $2i$ $2 \text{ cis } \frac{\pi}{2}$ or $2 \text{ cis } 90°$

22. $3i$ $3 \text{ cis } \frac{\pi}{2}$ or $3 \text{ cis } 90°$

23. -5 $5 \text{ cis } \pi$ or $5 \text{ cis } 180°$

24. -10 $10 \text{ cis } \pi$ or $10 \text{ cis } 180°$

25. $-4i$ $4 \text{ cis } \frac{3\pi}{2}$ or $4 \text{ cis } 270°$

26. $-5i$ $5 \text{ cis } \frac{3\pi}{2}$ or $5 \text{ cis } 270°$

Convert to trigonometric notation and then multiply or divide.

27. $(1 - i)(2 + 2i)$

28. $(\sqrt{3} + i)(1 + i)$

29. $(10\sqrt{3} + 10i)(\sqrt{3} - i)$

30. $(1 + i\sqrt{3})(1 + i)$

31. $(2\sqrt{3} + 2i)(2i)$

32. $(3\sqrt{3} - 3i)(2i)$

33. $\frac{1 + i}{1 - i}$

34. $\frac{1 - i}{1 + i}$

35. $\frac{-1 + i}{\sqrt{3} + i}$

36. $\frac{1 - i}{\sqrt{3} - i}$

37. $\frac{2\sqrt{3} - 2i}{1 + i\sqrt{3}}$

38. $\frac{3 - 3i\sqrt{3}}{\sqrt{3} - i}$

Raise the number to the power. Give your answer in polar notation.

39. $\left(2 \text{ cis } \frac{\pi}{3}\right)^3$

40. $\left(3 \text{ cis } \frac{\pi}{2}\right)^4$

41. $\left(2 \text{ cis } \frac{\pi}{6}\right)^6$

42. $\left(2 \text{ cis } \frac{\pi}{5}\right)^5$

43. $(1 + i)^6$

44. $(1 - i)^6$

Assignment Guide
Algebra: Omit

Alg w/Trig: Day 1: 1–35 m3, MR
Day 2: 36–64 m3, 65

Comprehensive: 1–64 m4, 65–67, MR

ADDITIONAL ANSWERS

Exercises

27. $4 \text{ cis } 0$
28. $2\sqrt{2} \text{ cis } \frac{5\pi}{12}$
29. $40 \text{ cis } 0$
30. $2\sqrt{2} \text{ cis } \frac{7\pi}{12}$
31. $8 \text{ cis } \frac{2\pi}{3}$
32. $12 \text{ cis } \frac{\pi}{3}$
33. $\text{cis } \frac{\pi}{2}$
34. $\text{cis } \frac{3\pi}{2}$
35. $\frac{\sqrt{2}}{2} \text{ cis } \frac{7\pi}{12}$
36. $\frac{\sqrt{2}}{2} \text{ cis } \frac{23\pi}{12}$
37. $2 \text{ cis } \frac{3\pi}{2}$
38. $3 \text{ cis } \frac{11\pi}{6}$
39. $8 \text{ cis } \pi$ or $8 \text{ cis } 180°$
40. $81 \text{ cis } 0$ or $81 \text{ cis } 0°$
41. $64 \text{ cis } \pi$ or $64 \text{ cis } 180°$
42. $32 \text{ cis } \pi$ or $32 \text{ cis } 180°$
43. $8 \text{ cis } \frac{3\pi}{2}$ or $8 \text{ cis } 270°$
44. $8 \text{ cis } \frac{\pi}{2}$ or $8 \text{ cis } 90°$

45. $-8-8i\sqrt{3}$
46. $-8+8i\sqrt{3}$
47. $-8-8i\sqrt{3}$
48. -64
49. i
50. -1
51. 1
52. $\frac{1}{2}-\frac{\sqrt{3}}{2}i$
53. $\sqrt{2}$ cis 60° and $\sqrt{2}$ cis 240° or $\sqrt{2}$ cis $\frac{\pi}{3}$ and $\sqrt{2}$ cis $\frac{4\pi}{3}$
54. $\sqrt{2}$ cis 105° and $\sqrt{2}$ cis 285° or $\sqrt{2}$ cis $\frac{7\pi}{12}$ and $\sqrt{2}$ cis $\frac{19\pi}{12}$
55. cis 30°, cis 150°, and cis 270° or cis $\frac{\pi}{6}$, cis $\frac{5\pi}{6}$, and cis $\frac{3\pi}{2}$
56. cis 90°, cis 210°, and cis 330° or cis $\frac{\pi}{2}$, cis $\frac{7\pi}{6}$, and cis $\frac{11\pi}{6}$
57. 2 cis 0°, 2 cis 90°, 2 cis 180°, and 2 cis 270° or 2 cis 0, 2 cis $\frac{\pi}{2}$, 2 cis π, and 2 cis $\frac{3\pi}{2}$
58. 2 cis 45°, 2 cis 135°, 2 cis 225°, and 2 cis 315° or 2 cis $\frac{\pi}{4}$, 2 cis $\frac{3\pi}{4}$, 2 cis $\frac{5\pi}{4}$, and 2 cis $\frac{7\pi}{4}$
59. $(1+0i)^3 = (\text{cis } 0)^3 = \text{cis } 0 = 1, \left(-\frac{1}{2}+\frac{\sqrt{3}}{2}i\right)^3 = (\text{cis } 120°)^3 = \text{cis } 0 = 1, \left(-\frac{1}{2}-\frac{\sqrt{3}}{2}i\right)^3 = (\text{cis } 240°)^3 = \text{cis } 0 = 1$
60. cis 60°, cis 180°, cis 300°, or $\frac{1}{2}+\frac{\sqrt{3}}{2}i, -1, \frac{1}{2}-\frac{\sqrt{3}}{2}i$
61. cis 90°, cis 180°, cis 270°, cis 0°, or $\pm 1, \pm i$

For Exercises 62 and 63, see Teacher's Answer Section

Mixed Review

68. 180°
69. 720°
70. −60°
71. 105°
72. $\frac{11}{12}\pi$
73. $\frac{5\pi}{12}$
74. $\frac{\pi}{8}$
75. $-\frac{\pi}{2}$
76. $1, -1, i, -i$
77. $2, -3, \pm\sqrt{2}$
78. $\frac{1}{2}, -2, 3$
79. a. 41.7 mg b. 13.9 mg c. 3.9mg

Raise the number to the power. Give your answer in rectangular notation.

45. $(2 \text{ cis } 240°)^4$
46. $(2 \text{ cis } 120°)^4$
47. $(1+\sqrt{3}i)^4$
48. $(-\sqrt{3}+i)^6$
49. $\left(\frac{1}{\sqrt{2}}+\frac{1}{\sqrt{2}}i\right)^{10}$
50. $\left(\frac{1}{\sqrt{2}}-\frac{1}{\sqrt{2}}i\right)^{12}$
51. $\left(\frac{\sqrt{3}}{2}+\frac{1}{2}i\right)^{12}$
52. $\left(\frac{\sqrt{3}}{2}-\frac{1}{2}i\right)^{14}$

Find the following.

53. the square roots of $-1+\sqrt{3}i$
54. the square roots of $-\sqrt{3}-i$
55. the cube roots of i
56. the cube roots of $-i$
57. the fourth roots of 16
58. the fourth roots of −16

B

59. Every complex number, including 1, has three different cube roots. Show that the three cube roots of 1 are 1, $-\frac{1}{2}+\frac{\sqrt{3}}{2}i$, and $-\frac{1}{2}-\frac{\sqrt{3}}{2}i$, by raising each to the third power. Locate them on a graph.

60. Write −1 as 1 cis 180° to find the three cube roots of −1. Graph the roots.

61. Find the fourth roots of 1.

62. Show that for any complex numbers z, w, $|z \cdot w| = |z| \cdot |w|$. (*Hint*: Let $z = r_1 \text{ cis } \theta_1$ and $w = r_2 \text{ cis } \theta_2$.)

63. Show that for any complex number z and any nonzero complex number w, $\left|\frac{z}{w}\right| = \frac{|z|}{|w|}$.

64. Find the cube roots of 68.4321. $\sqrt[3]{68.4321}$, $\sqrt[3]{68.4321}$ cis 120°, $\sqrt[3]{68.4321}$ cis 240°

65. ***Critical Thinking*** Find the number whose fourth roots are cis 0°, cis 90°, cis 180°, and cis 270°. 1

Challenge

66. Find polar notation for $(\cos\theta + i\sin\theta)^{-1}$. $\cos\theta - i\sin\theta$

67. Compute $\begin{bmatrix} i & 0 \\ 0 & -i \end{bmatrix}^3$. $\begin{bmatrix} -i & 0 \\ 0 & i \end{bmatrix}$

Mixed Review

Change radian measure to degrees. **68.** π **69.** 4π **70.** $-\frac{\pi}{3}$ **71.** $\frac{7\pi}{12}$

Change degree measure to radians. **72.** 165° **73.** 75° **74.** 22.5° **75.** −90°

For each polynomial find all rational roots. Find the other roots, if possible.

76. $x^4 - 1$ **77.** $x^4 + x^3 - 8x^2 - 2x + 12$ **78.** $2x^3 - 3x^2 - 11x + 6$

79. Radioactive Radon-222 is found in certain building materials. It has a half-life of 3.8 days. How much of a 50 mg sample will remain after
a. 1 day?
b. 7 days?
c. 14 days?

Problem Solving: Situational Problem Solving

Predicting Records

Past events can be used as models for making predictions for such events as athletic competitions. You can use the Problem-Solving Guidelines to help you solve a situational problem about predicting times for the mile run.

Situational Problem

The track record in 1875 for the mile run was set by Walter Slade of Great Britain. He ran a mile in 4 minutes, 24.5 seconds. Since that time, the record for the mile race has declined steadily. Use the data below to "predict" the time for 1985 (compare your results with the actual time for 1985), then make predictions for 2000 and 2100.

1875	Walter Slade, Britain	4:24.5	1944	Andersson	4:01.6
1880	Walter George, Britain	4:23.2	1945	Haegg	4:01.4
1882	George	4:21.4	1954	Roger Bannister, Britain	3:59.4
1882	George	4:19.4	1954	John Landry, Australia	3:58
1884	George	4:18.4	1957	Derek Ibbotson, Britain	3:57.2
1894	Fred Bacon, Scotland	4:18.2	1958	Herb Elliott, Australia	3:54.5
1895	Bacon	4:17	1962	Peter Snell, New Zealand	3:54.4
1911	Thomas Connett, U.S.	4:15.6	1964	Snell	3:54.1
1911	John Paul Jones, U.S.	4:15.4	1965	Michel Jazy, France	3:53.6
1913	Jones	4:14.6	1966	Jim Ryun, U.S.	3:51.3
1915	Norman Taber, U.S.	4:12.6	1967	Ryun	3:51.1
1923	Paavo Nurmi, Finland	4:10.4	1975	Filbert Bayi, Tanzania	3:51.0
1931	Jules Ladoumegue, France	4:09.2	1975	John Walker, New Zealand	3:49.4
1933	Jack Lovelock, New Zealand	4:07.6	1979	Sebastian Coe, Britain	3:49
1934	Glenn Cunningham, U.S.	4:06.8	1980	Steve Ovett, Britain	3:48.8
1937	Sydney Wooderson, Britain	4:06.4	1981	Coe	3:48.5
1942	Gunder Haegg, Sweden	4:06.2	1981	Ovett	3:48.4
1942	Arne Andersson, Sweden	4:06.2	1981	Coe	3:47.3
1942	Haegg	4:04.6	1985	Steve Cram, Britain	3:46.3
1943	Andersson	4:02.6			

Possible Assumption

Data in subsequent years follows this trend.

Possible Subproblems

1. Convert the track records to a workable unit of measure (minutes, seconds, etc.).
2. Graph the data. What curve best fits the data?
3. Can you determine an equation for the curve?
4. Use the equation to predict the times for subsequent years.

What do you predict that the record will be in the year 2000? 2100?

Problem Solving: Situational Problem Solving

Find data for other events and use that data to make predictions, if possible.

The data given for the mile can be approximated very well by a linear equation. The "least squares" line relating the record (in seconds) to the year has a correlation coefficient of better than -0.985. The equation of this line is

$$T = -0.346Y + 914.31$$

or, using the year 1875 as a base,

$$T = -0.346(Y - 1875) + 265.56$$

Predictions for 2000 and 2100 using this line are:

year	sec	min
2000	222.3	3:42.3
2100	187.7	3:07.7

How accurate will the linear model be for the future? For the year 2643, we would predict the record to be less than zero seconds!

It is likely that the record will follow more of an exponential curve. If we begin with the 1985 time and assume the record will decrease about 0.13% per year, we would estimate the following records:

year	sec	min
2000	221.9	3:41.9
2100	194.9	3:14.9
2600	101.7	1:41.7
2985	61.6	1:01.6

Even this curve has an unrealistic limit of 0. Some arbitrary limit must be set. The fastest a human has run over any distance has been about 30 mi/h. This would project to a 2-minute mile. Is this a reasonable limit?

Records have been decreasing more quickly than expected (thus linearly) due to faster tracks, improved training methods, better and lighter shoes, and increased interest in running. Could further advances make any limit reachable?

Problem Solving: Application

Students can do further research in this area and answer questions such as these:

What are the lowest and highest orbits possible for a satellite, and what determines these? How does an orbit decay? At what height will a satellite orbit geosynchronously (at the same rate as the earth's rotation), staying in one place relative to the earth? What purpose would it serve for a satellite to do so? What advantages does a lower orbit have (it takes less time to make one revolution)?

Problem Solving: Application

Satellite Tracking

Suppose a satellite is to be put in orbit over the equator 300 miles above the earth. Tracking stations are to be located along the equator. Each tracking station has a scanning screen that covers 180°, as illustrated below.

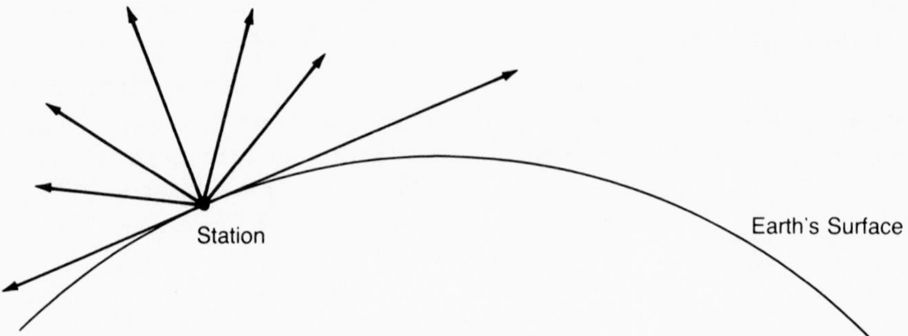

Tracking stations must be located close enough to each other so that there are no "blind spots" or regions where the satellite is not being observed by at least one scanner. The illustration below shows a satellite in a blind spot.

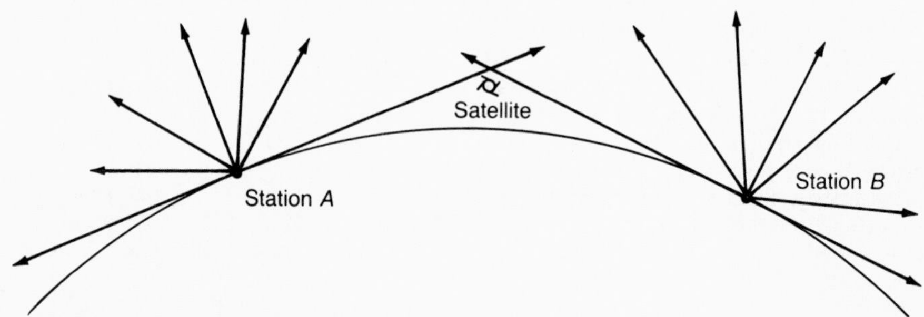

The illustration below shows the farthest distance apart that Stations A and B can be if they are to track the satellite.

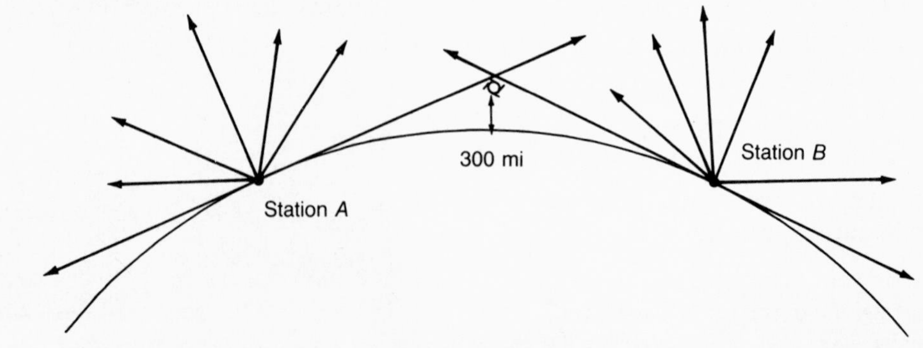

EXAMPLE

Find the maximum possible distance between two tracking stations if they are to scan a satellite in orbit 300 miles above the earth's surface. Use 4000 miles as the radius of the earth.

To solve the problem, first find the distance d, the ground distance from the satellite to one tracking station, and then double it.

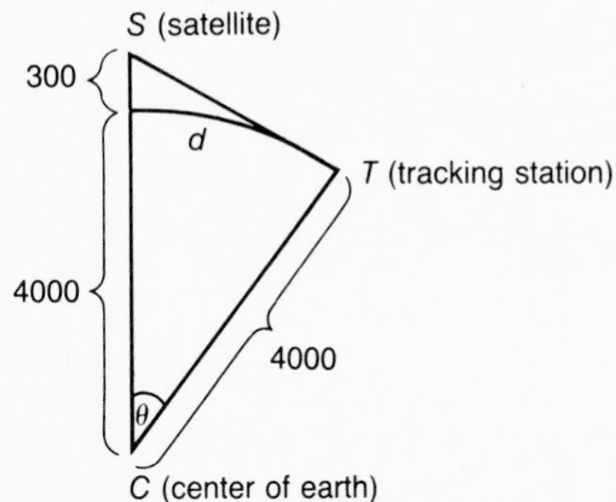

Since ST is tangent to the earth's surface we know that $\angle CTS$ is a right angle and thus

$$\cos\theta = \frac{4000}{4300}$$
$$\approx 0.9302$$

Thus, $\theta \approx 0.3758$ radians.

It follows that $\frac{d}{4000} \approx 0.3758$ or $d \approx 1503$ miles.

Hence, the maximum distance between the two tracking stations is about 3006 miles.

Problems

1. A satellite is to be placed in an equatorial orbit 558 miles above the earth's surface. Find the maximum possible distance between two tracking stations that are to scan the satellite.
2. A satellite is to be placed in an equatorial orbit 70 miles above the moon's surface. The moon has a diameter of 2160 miles. How far apart could tracking stations be placed on the moon's surface to track the satellite?
3. Given that the earth's circumference is approximately 25,000 miles, what is the fewest number of stations needed along the equator to track a satellite in orbit 300 miles above the earth?
4. Suppose only 7 stations could be built along the equator for the satellite in Problem 3. What would need to be done so that the satellite could be tracked through its orbit?
5. What is the lowest orbit possible for the given number of equally spaced stations located along the equator?
   a. 10 **b.** 6

ANSWERS

1. $\approx$ 4000 miles
2. $\approx$ 758 miles
3. $\frac{25,000}{3006} \approx 8.32$, so 9 stations are needed.
4. The satellite must be put into a higher orbit.
5. 203.6 mi, 611.4 mi

ANSWERS

1. $\cos x \cos y - \sin x \sin y$
2. $2 - \sqrt{3}$
3. $\frac{\sqrt{2} + \sqrt{6}}{4}$
4. $\frac{\sqrt{2} - \sqrt{6}}{4}$
5. $2 - \sqrt{3}$
6. $\sin 2\theta = \frac{24}{25}$, $\cos 2\theta = \frac{7}{25}$, $\tan 2\theta = \frac{24}{7}$, Quadrant I
7. $\sin 2\theta = \frac{24}{25}$, $\cos 2\theta = -\frac{7}{25}$, $\tan 2\theta = -\frac{24}{7}$, Quadrant II
8. $\frac{1}{2}\sqrt{2 + \sqrt{3}}$, or $\frac{\sqrt{2} + \sqrt{6}}{4}$
9. $\frac{\sqrt{2 - \sqrt{2}}}{2}$

Chapter 18 Summary and Review

18-1

These sum and difference identities can be used to change or simplify expressions.

$$\cos(\alpha - \beta) \equiv \cos\alpha\cos\beta + \sin\alpha\sin\beta$$
$$\cos(\alpha + \beta) \equiv \cos\alpha\cos\beta - \sin\alpha\sin\beta$$
$$\sin(\alpha - \beta) \equiv \sin\alpha\cos\beta - \cos\alpha\sin\beta$$
$$\sin(\alpha + \beta) \equiv \sin\alpha\cos\beta + \cos\alpha\sin\beta$$
$$\tan(\alpha - \beta) \equiv \frac{\tan\alpha - \tan\beta}{1 + \tan\alpha\tan\beta}$$
$$\tan(\alpha + \beta) \equiv \frac{\tan\alpha + \tan\beta}{1 - \tan\alpha\tan\beta}$$

Use sum and difference identities to simplify the following.

1. $\cos(x + y)$ **2.** $\tan(45° - 30°)$ **3.** $\sin 75°$

4. $\cos\frac{7\pi}{12}$ **5.** $\tan\frac{\pi}{12}$

18-2

These double-angle identities can be used to change or simplify expressions.

$$\sin 2\theta \equiv 2\sin\theta\cos\theta \qquad \cos 2\theta \equiv \cos^2\theta - \sin^2\theta$$
$$\cos 2\theta \equiv 1 - 2\sin^2\theta \qquad \cos 2\theta \equiv 2\cos^2\theta - 1$$
$$\tan 2\theta \equiv \frac{2\tan\theta}{1 - \tan^2\theta} \qquad \sin^2\theta \equiv \frac{1 - \cos 2\theta}{2}$$
$$\cos^2\theta \equiv \frac{1 + \cos 2\theta}{2}$$

Find $\sin 2\theta$, $\cos 2\theta$, $\tan 2\theta$, and the quadrant in which 2θ lies.

6. $\sin\theta = \frac{3}{5}$ (θ is in quadrant I) **7.** $\tan\theta = \frac{4}{3}$ (θ is in quadrant III)

These half-angle identities can be used to change or simplify expressions.

$$\sin\frac{\phi}{2} \equiv \pm\sqrt{\frac{1 - \cos\phi}{2}} \qquad \cos\frac{\phi}{2} \equiv \pm\sqrt{\frac{1 + \cos\phi}{2}}$$
$$\tan\frac{\phi}{2} \equiv \pm\sqrt{\frac{1 - \cos\phi}{1 + \cos\phi}} \qquad \tan\frac{\phi}{2} \equiv \frac{\sin\phi}{1 + \cos\phi}$$
$$\tan\frac{\phi}{2} \equiv \frac{1 - \cos\phi}{\sin\phi}$$

Find the following without using a table or calculator.

8. $\cos 15°$ **9.** $\sin\frac{\pi}{8}$

18-3

Memorizing certain trigonometric identities can help you prove other identities.

Prove the identity.

10. $\tan 2\theta \equiv \dfrac{2\tan\theta}{1-\tan^2\theta}$

18-4

There are several ways of denoting the inverse of the sine function $y = \sin x$. They are $x = \sin y$, $y = \sin^{-1} x$, and $y = \arcsin x$. Unit circles are useful in finding inverse values for trigonometric functions.

Find all values of the following.

11. $\sin^{-1}\dfrac{1}{2}$ **12.** $\arccos -\dfrac{\sqrt{2}}{2}$

Find the following.

13. $\text{Arcsin} -\dfrac{\sqrt{2}}{2}$ **14.** $\text{Cos}^{-1}\dfrac{\sqrt{3}}{2}$

18-5

In solving trigonometric equations, find all solutions from 0 to 2π that make the equation true. You may add any multiple of 2π to obtain other solutions.

Solve, finding all solutions from 0 to 2π.

15. $\sin^2 x - 7\sin x = 0$ **16.** $\sin 2x - \cos x = 0$

18-6

The guidelines for solving a triangle problem are as follows.

1. Draw a sketch of the problem situation.
2. Look for right triangles and sketch them.
3. Mark the known and unknown sides and angles.
4. Express the desired side or angle in terms of known trigonometric ratios, and then solve.

Solve the triangles. Use three-digit precision.

17.

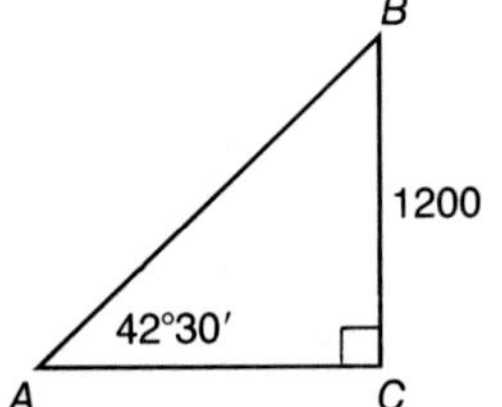

18.

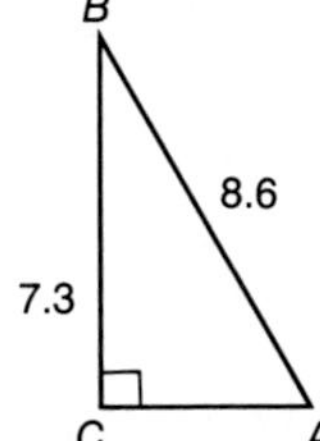

19.

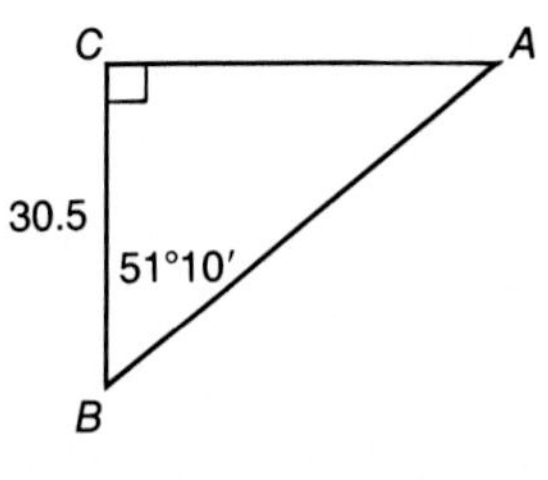

10.

$\tan 2\theta \equiv \dfrac{2\tan\theta}{1-\tan^2\theta}$	
$\tan(\theta+\theta)$	$\dfrac{2\tan\theta}{1-\tan^2\theta}$
$\dfrac{\tan\theta+\tan\theta}{1-\tan\theta\tan\theta}$	
$\dfrac{2\tan\theta}{1-\tan^2\theta}$	

11. $\frac{\pi}{6} + 2k\pi, \frac{5\pi}{6} + 2k\pi$

12. $\frac{3\pi}{4} + 2k\pi, \frac{5\pi}{4} + 2k\pi$

13. $-\frac{\pi}{4}$

14. $\frac{\pi}{6}$

15. $0, \pi, 2\pi$

16. $\frac{\pi}{6}, \frac{5\pi}{6}, \frac{\pi}{2}, \frac{3\pi}{2}$

17. $\angle B = 47°30'$, $b = 1310$, $c = 1776$

18. $\angle A = 58°10'$, $m\angle B = 31°50'$, $b = 4.55$

19. $\angle A = 38°50'$, $b = 37.9$, $c = 48.6$

20. 86.9 ft

21. 3708.8 mi

22. $m\angle C = 60$, $a = 16.3$, $c = 22.0$
23. $m\angle A = 34$, $a = 0.619$, $c = 0.514$
24. $\angle B = 49°30'$, $\angle C = 58°30'$, $c = 4.48$
25. $\angle A = 19°10'$, $\angle C = 25°50'$, $b = 7.96$
26. $\angle A = 33°30'$, $\angle B = 62°10'$, $\angle C = 84°20'$
27. 20.4
28. $-\sqrt{2} + i\sqrt{2}$
29. $\sqrt{2} \text{ cis } \frac{\pi}{4}$ or $\sqrt{2} \text{ cis } 45°$
30. $-1 + i\sqrt{3}$
31. $\sqrt[6]{2} \text{ cis } 15°$, $\sqrt[6]{2} \text{ cis } 135°$, $\sqrt[6]{2} \text{ cis } 255°$

20. A student was asked to estimate the height of a cliff. She stood at the bottom of the cliff and walked to a spot 100 ft away. From this distance, she used a protractor to estimate the angle to the top of the cliff as 41°. What did she calculate as the height of the cliff?

21. A Concorde jet flew from New York to Paris at a speed of 1000 mi/h in a direction of 8°30′ for $3\frac{3}{4}$ hrs. How far north did the jet travel?

18-7, 18-8

In triangles that are not right triangles, use the law of sines: In any triangle ABC, $\frac{a}{\sin A} = \frac{b}{\sin B} = \frac{c}{\sin C}$, or the law of cosines:

In any triangle ABC,
$$a^2 = b^2 + c^2 - 2bc \cos A$$
$$b^2 = a^2 + c^2 - 2ac \cos B$$
$$c^2 = a^2 + b^2 - 2ab \cos C$$

Solve triangle ABC.

22. $m\angle A = 40$, $m\angle B = 80$, $b = 25$

23. $\angle B = 118°20'$, $\angle C = 27°40'$, $b = 0.974$

24. $m\angle A = 72$, $a = 5$, $b = 4$

25.

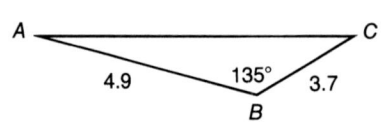

26.

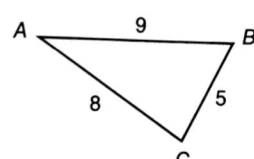

Use the formula $a = \frac{1}{2}bc \sin A$ to find the area of a triangle ABC.

27. $b = 5$, $c = 9$, $m\angle A = 65$

18-9

Trigonometric, or polar, notation for the complex number $a + bi$ is $r(\cos\theta + i\sin\theta)$, where r is the absolute value and θ is the argument. This is sometimes shortened to $r \text{ cis } \theta$ and is derived by using the formulas $a = r\cos\theta$ and $b = r\sin\theta$.

28. Find rectangular notation for $2(\cos 135° + i \sin 135°)$.

29. Find trigonometric notation for $1 + i$.

30. Find 2 cis 120°. Write your answer in rectangular notation.

Recall that the n-th roots of a complex number $r \text{ cis } \theta$ are given by

$$r^{\frac{1}{n}} \text{ cis } \left(\frac{\theta}{n} + k \cdot \frac{360°}{n}\right) \text{ where } k = 0, 1, 2, \cdots, n - 1$$

31. Find the cube roots of $1 + i$.

See also Problem 18, Computer-Assisted Problem Solving, page 853.

Chapter 18 Test

Use sum and difference identities to simplify the following.

1. $\sin(x - y)$ $\sin x \cos y - \cos x \sin y$

2. $\cos\left(\frac{\pi}{2} + \frac{\pi}{3}\right)$ $-\frac{\sqrt{3}}{2}$

3. $\tan 105°$ $-2 - \sqrt{3}$

4. $\sin 15°$ $\frac{\sqrt{2 - \sqrt{3}}}{2}$, or $\frac{\sqrt{6} - \sqrt{2}}{4}$

Find $\sin 2\theta$, $\cos 2\theta$, $\tan 2\theta$, and the quadrant in which 2θ lies.

5. $\cos\theta = \frac{4}{5}$ (θ in Quadrant I) $\frac{24}{25}, \frac{7}{25}, \frac{24}{7}$, Quadrant I

6. $\tan\theta = -\frac{3}{4}$ (θ in Quadrant II) $-\frac{24}{25}, \frac{7}{25}, -\frac{24}{7}$, Quadrant IV

Find the following without using tables.

7. $\sin\frac{\pi}{12}$ $\frac{1}{2}\sqrt{2 - \sqrt{3}}$

8. $\sin\frac{7\pi}{8}$ $\frac{\sqrt{2 - \sqrt{2}}}{2}$

9. Prove the identity $\tan\theta \equiv \frac{\sin 2\theta}{1 + \cos 2\theta}$.

Find the following.

10. $\arccos\frac{1}{2}$

11. $\text{Arccos}\,\frac{\sqrt{3}}{2}$

Solve, finding all solutions from 0 to 2π.

12. $2\cos^2 x + 1 = -3\cos x$

13. $\cos^2 x = 1 + \sin^2 x$

Solve the triangles. Angle C is a right triangle. Use three-digit precision.

14. $a = 9.2, c = 10.1$

15. $a = 28.5, m\angle B = 49°10'$

16. While walking through Chicago, Jenna estimated that the angle to the top of the 1454 ft tall Sears Tower was 15°. How far was she from the building?

Solve triangle ABC.

17. $\angle B = 117°10', \angle C = 26°50', b = 0.9763$

18. $m\angle A = 50, a = 9, b = 10$

19. $a = 3.8, c = 4.6, m\angle B = 132$

20.

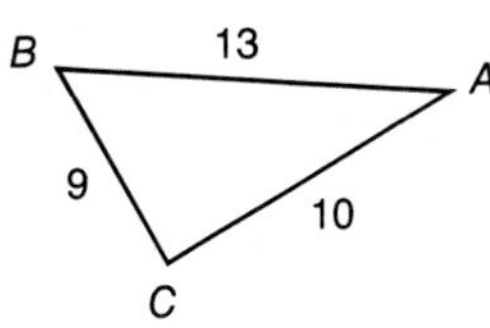

21. Find rectangular notation for $3(\cos 120° + i \sin 120°)$.

22. Find trigonometric notation for $1 - i$.

23. Find $(2 \text{ cis } 150°)^3$. Give your answer in rectangular notation.

Challenge

24. Solve $\sqrt{\sin x} = \frac{1}{2}\sqrt{2\sqrt{2}}$.

ADDITIONAL ANSWERS

9. $\tan\theta \equiv \frac{\sin 2\theta}{1 + \cos 2\theta}$

$\tan\theta$	$\frac{2\sin\theta\cos\theta}{1 + \cos^2\theta - \sin^2\theta}$
	$\frac{2\sin\theta\cos\theta}{2\cos^2\theta}$
	$\frac{\sin\theta}{\cos\theta}$
	$\tan\theta$

10. $\frac{\pi}{3} + 2k\pi, \frac{5\pi}{3} + 2k\pi$

11. $\frac{\pi}{6}$

12. $\frac{2\pi}{3}, \frac{4\pi}{3}, \pi$

13. $0, \pi, 2\pi$

14. $m\angle A = 65°40', m\angle B = 24°20', b = 4.16$

15. $m\angle A = 40°50', b = 33.0, c = 43.6$

16. 5426 ft

17. $m\angle A = 36°, a = 0.645, c = 0.495$

18. $m\angle B = 58°20', m\angle C = 71°40', c = 11.2$

19. $m\angle A = 21°30', m\angle C = 26°30', b = 7.68$

20. $m\angle A = 43°40', m\angle B = 50°10', m\angle C = 86°10'$

21. $-\frac{3}{2} + \frac{3\sqrt{3}}{2}i$

22. $\sqrt{2} \text{ cis } \frac{7\pi}{4}$

23. $8i$

24. $45° + 360°k, 135° + 360°k$

Test Item Analysis

Item	Lesson
1–4	18-1
5, 6	18-2
7, 8	18-1, 18-2
9	18-3
10, 11	18-4
12, 13, 24	18-5
14–16	18-6
17, 18	18-7
19, 20	18-8
21–23	18-9

ADDITIONAL ANSWERS

5. $a > 2$
6. $x < 1$
7. $-5 < x < 13$
8. $-6 \le y \le 14$
15. $3(2x - 11y)^2$
16. $\left(\frac{1}{3}x^3 + 7y\right)\left(\frac{1}{3}x^3 - 7y\right)$
17. $2(x + 2)(x - 2)(x + 3)$
18. 0, 6
19. 8, 1
20. $\frac{x + 6}{3(x - 2)}$
21. $\frac{a - 3}{5a + 2}$
22. $\frac{17}{4}$
23. $-5, 3$

Chapters 1-18 Cumulative Review

1-3 Evaluate each expression for $a = -2$ and $c = 7$.

1. $|a - 2c| - |2a - c| - ac$ 19
2. $-5|a^2 + ac| - 3|2ac - 1|$ −137

2-1 Solve.

3. $4x - 3[4(x + 6) + 1] = 2x - 5$ −7
4. $\frac{2}{3}x + \frac{3}{4} = 2(x - 11) + \frac{7}{4}$ $15\frac{3}{4}$

2-4, 2-6 Solve.

5. $4a + 3 < 9a - 7$
6. $6.1x - 1.1 < 0.8x + 4.2$
7. $-14 < 3x + 1 < 40$
8. $|4 - y| \le 10$

3-8

9. The cost of driving one new car 20,000 miles in a year is \$4380. The cost of driving 15,000 miles in a year is \$3690. Fit a linear function to the data, and predict the cost of driving the car 1000 miles in a year. \$0.138m + \$1620; \$1758

4-1, 4-4 Solve these systems.

10. $5a - b = -11$
    $4a + 12b = 4$ (−2, 1)
11. $a + b - 4c = -22$
    $-a - 2b + 3c = 13$
    $-2a + b + c = 11$ (−1, 3, 6)

5-1 – 5-3 Simplify.

12. $(8x^3 - 6x + 5) - (10x^4 + 4x^2 + 2x)$ $-10x^4 + 8x^3 - 4x^2 - 8x + 5$
13. $(4xy + 5y)(x^2 - 2)$ $4x^3y + 5x^2y - 8xy - 10y$
14. $(2x - 1)^3$ $8x^3 - 12x^2 + 6x - 1$

5-3, 5-5 Factor.

15. $12x^2 - 132xy + 363y^2$
16. $\frac{1}{9}x^6 - 49y^2$
17. $2x^3 + 6x^2 - 8x - 24$

5-7 Solve.

18. $6x - x^2 = 0$
19. $x^2 - 9x = -8$

6-1, 6-2 Simplify.

20. $\frac{x^2 + 4x - 12}{3x^2 - 12x + 12}$
21. $\frac{5a - 2}{a + 3} \div \frac{25a^2 - 4}{a^2 - 9}$

6-6 Solve.

22. $\frac{a - 3}{a + 2} = \frac{1}{5}$
23. $\frac{15}{m} - \frac{15}{m + 2} = 2$

7-1 – 7-9 Simplify.

24. $\sqrt[4]{32}$ **25.** $\sqrt{90x^3}$ **26.** $\sqrt{24}\sqrt{75}$ **27.** $\sqrt{x^2 + 6x + 9}$

28. $5\sqrt[3]{32} - 2\sqrt[3]{108} - 5\sqrt[3]{4}$ **29.** $(2\sqrt{7} - 3\sqrt{5})(\sqrt{7} + \sqrt{5})$

30. $(5 - 3i) - (6 - 4i)$ **31.** $(8 + 4i)(-5 - 3i)$ **32.** $\frac{2 + i}{3 - 2i}$

8-1, 8-3 Solve.

33. $9x^2 - 2 = 0$ **34.** $x^2 - 3x - 9 = 0$ **35.** $2x^{\frac{2}{3}} - x^{\frac{1}{3}} - 28 = 0$

8-7

36. The surface area of a sphere varies directly with the square of its radius. A sphere with radius $\frac{10}{\sqrt{\pi}}$ cm has a surface area of 400 cm². What is the surface area of a sphere with radius 2 cm? $k = 4\pi$, so the surface area is 16π.

9-1 Test for symmetry with respect to the *x*-axis and the *y*-axis.

37. $4y^2 = 2x - 1$
x-axis

38. $5x^2 - 2y^2 = 6$
Both axes

39. $y^3 - x^3 = -7$
Neither

9-6 For each of the following functions, graph the function and find the vertex, the line of symmetry, and the maximum or minimum value. See Additional Answers.

40. $f(x) = (x + 2)^2 - 4$
$(-2, -4)$, $x = -2$, min: -4

41. $f(x) = -2(x - 1)^2 + 3$
$(1, 3)$, $x = 1$, max: 3

10-1 – 10-4 Solve.

42. Find the midpoint of the segment with endpoints (4, 5) and (6, −7).

43. Find the center and radius of the circle $(x + 1)^2 + (y + 3)^2 = 4$.

44. Find the center, vertices, foci, and asymptotes for the hyperbola $\frac{(y + 3)^2}{25} - \frac{(x + 1)^2}{16} = 1$. Graph the hyperbola.

11-2 – 11-4 Solve.

45. Use synthetic division to find the quotient and remainder $(x^3 - 27) \div (x - 3)$.
Q: $x^2 + 3x + 9$, R 0

46. Suppose a polynomial of degree 5 with rational coefficients has roots 8, $6 - 7i$, $\frac{1}{2} + \sqrt{11}$. Find the other roots. $6 + 7i$, $\frac{1}{2} - \sqrt{11}$

47. Find the rational roots of $2x^3 - 3x^2 - x + 1$, if they exist. If possible, find the other roots. $\frac{1}{2}$, $\frac{1 + \sqrt{5}}{2}$, $\frac{1 - \sqrt{5}}{2}$

12-1 Write an equation of the inverse relation.

48. $2x + 3y - 7 = 0$
$2y + 3x - 7 = 0$

49. $y = 2x^2 + 3$
$x = 2y^2 + 3$

50. $f(x) = 2x$ $f^{-1}(x) = \frac{x}{2}$

12-3 Convert to logarithmic equations.

51. $10^{0.4771} = 3$
$\log_{10} 3 = 0.4771$

52. $y = 3^x$
$\log_3 y = x$

53. $x^y = z$
$\log_x z = y$

12-7 Solve.

54. $4^{3x + 5} = 16$ -1 **55.** $\log(x + 9) - \log x = 1$ 1 **56.** $9^{y^2} \cdot 3^{5y} = 27$ $-3, \frac{1}{2}$

---

24. $2\sqrt[4]{2}$
25. $3x\sqrt{10x}$
26. $30\sqrt{2}$
27. $x + 3$
28. $-\sqrt[3]{4}$
29. $-1 - \sqrt{35}$
30. $-1 + i$
31. $-28 - 44i$
32. $\frac{4 + 7i}{13}$
33. $\frac{\sqrt{2}}{3}, -\frac{\sqrt{2}}{3}$
34. $\frac{3 \pm 3\sqrt{5}}{2}$
35. $64, -\frac{343}{8}$

40.

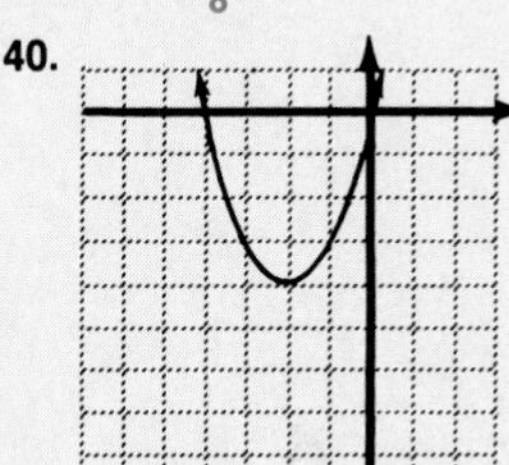

41.

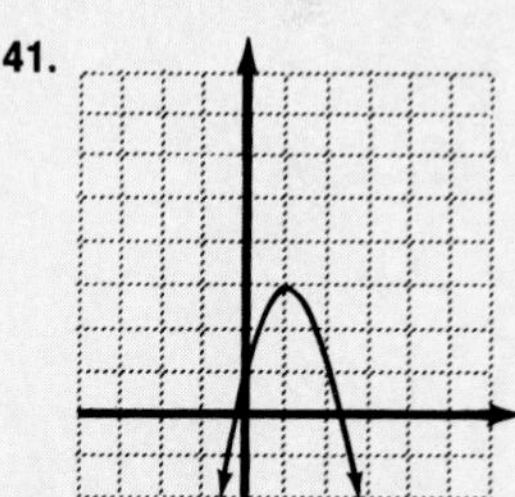

42. $(5, -1)$
43. Center: $(-1, -3)$, radius: 2
44. Center: $(-1, -3)$
Vertices: $(-1, 2)$, $(-1, -8)$
Foci: $(-1, -3 + \sqrt{41})$, $(-1, -3 - \sqrt{41})$

Asymptotes: $y + 3 = \frac{5}{4}(x + 1)$, $y + 3 = -\frac{5}{4}(x + 1)$

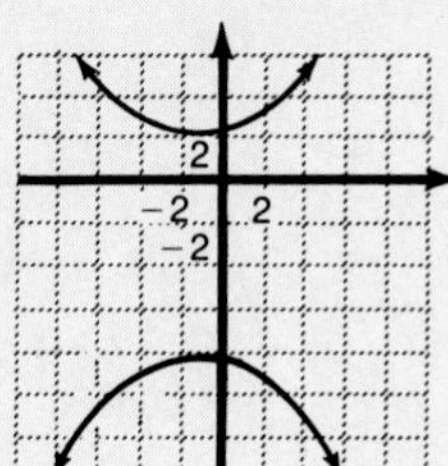

57. $\begin{bmatrix} -3 & 6 & 30 \\ 9 & -12 & 24 \\ 0 & 15 & -3 \end{bmatrix}$

58. $\begin{bmatrix} 28 & -7 \\ 58 & 15 \\ -29 & -15 \end{bmatrix}$

59. $\begin{bmatrix} -\frac{3}{16} & \frac{13}{48} & \frac{7}{24} \\ \frac{1}{64} & \frac{1}{192} & \frac{19}{96} \\ \frac{5}{64} & \frac{5}{192} & -\frac{1}{96} \end{bmatrix}$

62. Answers may vary; $(-1)^n(n+1)$

63. -41

64. $13\frac{13}{27}$

65. $\frac{27}{4}$

66. 15120

67. 120

68. 70

72.

Stem	Leaf
1	6, 7, 3
2	3, 4, 9, 8, 7, 3, 3, 9, 7, 2, 3, 2
3	1, 3, 1, 4

73. Answers may vary

Interval	Tally	Frequency
13–15	I	1
16–18	II	2
19–21		0
22–24	~~IIII~~ II	7
25–27	II	2
28–30	III	3
31–33	III	3
34–36	I	1

74. Mean: 25, mode: 23, median: 24

75.
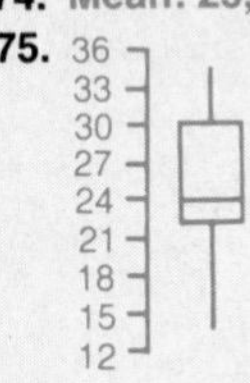

84. Cosine and secant are positive, the other four are negative

13-1 – 13-6

Let $A = \begin{bmatrix} -1 & 2 & 10 \\ 3 & -4 & 8 \\ 0 & 5 & -1 \end{bmatrix}$ and $B = \begin{bmatrix} 2 & 1 \\ -5 & -3 \\ 4 & 0 \end{bmatrix}$

57. Find $3A$. **58.** Find AB. **59.** Find A^{-1}. **60.** Evaluate $|A|$. 192

61. Solve using Cramer's rule. $7x - 2y = 10$
$9x + y = 20$ (2, 2)

14-1 – 14-4

62. State a rule for finding the n-th term of $-2, 3, -4, 5, \ldots$.

63. Find the 17th term of the arithmetic sequence 7, 4, 1, ...

64. Evaluate $\sum_{k=1}^{6} \left(\frac{1}{3}\right)^{k-3}$.

65. Find the sum of the infinite geometric series $9 - 3 + 1 - \cdots$.

15-1 – 15-4 Evaluate.

66. ${}_9P_5$ **67.** $5!$ **68.** $\binom{8}{4}$

69. Expand $(2a + 3y)^4$. $16a^4 + 96a^3y + 216a^2y^2 + 216ay^3 + 81y^4$

15-6

70. If one card is drawn from a deck of 52 cards, what is the probability of that card being black or a king? $\frac{7}{13}$

15-7

71. If a die is rolled, what is the probability of rolling an even number or a multiple of 3? $\frac{2}{3}$

16-1–16-3

For Problems 72 – 79, the scores on an English quiz are

16, 23, 24, 31, 33, 29, 28, 27, 23, 17, 13, 23, 31, 34, 29, 27, 22, 23, 22.

72. Construct a stem-and-leaf diagram.

73. Construct a frequency distribution showing the relative frequency.

74. Find the mean, mode, and median.

75. Construct a box and whisker plot.

76. What is the range? 21 **77.** Find the mean deviation. 4.6

78. Find the variance. 31.1 **79.** Find the standard deviation. 5.6

17-2 In which quadrant does the terminal side of each angle lie?

80. $-45°$ IV **81.** $240°$ III **82.** $-120°$ III **83.** $460°$ II

84. Give the signs of the six trigonometric function values for a rotation of $-420°$.

17-3

85. Convert 100° to radian measure.

86. Convert $\frac{2\pi}{3}$ radians to degree measure.

17-4–17-8

87. Graph the sine function between -2π and 2π.

88. Check the identity $\cos\left(\frac{\pi}{2} - \theta\right) \equiv \sin\theta$.

89. Sketch the graph of $y = \frac{1}{2}\cos(2\theta)$. Determine the amplitude and the period. $A = \frac{1}{2}$, period $= \pi$

90. Simplify $\tan y \sin y (\cot y - \csc y)$. $\sin y - \tan y$

18-1

91. Simplify $\cos(\alpha + \beta) + \cos(\alpha - \beta)$. $2\cos\alpha\cos\beta$

18-2

92. Simplify $\cos^2\frac{x}{2} - \sin^2\frac{x}{2}$. $\cos x$

18-3

93. Prove $\frac{1 - \cos x}{\sin x} \equiv \frac{\sin x}{1 + \cos x}$.

18-4

94. Find all values of $\arcsin\frac{1}{2}$.

18-5 Solve. Find all solutions from 0 to 2π.

95. $\cos^2 x - 1 = 2\sin x$ $0, \pi, 2\pi$

96. $2\tan x = 1 - \tan^2 x$ $\frac{\pi}{8}, \frac{5\pi}{8}, \frac{9\pi}{8}, \frac{13\pi}{8}$

18-6 Solve the triangle. Angle C is the right angle.

97. $a = 9.2, c = 10.1$

98. $m\angle A = 67°40', b = 135$

18-7 Solve triangle ABC.

99. $m\angle B = 150°, a = 3, b = 7$

18-8 Solve triangle ABC.

100. $a = 6, b = 7, c = 10$

18-9 Write in trigonometric, or polar, notation.

101. $-\sqrt{3} - i$ $2 \text{ cis } \frac{7\pi}{6}$

102. $\frac{1}{2} + \frac{\sqrt{3}}{2}i$ $1 \text{ cis } \frac{\pi}{3}$

Write in rectangular notation.

103. 10 cis 270° $-10i$

104. $4(\cos 135° + i\sin 135°)$ $-2\sqrt{2} + 2i\sqrt{2}$

---

85. $\frac{5\pi}{9}$

86. 120°

87.

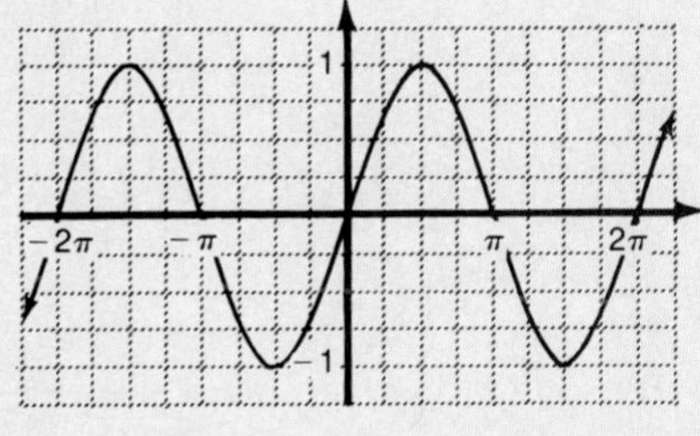

88. $\cos\left(\frac{\pi}{2} - \theta\right)$

$\equiv \cos\frac{\pi}{2}\cos\theta + \sin\frac{\pi}{2}\sin\theta$

$\equiv \quad 0 \quad + \quad 1 \quad \sin\theta$

$= \sin\theta$

89.

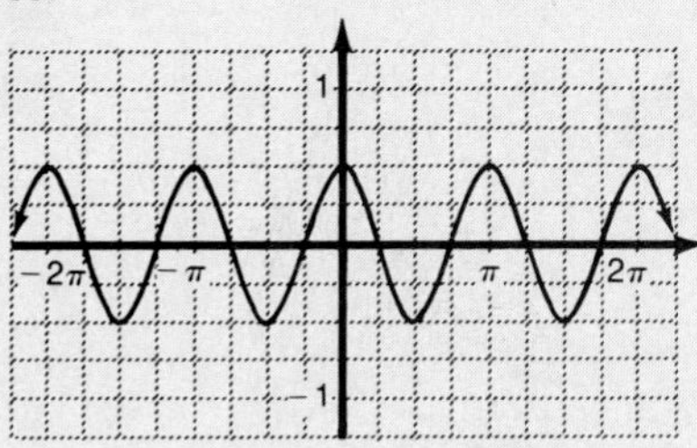

93.

$\frac{1 - \cos x}{\sin x}$	$\frac{\sin x}{1 + \cos x}$
$\frac{(1 - \cos x)(1 + \cos x)}{(\sin x)(1 + \cos x)}$	$\frac{(\sin x)(\sin x)}{(1 + \cos x)(\sin x)}$
$(1 - \cos x)(1 + \cos x)$	$(\sin x)(\sin x)$
$1 - \cos^2 x$	$\sin^2 x$
$\sin^2 x$	$\sin^2 x$

94. $\frac{\pi}{6} + 2k\pi, \frac{5\pi}{6} + 2k\pi$

97. $\angle A = 65°40'$
$\angle B = 24°20'$
$b = 4.2$

98. $\angle B = 22°20'$
$a = 328, c = 355$

99. $\angle A = 12°20'$
$\angle C = 17°40'$
$c = 4.25$

100. $\angle A = 36°10'$
$\angle B = 43°30'$
$\angle C = 100°20'$

Computer-Assisted Problem Solving

Some problems encountered in algebra require higher mathematics, such as calculus, to solve. Many of these problems, however, can be translated from algebra into computer programs in order to find a solution. While many languages exist for this purpose, the easiest to understand is BASIC (Beginner's All-purpose Symbolic Instruction Code). This appendix shows how problems that require tedious calculations to find an answer can be solved quickly using a computer.

As you input each program, look at the codes used in each line. These codes, often written as English words, give the computer instructions. Notice the FOR and NEXT statements in the programs. These allow the computer to make many repetitions of the lines in between.

The following lines will assist you in using the programs to solve each problem.

Before typing in a program, type NEW and press [return]. This will erase any program that is in memory.

Type each line and press [return].

If a mistake is noticed in a line, simply retype the line.

After inputting a program, check your work by typing LIST [return]. This will display the program on the screen. Compare it carefully with the program in the book. A mistake may cause a Syntax Error or an incorrect answer.

To save a program, first be sure there is a system disk in the drive. Think of a unique name for the program, such as MAXAREA for the program on the next page. Then type SAVE MAXAREA [return]. Any file already on the disk named MAXAREA will be replaced by the program, so be careful. You may want to save updated versions of a program as MAXAREA1, MAXAREA2, and so on.

To use a program later, save any program currently in memory, then type LOAD MAXAREA [return] at that time. (Note that loading a program also erases any program in memory.) Then type RUN [return].

Problem 1: Finding the Maximum Area

(for use after Chapter 1)

Windows are sold by "united" inches, that is, the sum of the height and the width. For the Clearys' new house, the developer will allow windows of 60 united inches. What dimensions should they choose to provide the maximum sunlight from each window?

Program

```
10  REM WINDOW AREA
15  REM "H", "W", AND "A" REPRESENT THE HEIGHT,
    WIDTH, AND AREA OF THE WINDOW
20  FOR H = 1 TO 59
30  W = 60 - H
40  A = H * W
45  REM "MAX" REPRESENTS THE MAXIMUM AREA OF THE
    WINDOW, "BH" AND "BW" REPRESENT THE HEIGHT
    AND WIDTH FOR THIS AREA
50  IF A > MAX THEN MAX = A:BH = H:BW = W
60  NEXT H
70  PRINT "MAKE WINDOWS ";BH;" INCHES BY ";BW;"
    INCHES"
```

Extension

Ampersand, Inc. charges $1.50 for each inch of window height and 95 cents for each inch of width. What is the cost of the window with the maximum area for 70 united inches?

Problem 2: Design Decisions Involving Area and Volume

(for use after Chapter 2)

A designer at the local paper-cup factory is asked to design a cup of 16 in^3 in the form of a right cylinder open at the top. What dimensions require the least amount of material to meet that criterion?

Program

```
10  REM CUP DESIGN
15  REM "MNA" REPRESENTS THE MINIMUM AREA OF THE
    CUP
20  MNA = 2000
```

Maximum Area

You may want to have students insert line 55 to see how the program works.

```
55 PRINT "FOR A HEIGHT
   OF ";H;" AND A WIDTH
   OF ";W;" THE AREA
   IS ";A
```

Program Notes

In line 30, we know $W + H = 60$. Solving for W, $W = 60 - H$.

In line 50, the variable *MAX* starts at 0. Every time we exceed it, we "remember" the values of the height and width with the variables *BH* and *BW*.

Answer to Problem

```
RUN
MAKE WINDOWS 30 INCHES BY
30 INCHES
```

A square creates a window with greatest area.

Answer to Extension

Replace the following lines.

```
20 FOR H = 1 TO 69
30 W = 70 - H
RUN
MAKE WINDOWS 35 INCHES BY
35 INCHES
```

The cost is $35 \cdot \$1.50 + 35 \cdot \$0.95 = \$85.75$.

Design Decisions

Review the formulas for the area and volume of a cylinder.

You may want students to insert line 65 to see the process the computer takes.

```
65 PRINT "THE RADIUS
   IS ";R;" THE HEIGHT
   IS ";H;" THE AREA
   IS ";A
```

Program Notes

In line 20, 2000 is an arbitrary large number.

In line 30, if $R > 2.26$, then the area of the base > 16 and H is 0.

In line 40, Volume $= \pi r^2 h = 16$.

Thus $h = \frac{16}{\pi r^2}$.

In line 50, Area $= A =$ lateral area + area bottom $= 2\pi rh + \pi r^2$.

Answer to Problem

```
RUN
THE RADIUS SHOULD BE
1.71999999 INCHES
THE HEIGHT SHOULD BE
1.72239774 INCHES
```

For a cup with minimum surface area, the radius should be 1.72 in. and the height should be 1.72 in.

Answer to Extension

Replace the following line.

```
50 A = 2 * 3.14 * R * H +
1.25 * 3.14 * R ^ 2
RUN
THE RADIUS SHOULD BE
1.59999999 INCHES
THE HEIGHT SHOULD BE
1.99044589 INCHES
```

For a cup with lowest cost, the radius should be 1.6 in. and the height should be 2.0 in.

Equations of Lines

This program can be used to do many of the exercises in Chapter 3, and can be easily modified to predict using a linear model.

Program Notes

lines 70 on print the point-slope equation once M and B are found. Formatting corrections in lines 75–100 are used to avoid printing equations like Y = 0X + 2, Y = 3X + 0, Y = 1X + 5, Y = 4X + −3, and so on.

Answer to Problem

```
RUN
ENTER X1,Y1 ?14,20
POINT OR SLOPE? POINT
ENTER X2,Y2, ?35,-6
THE POINT SLOPE EQUATION
IS Y = -1.23809524X +
37.3333333
RUN
ENTER X1,Y1 ?-12,5
POINT OR SLOPE? SLOPE
ENTER SLOPE -2.5
THE POINT SLOPE EQUATION
IS Y = -2.5X - 25
```

```
25  REM "R", "H", AND "A" REPRESENT THE RADIUS,
    HEIGHT, AND AREA OF THE CUP
30  FOR R = .1 TO 2.26 STEP .01
40  H = 16 / (3.14 * R ^ 2)
50  A = 2  3.14  R  H + 3.14  R ^ 2
55  REM "BR" AND "BH" REPRESENT THE RADIUS AND
    HEIGHT FOR THE MINIMUM AREA
60  IF A < (MNA) THEN MNA = A:BR = R:BH = H
70  NEXT R
80  PRINT " THE RADIUS SHOULD BE " ;BR;" INCHES"
90  PRINT " THE HEIGHT SHOULD BE " ;BH;" INCHES"
```

Extension

For the problem above, the stiffer material for the bottom of the cup is one-and-one-quarter times more expensive than the material for the sides. Find the dimensions of the cup with the lowest cost.

Problem 3: Equations of Lines

(for use after Chapter 3)

Find and display the equation of a line given either two points or one point and the slope. Then find the equation of **a.** The line through (14, 20) and (35, −6) **b.** The line with slope −2.5 through (−12, 5).

Program

```
10  REM   EQUATIONS OF LINES
15  PRINT "ENTER X1,Y1 ";: INPUT X1, Y1
20  INPUT "POINT OR SLOPE? ";X$
30  IF X$ = "SLOPE" THEN INPUT "ENTER SLOPE" ;M
    :GOTO 55
40  PRINT "ENTER X2,Y2 ";: INPUT X2,Y2
50 M = (Y2 - Y1) / (X2 - X1)
55 B = Y1 - M  X1
60  PRINT "THE POINT SLOPE EQUATION IS"
70  PRINT "Y =";
75  IF M < 0 THEN PRINT "-";
80  IF M < > 0 AND M < > 1 AND M < > - 1 THEN
    PRINT ABS (M);
85  IF M < > 0 THEN PRINT "X";
90  IF M < > 0 AND B > 0 THEN PRINT "+ ";
95  IF B < 0 THEN PRINT "- ";
```

```
100 IF B <  > 0 OR M = 0 THEN PRINT ABS (M);
105 PRINT
```

Extension

Find the equation of the lines through (x_1, y_1) perpendicular to the lines found above.

Problem 4: Systems of Equations

(for use after Chapter 4)

John Thomas plans to visit the Farmers' Livestock Market to buy pigs, cows, and sheep. His three objectives are to buy at least one of each animal, spend exactly $100, and buy exactly 100 animals. If the market charges $8 for each cow, $3 for a sheep, and 50 cents for a pig, how many of each type of animal should he buy?

Examining this problem, we might see two equations. If we let x represent the number of cows, let y be the number of sheep, and z stand for the number of pigs, we obtain

$$x + y + z = 100 \text{ (the number of animals must be 100)}$$
$$8x + 3y + 0.5z = 100 \text{ (the total cost must be \$100.00)}$$

We have a system of two equations with three unknowns.

Program

```
10  REM FARMER'S PROBLEM
15  REM X, Y, AND Z REPRESENT THE NUMBERS OF COWS,
    SHEEP, AND PIGS RESPECTIVELY
20  FOR X = 1 TO 12
30  FOR Y = 1 TO 30
40  FOR Z = 2 TO 98 STEP 2
50  IF X + Y + Z = 100 THEN GOTO 70
55  REM IF THE NUMBER OF ANIMALS DOES NOT TOTAL
    100 WE SKIP LINE 70
60  GOTO 80
65  REM IF THE COST OF THE ANIMALS IS $100 THEN WE
    PRINT THE NUMBER OF EACH KIND
70  IF 8 * X + 3 * Y + .5 * Z = 100 THEN PRINT
    X;" COWS, ";Y;" SHEEP, ";Z;" PIGS"
80  NEXT Z  90  NEXT Y  100 NEXT X
```

Extension

A school store sells pens for 9 cents, erasers for 6 cents, and paper clips at two for 1 cent. An algebra class is asked to determine how to buy at least one of each item while spending exactly $1 on exactly 100 items.

Answer to Extension

Add the following lines.

```
107 IF F = 1 THEN STOP
108 F = 1
110 M = -1  M: PRINT
    "FOR THE LINE
    PERPENDICULAR TO
    THIS ONE": GOTO 55
```

For a.,

```
FOR THE LINE
PERPENDICULAR TO THIS
ONE THE POINT SLOPE
EQUATION IS Y =
.807692308X + 8.69230769
```

For b.,

```
FOR THE LINE
PERPENDICULAR TO THIS
ONE THE POINT SLOPE
EQUATION IS Y =
.4X + 9.8
```

Systems of Equations

You may want to have students insert

```
45 PRINT "THE NUMBER OF
   ANIMALS TOTAL ";
   X + Y + Z
57 PRINT "THE COST OF
   THESE ANIMALS
   IS ";8 * x + 3 * y +
   5 * z
```

Program Notes

In line 30, the most we can spend on sheep is $100 − $8 − $1 = $91. Therefore, we can buy $\frac{91}{3}$ sheep or 30.

In line 40, since we must spend exactly $100, we can count by 2s. We cannot buy over 100 animals, hence we can stop at 98.

Answer to Problem

```
RUN
1 COWS, 17 SHEEP, 82 PIGS
2 COWS, 14 SHEEP, 84 PIGS
3 COWS, 11 SHEEP, 86 PIGS
4 COWS, 8 SHEEP, 88 PIGS
5 COWS, 5 SHEEP, 90 PIGS
6 COWS, 2 SHEEP, 92 PIGS
```

There are six different combinations, all of which are solutions.

See page 854 for Answer to Extension.

More Volume Problems

Finding the maximum capacity is equivalent to finding the maximum cross-sectional area.

The program will run faster if students change WIDTH TO WIDTH/2 in line 30.

Students can insert line 55 to see how the program is working.

```
55 PRINT "X IS ";X;
   " THE AREA IS ";AREA
```

Answer to Problem

```
RUN
INPUT THE WIDTH OF THE
GUTTER 8
TURN UP 1.99999998 INCHES
ON EACH SIDE
THE CROSS-SECTIONAL AREA
IS 7.99999995 SQUARE
INCHES
```

Turn sides up 2.00 in.

Answer to Extension

Replace the following lines.

```
40 AREA = X * (WIDTH / 2
   - X)
70 PRINT "THE DUCT
   SHOULD BE ";BESTX;
   " BY ";WIDTH / 2 -
   BESTX;" INCHES"
```

```
RUN
INPUT THE WIDTH OF THE
AIR DUCT 15
THE DUCT SHOULD BE
3.74999994 BY 3.75000006
INCHES
THE CROSS-SECTIONAL AREA
IS 14.0624999 SQUARE
INCHES
```

The dimensions are 3.75 in. by 3.75 in., a square.

Time and Distance Problems

You may want students to add line 75 to see the times for each iteration.

```
75 PRINT "LANDING ";10
   -X;" MILES FROM THE
   STORE, THIS TRIP
   TAKES ";T;" HOURS"
```

Problem 5: More Volume Problems

(for use after Chapter 5)

A gutter is to be made from a roll of aluminum 8 in. wide. How many inches should be turned vertically up at each side in order to obtain the maximum carrying capacity?

Program

```
10  REM MAX GUTTER
15  REM "X" REPRESENTS THE AMOUNT WE TURN UP
20  INPUT "INPUT THE WIDTH OF THE GUTTER ";WIDTH
30  FOR X = .1 TO WIDTH STEP .01
35  REM FINDING THE AREA OF A CROSS-SECTION
40  AREA = X * (WIDTH - 2 * X)
50  IF AREA > (MAXAREA) THEN MAXAREA = AREA:BESTX
    = X
60  NEXT X
70  PRINT "TURN UP ";BESTX;" INCHES ON EACH
    SIDE"
80  PRINT "THE CROSS-SECTIONAL AREA IS";
    MAXAREA;" SQUARE INCHES "
```

Extension

Sheet metal 15 in. wide is to be folded into a rectangular right prism to be used as an air duct. What are the width and height of the air duct with the greatest carrying capacity?

Problem 6: Time and Distance Problems

(for use after Chapter 6)

Fernando's island home is 4 miles offshore from a straight beach. There is a convenience store on the beach 10 miles north of the closest point to Fernando. If Fernando can row 4 mi/h and walk 5 mi/h, to what point on the beach should he row his boat in order to get to the store in the least possible time?

Program

```
10  REM ROW AND WALK PROBLEM
15  REM TIME REPRESENTS THE MINIMUM TIME FOR THE
    TRIP
20  TIME = 20
30  FOR X = .1 TO 10 STEP .1
```

```
33   REM R IS THE DISTANCE HE ROWS
37   REM USING THE PYTHAGOREAN THEOREM TO FIND R
40   R = SQR (16 + X ^ 2)
45   REM W IS THE DISTANCE HE WALKS
50   W = 10 - X
53   REM T IS THE TIME FOR THE TOTAL TRIP
57   REM USING TIME = RATE/DISTANCE TO FIND T
60   T = R / 4 + W / 5
65   REM C IS THE DISTANCE ALONG THE BEACH MEASURED
     FROM THE STORE
70   IF T < TIME THEN TIME = T:C = 10 - X
80   NEXT X
90   PRINT "HE SHOULD LAND AT A POINT ";C;" MILES
     FROM THE STORE."
100  PRINT "THE TRIP WILL TAKE ";TIME;" HOURS"
```

Extension

For the problem above, assume that Fernando's house is 3 miles offshore, that the store is 5 miles to the north, and that he can row at 3 mi/h and walk at 4 mi/h.

Problem 7: Chase Problems

(for use after Chapter 7)

A ship traveling due south at 17 mi/h is 5 miles east of a speedboat. The speedboat wants to intercept the ship by aiming at some point along the ship's intended path. If the speedboat averages 25 mi/h, how far ahead of the ship should its pilot aim?

Program

```
10   REM SHIP CHASE1
15   REM "T" REPRESENTS TIME
20   FOR T =.1 TO 5 STEP .1
25   REM "SHIPD" AND "SPDBTD" REPRESENT THE
     DISTANCE THE SHIP AND SPEEDBOAT TRAVEL
30   SHIPD = 17 * T
40   SPDBTD = 25 * T
50   IF SPDBTD > = SQR (5 ^ 2 + SHIPD ^ 2) THEN 70
60   NEXT T
70   PRINT "THE SPEEDBOAT SHOULD AIM ";SHIPD;"
     MILES AHEAD OF THE SHIP"
```

Program Notes

In line 20, 20 is an arbitrary number. In line 30, *x* represents miles measured north of the point on the beach closest to Sandy.

Answer to Problem

```
RUN
HE SHOULD LAND AT A POINT
4.70000001
MILES FROM THE STORE.
THE TRIP WILL TAKE
2.60000753 HOURS
```

He should land 4.7 miles from the store. The trip will take 2.6 hours, or 2 hours 36 minutes.

Answer to Extension

Replace the following lines.

```
30 FOR X = .1 TO 5 STEP
   .1
50 W = 5 - X
60 T = R / 3 + W / 4
70 IF T < TIME THEN TIME
   = T:C = 5 - X
RUN
HE SHOULD LAND AT A POINT
1.60000001 MILES FROM THE
STORE.
THE TRIP WILL TAKE
1.91143788 HOURS
```

He should land 1.6 miles from the store. The trip will take 1.9 hours, or 1 hour 54 minutes.

Chase Problems

Review the Pythagorean theorem. Students can insert line 45 to see the process the computer takes.

```
45 PRINT "AFTER ";T;
   " HOURS THE SPEEDBOAT
   WILL TRAVEL "
   ;SPDBTD;" MILES AND
   THE SHIP WILL TRAVEL "
   ;SHIPD;" MILES."
```

You may want students to insert line 55 to see if the speedboat will reach the ship.

```
55 PRINT "THE SPEEDBOAT
   MUST TRAVEL ";SQR
   (25 + SHIPD ^ 2);" TO
   INTERCEPT THE SHIP"
```

Program Notes

In line 20, 5 is an arbitrary number. In line 50, we use the Pythagorean theorem to find the distance the speedboat must travel. As soon as the speedboat meets or exceeds this distance, we jump out of the loop and print the distance the ship has traveled.

Answer to Problem

```
RUN
THE SPEEDBOAT SHOULD AIM
5.1 MILES AHEAD OF THE
SHIP
```

See page 854 for Answer to Extension.

Extension

A sailboat sailing east at 12 mi/h is 9 miles due north of a second sailboat traveling at 15 mi/h. How far ahead of the first boat should the second boat aim in order to intercept it in the least amount of time?

Problem 8: Predictions by Repeated Calculations

(for use after Chapter 8)

All 700 guests congregate on the main floor of a new museum. Every 15 minutes, the guests circulate in the following manner: one fourth of the people on the main floor go to the balcony, one half of the people in the balcony move to the lounge, and one half of the people in the lounge go to the main floor. How many people will be on the main floor after half an hour? 1 hour? 5 hours?

Program

```
10  REM MUSEUM CIRCULATION
20  M = 700
30  INPUT "INPUT THE NUMBER OF HOURS ";HOURS
35  REM "M", "L", AND "B" REPRESENT THE NUMBER
    OF PEOPLE ON THE MAIN FLOOR, LOUNGE, AND
    BALCONY RESPECTIVELY
40  FOR C = 1 TO HOURS * 4
50  B = B + 1 / 4 * M
60  M = 3 / 4 * M
70  L = L + 1 / 3 * B
80  B = 2 / 3 * B
90  M = M + 1 / 2 * L
100 L = 1 / 2 * L
110 NEXT C
120 PRINT M;" PEOPLE ON THE MAIN FLOOR AT THE END
    OF ";HOURS;" HOURS"
130 PRINT L;" PEOPLE IN THE LOUNGE ";B;" PEOPLE
    IN THE BALCONY"
```

Predictions

Students can add line 115 to view the computer process.

```
115 PRINT M;" PEOPLE ON
    THE MAIN FLOOR ";L;
    " PEOPLE IN THE
    LOUNGE ";B;" PEOPLE
    ON THE BALCONY"
```

Answer to Problem

```
RUN
INPUT THE NUMBER OF
HOURS .5
472.743056 PEOPLE ON THE
MAIN FLOOR AT THE END OF
.5 HOURS
57.1180556 PEOPLE IN THE
LOUNGE
170.138889 PEOPLE IN THE
BALCONY
RUN
INPUT THE NUMBER OF
HOURS 1
411.685897 PEOPLE ON THE
MAIN FLOOR AT THE END OF
1 HOURS
88.3080754 PEOPLE IN THE
LOUNGE
200.006028 PEOPLE IN THE
BALCONY
RUN
INPUT THE NUMBER OF
HOURS 5
400.000221 PEOPLE ON THE
MAIN FLOOR AT THE END OF
5 HOURS
99.999988 PEOPLE IN THE
LOUNGE
199.999793 PEOPLE IN THE
BALCONY
```

Extension

The next day, there are 700 patrons in the museum again. However, 100 go directly to the balcony and 150 to the lounge. The pattern of circulation proceeds as before. How many people are on the main floor after half an hour? 1 hour? 5 hours?

Problem 9: Maximizing Revenues

(for use after Chapter 9)

The Metro Bus Co. charges a 75 cent fare and carries 9000 passengers daily. Studies show that the number of riders decreases directly as the square of the fare increases, according to the function $RD(F) = \frac{5}{6}F^2$ where F represents the increase. What new fare would maximize the bus company's income?

Program

```
10  REM BUS FARES
15  REM "R" REPRESENTS THE MAXIMUM REVENUE
20  R = 75 * 9000
25  REM "RD(F)" IS A FUNCTION WHICH REPRESENTS
    THE REDUCTION IN THE NUMBER OF PASSENGERS
30  DEF FN RD(F) = 5 / 6 * F ^ 2
35  REM "F" AND "NR" REPRESENT THE FARE INCREASE
    AND THE REVENUE FOR THE NEW FARE
40  FOR F = 1 TO 104
50  NR = (75 + F) * (9000 - FN RD(F))
55  REM "MF" REPRESENTS THE FARE INCREASE FOR THE
    GREATEST REVENUE
60  IF NR > R THEN R = NR:MF = F
70  NEXT F
80  PRINT "A FARE OF ";75 + MF;" CENTS WOULD
    PROVIDE THE MOST REVENUE"
```

Extension

New studies show that the relation between the decrease in passengers and the increase in fare follows the linear function $RD(F) = 30F$. What new fare would maximize the bus company's income?

Problem 10: Distance Problems

(for use after Chapter 10)

Find the endpoints of the shortest segment through (1, 8) that ends on the x- and y- axes. Then enter and run the following program. Round the answers to the nearest tenth.

Program

```
10  REM SHORTEST SEGMENT
15  REM MINDIST WILL REPRESENT THE LENGTH OF THE
    SHORTEST SEGMENT
```

Maximizing Revenues

Review function notation.

Students can insert line 65 to view the computer process.

```
65 PRINT "THE FARE IS "
   ;75 + F;" THE
   DECREASE IN PASSENGERS
   IS ";FN RD(F); " THE
   REVENUE IS ";NR
```

Program Notes

In line 20, the company is now making $9000 \cdot 75 = 675{,}000$ cents = \$6750.
In line 40, if $F > 104$, then $RD(F) > 9000$ and the number of passengers falls below 0.
In line 50, Revenue = Fare (cost per passenger) · number of passengers.

Answer to Problem

```
RUN
A FARE OF 115 CENTS WOULD
PROVIDE THE MOST REVENUE
```

Answer to Extension

Replace the following lines.

```
30 DEF FN RD(F) = 30 * F
40 FOR F = 1 TO 300
RUN
A FARE OF 187 CENTS WOULD
PROVIDE THE MOST REVENUE
```

Distance Problems

You may want students to insert line 57 to see the process the computer takes.

```
57 PRINT "THE LENGTH IS "
   ;D;" THE Y-INTERCEPT
   IS ";Y/;" THE
   X-INTERCEPT IS ";X2
```

Students can insert line 65 to speed up the program.

```
65 IF MINDIST >D THEN
GOTO 80
```

Keep in mind that once the segment starts to grow, it will continue to grow.

Program Notes

In line 30, $y \neq 8$. Otherwise, we will divide by 0 in line 40.
In line 40, use the two-point formula $y - y_1 = \frac{y_2 - y_1}{x_2 - x_1}(x - x_1)$ where (x_1, y_1) is (0,YICP), (x_2, y_2) is (1, 8), and (x, y) is (XICP, 0).

Answer to Problem

```
RUN
THE SHORTEST SEGMENT IS
11.1803406 UNITS IN
LENGTH
THE ENDPOINTS ARE
(0, 10.001) AND
(4.99800095 ,0)
```

Answer to Extension

Replace the following lines.

```
30 FOR Y = 13.001 TO 50
   STEP .1
40 X = 4 * Y / (Y - 13)
80 PRINT "THE SHORTEST
   LADDER IS ";MINDIST;
   " FEET"
90 PRINT "PLACE THE
   LADDER ";XCRDNT -
   4;" FEET FROM THE
   FENCE"
RUN
THE SHORTEST LADDER IS
22.8341155 FEET
PLACE THE LADDER
8.81206563 FEET FROM THE
FENCE
```

Synthetic Division

You may want to have students add line 125 to see the coordinates of all the points.

```
125 PRINT "X = ";X;
    " Y = ";VLU
```

The program is intended first to make a rough estimate of the roots, and then to run again for closer approximations.

Students should insert line 180 GOTO 70 to prevent the program from stopping.

Program Notes

In line 140, if the curve crosses the *x*-axis, then we average the two *x* values to approximate a root.

Answer to Problem

```
RUN
INPUT TWO X-VALUES AND
THE ACCURACY -10, 10, 1
-7 IS A ROOT
-2 IS A ROOT
ONE ROOT IS APPROXIMATELY
3.5
```

```
20  MINDIST = 1000
25  REM YICP WILL BE THE Y-COORDINATE OF THE POINT
    ALONG THE Y-AXIS
30  FOR YICP = 8.001 TO 50 STEP .1
35  REM WE FIND THE X-COORDINATE OF THE POINT
    ALONG THE X-AXIS BY SOLVING THE EQUATION
    THROUGH (0,YICP) AND (1,8)
40  XICP = YICP / (YICP - 8)
45  REM USING THE PYTHAGOREAN THEOREM TO FIND THE
    DISTANCE OF THE SEGMENT
50  D = SQR (XICP ^ 2 + YICP ^ 2)
55  REM XCRDNT AND YCRDNT ARE THE VALUES OF THE X
    AND Y INTERCEPTS OF THE SHORTEST SEGMENT
    THROUGH (1,8)
60  IF D < MINDIST THEN MINDIST = D:YCRDNT =
    YICP:XCRDNT = XICP
70  NEXT YICP
80  PRINT "THE SHORTEST SEGMENT IS ";MINDIST;"
    UNITS IN LENGTH"
90  PRINT "THE ENDPOINTS ARE (0,";YCRDNT;") AND
    (";XCRDNT;",0)"
```

Extension

A fence 135 ft high is 4 ft from the side of a house. John wishes to know the length of the shortest ladder that will rest on the ground outside the fence and on the side of the house.

Problem 11: Synthetic Division

(for use after Chapter 11)

The method of synthetic division is an iterative process, which suggests that we can use the computer to find the solution. Use pencil and paper to estimate the roots to $P(x) = x^3 + 5.5x^2 - 17.5x - 49$ between -10 and 10. Now use the following program to estimate the roots to the nearest thousandth.

Program

```
10  REM SYNTHETIC DIVISION
15  REM "DG" REPRESENTS THE DEGREE OF THE
    FUNCTION
20  DG = 3
```

```
25  REM POLY(DG) IS AN ARRAY WHICH REPRESENTS THE
    COEFFICIENTS
30  DIM POLY(DG)
40  FOR X = 0 TO DG
50  READ POLY(X)
60  NEXT X
65  REM FIRST AND LAST ARE THE VALUES BETWEEN
    WHICH WE WISH TO EVALUATE THE FUNCTION
70  INPUT "INPUT TWO X-VALUES AND THE
    ACCURACY";FIRST, LAST, ACC
80  FOR X = FIRST TO LAST STEP ACC
90  VLU = 0
95  REM LINES 100-120 USE SYNTHETIC DIVISION TO
    ASSIGN "VLU" THE VALUE OF POLY(X)
100 FOR P = 0 TO DG
110 VLU = VLU * X + POLY(P)
120 NEXT P
130 IF VLU = 0 THEN PRINT X;" IS A ROOT"
135 REM PREVLU IS THE PREVIOUS VALUE OF THE
    FUNCTION "POLY"
140 IF SGN (PREVLU * VLU) = - 1 THEN PRINT "ONE
    ROOT IS APPROXIMATELY ";(X - ACC + X) / 2
150 PREVLU = VLU
160 NEXT X
170 DATA 1,5.5,-17.5,-49
```

Extension

Modify the program to find the roots to $x^4 + 9.734x^3 - 17.511x^2 - 304.052x - 332.563$.

Problem 12: Decisions Involving Distance

(for use after Chapter 12)

Sam plans a bicycle trip to his aunt's house by pedaling down his street and then veering across a large field to complete his trip. His velocity is 12 mi/h on the street and 4 mi/h across the field. If he does not take the shortcut, he has to ride 3 miles to the corner, make a left turn, and travel another 2 miles to his aunt's house. At what point should he begin his shortcut?

Program

```
10  REM SAM'S TRIP
```

```
RUN
INPUT TWO X-VALUES AND
THE ACCURACY 3, 4, .1
ONE ROOT IS APPROXIMATELY
3.55
RUN
INPUT TWO X-VALUES AND
THE ACCURACY 3.5, 3.6,
.01
3.5 IS A ROOT
```

The roots between −10 and 10 are −7, −2, and 3.5.

Answer to Extension

Replace the following lines.

```
 20 DG = 4
170 DATA 1, 9.734,
    -17.511, -304.052,
    -332.563
RUN
INPUT FIRST, LAST, AND
ACC -10, 10, .001
ONE ROOT IS APPROXIMATELY
-7.00050324
ONE ROOT IS APPROXIMATELY
-6.99950323
ONE ROOT IS APPROXIMATELY
-1.23350229
ONE ROOT IS APPROXIMATELY
5.50049844
```

Decisions Involving Distance

Review the distance formula.
You may want students to insert line 75 to see the process the computer takes.

```
75 PRINT X;" MILES FROM
   THE CORNER, THE TIME
   ON THE STREET IS "
   ;T2;" THE TIME ACROSS
   THE FIELD IS "
   ;T1
```

Program Notes

In line 20, if Sam stays on the street, the minimum time is 5 miles ÷ 12 mi/h.
In line 40, use the distance formula to find the distance across the field.
In line 50, Time = Distance ÷ Velocity.

Answer to Problem

```
RUN
HE SHOULD TURN .700000003
MILES FROM THE CORNER.
```

He should turn 0.7 miles from the corner.

Answer to Extension

Replace the following lines.

```
LIST
20 MNMT = 1 / 3
40 T1 = ( SQR (X ^ 2 +
   4)) / 8
50 T2 = (3 - X) / 15
RUN
HE SHOULD TURN 0 MILES
FROM THE CORNER.
```

He should stay on the street.

Matrix Inverses

Review dependent and independent equations.

Program Notes

Lines 80 through 120 compute the triangular matrix (zeros below the main diagonal).

Lines 170 through 210 print the elements in the inverse matrix.

Lines 220 through 260 obtain a zero in element *M*(*I*, *Z*).

Lines 270 through 350 switch rows until a nonzero element appears in the main diagonal. An error message appears if the matrix has no inverse.

Answer to Problem

```
RUN
THE ELEMENTS OF THE
INVERSE MATRIX ARE
-11 -4  6
  2  0 -1
  2  1 -1
```

Answer to Extension

Replace the following line.

```
360 DATA -2, 1, 2, 1, 0,
    -2, 0, 5, -8
RUN
THE ELEMENTS OF THE
INVERSE MATRIX ARE
-5    -9  1
-4    -8  1
-2.5  -5 .5
```

Using the inverse matrix, we find $x = 1.1$, $y = -3.2$, $z = 5.3$

```
15  REM "MNMT" REPRESENTS THE MINIMUM TIME FOR
    THE TRIP
20  MNMT = 5/12
30  FOR X = 3 TO 0 STEP - .1
35  REM "T1", "T2", AND "TT" REPRESENT THE TIME
    ACROSS THE FIELD, ON THE STREET, AND THE TOTAL
40  T1 = ( SQR (X ^ 2 + 4)) / 4
50  T2 = (3 - X) / 12
60  TT = T1 + T2
65  REM "BX" REPRESENTS THE DISTANCE AT WHICH
    TIME IS A MINIMUM
70  IF TT < MNMT THEN MNMT = TT:BX = X
80  NEXT X
90  PRINT "HE SHOULD TURN ";BX;" MILES FROM THE
    CORNER."
```

Extension

The next day Sam decides to take his sister's moped. The moped can travel at 15 mi/h on the street and 8 mi/h across the field. Based on this information, where should he begin his shortcut in order to arrive at his destination in the shortest amount of time?

Problem 13: Matrix Inverses

(for use after Chapter 13)

As we have seen, systems of equations can be solved using matrices. Matrix operations are easily adapted to computer programs, which quickly handle repetitive operations. Find the inverse of

$$\begin{bmatrix} 1 & 2 & 4 \\ 0 & -1 & 1 \\ 2 & 3 & 8 \end{bmatrix}$$

Program

```
10  REM INVERSE OF A MATRIX
20  X = 3: REM THE MATRIX IS 3 BY 3
30  DIM M(X,X): DIM I(X,X)
40  FOR R = 1 TO X: FOR C = 1 TO X
50  READ M(R,C): REM READING MATRIX ELEMENTS
60  IF R = C THEN I(R,C) = 1: REM I() IS THE
    INVERSE MATRIX
70  NEXT C: NEXT R
80  FOR Z = 1 TO X - 1
```

```
90  IF M(Z,Z) = 0 THEN GOSUB 270
100 FOR I = Z + 1 TO X
110 GOSUB 220: REM COMPUTE A ZERO IN M(I,Z)
120 NEXT I: NEXT Z
130 FOR Z = X TO 2 STEP - 1
140 FOR I = 1 TO Z - 1
150 GOSUB 220: REM COMPUTE A ZERO IN M(I,Z)
160 NEXT I: NEXT Z
170 PRINT "THE ELEMENTS OF THE INVERSE MATRIX
    ARE "
180 FOR R = 1 TO X: FOR C = 1 TO X
190 PRINT I(R,C) / M(R,R);" ";
200 NEXT C: PRINT : NEXT R
210 END
220 FIRST = M(I,Z): REM FIRST IS A DUMMY VARIABLE
230 FOR J = 1 TO X
240 M(I,J) = M(I,J) - M(Z,J) * FIRST / M(Z,Z)
250 I(I,J) = I(I,J) - I(Z,J) * FIRST / M(Z,Z)
260 NEXT J: RETURN
270 ZT = Z: REM ZT IS A DUMMY VARIABLE
280 FOR C = 1 TO X
290 DM = M(Z,C):DI = I(Z,C)
300 M(Z,C) = M(ZT + 1,C):I(Z,C) = I(ZT + 1,C)
310 M(ZT + 1,C) = DM:I(ZT + 1,C) = DI
320 NEXT C
330 ZT = ZT + 1
340 IF M(Z,Z) = 0 THEN GOTO 280
350 RETURN
360 DATA 1,2,4,0,-1,1,2,3,8
```

Extension

Solve the following system.

$$\begin{aligned} -2x + y + 2z &= 5.2 \\ x \quad\quad - 2z &= -9.5 \\ 5y - 8z &= -58.4 \end{aligned}$$

Problem 14: Repeated Calculations

(for use after Chapter 14)

The Colonial Insurance Company insures 45% of Kesseltown. Of the remaining citizens, 35% are covered by National and 20% by Wilderness. Each year, Colonial loses 5% of its insureds to each of its competitors, while National and Wilderness lose 7% of theirs to Colonial. In 3 years, what percent of Kesseltown will be insured by each insurance company? in 10 years?

Repeated Calculations

Students can add line 85 to see the process the computer takes.

```
85 PRINT "COLONIAL HAS "
   ;C;" NATIONAL HAS "
   ;N;" WILDERNESS HAS "
   ;W
```

Program Notes

In line 60, the percentage Colonial has after one year is equal to the original percentage minus twice what it loses to either company, plus what it gains from both companies.

Answer to Problem

```
RUN
INPUT THE NUMBER OF YEARS
3
IN 3 YEARS 43.362715%
WILL BE WITH COLONIAL
34.35132% WILL BE WITH
NATIONAL 22.285965% WILL
BE WITH WILDERNESS
RUN
INPUT THE NUMBER OF YEARS
10
IN 10 YEARS 41.769731%
WILL BE WITH COLONIAL
32.7450018% WILL BE WITH
NATIONAL 25.4852672% WILL
BE WITH WILDERNESS
```

Answer to Extension

Replace the following lines.

```
50 NC = C * .05:NN = N *
   .05:NW = W * .07
55 C2 = C * .08
60 C = C - NC - C2 +
   NN + NW
70 N = N - NN + C2
RUN
INPUT THE NUMBER OF YEARS
3
IN 3 YEARS 38.31457% WILL
BE WITH COLONIAL
39.680165% WILL BE WITH
NATIONAL 22.005265% WILL
BE WITH WILDERNESS
RUN
INPUT THE NUMBER OF YEARS
10
32.3111923% WILL BE WITH
COLONIAL
44.5460319% WILL BE
NATIONAL 23.1427758% WILL
BE WITH WILDERNESS
```

Probability

You may want students to add the following line to see the cards chosen for each trial

```
145 PRINT CARD$ (C1),CARD¢
     (C2)
```

Program Notes

We use 0–51 for the cards rather than 1–52 because it makes calculations in line 70 simpler. Similarly, the 4 suits are 0–3, the 13 ranks are 0–12.

Lines 70–90 give the cards numbered 0 to 51 names, for example, card 15, the suit is $\left[\frac{15}{13}\right] = 1$, the rank is $15 - 1 \cdot 13 = 2$. The card is thus the four of clubs.

In line 150, RIGHT$ (CARD$(C1),6)) represents the last 6 characters of CARD$(C1). The last 6 characters of ACE OF HEARTS is HEARTS. LEFT$ may be used similarly.

Answer to Problem

```
RUN
INPUT NUMBER OF TRIALS
1000 THE PROBABILITY IS
7E-03
```

Answers may vary. Note that the above answer is in scientific notation.

$7E\text{-}03 = 7 \times 10^{-3} = 0.007$

Answer to Extension

Replace the following lines.

```
150 IF CARD$ (C1) = "KING
    OF HEARTS" AND RIGHT$
    (CARD$ (C2),6) <>
    "HEARTS" AND LEFT$
    (CARD$ (C2),4) <>
    "KING" THEN S = S + 1
160 IF CARD$ (C2) = "KING
    OF HEARTS" AND RIGHT$
    (CARD$ (C1),6) <>
    "HEARTS" AND LEFT$
    (CARD$ (C1),4) <>
    "KING" THEN S = S + 1
```

```
RUN
INPUT NUMBER OF TRIALS
1000 THE PROBABILITY IS
0.29
```

Answers may vary.

Program

```
10  REM INSURANCE PROBLEM
20  C = .45:N = .35:W = .2
30  INPUT "INPUT THE NUMBER OF YEARS ";NMBR
40  FOR YEAR = 1 TO NMBR
50  NC = C * .05:NN = N * .07:NW = W * .07
60  C = C - 2 * NC + NN + NW
70  N = N - NN + NC
80  W = W - NW + NC
90  NEXT YEAR
100 PRINT "IN ";NMBR;" YEARS ";C * 100;"% WILL
    BE WITH COLONIAL"
110 PRINT N * 100;"% WILL BE WITH NATIONAL ";W *
    100;"% WILL BE WITH WILDERNESS"
```

Extension

In the problem above, a new pricing program helps National gain 8% of Colonial's insureds while losing only 5% of their own. The situation with Wilderness remains unchanged. What portion of the Kesseltown market can National expect to have in 3 years? 10 years?

Problem 15: Probability

(for use after Chapter 15)

Two cards are drawn from a standard 52-card deck. What is the probability that both are spades and one is the queen of spades?

Program

```
10  REM PROBABILITY AND CARDS
20  DIM CARD$ (51), RANK$ (12)
30  FOR I = 0 TO 3 : READ SUIT$ (I) : NEXT
40  DATA SPADES, CLUBS, HEARTS, DIAMONDS
50  FOR I = 0 TO 12: READ RANK$ (I) : NEXT
60  DATA TWO, THREE, FOUR, FIVE, SIX, SEVEN,
    EIGHT, NINE, TEN, JACK, QUEEN, KING, ACE
70  FOR I = 0 TO 51: SUIT = INT (I/13) : RANK =
    I - (SUIT  13)
80  CARD$ (I) = RANK$ (RANK) + "OF" + SUIT$
    (SUIT)
90  NEXT
```

```
100 INPUT "TRIALS? ";T
110 FOR I = 1 TO T
120 C1 = INT (52  RND(1))
130 C2 = INT (52  RND(1))
140 IF C2 = C1 THEN 130
150 IF CARD$ (C1) = "QUEEN OF SPADES" AND
    RIGHT$ (CARD$ (C2),6) = "SPADES" THEN
    S = S + 1
160 IF CARD$ (C2) = "QUEEN OF SPADES" AND
    RIGHT$ (CARD$ (C1),6) ="SPADES" THEN
    S = S + 1
170 NEXT
180 PRINT "THE PROBABILITY IS ";ST
```

Extension

What is the probability that one card is the king of hearts and the other is not a heart or king?

Problem 16: Statistics

(for use after Chapter 16)

Find the mean, median, mode, variance, and standard deviation for the victory margins of the first 22 Super Bowl winners.

Program

```
10  REM SUPER BOWL VICTORIES
20  DIM MARGIN (22)
30  DATA 25, 19, 9, 16,3, 21, 7, 17, 10, 4, 18,
    17, 4, 12, 17, 5, 10, 29, 22, 36, 19, 32
40  FOR I = 1 TO 22 : READ MARGIN (I) : SUM =
    SUM + MARGIN (I) : NEXT:
50  MEAN = SUM / 22: PRINT "MEAN = ";MEAN
60  REM SORT MARGINS FROM LEAST TO GREATEST
70  FLAG = 0
80  FOR I = 1 TO 21
90  IF MARGIN (I) < = MARGIN (I + 1) THEN 110
100 T = N(I) : N(I) = N(I + 1) : N(I + 1) = T :
    FLAG = 1
110 NEXT : IF FLAG = 1 THEN 70
120 PRINT "THE SORTED MARGINS ARE:": FOR I = 1
    TO 21: PRINT MARGIN (I);" ";: NEXT: PRINT
    MARGIN (22)
```

Statistics

Program Notes

Line 40 reads the margins of victory for the first 22 Super Bowls (Super Bowl I, which Green Bay won 35-10, had a 25-point margin.)

Lines 70–110 sort the margin from least to greatest using a bubble sort so that the median and mode can be found.

If a set of data is multimodal, the program will only find one mode.

Answer to Problem

```
RUN
MEAN = 16
THE SORTED MARGINS ARE:
3 4 4 5 7 9 10 10 12 16
17 17 18 19 19 21 22 25
29 32 36
MEDIAN = 17
MODE = 17
VARIANCE = 82.2727273
STANDARD DEVIATION =
9.07043148
```

Answer to Extension

For Super Bowl 23, suppose Seattle wins by 8 points. The following lines would need to be changed.

```
20  DIM MARGIN (23)
30  (ADD, 8 TO THE
    CURRENT LINE)
40  (CHANGE 22 TO 23)
50  (CHANGE 22 TO 23)
80  (CHANGE 21 TO 22)
120 (CHANGE 22 TO 23 AND
    21 TO 22)
130 MEDIAN = MARGIN(12):
    PRINT 'MEDIAN =
    ";MEDIAN
140 (CHANGE 22 TO 23)
170 (CHANGE 22 TO 23)
RUN
MEAN = 15.6521739
THE SORTED MARGINS ARE:
3 4 4 5 7 8 9 10 10 12
16 17 17 17 18 19 19 21
22 25 29 32 36
MEDIAN = 17
MODE = 17
VARIANCE = 82.2173913
STANDARD DEVIATION =
9.06738063
```

Answers may vary

```
130 MEDIAN = (MARGIN (11) + MARGIN (12)) / 2 :
    PRINT "MEDIAN = "; MEDIAN
140 FOR I = 1 TO 22: VAR = VAR +
    (MARGIN (I) - MEAN)^2
150 IF MARGIN (I) = MARGIN (I - 1) THEN
    SAME = SAME + 1 : IF SAME > HIGH THEN
    HIGH = SAME: MODE = MARGIN (I)
160 IF MARGIN (I) <> MARGIN (I - 1) THEN SAME =
    1
170 NEXT : PRINT "MODE = ";MODE : VAR = VAR/22
180 PRINT "VARIANCE = ";VAR: PRINT "STANDARD
    DEVIATION = ";SQR(VAR)
```

Extension

Change the program to include any Super Bowls that have been played since the January 1988 32-point victory by Washington over Denver.

Problem 17: Choosing the Best Angle for Motion

(for use after Chapter 17)

After Joe's mother leaves the house, he realizes that he needs to talk to her. She is driving her car to the corner, which is one-eighth mile away, and will make a right turn. She will average 18 mi/h. Joe can run 13 mi/h. At what angle to his street should he run in order to intercept his mother?

Program

```
10  REM JOE ON THE RUN
15  REM "ANG" REPRESENTS THE ANGLE IN RADIANS
20  FOR ANG = .01 TO 1.57 STEP .01
25  REM "TJ" AND "TM" REPRESENT THE TIME FOR JOE
    AND HIS MOTHER TO GET TO THE SAME POINT FOR A
    GIVEN ANGLE
30  TM = (.125 + .125 * TAN (ANG)) / 18
40  TJ = (.125 / COS (ANG)) / 13
50  IF TJ < = TM THEN 90
60  NEXT ANG
70  PRINT "JOE CAN NOT CATCH HIS MOM"
80  END
90  PRINT "JOE SHOULD RUN AT AN ANGLE OF ";ANG *
    180 / 3.14;" DEGREES TO HIS STREET"
```

Best Angle for Motion

You may want to have students add line 45 to see the process the computer takes.

```
45 PRINT "JOE TAKES "
   ;TJ;" HOURS AND HIS
   MOTHER TAKES ";
   " HOURS FOR AN ANGLE
   OF ";ANG
```

Program Notes

In line 20, 1.57 radians is 90°.
In line 40, Joe travels down the hypotenuse of a right triangle. We know one leg of the triangle is $\frac{1}{8}$ mile, and the angle is 'ANG', therefore
cos (ANG) = 0.125 ÷ hypotenuse.
Time = Distance ÷ Velocity
= hypotenuse ÷ velocity

Answer to Problem

```
RUN
JOE SHOULD RUN AT AN
ANGLE OF 33.8216561
DEGREES TO HIS STREET
```

Answer to Extension

Replace the following lines.

```
30 TM = (.125 + .125 *
   TAN (ANG)) / 24
40 TJ = (.125 / COS
   (ANG)) / 17
RUN
JOE SHOULD PEDAL AT AN
ANGLE OF 41.8471338
DEGREES TO HIS STREET
```

Extension

The next day, Joe is faced with the same need to catch up with his mother. This time, however, his mother is averaging 24 mi/h and Joe uses his bicycle, riding at 17 mi/h. What angle should Joe choose if he is to intercept his mother again?

Problem 18: Motion Problems

(for use after Chapter 18)

At noon, ship X was 90 miles due east of ship Y. Ship Y sailed north at 15 mi/h while ship X sailed west at 20 mi/h. At what time were they closest together?

Program

```
10  REM SHIPS PROBLEM
15  REM "MIN" AND "TIME" REPRESENT THE DISTANCE
    AND TIME AT WHICH THE SHIPS ARE CLOSEST
20  MIN = 90:TIME = 0
25  REM T REPRESENTS THE TIME THE SHIPS HAVE
    TRAVELED
30  FOR T = 1 TO 10 STEP 0.1
35  REM "X" IS THE HORIZONTAL DISTANCE BETWEEN
    THE TWO SHIPS
40  X = 90 - T * 20
45  REM "Y" IS THE DISTANCE SHIP Y HAS TRAVELED
    NORTH
50  Y = T * 15
53  REM "DIST" REPRESENTS THE DISTANCE BETWEEN
    THE TWO SHIPS
57  REM USING THE DISTANCE FORMULA TO FIND DIST
60  DIST = SQR (X ^ 2 + Y ^ 2)
70  IF DIST < (MIN) THEN MIN = DIST:TIME = T
80  NEXT T
90  PRINT "THEY WERE CLOSEST AFTER ";TIME;"
    HOURS"
100 PRINT "THEY ARE THEN ";MIN;" MILES APART."
```

Extension

On Sunday, ship Y was 100 miles, 300° from ship X. Ship Y sailed south at 10 mi/h while ship X sailed east at 17 mi/h. How many miles apart were the ships at their closest point?

Motion Problems

You may want students to insert line 73 to see the process the computer takes.

```
73 PRINT "THE SHIPS
   ARE ";DIST;" MILES
   APART AFTER ";T;"
   HOURS"
```

Students can insert line 77 to speed up the program.

```
77 IF DIST > (MIN) THEN
   GO TO 80
```

Program Notes

The coordinates in line 20 are the initial conditions, in case the ships never get closer.

In line 30, 10 is arbitrary, 0.1 determines the accuracy.

In line 40, T · 20 is the distance ship X has traveled $\left(\text{using } y = \frac{d}{t}\right)$.

Answer to Problem

```
RUN
THEY WERE CLOSEST AFTER
2.9 HOURS
THEY ARE THEN 54.0023148
MILES APART.
```

Answer to Extension

Replace the following lines.

```
10 MIN = 100:TIME = 0
30 X = 86.6 - T * 17
40 Y = 50 - T * 10
```

```
RUN
THEY WERE CLOSEST AFTER
5.09999999 HOURS
THEY ARE THEN 1.00498745
MILES APART.
```

Problem 4

Answer to Extension

Replace the following lines.

```
20 FOR X = 1 TO 11
30 FOR Y = 1 TO 16
70 IF .09 * X + .06 * Y +
   .01 * Z = 100
   THEN PRINT X;" PENS, "
   ;Y;" ERASERS, "
   ;Z;" PAPER CLIPS"
RUN
2 PENS, 6 ERASERS, 92
PAPER CLIPS
```

Only 1 combination satisfies the conditions of the problem.

Problem 7

Answer to Extension

Replace the following lines.

```
30 SHIPD = 12 * T
40 SPDBTD = 15 * T
50 IF SPDBTD > = SQR (9 ^
   2 + SHIPD ^ 2) THEN 70
RUN
THE SPEEDBOAT SHOULD AIM
13.2 MILES AHEAD OF THE
SHIP
```

Problem 8

Answer to Extension

Replace the following line.

```
20 M = 450:L = 150:B =
100
RUN
INPUT THE NUMBER OF
HOURS .5
433.420139 PEOPLE ON THE
MAIN FLOOR AT THE END OF
.5 HOURS
97.4826389 PEOPLE IN THE
LOUNGE
169.097222 PEOPLE IN THE
BALCONY
RUN
INPUT THE NUMBER OF
HOURS 1
410.858079 PEOPLE ON THE
MAIN FLOOR AT THE END OF
1 HOURS
95.8217292 PEOPLE IN THE
LOUNGE
193.320192 PEOPLE IN THE
BALCONY
RUN
INPUT THE NUMBER OF
HOURS 5
399.999968 PEOPLE ON THE
MAIN FLOOR AT THE END OF
5 HOURS
100.000085 PEOPLE IN THE
LOUNGE
199.999949 PEOPLE IN THE
BALCONY
```

After 5 hours the number of people on each floor is the same as before.

TI–81 INVESTIGATION 1

Exploring Rational Functions

(for use with Lesson 6–2)

Objective: Determine the characteristics of the graphs of rational functions.

The graphics capabilities of the *TI–81* allow you to take a careful look at the behavior of rational functions. By using the [ZOOM] and [RANGE] keys you can examine close-up or distant views of the features of the graphs.

EXAMPLE Plot the equation $\frac{x^3 - 10x^2 + 50}{x - 2}$. Find all its x-intercepts. Describe the graph of the function for all values of x.

(a) Press [Y=] and enter the function as Y1. Use the sequence

[(] [X|T] [∧] 3 [−] 10 [X|T] [x^2] [+] [X|T] [+] 50 [)] [÷] [(] [X|T] [−] 2 [)]

Press [MODE] to make sure all the left-side choices are highlighted. This is the "default" mode. Press [ZOOM] and select `6:Standard` to get the standard viewing window ($-10 \le x \le 10$, $-10 \le y \le 10$).

Note: The essential features of the graph are not all in the graphing window. To adjust the size of the window either reset the [RANGE] parameters or use `Zoom Out`.

(b) Press [RANGE] and change the settings to

`Xmin=−5` Use the [(−)] key, not [−].
`Xmax=15`
`Xscl=1` This sets tick marks one unit apart on the x-axis.
`Ymin=−25`
`Ymax=10`
`Yscl=1` This sets tick marks one unit apart on the y-axis.
`Xres=1`

(c) Press [GRAPH]. The key features of the graph are now in the viewing window. There are x-intercepts near -2, between 2 and 3, and between 9 and 10. There is also a vertical line showing at $x = 2$ that needs further investigation. There is a turning point, or **local minimum,** between $x = 5$ and $x = 6$.

(d) To find an approximation of the x-intercept between 9 and 10, press [ZOOM] and select `1:Box`. This feature allows you to zoom in for a closer look by drawing a rectangle around a point of interest. Use the arrow keys ([◀] and [▼]) to move the blinking cursor to a point just to the left and below the x-intercept that is between 9 and 10. Press [ENTER] to set this as the corner of the new viewing window. Use the arrow keys ([▲] and [▶]) to locate the diagonally opposite corner, making sure to include the x-intercept and part of the graph in the box. Press [ENTER] to complete the "zoom in." Repeat the box procedure two more times to zoom in closer.

Exploring Rational Functions

Students should experiment with the TI-81 calculator before they begin the investigation. Some examples:

1. Graph $y = 2x + 1$ and find some solutions.

   Press [Y=], enter 2 [x|T] + 1 [ENTER] [GRAPH], then press [TRACE] to find ordered pairs. (one is ≈ (.10526316, 1.2105263)). Press the right arrow until some integer values are found: (2, 5), (6, 13), etc.
2. Evaluate x^5 and x^{-3} for $x = -4$. On the home screen, press [(−)] 4 [STO▸] [x|T] [ENTER]. Then press [x|T] [∧] 5 [ENTER] −1024 [x|T] [∧] [(−)] 3 [ENTER] −.015625

ANSWERS

Try This

a. $x = 2.6$; $x = -2$

b., c., d., This graph does not touch $x = 2$.

(e) Press the [TRACE] key. Use the right or left arrow key to position the blinking cursor on the x-intercept. The x- and y-coordinates changes as the cursor moves. The x-intercept, rounded to the nearest hundredth, occurs at $x = 9.32$.

Note: To draw the box you can set any of the four corners first.

Try This

a. Return to the standard viewing window and use the "box" procedure to locate the other two x-intercepts. Round to the nearest hundredths place.

To investigate the behavior of the function in the Example around the vertical line $x = 2$, reset the RANGE to between -5 and 15 for x and between -25 and 10 for y. This vertical line, called an **asymptote,** is not part of the function because at $x = 2$ the denominator is equal to zero. (Recall that division by zero is undefined.) To see that the graph gets very close to but never touches the asymptote, set the following RANGE parameters.

Try This

b. Set Xmin=1, Xmax=3, Ymin=10, Ymax=20, Xscl=0.1, and Yscl=1.

c. Set x between 1 and 3, y between -20 and -40, Xscl=0.1, and Yscl=2.

d. Invent other locations further up or down on the y-axis around $x = 2$.

To look at the overall behavior of this rational function, return to the standard viewing window by pressing [ZOOM] and selecting 6. Press [ZOOM] again and select 4:Set Factors. The ZOOM FACTORS are the numbers by which the current minimum and maximum values of the range will be multiplied for the new viewing window. Set

XFact=5
YFact=25

Go the the [RANGE] and turn the tick marks off by changing both Xscl and Yscl to 0. Then press [ZOOM] and select 3:Zoom Out. Notice that the graph of this rational function resembles the graph of a 2nd degree (quadratic) polynomial except for the vertical "blip" in the graph around $x = 2$. Take a look at the [RANGE] to see the effect of zooming out.

Investigate

Enter and explore the graphs of the rational functions in exercises 1–4. Invent and graph others as needed to answer exercises 5–7.

1. $\dfrac{5}{2x - 3}$ 2. $\dfrac{1}{x^2 - 9}$ 3. $\dfrac{x + 2}{x^3}$ 4. $\dfrac{3}{x + 5}$

5. How are graphs of rational functions alike?
6. Where are the vertical asymptotes occurring?
7. Predict what will happen with a factorable third-degree, or **cubic,** polynomial in the denominator, as, for example,

$$\frac{1}{x^3 + 2x^2 - 11x - 12} \text{ where } x^3 + 2x^2 - 11x - 12 = (x - 3)(x + 1)(x + 4).$$

Use the ZOOM feature to look at the graphs of the following rational functions. What type of polynomial graph does each resemble, except for the blips?

8. $\dfrac{x^3 + 2x^2 - 5x - 6}{x + 4}$ 9. $\dfrac{x^4 - x^3 - 19x^2 + 49x - 30}{x^3}$

10. $\dfrac{2x^2 + 3x - 2}{x - 3}$ 11. $\dfrac{x^3 - x^2 - 14x + 24}{x - 1}$

12. Consider the graphs for exercises 8–11. Predict how to tell which polynomial the graph of a rational function will resemble without viewing the graph.
13. Locate the x-intercepts for each rational function in exercises 8–11.
    a. What determines the number of x-intercepts a rational function has?
    b. What determines the number of asymptotes?

Locate the x-intercepts (roots) to the nearest hundredths place.

14. $\dfrac{x^3 + 3x^2 - 2x - 6}{x + 1}$ 15. $\dfrac{4x^2 - 8x - 1}{x^2 - 4}$

Investigate

1.
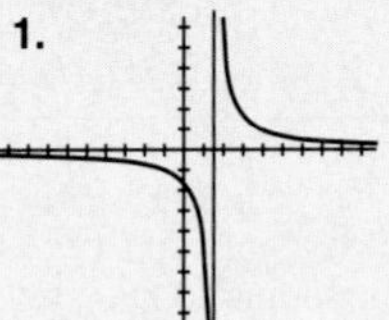

2.
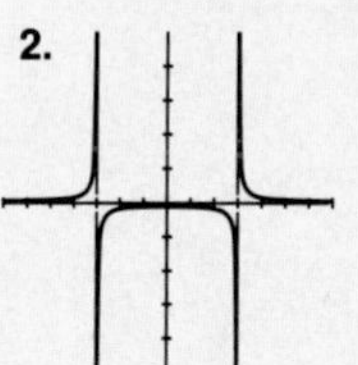

3.
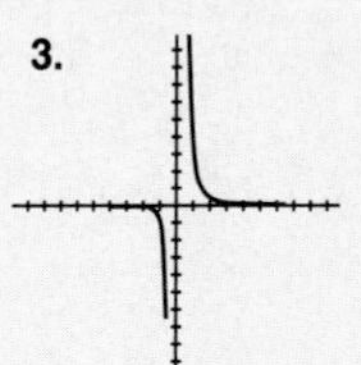

4.
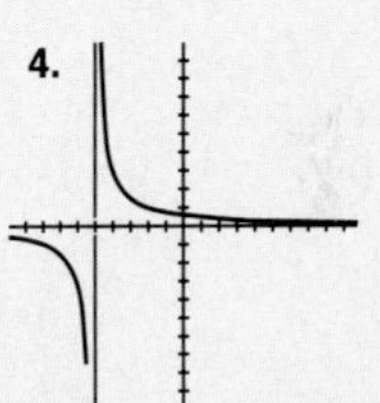

5. They have vertical asymptotes at values of x where the rational expression is undefined.
6. The asymptotes are occurring at values of x where the denominator equals zero.
7. There will be vertical asymptotes at $x = 3$, $x = -1$, and $x = -4$.
8. quadratic
9. linear
10. linear
11. quadratic
12. The ratio of the degree of the numerator to the degree of the denominator determines whether the graph resembles a quadratic or linear graph. For example, a 3rd-degree numerator with a 1st-degree denominator will resemble a 2nd-degree (quadratic) graph.
13. The roots are: 8. $\{-3, -1, 2\}$ 9. $\{-5, 1, 2, 3\}$ 10. $\{-2, 0.5\}$ 11. $\{-4, 2, 3\}$
    a. The roots of the numerator
    b. The roots of the denominator.
14. $\{-3.00, -1.41, 1.41\}$
15. $\{-0.12, 2.12\}$

Roots of Higher-Degree Polynomial Functions

Following Lesson 11-4, the TI-81 can check possible rational roots quickly and easily. After graphing and zooming in on the intercepts if necessary, the rational roots will be apparent.

TI–81 INVESTIGATION 2

Roots of Higher-Degree Polynomial Functions

(for use with Lesson 11–1)

Objective: Graphically identify, find, and/or approximate roots of higher-degree polynomial functions.

You can use the ZOOM, RANGE, and GRAPH features to explore the nature of a **root** of a polynomial function. The number and value of real roots are related to the x-intercepts of the graph of the polynomial.

EXAMPLE Find the number of real roots of $y = x^3 - 4x^2 + x + 6$ by graphing, and find their values.

Define under [Y=] `Y1=x³-4x²+x+6`.
View the graph on the standard settings ([ZOOM] and 6). There are three x-intercepts. Use [ZOOM] and select `1:Box` to draw a rectangle around each x-intercept for a closer look. In this case the intercepts can be concluded by inspection to be -1, 2, and 3.

Note: By using the [TRACE] key, you can get a decimal approximation for each intercept. The only way to be certain it is the exact value is to substitute the value into the equation to see if the y value equals 0. In many cases you will be able to get only a decimal approximation rounded to a certain place value.

The *three* x-intercepts relate to the *three* linear factors in number and value. The polynomial given above has three roots: -1, 2, and 3. These values for x each make the polynomial zero. The *TI–81* allows you to make a quick check as to whether a particular value is a root of the polynomial. For example, to try -1 for x, return to the Home screen ([2nd] [QUIT]) and press [(−)] 1 [STO➡] [X|T] [ENTER].

This stores the value of -1 in the variable x. Recall the polynomial by keying [2nd] [Y-VARS] and selecting `1:Y1`. When you press [ENTER], the calculator will substitute -1 for x in the polynomial $y = x^3 - 4x^2 + x + 6$ and evaluate. The value should be 0. The alternative is to re-enter the polynomial.

Try This **a.** Substitute 2 and 3 into the polynomial $y = x^3 - 4x^2 + x + 6$ by using the [STO➡] feature as above. Verify that each value of x gives $y = 0$.

Investigate

1. Graph the polynomials below. Invent others, as needed, to answer the questions.

$y = x^3 - 6x^2 + 11x - 6 = (x - 3)(x - 2)(x - 1)$
$y = x^3 - x^2 - 14x + 24 = (x - 3)(x - 2)(x + 4)$
$y = 2x^4 + 7x^3 + 4x^2 - 7x - 6 = (x - 1)(2x + 3)(x + 1)(x + 2)$

   a. How do the linear factors of a polynomial relate to its graph?

   b. What seems to determine how many real roots a polynomial function has?

   c. How could you formulate a polynomial function to cross the x-axis at -4, 3, and 7?

2. Observe the graphs of the following polynomials to answer the questions.

$y = x^2$ $\quad y = x^3$ $\quad y = x^4$ $\quad y = x^5$

   a. Predict what $y = x^6$ and $y = x^7$ will look like.

   b. Explain why there seems to be only one real root for each function.

   c. Under what conditions is a polynomial function of real variables an **even function;** that is, $P(x) = P(-x)$ for all x? (See Challenge in Lesson 11–1.)

   d. Under what conditions is a polynomial function of real variables an **odd function;** that is, $-P(x) = P(-x)$ for all x? (See Challenge in Lesson 11–1.)

3. Consider what a root is. Describe the possible shapes and positions of the graphs with respect to x-intercepts of

   a. quadratic polynomials. b. cubic polynomials. c. quartic polynomials.

4. a. Find the number of real roots of $y = x^3 + 6x^2 + x + 6$.

   b. How do you explain that there are *not* three real roots?

   c. What linear factor could you multiply y by to get a quartic polynomial which still has the same number of x-intercepts?

Find the roots of each polynomial to the nearest hundredths place.

5. $y = 3x^3 - 2x^2 - 8x - 3$

6. $y = 6x^4 - 29x^3 + 40x^2 - 7x - 12$

7. Find a polynomial with roots exactly double those of $y = x^3 - 7x^2 - 5x + 2$.

8. Find a pattern to predict the equation for doubling the roots of any third-degree equation. Can you generalize to a fourth-degree equation?

9. What happens to the roots of a polynomial when the coefficients of x are interchanged in reverse order? For example, consider

$y = 120x^4 - 154x^3 + 71x^2 - 14x + 1$ and
$y = x^4 - 14x^3 + 71x^2 - 154x + 120.$

Make up your own polynomials and generalize the results to any polynomial.

ANSWERS

Investigate

1. a. Linear factors determine where the graph crosses the x-axis.
b. The degree of the polynomial or the number of linear factors.
c. Make it by finding the product $(x + 4)(x - 3)(x - 7) = x^3 - 6x^2 - 19x + 84$.

2. a. x^6 will look like a narrower x^4; x^7 will look like a narrower x^5.
b. There is only one value of x, namely 0, that makes $y = 0$.
c. All exponents of x are even.
d. All exponents of x are odd.

3. a. Upward parabolas that are above the x-axis, downward parabolas that are below the x-axis; either upward or downward parabolas that touch the x-axis; either upward or downward parabolas that go through the axis at two points.
b. Curves that go up or down from the extreme left to the extreme right and go through or touch the axis at 1, 2, or 3 points.
c. Upward or downward parabolas, w shapes, or m shapes that may be above the x-axis, below the x-axis, or go through or touch the x-axis at 1, 2, or 3 points.

4. a. one real root
b. $x^3 + 6x^2 + x + 6 = (x^2 + 1)(x + 6)$; $x^2 + 1 = 0$ has no real solutions.
c. Any nonzero multiple of $(x + 6)$.

5. $\{-1, -0.47, 2.14\}$

6. $\{-0.41, 1.33, 1.50, 2.41\}$

7. $y = x^3 - 14x^2 - 20x + 16$

8. Multiply the coefficient of x^3 by 1, the coefficient of x^2 by 2, the coefficient of x by 4, and the constant by 8. For $ax^4 + bx^3 + cx^2 + dx + e$, multiply *a* by 1, *b* by 2, c by 4, *d* by 8, and e by 16.

9. The roots are the reciprocals of each other. $\left\{\frac{1}{2}, \frac{1}{3}, \frac{1}{4}, \frac{1}{5}\right\}$ and $\{2, 3, 4, 5\}$. If you know the roots of one polynomial, the roots of the second will be the multiplicative inverses (reciprocals) of the other.

Solving Systems of Equations Using Row Reduction or Cramer's Rule

To clear, or zero out, matrix *A* from the home screen, press 0 [STO▸] [2nd] [A].

Following entry of the last matrix element, press the [MATRIX] key to return to the matrix menu.

For Example 1, the first row operation should appear as
`*Row+(-2,[A],1,2)`
The argument is parentheses is (scalar, matrix, row multiplied, row added). The result is also stored in the row added.

TI–81 INVESTIGATION 3

Solving Systems of Equations Using Row Reduction or Cramer's Rule

(for use with Lesson 13–3)

Objective: Find the solutions of up to six equations and six variables by matrix operations.

For any system of up to six equations and six variables, you can use the *TI–81* to find solutions, when they exist. By pressing [MATRX], you access the two matrix menus: `MATRIX` (for performing functions or operations) and `EDIT` (for defining a new matrix or modifying an existing one). From a given system such as

$$x + 2y - 3z = 9$$
$$2x - y + 2z = -8$$
$$3x - y - 4z = 3$$

you can use the coefficients of the variables and the constants to form the matrix.

$$\begin{bmatrix} 1 & 2 & -3 & 9 \\ 2 & -1 & 2 & -8 \\ 3 & -1 & -4 & 3 \end{bmatrix}$$

Press [MATRX], then [▶] to enter the `EDIT` menu. Select `1:[A]` and change the dimensions of [*A*] to 3 × 4. Define each entry of the matrix by its row and column. When you finish with a position press [ENTER] to go to the next position.

EXAMPLE 1 Put the system of equations above in triangular form and solve.

To put the matrix [*A*] in triangular form, use the operations under the `MATRIX` menu. For example, to multiply row 1 by −2 and add the result to row 2, press

`MATRIX`
`4:*Row+(` [(−)] 2 [ALPHA] [,]
[2nd] [[A]] [ALPHA] [,] 1 [ALPHA] [,] 2 [)] [ENTER]

The resulting matrix is $\begin{bmatrix} 1 & 2 & -3 & 9 \\ 0 & -5 & 8 & -26 \\ 3 & -1 & 4 & 3 \end{bmatrix}$

The matrix is stored under the variable ANS. To multiply row 1 by −3 and add it to row 3

`MATRIX`
`4:*Row+(` [(−)] 3 [ALPHA] [,] [2nd] [ANS]
[ALPHA] [,] 1 [ALPHA] [,] 3 [)] [ENTER]

The resulting matrix is $\begin{bmatrix} 1 & 2 & -3 & 9 \\ 0 & -5 & 8 & -26 \\ 0 & -7 & 5 & -24 \end{bmatrix}$

To multiply row 2 by -0.2 press

MATRIX
3:Row([(−)] 0.2 [ALPHA] [,] [2nd]
[ANS] [ALPHA] [,] 2 [)] [ENTER]

The matrix is now $\begin{bmatrix} 1 & 2 & -3 & 9 \\ 0 & 1 & -1.6 & 5.2 \\ 0 & -7 & 5 & -24 \end{bmatrix}$

To obtain the triangular form, multiply row 2 by 7 and add it to row 3 by pressing

MATRIX
4:*Row+(7 [ALPHA] [,] [2nd] [ANS] [ALPHA] [,]
2 [ALPHA] [,] 3 [)] [ENTER]

The matrix is $\begin{bmatrix} 1 & 2 & -3 & 9 \\ 0 & 1 & -1.6 & 5.2 \\ 0 & 0 & -6.2 & 12.4 \end{bmatrix}$

At this point, you could re-enter the variables to solve for each. As an alternative, you can continue to use row operations to reduce the matrix to

$\begin{bmatrix} 1 & 0 & -1\text{E}-12 & -1 \\ 0 & 1 & 0 & 2 \\ 0 & 0 & 1 & -2 \end{bmatrix}$ $x = -1, y = 2, z = -2$

Note: $-1\text{E}-12$ is a very small number which should have been 0. All calculators have some error caused by rounding.

Try This Put each system of equations in triangular form and solve.

a. $x + y + z = 6$
$2x - 3y + 4z = 3$
$4x - 8y + 4z = 12$

b. $x - 2y + z = -4$
$3x + 2y - z = 8$
$-x + 3y + 5z = 0$

c. $x + 2y + z = 11$
$2x + y + z = 13$
$x + 3y + 3z = 19$

ANSWERS
Try This
a. (7, 1, −2)
b. (1, 2, −1)
c. (4, 2, 3)

You can use the *TI-81* to find the determinant of a matrix. You can then apply Cramer's rule to solve a system of equations such as

$$\begin{aligned} 4x + 3y + z &= -10 \\ x - 12y + 2z &= -5 \\ x + 18y + z &= 4 \end{aligned}$$

d. $\left(-\frac{1}{2}, \frac{1}{2}, 1\right)$
e. $(-6, 6, 4)$
f. $(-1, 2, -2, 1)$

Investigate

1. det = 0. There is no unique solution
2. det = 0. There is no unique solution
3. det ≠ 0. There is a unique solution
4. There is either no solution or an infinite number of solutions.
5. Both are −81. In general, the product of the diagonal of a matrix in triangular form is the determinant of that matrix.
6. det A = −det B

EXAMPLE 2 Solve the system above using the determinant and Cramer's rule.

To find $\begin{vmatrix} 4 & 3 & 1 \\ 1 & -12 & 2 \\ 1 & 18 & 1 \end{vmatrix}$ go to EDIT and define [A].

After entering the matrix, press the following keys to produce the determinant.

MATRIX 5:det [2nd] [[A]] [ENTER] = −159

Similarly, if you enter Dx, Dy, and Dz the values will be 477, −53, and −159, respectively. Then by Cramer's rule the solution is $(-3, \frac{1}{3}, 1)$. (Confirm Dx, Dy, and Dz).

Note: The *TI–81* allows only three matrices to be defined at any given time. You could modify Matrix [A] each time to save some entry work.

Try This Use Cramer's rule to find the solution.

d. $2x + 2y + z = 1$
$x + 3y - z = 0$
$-3x + y + 2z = 4$

e. $2x + y + 3z = 6$
$-6x + y + 5z = 62$
$7x - y + 4z = -32$

f. $x + y + z + w = 0$
$2x + 3y - z + w = 7$
$3x + 2y - 3z + 2w = 9$
$4x - y - z - w = -5$

Investigate

Use the determinant of the coefficient matrix [A] to decide whether each system of equations has a unique solution.

1. $x + y + z = 1$
$-3x + 7y + 2z = 0$
$-2x + 8y + 3z = 4$

2. $3x + 4y = 3$
$6x + 4z = 3$
$-3x + 4y - 4z = 2$

3. $2x - y + 3z - w = 5$
$-x - y + z + w = 4$
$x + y + z + w = 10$
$3x + y + z + w = 12$

4. Consider Exercises 1–3. What can be said about a system of equations if $|A| = 0$? Try any other systems if you need more information.

5. Use any matrices in triangular form from Lesson 13–1 or invent your own. How is the determinant of A related to the product of the elements in the main diagonal?

For example, how does $\begin{vmatrix} 3 & 0 & 5 \\ 0 & 9 & 4 \\ 0 & 0 & -3 \end{vmatrix}$ compare to $3 \cdot 9 \cdot -3$?

6. If any two matrices are identical except that two of the rows or columns have been interchanged, how are their determinants related?

TI–81 INVESTIGATION 4

Solving Systems of Equations Using Inverse Matrices

(for use with Lesson 13–6)

Objective: Find the solutions of up to six equations and six variables by matrix operations.

You can use the *TI–81* to solve systems of equations (up to 6 × 6) of the form $AX = B$, where A is the coefficient matrix, X is the variable matrix, and B is the constant matrix. If A^{-1} exists, you can find it by first entering A into the calculator.

EXAMPLE Find A^{-1}.

$$A = \begin{bmatrix} 1 & -1 & 1 \\ 2 & 0 & -3 \\ -1 & -1 & 2 \end{bmatrix}$$

Press [MATRX], `EDIT`, `1:[A]`, define A to be 3 × 3 matrix and enter each position (by row and column). Leave the matrix definition window and return to the Home screen by pressing [2nd] [QUIT] To verify the matrix entry press [2nd] [[A]] [ENTER]

Press [x^{-1}] [ENTER] to get

$$A^{-1} = \begin{bmatrix} 0.75 & -0.25 & -0.75 \\ 0.25 & -0.75 & -1.25 \\ 0.5 & -0.5 & -0.5 \end{bmatrix}$$

Note: You will sometimes need to use the arrow keys to scroll right in order to see the entire matrix, since the calculator uses decimal representation of rational numbers. For example, if

$$A = \begin{bmatrix} 4 & 2 & 2 \\ 0 & 1 & 2 \\ 1 & 0 & 3 \end{bmatrix},$$

$$\text{then } A^{-1} = \begin{bmatrix} 0.2142857143\ldots & -0.4285714286\ldots & 0.1428571429\ldots \\ 0.1428571429\ldots & 0.7142857143\ldots & -0.5714285714\ldots \\ -0.0714285714\ldots & 0.1428571429\ldots & 0.2857142857\ldots \end{bmatrix}$$

Try This Find A^{-1}.

a. $\begin{bmatrix} 3 & 2 \\ -3 & 4 \end{bmatrix}$ b. $\begin{bmatrix} 2 & 1 & 0 \\ 1 & 0 & 1 \\ 1 & -1 & 1 \end{bmatrix}$ c. $\begin{bmatrix} 0 & 2 & 1 & 3 \\ 2 & -1 & 3 & 4 \\ -2 & 1 & 5 & 2 \\ 0 & 1 & 0 & 2 \end{bmatrix}$

Solving Systems of Equations Using Inverse Matrices

In Lesson 9-8, we fit a 2nd-degree function to 3 points. You may show how a matrix may be used to fit an equation to up to 5 data points.

Fit an equation to (1, 9), (2, 15), (3, 27), (4, 51).

Four points determine a cubic equation: $y = ax^3 + bx^2 + cx + d$

$$A = \begin{bmatrix} 1 & 1 & 1 & 1 \\ 8 & 4 & 2 & 1 \\ 27 & 9 & 3 & 1 \\ 64 & 16 & 4 & 1 \end{bmatrix} \quad B = \begin{bmatrix} 3 \\ 5 \\ 9 \\ 17 \end{bmatrix}$$

so $X =$ [2nd] [A] [x^{-1}] [B] $= \begin{bmatrix} 1 \\ -3 \\ 8 \\ 3 \end{bmatrix}$

The equation is thus $y = x^3 - 3x^2 + 8x + 3$. The equation can then be graphed normally.

ANSWERS

Try This

a. $\begin{bmatrix} .2222222222\ldots & -.1111111111\ldots \\ .1666666667\ldots & .1666666667\ldots \end{bmatrix}$

b. $\begin{bmatrix} 0.5 & -0.5 & 0.5 \\ 0 & 1 & -1 \\ -0.5 & 1.5 & -0.5 \end{bmatrix}$

c. column 1
1.071428571...
1.142857143...
0.4285714286...
−0.5714285714...
column 2
0.1785714286...
−0.1428571429...
0.0714285714...
0.714285714...
column 3
−0.3214285714...
−0.1428571429...
0.0714285714...
0.0714285714...
column 4
−1.642857143...
−1.285714286...
−0.8571428571...
1.142857143...

When A^{-1} exists, the system of equations $AX = B$ can be solved by multiplying both sides of the equation by A^{-1}, as demonstrated in Lesson 13–6, to arrive at $X = A^{-1}B$.

So to get the solution with the *TI–81* you simply enter A and B into the calculator and use the key sequence [2nd] [[A]] [x^{-1}] [×] [2nd] [[B]]. For example, to solve the system

$$\begin{aligned} -2x + 3y - z &= 1 \\ x + 2y - z &= 4 \\ -2x - y + z &= -3 \end{aligned}$$

write it as

$$\underset{A}{\begin{bmatrix} -2 & 3 & -1 \\ 1 & 2 & -1 \\ -2 & -1 & 1 \end{bmatrix}} \times \underset{X}{\begin{bmatrix} x \\ y \\ z \end{bmatrix}} = \underset{B}{\begin{bmatrix} 1 \\ 4 \\ -3 \end{bmatrix}}$$

enter matrices A and B, then on the Home screen multiply x^{-1} by B. The result is given as

[2]
[3]
[4]

so $x = 2$, $y = 3$, and $z = 4$.

Investigate

Find the determinant and the inverse (if it exists) of each matrix.

1. $\begin{bmatrix} 3 & 9 \\ 7 & 21 \end{bmatrix}$

2. $\begin{bmatrix} 5 & 3 & -6 \\ 1 & -2 & 4 \\ 3 & -6 & 12 \end{bmatrix}$

3. $\begin{bmatrix} -2 & 1 \\ 0 & 0 \end{bmatrix}$

4. $\begin{bmatrix} 3 & -1 & 0 & 4 \\ 5 & 1 & 1 & -3 \\ 0 & 0 & 0 & 0 \\ 2 & 1 & 7 & -1 \end{bmatrix}$

5. $\begin{bmatrix} 2 & 0 & 8 & 3 \\ -1 & 0 & -3 & 7 \\ 6 & 0 & 1 & 0 \\ -2 & 0 & -6 & 14 \end{bmatrix}$

6. $\begin{bmatrix} 1 & 1 & 0 \\ -1 & -1 & 0 \\ 2 & 1 & 3 \end{bmatrix}$

7. How does the value of the determinant relate to the existence of an inverse matrix?

8. Consider the matrices in exercises 1–6. Where the inverse does *not* exist, what special characteristics exist, either in a row or column, or between rows or columns? Invent matrices of your own to test your conjecture.

Investigate

1. det = 0, A^{-1} does not exist
2. det = 0, A^{-1} does not exist
3. det = 0, A^{-1} does not exist
4. det = 0, A^{-1} does not exist
5. det = 0, A^{-1} does not exist
6. det = 0, A^{-1} does not exist
7. If the det = 0, then A^{-1} does not exist.
8. If a row or column is all zeros, det = 0 and A^{-1} does not exist. If one row or column is a multiple of another row or column, the det A = 0 and A^{-1} does not exist.

Note: If you are calculating det A and, due to rounding error, the calculator gets a very small value instead of 0, A^{-1} will show (be found) even though it does not exist in reality.

Solve the following systems using the $AX = B$ form and A^{-1}.

9. $2x + 4y + 2z = 3$
$4x + y - z = 4$
$2x - 3y + z = -3$

10. $x - 4y + z = 6$
$2x + 2y - 3z = -20$
$4x - y + 2z = -1$

11. $x + y + z + w = 2$
$2x + 3y + 2z - w = -2$
$2x - y - z + 2w = 7$
$3x - 2y - z - 3w = -2$

12. $2x - y - 3z + 2w = -2$
$x - 2y + z - 3w = 4$
$3x - 4y + 2z - 4w = 12$
$2x + 3y - z - 2w = -4$

Use A^{-1} to solve for the matrix X.

13. $\begin{bmatrix} 2 & 1 \\ -3 & 0 \end{bmatrix} X = \begin{bmatrix} 7 & 16 \\ -15 & -12 \end{bmatrix}$

14. $\begin{bmatrix} 0.5 & 1 & -1 \\ 0 & -0.5 & 1 \\ 2 & -1 & 1 \end{bmatrix} X = \begin{bmatrix} 1.5 & 3.5 & 3.5 \\ 0 & -1 & -3.5 \\ 1 & 9 & -6 \end{bmatrix}$

15. The following chart appeared in a newspaper following the 1990 baseball season:

FINAL RELIEF STANDINGS					
	Wins	Losses	Saves	Blown Saves	Points
Thigpen, Chi	4	6	57	8	151
Eckersley, Oak	4	2	48	2	144
D. Jones, Cle	5	5	43	8	113
Olsen, Bal	6	5	37	5	103
Righetti, NYY	1	1	36	3	102
Franco, NYM	5	3	33	6	91
Aguilera, Min	5	3	32	7	86
Henke, Tor	2	4	32	6	80
Myers, Cin	4	6	31	6	77
Schooler, Sea	1	4	30	4	76

a. How many equations are needed to determine the number of points each category contributes to the points column?

b. Write a system of equations to solve part a.

c. Solve the system using $X = A^{-1}B$. How many points is a win, loss, save, and blown save worth?

9. $\left(\frac{1}{2}, 1, -1\right)$
10. (−2.618181818, −1.109090909, 4.181818182)
11. (1, 0, −1, 2)
12. (2, −1, 3, 1)
13. $\begin{bmatrix} 5 & 4 \\ -3 & 8 \end{bmatrix}$
14. $\begin{bmatrix} 1 & 5 & -1 \\ 2 & 0 & 1 \\ 1 & -1 & -3 \end{bmatrix}$
15. a. 4
b. $4x + 6y + 57z + 8w = 151$
$4x + 2y + 48z + 2w = 144$
$5x + 5y + 43z + 8w = 113$
$6x + 5y + 37z + 5w = 103$
c. 2, −2, 3, −2

Analyzing Statistical Data

For Example 1, it is not necessary to count the frequency of each occurrence. Each individual data point may be entered with a *y*-value or frequency of 1. This will not produce an accurate scatter plot of frequencies, however.

TI–81 INVESTIGATION 5

Analyzing Statistical Data

(for use with Lesson 16–3)

Objective: Find and apply statistical measures of central tendency and variance. Find the "best fit" equation to explain a set of data and predict an expected result.

To access the statistical menus of the *TI–81*, press [2nd] [STAT]. The statistical operations are grouped functionally into three menus: `CALC` (for calculating statistical results), `DRAW` (for plotting the data), and `DATA` (for entering or editing the data). Before entering new data, be sure the statistical data memory is cleared by keying [2nd] [STAT] [◀] `2:ClrStat` [ENTER]

EXAMPLE 1 The cafeteria count by room on a given day was: 26, 19, 15, 26, 28, 13, 19, 22, 15, 19, 26, 18, 13, 26, and 21. Enter the data, find the statistical variables, and view the statistical graphs.

To enter data for statistical analysis, press [2nd] [STAT] [◀] to highlight the `DATA` menu. Select `1:Edit` by pressing 1 or [ENTER]. For one-variable statistics, enter new data as the *x*-variable and enter the frequency of that particular number as the *y*-variable.

x1=26		x2=19	x3=15	x4=28
y1=4	26 occurs 4 times	y2=3	y3=2	y4=1 . . .

Note: After keying in the number, press [ENTER] to move the cursor to the next line. Use the arrow keys to go back to edit any entries. Press [2nd] [STAT] `1:1-Var` [ENTER] to calculate the variables

x=20.4	the mean
Sx=306	sum of *x* values
Sx²= 6608	sum of the squares of *x* values
Sx=5.110213862	sample standard deviation of *x*
σx=4.936935622	population standard deviation of *x*
n=15	number of data points

There are three types of graphs that you can display by using the menu item `DRAW`: a histogram, a scatter plot, and a line graph. Before selecting a graph, set parameters of the `RANGE` so the graph will appear in the graphics window. For this example set

Xmin=10	The values range from 13 to 28.
Xmax=30	
Xscl=2	30 − 10 = 20 (range of *x*); 20 ÷ 10 tick marks = 2
Ymin=0	The frequency ranges from 1 to 4.
Ymax=5	
Yscl=0.5	5 − 0 = 5 (range of *y*); 5 ÷ 10 tick marks = 0.5.
Xres=1	

Press the [Y=] key and clear any equations so that no function is graphed at the same time as the statistical graph. Use the following sequence to display the histogram.

[2nd] [STAT] [▶] 1 [ENTER]

Note: To clear the statistical graph press [2nd] [DRAW] and select `1:ClrDraw`

Try This Enter the data, find the statistical variables, and view the three types of statistical graphs for Exercise 3 on page 692 of Lesson 16–1.

ANSWERS

Try This

$\bar{x}$ = 5.91875
Σx = 189.4
Σx^2 = 1157.26
Sx = 1.081348471
σx = 1.064318297
n = 32

The *TI–81* can also be used to find linear, logarithmic, power, or exponential "best fit" equations to explain the data's relationship.

EXAMPLE 2 The population and area of a sampling of cities in the U.S. is

Population	Area
467,000	116
566,000	181
352,000	138
370,000	78
192,000	66
374,000	185
1,000,000	333

Based on the observed data, what area would you predict for a city of 750,000 people?

(a) Press [2nd] [STAT] [◀] to display the `DATA` menu. Select `1:Edit` to enter the data points. Since we are trying to predict an area, enter the populations as x-values and the areas as y-values.

(b) Set the RANGE to view the scatter plot as follows.

```
Xmin=175000
Xmax=1250000
Xscl=100000
Ymin=50
Ymax=350
Yscl=30
Xres=1
```

After plotting, determine whether the data are best fit by a linear equation $y = a + bx$, a logarithmic equation $y = a + b \cdot \ln(x)$, an exponential equation $y = ab^x$, or a power equation $y = ax^b$.

(c) Press [2nd] [STAT] `2:LinReg`. Write down the value of r.

r is called the **correlation** coefficient. An r-value close to 0 means the equation fits the data poorly, an r-value close to 1 or -1 means the equation fits the data well (the minus sign just means that y decreases as x increases).

(d) Repeat step c for `3:LnReg`, for `4:ExReg`, and for `5:PwrReg`.

You should have found these r values:

Type of Equation	r-value
Linear	$r = .9180983371$
Logarithmic	$r = .8672275432$
Exponential	$r = .8487900744$
Power	$r = .8622864858$

(e) The r value whose absolute value is closest to 1 gives the best fit. So you can choose the linear equation, in the form $a + bx$. Press [2nd] [STAT] `2:LinReg`. The equation is thus 4.498903985 + 3.208394074E − 4x (approximately $4.5 + 0.00032x$).

We can now evaluate this equation for $x = 750{,}000$.

(f) Store 750,000 into the variable x. (Enter 750,000 and press [STO➡] [X|T].)

(g) Press [VARS]. Select the `LR` menu. Select `4:RegEq` to copy to the Home screen the linear regression equation: `4.498903985+3.208394074E-4x`

(h) Press [ENTER]. The prediction, based on the observed data, is that a city of 750,000 people would have an area of `245.1284595`, or about 245, square miles.

Investigate

1. 20 buildings
2. 9.36 years

Investigate

Find the "best fit" equation to predict the following.

1. The number of buildings of more than 300 feet in height found in a sampling of cities.

Population	Buildings
467,000	3
566,000	14
352,000	6
370,000	9
192,000	5
374,000	10
1,000,000	30

Based on the observed data, how many buildings of more than 300 feet in height would you expect to find a city of 750,000 people?

2. The amount of time in years it takes for an investment or deposit of money to double, using a sampling of interest rates is

% Interest	Years to Double
6	11.89
8	9.01
4	17.67
9	8.04
5	14.21

Predict the number of years (to the nearest hundredths place) it would take to double the money of an investment at 7.69% interest.

TI–81 INVESTIGATION 6

Trigonometric Identities

(for use with Lesson 18–3)

Objective: Find or verify trigonometric identities graphically.

The keys [SIN], [COS], and [TAN] allow you to directly access the sine, cosine, and tangent functions. You must use the variable X in an expression such as `sin(2X+1)`.

If the graphs of two trigonometric expressions are the same, then the expressions are equivalent. A trigonometric identity is formed when two trigonometric expressions are equivalent. You can use the RANGE and ZOOM features to verify if the graphs of two expressions are identical within the limitations of the graphing window.

One of the classic identities is $\sin^2(x) + \cos^2(x) = 1$. To get a picture of what the components look like, press [Y=] and define the following functions.

$y_1 = \sin^2(x)$ Press [(] [SIN] [(] [XIT] [)] [)] [x^2]

$y_2 = \cos^2(x)$ Use the same sequence as above with [COS].

$y_3 = \sin^2(x) + \cos^2(x)$ Enter the entire expression, as above, or use [2nd] [Y-VARS] and enter Y1+Y2.

$y_4 = 1$

Press [ZOOM] and select `7:Trig` to graph from -2π to 2π on the x-axis. The expressions are graphed one at a time if Sequence is highlighted under the [MODE] key. Notice that $\sin^2(x)$ and $\cos^2(x)$ both lie above the x-axis. Does it make sense that $\sin^2(x) + \cos^2(x) = 1$ graphically?

To test whether two trigonometric expressions are identities, graph each expression (each side of the equation) as a different function and compare the graphs.

Try This Identify whether the following are identities. Since cosecant, secant, and cotangent are the reciprocals of sine, cosine, and tangent, respectively, you can find their graphs by entering 1/SIN(x), 1/COS(x), and 1/TAN(x), respectively.

a. $\cos(3\pi + x) = -\cos(x)$

b. $\dfrac{\sin(2x) + \sin(x)}{\cos(2x) + \cos(x) + 1} = \tan(x)$

c. $\csc(x + \pi) = -\sec(x)$

d. $\dfrac{\sin(x) - \cos(x)}{\cos(x)} + 1 = \tan(x)$

Note: Because of the limitations of computer-generated graphs, two graphs may appear to coincide, but in reality be only very close. To be sure, ZOOM in and take a closer look. You can use algebraic proofs to verify identity candidates.

A trigonometric identity sometimes has domain restrictions which can be observed on the graph as vertical asymptotes. The lines are not part of the graph but show where the function is undefined (just as with rational expressions). For example, $\tan(2x)$ has vertical asymptotes at $\frac{\pi}{4}$ and $-\frac{\pi}{4}$ and every $\frac{\pi}{2}$ units to the left and right of those.

Trigonometric Identities

You may check identities by entering one side as Y1, the other as Y2, and graphing Y1−Y2. If the identity is true, the graph will be the graph of $y = 0$, so it will fall on the x-axis and not be apparent. Pressing [TRACE] and the left/right arrow keys will verify that the function is indeed $y = 0$.

ANSWERS

Try This

a. yes
b. yes
c. no
d. yes

Investigate

1. yes, restrictions at $-\frac{3\pi}{2}, -\frac{\pi}{2}, \frac{\pi}{2}, \frac{3\pi}{2}$
2. yes, restrictions at $-\frac{3\pi}{2}, -\frac{\pi}{2}, \frac{\pi}{2}, \frac{3\pi}{2}$
3. yes, restriction at $-\frac{3\pi}{2}, -\frac{\pi}{2}, \frac{\pi}{2}, \frac{3\pi}{2}$
4. no
5. Its maximum and minimum values occur at the x-coordinates of the intersection of the two graphs. It builds on the peaks and valleys halfway between.
6. It builds on the peaks and valleys of the two graphs, but the maximum and minimum values are skewed toward the $-3\sqrt{3}\cos(x)$ because it has a larger amplitude.
7. $a = 0.25$, $b = 4$, $c = 0$, $d = 0.75$
8. $a = 0.375$, $b = 4$, $c = 0$, $d = 0.625$
9. It appears by the pattern that a should be $\frac{7}{16}$, b should be 4, c should be 0, and d should be $\frac{9}{16}$. But it does not work. If you zoom in and look at the graphs around $\frac{\pi}{8}$ or $-\frac{\pi}{8}$, you will see that they are different.
10. It appears by the pattern that a should be $\frac{15}{32}$, b should be 4, c should be 0, and d should be $\frac{17}{32}$. If you zoom in and look at the graphs around $\frac{\pi}{8}$ or $-\frac{\pi}{8}$, you will see that they are different.
11. This pattern does not generalize. It is an example of a case where inductive reasoning fails. The pattern works for only the first three even powers.
12. a. Answers will vary.
    b. The conjecture works for Pythagorean identities, but there are several counterexamples to show it false in general. For example, $\cos(\alpha - \beta) = \cos\alpha\cos\beta + \sin\alpha\sin\beta$, but $\sin(\alpha - \beta) = \sin\alpha\cos\beta - \cos\alpha\sin\beta$. (See Lesson 17-1.)

Investigate

Determine if the following are identities. If so, identify the restrictions of the domain that appear in the standard "Trig" viewing window.

1. $\cos(x) + \sec(x) + 2 = 0$
2. $\tan^2(x) - \sin^2(x) = \tan^2(x)\sin^2(x)$
3. $\tan(x) \cdot \sin(x) + \cos(x) = \sec(x)$
4. $\dfrac{\sin(x) - \cos(x)}{\sec(x) - \csc(x)} = \dfrac{\csc(x)}{\cos(x)}$
5. Graph $y = 2\sin(x)$; $y = 2\cos(x)$ and $y = 2\sin(x) + 2\cos(x)$ on the same coordinate axes. How is the graph of $y = 2\sin(x) + 2\cos(x)$ related to the graphs of $y = 2\sin(x)$ and $y = 2\cos(x)$?
6. Graph $y = 3\sin(x)$, $y = -3\sqrt{3}\cos(x)$, and $y = 3\sin(x) - 3\sqrt{3}\cos(x)$ on the same coordinate axes. How is the graph of $y = 3\sin(x) - 3\sqrt{3}\cos(x)$ related to the graphs of $y = 3\sin(x)$ and $y = -3\sqrt{3}\cos(x)$?

Use the graphing features to find the values of a, b, c, and d that make an identity:

7. $\sin^4(x) + \cos^4(x) = a\cos(bx + c) + d$
8. $\sin^6(x) + \cos^6(x) = a\cos(bx + c) + d$
9. $\sin^8(x) + \cos^8(x) = a\cos(bx + c) + d$
10. $\sin^{10}(x) + \cos^{10}(x) = a\cos(bx + c) + d$
11. See if you can generalize to develop a formula for $\sin^{2n}(x) + \cos^{2n}(x)$.
12. A creative student claimed that if one replaces each function in an identity with its corresponding cofunction, the resulting equation will itself be an identity.
    a. Investigate the conjecture with some known identities from Lesson 18–3.
    b. If your data suggests that the technique may be valid, explain why it works. Otherwise, provide a counterexample.

TABLE 1 Squares and Square Roots

N	N^2	$\sqrt{N}$	N	N^2	$\sqrt{N}$
1	1	1	51	2,601	7.141
2	4	1.414	52	2,704	7.211
3	9	1.732	53	2,809	7.280
4	16	2	54	2,916	7.348
5	25	2.236	55	3,025	7.416
6	36	2.449	56	3,136	7.483
7	49	2.646	57	3,249	7.550
8	64	2.828	58	3,364	7.616
9	81	3	59	3,481	7.681
10	100	3.162	60	3,600	7.746
11	121	3.317	61	3,721	7.810
12	144	3.464	62	3,844	7.874
13	169	3.606	63	3,969	7.937
14	196	3.742	64	4,096	8
15	225	3.873	65	4,225	8.062
16	256	4	66	4,356	8.124
17	289	4.123	67	4,489	8.185
18	324	4.243	68	4,624	8.246
19	361	4.359	69	4,761	8.307
20	400	4.472	70	4,900	8.367
21	441	4.583	71	5,041	8.426
22	484	4.690	72	5,184	8.485
23	529	4.796	73	5,329	8.544
24	576	4.899	74	5,476	8.602
25	625	5	75	5,625	8.660
26	676	5.099	76	5,776	8.718
27	729	5.196	77	5,929	8.775
28	784	5.292	78	6,084	8.832
29	841	5.385	79	6,241	8.888
30	900	5.477	80	6,400	8.944
31	961	5.568	81	6,561	9
32	1,024	5.657	82	6,724	9.055
33	1,089	5.745	83	6,889	9.110
34	1,156	5.831	84	7,056	9.165
35	1,225	5.916	85	7,225	9.220
36	1,296	6	86	7,396	9.274
37	1,369	6.083	87	7,569	9.327
38	1,444	6.164	88	7,744	9.381
39	1,521	6.245	89	7,921	9.434
40	1,600	6.325	90	8,100	9.487
41	1,681	6.403	91	8,281	9.539
42	1,764	6.481	92	8,464	9.592
43	1,849	6.557	93	8,649	9.644
44	1,936	6.633	94	8,836	9.695
45	2,025	6.708	95	9,025	9.747
46	2,166	6.782	96	9,216	9.798
47	2,209	6.856	97	9,409	9.849
48	2,304	6.928	98	9,604	9.899
49	2,401	7	99	9,801	9.950
50	2,500	7.071	100	10,000	10

TABLE 2 Common Logarithms

x	0	1	2	3	4	5	6	7	8	9
1.0	.0000	.0043	.0086	.0128	.0170	.0212	.0253	.0294	.0334	.0374
1.1	.0414	.0453	.0492	.0531	.0569	.0607	.0645	.0682	.0719	.0755
1.2	.0792	.0828	.0864	.0899	.0934	.0969	.1004	.1038	.1072	.1106
1.3	.1139	.1173	.1206	.1239	.1271	.1303	.1335	.1367	.1399	.1430
1.4	.1461	.1492	.1523	.1553	.1584	.1614	.1644	.1673	.1703	.1732
1.5	.1761	.1790	.1818	.1847	.1875	.1903	.1931	.1959	.1987	.2014
1.6	.2041	.2068	.2095	.2122	.2148	.2175	.2201	.2227	.2253	.2279
1.7	.2304	.2330	.2355	.2380	.2405	.2430	.2455	.2480	.2504	.2529
1.8	.2553	.2577	.2601	.2625	.2648	.2672	.2695	.2718	.2742	.2765
1.9	.2788	.2810	.2833	.2856	.2878	.2900	.2923	.2945	.2967	.2989
2.0	.3010	.3032	.3054	.3075	.3096	.3118	.3139	.3160	.3181	.3201
2.1	.3222	.3243	.3263	.3284	.3304	.3324	.3345	.3365	.3385	.3404
2.2	.3424	.3444	.3464	.3483	.3502	.3522	.3541	.3560	.3579	.3598
2.3	.3617	.3636	.3655	.3674	.3692	.3711	.3729	.3747	.3766	.3784
2.4	.3802	.3820	.3838	.3856	.3874	.3892	.3909	.3927	.3945	.3962
2.5	.3979	.3997	.4014	.4031	.4048	.4065	.4082	.4099	.4116	.4133
2.6	.4150	.4166	.4183	.4200	.4216	.4232	.4249	.4265	.4281	.4298
2.7	.4314	.4330	.4346	.4362	.4378	.4393	.4409	.4425	.4440	.4456
2.8	.4472	.4487	.4502	.4518	.4533	.4548	.4564	.4579	.4594	.4609
2.9	.4624	.4639	.4654	.4669	.4683	.4698	.4713	.4728	.4742	.4757
3.0	.4771	.4786	.4800	.4814	.4829	.4843	.4857	.4871	.4886	.4900
3.1	.4914	.4928	.4942	.4955	.4969	.4983	.4997	.5011	.5024	.5038
3.2	.5051	.5065	.5079	.5092	.5105	.5119	.5132	.5145	.5159	.5172
3.3	.5185	.5198	.5211	.5224	.5237	.5250	.5263	.5276	.5289	.5307
3.4	.5315	.5328	.5340	.5353	.5366	.5378	.5391	.5403	.5416	.5428
3.5	.5441	.5453	.5465	.5478	.5490	.5502	.5514	.5527	.5539	.5551
3.6	.5563	.5575	.5587	.5599	.5611	.5623	.5635	.5647	.5658	.5670
3.7	.5682	.5694	.5705	.5717	.5729	.5740	.5752	.5763	.5775	5786
3.8	.5798	.5809	.5821	.5832	.5843	.5855	.5866	.5877	.5888	.5899
3.9	.5911	.5922	.5933	.5944	.5955	.5966	.5977	.5988	.5999	.6010
4.0	.6021	.6031	.6042	.6053	.6064	.6075	.6085	.6096	.6107	.6117
4.1	.6128	.6138	.6149	.6160	.6170	.6180	.6191	.6201	.6212	.6222
4.2	.6232	.6243	.6253	.6263	.6274	.6284	.6294	.6304	.6314	.6325
4.3	.6335	.6345	.6355	.6365	.6375	.6385	.6395	.6405	.6415	.6425
4.4	.6435	.6444	.6454	.6464	.6474	.6484	.6493	.6503	.6513	.6522
4.5	.6532	.6542	.6551	.6561	.6571	.6580	.6590	.6599	.6609	.6618
4.6	.6628	.6637	.6646	.6656	.6665	.6675	.6684	.6693	.6702	.6712
4.7	.6721	.6730	.6739	.6749	.6758	.6767	.6776	.6785	.6794	.6803
4.8	.6812	.6821	.6830	.6839	.6848	.6857	.6866	.6875	.6884	.6893
4.9	.6902	.6911	.6920	.6928	.6937	.6946	.6955	.6964	.6972	.6981
5.0	.6990	.6998	.7007	.7016	.7024	.7033	.7042	.7050	.7059	.7067
5.1	.7076	.7084	.7093	.7101	.7110	.7118	.7126	.7135	.7143	.7152
5.2	.7160	.7168	.7177	.7185	.7193	.7202	.7210	.7218	.7226	.7235
5.3	.7243	.7251	.7259	.7267	.7275	.7284	.7292	.7300	.7308	.7316
5.4	.7324	.7332	.7340	.7348	.7356	.7364	.7372	.7380	.7388	.7396

x	0	1	2	3	4	5	6	7	8	9
5.5	.7404	.7412	.7419	.7427	.7435	.7443	.7451	.7459	.7466	.7474
5.6	.7482	.7490	.7497	.7505	.7513	.7520	.7528	.7536	.7543	.7551
5.7	.7559	.7566	.7574	.7582	.7589	.7597	.7604	.7612	.7619	.7627
5.8	.7634	.7642	.7649	.7657	.7664	.7672	.7679	.7686	.7694	.7701
5.9	.7709	.7716	.7723	.7731	.7738	.7745	.7752	.7760	.7767	.7774
6.0	.7782	.7789	.7796	.7803	.7810	.7818	.7825	.7832	.7839	.7846
6.1	.7853	.7860	.7868	.7875	.7882	.7889	.7896	.7903	.7910	.7917
6.2	.7924	.7931	.7938	.7945	.7952	.7959	.7966	.7973	.7980	.7987
6.3	.7993	.8000	.8007	.8014	.8021	.8028	.8035	.8041	.8048	.8055
6.4	.8062	.8069	.8075	.8082	.8089	.8096	.8102	.8109	.8116	.8122
6.5	.8129	.8136	.8142	.8149	.8156	.8162	.8169	.8176	.8182	.8189
6.6	.8195	.8202	.8209	.8215	.8222	.8228	.8235	.8241	.8248	.8254
6.7	.8261	.8267	.8274	.8280	.8287	.8293	.8299	.8306	.8312	.8319
6.8	.8325	.8331	.8338	.8344	.8351	.8357	.8363	.8370	.8376	.8382
6.9	.8388	.8395	.8401	.8407	.8414	.8420	.8426	.8432	.8439	.8445
7.0	.8451	.8457	.8463	.8470	.8476	.8482	.8488	.8494	.8500	.8506
7.1	.8513	.8519	.8525	.8531	.8537	.8543	.8549	.8555	.8561	.8567
7.2	.8573	.8579	.8585	.8591	.8597	.8603	.8609	.8615	.8621	.8627
7.3	.8633	.8639	.8645	.8651	.8657	.8663	.8669	.8675	.8681	.8686
7.4	.8692	.8698	.8704	.8710	.8716	.8722	.8727	.8733	.8739	.8745
7.5	.8751	.8756	.8762	.8768	.8774	.8779	.8785	.8791	.8797	.8802
7.6	.8808	.8814	.8820	.8825	.8831	.8837	.8842	.8848	.8854	.8859
7.7	.8865	.8871	.8876	.8882	.8887	.8893	.8899	.8904	.8910	.8915
7.8	.8921	.8927	.8932	.8938	.8943	.8949	.8954	.8960	.8965	.8971
7.9	.8976	.8982	.8987	.8993	.8998	.9004	.9009	.9015	.9020	.9025
8.0	.9031	.9036	.9042	.9047	.9053	.9058	.9063	.9069	.9074	.9079
8.1	.9085	.9090	.9096	.9101	.9106	.9112	.9117	.9122	.9128	.9133
8.2	.9138	.9143	.9149	.9154	.9159	.9165	.9170	.9175	.9180	.9186
8.3	.9191	.9196	.9201	.9206	.9212	.9217	.9222	.9227	.9232	.9238
8.4	.9243	.9248	.9253	.9258	.9263	.9269	.9274	.9279	.9284	.9289
8.5	.9294	.9299	.9304	.9309	.9315	.9320	.9325	.9330	.9335	.9340
8.6	.9345	.9350	.9555	.9360	.9365	.9370	.9375	.9380	.9385	.9390
8.7	.9395	.9400	.9405	.9410	.9415	.9420	.9425	.9430	.9435	.9440
8.8	.9445	.9450	.9455	.9460	.9465	.9469	.9474	.9479	.9484	.9489
8.9	.9494	.9499	.9504	.9509	.9513	.9518	.9523	.9528	.9533	.9538
9.0	.9542	.9547	.9552	.9557	.9562	.9566	.9571	.9576	.9581	.9586
9.1	.9590	.9595	.9600	.9605	.9609	.9614	.9619	.9624	.9628	.9633
9.2	.9638	.9643	.9647	.9652	.9657	.9661	.9666	.9671	.9675	.9680
9.3	.9685	.9689	.9694	.9699	.9703	.9708	.9713	.9717	.9722	.9727
9.4	.9731	.9736	.9741	.9745	.9750	.9754	.9759	.9763	.9768	.9773
9.5	.9777	.9782	.9786	.9791	.9795	.9800	.9805	.9809	.9914	.9818
9.6	.9823	.9827	.9832	.9836	.9841	.9845	.9850	.9854	.9859	.9863
9.7	.9868	.9872	.9877	.9881	.9886	.9890	.9894	.9899	.9903	.9908
9.8	.9912	.9917	.9921	.9926	.9930	.9934	.9939	.9943	.9948	.9952
9.9	.9956	.9961	.9965	.9969	.9974	.9978	.9983	.9987	.9991	.9996

TABLE 3 Natural Logarithms (ln x)

x	0.00	0.01	0.02	0.03	0.04	0.05	0.06	0.07	0.08	0.09
1.0	0.0000	0.0100	0.0198	0.0296	0.0392	0.0488	0.0583	0.0677	0.0770	0.0862
1.1	0.0953	0.1044	0.1133	0.1222	0.1310	0.1398	0.1484	0.1570	0.1655	0.1740
1.2	0.1823	0.1906	0.1989	0.2070	0.2151	0.2231	0.2311	0.2390	0.2469	0.2546
1.3	0.2624	0.2700	0.2776	0.2852	0.2927	0.3001	0.3075	0.3148	0.3221	0.3293
1.4	0.3365	0.3436	0.3507	0.3577	0.3646	0.3716	0.3784	0.3853	0.3920	0.3988
1.5	0.4055	0.4121	0.4187	0.4253	0.4318	0.4383	0.4447	0.4511	0.4574	0.4637
1.6	0.4700	0.4762	0.4824	0.4886	0.4947	0.5008	0.5068	0.5128	0.5188	0.5247
1.7	0.5306	0.5365	0.5423	0.5481	0.5539	0.5596	0.5653	0.5710	0.5766	0.5822
1.8	0.5878	0.5933	0.5988	0.6043	0.6098	0.6152	0.6206	0.6259	0.6313	0.6366
1.9	0.6419	0.6471	0.6523	0.6575	0.6627	0.6678	0.6729	0.6780	0.6831	0.6881
2.0	0.6931	0.6981	0.7031	0.7080	0.7130	0.7178	0.7227	0.7275	0.7324	0.7372
2.1	0.7419	0.7467	0.7514	0.7561	0.7608	0.7655	0.7701	0.7747	0.7793	0.7839
2.2	0.7885	0.7930	0.7975	0.8020	0.8065	0.8109	0.8154	0.8198	0.8242	0.8286
2.3	0.8329	0.8372	0.8416	0.8459	0.8502	0.8544	0.8587	0.8629	0.8671	0.8713
2.4	0.8755	0.8796	0.8838	0.8879	0.8920	0.8961	0.9002	0.9042	0.9083	0.9123
2.5	0.9163	0.9203	0.9243	0.9282	0.9322	0.9361	0.9400	0.9439	0.9478	0.9517
2.6	0.9555	0.9594	0.9632	0.9670	0.9708	0.9746	0.9783	0.9821	0.9858	0.9895
2.7	0.9933	0.9969	1.0006	1.0043	1.0080	1.0116	1.0152	1.0188	1.0225	1.0260
2.8	1.0296	1.0332	1.0367	1.0403	1.0438	1.0473	1.0508	1.0543	1.0578	1.0613
2.9	1.0647	1.0682	1.0716	1.0750	1.0784	1.0818	1.0852	1.0886	1.0919	1.0953
3.0	1.0986	1.1019	1.1053	1.1086	1.1119	1.1151	1.1184	1.1217	1.1249	1.1282
3.1	1.1314	1.1346	1.1378	1.1410	1.1442	1.1474	1.1506	1.1537	1.1569	1.1600
3.2	1.1632	1.1663	1.1694	1.1725	1.1756	1.1787	1.1817	1.1848	1.1878	1.1909
3.3	1.1939	1.1970	1.2000	1.2030	1.2060	1.2090	1.2119	1.2149	1.2179	1.2208
3.4	1.2238	1.2267	1.2296	1.2326	1.2355	1.2384	1.2413	1.2442	1.2470	1.2499
3.5	1.2528	1.2556	1.2585	1.2613	1.2641	1.2669	1.2698	1.2726	1.2754	1.2782
3.6	1.2809	1.2837	1.2865	1.2892	1.2920	1.2947	1.2975	1.3002	1.3029	1.3056
3.7	1.3083	1.3110	1.3137	1.3164	1.3191	1.3218	1.3244	1.3271	1.3297	1.3324
3.8	1.3350	1.3376	1.3403	1.3429	1.3455	1.3481	1.3507	1.3533	1.3558	1.3584
3.9	1.3610	1.3635	1.3661	1.3686	1.3712	1.3737	1.3762	1.3788	1.3813	1.3838
4.0	1.3863	1.3888	1.3913	1.3938	1.3962	1.3987	1.4012	1.4036	1.4061	1.4085
4.1	1.4110	1.4134	1.4159	1.4183	1.4207	1.4231	1.4255	1.4279	1.4303	1.4327
4.2	1.4351	1.4375	1.4398	1.4422	1.4446	1.4469	1.4493	1.4516	1.4540	1.4563
4.3	1.4586	1.4609	1.4633	1.4656	1.4679	1.4702	1.4725	1.4748	1.4770	1.4793
4.4	1.4816	1.4839	1.4861	1.4884	1.4907	1.4929	1.4952	1.4974	1.4996	1.5019
4.5	1.5041	1.5063	1.5085	1.5107	1.5129	1.5151	1.5173	1.5195	1.5217	1.5239
4.6	1.5261	1.5282	1.5304	1.5326	1.5347	1.5369	1.5390	1.5412	1.5433	1.5454
4.7	1.5476	1.5497	1.5518	1.5539	1.5560	1.5581	1.5602	1.5623	1.5644	1.5665
4.8	1.5686	1.5707	1.5728	1.5748	1.5769	1.5790	1.5810	1.5831	1.5851	1.5872
4.9	1.5892	1.5913	1.5933	1.5953	1.5974	1.5994	1.6014	1.6034	1.6054	1.6074
5.0	1.6094	1.6114	1.6134	1.6154	1.6174	1.6194	1.6214	1.6233	1.6253	1.6273
5.1	1.6292	1.6312	1.6332	1.6351	1.6371	1.6390	1.6409	1.6429	1.6448	1.6467
5.2	1.6487	1.6506	1.6525	1.6544	1.6563	1.6582	1.6601	1.6620	1.6639	1.6658
5.3	1.6677	1.6696	1.6715	1.6734	1.6752	1.6771	1.6790	1.6808	1.6827	1.6845
5.4	1.6864	1.6882	1.6901	1.6919	1.6938	1.6956	1.6974	1.6993	1.7001	1.7029

x	0.00	0.01	0.02	0.03	0.04	0.05	0.06	0.07	0.08	0.09
5.5	1.7047	1.7066	1.7084	1.7102	1.7120	1.7138	1.7156	1.7174	1.7192	1.7210
5.6	1.7228	1.7246	1.7263	1.7281	1.7299	1.7317	1.7334	1.7352	1.7370	1.7387
5.7	1.7405	1.7422	1.7440	1.7457	1.7475	1.7492	1.7509	1.7527	1.7544	1.7561
5.8	1.7579	1.7596	1.7613	1.7630	1.7647	1.7664	1.7682	1.7699	1.7716	1.7733
5.9	1.7750	1.7766	1.7783	1.7800	1.7817	1.7834	1.7851	1.7867	1.7884	1.7901
6.0	1.7918	1.7934	1.7951	1.7967	1.7984	1.8001	1.8017	1.8034	1.8050	1.8066
6.1	1.8083	1.8099	1.8116	1.8132	1.8148	1.8165	1.8181	1.8197	1.8213	1.8229
6.2	1.8245	1.8262	1.8278	1.8294	1.8310	1.8326	1.8342	1.8358	1.8374	1.8390
6.3	1.8406	1.8421	1.8437	1.8453	1.8469	1.8485	1.8500	1.8516	1.8532	1.8547
6.4	1.8563	1.8579	1.8594	1.8610	1.8625	1.8641	1.8656	1.8672	1.8687	1.8703
6.5	1.8718	1.8733	1.8749	1.8764	1.8779	1.8795	1.8810	1.8825	1.8840	1.8856
6.6	1.8871	1.8886	1.8901	1.8916	1.8931	1.8946	1.8961	1.8976	1.8991	1.9006
6.7	1.9021	1.9036	1.9051	1.9066	1.9081	1.9095	1.9110	1.9125	1.9140	1.9155
6.8	1.9169	1.9184	1.9199	1.9213	1.9228	1.9242	1.9257	1.9272	1.9286	1.9301
6.9	1.9315	1.9330	1.9344	1.9359	1.9373	1.9387	1.9402	1.9416	1.9430	1.9445
7.0	1.9459	1.9473	1.9488	1.9502	1.9516	1.9530	1.9544	1.9559	1.9573	1.9587
7.1	1.9601	1.9615	1.9629	1.9643	1.9657	1.9671	1.9685	1.9699	1.9713	1.9727
7.2	1.9741	1.9755	1.9769	1.9782	1.9796	1.9810	1.9824	1.9838	1.9851	1.9865
7.3	1.9879	1.9892	1.9906	1.9920	1.9933	1.9947	1.9961	1.9974	1.9988	2.0001
7.4	2.0015	2.0028	2.0042	2.0055	2.0069	2.0082	2.0096	2.0109	2.0122	2.0136
7.5	2.0149	2.0162	2.0176	2.0189	2.0202	2.0215	2.0229	2.0242	2.0255	2.0268
7.6	2.0282	2.0295	2.0308	2.0321	2.0334	2.0347	2.0360	2.0373	2.0386	2.0399
7.7	2.0412	2.0425	2.0438	2.0451	2.0464	2.0477	2.0490	2.0503	2.0516	2.0528
7.8	2.0541	2.0554	2.0567	2.0580	2.0592	2.0605	2.0618	2.0631	2.0643	2.0665
7.9	2.0669	2.0681	2.0694	2.0707	2.0719	2.0732	2.0744	2.0757	2.0769	2.0782
8.0	2.0794	2.0807	2.0819	2.0832	2.0844	2.0857	2.0869	2.0882	2.0894	2.0906
8.1	2.0919	2.0931	2.0943	2.0956	2.0968	2.0980	2.0992	2.1005	2.1017	2.1029
8.2	2.1041	2.1054	2.1066	2.1078	2.1090	2.1102	2.1114	2.1126	2.1138	2.1150
8.3	2.1163	2.1175	2.1187	2.1199	2.1211	2.1223	2.1235	2.1247	2.1258	2.1270
8.4	2.1282	2.1294	2.1306	2.1318	2.1330	2.1342	2.1353	2.1365	2.1377	2.1389
8.5	2.1401	2.1412	2.1424	2.1436	2.1448	2.1459	2.1471	2.1483	2.1494	2.1506
8.6	2.1518	2.1529	2.1541	2.1552	2.1564	2.1576	2.1587	2.1599	2.1610	2.1622
8.7	2.1633	2.1645	2.1656	2.1668	2.1679	2.1691	2.1702	2.1713	2.1725	2.1736
8.8	2.1748	2.1759	2.1770	2.1782	2.1793	2.1804	2.1815	2.1827	2.1838	2.1849
8.9	2.1861	2.1872	2.1883	2.1894	2.1905	2.1917	2.1928	2.1939	2.1950	2.1961
9.0	2.1972	2.1983	2.1994	2.2006	2.2017	2.2028	2.2039	2.2050	2.2061	2.2072
9.1	2.2083	2.2094	2.2105	2.2116	2.2127	2.2138	2.2148	2.2159	2.2170	2.2181
9.2	2.2192	2.2203	2.2214	2.2225	2.2235	2.2246	2.2257	2.2268	2.2279	2.2289
9.3	2.2300	2.2311	2.2322	2.2332	2.2343	2.2354	2.2364	2.2375	2.2386	2.2396
9.4	2.2407	2.2418	2.2428	2.2439	2.2450	2.2460	2.2471	2.2481	2.2492	2.2502
9.5	2.2513	2.2523	2.2534	2.2544	2.2555	2.2565	2.2576	2.2586	2.2597	2.2607
9.6	2.2618	2.2628	2.2638	2.2649	2.2659	2.2670	2.2680	2.2690	2.2701	2.2711
9.7	2.2721	2.2732	2.2742	2.2752	2.2762	2.2773	2.2783	2.2793	2.2803	2.2814
9.8	2.2824	2.2834	2.2844	2.2854	2.2865	2.2875	2.2885	2.2895	2.2905	2.2915
9.9	2.2925	2.2935	2.2946	2.2956	2.2966	2.2976	2.2986	2.2996	2.3006	2.3016

TABLE 4 Function Values for e^x and e^{-x}

x	e^x	e^{-x}	x	e^x	e^{-x}	x	e^x	e^{-x}
0.00	1.0000	1.0000	0.55	1.7333	0.5769	3.6	36.598	0.0273
0.01	1.0101	0.9900	0.60	1.8221	0.5488	3.7	40.447	0.0247
0.02	1.0202	0.9802	0.65	1.9155	0.5220	3.8	44.701	0.0224
0.03	1.0305	0.9704	0.70	2.0138	0.4966	3.9	49.402	0.0202
0.04	1.0408	0.9608	0.75	2.1170	0.4724	4.0	54.598	0.0183
0.05	1.0513	0.9512	0.80	2.2255	0.4493	4.1	60.340	0.0166
0.06	1.0618	0.9418	0.85	2.3396	0.4274	4.2	66.686	0.0150
0.07	1.0725	0.9324	0.90	2.4596	0.4066	4.3	73.700	0.0136
0.08	1.0833	0.9231	0.95	2.5857	0.3867	4.4	81.451	0.0123
0.09	1.0942	0.9139	1.0	2.7183	0.3679	4.5	90.017	0.0111
0.10	1.1052	0.9048	1.1	3.0042	0.3329	4.6	99.484	0.0101
0.11	1.1163	0.8958	1.2	3.3201	0.3012	4.7	109.95	0.0091
0.12	1.1275	0.8869	1.3	3.6693	0.2725	4.8	121.51	0.0082
0.13	1.1388	0.8781	1.4	4.0552	0.2466	4.9	134.29	0.0074
0.14	1.1503	0.8694	1.5	4.4817	0.2231	5	148.41	0.0067
0.15	1.1618	0.8607	1.6	4.9530	0.2019	6	403.43	0.0025
0.16	1.1735	0.8521	1.7	5.4739	0.1827	7	1096.6	0.0009
0.17	1.1853	0.8437	1.8	6.0496	0.1653	8	2981.0	0.0003
0.18	1.1972	0.8353	1.9	6.6859	0.1496	9	8103.1	0.0001
0.19	1.2092	0.8270	2.0	7.3891	0.1353	10	22026	0.00005
0.20	1.2214	0.8187	2.1	8.1662	0.1225	11	59874	0.00002
0.21	1.2337	0.8106	2.2	9.0250	0.1108	12	162,754	0.000006
0.22	1.2461	0.8025	2.3	9.9742	0.1003	13	442,413	0.000002
0.23	1.2585	0.7945	2.4	11.023	0.0907	14	1,202,604	0.0000008
0.24	1.2712	0.7866	2.5	12.182	0.0821	15	3,269,017	0.0000003
0.25	1.2840	0.7788	2.6	13.464	0.0743			
0.26	1.2969	0.7711	2.7	14.880	0.0672			
0.27	1.3100	0.7634	2.8	16.445	0.0608			
0.27	1.3231	0.7558	2.9	18.174	0.0550			
0.29	1.3364	0.7483	3.0	20.086	0.0498			
0.30	1.3499	0.7408	3.1	22.198	0.0450			
0.35	1.4191	0.7047	3.2	24.533	0.0408			
0.40	1.4918	0.6703	3.3	27.113	0.0369			
0.45	1.5683	0.6376	3.4	29.964	0.0334			
0.50	1.6487	0.6065	3.5	33.115	0.0302			

TABLE 5 Values of Trigonometric Functions

Degrees	Radians	Sin	Cos	Tan	Cot	Sec	Csc		
0° 00′	0.0000	0.0000	1.0000	0.0000	—	1.000	—	1.5708	90° 00′
10	029	029	000	029	343.8	000	343.8	679	50
20	058	058	000	058	171.9	000	171.9	650	40
30	0.0087	0.0087	1.0000	0.0087	114.6	1.000	114.6	1.5621	30
40	116	116	0.9999	116	85.94	000	85.95	592	20
50	145	145	999	145	68.75	000	68.76	563	10
1° 00′	0.0175	0.0175	0.9998	0.0175	57.29	1.000	57.30	1.5533	89° 00′
10	204	204	998	204	49.10	000	49.11	504	50
20	233	233	997	233	42.96	000	42.98	475	40
30	0.0262	0.0262	0.9997	0.0262	38.19	1.000	38.20	1.5446	30
40	291	291	996	291	34.37	000	34.38	417	20
50	320	320	995	320	31.24	001	31.26	388	10
2° 00′	0.0349	0.0349	0.9994	0.0349	28.64	1.001	28.65	1.5359	88° 00′
10	378	378	993	378	26.43	001	26.45	330	50
20	407	407	992	407	24.54	001	24.56	301	40
30	0.0436	0.0436	0.9990	0.0437	22.90	1.001	22.93	1.5272	30
40	465	465	989	466	21.47	001	21.49	243	20
50	495	494	988	495	20.21	001	20.23	213	10
3° 00′	0.0524	0.0523	0.9986	0.0524	19.08	1.001	19.11	1.5184	87° 00′
10	553	552	985	553	18.07	002	18.10	155	50
20	582	581	983	582	17.17	002	17.20	126	40
30	0.0611	0.0610	0.9981	0.0612	16.35	1.002	16.38	1.5097	30
40	640	640	980	641	15.60	002	15.64	068	20
50	669	669	978	670	14.92	002	14.96	039	10
4° 00′	0.0698	0.0698	0.9976	0.0699	14.30	1.002	14.34	1.5010	86° 00′
10	727	727	974	729	13.73	003	13.76	981	50
20	756	756	971	758	13.20	003	13.23	952	40
30	0.0785	0.7785	0.9969	0.0787	12.71	1.003	12.75	1.4923	30
40	814	814	967	816	12.25	003	12.29	893	20
50	844	843	964	846	11.83	004	11.87	864	10
5° 00′	0.0873	0.0872	0.9962	0.0875	11.43	1.004	11.47	1.4835	85° 00′
10	902	901	959	904	11.06	004	11.10	806	50
20	931	929	957	934	10.71	004	10.76	777	40
30	0.0960	0.0958	0.9954	0.0963	10.39	1.005	10.43	1.4748	30
40	989	987	951	992	10.08	005	10.13	719	20
50	0.1018	0.1016	948	0.1022	9.788	005	9.839	690	10
6° 00′	0.1047	0.1045	0.9945	0.1051	9.514	1.006	9.567	1.4661	84° 00′
10	076	074	942	080	9.255	006	9.309	632	50
20	105	103	939	110	9.010	006	9.065	603	40
30	0.1134	0.1132	0.9936	0.1139	8.777	1.006	8.834	1.4573	30
40	164	161	932	169	8.556	007	8.614	544	20
50	193	190	929	198	8.345	007	8.405	515	10
7° 00′	0.1222	0.1219	0.9925	0.1228	8.144	1.008	8.206	1.4486	83° 00′
10	251	248	922	257	7.953	008	8.016	457	50
20	280	276	918	287	7.770	008	7.834	428	40
30	0.1309	0.1305	0.9914	0.1317	7.596	1.009	7.661	1.4399	30
40	338	334	911	346	7.429	009	7.496	370	20
50	367	363	907	376	7.269	009	7.337	341	10
8° 00′	0.1396	0.1392	0.9903	0.1405	7.115	1.010	7.185	1.4312	82° 00′
10	425	421	899	435	6.968	010	7.040	283	50
20	454	449	894	465	6.827	011	6.900	254	40
30	0.1484	0.1478	0.9890	0.1495	6.691	1.011	6.765	1.4224	30
40	513	507	886	524	6.561	012	6.363	195	20
50	542	536	881	554	6.435	012	6.512	166	10
9° 00′	0.1571	0.1564	0.9877	0.1584	6.314	1.012	6.392	1.4137	81° 00′
		Cos	Sin	Cot	Tan	Csc	Sec	Radians	Degrees

Degrees	Radians	Sin	Cos	Tan	Cot	Sec	Csc		
9° 00′	0.1571	0.1564	0.9877	0.1584	6.314	1.012	6.392	1.4137	81° 00′
10	600	593	872	614	197	013	277	108	50
20	629	622	868	644	084	013	166	079	40
30	0.1658	0.1650	0.9863	0.1673	5.976	1.014	6.059	1.4050	30
40	687	679	858	703	871	014	5.955	1.4021	20
50	716	708	853	733	769	015	855	992	10
10° 00′	0.1745	0.1736	0.9848	0.1763	5.671	1.015	5.759	1.3963	80° 00′
10	774	765	843	793	576	016	665	934	50
20	804	794	838	823	485	016	575	904	40
30	0.1833	0.1822	0.9833	0.1853	5.396	1.017	5.487	1.3875	30
40	862	851	827	883	309	018	403	846	20
50	891	880	822	914	226	018	320	817	10
11° 00′	0.1920	0.1908	0.9816	0.1944	5.145	1.019	5.241	1.3788	79° 00′
10	949	937	811	974	066	019	164	759	50
20	978	965	805	0.2004	4.989	020	089	730	40
30	0.2007	0.1994	0.9799	0.2035	4.915	1.020	5.016	1.3701	30
40	036	0.2022	793	065	843	021	4.945	672	20
50	065	051	787	095	773	022	876	643	10
12° 00′	0.2094	0.2079	0.9781	0.2126	4.705	1.022	4.810	1.3614	78° 00′
10	123	108	775	156	638	023	745	584	50
20	153	136	769	186	574	024	682	555	40
30	0.2182	0.2164	0.9763	0.2217	4.511	1.024	4.620	1.3526	30
40	211	193	757	247	449	025	560	497	20
50	240	221	750	278	390	026	502	468	10
13° 00′	0.2269	0.2250	0.9744	0.2309	4.331	1.026	4.445	1.3439	77° 00′
10	298	278	737	339	275	027	390	410	50
20	327	306	730	370	219	028	336	381	40
30	0.2356	0.2334	0.9724	0.2401	4.165	1.028	4.284	1.3352	30
40	385	363	717	432	113	029	232	323	20
50	414	391	710	462	061	030	182	294	10
14° 00′	0.2443	0.2419	0.9703	0.2493	4.011	1.031	4.134	1.3265	76° 00′
10	473	447	696	524	3.962	031	086	235	50
20	502	476	689	555	914	032	039	206	40
30	0.2531	0.2504	0.9681	0.2586	3.867	1.033	3.994	1.3177	30
40	560	532	674	617	821	034	950	148	20
50	589	560	667	648	776	034	906	119	10
15° 00′	0.2618	0.2588	0.9659	0.2679	3.732	1.035	3.864	1.3090	75° 00′
10	647	616	652	711	689	036	822	061	50
20	676	644	644	742	647	037	782	032	40
30	0.2705	0.2672	0.9636	0.2773	3.606	1.038	3.742	1.3003	30
40	734	700	628	805	566	039	703	974	20
50	763	728	621	836	526	039	665	945	10
16° 00′	0.2793	0.2756	0.9613	0.2867	3.487	1.040	3.628	1.2915	74° 00′
10	822	784	605	899	450	041	592	886	50
20	851	812	596	931	412	042	556	857	40
30	0.2880	0.2840	0.9588	0.2962	3.376	1.043	3.521	1.2828	30
40	909	868	580	994	340	044	487	799	20
50	938	896	572	0.3026	305	045	453	770	10
17° 00′	0.2967	0.2924	0.9563	0.3057	3.271	1.046	3.420	1.2741	73° 00′
10	996	952	555	089	237	047	388	712	50
20	0.3025	979	546	121	204	048	356	683	40
30	0.3054	0.3007	0.9537	0.3153	3.172	1.049	3.326	1.2654	30
40	083	035	528	185	140	049	295	625	20
50	113	062	520	217	108	050	265	595	10
18° 00′	0.3142	0.3090	0.9511	0.3249	3.078	1.051	3.236	1.2566	72° 00′
		Cos	Sin	Cot	Tan	Csc	Sec	Radians	Degrees

Degrees	Radians	Sin	Cos	Tan	Cot	Sec	Csc		
18° 00′	0.3142	0.3090	0.9511	0.3249	3.078	1.051	3.236	1.2566	72° 00′
10	171	118	502	281	047	052	207	537	50
20	200	145	492	314	018	053	179	508	40
30	0.3229	0.3173	0.9483	0.3346	2.989	1.054	3.152	1.2479	30
40	258	201	474	378	960	056	124	450	20
50	287	228	465	411	932	057	098	421	10
19° 00′	0.3316	0.3256	0.9455	0.3443	2.904	1.058	3.072	1.2392	71° 00′
10	345	283	446	476	877	059	046	363	50
20	374	311	436	508	850	060	021	334	40
30	0.3403	0.3338	0.9426	0.3541	2.824	1.061	2.996	1.2305	30
40	432	365	417	574	798	062	971	275	20
50	462	393	407	607	773	063	947	246	10
20° 00′	0.3491	0.3420	0.9397	0.3640	2.747	1.064	2.924	1.2217	70° 00′
10	520	448	387	673	723	065	901	188	50
20	549	475	377	706	699	066	878	159	40
30	0.3578	0.3502	0.9367	0.3739	2.675	1.068	2.855	1.2130	30
40	607	529	356	772	651	069	833	101	20
50	636	557	346	805	628	070	812	072	10
21° 00′	0.3665	0.3584	0.9336	0.3839	2.605	1.071	2.790	1.2043	69° 00′
10	694	611	325	872	583	072	769	1.2014	50
20	723	638	315	906	560	074	749	985	40
30	0.3752	0.3665	0.9304	0.3939	2.539	1.075	2.729	1.1956	30
40	782	692	293	973	517	076	709	926	20
50	811	719	283	0.4006	496	077	689	897	10
22° 00′	0.3840	0.3746	0.9272	0.4040	2.475	1.079	2.669	1.1868	68° 00′
10	869	773	261	074	455	080	650	839	50
20	898	800	250	108	434	081	632	810	40
30	0.3927	0.3827	0.9239	0.4142	2.414	1.082	2.613	1.1781	30
40	956	854	228	176	394	084	595	752	20
50	985	881	216	210	375	085	577	723	10
23° 00′	0.4014	0.3907	0.9205	0.4245	2.356	1.086	2.559	1.1694	67° 00′
10	043	934	194	279	337	088	542	665	50
20	072	961	182	314	318	089	525	636	40
30	0.4102	0.3987	0.9171	0.4348	2.300	1.090	2.508	1.1606	30
40	131	0.4014	159	383	282	092	491	577	20
50	160	041	147	417	264	093	475	548	10
24° 00′	0.4189	0.4067	0.9135	0.4452	2.246	1.095	2.459	1.1519	66° 00′
10	218	094	124	487	229	096	443	490	50
20	247	120	112	552	211	097	427	461	40
30	0.4276	0.4147	0.9100	0.4557	2.194	1.099	2.411	1.1432	30
40	305	173	088	592	177	100	396	403	20
50	334	200	075	628	161	102	381	374	10
25° 00′	0.4363	0.4226	0.9063	0.4663	2.145	1.103	2.366	1.1345	65° 00′
10	392	253	051	699	128	105	352	316	50
20	422	279	038	734	112	106	337	286	40
30	0.4451	0.4305	0.9026	0.4770	2.097	1.108	2.323	1.1257	30
40	480	331	013	806	081	109	309	228	20
50	509	358	001	841	066	111	295	199	10
26° 00′	0.4538	0.4384	0.8988	0.4877	2.050	1.113	2.281	1.1170	64° 00′
10	567	410	975	913	035	114	268	141	50
20	596	436	962	950	020	116	254	112	40
30	0.4625	0.4462	0.8949	0.4986	2.006	1.117	2.241	1.1083	30
40	654	488	936	0.5022	1.991	119	228	054	20
50	683	514	923	059	977	121	215	1.1025	10
27° 00′	0.4712	0.4540	0.8910	0.5095	1.963	1.122	2.203	1.0996	63° 00′
		Cos	Sin	Cot	Tan	Csc	Sec	Radians	Degrees

Degrees	Radians	Sin	Cos	Tan	Cot	Sec	Csc		
27° 00′	0.4712	0.4540	0.8910	0.5095	1.963	1.122	2.203	1.0966	63° 00′
10	741	566	897	132	949	124	190	966	50
20	771	592	884	169	935	126	178	937	40
30	0.4800	0.4617	0.8870	0.5206	1.921	1.127	2.166	1.0908	30
40	829	643	857	243	907	129	154	879	20
50	858	669	843	280	894	131	142	850	10
28° 00′	0.4887	0.4695	0.8829	0.5317	1.881	1.133	2.130	1.0821	62° 00′
10	916	720	816	354	868	134	118	792	50
20	945	746	802	392	855	136	107	763	40
30	0.4974	0.4772	0.8788	0.5430	1.842	1.138	2.096	1.0734	30
40	0.5003	797	774	467	829	140	085	705	20
50	032	823	760	505	816	142	074	676	10
29° 00′	0.5061	0.4848	0.8746	0.5543	1.804	1.143	2.063	1.0647	61° 00′
10	091	874	732	581	792	145	052	617	50
20	120	899	718	619	780	147	041	588	40
30	0.5149	0.4924	0.8704	0.5658	1.767	1.149	2.031	1.0559	30
40	178	950	689	696	756	151	020	530	20
50	207	975	675	735	744	153	010	501	10
30° 00′	0.5236	0.5000	0.8660	0.5774	1.732	1.155	2.000	1.0472	60° 00′
10	265	025	646	812	720	157	1.990	443	50
20	294	050	631	851	709	159	980	414	40
30	0.5323	0.5075	0.8616	0.5890	1.698	1.161	1.970	1.0385	30
40	352	100	601	930	868	163	961	356	20
50	381	125	587	969	675	165	951	327	10
31° 00′	0.5411	0.5150	0.8572	0.6009	1.664	1.167	1.942	1.0297	59° 00′
10	440	175	557	048	653	169	932	268	50
20	469	200	542	088	643	171	923	239	40
30	0.5498	0.5225	0.8526	0.6128	1.632	1.173	1.914	1.0210	30
40	527	250	511	168	621	175	905	181	20
50	556	275	496	208	611	177	896	152	10
32° 00′	0.5585	0.5299	0.8480	0.6249	1.600	1.179	1.887	1.0123	58° 00′
10	614	324	465	289	590	181	878	094	50
20	643	348	450	330	580	184	870	065	40
30	0.5672	0.5373	0.8434	0.6371	1.570	1.186	1.861	1.0036	30
40	701	398	418	412	560	188	853	1.007	20
50	730	422	403	453	550	190	844	977	10
33° 00′	0.5760	0.5446	0.8387	0.6494	1.540	1.192	1.836	0.9948	57° 00′
10	789	471	371	536	530	195	828	919	50
20	818	495	355	577	520	197	820	890	40
30	0.5847	0.5519	0.8339	0.6619	1.511	1.199	1.812	0.9861	30
40	876	544	323	661	501	202	804	832	20
50	905	568	307	703	1.492	204	796	803	10
34° 00′	0.5934	0.5592	0.8290	0.6745	1.483	1.206	1.788	0.9774	56° 00′
10	963	616	274	787	473	209	781	745	50
20	992	640	258	830	464	211	773	716	40
30	0.6021	0.5664	0.8241	0.6873	1.455	1.213	1.766	0.9687	30
40	050	688	225	916	446	216	758	657	20
50	080	712	208	959	437	218	751	628	10
35° 00′	0.6109	0.5736	0.8192	0.7002	1.428	1.221	1.743	0.9599	55° 10′
10	138	760	175	046	419	223	736	570	50
20	167	783	158	089	411	226	729	541	40
30	0.6196	0.5807	0.8141	0.7133	1.402	1.228	1.722	0.9512	30
40	225	831	124	177	393	231	715	483	20
50	254	854	107	221	385	233	708	454	10
36° 00′	0.6283	0.5878	0.8090	0.7265	1.376	1.236	1.701	0.9425	54° 00′
		Cos	Sin	Cot	Tan	Csc	Sec	Radians	Degrees

Degrees	Radians	Sin	Cos	Tan	Cot	Sec	Csc		
36° 00′	0.6283	0.5878	0.8090	0.7265	1.376	1.236	1.701	0.9425	54° 00′
10	312	901	073	310	368	239	695	396	50
20	341	925	056	355	360	241	688	367	40
30	0.6370	0.5948	0.8039	0.7400	1.351	1.244	1.681	0.9338	30
40	400	972	021	445	343	247	675	308	20
50	429	995	004	490	335	249	668	279	10
37° 00′	0.6458	0.6018	0.7986	0.7536	1.327	1.252	1.662	0.9250	53° 00′
10	487	041	969	581	319	255	655	221	50
20	516	065	951	627	311	258	649	192	40
30	0.6545	0.6088	0.7934	0.7673	1.303	1.260	1.643	0.9163	30
40	574	111	916	720	295	263	636	134	20
50	603	134	898	766	288	266	630	105	10
38° 00′	0.6632	0.6157	0.7880	0.7813	1.280	1.269	1.624	0.9076	52° 00′
10	661	180	862	860	272	272	618	047	50
20	690	202	844	907	265	275	612	0.9018	40
30	0.6720	0.6225	0.7826	0.7954	1.257	1.278	1.606	0.8988	30
40	749	248	808	0.8002	250	281	601	959	20
50	778	271	790	050	242	284	595	930	10
39° 00′	0.6807	0.6293	0.7771	0.8098	1.235	1.287	1.589	0.8901	51° 00′
10	836	316	753	146	228	290	583	872	50
20	865	338	735	195	220	293	578	843	40
30	0.6894	0.6361	0.7716	0.8243	1.213	1.296	1.572	0.8814	30
40	923	383	698	292	206	299	567	785	20
50	952	406	679	342	199	302	561	756	10
40° 00′	0.6981	0.6428	0.7660	0.8391	1.192	1.305	1.556	0.8727	50° 00′
10	0.7010	450	642	441	185	309	550	698	50
20	039	472	623	491	178	312	545	668	40
30	0.7069	0.6494	0.7604	0.8541	1.171	1.315	1.540	0.8639	30
40	098	517	585	591	164	318	535	610	20
50	127	539	566	642	157	322	529	581	10
41° 00′	0.7156	0.6561	0.7547	0.8693	1.150	1.325	1.524	0.8552	49° 00′
10	185	583	528	744	144	328	519	523	50
20	214	604	509	796	137	332	514	494	40
30	0.7243	0.6626	0.7490	0.8847	1.130	1.335	1.509	0.8465	30
40	272	648	470	899	124	339	504	436	20
50	301	670	451	952	117	342	499	407	10
42° 00′	0.7330	0.6691	0.7431	0.9004	1.111	1.346	1.494	0.8378	48° 00′
10	359	713	412	057	104	349	490	348	50
20	389	734	392	110	098	353	485	319	40
30	0.7418	0.6756	0.7373	0.9163	1.091	1.356	1.480	0.8290	30
40	447	777	353	217	085	360	476	261	20
50	476	799	333	271	079	364	471	232	10
43° 00′	0.7505	0.6820	0.7314	0.9325	1.072	1.367	1.466	0.8203	47° 00′
10	534	841	294	380	066	371	462	174	50
20	563	862	274	435	060	375	457	145	40
30	0.7592	0.6884	0.7254	0.9490	1.054	1.379	1.453	0.8116	30
40	621	905	234	545	048	382	448	087	20
50	650	926	214	601	042	386	444	058	10
44° 00′	0.7679	0.6947	0.7193	0.9657	1.036	1.390	1.440	0.8029	46° 00′
10	709	967	173	713	030	394	435	999	50
20	738	988	153	770	024	398	431	970	40
30	0.7767	0.7009	0.7133	0.9827	1.018	1.402	1.427	0.7941	30
40	796	030	112	884	012	406	423	912	20
50	825	050	092	942	006	410	418	883	10
45° 00′	0.7854	0.7071	0.7071	1.000	1.000	1.414	1.414	0.7854	45° 00′
		Cos	Sin	Cot	Tan	Csc	Sec	Radians	Degrees

TABLE 6 Random Numbers

ROW 1	82350	90391	34806	35773	37006	34566	12787	35876	01956	45032
ROW 2	88640	70497	48430	23118	28843	63970	27630	48165	75403	56046
ROW 3	88866	78271	21214	37408	13072	74208	46567	72124	21437	58899
ROW 4	22024	15249	05312	06293	89938	86283	37555	47539	45303	79801
ROW 5	78557	94906	43513	91811	65765	57999	04300	42085	14656	63862
ROW 6	00614	15626	32753	52056	40241	38191	38697	95113	87484	07445
ROW 7	60592	31356	78993	71554	67376	89165	83024	04971	33173	10565
ROW 8	99577	72094	87220	93468	12634	73241	90887	81145	44514	74872
ROW 9	41315	42978	08197	63928	39692	54237	62467	68393	50329	08419
ROW 10	24822	55560	78253	28041	15083	23942	02291	35719	81950	15762
ROW 11	06944	49907	61851	15463	39526	69032	07495	59166	50508	45936
ROW 12	80275	62418	44439	46123	10849	85380	08856	99522	69693	85205
ROW 13	85627	88368	81809	37340	77503	38405	78698	48913	10950	89533
ROW 14	51362	50793	29447	27773	30305	39479	40929	07584	86797	33690
ROW 15	78651	52923	63819	65496	52373	63226	97608	62619	11184	59319
ROW 16	43661	42921	70123	33169	37210	93951	37789	62622	36278	90576
ROW 17	83917	70635	53187	85377	09437	67836	00119	52705	09146	40761
ROW 18	08353	94629	74422	38676	11789	14744	37819	18874	43442	83293
ROW 19	10175	66887	35564	02091	83380	49556	89774	80413	67593	88292
ROW 20	62685	25884	93733	82093	77453	56403	31764	89720	18365	17074
ROW 21	90744	10792	94318	09771	30806	06889	57351	65908	73715	52729
ROW 22	10970	86189	75787	23891	91605	27770	22993	14397	93809	99067
ROW 23	89348	98603	04061	24420	29620	12504	35604	33671	14026	79021
ROW 24	97567	08941	18747	28969	53541	62222	57756	27990	04849	95722
ROW 25	93364	93512	86803	45856	97968	32641	24790	14548	79975	93491
ROW 26	95184	87663	74975	32858	02713	03348	91694	15908	78438	17265
ROW 27	21634	20106	93095	63081	04331	86360	48376	35879	90502	04342
ROW 28	35119	47963	25706	70328	90299	59639	96541	14381	71896	63691
ROW 29	10645	91688	35173	49893	18670	61188	53479	49512	19594	89066
ROW 30	20301	52310	28855	98311	75943	61868	66021	26565	37821	95791
ROW 31	70882	53420	46615	24653	91161	95603	89257	58094	44898	39646
ROW 32	71622	29832	57867	76963	52298	53556	42094	70948	20460	41980
ROW 33	32564	94559	90961	40398	50486	78439	12035	03923	27190	29849
ROW 34	19517	22450	62071	42815	64508	57543	00781	19440	21033	51421
ROW 35	91023	99839	93150	85480	09602	18857	36956	26273	97932	59352
ROW 36	74723	30908	83036	79236	46616	19522	30264	07118	61968	34319
ROW 37	04075	39146	98046	27426	27975	42670	48233	81370	93529	14139
ROW 38	60422	91391	96638	21680	31257	52601	64065	22417	32568	17772
ROW 39	20803	27478	44995	57419	58728	91408	86083	90531	62338	07438
ROW 40	20891	51357	73166	42323	42263	58243	77894	94763	49214	54829
ROW 41	36866	24285	45072	92763	69855	81929	33035	49712	34754	55166
ROW 42	75062	79115	89308	57338	01250	18914	10440	28981	67780	16264
ROW 43	09254	46288	72174	68439	05838	49878	56368	29642	16889	65994
ROW 44	69812	85750	77334	23167	63327	60612	58371	49078	35413	67035
ROW 45	88377	33535	02459	88695	88054	23776	54180	41184	59714	08985
ROW 46	49407	69576	87952	72323	94393	27844	79365	37197	35972	35367
ROW 47	94187	44459	93685	12069	32502	55403	08306	35970	96564	23604
ROW 48	23735	49509	49844	54546	68312	89793	38860	45076	82780	52100
ROW 49	51275	75658	61962	11966	49096	06965	48613	58890	59220	07371
ROW 50	09569	28121	93532	97064	03536	49673	35029	59577	63577	08083

TABLE 7 Normal Curve

AREAS UNDER THE STANDARD NORMAL CURVE (AREAS TO THE LEFT)

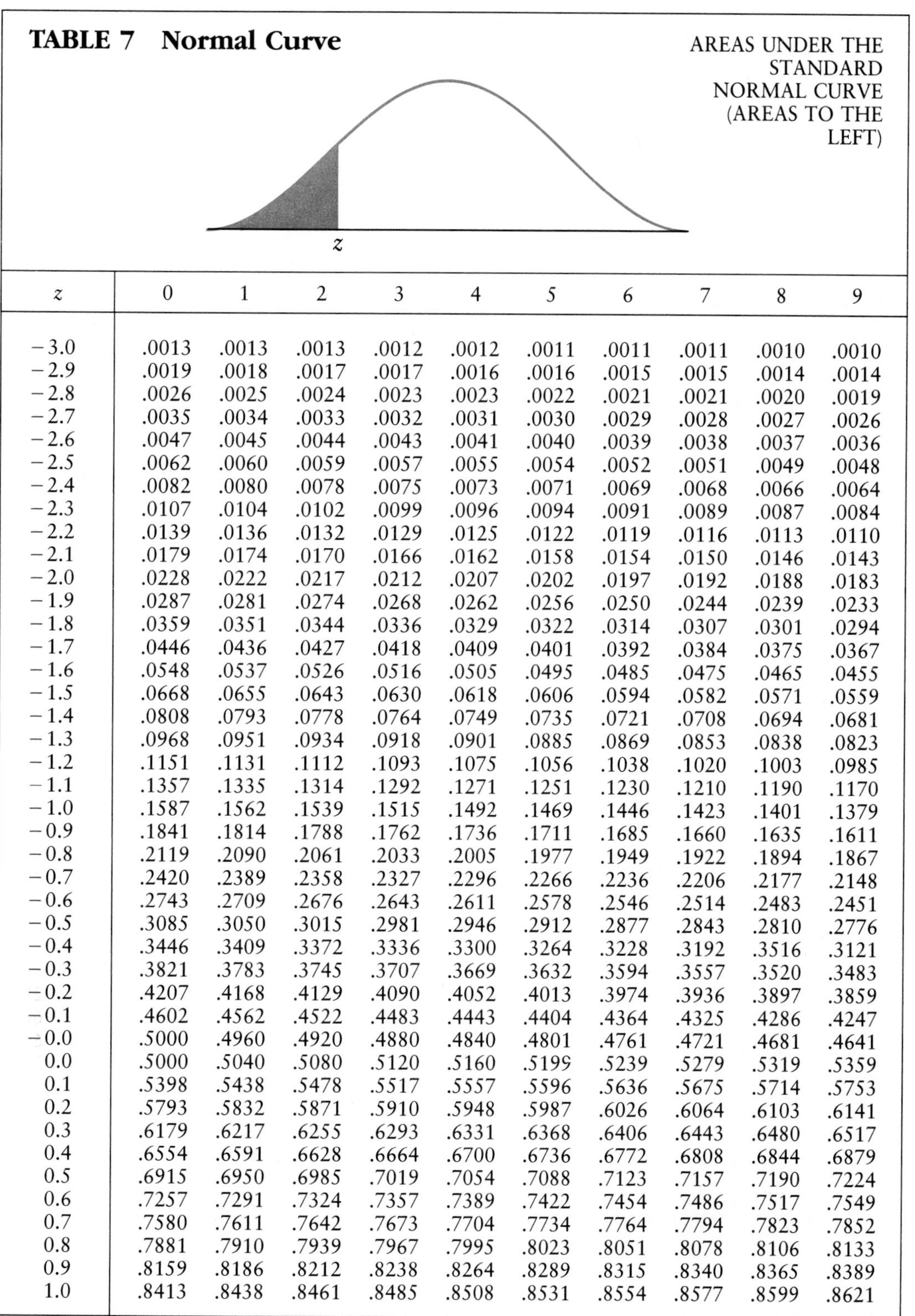

z	0	1	2	3	4	5	6	7	8	9
−3.0	.0013	.0013	.0013	.0012	.0012	.0011	.0011	.0011	.0010	.0010
−2.9	.0019	.0018	.0017	.0017	.0016	.0016	.0015	.0015	.0014	.0014
−2.8	.0026	.0025	.0024	.0023	.0023	.0022	.0021	.0021	.0020	.0019
−2.7	.0035	.0034	.0033	.0032	.0031	.0030	.0029	.0028	.0027	.0026
−2.6	.0047	.0045	.0044	.0043	.0041	.0040	.0039	.0038	.0037	.0036
−2.5	.0062	.0060	.0059	.0057	.0055	.0054	.0052	.0051	.0049	.0048
−2.4	.0082	.0080	.0078	.0075	.0073	.0071	.0069	.0068	.0066	.0064
−2.3	.0107	.0104	.0102	.0099	.0096	.0094	.0091	.0089	.0087	.0084
−2.2	.0139	.0136	.0132	.0129	.0125	.0122	.0119	.0116	.0113	.0110
−2.1	.0179	.0174	.0170	.0166	.0162	.0158	.0154	.0150	.0146	.0143
−2.0	.0228	.0222	.0217	.0212	.0207	.0202	.0197	.0192	.0188	.0183
−1.9	.0287	.0281	.0274	.0268	.0262	.0256	.0250	.0244	.0239	.0233
−1.8	.0359	.0351	.0344	.0336	.0329	.0322	.0314	.0307	.0301	.0294
−1.7	.0446	.0436	.0427	.0418	.0409	.0401	.0392	.0384	.0375	.0367
−1.6	.0548	.0537	.0526	.0516	.0505	.0495	.0485	.0475	.0465	.0455
−1.5	.0668	.0655	.0643	.0630	.0618	.0606	.0594	.0582	.0571	.0559
−1.4	.0808	.0793	.0778	.0764	.0749	.0735	.0721	.0708	.0694	.0681
−1.3	.0968	.0951	.0934	.0918	.0901	.0885	.0869	.0853	.0838	.0823
−1.2	.1151	.1131	.1112	.1093	.1075	.1056	.1038	.1020	.1003	.0985
−1.1	.1357	.1335	.1314	.1292	.1271	.1251	.1230	.1210	.1190	.1170
−1.0	.1587	.1562	.1539	.1515	.1492	.1469	.1446	.1423	.1401	.1379
−0.9	.1841	.1814	.1788	.1762	.1736	.1711	.1685	.1660	.1635	.1611
−0.8	.2119	.2090	.2061	.2033	.2005	.1977	.1949	.1922	.1894	.1867
−0.7	.2420	.2389	.2358	.2327	.2296	.2266	.2236	.2206	.2177	.2148
−0.6	.2743	.2709	.2676	.2643	.2611	.2578	.2546	.2514	.2483	.2451
−0.5	.3085	.3050	.3015	.2981	.2946	.2912	.2877	.2843	.2810	.2776
−0.4	.3446	.3409	.3372	.3336	.3300	.3264	.3228	.3192	.3516	.3121
−0.3	.3821	.3783	.3745	.3707	.3669	.3632	.3594	.3557	.3520	.3483
−0.2	.4207	.4168	.4129	.4090	.4052	.4013	.3974	.3936	.3897	.3859
−0.1	.4602	.4562	.4522	.4483	.4443	.4404	.4364	.4325	.4286	.4247
−0.0	.5000	.4960	.4920	.4880	.4840	.4801	.4761	.4721	.4681	.4641
0.0	.5000	.5040	.5080	.5120	.5160	.5199	.5239	.5279	.5319	.5359
0.1	.5398	.5438	.5478	.5517	.5557	.5596	.5636	.5675	.5714	.5753
0.2	.5793	.5832	.5871	.5910	.5948	.5987	.6026	.6064	.6103	.6141
0.3	.6179	.6217	.6255	.6293	.6331	.6368	.6406	.6443	.6480	.6517
0.4	.6554	.6591	.6628	.6664	.6700	.6736	.6772	.6808	.6844	.6879
0.5	.6915	.6950	.6985	.7019	.7054	.7088	.7123	.7157	.7190	.7224
0.6	.7257	.7291	.7324	.7357	.7389	.7422	.7454	.7486	.7517	.7549
0.7	.7580	.7611	.7642	.7673	.7704	.7734	.7764	.7794	.7823	.7852
0.8	.7881	.7910	.7939	.7967	.7995	.8023	.8051	.8078	.8106	.8133
0.9	.8159	.8186	.8212	.8238	.8264	.8289	.8315	.8340	.8365	.8389
1.0	.8413	.8438	.8461	.8485	.8508	.8531	.8554	.8577	.8599	.8621

z	0	1	2	3	4	5	6	7	8	9
1.1	.8643	.8665	.8686	.8708	.8729	.8749	.8770	.8790	.8810	.8830
1.2	.8849	.8869	.8888	.8907	.8925	.8944	.8962	.8980	.8997	.9015
1.3	.9032	.9049	.9066	.9082	.9099	.9115	.9131	.9147	.9162	.9177
1.4	.9192	.9207	.9222	.9236	.9251	.9265	.9279	.9292	.9306	.9319
1.5	.9332	.9345	.9357	.9370	.9382	.9394	.9406	.9418	.9429	.9441
1.6	.9452	.9463	.9474	.9484	.9495	.9505	.9515	.9525	.9535	.9545
1.7	.9554	.9564	.9573	.9582	.9591	.9599	.9608	.9616	.9625	.9633
1.8	.9641	.9649	.9656	.9664	.9671	.9678	.9686	.9693	.9699	.9706
1.9	.9713	.9719	.9726	.9732	.9738	.9744	.9750	.9756	.9761	.9767
2.0	.9772	.9778	.9783	.9788	.9793	.9798	.9803	.9808	.9812	.9817
2.1	.9821	.9826	.9830	.9834	.9838	.9842	.9846	.9850	.9854	.9857
2.2	.9861	.9864	.9868	.9871	.9875	.9878	.9881	.9884	.9887	.9890
2.3	.9893	.9896	.9898	.9901	.9904	.9906	.9909	.9911	.9913	.9916
2.4	.9918	.9920	.9922	.9925	.9927	.9929	.9931	.9932	.9934	.9936
2.5	.9938	.9940	.9941	.9943	.9945	.9946	.9948	.9949	.9951	.9952
2.6	.9953	.9955	.9956	.9957	.9959	.9960	.9961	.9962	.9963	.9964
2.7	.9965	.9966	.9967	.9968	.9969	.9970	.9971	.9972	.9973	.9974
2.8	.9974	.9975	.9976	.9977	.9977	.9978	.9979	.9979	.9980	.9981
2.9	.9981	.9982	.9982	.9983	.9984	.9984	.9985	.9985	.9986	.9986
3.0	.9987	.9987	.9987	.9988	.9988	.9989	.9989	.9989	.9990	.9990

Adapted from *Probability with Statistical Applications*, second edition, by F. Mosteller, R. E. K. Rourke, and G. B. Thomas, Jr. Reading, Mass.: Addison-Wesley, 1970, p. 473. Reprinted with permission.

TABLE 8 Symbols

Symbol	Meaning
$+$	positive
$-$	negative
$\cdot$	times
$\pm$	positive or negative
$=$	is equal to
$\neq$	is not equal to
$\approx$	is approximately equal to
$<$	is less than
$>$	is greater than
$\leq$	is less than or equal to
$\geq$	is greater than or equal to
$-n$	additive inverse of n
$\|n\|$	absolute value of n
b^n	nth power of b
$a:b$	ratio of a to b
%	percent
$^\circ$	degree
$\sqrt{}$	principal square root
π	pi, approximately 3.14
{ }	set braces
( )	set parentheses
[ ]	set brackets
$\in$	is a member of
$\cap$	the intersection of
$\cup$	the union of
$\emptyset$	the empty set
(x, y)	ordered pair
$f(x)$	f of x, the value of f at x
$\{x \mid x > 1\}$	the set of all numbers x such that $x > 1$
$\triangle$	triangle
$\angle$	angle
$\sim$	is similar to
$\overline{AB}$	segment AB
AB	the length of $\overline{AB}$
$P(A)$	the probability of event A
$\sin A$	the sine of A
$\cos A$	the cosine of A
$\tan A$	the tangent of A

TABLE 9 Geometric Formulas

<table>
<tr>
<td>

Rectangle
Area: $A = lw$
Perimeter: $P = 2l + 2w$

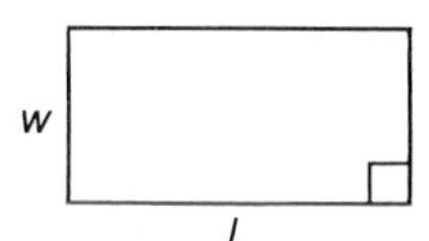

</td>
<td>

Parallelogram
Area: $A = bh$

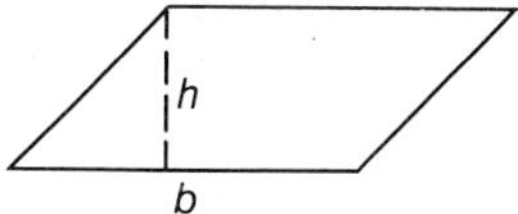

</td>
</tr>
<tr>
<td>

Square
Area: $A = s^2$
Perimeter: $P = 4s$

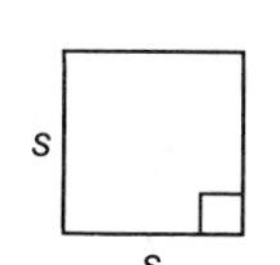

</td>
<td>

Trapezoid
Area: $A = \frac{1}{2}h(a + b)$

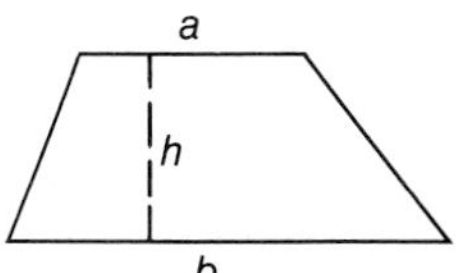

</td>
</tr>
<tr>
<td>

Triangle
Area: $A = \frac{1}{2}bh$
Sum of Angle Measures:
$A + B + C = 180°$

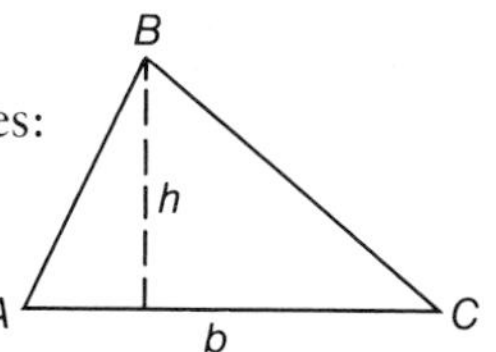

</td>
<td>

Circle
Area: $A = \pi r^2$
Circumference:
$C = \pi d = 2\pi r$

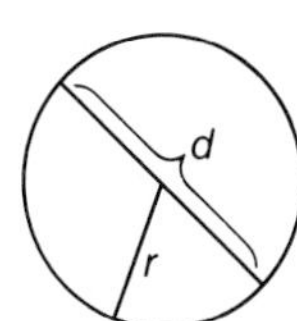

</td>
</tr>
<tr>
<td>

Right Triangle
Pythagorean Property:
$a^2 + b^2 = c^2$

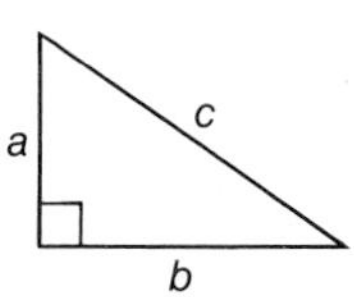

</td>
<td>

Rectangular Solid
Volume: $V = lwh$

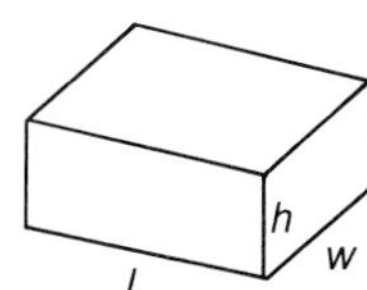

</td>
</tr>
<tr>
<td>

Polygon
Sum of Angle Measures:
$S = 180(n - 2)$
Number of Diagonals:
$N = \frac{n(n - 3)}{2}$

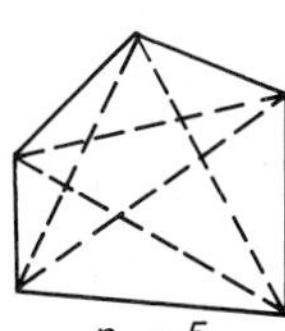

</td>
<td>

Cylinder
Volume: $V = \pi r^2 h$

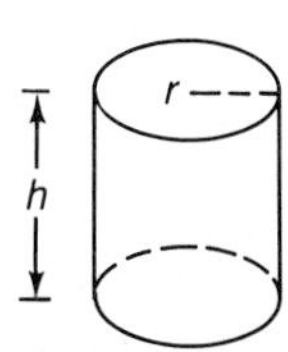

</td>
</tr>
<tr>
<td>

Prism
Volume: $V = Bh$
B = base area

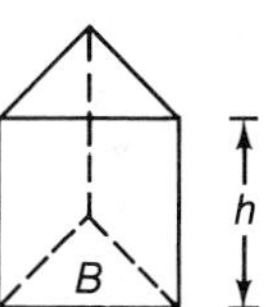

</td>
<td>

Cone
Volume: $V = \frac{1}{3}\pi r^2 h$

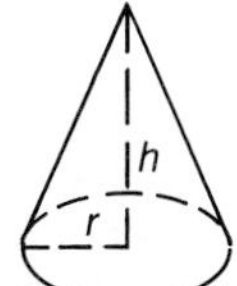

</td>
</tr>
</table>

Glossary

Abscissa (p. 110) The first number in an ordered pair; the x-coordinate.

Absolute value (p. 87) For any real number x, $|x| = x$ if x is nonnegative, and $|x| = -x$ if x is negative. The absolute value of a complex number $a + bi$ is denoted $|a + bi|$ and is defined to be $\sqrt{a^2 + b^2}$.

Addition property of equality (p. 26) For all numbers a, b, and c, if $a = b$, then $a + c = b + c$.

Addition property of inequality (p. 74) For all numbers a, b, and c, if $a < b$, then $a + c < b + c$. If $a > b$, then $a + c > b + c$. Similar statements hold for $\leq$ and $\geq$.

Additive identity (p. 17) Zero is the additive identity for addition. When we add 0 to any number we get that same number.

Additive inverse (p. 6) If the sum of two numbers is 0, they are additive inverses of each other.

Algorithm (p. 263) A systematic procedure for doing a computation.

Amplitude (p. 757) The amplitude of a periodic function is half the difference between its maximum and minimum function values. It is always positive.

Angle of depression or elevation (p. 805) The angle from the horizontal downward or upward to a line of sight.

Antecedent (p. 92) See *If-then statement.*

Antilogarithm (p. 436) Given $\log_a x = m$, the antilogarithm is the number m such that $m = a^x$.

Arcsine (p. 796) The inverse of the sine function; arcsin 0.5 is the angle whose sine is 0.5.

Arithmetic means (p. 619) Numbers $m_1, m_2, m_3, \ldots, m_n$ are arithmetic means between a and b if $a, m_1, m_2, m_3, \ldots, m_n, b$ form an arithmetic sequence.

Arithmetic sequence (p. 617) A sequence in which a constant d can be added to each term to get the next term. The constant d is called the common difference.

Arithmetic series (p. 620) A series associated with an arithmetic sequence.

Associative properties (p. 16) For any numbers a, b, and c,
Addition: $a + (b + c) = (a + b) + c$
Multiplication: $(a \cdot b) \cdot c = a \cdot (b \cdot c)$

Asymptote (p. 446) A line is an asymptote to a curve if the curve gets very close to the line as the distance from the center increases.

Augmented matrix (p. 593) A matrix containing the coefficients and constants of a system of linear equations.

Axes (p. 110) Two perpendicular number lines dividing a plane into four regions.

Axiom (p. 49) A property assumed or accepted without proof.

Base (p. 35) In exponential notation, n^x, n is the base. In logarithmic notation, $\log_a x$, a is the base.

Binomial (p. 206) A polynomial with exactly two terms.

Binomial coefficient (p. 660) The binomial coefficient

$$\binom{n}{a} \text{ means } \frac{n!}{a!(n-a)!}$$

Binomial expansion (p. 661) The sum of terms that results from multiplying out a power of a binomial.

Binomial theorem (p. 660) A theorem that tells how to expand a power of a binomial.

Boundary (p. 188) The edge of a half-plane.

Cartesian coordinate system (p. 110) When axes are placed on a plane perpendicular to each other so that ordered pairs of numbers are matched with the points of the plane, we have a Cartesian coordinate system.

Cartesian product (of sets) (p. 106) The cartesian product of two sets A and B, symbolized $A \times B$, is the set of all ordered pairs with first member from A and second member from B.

Characteristic (of logarithm) (p. 535) The integer part of a base 10 logarithm.

Chi-square test (p. 715) A hypothesis test used to determine whether a given set of data differs from what one would expect by chance.

Circle (p. 433) The set of all points in a plane that are at a constant distance from a fixed point in that plane. The fixed point is the *center* of the circle.

Closure (p. 49) A set is closed under an operation if, whenever the operation is done on elements within the set, the result is also in the set.

Coefficient (p. 21) In any term, the coefficient is the numeric factor of the term or the number that is multiplied by the variable. In $-3x$, the coefficient is -3; in x^4 the coefficient is 1.
Combination (p. 656) A selection of a group of objects from a set without regard to order.
Combinatorics (p. 644) The study of problems concerned with the number or ways a set of objects can be arranged, combined, or chosen, or the number of ways a succession of events can occur.
Common logarithm (p. 534) A base 10 logarithm.
Commutative properties (p. 15) For any numbers a and b,
Addition: $a + b = b + a$.
Multiplication: $a \cdot b = b \cdot a$.
Complement (p. 676) Suppose S is a sample space and A is an event in S. The complement of A, which is symbolized A', is the set of elements in S that are not in A.
Completing the square (p. 343) Adding one or more terms to an expression to make it the square of a binomial.
Complex number (p. 322) The complex numbers consist of all sums $a + bi$, where a and b are real numbers and i is the imaginary unit. The real part is a: the imaginary part is bi.
Complex rational expression (p. 256) One that has a rational expression in either its numerator or its denominator or in both.
Composition of functions (p. 149) If f and g are functions, the composition of f and g is given by $f(g(x))$.
Conditional statement (p. 92) A statement in the form *If a, then b.*
Conic section (p. 433) The nonempty intersection of any plane with a cone.
Conjugate (p. 327) Complex pairs such as $1 + 2i$ and $1 - 2i$.
Conjunction (p. 82) A sentence such as $x > 5$ *and* $x < 12$. A conjunction of two statements is formed by connecting them with "and" and is true when *both* statements are true.
Consequent (p. 92) See *If-then statement.*
Consistent system (p. 183) A system of equations or inequalities having at least one solution.
Constant of variation (p. 279) Whenever a situation results in a relation $y = kx$ or $y = \frac{k}{x}$ where x and y are the variables, k is the constant of variation.
Constant term (p. 14) A term with no variable.
Converge (p. 630) If, in an infinite series, S_n approaches some limit as n becomes very large, that limit is defined to be the sum of the series. If an infinite series has a sum, it is said to *converge* or be *convergent.*
Converse (p. 93) The converse of a sentence "if a, then b" is "if b, then a."
Coordinates (p. 88) The numbers in an ordered pair, used to locate a point on a plane.
Cosecant (p. 730) The reciprocal of the sine function $\csc \theta = \frac{1}{\sin \theta}$.
Cosine (p. 728) In a right triangle, the cosine of angle A is the ratio of the length of the side adjacent to A to the length of the hypotenuse.
Cotangent (p. 730) The reciprocal of the tangent function $\cot \theta = \frac{1}{\tan \theta}$.
Cramer's rule (p. 577) A rule for solving systems of equations using determinants.

Degree of a monomial (p. 206) The sum of the exponents of the variables in the monomial.
Degree of a polynomial (p. 206) The greatest degree of any of a polynomial's terms after it has been simplified.
Dependent system (p. 184) A consistent system of n equations and n variables is dependent if it is equivalent to a system of fewer than n equations.
Determinant (p. 576) A number assigned to a matrix that is a sum of certain products of its elements.
Dimensions of a matrix (p. 568) A matrix of m rows and n columns is called a matrix with dimensions $m \times n$.
Direct variation (p. 279) A function that can be described by an equation $y = kx$ where k is a constant.
Direct quadratic variation (p. 366) y varies directly as the square of x if there is some positive number k such that $y = kx^2$.
Discriminant (p. 354) For a quadratic equation $ax^2 + bx + c = 0$, the expression $b^2 - 4ac$ is called the discriminant.
Disjunction (p. 84) A sentence such as $x < -3$ or $x > 6$. A disjunction of two statements is formed by connecting them with "or." It is true when *one or both* statements are true.
Distance formula (p. 430) The distance between any two points (x_1, y_1) and (x_2, y_2) is given by $d = \sqrt{(x_1 - x_2)^2 + (y_1 - y_2)^2}$.
Distributive property (p. 20) The distributive property of multiplication over addition: For any real numbers a, b, and c, $(a + b) \cdot c = a \cdot c + b \cdot c$.
Domain (p. 107) See *Function.*

Element (of a set) (p. 106) Any member of a set.
Ellipse (p. 438) The set of all points P in a plane such that the sum of the distances from P to

two fixed points F_1 and F_2 is constant. Each fixed point is called a *focus*.

Empty set (p. 82) The set with no elements.

Equation (p. 26) A statement of equality between two expressions. An equation may be true or false.

Equivalent expressions (p. 15) Expressions that always result in the same number for all acceptable replacement values of their variables.

Even function (p. 388) If $f(x) = f(-x)$ for all x in the domain of a function f, then that function is even.

Event (p. 644) A set of outcomes that is a subset of the sample space resulting from an experiment. An event made up of several events is a *compound event.*

Exponent (p. 35) In exponential notation n^x, x is the exponent. The exponent tells how many times the base is used as a factor.

Exponential function (p. 521) The function $f(x) = a^x$, where a is some positive real-number constant different from 1, is called the exponential function, base a.

Extraneous roots (p. 318) A solution, found in the process of solving an equation, that is not a solution to the original equation.

Factorial (*n!*) (p. 646) For any natural number n, the product of the first n natural numbers. 0! is defined to be 1.

Factor theorem (p. 487) For a polynomial $P(x)$, if $P(r) = 0$, then the polynomial $x - r$ is a factor of $P(x)$.

Field (p. 50) Any number system, with two operations defined, in which certain axioms hold. The axioms are known as the *field axioms*.

Finite sequence (p. 620) A sequence with a last term.

Focus, Foci See *Ellipse, Hyperbola,* or *Parabola.*

Formula (p. 71) An equation that shows a relationship between two or more expressions.

Frequency distribution (p. 691) A table showing the frequency, or number of occurrences, of a particular set of data.

Function (p. 116) A relation or rule that assigns to each member of one set (called the *domain*) exactly one member of some set (called the *range*).

Fundamental counting principle (p. 645) In a compound event in which the first event may occur in n_1 different ways, the second event may occur in n_2 different ways, and the k-th event may occur in n_k different ways, the total number of ways the compound event may occur is $n_1 \cdot n_2 \cdot n_3 \ldots \cdot n_k$.

Fundamental theorem of algebra (p. 490) Every polynomial with complex coefficients and of degree n (where $n > 1$) can be factored into n linear factors.

General term (p. 612) The n-th term of a sequence.

Geometric means (p. 625) The numbers m_1, $m_2, m_3, \ldots$ are geometric means of a and b if $a, m_1, m_2, m_3, \ldots, b$ form a geometric sequence.

Geometric sequence (p. 624) A sequence in which a constant r can be multiplied by each term to get the next term. The constant r is called the *common ratio*.

Geometric series (p. 626) A series associated with a geometric sequence.

Graph (p. 110) The graph of an equation (or inequality) is the set of all points whose coordinates satisfy the equation (or inequality).

Greatest common factor (p. 21) The greatest integer that is a factor of two or more integers.

Greatest integer function (p. 148) $f(x) = [x]$; $[x]$ is the greatest integer that is less than or equal to x.

Half-plane (p. 188) One of the two regions into which a line separates a plane. The line itself is called a *boundary* and may or may not be included in the half-plane.

Harmonic sequence (p. 623) A sequence whose reciprocals form an arithmetic sequence.

Hyperbola (p. 445) The set of all points P in a plane such that the absolute value of the difference of the distances from P to two fixed points F_1 and F_2 is constant. The fixed points F_1 and F_2 are the *foci.*

Identity matrix (p. 589) A square matrix with ones in the upper left to the lower right along the main diagonal.

identity properties (p. 16) For any real number a,
Addition: $a + 0 = 0 + a = a$
Multiplication: $a \cdot 1 = 1 \cdot a = a$

If-then statement (p. 92) A conditional statement made up of two statements: "If . . ., then . . . ." The first statement, following *if,* is called the *antecedent.* The second statement, following *then,* is called the *consequent.*

Image (p. 384) Under a transformation, the point corresponding to a given point.

Imaginary number (p. 321) The square root of a negative number; expressed as $a + bi$, $b \neq 0$.

Inconsistent system (p. 183) A system of equations or inequalities having no solution.

Index (p. 294) The number k in $\sqrt[k]{\ }$, the k-th root, is called the index.

Inequality (p. 73) A mathematical sentence containing $>$, $<$, $\geq$, or $\leq$ between two expressions.

Infinite sequence (p. 612) A sequence with no last term.

Integer (p. 4) The numbers in the set $\{\ldots -3, -2, -1, 0, 1, 2, 3 \ldots\}$.

Intercept (p. 123) In the graph of an equation in two variables, the distance from the origin to the point where the graph crosses the axis.

Interpolation (p. 539) A process by which approximate function values can be determined between other values in a table.

Intersection (p. 82) The intersection of two sets is the set of all members that are common to both. The intersection of sets A and B is represented by the notation $A \cap B$.

Inverse of a sum (p. 22) The inverse of a sum is the sum of the inverses.

Inverse variation (p. 280) A function that can be described by an equation $y = \frac{k}{x}$, where $k \neq 0$ and k is a constant.

Irrational number (p. 4) A number that cannot be expressed using rational notation $\frac{a}{b}$ where $b \neq 0$ and a and b are integers.

Joint variation (p. 367) An equation of the form $z = kxy$ where k is a nonzero constant.

K-th root (p. 294) The k-th root of a number a is a number c such that $c^k = a$.

Least common denominator (p. 62) The smallest number that is a multiple of each denominator.

Least common multiple (p. 251) The smallest nonzero number that is a multiple of two or more given numbers.

Like terms (p. 21) Terms whose variable factors are exactly the same.

Line of symmetry (p. 384) In any figure, a line that divides the figure so that if it is folded on the line the two halves will match.

Linear equation (p. 122) An equation is linear if the variables occur to the first power only and its graph is a straight line.

Linear function (p. 143) A function defined by an equation in the form $y = mx + b$ where m and b are real numbers and $m \neq 0$.

Linear inequality (p. 188) An inequality in which the variables occur to the first power only.

Linear programming (p. 193) The mathematical theory of the minimization or maximization of a linear function subject to linear constraints.

Linear speed (p. 745) The linear speed v of a point that lies a distance of r from the center of rotation is given by $v = rw$ where w is the angular speed in radians per unit of time.

Logarithm (p. 523) If $a > 0$ and $x > 0$, $y = \log_a x$ if and only if $x = a^y$.

Logarithmic function (p. 523) The inverse of an exponential function.

Mantissa (p. 535) The portion of a base 10 logarithm between 0 and 1.

Matrix (p. 568) A rectangular array of numbers.

Mean (p. 694) The average of a set of values.

Mean deviation (p. 700) The measure of spread or variation; the average amount that a set of data deviates from the mean.

Median (p. 695) The middle value in a set of data when all the values are arranged in order.

Mode (p. 695) In a set of data, the value that occurs most often. Some sets of data have more than one mode and some have no mode.

Monomial (p. 206) An expression made up of a single term that is a product of numbers and variables.

Multiplication property of equality (p. 26) If an equation $a = b$ is true, then $a \cdot c = b \cdot c$ is true for any number c.

Multiplication property of inequality (p. 75) If we multiply by a positive number on both sides of a true inequality, we get another true inequality. If we multiply by a negative number and reverse the inequality, we get another true inequality.

Multiplicative identity (p. 17) The number 1 is the multiplicative identity. For any number n, $n \cdot 1 = n$.

Multiplicative inverse See *Reciprocal.*

Mutually exclusive (p. 668) Two events that cannot happen at the same time are mutually exclusive.

Natural logarithm (p. 551) Logarithm to the base e.

Natural numbers (p. 4) The numbers we use for counting. They are 1, 2, 3, 4, and so on.

Normal curve (p. 704) A symmetric bell shaped curve describing the normal distribution.

Normal distribution (p. 704) Describes the relative arrangement of a set of elements such that they fit the normal curve.

Odd function (p. 388) If $-f(x) = f(-x)$ for all x in the domain of a function (f), then that function is odd.

Ordered pair (p. 106) A pair of numbers in a particular order; the coordinates of a point in a plane.

Ordinate (p. 110) The y-coordinate or the second number of an ordered pair.

Origin (p. 110) The point at which the axes of a plane or graph cross; the point (0, 0) in the Cartesian coordinate system.

Outcome (p. 644) In situations in which we consider combinations of items or a succession of events such as flips of a coin or the drawing of cards, each result is called an *outcome.*

Parabola (p. 452) The set of all points equidistant from a fixed point (the focus) and a fixed line in a plane. The graph of the quadratic equation $ax^2 + bx + c = 0$, $a \neq 0$, is a parabola.

Partial sum (p. 614) The sum of a specified number of terms of a sequence.

Period (p. 304) The smallest horizontal distance needed for a graph to complete a cycle.

Periodic (p. 755) Functions with a repeating pattern.

Permutation (p. 645) A permutation of a set is an ordered arrangement of that set, without repetition.

Polar notation See *Trigonometric notation.*

Polynomial (p. 206) A sum of monomials.

Polynomial function (p. 207) A function that can be defined by a polynomial.

Power (p. 35) A number that can be named with exponential notation as n^x.

Prime factorization (p. 224) The expression of a composite number as the product of prime factors.

Principal square root (p. 293) The nonnegative square root of a number.

Principle of powers (p. 317) For any natural number n, if $a = b$ is true, then $a^n = b^n$.

Principle of zero products (p. 63) For any numbers a and b, if $ab = 0$, then $a = 0$ or $b = 0$, and if $a = 0$ or $b = 0$, then $ab = 0$.

Probability (p. 664) If an event E can occur m ways out of n equally-likely ways, the probability of that event is $P(E) = \frac{m}{n}$.

Proof (p. 49) A series of logical steps that lead from a hypothesis to a conclusion.

Quadrant (p. 110) One of the four regions into which coordinate axes divide a plane.

Quadratic equation (p. 342) An equation that can be written in the form $ax^2 + bx + c = 0$ where a, b, and c are real numbers and $a \neq 0$.

Quadratic formula (p. 350) A formula for finding the solutions of a quadratic equation $ax^2 + bx + c = 0$. The formula is

$$x = \frac{-b \pm \sqrt{b^2 - 4ac}}{2a}$$

Quadratic function (p. 400) A function defined by an equation of the form $y = ax^2 + bx + c$ where a, b, and c are real numbers and $a \neq 0$.

Quotient (p. 10) The quotient $\frac{a}{b}$ is the number (if it exists) which when multiplied by b gives a.

Radian (p. 741) A measure of angles. There are 2π radians in a circle.

Radical (p. 293) The symbol $\sqrt{}$ is called a radical symbol. Any expression that contains a radical is called a *radical expression.*

Radicand (p. 293) The expression under a radical.

Random sample (p. 710) A sample that is selected in such a fashion that each object in the population of interest has an equal chance of being selected and each object is chosen independently of any other objects in the sample.

Range See *Function.*

Rational expression (p. 244) The quotient of two polynomials.

Rational number (p. 4) Any number that can be expressed as the ratio of two integers in the form $\frac{a}{b}$ where $b \neq 0$.

Real number (p. 4) The real numbers consist of the rational numbers and the irrational numbers. There is a real number for each point of the number line.

Reciprocal (p. 9) Two expressions are reciprocals if their product is 1. A reciprocal is also called a *multiplicative inverse.*

Rectangular notation (p. 821) To change from trigonometric notation to rectangular notation $a + bi$, we use the formulas $a = r \cos \theta$ and $b = r \sin \theta$.

Recursion (p. 613) In a sequence, each term is related to the previous term or terms by a rule or formula.

Reference angle (p. 737) The acute angle that the terminal side of an angle makes with the x-axis.

Reflection (p. 384) A transformation in which points are reflected across a line.

Reflexive property of equality (p. 49) For every real number a, $a = a$.

Relation (p. 107) Any set of ordered pairs.

Replacement set (p. 26) The set of all values that may replace the variables in a sentence.

Root of a polynomial (p. 480) Any number that makes the polynomial zero.

Sample space (p. 664) The set of all possible outcomes of an experiment.

Scalar (p. 582) A constant k that is used as a multiplier for a matrix.

Scientific notation (p. 44) A number expressed as the product of a power of 10 and a numeral greater than or equal to 1 but less than 10. The numbers 4.25×10^3 and 2.3×10^{-2} are expressed using scientific notation.

Secant (p. 730) The reciprocal of the cosine function; $\sec \theta = \frac{1}{\cos \theta}$.

Sequence (p. 612) An ordered set of numbers.

Series (p. 614) An indicated sum of the terms of a sequence.

Sine (p. 728) In a right triangle, the sine of angle A is the ratio of the length of the side opposite to A to the length of the hypotenuse.

Sigma notation (p. 614) The Greek letter Σ (sigma) is the symbol for summation.

Slope of a line (p. 127) A number that tells how steeply the line slants; the ratio of rise to run.

Solution (p. 111) A replacement for a variable that makes an equation or inequality true.

Solution set (p. 26) The set of all replacements that make a sentence true.

Square root (p. 293) The number c is a square root of a if $c^2 = a$.

Standard deviation (p. 702) The square root of the variance.

Standard form (p. 135) Standard form of a linear equation is $ax + by + c = 0$. Standard form of a quadratic equation is $ax^2 + bx + c = 0$.

Statement (p. 92) A sentence that is either true or false.

Subset (p. 662) Set A is a subset of set B if every element of set A is an element of set B.

Subtrahend (p. 7) In subtraction, the number to be subtracted.

Synthetic division (p. 266) A method of division of a polynomial by a binomial, $x - a$, in which the variables are not written.

Symmetric property of equality (p. 49) For all numbers a and b, if $a = b$, then $b = a$.

System of equations (p. 160) A set of equations for which a common solution is sought.

Tangent (p. 728) In a right triangle, the tangent of angle A is the ratio of the length of the side opposite to A to the length of the side adjacent to A.

Terms (p. 21) The parts of an algebraic expression that are separated by an addition or subtraction sign.

Theorem (p. 7) A property that can be proved.

Transitive Property of Equality (p. 49) If $a = b$ and $b = c$, then $a = c$.

Translation (p. 391) A geometric transformation in which all points are moved the same distance in the same direction.

Trichotomy (p. 97) For any real number a, one and only one of the following is true: $a > 0$, $a = 0$, $a < 0$.

Trigonometric function (p. 728) A function that uses one of the six trigonometric ratios to assign values to the measures of the acute angles of a right triangle.

Trigonometric notation (p. 821) Trigonometric or polar notation for the complex number $a + bi$ is $r(\cos \theta + i \sin \theta)$, where $r = |a + bi|$ and θ is the argument. This is often shortened to $r \text{ cis } \theta$.

Trinomial (p. 206) A polynomial with three terms.

Trinomial square (p. 219) The square of a binomial; contains three terms.

Union (p. 84) The union of two sets is the set of all members that are in either or both sets. The union of sets A and B is represented by the notation $A \cup B$.

Variable (p. 14) A letter (or other symbol) used to represent one or several numbers.

Variance (p. 701) A measure of the amount of variation in a set of data. It is found by taking the mean of all the squared distances of the values from the mean.

***x*-coordinate** (p. 110) The first member of an ordered pair.

***x*-intercept** (p. 123) The x-coordinate of the point where the line intersects the x-axis.

***y*-coordinate** (p. 110) The second member of an ordered pair.

***y*-intercept** (p. 123) The y-coordinate of the point where the line intersects the y-axis.

z-score (p. 705) Used to define the number of standard deviations a point on the horizontal axis of the normal curve is from the mean.

Zero of a polynomial (p. 480) A number that when substituted into a polynomial function makes the function zero.

Selected Answers

Chapter 1

Lesson 1-1 Try This

a. Rational **b.** Rational **c.** Rational **d.** Irrational **e.** Rational **f.** Irrational **g.** -17 **h.** -18.6 **i.** $-\frac{7}{2}$ **j.** -14 **k.** 3.3 **l.** $-\frac{11}{24}$ **m.** 17 **n.** 17.8 **o.** $\frac{59}{48}$

Exercise Set 1-1

1. Rational **3.** Rational **5.** Rational **7.** Rational **9.** Rational **11.** Rational **13.** -28 **15.** -16 **17.** 5 **19.** -15 **21.** -34 **23.** -13.26 **25.** $-\frac{2}{3}$ **27.** $\frac{1}{10}$ **29.** -3 **31.** -21 **33.** 5 **35.** 44 **37.** -7.7 **39.** -34.80 **41.** $-\frac{13}{5}$ **43.** II, $\sqrt{4}$, $(\sqrt{2})^2$, $\sqrt[3]{8}$, $\frac{8}{4}$ **45.** $\frac{1}{2}$, $\sqrt{\frac{1}{4}}$, $\frac{8}{16}$, $\sqrt[3]{\frac{1}{8}}$, $\frac{2}{4}$ **49.** For example, 0.909009000900009. . . . **51.** $\frac{7}{24}$ **53.** $\frac{43}{40}$ **55.** 259.08 **57.** $\frac{1}{4}$ **59.** 2 **61.** 1 **63.** 60 **65.** 396

Lesson 1-2 Try This

a. -24 **b.** 28.35 **c.** -42.77 **d.** $\frac{5}{8}$ **e.** -3 **f.** -2 **g.** 0.25 **h.** $-\frac{6}{7}$ **i.** $\frac{36}{7}$ **j.** Possible **k.** Not possible **l.** Not possible **m.** Not possible

Exercise Set 1-2

1. -21 **3.** -8 **5.** 16 **7.** 126 **9.** -34.2 **11.** 26.46 **13.** 2 **15.** 60 **17.** 24 **19.** $-\frac{12}{35}$ **21.** 1 **23.** $-\frac{8}{27}$ **25.** $\frac{1}{5}$ **27.** -8 **29.** -4 **31.** 7 **33.** -7 **35.** 0.7 **37.** -3 **39.** 110 **41.** $-\frac{1}{10}$ **43.** $\frac{5}{4}$ **45.** $-\frac{4}{3}$ **47.** Possible **49.** Not possible **51.** $-\frac{1}{2}$ **53.** -2 **55.** Yes **57.** -1 **59. a.** The reciprocal of a, where a percent is a percent such that $a \cdot b = 100\%$. **b.** 250% **c.** 80% **61.** 7.875 **63.** $-4.\overline{6}$ **65.** Rational **67.** -3 **69.** -3 **71.** $-\frac{5}{9}$ **73.** $\frac{1}{2}$ **75.** 49 **77.** -3 **79.** 81 **81.** \$18.50

Lesson 1-3 Try This

a. 45 **b.** -8 **c.** 8 **d.** $-5x + (-3y)$ **e.** $17m + (-45)$ **f.** $-6p - (-5t)$ **g.** $8m + (5n + 6p)$ **h.** $(-9t)(17x)$ **i.** $16r(4q \cdot 9p)$ **j.** $\frac{171t}{27x}$ **k.** $2y$ **l.** $8a + x - b - x$

Exercise Set 1-3

1. 54 **3.** 11 **5.** 103 **7.** -4 **9.** -17 **11.** $-2 - 4a$ **13.** -15 **15.** 6 **17.** 115 **19.** 30 **21.** $8y + (-9x)$ **23.** $t + (-34s)$ **25.** $9x - (-7)$ **27.** $-18m - (-n)$ **29.** $73x + 9y$ **31.** $(12x + 9y) + 89z$ **33.** $(6x + 90) + \frac{y}{8}$, etc. **35.** $\frac{96x}{184y}$ **37.** $\frac{714}{35xy}$ **39.** $\frac{y}{x}$ **41.** $\frac{5}{-2x}$ **43.** $5 + |x|$ **45.** $-|2a|$ **47.** $|p| + |q|$ **49.** $3|p| = 8$ **53.** Yes **55.** -54 **57.** -4 **59.** 27 **61.** 19 **63.** $\frac{5}{16}$ **65.** $-\frac{2}{5}$ **67.** $\frac{91}{10}$ **69.** $\frac{-4}{1}$ **71.** Irrational **73.** Rational

Lesson 1-4 Try This

a. $5x + 45$ **b.** $8y - 80$ **c.** $ax + ay - az$ **d.** $2(l + w)$ **e.** $a(c - y)$ **f.** $6(x - 2)$ **g.** $5(-5y + 3w + 1)$ **h.** $20x$ **i.** $-7x$ **j.** $23.4x + 3.9$ **k.** $-7x$ **l.** $-y - 10$ **m.** $3x + 2y - 1$ **n.** $2x + 5z - 24$ **o.** $-\frac{1}{4}t - 41w + rd - 23$ **p.** $3x + 8$ **q.** $-x - 2y$ **r.** $23x - 10y$ **s.** $23x + 52$ **t.** $12a + 12$

Exercise Set 1-4

1. $3a + 3$ **3.** $4x - 4y$ **5.** $-10a - 15b$ **7.** $2ab - 2ac + 2ad$ **9.** $2\pi rh + 2\pi r$ **11.** $\frac{1}{2}ha + \frac{1}{2}hb$ **13.** $8(x + y)$ **15.** $9(p - 1)$ **17.** $7(x - 3)$ **19.** $x(y + 1)$ **21.** $2(x - y + z)$ **23.** $3(x + 2y - 1)$ **25.** $a(b + c - d)$ **27.** $\pi r(r + s)$ **29.** $9a$ **31.** $-3b$ **33.** $15y$ **35.** $11a$ **37.** $-8t$ **39.** $10x$ **41.** $13a - 10b$ **43.** $7a + 9b$ **45.** $9p + 12$ **47.** $4b$ **49.** $-a - 2$ **51.** $-b + 3$ **53.** $-t + y$ **55.** $-a - b - c$ **57.** $-8x + 6y - 13$ **59.** $2c - 5d + 3e - 4f$ **61.** $-a - 5$ **63.** $m + 1$ **65.** $5d - 12$ **67.** $-7x + 14$ **69.** $-9x + 21$ **71.** $44a - 22$ **73.** -190 **75.** $-12y - 145$ **77.** $17x + 14y + 129$ **79.** $-42x - 360y - 276$ **81.** 9 **83.** 8 **85.** $12x + 24y - 48z$ **87.** \$535.00 **89.** $-31a$ **91.** The answer is positive for an even number of minus signs, negative for an odd number of minus signs. **93.** 64 **95.** $(9y \cdot 8x)17z$ **97.** 0.5 **99.** $1.\overline{428571}$ **101.** $\frac{9}{20}$ **103.** $\frac{5}{4}$

Lesson 1-5 Try This

a. $y = 38$ **b.** $x = -16$ **c.** $x = \frac{4}{3}$ **d.** $y = 4$ **e.** $y = -\frac{4}{9}$ **f.** $x = -\frac{5}{2}$

Exercise Set 1-5

1. -3 **3.** 40 **5.** -15 **7.** -14 **9.** 39 **11.** 7 **13.** -9 **15.** -9 **17.** 36 **19.** 18 **21.** 5 **23.** 24 **25.** 7 **27.** 8 **29.** 21 **31.** 2 **33.** 2 **35.** $\frac{18}{5}$ **37.** 0 **39.** $\frac{4}{5}$ **41.** All real numbers **43.** No solution **45.** $w = 0$ **47.** All real numbers **49.** $\frac{45}{2}$ **51.** $\frac{5}{2}$ **55.** No **57.** Yes **59.** $-86a + 74$ **61.** $8(n - m)$ **63.** $6(n + 2)$ **65.** 5 **67.** Ex: $2x + \frac{1}{2}x + 5y + \frac{1}{5}y$

Lesson 1-6 Try This

a. \$7.42 **b.** $\approx$1.593 min **c.** 150% **d.** $\approx$11.1%

Exercise Set 1-6

1. \$14.75 **3.** \$169.60 **5.** $\approx$48,000,000 mi **7.** $\approx$341 m **9.** 622.45°F **11.** 37.2 sec **13.** 43.92 sec **15.** $\approx$85.3% **17.** $\approx$288.2% **19.** \$2.80 **21.** $\approx$55.6% **23.** 1:20 pm **25.** $15t$ **27.** $-8x$ **29.** $-\frac{1}{2}$ **31.** 14 **33.** -3 **35.** -3 **37.** 1

Lesson 1-7 Try This

a. $512x^3$ **b.** $81m^4$ **c.** 81 **d.** $243y^3$ **e.** $\frac{1}{10{,}000}$ **f.** $-\frac{1}{64}$ **g.** $\frac{1}{125y^3}$ **h.** $\frac{1}{625}$ **i.** 4^{-3} **j.** $(-5)^{-4}$ **k.** $(2x)^{-6}$ **l.** $(-8x)^5$

Exercise Set 1-7

1. $27y^3$ **3.** 1 **5.** $6m$ **7.** -125 **9.** $\frac{1}{9^5}$ **11.** $\frac{1}{11^1}$ **13.** $\frac{1}{(6x)^3}$ **15.** $\frac{1}{(3m)^4}$ **17.** $\frac{2a^2}{b^5}$ **19.** x^2y^2 **21.** 3^{-4} **23.** $(-16)^{-2}$ **25.** $(5y)^{-3}$ **27.** $\frac{y^{-4}}{3}$ **29.** x^2yz^{-7} **31.** $b^{-10}x^{-10}y^{-10}$ **33.** $\frac{1}{16}$ **35.** $-26\frac{15}{16}$ **37.** $25\frac{1}{4}$ **39.** 7 **41.** 16,807 **43.** $17(1 - 3y^2)$ **45.** 4 **47.** -1

Lesson 1-8 Try This

a. 4,096 **b.** $-75x^{-14}$ **c.** $-10x^{-12}y^2$ **d.** $30x^{m+7}y^{n+4}$ **e.** 5^6 **f.** 10^6 **g.** $-2y^{10}x^{-4}$ or $-\frac{2y^{10}}{x^4}$ **h.** $\frac{3}{2}a^{-2}b^2$ or $\frac{3b^2}{2a^2}$ **i.** -8 **j.** 3^{42} **k.** x^{-14} or $\frac{1}{x^{14}}$ **l.** t^6 **m.** $8x^3y^3$ **n.** $-32x^{20}y^{10}$ **o.** $1000x^{-12}y^{21}z^{-6}$ or $\frac{1000y^{21}}{x^{12}z^6}$ **p.** x^9y^{12} **q.** $\frac{9x^4}{4y^4}$ or $\frac{9}{4}x^4y^{-4}$ **r.** 16 **s.** 24 **t.** 27

Exercise Set 1-8

1. 5^9 **3.** 8^{-4} **5.** 8^{-6} **7.** b^{-3} **9.** a^3 **11.** $6x^5$ **13.** $-28m^5n^5$ **15.** $-14x^{-11}$ **17.** $-30(x^{a+5})(y^{b+9})$ **19.** 6^5 **21.** 4^5 **23.** 10^{-9} **25.** 9^2 **27.** a^5 **29.** 1 **31.** $-\frac{4x^9}{3y^2}$ **33.** $\frac{3x^3}{2y^2}$ **35.** $-10x^{5a}$ **37.** $-3x^{a-2}y^{b-5}$ **39.** 4^6 **41.** 8^{-12} **43.** 6^{12} **45.** $3^3x^6y^6$ or $27x^6y^6$ **47.** $(-2)^{-2}x^{-6}y^8$ or $\frac{y^8}{4x^6}$ **49.** $(-6)^{-2}a^4b^{-6}c^{-2}$, or $\frac{a^4}{36b^6c^2}$ **51.** $\frac{1}{4^9 \cdot 3^{12}}$ **53.** $\frac{8x^9y^3}{27}$ **55.** 10 **57.** 24 **59.** 2^{21} **61.** $\frac{1}{a^{14}b^{27}}$ **63.** $\frac{27x^4y^4}{26}$ **65.** x^{9y} **67.** a^{6b} **69.** $x^{ca+cb}y^{ca+cb}$ **71.** $4x^{2a}y^{2b}$ **73.** 68 **75.** $\frac{1}{5}$ **77.** 0

Lesson 1-9 Try This

a. 4.6×10^{11} **b.** 1.235×10^{-9} **c.** 1.7×10^{-24} g **d.** 1.5×10^8 km **e.** 789,300,000,000 **f.** 0.0000567 **g.** 7.462×10^{-13} **h.** 2.0×10^3 **i.** 5.5×10^2 **j.** 3×10^{-4}

Exercise Set 1-9

1. 4.7×10^{10} **3.** 8.63×10^{17} **5.** 1.6×10^{-8} **7.** 7×10^{-11} **9.** 9.11×10^{-28} g **11.** 4.8×10^{-10} eu **13.** 1×10^{-9} **15.** 3.0699×10^5 lb **17.** 0.0004 **19.** 673,000,000 **21.** 0.0000000008923 **23.** 9.66×10^{-5} **25.** 1.3338×10^{-11} **27.** 8.32×10^{10} **29.** 2.5×10^3 **31.** 5×10^4 **33.** 3×10^{11} **35.** 4.5×10^2 **37.** 1.1×10^{11} **39.** 6.5×10^1 **41.** 3.8715403×10^3 **43.** 2.0000000029×10^7 **45.** $\approx 1.4 \times 10^{12}$ mi **49.** $\approx 6.82 \times 10^{-1}$ mi/h **51.** 2.33×10^1 ft/sec **53.** 42.9% **55.** 3.05×10^{-7} sec **57.** $35y + 98$ **59.** -132 **61.** t^2 **63.** $-2(a + b)$ **65.** $(w - y)\left(\frac{x}{2}\right)$ **67.** $3\left(\frac{y}{5} + 2\right)$

Lesson 1-10 Try This

a. Assoc. prop. of addn. **b.** Dist. prop. **c.** Ident. prop. of addn. **d.** Ident. prop. of mult., prop. of mult. inv. **e.** No; no mult. inverse **f.** Yes **g.** Dist. prop.

Exercise Set 1-10

1. Dist. prop. **3.** Prop. of add. inv. **5.** None; subtr. thm. **7.** Assoc. prop. of addn. **9.** Symm. prop. of equality **11.** Comm. prop. of addn. **13.** None; subtr. thm. **15.** Comm. prop. of addn. **17.** No; there is no add. inv. or mult. inv. **19.** Yes **21.** Assoc. prop. of addn.; Ident. prop. for addn.

23. $-(a - b) = -(a + (-b))$; Theorem 1-1
$= -1(a + (-b))$; Ident. prop. of mult.
$= (-1)(a) + (-1)(-b)$; Dist. prop.
$= -a + b$; Mult. prop. of -1
$= b + (-a)$; Comm. prop. of addition
$= b - a$; Theorem 1-1
Therefore, $-(a - b) = b - a$; Statements 1–6

25. $\frac{a}{b} = \frac{a \cdot 1}{1 \cdot b}$; Ident. prop. of mult.
$= \frac{a}{1} \cdot \frac{1}{b}$; Assoc. prop. of mult.
$= a \cdot \frac{1}{b}$; Ident. prop. of mult.
Therefore, $\frac{a}{b} = a \cdot \frac{1}{b}$; Statements 1–3

29. $5xy + 15xz$ **31.** $2w - 6wx$ **33.** m^{-3} **35.** x^4 **37.** 305 **39.** -4 **41.** \$48 **43.** 9×10^{-3}

Problem Set 1-11

1. There are 16 spokes for a wheel with 16 spaces. **3.** 300 mi **5.** There will be 10 liters at 5 hours, so there would be less than 10 liters after 5 hours.

Chapter 1 Summary and Review

1. No, no, yes, yes **3.** Rational **5.** $-\frac{27}{10}$ **7.** $-\frac{1}{24}$

9. -19.7 **11.** -8.4 **13.** 6010 **15.** $\frac{7}{6}$ **17.** $7y \cdot 4x$

19. $\frac{5}{12}$ **21.** -4 **23.** $6x - 6y + 6z$

25. $6a - 4b + 3c$ **27.** $-5(4x - y + 2z)$
29. $-10y - 5z$ **31.** $-r + t$ **33.** $-a + 4$

35. $6x + 2$ **37.** 6 **39.** 0 **41.** 8^{-3} **43.** $\frac{y^{-5}}{3}$

45. $\frac{1}{(-4)^3}$ or $-\frac{1}{64}$ **47.** $\frac{3a^3}{c^5}$ **49.** $-\frac{14}{x}$ **51.** $-\frac{3y^5}{x^8}$

53. $-\frac{1}{8x^9}$ **55.** 8.0×10^7 **57.** 3.78×10^9

Chapter 2

Lesson 2-1 Try This

a. $y = \frac{2}{5}$ **b.** $x = 2$ **c.** $y = -\frac{19}{8}$ **d.** $\{19, -5\}$

e. $\left\{0, \frac{17}{3}\right\}$ **f.** $\left\{-\frac{2}{9}, \frac{1}{2}\right\}$

Exercise Set 2-1

1. $\frac{4}{3}$ **3.** $\frac{37}{5}$ **5.** 13 **7.** 2 **9.** 2 **11.** 7 **13.** 5

15. $-\frac{51}{31}$ **17.** 5 **19.** 2 **21.** $\{-2, 5\}$ **23.** $\{8, 9\}$

25. $\left\{\frac{3}{2}, \frac{2}{3}\right\}$ **27.** $\{0, 8\}$ **29.** $\{0, 1, -2\}$ **31.** $\left\{3, -\frac{4}{7}\right\}$

33. $-\frac{10}{31}$ **35.** $\frac{f + 4}{16}$ **37.** $\frac{3 + 5b}{7 - a}$ **39.** $\frac{19}{5 + a}$
43. $\{1, 0\}$ **45.** $\{0\}$ **47.** 4^5 **49.** x^{-2}
51. 3.9004×10^5 **53.** 2.4072×10^1 **55.** $-8{,}220{,}000$

Lesson 2-2 Try This

a. $5\frac{3}{4}$ ft; $17\frac{1}{4}$ ft **b.** $\frac{1}{2}$ **c.** $3x + 30 = 5x$; \$15
d. \$124 **e.** \$725 **f.** 17, 19 **g. 1.** Harold 22, Gunther 24 **2.** Harold 11, Gunther 12

Exercise Set 2-2

1. 8 cm; 4 cm **3.** $1\frac{3}{5}$m; $2\frac{2}{5}$m **5.** 5 **7.** \$45
9. \$650 **11.** 32°, 96°, 52° **13.** 31 m by 17 m
15. 11, 13, 15 **17.** \$15,000 **19.** \$3644 **21.** 98%
23. 84 **25.** 143 gal **27.** 20 cm, 32 cm **29.** 84 years
31. $3x^4 + 3x^2y - xy^2$ **33.** $2a^2 + 2b^2 + 2c^2$
35. $3ab^2(a - 3)$ **37.** $6xy(5x + y - 2x^2)$
39. $1.64 \cdot 10^3$

Lesson 2-3 Try This

a. $b = \frac{2A}{h}$ **b.** $c = \frac{5}{3}P - 10$ **c.** $m = \frac{H - 2r}{3}$

d. $p = \frac{Q - 3r}{5}$ **e.** $Q = \frac{T}{1 + iy}$ **f.** $G = \frac{x}{1 - r^2p}$

Exercise Set 2-3

1. $l = \frac{A}{w}$ **3.** $I = \frac{W}{E}$ **5.** $m = \frac{F}{a}$ **7.** $t = \frac{I}{Pr}$

9. $m = \frac{E}{c^2}$ **11.** $l = \frac{P - 2w}{2}$ **13.** $a^2 = c^2 - b^2$

15. $r^2 = \frac{A}{\pi}$ **17.** $F = \frac{9}{5}C + 32$ **19.** $r^3 = \frac{3V}{4\pi}$

21. $h = \frac{2A}{(a + b)}$ **23.** $m = \frac{rF}{v^2}$ **25.** $a = \frac{2s - 2v_it}{t^2}$

27. 0.4 yr **31.** $T_2 = \frac{P_2V_2T_1}{P_1V_1}$ **33.** 6^{-6} **35.** 8^6

37. $\frac{19}{11}$ **39.** 5 **41.** 4 or -5

Lesson 2-4 Try This

a. Solution **b.** Not a solution **c.** Solution

d. −2 0

e. 0 1

f. 0 5

g. $x > 3$ **h.** $3 \geq x$ **i.** $x \leq -2$ **j.** $y \leq \frac{3}{10}$

k. $y < -\frac{5}{12}$ **l.** $x \geq 12$ **m.** $y \leq -\frac{1}{5}$ **n.** $x < \frac{1}{2}$

o. $y \geq \frac{22}{13}$

Exercise Set 2-4

1. Solution **3.** Not a solution

5. −1 0

7. 0 3

9. $x > -3$ **11.** $y < 6$ **13.** $a \leq -20$ **15.** $x \leq 19$
17. $y > -9$ **19.** $y \leq 14$ **21.** $t < -9$ **23.** $x < 50$

25. $y \geq -0.4$ **27.** $y \geq \frac{9}{10}$ **29.** $y > 3$ **31.** $x \leq 4$

33. $x < -\frac{2}{5}$ **35.** $y < 5$ **37.** Real Numbers

39. $m \leq \frac{33}{10}$ **41.** $-3 < y < 3$ **43.** $x < -3$ or $x > 3$
45. a. False, because $a = 4$, $b = 5$, $c = 1$, $d = 4$
47. $36x^6y^{10}$ **49.** $4n^{2t}$ **51.** 62, 63, 64

Lesson 2-5 Try This

a. Score ≥ 71 **b.** $n < 100$ hr

Exercise Set 2-5

1. Less than 620.5 mi **3.** \$20,000 **5.** Less than \$2 (\$1.99) **7.** Less than 100 hr **9.** 10% **11.** 92
15. Never; maximum height is 3136 ft. **17.** Greater than $\frac{f}{3.75}$ hours **19.** $z = \frac{1}{xy}$ **21.** $r = \frac{A}{2\pi(1 + h)}$

Lesson 2-6 Try This

a. −1 0 4

b. −2 0 5

c. $\{x \mid -2 \le x \le 1\}$ **d.** $\{x \mid -1 \le x < 9\}$

e. 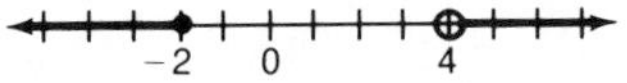 −2 0 4

f. 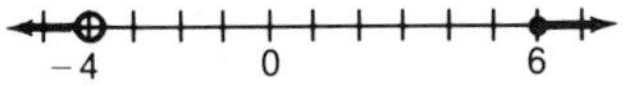 −4 0 6

g. $\{x \mid x < 1 \text{ or } x \ge 7\}$ **h.** $\left\{x \mid x < -2 \text{ or } x \ge \frac{7}{2}\right\}$

Exercise Set 2-6

1. 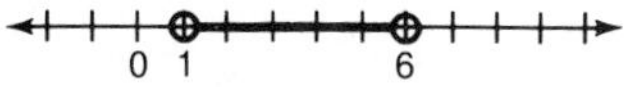 0 1 6

3. 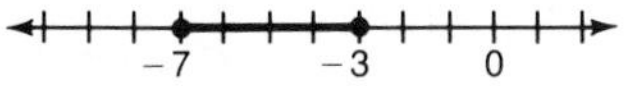 −7 −3 0

5. $-4 < x < 6$ **7.** $-2 < y \le 2$ **9.** $-\frac{5}{3} \le x \le \frac{4}{3}$
11. $0 < x < 14$

13. 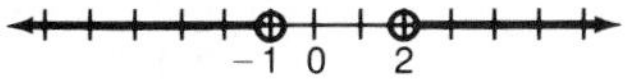 −1 0 2

15. 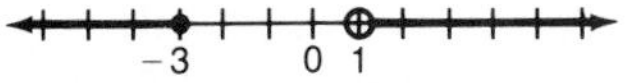 −3 0 1

17. 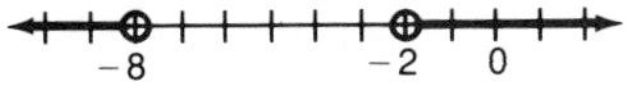 −8 −2 0

19. $x < -9$ or $x > -5$ **21.** $x \le \frac{5}{2}$ or $x \ge 11$

23. $x < \frac{4}{3}$ or $x > 15$ **25.** $x > 5$ **27.** $x > 1$ **29.** $x < 0$

31. $m < \frac{6}{5}$ **33.** $x < \frac{13}{40}$ or $x > \frac{17}{40}$ **35.** $x > \frac{21}{4}$

37. True **39.** False **41.** False **43.** $-\frac{2}{5} \le x \le 2$

45. $10 < x \le 18$ **47. a.** 1 **b.** p **49.** 3 **51.** −16
53. $9w^2$ **55.** $-64a^6b^3$ **57.** $121

Lesson 2-7 Try This

a. $7|x|$ **b.** x^8 **c.** $5a^2|b|$ **d.** $\frac{7|a|}{b^2}$ **e.** $9|x|$ **f.** 29

g. 5 **h.** 20 **i.** $\{6, -6\}$ **j.** $\left\{\frac{1}{2}, -\frac{1}{2}\right\}$

k. $\{x \mid -5 < x < 5\}$ **l.** $\{x \mid -6.5 \le x \le 6.5\}$

m. $\{y \mid y \le -8 \text{ or } y \ge 8\}$ **n.** $\left\{x \mid x < -\frac{1}{2} \text{ or } x > \frac{1}{2}\right\}$

o. $\left\{x \mid x = -\frac{13}{3} \text{ or } x = \frac{5}{3}\right\}$ **p.** $\{x \mid -2 \le x \le 5\}$

q. $\left\{x \mid < -\frac{3}{2} \text{ or } x > \frac{11}{2}\right\}$

Exercise Set 2-7

1. $3|x|$ **3.** y^8 **5.** $9x^2y^2|y|$ **7.** $\frac{a^2}{|b|}$ **9.** $16|m|$ **11.** $t^2|t|$
13. 34 **15.** 11 **17.** 33 **19.** 5 **21.** 3, −3
23. $-3 < x < 3$ **25.** $x \le -2$ or $x \ge 2$ **27.** $t \le -5.5$
or $t \ge 5.5$ **29.** −9, 15 **31.** $-\frac{1}{2} \le x \le \frac{7}{2}$ **33.** $y < -\frac{3}{2}$
or $y > \frac{17}{2}$ **35.** $x \le -\frac{5}{4}$ or $x \ge \frac{23}{4}$ **37.** $x > -\frac{3}{5}$ or
$x < -1$ **39.** $t \le 6$ or $t \ge 8$ **41.** 0, 7 **43.** All real
numbers **45.** $-\frac{13}{54} < x < -\frac{7}{54}$ **47.** All real numbers

49. $-\frac{1}{4}$, 1 **51.** $x \le 1$ **53.** m^{-2} **55.** $-8w^8n^{-6}$

57. $c = -2$ **59.** Answers may vary.

Lesson 2-8 Try This

a. **1.** $3x + 5 = 20$ Hypothesis (assumed true)
2. $3x = 15$ Add. property
3. $x = 5$ Mult. property
4. If $3x + 5 = 20$, then $x = 5$. Statements 1–3

b. **1.** $-3x + 8 > 23$ Hypothesis (assumed true)
2. $-3x > 15$ Add. prop. for inequalities
3. $x < -5$ Mult. prop. for inequalities
4. If $-3x + 8 > 23$, then $x < -5$ Statements 1–3

c. If $x = 10$, then $3x + 7 = 37$ **d.** If $x > 12$, then $x > 15$

e. **1.** $x = 5$ Hypothesis
2. $3x = 15$ Mult. property
3. $3x + 5 = 20$ Add. property
4. If $x = 5$, then $3x + 5 = 20$ Statements 1–3

f. **(1)**
1. $x < -5$ Hypothesis
2. $-3x > 15$ Multiply both sides by −3
3. $-3x + 8 > 23$ Add 8 to both sides
(2) Solution set of antecedent and consequent: $\{x \mid x < -5\}$ since the consequent is the solution set of the antecedent.

g. Statement
$7x - 1 > 34$
$7x > 35$ Add. property
$x > 5$ Mult. property
Converse
$x > 5$
$7x > 35$ Mult. property
$7x - 1 > 34$ Add. property

h. **(1)** Statement
$9x - 5 = 103$
$9x = 108$ Add. property
$x = 12$ Mult. property
Converse
$x = 12$
$9x = 108$ Mult. property
$9x - 5 = 103$ Add. property
(2) $9x - 5 = 103$
$9x = 108$
$x = 12$
$9(12) - 5 = 103$ Substituting
$108 - 5 = 103$
$103 = 103$

i. Yes **j.** No **k.** Yes **l.** Yes **m.** No **n.** No

Exercise Set 2-8

5. If $6y = 10$, then $3y = 5$. **7.** If $x < 20$, then $x < 12$.

9. If $x = 7$, then $7x - 12 = 37$. **11.** If $x \ge \frac{16}{17}$, then

$15x - 5 \ge 11 - 2x$. **13.** $\left\{x \mid -\frac{9}{2} < x\right\}$ **15.** $-\frac{4}{7}$

17. $-\frac{17}{2}$ **19.** $-\frac{5}{3}$ **21.** Yes **23.** Yes **25.** No

27. Yes **39.** $\frac{1}{8}$ **41.** $\frac{1}{6}$ **43.** 13 **45.** −43

Problem Set 2-9

1. They would use 905 kWh. **3.** There might be about 364 customers after 4 years. **5.** Some possible solutions: 20 km, 40 km, 60 km, 30 km, 60 km, 70 km.

Chapter 2 Summary and Review

1. 2 **3.** 1 **5.** $-5\frac{5}{6}$ **7.** −4, 3 **9.** 26°, 130°, 24°

11. $\frac{2A}{h}$ **13.** $y \geq 1$ **15.** $x \geq -27$ **17.** $x \leq 30$

19. 3, 5, 7 **21.** $x < -5$ or $x > 3$ **23.** $x < -2$ or $x > 1$
25. $x^2|xy|$ **27.** 26 **29.** 21 **31.** $-4 < y < 4$
33. $x \geq 8$ or $x \leq -2$

Chapter 3

Lesson 3-1 Try This

a. {(*d*, 1), (*d*, 2), (*e*, 1), (*e*, 2)} **b.** {(*x*, *x*), (*x*, *y*), (*x*, *z*), (*y*, *x*), (*y*, *y*), (*y*, *z*), (*z*, *x*), (*z*, *y*), (*z*, *z*)} **c.** {(1, 1), (2, 2)} **d.** Domain {*a*, *b*, *c*, *e*}; range {1, 2, 3} **e.** Domain {1, 2}; range {1, 2, 3} **f.** {6} **g.** {(3, 4), (3, 5), (4, 4), (4, 5), (5, 4), (5, 5)}

Exercise Set 3-1

1. {(chili, cheese), (chili, onions), (chili, peppers), (pizza, cheese), (pizza, onions), (pizza, peppers), (salad, cheese), (salad, onions), (salad, peppers)} **3.** {(*x*, 1), (*x*, 2), (*y*, 1), (*y*, 2), (*z*, 1), (*z*, 2)} **5.** {(5, 5), (5, 6), (5, 7), (5, 8), (6, 5), (6, 6), (6, 7), (6, 8), (7, 5), (7, 6), (7, 7), (7, 8), (8, 5), (8, 6), (8, 7), (8, 8)} **7.** {(−7, −3), (−7, 1), (−7, 2), (−7, 5), (−3, 1), (−3, 2), (−3, 5), (1, 2) (1, 5), (2, 5)} **9.** {(−7, −7), (−7, −3), (−7, 1), (−7, 2), (−7, 5), (−3, −3), (−3, 1), (−3, 2), (−3, 5), (1, 1), (1, 2), (1, 5), (2, 2), (2, 5), (5, 5)} **11.** {(−7, −7), (−3, −3), (1, 1), (2, 2), (5, 5)} **13.** Domain {5, 6, 8}; range {2, 4, 6} **15.** Domain {6, 7, 8}; range {0, 5} **17.** Domain {8, 5}; range {1} **19.** Domain {5}; range {6} **21.** {8, 10, 12} **23.** {2, 8, 10, 12} **25.** {(5, 2), (5, 3)} **27.** {(2, 4), (2, 5), (3, 4), (3, 5)} **29.** {(3, 3), (3, 4)} **31. d.** {(−1, 3), (−1, 5), (1, 3), (1, 5), (3, 5)}

35. 4 **37.** 1 **39.** c^6 **41.** $y < 12$ **43.** $t > -\frac{5}{16}$

Lesson 3-2 Try This

a. **b.**

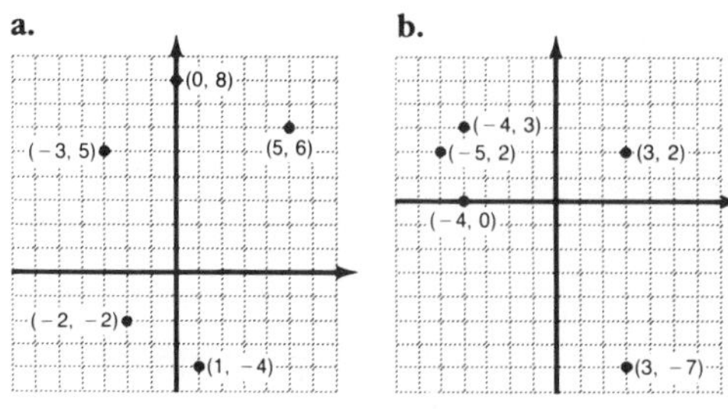

c. Yes; yes **d.** No; no **e.** No; yes

f. **g.**

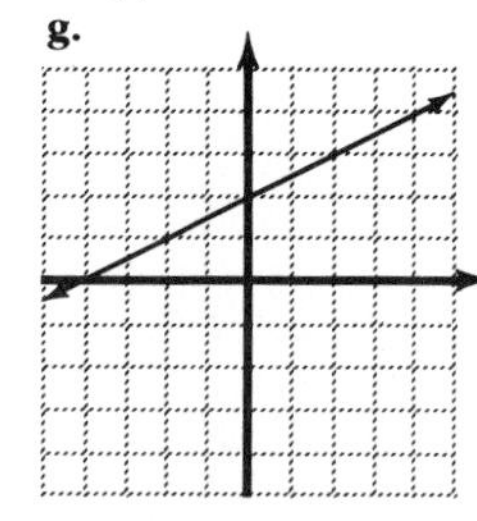

h. **i.**

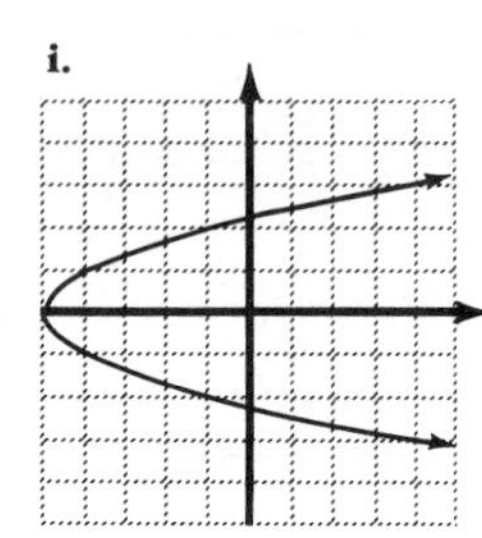

The shapes are the same, but this curve opens to the right instead of upward.

Exercise Set 3-2

1. **3.**

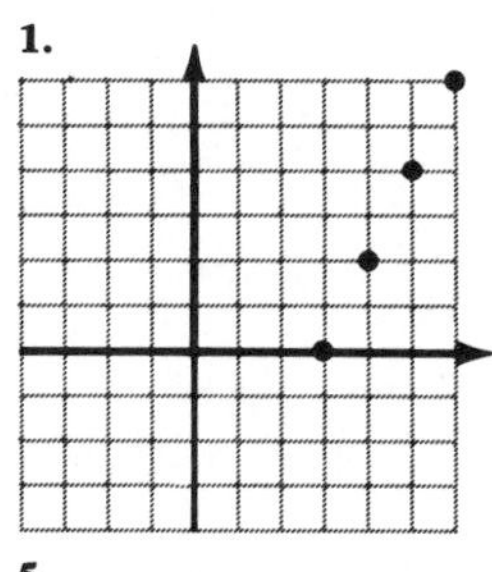

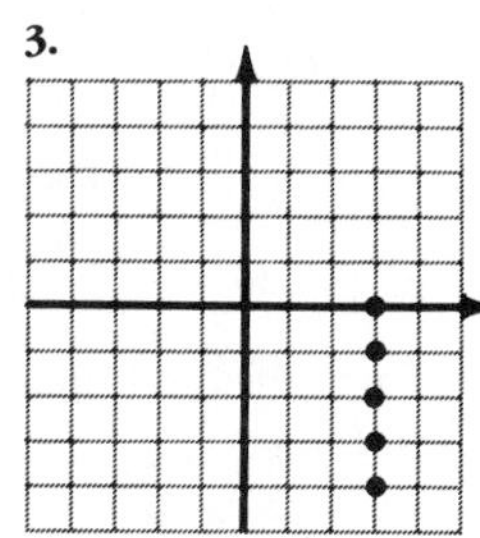

5. **7.**

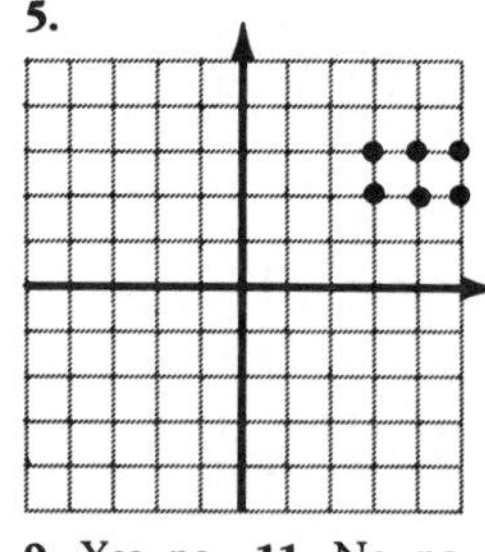

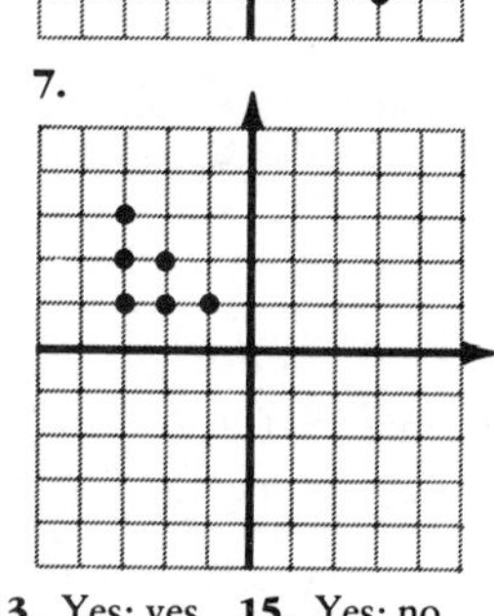

9. Yes; no **11.** No; no **13.** Yes; yes **15.** Yes; no **17.** Yes; no **19.** No; yes

21. **23.**

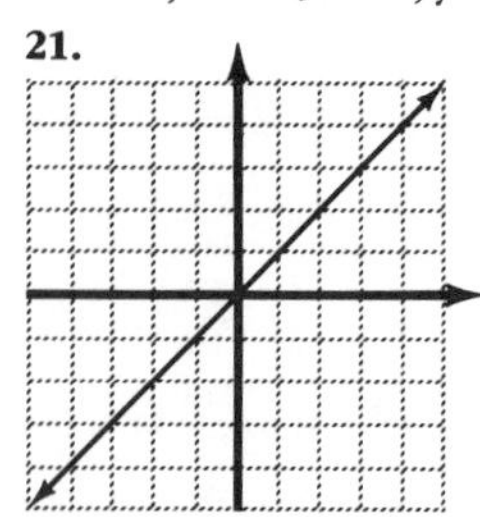

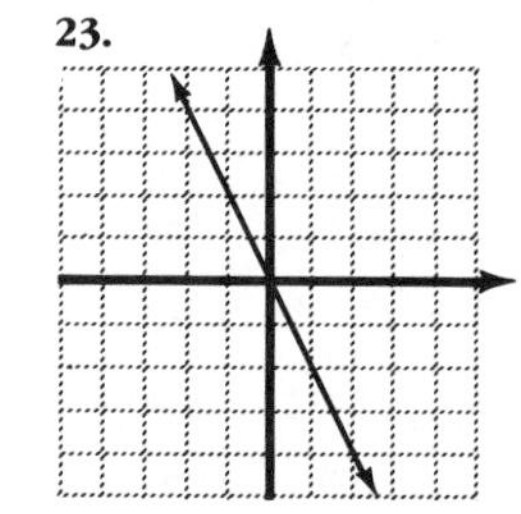

25.

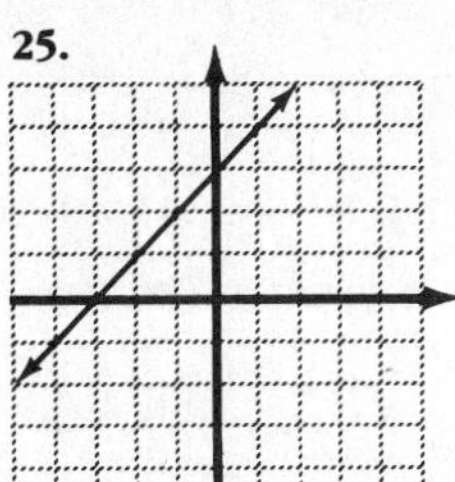

27.

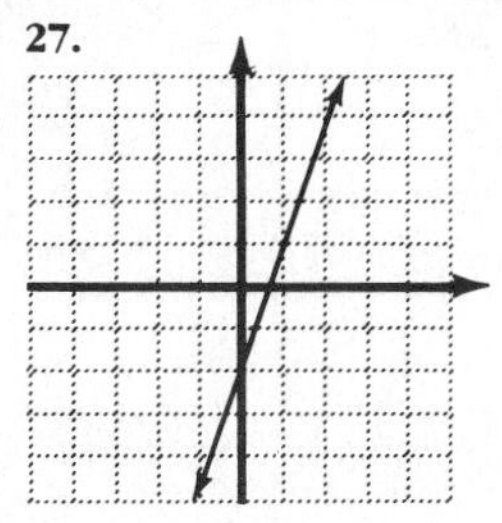

29.

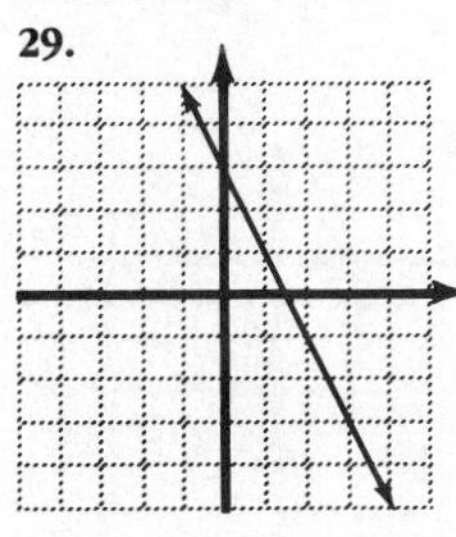

31.

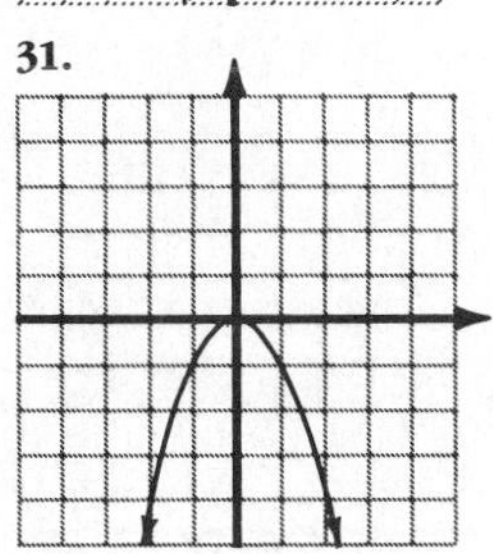

33.

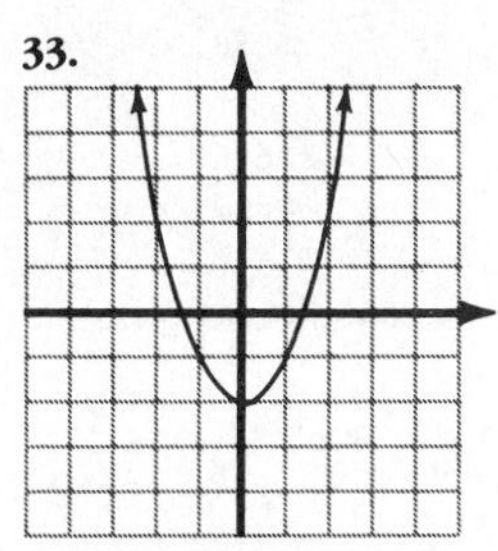

35.

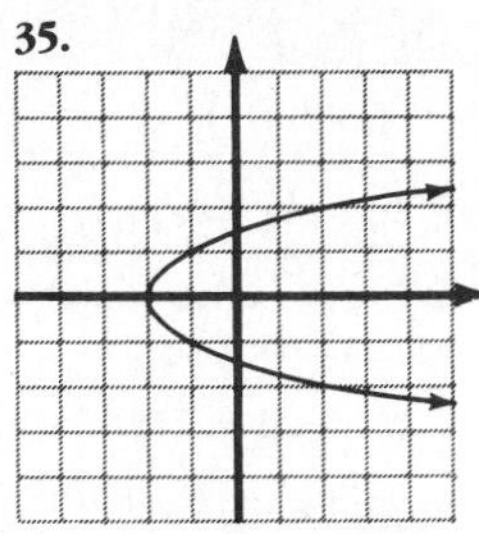

37. Domain R; range $\{y|y \leq 0\}$ **39.** Domain R; range $\{y|y \geq -2\}$ **41.** Domain $\{x|x \geq -2\}$; range R

43. a. $\{x|2 \leq x \leq 6\}$, **b.** $\{y|1 \leq y \leq 5\}$ **61.** $y = -\frac{5}{2}$

63. 6 in., 24 in.

Lesson 3-3 Try This

a. A. Not a function **B.** Function **C.** Function **D.** Function **E.** Function **b. (1)** Yes **(2)** Yes **(3)** Yes **(4)** No **c.** $h(9) = 1$; $h(6) = 6$; $h(0) = -2$ **d.** 1 **e.** 4 **f.** 4 **g.** $12a^2 + 1$ **h.** $\{x|x \neq 1$ and $x \neq -3\}$ **i.** $\{x|x$ is a real number$\}$ **j.** $\{x|x \neq 0\}$

Exercise Set 3-3

1. Yes **3.** No **5.** Yes **7.** Yes **9.** No **11.** Yes **13. a.** 1 **b.** −3 **15. a.** 0 **b.** 1 **17. b.** 32 **c.** 20 **19. d.** Not possible **21.** R **23.** $\{x|x \neq 0\}$

25. $\left\{x|x \neq -\frac{8}{5}\right\}$ **27.** $\{x|x \neq 0, x \neq -2$, and $x \neq 1\}$

29. c. $-\frac{1}{2}$ **d.** Not possible **31.** 0, 1 **35. a.** 0

b. Not possible **c.** Not possible **d.** $\{x|x \neq 0$ and $x \neq 2\}$ **37.** 8 **39.** 47.5 **41.** $x > 3$ or $x < 2$ **43.** $11 > x > 6$ **45.** None

Lesson 3-4 Try This

a. Yes **b.** Yes **c.** No, has a variable to a power **d.** No, has a variable in a denominator **e.** No, has a product of variables **f.** Yes

g.

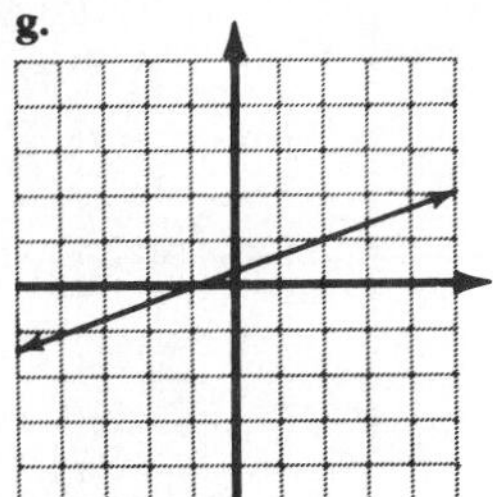

h.

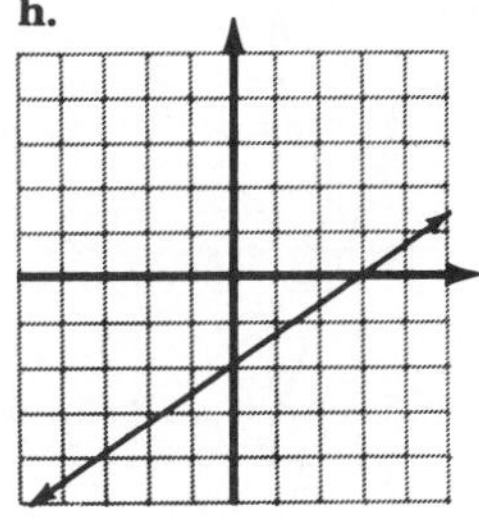

i.

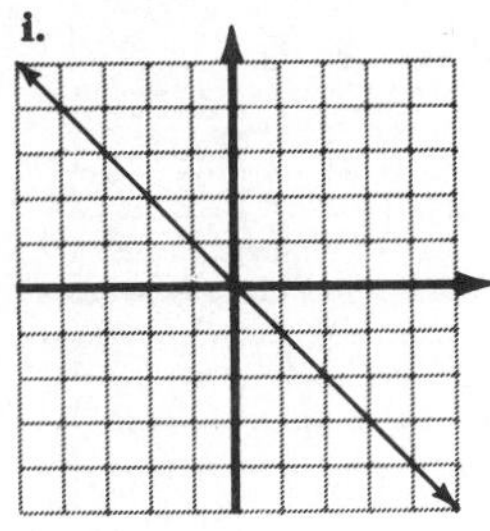

j.

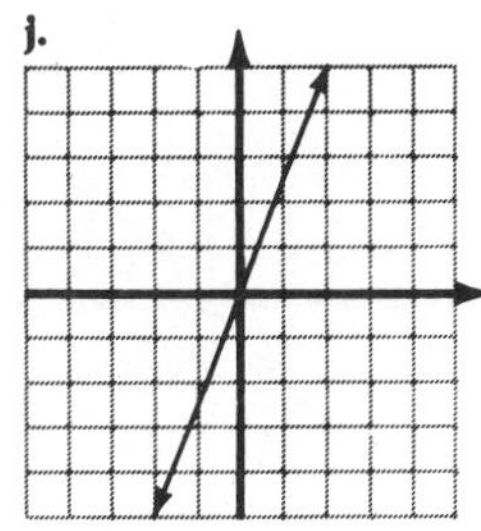

k. The graph of $y = 2x + 1$ is a line moved up 1 unit from the graph of $y = 2x$. **l.** The graph of $y = 2x - 4$ is a line moved down 4 units from the graph of $y = 2x$.

m. – o.

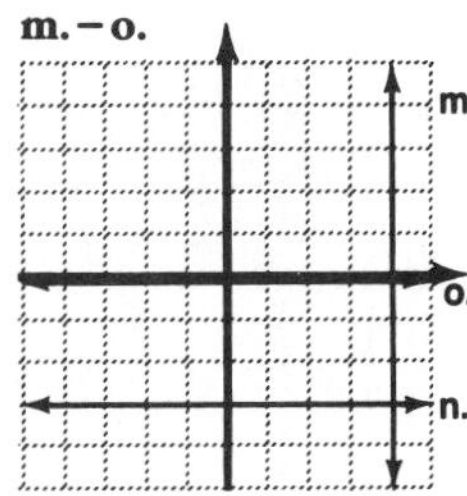

Exercise Set 3-4

1. Yes **3.** No; 2nd degree **5.** Yes **7.** Yes **9.** Yes

11.

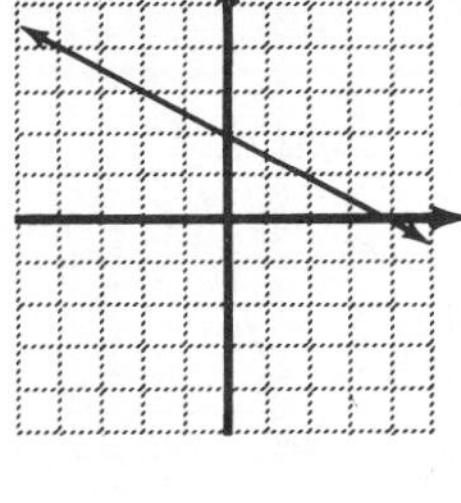

13.

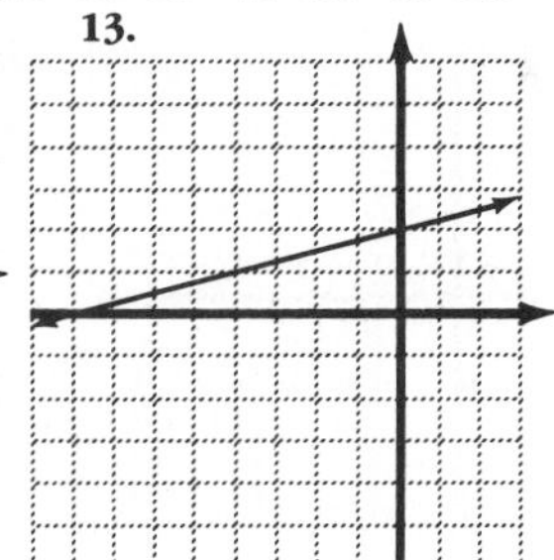

15.

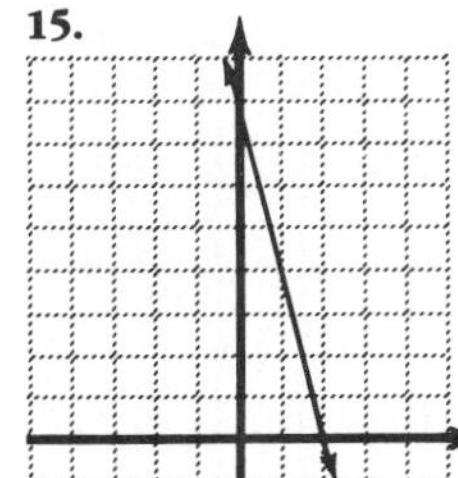

17.

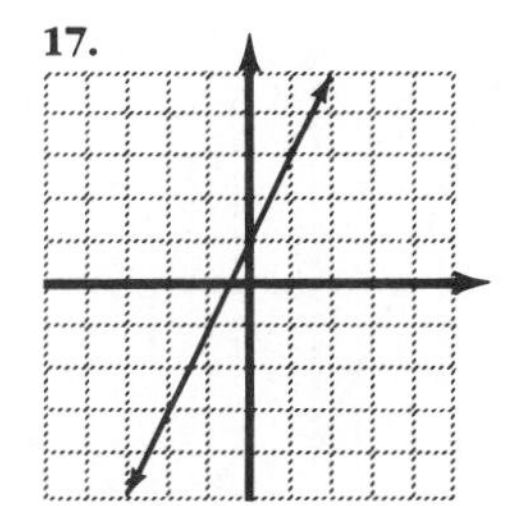

19.
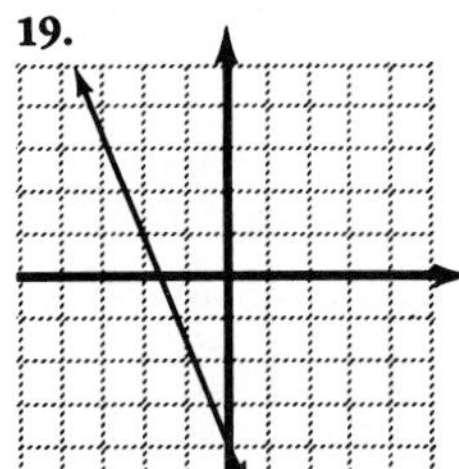

21.
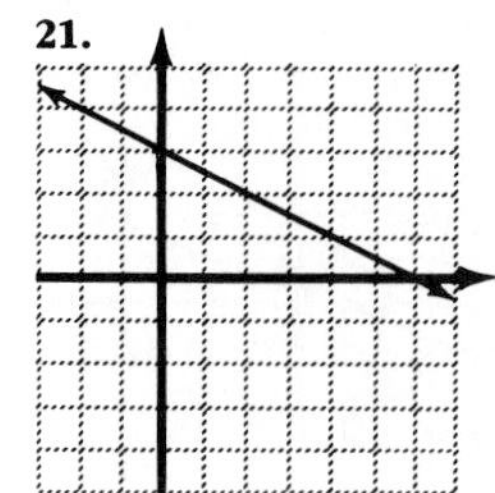

23.
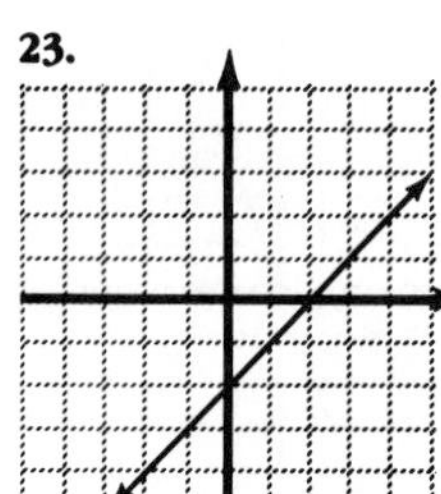

25.
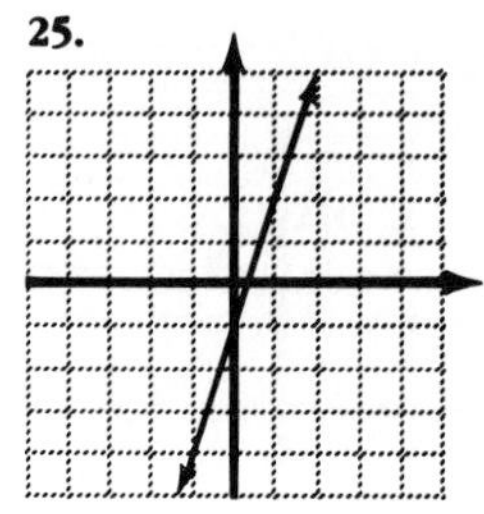

27.
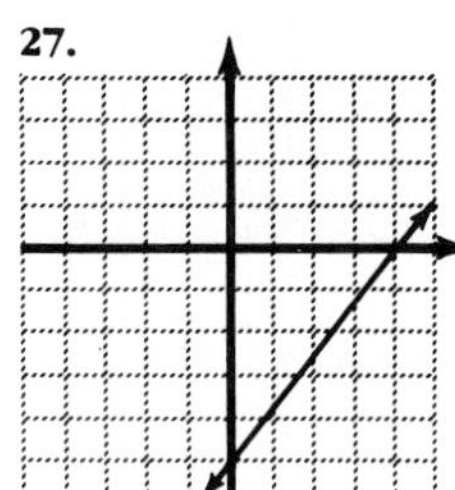

29.
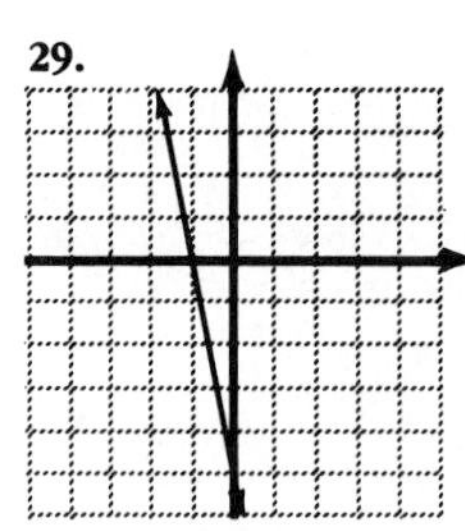
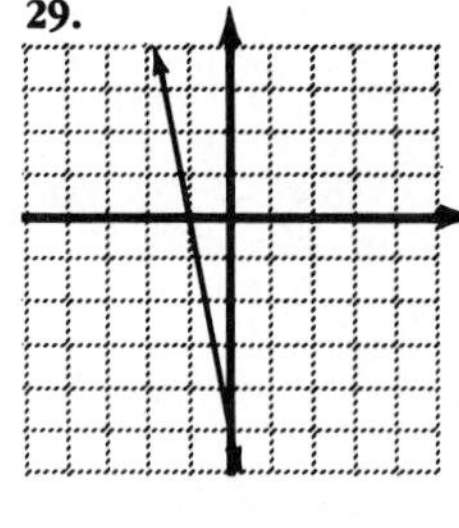

31.
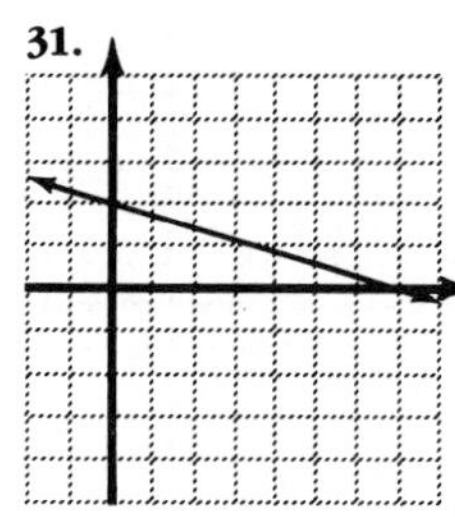

33.
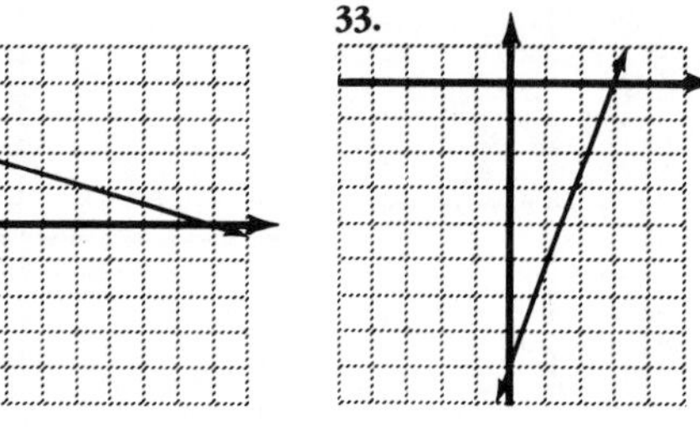

35.
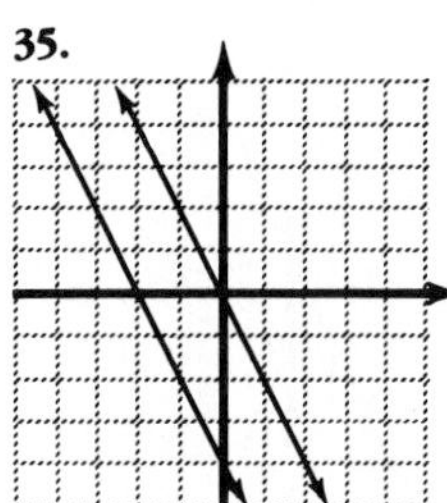

37.
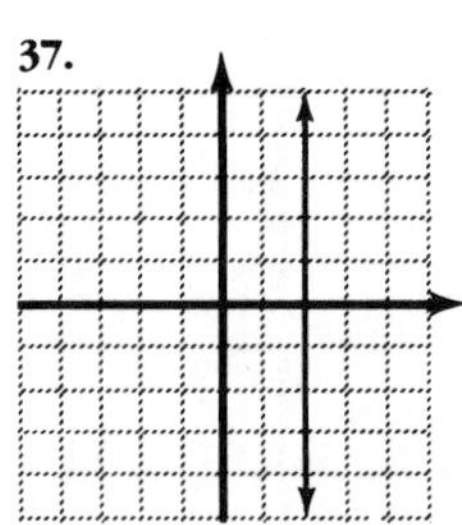

39.
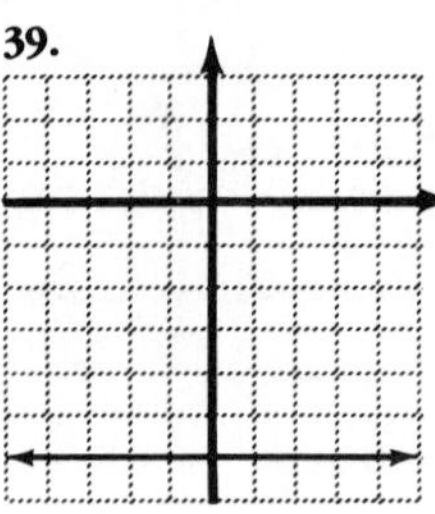

41.
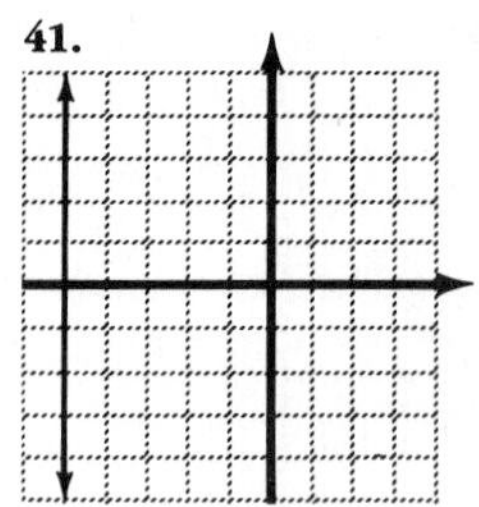

43.
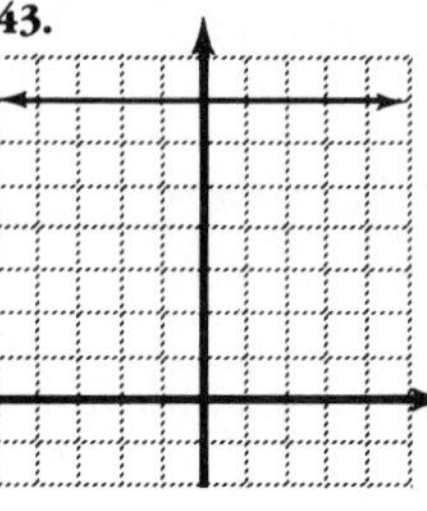

45.
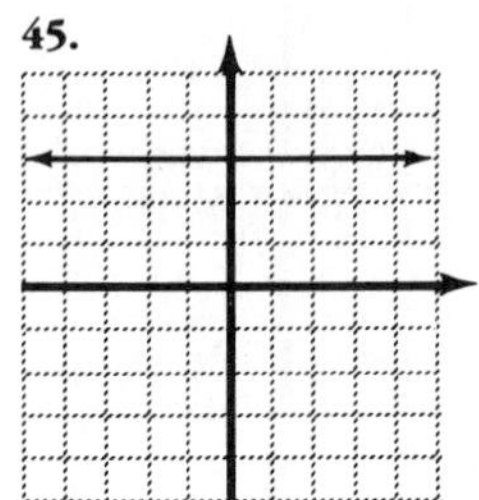

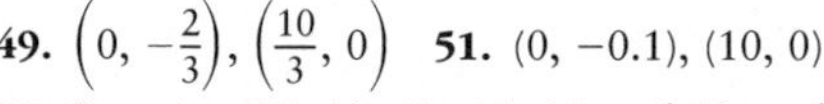

49. $\left(0, -\frac{2}{3}\right), \left(\frac{10}{3}, 0\right)$ **51.** (0, −0.1), (10, 0)

53. Exercises 39, 40, 43, 44, 45, and 48 are horizontal lines and, therefore, functions.

55. c. $y - 3 = k(x + 5)$ **57.** $\frac{1}{a^{-6}}$ or a^6

59. $\{(a, 0), (a, 1), (b, 0), (b, 1), (c, 0), (c, 1)\}$
61. $\{(-1, 0), (-1, 1), (0. 1)\}$

Lesson 3-5 Try This
a. $\frac{13}{11}$ **b.** 1 **c.** $\frac{11}{5}$ **d.** −1 **e.** 0 **f.** No slope

g. $y = -3x - 2$ **h.** $y = \frac{1}{4}x - 9$ **i.** $y = -\frac{1}{2}x + \frac{5}{2}$

Exercise Set 3-5
1. 8 **3.** −1 **5.** $-\frac{1}{2}$ **7.** 2 **9.** $\frac{3}{7}$ **11.** $\frac{1}{2}$ **13.** $\frac{2}{5}$

15. No slope **17.** No slope **19.** 0 **21.** No slope
23. 0 **25.** No slope **27.** 0 **29.** 0 **31.** No slope

33. $y = 4x - 10$ **35.** $y = -x - 7$ **37.** $y = \frac{1}{2}x + 7$

39. $y = -7$ **41.** 1.7441860

43. $y = 3.516x - 13.1602$ **45.** Yes **47.** $\frac{5}{8}$

51. $m = -\frac{3}{5}$ **53.** Figure *ABCD* is a parallelogram, and its opposite sides are parallel.
55. a. Grade = 4%; $y = 0.04x$ **b.** Grade = 6.7%; $y = 0.067x$ **57.** *R* **59.** 15 **61.** $-\frac{1}{6}$ **63.** $-\frac{36}{5}$

Lesson 3-6 Try This
a. $y = -3x + 7$ **b.** $y = -\frac{10}{3}x + 4$

c. $m = -5; b = \frac{1}{3}$ **d.** $m = \frac{2}{3}; b = 2$

e. $m = 0; b = 3$

f.

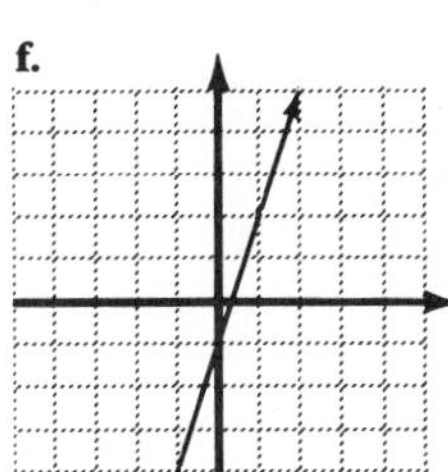

g.

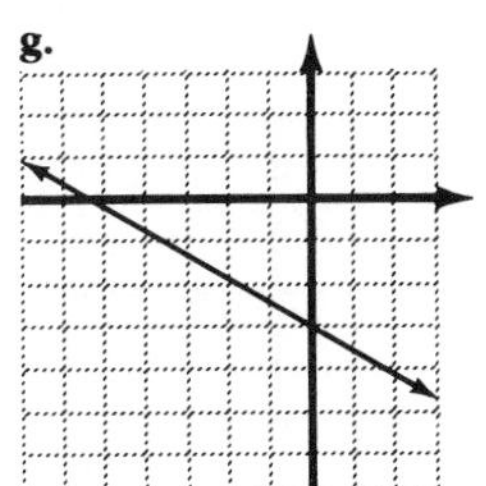

h.

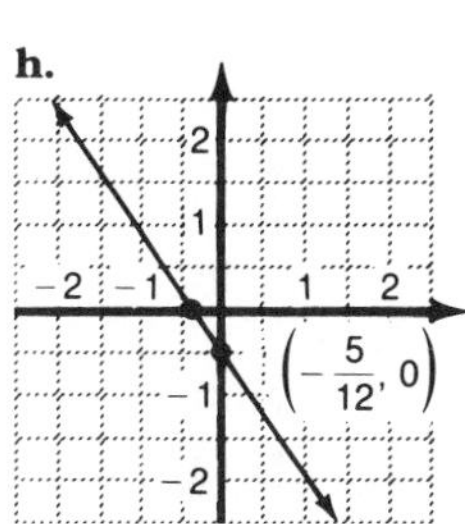

i. $5x - 5y + \frac{1}{2} = 0$; $m = 1$

j. $8x - 5y - 10 = 0$; $m = \frac{8}{5}$

Exercise Set 3-6

1. $y = \frac{1}{2}x + \frac{7}{2}$ **3.** $y = x$ **5.** $y = \frac{5}{2}x + 5$

7. $y = \frac{1}{4}x + \frac{17}{4}$ **9.** $y = \frac{2}{5}x$ **11.** $y = 3x + 5$

13. $m = 2$; $b = 3$ **15.** $m = -4$; $b = 9$

17. $m = -1$; $b = 6$ **19.** $m = -3$; $b = 5$

21. $m = \frac{3}{4}$; $b = -3$ **23.** $m = -3$; $b = 4$

25. $m = -\frac{7}{3}$; $b = -3$ **27.** $m = 0$; $b = 7$

29. $m = 0$; $b = -\frac{10}{3}$

31.

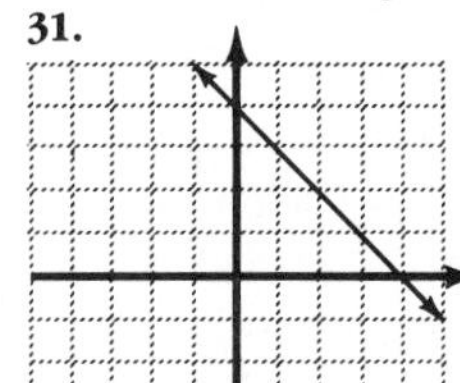

33.

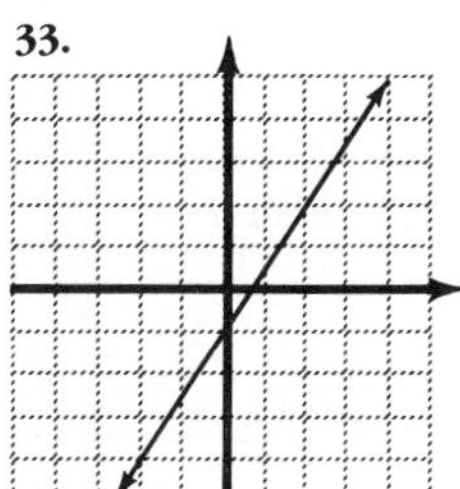

35.

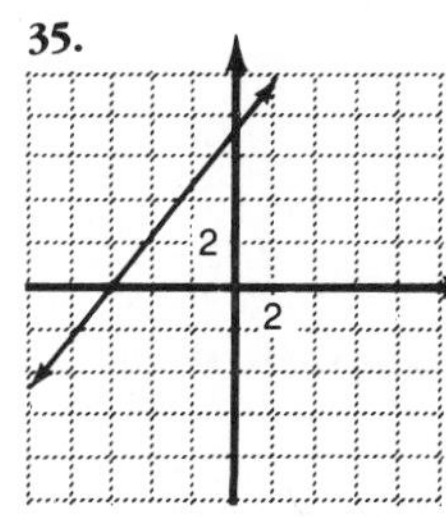

37. $4x - y - 8 = 0$; $m = 4$
39. $2x - y + 3 = 0$; $m = 2$
41. $x - 6 = 0$; no slope
43. $x - y - 2 = 0$; $m = -1$
45. $2x - 6 = 0$; no slope
47. Not a linear equation

49. $y = \frac{2}{5}x - 4$

51. $y = -0.36x + 10$

53. $y = \frac{5}{2}x + \frac{3}{11}$ **55.** $y = -2x + 2$; $a = -3$, $b = -8$

59. $a = \frac{7}{5}$, $b = -\frac{7}{4}$, $m = \frac{5}{4}$ **61.** $a = -5$, $b = -14.4$, $m = -2.88$ **63.** Function **65.** Function **67.** Not a function **69.** Domain {1}; range {2, 6} **71.** Domain R; range {3} **73.** 9.80 or more

Lesson 3-7 Try This

a. Yes **b.** No **c.** No **d.** $y = -4x - 12$ **e.** Yes

f. No **g.** $y = -\frac{8}{7}x + \frac{6}{7}$ **h.** $y = \frac{1}{2}x + \frac{5}{2}$

Exercise Set 3-7

1. Yes **3.** No **5.** Yes **7.** $y = -\frac{1}{2}x + \frac{17}{2}$

9. $y = \frac{5}{7}x - \frac{17}{7}$ **11.** $y = \frac{1}{3}x + 4$ **13.** Yes **15.** No

17. $y = \frac{1}{2}x + 4$ **19.** $y = \frac{4}{3}x - 6$ **21.** $y = \frac{5}{2}x + 9$

23. $y = -\frac{7}{3}x + \frac{22}{3}$ **27.** $y = -0.5x - 0.6$

29. c. $y = mx + c$, $c \neq b$ **31.** $k = 7$ **33.** Yes
35. Yes **37.** 6 **39.** 27 **41.** 126

Lesson 3-8 Try This

a. (1) $R = -0.0079t + 10.43$ **(2)** ≈9.79 sec, ≈9.395 sec **(3)** ≈2099 **b.** Answers may vary. $T = 5t + 50$; 90°; 2 min

Exercise Set 3-8

1. a. $E = \frac{3}{20}t + 72$ **b.** 78.45 years in 1993, 80.7 in 2008 **3. a.** $D = \frac{1}{5}t + 20$ **b.** 28.2 in 1991, 31 in 2005 **5. a.** $R = -0.075t + 46.8$ **b.** 41.85 sec in 1996, 41.325 sec in 2003 **c.** 2021
7. a. $C = 0.15m + 15$ **b.** $45.00
13. 100.03916 cm; 99.96796 cm **17. c.** 87.98 cm
19. No Slope **21.** $y = -x + 5$ **23.** $-7c$
25. $5x + 9$ **27.** $14r - 12s$ **29.** p^4

Lesson 3-9 Try This

a. & b.

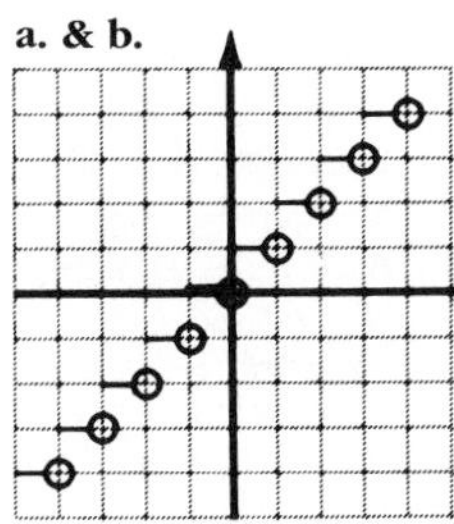

c.

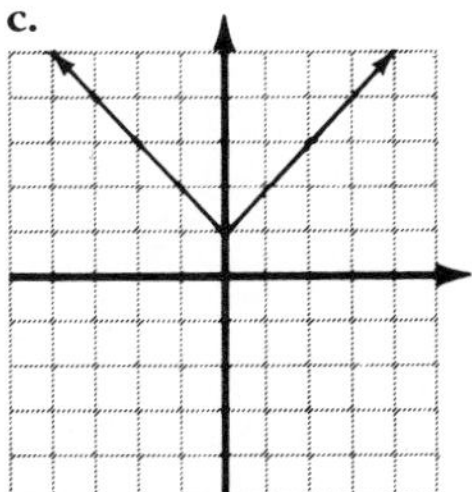

d.

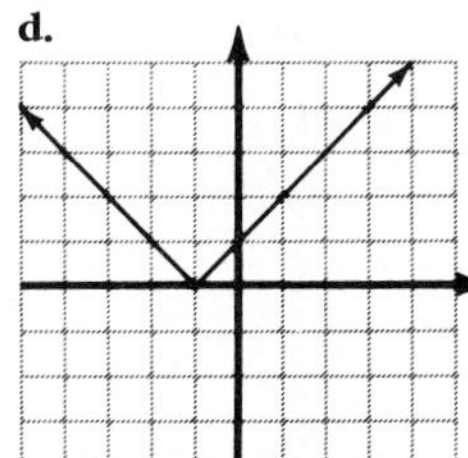

e. −10 **f.** −3 **g.** −7
h. −24 **i.** $-3x + 12$
j. $-3x - 4$ **k.** $9x$
l. $x - 8$

Exercise Set 3-9

1.

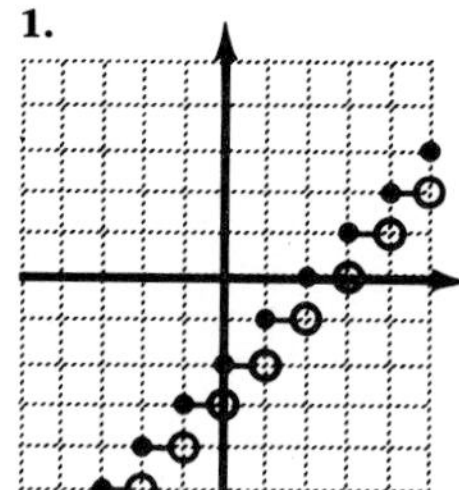

3.

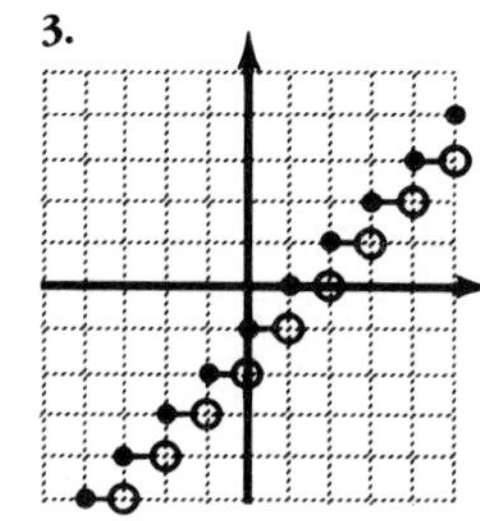

5.

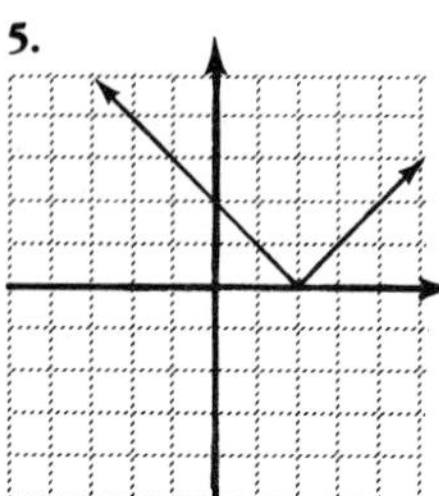

7.

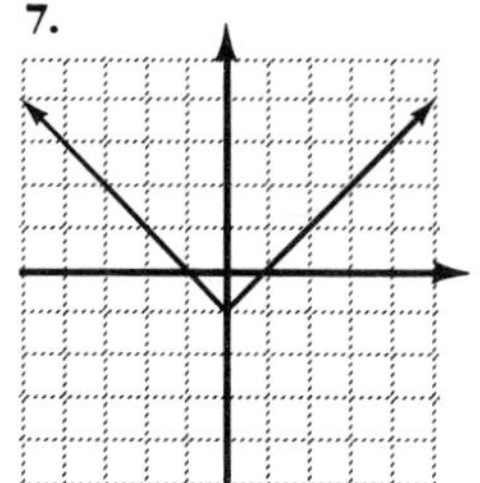

9.

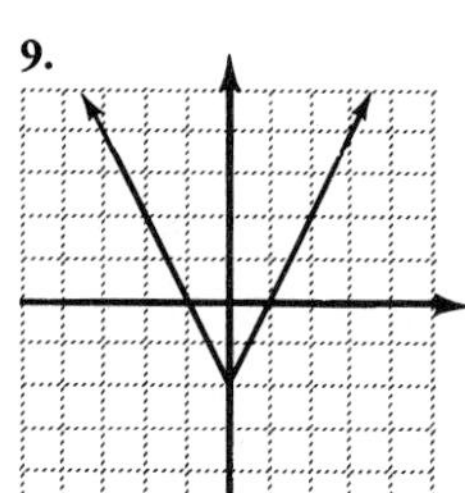

11. 0 **13.** 64 **15.** 35 **17.** −52 **19.** $4x - 1$ **21.** $x^2 - 1$ **23.** x^4 **29.** 10 **31.** 36 **33.** −49 **35.** −25 **37.** 38 **39.** $10x + 45$ **41.** $10x + 4$ **43. a.** $K(F) = \frac{5}{9}F + 255\frac{2}{9}$ **b.** 248° K **47.** No **49.** 14 **51.** $y = 2x + 1$ **53.** $y = -\frac{3}{2}x$ **55.** $\frac{1}{(2w)^3}$ **57.** −3 **59.** $8, -\frac{14}{3}$

Problem Set 3-10

1.

\$6 tapes	\$4 tapes
8	0
6	3
4	6
2	9
0	12

3. There can be 11 rows of letters in the poster. **5.** There could be 60 people **7.** \$1.19 (3 quarters, 4 dimes, 4 pennies, or 1 quarter, 9 dimes, 4 pennies) **9.** 27

Chapter 3 Summary and Review

1. {(*a*, 1), (*a*, 2), (*b*, 1), (*b*, 2), (*c*, 1), (*c*, 2)} **3.** Domain {−6, −1, 0, 1, 2}; range {−4, 1, 2, 4, 5} **5.**

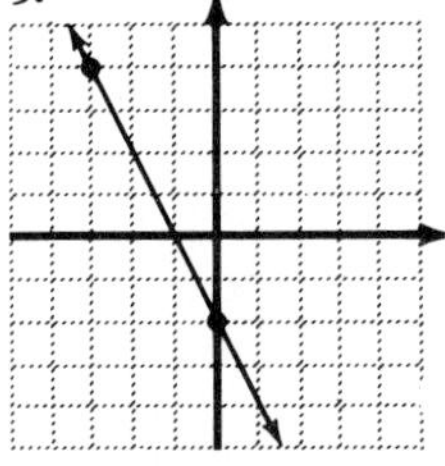

7. No **9.** Yes **11.** Yes **13.**

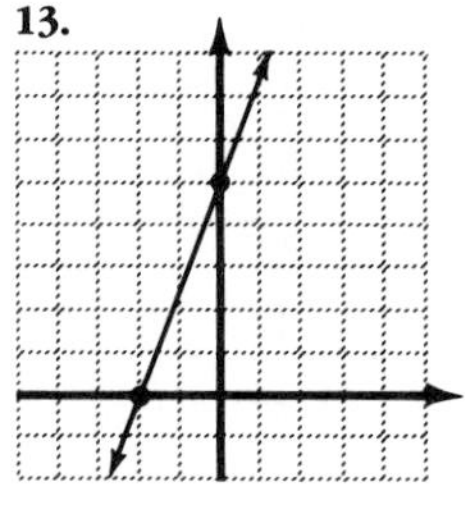

15.

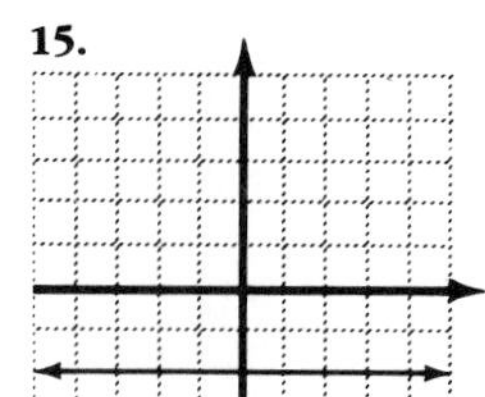

17. $y = \frac{1}{2}x + 4$ **19.** $m = \frac{5}{2}$; $b = -2$ **21. a.** $y = -\frac{5}{3}x + 2$ **b.** $y = \frac{3}{5}x + \frac{44}{5}$ **23.** 18.728 sec **25.**

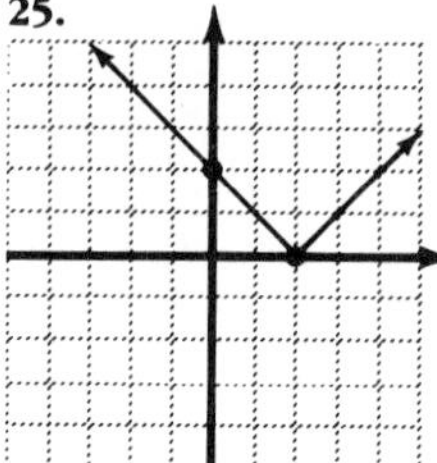

27. 16 **29.** $2x^2 + 4x$

Chapter 4

Lesson 4-1 Try This

a. (4, 7) **b.** (3, −1)

Exercise Set 4-1

1. (3, 1) **3.** (3, −2) **5.** (1, −5) **7.** (2, 1) **9.** $\left(\frac{5}{2}, -2\right)$ **11.** (3, −2) **13.** No solution **17.** $\{(x, y) | x = y \text{ and } x \geq 0\}$ **19.** 15 **21.** 3 **23.** 21 **25.** $m = -2$, $b = 4$ **27.** $\left\{a \middle| a > 2 \text{ or } a < -\frac{8}{5}\right\}$

Lesson 4-2 Try This

a. (−3, 2) **b.** $\left(\frac{3}{8}, \frac{11}{8}\right)$ **c.** (1, 4) **d.** (−3, 1) **e.** (5, 3) **f.** (2, −1) **g.** (20, 3)

Exercise Set 4-2

1. (2, −2) **3.** (−2, 1) **5.** (1, 2) **7.** (3, 0) **9.** (−1, 2) **11.** (−3, 2) **13.** (6, 2) **15.** (3, −3) **17.** $\left(\frac{1}{2}, -\frac{1}{2}\right)$ **19.** $\left(-\frac{4}{3}, -\frac{19}{3}\right)$ **21.** (90.91, −90.91) **23.** $\left(-\frac{1}{4}, -\frac{1}{2}\right)$ **25.** {(5, 3), (5, −3), (−5, 3), (−5, −3)} **27.** $m = -\frac{1}{2}$; $b = \frac{5}{2}$ **29.** $2x - y = -6$ **31.** Not linear **33.** Not linear **35.** \$3250

Lesson 4-3 Try This

a. 35, 140 **b.** 30 L of 5%, 70 L of 15% **c.** 280 km

Exercise Set 4-3

1. 5, −47 **3.** 24, 8 **5.** 150 lb soybean meal, 200 lb corn meal **7.** 5 L of each **9.** \$4100 at 14%, \$4700 at 16% **11.** \$725 at 12%, \$425 at 11% **13.** 375 km **15.** $1\frac{3}{4}$ **17.** 8 white, 22 yellow **19.** 13 at \$9.75, 32 at \$850 **21.** Maria 20, Carlos 28 **23.** $l = 160$ m, $w = 154$ m **25.** $l = 31$ cm, $w = 12$ cm **27.** Irwin, 32 yrs; Lippi, 14 years **29.** 82 **31.** 137° **33.** $4\frac{4}{7}$ L

35. m^4 **37.** $w^6|w|$ **39.** $75a^2|a|$ **41.** -1

43. $y = -x + 3$ **45.** $x + 1$ **47.** $x + \frac{1}{2}$

Lesson 4-4 Try This

a. $\left(2, \frac{1}{2}, -2\right)$ **b.** $(1, -2, 3)$ **c.** $(5, -1, 2)$

Exercise Set 4-4

1. $(1, 2, 3)$ **3.** $(-1, 5, -2)$ **5.** $(3, 1, 2)$ **7.** $(-3, -4, 2)$ **9.** $(2, 4, 1)$ **11.** $(-3, 0, 4)$ **13.** $(2, 2, 4)$ **15.** $\left(\frac{1}{2}, 4, -6\right)$ **17.** $\left(\frac{1}{2}, \frac{1}{3}, \frac{1}{6}\right)$ **19.** $\left(\frac{1}{2}, \frac{2}{3}, -\frac{5}{6}\right)$ **21.** $(1, -1, 2)$ **23.** $(1, -2, 4, -1)$ **25.** $\left(-1, \frac{1}{5}, -\frac{1}{2}\right)$ **29.** $3x + 4y + 2z = 12$ **31.** $y = -\frac{1}{3}x + \frac{8}{3}$ **33.** $\{x|x \neq 0\}$ **35.** $-2x + 4y + 8 = 0$; $y = \frac{1}{2}x - 2$ **37. b.** \$132

Lesson 4-5 Try This

a. A: 112, B: 90, C: 85

Exercise Set 4-5

1. 17, 9, 79 **3.** 4, 2, −1 **5.** A = 34°, B = 104°, C = 42° **7.** T = 25°, U = 50°, V = 105° **9.** \$21 on Thurs.; \$18 on Fri.; \$27 on Sat. **11.** First score: 74.5; second score: 68.5; third score: 82 **13.** A: 2200, B: 2500, C: 2700 **15.** Todd 10; Don 12; Carla 15 **17.** 464 **19.** Adults': 2050; senior citizens': 845; children's: 210 **21.** 25 **23.** 8 **25.** 6 **27.** Not parallel

Lesson 4-6 Try This

a. Inconsistent **b.** Consistent **c.** Inconsistent **d.** Consistent **e.** Dependent **f.** Not dependent **g.** Dependent **h.** Not dependent

Exercise Set 4-6

1. Inconsistent **3.** Consistent **5.** Consistent **7.** Inconsistent **9.** Consistent **11.** Dependent **13.** Not dependent **15.** Dependent **17.** Not dependent **19.** Dependent **21.** $(0, -5)$, $(1, -2)$, $(-1, -8)$ **23.** No solution **25.** No solution **27.** 21: Consistent and dependent; 23: Inconsistent; 25: Inconsistent **31.** 25 **33.** $\left(\frac{2y - 5}{3}, y\right)$ **35.** $\{x|x \neq 1$ and $x \neq 0\}$ **37.** $m = -\frac{2}{3}$, $b = \frac{5}{3}$ **39.** $m = \frac{5}{2}$, $b = \frac{11}{2}$ **41.** 2 **43.** −6

Lesson 4-7 Try This

a.

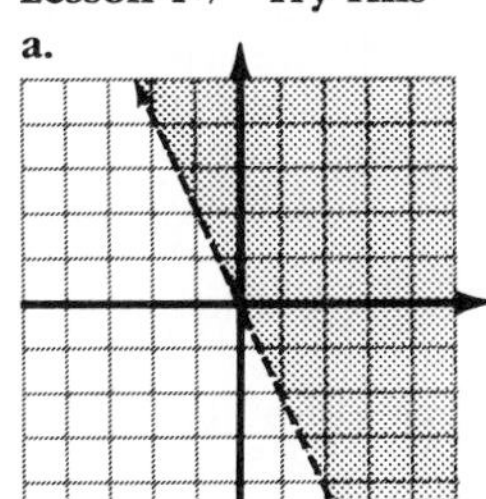

b.

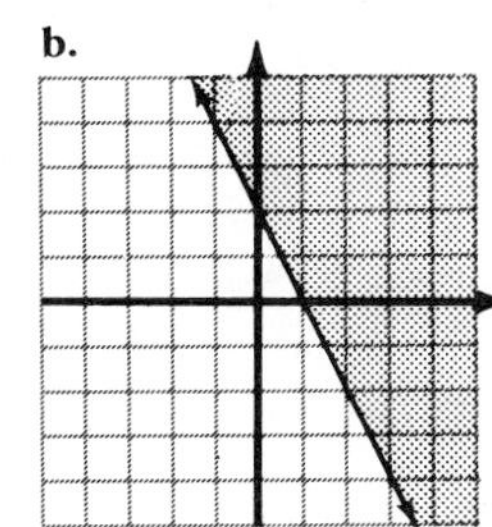

c.

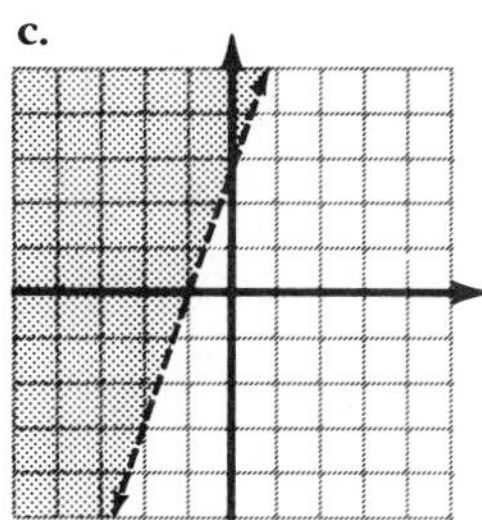

d.

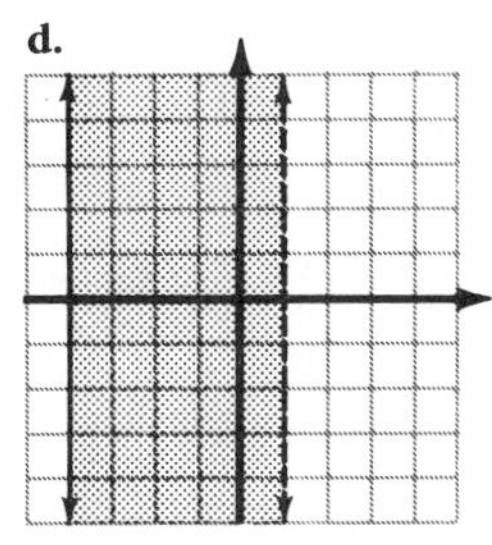

e.

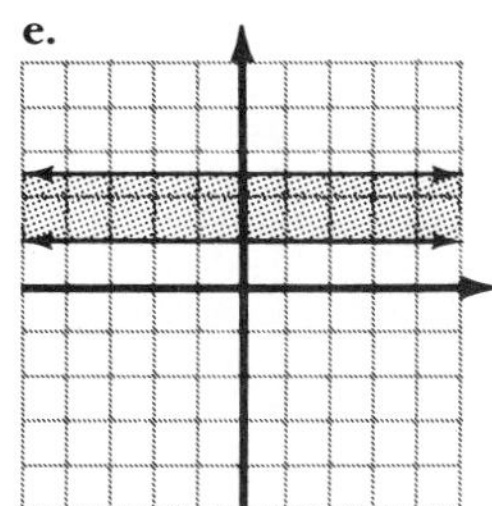

f.

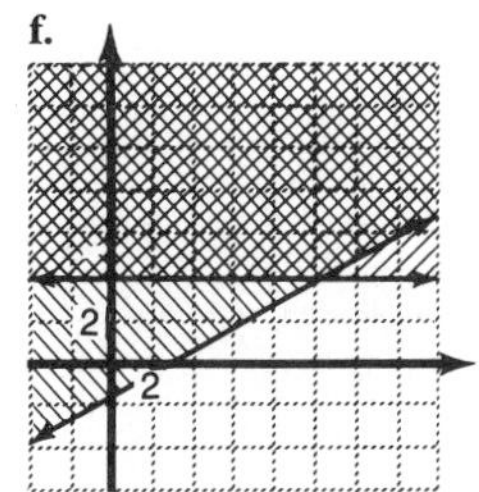

g.

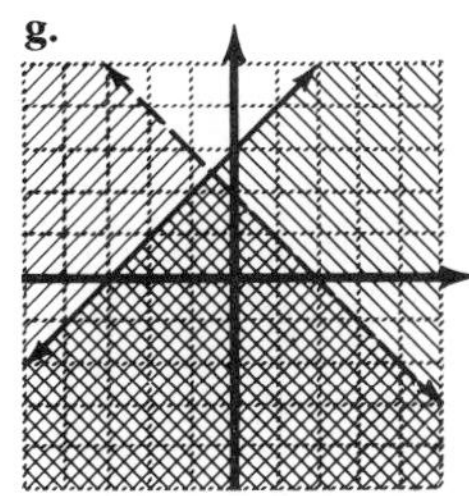

h.

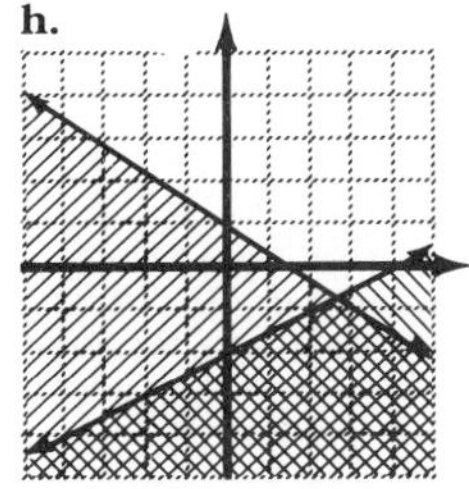

i. 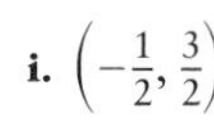 $\left(-\frac{1}{2}, \frac{3}{2}\right)$

j. 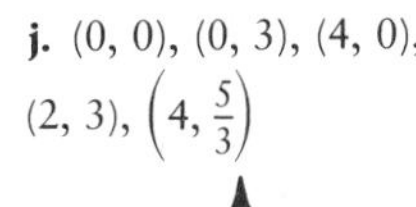 $(0, 0)$, $(0, 3)$, $(4, 0)$, $(2, 3)$, $\left(4, \frac{5}{3}\right)$

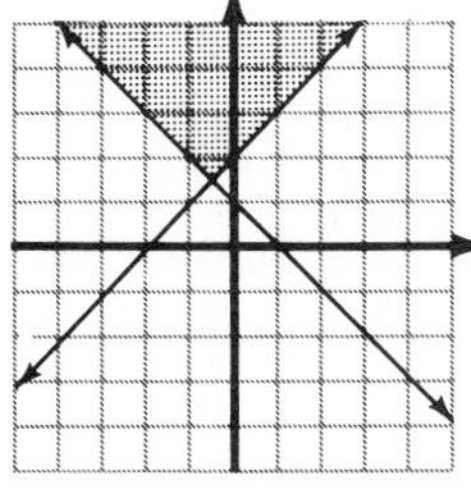

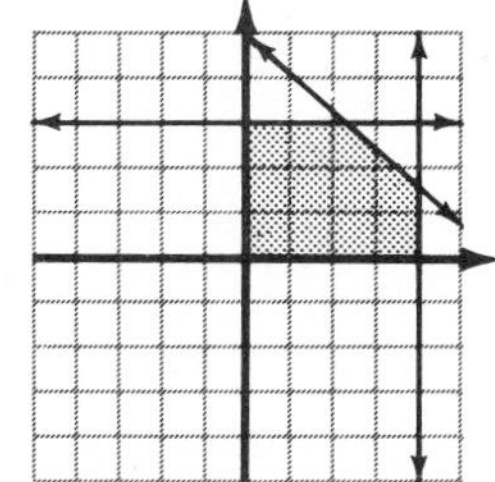

Exercise Set 4-7

1.

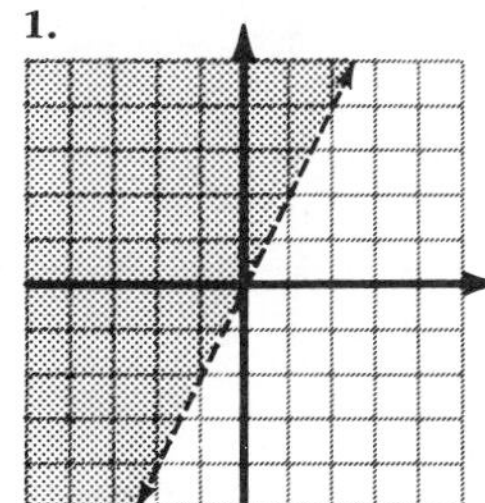

3.

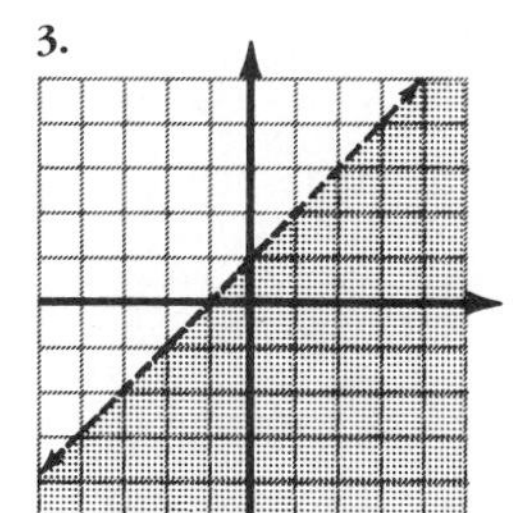

5.

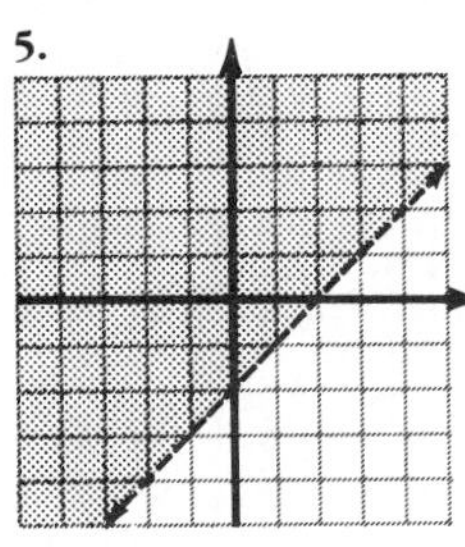

7.

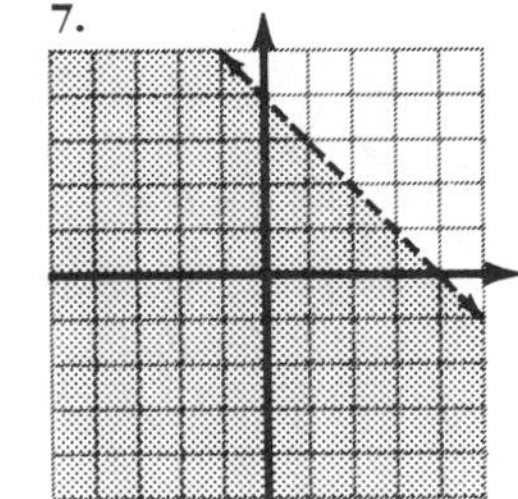

9.

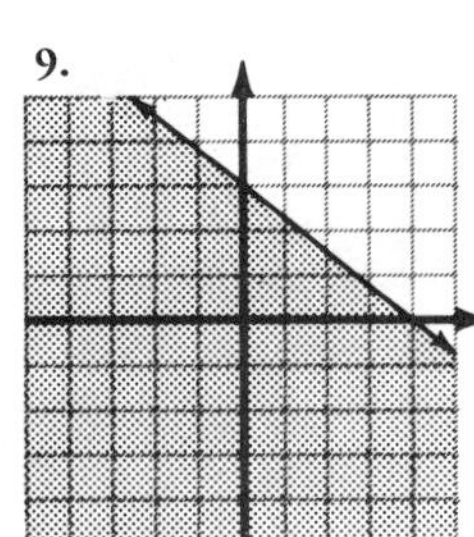

11.

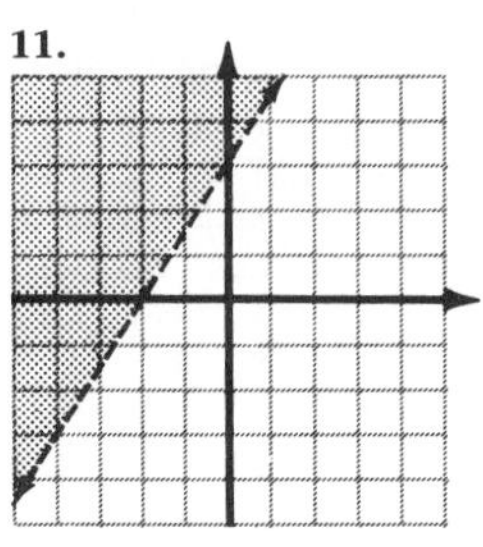

13.

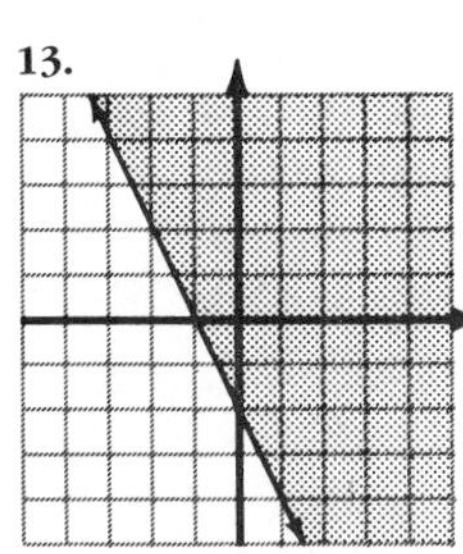

15.

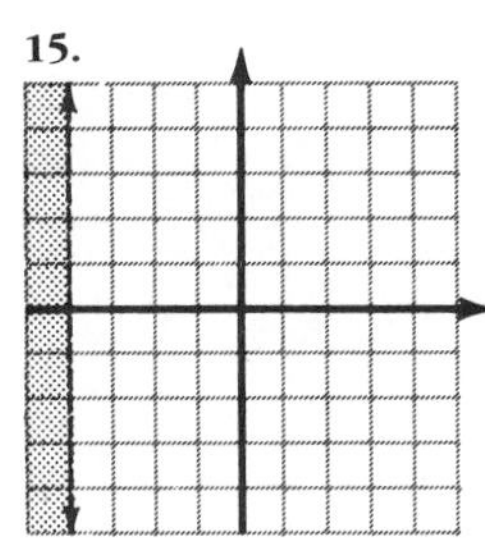

17.

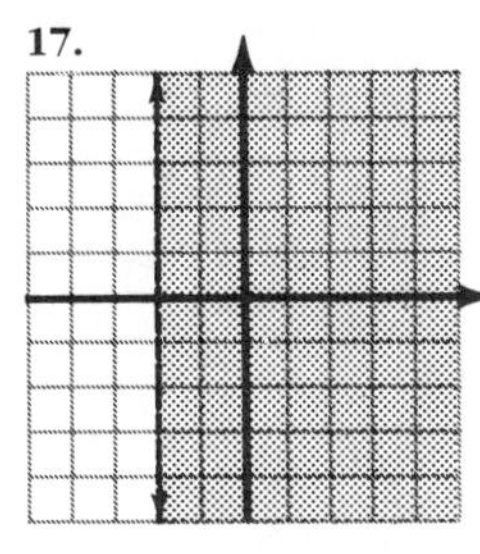

19.

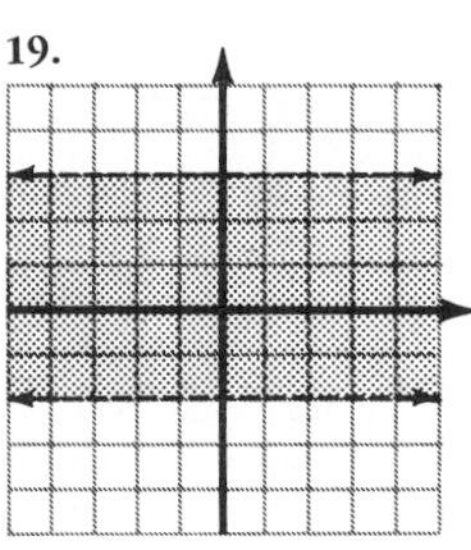

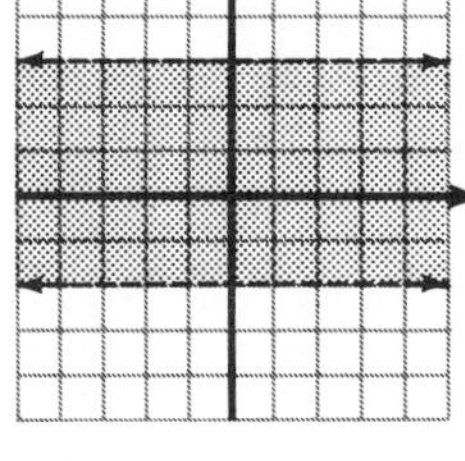

21.

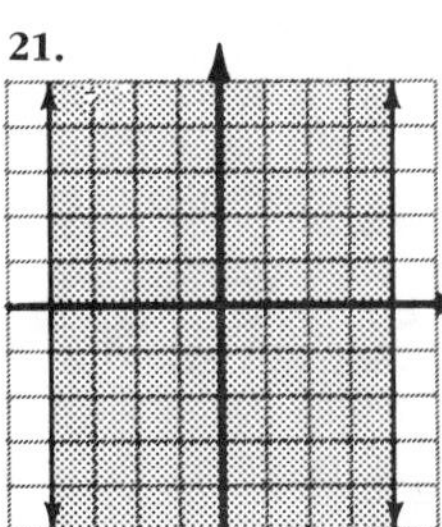

23.

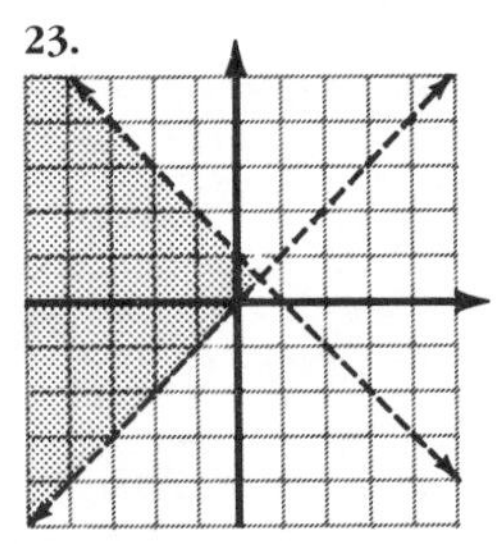

25.

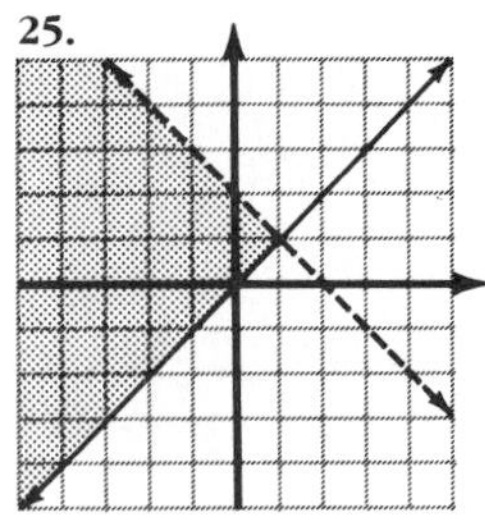

27.

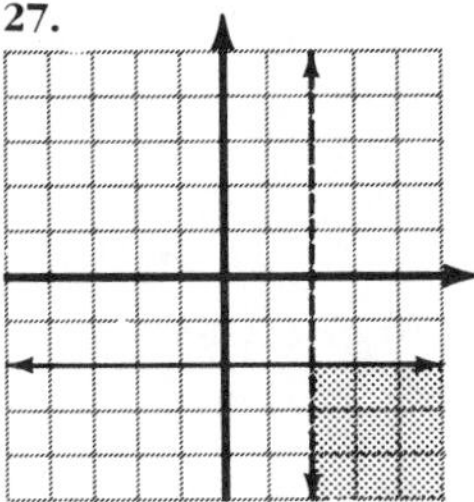

29.

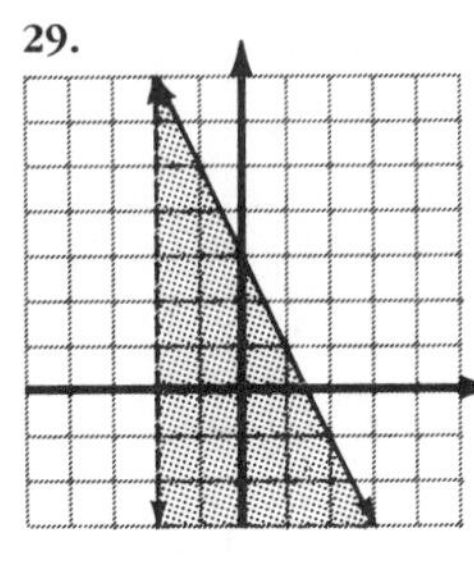

31.

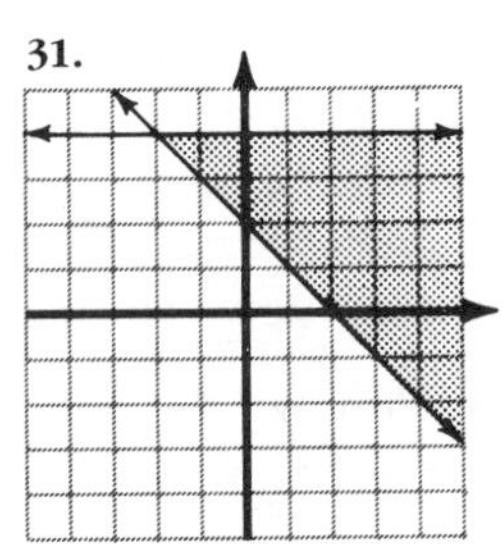

33.

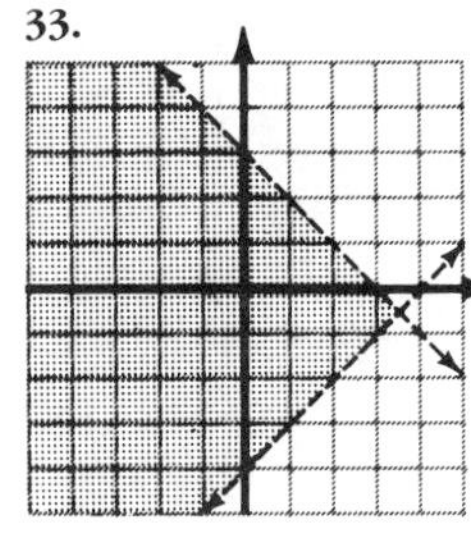

35.

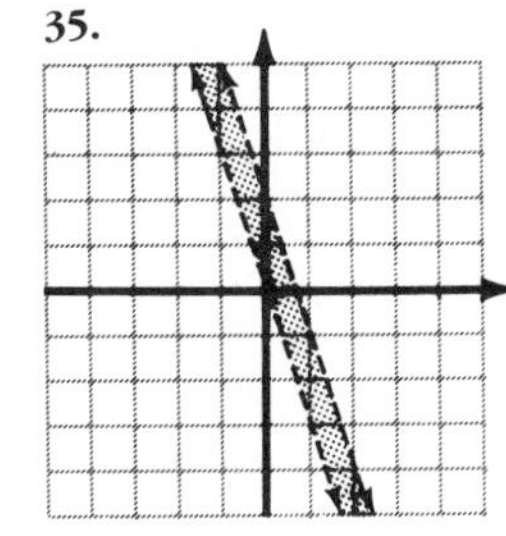

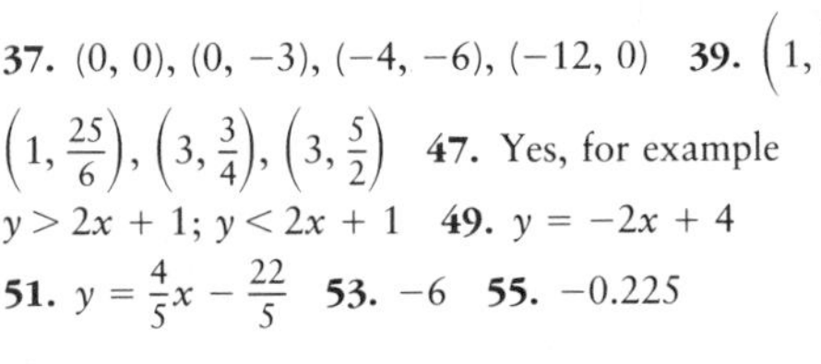

37. (0, 0), (0, −3), (−4, −6), (−12, 0) **39.** $\left(1, \frac{9}{4}\right)$, $\left(1, \frac{25}{6}\right)$, $\left(3, \frac{3}{4}\right)$, $\left(3, \frac{5}{2}\right)$ **47.** Yes, for example $y > 2x + 1$; $y < 2x + 1$ **49.** $y = -2x + 4$ **51.** $y = \frac{4}{5}x - \frac{22}{5}$ **53.** −6 **55.** −0.225

Lesson 4-8 Try This

a. 40 hamburgers, 50 hot dogs

Exercise Set 4-8

1. You must correctly answer 8 questions of type A and 10 of type B to maximize your score. The maximum score is 102. **3.** \$7000 should be invested at bank X and \$15,000 at bank Y to maximize income at \$1395 **5.** 2 knit suits; 4 worsted suits; maximum profit is \$192. **7.** 30 P-1 airplanes and 10 P-2 airplanes should be used to minimize the cost at \$460,000. **9.** $r > 4$

Chapter 4 Summary and Review

1. (0, 1) **3.** (−5, −1) **5.** (5, 2) **7.** $\left(\frac{7}{5}, \frac{10}{3}\right)$ **9.** Carol's speed = 51 km/h; Ellie's speed = 68 km/h **11.** $\left(2, -2, \frac{1}{2}\right)$ **13.** Inconsistent

15.

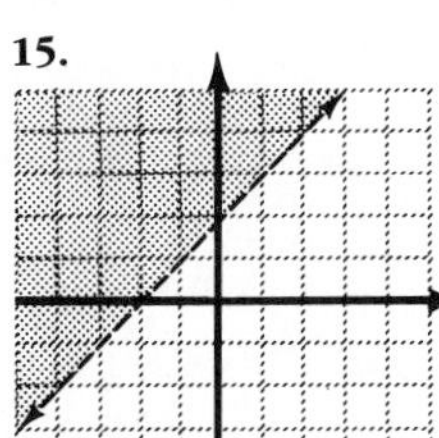

17.

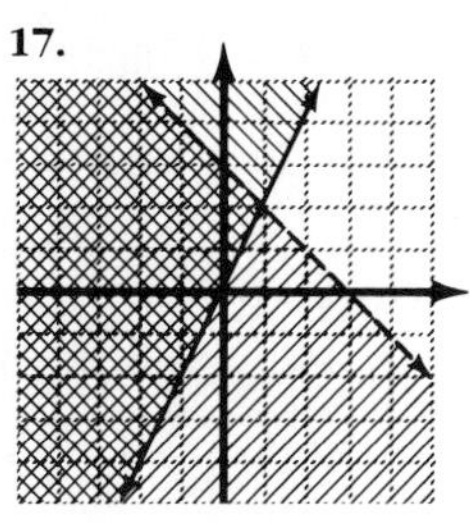

19. \$40,000 in municipal bonds and \$20,000 in mutual funds; \$6800 maximum income.

Chapters 1-4 Cumulative Review

1. $-\frac{107}{65}$ **3.** $17\frac{4}{31}$ **5.** 12.65 **7.** 12 **9.** -9
11. $11y - 7$ **13.** 5 **15.** \$260 **17.** $81x^4$
19. $-10x^{-3}y^7$ **21.** $\frac{1}{64}x^{-6}$ **23.** 1.5×10^{-3} **25.** -1
27. $7, -\frac{1}{2}$ **29.** $\frac{e}{c^2}$ **31.** $x > 7$ **33.** $x < \frac{12}{5}$
35. $-1 < x < \frac{5}{4}$ **37.** $-\frac{1}{2} < x < \frac{1}{2}$ **39.** $x \leq 4$ or $x \geq 10$
41. {(−1, −1), (−1, 0), (−1, 1), (−1, 2), (−1, 3), (0, 0), (0, 1), (0, 2), (0, 3), (1, 1), (1, 2), (1, 3), (2, 2), (2, 3), (3, 3)}
43.

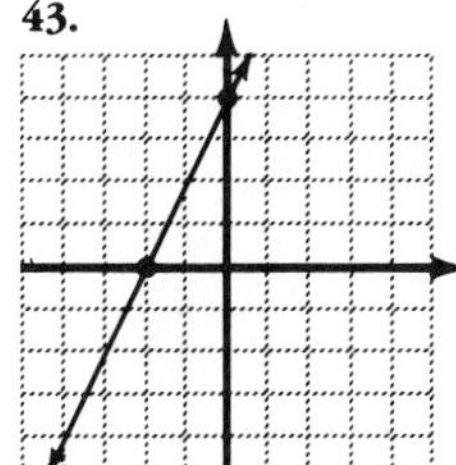

45. *R*
47.

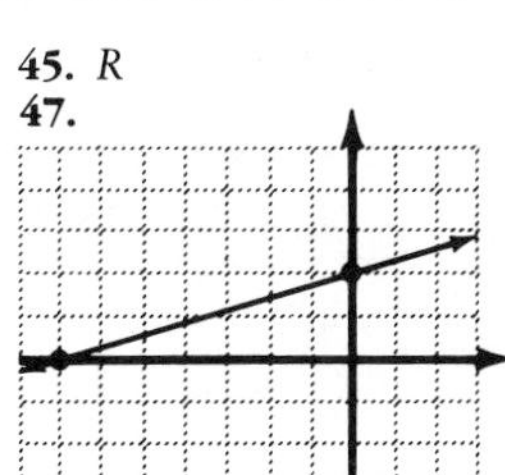

49. $8x + y + 17 = 0$ **51.** Slope $= \frac{3}{5}$, y-intercept $= -\frac{8}{5}$
53. $2x - y = 7$ **55.** -20 **57.** $(-2, -3)$ **59.** Rice \$0.28/lb, seeds \$0.98/lb **61.** $(-2, 5, -1)$
63. Inconsistent
65.

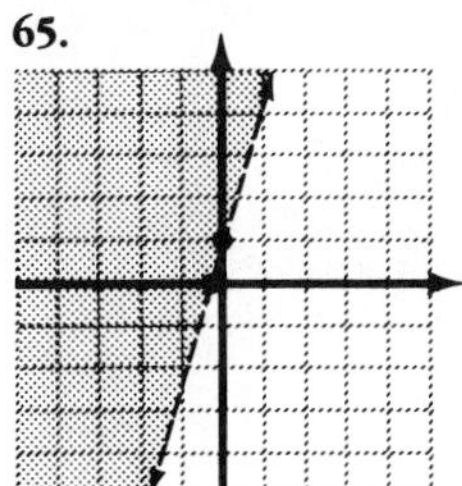

67. 0 windows, 6 doors

Chapter 5

Lesson 5-1 Try This

a. (1) 5 (2) 85 (3) -23 **b.** $3x^2 + 2x^4$
c. $9x^3y^2 - 2x^2y^3$ **d.** $7xy^2 + 3x^2 - y^2$

Exercise Set 5-1

1. 54, 2 **3.** $-45, -\frac{235}{27}$ **5.** $2x^2$ **7.** $3x + y$
9. $a + 6$ **11.** $-6a^2b - 2b^2$ **13.** $9x^2 + 2xy + 15y^2$
15. $-x^2y + 9xy^2 + 4y$ **17.** $-4a^3 + 2a^2 - 7a + 5$
19. $8a^3 - 16a^2 + 6a - 7$
21. $-3x^2 - 6ax + 6x - 3a^2 + 6a - 4$
23. $55x^5 - 59x^4 + 14x^3 + 12x^2 + 18x + 175$
25. $29x^5 - 15x^4 + 86x^3 - 68x^2 + 50x + 25$
27. 160 **29.** 18,562.3 in.^{3} or 10.7 ft^3 **31.** 7.36%
35. 2 **41.** $3m(2m + 1)$ **43.** $17(1 + 3c)$
45. $y = -3x + 1$ **47.** $y = x + 2$ **49.** -0.5

Lesson 5-2 Try This

a. $-4x^3 + 2x^2 - 4x - \frac{3}{2}$
b. $5p^2q^4 + p^2q^2 - 6pq^2 - 3q + 5$
c. $-5x^2t^2 + 4xy^2t + 3xt - 6x + 5$
d. $3x^2y - 5xy + 7x - 4y - 2$
e. $8xy^4 - 9xy^2 + 4x^2 + 2y - 7$
f. $7x^2y - 9x^3y^2 + 5x^2y^3 - x^2y + 9y$

Exercise Set 5-2

1. $3x^3 - x^2 + 7x$ **3.** $3x^2y - 5xy^2 + 7xy + 2$
5. $3x + 2y - 2z - 3$ **7.** $9.46y^4 + 2.5y^3 - 11.8y - 3.1$
9. $\frac{3}{4}x^3 + \frac{1}{4}x^2 + \frac{1}{16}x + \frac{23}{24}$ **11.** $4y^4 - 7y^2 + 2y + 1$
13. $-20x^4y^4 + 12x^3y^3 - 5x^2y^2 + 3xy - 19$
15. $-2x^3 - 6x^2 - x + 11$ **17.** $-4x^2 - 5y^2 + 3$
19. $6x^4 - 8x^2 + 9x - 4$
21. $0.06y^4 + 0.032y^3 - 0.94y^2 + 0.93$
23. $-\frac{4}{9}y^3 + \frac{4}{9}y^2 + \frac{26}{27}y + \frac{4}{9}$
25. $47x^{4a} + 40x^{3a} + 30x^{2a} + x^a + 4$
27. $x^{5b} + 4x^{4b} + x^{3b} - 6x^{2b} - 9x^b$
29. $5x^3y^2z - 4x^2y^2z^2 + 2xyz - 12x^3yz + 4x^2y^2z - xyz^2 - 9$ **31.** $17 - 30pq^2 + 8p^2qr + 3pqr$
35. $-2a^4 + 12a^3 + 3a^2$ **37.** $\frac{1}{64}$
39. $-2x - 4y + 6 = 0$ or $2x + 4y - 6 = 0$
41. -2 **43.** 10 **45.** 47

Lesson 5-3 Try This

a. $3x^3y^2 + 4x^2y^2 - xy^2 + 6y^2$
b. $2p^4q^2 + 3p^2q^2 + 2q^2$ **c.** $2x^3y - 4xy + 3x^3 - 6x$
d. $15x^2 - xy - 6y^2$ **e.** $6xy - 40x + 60y - 400$
f. $16x^2 - 40xy + 25y^2$ **g.** $4y^4 + 24x^2y^3 + 36x^4y^2$
h. $16x^2 - 49$ **i.** $25x^4y^2 - 4y^2$
j. $4x^2 + 12x + 9 - 25y^2$ **k.** $25t^2 - 4x^6y^4$
l. $x^3 + 3x^2 + 3x + 1$ **m.** $x^3 - 3x^2 + 3x - 1$
n. $t^6 + 9t^4b + 27t^2b^2 + 27b^3$
o. $8a^9 - 60a^6b^2 + 150a^3b^4 - 125b^6$

Exercise Set 5-3

1. $6x^3 + 4x^2 + 32x - 64$
3. $4a^3b^2 - 10a^2b^2 + 3ab^3 + 4ab^2 - 6b^3 + 4a^2b - 2ab + 3b^2$ **5.** $a^3 - b^3$ **7.** $4x^2 + 8xy + 3y^2$
9. $12x^3 + x^2y - \frac{3}{2}xy - \frac{1}{8}y^2$
11. $4x^3 - 4x^2y - 2xy^2 + 2y^3$ **13.** $4x^2 + 12xy + 9y^2$

15. $4x^4 - 12x^2y + 9y^2$ **17.** $4x^6 + 12x^3y^2 + 9y^4$
19. $9x^2 - 4y^2$ **21.** $x^4 - y^2z^2$ **23.** $9x^4 - 4$
25. $y^3 + 15y^2 + 75y + 125$
27. $m^6 - 6m^4n + 12m^2n^2 - 8n^3$
29. $\frac{1}{4}x^4 - \frac{3}{5}x^2y + \frac{9}{25}y^2$
31. $0.25x^2 + 0.70xy^2 + 0.49y^4$
33. $4x^2 + 12xy + 9y^2 - 16$ **35.** $x^4 - 1$
37. $16x^4 - y^4$ **39.** $16x^4 - 32x^3 + 16x^2$
41. $x^{4a} - y^{4b}$ **43.** **d.** $b = 2$,
$A(r) = 1000(r^2 + 2r + 1)$
$b = 3$, $A(r) = 1000(r^3 + 3r^2 + 3r + 1)$
$b = 4$, $A(r) = 1000(r^4 + 4r^3 + 6r^2 + 4r + 1)$
45. $16x^4 - 32x^3 + 16x^2$ **47.** $x^6 - 1$
49. $y^6 - 3y^4 + 3y^2 - 1$
51. $a^2 + 2ac + c^2 - b^2 - 2bd - d^2$
53. $y^{3+3n}z^{n+3} - 4y^4z^{3n}$ **55.** $(2c)^{-3}$ **57.** m^{-1}
59. $-8x^{3+a}y^8$ **61.** $3y^2|y|$

Lesson 5-4 Try This

a. $3x(x - 2)$ **b.** $P(1 + rt)$ **c.** $3y^2(3y^2 - 5y + 1)$
d. $3x^2y(2 - 7xy + y^2)$ **e.** $(x + 7)^2$ **f.** $(3y - 5)^2$
g. $(9y + 4x)^2$ **h.** Not a trinomial square
i. $(4x^2 - 5y^3)^2$ **j.** $-4(2a^2 - 3b^2)^2$
k. $-3y^2(2x^2 - 5y^3)^2$ **l.** $(y + 2)(y - 2)$
m. $(7x^2 + 5y^5)(7x^2 - 5y^5)$ **n.** $(6x^2 + 4y^3)(6x^2 - 4y^3)$
o. $(x + 1 + p)(x + 1 - p)$ **p.** $(12 + x)(4 - x)$
q. $(x + 4)(x + 5)$ **r.** $(5y + 2)(y + 2)$
s. $(p - q)(x + y)$

Exercise Set 5-4

1. $y(y - 5)$ **3.** $3y(2y + 1)$ **5.** $x^2(x + 8)$
7. $5(x^2 - x + 3)$ **9.** $4y^2(2 + y^2)$
11. $2x(4y + 5z - 7w)$ **13.** $5x^2y^2(y + 3x)$
15. $y(y^3 - y^2 + y + 1)$ **17.** $5(2a^4 + 3a^2 - 5a - 6)$
19. $(x - 4)^2$ **21.** $(x + 8)^2$ **23.** $(x - 1)^2$ **25.** $(a - 2)^2$
27. $(y + 6)^2$ **29.** $a(a + 12)^2$ **31.** $5(2y + 5)^2$
33. $2(4x + 3)^2$ **35.** $(5y - 8)^2$ **37.** $(y + 3)(y - 3)$
39. $(2a + 7)(2a - 7)$ **41.** $(10y + 9)(10y - 9)$
43. $8(x + y)(x - y)$ **45.** $5(x^2 + y^2)(x + y)(x - y)$
47. $a^2(3a + b)(3a - b)$ **49.** $(x - y - 5)(x - y + 5)$
51. $(c + 2d - 3p)(c + 2d + 3p)$
53. $3(2x + 1 - y)(2x + 1 + y)$
55. $(4 - x + y)(4 + x - y)$ **57.** $(x + w)(y + z)$
59. $(y^2 + 3)(y - 1)$ **61.** $(t - 2)(t + 6)$
63. $(xy - 3)(2 - x)$ **65.** $2(2y^{2a} + 5)(y^{2a} + 3)$
67. $(0.2x + 0.3y)(0.2x - 0.3y)$
69. $\left(\frac{1}{6}y^2 + \frac{1}{9}x\right)\left(\frac{1}{6}y^2 - \frac{1}{9}x\right)$
83. 7 **85.** 28 **87.** $m = -5, b = 6$ **89.** $m = -2$,
$b = 3$ **91.** -3 **93.** 2

Lesson 5-5 Try This

a. $(10x + 1)(100x^2 - 10x + 1)$
b. $(y + 4x)(y^2 - 4xy + 16x^2)$
c. $(x - 2)(x^2 + 2x + 4)$
d. $(3y - 2x)(9y^2 + 6xy + 4x^2)$ **e.** $(x + 7)(x - 2)$
f. $(x - 7)(x - 3)$ **g.** $(y - 2)(y + 1)$
h. $(y + 16)(y + 2)$ **i.** $(3x + 2)(x + 1)$
j. $(2x + 3)(2x - 1)$ **k.** $2(4y - 1)(3y - 5)$
l. $(2x^2y^3 + 5)(x^2y^3 - 4)$

Exercise Set 5-5

1. $(x + 2)(x^2 - 2x + 4)$ **3.** $(y - 4)(y^2 + 4y + 16)$
5. $(w + 1)(w^2 - w + 1)$ **7.** $(2a + 1)(4a^2 - 2a + 1)$
9. $(y - 2)(y^2 + 2y + 4)$ **11.** $(2 - 3b)(4 + 6b + 9b^2)$
13. $(4y + 1)(16y^2 - 4y + 1)$
15. $(7x + 3)(49x^2 - 21x + 9)$
17. $(a - b)(a^2 + ab + b^2)$
19. $\left(a + \frac{1}{2}b\right)\left(a^2 - \frac{1}{2}ab + \frac{1}{4}b^2\right)$
21. $(2x - 3y)(4x^2 + 6xy + 9y^2)$ **23.** $(y + 5)(y + 3)$
25. $(a - 5)^2$ **27.** $(t - 5)(t + 3)$ **29.** $(x - 4)(x + 2)$
31. $(y + 8)(y + 4)$ **33.** $(x + 8)(x - 5)$
35. $(y - 5)(y - 9)$ **37.** $(x + 3)(x - 2)$
39. $(y + 7)(y + 1)$ **41.** $(8 - x)(7 + x)$
43. $(3b + 2)(b + 2)$ **45.** $(3y - 2)(2y + 1)$
47. $(6a + 5)(a - 2)$ **49.** $(3a + 4)(3a - 2)$
51. $(3x + 2)(x - 6)$ **53.** $(3x - 5)(2x + 3)$
55. $(3a - 4)(a - 2)$ **57.** $(5y + 2)(7y + 4)$
59. $(5t - 3)(t + 1)$ **61.** $4(2x + 1)(x - 4)$
63. $x(3x + 1)(x - 2)$ **65.** $(24x + 1)(x - 2)$
67. $(7x + 3)(3x + 4)$ **69.** $(5x + 4)(8x - 3)$
71. $(4a - 3)(3a - 2)$ **73.** $(x^2 + 16)(x^2 - 5)$
75. $\left(x + \frac{4}{5}\right)\left(x - \frac{1}{5}\right)$ **77.** $(y - 0.1)(y + 0.5)$
79. $(2x - 3y)(x + 2y)$ **81.** $(2x - 3y)(4x + 3y)$
83. $(7ab + 6)(ab + 1)$ **85.** $r(s + 4)(s^2 - 4s + 16)$
87. $5(x - 2z)(x^2 + 2xz + 4z^2)$
89. $(x + 0.1)(x^2 - 0.1x + 0.01)$
91. $8(2x^2 - t^2)(4x^4 + 2x^2t^2 + t^4)$ **107.** $(2, 8, -1)$
109. $y = -2x + 3$ **111.** $y = 2x + 4$ **113.** \$285

Lesson 5-6 Try This

a. $2(1 + 4x^2)(1 + 2x)(1 - 2x)$
b. $7(a + 1)(a - 1)(a^2 - a + 1)(a^2 + a + 1)$
c. $(3 + x)(4 + x)$ **d.** $(c - d + t + 4)(c - d - t - 4)$
e. $5(y^4 + 4x^6)$ **f.** $3(2x + 3)(x - 2)$
g. $(a + b)(a - b)^2$ **h.** $3(x + 3a)^2$
i. $(a + b - c)(a + b + c)$

Exercise Set 5-6

1. $(x + 12)(x - 12)$ **3.** $3(x^2 + 2)(x^2 - 2)$ **5.** $(a + 5)^2$
7. $2(x - 11)(x + 6)$ **9.** $(3x + 5y)(3x - 5y)$
11. $(2c - d)^2$ **13.** $(x^2 + 2)(2x - 7)$
15. $(4x - 15)(x - 3)$ **17.** $(m^3 + 10)(m^3 - 2)$
19. $(c - b)(a + d)$
21. $(m + 1)(m^2 - m + 1)(m - 1)(m^2 + m + 1)$
23. $(x + y + 3)(x - y + 3)$ **25.** $(6y - 5)(6y + 7)$
27. $(a^4 + b^4)(a^2 + b^2)(a + b)(a - b)$
29. $(2p + 3q)(4p^2 - 6pq + 9q^2)$
31. $(4p - 1)(16p^2 + 4p + 1)$ **33.** $ab(a + 4b)(a - 4b)$
35. $(4xy - 3)(5xy - 2)$ **37.** $2(x + 2)(x - 2)(x + 3)$
39. $2(5x - 4y)(25x^2 + 20xy + 16y^2)$
41. $2(2x + 3y)(4x^2 - 6xy + 9y^2)$
43. $(5y^2 - 12x)(6y^2 - 5x)$
45. $3(a + b + c + d)(a + b - c - d)$
47. $(y^2 + 11)(2 - y)(2 + y)$ **55.** $y = -2x - 3$
57. 0 **59.** -1

Lesson 5-7 Try This

a. 2, 4 **b.** 1, $-\frac{3}{4}$ **c.** −5 **d.** 0, 2 **e.** 0, −3 **f.** 3, 1, −1

Exercise Set 5-7

1. −7, 4 **3.** 4 **5.** 6 **7.** −5, −4 **9.** 0, −8 **11.** −3, 3 **13.** −6, 6 **15.** −5, −9 **17.** −9, 7 **19.** 7, 4 **21.** 8, −4 **23.** $-\frac{2}{3}$, −2 **25.** $\frac{3}{4}, \frac{1}{2}$ **27.** 0, 6 **29.** $-\frac{3}{4}, \frac{2}{3}$ **31.** −2, 2 **33.** $\frac{1}{2}$, 7 **35.** $-\frac{5}{7}, \frac{2}{3}$ **37.** 0, $\frac{1}{5}$ **39.** $-\frac{9}{10}, \frac{9}{10}$ **41.** $-\frac{1}{8}, \frac{1}{8}$ **43.** 0, $\frac{1}{3}, -\frac{1}{3}$ **45.** −5, 4 **47.** −3, 15 **49.** 1 **51.** $-2a$, 3 **53.** $a, -a$ **55.** (−1, 1) **57.** (1, 2)

Lesson 5-8 Try This

a. 8 or −6 **b.** Length is 8 cm; width is 3 cm.

Exercise Set 5-8

1. $\frac{7}{2}$ or $-\frac{3}{2}$ **3.** −12 or 11 **5.** Length is 12 ft; width is 7 ft. **7.** Length is 100 m; width is 75 m. **9.** 9 and 11 **11.** 3 cm **13.** Height is 7 cm; base is 16 cm. **15.** 16, 18, and 20 **17.** 9, 10, and 11; 3, 4, and 5 **19.** Length is 28 cm; width is 14 cm. **21.** Width is 30 in., length is 40 in.; depth is 20 in. **23.** 54 cm^2 **25.** $8x^6 - 12x^4 + 6x^2 - 1$ **27.** $(x + 2)(x - 2)$ **29.** $2y(2y - 1)$ **31.** −6

Chapter 5 Summary and Review

1. −9 **3.** $4a + 7$ **5.** $-4x^3 + 10x^2 + 2x + 7$ **7.** $5p^3 + pq + 4pq^2 + 3pq^3 - 5q$ **9.** $4y^4 + 16x^3y^3 - 13xy^2$ **11.** $6p - 10q + 11r$ **13.** $10a - 4b - 9c$ **15.** $3x^3y + 4x^2y - 6xy - 8y$ **17.** $30y^6 - 2y^4 - y^3 - 12y^2 + 45y - 42$ **19.** $-9x^4y^6 + 4t^2$ **21.** $8x^3 + 12x^2 + 6x + 1$ **23.** $7t^2(4t^2 - 5t + 2)$ **25.** $(3y - 8)(3y + 8)$ **27.** $9(x + y)(x - y)$ **29.** $(y - 2 - 2x)(y - 2 + 2x)$ **31.** $(5x - 2y)^2$ **33.** $(a - 4)(a - 6)$ **35.** $(9 + x)(8 - x)$ **37.** $(4x - 3)(2x - 3)$ **39.** $3(x + 3)(x - 3)$ **41.** $4(y + 7)(y - 2)$ **43.** $(2x - 3y)(4x^2 + 6xy + 9y^2)$ **45.** $(w + y)(k - t)$ **47.** $-\frac{1}{2}$, −4 **49.** 9 cm by 6 cm

Chapter 6

Lesson 6-1 Try This

a. $\frac{3x^2 + 2xy}{5x^2 + 4xy}$ **b.** $\frac{6x^3 + 4x^2 - 3xy - 2y}{9x^2 + 18x + 8}$ **c.** $\frac{5 - 2a}{b - a}$ **d.** $7x$ **e.** $2a + 3$ **f.** $5y + 8$ **g.** $\frac{3x + 2}{x + 2}$ **h.** $\frac{y + 2}{y - 1}$ **i.** $\frac{5(2x - 3y)}{7(x + 2y)}$ **j.** $\frac{3(x - y)}{x + y}$ **k.** $a - b$ **l.** $\frac{x - 5}{x + 3}$ **m.** $\frac{1}{x + 7}$ **n.** $y^3 - 9$ **o.** $\frac{(x + 5)}{2(x - 5)}$ **p.** $\frac{2ab(a + b)}{(a - b)}$

Exercise Set 6-1

1. $\frac{3x(x + 1)}{3x(x + 3)}$ **3.** $\frac{(t - 3)(t + 3)}{(t + 2)(t + 3)}$ **5.** $a - 2$ **7.** $\frac{x + 2}{x - 2}$ **9.** $\frac{p - 5}{p + 5}$ **11.** $\frac{y + 6}{3(y - 2)}$ **13.** $\frac{a^2 + ab + b^2}{a + b}$ **15.** $\frac{(x + 4)(x - 4)}{x(x + 3)}$ **17.** $\frac{y + 4}{2}$ **19.** $\frac{(x + 5)(2x + 3)}{7x}$ **21.** $\frac{1}{x + y}$ **23.** 3 **25.** $\frac{(y - 3)(y + 2)}{y}$ **27.** $\frac{2a + 1}{a + 2}$ **29.** $\frac{(x + 4)(x + 2)}{3(x - 5)}$ **31.** $\frac{x^2 + 4x + 16}{(x + 4)^2}$ **33.** $\frac{x - 3}{(x + 1)(x + 3)}$ **35.** $\frac{m - t}{m + t + 1}$ **37.** $\frac{x^2 + xy + y^2 + x + y}{x - y}$ **45.** $-x^7 + x^4 + 4x^3y^3 + 2xy^2 - \frac{1}{2}$ **47.** $(x - 2 + y)(x - 2 - y)$

Lesson 6-2 Try This

a. $\frac{12 + y}{y}$ **b.** $3x + 1$ **c.** $\frac{a - b}{b + 2}$ **d.** $\frac{y + 12}{x^2 + y^2}$ **e.** $\frac{2x^2 + 11}{x - 5}$ **f.** $\frac{11x^2}{2x - y}$ **g.** $\frac{9x^2 + 28y}{21x}$ **h.** $\frac{3y^2 + 12y + 3}{(y - 4)(y - 3)(y + 5)}$ **i.** $\frac{a + 12}{a(a + 3)}$ **j.** $\frac{2}{x - 1}$ **k.** $\frac{4y^2 - y + 18}{(y - 1)(2 - y)(y + 2)}$

Exercise Set 6-2

1. $\frac{8y}{x}$ **3.** $\frac{7y}{x + y}$ **5.** $\frac{9xy}{x^2 + y^2}$ **7.** 2 **9.** $\frac{3y + 5}{y - 2}$ **11.** $a + b$ **13.** $\frac{11}{x}$ **15.** $\frac{1}{x + 5}$ **17.** $\frac{x + y}{x - y}$ **19.** $\frac{3x - 4}{(x - 2)(x - 1)}$ **21.** $\frac{8x + 1}{x^2 - 1}$ **23.** $\frac{2x - 14}{15x + 75}$ **25.** $\frac{-a^2 + 7ab - b^2}{a^2 - b^2}$ **27.** $\frac{y}{(y - 2)(y - 3)}$ **29.** $\frac{3y - 10}{y^2 - y - 20}$ **31.** $\frac{3y^2 - 3y - 29}{(y - 3)(y + 8)(y - 4)}$ **33.** $\frac{2x^2 - 13x + 7}{(x + 3)(x - 1)(x - 3)}$ **35.** 0 **37.** $\frac{-3x^2 - 3x - 4}{x^2 - 1}$ **39.** $\frac{2y^2 + 3 - 7x^3y}{x^2y^2}$ **41.** $\frac{5y + 23}{5 - 2y}$ **43.** $\frac{x - y + x^2 + xy}{x + y - x^2 + xy}$ **45.** $\frac{x - 4}{x - 5}$ **47.** $\frac{x^2 - 30}{x^2 - 11}$ **53.** Dependent; $25x + 125y = 84$ **55.** 1, 11 **57.** 0, −1, 4

Lesson 6-3 Try This

a. $\frac{14y + 7}{14y - 2}$ **b.** $\frac{x}{x + 1}$ **c.** $\frac{c + 1}{4}$ **d.** $a - b$ **e.** $\frac{y + x}{y + 3x}$ **f.** $\frac{x + 2}{(x - 2)(x - 1)}$

Exercise Set 6-3

1. $\frac{1 + 4x}{1 - 3x}$ **3.** $\frac{(x + 1)(x - 1)}{x^2 + 1}$ **5.** $\frac{3y + 4x}{4y - 3x}$ **7.** $\frac{x + y}{x}$ **9.** $\frac{a^2(b - 3)}{b^2(a - 1)}$ **11.** $\frac{1}{a - b}$ **13.** $\frac{1 + x^2}{x}$ **15.** $\frac{y - 3}{y + 5}$ **17.** $\frac{1 + x}{1 - x}$ **19.** $\frac{5(y - x + 2)}{6(x + 2)}$ **21.** $\frac{x}{x + 1}$ **23.** a **27.** $\frac{x - 1}{x}$, x **29.** −6 or 7

Lesson 6-4 Try This

a. $\frac{x^2}{2} + 8x + 3$ **b.** $4x^2 + x + 2$ **c.** $2x^6 + \frac{3}{2}x^5 + 3x^4 + 6x^3 + x^2 + \frac{1}{2}x + 1$ **d.** $5y^3 - 2y^2 + 6y$ **e.** $\frac{x^2}{2} + 5x + 8$

f. $4y^3 + y^2 + \frac{1}{2}y$ g. $x + 5$ h. $3y^3 - 2y^2 + 6y - 4$

i. $y^2 - 8y - 24$, R: -66 j. $y - 11 + \frac{3y - 27}{y^2 - 3}$

Exercise Set 6-4

1. $6x^4 - 3x^2 + 8$ 3. $-2a^2 + 4a - 3$ 5. $y^3 - 2y^2 + 3y$ 7. $-6x^5 + 3x^3 + 2x$ 9. $1 - ab^2 - a^3b$ 11. $-2pq + 3p - 4q$ 13. $x + 7$ 15. $a - 12$, R: 32 17. $y - 5$ 19. $y^2 - 2y - 1$, R: -8 21. $a^2 + 4a + 15$, R: 72 23. $4x^2 - 6x + 9$ 25. $x^2 + 6$ 27. $4x^2 - 1$, R: $-2x + 1$ 29. $2y^2 + 2y - 1 + \frac{8}{5y - 2}$ 31. $x^2 + 2y$ 33. $x^3 + x^2y + xy^2 + y^3$ 37. $-\frac{3}{2}$ 39. 1 41. $\frac{n^9}{8m^6}$ 43. 0.000634 45. $4(2x + y)^2$

Lesson 6-5 Try This

a. Q: $x^2 + 8x + 15$, R: 0 b. Q: $8x + 12$, R:40 c. Q: $x^2 - 4x + 13$, R: -30 d. Q: $y^2 - y + 1$, R: 0

Exercise Set 6-5

1. Q: $x^2 - x + 1$, R: 6 3. Q: $a + 7$, R: -47 5. Q: $x^2 - 5x - 23$, R: -43 7. Q: $3x^2 - 2x + 2$, R: -3 9. Q: $y^2 + 2y + 1$, R: 12 11. Q: $3x^3 + 9x^2 + 2x + 6$, R: 0 13. Q: $x^2 + 3x + 9$, R: 0 15. Q: $y^3 + y^2 + y + 1$, R: 2 17. Q: $5x + 8$, R: 24 19. Q: $3x^3 + 21x^2 + 142x + 994$, R: 6968 21. Q: $4x^2 + 12x + 52$, R: 199 23. Q: $3x^3 + 7.23x^2 - 6.58x - 15.85$, R: -51.19 27. Q: $7x^6 + 6x^3 + 15$, R: 55 29. $\{x | x \neq -3\}$ 31. $\{x | x \neq 0, x \neq -3\}$ 33. $2(2x - y)^2$ 35. $(3x - 1)(9x^2 + 3x + 1)$

Lesson 6-6 Try This

a. $\frac{2}{3}$ b. $-\frac{120}{11}$ c. $y = 57$ d. No solution e. 3 f. $-3, 4$ g. $1, -\frac{1}{2}$ h. $1, -\frac{1}{2}$ i. $x = 7$ j. $x = -13$

Exercise Set 6-6

1. $\frac{51}{2}$ 3. $\frac{40}{9}$ 5. $-5, -1$ 7. -1 9. $\frac{17}{4}$ 11. No solution 13. 2 15. $\frac{3}{5}$ 17. 6 19. -145 21. $-\frac{10}{3}$ 23. -3 25. $-6, 5$ 27. No solution 29. Yes 35. $2.5y$ 37. $\frac{x + 3}{x - 3}$ 39. -1 41. -2.75

Lesson 6-7 Try This

a. $2\frac{2}{5}h$ b. A, 32 h; B, 96 h c. 35.5 mi/h

Exercise Set 6-7

1. $3\frac{3}{14}$h 3. $2\frac{2}{9}$h 5. 30 h 7. 3.173 h 9. 7 km/h 11. A, 46 km/h; B, 58 km/h 13. 9 km/h 15. 2 km 17. 50 km/h and 75 km/h 19. $\frac{35}{12}$ 21. $-3, -2$ 23. $\frac{7}{4}$ 25. 53.26 mi/h 27. $51\frac{3}{7}$ mi/h 29. $4{:}21\frac{9}{11}$ 31. a. 12 mi 33. $\frac{1 + 2x}{1 - 5x}$ 35. $\frac{3y + 2x}{2y - 3x}$ 37. $(2x + 3)(x - 1)$ 39. $-1, -2$ 41. 7.5

Lesson 6-8 Try This

a. $T = \frac{PV}{k}$ b. 6 cm

Exercise Set 6-8

1. $d_1 = \frac{d_2W_1}{W_2}$ 3. $t = \frac{2S}{v_1 + v_2}$ 5. $r_2 = \frac{Rr_1}{r_1 - R}$ 7. $s = \frac{Rg}{g - R}$ 9. $r = \frac{2V - IR}{2I}$ 11. $r = \frac{nE - IR}{In}$ 13. $H = m(t_1 - t_2)S$ 15. $e = \frac{Er}{R + r}$ 17. $a = \frac{S - Sr}{1 - r^n}$ 19. $\frac{120}{23}$ ohms 21. 12 cm 23. a. $t = \frac{ab}{b + a}$ c. $b = \frac{ta}{a - t}$ 25. 2 m 27. $42ab$ 29. $-7, -3$

Lesson 6-9 Try This

a. $k = 0.4, y = 0.4x$ b. $k = 0.6, y = \frac{0.6}{x}$ c. 50 volts d. $7\frac{1}{2}$ h

Exercise Set 6-9

1. $k = 8, y = 8x$ 3. $k = 16, y = 16x$ 5. $k = 5$, $y = 5x$ 7. $k = 1, y = x$ 9. $k = 60, y = \frac{60}{x}$ 11. $k = 36, y = \frac{36}{x}$ 13. $k = 9, y = \frac{9}{x}$ 15. 6 amperes 17. $\frac{2}{9}$ ampere 19. 125,000 21. 160 cm^3 23. 532,500 tons 25. 40 kg 27. 450 m 29. 2074 33. $A = \frac{k}{B}$, so $B = \frac{k}{A}$, and $\frac{1}{A} = \frac{B}{k} = \frac{1}{k} \cdot B$ 35. $40x^{2+a}y^2$ 37. $7a^3b$ 39. 2×10^{-2} 41. $4(2x - 3)(2x + 3)$

Problem Set 6-10

1. There are $10(10 + 1) = 10 \cdot 11 = 110$ dots. 3. One can buy one 3 lb and nine 5 lb bags, or six of each, or eleven 3 lb bags and three 5 lb bags, or sixteen 3 lb bags. 5. One worked 10 days and the other worked 15 days. 7. They could have scored 34 points 7 different ways.

Chapter 6 Summary and Review

1. $\frac{4y^2 - 3y}{2y^2 + 5y}$ 3. $\frac{3(a - b)}{4(a + b)}$ 5. $\frac{(x - 4)(2x - 1)}{4x^2 - 2x + 1}$ 7. $\frac{-4a + 21}{a + 3}$ 9. $\frac{-x^2 + 16x + 50}{(x + 9)(x - 9)(3x + 2)}$ 11. $\frac{b + a}{b - a}$ 13. $\frac{ab}{b + a}$ 15. $2x^3 + 3x^2 + 2x + 4 + \frac{2}{2x - 3}$ 17. Q: $3x^2 + 2x - 2$, R: -1 19. $5, -3$ 21. 30 km/h and 20 km/h 23. 84 mi/h 25. $q = \frac{fp}{p - f}$ 27. 168.75 kg 29. 40 days

Chapter 7

Lesson 7-1 Try This

a. $3, -3$ b. $6, -6$ c. $11, -11$ d. 1 e. -6

f. $\frac{9}{10}$ **g.** -0.08 **h.** 24 **i.** $5|y|$ **j.** $4|y|$ **k.** $|x+7|$
l. -4 **m.** $3y$ **n.** $-\frac{7}{4}$ **o.** $b^5 = a$ **p.** $c^{12} = 63$
q. $n^9 = 16a$ **r.** -3 **s.** -3 **t.** $-2x$ **u.** $3x + 2$
v. 3 **w.** -3 **x.** No real root **y.** $2|x-2|$ **z.** $|x+3|$

Exercise Set 7-1

1. 4, -4 **3.** 12, -12 **5.** 20, -20 **7.** $-\frac{7}{6}$ **9.** 14
11. $\frac{3}{4}$ **13.** -0.07 **15.** $4|x|$ **17.** $5|t|$ **19.** $|a+1|$
21. $|x-2|$ **23.** 3 **25.** $-4x$ **27.** 10 **29.** $0.7(x+1)$
31. $p^4 = 10$ **33.** $r^{28} = 500h$ **35.** 5 **37.** -1
39. $-\frac{2}{3}$ **41.** $|x|$ **43.** $5|a|$ **45.** 6 **47.** y **49.** $x-2$
51. **a.** 13 **c.** 18 **53.** All real numbers **55.** $\left\{x \mid x \le \frac{4}{3}\right\}$
57. All real numbers **63.** 4, -1 **65.** 3 or -2

Lesson 7-2 Try This

a. $\sqrt{133}$ **b.** $\sqrt{x^2 - 4y^2}$ **c.** $\sqrt[4]{2821}$ **d.** $\sqrt[3]{8x^5 + 40x}$
e. $4\sqrt{2}$ **f.** $2\sqrt[3]{10}$ **g.** $10\sqrt{3}$ **h.** $|x+2|\sqrt{3}$
i. $2|bc|\sqrt{3ab}$ **j.** $2\sqrt[3]{2}$ **k.** $3|x|y^2$ **l.** $(a+b)\sqrt[3]{a+b}$
m. $3\sqrt{2}$ **n.** $6|y|\sqrt{7}$ **o.** $3x\sqrt[3]{4y}$ **p.** $7\sqrt{3ab}$

Exercise Set 7-2

1. $\sqrt{6}$ **3.** $\sqrt[3]{10}$ **5.** $\sqrt[4]{72}$ **7.** $\sqrt{30ab}$ **9.** $\sqrt[5]{18t^3}$
11. $\sqrt{x^2 - a^2}$ **13.** $\sqrt[3]{0.06x^2}$ **15.** $\sqrt[4]{x^3 - 1}$ **17.** $\sqrt{\frac{6y}{5x}}$
19. $2\sqrt{5}$ **21.** $5|y^3|\sqrt{7}$ **23.** $2y\sqrt[3]{5}$ **25.** $3m\sqrt[3]{4m^2}$
27. $2\sqrt[4]{5}$ **29.** $3x^2y^2\sqrt[4]{3y^2}$ **31.** $2xy\sqrt[5]{2xy^4}$
33. $2y\sqrt[9]{x^3y^3}$ **35.** $5\sqrt{2}$ **37.** $4\sqrt{3}$ **39.** $30\sqrt{3}$
41. $5|b|c^2\sqrt{2b}$ **43.** $2y^3\sqrt[3]{2}$ **45.** $(b+3)^2$
47. 20 mi/h **49.** 56 mi/h **51.** $-3.3°$ C
53. $-54.0°$ C **55.** $(3y+1)(y-5)$ **57.** $x + 7$

Lesson 7-3 Try This

a. $\frac{5}{6}$ **b.** $\frac{10}{3}$ **c.** $\frac{|x|}{10}$ **d.** $\frac{2|a|\sqrt{a}}{b^2}$ **e.** 5 **f.** $56\sqrt{xy}$
g. $\frac{20}{7}$ **h.** $\frac{2ab}{3}$ **i.** $13\sqrt{2}$ **j.** $10\sqrt[4]{5x} - \sqrt{7}$ **k.** $19\sqrt{5}$
l. $(3y+4)\sqrt[3]{y^2} + 2y^2$ **m.** $2\sqrt{x-1}$ **n.** $3(\sqrt[3]{2} - \sqrt{6})$

Exercise Set 7-3

1. $\frac{4}{5}$ **3.** $\frac{4}{3}$ **5.** $\frac{7}{|y|}$ **7.** $\frac{5|y|\sqrt{y}}{x^2}$ **9.** $\frac{2x\sqrt[3]{x^2}}{3y}$ **11.** $\sqrt{7}$
13. 3 **15.** $|y|\sqrt{5y}$ **17.** $2\sqrt[3]{a^2b}$ **19.** $3\sqrt{xy}$
21. $\sqrt{x^2 + xy + y^2}$ **23.** $8\sqrt{3}$ **25.** $3\sqrt[3]{5}$ **27.** $13\sqrt[3]{y}$
29. $7\sqrt{2}$ **31.** $6\sqrt[3]{5}$ **33.** $23\sqrt{2}$ **35.** $21\sqrt{3}$
37. $38\sqrt{5}$ **39.** $122\sqrt{2}$ **41.** $9\sqrt[3]{2}$ **43.** $4\sqrt[3]{4}$
45. $29\sqrt{2}$ **47.** $(1 + 6|a|)\sqrt{5a}$ **49.** $(2-x)\sqrt[3]{3x}$
51. $10(a-1)\sqrt[3]{a}$ **53.** $3\sqrt{2y-2}$
55. $(|x| + 3)\sqrt{x-1}$ **57.** 1.62 sec **59.** 2.20 sec
61. $a = -b$ or $a = 0$ or $b = 0$ **63.** $\frac{5}{2}\sqrt{2} + 3\sqrt[3]{2}$
65. $5\sqrt[3]{2}$ **67.** $y = -2x$ **69.** 2×10^{-7} **71.** 3.5×10^3
73. 7, -3 **75.** **a.** $f(x) = 2 + 1.5x$ **b.** \$18.50

Lesson 7-4 Try This

a. $5\sqrt{6} + 3\sqrt{14}$ **b.** $3\sqrt{ab} - 4\sqrt{3a} + 6\sqrt{3b} - 24$
c. $20 - 4y\sqrt{5} + y^2$ **d.** $64 - 25|x|$ **e.** $\frac{\sqrt{6}}{3}$ **f.** $\frac{\sqrt{70}}{7}$
g. $\frac{\sqrt[3]{4}}{2}$ **h.** $\frac{2\sqrt{3ab}}{3|b|}$ **i.** $\frac{2x^2\sqrt{3xy}}{3y^2}$ **j.** $\frac{\sqrt[3]{28}}{2}$ **k.** $\frac{\sqrt[7]{192y^6x^5}}{2|y|}$
l. $-5(1+\sqrt{2})$ **m.** $-\sqrt{2} + \sqrt{3}$
n. $\frac{\sqrt{15} + \sqrt{3} + \sqrt{5} + 1}{2}$ **o.** $\frac{3 - \sqrt{3}}{6}$

Exercise Set 7-4

1. $2\sqrt{6} - 18$ **3.** $\sqrt{6} - \sqrt{10}$ **5.** $2\sqrt{15} - 6\sqrt{3}$
7. -6 **9.** $3a\sqrt[3]{2}$ **11.** 1 **13.** -12 **15.** $|a| - |b|$
17. $1 + \sqrt{5}$ **19.** $7 + 3\sqrt{3}$ **21.** -6
23. $|a| + \sqrt{3a} + \sqrt{2a} + \sqrt{6}$
25. $2\sqrt[3]{9} - 3\sqrt[3]{6} - 2\sqrt[3]{4}$ **27.** $7 + 4\sqrt{3}$
29. $21 - 6\sqrt{6}$ **31.** $\frac{\sqrt{30}}{5}$ **33.** $\frac{\sqrt{70}}{7}$ **35.** $\frac{2\sqrt{15}}{5}$
37. $\frac{2\sqrt[3]{6}}{3}$ **39.** $\frac{\sqrt[3]{75ac^2}}{5c}$ **41.** $\frac{y\sqrt[3]{9yx^2}}{3x^2}$ **43.** $\frac{\sqrt[3]{x^2y^2}}{xy}$
45. $\frac{5(8 + \sqrt{6})}{58}$ **47.** $-2\sqrt{7}(\sqrt{5} + \sqrt{3})$
49. $-\frac{\sqrt{15} + 20 - 6\sqrt{3} - 8\sqrt{30}}{77}$
51. $\frac{x - 2\sqrt{xy} + y}{x - y}$ **53.** $\frac{3\sqrt{6} + 4}{2}$ **55.** $\frac{4\sqrt{ab} - 12b}{a - 9b}$
57. $\frac{x + 8\sqrt{xy} + 15y}{x - 25y}$ **59.** $\frac{2}{\sqrt{6}}$ **61.** $\frac{7}{\sqrt[3]{98}}$
63. $\frac{5y^2}{x\sqrt[3]{150x^2y^2}}$ **65.** $\frac{-22}{\sqrt{6} + 5\sqrt{2} + 5\sqrt{3} + 25}$
67. $x - 6$ **71.** 1 **73.** $\frac{\sqrt{p^2 - 16q^2}}{p + 4q}$ **75.** $y = \frac{28}{x}$
77. $(3y - x - 1)(3y + x + 1)$ **79.** 5
81. $\frac{1}{4}x^2 - 3x + 10$ **83.** 4, 6, and -6, -4
85. \$50,000

Lesson 7-5 Try This

a. $\sqrt[3]{8^2} = 4$; $(\sqrt[3]{8})^2 = 4$ **b.** $(\sqrt{6y})^3 = 6|y|\sqrt{6y}$;
$\sqrt{(6y)^3} = 6|y|\sqrt{6y}$ **c.** $\sqrt[4]{y}$ **d.** $\sqrt{3a}$ **e.** $\sqrt[4]{16}$ or 2
f. $(a^3b^2c)^{\frac{1}{4}}$ **g.** $\left(\frac{x^2y}{16}\right)^{\frac{1}{5}}$ **h.** $x\sqrt{x}$ **i.** 4 **j.** $(7abc)^{\frac{4}{3}}$
k. $6^{\frac{7}{5}}$ **l.** $(x^2y^3)^{\frac{1}{4}}$ or $x^{\frac{1}{2}}y^{\frac{3}{4}}$ **m.** $\frac{1}{5^{\frac{1}{4}}}$ **n.** $\frac{1}{(3xy)^{\frac{7}{8}}}$ **o.** $7^{\frac{14}{15}}$
p. $5^{\frac{1}{3}}$ **q.** $9^{\frac{2}{5}}$ **r.** $\sqrt{a}$ **s.** x **t.** $\sqrt{2}$ **u.** xy^3
v. $\sqrt[4]{xy^2}$ **w.** $\sqrt[4]{63}$ **x.** $\sqrt[4]{a-b}$ **y.** $\sqrt[6]{x^{-4}y^3z^5}$
z. $\sqrt[4]{ab}$

Exercise Set 7-5

1. $6a\sqrt{6a}$ **3.** $4b\sqrt[3]{4b}$ **5.** $54a^3b\sqrt{2b}$ **7.** $2c\sqrt[3]{18cd^2}$
9. $\sqrt[4]{x}$ **11.** 2 **13.** $\sqrt[5]{a^2b^2}$ **15.** $\sqrt[3]{a^2}$ **17.** 8
19. $\sqrt{a^5t^3}$ **21.** $\sqrt[2]{y^7}$ **23.** $\sqrt[4]{m^3n^5}$ **25.** $19^{\frac{1}{3}}$ **27.** $6^{\frac{1}{2}}$
29. $(xy)^{\frac{1}{5}}$ **31.** $(x^3y^2z^2)^{\frac{1}{7}}$ **33.** $(7xy)^{\frac{4}{3}}$ **35.** $(2a^5b)^{\frac{7}{6}}$
37. $(12ab)^{\frac{1}{2}}$ or $2(3ab)^{\frac{1}{2}}$ **39.** $(3a^4b^3)^{\frac{4}{7}}$ **41.** $\frac{1}{y^{\frac{1}{4}}}$
43. $\frac{1}{(5xy)^{\frac{5}{6}}}$ **45.** $8^{\frac{3}{4}}$ **47.** $x^{\frac{5}{6}}$ **49.** $11^{\frac{7}{6}}$ **51.** $9^{\frac{2}{11}}$
53. $3.9^{\frac{7}{20}}$ **55.** $5^{\frac{15}{28}}$ **57.** $\sqrt[3]{y}$ **59.** x^2y^3 **61.** $2x^3y^4$
63. $\frac{x^3y^4}{2}$ **65.** $3ab^3$ **67.** $3x^2y^2$
69. $\sqrt[4]{3xy^2 + 24xy + 48x}$ **71.** $\sqrt[12]{(x+y)^{-1}}$

73. $\sqrt[12]{x^4y^3z^2}$ **75.** $\sqrt[5]{xy^5}$ **77.** $\sqrt{(a^2 - b^2)}$
79. $\frac{\sqrt{a-b}}{(a-b)^2}$ **81.** $\frac{1}{a+2b}$ **83.** $a^{\frac{2}{15}}$ **85.** $(x+6)^{\frac{1}{2}}$
89. 45.9 m **91.** 79.4 m **93.** No **95.** $4x^3 + 3x^2$

Lesson 7-6 Try This

a. 100 **b.** No solution **c.** 9 **d.** 5
e. $h = \frac{1}{\pi r}\sqrt{s^2 - \pi^2 r^4}$; $h = 4$

Exercise Set 7-6

1. 2 **3.** 168 **5.** 3 **7.** 19 **9.** $\frac{80}{3}$ **11.** 4 **13.** -27
15. 397 **17.** No solution **19.** $\frac{1}{64}$ **21.** -6 **23.** 5
25. $-\frac{1}{4}$ **27.** 3 **29.** 9 **31.** 7 **33.** $\frac{80}{9}$ **35.** -1
37. 6, 2 **39.** No solution **41.** $s = \frac{v^2}{2g}$; $512g$ **43.** 8
45. $5 \pm 2\sqrt{2}$ **47.** 2 **49.** $\frac{5}{4}$ **55.** $2|y|\sqrt{3}$ **57.** 4

Lesson 7-7 Try This

a. $i\sqrt{7}$ **b.** $-6i$ **c.** $4i\sqrt{10}$ **d.** -18 **e.** $-3\sqrt{3}$
f. $-3\sqrt{2}$ **g.** 0 **h.** $-i$ **i.** $-2 + 7i$

Exercise Set 7-7

1. $i\sqrt{2}$ **3.** $6i$ **5.** $-3i$ **7.** $8i\sqrt{2}$ **9.** $\frac{3}{4}i$ **11.** $-4i\sqrt{5}$
13. $92i$ **15.** $-4\sqrt{3}$ **17.** $-\sqrt{6}$ **19.** 6 **21.** $-3\sqrt{5}$
23. -10 **25.** $3i$ **27.** $8 + i$ **29.** $9 - 5i$ **31.** $-5 + 5i$
33. $-9 + 5i$ **35.** i **37.** -1 **39.** $-i$ **41.** 0 **43.** $-i$
45. i **47.** i **49.** $-i$ **51.** i **53.** $-i$ **55.** i
57. $\sqrt{m^2 - n^2}$ **59.** $\frac{(x+3)}{(x+5)}$ **61.** $\frac{x-2}{4x+1}$ **63.** 3, $-\frac{1}{4}$

Lesson 7-8 Try This

a. – e.

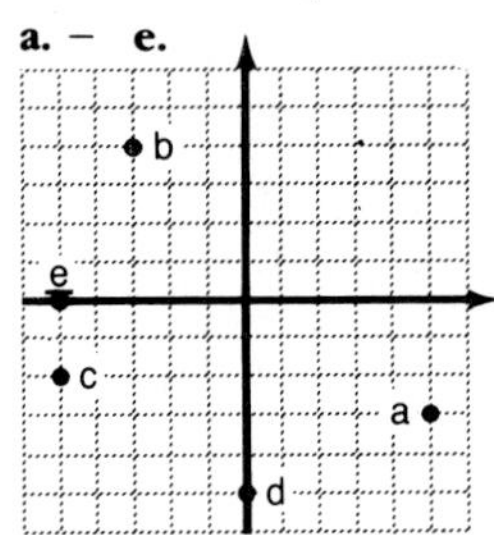

f. 5 **g.** 13 **h.** $\sqrt{2}$

Exercise Set 7-8

1. **3.**

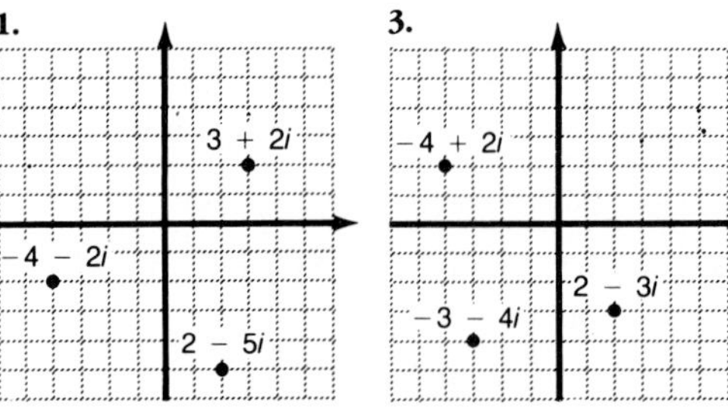

5.

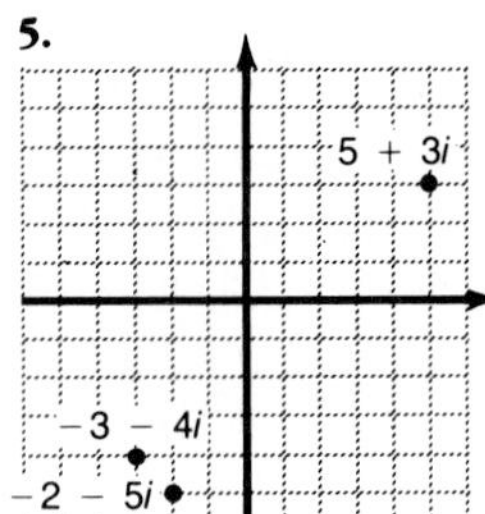

7. 5 **9.** 17 **11.** $\sqrt{10}$
13. 3 **15.** $\sqrt{c^2 + d^2}$
17. $2\sqrt{4c^2 + 1}$

19. a.

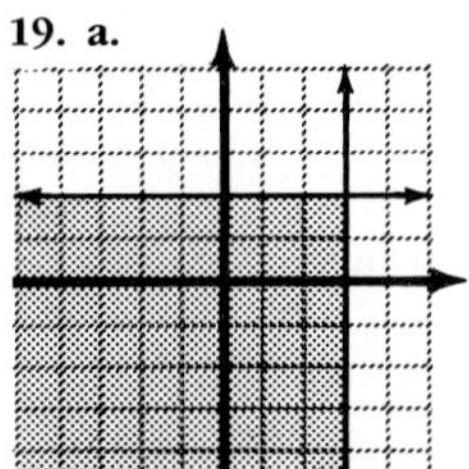

19. b.

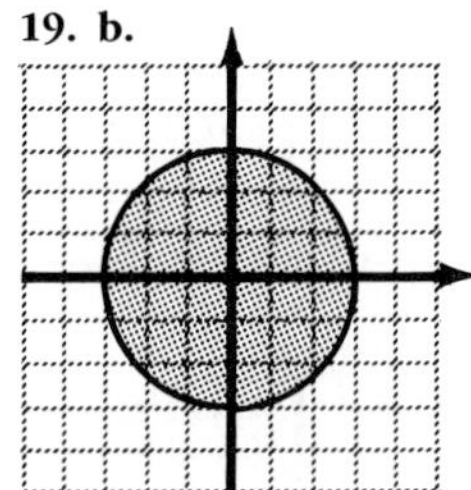

23. $3\sqrt{3}$ **25.** $2a\sqrt[3]{2}$ **27.** $(a+3)(a^2 - 3a + 9)$
29. $(x-4)^3$

Lesson 7-9 Try This

a. $x = -1, y = 2$ **b.** -30 **c.** -100 **d.** $3 - 28i$
e. $6 - 3i$ **f.** $-9 + 5i$ **g.** $7i$ **h.** -8 **i.** 53 **j.** 10
k. $9p^2 + 4q^2$ **l.** $2i$ **m.** $\frac{10}{17} - \frac{11}{17}i$ **n.** $\frac{3}{25} - \frac{4}{25}i$

Exercise Set 7-9

1. $x = -\frac{3}{2}, y = 7$ **3.** $x = -2, y = -8$ **5.** -3
7. -25 **9.** $5 + 10i$ **11.** $-8i$ **13.** $7 + i$
15. $-m - ni$ **17.** 45 **19.** $\frac{8}{5} + \frac{1}{5}i$ **21.** $-\frac{11}{5} + \frac{2}{5}i$
23. $-i$ **25.** $\frac{1}{10} + \frac{1}{5}i$ **27.** $-\frac{4}{65} - \frac{7}{65}i$ **29.** -1
31. $-\frac{1}{2} + \frac{1}{2}i$ **33.** For example, $\sqrt{-1}\sqrt{-1} = i^2 = -1$, but $\sqrt{(-1)(-1)} = \sqrt{1} = 1$ **35.** $-\frac{1}{8} - \frac{\sqrt{3}}{8}i$
37. $\frac{1}{100} - \frac{7i}{100}$ **39.** $\frac{3\sqrt{15}}{10}$ **41.** $y = 3x - 3$

Lesson 7-10 Try This

a. $(1-i)^2 + 2(1-i) + 1 = 1 - 2i + i^2 + 2 - 2i + 1 = 3 - 4i$; therefore $(1-i)$ is not a solution of $x^2 + 2x + 1 = 0$. **b.** $x^2 - 2x + 2 = 0$
c. $x^2 - 4x + 13 = 0$ **d.** $2 + 5i$
e. $(x + 2i)(x - 2i) = x^2 + 2ix - 2ix - 4i^2 = x^2 + 4$
f. $(-1 + i)^2 = 1 - 2i + i^2 = 1 - 2i - 1 = -2i$; $1 - i$

Exercise Set 7-10

1. Yes, yes **3.** No, yes **5.** Yes, yes **7.** $x^2 + 25 = 0$
9. $x^2 - 4x + 13 = 0$ **11.** $x^2 + 3 = 0$
13. $x^2 - 12x + 42 = 0$ **15.** $x^2 - 6x + 26 = 0$
17. $\frac{12}{5} - \frac{1}{5}i$ **19.** $\frac{8}{29} + \frac{9}{29}i$ **21.** $\frac{11}{25} + \frac{2}{25}i$
23. $(2x + i)(2x - i) = 4x^2 - 2ix + 2ix - i^2 = 4x^2 + 1$ **25.** $(2 + i)^2 = 4 + 4i + i^2 = 3 + 4i$; $-2 - i$
29. $x^3 - 2ix^2 - 3x^2 + 5ix + x - 2i + 2 = 0$

33. $2 - i, -2 + i$ **35.** 4,441,000 **37.** $\frac{m^2 - 3}{m^2 + 3}$

39. $\frac{3c^2 + 2}{3c^2 - 2}$

Chapter 7 Summary and Review

1. 36 **3.** $-\frac{2x}{3}$ **5.** $2|x|$ **7.** $a^2b^2\sqrt[3]{b}$ **9.** $2\sqrt[3]{2}$

11. $\frac{x^2\sqrt{5}}{2}$ **13.** $-\sqrt[3]{3}$ **15.** 1

17. $2\sqrt[3]{4} + 7\sqrt[3]{6} + 3\sqrt[3]{9}$ **19.** $\frac{9 + 3\sqrt{17}}{-4}$ **21.** $4\sqrt[3]{4}$

23. $|a^3|b^2$ **25.** $\sqrt[3]{x^2}$ **27.** 4 **29.** $15^{\frac{1}{3}}$ **31.** $x^1y^{\frac{4}{3}}z^{\frac{5}{3}}$

33. $\frac{1}{x^{\frac{1}{2}}}$ **35.** 4 **37.** $\sqrt{x}$ **39.** $\frac{|y^3|}{2x^2}$ **41.** $-\frac{31}{3}$

43. $L = \frac{gT^2}{16\pi^2}$ **45.** $w_2 = \frac{w_1}{A^2}$ **47.** $-5i$ **49.** $2 - i$

51.

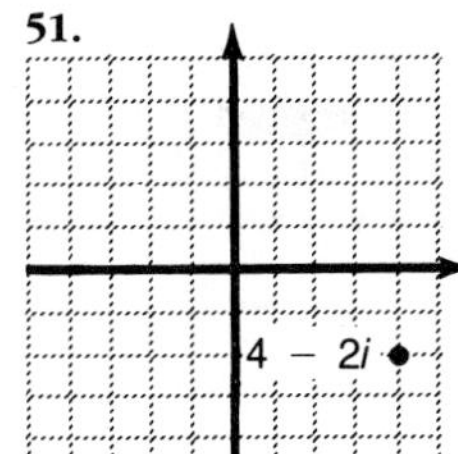

53. $\sqrt{34}$ **55.** $14 + 2i$

57. 13 **59.** $\frac{8 - i}{5}$

61. $\frac{1}{10} - \frac{1}{5}i$ **63.** $-\frac{16}{13} - \frac{11}{13}i$

Chapter 8

Lesson 8-1 Try This

a. $0, -\frac{8}{5}$ **b.** $\frac{7}{2}, \frac{1}{2}$ **c.** $-3, 2$ **d.** $\pm\frac{\sqrt{35}}{7}$ **e.** $\pm\frac{\sqrt{2}}{2}i$

f. $\pm\frac{2}{7}i$ **g.** $x^2 + 14x + 49$ **h.** $y^2 - 11y + \frac{121}{4}$

i. $x^2 - \frac{2}{5}x + \frac{1}{25}$ **j.** $x^2 + 2ax + a^2$ **k.** $\frac{-1 \pm \sqrt{5}}{2}$

l. $-\frac{1}{2}, 1$ **m.** $\frac{1 \pm \sqrt{33}}{16}$ **n.** $\frac{2}{3}, -\frac{5}{3}$

Exercise Set 8-1

1. $0, \frac{3}{7}$ **3.** $0, -\frac{8}{19}$ **5.** $-7, -2$ **7.** $-\frac{3}{2}, -5$

9. $\frac{2}{3}, -4$ **11.** $\frac{5}{3}, -4$ **13.** $-\frac{7}{2}, -1$ **15.** 4 **17.** 10, 5

19. $\pm\sqrt{7}$ **21.** 0 **23.** $\pm\frac{\sqrt{21}}{3}$ **25.** $\pm\frac{\sqrt{2}}{2}$ **27.** $\pm\frac{4}{3}i$

29. $\pm\frac{i\sqrt{5}}{5}$ **31.** $\pm i\sqrt{6}$ **33.** $\pm i\sqrt{5}$ **35.** $\pm\frac{5}{4}$

37. $y^2 - 20y + 100$ **39.** $y^2 - \frac{1}{5}y + \frac{1}{100}$

41. $x^2 - 2.6kx + 1.69k^2$ **43.** $-3, -4$ **45.** $2 \pm \sqrt{3}$

47. $\frac{-1 \pm \sqrt{69}}{2}$ **49.** $\frac{5 \pm \sqrt{145}}{6}$ **51.** $3 \pm 3i$

53. $-\frac{5}{3}, 4, \frac{5}{2}$ **55.** $\pm\sqrt{\frac{b}{a}}$ or $\frac{\sqrt{ab}}{a}$ **57.** $\frac{1}{18}, \frac{1}{3}$

59. $\sqrt{3} \pm 1$ **61.** $0, -\frac{b}{a}$ **65.** $2a^3\sqrt{15}$

67. $\sqrt{2} - 4\sqrt{10}$ **69.** $7 - \sqrt{21} + \sqrt{14} - \sqrt{6}$
71. 13 **73.** 4

Lesson 8-2 Try This

a. 2 cm **b.** A: 16 km/h; B: 12 km/h

Exercise Set 8-2

1. 2 cm **3.** Length 6 m; width 2 m **5.** Length 24 m; width 12 m **7.** 24 m and 10 m **9.** A: 15 km/h; B: 8 km/h **11.** 35 km/h **17.** 5 **19.** 100 **21.** 20

Lesson 8-3 Try This

a. $\frac{-1 \pm \sqrt{22}}{3}$ **b.** $\frac{-3 \pm 3\sqrt{21}}{10}$ **c.** $\frac{1 \pm i\sqrt{7}}{2}$

d. $\frac{-1 \pm i\sqrt{5}}{3}$ **e.** $1.21, -1.88$

Exercise Set 8-3

1. $-3 \pm \sqrt{5}$ **3.** $1, -5$ **5.** $3, -10$ **7.** $2, -\frac{1}{2}$

9. $-1, -\frac{5}{3}$ **11.** $\frac{1 \pm i\sqrt{3}}{2}$ **13.** $-1 \pm 2i$ **15.** $1 \pm 2i$

17. $2 \pm 3i$ **19.** $\pm i\sqrt{5}$ **21.** $\frac{-3 \pm \sqrt{41}}{2}$ **23.** $\pm\frac{\sqrt{10}}{2}$

25. $0, -1$ **27.** $\frac{-1 \pm 2i}{5}$ **29.** $\frac{3}{4}, -2$ **31.** $\frac{1 \pm 3i}{2}$

33. $\frac{3}{2}, \frac{2}{3}$ **35.** $1.32, -5.32$ **37.** $5.24, 0.76$

39. $2.77, -1.27$ **41.** $\frac{-1 \pm \sqrt{1 + 4\sqrt{2}}}{2}$

43. $\frac{-5\sqrt{2} \pm \sqrt{34}}{4}$ **45.** $\frac{-3 \pm \sqrt{9 - 4}}{2}$ **47.** 4.8 km/h

49. $x = \frac{-y \pm \sqrt{-47y^2 + 108}}{6}$ **53.** 3 **55.** $-i$

57. $\frac{3 - i}{10}$ **59.** $2 + 3i$ **61.** $3, -3$

Lesson 8-4 Try This

a. Two real **b.** One real **c.** Two nonreal

d. Sum = 4; product = $\frac{4}{3}$ **e.** Sum = $-\sqrt{2}$; product = -4 **f.** $4x^2 - 12x - 1 = 0$
g. $3x^2 + 7x - 20 = 0$ **h.** $x^2 - x - 56 = 0$
i. $x^2 - (m + n)x + mn = 0$ **j.** $x^2 + x - 72 = 0$
k. $x^2 - 6x + 7 = 0$ **l.** $4x^2 - 8x - 1 = 0$

Exercise Set 8-4

1. One real **3.** Two nonreal **5.** Two real
7. One real **9.** Two nonreal **11.** Two real
13. Two real **15.** One real **17.** Sum = 2; product = 10 **19.** Sum = −1; product = −1

21. Sum = $-\frac{1}{2}$; product = 2 **23.** Sum = 0; product = −49 **25.** Sum = $\frac{12}{25}$; product = $\frac{2}{25}$

27. Sum = −4; product = −2
29. $4x^2 + 4\pi x + 1 = 0$ **31.** $x^2 - 5x - \sqrt{2} = 0$
33. $x^2 - 16 = 0$ **35.** $x^2 + 10x + 25 = 0$
37. $8x^2 + 6x + 1 = 0$
39. $12x^2 - (4k + 3m)x + km = 0$
41. $x^2 - \sqrt{3}x - 6 = 0$ **43.** $x^2 - \pi x - 12\pi^2 = 0$
45. $x^2 - 11x + 30 = 0$ **47.** $4x^2 + 23x - 6 = 0$
49. $x^2 - 4x + 1 = 0$ **51.** $x^2 - x - 3 = 0$
53. $ghx^2 - (g^2 - h^2)x - gh = 0$

55. $x^2 - 8x + 25 = 0$ **57. a.** $k < \frac{1}{4}$ **b.** $k = \frac{1}{4}$

c. $k > \frac{1}{4}$ **59. a.** $k < 1$ **b.** $k = 1$ **c.** $k > 1$

61. **a.** $k > \frac{11}{3}$ **b.** $k = \frac{11}{3}$ **c.** $k < \frac{11}{3}$ **63.** $-\frac{1}{3}$, $k = -\frac{3}{5}$ **65.** -1 **71.** $h = -36$, $k = 15$
73. $(5x + 2)(3x + 1)$ **75.** $a(a + 1)(a - 1)$ **77.** 2, 0
79. 4, 6 **81.** 5, -5

Lesson 8-5 Try This

a. $\pm 3, \pm 1$ **b.** $\pm\sqrt{2}, \pm i\sqrt{2}$ **c.** 4 **d.** 4, 2, -1, -3
e. 125, -8 **f.** -128

Exercise Set 8-5

1. 81, 1 **3.** $\pm\sqrt{5}$ **5.** 7, -1, 5, 1 **7.** 4, 1, 6, -1
9. $\pm\sqrt{6}, \pm i\sqrt{2}$ **11.** $\frac{1}{3}, -\frac{1}{2}$ **13.** 2, -1 **15.** -27, 8
17. 16 **19.** $x = 16$ **21.** $1 \pm \sqrt{2}, \frac{-1 \pm \sqrt{5}}{2}$
23. $\frac{5 \pm \sqrt{21}}{2}, \frac{3 \pm \sqrt{5}}{2}$ **25.** $\frac{1}{3}$ **35.** $\frac{\sqrt{ab}}{ab}$ **37.** $x^2 = -16$
39. $x^2 - 4x + 29 = 0$ **41.** $-\frac{5}{2}$, 3 **43.** 8, -3

Lesson 8-6 Try This

a. $r = \sqrt{\frac{V}{\pi h}}$ **b.** $r = \frac{-\pi h + \sqrt{\pi^2 h^2 + 2\pi}}{2\pi}$
c. (1) 4.33 sec (2) 1.87 sec (3) 44.9 m

Exercise Set 8-6

1. $s = \frac{\sqrt{P}}{2}$ **3.** $r = \sqrt{\frac{Gm_1m_2}{F}}$ **5.** $r = \sqrt{x^2 + y^2}$
7. $z = \sqrt{d^2 - x^2 - y^2}$ **9.** $t = \frac{v_o \pm \sqrt{v_o^2 - 64h}}{32}$
11. $t = \sqrt{\frac{2S}{g}}$ **13.** $r = \frac{-\pi h \pm \sqrt{\pi^2 h^2 + 2\pi A}}{2\pi}$
15. $t = \frac{\pi \pm \sqrt{\pi^2 - 12k\sqrt{2}}}{2\sqrt{2}}$ **17.** **a.** 3.91 sec
19. **a.** 18.75% **c.** 11% **21.** 7 ft **23.** A: 24 km/h; B: 10 km/h **25.** 2.2199 cm; 8.0101 cm
27. $a = \frac{b}{\sqrt{T^2 - 1}}$ **29.** 12 **31.** 3 cm × 4 cm
33. $-i$ **35.** -36 **37.** $-2 + 2i$ **39.** 4, 15 **41.** 0, -4
43. $\frac{5\sqrt{6}}{6}, \frac{-5\sqrt{6}}{6}$ **45.** $-2 \pm 2i$
47.

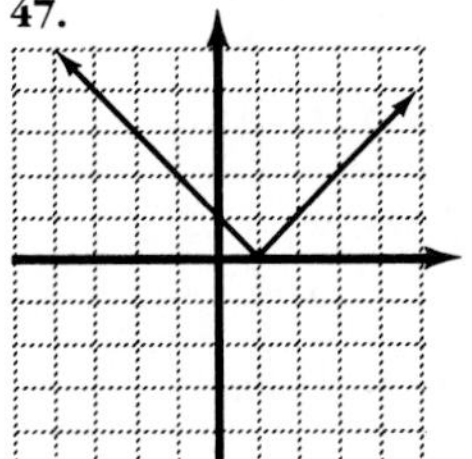

Lesson 8-7 Try This

a. $y = 7x^2$ **b.** $y = \frac{9}{x^2}$ **c.** $y = \frac{1}{2}xz$ **d.** $y = \frac{5xz^2}{w}$
e. 490 m

Exercise Set 8-7

1. $y = \frac{54}{x^2}$ **3.** $y = \frac{0.256}{x^2}$ **5.** $y = \frac{2}{3}x^2$ **7.** $y = xz$
9. $y = 187.5\frac{x}{z^2}$ **11.** $y = \frac{xz}{5wp}$ **13.** 180 m
15. 94.03 kg **17.** If p varies directly as q, then $p = kq$. Thus $q = \frac{1}{k}p$ so q varies directly as p. **19.** $\frac{\pi}{4}$
21. Division by zero is undefined. **23c.** $d = 1147$ km
25. 2 nonreal **27.** Sum $= -5$; product $= -2$
29. Sum $= -4$; product $= -\frac{3}{2}$ **31.** 3, $\frac{1}{3}$ **33.** $-x - yi$

Problem Set 8-8

1. There were 51 companies contacted. **3.** Tracy: Illinois; Sally: Hawaii; Juan: California; Herb: New York; Rick: Indiana; Terry: Florida. **5.** $10^2 = 100$

Chapter 8 Summary and Review

1. 0, $-\frac{6}{7}$ **3.** $\frac{2}{3}$, -4 **5.** $\pm\frac{i\sqrt{2}}{2}$ **7.** $x^2 + 16x + 64$
9. $-2 \pm \sqrt{10}$ **11.** 25 m, 20 m, 15 m **13.** $\frac{-3 \pm \sqrt{29}}{2}$
15. $\frac{-1 \pm i\sqrt{15}}{2}$ **17.** Discriminant = 9. There are two real roots. **19.** $10x^2 + 5x + 6 = 0$ **21.** ± 1
23. $A = \sqrt{1 - a^2}$ **25.** 4.67 sec **27.** $y = \frac{5}{2}x^2$
29. $y = \frac{-10}{x^2}$

Chapters 1–8 Cumulative Review

1. $8x - 5$ **3.** $\frac{5}{3}$ **5.** \$9.25 **7.** $-\frac{3y^3z^4}{x^2}$
9. 3.24×10^{-2} **11.** $x \leq 5$ **13.** Less than 275 mi
15. $x \geq 6$ or $x \leq -1$ **17.** 1
19.
21. $y = -\frac{5}{4}x - \frac{5}{2}$
23. $m = \frac{3}{4}$, $b = -3$
25. $y = -\frac{4}{5}x - \frac{17}{5}$
27. $y = \frac{25}{7}x + \frac{10}{7}$
29. 52
31. $\left(-\frac{1}{3}, -\frac{19}{3}\right)$ **33.** 6, -4 **35.** $(-2, 1, 4)$ **37.** $-7y$
39. $4x - 2$ **41.** $x^4 - 6x^2y + 9y^2$
43. $12x(2x - 3)(x - 2)$ **45.** $(x - y + 6)(x - y - 6)$
47. $-3y(2y^2 - 1)(2y^2 - 1)$
49. $2(x - y + 3t)(x - y - 3t)$ **51.** $-2, -\frac{3}{4}$
53. $2\frac{1}{2}$ ft by 6 ft **55.** $\frac{(4x + 1)(4x^2 + 6x + 9)}{(2x - 3)(16x^2 - 4x + 1)}$
57. $\frac{1}{x - y}$ **59.** $16x^2 + 12x + 9$ **61.** Q: $x^2 - 4$; R: -14 **63.** -1 **65.** $13\frac{5}{7}$h **67.** $y_2 = \frac{x_2y_1}{x_1}$ **69.** 1166
71. 2 **73.** $2x^2\sqrt[3]{3x}$ **75.** $\sqrt{x^2 - xy + y^2}$
77. $x\sqrt[3]{3} + \sqrt[3]{12x^2}$ **79.** $\frac{2x}{y^{\frac{3}{4}}}$ **81.** 6, 2 **83.** $9 - 8i$
85. $\sqrt{13}$ **87.** 89 **89.** $\frac{i}{-2}$ **91.** $x^2 + 4 = 0$

93. $-i + 2$ **95.** $\pm\sqrt{5}$ **97.** $y^2 - \frac{1}{3}y + \frac{1}{36}$
99. 25 m by 40 m **101.** $\frac{1 \pm i\sqrt{19}}{4}$
103. Discriminant = 116; there are two irrational roots. **105.** 16, 1 **107.** $\frac{1}{3}, -\frac{1}{2}$ **109.** $y = \frac{\sqrt{x+2}}{k}$
111. $xz^2 = 1440y$

Chapter 9

Lesson 9-1 Try This

a. Symmetric with respect to the y-axis **b.** Symmetric with respect to both axes **c.** Yes **d.** Yes **e.** No **f.** No **g.** Even **h.** Neither **i.** Odd

Exercise Set 9-1

1. y-axis **3.** Both axes **5.** Neither axis **7.** y-axis **9.** Both axes **11.** Neither axis **13.** Yes **15.** Yes **17.** Yes **19.** Yes **21.** No **23.** No **25.** Neither **27.** Even **29.** Even **31.** Odd **33.** Neither **35.** Even **37.** Even **39.** Even **41.** Odd **43.** Odd

45.

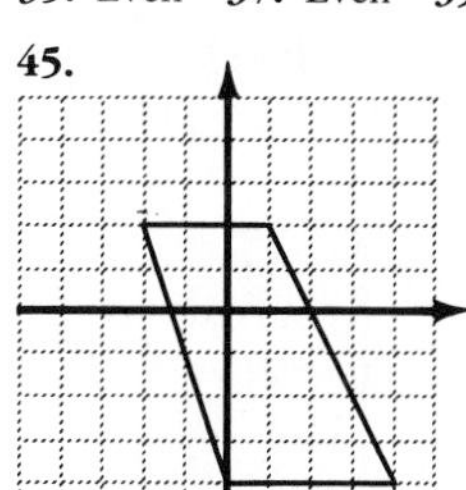

47.

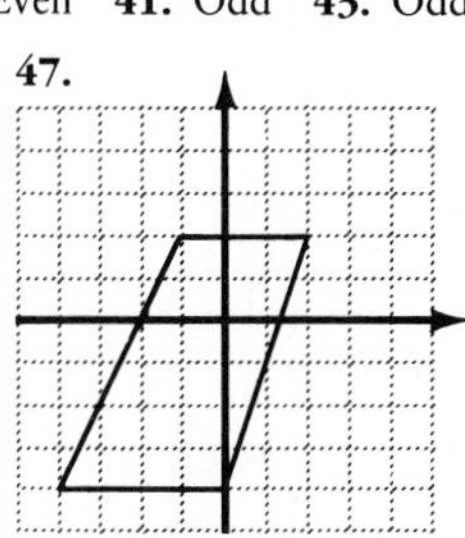

49. y-axis **51.** Both axes **53.** Both axes **55.** $4\sqrt{15}$
57. $4\sqrt{5}$ **59.** $-4, -\frac{3}{2}$ **61.** $-5, 6$ **63.** $x^2 + 4x = 0$
65. $x^2 - 6x + 13 = 0$

Lesson 9-2 Try This

a.

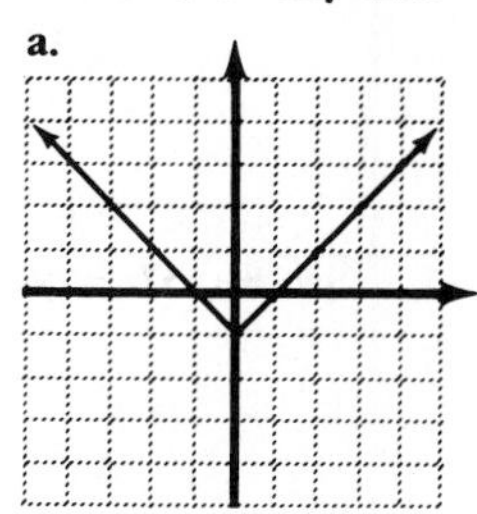

b.

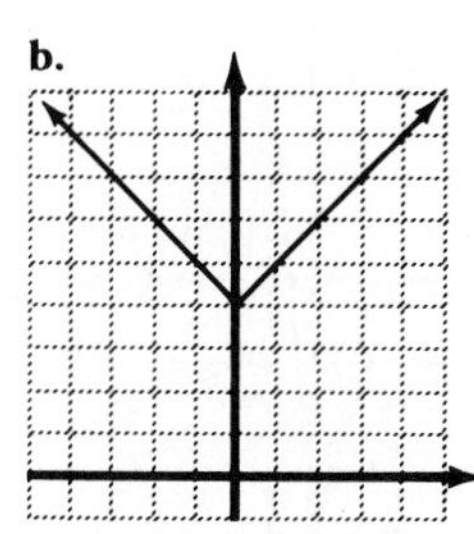

c.

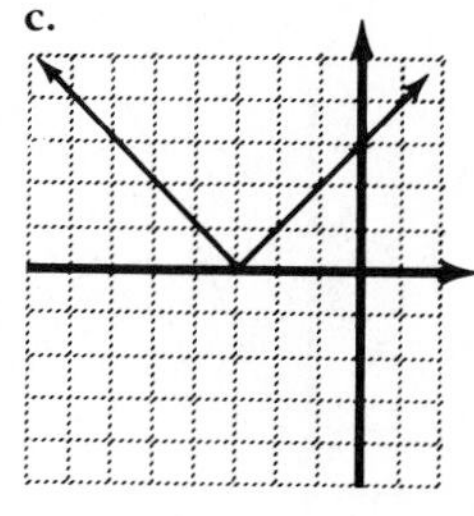

d.

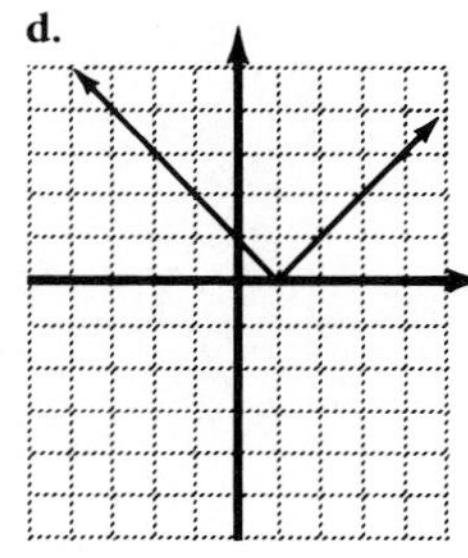

Exercise Set 9-2

1.

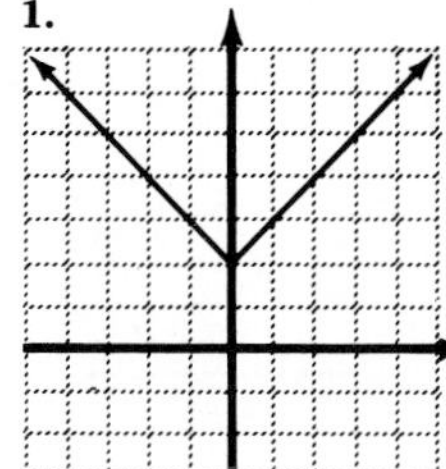

3.

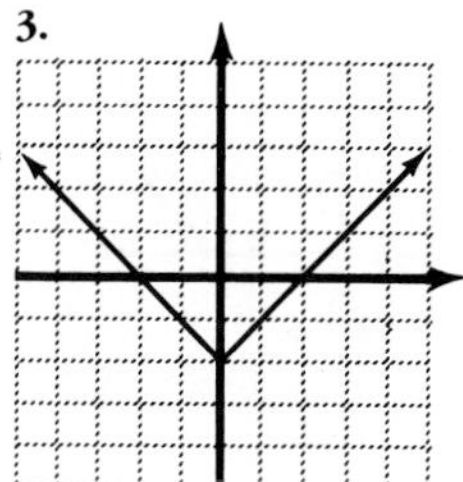

5.

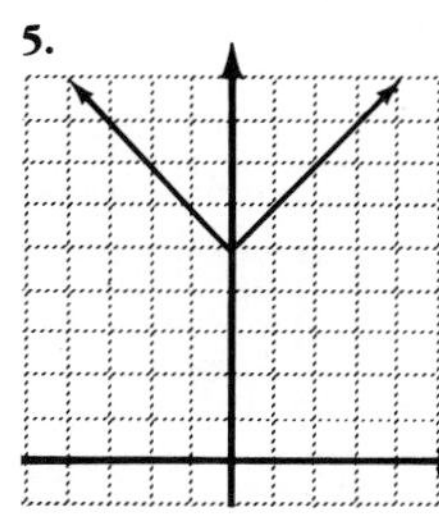

7.

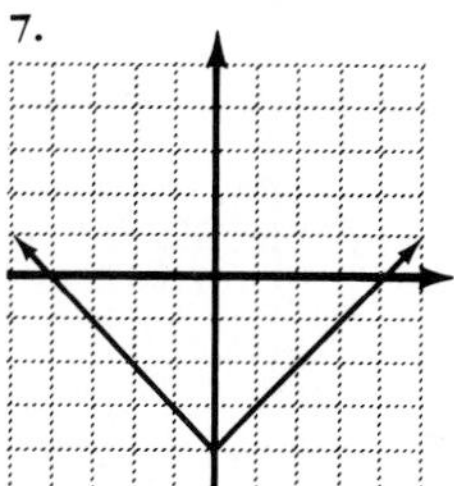

9.

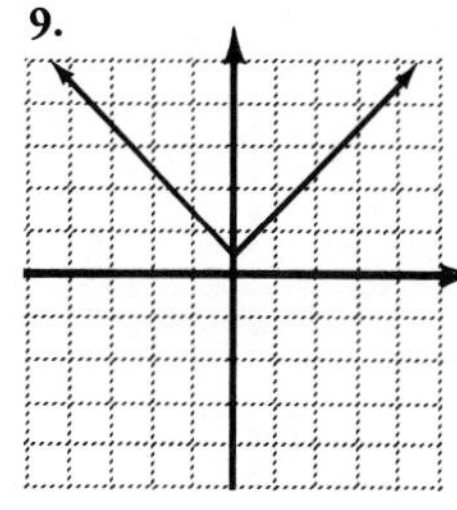

11.

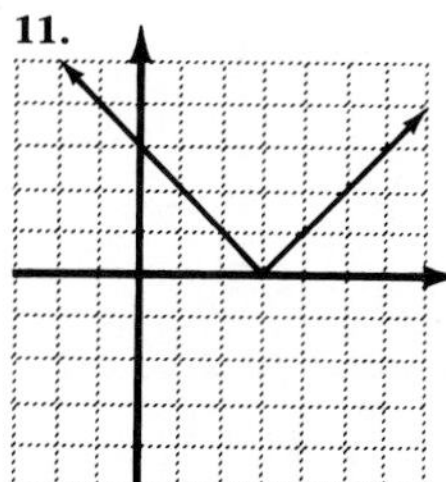

13.

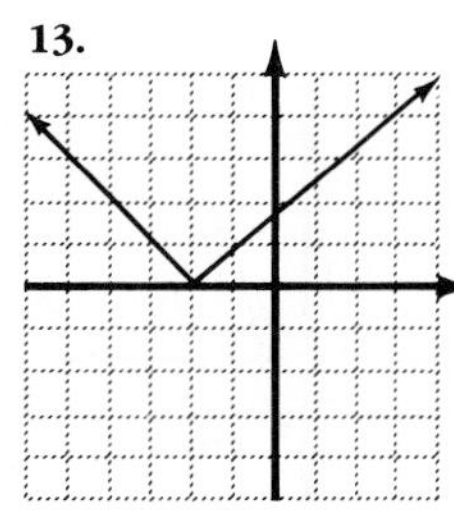

15.

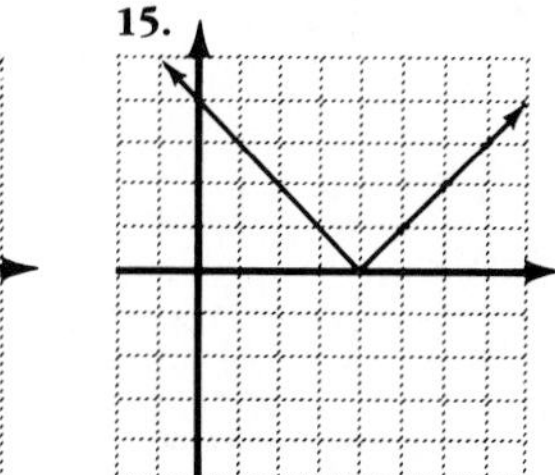

17.

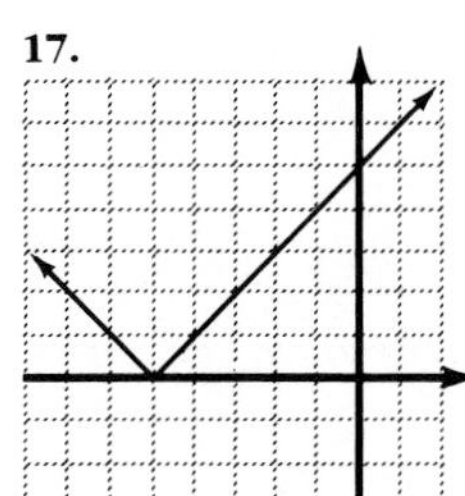

19.

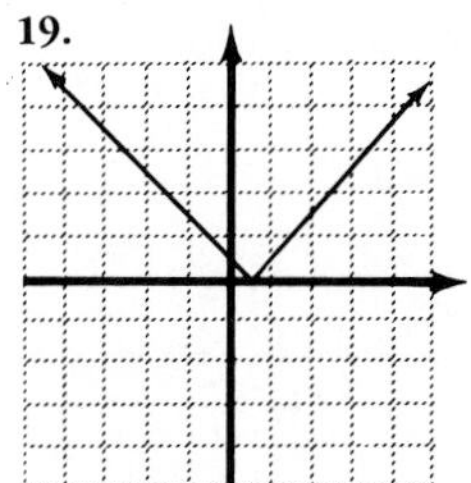

21.

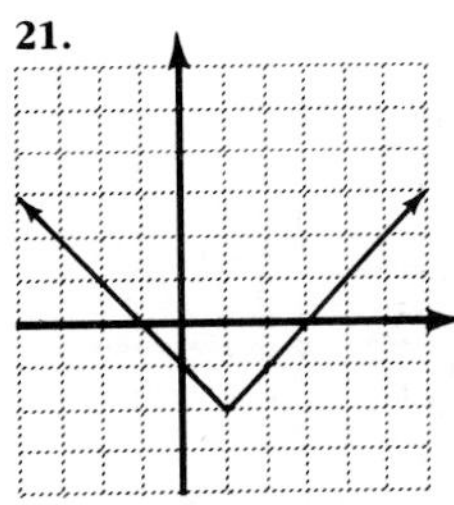

23.

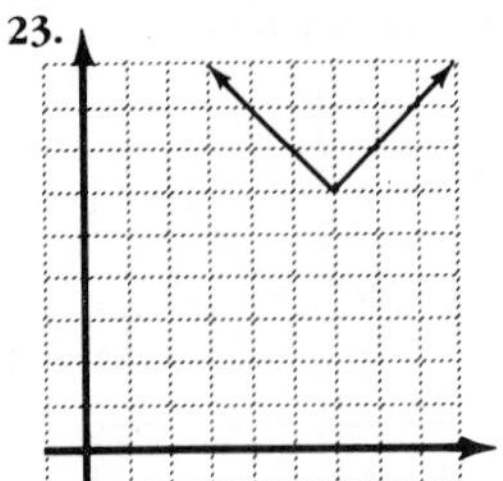

25.

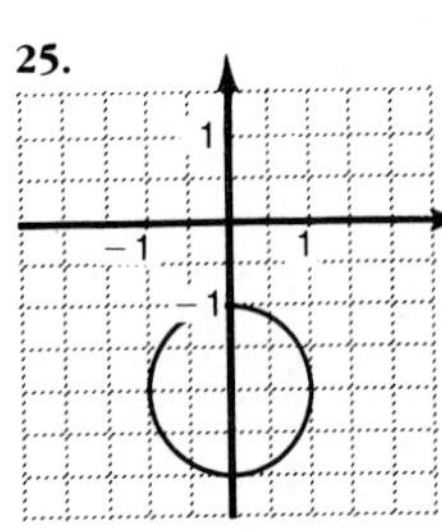

27.

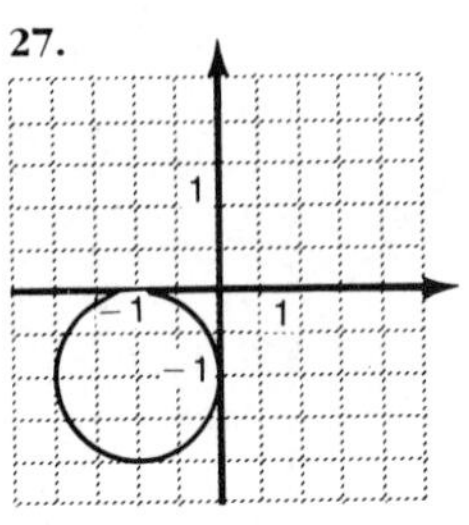

29. $(5, -1)$ **35.** $x^2 + 3x + 2 = 0$ **37.** 26
39. $\sqrt{m^2 + n^2}$ **41.** 3 **43.** $0, \pm 3$

Lesson 9-3 Try This

a.

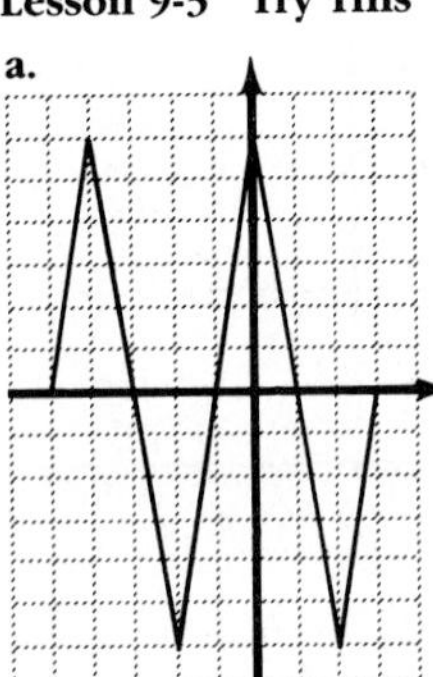

b.

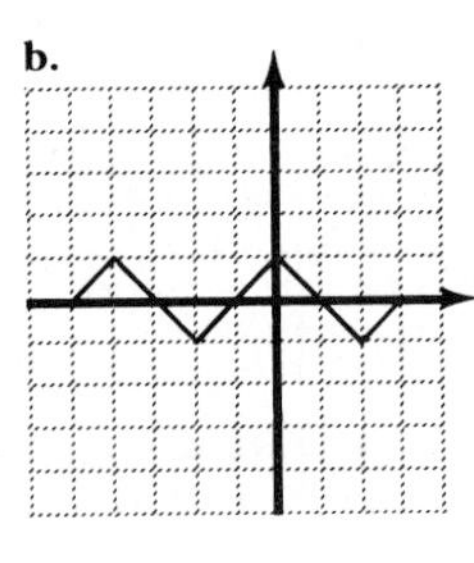

c.

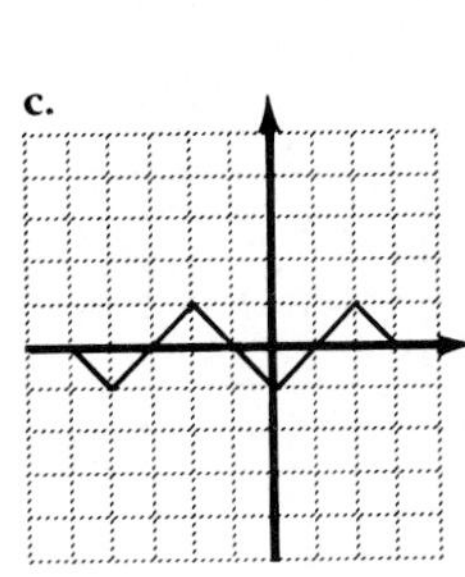

d.

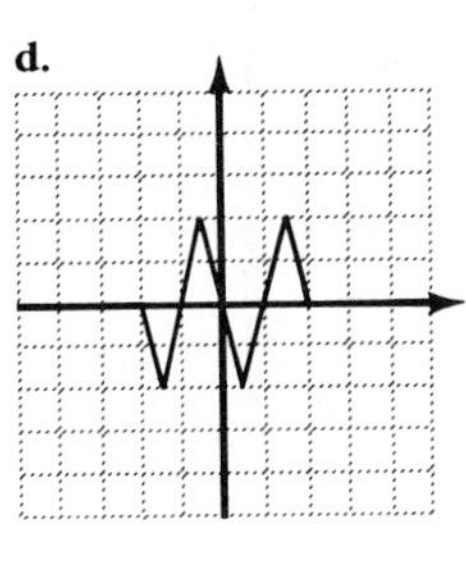

e.

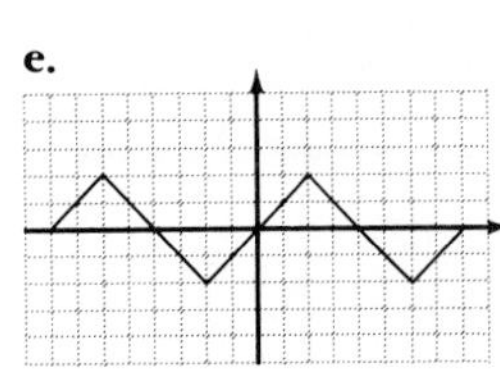

f.

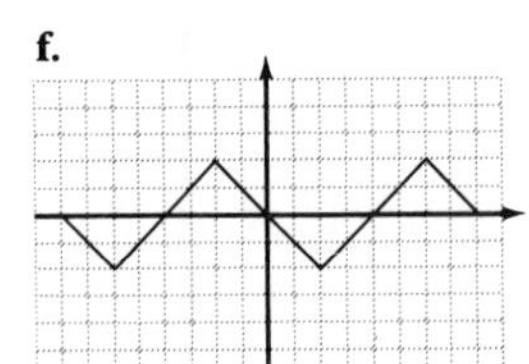

Exercise Set 9-3

1.

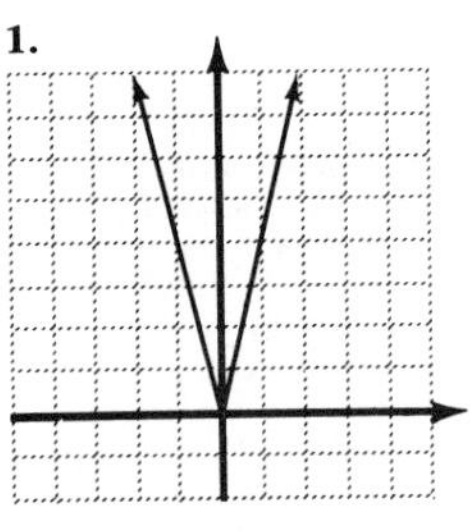

3.

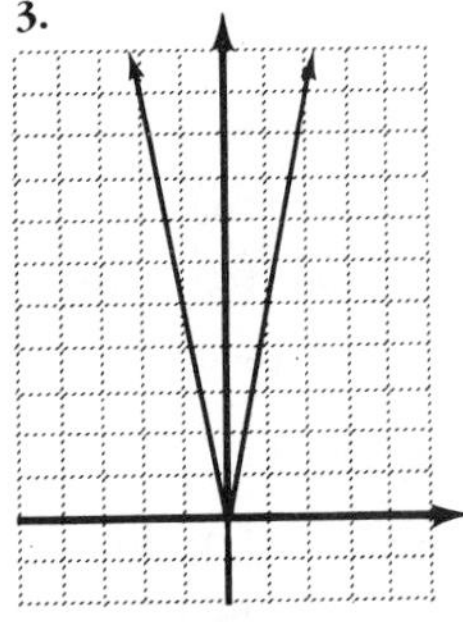

5.

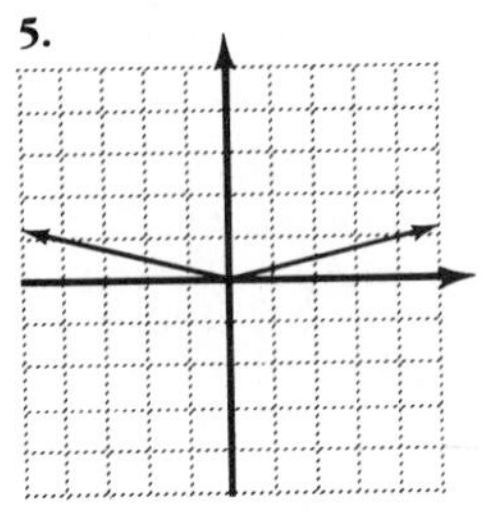

7.

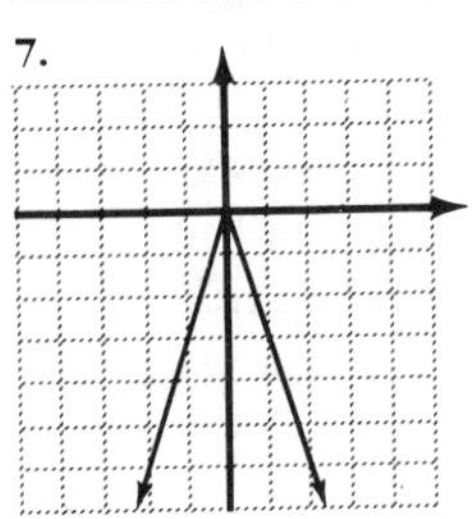

9.

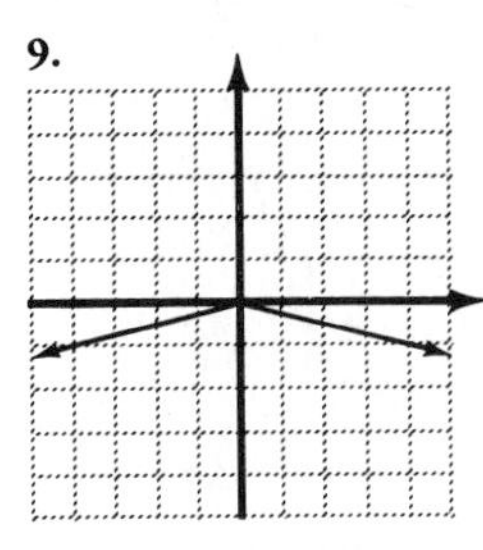

11.

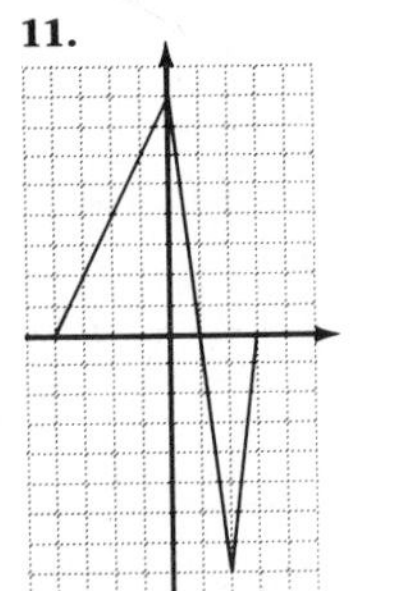

13.

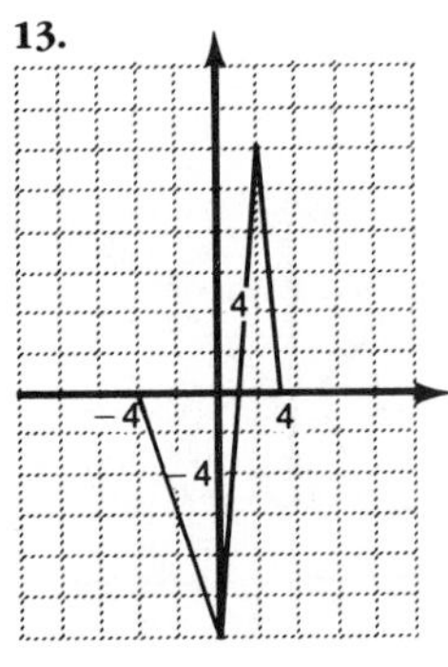

15.

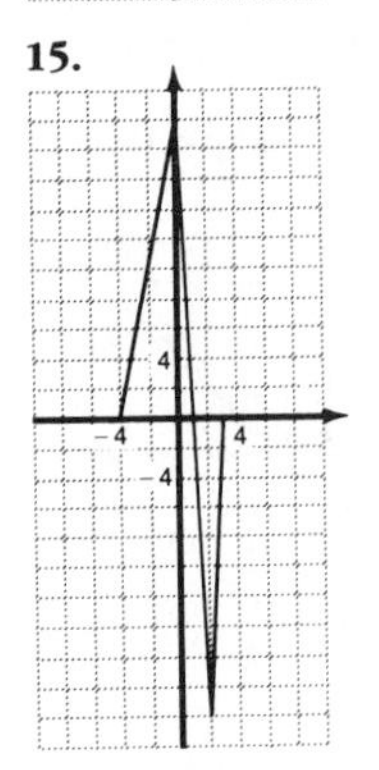

17.

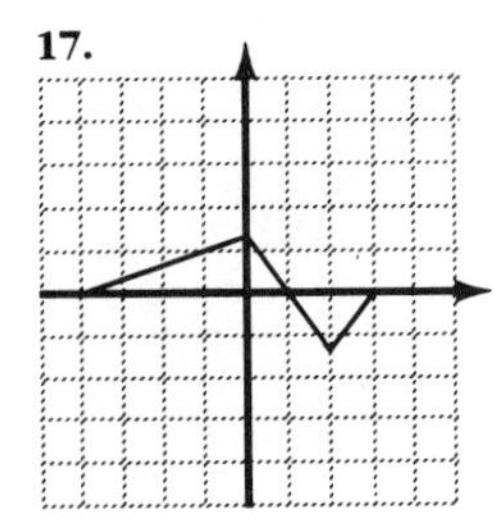

19.

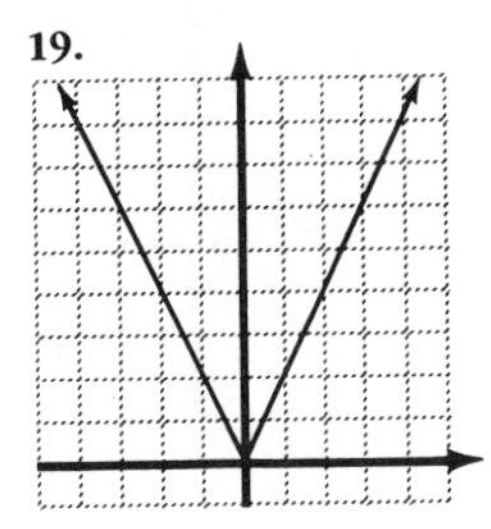

21.

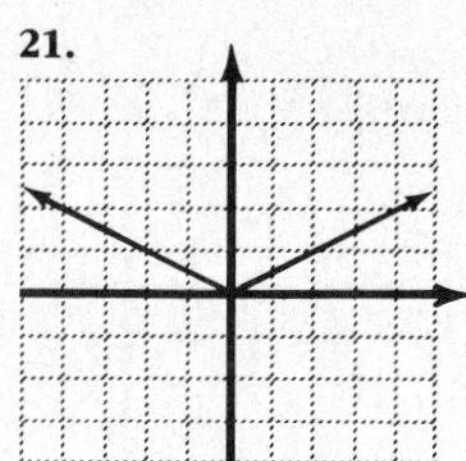

23.

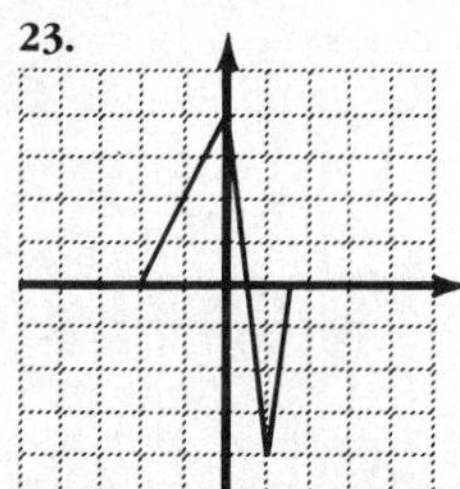

25.

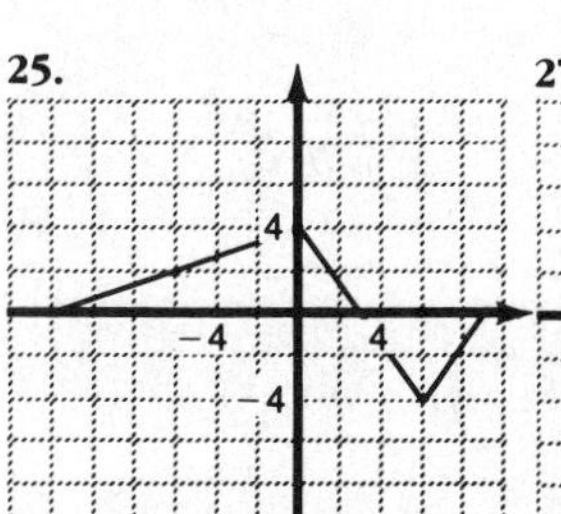

27.

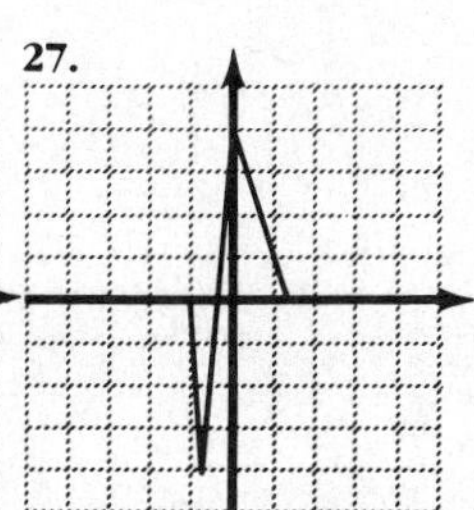

29.

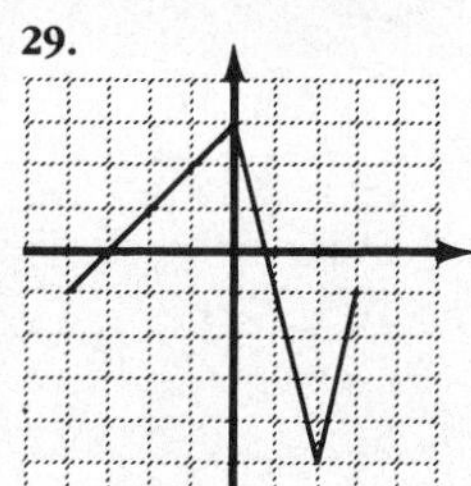

31.

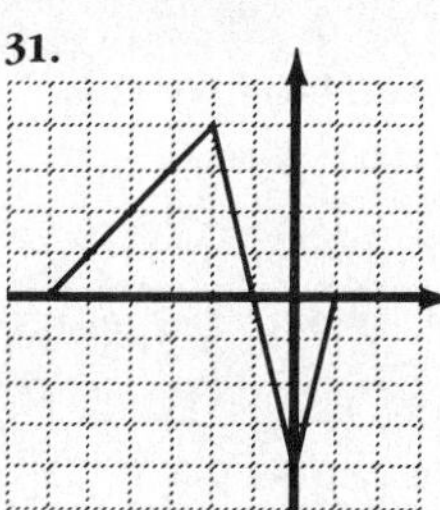

33.

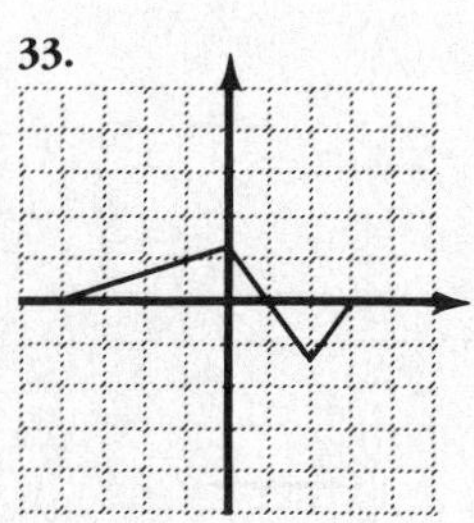

35.

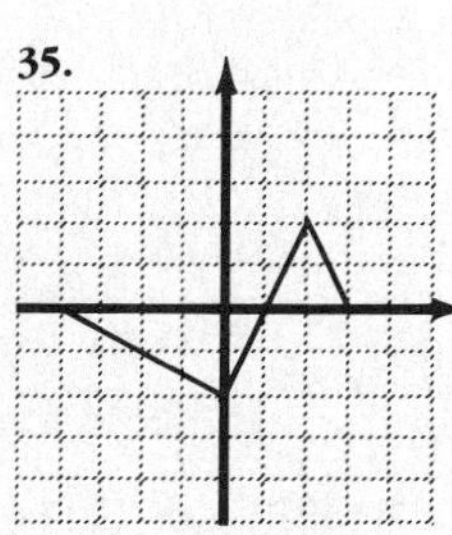

45. Yes, Yes **47.** $6x^2 - 5x + 1 = 0$ **49.** $-1 - 2i$
51. 1 **53.** 3, −8

Lesson 9-4 Try This

a. **1)**

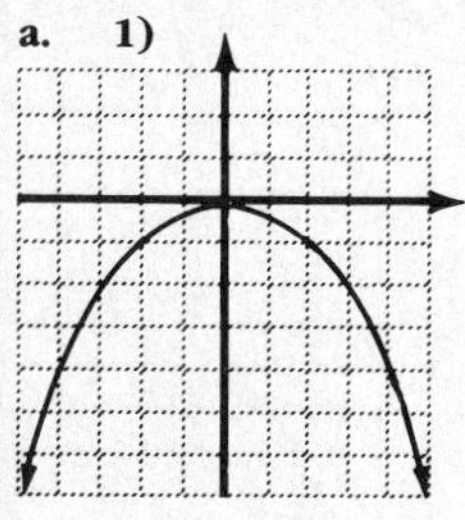

2) y-axis ($x = 0$); **3)** (0, 0)

b. **1)**

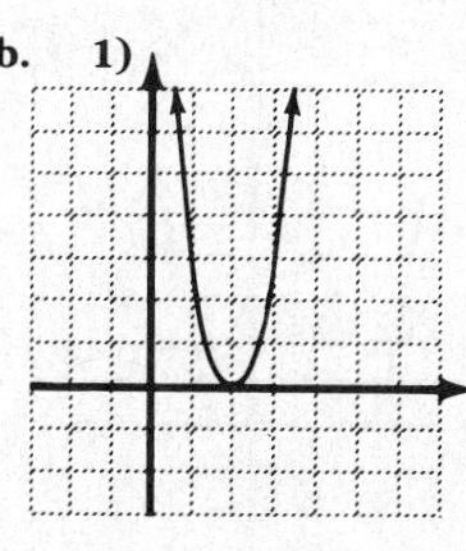

2) $x = 2$ **3)** (2, 0)

Exercise Set 9-4

1. Vertex: (0, 0),
Line of sym: $x = 0$

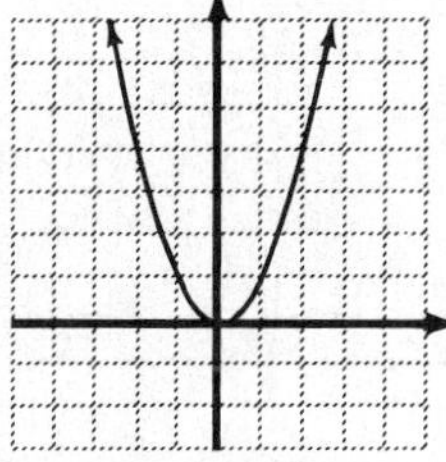

3. Vertex: (0, 0),
Line of sym: $x = 0$

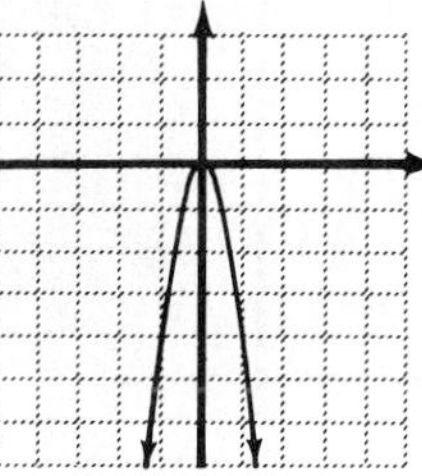

5. Vertex: (0, 0),
Line of sym: $x = 0$

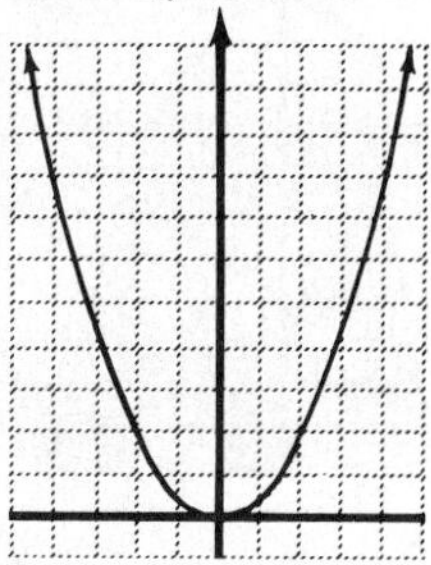

7. Vertex: (0, 0),
Line of sym: $x = 0$

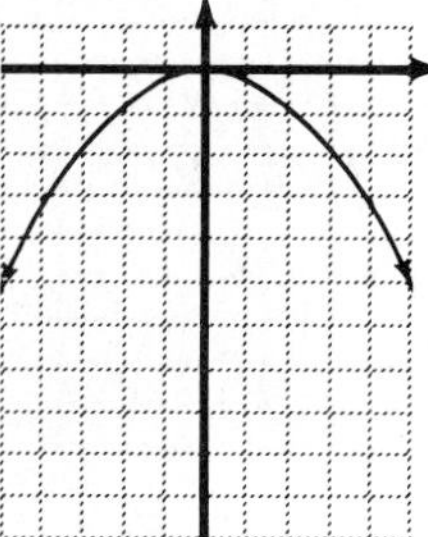

9. Vertex: (7, 0),
Line of sym: $x = 7$

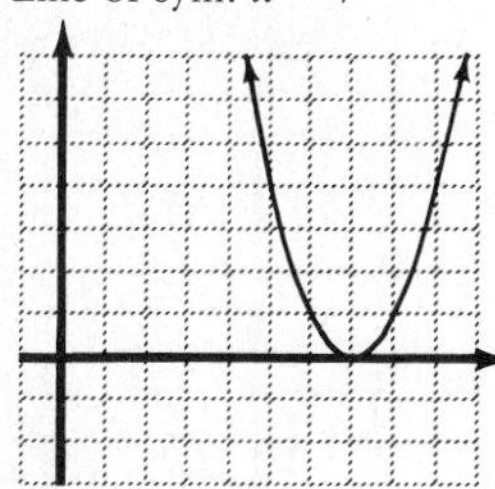

11. Vertex: (2, 0),
Line of sym: $x = 2$

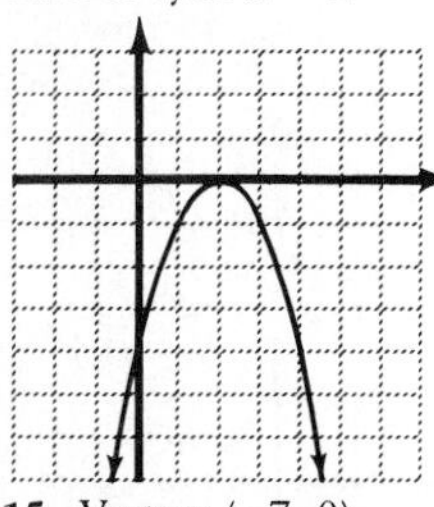

13. Vertex: (7, 0),
Line of sym: $x = 7$

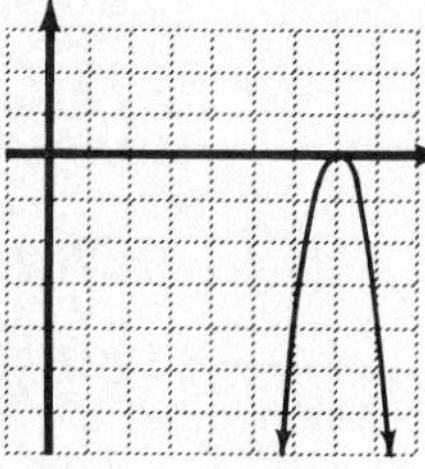

15. Vertex: (−7, 0),
Line of sym: $x = -7$

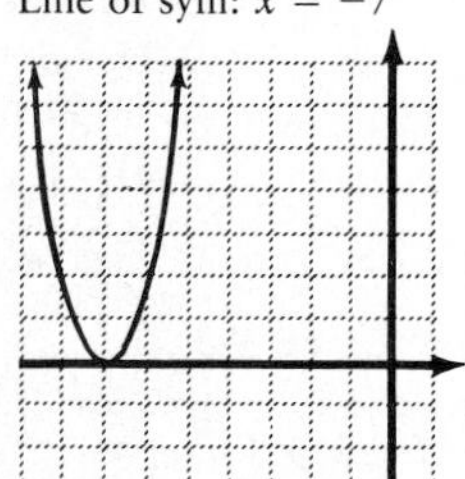

17. Vertex: (2, 0),
Line of sym: $x = 2$

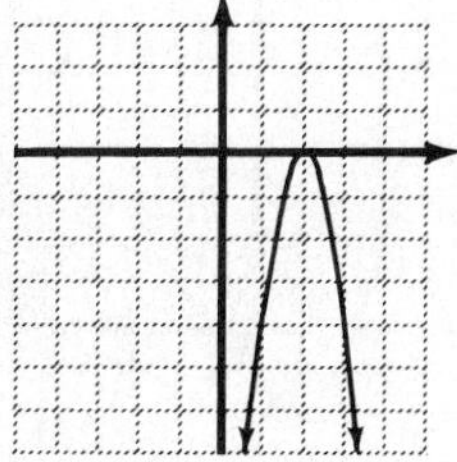

19. Vertex: (−1, 0),
Line of sym: $x = -1$

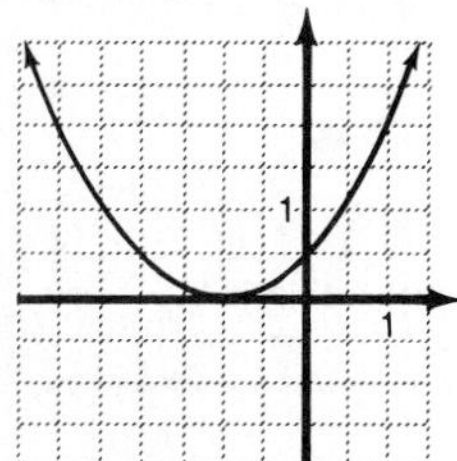

21.

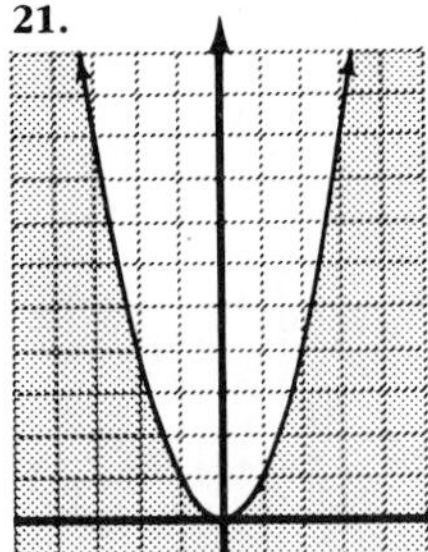

23.

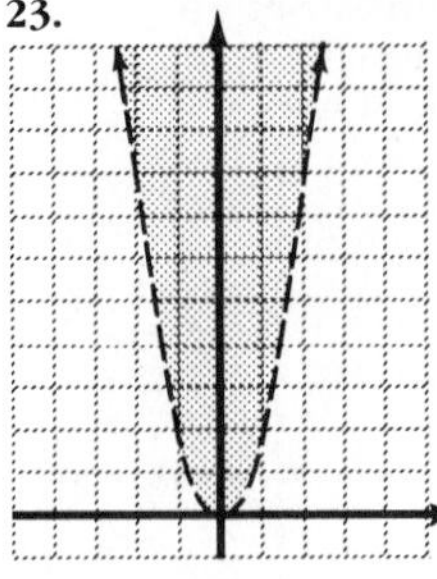

25.

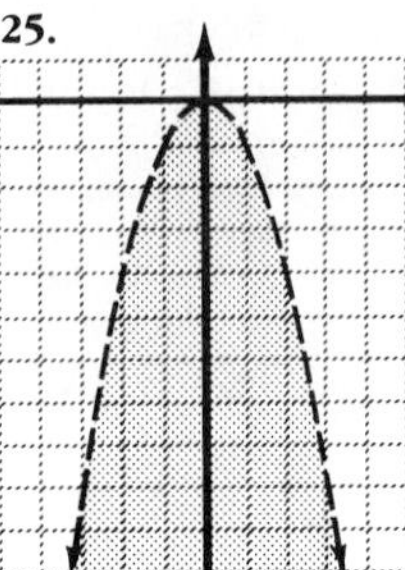

27.

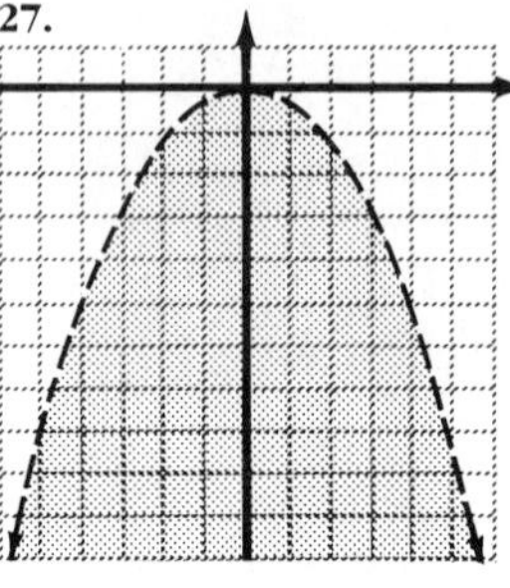

35. 2 nonreal **37.** $-3 \pm \sqrt{5}$ **39.** $\frac{1}{4}$

Lesson 9-5 Try This

a. Vertex: (2, 4); Line of sym: $x = 2$; Min: 4

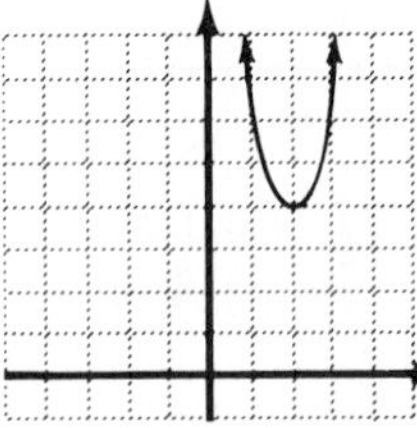

b. Vertex: (−2, −1); Line of sym: $x = -2$; Max: −1

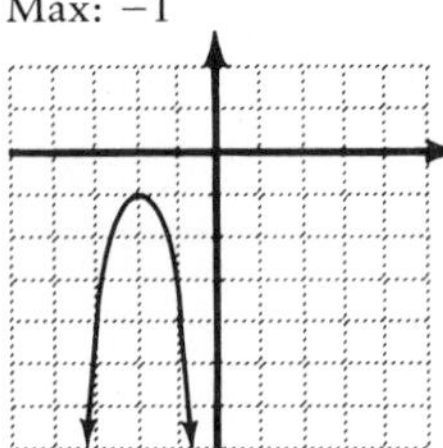

c. Vertex: (5, 40); Line of sym: $x = 5$; Min: 40
d. Vertex: (5, 0); Line of sym: $x = 5$; Max: 0
e. Vertex: $\left(-\frac{3}{4}, -6\right)$; Line of sym: $x = -\frac{3}{4}$; Min: −6
f. Vertex: (−9, 3); Line of sym: $x = -9$; Max: 3

Exercise Set 9-5

1. Vertex: (3, 1); Line of sym: $x = 3$ Min: 1

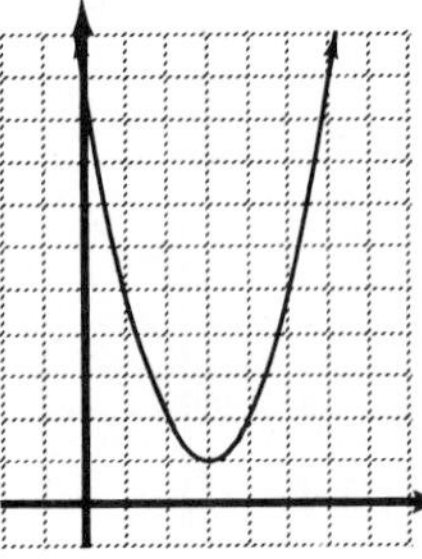

3. Vertex: (−1, −2); Line of sym: $x = -1$ Min: −2

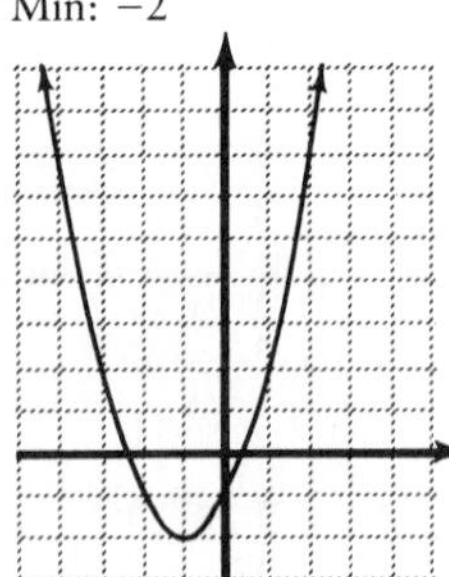

5. Vertex: (1, −3); Line of sym: $x = 1$; Min: −3

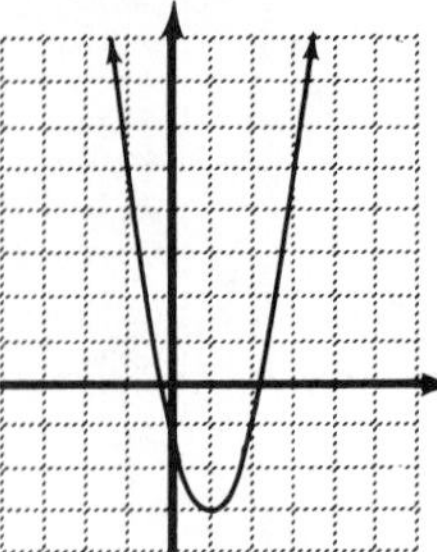

7. Vertex: (−4, 1); Line of sym: $x = -4$; Max: 1

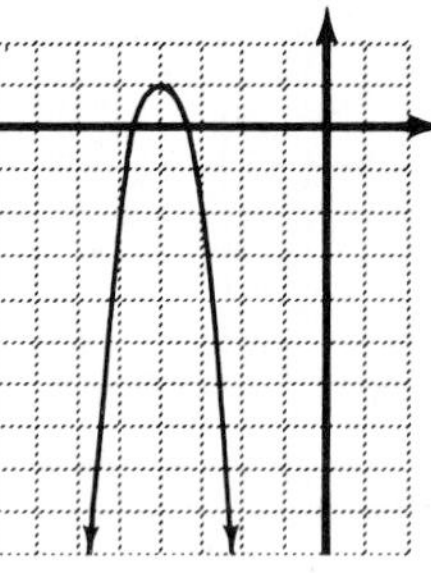

9. (9, 5); $x = 9$; min = 5 **11.** $\left(-\frac{1}{4}, -13\right)$; $x = -\frac{1}{4}$; min = −13 **13.** (10, −20); $x = 10$; max = −20
15. $(-4.58, 65\pi)$; $x = -4.58$; min 65π
17. $f(x) = -2x^2 + 4$ **19.** $f(x) = 2(x - 6)^2$
21. $f(x) = -2(x - 3)^2 + 8$ **23.** $f(x) = 2(x + 3)^2 + 5$
25. $f(x) = 2(x - 2)^2 - 3$ **27.** $g(x) = 6(x - 4)^2$
31. $g(x) = -2(x - 5)^2 - 11$ **33.** $c = \pm\sqrt{a^2 + b^2}$
35. $c = \pm\frac{\sqrt{Em}}{m}$ **37.** $y = 2xz$

Lesson 9-6 Try This

a. (1) $f(x) = (x - 2)^2 + 3$ **(2)** (2, 3), $x = 2$, min = 3 **b. (1)** $f(x) = -4\left(x - \frac{3}{2}\right)^2 + 4$
(2) $\left(\frac{3}{2}, 4\right)$, $x = \frac{3}{2}$, max = 4 **c.** 225
d. 25 m by 25 m

Exercise Set 9-6

1. $f(x) = (x - 1)^2 - 4$; Vertex: (1, −4); Line of sym: $x = 1$; Min: −4 **3.** $f(x) = -(x - 2)^2 + 10$; Vertex: (2, 10); Line of sym: $x = 2$; Max: 10
5. $f(x) = \left(x + \frac{3}{2}\right)^2 - \frac{49}{4}$; Vertex: $\left(-\frac{3}{2}, -\frac{49}{4}\right)$; Line of sym: $x = -\frac{3}{2}$; min: $-\frac{49}{4}$ **7.** $f(x) = \left(x - \frac{9}{2}\right)^2 - \frac{81}{4}$; Vertex: $\left(\frac{9}{2}, -\frac{81}{4}\right)$; Line of sym: $x = \frac{9}{2}$; min: $-\frac{81}{4}$
9. $f(x) = 3(x - 4)^2 + 2$; Vertex: (4, 2); Line of sym: $x = 4$; Min: 2 **11.** $f(x) = \frac{3}{4}(x + 6)^2 - 27$; Vertex: (−6, −27); Line of sym: $x = -6$; Min: −27
13. 19 m by 19 m; 361 m^2 **15.** 121; 11 and 11
17. −4; 2 and −2 **19.** $-\frac{25}{4}$, $\frac{5}{2}$ and $-\frac{5}{2}$
21. $f(x) = 3\left[x - \left(-\frac{m}{6}\right)\right]^2 + \frac{11m^2}{12}$
23.

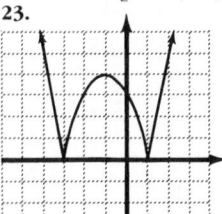

25. Max: 7.014
27. Max: 114.009; both 10.6775 **31.** \$6
33. 1800 ft^2
35. $11\sqrt{2}$ ft **37.** Both
39. x-axis **41.** 4
43. $16i$ **45.** 10
47. 3.40956×10^7

Lesson 9-7 Try This

a. $1 + \sqrt{6}, 1 - \sqrt{6}$ **b.** -4 **c.** None

Exercise Set 9-7

1. $2 + \sqrt{3}, 2 - \sqrt{3}$ **3.** $3, -1$ **5.** $4, -1$ **7.** $4, -1$
9. $\frac{-2 \pm \sqrt{6}}{2}$ **11.** None **13.** None **15.** $\frac{3 \pm \sqrt{6}}{3}$

17.

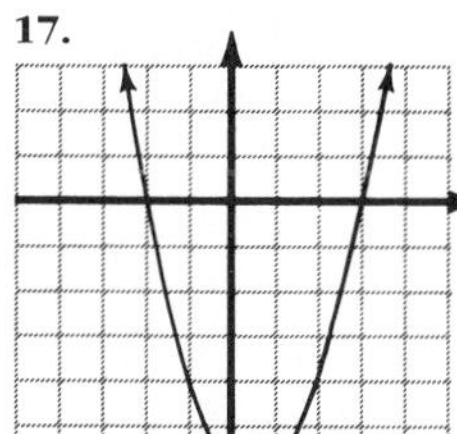

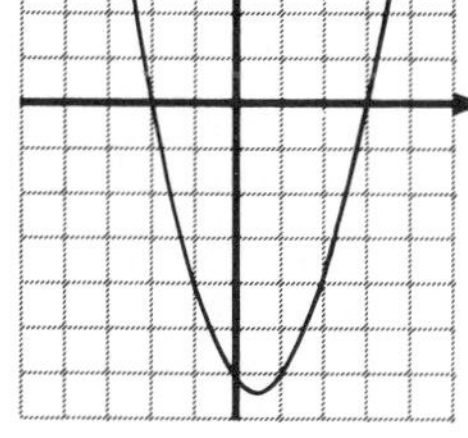

a. 3.4, −2.4
b. 2.3, −1.3

21. None
23. No
25. Yes
27. Vertex: $(-3, 0)$; Line of sym: $x = -3$

29.

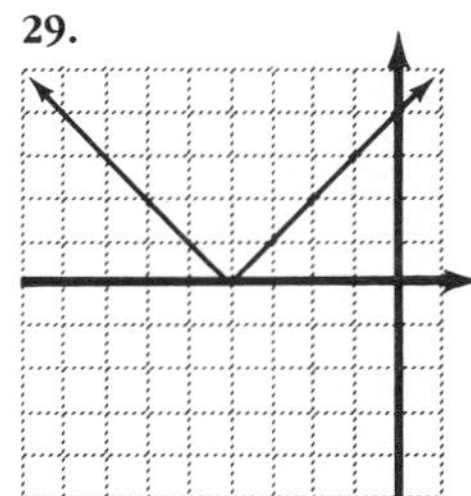

Lesson 9-8 Try This

a. $f(x) = x^2 - 2x + 1$ **b.** $f(x) = x^2 + 2x + 3$
c. **(1)** $f(x) = 0.1875x^2 - 16.25x + 500$ **(2)** 288
d. **(1)** 12.4 m in 0.286 sec **(2)** 1.876 sec

Exercise Set 9-8

1. $f(x) = 2x^2 + 3x - 1$ **3.** $f(x) = -3x^2 + 13x - 5$
5. **a.** $-4x^2 + 40x + 2$ **b.** \$98
7. **a.** $0.0875r^2 - 10.5r + 436.25$ **b.** 121.25
9. **a.** 30.77 m at 25 sec **b.** 50.1 sec
11. 156.25, 40 km/h **13.** **a.** 5 amperes
b. 300 watts **19.** Neither **21.** y-axis
23. Vertex: $(0, 0)$; Line of sym: y-axis
25. Vertex: $(-1, 0)$; Line of sym: $x = -1$

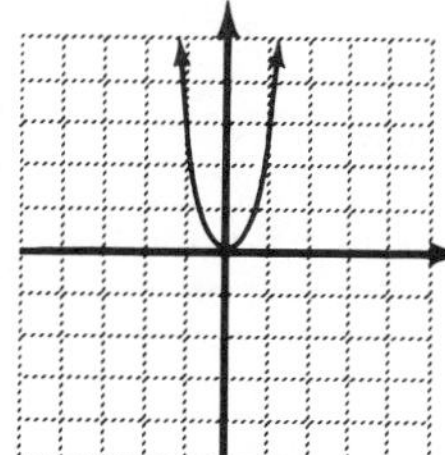

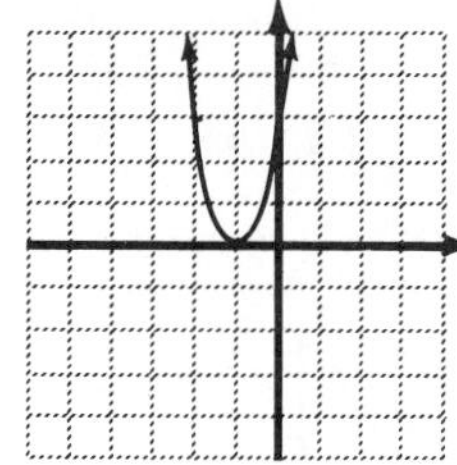

27. $\pm 3, \pm 2i$

Chapter 9 Summary and Review

1. Both **3.** Neither **5.** Neither **7.** No **9.** No
11. Yes

13.

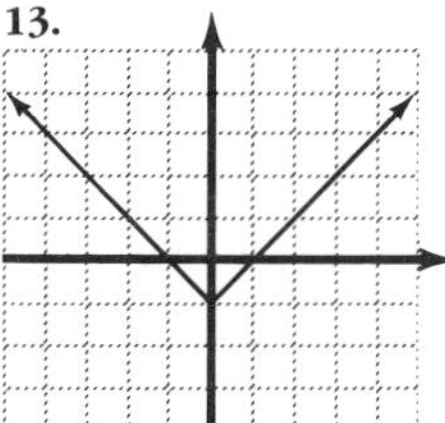

15.

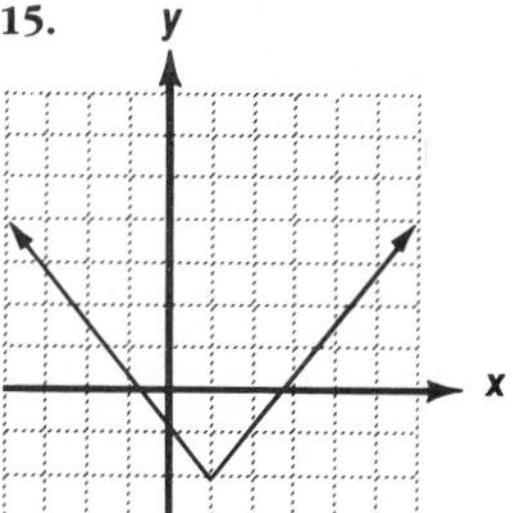

17.

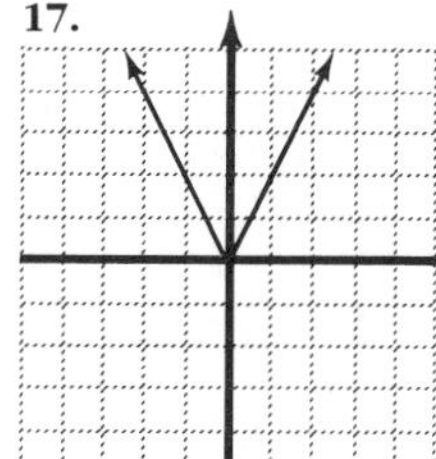

19.

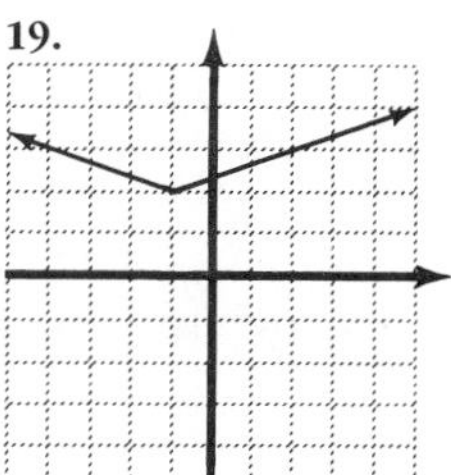

21. Vertex: $(0, 0)$; Line of sym: $x = 0$ **23.** Vertex: $(2, 0)$; Line of sym: $x = 2$ **25.** Vertex: $(1, 5)$; Line of sym: $x = 1$; Min: 5 **27.** $(x - 4)^2 - 11$
29. $-2(x + 1)^2 + 5$ **31.** -16; 4 and -4
33. $-1 \pm \sqrt{5}$ **35.** $f(x) = -2x^2 - 4x + 3$
37. $f(x) = -x^2 + 8x - 8$

Chapter 10

Lesson 10-1 Try This

a. $\sqrt{149}$ **b.** $6\sqrt{2}$ **c.** $\left(\frac{3}{2}, -\frac{5}{2}\right)$ **d.** $(9, -5)$

Exercise Set 10-1

1. 5 **3.** $3\sqrt{2}$ **5.** 5 **7.** 8 **9.** $\sqrt{a^2 + 64}$
11. $\sqrt{a^2 + b^2}$ **13.** $2\sqrt{a}$ **15.** $\left(-\frac{1}{2}, -1\right)$
17. $\left(-\frac{7}{2}, -\frac{15}{2}\right)$ **19.** $(4, 4)$ **21.** $(a, 0)$ **23.** Yes
35. $-6, 0$ **37.** No **39.** No **41.** $x^2 - 6x + 9$
43. $x^2 + 3x + \frac{9}{4}$ **45.** $m^2 + 7.4m + 13.69$
47. $c^2 - c + \frac{1}{4}$

Lesson 10-2 Try This

a. $x^2 + y^2 = 6$ **b.** $(x + 3)^2 + (y - 7)^2 = 25$
c. $(x - 5)^2 + (y + 2)^2 = 3$
d. $(x + 2)^2 + (y + 6)^2 = 28$ **e.** $(-1, 3)$; 2

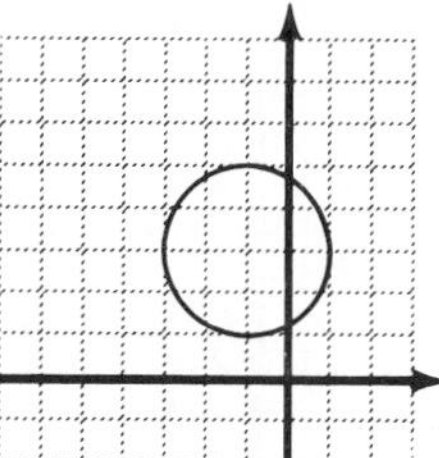

f. $(7, -2)$; 8 **g.** $(6, 4)$; 5

Exercise Set 10-2

1. $x^2 + y^2 = 49$ **3.** $(x + 2)^2 + (y - 7)^2 = 5$

5. $(-1, -3), 2$ **7.** $(8, -3), 2\sqrt{10}$

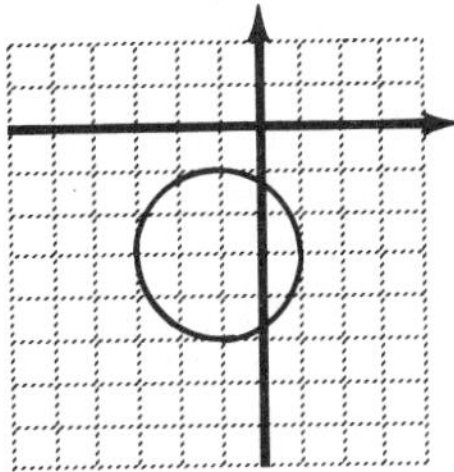

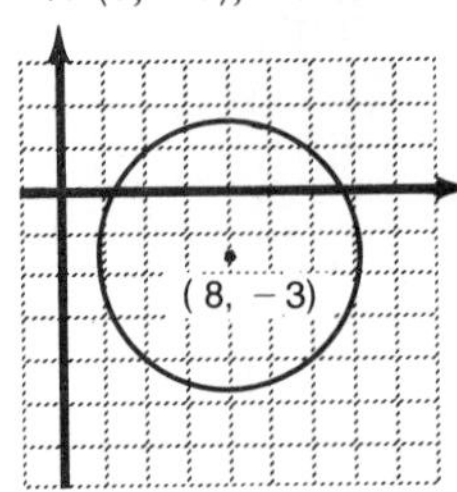

9. $(0, 0), \sqrt{2}$ **11.** $(5, 0), \frac{1}{2}$

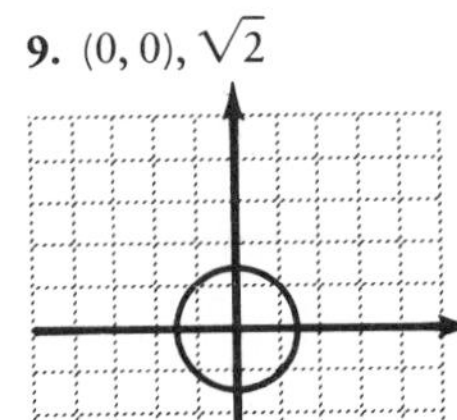

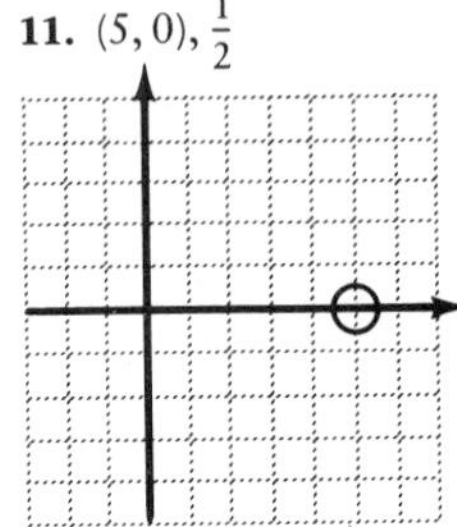

13. $(-4, 3); 2\sqrt{10}$ **15.** $(4, -1); 2$ **17.** $(2, 0); 2$ **19.** $x^2 + y^2 = 25$ **21.** $(x - 2)^2 + (y - 4)^2 = 16$ **23.** $1 \pm \sqrt{77}, 2 \pm 4\sqrt{5}$ **25.** $2, -3 \pm \sqrt{5}$ **27.** The origin **35.** x-axis **37.** y-axis **39.** $(5, 0), (1, 0)$ **41.** $f(x) = 2x^2 - 6x$ **43.** $\frac{5}{2}, -\frac{3}{4}$ **45.** 9 **47.** $2\sqrt{2}, 0, -2\sqrt{2}$

Lesson 10-3 Try This

a. Vertices: $(\pm 3, 0)$, $(0, \pm 1)$; foci: $(\pm 2\sqrt{2}, 0)$

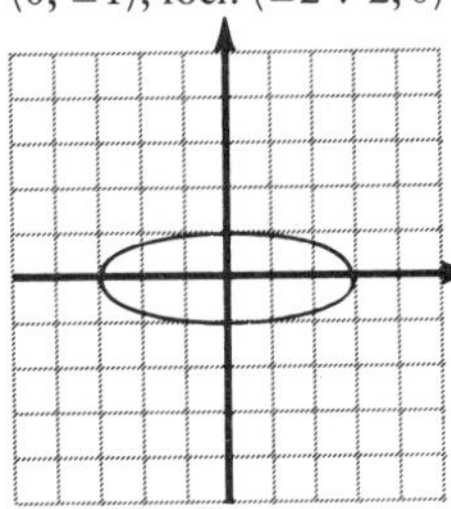

b. Vertices: $(\pm 5, 0)$, $(0, \pm 3)$; foci: $(\pm 4, 0)$

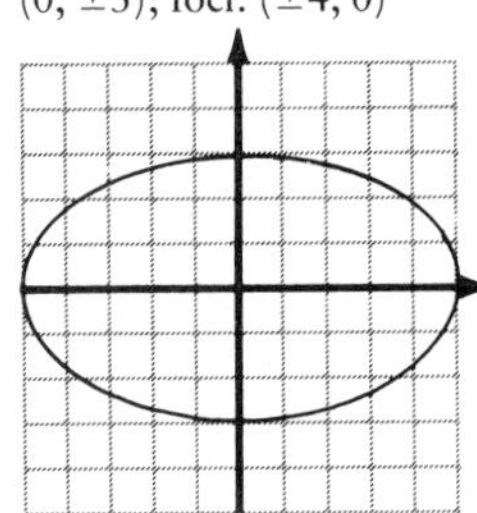

c. Vertices: $(\pm 2, 0)$, $(0, \pm\sqrt{2})$; foci: $(\pm\sqrt{2}, 0)$

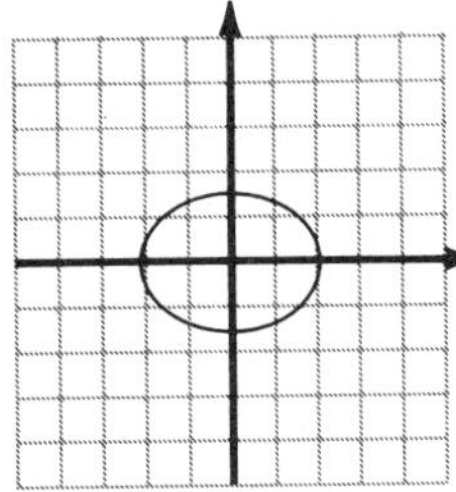

d. Center: $(0, 0)$; vertices: $(\pm 1, 0)$, $(0, \pm 3)$; foci: $(0, \pm 2\sqrt{2})$

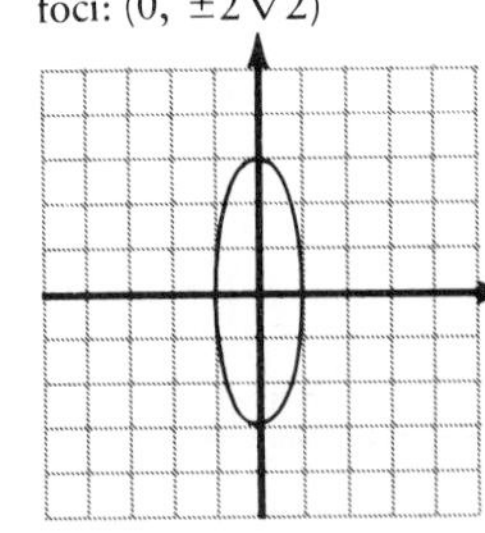

e. Center: $(0, 0)$; vertices: $(\pm 3, 0)$, $(0, \pm 5)$; foci: $(0, \pm 4)$

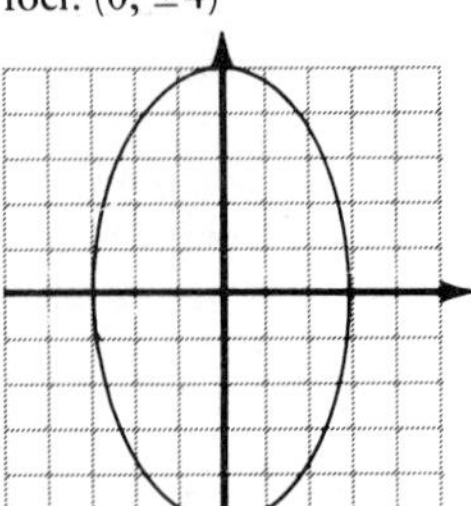

f. Center: $(0, 0)$; vertices: $(\pm\sqrt{2}, 0)$, $(0, \pm 2)$; foci: $(0, \pm\sqrt{2})$

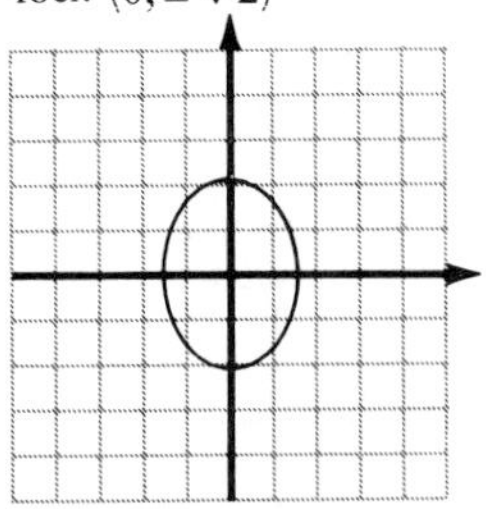

g. Center: $(0, 0)$; vertices: $(\pm 4\sqrt{3}, 0)$, $(0, \pm 4)$; foci: $(\pm 4\sqrt{2}, 0)$

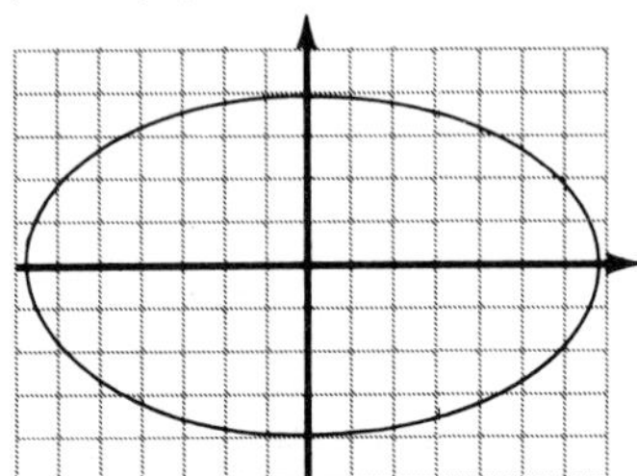

h. Center: $(-3, 2)$; vertices; $\left(-3\frac{1}{5}, 2\right)$, $\left(-3, 2\frac{1}{3}\right)$, $\left(-3, 1\frac{2}{3}\right)$, $\left(-2\frac{4}{5}, 2\right)$; foci: $\left(-3, 2\frac{4}{15}\right)$, $\left(-3, 1\frac{11}{15}\right)$

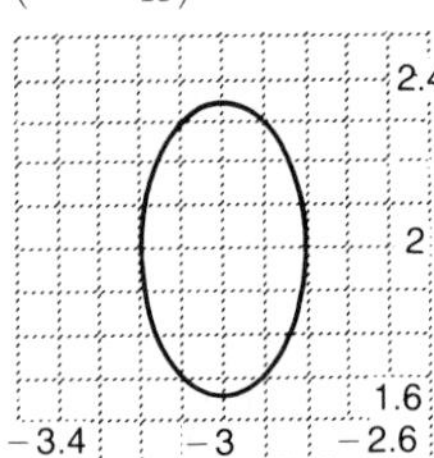

i. Center: $(2, -3)$; vertices: $\left(2\frac{1}{3}, -3\right)$, $\left(2, -3\frac{1}{5}\right)$, $\left(2, -2\frac{4}{5}\right)$, $\left(1\frac{2}{3}, -3\right)$; foci: $\left(2\frac{4}{15}, -3\right)$, $\left(1\frac{11}{15}, -3\right)$

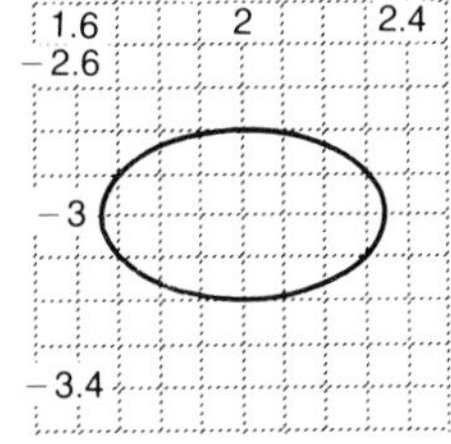

Exercise Set 10-3

1. Vertices: $(\pm 2, 0)$, $(0, \pm 1)$; foci: $(\pm\sqrt{3}, 0)$

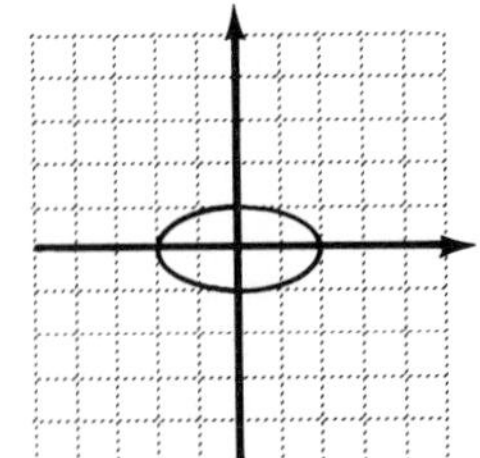

3. Vertices: $(\pm 3, 0)$, $(0, \pm 4)$; foci: $(0, \pm\sqrt{7})$

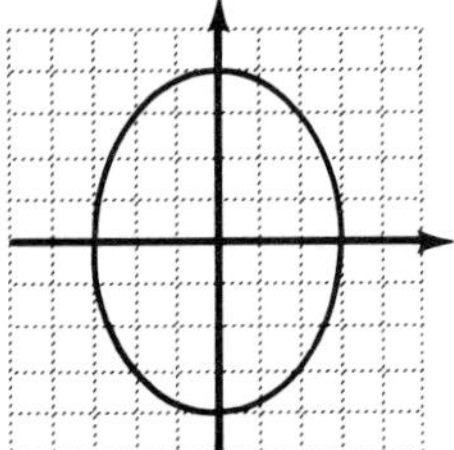

5. Vertices: $(\pm\sqrt{3}, 0)$, $(0, \pm\sqrt{2})$; foci: $(\pm1, 0)$

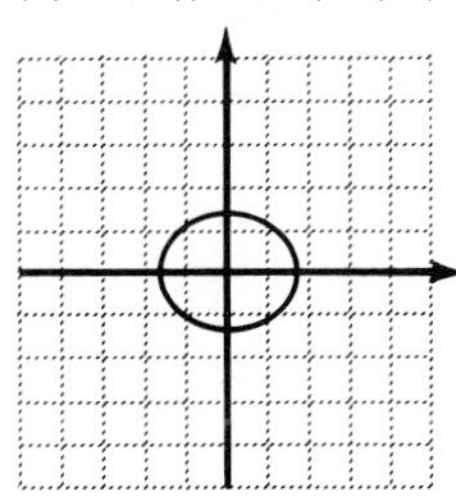

7. Vertices: $\left(\pm\frac{1}{2}, 0\right)$, $\left(0, \pm\frac{1}{3}\right)$; foci: $\left(\pm\frac{\sqrt{5}}{6}, 0\right)$

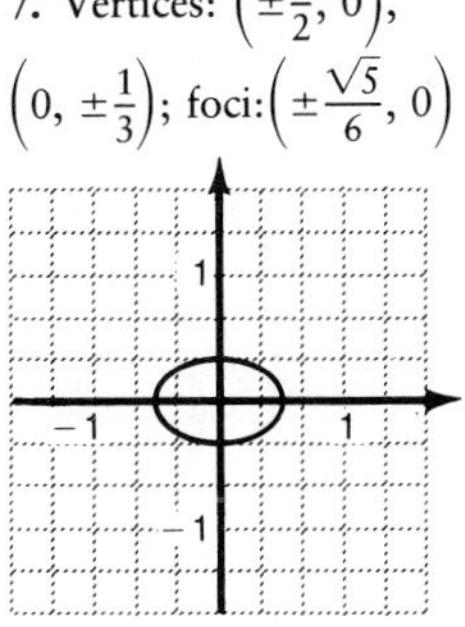

9. Center: $(1, 2)$; vertices: $(-1, 2)$, $(3, 2)$, $(1, 1)$, $(1, 3)$; foci: $(1 \pm \sqrt{3}, 2)$

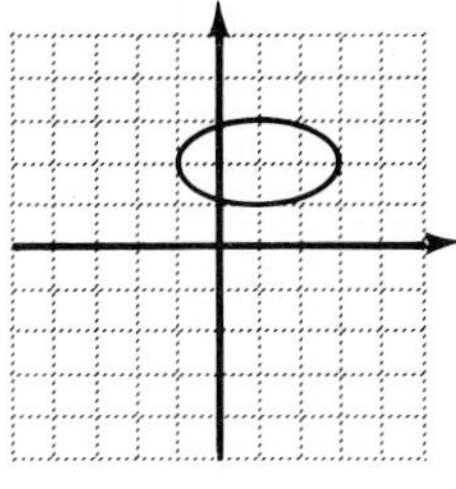

11. Center: $(-3, 2)$; vertices: $(-8, 2)$, $(2, 2)$, $(-3, -2)$, $(-3, 6)$; foci: $(-6, 2)$, $(0, 2)$

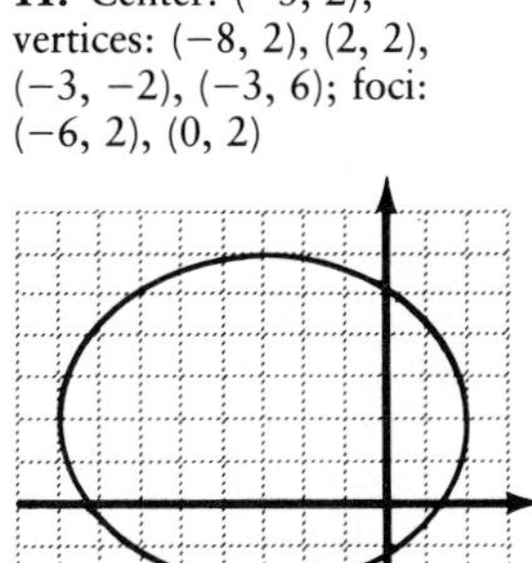

13. Center: $(-2, 1)$; vertices: $(-10, 1)$, $(6, 1)$, $(-2, 1 \pm 4\sqrt{3})$; foci: $(-6, 1)$, $(2, 1)$

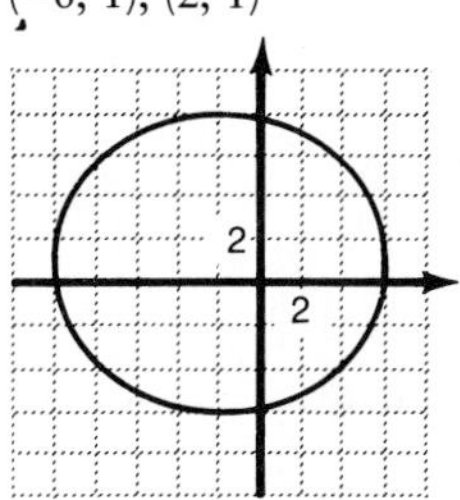

15. Center: $(2, -1)$; vertices: $(-1, -1)$, $(5, -1)$, $(2, -3)$, $(2, 1)$; foci: $(2 \pm \sqrt{5}, -1)$

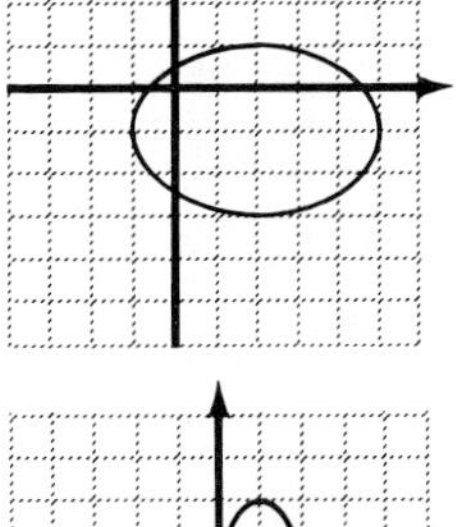

17. Center: $(1, 1)$; vertices: $(0, 1)$, $(2, 1)$, $(1, -1)$, $(1, 3)$; foci: $(1, 1 \pm \sqrt{3})$

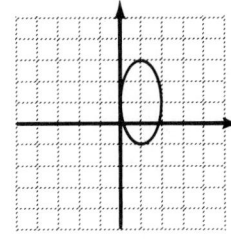

19. Center $(2.5, -0.95)$; vertices $(6, -0.95)$, $(-1, 0.95)$, $(2.5, 1.02)$, $(2.5, -2.93)$ **21.** $\frac{x^2}{4} + \frac{y^2}{9} = 1$

23. $\frac{(x-3)^2}{4} + \frac{(y-1)^2}{25} = 1$

25. $(x+2)^2 + \frac{(y-3)^2}{16} = 1$

27. a. No **c.** Yes; domain $\{x \mid -1 \le x < 1\}$; range $\{y \mid 0 \le y \le 3\}$ **29.** 2.0×10^6 miles **33.** $0 < e < 1$ **35. a.** $A = \pi ab$ **c.** $2\pi\sqrt{3}$ **41.** $f(x) = (x + 2.5)^2 - 7.25$; Vertex: $(-2.5, -7.25)$; Line of sym: $x = -2.5$; Min: -7.25

43. $\left(-1 + \frac{\sqrt{6}}{2}, 0\right), \left(-1 - \sqrt{6}, 0\right)$ **45.** $\sqrt{34}$

47. $f(x) = 3x^2 + 2x - 4$

Lesson 10-4 Try This

a. Vertices: $(-3, 0)$, $(3, 0)$; foci: $(-\sqrt{13}, 0)$, $(\sqrt{13}, 0)$; asymptotes: $y = -\frac{2}{3}x$, $y = \frac{2}{3}x$

b. Vertices: $(-4, 0)$, $(4, 0)$; foci: $(-4\sqrt{2}, 0)$, $(4\sqrt{2}, 0)$; asymptotes: $y = x$, $y = -x$

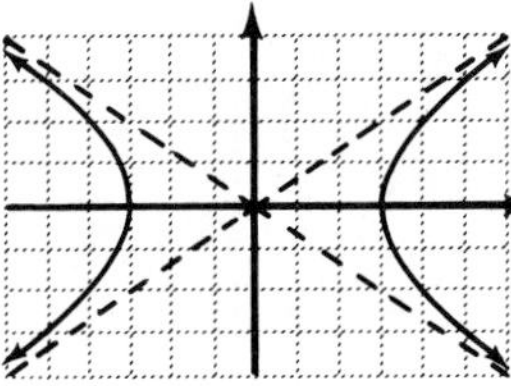

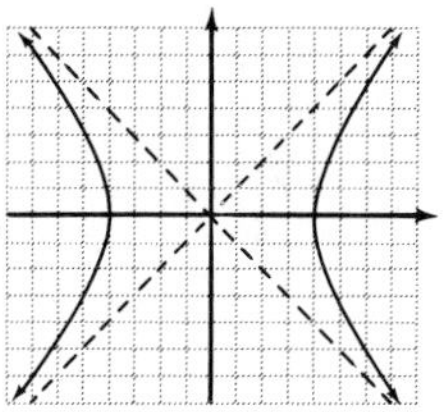

c. Vertices: $(0, -5)$, $(0, 5)$; foci: $(0, -\sqrt{34})$, $(0, \sqrt{34})$; asymptotes: $y = -\frac{5}{3}x$, $y = \frac{5}{3}x$

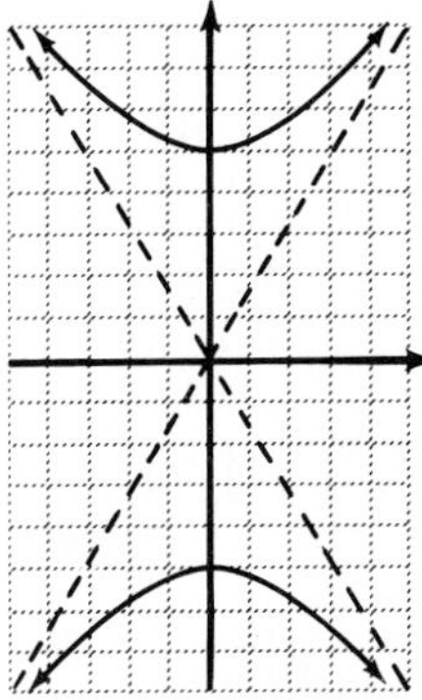

d. Vertices: $(0, 5)$, $(0, -5)$; foci: $(0, -5\sqrt{2})$, $(0, 5\sqrt{2})$; asymptotes: $y = x$, $y = -x$

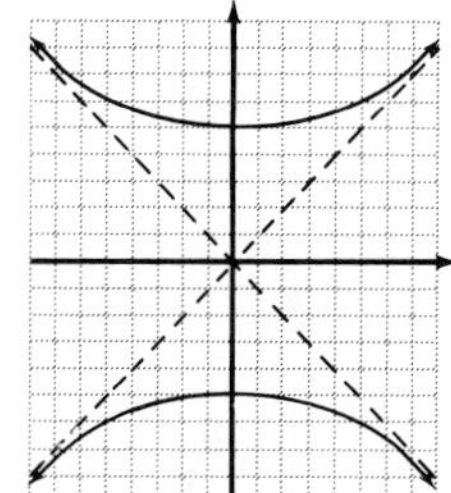

e. Center: $(1, -2)$; vertices: $(-4, -2)$, $(6, -2)$; foci: $(1 - \sqrt{29}, -2)$, $(1 + \sqrt{29}, -2)$; asymptotes: $y + 2 = -\frac{2}{5}(x - 1)$, $y + 2 = \frac{2}{5}(x - 1)$

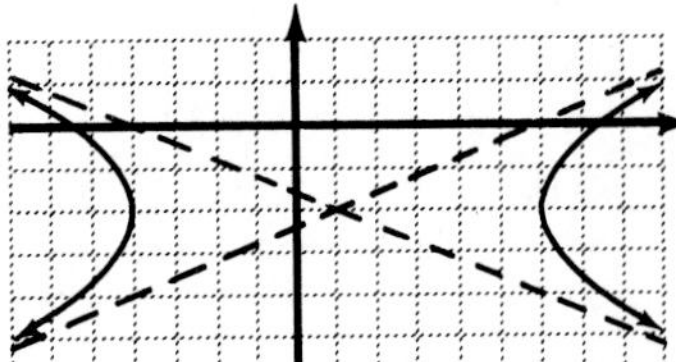

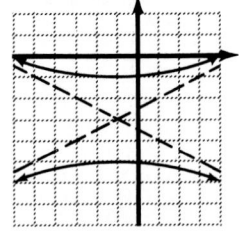

f. Center $(-1, 2)$; vertices: $(-1, -1)$, $(-1, 5)$; foci: $(-1, -3)$, $(-1, 7)$; asymptotes: $y - 2 = \pm\frac{3}{4}(x + 1)$

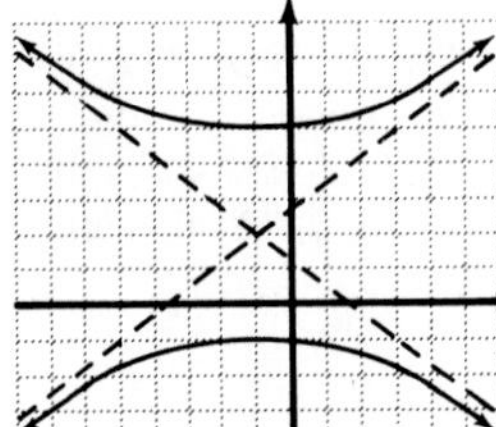

g.

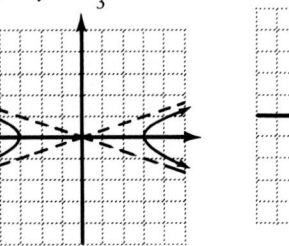

h.

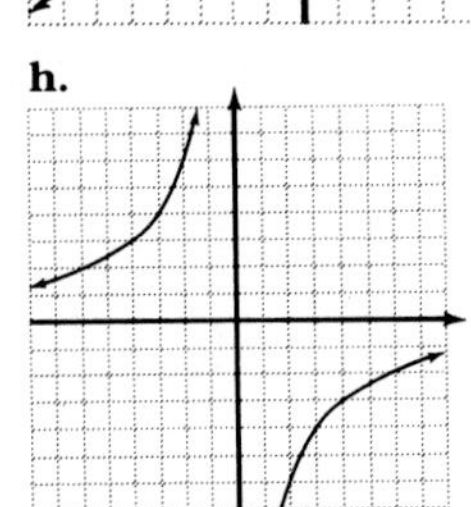

Exercise Set 10-4

1. Center: $(0, 0)$; foci: $(\pm\sqrt{10}, 0)$; vertices: $(\pm 3, 0)$; asym: $y = \pm\frac{1}{3}x$

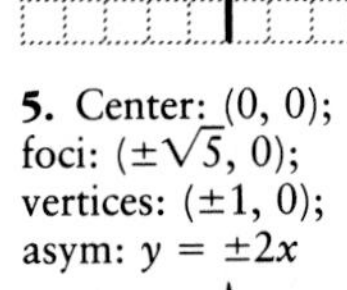

3. Center: $(0, 0)$; foci: $(0, \pm 2\sqrt{5})$; vertices: $(0, \pm 4)$; asym: $y = \pm 2x$

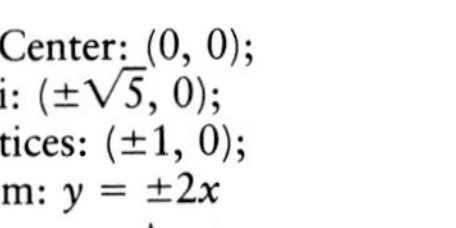

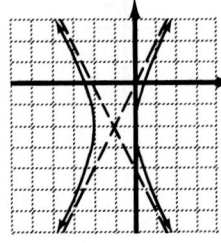

5. Center: $(0, 0)$; foci: $(\pm\sqrt{5}, 0)$; vertices: $(\pm 1, 0)$; asym: $y = \pm 2x$

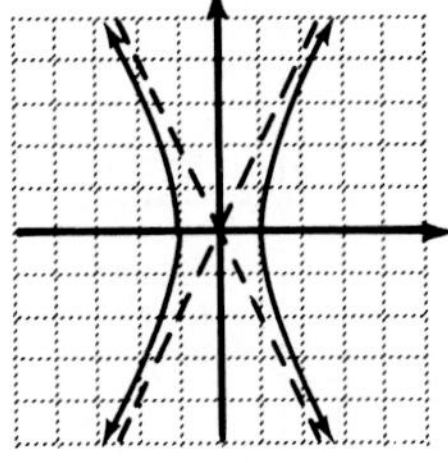

7. Center: $(0, 0)$; foci: $(0, \pm\sqrt{5})$; vertices: $(0, \pm 2)$; asym: $y = \pm 2x$

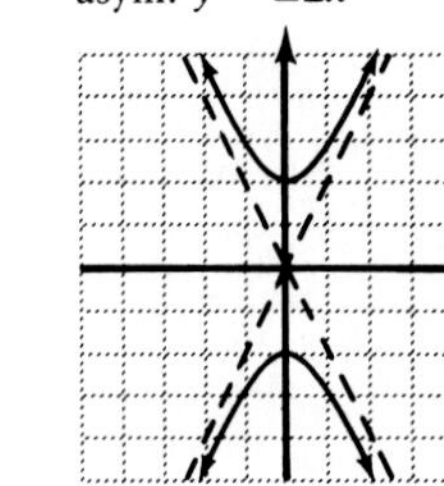

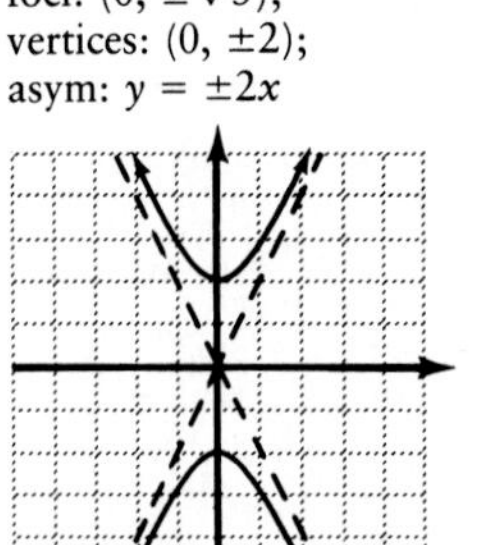

9. Center: $(0, 0)$; foci: $(\pm\sqrt{6}, 0)$; vertices: $(\pm\sqrt{3}, 0)$; asym: $y = \pm x$

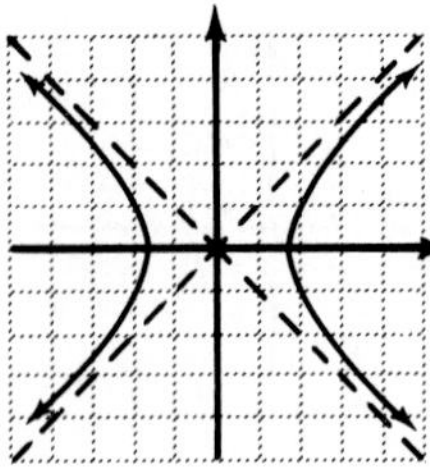

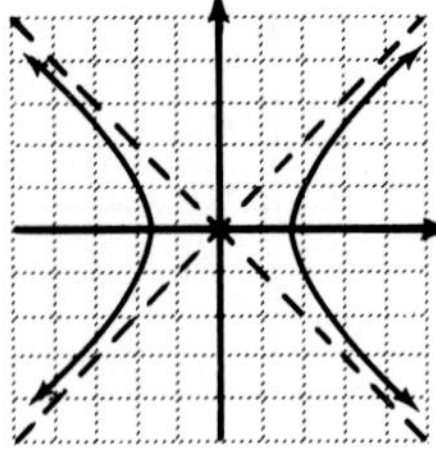

11. Center: $(-1, -3)$; foci: $(-1, -3 \pm 2\sqrt{5})$; vertices: $(-1, -1)$ and $(-1, -5)$; asym: $y = \frac{1}{2}x - \frac{5}{2}$ and $y = -\frac{1}{2}x - \frac{7}{2}$

13. Center: $(-1, -3)$; foci: $(-1, -3 \pm \sqrt{41})$; vertices: $(-1, -8)$ and $(-1, 2)$; asym: $y = \frac{5}{4}x - \frac{7}{4}$ and $y = -\frac{5}{4}x - \frac{17}{4}$

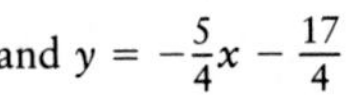

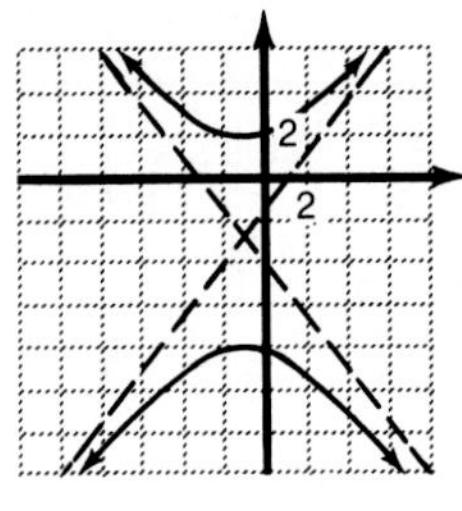

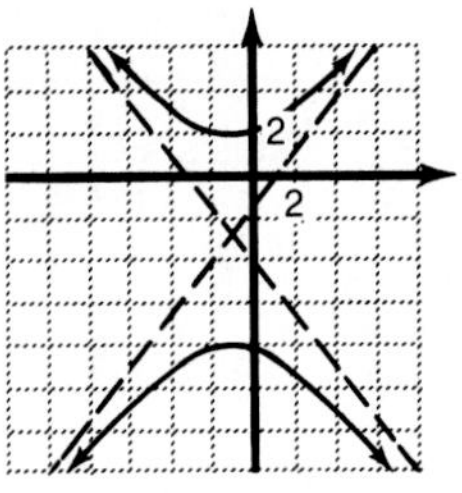

15. Center: $(-1, -2)$; foci: $(-1 \pm \sqrt{5}, -2)$; vertices: $(-2, -2)$ and $(0, -2)$; asym: $y = 2x$ and $y = -2x - 4$

17. Center: $(-3, 1)$; foci: $(-3 \pm \sqrt{13}, 1)$; vertices: $(-1, 1)$ and $(-5, 1)$; asym: $y = \frac{3}{2}x + \frac{11}{2}$ and $y = -\frac{3}{2}x - \frac{7}{2}$

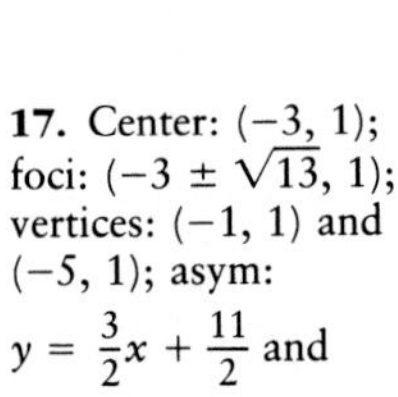

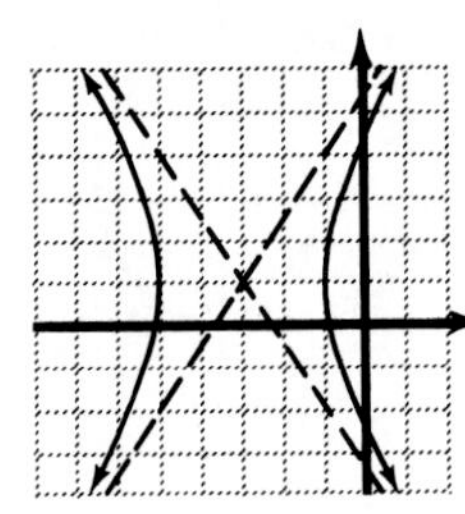

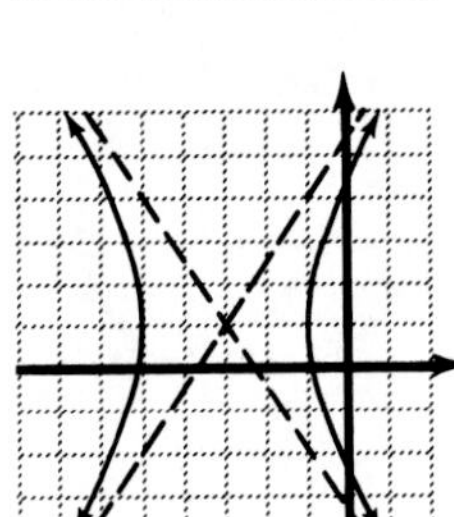

19.

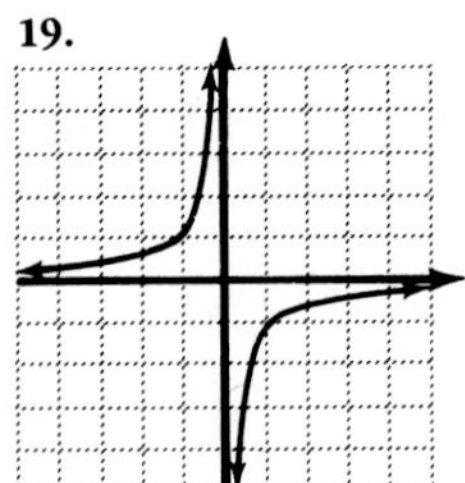

21.

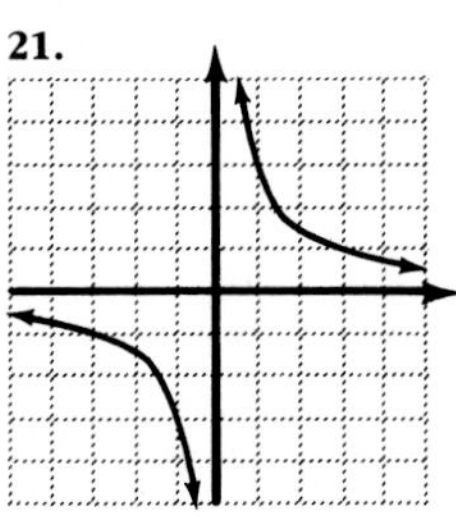

23. $\frac{x^2}{4} - \frac{y^2}{9} = 1$ **27.** $e > 1$ **29.** The graph gets closer to the coordinate axes. **33.** $(3, 6)$ **35.** $(6, 0)$ **37.** 10 **39.** 5 **41.** Neither **43.** Yes **45.** 138.24 m^2

Lesson 10-5 Try This

a. Vertex (0, 0); focus (0, 2); directrix $y = -2$

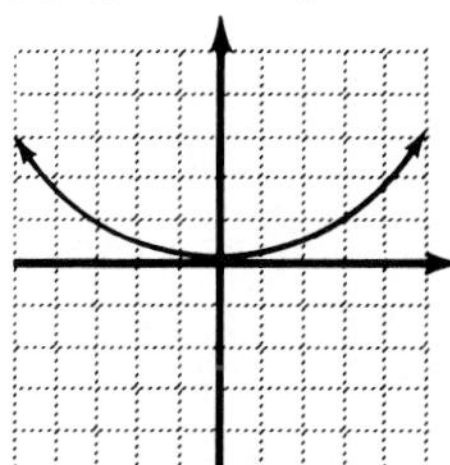

b. Vertex (0, 0); focus $\left(0, -\frac{1}{2}\right)$; directrix $y = \frac{1}{2}$

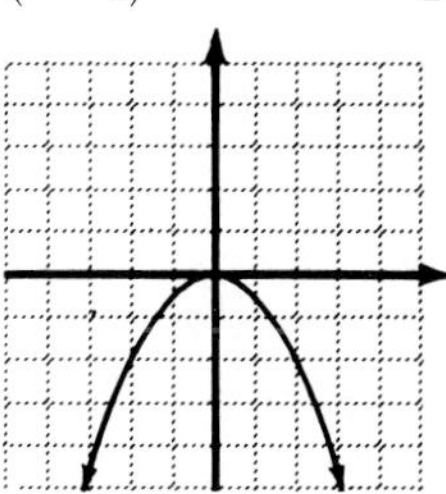

c. Vertex (0, 0); focus $\left(\frac{1}{2}, 0\right)$; directrix $x = -\frac{1}{2}$

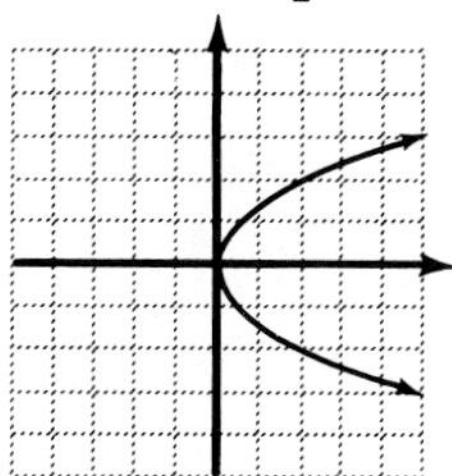

d. Vertex (0, 0); focus (−1, 0); directrix $x = 1$

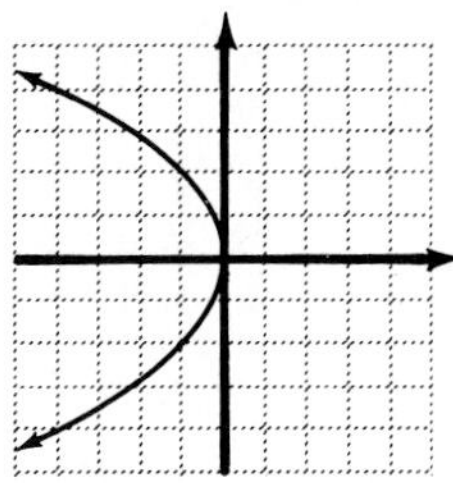

e. Vertex: $\left(-1, -\frac{1}{2}\right)$; focus: $\left(-1, \frac{3}{2}\right)$; dir: $y = -\frac{5}{2}$

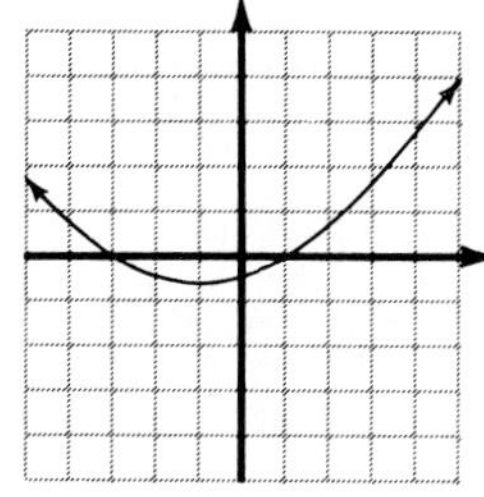

f. Vertex: (2, −1); focus: (1, −1); dir: $x = 3$

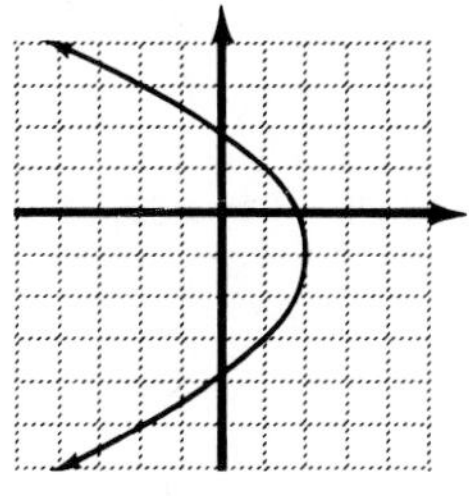

Exercise Set 10-5

1. V: (0, 0); F(0, 2); $y = -2$

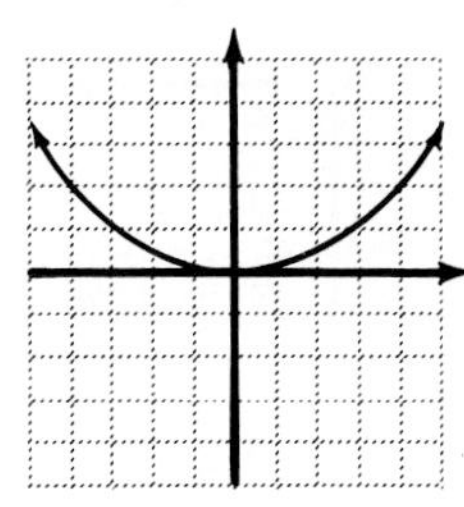

3. V: (0, 0) $F\left(-\frac{3}{2}, 0\right)$; $x = \frac{3}{2}$

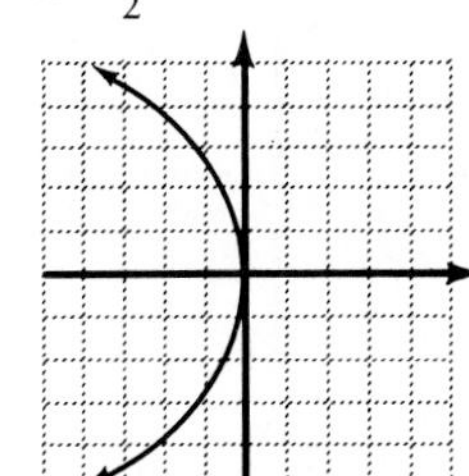

5. V (0, 0) F(0, 1); $y = -1$

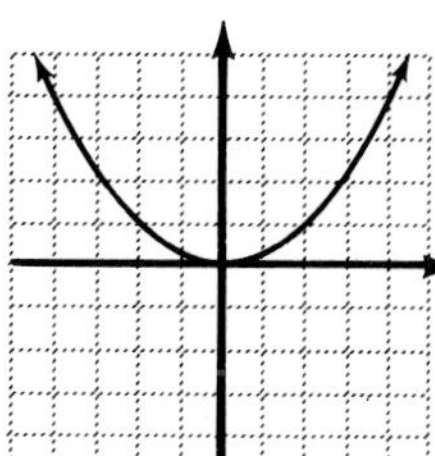

7. V: (0, 0) $F\left(0, \frac{1}{8}\right)$; $y = -\frac{1}{8}$

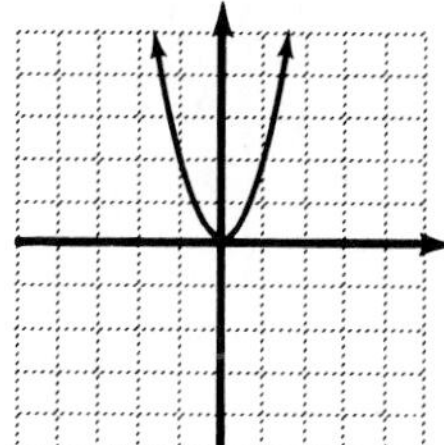

9. V (−2, 1); $F\left(-2, -\frac{1}{2}\right)$; $y = \frac{5}{2}$

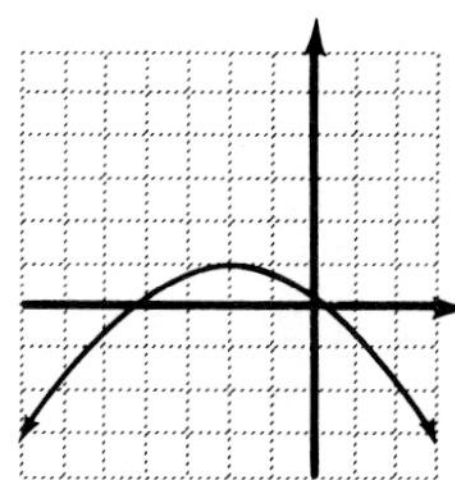

11. V (−1, −3); $F\left(-1, -\frac{7}{2}\right)$; $y = -\frac{5}{2}$

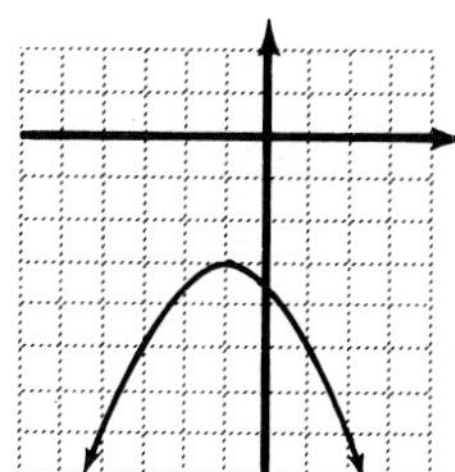

13. V (0, −2); $F\left(0, -\frac{7}{4}\right)$; $y = -\frac{9}{4}$

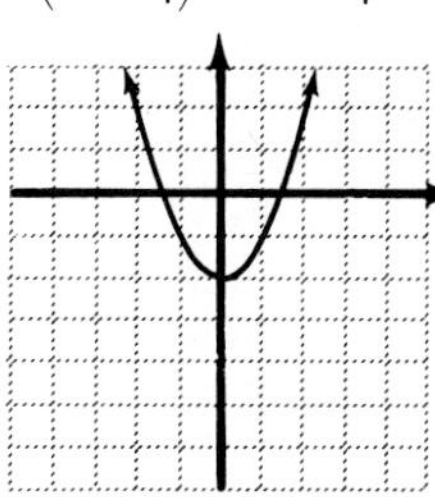

15. V (−2, −1); $F\left(-2, -\frac{3}{4}\right)$; $y = -\frac{5}{4}$

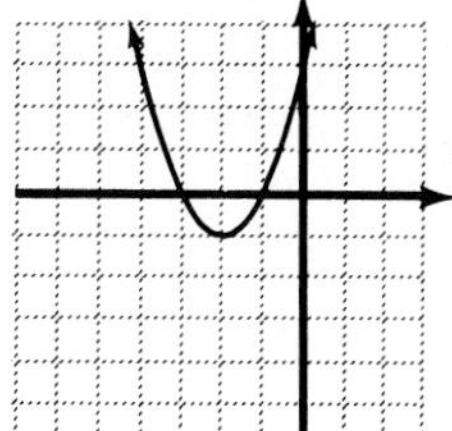

17. $V\left(\frac{23}{4}, \frac{1}{2}\right)$; $F\left(6, \frac{1}{2}\right)$; $x = \frac{11}{2}$

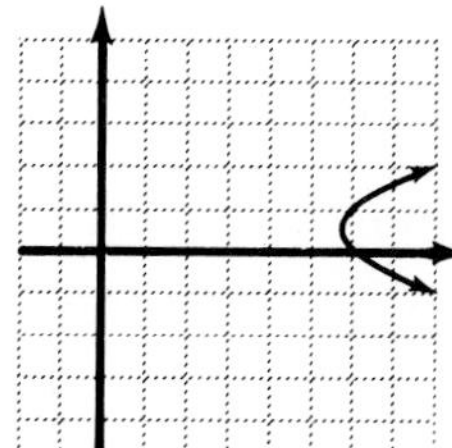

19. $y^2 = 16x$
21. $y^2 = -4\sqrt{2}x$
23. $x^2 = 12\sqrt{3}y$
25. $(y - 2)^2 = 14\left(x + \frac{1}{2}\right)$
27. $(x - 3)^2 = -12(y - 7)$
29. Vertex: (0, 0); focus: (0, 2014.0625); directrix: $y = 2014.0625$

31.

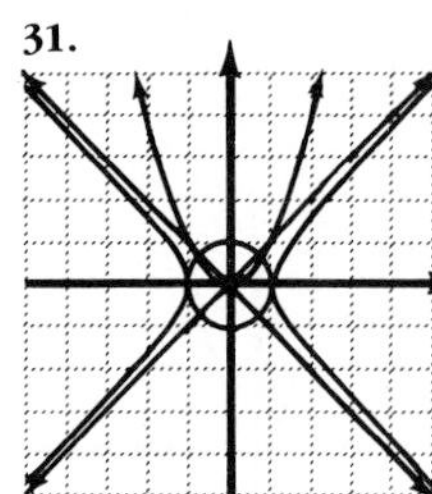

33. $(x + 1)^2 = -4(y - 2)$
35. 10 ft, 11.6 ft, 16.4 ft, 24.4 ft, 35.6 ft, 50 ft
41. Vertex: (3, 11), min: 11
43. $y^2 - 8y + 16$
45. $a^2 - 0.2a + 0.01$
47. $-\frac{4}{3}, -3$ **49.** $\frac{2}{5}, -\frac{1}{2}$
51. $-\frac{5}{2}, \frac{1}{3}$

Lesson 10-6 Try This

a. Ellipse **b.** Circle **c.** Parabola **d.** Hyperbola
e. $(x - 3)^2 + (y + 1)^2 = 16$ **f.** $x^2 = -\frac{2}{3}y$
g. $\frac{(y + 3)^2}{4} - \frac{(x + 1)^2}{1} = 1$ **h.** (4, 3), (−3, −4)
i. (4, 7), (−1, 2) **j.** (±2, 0) **k.** (±4, 0)

Exercise Set 10-6

1. Hyperbola **3.** Parabola **5.** Hyperbola
7. Hyperbola **9.** Does not exist **11.** $x^2 + y^2 = 9$
13. $x = 2y^2$ **15.** $\frac{x^2}{4} + \frac{(y + 1)^2}{9} = 1$
17. $\frac{(y - 4)^2}{9} - \frac{(x - 2)^2}{36} = 1$ **19.** $\frac{(x + 1)^2}{9} + \frac{(y + 3)^2}{4} = 1$
21. (−8, −6), (6, 8) **23.** (−7, 1), (1, −7)
25. (0, 3), (2, 0) **27.** (1, 1), (2, 4) **29.** (1, 1), (0, 0)
31. (0, −2), (0, 2) **33.** (−5, −3), (−5, 3), (4, 0)
35. (0, −5), (0, 5)
37.

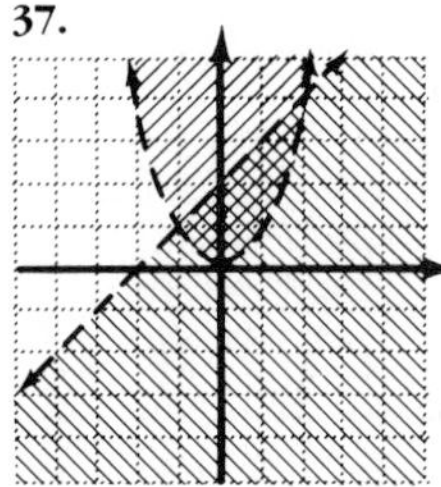

43. b. (−2, −3)
45. 4, 0, −4 **47.** No
49. 3 **51.** $\sqrt{m + n}$
53. $\left(\frac{5}{2}, \frac{25}{2}\right)$

Lesson 10-7 Try This

a. (−3, −4), (4, 3) **b.** (4, 7), (−1, 2)
c. (2, 1), (−4, 4) **d.** (0, −2), (0, 2)
e. (−2, −3), (−2, 3), (2, −3), (2, 3)
f. (2, −3), $\left(-\frac{14}{3}, \frac{1}{3}\right)$
g. (−3, −2), (−2, −3), (3, 2), (2, 3)
h. (2, 4), (−2, −4)

Exercise Set 10-7

1. (3, 2), $\left(4, \frac{3}{2}\right)$ **3.** $\left(\frac{7}{3}, \frac{1}{3}\right)$, (1, −1)
5. (1, 4), $\left(\frac{11}{4}, -\frac{5}{4}\right)$ **7.** (0, 2), (3, 1)
9. (2, −8), $\left(-\frac{40}{3}, -\frac{6}{5}\right)$
11. $(-3, -\sqrt{5}), (-3, \sqrt{5}), (3, -\sqrt{5}), (3, \sqrt{5})$
13. (−4, −2), (−2, −4), (2, 4), (4, 2)
15. (−2, −2), (2, 2), (4, 1), (−4, −1)
17. (−2, −1), (2, 1) **19.** No solution
21. $\left(\frac{1}{3}, \frac{1}{3}\right), \left(-\frac{1}{3}, \frac{1}{3}\right)$ (0, 0)

25. There is no number x such that $\frac{x^2}{a^2} - \frac{\left(\frac{b}{a}x\right)^2}{b^2} = 1$, because the left side simplifies to $\frac{x^2}{a^2} - \frac{x^2}{a^2}$, which is 0.
27. $(x + 1)^2 + (y + 3)^2 = 100$ **29.** 2 **31.** (0, 0); 7
33. 2 km **35.** No **37.** No **39.** Yes

Lesson 10-8 Try This

a. 14 m, 9 m **b.** $l = 12, w = 5$ **c.** $w = 1$ ft, $l = 2$ ft

Exercise Set 10-8

1. 6 cm, 8 cm **3.** 4 in., 5 in.
5. 12, 13 and −12, −13 **7.** $l = \sqrt{3}$ m, $w = 1$ m
9. 16 ft, 24 ft **11.** 9.7 **13.** 30 cm, 40 cm
17. Carpenter: 8.3 days, helper: 12.3 days
19. (3, 10) **21.** $f(x) = 2x^2 + 6x - 3$

Problem Set 10-9

1. 22 sections with 6 paths **3.** 63 games (1 less game than the number of teams) **5.** Roosevelt 195, Riverside 125, Central 190.

Chapter 10 Summary and Review

1. $2\sqrt{29}$ **3.** $\sqrt{221}$ **5.** (2, 6) **7.** (5, 5)
9. $(x - 3)^2 + (y + 1)^2 = 4$ **11.** Center (0, 0); radius 6
13. Center: $\left(\frac{3}{4}, \frac{5}{4}\right)$; radius: $\frac{\sqrt{10}}{4}$
15. Center: (−2, 1); vertices: (−6, 1), (2, 1), (−2, 4), (−2, −2); foci: $(-2 + \sqrt{7}, 1)$, $(-2 - \sqrt{7}, 1)$

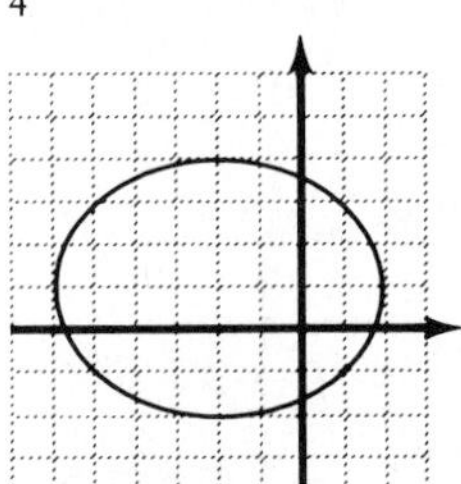

17. Center: (0, 0); vertices: $(\sqrt{6}, 0)$, $(-\sqrt{6}, 0)$; foci: $(\sqrt{22}, 0)$, $(-\sqrt{22}, 0)$; asymptotes: $y = \pm\frac{2\sqrt{6}}{3}x$

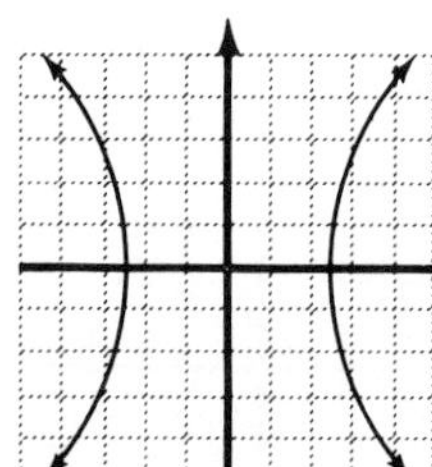

19. Vertex: (1, −1); focus: $\left(1, -\frac{1}{2}\right)$; directrix: $y = -\frac{3}{2}$

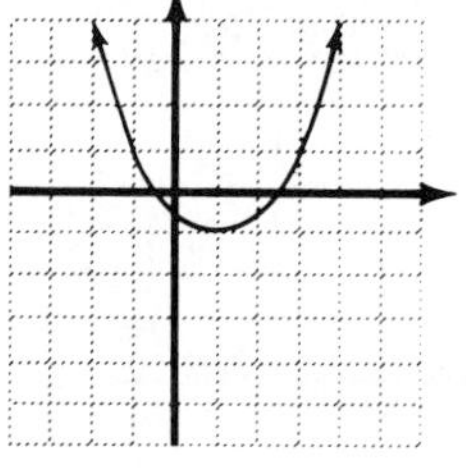

21. Hyperbola **23.** Circle **25.** No conic

27. $(1, 2), \left(-\frac{3}{2}, \frac{13}{4}\right)$ **29.** $(4, 0), (0, 3)$

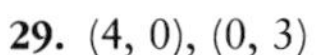

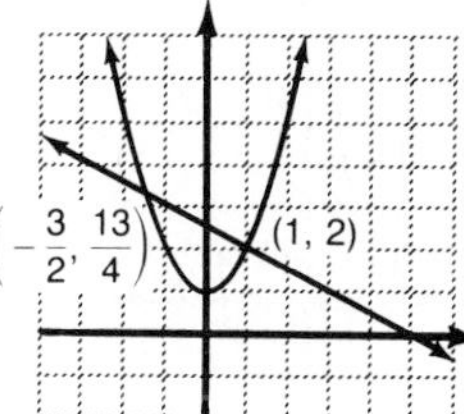

31. $(6, -2), (-6, 2)$ **33.** $3, -16$ or $-3, 16$

Chapter 11

Lesson 11-1 Try This

a. **(1)** Yes **(2)** No **b.** **(1)** Yes **(2)** No
c. **(1)** No **(2)** Yes **d.** **(1)** Yes **(2)** No
e. $x^3 + 2x^2 - 5x - 6 = (x - 3)(x^2 + 5x + 10) + 24$

Exercise Set 11-1

1. Yes, no, no **3.** Yes, no, yes, yes **5.** **a.** Yes **c.** No
7. **a.** Yes **c.** No **9.** **a.** Yes **c.** Yes
11. **a.** $x^3 + 6x^2 - x - 30 = (x - 2)(x^2 + 8x + 15) + 0$
13. $x^3 - 8 = (x + 2)(x^2 - 2x + 4) + (-16)$
15. $x^4 + 9x^2 + 20 = (x^2 + 4)(x^2 + 5) + 0$
17. $5x^5 - 3x^4 + 2x^2 - 3 =$
$(2x^2 - x + 1)\left(\frac{5}{2}x^3 - \frac{1}{4}x^2 - \frac{11}{8}x + \frac{7}{16}\right) + \frac{29x - 55}{16}$
19. $2x^3 + 7x^2 - 5$ **21.** $6x^3 - 8x^2 + 23x - 4$
23. **b.** -2 **25.** All exponents even; yes **27.** Even
29. Neither
31. **33.**

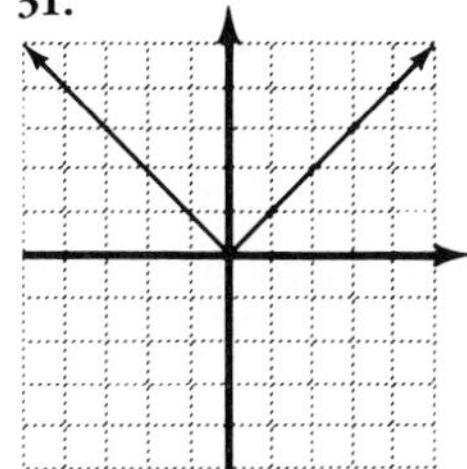

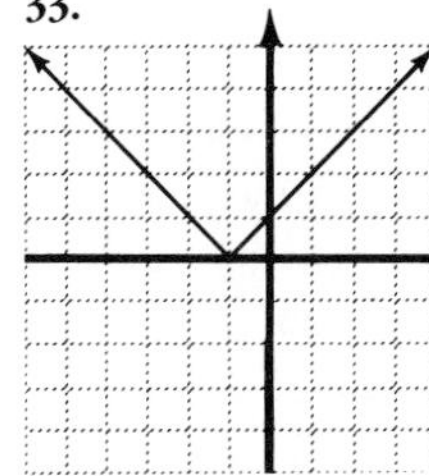

35. $\frac{1 \pm \sqrt{10}}{3}$ **37 b.** 88 points

Lesson 11-2 Try This

a. 73,120; $-37{,}292$ **b.** Yes **c.** No **d.** Yes **e.** No
f. Yes **g.** $P(x) = (x - 2)(x + 3)(x + 5)$; $2, -3, -5$

Exercise Set 11-2

1. $P(1) = 0$; $P(-2) = -60$; $P(3) = 0$
3. $P(20) = 5{,}935{,}988$; $P(-3) = -722$
5. Yes, no **7.** No, no **9.** No **11.** Yes **13.** Yes
15. **a.** Yes **b.** $x^2 + 3x + 2$
c. $(x - 1)(x + 2)(x + 1)$ **d.** $1, -2, -1$
17. $P(x) = (x - 1)(x + 2)(x + 3)$; $1, -2, -3$
19. $P(x) = (x - 2)(x - 5)(x + 1)$; $2, 5, -1$
21. $P(x) = (x - 2)(x - 3)(x + 4)$; $2, 3, -4$
23. $P(x) = (x - 1)(x - 2)(x - 3)(x + 5)$; $1, 2, 3, -5$
25. $-5 < x < 1$ or $x > 2$ **27.** 4 **29.** 0

35. $f(x) = 2\left(x - \frac{5}{2}\right)^2 - \frac{41}{2}$; Vertex: $\left(\frac{5}{2}, -\frac{41}{2}\right)$; Line of sym: $x = \frac{5}{2}$; Min: $-\frac{41}{2}$ **37.** Center $(-1, 0)$; radius 8
39. Center $(-1, 1)$; radius $3\sqrt{5}$

Lesson 11-3 Try This

a. -7 (multiplicity 2), 3 (multiplicity 1)
b. 4 (multiplicity 2), 3 (multiplicity 2)
c. 1 (multiplicity 1), -1 (multiplicity 1)
d. $7 + 2i$ and $3 - 7\sqrt{5}$ are the other roots.
e. $i, -i, -2, 1$ **f.** $P(x) = x^3 - 6x^2 + 3x + 10$
g. $P(x) = x^5 + 6x^4 + 12x^3 + 8x^2$
h. $P(x) = x^4 - 6x^3 + 11x^2 - 10x + 2$
i. $P(x) = x^3 - 2x^2 + 4x - 8$

Exercise Set 11-3

1. -3 (multiplicity 2), 1 (multiplicity 1)
3. 3 (multiplicity 2), -4 (multiplicity 3), 0 (multiplicity 4) **5.** 2 (multiplicity 2), 3 (multiplicity 2) **7.** $5 - i$, $2i$ are the other roots.
9. $-3 - 4i$, $4 + \sqrt{5}$ **11.** $1 + i$ **13.** $i, 3, 2$
15. $-2i, 2, -2$ **17.** $2 + i, 2 - i$ **19.** $-1 + i\sqrt{3}$, $-1 - i\sqrt{3}$ **21.** $\sqrt{3}, 1 + 3i, 1 - 3i$
23. $P(x) = x^3 - 6x^2 - x + 30$
25. $P(x) = x^3 - 2x^2 + x - 2$
27. $P(x) = x^3 - 7x^2 + 17x - 15$
29. $P(x) = x^3 - \sqrt{3}x^2 - 2x + 2\sqrt{3}$; no
31. $P(x) = x^4 - 10x^3 + 25x^2$
33. $P(x) = x^4 - 3x^3 - 7x^2 + 15x + 18$
35. $P(x) = x^3 - 4x^2 + 6x - 4$
37. $P(x) = x^3 + 2x^2 + 9x + 18$
39. $P(x) = x^4 - 6x^3 + 11x^2 - 10x + 2$
41. $P(x) = x^4 + 4x^2 - 45$
43. $P(x) = x^4 - 4x^3 + 9x^2 + 8x - 22$
45. $i, -i, -\frac{b}{a}$ **47.** $i, -i, 1 + \sqrt{2}, 1 - \sqrt{2}$
55. Vertex: $(-1, 1)$; Line of sym: $x = -1$; Max: -1
57. Vertex: $(0, 1)$; focus: $(0, 3)$; directrix: $y = -1$
59. $11\frac{1}{4}$ lb of Mocha-Java, $8\frac{3}{4}$ lb of Manager's Blend
61. **a.** 12.76 **c.** 122 lb

Lesson 11-4 Try This

a. $\frac{1}{2}, -2, \sqrt{3}, -\sqrt{3}$ **b.** $-7, 2i, -2i$ **c.** None **d.** 2

Exercise Set 11-4

1. -3; $\sqrt{2}, -\sqrt{2}$ **3.** $1, -\frac{1}{5}, 2i, -2i$
5. $-1, -2$; $3 + \sqrt{13}, 3 - \sqrt{13}$ **7.** $1, 2$; $-4 + \sqrt{21}$, $-4 - \sqrt{21}$ **9.** -2; $1 + i\sqrt{3}, 1 - i\sqrt{3}$ **11.** $\frac{3}{4}$; $i, -i$
13. $1, 2, -2$ **15.** No rational **17.** No rational
19. No rational
21. **a.** 2 (multiplicity 2), -3 (multiplicity 1) **c.** $\frac{1}{2}$
23. 5 cm, $\frac{15 - 5\sqrt{5}}{2}$ cm ($\approx$1.9098 cm)
29. $4\sqrt{2}$ **31.** 12 **33.** $(0, -4), (1, -3)$
35. Yes, no, yes

Lesson 11-5 Try This

a. 1 **b.** 5, 3, or 1 **c.** 2 or 0 **d.** 2 or 0 **e.** 1 **f.** 0

Exercise Set 11-5

1. 3 or 1 **3.** 0 **5.** 2 or 0 **7.** 3 or 1 **9.** 2 or 0
11. 0 **13.** 3 or 1 **15.** 2 or 0 **17.** 0 **19.** 1
21. 1 positive, 1 negative, 2 complex
23. 0 positive, 0 negative, 4 complex
25. 1 positive, 1 negative, $2n - 2$ complex
31. (3, −4), (−3, −4), (4, 3), (−4, 3)

Lesson 11-6 Try This

a.

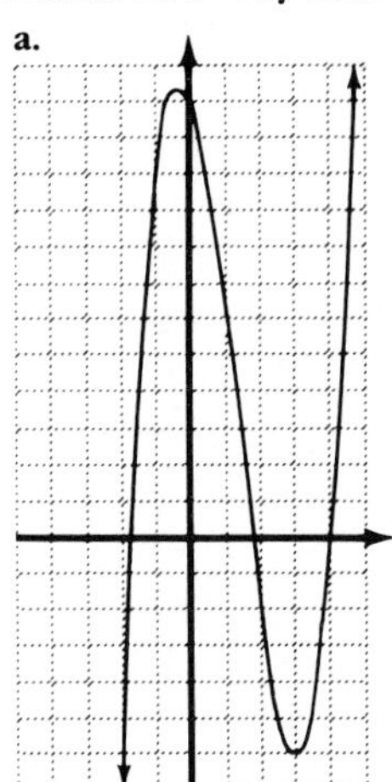

b. 0.7, −0.5, 2.9

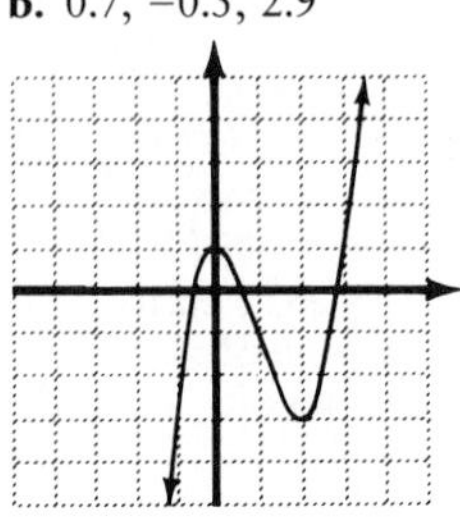

c. No real solution.

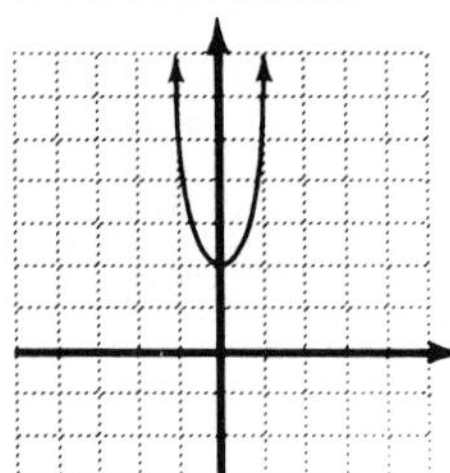

Exercise Set 11-6

1.

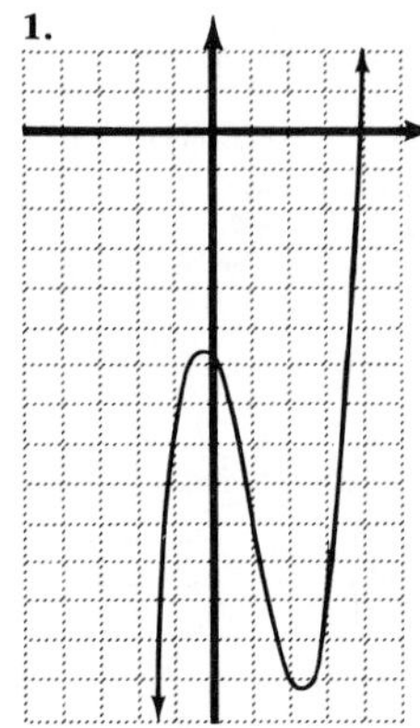

3.

5.

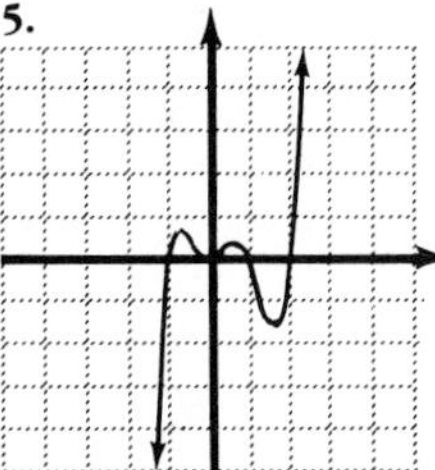

7. −1, 2

9. 2.2

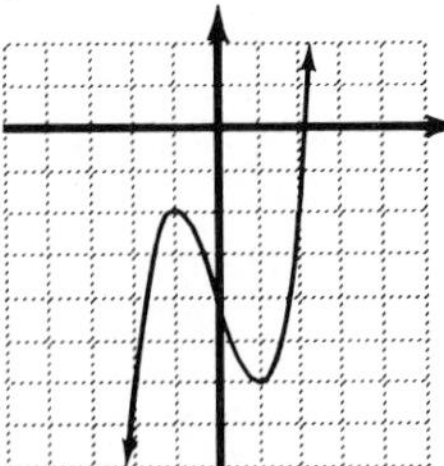

11. ±1.4, ±2

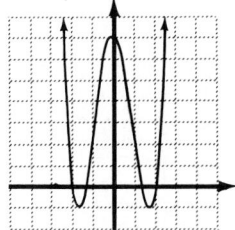

13. −1, ±1.4

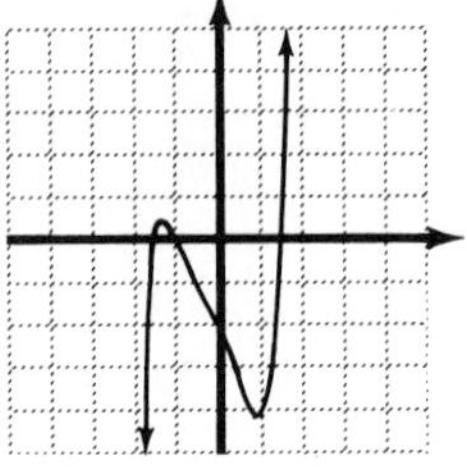

15. No real solution

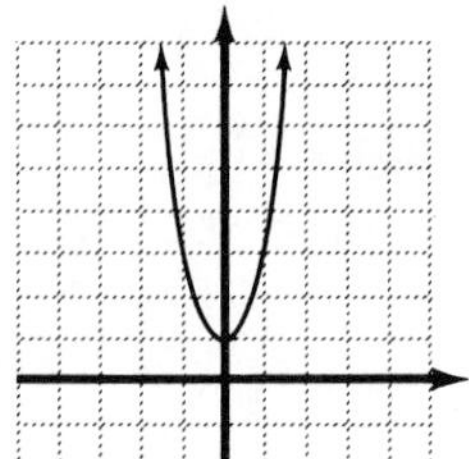

17. 0.79
19. −1.27

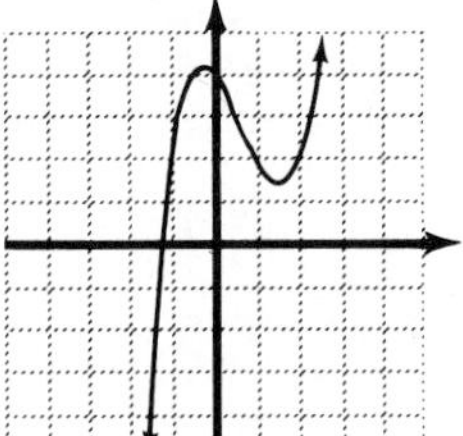

23. $P(x) = 3x^4 - 5x^3 + 4x^2 - 5$. Perform synthetic division using a as the divisor and 3, −5, 4, 0, and −5 as the coefficients to find $P(a) = a[a(a(3a - 5) + 4)] - 5$. This expression is the same expression obtained by factoring to find nested form.

25. $y = -\frac{1}{2}x + 3$ **27.** $x \leq -\frac{7}{3}$ or $x \geq 1$
29. No solution **31.** 6, 2, −1 **33.** (3, 6)

Problem Set 11-7

1. 65, 35, and 20 points. **3.** 4094 people in the 11 generations **5.** 24, 28, 32, 36, 41 lb. **7.** 105

Chapter 11 Summary and Review

1. No, yes **3.** Yes, no **5.** Yes
7. $x^3 - 2x^2 + 4 = (x - 1)(x^2 - x - 1) + 3$
9. 1, −7, 53, 73 **11.** −1, 1, 18
13. 1 (multiplicity 2), 11 (multiplicity 2)
15. $P(x) = x^4 - 6x^3 + 11x^2 - 10x + 2$
17. $\frac{1}{2}, \frac{5 + \sqrt{15}}{10}, \frac{5 - \sqrt{15}}{10}$
19. Positive 3 or 1, negative 0
21. −3, 1.4, −1.4

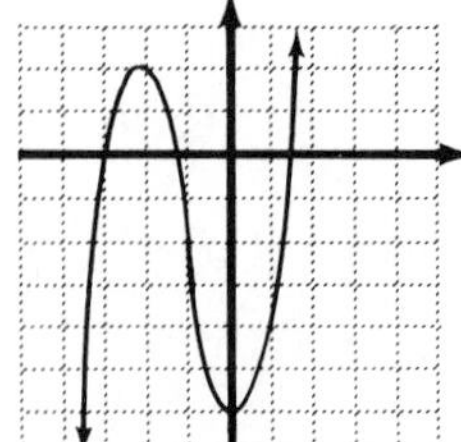

Chapter 12

Lesson 12-1 Try This

a. $x = y^2 + 4$ **b.** Yes **c.** No **d.** $g^{-1}(x) = x - 2$

e. $g^{-1}(x) = \frac{1}{5}(x - 2)$ **f.** $f^{-1}(x) = x^2 - 1, x \geq 0$

g. $f^{-1}(f(579)) = 579, f(f^{-1}(-83{,}479)) = -83{,}479$

Exercise Set 12-1

1. $x = 4y - 5$ **3.** $x = 3y^2 + 2$ **5.** $y^2 - 3x^2 = 3$

7. $y \cdot x = 7$ **9.** $yx^2 = 1$ **11.** $x = \frac{5}{y}$ **13.** No

15. Yes **17.** Yes **19.** Yes **21.** Yes **23.** No

25. $f^{-1}(x) = x + 1$ **27.** $f^{-1}(x) = x - 4$

29. $f^{-1}(x) = x - 8$ **31.** $f^{-1}(x) = \frac{x - 5}{2}$

33. $f^{-1}(x) = \frac{x + 1}{3}$ **35.** $f^{-1}(x) = 2(x - 2)$

37. $f^{-1}(x) = x^2 + 1; x \geq 0$

39. $f^{-1}(x) = x^2 - 2; x \geq 0$ **41.** 5, −12

43. 489, −17,422

45.

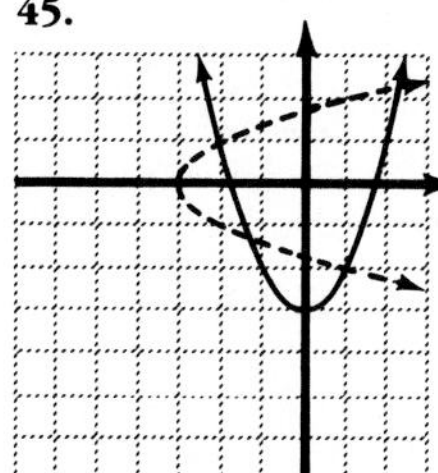

47.

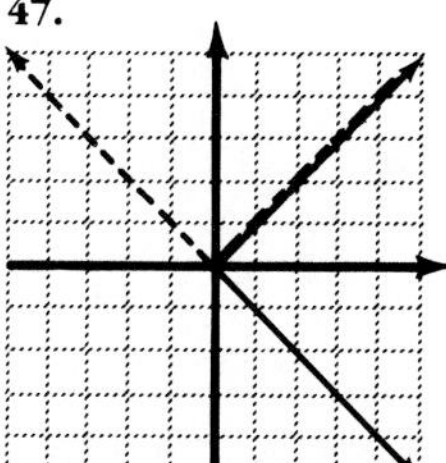

49. x, x **51.** $x^2 + 6x + 9; x^2 + 3$

53. $12x^2 - 12x + 5; 6x^2 + 3$

55. $x^4 - 2x^2; x^4 - 2x^2$ **57.** x-axis: no; y-axis: yes; origin: no; $y = x$: no **59.** x-axis: no; y-axis: no; origin: yes; $y = x$: no **61.** 3^8 **63.** 9 **65.** m^{15}

67. $\frac{m^6}{16n^{14}}$

Lesson 12-2 Try This

a. $3^{\frac{1}{2}} \approx 1.7$

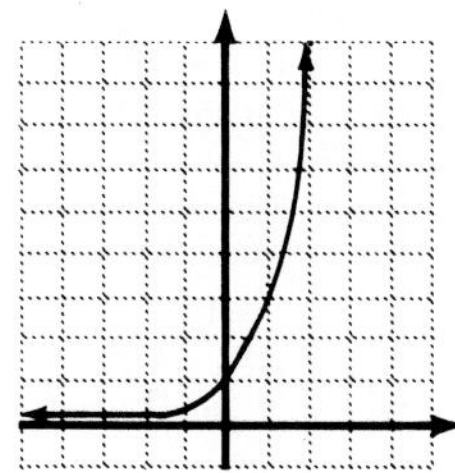

b.

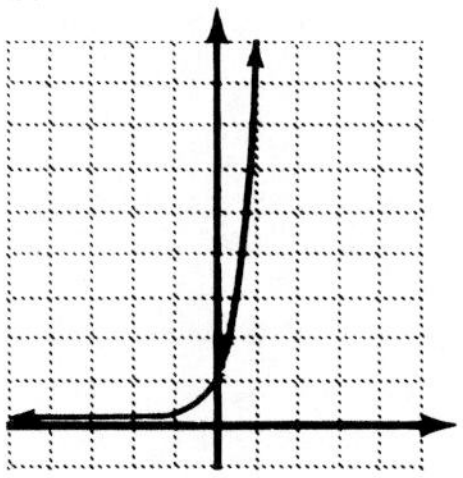

c.

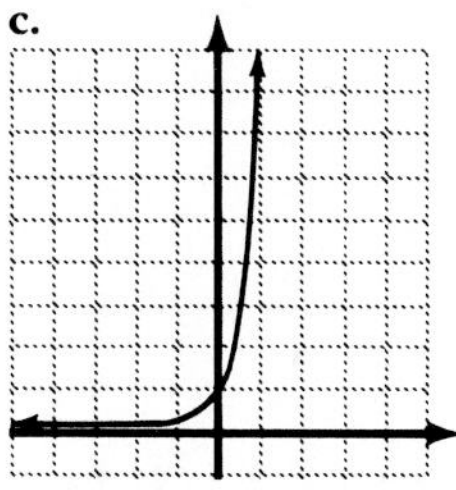

d.

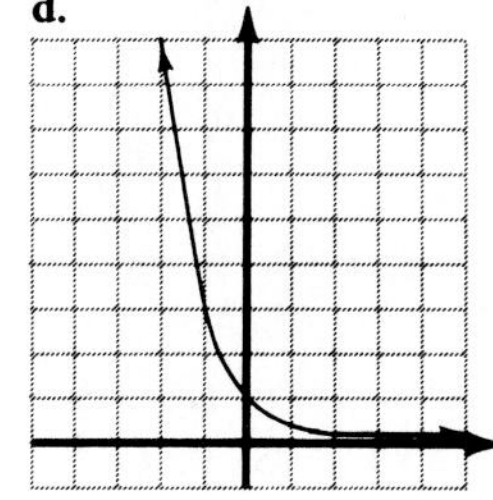

e. D: positive real nos.; R: all real nos.

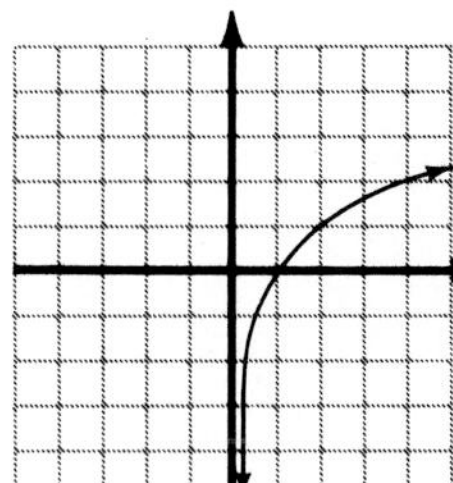

f. D: positive real nos.; R: all real nos.

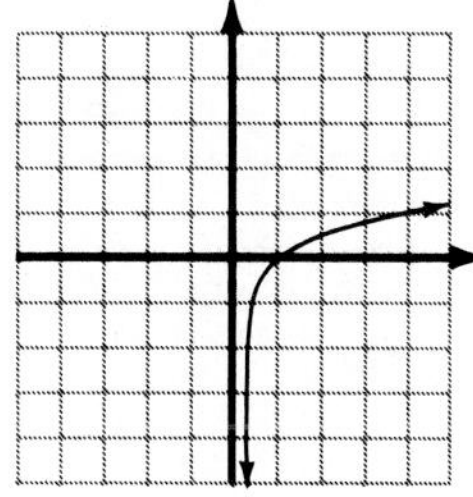

Exercise Set 12-2

1.

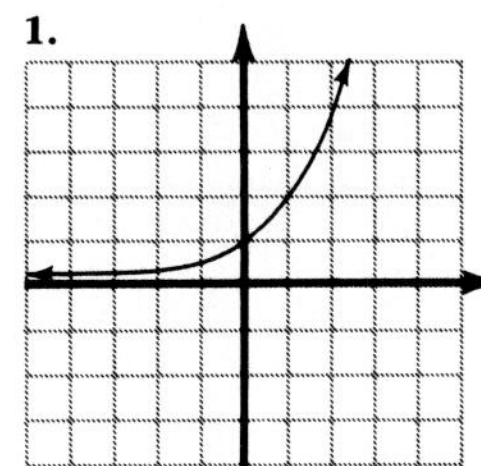

3.

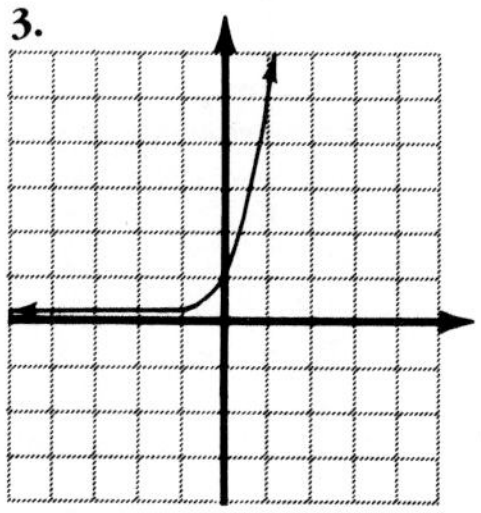

5.

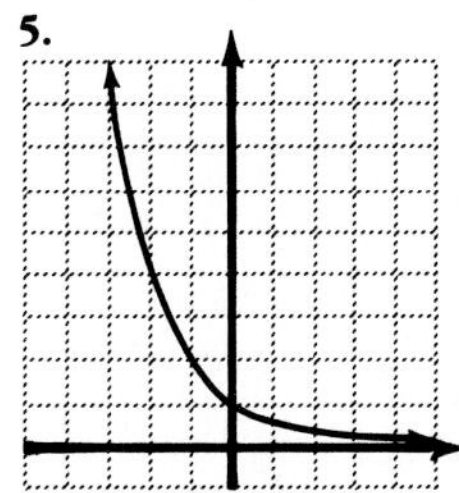

7.

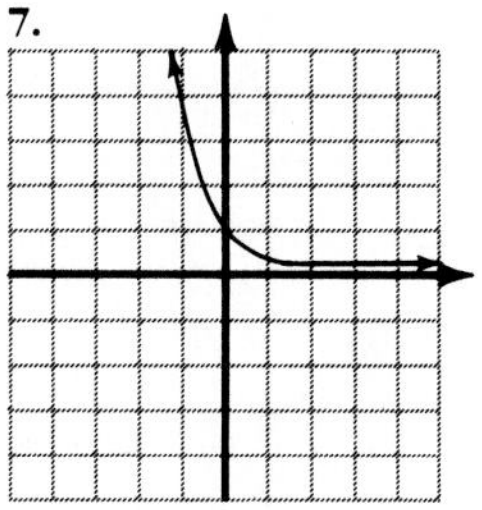

9.

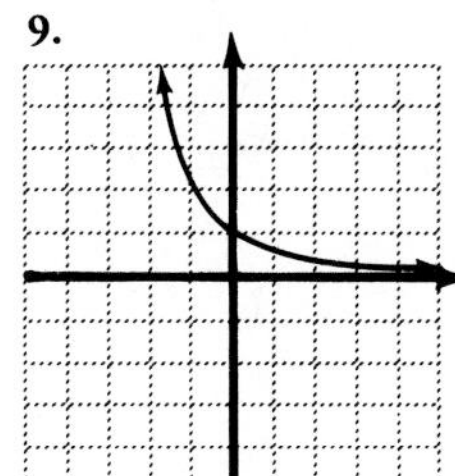

11.

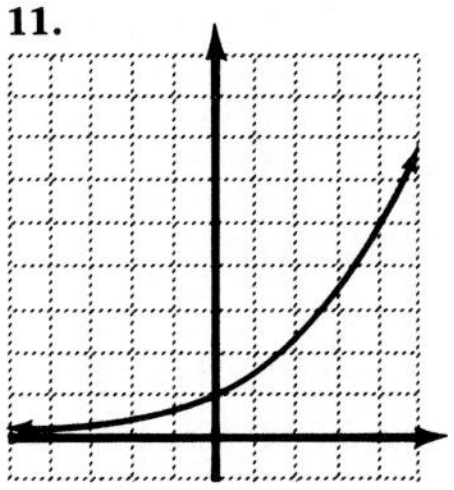

13.

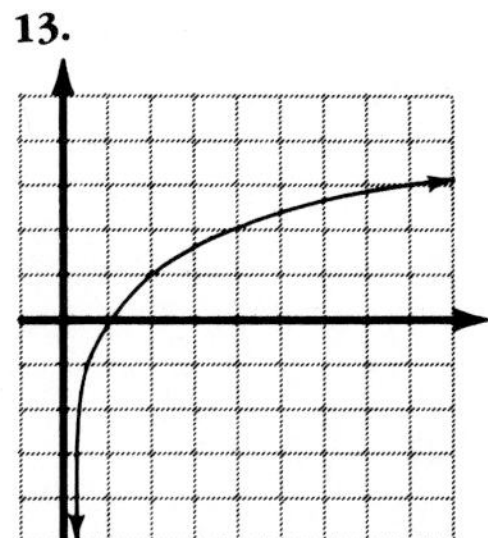

15.

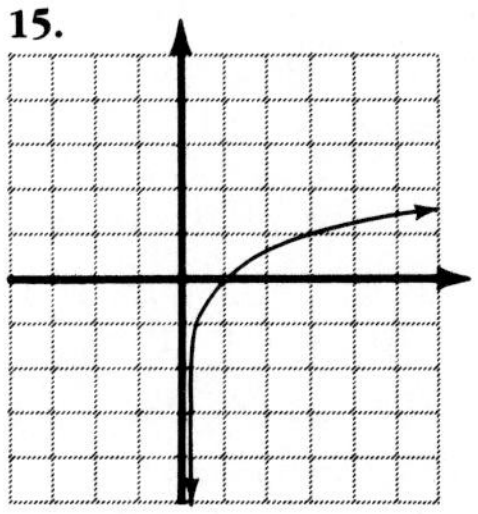

17.

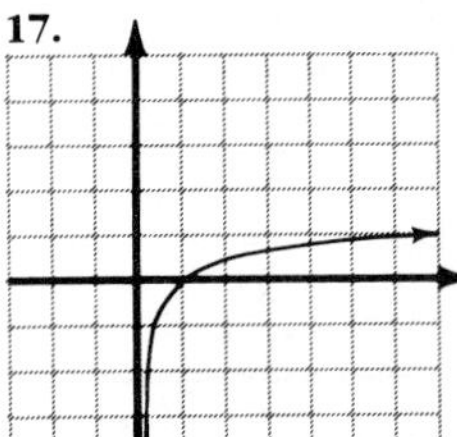

19.

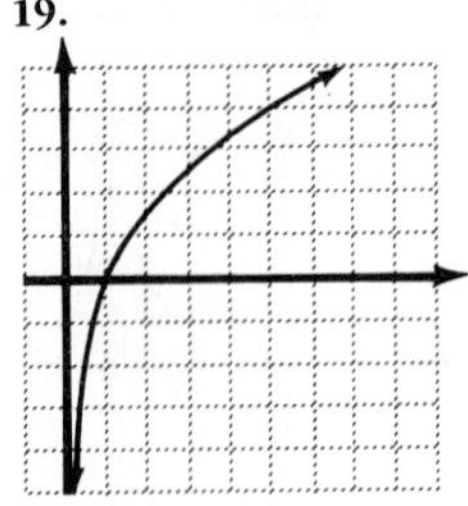

21. Set of all real numbers **23.** 1

25.

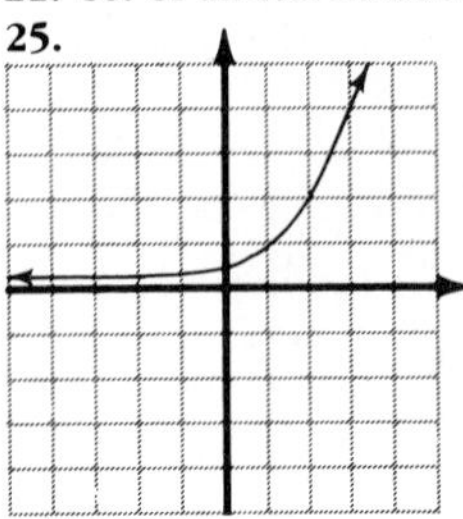

27.

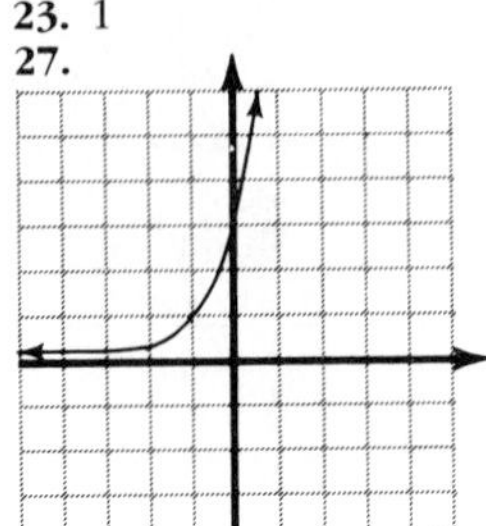

29.

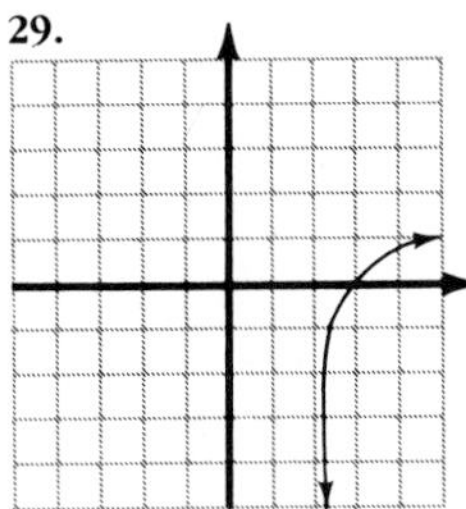

31.

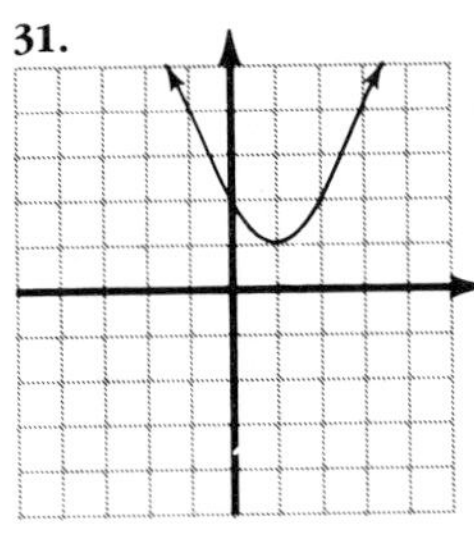

33.

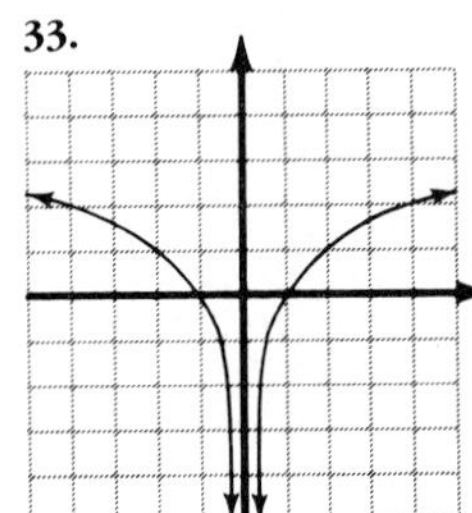

35. $\{x|x > 0\}$
37. $\{x|x > 0\}$
39. $\{x|x \neq 0\}$
41. π^5
47. 3.007114×10^6
49. 0.00005709
51. $y^2 = 24x$

Lesson 12-3 Try This

a. $\log_6 1 = 0$ **b.** $\log_{10} 0.001 = -3$ **c.** $\log_{16} 2 = \frac{1}{4}$
d. $\log_{\frac{6}{5}} \frac{25}{36} = -2$ **e.** $2^5 = 32$ **f.** $10^3 = 1000$
g. $10^{-2} = 0.01$ **h.** $(\sqrt{5})^2 = 5$ **i.** 10,000 **j.** 3 **k.** 4
l. −2 **m.** 3 **n.** 42 **o.** 37 **p.** 3.2

Exercise Set 12-3

1. $5 = \log_{10} 100{,}000$ **3.** $\frac{1}{3} = \log_8 2$ **5.** $-3 = \log_5 \frac{1}{125}$
7. $0.3010 = \log_{10} 2$ **9.** $3^t = 8$ **11.** $5^2 = 25$
13. $10^{-1} = 0.1$ **15.** $10^{0.845} = 7$ **17.** $k^c = A$
19. 64 **21.** 4 **23.** $\frac{1}{9}$ **25.** 2 **27.** 4 **29.** 9
31. 6 **33.** 2 **35.** −1 **37.** 0 **39.** $\{x|x > 0\}$

41. $\{x|0 < x < 1\}$ **45.** $-\frac{1}{2}$
47. $x^5 - x^4 - 2x^3 + 2x^2 + x - 1$
49. $f(x) = 3x^2 - 6x - 5$

Lesson 12-4 Try This

a. (1) $\log_a M + \log_a N$ **(2)** $\log_5 25 + \log_5 5 = 3$
b. (1) $\log_3 35$ **(2)** $\log_a CABIN$ **c.** $5 \log_7 4$
d. $\frac{1}{2} \log_a 5$ **e. (1)** $\log_a M - \log_a N$
(2) $\log_c 1 - \log_c 4$ **f.** $\log_{10} 4 + \log_{10} \pi - \frac{1}{2}\log_{10} 23$
g. $\frac{3}{2}\log_a z - \frac{1}{2}\log_a x - \frac{1}{2}\log_a y$ **h.** $\log_a \frac{x^5 \sqrt[4]{z}}{y}$
i. (1) 0.954 **(2)** 0.1505 **(3)** 0.1003 **(4)** 0.176
(5) 1.585

Exercise Set 12-4

1. $\log_2 32 + \log_2 8 = 5 + 3 = 8$
3. $\log_4 64 + \log_4 16 = 3 + 2 = 5$
5. $\log_c B + \log_c x$ **7.** $\log_a (6 \cdot 70)$ **9.** $\log_c (K \cdot y)$
11. $5 \log_b t$ **13.** $\log_a 67 - \log_a 5$ **15.** $\log_b 3 - \log_b 4$
17. $\log_a 5 + \log_a x + 4 \log_a y + 3 \log_a z$
19. $\log_a \frac{\sqrt[3]{x^2}\sqrt{y}}{y}$ **21.** $\log_a \frac{2x^4}{y^3}$ **23.** $\log_a \frac{\sqrt{a}}{x}$
25. 0.602 **27.** 1.699 **29.** 1.778 **31.** −0.088
33. 1.954 **35.** −0.602 **37.** False **39.** False
41. False **43.** $\frac{1}{2}$ **45.** $\sqrt{7}$ **47.** −2, 0 **51.** −2
55. $i, -i, 2$ **57.** 5, 1; $\sqrt{5}, -\sqrt{5}$

Lesson 12-5 Try This

a. 2.3238 **b.** 5.8186 **c.** 0.4625 **d.** −4.3665
e. 0.8506 **f.** 0.6021 **g.** 0.9996 **h.** 0.4609 + 2
i. 0.4609 + (−4) **j.** 8.6646 − 10 **k.** 9.7832 − 10
l. 6.8055 − 10 **m.** 22,003.92 **n.** 1022.8219
o. 0.00098469 **p.** 0.00000017 **q.** 64106.2
r. 4.25×10^{-4} **s.** 0.0105

Exercise Set 12-5

1. 0.3909 **3.** 0.7251 **5.** 0.5705 **7.** 0.0294
9. 0.8007 **11.** 3.9405 **13.** 1.3139 **15.** 1.9657
17. 5.7952 **19.** 8.8463 − 10, or −1.1537
21. 6.3345 − 10, or −3.6655 **23.** 7.5403 − 10, or
−2.4597 **25.** 7.34 **27.** 4.79 **29.** 5.72 **31.** 2330
33. 18 **35.** 0.0973 **37.** 0.0346 **39.** 0.00000426
41. 15,500 **43.** 0.0951 **45.** 3.7536 **47.** $10^{\frac{1}{3}\log 8} = 2$
49. $10^{\log 14 - \log 2} = 7$ **51.** Parabola

Lesson 12-6 Try This

a. 3.6592 **b.** 8.3779 − 10 or 1.6221 **c.** 2856
d. 0.0005956

Exercise Set 12-6

1. 1.6194 **3.** 0.4689 **5.** 2.8130 **7.** 9.1538 − 10
9. 7.6291 − 10 **11.** 9.2494 − 10 **13.** 2.7786
15. 2.9031 **17.** 224.5 **19.** 14.53 **21.** 70,030
23. 0.09245 **25.** 0.5343 **27.** 0.007295
29. 9.8445 − 10 **33.** 0.8268 **35.** 3 or 1 **37.** 0
39. Yes **41.** Yes **43.** $f^{-1}(x) = x^2 - 3$

Lesson 12-7 Try This

a. 2.8074 **b.** 1.2925 **c.** 3 **d.** 125 **e.** 8.75 **f.** 2

g. $\approx$10 years **h.** 34 db. **i.** 60 db. **j.** $\approx$8.4

Exercise Set 12-7

1. 3 **3.** 3.3219 **5.** $\frac{5}{2}$ **7.** $-3, -1$ **9.** 1.4036

11. 2.7093 **13.** 3.6064 **15.** 5.6467 **17.** 1 **19.** 1

21. $\sqrt{41}$ **23.** $1, 10^{16}$ **25.** $\pm\frac{\sqrt{2}}{4}$ **27.** 22.5

29. 64 dec. **31.** 120 dec. **33.** $\approx$8.25

35. $\approx 6.3 \times 10^7 I_0$ **37.** 7.8 **39.** $\pm 4\sqrt{39}$ **41.** $25, \frac{1}{25}$

43. $100, \frac{1}{100}$ **45.** $-\frac{1}{2}$ **47.** $t = \frac{\log_b y - \log_b k}{a}$

49. $n = \log_v c - \log_v P$, or $\log_v \frac{c}{P}$ **51.** $y = xa^{2x}$

53. 10,100 **55.** 5 **57.** $\left\{x \middle| x < \frac{\log 0.8}{\log 0.5} \approx 0.3219\right\}$

61. 4 **63.** 4 **65.** $f^{-1} = 5x + 5$ **67.** $3 = \log_{10} 1000$

69. $\frac{1}{2} = \log_{81} 9$ **71.** $8^1 = 8$ **73.** $2^6 = 64$ **75.** None

77. $1, 2, -2$

Lesson 12-8 Try This

a.

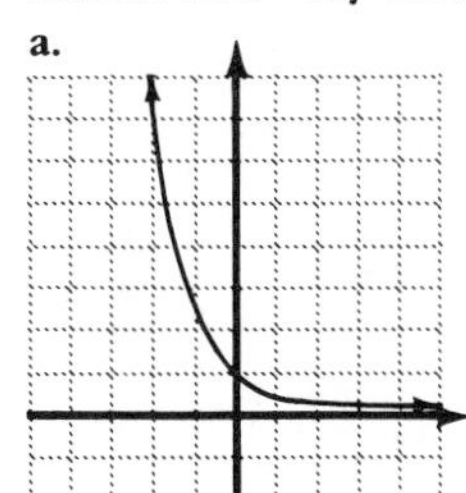

b.

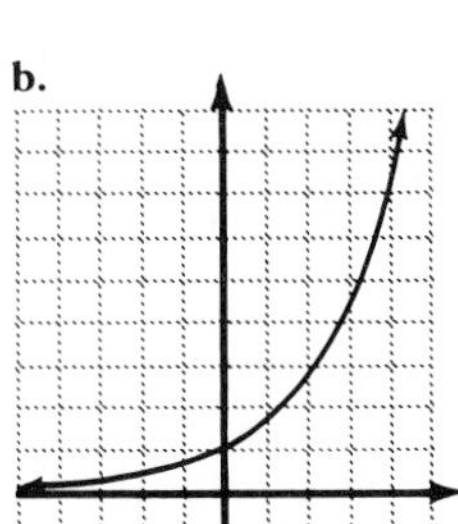

c. 0.693147 **d.** 4.605170 **e.** -2.599375
f. 0.000100 **g. (1)** 0.0514 **(2)** 231,000
h. 3.5 grams **i.** 3 **j.** 4.7385 **k.** 0.4342
l. 6.937 **m.** -0.783 **n.** 2.8076

Exercise Set 12-8

1.

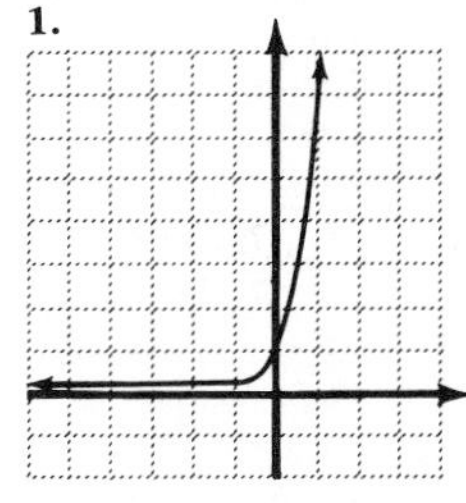

3.

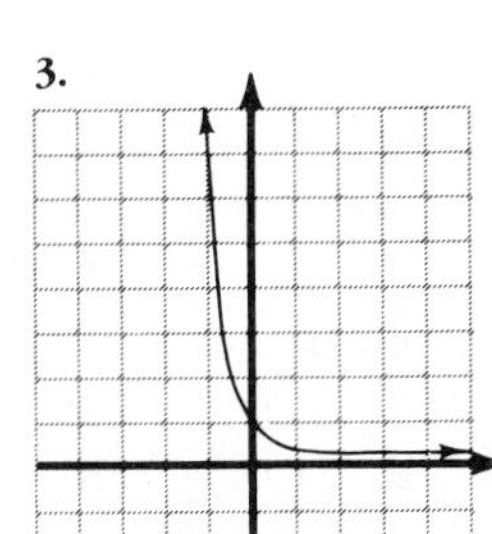

5.

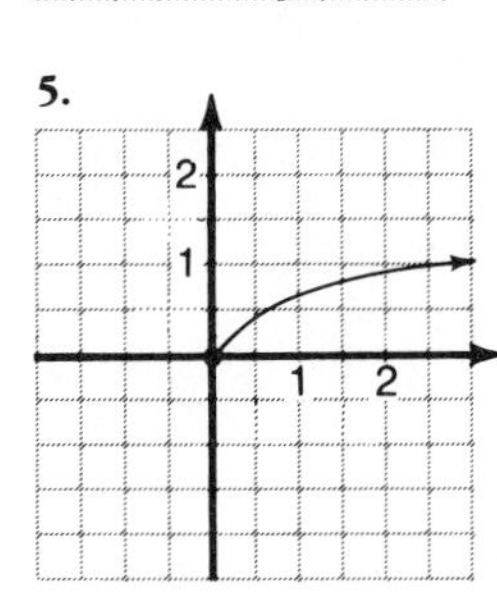

7. 0.6313 **9.** -3.9739
11. 0.7561
13. -1.5465
15. 8.4119
17. -7.4872
19. -2.5256
21. 13.7953
23. $k \approx 0.03148$; $P \approx 1{,}182{,}000$
25. 125 grams
27. 248,000 years

29. 7997 years **31.** 2.1610 **33.** -0.1544

35. 2.4849 **37.** $t = \frac{\ln P - \ln P_0}{k}$ **39. a.** \$1.1255

c. \$1.1274746 **41.** $N = N_0 2^{-\frac{t}{H}}$

45. $\log_a(\log_a x) = \log_a\left(\frac{\log_b x}{\log_b a}\right)$, by Theorem 12-7,

$\log_a(\log_a x) = \log_a(\log_b x - \log_b a)$, by Theorem 12-6.
47. No, yes, no **49.** -9

Chapter 12 Summary and Review

1. $y = \frac{1}{3}x + \frac{1}{3}$ **3.** $(1, 4), (8, -3), (-5, -1)$

5. Yes **7.** $g^{-1}(x) = x^2 - 4x + 4, x \geq 2.$
9. Set of all real numbers, set of all positive numbers; $(0, 1)$.

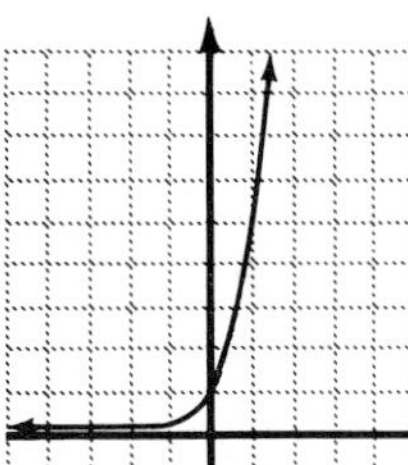

11. $2.3 = \log_7 x$
13. $3^4 = 81$
15. 4 **17.** 3
19. $\log_b \frac{(ac^3)^{\frac{1}{2}}}{d^4}$
21. 1.255 **23.** -0.602
25. 1.4183

27. 0.7649 **29.** 0.00230 **31.** 1.2730 **33.** $-\frac{1}{5}$

35. 9 **37.** 14.2 years **39.** 7.3778

Chapters 1–12 Cumulative Review

1. 10 **3.** -4
5. $-5 \leq x$
7. $x > 60$
9. $x - 6 = 0$
11. $\left(-\frac{1}{2}, -\frac{1}{2}\right)$
13. 5 liters of A and 19 liters B

15.

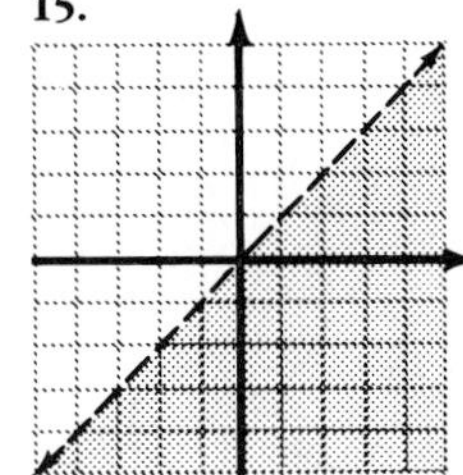

17. $4z^2 + 16yz + 16y^2$
19. $a^6 + 6a^4b + 12a^2b^2 + 8b^3$
21. $(a^8 + 1)(a^4 + 1)(a^2 + 1)(a + 1)(a - 1)$
23. $(y + 5)(y^2 - 5y + 25)$

25. $(x - 4)(2x + 3)(2x - 3)$ **27.** $\frac{1}{3}, 6$

29. $\frac{x^2(y - 3)}{y^2(x - 1)}$ **31.** $x^3 + 3x^2 + x - 9$

33. $x = \frac{1}{2}, x = -\frac{2}{7}$ **35.** -5 **37.** 3 **39.** $4y\sqrt{3y}$

41. $6 + \sqrt{35}$ **43.** $\frac{2}{3}a\sqrt{3}$ **45.** $x = 21$ **47.** $21 + 20i$

49. i **51.** $0, \frac{4}{5}$ **53.** $12x^2 + 11x - 15 = 0$

55. y-axis **57.** Neither axis **59.** Odd
61. a. $f(x) = -3(x - 2)^2 + 7$ **b.** $(2, 7)$, $x = 2$, max 7
63. $\sqrt{106}$

65. Vertex: $(-1, 2)$; focus: $\left(-1, \frac{1}{2}\right)$; directrix: $y = \frac{7}{2}$

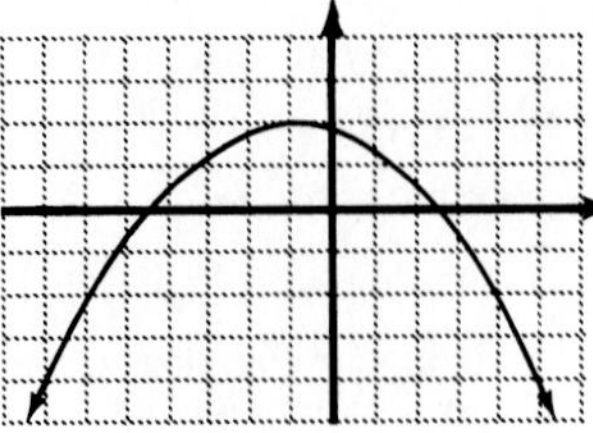

67. $(2, 4), (-2, -4), (4, 2), (-4, -2)$
69. $x^3 - 3x^2 + x - 3 = 0$
71. 3 or 1 positive roots, 2 or 0 negative roots
73. 2 **75.** $\log_5\left(\frac{\sqrt{x}}{y^3}\right)$ **77.** -10 **79.** $\frac{5}{3}$ **81.** 4.2932

Chapter 13

Lesson 13-1 Try This

a. 3×2 **b.** 2×2 **c.** 3×3 **d.** 1×2 **e.** 2×1 **f.** 1×1 **g.** $(-8, 2)$ **h.** $(-1, 2, 3)$

Exercise Set 13-1

1. 2×3 **3.** 5×2 **5.** $\left(\frac{3}{2}, \frac{5}{2}\right)$ **7.** $\left(\frac{1}{2}, \frac{3}{2}\right)$
9. $(-1, 2, -2)$ **11.** $\left(2, \frac{1}{2}, -2\right)$ **13.** $(7, 4, 5, 6)$
15. $(2, -1, 3, 4, 1)$ **17.** $\frac{x(x - 21)}{(x + 3)(x - 3)}$ **19.** -0.3036
21. 0.9562 **23.** 12 or -12

Lesson 13-2 Try This

a. **(1)** $\begin{bmatrix} -2 & -6 \\ 13 & 0 \end{bmatrix}$ **(2)** $\begin{bmatrix} -2 & -6 \\ 13 & 0 \end{bmatrix}$ **(3)** $\begin{bmatrix} 4 & -1 \\ 6 & -3 \end{bmatrix}$
b. $\begin{bmatrix} -1 & 4 & -7 \\ -2 & -4 & 8 \end{bmatrix}$ **c.** $\begin{bmatrix} -6 & 6 \\ 1 & -4 \\ -7 & 5 \end{bmatrix}$
d. $\begin{bmatrix} -2 & 1 & -5 \\ -6 & -4 & 3 \end{bmatrix}$ **e.** $\begin{bmatrix} -1 & -3 & 5 \\ 2 & 0 & 0 \\ -6 & 10 & -7 \end{bmatrix}$
f. $\begin{bmatrix} 3 & 2 & 3 \\ 10 & 4 & 2 \end{bmatrix}$ **g.** $\begin{bmatrix} 11 & -2 & -7 \\ -3 & 13 & -5 \\ 7 & 2 & -6 \end{bmatrix}$

Exercise Set 13-2

1. 2×2 **3.** 2×3 **5.** $\begin{bmatrix} -2 & -3 \\ 6 & -4 \end{bmatrix}$ **7.** $\begin{bmatrix} -5 & 0 & 11 \\ 3 & 2 & 0 \end{bmatrix}$
9. $\begin{bmatrix} 0 & -2 & 3 \\ 1 & -1 & 2 \\ 1 & -5 & 5 \end{bmatrix}$ **11.** Cannot be added. **13.** $\begin{bmatrix} 4 & 7 \\ 2 & -2 \end{bmatrix}$
15. Cannot be subtracted. **17.** $\begin{bmatrix} 2 & 2 & -7 \\ -1 & -1 & 4 \\ 5 & 1 & 3 \end{bmatrix}$
19. Cannot be subtracted. **21.** $\begin{bmatrix} 3 & 3 & -7 \\ 5 & -2 & -1 \end{bmatrix}$
23. $\begin{bmatrix} 4 & -5 & 2 \\ -1 & 0 & 4 \\ 2 & 3 & 5 \end{bmatrix}$ **25.** $\begin{bmatrix} -3 & 7 & -7 \\ 0 & 0 & -3 \\ 0 & 0 & -6 \end{bmatrix}$
27. Cannot be subtracted. **29.** $\begin{bmatrix} -4 & 3 & 1 \\ 2 & -1 & -2 \\ -1 & -8 & 0 \end{bmatrix}$
33. 1.183 **35.** $\pm\frac{\sqrt{10}}{2}$ **37.** $-5, 3$

Lesson 13-3 Try This

a. 14 **b.** -2 **c.** $-2x + 12$ **d.** $(3, 1)$
e. $\left(-\frac{10}{41}, -\frac{13}{41}\right)$ **f.** 93 **g.** 60 **h.** 100 **i.** $(1, 3, -2)$
j. $\left(\frac{1}{3}, \frac{4}{5}, -\frac{1}{15}\right)$

Exercise Set 13-3

1. 3 **3.** 36 **5.** -10.3 **7.** 0 **9.** $(2, 0)$
11. $(-4, -5)$ **13.** $\left(\frac{1}{3}, -\frac{2}{3}\right)$ **15.** -10 **17.** -3
19. -11 **21.** $(2, -1, 4)$ **23.** $(1, 2, 3)$
25. $\left(\frac{3}{2}, \frac{13}{14}, \frac{33}{14}\right)$ **27.** $x^3 - 4x$ **29.** $z + 3z^2$
31. 2 or -2 **33.** $\left(\frac{15 - 4\pi}{-3\sqrt{3} - \pi^2}, \frac{4\sqrt{3} + 5\pi}{-3\sqrt{3} - \pi^2}\right)$
41. $8, -8$ **43.** $512, -216$ **45.** $y^3 - 2y^2 + 5$

Lesson 13-4 Try This

a. $\begin{bmatrix} 5 & -10 & 5x \\ 20 & 5y & 5 \\ 0 & -25 & 5x^2 \end{bmatrix}$ **b.** $\begin{bmatrix} -3t & 3t & -12t & -3xt \\ -3yt & -9t & 6t & -3yt \\ -3t & -12t & 15t & -3yt \end{bmatrix}$
c. $\begin{bmatrix} 12 \\ 13 \\ 5 \\ 16 \end{bmatrix}$ **d.** $\begin{bmatrix} 0 & 26 \\ -8 & 3 \\ -13 & 33 \\ -7 & 32 \end{bmatrix}$ **e.** $[8 \quad 5 \quad 4]$
f. $\begin{bmatrix} 2 & 8 & 6 \\ -29 & -34 & -7 \end{bmatrix}$ **g.** Undefined **h.** $\begin{bmatrix} 1 & 4 & 8 \\ -1 & 8 & 8 \end{bmatrix}$
i. $\begin{bmatrix} 3 & 4 & -2 \\ 2 & -2 & 5 \\ 6 & 7 & -1 \end{bmatrix}\begin{bmatrix} x \\ y \\ z \end{bmatrix} = \begin{bmatrix} 5 \\ 3 \\ 0 \end{bmatrix}$
j. $\begin{bmatrix} 5 & 7 & 0 \\ 3 & -2 & 1 \\ -2 & 3 & -1 \end{bmatrix}\begin{bmatrix} x \\ y \\ z \end{bmatrix} = \begin{bmatrix} 19 \\ 1 \\ -12 \end{bmatrix}$
k. $\begin{bmatrix} 3 & 0 & 2 & -7 \\ 0 & 1 & -2 & 0 \\ 5 & 5 & 0 & -3 \\ 0 & 0 & 10 & -3 \\ 1 & 0 & -1 & -1 \end{bmatrix}\begin{bmatrix} v \\ w \\ x \\ y \end{bmatrix} = \begin{bmatrix} 13 \\ 0 \\ -5 \\ 15 \\ 2 \end{bmatrix}$
l. $\begin{bmatrix} 4 & 0 & 0 & 0 \\ 4 & 1 & 0 & 0 \\ 4 & 2 & 1 & 0 \\ 4 & 3 & 2 & 1 \end{bmatrix}\begin{bmatrix} w \\ x \\ y \\ z \end{bmatrix} + \begin{bmatrix} 1 \\ 3 \\ 6 \\ 10 \end{bmatrix} = \begin{bmatrix} 0 \\ 0 \\ 0 \\ 0 \end{bmatrix}$

Exercise Set 13-4

1. $\begin{bmatrix} -2 & -4 \\ -8 & -6 \end{bmatrix}$ **3.** $\begin{bmatrix} 14 & -14 \\ -14 & 14 \end{bmatrix}$ **5.** $\begin{bmatrix} t & 3t \\ 2t & 6t \end{bmatrix}$
7. $\begin{bmatrix} 2 & -9 & -6 \\ 3 & -3 & -4 \\ -2 & 2 & -1 \end{bmatrix}$ **9.** $[-22]$ **11.** $[-36]$
13. $\begin{bmatrix} 1 & 3 \\ -6 & 17 \end{bmatrix}$ **15.** $\begin{bmatrix} 0 & 0 \\ 0 & 0 \end{bmatrix}$ **17.** $[-14 \quad -11 \quad -3]$
19. $[-13 \quad -1 \quad -4]$ **21.** $\begin{bmatrix} 3 & 3 \\ -1 & -1 \end{bmatrix}$
23. $\begin{bmatrix} -5 & 4 & 3 \\ 5 & -9 & 4 \\ 7 & -18 & 17 \end{bmatrix}$ **25.** $\begin{bmatrix} -7 \\ -18 \end{bmatrix}$ **27.** Not possible
29. $\begin{bmatrix} 3 & -2 & 4 \\ 2 & 1 & -5 \end{bmatrix}\begin{bmatrix} x \\ y \\ z \end{bmatrix} = \begin{bmatrix} 17 \\ 13 \end{bmatrix}$

31. $\begin{bmatrix} 1 & -1 & 2 & -4 \\ 2 & -1 & -1 & 1 \\ 1 & 4 & -3 & -1 \\ 3 & 5 & -7 & 2 \end{bmatrix}\begin{bmatrix} x \\ y \\ z \\ w \end{bmatrix} = \begin{bmatrix} 12 \\ 0 \\ 1 \\ 9 \end{bmatrix}$

33. $\begin{bmatrix} 13 & 5 & 0 \\ 24 & 18 & 18 \\ 18 & 17 & 15 \end{bmatrix}; \begin{bmatrix} -4 & -1 & 0 \\ -9 & -5 & 9 \\ 2 & -2 & 4 \end{bmatrix}$

35. I is a multiplicative identity. **37.** No

47. $x^4 - 6x^2y + 9y^2$ **49.** $\frac{4m^2\sqrt[3]{z}}{9n^4z^5}$ **51.** 1 positive, 1 or 3 negative **53.** $P(3) = 325$; $P(-1) = -15$; $P(0) = -8$; $P\left(\frac{1}{2}\right) = 0$

Lesson 13-5 Try This

a. No, $AB = \begin{bmatrix} 1 & 0 \\ 0 & -1 \end{bmatrix}$ **b.** Yes, $AB = BA = I$

c. Does not exist. **d.** $\begin{bmatrix} \frac{2}{5} & -\frac{3}{5} \\ \frac{1}{5} & \frac{1}{5} \end{bmatrix}$ **e.** $\begin{bmatrix} \frac{1}{6} & -\frac{1}{6} \\ \frac{1}{10} & \frac{1}{10} \end{bmatrix}$

Exercise Set 13-5

1. Yes **3.** No **5.** $\begin{bmatrix} -3 & 2 \\ 5 & -3 \end{bmatrix}$ **7.** $\begin{bmatrix} 2 & -3 \\ -7 & 11 \end{bmatrix}$

9. $\begin{bmatrix} \frac{2}{11} & \frac{3}{11} \\ -\frac{1}{11} & \frac{4}{11} \end{bmatrix}$ **11.** Does not exist.

13. Does not exist.

15. $-\frac{1}{0.05}\begin{bmatrix} 0.2 & -0.1 \\ -1.5 & 0.5 \end{bmatrix}$ or $\begin{bmatrix} -4 & 2 \\ 30 & -10 \end{bmatrix}$

17. $-\frac{1}{xy}\begin{bmatrix} 0 & -x \\ -y & 0 \end{bmatrix}$ or $\begin{bmatrix} 0 & \frac{1}{y} \\ \frac{1}{x} & 0 \end{bmatrix}$, $xy \neq 0$

21. Let $A = \begin{bmatrix} a & a \\ b & b \end{bmatrix}$. Then $|A| = ab - ba = 0$ and A^{-1} does not exist. Let $A = \begin{bmatrix} a & b \\ a & b \end{bmatrix}$. Then $|A| = ab - ab = 0$ and A^{-1} does not exist.

23. $(x^2 + 9y^4)(x + 3y^2)(x - 3y^2)$

25. $(2m - 3n)(3m - 2n)$ **27.** $3yz^3\sqrt[3]{2y}$ **29.** $-\frac{8n^{12}}{m^{12}}$

31. 30 m × 30 m; 900 m^2

Lesson 13-6 Try This

a. $A^{-1} = \begin{bmatrix} -\frac{1}{2} & \frac{1}{2} & \frac{1}{2} \\ 1 & 0 & -1 \\ \frac{3}{2} & -\frac{1}{2} & -\frac{1}{2} \end{bmatrix}$ **b.** Does not exist.

c. $\left(-\frac{3}{22}, \frac{5}{22}\right)$ **d.** $\left(-\frac{14}{5}, -\frac{24}{5}, -\frac{4}{5}\right)$

Exercise Set 13-6

1. $A^{-1} = \begin{bmatrix} -1 & 1 & 0 \\ -1 & 0 & 1 \\ 6 & -2 & -3 \end{bmatrix}$ **3.** $A^{-1} = \begin{bmatrix} -\frac{4}{3} & -\frac{5}{3} & 1 \\ -\frac{4}{3} & -\frac{8}{3} & 1 \\ \frac{1}{3} & \frac{2}{3} & 0 \end{bmatrix}$

5. $A^{-1} = \begin{bmatrix} -\frac{1}{2} & \frac{1}{2} & \frac{1}{2} \\ 1 & 0 & -1 \\ \frac{3}{2} & -\frac{1}{2} & -\frac{1}{2} \end{bmatrix}$ **7.** (2, 2) **9.** (−2, 3)

11. (3, −3, −2) **13.** $A^{-1} = \begin{bmatrix} \frac{1}{x} & 0 & 0 \\ 0 & \frac{1}{y} & 0 \\ 0 & 0 & \frac{1}{z} \end{bmatrix}$; $x, y, z \neq 0$

15. $x = \begin{bmatrix} -7 & -6 \\ 12 & 10 \end{bmatrix}$ **21.** (−4, 9) **23.** $\frac{40 + 5\sqrt{6}}{58}$

25. $\frac{u\sqrt[3]{9uv^2}}{3v^2}$ **27.** $1 < x$ **29.** 80, 78, 86

Lesson 13-7 Try This

a. A: \$1467; B: \$1507.50; C: \$2137.50

Exercise Set 13-7

1. A: \$248.50; B: \$298.75; C: \$370; D: \$180
3. H: 29; E: 32; A: 31, T: 36; C: 43; Z: 38; J: 40; D: 37 **9.** $-5 \leq x \leq 5$ **11.** $s \geq 90$

Chapter 13 Summary and Review

1. 2 × 3 **3.** (1, −2) **5.** $\begin{bmatrix} -2 & 0 \\ 1 & -4 \end{bmatrix}$ **7.** 14

9. (2, −1) **11.** −1 **13.** (2, 3, 1) **15.** $\begin{bmatrix} 9 & 0 \\ -6 & 3 \end{bmatrix}$

17. $\begin{bmatrix} -6 & -3 & 3 \\ 5 & 2 & -4 \end{bmatrix}$ **19.** Does not exist.

21. $\begin{bmatrix} 2 & -3 \\ -1 & 2 \end{bmatrix}$ **23.** $\begin{bmatrix} \frac{2}{3} & -\frac{1}{6} & -\frac{1}{6} \\ 0 & -\frac{1}{2} & \frac{1}{2} \\ -\frac{1}{3} & \frac{1}{3} & \frac{1}{3} \end{bmatrix}$ **25.** (1, −2)

27. Pens \$7.20, pencils \$7.00, erasers \$28.00

Chapter 14

Lesson 14-1 Try This

a. $a_1 = 1, a_2 = 3, a_3 = 7, a_{10} = 1023, a_{15} = 32{,}767$
b. $a_1 = -1, a_2 = 4, a_3 = -9, a_{10} = 100, a_{15} = -225$
c. 0, 4, 8, 12, 16 **d.** 4, 2, 0, −2, −4 **e.** $a_n = 2n$
f. $a_n = (-1)^n(n)$ **g.** $a_n = n^3$ **h.** $a_n = 2^{n-1}$

i. $S_1 = \frac{1}{2}, S_2 = \frac{3}{4}, S_3 = \frac{7}{8}, S_4 = \frac{15}{16}$ **j.** $7\frac{5}{6}$ **k.** 776

l. $\sum_{n=1}^{5} 2n$ **m.** $\sum_{n=1}^{\infty} (-1)^{n+1}(n + 1)$

Exercise Set 14-1

1. 4, 7, 10, 13; 31; 46 **3.** $\frac{1}{2}, \frac{2}{3}, \frac{3}{4}, \frac{4}{5}; \frac{10}{11}; \frac{15}{16}$

5. −1, 0, 3, 8; 80; 195 **7.** $2, 2\frac{1}{2}, 3\frac{1}{3}, 4\frac{1}{4}; 10\frac{1}{10}; 15\frac{1}{15}$

9. 2, 5, 17, 65, 257 **11.** $8, 6, 5, 4\frac{1}{2}, 4\frac{1}{4}$

13. $a_n = 2n - 1$ **15.** $a_n = \frac{n + 1}{n + 2}$ **17.** $a_n = 3^{\frac{n}{2}}$

19. $a_n = -3n + 2$ **21.** $S_1 = \frac{1}{3}, S_2 = \frac{1}{2}, S_3 = \frac{7}{12}, S_4 = \frac{5}{8}$

23. $S_1 = 4, S_2 = 11, S_3 = 21, S_4 = 34$
25. $\frac{1}{2} + \frac{1}{4} + \frac{1}{6} + \frac{1}{8} + \frac{1}{10} + \frac{137}{120}$
27. $2^1 + 2^2 + 2^3 + 2^4 + 2^5 = 62$
29. $\log 7 + \log 8 + \log 9 + \log 10 = \log(7 \cdot 8 \cdot 9 \cdot 10) = \log 5040$
31. $\sum_{n=1}^{6} \frac{n}{n+1}$ **33.** $\sum_{n=1}^{6} (-1)^n 2^n$ **35.** $\sum_{n=2}^{\infty} (-1)^n n^2$
37. $\frac{3}{2}, \frac{3}{2}, \frac{3}{2}, \frac{3}{2}, \frac{3}{2}$ **39.** 0, 0.0693, 1.792, 3.178, 4.787
41. 1.645751 **43.** $1 - \frac{1}{n+1}$ **45.** $\begin{bmatrix} 15 & 14 & 20 \\ 8 & 2 & 22 \\ 9 & 32 & 26 \end{bmatrix}$
47. $\begin{bmatrix} 13 & 33 & 27 \\ 4 & 4 & 16 \\ 31 & 33 & 69 \end{bmatrix}$ **49.** Not possible

Lesson 14-2 Try This

a. $a_1 = 2, d = 1$ **b.** $a_1 = 1, d = 3$
c. $a_1 = 19, d = -5$ **d.** $a_1 = 10, d = -\frac{1}{2}$
e. 50 **f.** a_{72} **g.** $a_1 = 7, d = 12$; 7, 19, 31, 43, . . .
h. 3, 10, 17, 24 **i.** 20,100 **j.** 112,101 **k.** 225
l. 455

Exercise Set 14-2

1. $a_1 = 2, d = 5$ **3.** $a_1 = 7, d = -4$ **5.** $a_1 = \frac{3}{2}$, $d = \frac{3}{4}$ **7.** $a_{12} = 46$ **9.** $a_{17} = -41$ **11.** a_{27} **13.** a_{102}
15. $a_1 = 8, d = -3$; 8, 5, 2, −1, . . . **17.** 2, 7, 12, 17, 22 **19.** 2550 **21.** 670 **23.** 432 **25.** 855
27. 465 **29.** $S_n = n^2$ **31.** 16 means, $d = \frac{49}{17}$
33. $a_1 = p - 5q, d = 3p + 2q$ **35.** 51,679.65
37. $\frac{1}{8}, \frac{1}{11}, \frac{1}{14}, \frac{1}{17}$ **41.** $x + d = y$ or $x = y - d$; $z = y + d$; $x + y + z = y - d + y + y + d = 3y$
43. $x \leq -5$ or $x \geq 5$ **45.** −11 **47.** $-\frac{1}{11}\begin{bmatrix} 3 & -1 \\ -5 & -2 \end{bmatrix}$
49. $\sqrt[3]{x - 8}$ **51.** $f^{-1}(x) = x^{\frac{1}{3}}$ **53.** $f^{-1}(x) = 3^x$
55. $\log_x 7 = 5$ **57.** $\angle A = 70°; \angle B = 60°; \angle C = 50°$

Lesson 14-3 Try This

a. 5 **b.** −3 **c.** $-\frac{1}{4}$ **d.** $\frac{1}{3}$ **e.** −9375 **f.** 10
g. \$507.89 **h.** 11,718 **i.** $\frac{341}{256}$ **j.** 363 **k.** $\frac{65}{27}$

Exercise Set 14-3

1. 2 **3.** −1 **5.** $\frac{1}{x}$ **7.** 243 **9.** 1250 **11.** 3, 12, 48
13. $\frac{1}{4}, \frac{1}{8}, \frac{1}{16}, \frac{1}{32}, \frac{1}{64}$ **15.** \$1015.79 **17.** 762 **19.** $\frac{547}{18}$
21. $\frac{1 - x^8}{1 - x}$, or $(1 + x)(1 + x^2)(1 + x^4)$ **23.** $\frac{63}{32}$
25. 21,844 **27. a.** $\frac{1}{256}$ ft **29. a.** \$5866.60 **33.** Yes
37. \$1,529,908.60 **41.** (5, 0), (3, 4), (3, −4)
43. 9 cm

Lesson 14-4 Try This

a. No **b.** No **c.** Yes **d.** $\frac{3}{2}$ **e.** $\frac{16}{5}$

Exercise Set 14-4

1. No **3.** Yes **5.** Yes **7.** Yes **9.** 8 **11.** 2
13. $\frac{160}{9}$ **15.** $\frac{7}{9}$ **17.** $\frac{7}{33}$ **19.** $\frac{170}{33}$ **21.** 24 m
23. 512 cm^2 **25.** $\frac{1}{3}$ decimal, or $\frac{1}{11}$ binary
27. ±80, ±40, ±20, ±16, ±10, ±8, ±5, ±4, ±2, ±1
29. $P(2) = -336$; $P(5) = 1740$; $P(0) = -80$; $P(-5) = 0$ **31.** −1, −5, 4; −1, −5, 4, $2i$, $-2i$
33. −6, −3, 2, 137

Lesson 14-5 Try This

a. A. Show true for $n = 1$; $\frac{1(1+1)}{2} = \frac{1 \cdot 2}{2} = 1$

B. Assume true for $n = k$; $1 + 2 + 3 + 4 + \cdots + k = \frac{k(k+1)}{2}$

Show true for $k + 1$; $1 + 2 + 3 + 4 + \cdots + k + k + 1 = \frac{k(k+1)}{2} + k + 1$

$= \frac{k(k+1)}{2} + \frac{2(k+1)}{2} = \frac{k(k+1) + 2(k+1)}{2}$

$= \frac{(k+1)(k+2)}{2} = \frac{(k+1)[(k+1)+1]}{2}$

b. A. Show true for $n = 1$; $2^{1+1} - 1 - 2 = 4 - 1 - 2 = 1$

B. Assume true for $n = k$;
$1 + 3 + 7 + 15 + \cdots + (2^k - 1) = 2^{k+1} - k - 2$
Show true for $n = k + 1$;
$1 + 3 + 7 + 15 + \cdots + (2^k - 1) + (2^{k+1} - 1)$
$= 2^{k+1} - k - 2 + 2^{k+1} - 1$
$= 2 \cdot 2^{k+1} - k - 1 - 2$
$= 2^{(k+1)+1} - (k + 1) - 2$

Exercise Set 14-5

1. A. $\frac{1}{2} \cdot 1(1 + 5) = \frac{6}{2} = 3$

B. Assume true for $n = k$, show true for $n = k + 1$.
$3 + 4 + 5 + \cdots + (k + 2) + (k + 3)$
$= \frac{k(k+5)}{2} + k + 3 = \frac{k(k+5) + 2(k+3)}{2}$
$= \frac{k^2 + 7k + 6}{2} = \frac{(k+1)(k+6)}{2}$
$= \frac{1}{2}(k + 1)[(k + 1) + 5]$

3. A. $-\frac{1(1+3)}{2} = \frac{-4}{2} = -2$

B. Assume true for $n = k$, show true for $n = k + 1$.
$-2 - 3 - 4 - \cdots - (k + 1) - (k + 2)$
$= \frac{-k(k+3)}{2} - (k + 2) = \frac{-k(k+3) - 2(k+2)}{2}$
$= \frac{-(k^2 + 5k + 4)}{2}$
$= \frac{-(k+1)(k+4)}{2}$
$= -\frac{1}{2}(k + 1)[(k + 1) + 3]$

7. A. $\frac{1}{1+1} = \frac{1}{2}$

B. Assume true for $n = k$, show true for $n = k + 1$.
$\frac{1}{1 \cdot 2} + \frac{1}{2 \cdot 3} + \cdots \frac{1}{k(k+1)} + \frac{1}{(k+1)(k+2)}$

$= \frac{k}{k+1} + \frac{1}{(k+1)(k+2)}$
$= \frac{k(k+2)}{(k+1)(k+2)} + \frac{1}{(k+1)(k+2)}$
$= \frac{(k+1)^2}{(k+1)(k+2)} = \frac{(k+1)}{(k+2)} = \frac{(k+1)}{[(k+1)+1]}$

11. A. $2 \cdot 1 + 3 = 5$; $1(1 + 4) = 5$
B. Assume true for $n = j$, show true for $n = j + 1$.
$\sum_{k=1}^{j} (2k + 3) + [2(j + 1) + 3]$
$= j(j^2 + 4) + (2j + 5) = j^2 + 6j + 5$
$= (j + 1)[(j + 1) + 4]$
17. $2, -2, 2i, -2i, -1$ **19.** $10\sqrt{2}$ **21.** $5, -5$
23. $3, -3, 3i, -3i$

Problem Set 14-6

1. 25% **3.** $a = 4$, $b = 5$, and $c = 6$, or $a = -4$, $b = -5$, and $c = -6$ **5.** 12

Chapter 14 Summary and Review

1. $0, \frac{1}{3}, \frac{2}{4}, \frac{3}{5}; \frac{9}{11}; \frac{14}{16}$ **3.** $2, -2, -\frac{2}{3}, -\frac{2}{5}, -\frac{2}{7}$
5. $\frac{n+1}{n}$ **7.** $\sum_{n=1}^{6} (4n)(-1)^{n+1}$ **9.** 15th term **11.** 465
13. -2 **15.** 8th term **17.** $3\frac{15}{16}$ **19.** No **21.** 40
23. A. True for $n = 1$. **B.** Assume that statement is true for $n = k$. Show true for $n = k + 1$.
$1 + 4 + 7 + \cdots + (3k - 2) + [3(k + 1) - 2]$
$= \frac{k(3k-1)}{2} + [3(k+1) - 2] = \frac{3k^2 - k + 6k + 2}{2}$
$= \frac{3k^2 + 5k + 2}{2} = \frac{(k+1)(3k+2)}{2} = \frac{(k+1)[3(k+1) - 1]}{2}$

Chapter 15

Lesson 15-1 Try This

a. 24 **b.** 64 **c.** 6 **d.** 120 **e.** 720 **f.** 720
g. 362,880 **h.** 18! **i.** $10 \cdot 9!$ **j.** $11 \cdot 10 \cdot 9 \cdot 8!$
k. 210 **l.** 5040 **m.** 56 **n.** 55,440 **o.** 151,200
p. 2880

Exercise Set 15-1

1. 24 **3.** 720 **5.** 336 **7.** 720 **9.** 24 **11.** 5040
13. 720 **15.** 40,320 **17.** 120 **19.** 1 **21.** $9 \cdot 8!$
23. $a \cdot (a - 1)!$ **25.** $27 \cdot 26 \cdot 25 \cdot 24 \cdot 23 \cdot 22!$ **27.** 24
29. 604,800 **31.** 380 **33.** 336 **35.** 120, 60
37. ${}_6P_4 = 360$ **39.** 20,160 **41.** $9 \cdot 9 \cdot 8 \cdot 7 \cdot 6 \cdot 5 \cdot 4$, or 544,320 **45.** 8 **47.** 11 **53.** $\pm 3, \pm 6i$ **55.** 100
57. -98 **59.** 1581 **61.** 2132 **63.** $\approx 8.34 \times 10^{15}$
65. A:31, B:28, C:27

Lesson 15-2 Try This

a. 26^5 **b. (1)** 2652 **(2)** 2704 **c.** 420 **d.** 210
e. 5040

Exercise Set 15-2

1. 1296; 360 **3.** 11,880 **5.** 648; 180 **7.** 648; 180
9. $80 \cdot 26 \cdot 9999 = 20{,}797{,}920$ **11.** 6 **13.** 34,650
15. 151,200 **17.** 180 **19.** 1260 **21.** 24 **23.** 5040
25. a. 120 **c.** 24 **27.** 36 **31.** 5040 **33.** $2n - 1$

35. ${}_nP_r = \frac{n!}{(n-r)!} = \frac{n(n-1)(n-2)\cdots(n-r+1)(n-r)!}{(n-r)!}$
$= n(n - 1)(n - 2)\cdots(n - r + 1)$ **37.** No, yes, yes
39. $P(x) = (x - 1)(x + 2)(x - 3)(x + 4)$;
$1, -2, 3, -4$

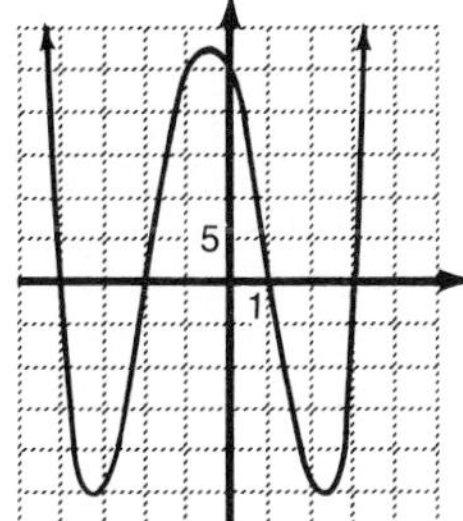

41. 1
43. $x^{\frac{5}{2}}, x^3, x^{\frac{7}{2}}$

Lesson 15-3 Try This

a. (1) 1 **(2)** 4 **(3)** 6 **(4)** 4 **(5)** 1 **b.** 45 **c.** 45
d. n **e.** 792 **f.** $\binom{9}{0} + \binom{9}{1} + \binom{9}{2} + \cdots + \binom{9}{9}$ or 512

Exercise Set 15-3

1. 126 **3.** 1225 **5.** 495 **7.** $\frac{n(n-1)(n-2)}{6}$
9. 8885 **11.** 72 **13.** 28, 56 **15.** 1200
17. $\binom{58}{6} \cdot \binom{42}{4}$ **19.** 56 **21.** 1 **23.** $\frac{(n+1)n}{2}$ **25.** 4
27. 8 **29.** $\frac{n(n-1)}{2}; \frac{n(n-3)}{2}$ **31.** $\begin{bmatrix} 7 & 4 & 13 \\ 10 & 2 & 23 \\ 14 & 16 & 18 \end{bmatrix}$
33. -1 **35.** $\begin{bmatrix} 9 & 6 & 17 \\ 16 & 11 & 30 \\ 7 & 2 & 15 \end{bmatrix}$ **37.** $f^{-1}(x) = x^{\frac{3}{2}}, x \geq 0$
39. $f^{-1}(x) = \frac{1}{3}x - \frac{1}{2}$ **41.** 10 **43.** $-\frac{14}{3} \leq x \leq 2$
45. 12 m, 10 m

Lesson 15-4 Try This

a. $-1512x^5$ **b.** $8064y^{10}$
c. $x^{10} - 5x^8 + 10x^6 - 10x^4 + 5x^2 - 1$
d. $16x^4 + 32\frac{x^3}{y} + 24\frac{x^2}{y^2} + 8\frac{x}{y^3} + \frac{1}{y^4}$ **e.** 2^{50} **f.** 2^{10}

Exercise Set 15-4

1. $15a^4b^2$ **3.** $-745{,}472a^3$ **5.** $-1{,}959{,}552u^5v^{10}$
7. $m^5 + 5m^4n + 10m^3n^2 + 10m^2n^3 + 5mn^4 + n^5$
9. $x^{10} - 15x^8y + 90x^6y^2 - 270x^4y^3 + 405x^2y^4 - 243y^5$ **11.** $\binom{n}{0} - \binom{n}{1} + \binom{n}{2} - \binom{n}{3} + \cdots + \binom{n}{n}(-1)^n$ **13.** $99 + 70\sqrt{2}$ **15.** 128 **17.** 2^{26}
19. $-7 - 4i\sqrt{2}$ **21.** $\sum_{r=0}^{n} \binom{n}{r}(-1)^r a^{n-r} b^r$
25. $-5 \pm \sqrt{8}$ **29.** $\pm 16, \pm 8, \pm 4, \pm 2, \pm 1$
31. $P(-3) = 625$; $P(-1) = 81$; $P(0) = 16$; $P(2) = 0$; $P(30) = 614{,}656$ **33.** $\frac{1}{4} - \frac{i}{4}$ **35.** 3,628,800
37. \$10,000

Lesson 15-5 Try This

a. $\frac{1}{2}$ **b.** $\frac{11}{850}$ **c.** $\frac{1}{6}$

Exercise Set 15-5

1. $\frac{1}{4}$ **3.** $\frac{1}{13}$ **5.** $\frac{1}{2}$ **7.** $\frac{2}{13}$ **9.** $\frac{2}{7}$ **11.** 0 **13.** $\frac{11}{4165}$

15. $\frac{1}{18}$ **17.** $\frac{28}{65}$ **19.** $\frac{30}{323}$ **21. a.** $13 \cdot 48 = 624$

23. b. 0.0423 **25.** Vertex: $(4, -3)$; Line of sym: $x = 4$; Focus: $(4, -2)$; Dir: $y = -4$ **27.** 360,360 **29.** 504 **31.** $2500

Lesson 15-6 Try This

a. $\frac{5}{6}$ **b.** $\frac{7}{13}$ **c.** $\frac{1}{4}$ **d.** $\frac{1}{12}, \frac{1}{18}$

Exercise Set 15-6

1. $\frac{15}{22}$ **3.** $\frac{6}{11}$ **5.** $\frac{1}{2}$ **7.** $\frac{2}{3}$ **9.** $\frac{1}{2}$ **11.** $\frac{4}{13}$ **13.** $\frac{9}{13}$

15. $\frac{1}{12}$ **17.** $\frac{1}{8}$ **19.** $\frac{5}{24}$ **21.** $\frac{3}{7}$ **23.** $\frac{1}{120}$ **25.** $\frac{5}{8}$

27. $\frac{1325}{1326}$ **29.** $\frac{3}{7}$ **31.** $(y + 2)^2 = -16(x + 4)$

33. $(y + 2)^2 = 16(x - 4)$ or $(x - 4)^2 = \frac{1}{4}(y + 2)$

35. a. $y = \frac{1}{2}x$ **c.** $y = \frac{4}{7}x$

Lesson 15-7 Try This

a. Theoretical probability is 0.375 **b.** Theoretical probability is 0.375 **c.** Theoretical probability is 0.625 **d.** 0.80

Exercise Set 15-7

Note: Answers may vary for exercises 1–28. Theoretical probabilities are given.

1. ≈0.64 **3.** ≈0.563 **5.** ≈0.313 **7.** ≈0.06 **9.** ≈0.22 **11.** ≈0.55 **13.** ≈0.13 **15.** ≈0.14 **17.** ≈0.075 **19.** ≈0.08 **23.** 0.42 **25.** 0.083 **27.** ≈0.34

29. $\frac{x - 7}{x + 7}$ **31.** $e^8 = u$ **33.** $\ln t = t + 1$

Lesson 15-8 Try This

a. ≈0.29 **b.** ≈0.42 **c.** ≈0.08 **d.** ≈0.94

Exercise Set 15-8

1. ≈0.64 **3.** ≈0.38 **5.** ≈0.52 **7.** ≈0.47 **9.** ≈0.18 **11.** ≈0.504 **17.** ≈0.4 **19.** ≈0.016 **21.** ≈0.19

23. ≈0.33 **25.** $\frac{3 - a}{a(a + 3)}$ **27.** 36

Chapter 15 Summary and Review

1. 24 **3.** 720 **5.** 1 **7.** $14 \cdot 13!$ **9.** 1,814,400 **11.** 3360 **13.** 3003 **15.** 120 **17.** $32x^5 - 320x^4 + 1280x^3 - 2560x^2 + 2560x - 1024$ **19.** $\frac{25}{102}$ **21.** $\frac{4}{13}$ **23.** ≈0.65

Chapter 16

Lesson 16-1 Try This

a.

Stem	Leaf
12	2, 6, 6, 1, 5, 0, 9, 7, 3, 8, 6, 5, 3
13	2, 2, 5, 7, 2, 2, 2, 1
14	3, 8, 5, 3, 8, 4, 3
15	4, 4, 3, 3
16	4, 4
17	3

b.

Stem	Leaf
1	77
2	98, 93, 89
3	89, 09, 91, 93, 12, 85, 31, 38, 54, 21
4	39, 66, 86, 38, 41
5	01
6	65, 11

c.

Interval	Frequency	Rel f
14–15	3	0.08
16–17	2	0.05
18–19	2	0.05
20–21	4	0.11
22–23	5	0.13
24–25	3	0.08
26–27	4	0.11
28–29	2	0.05
30–31	1	0.03
32–33	4	0.11
34–35	3	0.08
36–37	2	0.05
38–39	2	0.05
40–41	1	0.03

Exercise Set 16-1

1.

Stem	Leaf
0	0, 4, 3, 2, 6
1	1
2	9, 5, 2
3	5, 4
4	1, 6, 7, 6, 9, 6, 1
5	4, 9, 4
6	0

5.

Interval	Frequency	Rel f
801–900	1	0.025
901–1000	5	0.125
1001–1100	1	0.025
1101–1200	0	0
1201–1300	6	0.15
1301–1400	8	0.2
1401–1500	7	0.175
1501–1600	8	0.2
1601–1700	4	0.1

13. Center: $(2, -5)$; vertices: $(-1, -5)$, $(5, -5)$; foci: $(2 - 3\sqrt{2}, -5)$, $(2 + 3\sqrt{2}, -5)$; asymptotes: $y + 5 = \pm(x - 2)$ **15.** 4.35891×10^{11} **17.** 1.2108×10^9

Lesson 16-2 Try This

a. 189.4 pounds **b.** 78 **c.** 31.5

d.

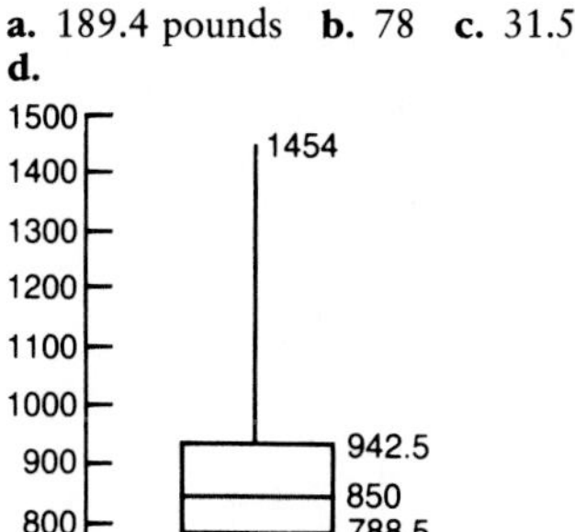

Exercise Set 16-2

1. Mean 831, median 794, mode 794 **3.** Mean 99.97, median 98.7, mode 98.6 **5.** Mean 273.6, median 106, mode none

7. **9.**

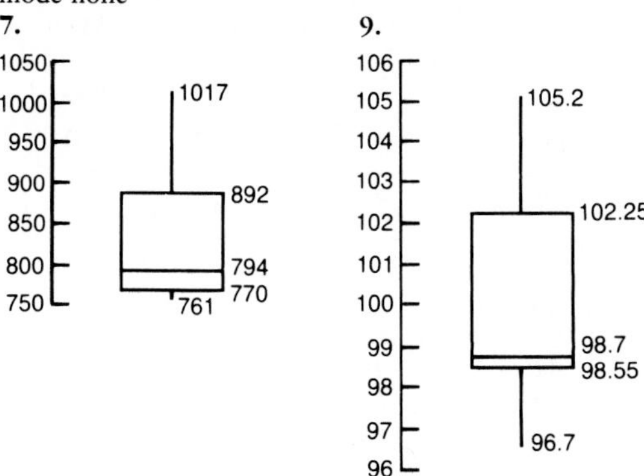

11.

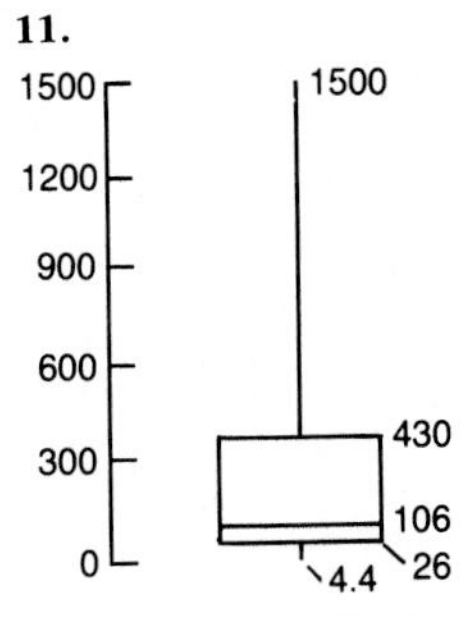

13. The median decreases to 85; the mean decreases to 215.2 **15.** No **17.** 203.1; 18.2% **19.** Center: (1, 2); Vertices: (−1, 2), (3, 2), (1, 1), (1, 3); Foci: $(1 - \sqrt{3}, 2)$, $(1 + \sqrt{3}, 2)$ **21.** $f(x) = x^4 - 6x^3 + 7x^2 + 36x - 78$

Lesson 16-3 Try This

a. 5, 1.3 **b.** 73.4 **c.** 8.57

Exercise Set 16-3

1. Range = 1642; mean deviation = 537.7; variance = 366337.49; standard deviation = 605.3 **3.** Range = 5.9; mean deviation = 1.68; variance = 4.01; standard deviation = 2.00 **5.** Range = 34; mean deviation = 9.9; variance = 120.4; standard deviation = 10.97

11. $\frac{4}{3}$ **13.** (1, −2)

Lesson 16-4 Try This

a. 16% **b.** 84% **c.** −1.25 **d.** 2.5 **e.** −0.4 **f.** 0 **g.** 0.9505 **h.** 0.7580 **i.** 0.0062 **j.** ≈11 times in 100

Exercise Set 16-4

1. ≈34% **3.** ≈81.5% **5.** ≈95% **7.** 1.7 **9.** −0.75 **11.** 0.0367 **13.** 0.0274 **15.** 0.9980 **17.** 0.0446 **19.** 0.2742 **21.** 1.32 **23.** −1.25 **25.** 0.35 **27.** 0.2258 **29.** 0.2511 **31.** 0.9817 **33.** 0.0990 **35.** 0.7745 **37.** 0.6915 **39.** 0.0062 **43.** 4.56% **45.** $x^5 + 10x^4y + 40x^3y^2 + 80x^2y^3 + 80xy^4 + 32y^5$ **47.** $x^3 - 3x^2 + 3x - 1$ **49.** $189x^5$, $5103x$ **51.** $f(x) = x^4 - x^3 - 21x^2 + 9x + 108$

Lesson 16-5 Try This

a. No **b.** Answers may vary. For example, for an audience of 120 people, choose every twelfth person as they exit the theater **c.** Answers may vary. For example, use a random number table to generate the last four digits of telephone numbers for prefixes in your community. **d.** Answers may vary. **(1)** This sample is likely to be biased against irradiation. **(2)** This sample might be representative. **(3)** This sample might be biased in favor of irradiation. **e.** Answers may vary. For a sample of 200 voters, interview the following: 80 voters under age 35; 40 voters age 35–44; 40 voters age 45–54; 30 voters age 55–64; 10 voters age 65 or older.

Exercise Set 16-5

1. Not a random sample because each student at the high school did not have an equal chance of participating. **3.** Not a random sample because each student did not have a chance to be selected. **5.** Not a random sample because there are 99 possible selections for the first number, 100 for the second, and 101 for the third. **7.** The scientist could have given each mouse a number between 1 and 30, then used a random number table to select 5 numbers between 1 and 30. **9.** This is only representative of people who walk past the county court building. This may be biased because not everyone will walk past the building. **11.** This is only representative of individuals who attend wrestling meets. **13.** This is only representative of people who live in densely populated areas. It would be biased because it does not include voters living in rural areas. **15.** By randomly selecting 33 people from Kent County, 134 people from New Castle County, and 33 from Sussex County. **17.** Assign each of the 20,000 people a number, then use a random number generator to select 12 people. **21.** $(y + 1)^3$ **23.** 4 oz of Happy Trail Mix and 8 oz of Mountain Top Trail Mix

Lesson 16-6 Try This

a. We expect 15 sixes and 75 other numbers.

$$\chi^2 = \frac{16}{15} + \frac{16}{75} + \frac{96}{75} \approx 1.28$$

b. No. $\chi^2 = 11.58$, which is greater than 9.21, the table value for 3 possible outcomes at the 1% level. **c.** $\chi^2 = 11.36$; it is significant at both the 5% and 1% levels. We would conclude that there is a difference between the pairs of lanes at three levels, and reject the null hypothesis.

Exercise Set 16-6

1. $\frac{2}{25} = 0.08$ **3.** $\frac{9441}{80} = 118.0125$ **5.** $\chi^2 = 12.5$
7. $\chi^2 \approx 11.546$ **9.** $\chi^2 \approx 31.83$; we reject the null hypothesis at the 1% level of significance.
11. No. **13.** Small expected values have too much effect on the value of χ^2. We can group the data so that expected values are greater than 5. **15.** $\frac{9}{4}$

Chapter 16 Summary and Review

1.

Stem	Leaf
4	9
5	3, 0
6	7, 3, 3, 5
7	3, 7, 8, 1, 4, 6, 2, 3, 4, 7, 0, 2
8	2, 0, 1, 0, 0, 3
9	2, 3, 6, 0, 1

3. Mean 935, mode 720, median 720 **5.** 13
7. 195.8 **9.** 16% **11.** 0.1056 **13.** Assign each of the 200 doctors a number between 1 and 200, then randomly select five numbers between 1 and 200.
15. $\chi^2 = 3.30625$ **17.** $\chi^2 = 31.63$, so we reject the null hypothesis.

Chapter 17

Lesson 17-1 Try This

a. $\sin\theta = \frac{4}{5}$, $\cos\theta = \frac{3}{5}$, $\tan\theta = \frac{4}{3}$ **b.** $r = 12\sqrt{2}$ ft
c. $\cot\theta \approx 1.33$, $\sec\theta = 1.25$, $\csc\theta \approx 1.67$
d. $\sin\theta = \frac{15}{17}$; $\tan\theta = \frac{15}{8}$; $\csc\theta = \frac{17}{15}$; $\sec\theta = \frac{17}{8}$; $\cot\theta = \frac{8}{15}$

Exercise Set 17-1

1. $\sin\theta = \frac{7}{25}$; $\cos\theta = \frac{24}{25}$; $\tan\theta = \frac{7}{24}$ **3.** $\sin\theta = \frac{8}{17}$; $\cos\theta = \frac{15}{17}$; $\tan\theta = \frac{8}{15}$ **5.** $a = 3$ **7.** $b = 2$
9. $\cot\theta = 3.43$; $\sec\theta = 1.04$; $\csc\theta = 3.57$
11. $\cot\theta = 1.88$; $\sec\theta = 1.13$; $\csc\theta = 2.13$
13. $\sin\theta = \frac{\sqrt{3}}{2}$; $\sec\theta = 2$; $\cos\theta = \frac{1}{2}$; $\csc\theta = \frac{2\sqrt{3}}{3}$; $\cot\theta = \frac{\sqrt{3}}{3}$ **15.** $\cos\theta = \frac{\sqrt{3}}{2}$; $\tan\theta = \frac{\sqrt{3}}{3}$; $\cot\theta = \sqrt{3}$; $\sec\theta = \frac{2\sqrt{3}}{3}$; $\csc\theta = 2$ **17.** $\sin\theta = \frac{1}{2}$; $\cos\theta = \frac{\sqrt{3}}{3}$; $\tan\theta = \frac{\sqrt{3}}{3}$; $\cot\theta = \sqrt{3}$; $\sec\theta = \frac{2\sqrt{3}}{3}$; $\csc\theta = 2$ **19.** $\sin\theta = \frac{\sqrt{2}}{2}$; $\cos\theta = \frac{\sqrt{2}}{2}$; $\tan\theta = 1$; $\cot\theta = 1$; $\sec\theta = \sqrt{2}$; $\csc\theta = \sqrt{2}$ **21. a.** $\frac{28\sqrt{3}}{3}$ ft
25. $13\sqrt{13} - 7\sqrt[4]{7}$ **27.** $\sqrt[20]{a^8b^{15}}$ **29.** 128 **31.** π

Lesson 17-2 Try This

a. First **b.** Third **c.** Fourth **d.** Third **e.** First
f. First **g.** $\sin\theta = -\frac{1}{2}$; $\cos\theta = \frac{\sqrt{3}}{3}$; $\tan\theta = -\frac{\sqrt{3}}{3}$
h. Cosine and secant values are positive; the other four function values are negative. **i.** $\sin 180° = 0$; $\cos 180° = -1$; $\tan 180° = 0$; $\sin 270° = -1$; $\cos 270° = 0$; $\tan 270°$ is undefined. **j.** 30° **k.** 30°
l. $-\frac{1}{2}, -\frac{\sqrt{3}}{2}, \frac{\sqrt{3}}{3}$ **m.** $-\frac{\sqrt{2}}{2}, \frac{\sqrt{2}}{2}, -1$ **n.** 0, −1, 0

Exercise Set 17-2

1. First **3.** Third **5.** First **7.** Second **9.** Second
11. Fourth **13.** $\sin\theta = -\frac{3}{5}$; $\cos\theta = -\frac{4}{5}$; $\tan\theta = \frac{3}{4}$
15. $\sin\theta = -\frac{3}{5}$; $\cos\theta = \frac{4}{5}$; $\tan\theta = -\frac{3}{4}$
17. $\sin\theta = \frac{\sqrt{3}}{2}$; $\cos\theta = -\frac{1}{2}$; $\tan\theta = -\sqrt{3}$ **19.** All function values are positive. **21.** The cosine and secant function values are positive; the other four are negative.
23. All function values are positive

25.

θ	cot θ	sec θ	csc θ
0°	—	1	—
90°	0	—	1
180°	—	−1	—
270°	0	—	−1

27. 30° **29.** 45° **31.** 45° **33.** 0 **35.** Undefined **37.** Undefined **39.** $-\frac{\sqrt{2}}{2}$ **41.** $-\frac{\sqrt{3}}{2}$ **43.** $\frac{\sqrt{3}}{3}$
45. $-\sqrt{2}$ **47.** 1 **49.** $-\frac{\sqrt{3}}{2}, -\frac{1}{2}, \sqrt{3}$ **51.** 0, −1, 0
53. $\sin 30° = 0.500$; $\cos 30° = 0.866$; $\tan 30° = 0.577$; $\csc 30° = 2.000$; $\sec 30° = 1.155$; $\cot 30° = 1.732$
55. $\sin 120° = 0.866$; $\cos 120° = -0.500$; $\tan 120° = -1.732$; $\csc 120° = 1.155$; $\sec 120° = -2.000$; $\cot 120° = -0.577$
57. $\sin\theta = 0.866$; $\cos\theta = 0.5$; $\tan\theta = 1.732$; $\sec\theta = 2$; $\csc\theta = 1.155$; $\cot\theta = 0.577$
59. $\sin\theta = -\frac{8}{17}$; $\cos\theta = -\frac{15}{17}$; $\tan\theta = -\frac{8}{15}$; $\csc\theta = -\frac{17}{8}$; $\sec\theta = -\frac{17}{15}$; $\cot\theta = \frac{15}{8}$
61. $\sin\theta = -\frac{5}{13}$; $\cos\theta = \frac{12}{13}$; $\tan\theta = -\frac{5}{12}$; $\csc\theta = -\frac{13}{5}$; $\sec\theta = \frac{13}{12}$; $\cot\theta = -\frac{12}{5}$ **63.** 38.25 in.
65. No **67.** $\pm\frac{1}{5}$ **69.** $\frac{7}{13}$ **71.** $\frac{11}{26}$

Lesson 17-3 Try This

a. $\frac{5}{4}\pi$ **b.** $\frac{5}{3}\pi$ **c.** $-\frac{7}{4}\pi$ **d.** 240° **e.** 450° **f.** −144°
g. 57.6 cm **h.** 6 radians **i.** 2 **j.** $\sqrt{3}$ **k.** $\sqrt{2}$
l. 377 cm/sec **m.** 3.6 radians/sec

Exercise Set 17-3

1. $\frac{\pi}{6} \approx 0.52$ **3.** $\frac{5\pi}{9} \approx 1.74$ **5.** $\frac{5\pi}{12} \approx 1.31$
7. $\frac{2\pi}{3} \approx 2.09$ **9.** $-\frac{16\pi}{9} \approx -5.58$ **11.** $-\frac{17\pi}{36} \approx -1.48$
13. 57.3° **15.** 1440° **17.** 135° **19.** 20.9 cm
21. 5.7 **23.** $\sqrt{3}$ **25.** $\frac{2\sqrt{3}}{3}$ **27.** 1 **29.** $\frac{\sqrt{3}}{3}$ **31.** 0
33. 54 m/min **35.** 41.0 cm/sec **37.** 66,626 mi/h
39. 1429 radian/hr **41.** 11.4 mi/h **43. a.** 53.33

c. 25 **45.** 111.6 km; 69.8 mi **49.** 25,000 mi
51. No **53.** $f^{-1}(x) = x^{\frac{1}{3}}$ **55.** $f^{-1}(x) = \sqrt[4]{x^2 + 1}$
57. e **59.** $\frac{10}{9}$

Lesson 17-4 Try This

a. 0.2644 **b.** 0.4699 **c.** 0.6383 **d.** −0.9868
e. 52°50′ **f.** 32°27′ **g.** 43.917° **h.** 0.6264
i. 1.900 **j.** ≈21°15′ **k.** ≈31°47′

Exercise Set 17-4

1. 0.2306 **3.** 0.5519 **5.** 0.5467 **7.** 1.127
9. −0.7969 **11.** 0.6383 **13.** 0.5392 **15.** 3.689
17. 81°10′ **19.** 45°50′ **21.** 13°40′ **23.** 46°39′
25. 67°3′ **27.** −48°57′ **29.** 412°33′ **31.** 45.42°
33. 76.88° **35.** −68.78° **37.** 225.55° **39.** 0.4775
41. 0.5889 **43.** 0.4494 **45.** 39°43′ **47.** 45°44′
49. 74°53′ **51.** 0.2095π **53.** 1.1922222π
55. 74.694267° **57.** 2172.0382° **59.** 1477.08°
61. 135.576° **63.** 0.5708 **65.** −0.5582
67. −22.4013 **69.** 0.0864 **71.** −0.0089
75. $\sin\theta \approx \theta$ for small angles **77.** 61.63944°
79. 8.65689×10^5 mi is the diameter **81.** Yes, yes
83. Yes, no **85.** (−1, −2, 3) **87.** All real numbers
89. 242 **91.** 0.05556, or $\frac{1}{18}$

Lesson 17-5 Try This

a. 3 **b.** D: set of all real numbers; R: $-1 \le \sin x \le 1$
c. Yes; 2π **d.** Odd **e.** 2π **f.** $\{y \mid y \ge 1 \text{ or } y \le -1\}$
g.

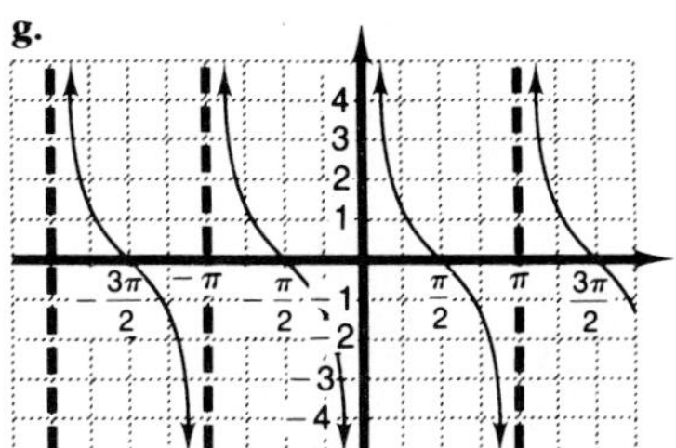

h. π **i.** D: $\{x \mid x \ne k\pi, k \text{ an integer}\}$; R: All reals
j. Odd

Exercise Set 17-5

1. No **3.** Yes **5.** Yes **7.** 4
9.

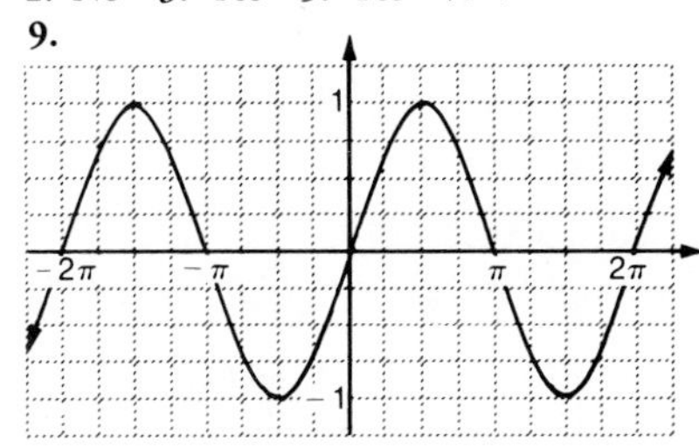

13.

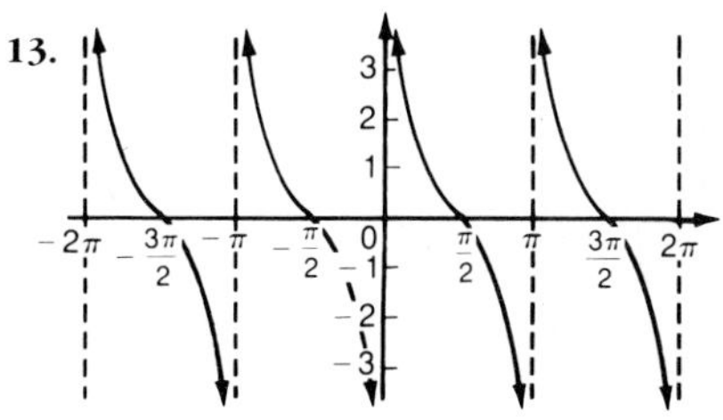

15.

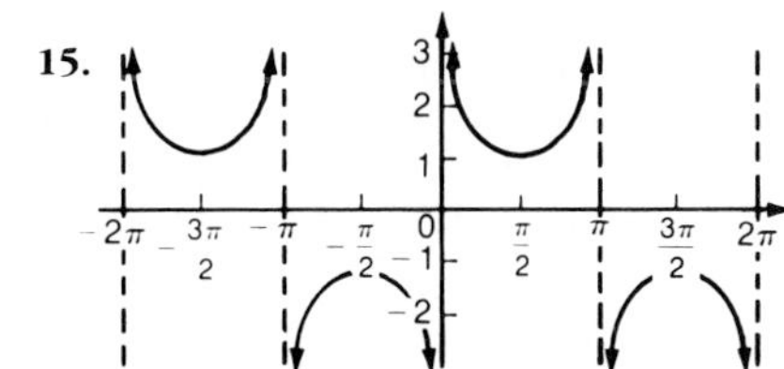

17. a. cosine curve **c.** curve through $(-\pi, 1)$, $\left(-\frac{\pi}{2}, 0\right)$, $(0, -1)$, $\left(\frac{\pi}{2}, 0\right)$, $(\pi, 1)$ **19. a.** sine curve
c. curve through $(-\pi, 0)$, $\left(-\frac{\pi}{2}, 1\right)$, $(0, 0)$, $\left(\frac{\pi}{2}, -1\right)$, $(\pi, 0)$ **21. a.** cosine curve **d.** They are the same.
23.

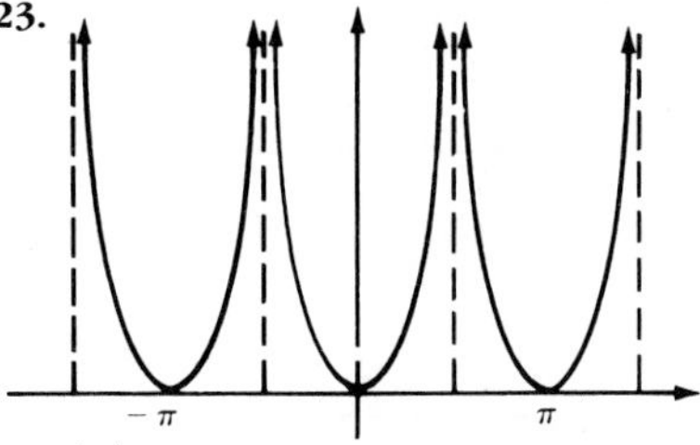

25. $\left\{x \,\middle|\, -\frac{\pi}{2} + 2k\pi < x < \frac{\pi}{2} + 2k\pi, k \text{ an integer}\right\}$
27.

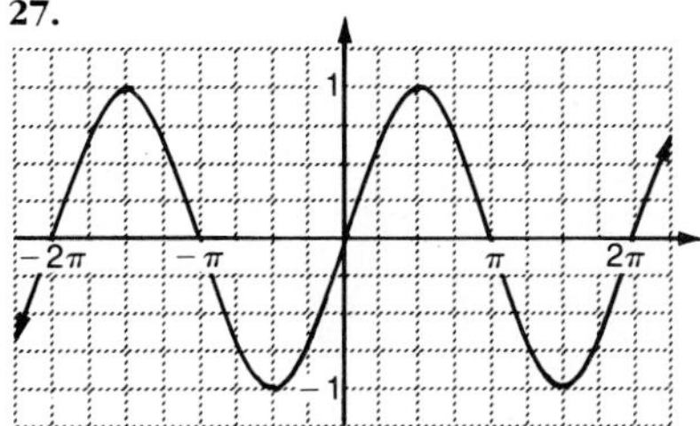

29. Odd **31.** Even **33.** 10

Lesson 17-6 Try This

a. $\cos\theta \equiv \cot\theta \cdot \sin\theta$ **b.** $\sin^2\theta \equiv 1 - \cos^2\theta$
c. $\sin\theta \equiv \sqrt{1 - \cos^2\theta}$ **d.** $\sec^2\theta - \tan^2\theta \equiv 1$;
$\tan^2\theta \equiv \sec^2\theta - 1$ **e.** $\sec\theta \equiv \pm\sqrt{1 + \frac{\sin^2\theta}{\cos^2\theta}}$
f. $\cos\left(0 - \frac{\pi}{2}\right) = \cos -\frac{\pi}{2} = 0 = \sin 0$
g. $\cot\left(\theta + \frac{\pi}{2}\right) \equiv -\tan\theta$

Exercise Set 17-6

1. $\cos\theta \equiv \frac{\sin\theta}{\tan\theta}$ **3.** $\csc\theta \equiv \pm\sqrt{1 + \cot^2\theta}$

5. $\cot\theta \equiv \pm\sqrt{\csc^2\theta - 1}$ **7.** $\tan\theta \equiv \pm\sqrt{\frac{1}{\cos^2\theta} - 1}$

9. $\sin\left(\frac{\pi}{4} - \frac{\pi}{2}\right) = \sin\left(-\frac{\pi}{4}\right) = -\frac{\sqrt{2}}{2} = -\cos\frac{\pi}{4}$

11. $\sin\left(\frac{\pi}{2} - \frac{5\pi}{4}\right) = \sin\left(-\frac{3\pi}{4}\right) = -\frac{\sqrt{2}}{2} = \cos\frac{5\pi}{4}$

13. $\tan\left(\theta - \frac{\pi}{2}\right) \equiv -\cot\theta$ **15.** $\sec\left(\frac{\pi}{2} - \theta\right) \equiv \csc\theta$

17. $\sin 25° = 0.4226$; $\cos 25° = 0.9063$; $\tan 25° = 0.4663$; $\cot 25° = 2.145$; $\sec 25° = 1.103$; $\csc 25° = 2.366$ **19.** $-\sin\theta$ **21.** $-\cos\theta$ **23.** $\cos\theta$ **25.** $-\cos\theta$ **27.** 0.92388 **29.** 0.92388 **31.** 0.38268 **39.** $(x^2 + 25)(x + 5)(x - 5)$ **41.** $(x + 4)(x + 5)(x + 6)$

43. $x^3 - x^2 + x - 1$ **45.** $\frac{-3125l^{10}n^6\sqrt[3]{n^2}}{16{,}807m^{15}}$

47. $\sin\alpha = \frac{12}{13}$; $\sin\theta = \frac{5}{13}$; $\cos\alpha = \frac{5}{13}$; $\cos\theta = \frac{12}{13}$; $\tan\alpha = \frac{12}{5}$; $\tan\theta = \frac{5}{12}$; $\cot\alpha = \frac{5}{12}$; $\cot\theta = \frac{12}{5}$; $\csc\alpha = \frac{13}{12}$; $\csc\theta = \frac{13}{5}$; $\sec\alpha = \frac{13}{5}$; $\sec\theta = \frac{13}{12}$

49. $a = \sqrt{2}$, $b = 2$

Lesson 17-7 Try This

a. 2,

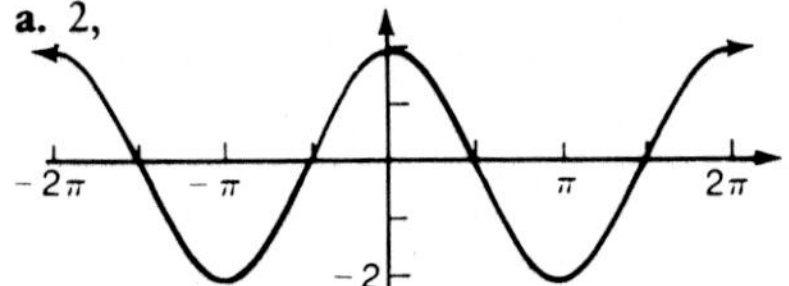

b. π,

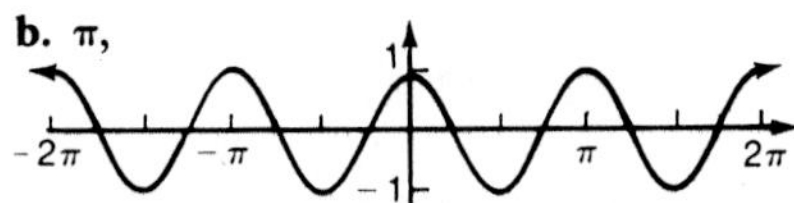

c. $A = 3$, period $= \pi$,

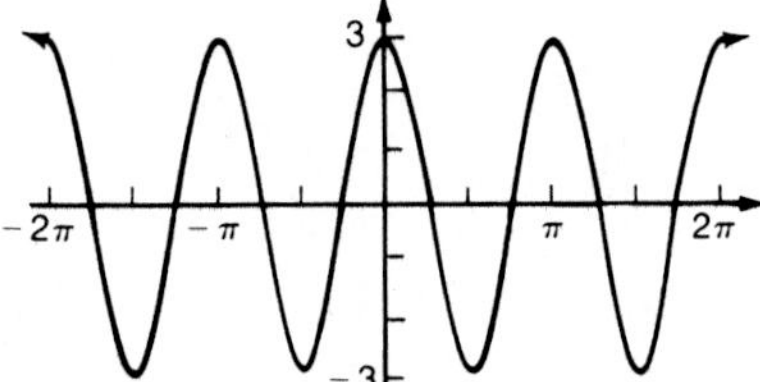

Exercise Set 17-7

1. $\frac{1}{2}$ **3.** 3 **5.** $\frac{1}{3}$

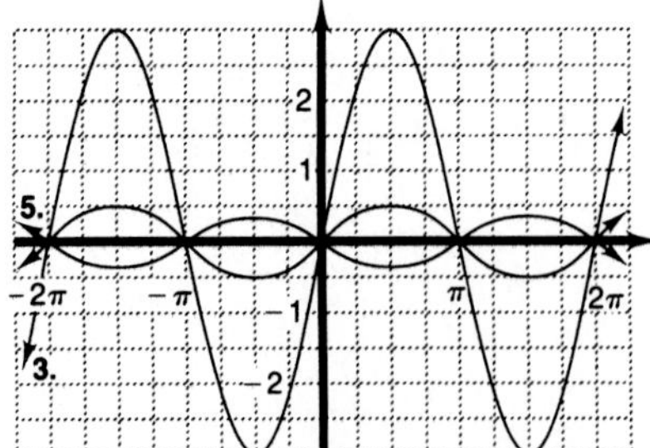

7. 4 **8.** 4 **9.** 2

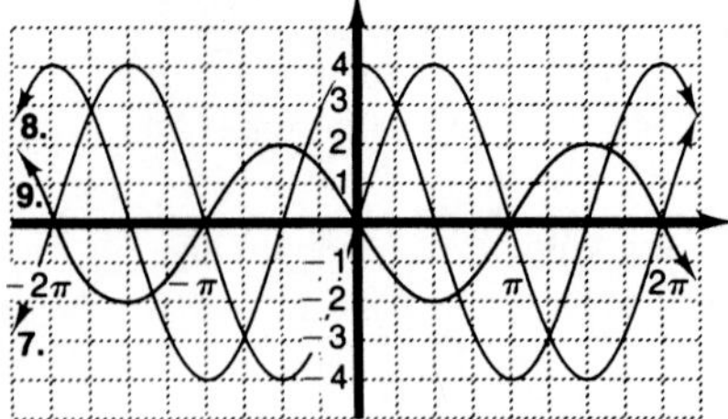

11. $\frac{2\pi}{3}$

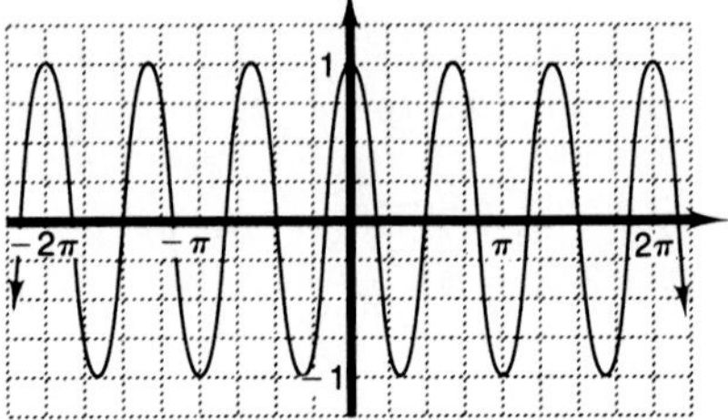

13. 4π **15.** 6π

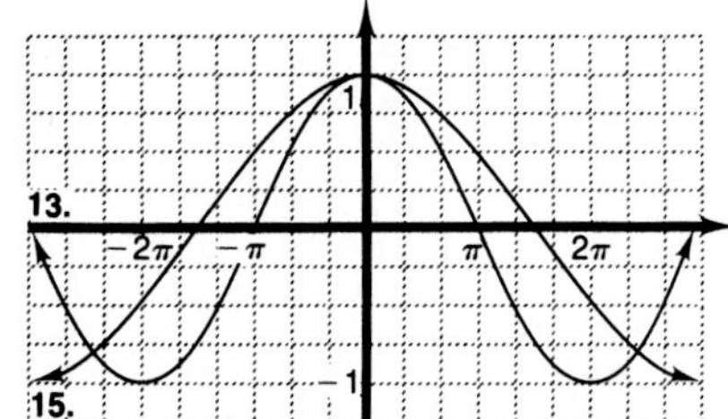

19. 2; π **21.** $\frac{1}{2}$; π

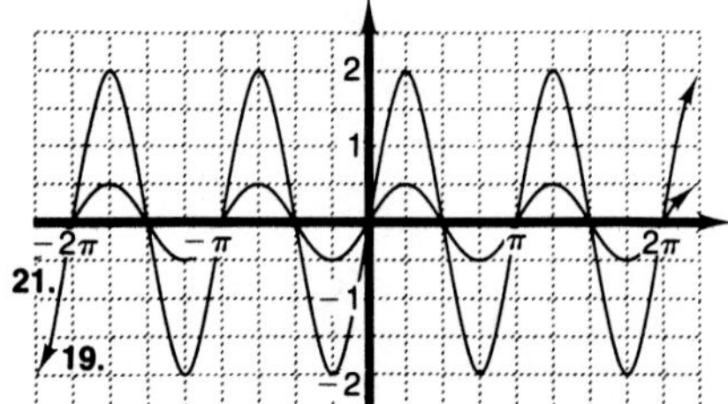

25. $\frac{1}{2}$; π **27.** $\frac{1}{2}$; π

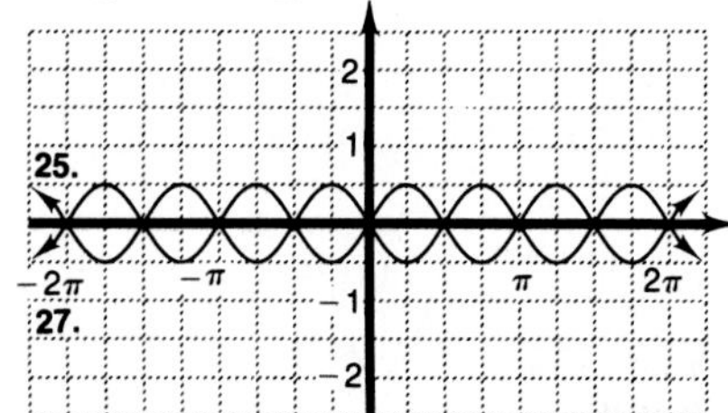

28, 29.

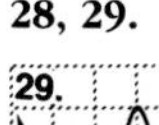

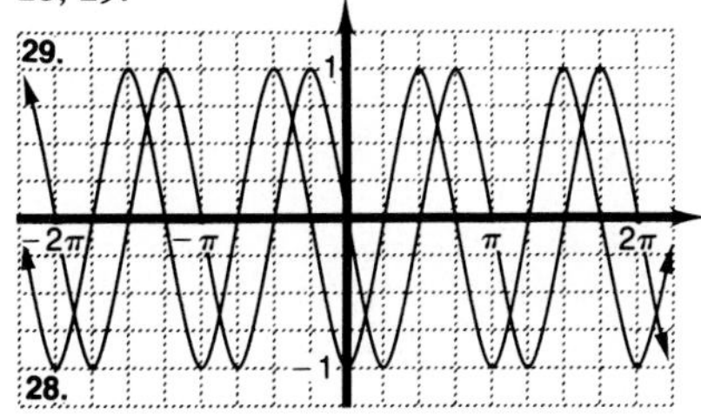

35. No, yes, no **37.** $P(-5) = -24$; $P(-3) = 0$; $P(2) = 60$; $P(4) = 210$

Lesson 17-8 Try This

a. $\cos x + 1$ **b.** $\sin\theta$ **c.** $\sin x$ **d.** $\cot x = -4$ or $\cot x = 3$

Exercise Set 17-8

1. $\sin^2 x - \cos^2 x$ **3.** $\sin x - \sec x$ **5.** $\sin\theta + \cos\theta$ **7.** $\cot x - \tan x$ **9.** $1 - 2\sin y \cos y$ **11.** $\sec^2\theta + 2\tan\theta$ **13.** $\cos x(\sin x + \cos x)$ **15.** $(\sin y - \cos y)(\sin y + \cos y)$ **17.** $\cos^2 x$ **19.** $\sin^2\theta - \cos^2\theta$ **21.** $3(\cot y + 1)^2$ **23.** $(\csc^2\theta + 5)(\cot^2\theta)$ **25.** $\tan x$ **27.** $\frac{2}{9}\cos\theta\cot\theta$ **29.** $\cos x - 1$ **31.** $\cos x + 1$ **33.** $\tan x = -7$ or $\tan x = 3$ **35.** $\sin\theta = \frac{3}{4}$ or $\sin\theta = -\frac{1}{2}$ **37.** $\cot x = -10$ or $\cot x = 1$ **39.** No solution **41.** $\csc x = \frac{3 + \sqrt{41}}{4}$ **53.** $(x + 2)^4$ **55.** $\frac{2\pi}{5}$ **57.** $\frac{7\pi}{6}$ **59.** 315° **61.** 30°

Chapter 17 Summary and Review

1. 20 cm **3.** First **5.** Second **7.** $\sin\theta = -\frac{4}{7}$; $\cos\theta = \frac{\sqrt{33}}{7}$; $\tan\theta = \frac{-4\sqrt{33}}{33}$; $\cot\theta = -\frac{\sqrt{33}}{4}$; $\csc\theta = -\frac{7}{4}$; $\sec\theta = \frac{7\sqrt{33}}{33}$ **9.** 30° **11.** Undefined **13.** $\frac{\sqrt{2}}{2}$ **15.** $\frac{5\pi}{6}$ **17.** $-\frac{\pi}{3}$ **19.** −60° **21.** $\sqrt{2}$ **23.** 1 **25.** 0.1449 **27.** 0.515 **29.** 24°35′

31.

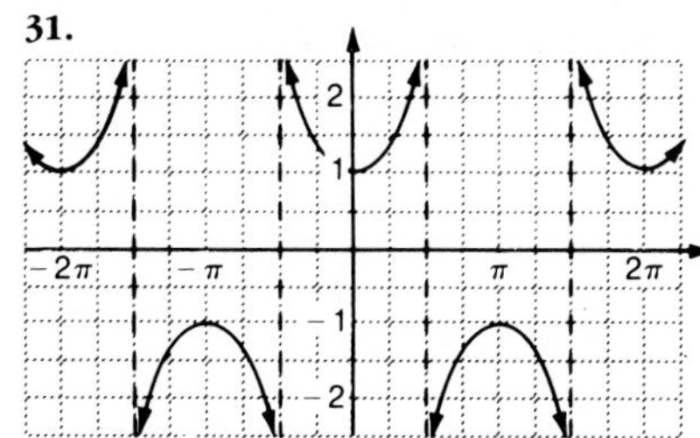

33. $\sin\left(\frac{\pi}{2} - \frac{\pi}{4}\right) = \sin\frac{\pi}{4} = \frac{\sqrt{2}}{2} = \cos\frac{\pi}{4}$ **35.** $\csc\theta \equiv \pm\sqrt{\frac{1}{1 - \cos^2\theta}}$ **37.** $\sin 15° = 0.2588$ **39.** $\tan 15° = 0.2679$ **41.** $\sec 15° = 1.035$

43. 3

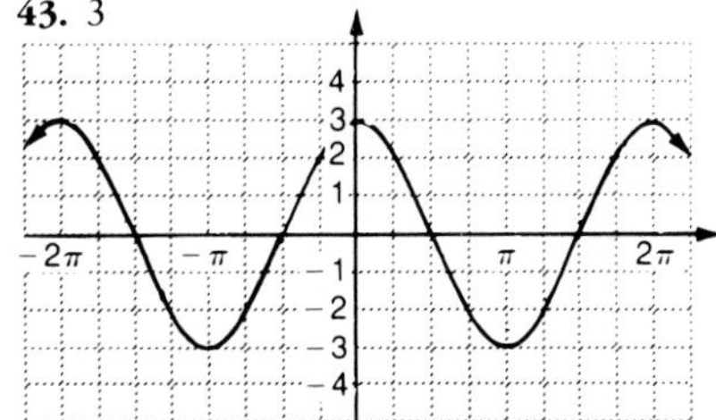

45. $\csc\theta$

Chapter 18

Lesson 18-1 Try This

a. $\frac{1}{2}$ **b.** $\frac{\sqrt{2} - \sqrt{6}}{4}$ **c.** $\frac{\sqrt{6} - \sqrt{2}}{4}$ **d.** $\frac{\sqrt{2} + \sqrt{6}}{4}$ **e.** $-2 - \sqrt{3}$

Exercise Set 18-1

1. $\cos A \cos B + \sin A \sin B$ **3.** $\frac{\sqrt{2} + \sqrt{6}}{4}$ **5.** $\frac{\sqrt{2} - \sqrt{6}}{4}$ **7.** $-\frac{\sqrt{3}}{2}$ **9.** $\frac{-\sqrt{2} - \sqrt{6}}{4}$ **11.** $-\frac{\sqrt{2}}{2}$ **13.** $\sin P \cos Q + \cos P \sin Q$ **15.** $\frac{\tan P - \tan Q}{1 + \tan P \tan Q}$ **17.** $\frac{\sqrt{2} + \sqrt{6}}{4}$ **19.** $2 - \sqrt{3}$ **21.** $\frac{\sqrt{6} - \sqrt{2}}{4}$ **23.** $2 + \sqrt{3}$ **25.** $\frac{\sqrt{6} - \sqrt{2}}{4}$ **27.** $\frac{\sqrt{2}}{2}$ **29.** $2 + \sqrt{3}$ **31.** $2 - \sqrt{3}$ **33.** $\cos 3\pi = -1$ **35.** $\cos(A - B)$ **37.** $2\cos\alpha\cos\beta$ **39.** $\tan(A - B)$ **41.** $\tan 52° = 1.280$ **43.** $2\sin\alpha\cos\beta$ **45.** $-\frac{\sqrt{3}}{2}$ **47.** $\frac{\cot\alpha\cot\beta - 1}{\cot\beta + \cot\alpha}$ **53.** 1.2071; 0.9659 **63.** $-m$ **65.** $\frac{5\sqrt{6}}{6}$ **67.** 0.3488 **69.** 0.8420 **71.** 243 **73.** 1102.5 m

Lesson 18-2 Try This

a. $\frac{24}{25}$ **b.** $\sin 2\theta = \frac{120}{169}$; $\cos 2\theta = -\frac{119}{169}$; $\tan 2\theta = -\frac{120}{119}$; second quadrant **c.** $\cos^3\theta - 3\sin^2\theta\cos\theta$ or $\cos\theta - 4\sin^2\theta\cos\theta$ or $2\cos^3\theta - \cos\theta - 2\sin^2\theta\cos\theta$ **d.** $\frac{\sqrt{2 + \sqrt{3}}}{2}$ **e.** 1

Exercise Set 18-2

1. $\frac{24}{25}, -\frac{7}{25}, -\frac{24}{7}$, II **3.** $\frac{24}{25}, \frac{7}{25}, \frac{24}{7}$, I **5.** $\frac{24}{25}, -\frac{7}{25}, -\frac{24}{7}$, II **7.** $\frac{\sqrt{2 + \sqrt{3}}}{2}$ **9.** $2 + \sqrt{3}$ **11.** $\frac{\sqrt{2 + \sqrt{2}}}{2}$ **13.** $\frac{\sqrt{2 + \sqrt{2}}}{2}$ **15.** $\sqrt{2} - 1$ **17.** $\cos x$ **19.** $\sin 4x$ **21.** 1 **23.** 1 **25.** $\sin 2x$ **31.** $f^{-1}(x) = \sqrt{x^3 - 1}$ **33.** $f^{-1}(x) = \ln x$

Lesson 18-3 Try This

a.

$\cot^2 x - \cos^2 x \equiv$	$\cos^2 x \cot^2 x$
$\dfrac{\cos^2 x}{\sin^2 x} - \cos^2 x$	$\cos^2 x \dfrac{\cos^2 x}{\sin^2 x}$
$\dfrac{\cos^2 x - \cos^2 x \sin^2 x}{\sin^2 x}$	
$\dfrac{\cos^2 x(1 - \sin^2 x)}{\sin^2 x}$	
$\dfrac{\cos^2 x \cos^2 x}{\sin^2 x}$	

b.

$\dfrac{\sin 2\theta + \sin\theta}{\cos 2\theta + \cos\theta + 1} \equiv$	$\tan\theta$
$\dfrac{2\sin\theta\cos\theta + \sin\theta}{2\cos^2\theta + \cos\theta}$	$\dfrac{\sin\theta}{\cos\theta}$
$\dfrac{\sin\theta(2\cos\theta + 1)}{\cos\theta(2\cos\theta + 1)}$	
$\dfrac{\sin\theta}{\cos\theta}$	

Exercise Set 18-3

1.

$\csc x - \cos x \cot x \equiv$	$\sin x$
$\dfrac{1}{\sin x} - \cos x \dfrac{\cos x}{\sin x}$	$\sin x$
$\dfrac{1 - \cos^2 x}{\sin x}$	
$\dfrac{\sin^2 x}{\sin x}$	
$\sin x$	

5.

$\dfrac{1 - \sin x}{\cos x} \equiv$	$\dfrac{\cos x}{1 + \sin x}$
$\dfrac{1 - \sin x}{\cos x} \cdot \dfrac{\cos x}{\cos x}$	$\dfrac{\cos x}{1 + \sin x} \cdot \dfrac{1 - \sin x}{1 - \sin x}$
$\dfrac{\cos x - \sin x \cos x}{\cos^2 x}$	$\dfrac{\cos x - \cos x \sin x}{1 - \sin^2 x}$
	$\dfrac{\cos x - \sin x \cos x}{\cos^2 x}$

11.

$\dfrac{1 + \tan\theta}{1 - \tan\theta} + \dfrac{1 + \cot\theta}{1 - \cot\theta} \equiv$	0
$\dfrac{1 + \frac{\sin\theta}{\cos\theta}}{1 - \frac{\sin\theta}{\cos\theta}} + \dfrac{1 + \frac{\cos\theta}{\sin\theta}}{1 - \frac{\cos\theta}{\sin\theta}}$	0
$\dfrac{\frac{\cos\theta + \sin\theta}{\cos\theta}}{\frac{\cos\theta - \sin\theta}{\cos\theta}} + \dfrac{\frac{\sin\theta + \cos\theta}{\sin\theta}}{\frac{\sin\theta - \cos\theta}{\sin\theta}}$	
$\dfrac{\cos\theta + \sin\theta}{\cos\theta - \sin\theta} + \dfrac{\sin\theta + \cos\theta}{\sin\theta - \cos\theta}$	
$\dfrac{\cos\theta + \sin\theta}{\cos\theta - \sin\theta} - \dfrac{\cos\theta + \sin\theta}{\cos\theta - \sin\theta}$	

23.

$\dfrac{\tan 3\theta - \tan\theta}{1 + \tan 3\theta \tan\theta} \equiv$	$\dfrac{2\tan\theta}{1 - \tan^2\theta}$
$\tan(3\theta - \theta)$	$\tan 2\theta$
$\tan 2\theta$	

37. 4 **39.** 5 ft

Lesson 18-4 Try This

a. Not a function;

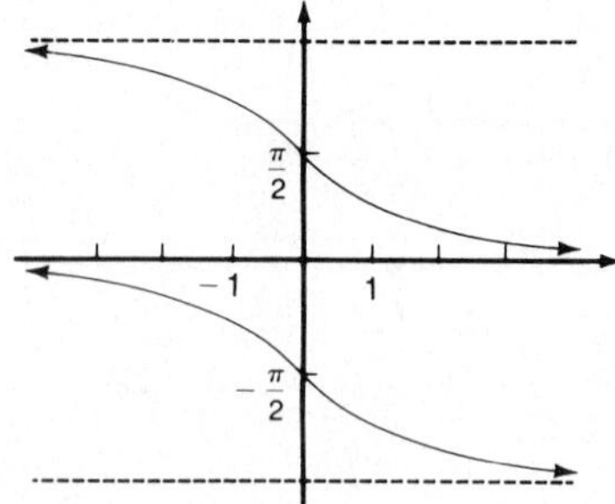

b. $\frac{\pi}{4} + 2k\pi, \frac{7\pi}{4} + 2k\pi$ **c.** $\frac{\pi}{3} + 2k\pi, \frac{2\pi}{3} + 2k\pi$

d. $25° + k \cdot 360°, 155° + k \cdot 360°$ **e.** $\frac{3\pi}{4} + k\pi$

f. $\frac{\pi}{3}$ **g.** $\frac{3\pi}{4}$ **h.** $\frac{3\pi}{4}$ **i.** $-\frac{\pi}{4}$

Exercise Set 18-4

1. $\frac{\pi}{4} + 2k\pi, \frac{3\pi}{4} + 2k\pi$ **3.** $\frac{\pi}{4} + 2k\pi, -\frac{\pi}{4} + 2k\pi$

5. $\frac{5\pi}{4} + 2k\pi, -\frac{\pi}{4} + 2k\pi$ **7.** $\frac{3\pi}{4} + 2k\pi, \frac{5\pi}{4} + 2k\pi$

9. $\frac{\pi}{3} + k\pi$ **11.** $\frac{\pi}{4} + k\pi$ **13.** $\frac{5\pi}{6} + k\pi$ **15.** $\frac{3\pi}{4} + k\pi$

17. $0 + 2k\pi$ **19.** $\frac{\pi}{2} + 2k\pi$ **21.** $23° + k \cdot 360°$, $157° + k \cdot 360°$ **23.** $39° + k \cdot 360°, 141° + k \cdot 360°$
25. $36°58' + k \cdot 360°, 323°02' + k \cdot 360°$
27. $21°25' + k \cdot 360°, 338°35' + k \cdot 360°$
29. $20°10' + k \cdot 180°$ **31.** $38°20' + k \cdot 180°$
33. $31° + k \cdot 360°, 329° + k \cdot 360°$

35. $9°10' + k \cdot 360°, 170°50' + k \cdot 360°$ **37.** $\frac{\pi}{4}$ **39.** $\frac{\pi}{3}$

41. $-\frac{\pi}{3}$ **43.** $\frac{3\pi}{4}$ **45.** $-\frac{\pi}{6}$ **47.** $\frac{2\pi}{3}$ **49.** $\frac{3\pi}{4} + k\pi$

77. $1, -1, \frac{-1 + i\sqrt{3}}{2}, \frac{-1 - i\sqrt{3}}{2}$ **79.** 12 km/h; 5 km/h

Lesson 18-5 Try This

a. $\frac{\pi}{6}, \frac{5\pi}{6}, \frac{7\pi}{6}, \frac{11\pi}{6}$ plus $2k\pi$ **b.** $\frac{\pi}{6}, \frac{5\pi}{6}, \frac{7\pi}{6}, \frac{11\pi}{6}$
c. 75°30′, 284°30′, 120°, 240° **d.** 90°, 120°, 240°, 270°

Exercise Set 18-5

1. $\frac{4\pi}{3}, \frac{5\pi}{3}$ or 240°, 300° **3.** $\frac{\pi}{6}, \frac{5\pi}{6}, \frac{7\pi}{6}, \frac{11\pi}{6}$ or 30°, 150°, 210°, 330° **5.** $\frac{\pi}{6}, \frac{5\pi}{6}, \frac{3\pi}{2}$ or 30°, 150°, 270°

7. $0, 2\pi$ or 0°, 360° **9.** $\frac{\pi}{6}, \frac{5\pi}{6}$ or 30°, 150°

11. 123°41′, 303°41′ **13.** 109°28′, 120°, 240°, 250°32′

15. $0, \frac{\pi}{2}, \pi, \frac{3\pi}{2}, 2\pi$ **17.** $0, \pi, 2\pi$ **19.** $\frac{3\pi}{4}, \frac{7\pi}{4}$

21. $\frac{\pi}{4}, \frac{\pi}{2}, \frac{3\pi}{4}, \frac{5\pi}{4}, \frac{3\pi}{2}, \frac{7\pi}{4}$ **23.** $0, \frac{\pi}{2}, \pi, \frac{3\pi}{2}, 2\pi$

25. $0, 2\pi$ **51.** 720 **53.** 3024 **55.** 252

Lesson 18-6 Try This

a. $a \approx 38.43$, $b \approx 54.88$ **b.** $\angle A \approx 56°19'$, $\angle B \approx 33°41'$, $c \approx 7.211$ **c.** ≈ 75.8 m **d.** $\approx 28°30'$ **e.** 240.3 ft **f.** 136 km; 63.4 km

Exercise Set 18-6

1. $\angle B = 53°50'$, $b = 37.2$, $c = 46.1$ **3.** $\angle A = 77°20'$, $a = 436.5$, $c = 447.4$ **5.** $\angle B = 77°40'$, $a = 4.2$, $c = 14.2$ **7.** $\angle A = 66°50'$, $b = 0.0148$, $c = 0.0375$ **9.** $\angle A = 20°40'$, $b = 0.0129$, $c = 0.0138$ **11.** $\angle A = 33°30'$, $a = 0.0247$, $b = 0.0373$ **13.** $c = 21.6$, $\angle A = 33°40'$, $\angle B = 56°20'$ **21.** 239 ft **23.** 1°40′ **25.** 30°10′ **27.** 18,572 **29.** 328 ft **31.** 109 km **33.** 25.9 cm **35.** 8.33 cm **37.** 355 ft **39.** 7.92 km **41.** 3.45 km **47.** $\pm\frac{7}{5}i$

Lesson 18-7 Try This

a. $m\angle B = 87$, $b \approx 9.94$, $c \approx 7.84$ **b.** $m\angle A = 59$, $a \approx 221.05$, $c \approx 225.55$ **c.** No solution **d.** $\angle B = 36°52'$, $\angle C = 90°$, $c = 5$ **e.** $m\angle A \approx 43$, $\angle C \approx 104$, $c \approx 35.6$ or $m\angle A \approx 137$, $m\angle C \approx 10$, $c \approx 6.4$ **f.** $m\angle A \approx 124$, $m\angle C \approx 18$, $a \approx 26.9$ **g.** ≈ 8.452

Exercise Set 18-7

1. $m\angle C = 50$, $a = 18.4$, $c = 16.3$ **3.** $m\angle C = 96$, $b = 15.2$, $c = 20.3$ **5.** $m\angle C = 17$, $a = 26.3$, $c = 10.5$ **7.** $m\angle A = 121$, $a = 33.4$, $c = 14.0$ **9.** $\angle B = 68°50'$, $a = 13.2$, $b = 32.3$ **11.** $\angle A = 12°20'$, $\angle C = 17°40'$, $c = 4.25$ **13.** $\angle A = 20°20'$, $\angle B = 99°40'$, $b = 34.1$ **15.** $\angle B = 56°20'$, $\angle C = 87°40'$, $c = 40.8$ or $\angle B = 123°40'$, $\angle C = 20°20'$, $c = 14.2$ **17.** $\angle C = 44°40'$, $m\angle B = 19$, $b = 6.25$ **37.** $\frac{36b^2d^2\sqrt[3]{d^2}}{a^4c^4}$ **39.** 1 **41.** 54 **43.** −209,715

Lesson 18-8 Try This

a. $a = 40.5$, $\angle B = 22°10'$, $\angle C = 35°50'$ **b.** $\angle A = 108°10'$, $\angle B = 22°20'$, $\angle C = 49°30'$

Exercise Set 18-8

1. $c = 12.0$, $\angle A = 20°40'$, $\angle B = 24°20'$ **3.** $a = 14.9$, $\angle B = 23°40'$, $\angle C = 126°20'$ **5.** $a = 24.8$, $\angle B = 20°40'$, $\angle C = 26°20'$ **7.** $b = 74.8$, $\angle A = 95°30'$, $\angle C = 11°50'$ **9.** $\angle A = 29°$, $\angle B = 46°30'$, $\angle C = 104°30'$ **11.** $\angle A = 34°50'$, $\angle B = 58°50'$, $\angle C = 86°20'$ **13.** $\angle A = 36°10'$, $\angle B = 43°30'$, $\angle C = 100°20'$ **15.** $\angle A = 73°40'$, $\angle B = 51°50'$, $\angle C = 54°30'$ **33.** 2 **43.** $2(c - 15)(c + 1)$

Lesson 18-9 Try This

a. $1 - i$ **b.** $\sqrt{2}(\cos 315° + i \sin 315°)$ **c.** 20 cis 55° **d.** $2 \text{ cis } \frac{\pi}{4}$ **e.** 32 cis 270° **f.** 16 cis 120° **g.** $1 + i, -1 - i$ **h.** $\sqrt{3} + i, -\sqrt{3} + i, -2i$

Exercise Set 18-9

1. $\frac{3\sqrt{3}}{2} + \frac{3}{2}i$ **3.** $-2\sqrt{2} + 2i\sqrt{2}$ **5.** $-10i$ **7.** $\frac{5\sqrt{2}}{2} - \frac{5\sqrt{2}}{2}i$ **9.** $2 + 2i$ **11.** $2\sqrt{3} + 2i$ **13.** $-2 - 2i$ **15.** $\sqrt{2} \text{ cis } \frac{3\pi}{4}$ or $\sqrt{2}$ cis 135° **17.** $2 \text{ cis } \frac{\pi}{6}$ or 2 cis 30° **19.** $20 \text{ cis } \frac{11\pi}{6}$ or 20 cis 330° **21.** $2 \text{ cis } \frac{\pi}{2}$ or 2 cis 90° **23.** 5 cis π or 5 cis 180° **25.** $4 \text{ cis } \frac{3\pi}{2}$ or 4 cis 270° **27.** 4 cis 0 **29.** 40 cis 0 **31.** $8 \text{ cis } \frac{2\pi}{3}$ **33.** $\text{cis } \frac{\pi}{2}$ **35.** $\frac{\sqrt{2}}{2} \text{ cis } \frac{7\pi}{12}$ **37.** $2 \text{ cis } \frac{3\pi}{2}$ **39.** 8 cis π or 8 cis 180° **41.** 64 cis π or 64 cis 180° **43.** $8 \text{ cis } \frac{3\pi}{2}$ or 8 cis 270° **45.** $-8 - 8i\sqrt{3}$

69. 720° **71.** 105° **73.** $\frac{5\pi}{12}$ **75.** $-\frac{\pi}{2}$ **77.** $2, -3, \pm\sqrt{2}$ **79. c.** 3.9 mg

Chapter 18 Summary and Review

1. $\cos x \cos y - \sin x \sin y$ **3.** $\frac{\sqrt{2} + \sqrt{6}}{4}$ **5.** $2 - \sqrt{3}$ **7.** $\sin 2\theta = \frac{24}{25}$, $\cos 2\theta = -\frac{7}{25}$, $\tan 2\theta = -\frac{24}{7}$, Quadrant II **9.** $\frac{\sqrt{2 - \sqrt{2}}}{2}$ **11.** $\frac{\pi}{6} + 2k\pi, \frac{5\pi}{6} + 2k\pi$ **13.** $-\frac{\pi}{4}$ **15.** $0, \pi, 2\pi$ **17.** $\angle B = 47°30'$, $b = 1310$, $c = 1776$ **19.** $\angle A = 38°50'$, $b = 37.9$, $c = 48.6$ **21.** 3708.8 mi **23.** $m\angle A = 34$, $a = 0.619$, $c = 0.514$ **25.** $\angle A = 19°10'$, $\angle C = 25°50'$, $b = 7.96$ **27.** 20.4 **29.** $\sqrt{2} \text{ cis } \frac{\pi}{4}$ or $\sqrt{2}$ cis 45° **31.** $\sqrt[6]{2}$ cis 15°, $\sqrt[6]{2}$ cis 135°, $\sqrt[6]{2}$ cis 255°

Chapters 1–18 Cumulative Review

1. 19 **3.** −7 **5.** $a > 2$ **7.** $-5 < x < 13$ **9.** $\$0.138m + \$1620$; \$1758 **11.** $(-1, 3, 6)$ **13.** $8x^3 - 12x^2 + 6x - 1$ **15.** $3(2x - 11y)^2$ **17.** $2(x + 2)(x - 2)(x + 3)$ **19.** 8, 1 **21.** $\frac{a - 3}{5a + 2}$ **23.** −5, 3 **25.** $3x\sqrt{10x}$ **27.** $x + 3$ **29.** $-1 - \sqrt{35}$ **31.** $-28 - 44i$ **33.** $\frac{\sqrt{2}}{3}, -\frac{\sqrt{2}}{3}$ **35.** $64, -\frac{343}{8}$ **37.** x-axis **39.** Neither **41.** $(1, 3)$, $x = 1$, max: 3 **47.** $\frac{1}{2}, \frac{1 + \sqrt{5}}{2}, \frac{1 - \sqrt{5}}{2}$ **49.** $x = 2y^2 + 3$ **51.** $\log_{10} 3 = 0.4771$ **53.** $\log_x z = y$ **55.** 1 **57.** $\begin{bmatrix} -3 & 6 & 30 \\ 9 & -12 & 24 \\ 0 & 15 & -3 \end{bmatrix}$ **61.** $(2, 2)$ **63.** −41 **65.** $\frac{27}{4}$ **67.** 120 **69.** $16a^4 + 96a^3y + 216a^2y^2 + 216ay^3 + 81y^4$ **71.** $\frac{2}{3}$ **77.** 4.6 **79.** 5.6 **81.** III **83.** II **85.** $\frac{5\pi}{9}$ **89.** $A = \frac{1}{2}$, period $= \pi$ **91.** $2 \cos \alpha \cos \beta$ **95.** $0, \pi, 2\pi$ **97.** $\angle A = 65°40'$, $\angle B = 24°20'$, $b = 4.2$ **99.** $\angle A = 12°20'$, $\angle C = 17°40'$, $c = 4.25$ **101.** $2 \text{ cis } \frac{7\pi}{6}$ **103.** $-10i$

Index